TEACHER'S EDITION

PRENTICE HALL MATHEMATICS

PRE-ALGEBRA

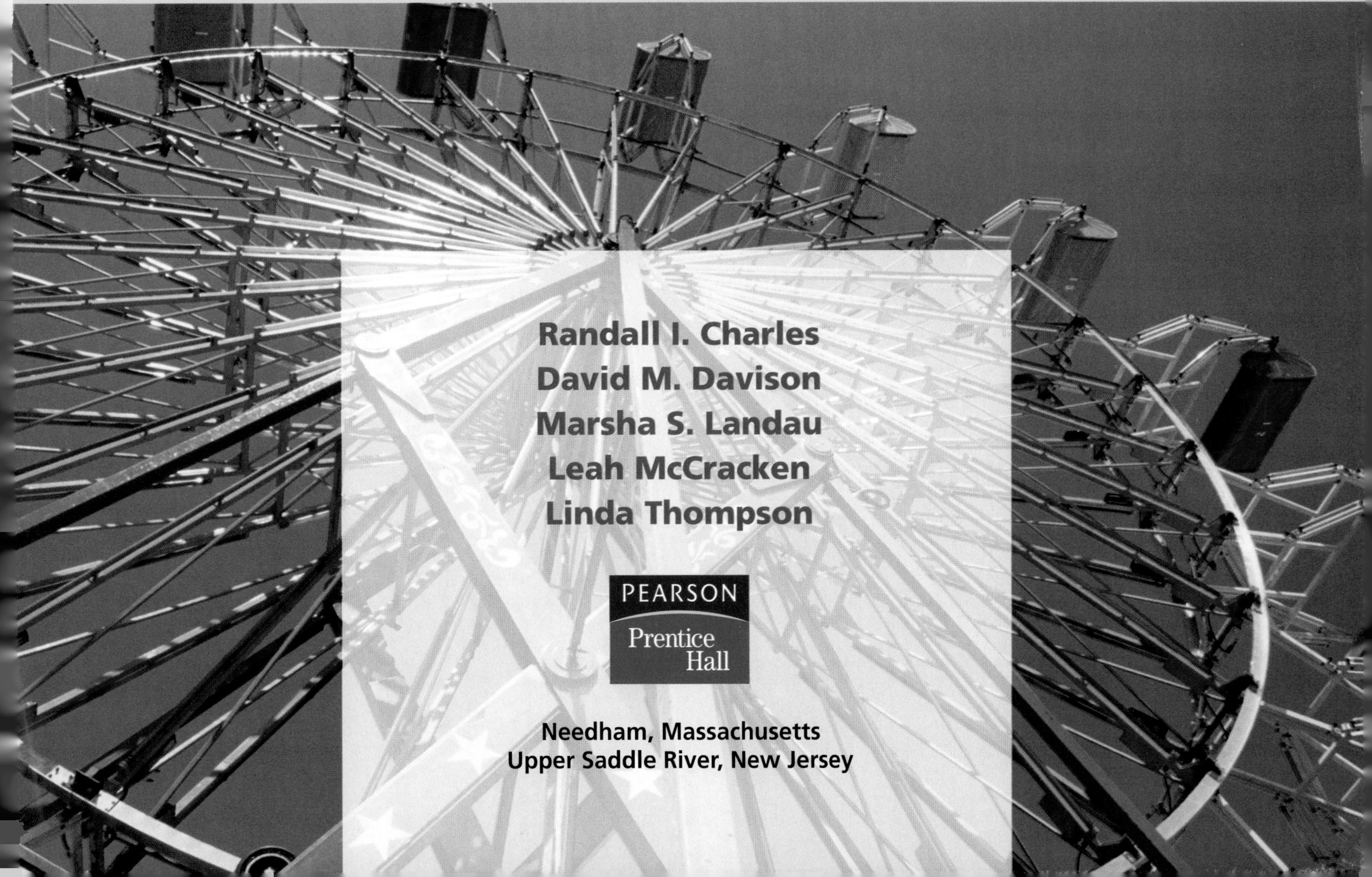

Randall I. Charles

David M. Davison

Marsha S. Landau

Leah McCracken

Linda Thompson

PEARSON

Prentice
Hall

Needham, Massachusetts
Upper Saddle River, New Jersey

ISBN 0-13-037918-2

6 7 8 9 10   07 06 05

Teacher's Edition Contents

Teacher Handbook

Student Edition with Teacher Notes

PRENTICE HALL
The *right path* makes

The right path
across the grade levels . . .

Vertical Alignment K–12

Prentice Hall Mathematics is the grades 6–12 companion of the Scott Foresman elementary series. The continuity of design, content, and pedagogy extends from K–12. The scope and sequence of the series addresses both today's curriculum guidelines and teacher expectations.

PEARSON
Prentice Hall

Proven Authorship

Series author Randy Charles ensures continuity of content from course to course, while program authors ensure integrity of content within each course. (See page T14.)

Proven Track Record

Prentice Hall Mathematics builds on the combined experience and heritage of three respected names in mathematics publishing—Prentice Hall, Scott Foresman, and Addison Wesley.

MATHEMATICS all the difference

The right path every day, in every lesson . . .

Reach Your Students

Math is made relevant and meaningful through *Dorling Kindersley Real-World Snapshots*. Watch students' excitement build as they make the connection between mathematics and real-world situations. (See pages T6–T7.)

Empower Your Students

Every student has the opportunity to excel through our unique *Instant Check System™*. No other program makes it this easy for you to assess readiness, progress, and mastery. (See pages T8–T9.)

Prepare Your Students

Daily Test Prep allows students to approach high-stakes tests with confidence. And because it's built into every lesson, you don't have to stop teaching to prepare them for the test! (See pages T10–T11.)

. . . and *Prentice Hall Mathematics* provides you with the **teaching support** you deserve—every day, in every lesson.

Grab Their Attention

Dorling Kindersley Real-World Snapshots grab students' attention with a captivating visual style.

■ **Activities**

Students gather data to apply the mathematics from the chapter to real-world situations.

DK Real-World Snapshots

Wireless Style

Applying Equations Cell-phone use has increased dramatically since the mid-1990s. Millions of people worldwide own cell phones. If you are one of them, you probably purchased a calling plan from a service provider. These providers charge different fees for a variety of services.

Throw It Away!
A credit-card-sized disposable cell phone offers approximately one hour of talk time.

The circuits are printed metallic ink instead of tiny wires.

Activity

1. Suppose you are shopping for a calling plan. You expect to use 10 long-distance minutes per month.
   a. Use the table below and the total-cost equation to find out how much you will pay for the first month of each calling plan.
   b. **Writing in Math** Which plan would you choose? Explain.
2. Suppose a friend is also shopping for a calling plan. Your friend expects to use 60 long-distance minutes each month.
   a. Use the table below and the total-cost equation to find out how much your friend will pay for the first month of each calling plan.
   b. Which plan do you think your friend would choose? Explain.
3. **Number Sense** Without calculating, which plan would be the least expensive to use in the second month? Explain.

Calling Plan	A	B	C	D
Monthly Fee	$19.99	$34.99	$19.99	$29.99
Long-Distance Rate	$.15	$.15	$.00	$.20
Activation Fee	$36.00	$24.00	$30.00	$35.00

Total-Cost Equation
$c = m + d\ell + a$

c = total cost
m = monthly fee
ℓ = long-distance rate
d = long-distance minutes
a = activation fee

Monthly Fee The amount a customer pays each month for basic service

Long-Distance Rate The amount a customer pays for each minute of a call made outside the local calling area

Activation Fee A one-time fee paid to start phone service

Where's the Cell-Phone Tower?
Cell phone companies often camouflage their towers to make them blend in with the surrounding landscape.

Antenna

Antenna

Take It to the NET For more information about cell phones, go to www.PHSchool.com.
Web Code ade-0753

394

395

■ **Take It to the Net**

Data at PHSchool.com further develop concepts.

all of my students?"

Connect to Their World

2 EXAMPLE <u>Real-World</u> <u>Problem Solving</u>

Bicycling Beth leaves home on her bicycle, riding at a steady rate of 8 mi/h. Her brother Ted leaves home on his bicycle half an hour later, following Beth's route. He rides at a steady rate of 12 mi/h. How long after Beth leaves home will Ted catch up?

distance Beth travels = distance Ted travels

Words   8 mi/h · Beth's time   =   12 mi/h · Ted's time

Equation

<u>Real-World</u> <u>Connection</u>

An estimated 80.6 million people in the United States ride bicycles. About 14.5% of the nation's bicycle riders live in California.

Real-World Connections
within each lesson make skills and concepts relevant.

More Than One Way

Telephone Services For local telephone service, the McNeils pay $9.95/month plus $.035/min for local calls. Last month, they paid $12.75 for local service. To find the minutes m of local calls, solve the equation $0.035m + 9.95 = 12.75$.

Nicole's Method

I can work with decimals as I have before.

$$0.035m + 9.95 = 12.75$$
$$0.035m + 9.95 - 9.95 = 12.75 - 9.95$$
$$0.035m = 2.8$$
$$\frac{0.035m}{0.035} = \frac{2.8}{0.035}$$
$$m = 80$$

The McNeils made 80 min of local calls.

Daryl's Method

Use multiplication to clear the decimals. Use the decimals with the greatest number of decimal places to decide what power of 10 to use.

Plus...

Take It to the NET

Online lesson quiz at
www.PHSchool.com

Web Code: abg-0804

Built-in Web Support

PHSchool.com supports students as they learn. Built-in **Web Codes** take them directly to components of the Web site, including:

- Self-grading tests and lesson quizzes
- Updated data sources
- Support for chapter projects

“How can I *empower* to learn

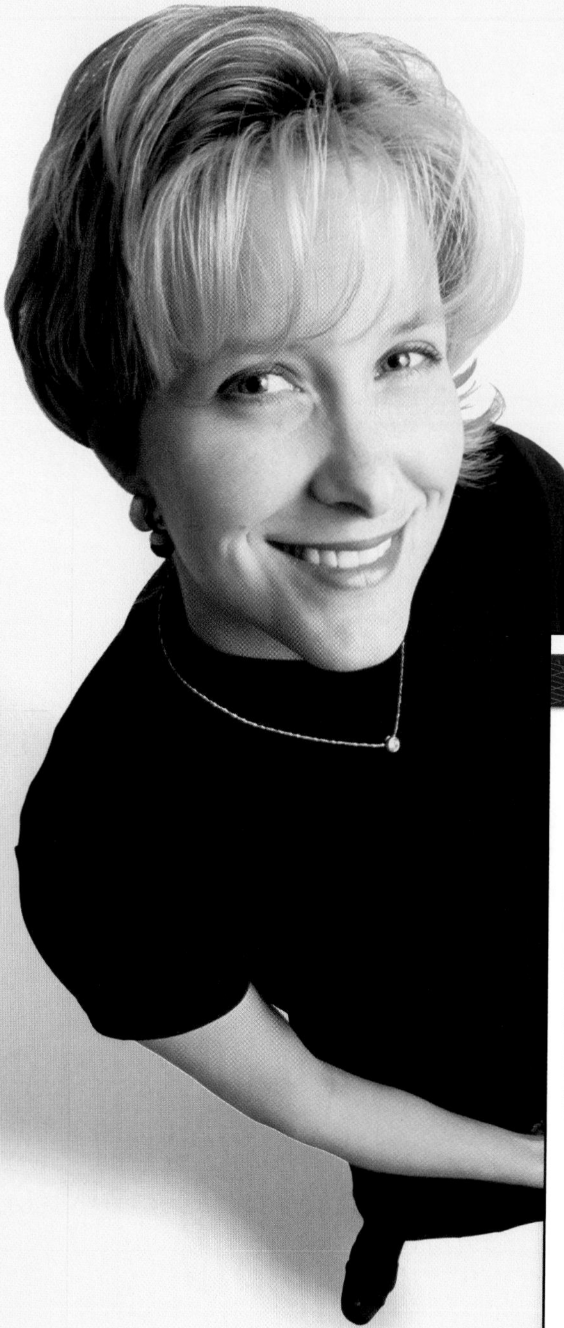

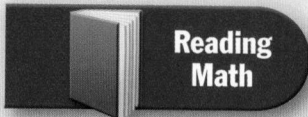

Ongoing Assessment

Instant Check System™

enables students to check their understanding at key points during instruction. No other program provides such an easy-to-use way to measure students' progress.

7-7 Transforming Formulas

What You'll Learn

- To solve a formula for a given variable
- To use formulas to solve problems

... And Why

To find travel times in real-world situations

Check Skills You'll Need

Use each formula for the values given.

1. Use the formula $d = rt$ to find d when $r = 80$ km/h and $t = 4$ h.
2. Use the formula $P = 2\ell + 2w$ to find P when $\ell = 9$ m and $w = 7$ m.
3. Use the formula $A = \frac{1}{2}bh$ to find A when $b = 12$ ft and $h = 8$ ft.

For help, go to Lesson 3-4.

OBJECTIVE 1 Solving Formulas for a Given Variable

Remember that a formula shows the relationship between two or more quantities. You can use the properties of equality to transform a formula to represent one quantity in terms of another.

1 EXAMPLE Transforming in One Step

Solve the area formula $A = \ell w$ for ℓ.

$A = \ell w$

$\frac{A}{w} = \frac{\ell w}{w}$ Divide each side by w.

$\frac{A}{w} = \ell$, or $\ell = \frac{A}{w}$ Simplify.

Check Understanding Example 1

1. Solve for the variable indicated in red.

a. $p = s - c$ b. $h = \frac{k}{j}$ c. $I = prt$

Sometimes you need to use more than one step.

2 EXAMPLE Using More Than One Step

Solve the perimeter formula $P = 2\ell + 2w$ for ℓ.

$P = 2\ell + 2w$

$P - 2w = 2\ell + 2w - 2w$

$P - 2w = 2\ell$

$\frac{1}{2}(P - 2w) = \frac{1}{2}(2\ell)$

$\frac{1}{2}P - w = \ell$

Check Understanding Example 2

2. Solve for the variable indicated

a. $5a + 7 = b$ b. $P = 2$

Interactive lesson includes instant self-check, tutorials, and activities.

378 Chapter 7 Solving Equations and Inequalities

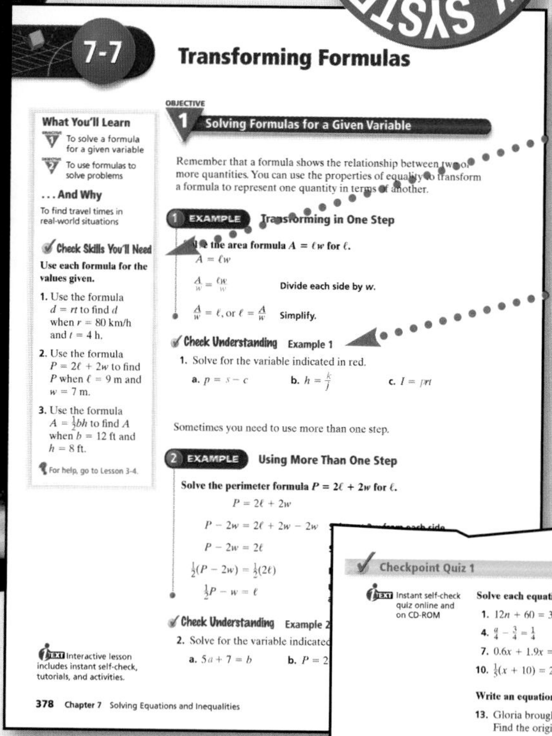

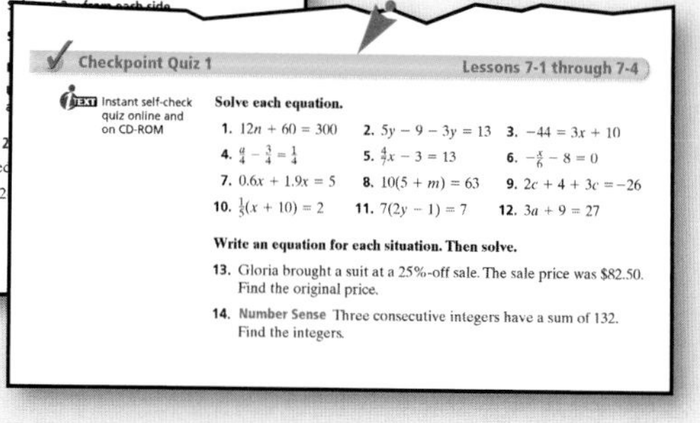

Checkpoint Quiz 1 Lessons 7-1 through 7-4

Instant self-check quiz online and on CD-ROM

Solve each equation.

1. $12n + 60 = 300$
2. $5y - 9 - 3y = 13$
3. $-44 = 3x + 10$
4. $\frac{a}{4} - \frac{3}{4} = \frac{1}{4}$
5. $\frac{4}{7}x - 3 = 13$
6. $-\frac{x}{6} - 8 = 0$
7. $0.6x + 1.9x = 5$
8. $10(5 + m) = 63$
9. $2c + 4 + 3c = -26$
10. $\frac{1}{5}(x + 10) = 2$
11. $7(2y - 1) = 7$
12. $3a + 9 = 27$

Write an equation for each situation. Then solve.

13. Gloria brought a suit at a 25%-off sale. The sale price was $82.50. Find the original price.
14. Number Sense Three consecutive integers have a sum of 132. Find the integers.

Before lessons
Check Skills You'll Need

During lessons
Check Understanding after every example

After lessons
Checkpoint Quizzes

Reading Math — Reading for Problem Solving

For Use With Page 364, Exercise 4

Read through the problem below. Then follow along with what Elena thinks as she solves the problem. Check your understanding with the exercise at the bottom of the page.

Wendy bought a drill at a 10%-off sale. The sale price was $75.60. Find the original price p.

What Elena Thinks	What Elena Writes
What information is given in the problem? I'll write it down.	A drill was on sale for 10% off. The sale price was $75.60.
What am I trying to find out? I'll write out the question.	What was the original price?
I know that 10% off means that you subtract 10% of the original price from the original price. I'll write this as an equation in words.	Original price minus 10% of the original price is the sale price, $75.60.

Reading Math

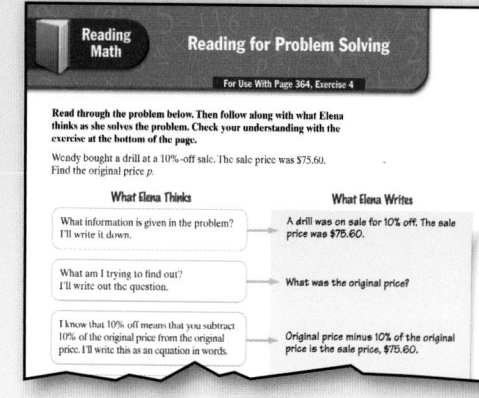

Built-in Reading Help

Reading Math lessons and side-column features provide help where students often struggle:

- Math Vocabulary
- Understanding Word Problems
- Understanding Formulas and Symbols

students independently?"

Built-in Homework Help

Leveled exercise sets

allow you to easily craft just the right assignments for your classes. Plus, we've built in homework helpers along the way.

■ **Student Help features**
throughout the text—consistently labeled in green—assist your students in becoming independent learners.

(A) Practice by Example
refers students directly back to the examples in the lesson. (Also great for parents trying to help with homework!)

(B) Apply Your Skills
Richer skill exercises and multi-step application problems combine skills from earlier lessons.

(C) Challenge
Exercises extend and stretch students' thinking.

EXERCISES

Practice and Problem Solving

For more exercises, see *Extra Practice*.

(A) Practice by Example
Examples 1 and 2 (page 378)

Complete the steps to solve each equation for the variable indicated in red.

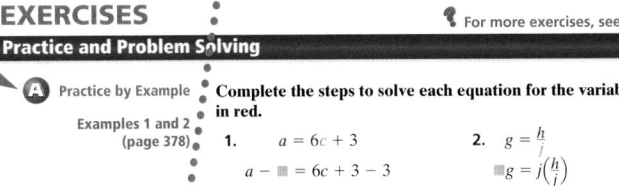

1.
$a = 6c + 3$
$a - \blacksquare = 6c + 3 - 3$
$a - \blacksquare = 6c$
$\dfrac{a - 3}{\blacksquare} = \dfrac{6c}{\blacksquare}$
$\dfrac{a - 3}{\blacksquare} = \blacksquare$

2.
$g = \dfrac{h}{j}$
$\blacksquare g = j\left(\dfrac{h}{j}\right)$
$jg = \blacksquare$
$\dfrac{jg}{\blacksquare} = \dfrac{h}{g}$
$\blacksquare = \dfrac{h}{g}$

Solve for the variable indicated in red.

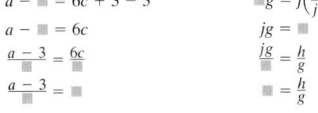

3. $V = \ell wh$ **4.** $P = 4s$ **5.** $q = \dfrac{p}{d}$

6. $r = 2s - 8$ **7.** $\frac{2}{3}m - 5 = n$ **8.** $m = \dfrac{a + b}{2}$

Examples 3 and 4 (page 379)

9. Commissions LaTanya sells business suits and gets a 4% commission on her sales. Last week, she received a paycheck that included $196 in commissions. Solve the formula $C = 0.04s$ for s, where C is the amount of commission and s is the amount of sales. Substitute to find LaTanya's sales.

10. Renting You have $12.00 to rent a pair of in-line skates. They rent for $3.00 plus $1.50 per hour. To determine the maximum length of time you can rent the in-line skates, solve the formula $C = 3 + 1.5h$ for h. Then substitute 12 for C.

(B) Apply Your Skills

Solve for the variable indicated in red.

11. $V = \frac{1}{2}\pi r^2 h$ **12.** $d^2 = \frac{3}{2}h$ **13.** $A = \frac{1}{2}(a + b)h$

14. a. Construction Bricklayers use the formula $N = 7LH$ to estimate the number N of bricks needed in a wall. L is the length of the wall and H is the height. Solve the formula for H.
   b. If 1,134 bricks are used to build a wall that is 18 ft long, how high is the wall?

15. Writing in Math A formula for the perimeter of a rectangle is $P = 2(b + h)$. Explain how you would find the height of the rectangle if you knew the perimeter and the base.

(C) Challenge

16. a. Economics Joe uses the formula $p = wh + 1.5wv$ to figure his weekly pay. In the formula, p is the weekly pay, w is the hourly wage, h is the number of regular hours, and v is the number of overtime hours. Solve the formula for v.
   b. Joe's hourly wage is $6.24/h. If he earned $282.36 last week working 40 regular hours plus overtime, how many hours overtime did he work?

380   Chapter 7   Solving Equations and Inequalities

"How can I prepare

Test Prep Every Day Builds Readiness

Standardized Test Prep

in *every lesson* makes test prep a powerful part of everyday instruction. Includes all major problem types:

- **Multiple Choice**
- **Gridded Response**
- **Short and Extended Response (rubric-based)**
- **Reading Comprehension**

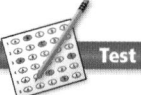

Test Prep

Multiple Choice

For Exercises 17–19, what is the correct result when you solve for the variable indicated in red?

17. $z = xy$
- **A.** $x = \frac{z}{y}$
- **B.** $x = \frac{y}{z}$
- **C.** $x = yz$
- **D.** $y = xz$

18. $r = 2s - 8$
- **F.** $s = \frac{r+2}{8}$
- **G.** $s = r + 4$
- **H.** $s = \frac{r+8}{2}$
- **I.** $s = 2r + 16$

19. $\frac{2}{3}m - 5 = n$
- **A.** $m = \frac{2}{3}(n + 5)$
- **B.** $m = \frac{3}{2}(n + 5)$
- **C.** $m = \frac{3}{2}n + 5$
- **D.** $m = \frac{2}{3}n + 5$

Take It to the NET
Online lesson quiz at
www.PHSchool.com
Web Code: ada-0707

20. Use the batting average formula, $a = \frac{h}{n}$. What is the number of hits h for $a = 0.245$ and $n = 25$?
- **F.** 98
- **G.** 7
- **H.** 6
- **I.** 0

Extended Response

21. Solve $A = \frac{1}{2}(a + b)h$ twice, once for b and once for h. Explain your process for each solution. Then compare the two processes, stating similarities and differences.

Writing in Math

Writing to Explain

For Use With Page 270, Exercise 49

In this book, there are many exercises that ask you to explain your work. One type of exercise that asks for an explanation is Error Analysis. For an Error Analysis exercise, you often need to do three things:

- Identify the error.
- Explain the error.
- Show a correct solution.

You do not have to do them in the above order, however. Often, showing a correct solution first will help you find and understand the error.

EXAMPLE

Error Analysis A student solved the equation $-\frac{7}{10}h = 5\frac{3}{5}$ and found the solution 8. Describe and correct the student's error.

- Show a correct solution.

$$-\frac{7}{10}h = 5\frac{3}{5}$$

Writing in Math

Writing Math Strand

No other program provides this unique combination of practice and instruction.

- **Daily Writing Practice**—Every lesson contains Writing in Math exercises.
- **Writing Instruction**—Special Writing in Math lessons provide direct instruction in how to more effectively communicate using words and mathematics.

my students for high-stakes tests?"

Test-Taking Strategies Build Confidence

Test-Taking Strategies   **Eliminating Answers**

Before you do all the work involved in solving a multiple-choice problem, you usually can eliminate some answer choices. This can save you time in finding the correct answer. Also, it improves your chances of making a correct guess.

1 EXAMPLE

What is the solution to $\frac{3}{4}(x - 2) = \frac{3}{2}$?

A. -2 **B.** 2 **C.** 3 **D.** 4

The product on the left must equal the positive number on the right. Thus, since $\frac{3}{4}$ is positive, the value of $(x - 2)$ must also be positive.

The choices -2 and 2 do not give positive values for $(x - 2)$. You can eliminate choices A and B. Then substitute 4 for x and use mental math to find that D is the correct choice.

2 EXAMPLE

What is the solution to $x + 0.05x = 420$?

F. 400 **G.** 410 **H.** 420 **I.** 450

On the left, a fraction of x is added to x and the result is 420. Thus the value of x must be less than 420. You can eliminate choices H and I. Then check 400 in the equation to find that F is the correct choice.

Test-Taking Strategies

give students the tools they need to approach tests with confidence. Each mini-lesson is supported with transparencies and practice masters.

Plus...

Prentice Hall Assessment System

enables you to easily prescribe a unique plan for each of your classes through a three-step process:

1. **Diagnose & Prescribe**
2. **Review & Reteach**
3. **Practice & Assess**

The teaching *support*

Only Prentice Hall brings you . . .

Presentation Assistant Plus!

All the materials you need to teach a lesson from beginning to end—in two easy-to-use formats: transparencies and PowerPoint®.

1. Introduce

Check Skills You'll Need questions assess student understanding of prerequisite skills.

2. Teach

Additional Examples have been reproduced from the Teacher's Edition.

3. Check Homework

All answers are provided for all the homework exercises in the Student Edition.

4. Assess

Lesson Quizzes are reproduced from the Teacher's Edition and include answers.

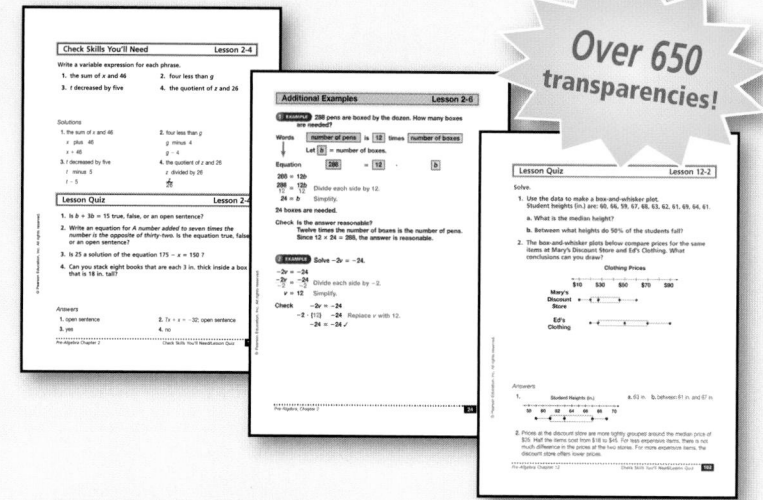

Over 650 transparencies!

Here's the "Plus!"

Presentation Pro CD-ROM

contains all the transparencies on **PowerPoint** to allow you to tailor your presentations for maximum effectiveness.

![iTEXT]

The interactive text online and on CD-ROM takes learning to a new level.

Try iText today at PHSchool.com/Math

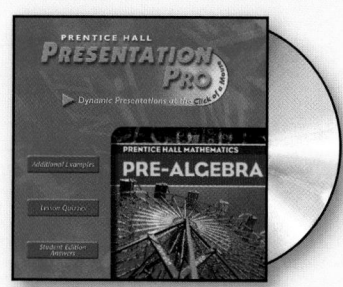

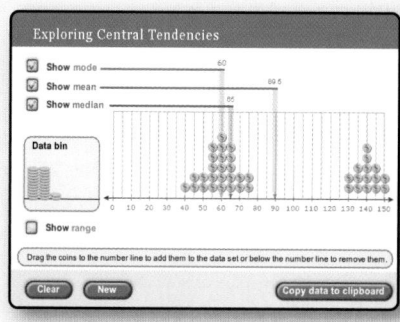

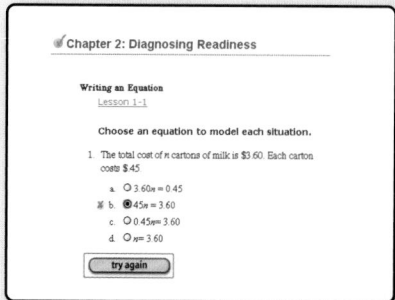

iText includes:

- ## Activities and videos
  at point-of-use bring math to life.

- ## Reading support with audio
  helps you reach students struggling with math vocabulary.

- ## Instant-feedback assessments
  let students know right away whether they're on track.

you deserve

Complete Program Resources

Student Edition
iText—Interactive text
online and on CD-ROM
Teacher's Edition
Teaching Resources
- Grab & Go
Chapter Support Files
  – Practice
  – Reteaching
  – Enrichment
  – Chapter Projects
  – Checkpoint Quizzes
  – Chapter Tests
  – Alternative Assessment
  – Cumulative Review
- Cumulative Assessment
- Solution Key

Reaching All Students

Practice Workbook
Reading and Math Literacy Masters
Guided Problem Solving Masters
Hands-On Activities
Technology Activities
Prentice Hall MathNotes Folders
Skills Intervention Kit

Teacher Time Savers

Presentation Assistant Plus!
- Additional Examples on Transparencies
- Daily Skills Check and Lesson Quiz Transparencies
- Student Edition Answers on Transparencies
- Classroom Aid Transparencies
- Prentice Hall Presentation Pro CD-ROM

Assessment and Test Prep

Prentice Hall Assessment System
- Computer Test
Generator CD-ROM
- Algebra Readiness Tests
- Assessment Resources
  – Checkpoint Quizzes
  – Chapter Tests, Forms A & B
  – Alternative Assessment
  – Cumulative Assessment
- Content Diagnostic Tests
- Skills and Concepts Review
- Test Preparation Workbook, with Teacher's Guide
- Test-Taking Strategies With Transparencies

Spanish Support

Student Edition, Spanish Version
Spanish Practice Workbook
Spanish Reading and Math Literacy Masters
Spanish Assessment Resources

Technology

iText—Interactive text online
and on CD-ROM
Prentice Hall
Presentation Pro CD-ROM
Resource Pro® with
Planning Express® CD-ROM
Computer Test Generator CD-ROM
PH SuccessNet
Teacher Center Web Site
PHSchool.com
Textbook Site
Scientific Calculator
TI–34 II
Graphing Calculator
TI-73, TI-83 Plus

Take a virtual tour
of the program at
PHSchool.com/Math

Authors

Randall I. Charles, Ph.D., is Professor Emeritus in the Department of Mathematics and Computer Science at San Jose State University, San Jose, California. He began his career as a high school mathematics teacher, and he was a mathematics supervisor for five years. Dr. Charles has been a member of several NCTM committees and is the former Vice President of the National Council of Supervisors of Mathematics. Much of his writing and research has been in the area of problem solving. He has authored more than 75 mathematics textbooks for kindergarten through college.

David M. Davison, Ph.D., is a Professor of Mathematics Education at Montana State University in Billings, Montana. One of Dr. Davison's areas of special focus is the integration of mathematics with other disciplines, especially science. He is also the author of a book and several articles on integrating mathematics and science and teaching mathematics to Native Americans.

Marsha Landau, Ph.D., is a mathematics education specialist from Evanston, Illinois. Dr. Landau works with teachers and students in grades K–9 to support mathematics learning, and is particularly active with individual students talented in mathematics.

Leah McCracken has more than 30 years experience in mathematics classrooms, Grade 5 through college. She currently works with students, teachers, and school leaders across the country, especially in the area of integrating technology into the curriculum. Ms. McCracken is a past recipient of the Montana Mathematics Teacher of the Year award as well as the Presidential Award for Excellence in Mathematics Teaching.

Linda Thompson is a mathematics consultant from Warrenton, Oregon. Ms. Thompson, who is listed in *Who's Who's in American Education,* is a contributing author of elementary and secondary mathematics textbooks, as well as numerous articles on mathematics education.

PEARSON
Prentice Hall

ISBN 0-13-068608-5

6 7 8 9 10   07 06 05

Reviewers

Chandler Cox
White Knoll Middle School
West Columbia, South Carolina

Fred Ferguson
Yough High School
Herminie, Pennsylvania

Nancy Hughes
Indian Hills Middle School
Shawnee Mission, Kansas

Dorothy (Dot) Johnson-Manning
Siwell Road Middle School
Jackson, Mississippi

Ellice P. Martin, Ed.D.
Lanier County Middle School
Lakeland, Georgia

Desireé Marcelin McNeal
Susan Miller Dorsey High School
Los Angeles, California

Consultants

Reading Consultant

Bonnie B. Armbruster, Ph.D.
Department of Curriculum and Instruction
University of Illinois at Champaign-Urbana
Champaign, Illinois

Content Consultants

Courtney Lewis
Mathematics
Prentice Hall Senior National Consultant
Baltimore, Maryland

Kimberly Margel
Mathematics
Prentice Hall National Consultant
Scottsdale, Arizona

Deana Cerroni
Mathematics
Prentice Hall National Consultant
Las Vegas, Nevada

Sandra Mosteller
Mathematics
Prentice Hall National Consultant
Anderson, South Carolina

Rita Corbett
Mathematics
Prentice Hall Consultant
Elgin, Illinois

Addie Martin
Mathematics
Prentice Hall Consultant
Upper Marlboro, Maryland

Charlotte Samuels
Mathematics
Prentice Hall Consultant
Lafayette Hill, Pennsylvania

Cathy Davies
Mathematics
Prentice Hall Consultant
Laguna Niguel, California

Rose Primiani
Mathematics
Prentice Hall Consultant
Brick, New Jersey

Margaret Thomas
Mathematics
Prentice Hall Consultant
Indianapolis, Indiana

Sally Marsh
Mathematics
Prentice Hall Consultant
Baltimore, Maryland

Loretta Rector
Mathematics
Prentice Hall Consultant
Foresthill, California

Contents in Brief

Algebraic Expressions and Integers

Solving One-Step Equations and Inequalities

Student Support

 Instant Check System

Diagnosing Readiness, 64

Check Skills You'll Need, 66, 71, 76, 80, 86, 92, 96, 102, 106, 110

Check Understanding, 67, 68, 72, 73, 76, 77, 80, 81, 87, 88, 92, 93, 97, 102, 103, 106, 107, 111, 112

Checkpoint Quiz, 79, 109

Comprehensive Test Prep

Daily Test Prep, 70, 75, 79, 83, 90, 95, 99, 105, 109, 114

Test-Taking Tip, 67, 107, 112

Test-Taking Strategies, 116

Cumulative Test Prep, 121

Reading Math

Reading Math, 73, 89, 93, 103

Reading for Problem Solving, 91

Understanding Vocabulary, 117

Reading Comprehension, 70

Writing in Math

Daily Writing Practice, 69, 75, 79, 83, 90, 95, 101, 105, 109, 113, 120

Writing to Compare, 115

Real-World Problem Solving

Strategy: Try, Test, Revise, 96–99
Golf, 66
Fundraising, 72
Scuba Diving, 81
Math at Work, 99
. . . and more!

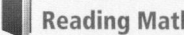

Decimals and Equations

Chapter 4

Factors, Fractions, and Exponents

Chapter 5

Operations With Fractions

Table of Contents

Ratios, Proportions, and Percents

Solving Equations and Inequalities

Table of Contents

Chapter 8

Linear Functions and Graphing

Chapter 9

Spatial Thinking

Student Support

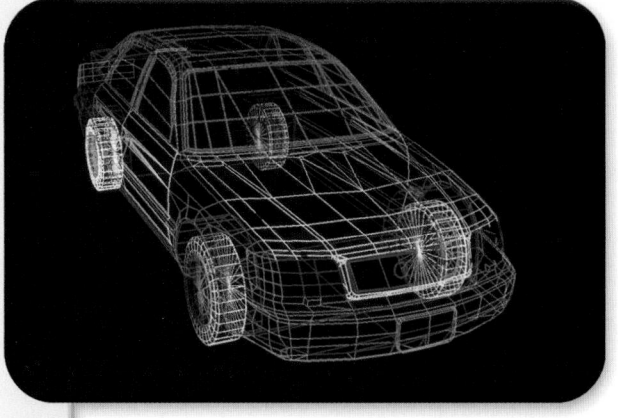

Chapter 10

Area and Volume

Student Support

 Instant Check System

Diagnosing Readiness, 520

Check Skills You'll Need, 522, 527, 532, 539, 545, 552, 557, 562, 566

Check Understanding, 523, 527, 528, 529, 533, 534, 540, 545, 546, 547, 553, 554, 558, 563, 566, 567

Checkpoint Quiz, 537, 565

 **Comprehensive Test Prep**

Daily Test Prep, 525, 531, 536, 543, 550, 556, 560, 565, 569

Test-Taking Tip, 550

Test-Taking Strategies, 570

Cumulative Test Prep, 575

Reading Math

Reading Math, 523, 541, 546

Reading a Formula, 551

Understanding Vocabulary, 571

Reading Comprehension, 526

Writing in Math

Daily Writing Practice, 525, 530, 536, 542, 549, 555, 559, 564, 568, 574

Real-World Problem Solving

Strategy: Make a Model, 562–565
Parades, 522
Math at Work, 526
Landscaping, 534
Architecture, 556
. . . and more!

Chapter 11

Right Triangles in Algebra

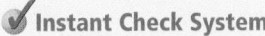

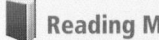

Table of Contents

Data Analysis and Probability

Chapter 13

Nonlinear Functions and Polynomials

Connect Your Learning
Through Problem Solving, Activities, and the Web

Applications: Real-World Applications

**And Over 100 More Topics!
See Real-World
Applications in the
Index, Page 879**

Applications: Math at Work

Applications: Interdisciplinary Connections

Problem-Solving Strategies

The Problem-Solving Lessons included in Prentice Hall *Pre-Algebra* progress in depth and sophistication throughout the course. You will learn to combine and compare strategies to solve problems. Throughout the text, a greater focus on the strategy "Write an Equation" helps prepare you for success in algebra.

The Problem-Solving Lessons in each chapter of Prentice Hall Mathematics progress in depth and sophistication within a course and from course to course.

Take It to the Net

Throughout this book you will find links to the Prentice Hall Web site. Use the Web Code provided with each link to gain direct access to online material.

Here's how to **Take It to the NET**:
- Go to **PHSchool.com**.
- Enter the Web Code.
- Click Go!

For a complete list of online features, use Web Code adk-0099

Lesson Quiz Web Codes

There is an online quiz for each lesson. Access these quizzes with Web Codes ada-0101 through ada-1308 for Lesson 1-1 through Lesson 13-8. *See page 22.*

115 Lesson Quizzes
Web Code format: ada-0204
02 = Chapter 2   04 = Lesson 4

Chapter Resource Web Codes

Chapter	Vocabulary Quizzes *See page 57.*	Chapter Tests *See page 60.*	Dorling Kindersley Real-World Snapshots *See pages 62–63.*	Chapter Projects
1	adj-0151	ada-0152	ade-0153	add-0161
2	adj-0251	ada-0252	ade-0253	add-0261
3	adj-0351	ada-0352	ade-0353	add-0361
4	adj-0451	ada-0452	ade-0453	add-0461
5	adj-0551	ada-0552	ade-0553	add-0561
6	adj-0651	ada-0652	ade-0653	add-0661
7	adj-0751	ada-0752	ade-0753	add-0761
8	adj-0851	ada-0852	ade-0853	add-0861
9	adj-0951	ada-0952	ade-0953	add-0961
10	adj-1051	ada-1052	ade-1053	add-1061
11	adj-1151	ada-1152	ade-1153	add-1161
12	adj-1251	ada-1252	ade-1253	add-1261
13	adj-1351	ada-1352	ade-1353	add-1361
End-of-Course		ada-1154		

Additional Resource Web Codes

Data Updates   Use Web Code adg-2041 to get up-to-date government data for use in examples and exercises. *See page 95.*

Math at Work   For information about each Math at Work feature, use Web Code adb-2031. *See page 29.*

*i***TEXT** Complete student textbok available online. Includes interactivities and videos.

Prentice Hall Mathematics programs are research-based and proven to work

The stakes for mathematics educators are high. You are expected to raise student achievement. Prentice Hall understands your dedicated efforts and gives you the confidence to meet this challenge. In developing Prentice Hall programs, the use of research studies is a central, guiding construct. Research on *Prentice Hall Mathematics* indicated key elements of a textbook program that ensure student success: constant review within instruction, support for reading and writing in mathematics, and an ongoing assessment strand. This research was conducted in three phases:

Phase ❶: Exploratory Needs Assessment

Phase ❷: Formative, Prototype Development and Field Testing

Phase ❸: Summative, Validation Research

1 Exploratory Needs Assessment

Along with periodic surveys concerning curriculum issues and challenges, we conducted specific product development research, which included discussions with teachers and advisory panels, focus groups, and quantitative surveys. We explored the specific needs of teachers, students, and other educators regarding each book we developed in *Prentice Hall Mathematics*.

In conjunction with Prentice Hall authors, secondary research was done to explore educational research about learning. This research was incorporated into our instructional strategy and pedagogy to make a more effective mathematics program.

2 Formative, Prototype Development and Field Testing

During this phase of research, we worked to develop prototype materials for each course in *Prentice Hall Mathematics*. Then we tested the materials, including field testing with students and teachers, and qualitative and quantitative evaluations of different kinds. We received solid feedback about our lesson structure in our early prototype testing. Results were channeled back into the program development for improvement. For example, teachers commented positively on motivational quality and richness of the mathematics in the Dorling Kindersley features.

3 Summative, Validation Research

Finally, we conducted and continue to conduct longer-term research based on scientific, experimental designs under actual classroom conditions. This research identifies what works and what can be improved in revisions. We also continue to monitor the program in the market. We talk to our users about what works, and then we begin the cycle over again. Highlights of this research follow in the next section.

The new federal education law "No Child Left Behind" dictates that math programs be supported by research showing their efficacy. The research behind *Prentice Hall Mathematics* provides the evidence you deserve.

Prentice Hall Research Time Line

Market Needs Assessment
(Quantitative & Qualitative)
- Teacher Interviews
- Classroom Observations
- Mail Surveys
- Conference Participation

Formative Research
(Quantitative & Qualitative)
- Field Testing of Prototypes
- Classroom Observations
- Teacher Reviews
- Supervisor Reviews
- Educator Advisory Panels
- Prentice Hall Sales Force Input

Summative Research
(Experimental and Quasi-Experimental Study Designs & Qualitative Research)
- Pre-Publication Learner Verification Research
- Post-Publication Validation Studies
- Classroom Observations
- Evaluation of In-Market Results on Standardized Tests

Prentice Hall Math Pre-Algebra gets results!

Standardized Pre- to Post-Test Results

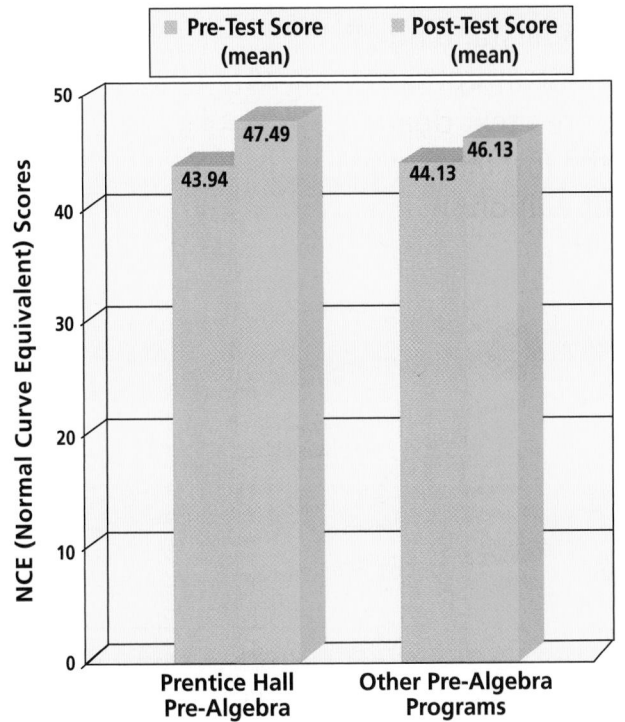

Legend:
- Pre-Test Score (mean)
- Post-Test Score (mean)

NCE (Normal Curve Equivalent) Scores

Prentice Hall Pre-Algebra: 43.94, 47.49
Other Pre-Algebra Programs: 44.13, 46.13

Prentice Hall mathematics programs are continually researched to determine "what works." Our programs are regularly revised to keep the best of what has worked in prior editions, and to improve them to meet changing market and curriculum needs. For example . . .

In a year-long study conducted in three states, 8th grade students using the Prentice Hall Pre-Algebra program outscored students using other pre-algebra programs on a nationally normed standardized test.

The study followed a scientific, experimental design with two classes per school. The classes selected were of similar ability levels and the assignment of the Prentice Hall program was done randomly. A total of four schools (a mix of rural, suburban, and urban) participated, with 120 students involved in the study.

Classes were tested at the beginning of the school year using the TerraNova™ Complete Battery Plus, and they were re-tested at the end of the school year. The final results are shown in the graph at the left.

All tests were scored by CTB/McGraw-Hill, the publisher of the TerraNova™ exam. Statistical analyses were conducted by an independent statistician from Pulse Analytics, Inc.

Additional studies of program effectiveness are under way, and many districts have demonstrated math improvement since adopting Prentice Hall mathematics programs.

Detailed results of this study can be obtained at **www.PHSchool.com/MathResearch**.

A unique progress-monitoring system that gives every student the opportunity to excel

What Research Indicates: Students' learning progresses to higher levels of understanding only if they have mastered a foundational understanding of preliminary concepts. If students are not functioning at a particular level of understanding, they are not ready to move on. Review plays a key role in promoting retention. Research clearly indicates that review should be systematically planned and incorporated into instruction. Before a new chapter or topic is begun, an inventory can help you ascertain whether any prerequisite knowledge is missing. Review should be continuous for students to attain mastery.

(Suydam, Marilyn N. *The Role of Review in Mathematical Instruction*. Columbus, Ohio: ERIC Clearinghouse for Science, Mathematics, and Environmental Education.)

Prentice Hall's Response: *Prentice Hall Mathematics* provides a unique **Instant Check System**™ that is built right into the text to assess mastery and diagnose weaknesses before, during, and after each lesson's instruction. This ongoing monitoring strand allows students to check their understanding of skills before moving on to the next topic. If students have misconceptions or need to reinforce their skills, the green type throughout the text clearly indicates where they can go for help. All the answers for the *Instant Check System*™ questions are available at the back of the student edition so students can check their work.

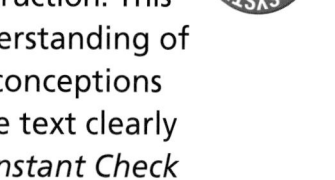

✓ Diagnosing Readiness

At the beginning of every chapter, students complete the *Diagnosing Readiness* exercises to see what prerequisite skills they may need to review before they begin the chapter. The Teacher's Edition prescribes specific *Examples* and *Exercises* that students can do for intervention.

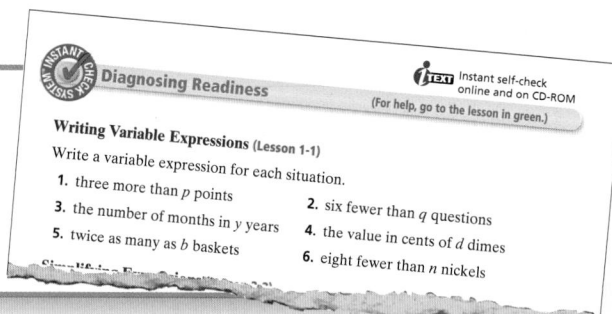

✓ Check Skills You'll Need

To begin each lesson, students complete the *Check Skills You'll Need* exercises to make sure they have the skills needed to successfully learn the concepts in the lesson. These questions with worked-out solutions are conveniently available as transparencies and on CD-ROM.

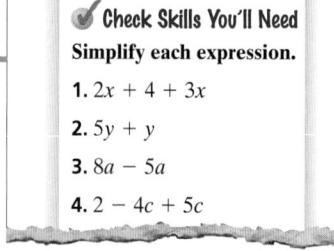

> "If students do not have the proper level of understanding, they cannot further their knowledge of concepts and relationships in mathematics. Both the Instant Check System and the Diagnosing Readiness feature help teachers assess how well students have achieved understanding of related skills before having them move on to subsequent concepts."
>
> —Art Johnson, *Prentice Hall Geometry* author

✓ Check Understanding

Every lesson includes numerous *Examples*, each followed by *Check Understanding* questions that students can do on their own. As skills and concepts are introduced, these questions focus students on the mathematics being presented and allow them to assess their understanding. More importantly, these questions will raise misconceptions that students have so that you may immediately address them.

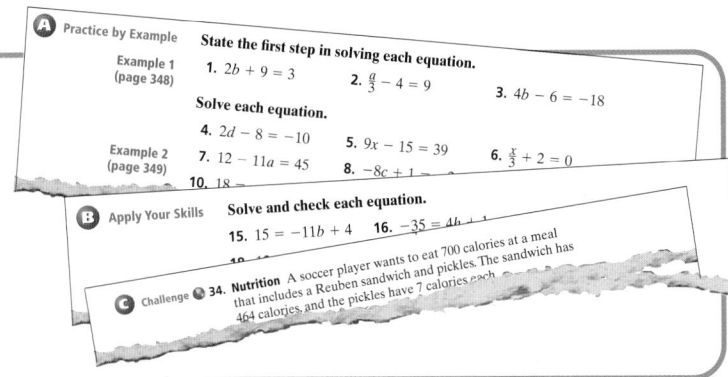

$$9(-4) + 2 \overset{?}{=} 4(-4) - 18 \qquad \text{Substitute } -4 \text{ for } a.$$
$$-36 + 2 \overset{?}{=} -16 - 18 \qquad \text{Multiply.}$$
$$-34 = -34 \checkmark$$

✓ Check Understanding Example 1

1. Solve and check each equation.

a. $4x + 4 = 2x + 36$ b. $-15 + 6b = -8b + 13$

Leveled Exercises

The abundant *Exercises* in every lesson are organized by level to provide ample opportunity for students of all abilities to master the concepts. The *A: Practice by Example* exercises directly relate to the *Examples* in the lesson. Some *A* exercises are partially solved to help students get started. The *B: Apply Your Skills* and *C: Challenge* exercises provide richer skill and application problems to extend students' thinking.

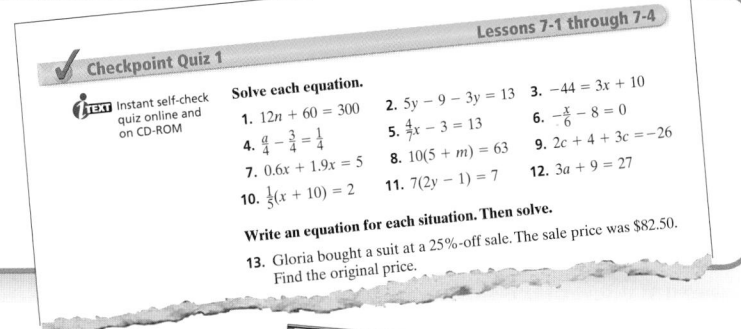

A Practice by Example   State the first step in solving each equation.

Example 1
(page 348)   **1.** $2b + 9 = 3$ **2.** $\frac{a}{3} - 4 = 9$ **3.** $4b - 6 = -18$

Solve each equation.

4. $2d - 8 = -10$ **5.** $9x - 15 = 39$ **6.** $\frac{x}{3} + 2 = 0$

Example 2
(page 349)   **7.** $12 - 11a = 45$ **8.** $-8c + 1 =$

10. $18 =$

B Apply Your Skills   Solve and check each equation.

15. $15 = -11b + 4$ **16.** $-35 = 4b$

C Challenge **34. Nutrition** A soccer player wants to eat 700 calories at a meal that includes a Reuben sandwich and pickles. The sandwich has 464 calories, and the pickles have 7 calories each

✓ Checkpoint Quizzes

Two *Checkpoint Quizzes* in every chapter provide students with opportunities for ongoing assessment. Each quiz provides a cumulative review of skills within specific lessons. Alternate versions are available in the Teaching Resources and online.

✓ Checkpoint Quiz 1 Lessons 7-1 through 7-4

Instant self-check quiz online and on CD-ROM

Solve each equation.

1. $12n + 60 = 300$ **2.** $5y - 9 - 3y = 13$ **3.** $-44 = 3x + 10$

4. $\frac{a}{4} - \frac{3}{4} = \frac{1}{4}$ **5.** $\frac{4}{7}x - 3 = 13$ **6.** $-\frac{x}{6} - 8 = 0$

7. $0.6x + 1.9x = 5$ **8.** $10(5 + m) = 63$ **9.** $2c + 4 + 3c = -26$

10. $\frac{1}{5}(x + 10) = 2$ **11.** $7(2y - 1) = 7$ **12.** $3a + 9 = 27$

Write an equation for each situation. Then solve.

13. Gloria bought a suit at a 25%-off sale. The sale price was $82.50. Find the original price.

Prentice Hall Mathematics *iTEXT* with Self-Grading Assessments

The *iText* provides the complete Student Edition online and on CD-ROM. The unique *Instant Check System*™ is made interactive in the *iText* to allow students ongoing opportunities for checking their learning. Also, the click of a button lets students go back to a lesson or Example for additional help. Students get instant feedback so they know whether they're on track and where to go to get help.

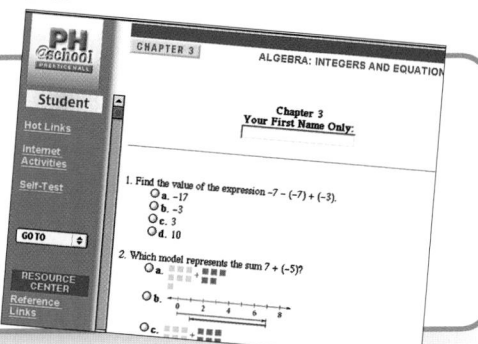

Reading and Writing throughout build communication skills

What Research Indicates: Reading mathematics requires the same skills as reading in other content areas—decoding and comprehending what is read, analyzing and evaluating the content based on one's prior knowledge, and making inferences and generating conclusions. Mathematics text demands that readers also use additional, content-specific reading skills, for example, reading graphs. Students need to learn to focus on significant details, explanations, and the underlying logic in texts where there are more concepts per word, per sentence, and per paragraph than in any other kind of text.

(Barton, Mary Lee & Heidema, Clare. *Teaching Reading in Mathematics:* A Supplement to Teaching Reading in the Content Areas Teacher's Manual, 2nd Ed. Aurora, Colorado: Mid-continent Research for Education and Learning.)

The development of a student's power to use mathematics also involves learning the signs, symbols, and terms of mathematics. This is best accomplished in problem-solving situations in which students have an opportunity to read, write, and discuss ideas so that the use of the language of mathematics becomes natural. As students communicate their ideas, they learn to clarify, refine, and consolidate their thinking.

(*Curriculum and Evaluation Standards for School Mathematics.* Reston, Virginia: The National Council of Teachers of Mathematics, Inc.)

Prentice Hall's Response: *Prentice Hall Mathematics* provides a consistent emphasis on mathematics literacy with a special focus on reading and writing in mathematics. This program integrates even more ways for you to develop your students' ability to read and write mathematically so that they are successful in this course and on state tests.

Reading Math

The *Reading Math* hints within lessons help students to read and understand the language of mathematics. The *Reading Math* lessons help students read more effectively, so that they can write, speak, and think mathematically. Reading for Problem Solving, Reading a Diagram, and Reading an Example are just a few of the strategies included.

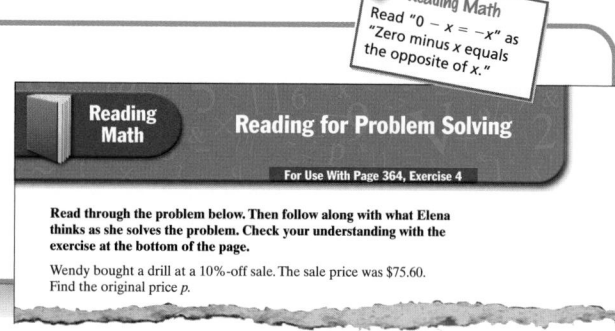

Writing in Math

Writing in Math lessons help students learn to explain, persuade, justify, or compare in a mathematical situation. Every lesson incorporates *Writing in Math* exercises to give students daily writing practice. Instruction in writing answers to rubric-scored questions helps students communicate successfully on today's tests.

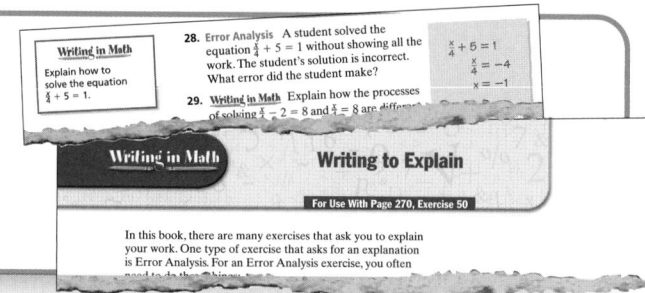

> *"Success in subsequent mathematics courses and on standardized tests depends greatly on a student's ability to communicate in mathematics. The emphasis on reading and writing in Prentice Hall Mathematics through the Reading Tips and Reading Math features and through the Writing in Math opportunities enables all students to develop their communication skills."*
>
> —Randy Charles, *Prentice Hall Mathematics* series author

Understanding Vocabulary

The text carefully develops the skill of reading math vocabulary. New vocabulary is conveniently listed at the beginning of each chapter and each lesson. Each new term is highlighted in yellow. The Chapter Review exercises help students to correctly use the chapter vocabulary. The **iTEXT** reinforces students' vocabulary skills with an online vocabulary quiz for every chapter and an audio version of all glossary terms.

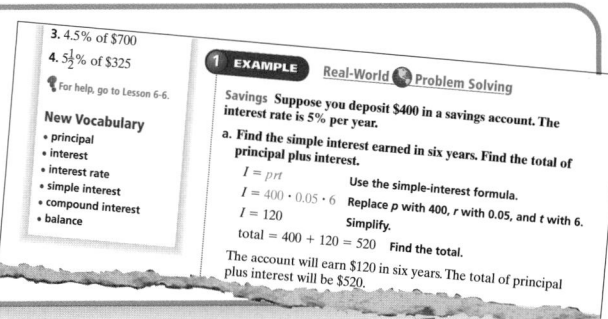

Reading and Math Literacy Masters

These unique blackline masters supplement the coverage of reading and math in the textbook. Students learn a variety of techniques to master mathematics vocabulary and symbols, read for problem solving, and increase comprehension.

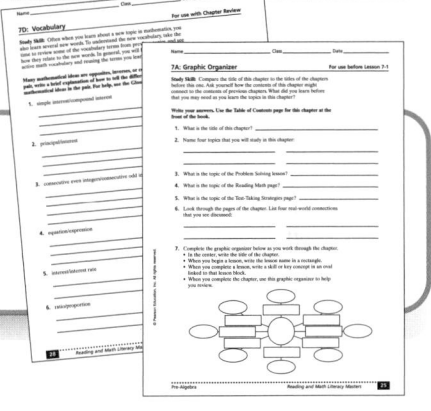

Guided Problem Solving Masters

Within the text, students learn to use a wealth of problem solving strategies. More importantly, they learn when to choose an appropriate strategy. The *Guided Problem Solving Masters* provide a step-by-step guide to help students read and understand, plan and solve, and look back and check a problem. With one master for each lesson, students can help develop their reading and problem-solving skills on a daily basis.

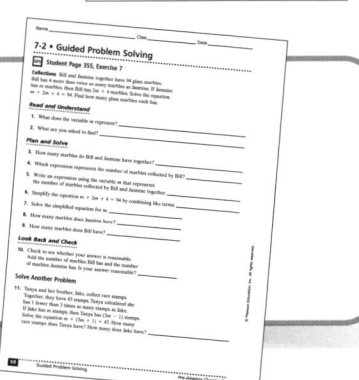

Reading for problem solving through Real-World Connections

Prentice Hall Mathematics incorporates abundant real-world connections within *Examples* and *Exercises* to provide a problem-solving context for applications of mathematics. Dorling Kindersley Real-World Snapshots bring math to life, with activities in which students gather data they need by reading graphic displays and captions.

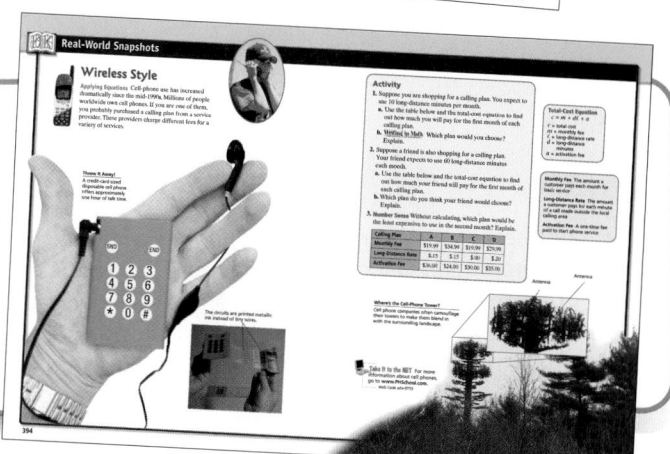

Ongoing assessment and test preparation guarantee testing success

What Research Indicates: We assess students most fairly when we assess often and with a variety of different answers. Research also shows that assessment needs to measure and describe a student's growth and achievement in all domains of mathematics and at three levels of thinking. Because of this, there should be questions at all levels of thinking, of varying degrees of difficulty, and in all content domains.

(Shafer, Mary C. & Foster, Sherian. "The Changing Faces of Assessment." *Principled Practice in Mathematics and Science Education,* Volume 1, No. 2.)

Prentice Hall's Response: *Prentice Hall Mathematics* provides an ongoing assessment strand that begins within the lesson instruction and continues throughout the program components. The program exposes students to questions of varying difficulty and at different levels of thinking in the daily *Check Understanding* questions and in the leveled *Exercises.*

A variety of question formats, including those found on today's standardized tests, is built into the Student Edition to assess student learning and prepare students for high-stakes tests. The ability to demonstrate knowledge in short-answer and open-ended formats increases opportunities for students to be successful on today's tests and in gaining admission to higher schooling and to the workplace.

✓ Check Understanding

Check Understanding questions after worked-out *Examples* allow students to assess their progress on a daily basis while they learn. The *Exercises* in every lesson include questions that emphasize the processes of explaining or reasoning—mirroring the types of questions that students will encounter on today's tests.

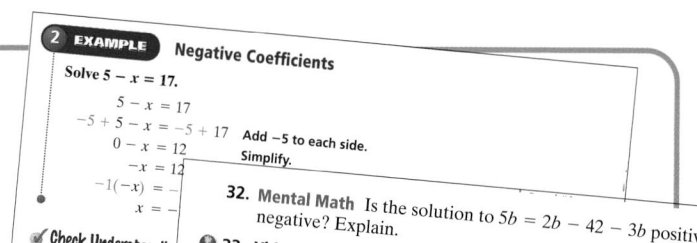

Quizzes and Tests—In Print and Online

You can assess student progress at key points with the *Lesson Quizzes, Checkpoint Quizzes,* and *Chapter Tests.* The Teaching Resources provides additional quizzes and tests, as well as alternative assessments. Online self-grading quizzes and tests are available on the Prentice Hall Web site at **www.PHSchool.com**.

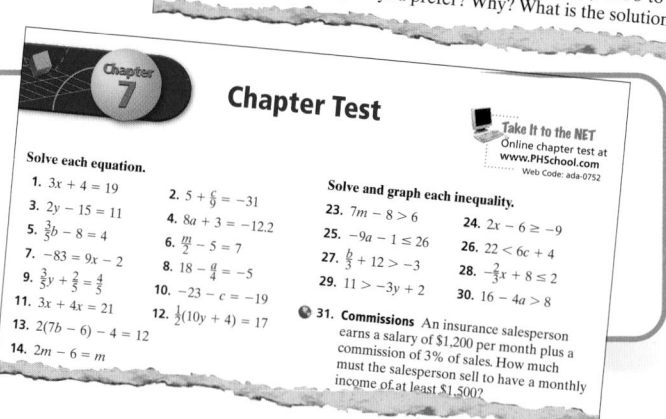

> "Assessment is an integral part of a mathematics program. *Prentice Hall Mathematics* provides a strong formative and summative assessment strand. The formative assessment features—before and during instruction—offer a variety of modalities that speak to different kinds of learners. The summative assessment features—after instruction—further prepare students for success on today's tests."
>
> —Sadie Chavis Bragg, *Prentice Hall Algebra* author

Standardized Test Prep Exercises

Test Prep exercises in every lesson give students daily practice with the types of test-item formats that they will encounter on state tests. You can also provide students with the *Test Prep* page at the end of each chapter.

The daily exercises and the test prep pages include these most common test-item formats:

- Multiple Choice
- Gridded Response
- Reading Comprehension
- Short Response
- Extended Response

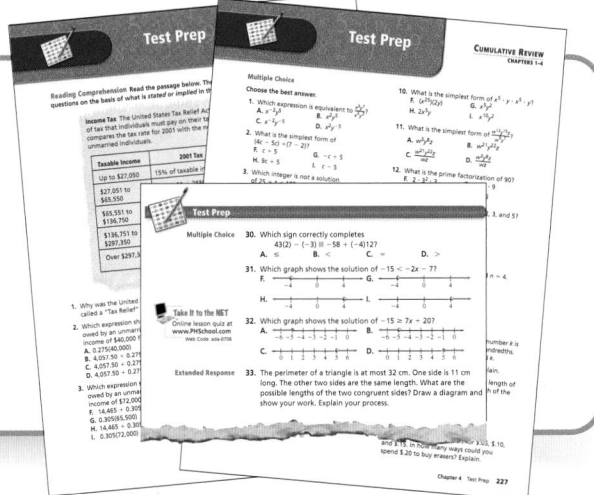

Test-Taking Strategies

Test-Taking Strategies in every chapter teach students strategies to be successful and give them practice in the skills they need to pass state tests and standardized national exams. Several lessons focus on helping students answer rubric-based questions.

The *Test-Taking Strategies With Transparencies* provide instruction on overheads and include additional practice sheets for the strategies taught in each chapter.

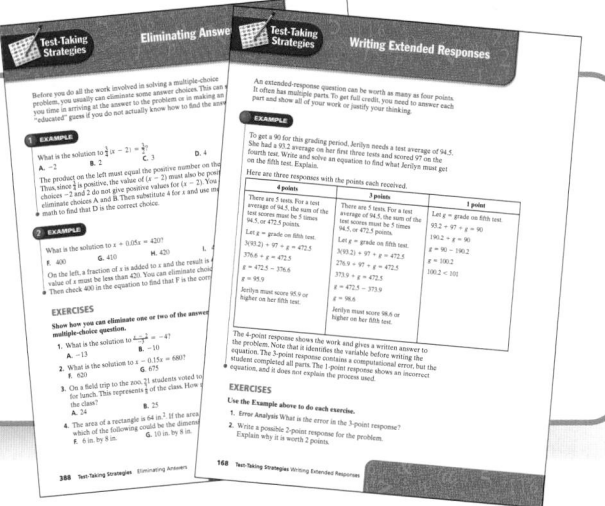

Prentice Hall Assessment System

An innovative *Assessment System* gives you everything you need to assess student progress on the content covered in the course, and to prepare students for high-stakes testing. The system contains the program Assessment Resources and the Computer Test Generator CD-ROM with unlimited questions and ready-to-use Instant Chapter Tests™.

You can diagnose and monitor student progress with *Diagnostic and Benchmark Tests*, prescribe intervention with the *Skills and Concepts Review*, and provide practice for standardized assessments with the *Test Prep* booklet. A *Teacher's Guide* gives correlations and answers. Also included is the *Test-Taking Strategies With Transparencies* described above.

Mathematical Strands

Overview and Background

Number and Operations

NCTM Standard for Grades 6–12

- Understand numbers, ways of representing numbers, relationships among numbers, and number systems
- Understand meanings of operations and how they relate to one another
- Compute fluently and make reasonable estimates

Key Content in Prentice Hall *Pre-Algebra*

- Represent, compare, compute, and solve problems with fractions and rational numbers (Chapters 4, 5)
- Represent, compare, compute, and solve problems with decimals (Chapters 3, 6)
- Represent, compare, compute, and solve problems with integers (Chapters 1, 2)
- Represent, compute, and solve problems with ratios, proportions, and percents (Chapters 6, 11)
- Represent large numbers in various forms; use exponents (Chapter 4)
- Use mental math and estimation to solve problems and to judge the reasonableness of computations (throughout *Pre-Algebra*)
- Use properties of numbers to simplify computations and understand relationships (throughout *Pre-Algebra*)

Background and Progression

Students usually enter Pre-Algebra with computational facility with whole numbers, fractions and decimals. They have varying degrees of mastery with percents, rates, ratios, proportions and estimation.

In *Pre-Algebra,* students reach mastery of integer operations, rates, ratios, proportions and percents, both computations and applications. They master computation with exponents (including scientific notation). Estimation skills are maintained.

In *Algebra 1,* students build an understanding of real numbers by using symbolic, graphic, and numeric representations as they solve equations and inequalities. Work with rational and radical expressions, equations, and functions builds a wide base of experience with rational and irrational numbers. Matrices are introduced.

Data Analysis and Probability

NCTM Standard for Grades 6–12

- Formulate questions that can be addressed with data and collect, organize, and display relevant data to answer them
- Select and use appropriate statistical methods to analyze data
- Develop and evaluate inferences and predictions that are based on data
- Understand and apply basic concepts of probability

Key Content in Prentice Hall *Pre-Algebra*

- Select, make, and use appropriate graphical representations of data (Chapters 8, 9, 12)
- Find, use, and interpret measures of center and spread (Chapter 3)
- Compute probabilities for simple, compound, and complementary events (Chapters 6, 12)
- Use observations about samples to make conjectures about the parent populations (Chapter 12)
- Use scatter plots and approximate lines of fit to make conjectures (Chapter 8)

Background and Progression

Students usually enter Pre-Algebra having experience with gathering, displaying, and analyzing data. They have mastered measures of center, simple line graphs, bar graphs, and probabilities. They have made circle graphs, stem-and-leaf plots, and box-and-whisker plots.

In *Pre-Algebra,* students work with double bar graphs and double line graphs. They analyze survey techniques for bias, group data into intervals, and make scatter plots to analyze relationships between two sets of data.

Students continue working with stem-and-leaf plots, histograms and circle graphs. They master box-and-whisker plots. Tree diagrams and organized lists are used to develop probability concepts for compound events

In *Algebra 1,* students work with scatter plots and functions to model the relationships between sets of data. They compute probabilities for simple and compound events. Compound events involve the occurrence of two outcomes.

 *For more **Math Background** on every lesson, see pages C-D before each chapter and see each lesson's teaching notes.*

Algebra

NCTM Standard for Grades 6–12

- Understand patterns, relations, and functions
- Represent and analyze mathematical situations and structures using algebraic symbols
- Use mathematical models to represent and understand quantitative relationships
- Analyze change in various contexts

Key Content in Prentice Hall *Pre-Algebra*

- Represent, analyze, and generalize a variety of patterns with tables, graphs, words, and symbolic rules (Chapters 1, 8, 13)
- Use graphs, tables, and patterns to analyze the changes in quantities in linear relationships (Chapter 8)
- Explore properties of nonlinear relationships (Chapter 13)
- Model and solve problems using diagrams, tables, and graphs (throughout *Pre-Algebra*)
- Use symbolic algebra to represent and solve problems (throughout *Pre-Algebra*)
- Recognize and generate equivalent forms for simple algebraic expressions (Chapters 2, 7, 13)
- Solve linear equations (Chapters 2, 3, 5, 7, 8)

Background and Progression

Students usually enter Pre-Algebra having represented patterns and relationships through words, tables, and graphs. They also have experience using variables to (1) represent specific unknown numbers (as in equations), and (2) generalize patterns in numeric relationships (as in input/output tables). Students have worked with models that support algebraic notation in the context of percents, proportions, integers, and properties of equality.

In **Pre-Algebra,** students continue to use models, tables, graphs, and symbolic notation to represent algebraic relationships. They solve multi-step equations, and use equivalent forms for expressions involving parentheses, like terms, and exponents. Students relate rate of change, slope, and *y*-intercept to graphs, tables, and symbolic forms. They explore nonlinear relationships through tables, graphs, and equations.

In **Algebra 1,** students use tables, graphs, verbal rules, and symbolic rules to describe linear, quadratic, and exponential functions. They choose a best model for data from among these functions. Rate of change is studied in the context of direct variation, linear equations, and arithmetic and geometric sequences. Students learn how to write equivalent forms of polynomial, radical, and rational expressions.

Geometry

NCTM Standard for Grades 6–12

- Analyze characteristics and properties of two- and three-dimensional geometric shapes and develop mathematical arguments about geometric relationships
- Specify locations and describe spatial relationships using coordinate geometry and other representational systems
- Apply transformations and use symmetry to analyze mathematical situations
- Use visualization, spatial reasoning, and geometric modeling to solve problems

Key Content in Prentice Hall *Pre-Algebra*

- Describe, classify, and use relationships among two- and three-dimensional objects (Chapters 6, 9, 10, 11)
- Draw inferences about angles, side lengths, perimeters, areas, and volumes of similar objects (Chapters 6, 10, 11)
- Use two-dimensional representations of three-dimensional objects to visualize and solve problems (Chapters 10, 11)
- Use number lines to represent various types of numbers and operations (Chapters 1, 2, 4, 5, 6, 11)
- Use coordinate geometry to represent geometric shapes (Chapters 9, 11)
- Describe sizes, positions, and orientations of shapes under various transformations (Chapter 9)
- Recognize and describe symmetries within objects and congruence and similarity among objects (Chapters 6, 9)
- Use geometric models to represent and explain numerical and algebraic relationships (throughout *Pre-Algebra*)

Background and Progression

Students enter Pre-Algebra having named and classified angles and polygons. They have used grids, nets, and block diagrams to build concepts of area and volume. Transformations and symmetry have been introduced. Students have experience with number lines and other geometric models used to represent fractions, decimals, and integers. The coordinate plane is introduced.

In **Pre-Algebra,** students continue using two-dimensional representations to explore three-dimensional relationships. They draw inferences about lengths, areas, and volumes of similar figures. Congruent and similar figures are studied and transformations occur on a coordinate plane. Students use number lines to model numbers and operations.

In **Algebra 1,** students begin to use geometric models with proportions, percent, and probability. They also explore ways to describe translations of familiar functions.

 *For more **Math Background** on every lesson, see pages C-D before each chapter and see each lesson's teaching notes.*

Measurement

NCTM Standard for Grades 6–12

- Understand measurable attributes of objects and the units, systems, and processes of measurement
- Apply appropriate techniques, tools, and formulas to determine measurements

Key Content in Prentice Hall *Pre-Algebra*

- Understand and use metric and customary systems of measurement (Chapters 3, 5, 6)
- Convert among units within a system of measurement (Chapters 3, 5)
- Select and use units of the appropriate sizes and types to measure angles, perimeters, areas, surface areas, and volumes (Chapters 9, 10, 11)
- Estimate measures (Chapters 9, 10)
- Develop strategies and use formulas to find the perimeters (circumferences) and areas of triangles, various quadrilaterals, circles, and compound plane figures (Chapters 3, 9, 10)
- Develop strategies and use formulas to find the surface areas and volumes of various prisms, pyramids, cylinders, cones, and spheres (Chapter 10)
- Solve problems involving scale factors and rates (Chapters 3, 6)

Background and Progression

Students entering Pre-Algebra can usually choose appropriate units, convert units, and estimate measures within the customary system and the metric system. They have developed and worked with formulas for measurement of triangles, rectangles, squares, parallelograms, and circles. Students have explored surface area and volume of three-dimensional figures.

In **Pre-Algebra,** students use dimensional analysis to convert units within the customary system and metric system. They apply formulas for rectangles, triangles, and trapezoids to find areas of irregular figures. Students develop the formula for area of a circle and use formulas to find surface areas and volumes of prisms, cylinders, pyramids, cones, and spheres. They apply scale factors in similar figures to find changes in lengths, areas, and volumes.

In **Algebra 1,** students make decisions about appropriate scales with graphical representations of data. They use formulas for the perimeters and areas of figures to find missing measures, and use appropriate conversion factors to help set up proportions and other equations.

Problem Solving

NCTM Standard for Grades 6–12

- Build new mathematical knowledge through problem solving
- Solve problems that arise in mathematics and in other contexts
- Apply and adapt a variety of appropriate strategies to solve problems
- Monitor and reflect on the process of mathematical problem solving

Key Processes in Prentice Hall *Pre-Algebra*

- Solve problems taken from the student's current and future world (Examples throughout *Pre-Algebra*)
- Use a problem-solving plan (Read and Understand, Plan and Solve, Look Back and Check) that supports analysis, choice of strategies, evaluation, and reasonableness checks (Problem Solving lessons in every chapter)
- Choose from and use a variety of appropriate methods to solve problems (More Than One Way features, and Problem Solving lessons that compare strategies throughout *Pre-Algebra*)
- Construct an expression or equation to solve a problem (Examples using the "Words to Equation" or "Words to Expression" models throughout *Pre-Algebra*)
- Build understanding of new topics through problem solving (Investigations, Understanding Word Problems, and Real-World Snapshots throughout *Pre-Algebra*)
- Reflect on the process of problem solving (Look Back and Check, Writing in Math, and Error Analysis exercises throughout *Pre-Algebra*)

Background and Progression

Throughout Prentice Hall Mathematics, students use a consistent framework for problem solving. The framework identifies three phases in the problem-solving process: Read and Understand, Plan and Solve, Look Back and Check.

In **Pre-Algebra,** students learn 13 specific strategies and apply them to a variety of problems. They use checks for both reasonableness and accuracy. Students also learn to use more than one strategy to solve a problem, and compare strategies to determine which one is most appropriate in a given situation. Throughout the text, the use of the strategy Write an Equation helps prepare students for algebra.

In **Algebra 1,** students are supported in the critical skill of expressing the mathematical relationships from real-world problems with appropriate symbolic models. Each chapter contains numerous real-world examples, many of which use the "relate, define, write" format to guide the student in choosing and writing a correct model.

 *For more **Math Background** on every lesson, see pages C-D before each chapter and see each lesson's teaching notes.*

Reasoning and Proof

NCTM Standard for Grades 6–12

- Recognize reasoning and proof as fundamental aspects of mathematics
- Make and investigate mathematical conjectures
- Develop and evaluate mathematical arguments and proofs
- Select and use various types of reasoning and methods of proof

Key Processes in Prentice Hall *Pre-Algebra*

- Use inductive reasoning to make and investigate conjectures (Investigations throughout *Pre-Algebra*)
- Apply appropriate reasoning to analyze mathematical statements (Reasoning exercises throughout *Pre-Algebra*)
- Explain work, and justify conclusions (Writing in Math, Error Analysis, Short Response, and Extended Response exercises throughout *Pre-Algebra*)
- Construct logical arguments to support conclusions (Writing in Math lessons and exercises throughout *Pre-Algebra*)

Background and Progression

Prior to a Pre-Algebra course, students use mathematical reasoning in the development of number sense with operations, classification skills in geometry, and the use of variables in algebraic notation. Problem solving strategies such as work backward or solve a simpler problem also require reasoning skills.

In **Pre-Algebra,** reasoning is an integral part of students' daily work. Every lesson contains a mix of Reasoning, Number Sense, and Error Analysis exercises. These exercises are found both in the Check Understanding questions that follow each worked-out Example and in the B-level practice exercises.

Investigations throughout *Pre-Algebra* provide students with opportunities to use inductive reasoning. Investigations cover topics in number sense, operations, algebraic patterns, geometric properties, data analysis, and probability.

Throughout the text, students are encouraged to state properties both as specific instances as well as generalizations using variables. Students also have the opportunity to justify steps in various procedures by citing the supporting properties.

Most lessons contain Writing in Math exercises, Short Response questions, or Extended Response questions. These require students to justify their conclusions, and explain their steps.

Communication

NCTM Standard for Grades 6–12

- Organize and consolidate their mathematical thinking through communication
- Communicate their mathematical thinking coherently and clearly to peers, teachers, and others
- Analyze and evaluate the mathematical thinking and strategies of others
- Use the language of mathematics to express mathematical ideas precisely

Key Processes in Prentice Hall *Pre-Algebra*

- Write about mathematical concepts by summarizing, comparing, analyzing, and explaining (Writing in Math exercises and lessons; Reasoning, Short Response, and Extended Response exercises throughout *Pre-Algebra*)
- Understand the language and notations of mathematics (Reading Math hints and lessons, Vocabulary and Reading Comprehension exercises throughout *Pre-Algebra*)
- Use appropriate notation to express mathematical relationships in real-world contexts (Examples using "Words to Equation" model throughout *Pre-Algebra*)
- Analyze sample work to find errors (Error Analysis exercises throughout *Pre-Algebra*)

Background and Progression

To effectively communicate within the language of mathematics, students need ample opportunity to express math in words, in symbols, through models, and orally.

Pre-Algebra integrates a Reading Math strand that includes short help tips related to math vocabulary and symbols as well as full-page lessons that focus on vocabulary and how to read critical elements of a math textbook.

Students also have multiple opportunities to write about the mathematics they do. Writing in Math exercises ask students to justify their work, explain a process, compare concepts, or draw a conclusion about the mathematics contained in the lesson. Full-page Writing In Math lessons focus on writing to explain, compare, justify, or persuade.

Many examples use Prentice Hall's "Words to Equation" model to help students translate real-world situations into precise mathematical language.

Test Prep exercises in every lesson and at the end of each chapter include Short Response, Extended Response, and Reading Comprehension. These exercises require students to explain their work, justify their conclusions, and interpret mathematics found in everyday situations. Students also learn how to write rubric-based responses.

 *For more **Math Background** on every lesson, see pages C-D before each chapter and see each lesson's teaching notes.*

Mathematical Strands

Connections

NCTM Standard for Grades 6–12

- Recognize and use connections among mathematical ideas
- Understand how mathematical ideas interconnect and build on one another to produce a coherent whole
- Recognize and apply mathematics in contexts outside of mathematics

Key Processes in Prentice Hall *Pre-Algebra*

- Solve problems in more than one way (Problem-Solving Strategy lessons, More Than One Way features throughout *Pre-Algebra*)
- Solve problems arising from real-world contexts (Real-World examples and exercises, Real-World Snapshots, and Reading Comprehension exercises throughout *Pre-Algebra*)
- Use various models to represent numeric, geometric, and algebraic concepts (throughout Pre-Algebra)
- Use symbolic algebra to represent generalizations and problems about numbers (throughout *Pre-Algebra*)
- Use algebraic formulas to represent properties of geometric figures (Chapters 9, 10, 11)
- Use concepts of ratio and proportionality to solve problems in geometry, probability, and algebra (Chapters 6, 8, 9, 10, 11, 13)

Background and Progression

Most students enter a Pre-Algebra course able to master alternative methods for various procedures and to distinguish which one of several approaches might be best.

In **Pre-Algebra,** students use alternative methods in More Than One Way features (every chapter) and in Problem Solving lessons. These situations give a rich mix of numeric, algebraic, geometric, and experimental approaches to problems.

Every lesson contains real-world applications that provide contexts for mathematics. In addition, Real-World Snapshots in each chapter provide more complex contexts that require students to apply what they have learned.

Consistent modeling for decimals, fractions, percents, and proportions helps students make connections among numbers and operations. Mathematical properties are summarized with dual examples to relate arithmetic and algebraic representations.

Two-dimensional nets provide a critical link between an object and its surface area. Students also make connections from the coordinate plane to both algebraic equations and geometric transformations.

Representation

NCTM Standard for Grades 6–12

- Create and use representations to organize, record, and communicate mathematical ideas
- Select, apply, and translate among mathematical representations to solve problems
- Use representations to model and interpret physical, social, and mathematical phenomena

Key Processes in Prentice Hall *Pre-Algebra*

- Organize mathematical information in order to make and support conjectures (Investigations throughout *Pre-Algebra*)
- Make and use tables, graphs or other visual models, verbal rules, and symbolic rules to represent operations and relationships (throughout *Pre-Algebra*)
- Choose an appropriate graphical display for data; use one and two variables to express relationships within data (Chapters 2, 8, 12)
- Solve real-world problems by creating a mathematical model to represent the essential mathematics involved (Examples using the "Words to Equations" or "Words to Inequalities" models, Reading Comprehension exercises, and Real-World Snapshots throughout *Pre-Algebra*)

Background and Progression

Students entering a Pre-Algebra course have experience with many forms of representation. They use concrete and visual models to help develop number concepts and solve problems.

In **Pre-Algebra,** visualization continues as a strong strand with consistent modeling of numbers, operations, and relationships. Visual models are presented for fractions, percents, addition, subtraction, multiplication, division, equations, probabilities, and algebraic expressions.

Function relationships are represented through tables, patterns, graphs, words, and variables.

The presentation of data also includes a wide range of choices. Students learn to identify the most appropriate vehicle for presenting data involving one or two variables and for comparing data. This means choosing from among bar graphs, histograms, line graphs, circle graphs, box-and-whisker plots, stem-and-leaf plots, and scatter plots.

Finally, students are given many opportunities to choose their own representation for real-life contextual mathematics in the Real-World Snapshots and numerous Real-World Problem-Solving examples.

 *For more **Math Background** on every lesson, see pages C-D before each chapter and see each lesson's teaching notes.*

Pacing Options for Pre-Algebra

Pacing Guide

This chart is provided merely as a guide to help you customize your course. To accommodate flexible scheduling, most lessons are subdivided into objectives. Within the lessons of the Student Edition, these objectives are indicated in red by the symbol ▼. The Assignment Guide for each lesson indicates which exercises in the Student Edition correspond to each objective of the lesson.

Detailed Chapter Pacing Options precede each chapter and give you lesson-by-lesson pacing suggestions for that specific chapter.

CHAPTER	Traditional (45-minute class periods)	Two-Year (45-minute class periods)	Block (90-minute class periods)	Two-Year Block (90-minute class periods)
1	15 days	27 days	7 days	15 days
2	15 days	26 days	6 days	15 days
3	11 days	25 days	6 days	11 days
4	13 days	26 days	6 days	13 days
5	14 days	26 days	7 days	14 days
6	14 days	26 days	7 days	14 days
7	13 days	26 days	6 days	13 days
8	13 days	26 days	6 days	13 days
9	14 days	26 days	7 days	14 days
10	13 days	26 days	6 days	13 days
11	10 days	24 days	5 days	10 days
12	14 days	26 days	6 days	14 days
13	11 days	25 days	5 days	11 days
Total	170 days	335 days	80 days	170 days

Differentiated Scope of Course

B = Basic Course   C = Core Course   A = Advanced Course

Chapter 1 Algebraic Expressions and Integers	B	C	A
1-1: Variables and Expressions	✓	✓	✓
1-2: The Order of Operations	✓	✓	✓
1-3: Evaluating Expressions	✓	✓	✓
1-4: Integers and Absolute Value	✓	✓	✓
• Investigation: Modeling Integers	✓	✓	
1-5: Adding Integers	✓	✓	✓
1-6: Subtracting Integers	✓	✓	✓
1-7: Inductive Reasoning	✓	✓	✓
1-8: Look for a Pattern	✓	✓	✓
1-9: Multiplying and Dividing Integers	✓	✓	✓
1-10: The Coordinate Plane	✓	✓	✓
• Technology: Graphing Ordered Pairs	✓	✓	✓

Chapter 2 Solving One-Step Equations and Inequalities	B	C	A
2-1: Properties of Numbers	✓	✓	✓
2-2: The Distributive Property	✓	✓	✓
2-3: Simplifying Variable Expressions	✓	✓	✓
2-4: Variables and Equations	✓	✓	✓
• Investigation: Using Models With Equations	✓	✓	
2-5: Solving Equations by Adding or Subtracting	✓	✓	✓
2-6: Solving Equations by Multiplying or Dividing	✓	✓	✓
2-7: Try, Test, Revise	✓	✓	✓
• Technology: Data and Graphs	✓	✓	✓
2-8: Inequalities and Their Graphs	✓	✓	✓
2-9: Solving One-Step Inequalities by Adding or Subtracting	✓	✓	✓
2-10: Solving One-Step Inequalities by Multiplying or Dividing	✓	✓	✓

Chapter 3 Decimals and Equations	B	C	A
• Investigation: Exploring Decimals	✓	✓	
3-1: Rounding and Estimating	✓	✓	✓
3-2: Estimating Decimal Products and Quotients	✓	✓	✓
3-3: Mean, Median, and Mode	✓	✓	✓
• Technology: Mean and Median on a Graphing Calculator	✓	✓	✓
3-4: Using Formulas	✓	✓	✓
• Technology: Formulas in a Spreadsheet		✓	✓
3-5: Solving Equations by Adding or Subtracting Decimals	✓	✓	✓
3-6: Solving Equations by Multiplying or Dividing Decimals	✓	✓	✓
3-7: Using the Metric System	✓	✓	✓
• Extension: Precision and Significant Digits			✓

	B	C	A
3-8: Simplify the Problem	✓	✓	✓

Chapter 4 Factors, Fractions, and Exponents	B	C	A
4-1: Divisibility and Factors	✓	✓	✓
4-2: Exponents	✓	✓	✓
4-3: Prime Factorization and Greatest Common Factor	✓	✓	✓
• Extension: Venn Diagrams	✓	✓	✓
4-4: Simplifying Fractions	✓	✓	✓
4-5: Account for All Possibilities	✓	✓	✓
4-6: Rational Numbers	✓	✓	✓
4-7: Exponents and Multiplication	✓	✓	✓
• Technology: Evaluating Expressions With Graphing Calculators	✓	✓	✓
4-8: Exponents and Division	✓	✓	✓
4-9: Scientific Notation	✓	✓	✓
• Technology: Scientific Notation With Calculators	✓	✓	✓

Chapter 5 Operations With Fractions	B	C	A
5-1: Comparing and Ordering Fractions	✓	✓	✓
5-2: Fractions and Decimals	✓	✓	✓
• Review: Estimating With Fractions and Mixed Numbers	✓	✓	
5-3: Adding and Subtracting Fractions	✓	✓	✓
5-4: Multiplying and Dividing Fractions	✓	✓	✓
5-5: Using Customary Units of Measurement	✓	✓	✓
• Extension: Greatest Possible Error			✓
5-6: Work Backward	✓	✓	✓
5-7: Solving Equations by Adding or Subtracting Fractions	✓	✓	✓
5-8: Solving Equations by Multiplying Fractions	✓	✓	✓
5-9: Powers of Products and Quotients	✓	✓	✓

Chapter 6 Ratios, Proportions, and Percents	B	C	A
6-1: Ratios and Unit Rates	✓	✓	✓
• Extension: Converting Between Measurement Systems	✓	✓	✓
6-2: Proportions	✓	✓	✓
6-3: Similar Figures and Scale Drawings	✓	✓	✓
• Technology: Dilations		✓	✓
6-4: Probability	✓	✓	✓
6-5: Fractions, Decimals, and Percents	✓	✓	✓
6-6: Proportions and Percents	✓	✓	✓
6-7: Percents and Equations	✓	✓	✓
6-8: Percent of Change	✓	✓	✓
6-9: Markup and Discount	✓	✓	✓
• Technology: Making a Table	✓	✓	✓
6-10: Make a Table	✓	✓	✓

Chapter 7 Solving Equations and Inequalities

	B	C	A
7-1: Solving Two-Step Equations	✓	✓	✓
7-2: Solving Multi-Step Equations	✓	✓	✓
7-3: Multi-Step Equations With Fractions and Decimals	✓	✓	✓
7-4: Write an Equation	✓	✓	✓
7-5: Solving Equations With Variables on Both Sides	✓	✓	✓
• Technology: Using Tables to Solve Equations		✓	✓
7-6: Solving Two-Step Inequalities	✓	✓	✓
• Extension: Compound Inequalities	✓	✓	✓
7-7: Transforming Formulas	✓	✓	✓
7-8: Simple and Compound Interest			✓
• Technology: Credit Card Interest			✓

Chapter 8 Linear Functions and Graphing

	B	C	A
• Investigation: Relating Graphs to Events	✓	✓	✓
8-1: Relations and Functions	✓	✓	✓
8-2: Equations With Two Variables	✓	✓	✓
• Extension: Direct Variation	✓	✓	✓
8-3: Slope and y-intercept	✓	✓	✓
• Technology: Graphing Lines	✓	✓	✓
8-4: Writing Rules for Linear Functions	✓	✓	✓
8-5: Scatter Plots	✓	✓	✓
8-6: Solve by Graphing	✓	✓	✓
8-7: Solving Systems of Linear Equations	✓	✓	✓
8-8: Graphing Linear Inequalities	✓	✓	✓
• Technology: Graphing Inequalities		✓	✓

Chapter 9 Spatial Thinking

	B	C	A
9-1: Introduction to Geometry: Points, Lines, and Planes	✓	✓	✓
• Review: Drawing and Measuring Angles	✓	✓	
9-2: Angle Relationships and Parallel Lines	✓	✓	✓
9-3: Classifying Polygons	✓	✓	✓
• Extension: Angles of a Polygon	✓	✓	✓
9-4: Draw a Diagram	✓	✓	✓
9-5: Congruence	✓	✓	✓
9-6: Circles	✓	✓	✓
9-7: Constructions	✓	✓	✓
• Technology: Exploring Constructions			✓
9-8: Translations		✓	✓
• Extension: Matrices and Translations			✓
9-9: Symmetry and Reflections		✓	✓
9-10: Rotations		✓	✓
• Extension: Tessellations		✓	✓

Chapter 10 Area and Volume

	B	C	A
10-1: Area: Parallelograms	✓	✓	✓
10-2: Area: Triangles and Trapezoids	✓	✓	✓
10-3: Area: Circles	✓	✓	✓
• Extension: Three Views of an Object	✓	✓	✓

	B	C	A
10-4: Space Figures	✓	✓	✓
• Extension: Cross Sections of Space Figures	✓	✓	✓
10-5: Surface Area: Prisms and Cylinders	✓	✓	✓
10-6: Surface Area: Pyramids, Cones, and Spheres	✓	✓	✓
10-7: Volume: Prisms and Cylinders	✓	✓	✓
• Technology: Rounding Error	✓	✓	✓
10-8: Make a Model	✓	✓	✓
10-9: Volume: Pyramids, Cones, and Spheres	✓	✓	✓

Chapter 11 Right Triangles in Algebra

	B	C	A
11-1: Square Roots and Irrational Numbers	✓	✓	✓
11-2: The Pythagorean Theorem	✓	✓	✓
• Extension: The Pythagorean Theorem and Circles	✓	✓	✓
11-3: Distance and Midpoint Formulas	✓	✓	✓
11-4: Write a Proportion	✓	✓	✓
11-5: Special Right Triangles	✓	✓	✓
• Extension: Squares Roots of Expressions With Variables			✓
11-6: Sine, Cosine, and Tangent Ratios			✓
• Extension: Finding the Angles of a Right Triangle			
11-7: Angles of Elevation and Depression			✓

Chapter 12 Data Analysis and Probability

	B	C	A
12-1: Frequency Tables and Line Plots	✓	✓	✓
• Technology: Making Histograms		✓	✓
12-2: Box-and-Whisker Plots	✓	✓	✓
• Extension: Stem-and-Leaf Plots	✓	✓	✓
12-3: Using Graphs to Persuade	✓	✓	✓
12-4: Counting Outcomes and Theoretical Probability	✓	✓	✓
12-5: Independent and Dependent Events	✓	✓	✓
12-6: Permutations and Combinations	✓	✓	✓
• Extension: Pascal's Triangle			✓
12-7: Experimental Probability	✓	✓	✓
12-8: Random Samples and Surveys	✓	✓	✓
• Technology: Using Random Numbers	✓	✓	✓
12-9: Simulate the Problem	✓	✓	✓

Chapter 13 Nonlinear Functions and Polynomials

	B	C	A
13-1: Patterns and Sequences	✓	✓	✓
• Technology: Displaying Sequences		✓	✓
13-2: Graphing Nonlinear Functions	✓	✓	✓
13-3: Exponential Growth and Decay	✓	✓	✓
• Technology: Nonlinear Functions and Graphing Calculators			✓
13-4: Polynomials		✓	✓
• Extension: Degree of a Polynomial		✓	✓
13-5: Adding and Subtracting Polynomials		✓	✓
13-6: Multiplying a Polynomial by a Monomial		✓	✓
13-7: Multiplying Binomials		✓	✓
• Extension: Binomial Factors of a Trinomial			✓
13-8: Use Multiple Strategies	✓	✓	✓

Using Your Book for Success

Welcome to Prentice Hall *Pre-Algebra.* There are many features built into the daily lessons of this text that will help you learn the important skills and concepts you will need to be successful in this course. Look through the following pages for some study tips that you will find useful as you complete each lesson.

Instant Check System™
An *Instant Check System™*, built into the text and marked with a ✔, allows you to check your understanding of skills before moving on to the next topic.

✔ Diagnosing Readiness
Complete the *Diagnosing Readiness* exercises to see what topics you may need to review before you begin the chapter.

✔ Check Skills You'll Need
Complete the *Check Skills You'll Need* exercises to make sure you have the skills needed to successfully learn the concepts in the lesson.

✔ Check Understanding
Every lesson includes numerous *Examples*, each followed by a *Check Understanding* question that you can do on your own to see if you understand the skill being introduced. Check your progress with the answers at the back of the book.

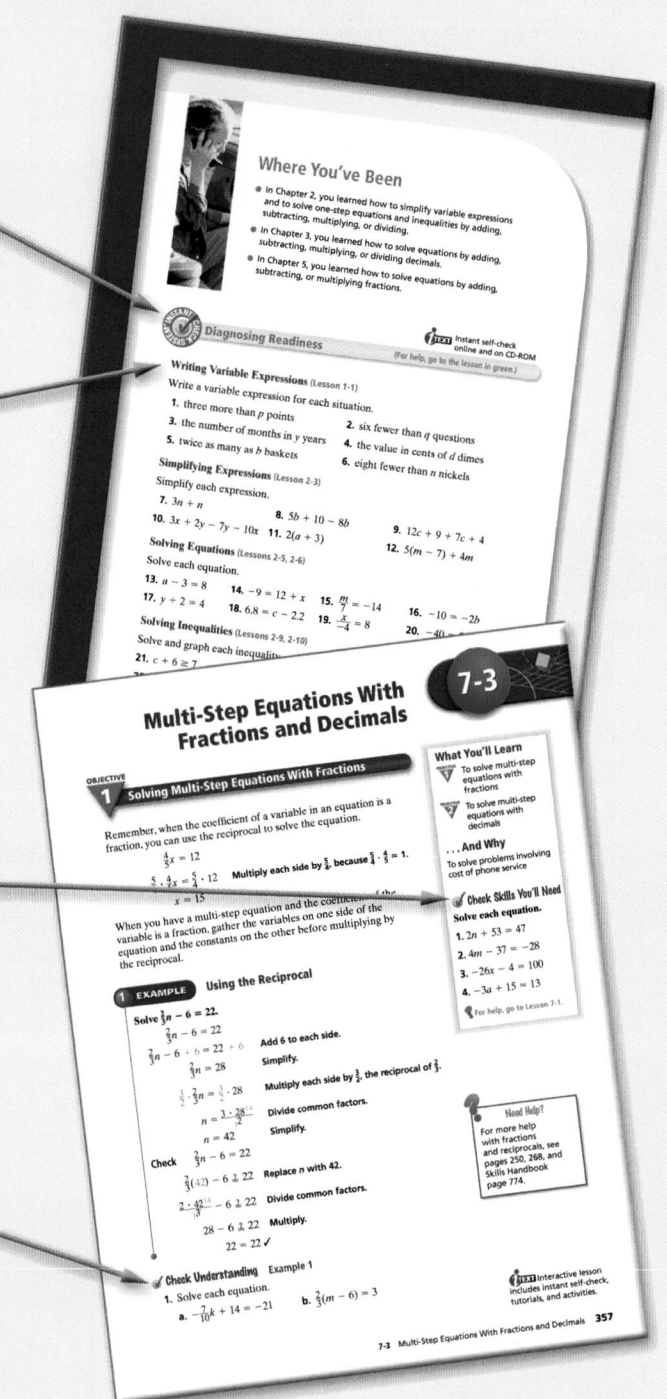

Need Help?

Need Help? notes provide a quick review of a concept you need to understand the topic being presented. Look for the green labels throughout your book to tell you where to "Go" for help.

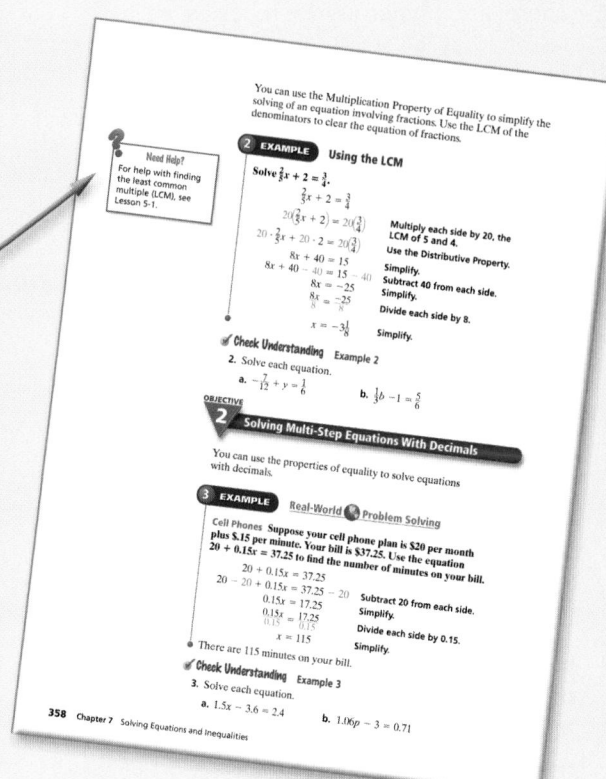

More Than One Way

The *More Than One Way* feature shows you two different methods to solve a problem. By analyzing each student's method, you can think critically about the solution and then choose a method you would use to solve a similar problem.

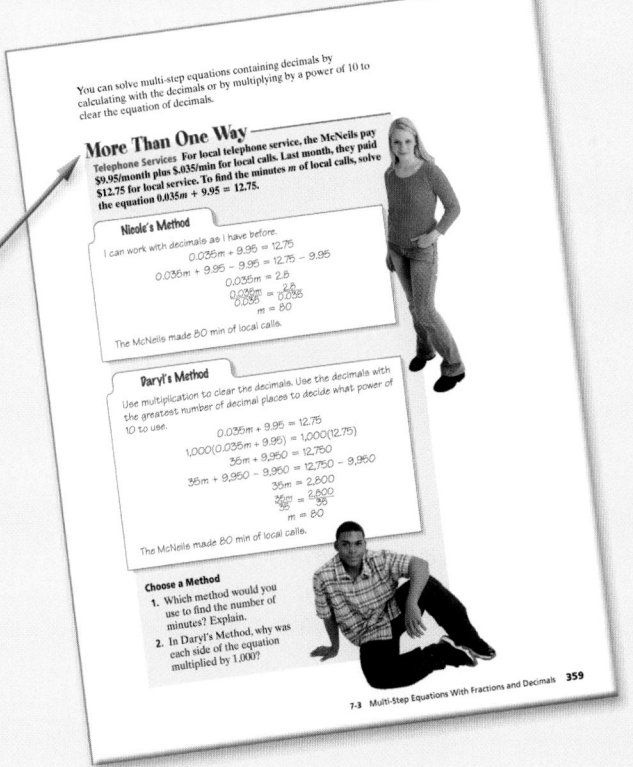

Exercise Sets

Exercises

There are numerous *Exercises* in each lesson that give you the practice you need to master the concepts in the lesson. Each practice set includes the following sections.

A: Practice by Example

The *A: Practice by Example* exercises refer you back to the Examples in the lesson, in case you need help with completing these exercises.

B: Apply Your Skills

The *B: Apply Your Skills* exercises combine skills from earlier lessons to offer you richer skill exercises and multi-step application problems.

C: Challenge

The *C: Challenge* exercises give you an opportunity to solve problems that extend and stretch your thinking.

Test Prep

Test Prep exercises give you daily practice with all the types of test question formats that you will encounter on state and national tests.

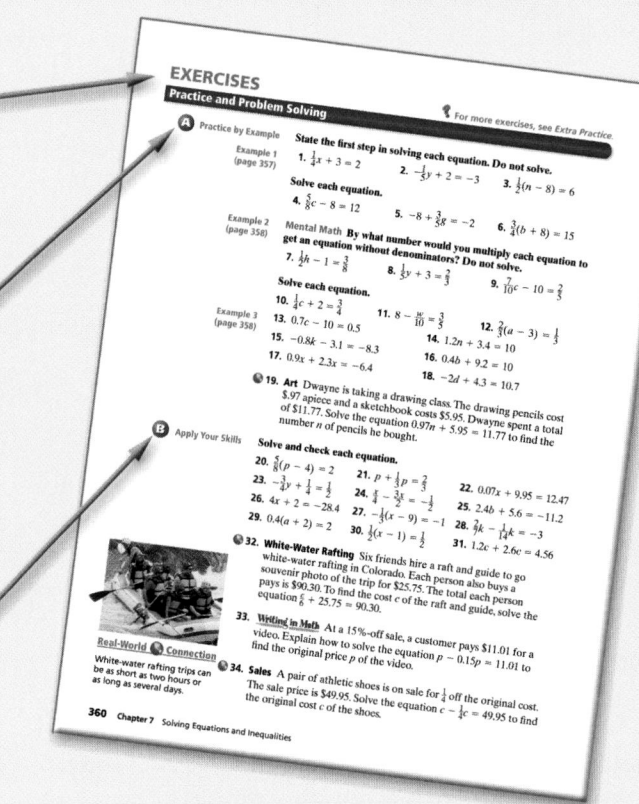

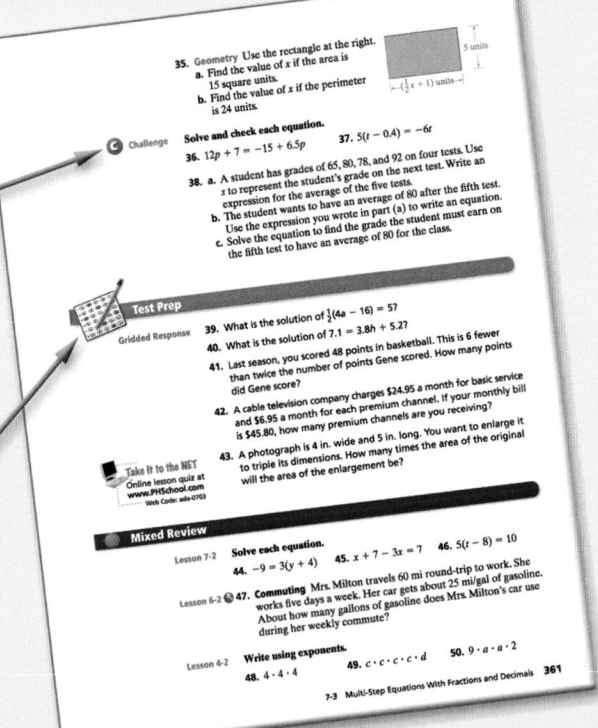

Preparing for Tests

Test-Taking Strategies

Test-Taking Strategies in every chapter teach you strategies to be successful and give you practice in the skills you need to pass state tests and standardized national exams.

Test Prep

In addition to the exercises in every lesson, the *Test Prep* pages in every chapter give you more opportunities to prepare for the tests you will have to take.

Test Item Formats

The *Test Prep* exercises in your book give you the practice you need to answer all types of test questions.
- *Multiple Choice*
- *Gridded Response*
- *Short Response* (scored with a rubric)
- *Extended Response* (scored with a rubric)
- *Reading Comprehension*

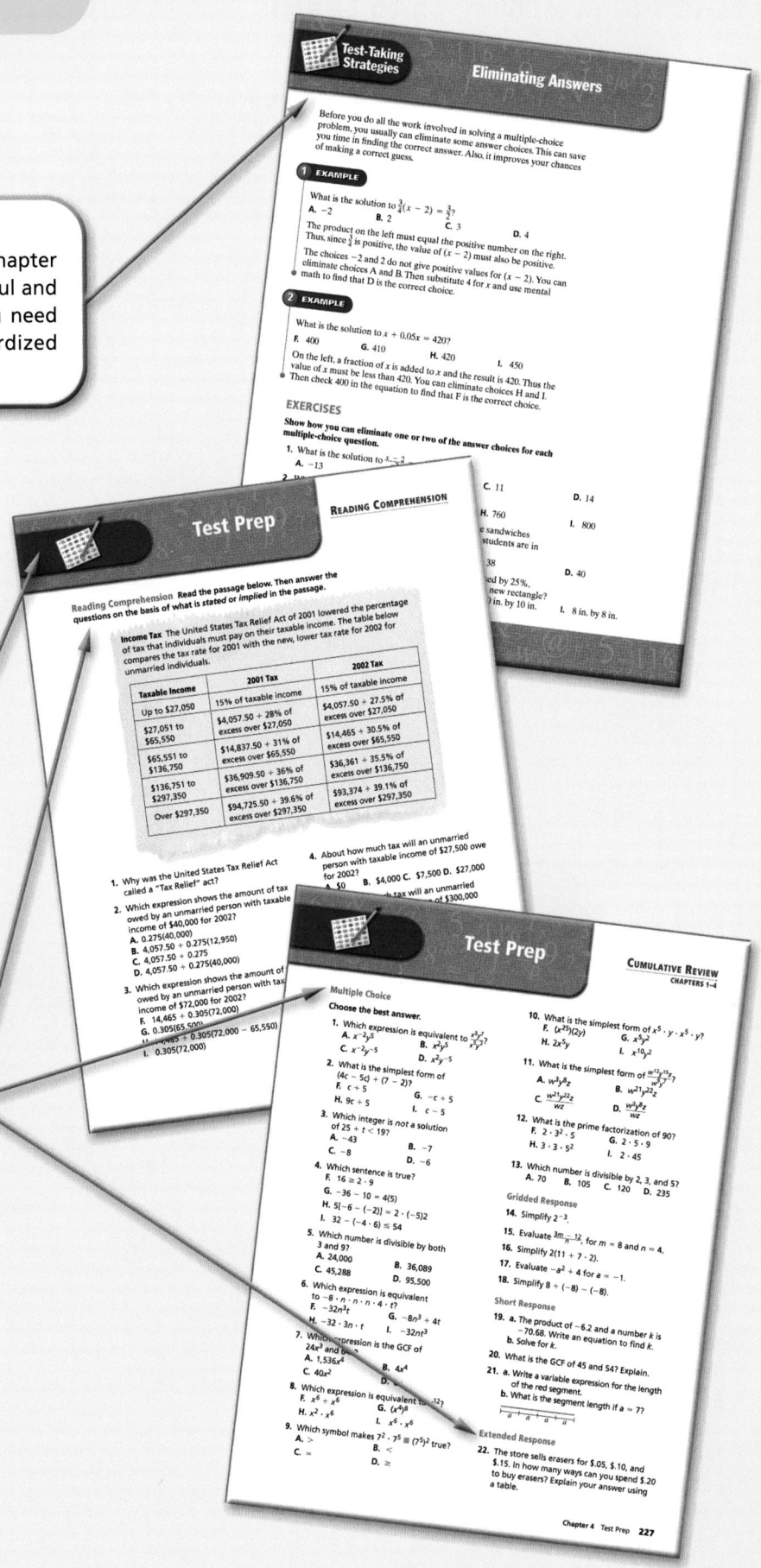

Reading and Writing to Learn

Your *Pre-Algebra* text provides even more ways for you to develop your ability to read and write mathematically so that you are successful in this course and on state tests.

New Vocabulary
New Vocabulary is listed for each lesson so you can pre-read the text. As each term is introduced, it is highlighted in yellow.

Reading Math hints
These *hints* help you to use mathematical notation correctly, understand vocabulary, and translate symbols into everyday English so you can talk about what you've learned.

Reading Math lessons
Reading Math lessons focus on a variety of topics to help you read more effectively, so that you can write, speak, and think mathematically.

Writing in Math lessons
Writing in Math lessons help you to write more effectively about the mathematics you are learning.

For more help:

- **Reading Math exercises**
  Reading Math exercises in the Chapter Review help you to understand and correctly use the vocabulary presented in the chapter.

- **English/Spanish Illustrated Glossary**
  While you are learning, use this handy reference that contains a written explanation and an illustrated example to help you understand and remember. each term.

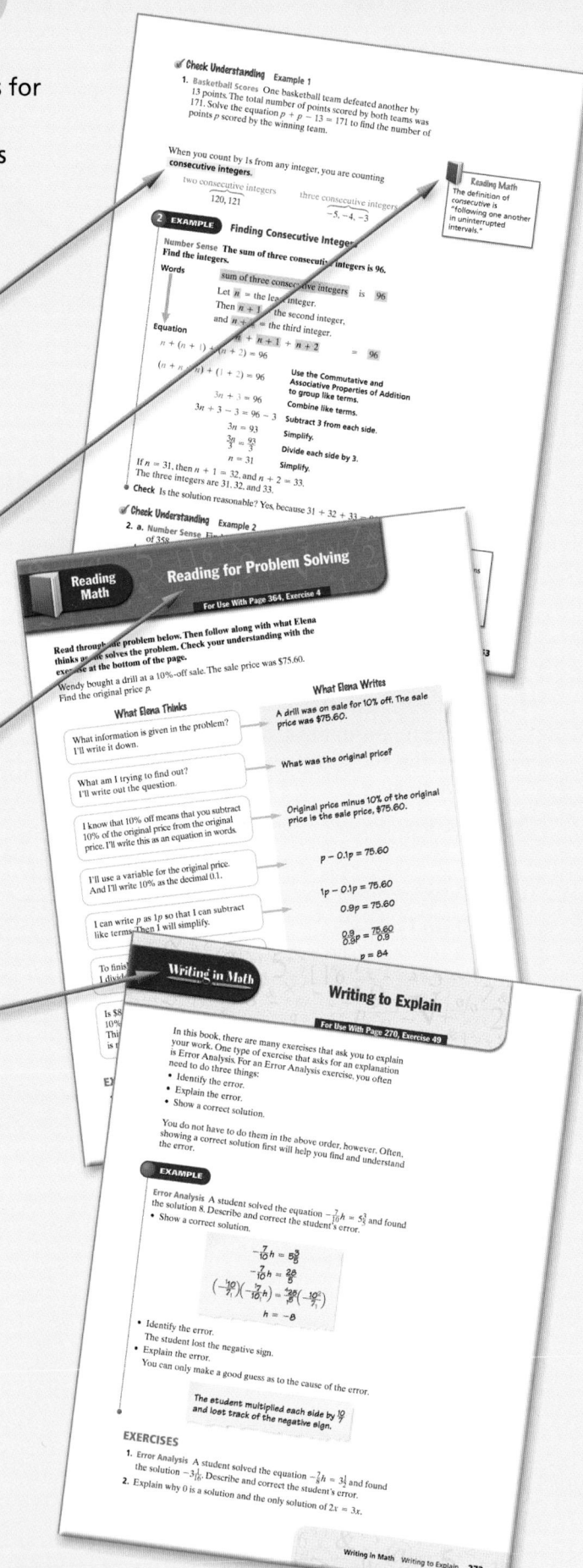

Dorling Kindersley (DK) Real-World Snapshots

Dorling Kindersley (DK) is an international publishing company that specializes in the creation of high-quality, illustrated information books for children and adults. DK is part of the Pearson family of companies.

Real-World Snapshots
The *Real-World Snapshots* feature applies the exciting and unique graphic presentation style found in Dorling Kindersley books to show you how mathematics is used in real life.

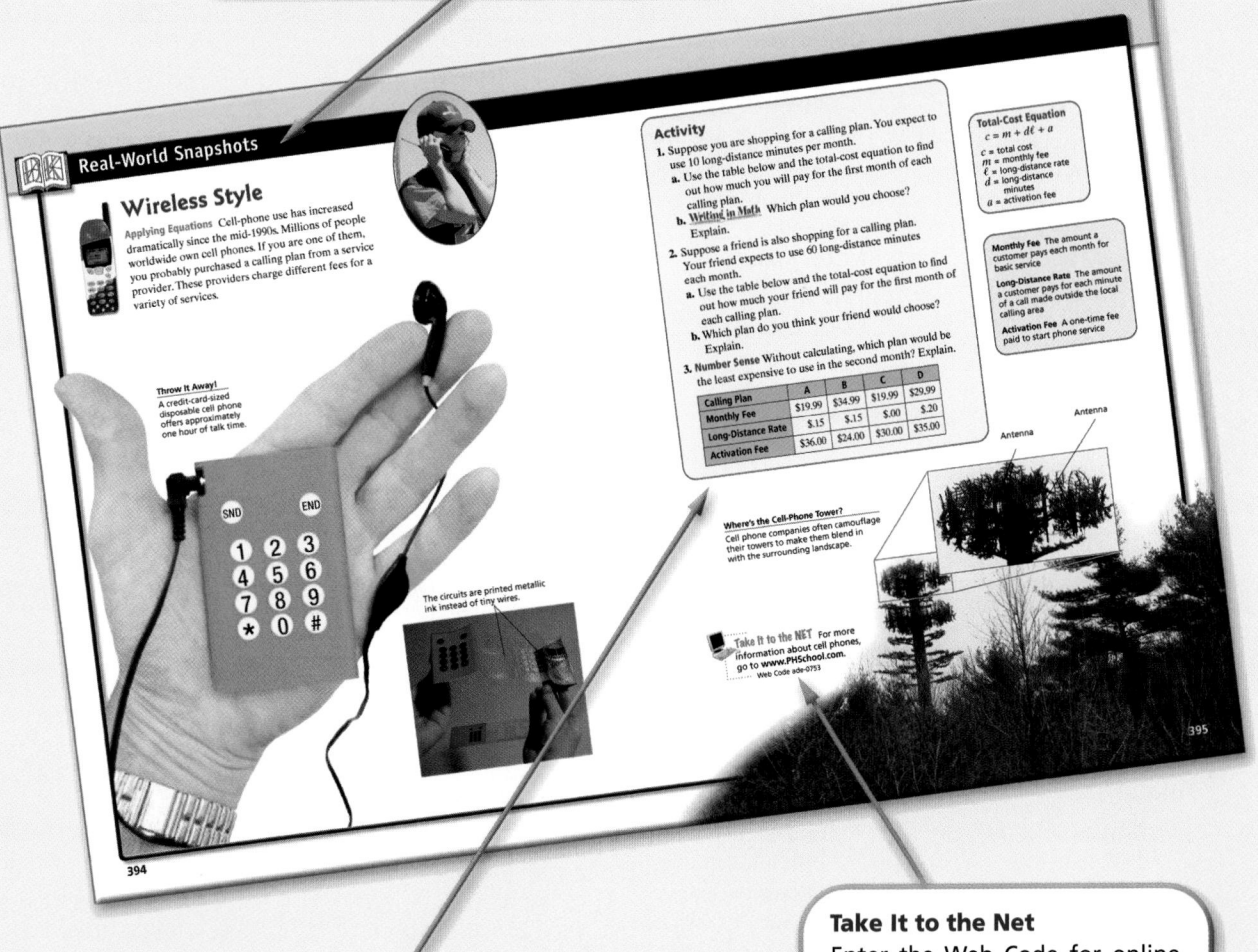

Activities
Using data from these pages and data that you gather, complete the hands-on *Activities* to apply the mathematics you are learning in real-world situations.

Take It to the Net
Enter the Web Code for online information you can use to learn more about the topic of the feature.

Algebraic Expressions and Integers

Chapter at a Glance

1-1

Variables and Expressions

pp. 4–7

Objectives

▼ Identifying Numerical and Variable Expressions

▼ Writing Variable Expressions

New Vocabulary
variable, variable expression

NCTM Standards
1, 2, 6, 10

Local Standards

1-2

The Order of Operations

pp. 8–12

Objectives

▼ Using the Order of Operations

▼ Using Grouping Symbols

New Vocabulary
order of operations

NCTM Standards
1, 2, 3, 6, 10

Local Standards

1-3

Evaluating Expressions

pp. 14–17

Objectives

▼ Evaluating Variable Expressions

▼ Solving Problems by Evaluating Expressions

New Vocabulary
evaluate

NCTM Standards
1, 2, 5, 6, 10

Local Standards

1-4

Integers and Absolute Value

pp. 18–22

Objectives

▼ Represent and Order Integers

▼ Finding Absolute Value

New Vocabulary
opposites, integers, absolute value

NCTM Standards
1, 2, 4, 6, 8, 9, 10

Local Standards

1-5

Adding Integers

pp. 24–29

Objectives

▼ Using Models to Add Integers

▼ Using Rules to Add Integers

Materials
algebra tiles

NCTM Standards
1, 2, 4, 6, 8, 9, 10

Local Standards

✔ **Checkpoint Quiz 1**

1-6

Subtracting Integers

pp. 30–34

Objectives

▼ Using Models to Subtract Integers

▼ Using Rules to Subtract Integers

Materials
algebra tiles

NCTM Standards
1, 2, 4, 6, 8, 9, 10

Local Standards

1-7

Inductive Reasoning

pp. 35–39

Objectives

▼ Writing Rules for Patterns

▼ Making Predictions and Testing Conjectures

New Vocabulary
inductive reasoning, conjecture, counterexample

NCTM Standards
1, 2, 3, 6, 7, 9, 10

Local Standards

1-8 Problem Solving

Look for a Pattern

pp. 40–43

Objective

▼ Finding Number Patterns

NCTM Standards
1, 2, 3, 5, 6, 10

Local Standards

1-9

Multiplying and Dividing Integers

pp. 44–49

Objectives

▼ Multiplying Integers

▼ Dividing Integers

NCTM Standards
1, 2, 5, 6, 9, 10

Local Standards

✔ **Checkpoint Quiz 2**

1-10

The Coordinate Plane

pp. 50–54

Objectives

▼ Naming Coordinates and Quadrants

▼ Graphing Points

New Vocabulary
coordinate plane, x-axis, y-axis, quadrants, origin, ordered pair, x-coordinate, y-coordinate

NCTM Standards
2, 3, 6, 8, 9, 10

Local Standards

Correlation to Standardized Tests

Lesson	NAEP	Terra Nova CAT/6	Terra Nova CTBS	ITBS	SAT10	Local Test
1-1	A3a		■		■	
1-2	N5e		■	■	■	
1-3	A3a, A3b		■		■	
1-4	N1g, N1i	■	■		■	
1-5	N3a	■	■		■	
1-6	N3a	■	■		■	
1-7	A1a					
1-8	A1a	■	■		■	
1-9	N3a, N3d	■	■		■	
1-10	A2c, A2d	■	■			

NAEP National Assessment of Educational Progress
- N = Number Sense, Properties, and Operations
- M = Measurement
- G = Geometry and Spatial Sense
- D = Data Analysis, Statistics and Probability
- A = Algebra and Functions

CAT/6 California Achievement Test, 6th Ed.
CTBS Comprehensive Test of Basic Skills
ITBS Iowa Test of Basic Skills, Form M
SAT10 Stanford Achievement Test, 10th Ed.

NCTM STANDARDS 2000

1	Number and Operations	6	Problem Solving
2	Algebra	7	Reasoning and Proof
3	Geometry	8	Communication
4	Measurement	9	Connections
5	Data Analysis and Probability	10	Representation

Pacing Options

This chart suggests pacing for only the core lessons and their parts. It is provided as a possible guide. It will help you determine how much time you have in your schedule to cover other components, such as the features, chapter projects, Chapter Review, and Chapter Test.

Day	Traditional 45-minute class periods	Two-Year 45-minute class periods	Block 90-minute class periods
1	1-1 ⅤⅤ	1-1 Ⅴ	1-1 ⅤⅤ / 1-2 ⅤⅤ
2	1-2 ⅤⅤ	1-1 Ⅴ	1-3 ⅤⅤ
3	1-3 ⅤⅤ	1-2 Ⅴ	1-4 ⅤⅤ / 1-5 Ⅴ
4	1-4 ⅤⅤ	1-2 Ⅴ	1-5 Ⅴ / 1-6 ⅤⅤ
5	1-5 Ⅴ	1-2 Ⅴ	1-7 ⅤⅤ / 1-8 Ⅴ
6	1-5 Ⅴ	1-3 Ⅴ	1-9 ⅤⅤ
7	1-6 ⅤⅤ	1-3 Ⅴ	1-10 ⅤⅤ
8	1-7 Ⅴ	1-3 Ⅴ	
9	1-7 Ⅴ	1-4 Ⅴ	
10	1-8 Ⅴ	1-4 Ⅴ	
11	1-9 Ⅴ	1-5 Ⅴ	
12	1-9 Ⅴ	1-5 Ⅴ	
13	1-10 ⅤⅤ	1-5 Ⅴ	
14		1-6 Ⅴ	
15		1-6 Ⅴ	
16		1-7 Ⅴ	
17		1-7 Ⅴ	
18		1-7 Ⅴ	
19		1-8 Ⅴ	
20		1-8 Ⅴ	
21		1-9 Ⅴ	
22		1-9 Ⅴ	
23		1-9 Ⅴ	
24		1-10 ⅤⅤ	

Math Background

Skills Trace

BEFORE Chapter 1
Students have encountered all of the topics in Chapter 1 in previous courses.

DURING Chapter 1
This chapter reviews key concepts and skills needed as a foundation for algebra.

AFTER Chapter 1
Every chapter throughout Pre-Algebra uses variables, expressions, equations, and integers. These topics are extended to more complex situations in algebra.

1-1 Variables and Expressions

Mathematics, in many ways, is a language. Students see that writing algebra involves the same operation symbols $(+, -, \times, \div)$ as arithmetic, but it also involves using one or more letters as "placeholders" in order to generalize a specific arithmetic statement. So $3 + 17$ becomes the more general $x + 17$.

In algebra, letters, called *variables,* act as placeholders. These placeholders were introduced in previous grades as boxes. For example, $\blacksquare + 17 = 20$. This becomes $x + 17 = 20$ in the language of algebra. The phrase $x + 17$ is called an *algebraic expression.*

An algebraic expression does not contain a verb, such as equals $(=)$, is greater than $(>)$, is less than $(<)$, is greater than or equal to $(\geq)$, or is less than or equal to $(\leq)$. So $3b - 9$ is an algebraic expression. Because $3b \geq 9$ does contain a verb, it is an algebraic sentence, or inequality, rather than an expression.

1-2 The Order of Operations

Algebra is a mathematical system with certain rules. One of these rules is consistency. To ensure that everyone will find the same value for an expression such as $3 + 4 \cdot 2$, mathematicians have agreed upon a rule called the *order of operations.* Without the order of operations, one person might choose to add first and another person might choose to multiply first.

Using the order of operations, you first simplify any operations within grouping symbols. Then simplify numbers with exponents. (Exponents will be covered in a later chapter.) Then multiply and divide from left to right. Finally add and subtract from left to right.

In the case of $3 + 4 \cdot 2$, the order of operations says that you multiply first (in order from left to right), and only then do you add (in order from left to right). This means that the correct value of the expression $3 + 4 \cdot 2$ is 11. If parentheses are inserted into the expression, such as $(3 + 4) \cdot 2$, then perform the operations within the parentheses first, so that you end up with $7 \cdot 2$, or 14.

1-3 Evaluating Expressions

There is more than one way to simplify a fraction like $\frac{120}{24}$. One way is to divide 120 by 24. Another is to write the prime factorization of the numerator and denominator and then divide common factors. For example,

$$\frac{120}{24} = \frac{2 \cdot 2 \cdot 2 \cdot 3 \cdot 5}{2 \cdot 2 \cdot 2 \cdot 3}$$
$$= \frac{2}{2} \cdot \frac{2}{2} \cdot \frac{2}{2} \cdot \frac{3}{3} \cdot \frac{5}{1}$$

This process works because a quotient of common factors is 1. That is, $\frac{2}{2} = 1$ and $\frac{3}{3} = 1$. Then, by the Identity Property for Multiplication, $1 \cdot \frac{5}{1} = \frac{5}{1}$, or 5.

1-4 Integers and Absolute Value

Students know that the counting numbers to the right of zero on a number line $(1, 2, 3, 4, \ldots)$, together with 0, are called the *whole numbers.* In Lesson 1-4, they learn that the opposites of the counting numbers $(-1, -2, -3, -4, \ldots)$ are to the left of zero on a number line. Together, the (positive) whole numbers and their (negative) opposites form the set of integers. The number 0 is neither positive nor negative.

Integers on the number line have two qualities: each has a distance from zero (such as 3 or 4), and each has a direction from zero indicated by its sign $(+$ or $-)$.

The distance an integer is from 0 is the *absolute value* of the integer. The absolute value of 0 is 0. On the number line, -3 and 3 are the same distance from zero, so 3 and -3 have the same absolute value, even though they have opposite signs.

1-5 1-6 Adding and Subtracting Integers

Adding and subtracting integers may actually be more difficult for students than multiplying or dividing integers. There are a few steps you can take to make adding and subtracting integers more straightforward: 1) To subtract an integer, always add its opposite. 2) To add integers, learn how to use their absolute values.

To add integers, you have to find either the sum or the difference of the absolute values, depending on the signs of the numbers in the expression. Once you have performed the operation, you can determine the sign by using the rules for adding integers.

1-7 1-8 Inductive Reasoning and Look for a Pattern

In *inductive reasoning* you make conclusions based on patterns you observe. For example, if you are given a number pattern such as 2, 4, 6, 8, . . . , you observe how the numbers change and you can predict, through inductive reasoning, that the next number in the pattern will be 10. You make this prediction, or *conjecture*, because the numbers you see in the pattern increase by 2.

In contrast, in *deductive reasoning* you draw a conclusion by reasoning logically from given facts. For example, given the fact that $2x = 24$, you can reason logically using mathematical properties to conclude that $x = 12$.

Inductive and deductive reasoning are very important skills in mathematics. You solve most problems in mathematics either by observing a pattern and making a conjecture (inductive reasoning) or by using given facts to draw a conclusion (deductive reasoning).

1-9 Multiplying and Dividing Integers

Like adding and subtracting integers, multiplying and dividing integers can be simplified if you first perform the multiplication or division on the absolute values of the numbers involved. Once the product or quotient is found, you may then look at the signs in the original expression and use the rules for multiplying and dividing integers to determine the correct sign for the product or quotient.

1-10 The Coordinate Plane

The concept of the coordinate plane should be easy enough to grasp for students who have already learned how to graph integers on a number line. As of this point in your study of algebra, you can apply what you learn about the coordinate plane in this chapter to real-world situations of finding points on maps, or identifying a place on a map by its coordinates.

Explain that in their future studies of algebra, students will use what they learn in this lesson to make graphical representations of many different types of algebraic equations. These representations, or graphs, will aid in solving algebraic equations.

Additional Professional Development Opportunities

Chapter 1 Math Background notes:
pp. 5, 9, 15, 19, 25, 31, 36, 41, 45, 51

Professional Development, Content Facilitator Guide: Pre-Algebra, Chapter 1

Additional resources available from SkyLight Professional Development: On-site courses, workshops, summer institutes. Online courses and chat rooms. Videocassettes and books. Visit www.skylightedu.com.

# Ongoing Assessment and Intervention

The *Prentice Hall Pre-Algebra* program provides many options for assessment in the Student Edition, Teacher's Edition, and teaching resources. From these options you may choose instructional materials that are appropriate for your students and support your district's curriculum requirements.

Daily Assessment

 ### Instant Check System™ in Chapter 1

Allows students to check their own learning before, during, and after each lesson.

Diagnosing Readiness before the chapter (p. 2)

Check Skills You'll Need exercises in each lesson (pp. 4, 8, 14, 18, 24, 30, 35, 40, 44, 50)

Check Understanding questions with each Example (pp. 5, 8, 9, 13, 14, 15, 18, 19, 24, 25, 26, 30, 31, 35, 36, 37, 41, 44, 45, 46, 51)

Checkpoint Quiz (pp. 22, 49)

Formal Assessment

In Chapter 1 and Additional Resources

Assesses student progress throughout the *Pre-Algebra* text and with blackline masters and CD-ROM.

Student Edition

- Chapter 1 Review, with Vocabulary Skills and Concepts Review, pp. 57–59
- Chapter 1 Test, p. 60

Assessment Resources *Spanish versions available.*

- Checkpoint Quizzes 1 & 2
- Chapter Test, Forms A & B
- Chapter Alternative Assessment

 Computer Test Generator CD-ROM

- Instant Chapter Tests™ — pre-made tests with items that vary every time you print.
- Online Testing allows you to give tests online and receive progress reports.
- Diagnose readiness with questions on prerequisite skills.
- Prepare students by making tests based on standardized test objectives.

Algebra Readiness Tests

- Includes Basic Skills Tests and Concept-Readiness Tests.
- Assess understanding of skills and concepts needed for success in algebra.

Standardized Test Preparation

 ### Test Prep in Chapter 1

Teaches students strategies and gives them practice with all the test item formats they will encounter on high-stakes tests.

Test Prep exercises in each lesson (pp. 7, 12, 17, 22, 28, 34, 39, 43, 49, 54)

Test-Taking Strategies (p. 56: Writing Gridded Responses)

Test Prep (p. 61: Reading Comprehension)

PRENTICE HALL ASSESSMENT *SYSTEM*

Provides a three-step approach to preparing students for high-stakes, national, and state exams.

❶ Diagnose & Prescribe

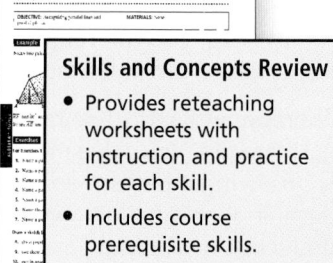

Content Diagnostic Tests
- Diagnose strengths and weaknesses with ongoing benchmark tests.
- Prescribe individualized reteaching opportunities.

❷ Review & Reteach

Skills and Concepts Review
- Provides reteaching worksheets with instruction and practice for each skill.
- Includes course prerequisite skills.

❸ Practice & Assess

Standardized Test Preparation
- Features practice for national standardized exams.
- Includes practice tests for NAEP, SAT10, ITBS, and Terra Nova.

Test-Taking Strategies With Transparencies
- Support the Test-Taking Strategies pages in the Student Edition.
- Provide a transparency and a worksheet for each strategy.

Reaching All Students

The textbook, the iText, and other technology components provide numerous opportunities to reach students of various ability levels and learning styles. Each Teacher's Edition lesson suggests how you can help all your students be successful and understand the mathematics in Chapter 1.

Below Level

Student Edition
- Diagnosing Readiness*: p. 2
- Check Skills You'll Need*: pp. 4, 8, 14, 18, 24, 30, 35, 40, 44, 50

Reteaching
Chapter 1 Grab & Go™ File: pp. 11–20

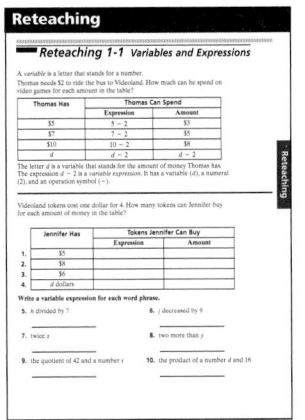

* Can be used with all ability levels to ensure mastery of prerequisite skills.

Advanced Learners

Student Edition
- Challenge exercises: pp. 7, 12, 17, 21, 28, 33, 34, 39, 43, 48, 54

Enrichment
Chapter 1 Grab & Go™ File: pp. 21–30

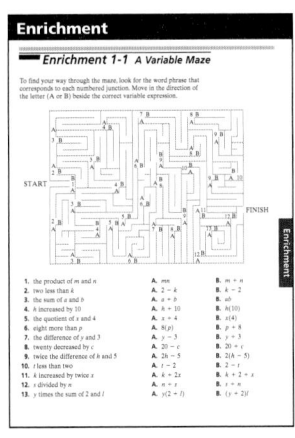

Problem Solving

Student Edition
- Strategies: pp. 40–43
- Real-World Problem Solving: pp. 5, 15, 26, 31, 36, 40, 44, 46

Guided Problem Solving Masters
Chapter 1: pp. 1–10

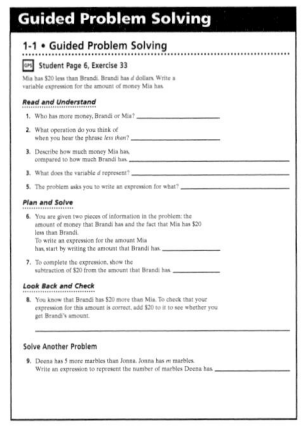

Reading and Math Literacy

Student Edition
- Vocabulary: pp. 3, 57, plus in most lessons
- Reading Math: pp. 9, 13, 15, 35
- Writing in Math: pp. 7, 11, 17, 21, 28, 33, 39, 48, 53, 60
- Illustrated Glossary: pp. 782–826

Reading and Math Literacy Masters
Chapter 1: pp. 1–4

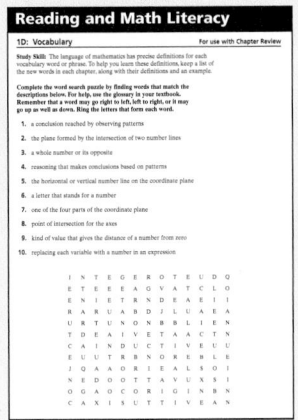

English Learners

Student Edition
- English/Spanish Illustrated Glossary: pp. 782–826

Workbook and Masters
Spanish Practice Workbook: pp. 1–10
Spanish Reading and Math Literacy Masters: pp. 1–4

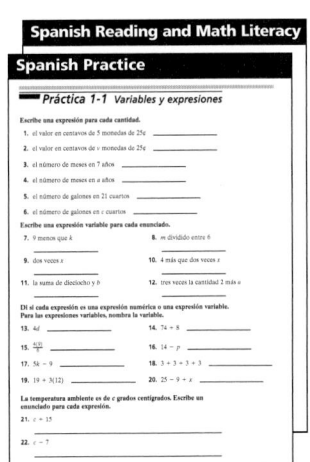

Learning Styles

Student Edition
- Investigation: pp. 8, 23, 44
- Technology: p. 55
- DK Activities: pp. 62–63
- Chapter Project: p. 738

Activity Masters
Hands-On Activities: 1, 26, 29
Technology Activities: 1, 2, 3

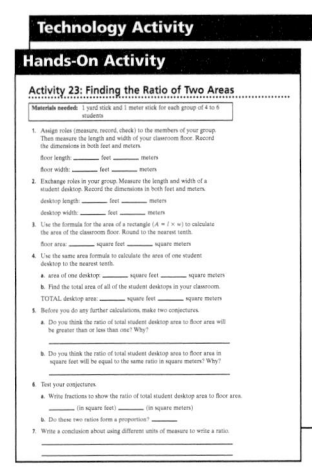

Program Resources

	Resources in Grab & Go™ Files				Resources for Reaching All Students				Spanish Resources			Transparencies				Presentation Assistant Plus!
	Practice	Reteach	Enrich	Checkpt Quiz	Reading & Math Literacy	Technology Activities	Hands-On Activities	Guided Problem Solving	Practice	Reading & Math Literacy	Checkpt Quiz	Skills Check	Additional Examples	Answers to Exercises	Lesson Quiz	Prentice Hall Presentation Pro CD-ROM
1-1	■	■	■		■			■	■	■		■	■	■	■	■
1-2	■	■	■			■		■	■			■	■	■	■	■
1-3	■	■	■			■		■	■			■	■	■	■	■
1-4	■	■	■	■	■			■	■		■	■	■	■	■	■
1-5	■	■	■			■		■	■			■	■	■	■	■
1-6	■	■	■			■		■	■			■	■	■	■	■
1-7	■	■	■					■	■			■	■	■	■	■
1-8	■	■	■					■	■			■	■	■	■	■
1-9	■	■	■	■		■		■	■		■	■	■	■	■	■
1-10	■	■	■				■	■	■			■	■	■	■	■
For the Chapter	Chapter Projects, Chapter Tests, Alternative Assessment, Cumulative Review, Cumulative Assessment				**On Web site only:** Home Activities, Algebra Readiness Puzzles, Interdisciplinary Activities				Spanish Chapter Tests, Alternative Assessment, Cumulative Review, Cumulative Assessment			Classroom Aid Transparencies				

Also available for use with the chapter:
- Practice Workbook
- Solution Key
- MathNotes folder
- For additional online and technology resources, see below.
- For teacher support and access to student Web site materials, use Web Code adk-5500.

PRENTICE HALL ASSESSMENT SYSTEM

Program assessment and test preparation, all in one place.

See page 2E.

Skills Intervention Kit

A *complete* system for the student who is struggling with course-level work

How to Use With Chapter 1

| 1-3, 1-9 | Whole Numbers |
| 1-10 | Pre-Algebra Basics |

Online Intervention

Integrated within the iText, this online intervention system includes diagnostic tests and prescribed remediation, plus reports to track student mastery.

Technology

iTEXT Online and on CD-ROM

Complete Interactive Student Text online and on CD-ROM—with instant-feedback assessment, tutorial help, dynamic activities, instructional and real-world videos, audio, and additional practice.

 www.PHSchool.com For Students

Use Web Codes for easy access to online activities, chapter projects, self-grading lesson quizzes, chapter tests, vocabulary quizzes, updated data sources, graphing calculator procedures, and more.

PH SuccessNet For Teachers

Online lesson planning with built-in state correlations, all the teaching resources, complete reference library, your own calendar and Teacher Web page, professional development, and more.

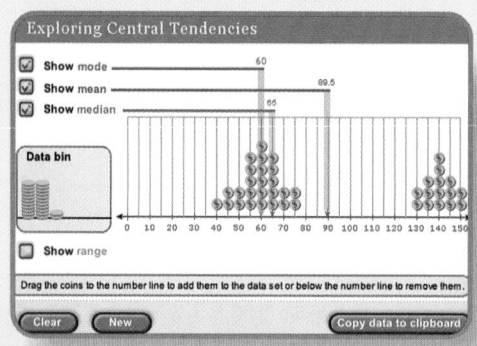

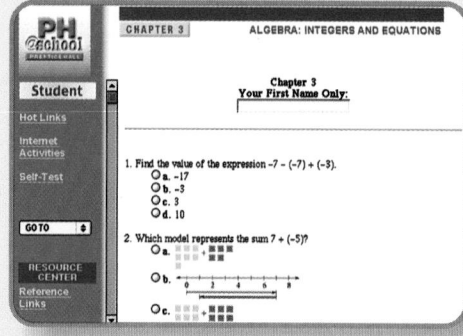

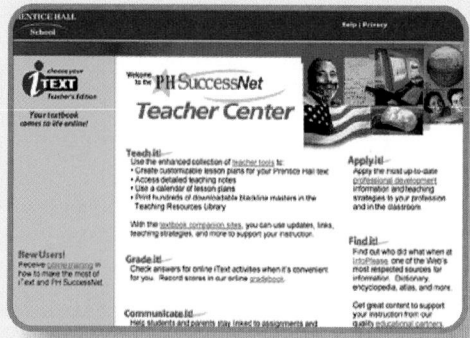

Presentation Assistant Plus!

The Prentice Hall *Presentation Assistant Plus!* provides you with the material you need to teach a lesson from beginning to end. Two easy-to-use formats—Transparencies and CD-ROM—allow you to present a lesson the way you are most comfortable.

Transparencies

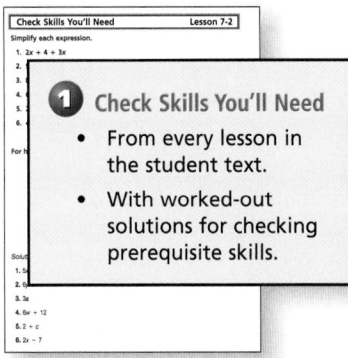

1 Check Skills You'll Need
- From every lesson in the student text.
- With worked-out solutions for checking prerequisite skills.

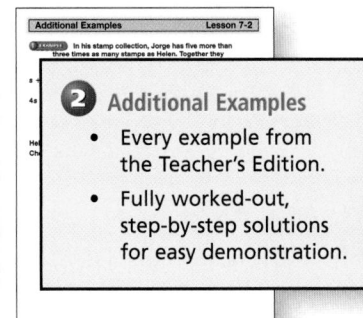

2 Additional Examples
- Every example from the Teacher's Edition.
- Fully worked-out, step-by-step solutions for easy demonstration.

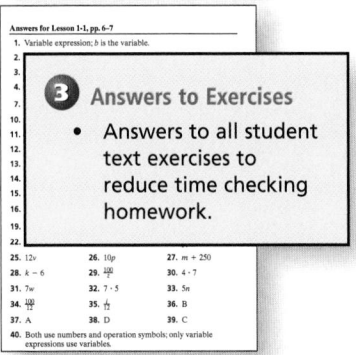

3 Answers to Exercises
- Answers to all student text exercises to reduce time checking homework.

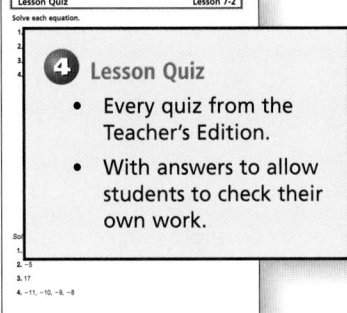

4 Lesson Quiz
- Every quiz from the Teacher's Edition.
- With answers to allow students to check their own work.

 Throughout the Teacher's Edition, this symbol indicates material that is available in the Presentation Assistant Plus!

 PowerPoint Prentice Hall Presentation Pro CD-ROM

- Includes all Transparencies as PowerPoint® presentations.
- Conveniently organized by lesson so you can easily **1** Introduce, **2** Teach, **3** Check Homework, and **4** Assess each lesson.
- Animated examples allow step-by-step instruction at your own pace.
- Easy to edit so you can create custom presentations.

Teaching Chapter 1 Using Presentation Assistant Plus!

	1 Introduce	**2 Teach**	**3 Check Homework**	**4 Assess**
	Check Skills You'll Need	Additional Examples	Student Edition Answers	Lesson Quiz
1-1	p. 1	p. 1	✔	p. 1
1-2	p. 2	p. 2	✔	p. 2
1-3	p. 3	pp. 3–4	✔	p. 3
1-4	p. 4	p. 5	✔	p. 4
1-5	p. 5	pp. 6–7	✔	p. 5
1-6	p. 6	p. 8	✔	p. 6
1-7	p. 7	pp. 9–10	✔	p. 7
1-8	p. 8	p. 11	✔	p. 8
1-9	p. 9	pp. 11–13	✔	p. 9
1-10	p. 10	p. 14	✔	p. 10

Prentice Hall Presentation Pro

CD-ROM with dynamic Powerpoint® presentations for every lesson. Helps you introduce and develop concepts, check homework, and assess progress. Part of Presentation Assistant Plus! *(See above.)*

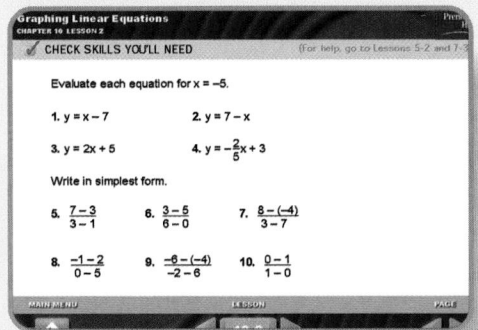

Computer Test Generator

CD-ROM to create practice sheets and tests for course objectives and standardized tests. Includes Instant Chapter Tests™, online testing, and student reports. Part of the PH Assessment System. *(See page 2E.)*

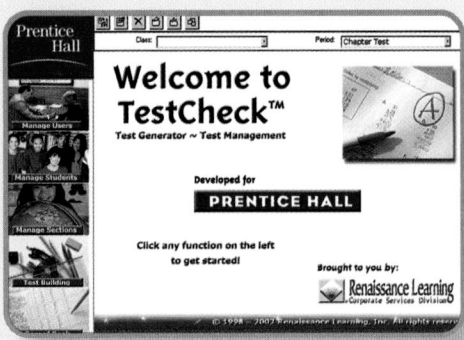

Resource Pro® with Planning Express®

CD-ROM with a lesson planning tool that allows you to import state and local objectives. Includes electronic versions of all the teaching resources.

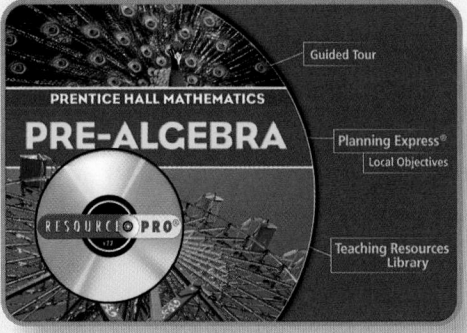

Algebraic Expressions and Integers

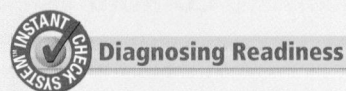

Diagnosing Readiness

Students will find answers to these exercises in the back of their textbooks.

Prescribing Intervention
For intervention, direct students to:

Adding and Subtracting Whole Numbers
Pre-Course skills.

Comparing Whole Numbers
Skills Handbook: p. 757;
Example 1; Exercises 1–10.

Multiplying and Dividing Whole Numbers
Skills Handbook: p. 759;
Example 2; Exercises 1–12.
Skills Handbook: p. 760;
Example; Exercises 1–10.

Reading Numbers on a Number Line
Previous Course

Where You've Been

In previous courses you learned:

● How to evaluate expressions using the order of operations.

● How to add, subtract, multiply, and divide whole numbers.

● How to compare whole numbers.

● How to relate numbers to points on a number line.

 Instant self-check
online and on CD-ROM

Diagnosing Readiness   (For help, go to the Skills Handbook.)

Adding and Subtracting Whole Numbers (Previous Course)

Find each sum or difference.

1. $7 - 6$ 1	**2.** $9 + 2$ 11	**3.** $15 - 4$ 11	**4.** $11 + 8$ 19
5. $20 - 7$ 13	**6.** $32 + 8$ 40	**7.** $32 - 15$ 17	**8.** $26 + 17$ 43
9. $67 + 109$ 176	**10.** $82 - 54$ 28	**11.** $44 + 122$ 166	**12.** $91 - 16$ 75

Comparing Whole Numbers (Skills Handbook, p. 757)

Compare. Use $>$, $<$, or $=$ to complete each statement.

13. $5 \blacksquare 2$ $>$ **14.** $1 \blacksquare 0$ $>$ **15.** $14 \blacksquare 17$ $<$

16. $6 + 12 \blacksquare 7 + 13$ $<$ **17.** $10 - 2 \blacksquare 27 - 18$ $<$ **18.** $4 \times 7 \blacksquare 2 \times 14$ $=$

Multiplying and Dividing Whole Numbers (Skills Handbook, pp. 759, 760)

Find each product or quotient.

19. $36 \div 3$ 12	**20.** 10×3 30	**21.** $7(4)$ 28	**22.** $25 \div 5$ 5
23. $12 \cdot 8$ 96	**24.** $7\overline{)35}$ 5	**25.** $20 \cdot 10$ 200	**26.** $9\overline{)720}$ 80
27. $124 \div 4$ 31	**28.** $12\overline{)156}$ 13	**29.** $4 \cdot 12 \cdot 10$ 480	**30.** $132 \div 11$ 12

Reading Numbers on a Number Line (Skills Handbook, p. 757)

What is the distance of each point from zero on the number line?

31. A 1   **32.** B 4

33. C 7   **34.** D 10

Algebraic Expressions and Integers

Key Vocabulary

- absolute value (p. 19)
- conjecture (p. 35)
- coordinate plane (p. 50)
- counterexample (p. 37)
- evaluate (p. 14)
- inductive reasoning (p. 35)
- integers (p. 19)
- opposites (p. 19)
- order of operations (p. 8)
- ordered pair (p. 50)
- origin (p. 50)
- quadrants (p. 50)
- variable (p. 4)
- variable expression (p. 4)
- x-axis (p. 50)
- x-coordinate (p. 50)
- y-axis (p. 50)
- y-coordinate (p. 50)

3

Where You're Going

In this chapter, you will learn how to

- Use variables and variable expressions.
- Perform operations with integers.
- Graph points in the coordinate plane.
- Solve a problem by looking for a pattern.

Real-World Snapshots Applying what you learn, on pages 62–63 you will solve problems about sunken ships.

Chapter 1 Overview

In this chapter, the basic language of algebra is introduced. First, students learn to represent unknown quantities with variables and to write numerical and variable expressions. Students learn the order of operations to simplify and evaluate numerical expressions. Students learn to represent, graph, and order integers, as well as find absolute values. They simplify expressions containing integers using all four mathematical operations. Students find patterns, and then use inductive reasoning to solve problems. Last, the students explore coordinate planes. They name coordinates and quadrants, and graph points.

Activating Prior Knowledge
Students build upon skills they learned in previous courses to begin their study of algebraic expressions and integers.
Ask: *What is an expression?*
a mathematical phrase with numbers and operation symbols

Reading Math
- Reading an Example, p. 13.
- **Vocabulary** A complete list of terms, plus vocabulary exercises, appears in the Chapter Review on p. 57.
- **Illustrated Glossary** Examples for each vocabulary term, plus definitions in both English and Spanish, appear starting on p. 782.

Test Taking Strategies
Writing Gridded Responses, p. 56

Real-World Problem Solving
- **Strategy:** Look for a Pattern, pp. 40–43
- **DK Real-World Snapshots:** Applying Integers, pp. 62–63
- **Chapter Project:** Cure for the Common Code, p. 738

 **www.PHSchool.com**
Internet support includes:
- Self-grading Vocabulary and Chapter 1 Tests
- Activity Masters
- Chapter Project support
- Chapter Planner
- Chapter 1 Resources

Plus

3

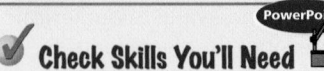

1-1

1. Plan

Lesson Preview

✓ **Check Skills You'll Need**

Converting Measurements
Table 1, p. 776

Lesson Resources

📁 **Teaching Resources**
Practice, Reteaching, Enrichment

👥 **Reaching All Students**
Practice Workbook 1-1
Spanish Practice Workbook 1-1
Reading and Math Literacy 1A
Spanish Reading and Math
  Literacy 1A
Guided Problem Solving 1-1

⏱ **Presentation Assistant Plus!**
Transparencies and PowerPoint™
• Check Skills You'll Need 1-1
• Additional Examples 1-1
• Student Edition Answers 1-1
• Lesson Quiz 1-1
• Classroom Aid 7
PH Presentation Pro CD-ROM 1-1

ASSESSMENT SYSTEM

Computer Test Generator CD-ROM

💻 **Technology**
Resource Pro® CD-ROM
Computer Test Generator CD-ROM
PH Presentation Pro CD-ROM

💻 **www.PHSchool.com**
Student Site
• Teacher Web Code: adk-5500
• Algebra Readiness Puzzles 1, 24
• Self-grading Lesson Quiz
PH SuccessNet Teacher Center
• Lesson Planner
• Resources

Plus  **TEXT**

1-1 Variables and Expressions

What You'll Learn

 OBJECTIVE 1 To identify variables, numerical expressions, and variable expressions

 OBJECTIVE 2 To write variable expressions for word phrases

. . . And Why

To use the language of algebra to model real-world problems

✓ **Check Skills You'll Need**

Complete each equation.

1. 1 week = ▪ days **7**

2. 1 foot = ▪ inches **12**

3. 1 nickel = ▪ cents **5**

4. 1 gallon = ▪ quarts **4**

5. 1 yard = ▪ feet **3**

📖 For help, go to Table 1, p. 776.

New Vocabulary

• variable
• variable expression

📖 **TEXT** Interactive lesson includes instant self-check, tutorials, and activities.

OBJECTIVE

1 Identifying Numerical and Variable Expressions

Gas Mileage How many miles can you drive on ten gallons of gas? The answer depends on the type of vehicle you drive. The table shows some typical data.

Vehicle Type	Miles	Gallons	Miles per Gallon
Subcompact	330	10	$330 \div 10$
Compact	300	10	$300 \div 10$
Mid-size sedan	245	10	$245 \div 10$
Sport utility vehicle	175	10	$175 \div 10$
Pickup truck	160	10	$160 \div 10$

The last column gives a *numerical expression* ↑ for each vehicle's miles per gallon.

If you don't know the number of miles, you can use a *variable* to stand for the number. Then you can write a *variable expression* for miles per gallon.

variable → m ← miles on 10 gallons

variable expression → $m \div 10$ ← miles per gallon

A **variable** is a letter that stands for a number.
A **variable expression** is a mathematical phrase that uses variables, numerals, and operation symbols.

1 EXAMPLE **Identifying Expressions**

Identify each expression as a *numerical expression* or a *variable expression*. For a variable expression, name the variable.

a. $5 - 5$
  numerical expression

b. $c - 5$
  Variable expression; c is the variable.

4 **Chapter 1** Algebraic Expressions and Integers

✓ Ongoing Assessment and Intervention

Before the Lesson
Diagnose prerequisite skills using:
• Check Skills You'll Need

During the Lesson
Monitor progress using:
• Check Understanding
• Additional Examples
• Test Prep

After the Lesson
Assess knowledge using:
• Lesson Quiz
• Computer Test Generator
  CD-ROM

✓ Check Understanding Example 1

1. Identify each expression as a *numerical expression* or a *variable expression*. For a variable expression, name the variable.

   a. $8 \div x$
   Variable expression; x is the variable.

   b. 100×6
   numerical expression

   c. $d + 43 - 9$
   Variable expression; d is the variable.

OBJECTIVE

2 Writing Variable Expressions

You can translate word phrases into variable expressions.

Word Phrase	Variable Expression
Nine more than a number y	$y + 9$
4 less than a number n	$n - 4$
A number z times three	$z \cdot 3$ or $3z$ or $3(z)$
A number a divided by 12	$a \div 12$ or $\frac{a}{12}$
5 times the quantity 4 plus a number c	$5 \cdot (4 + c)$ or $5(4 + c)$

> **Writing in Math**
>
> You can translate many words for operations into operation symbols.
>
> total $+$
> more than $+$
> increased by $+$
> difference $-$
> fewer than $-$
> less than $-$
> decreased by $-$
> product $\times$ or $\cdot$ or ( )
> times $\times$ or $\cdot$ or ( )
> quotient $\div$ or —
> divided by $\div$ or —

2 EXAMPLE Real-World 🌐 Problem Solving

Science The fastest dinosaur may have been *Ornithomimus*, which could run about 60 ft in a second. Write a variable expression for the distance Ornithomimus could run in a given time.

Words | 60 | times | number of seconds |

Let s = number of seconds.

Expression   60   · s

The variable expression $60 \cdot s$, or $60s$, describes the distance in feet Ornithomimus could run in s seconds.

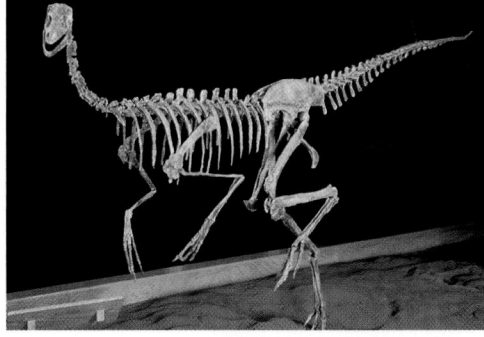

Real-World 🌐 Connection

Ornithomimus was an ostrich-like oviraptor about 7 ft tall. Its long tail acted as a counterbalance and as a stabilizer during fast turns.

✓ Check Understanding Example 2

2. **a.** Bagels cost $.50 each. Write a variable expression for the cost of b bagels. $0.50b$

   b. **Measurement** Write a variable expression for the number of hours in m minutes. $\frac{m}{60}$

👥 Reaching All Students

| **Below Level** Explain that variables are useful for representing unknown amounts. For example, your students don't know what their heights will be two years from now. The amount each student will grow is a variable. | **Advanced Learners** Ask students how 6 divided by 2 plus 1 differs from 6 divided by the quantity 2 plus 1. You simplify the former to 3 plus 1, or 4. For the latter, simplify to 6 divided by 3, or 2. | **Visual Learners** See note on page 5. **English Learners** See note on page 5. |

Professional Development

Math Background

The variable h occurs twice in the expression $3h + 5 + 2h$. If a variable occurs more than once in an expression, you regard it as having the same value each time it occurs.

Teaching Notes

1 EXAMPLE Visual Learners

Have students copy each expression on their papers and circle any variables.

Error Prevention!

A common error is to write the phrase "4 less than a number n" as "4 − n." Point out that *less than* is not the same as *less*. Suggest that students think of a value for the variable, such as "4 less than 10." Then they can use that same value to check their variable expression.

1 EXAMPLE English Learners

Ask: *What letter is left out when the word "number" is changed into the word "numerical?"* the letter b

🖳 PowerPoint Additional Examples

1 Identify each expression as a *numerical expression* or a *variable expression*. For a variable expression, name the variable.
   a. 7×3 **b.** $4t$
   a. numerical expression
   b. variable expression; t

2 Write a variable expression for the cost of p pens priced at 29¢ each. 29p

Closure

Ask: *What is a variable?* a letter that stands for a number *What is a variable expression?* a mathematical phrase that uses variables, numerals, and operation symbols Have students write a variable expression for the number of days in m weeks. 7m

5

Assignment Guide

1 Objective 1
  Ⓐ Ⓑ Core 1–6, 23–26
  Ⓒ Extension 40

2 Objective 2
  Ⓐ Ⓑ Core 7–22, 27–39
  Ⓒ Extension 41

Test Prep 42–45
Mixed Review 46–52

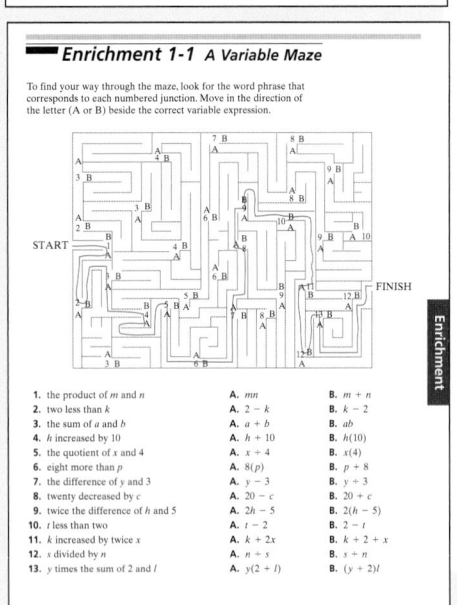

EXERCISES

? For more exercises, see *Extra Practice.*

Practice and Problem Solving

Ⓐ **Practice by Example**

Example 1
(page 4)

Identify each expression as a *numerical expression* or a *variable expression*. For a variable expression, name the variable.

1. $b + 6$
See left.

2. $80 \div 8$
numerical expression

3. $14 - n$
See left.

4. 14×14
numerical expression

5. $100x$
See left.

6. $8 + 8 + 8 + 8$
numerical expression

Example 2
(page 5)

1. Variable expression; b is the variable.
3. Variable expression; n is the variable.
5. Variable expression; x is the variable.

Write a variable expression for each word phrase.

7. 16 more than m $m + 16$

8. 6 divided by z $\frac{6}{z}$

9. the product of c and 3 $3c$

10. 2 less than p $p - 2$

11. b times 3 $3b$

12. 4 fewer than j $j - 4$

13. n divided by 3 $\frac{n}{3}$

14. 3 divided by n $\frac{3}{n}$

15. x less than 2 $2 - x$

16. 8 less than z $z - 8$

Write a numerical or variable expression for each quantity.

17. two dozen eggs $2 \cdot 12$

18. d dozen eggs $d \cdot 12$

19. the value in cents of 7 nickels $5 \cdot 7$

20. the value in cents of n nickels $5n$

21. number of quarts in 3 gallons $4 \cdot 3$

22. number of quarts in g gallons $4g$

Ⓑ **Apply Your Skills**

23. Variable expression; d is the variable.
25. Variable expression; g is the variable.

Identify each expression as a *numerical expression* or a *variable expression*. For a variable expression, name the variable.

23. $d + 53$
See left.

24. $12 - 7$
numerical expression

25. $\frac{g}{9}$
See left.

26. $4(5)$
numerical expression

Measurement **Write an expression for each quantity.**

27. the number of days in 4 weeks $7 \cdot 4$

28. the number of days in w weeks $7w$

29. number of pounds in 160 ounces $\frac{160}{16}$

30. number of pounds in z ounces $\frac{z}{16}$

31. the number of feet in 100 inches $\frac{100}{12}$

32. the number of feet in i inches $\frac{i}{12}$

33. Mia has $20 less than Brandi. Brandi has d dollars. Write a variable expression for the amount of money Mia has. $d - 20$

Use the calorie chart at the left for Exercises 34 and 35.

34. Write a variable expression for the number of calories in e eggs and one slice of bread. $110e + 55$

35. Write a variable expression for the number of calories in a fruit salad made from a apples and b bananas. $70a + 100b$

Calorie Chart

Food	Calories
Bread slice	55
Apple	70
Banana	100
Egg	110

Use the Guided Problem Solving worksheet with Exercise 33.

Modeling In each model, the red line represents a variable expression. Match each model with its expression.

A. $\frac{x}{4}$ B. $4 + x$ C. $4x$ D. $x - 4$

36.  B

37. C

38. D

39. A

C **Challenge**

40. 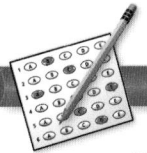 **Writing in Math** How are numerical expressions and variable expressions similar? How are they different? **Both use numbers and operation symbols; only variable expressions use variables.**

41. **Error Analysis** A student wrote the variable expression $n - 5$ for the word phrase *n less than five*. Explain the student's error. **Answers may vary. Sample: The student confused the positions of *n* and 5.**

Test Prep

Multiple Choice A hot-air balloon is at an altitude of m meters. In Exercises 42–44, which expression matches the given word phrase?

42. the balloon's new altitude after rising 34 meters **B**
    A. $m - 34$ **B.** $m + 34$ **C.** $3m$ **D.** $34m$

43. the balloon's new altitude after falling 2,000 meters **I**
    F. $m + 2{,}000$ **G.** $2{,}000 - m$ **H.** $2{,}000m$ **I.** $m - 2{,}000$

44. the balloon's new altitude after tripling its altitude **C**
    A. $m - 34$ **B.** $m + 34$ **C.** $3m$ **D.** $34m$

45. Pam is 15 years old. Which expression gives Pam's age p years ago? **H**
    F. $p - 15$ **G.** $p + 15$ **H.** $15 - p$ **I.** $\frac{p}{15}$

Take It to the NET
Online lesson quiz at
www.PHSchool.com
Web Code: ada-0101

Mixed Review

Previous Course **Compute.**

46. $105 + 25 + 95$ **225** **47.** $3 \times 6 \times 4$ **72**   **48.** $8 + 1 - 1$ **8**

49. $648 - 573$ **75**   **50.** $169 \div 13$ **13**   **51.** $22{,}534 - 12{,}971$
                                                           9,563

52. **Purchasing** A customer buys orange juice for $.95 and two apples for $.55 each. She gives the cashier a five-dollar bill. How much change should the cashier give the customer? **$2.95**

53. a. Recall the *counting numbers*, 1, 2, 3, 4, . . . Of the first 1,000 counting numbers, how many end in 1, 3, 5, 7, or 9? **500**
    b. How many end in 2, 4, 6, or 8? **400**

4. Assess

 **Lesson Quiz 1-1**

Write a variable expression for each word phrase.

1. the total of h and 56 $h + 56$

2. three less than d $d - 3$

3. p decreased by three $p - 3$

4. a divided by 7 $a \div 7$

Alternative Assessment

Have students write an explanation of the differences between a *variable*, a *variable expression*, and a *numerical expression.* Have students share their explanations with a partner to check whether they agree with each other. **A variable is a letter. A variable expression uses variables, numerals, and operation symbols. A numerical expression uses numerals and operation symbols, but no variables.**

Test Prep

Resources
For additional practice with a variety of test item formats:

• Test Prep, p. 61
• Test-Taking Strategies, p. 56
• Test-Taking Strategies With Transparencies

Reteaching 1-1 *Variables and Expressions*

A *variable* is a letter that stands for a number.
Thomas needs $2 to ride the bus to Videoland. How much can he spend on video games for each amount in the table?

Thomas Has	Thomas Can Spend	
	Expression	Amount
$5	5 − 2	$3
$7	7 − 2	$5
$10	10 − 2	$8
d	d − 2	d − 2

The letter d is a variable that stands for the amount of money Thomas has. The expression d − 2 is a *variable expression*. It has a variable (d), a numeral (2), and an operation symbol (−).

Videoland tokens cost one dollar for 4. How many tokens can Jennifer buy for each amount of money in the table?

	Jennifer Has	Tokens Jennifer Can Buy	
		Expression	Amount
1.	$5	4(5)	20
2.	$8	4(8)	32
3.	$6	4(6)	24
4.	d dollars	4(d)	4d

Write a variable expression for each word phrase.

5. h divided by 7   **6.** j decreased by 9
    $\frac{h}{7}$ $j - 9$

7. twice x **8.** two more than y
    $2x$ $y + 2$

9. the quotient of 42 and a number s **10.** the product of a number d and 16
    $\frac{42}{s}$ 16d

1-2

Lesson Preview

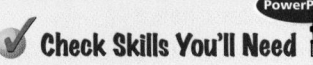

✓ **Check Skills You'll Need** PowerPoint

Dividing Whole Numbers
Skills Handbook: p. 760;
Exercises 26–48.

Lesson Resources

📁 **Teaching Resources**
Practice, Reteaching, Enrichment

👥 **Reaching All Students**
Practice Workbook 1-2
Spanish Practice Workbook 1-2
Guided Problem Solving 1-2
Technology Activities 1
Hands-On Activities 26

⏰ **Presentation Assistant Plus!**
Transparencies and PowerPoint™
• Check Skills You'll Need 1-2
• Additional Examples 1-2
• Student Edition Answers 1-2
• Lesson Quiz 1-2
PH Presentation Pro CD-ROM 1-2

ASSESSMENT SYSTEM

Computer Test Generator CD-ROM

💻 **Technology**
Resource Pro® CD-ROM
Computer Test Generator CD-ROM
PH Presentation Pro CD-ROM

💻 **www.PHSchool.com**
Student Site
• Teacher Web Code: adk-5500
• Algebra Readiness Puzzles 2
• Graphing Calculator, Procedure 1
• Self-grading Lesson Quiz
PH SuccessNet Teacher Center
• Lesson Planner
• Resources

Plus

8

1-2 The Order of Operations

What You'll Learn

OBJECTIVE **1** To use the order of operations

OBJECTIVE **2** To use grouping symbols

. . . And Why

To find the value of an expression with more than one operation

✓ **Check Skills You'll Need**

Find each quotient.

1. $164 \div 2$ 82   **2.** $344 \div 8$ 43
3. $284 \div 4$ 71   **4.** $133 \div 7$ 19
5. $182 \div 13$ 14 **6.** $650 \div 25$ 26

❓ For help, go to Skills Handbook, p. 760.

New Vocabulary

• order of operations

Investigation

Experimenting With Order

In most languages, the meaning of words depends on their order. For example, "sign the check" is not the same as "check the sign."

Similarly, order is important in the language of mathematics.

1. **Mental Math** Find the value of the expression $3 + 5 \times 2$.
   13 or 16
2. **Analyze** What answer do you get to Question 1 if you multiply before adding? If you add before multiplying?
   13; 16
3. **Reasoning** How does the order in which you do the operations affect your answer?
   Answers may vary. Sample: Different orders of operations can give different answers.

The order in which you perform operations can affect the value of an expression. To avoid confusion, mathematicians have agreed on an **order of operations.** Multiply and divide first. Then add and subtract.

To *simplify* a numerical expression, you use the order of operations and replace the expression with the simplest name for its value.

1 EXAMPLE **Simplifying Expressions**

Simplify $4 + 15 \div 3$.

$4 + 15 \div 3$
$4 + 5$ **First divide.**
9 **Then add.**

✓ **Check Understanding** Example 1

1. Simplify each expression.

   a. $2 + 5 \times 3$ 17   **b.** $12 \div 3 - 1$ 3   **c.** $10 - 1 \cdot 7$ 3

When operations have the same rank in the order of operations, do them from left to right.

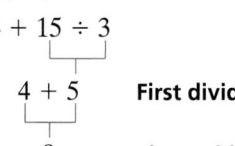
iTEXT Interactive lesson includes instant self-check, tutorials, and activities.

✓ **Ongoing Assessment and Intervention**

Before the Lesson	**During the Lesson**	**After the Lesson**
Diagnose prerequisite skills using:	Monitor progress using:	Assess knowledge using:
• Check Skills You'll Need	• Check Understanding	• Lesson Quiz
	• Additional Examples	• Computer Test Generator
	• Test Prep	CD-ROM

② EXAMPLE **Using the Order of Operations**

Simplify $3 \cdot 5 - 8 \div 4 + 6$.

$3 \cdot 5 - 8 \div 4 + 6$

$15 \quad - \quad 2 \quad + \quad 6$ **Multiply and divide from left to right.**

$13 + 6$ **Add and subtract from left to right.**

19 **Add.**

✓ Check Understanding   Example 2

2. Simplify each expression.

   a. $4 - 1 \cdot 2 + 6 \div 3$ 4   **b.** $5 + 6 \cdot 4 \div 3 - 1$ 12

OBJECTIVE

2 **Using Grouping Symbols**

Grouping symbols, such as parentheses, ( ), and brackets, [ ], indicate order. A fraction bar also is a grouping symbol, since $\frac{4+2}{3} = (4+2) \div 3$. Always work inside grouping symbols first.

Key Concepts   **Order of Operations**

   1. Work inside grouping symbols.
   2. Multiply and divide in order from left to right.
   3. Add and subtract in order from left to right.

③ EXAMPLE **Simplifying With Grouping Symbols**

Simplify $10 \div [9 - (2 \cdot 2)]$.

$10 \div [9 - (2 \cdot 2)]$

$10 \div [9 \quad - \quad 4]$ **Multiply within parentheses.**

$10 \quad \div \quad 5$ **Subtract within brackets.**

2 **Divide.**

✓ Check Understanding   Example 3

3. Simplify each expression.

   a. $2[(13 - 4) \div 3]$ 6   **b.** $1 + \frac{10 - 2}{4}$ 3

Calculator Hint

Many calculators use the order of operations. To test yours, enter $10 - 4 \div 2$. If the answer is 8, then your calculator uses the order of operations.

If the answer is 3, then your calculator does not use the order of operations.

Reading Math

For help with reading an Example, see page 13.

---

2. Teach

Professional Development

Math Background

Ask students what would happen if there were no rule about whether to drive on the right side or the left side of the road. Explain to students that the side to drive on is not important as long as everybody follows the same rule. Similarly, the rules for the order of operations are neither right nor wrong, but simply a way of doing things that everybody follows to avoid confusion.

Teaching Notes

Investigation (Optional)
Discuss with students the importance of consistency in mathematics. For example, $2 + 12 \div 6$ must have the same value, 4, for everyone. The order of operations ensures that the value of an expression is always calculated in one way.

③ EXAMPLE **Auditory Learners**

A popular mnemonic device for the order of operations is PMDAS (Please, My Dear Aunt Sally). The letters stand for Parentheses first, then Multiplication and Division (in order from left to right), and finally, Addition and Subtraction (in order from left to right). Have students make their own mnemonic devices for the order of operations.

③ EXAMPLE **Diversity**

Ask students if they have lived in or visited cultures that read in an order different from left to right. If not, ask them to research this matter. Have them find whether these cultures read their mathematics in the same order as they read words.

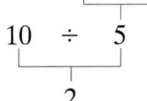 **Additional Examples**

❶ Simplify $8 - 2 \cdot 2$.   4

❷ Simplify $12 \div 3 - 1 \cdot 2 + 1$.   3

❸ Simplify $20 - 3[(5 + 2) - 1]$.   2

👥 Reaching All Students

| **Below Level** Encourage students to take time to write down intermediate steps. Remind them that, in math, accuracy is more important than speed. | **Advanced Learners** Have students simplify $9 \div (0 + 3)$. **3** Ask: *What would be the result if the parentheses were not there? Explain your answer.* There would be no result. $9 \div 0$ has no meaning. | **Auditory Learners** See note on page 9. **Diversity** See note on page 9. |

9

You can use the order of operations to find the area of an irregular figure by more than one method.

More Than One Way

Urban Planning Some urban planners specialize in planning entire new towns. These towns are designed for livability, with plenty of open space. The sketch shows the dimensions for a new town called Panorama. Find Panorama's area.

Kevin's Method

Divide the figure into rectangles. Then add their areas.

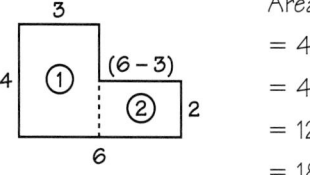

$$Area = Area① + Area②$$
$$= 4 \cdot 3 + (6 - 3) \cdot 2$$
$$= 4 \cdot 3 + 3 \cdot 2$$
$$= 12 + 6$$
$$= 18$$

Panorama's area is 18 km².

Tina's Method

Visualize attaching a small rectangle to complete a large rectangle. Then subtract the small area from the large area.

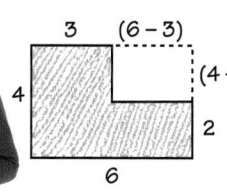

$$Area = \begin{array}{c} \text{Area of large} \\ \text{rectangle} \end{array} - \begin{array}{c} \text{Area of small} \\ \text{rectangle} \end{array}$$
$$= 6 \cdot 4 - (6 - 3) \cdot (4 - 2)$$
$$= 6 \cdot 4 - 3 \cdot 2$$
$$= 24 - 6$$
$$= 18$$

Panorama's area is 18 km².

Choose a Method

1. Answers may vary. Sample: Kevin's method. It is a simpler computation.

1. **Which method would you use to find the town's area? Explain.** See left.
2. **Can you think of another way to solve the problem? Explain.** Answers may vary. Sample: Put a grid on the figure and count squares.

EXERCISES

 For more exercises, see *Extra Practice*.

Practice and Problem Solving

A Practice by Example

Examples 1 and 2
(pages 8 and 9)

Simplify each expression.

1. $3 + 6 \times 4$ 27
2. $35 \div 7 - 2$ 3
3. $8 - 2 \cdot 3$ 2

4. $6 - 6 \div 3$ 4
5. $21 - 13 + 8$ 16
6. $6 \cdot 2 + 4$ 16

7. $12 - 8 \div 2 + 3$ 11
8. $21 \div 7 + 14 \times 2$ 31
9. $2 \cdot 2 + 0 \cdot 4$ 4

10. $4(4) - 2(5)$ 6
11. $2 + 3 \cdot 24 \div 6$ 14
12. $4 \div 4 \cdot 4 + 4 - 4$ 4

Example 3
(page 9)

13. $7 + 3 \cdot (8 \div 4)$ 13
14. $2(15 - 9) \cdot 9$ 108
15. $[2 + (6 \cdot 8)] - 1$ 49

16. $2(6) + \dfrac{7 + 8}{3}$ 17
17. $3(7 + 4)$ 33
18. $12 \div (3 - 2) + 1$ 13

19. $6 + \dfrac{6 + 2}{4}$ 8
20. $\dfrac{21 + 15}{3 + 6}$ 4
21. $(21 + 3) \div 4 \div 2$ 3

B Apply Your Skills

22. The student subtracted 1 from 6 before dividing, instead of dividing and then subtracting.

22. Error Analysis A student found the value of the expression $30 \div 6 - 1$ to be 6. Explain the student's error. **See left.**

23. Writing in Math Why do we need to agree on an order of operations? We must agree on an order of operations to ensure that everyone gets the same value for an expression.

Simplify each expression.

24. $(56 - 5) \div 17$ 3
25. $60 \div 4 + 9$ 24
26. $2[8 + (5 - 3)] - 8$ 12

27. $12 \div 3 \times 4$ 16
28. $36 - 27 \div 9 \div 1$ 33
29. $6(4 + 1) - 5$ 25

30. $14 + 5 \times 2$ 24
31. $440 \div (2 + 18)$ 22
32. $16 \div 8 \times 2$ 4

Compare. Use >, <, or = to complete each statement.

33. $15 \cdot 3 - 2 \;\blacksquare\; 15 \cdot (3 - 2)$ >

34. $18 - 6 \div 3 \;\blacksquare\; (18 - 6) \div 3$ >

35. $8 + 12 \div 4 \;\blacksquare\; (8 + 12) \div 4$ >

36. $22 - 7 \cdot 2 \;\blacksquare\; (22 - 7) \cdot 2$ <

37. $12 \div 3 + 9 \cdot 4 \;\blacksquare\; 12 \div (3 + 9) \cdot 4$ >

38. $(19 - 15) \div (3 + 1) \;\blacksquare\; 19 - 15 \div 3 + 1$ <

Insert grouping symbols to make each number sentence true.

39. $7 + 4 \cdot 6 = 66$
$(7 + 4) \cdot 6 = 66$
40. $7 \cdot 8 - 6 + 3 = 17$
$[7 \cdot (8 - 6)] + 3 = 17$
41. $3 + 8 - 2 \cdot 5 = 45$
$(3 + 8 - 2) \cdot 5 = 45$
42. $6 \cdot 3 + 9 - 4 = 23$
$(6 \cdot 3) + (9 - 4) = 23$

Write a numerical expression for each phrase. Then simplify.

43. five added to the product of four and nine $4 \cdot 9 + 5$; 41

44. twenty-one minus the sum of fifteen and five $21 - (15 + 5)$; 1

45. seventeen minus the quotient of twenty-five and five
$17 - (25 \div 5)$; 12

Assignment Guide

1 Objective 1
A B Core 1–12, 22, 23, 46
C Extension 47–49

2 Objective 2
A B Core 13–21, 24–45
C Extension 50, 51

Test Prep 52–55
Mixed Review 56–60

Error Prevention!

Exercises 33–38 Review the meanings of the symbols < and >. Point out that the symbol points to the lesser number.

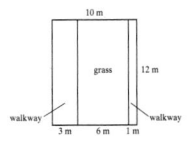

Practice 1-2 *The Order of Operations*

Simplify each expression.

1. $3 + 15 - 5 \cdot 2$ ___8___   2. $5 \cdot 6 + 2 \cdot 4$ ___38___
3. $48 \div 8 - 1$ ___5___   4. $68 - 12 \div 2 + 3$ ___66___
5. $6(2 + 7)$ ___54___   6. $25 - (6 \cdot 4)$ ___1___
7. $3[9 - (6 - 3)] - 10$ ___8___   8. $60 \div (3 + 12)$ ___4___
9. $4 - 2 + 6 \cdot 2$ ___14___   10. $18 \div (5 - 2)$ ___6___
11. $\frac{16 + 24}{30 - 22}$ ___5___   12. $2[4(9 - 7) + 1]$ ___18___
13. $(8 \div 8 + 2 + 11) \div 2$ ___7___   14. $9 + 3 \cdot 4$ ___21___
15. $18 \div 3 \cdot 5 - 4$ ___26___   16. $10 + 28 \div 14 - 5$ ___7___

Insert grouping symbols to make each number sentence true.
17. $(3 + 5) \cdot 8 = 64$ 18. $4 \cdot (6 - 2) + 7 = 23$
19. $10 \div (3 + 2) \cdot 4 = 8$ 20. $(3 + 6) \cdot 2 = 18$

A city park has two walkways with a grassy area in the center, as shown in the diagram.
21. Write an expression for the area of the sidewalks, using subtraction.
___$12 \cdot 10 - 12 \cdot 6$___
22. Write an expression for the area of the sidewalks, using addition.
___$3 \cdot 12 + 1 \cdot 12$___

Compare. Use >, <, or = to complete each statement.
23. $(24 - 8) \div 4$ _<_ $24 - 8 \div 4$ 24. $3 \cdot (4 - 2) \cdot 5$ _>_ $3 \cdot 4 - 2 \cdot 5$
25. $(22 + 8) \div 2$ _<_ $22 + 8 \div 2$ 26. $20 \div 2 + 8 \cdot 2$ _>_ $20 \div (2 + 8) \cdot 2$
27. $11 \cdot 4 - 2$ _>_ $11 \cdot (4 - 2)$ 28. $(7 \cdot 3) - (4 \cdot 2)$ _=_ $7 \cdot 3 - 4 \cdot 2$

Enrichment 1-2 *Binary Operations*

A *binary operation* is an operation performed on two numbers. Addition, subtraction, multiplication, and division are all binary operations. Once you known how to use a binary operation, you can perform it on any two numbers.
Here is a new binary operation. # means "multiply the numbers, then add the second number to the product."
Example $5 \# 4 = 5 \times 4 + 4 = 24$

Use the operation # to solve.
1. $3 \# 2$ ___8___   2. $8 \# 5$ ___45___   3. $1 \# 7$ ___14___
4. $10 \# 9$ ___99___   5. $4 \# (2 \# 7)$ ___105___   6. $(3 \# 4) \# 5$ ___85___
7. Evaluate $3 \# 5 + 2$ doing the operation # first. ___22___
8. Evaluate $3 \# 5 + 2$ doing the operation + first. ___28___
9. Complete the following order of operation rule, guaranteeing that the value of $3 \# 5 + 2$ will be 28: When evaluating an expression involving # and +, ___do the operation + first___
10. Use your rule to evaluate $8 \# 6 + 3$. ___81___

Discover how to use each binary operation by studying the examples. Then perform the operation on the given numbers.
Example $2 * 5 = 20$ $4 * 3 = 24$ $7 * 5 = 70$ $10 * 10 = 200$
11. $3 * 6$ ___36___   12. $5 * 5$ ___50___   13. $8 * 2$ ___32___
14. $12 * 12$ ___288___   15. $(2 * 2) * 4$ ___64___   16. $2 *(2 * 4)$ ___64___

Example $4 \$ 1 = 17$ $6 \$ 3 = 39$ $9 \$ 2 = 83$ $10 \$ 1 = 101$
17. $5 \$ 3$ ___28___   18. $2 \$ 7$ ___11___   19. $7 \$ 13$ ___62___
20. $12 \$ 10$ ___154___   21. $(2 \$ 3) \$ 4$ ___53___   22. $2 \$ (3 \$ 4)$ ___17___

11

Lesson Quiz 1-2

Simplify each expression.

1. $7(3) - 2 \cdot 4$ 13

2. $6 \div 2 + 1 \cdot 5$ 8

3. $10 \div (4 + 1)$ 2

4. $3[9 \cdot 2 \div (10 - 4)]$ 9

Alternative Assessment

Have students work with partners to write a numerical expression involving two or more operations. Write the expression on one side of an index card and its value on the other side. Have partners exchange cards and simplify the expression. They can check their answer by looking on the back of the card.

Test Prep

 **Resources**

For additional practice with a variety of test item formats:

• Test Prep, p. 61
• Test-Taking Strategies, p. 56
• Test-Taking Strategies With Transparencies

Reteaching 1-2 *The Order of Operations*

Simplify $\frac{18 + 4}{2} - 3(10 \cdot 2 - 3 \cdot 6)$

$\frac{18 + 4}{2} - 3(10 \cdot 2 - 3 \cdot 6)$ Work inside grouping symbols first.

$= \frac{22}{2} - 3(10 \cdot 2 - 3 \cdot 6)$ A fraction bar is a grouping symbol.

$= 11 - 3(10 \cdot 2 - 3 \cdot 6)$ Divide the fraction.

$= 11 - 3(20 - 18)$ Multiply within the parentheses.

$= 11 - 3(2)$ Subtract within the parentheses.

$= 11 - 6$ Multiply.

$= 5$

Simplify each expression.

1. $8 + 2 \times 7$ 22
2. $16 \div 2 - 5$ 3
3. $\frac{8 + 12}{5}$ 4
4. $4 - 24 \div 8$ 1
5. $3 + 2 \cdot 5 - 4$ 9
6. $15 - 2(5 - 2)$ 9
7. $9 \cdot 3 + 2 \cdot 5$ 37
8. $12 \div 4 - 6 \div 3$ 1
9. $5(2 + 4) + 15 \div (9 - 6)$ 35
10. $3 \cdot 2 + 16 \div 4 - 3$ 7
11. $(18 + 7) \div (3 + 2)$ 5
12. $3[8 - 3 \cdot 2 + 4(5 - 2)]$ 42
13. $4 \cdot 9 + 8 \div 2 - 6 \cdot 5$ 10
14. $[7 + 3 \cdot 2 + 8] \div 7$ 3
15. $53 - [3(8 + 2) + 5(9 - 5)]$ 3
16. $(20 + 22) \div 6 + 1$ 8
17. $2[9(6 - 5)]$ 18
18. $5 + 3 \cdot 4 - 8 \div 2 \cdot 7$ 23

---

46. On the Job A part-time employee worked 4 hours on Monday and 7 hours each day for the next 3 days. Write and simplify an expression that shows the total number of hours worked.
$4 + 7 \cdot 3$; 25 hours

C Challenge
Write two expressions you could use to find the area of each shaded figure. Find the area. 47–49. Answers may vary. See left.

47. Sample:
$(6 \times 5) - (4 \times 2)$ and
$(6 \times 3) + (2 \times 2)$;
22 in.^{2}

48. Sample:
$(6 \times 6) - (2 \times 2)$ and
$(2 \times 6) + (2 \times 2) + (2 \times 2) + (2 \times 2)$; 32 m^2

49. Sample: $(5 \times 4) - (3 \times 3)$ and
$(4 \times 1) + (4 \times 1) + (3 \times 1)$; 11 ft^2

47.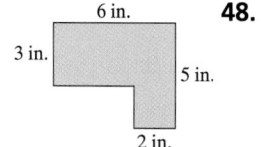
3 in. | 6 in. | 5 in. | 2 in.

48.
2 m | 2 m | 6 m | 2 m | 2 m | 6 m

49.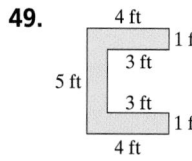
4 ft | 1 ft | 3 ft | 5 ft | 3 ft | 1 ft | 4 ft

50. Open-Ended Write a word problem for the numerical expression $3(4 + 3) + 2$. Then simplify the expression. **See margin.**

51. Number Sense Use the digits 1–9 in order. Insert operation signs and grouping symbols to get a value of 100.
Answers may vary. Sample: $1 + 2 + 3 + 4 + 5 + 6 + 7 + (8 \cdot 9)$

Test Prep

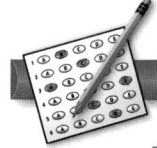

Multiple Choice

52. Which expression has a value of 18? **D**
A. $3 \cdot 2 + 4$
B. $(18 - 10) \div 4 + 15$
C. $4 \cdot 2 + 3 - 2$
D. $27 - 13 \cdot 2 + 17(6 - 5)$

53. Which expression gives the area of the garden? **G**
F. $4(2 + 5) + 5 \cdot 5$
G. $(2 + 5 + 2) \cdot (2 + 5 + 2) - 4(2 \cdot 2)$
H. $(2 + 5 + 2) - (2 \cdot 2)$
I. $4(2 \cdot 2) + 4(5 \cdot 2) + 5 \cdot 5$

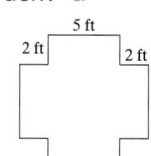
5 ft | 2 ft | 2 ft

54. Which set of grouping symbols makes the equation true? $2 \cdot 3 + 5 - 2 \cdot 2 = 12$ **D**
A. $(2 \cdot 3) + 5 - (2 \cdot 2)$
B. $2 \cdot [3 + (5 - 2)] \cdot 2$
C. $2 \cdot [3 + (5 - 2 \cdot 2)]$
D. $2 \cdot (3 + 5) - 2 \cdot 2$

55. What is the value of $8 \cdot 5 - 3(24 \div 6)$? **F**
F. 28
G. 64
H. 111
I. 148

Test-Taking Tip
You should consider all answer choices before deciding on the appropriate one.

Take It to the NET
Online lesson quiz at
www.PHSchool.com
Web Code: ada-0102

Mixed Review

Lesson 1-1 **Write a variable expression for each word phrase.**

56. the product of a number n and 8 **8n**

57. k divided by 20 $\frac{k}{20}$

58. six less than a number h **h − 6**

59. the value, in cents, of d dimes **10d**

60. A telephone call costs c cents per minute. Write a variable expression for the cost of a 15-minute call. **15c**

 Use the Guided Problem Solving worksheet with Exercise 46.

50. Answers may vary. Sample: Payton bought 4 pairs of blue socks and 3 pairs of red socks at $3 a pair. She also bought a hat for $2. What was the total cost of her purchases? $23

The description below explains how to read an example. Read the description. Study the Example. Then do the exercises at the bottom of the page to check your understanding.

Before an example, there usually is information that will help you understand what the example is teaching. For Example 3 on page 9, the paragraph before the Key Concepts box describes grouping symbols and how to work with them.

The Key Concepts box shows you that your work with grouping symbols occurs first in the order of operations:

1. Work inside grouping symbols.

2. Multiply and divide in order from left to right.

3. Add and subtract in order from left to right.

Examples show you how to use the concepts taught in the lesson. In an example, the steps are on the left and the explanations are in **bold** on the right. As you read an example, make sure you understand each step and its explanation.

EXAMPLE **Simplifying With Grouping Symbols**

Simplify $10 \div [9 - (2 \cdot 2)]$.

$10 \div [9 - (2 \cdot 2)]$ Read the problem and locate the grouping symbols.

The **red** lines show the work inside the innermost grouping symbols.

$10 \div [9 - 4]$ **Multiply within parentheses.** The text in bold explains the step.

$10 \div 5$ **Subtract within brackets.** Make mental math checks while you read:
$2 \cdot 2 = 4 \checkmark$
$9 - 4 = 5 \checkmark$

2 **Divide.** $10 \div 5 = 2 \checkmark$

✓ **Check Understanding** appears after each Example. It provides exercises like the following to let you instantly check how well you understand what is being taught in the Example.

EXERCISES

Simplify each expression.

1. $2[(13 - 4) \div 3]$ 6

2. $1 + \dfrac{10 - 2}{4}$ 3

3. $3[(8 + 4) \div 6]$ 6

4. $\dfrac{6 + 9}{3} - 2$ 3

5. $4 \cdot [3 + (2 \cdot 3)]$ 36

6. $16 \div (8 - 4) - 2$ 2

Reading an Example

In this feature, students "read" an example to understand and learn how to simplify an expression.

Teaching Notes

Teaching Tip
Explain to students that there is a hierarchy in grouping symbols. You first do the work inside the parentheses ( ), then inside the brackets [ ], and finally inside the braces { }, if these symbols are included in the problem.

Teaching Tip
The text in bold black at the right of the steps in an Example is "teaching text." Each line of teaching text gives the reason why its solution step follows from the preceding one.

Inclusion
Some students may not "see" how the problem changes between the first step and the second step. Have students place a finger on $(2 \cdot 2)$ in the first step. Ask: *What is two times two?* 4 Then have students drag the finger down to the 4 below it. Repeat for the other steps.

1. Plan

Lesson Preview

 Check Skills You'll Need

The Order of Operations
Lesson 1-2: Example 3;
Exercises 13–21.
Extra Practice, p. 744.

Lesson Resources

 **Teaching Resources**
Practice, Reteaching, Enrichment

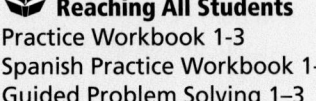 **Reaching All Students**
Practice Workbook 1-3
Spanish Practice Workbook 1-3
Guided Problem Solving 1–3
Technology Activities 2

 **Presentation Assistant Plus!**
Transparencies and PowerPoint™
• Check Skills You'll Need 1-3
• Additional Examples 1-3
• Student Edition Answers 1-3
• Lesson Quiz 1-3
PH Presentation Pro CD-ROM 1-3

ASSESSMENT SYSTEM

Computer Test Generator CD-ROM

 Technology
Resource Pro® CD-ROM
Computer Test Generator CD-ROM
PH Presentation Pro CD-ROM

 www.PHSchool.com

Student Site
• Teacher Web Code: adk-5500
• Algebra Readiness Puzzles 25, 26
• Self-grading Lesson Quiz
PH SuccessNet Teacher Center
• Lesson Planner
• Resources

Plus

What You'll Learn

OBJECTIVE 1 To evaluate variable expressions

OBJECTIVE 2 To solve problems by evaluating expressions

. . . And Why

To solve real-world problems involving packaging and shopping

 Check Skills You'll Need

Simplify each expression.

1. $6(9 + 1)$ 60

2. $17 - 2 + 3$ 18

3. $9 + 8 \cdot 2 + 4$ 29

4. $[3(5) + 1] \cdot 2$ 32

 For help, go to Lesson 1-2.

New Vocabulary

• evaluate

To **evaluate** a variable expression, you first replace each variable with a number. Then, you use the order of operations to simplify.

1 EXAMPLE **Evaluating a Variable Expression**

Evaluate $4y - 15$ for $y = 9$.

$$4y - 15 = 4(9) - 15 \quad \text{Replace } y \text{ with 9.}$$
$$= 36 - 15 \quad \text{Multiply.}$$
$$= 21 \quad \text{Subtract.}$$

 Check Understanding **Example 1**

1. Evaluate each expression.

a. $63 - 5x$, for $x = 7$ 28   **b.** $4(t + 3) + 1$, for $t = 8$ 45

Sometimes expressions have more than one variable.

2 EXAMPLE **Replacing More Than One Variable**

Evaluate $3ab + \frac{c}{2}$ for $a = 2$, $b = 5$, and $c = 10$.

$$3ab + \frac{c}{2} = 3 \cdot 2 \cdot 5 + \frac{10}{2} \quad \text{Replace the variables.}$$
$$= 3 \cdot 2 \cdot 5 + 5 \quad \text{Work within grouping symbols.}$$
$$= 6 \cdot 5 + 5 \quad \text{Multiply from left to right.}$$
$$= 30 + 5 \quad \text{Multiply.}$$
$$= 35 \quad \text{Add.}$$

 Check Understanding **Example 2**

2. Evaluate each expression.

a. $6(g + h)$, for $g = 8$ and $h = 7$ 90
b. $2xy - z$, for $x = 4$, $y = 3$, and $z = 1$ 23
c. $\frac{r + s}{2}$, for $r = 13$ and $s = 11$ 12

iTEXT Interactive lesson includes instant self-check, tutorials, and activities.

Ongoing Assessment and Intervention

Before the Lesson
Diagnose prerequisite skills using:
• Check Skills You'll Need

During the Lesson
Monitor progress using:
• Check Understanding
• Additional Examples
• Test Prep

After the Lesson
Assess knowledge using:
• Lesson Quiz
• Computer Test Generator CD-ROM

2 Solving Problems by Evaluating Expressions

You can write and evaluate variable expressions to solve problems.

---

3 EXAMPLE   Real-World Problem Solving

Purchasing Energy drinks come in cases of 24 bottles.
a. Write a variable expression for the number of cases a store should order to get *b* bottles of energy drinks.
b. Evaluate the expression for 120 bottles.

a. *b* bottles

$$\frac{b}{24}$$

b. 120 bottles

$$\frac{b}{24} = \frac{120}{24}$$ Evaluate for *b* = 120.

$$= 5$$ Divide.

● The store should order five cases to get 120 bottles.

✔ **Check Understanding**   Example 3

3. The store in Example 3 pays $29 for each case of energy drinks. Write a variable expression for the cost of *c* cases. Evaluate the expression to find the cost of five cases. 29*c*; $145

---

4 EXAMPLE   Real-World Problem Solving

Online Shopping An online music store charges $14 for each CD. Shipping costs $6 per order. Write a variable expression for the cost of ordering CDs. Find the cost of ordering four CDs.

Words	$14	for each	CD	plus	$6 shipping

Let *n* = number of CDs.

Expression	14	·	*n*	+	6

Evaluate the expression for *n* = 4.

$$14 \cdot n + 6 = 14 \cdot 4 + 6$$ **Replace *n* with 4.**

$$= 56 + 6$$ **Multiply.**

$$= 62$$ **Add.**

● It costs $62 to order four CDs.

✔ **Check Understanding**   Example 4

4. Evaluate the expression in Example 4 to find the cost of ordering seven CDs. $104

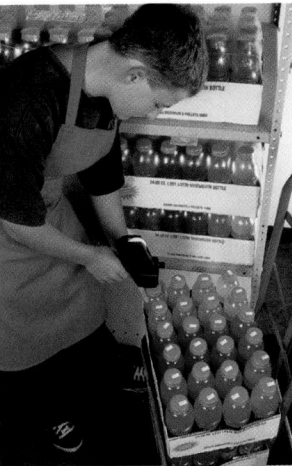

Real-World Connection

In a case, bottles are often arranged in 4 rows of 6 (or 6 rows of 4).

Reading Math

In Example 4, the phrase *for each* implies multiplication. So *$14 for each CD* means "$14 times the number of CDs."

---

2. Teach

Math Background

You may wish to introduce *term* and *coefficient* at this time (see Lesson 2-3). In the expression (or term) 4*y*, 4 is the coefficient of *y*. In any term with one variable, the coefficient is the number that multiplies the variable. When you do not see the number, such as in *x*, it is understood to be 1.

Teaching Notes

1 EXAMPLE English Learners

Explain that *evaluate* means to find the numerical *value*.

2 EXAMPLE Error Prevention

Students sometimes replace a variable with the wrong number. Encourage students to cross out each variable and write its replacement number above it.

Additional Examples

1 Evaluate 18 + 2*g* for *g* = 3. **24**

2 Evaluate $2ab - \frac{c}{3}$ for *a* = 3, *b* = 4, and *c* = 9. **21**

3 The Omelet Café buys cartons of 36 eggs.
   a. Write a variable expression for the number of cartons needed for *x* eggs. $\frac{x}{36}$
   b. Evaluate the expression for 180 eggs. **5 cartons**

4 The One Pizza restaurant makes only one kind of pizza, which costs $16. The delivery charge is $2. Write a variable expression for the cost of having pizzas delivered. Evaluate the expression to find the cost of having two pizzas delivered. **16 · *p* + 2; $34**

Closure

Ask students to give examples of how they could use variable expressions in their lives. Have them select one example and then write and evaluate a variable expression for it.

👥 **Reaching All Students**

Below Level Have students write an expression representing how much they would make if paid $3 per hour for a job. Then have them evaluate the expression for 8 hours of work. 3*t*; $24	**Advanced Learners** Challenge students to write a problem that is similar to Example 4 using shipping rates of some other online store.	**English Learners** See note on page 15. **Error Prevention** See note on page 15.

Assignment Guide

1 Objective 1
Ⓐ Ⓑ Core 1–14, 17–26, 29, 30
Ⓒ Extension 33

2 Objective 2
Ⓐ Ⓑ Core 15, 16, 27, 28, 31
Ⓒ Extension 32

Test Prep 34–37
Mixed Review 38–44

Practice 1-3 *Evaluating Expressions*

Evaluate each expression.

1. xy, for $x = 3$ and $y = 5$ ___15___
2. $24 - p \cdot 5$, for $p = 4$ ___4___
3. $5a + b$, for $a = 6$ and $b = 3$ ___33___
4. $6x$, for $x = 3$ ___18___
5. $9 - k$, for $k = 2$ ___7___
6. $63 \div p$, for $p = 7$ ___9___
7. $2 + n$, for $n = 3$ ___5___
8. $3m$, for $m = 11$ ___33___
9. $10 - r + 5$, for $r = 9$ ___6___
10. $m + n + 6$, for $m = 12$ and $n = 18$ ___15___
11. $1,221 + x$, for $x = 37$ ___33___
12. $10 - x$, for $x = 3$ ___7___
13. $4m + 3$, for $m = 5$ ___23___
14. $35 - 3x$, for $x = 10$ ___5___
15. $851 - p$, for $p = 215$ ___636___
16. $18a - 9b$, for $a = 12$ and $b = 15$ ___81___
17. $3ab - c$, for $a = 4, b = 2$, and $c = 5$ ___19___
18. $\frac{ab}{2} + 4c$, for $a = 6, b = 5$, and $c = 3$ ___27___
19. $\frac{rst}{2}$, for $r = 9, s = 2$, and $t = 4$ ___24___
20. $x(y + 5) - z$, for $x = 3, y = 2$, and $z = 7$ ___14___
21. Elliot is 58 years old.
   a. Write an expression for the number of years by which Elliot's age exceeds that of his daughter, who is y years old. ___$58 - y$___
   b. If his daughter is 25, how much older is Elliot? ___33 years___
22. A tree grows 5 in. each year.
   a. Write an expression for the tree's height after x years. ___$5x$___
   b. When the tree is 36 years old, how tall will it be? ___180 in.___

Enrichment 1-3 *Equal Expressions*

The value of a variable expression depends upon the value of the variable. By choosing the correct value, you can cause two expressions to be equal. The expressions $x - 6$ and $2x - 11$, for example, both have the same value when $x = 5$.

$$x - 6 = 5 - 6 \qquad 2x - 11 = 2(5) - 11$$
$$= -1 \qquad\qquad = 10 - 11$$
$$\qquad\qquad = -1$$

Complete the tables for the given values of the variables. Then in the space to the right, name the value of the variable for which the two expressions are equal.

1.
k	10	11	12	13	14	15	16	17
$5 + k$	15	16	17	18	19	20	21	22
$2k - 9$	11	13	15	17	19	21	23	25

$k =$ ___14___

2.
x	1	2	3	4	5	6	7	8
$10 - x$	9	8	7	6	5	4	3	2
$3x - 2$	1	4	7	10	13	16	19	22

$x =$ ___3___

3.
n	2	3	4	5	6	7	8	9
$2n - 3$	1	3	5	7	9	11	13	15
$27 - 3n$	21	18	15	12	9	6	3	0

$n =$ ___6___

4.
h	0	1	2	3	4	5	6	7
$5h + 7$	7	12	17	22	27	32	37	42
$6h + 1$	1	7	13	19	25	31	37	43

$h =$ ___6___

5.
a	0	1	2	3	4	5	6	7
$29 - 2a$	29	27	25	23	21	19	17	15
$3a + 4$	4	7	10	13	16	19	22	25

$a =$ ___5___

6. Explain why there is no value of x for which the expressions $x + 3$ and $x + 4$ are equal.
For every value of x, $x + 3 < x + 4$.

EXERCISES

Practice and Problem Solving

For more exercises, see *Extra Practice.*

Ⓐ **Practice by Example**

Example 1 (page 14)

Evaluate each expression.

1. $7b$, for $b = 5$ **35**
2. $5 - c$, for $c = 3$ **2**
3. $x \div 8$, for $x = 40$ **5**
4. $3n + 2$, for $n = 7$ **23**
5. $41 - 4h$, for $h = 10$ **1**
6. $5a + 7$, for $a = 20$ **107**

Example 2 (page 14)

Evaluate each expression for $x = 2, y = 3$, and $z = 10$.

7. xyz **60**
8. $8y \div x$ **12**
9. $\frac{z}{5} + 2$ **4**
10. $4y - x$ **10**
11. $2z + xy$ **26**
12. $\frac{9 + y}{x}$ **6**
13. $4xy - z$ **14**
14. $5(y + z)$ **65**

Examples 3 and 4 (page 15)

15. **Word Processing** An office assistant types 55 words per minute.
   a. Write a variable expression for the number of words the office assistant types in m minutes. **55m**
   b. Evaluate the expression for 20 minutes. **1,100 words**

16. **Online Purchasing** An online video store charges $24 for each DVD. Shipping costs $4 per order.
   a. Write a variable expression for the cost of ordering DVDs.
   b. Find the cost of ordering 3 DVDs. **$76**   **24d + 4**

Ⓑ **Apply Your Skills**

Evaluate each expression.

17. $2a + 5$, for $a = 5$ **15**
18. $105z$, for $z = 7$ **735**
19. $6 \div a + 8$, for $a = 2$ **11**
20. $19 - (a - 4)$, for $a = 8$ **15**
21. $13ab$, for $a = 1$ and $b = 7$ **91**
22. $16 - 4mn$, for $m = 0$ and $n = 3$ **16**
23. $j(5 + k)$, for $j = 11$ and $k = 4$ **99**
24. rst, for $r = 5, s = 5$, and $t = 5$ **125**
25. $\frac{150}{z + y}$, for $y = 25$ and $z = 50$ **2**
26. $\frac{x - y}{4}$, for $x = 52$ and $y = 12$ **10**

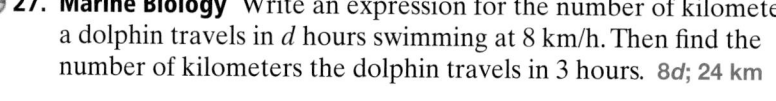

27. **Marine Biology** Write an expression for the number of kilometers a dolphin travels in d hours swimming at 8 km/h. Then find the number of kilometers the dolphin travels in 3 hours. **8d; 24 km**

28. **Data Analysis** Use the chart to find how many calories a 100-lb person uses in an hour of moderate walking.
   a. Write an expression for the number of calories a 100-lb person uses in moderate walking for w hours. **153w**
   b. Evaluate the expression to find the number of calories a 100-lb person uses in moderate walking for 2 hours. **306 calories**

Calories per Hour Used by a 100-lb Walker

Type of Walking	Calories
Slow	110
Moderate	153
Brisk	175
Racing	295

SOURCE: www.nutristrategy.com

Real-World Connection

By *porpoising* (jumping clear of the water), dolphins can travel as fast as 26 km/h.

29. **Error Analysis** Your friend evaluates $(10 - k) \div 5$ for $k = 5$, and gets 9 for an answer. Explain your friend's error. **Answers may vary. Sample: You did not work within the grouping symbols first.**

30. Evaluate $4a - b + \frac{b}{2}$, for $a = 3$ and $b = 4$. 10

31. A fitness club requires a $100 initiation fee and dues of $25 each month. Write an expression for the cost of membership for n months. Then find the cost of membership for one year.

$100 + 25n$; $400

C Challenge

32. A carnival charges $5 for admission plus $2 per ride. $5 + 2r$
  a. Write an expression for the cost of admission plus r rides.
  b. Find the cost of admission plus six rides. $17
  c. How many rides can you afford if you have $15 to spend?
  5 rides

33. <u>**Writing in Math**</u> Write a word problem that could be solved by evaluating the expression $3x - 5$ for $x = 5$. Answers may vary. Sample: Liam has 5 fewer than 3 times the number of cards that Jamie has. Jamie has 5 cards. How many cards does Liam have?

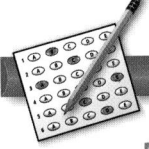

Test Prep

Multiple Choice

In Exercises 34–37, use the following fact to answer the questions: Every minute, about 145 babies are born in the world.

34. Which expression shows how many babies are born in the world in m minutes? **D**
  A. $60m$ **B.** $145m + 60$
  C. $60m + 145$ **D.** $145m$

35. How many babies are born in the world in 6 minutes? **H**
  F. 360 babies   **G.** 505 babies
  H. 870 babies   **I.** 930 babies

36. How many babies are born in the world in one day? **D**
  A. 3,480 babies   **B.** 86,400 babies
  C. 104,400 babies   **D.** 208,800 babies

Take It to the NET
Online lesson quiz at
www.PHSchool.com
Web Code: ada-0103

37. How many babies are born in the world in one week? **F**
  F. 1,461,600 babies   **G.** 522,000 babies
  H. 60,900 babies   **I.** 10,080 babies

Mixed Review

Lesson 1-2   **Simplify each expression.**

38. $(60 - 6) \div 9$ 6   **39.** $80 \div 2 + 13$ 53   **40.** $5 \div 5 \cdot 5 - 5$ 0

Lesson 1-1   **Write a variable expression for each word phrase.**

41. t fewer than 19   **42.** d divided by 20   **43.** the sum of 8 and n
$19 - t$ $\frac{d}{20}$ $8 + n$

Previous Course

44. Error Analysis Valerie has test grades of 96, 82, 78, and 76. Using a calculator, she found her average grade to be 275. Is Valerie's answer reasonable? Explain Valerie's error. No; Valerie's average grade should be in the 80s. Valerie evaluated $96 + 82 + 78 + 76 \div 4$ on her calculator instead of $\frac{96 + 82 + 78 + 76}{4}$.

1-3 Evaluating Expressions   **17**

 Use the Guided Problem Solving worksheet with Exercise 31.

1. Plan

Lesson Preview

✔ Check Skills You'll Need

Working With Integers
Skills Handbook: p. 775;
Example 1; Exercises 1–8.

Lesson Resources

📁 **Teaching Resources**
Practice, Reteaching, Enrichment
Checkpoint Quiz 1

🌱 **Reaching All Students**
Practice Workbook 1-4
Spanish Practice Workbook 1-4
Reading and Math Literacy 1B
Spanish Reading and Math
  Literacy 1B
Spanish Checkpoint Quiz 1
Guided Problem Solving 1-4
Hands-On Activities 29

🕐 **Presentation Assistant Plus!**
Transparencies and PowerPoint™
• Check Skills You'll Need 1-4
• Additional Examples 1-4
• Student Edition Answers 1-4
• Lesson Quiz 1-4
• Classroom Aid 6
PH Presentation Pro CD-ROM 1-4

ASSESSMENT SYSTEM

Checkpoint Quiz 1
Computer Test Generator CD-ROM

💻 **Technology**
Resource Pro® CD-ROM
Computer Test Generator CD-ROM
PH Presentation Pro CD-ROM

💻 **www.PHSchool.com**
Student Site
• Teacher Web Code: adk-5500
• Algebra Readiness Puzzles 27
• Self-grading Lesson Quiz
PH SuccessNet Teacher Center
• Lesson Planner
• Resources

Plus 🔲TEXT

18

What You'll Learn

OBJECTIVE 1 To represent, graph, and order integers

OBJECTIVE 2 To find opposites and absolute values

. . . And Why

To represent real-world quantities that are less than zero, such as cold temperatures

✔ Check Skills You'll Need

Write an integer for each situation.

1. lose $7   −7

2. find $9   9

3. 8 steps forward   8

4. 3 yards gained   3

5. 5 floors down   −5

❓ For help, go to Skills Handbook, p. 775.

New Vocabulary

• opposites
• integers
• absolute value

🔲TEXT Interactive lesson includes instant self-check, tutorials, and activities.

Antifreeze is mixed with the water in a car's radiator to prevent the water from freezing. Pure water freezes at about 32 degrees Fahrenheit (°F) *above* zero. A mixture of equal parts water and antifreeze freezes at about 32 degrees *below* zero.

Freezing Points

Substance	Freezing Temperature (°F)
Water	32
Antifreeze and water	−32
Seawater	28
Gasoline	−36

You can write 32 degrees above zero as +32°F or 32°F. You can write 32 degrees below zero as −32°F. Read the numbers 32 and −32 as "*positive* 32" and "*negative* 32," respectively.

1 EXAMPLE   **Representing Negative Numbers**

Temperature Write a number to represent the temperature shown by the thermometer.

The temperature of the liquid in the thermometer is 4 degrees Celsius below zero, ● or −4°C.

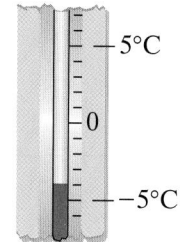

✔ Check Understanding   Example 1

1. Temperature Seawater freezes at about 28°F, or about 2 degrees Celsius below zero. Write a number to represent the Celsius temperature. −2

You can graph positive and negative numbers on a number line. A number line helps you compare numbers and arrange them in order.

Numbers increase in value from left to right.

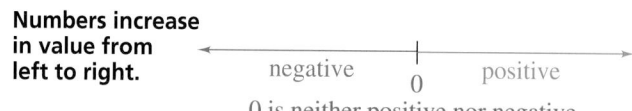

0 is neither positive nor negative.

Ongoing Assessment and Intervention

Before the Lesson
Diagnose prerequisite skills using:
• Check Skills You'll Need

During the Lesson
Monitor progress using:
• Check Understanding
• Additional Examples
• Test Prep

After the Lesson
Assess knowledge using:
• Lesson Quiz
• Computer Test Generator CD-ROM
• Chapter Checkpoint 1 (p. 22)

2 EXAMPLE Graphing on a Number Line

Graph −1, 4, and −5 on a number line. Order the numbers from least to greatest.

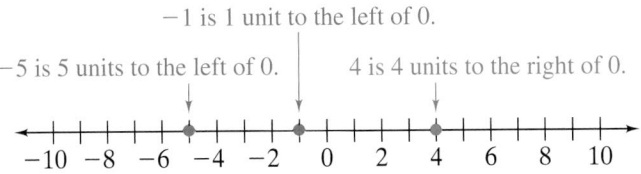

−1 is 1 unit to the left of 0.

−5 is 5 units to the left of 0.

4 is 4 units to the right of 0.

● The numbers from least to greatest are −5, −1, and 4.

✓ Check Understanding Example 2

2. Graph 0, 2, and −6 on a number line. Order the numbers from least to greatest.

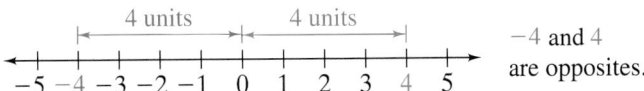

−6

−1 0 1 2

−6, 0, 2

OBJECTIVE

2 Finding Absolute Value

Numbers that are the same distance from zero on a number line but in opposite directions are called **opposites.**

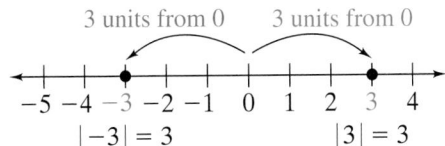

4 units | 4 units

−5 −4 −3 −2 −1 0 1 2 3 4 5

−4 and 4 are opposites.

Integers are the whole numbers and their opposites. A number's distance from zero on the number line is called its **absolute value.** You write *the absolute value of 3* as |3|.

> **Need Help?**
> Recall: The whole numbers, 0, 1, 2, 3, 4, . . . , are the counting numbers and zero.

3 EXAMPLE Finding Absolute Value

Use a number line to find |−3| and |3|.

3 units from 0 | 3 units from 0

−5 −4 −3 −2 −1 0 1 2 3 4

|−3| = 3 | |3| = 3

✓ Check Understanding Example 3

3. Write |−10| in words. Then find |−10|.
   the absolute value of negative ten; 10

Professional Development

Math Background

Integers are the whole numbers and their opposites. Zero separates positive and negative integers on a number line. Zero is neither positive nor negative and is its own opposite.

Teaching Notes

English Learners
Students may confuse minus signs and negative signs when reading problems. There is a space after the minus sign, whereas the negative sign sits next to its number.

2 EXAMPLE Visual Learners
On the chalkboard, draw a number line with tick marks, but with 0 as the only number shown. Point to places on the number line for integers and ask the students to name each integer.

3 EXAMPLE Teaching Tip
Students can read the first vertical line in an absolute value as "the distance that," and read the second vertical line as "is from zero." So |3| is read as "the distance that three is from zero."

PowerPoint

📃 Additional Examples

❶ Write a number to represent the temperature shown by the thermometer.
2 degrees Celsius below zero, or −2°C

5°C
0
−5°C

❷ Graph 2, −2, and −3 on a number line. Order the numbers from least to greatest. −3, −2, 2

−6 −5 −4 −3 −2 −1 0 1 2 3 4 5

❸ Use a number line to find |−5| and |5|. 5, 5

Closure

Ask: *What are integers?* the set of whole numbers and their opposites *What is the absolute value of −5?* 5 *What number is neither positive nor negative?* 0

👥 Reaching All Students

Below Level Give each student a number line. Have them practice finding numbers on the number line. Practice counting the distance between numbers.

Advanced Learners Have students evaluate |−12|−|12|. 0 Ask: *Will the value be the same for any integer in place of 12 and its opposite in place of −12?* yes

English Learners See note on page 19. **Error Prevention** See note on page 21.

19

Assignment Guide

 **Objective 1**
- **Ⓐ Ⓑ Core** 1–15, 28–34, 41–43, 47–54
- **Ⓒ Extension** 56–60

Objective 2
- **Ⓐ Ⓑ Core** 16–27, 35–40, 44–46, 55
- **Ⓒ Extension** 61

Test Prep 62–65
Mixed Review 66–71

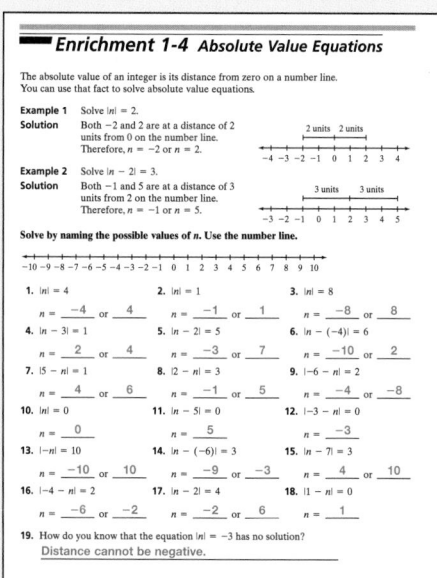

EXERCISES

For more exercises, see *Extra Practice*.

Practice and Problem Solving

Ⓐ Practice by Example

Write a number to represent each quantity.

Example 1
(page 18)

1. a profit of $250
250

2. 18°C below zero
−18

3. 45 s before launch
−45

4. a deposit of $110
110

5. a debt of $50
−50

6. win by 7 points
7

7. 300 ft below sea level −300

8. a loss of 8 yd
−8

9. an elevation of 3,400 ft 3,400

Example 2
(page 19)

Write the number represented by each point on the number line.

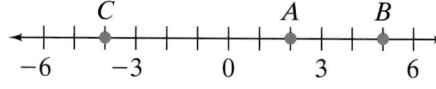

10. *A* 2

11. *B* 5

12. *C* −4

Graph each set of numbers on a number line. Then order the numbers from least to greatest. 13–15. Graphs. See margin.

 13. −2, 8, −9
−9, −2, 8

14. −3, −12, −9
−12, −9, −3

15. 0, 6, −6
−6, 0, 6

Example 3
(page 19)

Use a number line to find the absolute values of the integers in each pair.

16. 1, −1
1, 1

17. −2, 2
2, 2

18. −8, 8
8, 8

19. −7, 7
7, 7

20. 6, −6
6, 6

21. −4, 4
4, 4

Simplify each expression.

22. |18| 18

23. the absolute value of −9 9

24. |−3| 3

25. the absolute value of 6 6

26. |−7| 7

27. the absolute value of −2 2

Ⓑ Apply Your Skills

Open-Ended Describe a quantity each integer could represent.
28–30. See left.

28. Answers may vary. Sample: loss of 1,000 points in a board game

29. Answers may vary. Sample: 28 golf strokes over par

30. Answers may vary. Sample: checkbook balance for checks totalling $126 more than is in the account.

28. −1,000

29. 28

30. −126

Write the integer represented by each point.

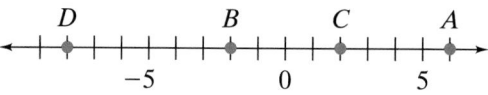

31. *A* 6

32. *B* −2

33. *C* 2

34. *D* −8

Simplify each expression.

35. |0| 0

36. |−1,000| 1,000

37. −|−13| −13

38. |−56| 56

39. −|−23| −23

40. −|12| −12

Compare. Use >, <, or = to complete each statement.

41. −8 ■ 0 <

42. 4 ■ −25 >

43. −9 ■ −2 <

44. |−1| ■ |50| <

45. |−6| ■ |−12| <

46. |10| ■ |−10| =

20 Chapter 1 Algebraic Expressions and Integers

 Use the Guided Problem Solving worksheet with Exercise 13.

13.
−9 −2 0 8

14.
−12 −9 −3 0

15.
−6 0 6

Write an expression to represent each quantity.

47. 10 times your height *h* in inches 10*h*

48. a loss of $\frac{1}{3}$ of an investment of *d* dollars $-\frac{1}{3}d$

49. *n* degrees Fahrenheit above *r*°F room temperature *r* + *n*

Read the passage below before doing Exercises 50 and 51.

Finding Famous Ships

Scientist-explorer Robert D. Ballard led the expeditions that found two famous ships deep in the North Atlantic Ocean.

In 1912, the luxury passenger liner *Titanic* struck an iceberg. It came to rest 12,500 ft below sea level. *Titanic* was 882 ft long and 92 ft wide.

In 1941, the mighty warship *Bismarck* sank in battle. *Bismarck* was 823 ft long and 118 ft wide.

Star Hercules, only 269 ft long, towed the underwater camera sled that found *Bismarck* under 15,617 ft of water.

50. Write integers that represent the positions of *Titanic* and *Bismarck*. −12,500; −15,617

51. A friend says that *Bismarck*'s resting place is higher than *Titanic*'s, since 15,617 is higher than 12,500. Explain your friend's error. Answers may vary. Sample: My friend did not take into account the signs of the numbers.

Complete each sentence with a word that makes it true.

52. An integer is negative, positive, or ? . zero

53. All ? integers are less than zero. negative

54. The opposite of a ? number is negative. positive

55. The absolute value of an integer is never ? . negative

C Challenge **Open-Ended Name two consecutive integers between the given integers.** 56–58. Answers may vary. Samples are given.

56. −6, 2 −3, −2 **57.** 0, −4 −2, −1 **58.** −8, −12 −11, −10

Record Low Temperatures for Three States

State	Temperature (°C)
California	−45
Nevada	−50
Georgia	−17

59. a. Data Analysis Use a number line to graph the temperatures in the chart at the left. Label each temperature with the name of the state where it was recorded. See margin.
   b. Which state recorded the lowest temperature? Nevada

60. Writing in Math How can you use integers to describe elevations above and below sea level? See margin.

61. Reasoning Explain why $|x + y|$ and $|x| + |y|$ are not the same. Give examples to show that $|x + y| = |x| + |y|$ for some values of *x* and *y*, and $|x + y| \neq |x| + |y|$ for other values of *x* and *y*.
   See margin.

59a.

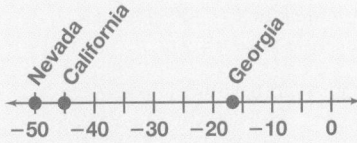

Nevada California Georgia

−50 −40 −30 −20 −10 0

60. Answers may vary. Sample: If sea level is zero, then water levels above sea level can be described by positive integers, and water levels below sea level can be described by negative integers.

61. No. Explanations may vary. Sample: If *x* and *y* have opposite signs, $|x + y| \neq |x| + |y|$. For *x* = −1 and *y* = 3, $|-1 + 3| = 2$ while $|-1| + |3| = 4$.

Lesson Quiz 1-4

Write an integer to represent each situation.

1. a debt of $50 -50

2. a dive of 23 feet below the surface -23

Simplify.

3. $|-12|$ 12

4. $|8|$ 8

✓ Chapter Checkpoint 1

To check understanding of Lessons 1-1 to 1-4:

Checkpoint Quiz 1 (p. 22)

  Teaching Resources
Checkpoint Quiz 1 (also in Prentice Hall Assessment System)

Reaching All Students
Reading and Math Literacy 1B

Spanish versions available.

Reteaching 1-4 Integers and Absolute Value

Compare. Use >, <, or = to complete each statement.

a. $-4 \square -2$

Graph -4 and -2 on the number line.

A number on the left is less than a number on the right.
Thus, -4 is less than -2.
$-4 < -2$

b. $|-4| \square |-2|$

The *absolute value* of a number is its distance from zero on the number line.

Thus $|-4| = 4$ and $|-2| = 2$.
Since $4 > 2$, $|-4| > |-2|$.

Compare. Use >, <, or = to complete each statement.

1. $-3 \boxed{<} -2$	2. $-5 \boxed{<} 1$	3. $0 \boxed{>} -2$
4. $1 \boxed{>} 0$	5. $1 \boxed{>} -1$	6. $-5 \boxed{<} -3$
7. $|-3| \boxed{>} 0$	8. $|-2| \boxed{<} |-5|$	9. $|-3| \boxed{>} 2$
10. $|-6| \boxed{=} 6$	11. $|3| \boxed{>} |-2|$	12. $|-7| \boxed{>} 0$
13. $-3 \boxed{<} |-3|$	14. $4 \boxed{>} |-2|$	15. $|-2| \boxed{<} 3$
16. $|-5| \boxed{>} 3$	17. $|8| \boxed{=} |-8|$	18. $-6 \boxed{<} -4$
19. $5 \boxed{>} |-4|$	20. $-3 \boxed{>} -5$	21. $|2| \boxed{<} |-3|$
22. $|-1| \boxed{=} |1|$	23. $|-3| \boxed{>} |-1|$	24. $-1 \boxed{<} 2$

Test Prep

Multiple Choice

62. Which list shows the values in order from least to greatest? **B**
 A. $0, 3, -17, -25$ **B.** $-25, -17, 0, 3$
 C. $0, -17, -25, 3$ **D.** $-25, 0, 3, -27$

63. Which expression has the value -90? **I**
 F. $|-90|$ **G.** 90 **H.** $|90|$ **I.** $-|90|$

64. Which list shows the values in order from least to greatest? **B**
 A. $|-6|, 6, |-3|, 3$ **B.** $-6, -|-3|, 3, |-6|$
 C. $|-6|, |-3|, |3|, |6|$ **D.** $-3, -|-6|, -|3|, 6$

65. Which two integers are between -5 and 2? **F**
 F. $-4, 1$ **G.** $-3, 3$ **H.** $-6, 1$ **I.** $0, 4$

Take It to the NET
Online lesson quiz at
www.PHSchool.com
Web Code: ada-0104

Mixed Review

Lesson 1-3 **Evaluate each expression.**

66. $p - 5$, for $p = 19$ **67.** $3d + 3$, for $d = 7$ **68.** $55y$, for $y = 8$
 14 24 440

Lesson 1-2 **Compare. Use >, <, or = to complete each statement.**

69. $5 + 10 \div 5 \blacksquare (5 + 10) \div 5$ $>$

70. $(9 - 6) \div (2 + 1) \blacksquare 9 - 6 \div 2 + 1$ $<$

Lesson 1-1 **71.** Suppose you have c CDs. Your friend has 6 more CDs than you do. Write an expression for the number of CDs your friend has.
 $c + 6$

✓ Checkpoint Quiz 1   Lessons 1-1 through 1-4

 Instant self-check quiz online and on CD-ROM

Write a variable expression for each word phrase.

1. 23 more than f **2.** g divided by 34 **3.** product of 9 and p
 $f + 23$ $\frac{g}{34}$ $9p$

Simplify each expression.

4. $17 + 16 - 13$ 20 **5.** $70 \div [5(3 + 4)]$ 2 **6.** $9 \times 6 \div 3 + 1$ 19

Evaluate each expression for $x = 4$, $y = 6$, and $z = 12$.

7. $2x - 8$ 0 **8.** $3(z + y)$ 54 **9.** $4y - z + \frac{z}{x}$ 15

🌐 **10. Temperature** On Monday the average temperature was $-10°F$. On Tuesday it was $-15°F$. On Wednesday it was $-13°F$. On Thursday it was $0°F$.
 a. Graph the temperatures on a number line. 10a–b. See margin.
 b. Write the days in order from coldest to warmest.

Checkpoint Quiz 1
10a.

$-15 \; -13 \; -10 \qquad -2 \; 0$

10b. Tuesday, Wednesday, Monday, Thursday

Alternative Assessment

Ask students to write a weather report in which the low temperature for the day is a negative integer and the high temperature for the day is a positive integer. Have them draw a thermometer for each temperature.

Test Prep

 **Resources**
For additional practice with a variety of test item formats:
• Test Prep, p. 61
• Test-Taking Strategies, p. 56
• Test-Taking Strategies With Transparencies

Modeling Integers

For Use With Lesson 1-5

You can use models, such as colored tiles, to represent integers.
Use a yellow tile ☐ to represent a positive integer.
Use a red tile ■ to represent a negative integer.

1 EXAMPLE

Use models to represent the integers 3, −1, and −4.

☐☐☐ 3   ■ −1   ■■■■ −4

An equal number of yellow tiles and red tiles combine to make zero.

These tiles make a zero pair. ⟶ ☐■ represents zero, or ☐ + ■ = 0.

You can remove zero pairs in sets of mixed tiles.

2 EXAMPLE

Write the integer that is represented by ■■■■■☐☐.

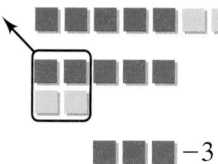

Group the zero pairs.
Then remove them.

Write the integer that the remaining tiles represent.

■■■ −3

EXERCISES

Use tiles to model each integer. 1–8. Models may vary. Samples are shown.

1. −3 ■■■   **2.** 5 ☐☐☐☐☐   **3.** −2 ■■   **4.** 7 ☐☐☐☐☐☐☐

5. 0 ☐■   **6.** −6 ■■■■■■   **7.** 2 ☐☐   **8.** −8
                                                                              ■■■■■■■■

Write an integer for each model.

9. ☐☐ 2   **10.** ■■■■■■ −5   **11.** ■■ −2   **12.** ☐☐☐☐☐☐ 6

13. ■■☐☐   **14.** ■■☐☐   **15.** ☐☐☐☐   **16.** ■■☐☐■■
☐☐■■ 0   ☐ 1   ☐☐■■ 4   −1

Investigation

Modeling Integers

This Investigation shows students how to use tile models for integers.

Teaching Notes

Teaching Tip
Some students may have never used tiles for modeling. Explain to them that each yellow tile represents 1 and each red tile represents −1.

A yellow tile and a red tile together are called a *zero pair* since the sum of −1 and 1 is zero. You can remove zero pairs without changing the value of the integer that is being modeled.

1 EXAMPLE **Error Prevention**

Remind students that the value of the 4 red tiles is less than the value of the 3 yellow tiles. In each model, the color of the tiles represents the sign of the integer.

2 EXAMPLE **Error Prevention**

Students may not understand how to model the combining of zero pairs. Demonstrate with transparent tiles on a projector. Encourage students to work in pairs or groups to help each other.

Adding Integers

1. Plan

Lesson Preview

 Check Skills You'll Need

Integers and Absolute Value
Lesson 1-4: Example 3;
Exercises 22–27.
Extra Practice, p. 744.

Lesson Resources

 Teaching Resources
Practice, Reteaching, Enrichment

 Reaching All Students
Practice Workbook 1-5
Spanish Practice Workbook 1-5
Guided Problem Solving 1-5
Technology Activities 3

 Presentation Assistant Plus!
Transparencies and PowerPoint™
• Check Skills You'll Need 1-5
• Additional Examples 1-5
• Student Edition Answers 1-5
• Lesson Quiz 1-5
• Classroom Aid 6, 13
PH Presentation Pro CD-ROM 1-5

 ASSESSMENT SYSTEM

Computer Test Generator CD-ROM

 Technology
Resource Pro® CD-ROM
Computer Test Generator CD-ROM
PH Presentation Pro CD-ROM

 www.PHSchool.com
Student Site
• Teacher Web Code: adk-5500
• Algebra Readiness Puzzles 3, 4
• Self-grading Lesson Quiz
PH SuccessNet Teacher Center
• Lesson Planner
• Resources

Plus

What You'll Learn

OBJECTIVE 1 To use models to add integers

OBJECTIVE 2 To use rules to add integers

. . . And Why

To use integers to solve real-world problems in sports and Earth science

 Check Skills You'll Need

Compare. Use >, <, or = to complete each statement.

1. $-6 \blacksquare -3$ <
2. $2 \blacksquare -15$ >
3. $-5 \blacksquare |5|$ <
4. $|10| \blacksquare |-10|$ =
5. $|9| \blacksquare |-2|$ >
6. $|-8| \blacksquare |0|$ >

 For help, go to Lesson 1-4.

 TEXT Interactive lesson includes instant self-check, tutorials, and activities.

OBJECTIVE

 1 **Using Models to Add Integers**

If a car goes forward 20 ft and then backs up 20 ft, it ends where it started. Using opposite integers, you can represent this situation as $20 + (-20) = 0$.

When you add opposites, the sum is zero. So, opposites are also called *additive inverses*.

Key Concepts **Addition of Opposites**

The sum of an integer and its opposite is zero.

Arithmetic	Algebra
$1 + (-1) = 0$	$x + (-x) = 0$
$-1 + 1 = 0$	$-x + x = 0$

You can use tiles to add integers. One positive tile and one negative tile combine to make a zero pair, since 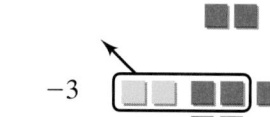.

To add integers using tiles, combine tiles and remove the zero pairs.

1 **EXAMPLE** **Using Tiles to Add Integers**

Modeling Use tiles to find $2 + (-5)$.

$2 + (-5)$ Model the sum.

-3 Group and remove zero pairs. There are three negative tiles left.

$2 + (-5) = -3$

 Check Understanding **Example 1**

1. Use tiles to find each sum.

   a. $-1 + 4$ 3   **b.** $7 + (-3)$ 4   **c.** $-2 + (-2)$ -4

Ongoing Assessment and Intervention

Before the Lesson
Diagnose prerequisite skills using:
• Check Skills You'll Need

During the Lesson
Monitor progress using:
• Check Understanding
• Additional Examples
• Test Prep

After the Lesson
Assess knowledge using:
• Lesson Quiz
• Computer Test Generator CD-ROM

A number line provides another model that you can use to add integers, as shown in Example 2.

2 EXAMPLE   **Using a Number Line**

Football On two plays, a football team first loses 8 yd and then gains 3 yd. Find $-8 + 3$ to find the result of the two plays.

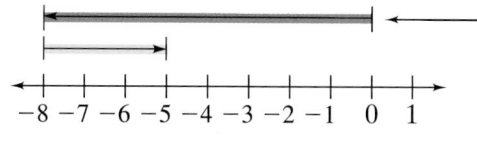

Start at 0. To represent -8, move left 8 units. To add positive 3, move right 3 units to -5.

$$-8 + 3 = -5$$

● The result of the two plays is a loss of 5 yd.

✓ Check Understanding   Example 2

2. Use a number line to find each sum.

   a. $2 + (-6)$ -4 **b.** $-4 + 9$ 5 **c.** $-5 + (-1)$ -6

OBJECTIVE

2   Using Rules to Add Integers

You can also use rules to find the sum of two integers.

Key Concepts   **Adding Integers**

Same Sign The sum of two positive integers is positive. The sum of two negative integers is negative.

Different Signs To add two integers with different signs, find the difference of their absolute values. The sum has the sign of the integer with the greater absolute value.

3 EXAMPLE   **Applying Rules to Add Integers**

Find each sum.

a. $-12 + (-31)$

$-12 + (-31) = -43$ Since both integers are negative, the sum is negative.

b. $7 + (-18)$

$|-18| - |7| = 18 - 7$ Find the difference of the absolute values.

$\quad\quad\quad\quad = 11$ Simplify.

$7 + (-18) = -11$ Since -18 has the greater absolute value, the sum is negative.

1-5 Adding Integers   **25**

👥 Reaching All Students

Below Level Have the students think of words that represent opposites. An example is *hot* and *cold*.	**Advanced Learners** Challenge students to give an example of a number whose absolute value equals the opposite of the number. any negative number	**Tactile Learners** See note on page 25. **English Learners** See note on page 26.

2. Teach

Professional Development

Math Background

You can model the sum of two integers with tiles. Use one color to represent positive integers and a second color to represent negative integers. To model the addition of two integers, represent each integer in tiles and then put these tiles together. Match a positive tile with a negative tile to form a zero pair. Remove the zero pairs. The remaining tiles represent the integer sum.

Teaching Notes

1 EXAMPLE   **Teaching Tip**

Ask: *Why can you remove the zero pair tiles?* because zero pairs have no effect on the value represented

2 EXAMPLE   **Tactile Learners**

Have students use their fingers to trace the operations performed on the number line.

3 EXAMPLE   **Error Prevention**

A common error is thinking that the absolute value of a number is its opposite. This is true for some numbers, but not all. Remind students that the absolute value of a number is its distance from zero, without regard to its direction from zero.

PowerPoint

🖥 Additional Examples

1 Use tiles to find $(-7) + 3$. -4

2 From the surface, a diver goes down 20 feet and then comes back up 4 feet. Find $-20 + 4$ to find where the diver is. 16 feet below the surface

3 Find each sum.
   a. $-20 + (-15)$ -35
   b. $13 + (-17)$ -4

25

Closure

Real-World Connection

A worldwide network of monitors keeps track of earthquake activity. Here technicians check the monitor in Albuquerque.

✓ **Check Understanding**   Example 3

3. Find each sum.

   a. −22 + (−16) −38 **b.** 60 + (−13) 47 **c.** −125 + 35 −90

④ **EXAMPLE**   Real-World 🌐 Problem Solving

Earth Science The earthquake monitor in Hockley, Texas, is located in a salt mine at an elevation of −416 m. The elevation of the monitor in Albuquerque, New Mexico, is 2,156 m higher than the one in Hockley. Find the elevation of the monitor in Albuquerque.

$-416 + 2,156$	Write an expression.
$\|2,156\| - \|-416\| = 2,156 - 416$	Find the difference of the absolute values.
$= 1,740$	Simplify.
$-416 + 2,156 = 1,740$	Since 2,156 has the greater absolute value, the sum is positive.

● The elevation of the monitor in Albuquerque is 1,740 m.

✓ **Check Understanding**   Example 4

4. The elevation of a monitor in Piñon Flat, California, is 1,696 m higher than the monitor in Hockley, Texas. Find the elevation of the monitor in Piñon Flat. 1,280 m

To add several integers, use the order of operations.

⑤ **EXAMPLE**   Using the Order of Operations

Find −12 + (−6) + 15 + (−2).

$-12 + (-6) + 15 + (-2)$	Add from left to right.
$-18 \quad + \quad 15 + (-2)$	The sum of two negative integers is negative.
$-3 \quad + \quad (-2)$	$\|-18\| - \|15\| = 3$. Since −18 has the greater absolute value, the sum is negative.
-5	The sum of two negative integers is negative.

● $-12 + (-6) + 15 + (-2) = -5$

✓ **Check Understanding**   Example 5

5. Find each sum.

   a. 1 + (−3) + 2 + (−10) −10 **b.** −250 + 200 + (−100) + 220 70

EXERCISES

Practice and Problem Solving

For more exercises, see *Extra Practice*.

 Practice by Example

Examples 1 and 2
(pages 24 and 25)

Modeling Write an expression for each model. Find the sum.

1.
$-4 + 7; 3$

2. $5 + 0; 5$

3.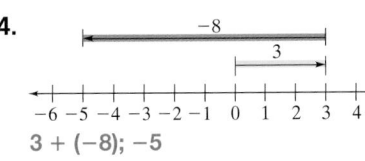
$-4 + (-2); -6$

4.
$3 + (-8); -5$

Draw a model and find each sum.

5. $2 + (-5)$ -3 6. $-5 + 2$ -3 7. $5 + (-2)$ 3 8. $-5 + (-2)$ -7

9. $-6 + 1$ -5 10. $-3 + (-6)$ -9 11. $-3 + 2$ -1 12. $-3 + 4$ 1

Example 3
(page 25)

Find each sum.

13. $14 + (-11)$ 3 14. $0 + (-9)$ -9 15. $-6 + (-7)$ -13

16. $-18 + 4$ -14 17. $-40 + 93$ 53 18. $-26 + (-39)$ -65

19. $450 + (-350)$ 100 20. $100 + (-100)$ 0 21. $235 + (-420)$ -185

Example 4 22. **Geography** The highest peak at Mount Ellsworth in Montana is
(page 26) 3,275 m lower than the highest peak of Mount Kilimanjaro in Kenya, at 5,895 m. Find the elevation of the highest peak at Mount Ellsworth. **2,620 m**

Example 5
(page 26)

Find each sum.

23. $19 + (-9) + 45 + (-32)$ 23 24. $-3 + 2 + (-7) + 7 + 13$ 12

25. $-94 + 68 + (-22) + (-13)$ -61 26. $-20 + (-89) + 112 + 9$ 12

 Apply Your Skills

Reasoning Without adding, tell whether each sum is positive, negative, or zero. Explain how you found your answer.
27–29. See left.

27. **Negative; both numbers are negative.**
28. **Positive; the number with greater absolute value is positive.**
29. **Zero; the numbers are opposites.**

27. $-4 + (-10)$ 28. $11 + (-3)$ 29. $6 + (-6)$

Mental Math Find each sum.

30. $-5 + 20$ 15 31. $9 + (-9)$ 0 32. $-4 + (-2) + (-2)$ -8

33. $10 + (-3)$ 7 34. $-5 + 5 + 16$ 16 35. $-120 + 100 + (-20)$ -40

Compare. Use >, <, or = to complete each statement.

36. $-6 + 1$ ▮ $5 + 1$ $<$ 37. $0 + 3$ ▮ $-2 + 0$ $>$

38. $10 + (-2)$ ▮ $-4 + 12$ $=$ 39. $-1 + 1$ ▮ $-2 + 0$ $>$

40. $49 + (-21)$ ▮ $|-18|$ $>$ 41. $|-20| + (-7)$ ▮ $-11 + (-11)$ $>$

Assignment Guide

1 Objective 1
- Ⓐ Ⓑ **Core** 1–12, 52, 53
- Ⓒ **Extension** 56–58

2 Objective 2
- Ⓐ Ⓑ **Core** 13–51, 54, 55
- Ⓒ **Extension** 59

Test Prep 60–63
Mixed Review 64–71

Practice 1-5 *Adding Integers*

Write a numerical expression for each of the following. Then find the sum.

1. climb up 26 steps, then climb down 9 steps
   $26 + (-9) = 17$

2. earn $100, spend $62, earn $35, spend $72
   $100 + (-62) + 35 + (-72) = 1$

Find each sum.

3. $-8 + (-3)$ -11 4. $6 + (-6)$ 0 5. $-12 + (-17)$ -29

6. $9 + (-11)$ -2 7. $-4 + (-6)$ -10 8. $18 + (-17)$ 1

9. $-8 + 8 + (-11)$ -11 10. $12 + (-7) + 3 + (-8)$ 0 11. $-15 + 7 + 15$ 7

12. $0 + (-11)$ -11 13. $6 + (-5) + (-4)$ -3 14. $-5 + (-16) + 5 + 8 + 16$ 8

Without adding, tell whether each sum is positive, negative, or zero.

15. $192 + (-129)$ positive   16. $-417 + (-296)$ negative   17. $-175 + 87$ negative

Evaluate each expression for $n = -12$.

18. $n + 8$ -4 19. $n + (-5)$ -17 20. $12 + n$ 0

Compare. Write >, <, or = to complete each statement.

21. $-7 + 5$ ⊳ $3 + (-6)$ 22. $4 + (-9)$ = $6 + (-7) + (-4)$

23. An elevator went up 15 floors, down 9 floors, up 11 floors, and down 19 floors. Find the net change. down 2 floors

24. The price of a share of stock started the day at $37. During the day it went down $3, up $1, down $7, and up $4. What was the price of a share at the end of the day? $32

Enrichment 1-5 *Clock Numbers*

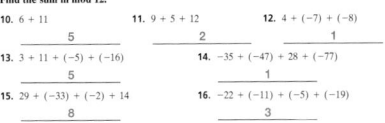

A *finite number system* is one that contains a limited number of numbers. The finite number system on a clock face consists of the numbers from 1 to 12. The clock system is called Modulo-twelve, which is abbreviated *mod 12*.

Since "14" o'clock equals 2 o'clock, we can write $14 = 2 \pmod{12}$.
The integer 14 is equivalent to the number 2 in the mod 12 system. Every integer has an equivalent in mod 12. To find the equivalent of an integer, add or subtract a multiple of 12 to obtain a number between 1 and 12.

Examples $55 = 55 - 4(12) = 55 - 48 = 7 \pmod{12}$
$-13 = -13 + 2(12) = -13 + 24 = 11 \pmod{12}$

Find the mod 12 equivalent. Each answer must be a number from 1 to 12.

1. 18 6 2. 85 1 3. -5 7

4. -64 8 5. 149 5 6. -97 11

The numbers 13, 25, and 37 are all equivalent to 1 (mod 12). When integers have the same equivalent, they are said to be *congruent*. The numbers 13, 25, and 37 are congruent in mod 12.

Write four integers, two positive and two negative, that are congruent in mod 12 to the given number. Answers may vary; examples are given.

7. 3 $15, 27, -9, -21$ 8. 8 $20, 32, -4, -16$ 9. 12 $24, 36, -12, -24$

To add in mod 12, find the sum in the usual manner. Then write the mod 12 equivalent.

Find the sum in mod 12.

10. $6 + 11$ 5 11. $9 + 5 + 12$ 2 12. $4 + (-7) + (-8)$ 1

13. $3 + 11 + (-5) + (-16)$ 5 14. $-35 + (-47) + 28 + (-77)$ 1

15. $29 + (-33) + (-2) + 14$ 8 16. $-22 + (-11) + (-5) + (-19)$ 3

Evaluate each expression for $n = -15$.

42. $n + (-7) - n$ **43.** $15 + n + (-8)$ **44.** $n + (-15) + n$ -45
  -7 -8

Write a numerical expression for each of the following. Then find the sum.

45. You borrow $20, and then pay back $18. $-20 + 18; -2$

46. You save $200, and then spend $75. $200 + (-75); 125$

47. A man deposits $120, and then writes a check for $25.
$120 + (-25); 95$

48. A submarine at 35 ft below sea level moves up 10 ft.
$-35 + 10; -25$

Use the order of operations to find each sum.

49. $4 + (-6) + 3$ 1   **50.** $-1 + 1 + (-3)$ -3

51. $-72 + 36 + (-6) + (-18)$ -60

 **52. Football** A football team gained 4 yd, lost 2 yd, gained 11 yd, lost 8 yd, and then lost 9 yd. Find the net gain or loss. **4 yd loss**

55. Answers may vary.
Sample: First find the
difference of the
absolute values of the
two numbers. Then
give the answer the
sign of the number
with the greater
absolute value.

 **53. Finance** Maria had $123. She spent $35, loaned $20 to a friend,
and received her $90 paycheck. How much does she have now?
GPS **$158**

54. Error Analysis A friend says that the value of $-17 + 5$ is -22.
Explain how your friend may have made this error.
Answers may vary. Sample: My friend subtracted 5 instead of adding 5.

55. Writing in Math A friend is having trouble finding the sum of -84
and 28. What explanation would you give to help your friend?
See left.

C **Challenge**   **Reasoning** For Exercises 56–59, use the number line and tell whether
the value of each expression is positive or negative.

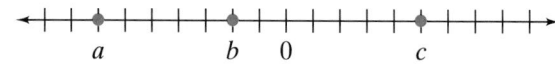

56. $a + b$ **57.** $b + c$ **58.** $a + a$ **59.** $|a + b + c|$
  negative   **positive**   **negative**   **positive**

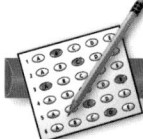

Test Prep

Multiple Choice   **60.** The temperature starts at $-10°F$, drops 2°, drops 5°, and rises 1°.
Which expression gives the current temperature? **B**
A. $(-10) + 2 + 5 + 1$ **B.** $-10 + (-2) + (-5) + 1$
C. $10 + 2 + 5 + (-1)$ **D.** $10 + 2 + 5 + 1$

61. A stock price starts at $6, rises $3, falls $1, and falls $1 again. What
is the current price of the stock? **H**
F. $1   **G.** $5   **H.** $7   **I.** $11

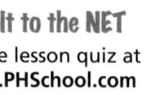
Take It to the NET
Online lesson quiz at
www.PHSchool.com
Web Code: ada-0105

62. Which statement shows an example of additive inverses? **B**
A. $xy = yx$ **B.** $x[(y + (-y)] = x(0)$
C. $x + y = y + x$ **D.** $x\left(\frac{y}{y}\right) = x(1)$

  Use the Guided Problem
GPS Solving worksheet with
Exercise 53.

63. Refer to the map at the right. The lowest temperature recorded in South America is 54 degrees higher than the lowest temperature recorded in North America. What is the lowest temperature recorded in South America? **G**

 F. $-135°F$ **G.** $-27°F$
 H. $-17°F$ **I.** $-138°F$

Lowest Recorded Temperatures

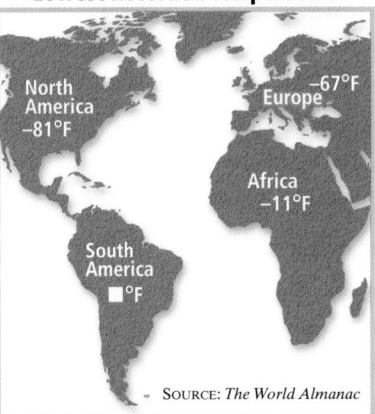

North America $-81°F$
Europe $-67°F$
Africa $-11°F$
South America ■°F

— SOURCE: *The World Almanac*

Mixed Review

Lesson 1-4   **Compare. Use >, <, or = to complete each statement.**

64. -90 ■ -6 $<$ **65.** -2 ■ -7 $>$ **66.** $|-15|$ ■ -15 $>$

67. 0 ■ -8 $>$ **68.** -45 ■ -44 $<$ **69.** 100 ■ $|-101|$ $<$

70. Write a numerical expression for the phrase *one hundred thirty added to the difference of one hundred sixteen and eight.* Then simplify the expression. $(116 - 8) + 130$, or $130 + (116 - 8)$; 238

Lesson 1-3   **71. Repairs** A repair center charges a $25 flat fee plus $10 per hour for labor. Write an expression for the cost of a repair that takes *n* hours. Then evaluate the expression to find the cost of an oven repair that takes 3 hours. $25 + 10n$; $55

Math at Work

Weaver

Weaver A sturdy four-shaft floor loom, a 10-dent reed, a ski shuttle, two boat shuttles—these are some of the tools and terms of the ancient craft of weaving. Weavers use yarn, ribbon, and thread. They design and make colorful, unique items such as rugs, tapestries, and handbags. Like a pattern in algebra, each design has rules that must be followed for the desired result.

Take It to the NET For more information about weavers, go to **www.PHSchool.com**.
Web Code: adb-2031

---

4. Assess

 **Lesson Quiz 1-5**

Find each sum.

1. $-37 + (-5)$ -42

2. $14 + (-4)$ 10

3. $-100 + 5 + (-3)$ -98

4. Evaluate $33 + t$ for $t = -11$.   22

Alternative Assessment

Group students in pairs. Instruct one student to use tiles to set up an addition problem involving integers. Have the partner describe the problem and then find and describe the sum.

Test Prep

Resources
For additional practice with a variety of test item formats:
• Test Prep, p. 61
• Test-Taking Strategies, p. 56
• Test-Taking Strategies With Transparencies

Exercise 63 Suggest that students first represent the problem by writing an expression with integers.

Reteaching 1-5 *Adding Integers*

Use tiles and the rules for adding integers to find each sum.

a. $-4 + -3$

Four negative tiles plus 3 negative tiles gives 7 negative tiles.
$-4 + -3 = -7$
The sum of two negative integers is negative.

b. $-8 + 3$

Remove zero pairs.

Since the signs of the integers are different, you must remove zero pairs. The number of tiles left is the number of negative tiles $|-8|$ minus the number of positive tiles $|3|$. Thus, you can always subtract the absolute values of the numbers to find how many tiles will be left.
$|-8| - |3| = 5$
Since there are more negative tiles than positive tiles, $|-8| > |3|$, there are negative tiles left after you subtract zero pairs. Thus, the sum is negative.
$-8 + 3 = -5$

Use rules or tiles to find each sum.

1. $9 + (-12)$ -3 **2.** $-4 + 10$ 6   **3.** $-1 + (-8)$ -9

4. $-6 + (-11)$ -17 **5.** $-5 + 15$ 10   **6.** $2 + (-14)$ -12

7. $(-3) - 6$ -9 **8.** $-(-2) + 9$ 11   **9.** $(-2) - 4$ -6

10. $-5 - (-4)$ -1 **11.** $7 + (-2)$ 5   **12.** $16 + (-6)$ 10

29

1-6

1. Plan

Lesson Preview

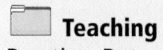 **Check Skills You'll Need**

Adding Integers
Lesson 1-5: Example 3;
Exercises 13–21.
Extra Practice, p. 744.

Lesson Resources

 Teaching Resources
Practice, Reteaching, Enrichment

 Reaching All Students
Practice Workbook 1-6
Spanish Practice Workbook 1-6
Guided Problem Solving 1-6
Technology Activities 3

 Presentation Assistant Plus!
Transparencies and PowerPoint™
• Check Skills You'll Need 1-6
• Additional Examples 1-6
• Student Edition Answers 1-6
• Lesson Quiz 1-6
• Classroom Aid 13
PH Presentation Pro CD-ROM 1-6

 ASSESSMENT SYSTEM

Computer Test Generator CD-ROM

 Technology
Resource Pro® CD-ROM
Computer Test Generator CD-ROM
PH Presentation Pro CD-ROM

 **www.PHSchool.com**

Student Site
• Teacher Web Code: adk-5500
• Self-grading Lesson Quiz
PH SuccessNet Teacher Center
• Lesson Planner
• Resources

Plus **iTEXT**

Subtracting Integers

1 Using Models to Subtract Integers

You can use tiles to help you understand subtraction of integers.

What You'll Learn

 OBJECTIVE 1 To use models to subtract integers

 OBJECTIVE 2 To use a rule to subtract integers

. . . And Why

To use integers to solve real-world problems involving weather

 **Check Skills You'll Need**

Find each sum.

1. $8 + (-9)$ **−1**

2. $-11 + (-18)$ **−29**

3. $-4 + (-6)$ **−10**

4. $14 + (-3)$ **11**

5. $6 + (-6)$ **0**

6. $-13 + (-10)$ **−23**

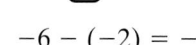 For help, go to Lesson 1-5.

---

1 EXAMPLE Using Tiles to Subtract Integers

Find $-6 - (-2)$.

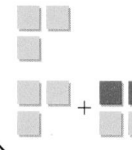

Start with 6 negative tiles.

Take away 2 negative tiles.
There are 4 negative tiles left.

• $-6 - (-2) = -4$

✔ **Check Understanding** Example 1

1. Use tiles to find each difference.

   a. $-7 - (-2)$ **−5**   **b.** $-4 - (-3)$ **−1**   **c.** $-8 - (-5)$ **−3**

You can use zero pairs to subtract an integer from a smaller integer.

2 EXAMPLE Using Zero Pairs to Subtract Integers

Find $3 - 5$.

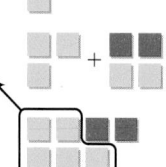

Start with 3 positive tiles.

There are not enough positive tiles to take away 5. Add 2 zero pairs.

Take away 5 positive tiles.
There are 2 negative tiles left.

• $3 - 5 = -2$

✔ **Check Understanding** Example 2

2. Use tiles to find each difference.

   a. $4 - 8$ **−4**   **b.** $-1 - 5$ **−6**   **c.** $-2 - (-7)$ **5**

iTEXT Interactive lesson includes instant self-check, tutorials, and activities.

Ongoing Assessment and Intervention

Before the Lesson
Diagnose prerequisite skills using:
• Check Skills You'll Need

During the Lesson
Monitor progress using:
• Check Understanding
• Additional Examples
• Test Prep

After the Lesson
Assess knowledge using:
• Lesson Quiz
• Computer Test Generator CD-ROM

You can use models to show the relationship between adding and subtracting integers.

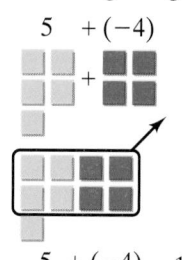

$5 + (-4)$

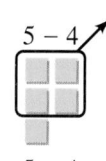

$5 - 4$

$5 - 4 = 1$

$5 + (-4) = 1$

Both $5 + (-4)$ and $5 - 4$ equal 1. So, $5 + (-4) = 5 - 4$.

The models suggest the following rule for subtracting integers.

Key Concepts | **Subtracting Integers**

To subtract an integer, add its opposite.

Arithmetic	**Algebra**
$2 - 5 = 2 + (-5) = -3$	$a - b = a + (-b)$
$2 - (-5) = 2 + 5 = 7$	$a - (-b) = a + b$

3 **EXAMPLE** **Real-World**  **Problem Solving**

Weather In January, 1916, the temperature in Browning, Montana, dropped 100 degrees overnight. The initial temperature was 44°F. What was the final temperature?

$44 - 100$ **Write an expression.**

$44 - 100 = 44 + (-100)$ **To subtract 100, add its opposite.**

$\qquad\qquad = -56$ **Simplify.**

● The final temperature was −56°F.

✓ **Check Understanding** Example 3

3. Find each difference.

    a. $32 - (-3)$ **35**   **b.** $-40 - 66$ **−106**   **c.** $2 - 48$ **−46**
    d. The lowest temperature ever recorded on the moon was about −170°C. The lowest temperature ever recorded in Antarctica was −89°C. Find the difference in the temperatures. **−81°C**

Real-World  **Connection**

The lowest temperature ever recorded on Earth was −129°F (−89°C) in Vostok, Antarctica. Scientists there are taking ice-core samples to depths of −3,600 m.

---

2. Teach

 Professional Development

Math Background

You can read the expression $- (-3)$ as *the opposite of (the opposite of three)*. It seems reasonable that the opposite of the opposite gets you back to where you started. Mathematically, this means that $- (-3)$ is the same as 3. So you can read the expression $8 - (-3)$ as "8 plus the opposite of the opposite of 3," which you can write as $8 + 3$.

Teaching Notes

1 **EXAMPLE** **Tactile Learners**
Encourage even those students who can do the math mentally to model the expressions with tiles. This will help them understand and remember the concepts of subtracting integers.

2 **EXAMPLE** **Inclusion**
Pair students who may not have good eye/hand coordination with students who do. A student who does not have good coordination can instruct his or her partner on how to use tiles to solve the problem and will benefit from it visually.

PowerPoint

Additional Examples

1 Find $-7 - (-5)$. **−2**

2 Find $2 - 8$. **−6**

3 An airplane left Houston, Texas, where the temperature was 42°F. When the airplane landed in Anchorage, Alaska, the temperature was 50°F lower. What was the temperature in Anchorage? **−8°F**

Closure

Ask: *What are two things you do to subtract an integer?* Find its opposite, then add.

👥 Reaching All Students

Below Level Have students do the opposite of what you say. Possible phrases are: stand up, face the front of the room, and look up. Then, give them an integer and instruct them to say the opposite of it.	**Advanced Learners** Ask: *What is the sum if you add the absolute value of an integer (other than zero) to the absolute value of its opposite?* twice the absolute value of the integer	**Tactile Learners** See note on page 31. **Inclusion** See note on page 31.

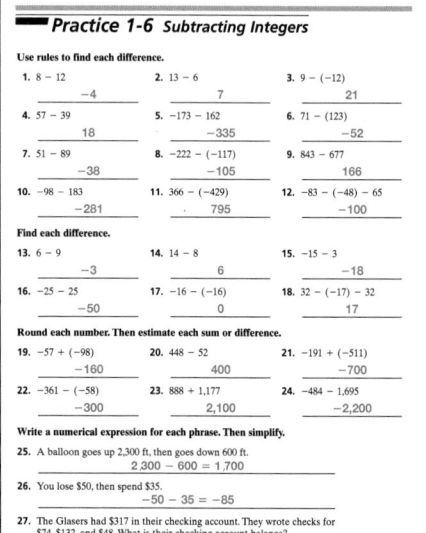

EXERCISES

? For more exercises, see *Extra Practice*.

Practice and Problem Solving

Ⓐ **Practice by Example**

Examples 1 and 2
(page 30)

Write a number sentence for each model.

1. 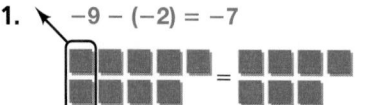 $-9 - (-2) = -7$

2. 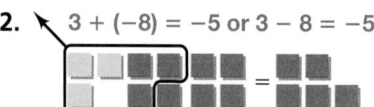 $3 + (-8) = -5$ or $3 - 8 = -5$

Modeling Use tiles to help you find each difference.

3. $-7 - (-3)$ −4 **4.** $-15 - (-7)$ −8 **5.** $-5 - (-6)$ 1

6. $-9 - (-7)$ −2 **7.** $-7 - (-9)$ 2 **8.** $-16 - (-9)$ −7

9. $-8 - (-3)$ −5 **10.** $-1 - (-3)$ 2 **11.** $10 - (-5)$ 15

12. $9 - (-8)$ 17 **13.** $-14 - (-8)$ −6 **14.** $-7 - (-7)$ 0

15. $2 - 3$ −1 **16.** $-2 - 3$ −5 **17.** $-10 - 2$ −12

Example 3
(page 31)

Write each difference as a sum. Then simplify.

18. $6 - 2$
$6 + (-2)$; 4

19. $6 - (-2)$
$6 + 2$; 8

20. $-6 - 2$
$-6 + (-2)$; −8

21. $2 - 6$
$2 + (-6)$; −4

22. $2 - (-6)$
$2 + 6$; 8

23. $-2 - 6$
$-2 + (-6)$; −8

24. $5 - 11$
$5 + (-11)$; −6

25. $75 - (-25)$
$75 + 25$; 100

26. $22 - (-7)$
$22 + 7$; 29

27. $87 - (-9)$
$87 + 9$; 96

28. $35 - 15$
$35 + (-15)$; 20

29. $100 - (-91)$
$100 + 91$; 191

🌐 **30. Account Balances** Terry has $43 in a checking account. If Terry writes a check for $62, what is the new account balance? −$19

🌐 **31. Scores** Suppose you have a score of 35 in a game. You get a [GPS] 50-point penalty. What is your new score? −15

Ⓑ **Apply Your Skills**

Find each difference.

32. $-49 - 75$ −124 **33.** $-65 - 15$ −80 **34.** $16 - (-3)$ 19

35. $120 - (-50)$ 170 **36.** $989 - 76$ 913 **37.** $-35 - 25$ −60

38. $-92 - (-9)$ −83 **39.** $-81 - (-13)$ −68 **40.** $36 - 88$ −52

45–50. Answers may vary. Samples are given.

45. $3 - 3 = 0$;
$(-4) - (-4) = 0$

46. $15 - 5 = 10$;
$-5 - (-15) = 10$

47. $1 - 7 = -6$;
$-10 - (-4) = -6$

48. $5 - 20 = -15$;
$-20 - (-5) = -15$

49. $7 - 4 = |-3|$;
$-2 - (-5) = |-3|$

50. $12 - 1 = |11|$;
$-5 - (-16) = |11|$

Simplify.

41. $-90 - (-80) - 20$ −30 **42.** $810 - 30 - (-70)$ 850

43. $23 - (-15) - 28$ 10 **44.** $-17 + 25 - (-58)$ 66

Open-Ended Use positive and negative integers to write two different subtraction number sentences for each difference. 45–50. See left.

SAMPLE ■ − ■ = −5 $17 - 22 = -5$
$-20 - (-15) = -5$

45. ■ − ■ = 0   **46.** ■ − ■ = 10   **47.** ■ − ■ = −6

48. ■ − ■ = −15   **49.** ■ − ■ = $|-3|$ **50.** ■ − ■ = $|11|$

32 Chapter 1 Algebraic Expressions and Integers

 Use the Guided Problem Solving worksheet with Exercise 31.

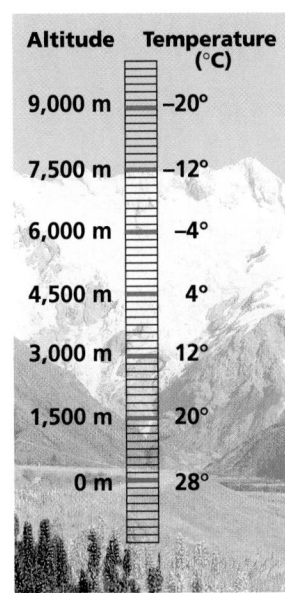

Altitude	Temperature (°C)
9,000 m	−20°
7,500 m	−12°
6,000 m	−4°
4,500 m	4°
3,000 m	12°
1,500 m	20°
0 m	28°

🌐 **Meteorology** **The graph at the left shows how temperature changes with altitude. Use this graph for Exercises 51–53.**

51. As the altitude increases, what happens to the temperature?
It decreases.

52. What is the change in temperature from 1,500 m to 6,000 m? −24°C

53. What is the change in temperature for every 1,500-m increase in altitude? −8°C

Mental Math **Simplify each expression.**

54. $-6 - (-8)$ 2   55. $-45 - 15$ −60   56. $-7 - (-7) + (-7)$ −7

57. $100 - (-50)$ 150   58. $20 - (-10) - 20$ 10   59. $-11 + 22 - (-55)$ 66

60. $3 - (-3) + 6$ 12   61. $-32 + 2 + (-10)$ −40   62. $-87 + (-3) + 90$ 0

63. $6 - (-6) + 6$ 18   64. $0 + (-15) - 15$ −30   65. $-13 - 17 + 10$ −20

Write a numerical expression for each phrase. Then simplify and answer the question.

66. You are $2 in debt. You borrow $4 more. What is the total amount of your debt? −2 − 4; −6; $6

67. An airplane takes off, climbs 3,000 ft, and then descends 600 ft. What is the airplane's current height? 3,000 − 600; 2,400; 2,400 ft

68. From 0°F, the temperature increases 15 degrees and then drops 25 degrees. What is the current temperature?
0 + 15 − 25; −10; −10°F

 **Challenge**

Estimation **Round each number. Then estimate the sum or difference.**
69–74. Answers may vary. Samples are given.
SAMPLE $-2,216 - 488 \approx -2,200 - 500 = -2,700$

69. $-41 - (-86)$ 50   70. $-227 - 49$ −280   71. $-398 - 67$ −470

72. $-86 - 22$ −110   73. $288 - 59$ 230   74. $63 - (-21)$ 80

75. **a.** **Writing in Math** A thermometer is like a vertical number line. Use the one at the right to write a subtraction problem. See left.
b. Write and simplify a numerical expression for your problem. 5 + (−7); −2°C

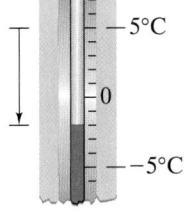

76. **a.** **Patterns** Copy and complete. The first one is done for you.
$8 - (-4) = 12$
$12 - (-4) = \blacksquare$ 16
$16 - (-4) = \blacksquare$ 20
$20 - (-4) = \blacksquare$ 24
$24 - (-4) = \blacksquare$ 28
b. If you begin at 8 and subtract −4 five times, the result is $\blacksquare$. 28
c. Begin at 0 and subtract −4 six times. What is the result? 24

77. **Reasoning** For what values of a is each statement true? Give an example, if possible. See left.
a. $|a - 5| = |a| - 5$ **b.** $|a - 5| > |a| - 5$ **c.** $|a - 5| < |a| - 5$

75a. Answers may vary. Sample: The temperature at 5:00 P.M. was 5°C, but it dropped 7 degrees after sundown. What is the temperature after sundown?

77a. $a \geq 5$
Example: When $a = 6$, $|6 - 5| = |6| - 5$.

77b. $a < 5$
Example: When $a = 4$, $|4 - 5| > |4| - 5$.

77c. none

Error Prevention!

Exercises 18–29 When subtracting an integer by adding the opposite, students may forget to replace the integer by its opposite. Remind students that there are two changes to be made: change subtraction to addition, and use the opposite of the second integer. Point out that they are performing two actions that, in effect, cancel each other so that the value of the expression remains unchanged.

Teaching Tip
Exercises 69–74 If students have difficulty rounding, suggest that they ask themselves questions such as, "Is 86 closer to 80 or 90?"

Find each difference.

1. $-24 - (-5)$ -19

2. $19 - (-4)$ 23

3. $-33 - 11$ -44

4. $14 - 46$ -32

5. $-200 - 50 - (-10)$ -240

Test Prep

📁 **Resources**

For additional practice with a variety of test item formats:

• Test Prep, p. 61

• Test-Taking Strategies, p. 56

• Test-Taking Strategies With Transparencies

Exercise 82 Point out to students that evaluating two of the expressions cannot give them the answer, but evaluating three of the expressions will. Ask why. If the first two values are the same, the third value will identify which of the third and fourth choices is correct. If the first two values are different, the third value will identify which of the first and second choices is correct.

Reteaching 1-6 *Subtracting Integers*

a. Find $-7 - (-3)$ and $-7 + 3$. Compare.

$-7 - (-3)$ $-7 + 3$

Start with 7 negative tiles and take away 3 negative tiles. Add three positive tiles. Remove zero pairs.

With both you start with 7 negative tiles. Taking away 3 negative tiles has the same effect as adding 3 positive tiles and removing zero pairs.
$-7 - (-3) = -7 + 3 = -4$

b. Find $-4 - 2$ and $-4 + (-2)$. Compare.

$-4 - 2$ $-4 + (-2)$

With both you start with 4 negative tiles. Adding two zero pairs and taking away two positive tiles has the same effect as adding two negative tiles.
$-4 - 2 = -4 + (-2) = -6$

Use rules for subtracting integers to find each difference. Use tiles to help.

1. $-5 - (-3) = -5 + \underline{}3 = \underline{}-2$

2. $-8 - 6 = -8 + \underline{}-6 = \underline{}-14$

3. $3 - (-9) = 3 + \underline{}9 = \underline{}12$

4. $-2 - (-7) = -2 + \underline{}7 = \underline{}5$

5. $4 - 10 = 4 + \underline{}-10 = \underline{}-6$

6. $1 - (-6) = 1 + \underline{}6 = \underline{}7$

7. $-9 - 5 = -9 + \underline{}-5 = \underline{}-14$

8. $-6 - (-2) = -6 + \underline{}2 = \underline{}-4$

9. $7 - 8 = 7 + \underline{}-8 = \underline{}-1$

In each number square, the rows, columns, and diagonals have the same sum. Copy and complete each number square.

78.

5	-9	▓
▓	-1	▓
-3	▓	-7

5	-9	1
-5	-1	3
-3	7	-7

sum = ▓ -3

79.

-2	▓	▓
-9	-5	▓
-4	▓	▓

-2	-7	-6
-9	-5	-1
-4	-3	-8

sum = ▓ -15

80.

9	-5	-4	6
-2	4	3	1
2	0	-1	5
-3	7	8	-6

81.

-6	4	5	-9
2	-4	-1	-3
-5	1	-2	0
3	-7	-8	6

80. See left.

▓	-5	▓	6
▓	4	3	▓
2	0	▓	5
-3	▓	▓	-6

sum = ▓ 6

81. See left.

-6	4	5	-9
2	▓	-1	-3
-5	1	▓	0
▓	-7	-8	▓

sum = ▓ -6

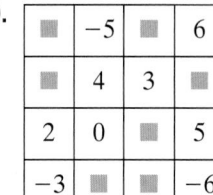

Test Prep

Multiple Choice

82. Three of the four expressions have the same value. Which one has a different value? **D**
  A. $6 + (-4)$ **B.** $6 - 4$ **C.** $|4 - 6|$ **D.** $-6 - 4$

83. Suppose you have a score of 25 in a game. You get a penalty that lowers your score by 60 points. What is your new score? **H**
  F. -85 **G.** -40 **H.** -35 **I.** 15

84. How many degrees warmer is a temperature of 20°C than a temperature of -7°C? **D**
  A. -27°C   **B.** -13°C   **C.** 13°C   **D.** 27°C

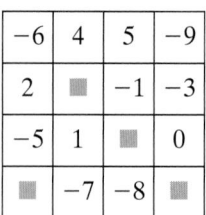

Take It to the NET
Online lesson quiz at **www.PHSchool.com**
Web Code: ada-0106

85. What is the value of $-23 + -(-15) + |-17| + (-35)$? **G**
  F. -56 **G.** -26 **H.** $|-26|$ **I.** 56

Mixed Review

Lesson 1-5 **Find each sum.**

86. $-17 + 12$ -5 **87.** $-8 + 15$ 7 **88.** $-9 + (-4) + 7$ -6

Lesson 1-4 **Open-Ended Complete each statement with an integer.**
89–92. Answers may vary. Samples are given.
  89. $-5 > $ ▓ -7 **90.** ▓ < 6 3 **91.** $|-1| > $ ▓ 0 **92.** $|$▓$| < 8$ -6

Lesson 1-1 **93.** Write an expression for the phrase *one hundred plus the product of six and nine*. Simplify the expression. $100 + 6 \cdot 9; 154$

34 Chapter 1 Algebraic Expressions and Integers

Alternative Assessment

Have each student make a poster displaying the rules for adding and subtracting integers. Encourage students to include examples and use colors to help explain the rules visually.

Inductive Reasoning

OBJECTIVE 1 — Writing Rules for Patterns

Inductive reasoning is making conclusions based on patterns you observe. A conclusion you reach by inductive reasoning is a **conjecture**.

1 EXAMPLE Reasoning Inductively

Visual Patterns Use inductive reasoning. Make a conjecture about the next figure in the pattern. Then draw the figure.

Observation: The shaded triangle is rotating clockwise around the square.

Conjecture: The next figure will have a shaded triangle in the bottom-right corner.

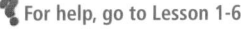

✓ Check Understanding Example 1

1. Make a conjecture about the next figure in the pattern at the right. Then draw the figure.
   A six-sided figure with all vertices on a circle.

For a number pattern, a conjecture can be a rule that explains how to make the pattern.

2 EXAMPLE Writing Rules for Patterns

Number Patterns Write a rule for each number pattern.

a. 30, 25, 20, 15, . . .   Start with 30 and subtract 5 repeatedly.

b. 2, −2, 2, −2, . . .   Alternate 2 and its opposite.

c. 1, 3, 4, 12, 13, . . .   Start with 1. Alternate multiplying by 3 and adding 1.

✓ Check Understanding Example 2

2. Write a rule for each pattern.

   a. 4, 9, 14, 19, . . .
   Start with 4 and add 5 repeatedly.

   b. 3, 9, 27, 81, . . .
   Start with 3 and multiply by 3 repeatedly.

   c. 1, 1, 2, 3, 5, 8, . . .
   Start with 1, 1. Then each number is the sum of the previous two numbers.

What You'll Learn

OBJECTIVE 1 To write rules for patterns

OBJECTIVE 2 To make predictions and test conjectures

. . . And Why

To use inductive reasoning in finding patterns and in making conjectures about economic data

✓ Check Skills You'll Need

Find each difference.

1. $-3 - 4$
   -7

2. $-7 - 4$
   -11

3. $-11 - 4$
   -15

4. $-15 - 4$
   -19

 For help, go to Lesson 1-6.

New Vocabulary

- inductive reasoning
- conjecture
- counterexample

 Reading Math

The three dots in a pattern tell you that the pattern continues.

 Interactive lesson includes instant self-check, tutorials, and activities.

Lesson Preview

✓ **Check Skills You'll Need**

Adding Integers
Lesson 1-6: Example 1;
Exercises 3–17.
Extra Practice, p. 744.

Lesson Resources

📁 **Teaching Resources**
Practice, Reteaching, Enrichment

Reaching All Students
Practice Workbook 1-7
Spanish Practice Workbook 1-7
Guided Problem Solving 1-7

⏱ **Presentation Assistant Plus!**
Transparencies and PowerPoint™
- Check Skills You'll Need 1-7
- Additional Examples 1-7
- Student Edition Answers 1-7
- Lesson Quiz 1-7
PH Presentation Pro CD-ROM 1-7

 **ASSESSMENT SYSTEM**

Computer Test Generator CD-ROM

💻 **Technology**
Resource Pro® CD-ROM
Computer Test Generator CD-ROM
PH Presentation Pro CD-ROM

💻 **www.PHSchool.com**

Student Site
- Teacher Web Code: adk-5500
- Algebra Readiness Puzzles 102
- Self-grading Lesson Quiz
PH SuccessNet Teacher Center
- Lesson Planner
- Resources

Plus

Ongoing Assessment and Intervention

Before the Lesson
Diagnose prerequisite skills using:
- Check Skills You'll Need

During the Lesson
Monitor progress using:
- Check Understanding
- Additional Examples
- Test Prep

After the Lesson
Assess knowledge using:
- Lesson Quiz
- Computer Test Generator CD-ROM

Inductive reasoning assumes that a pattern will continue. Sometimes this is true, but sometimes it's not. When you make a *conjecture based on a pattern*, you are using *inductive reasoning*. Because the *conjectures* you make are not always true, you should check your conjectures whenever possible. All you need is one counterexample to prove a conjecture is not true.

Teaching Notes

Science Connection
Encourage students to interview a science teacher to find out about the role of inductive reasoning in science. Have them find an example of how conjectures change as more knowledge is gained.

2 EXAMPLE Visual Learners
Encourage students to write the change below each pair of numbers to help them see any pattern.

3 EXAMPLE Auditory Learners
Encourage students to ask a partner to describe his or her thinking that leads to seeing the pattern.

5 EXAMPLE Error Prevention
Students may think that one, two, or three examples are enough to prove that a statement is true. Remind them that seeing three red birds, for example, does not mean that all birds are red.

---

3 EXAMPLE Extending a Pattern

Number Patterns Write a rule for the number pattern 640, 320, 160, 80, . . . Find the next two numbers in the pattern.

$$640, \quad 320, \quad 160, \quad 80$$
$$\div 2 \qquad \div 2 \qquad \div 2$$

The first number is 640. The next numbers are found by dividing by 2.

The rule is *Start with 640 and divide by 2.* The next two numbers in the pattern are $80 \div 2 = 40$ and $40 \div 2 = 20$.

✓ **Check Understanding** Example 3

3. Write a rule for the pattern 1, 3, 5, 7, . . . Find the next two numbers in the pattern. **Start with 1 and add 2 repeatedly; 9, 11**

OBJECTIVE

2 Predictions and Counterexamples

With sufficient information, you can make predictions based on reasonable conjectures. Such predictions will probably—but not necessarily—turn out to be accurate.

4 EXAMPLE Real-World Problem Solving

Statistics See the graph below. Is a conjecture that average hourly earnings in the year 2005 will be about $15.75 reasonable?

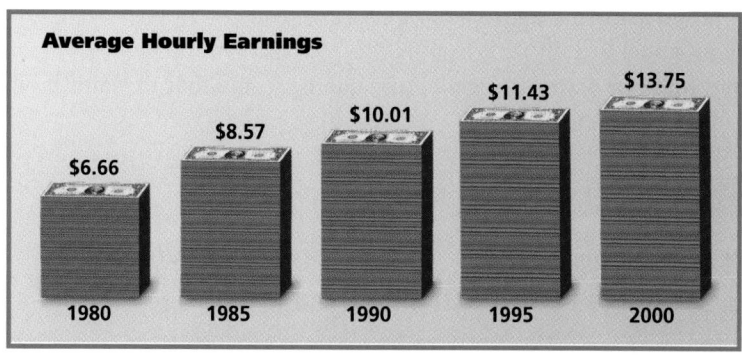

Average hourly earnings appear to increase by $1.50 to $2.50 every five years. The conjecture of $15.75 in 2005 is reasonable, since it is about $2.00 more than the earnings for 2000.

✓ **Check Understanding** Example 4

4. You toss a coin four times, and it comes up heads each time. Is the conjecture *The coin will come up heads on every toss* reasonable? Explain. **No; if the coin is fair, the coin can come up tails on any toss.**

👥 Reaching All Students

| **Below Level** Have students think of number patterns. An example is 2, 4, 6, 8, . . . Have them describe the pattern in words. **Anwers may vary. Sample: This pattern starts with 2 and adds 2 repeatedly.** | **Advanced Learners** Ask: *Is this conjecture correct? 2x is always greater than x.* If incorrect, give a counterexample. **Incorrect; if x < 0, then x will be greater than 2x.** | **Visual Learners** See note on page 36. **Auditory Learners** See note on page 36. |

An example that proves a statement false is a **counterexample.**
You need only one counterexample to prove that a conjecture
is incorrect.

5 EXAMPLE Analyzing Conjectures

Inductive Reasoning Is each conjecture correct or incorrect? If it
is incorrect, give a counterexample.

a. Every four-sided figure is a rectangle.
The conjecture is incorrect. The figure below has four sides, but
it is not a rectangle.

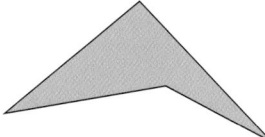

b. The absolute value of any integer is positive.
The conjecture is incorrect. The absolute value of zero is zero,
which is neither positive nor negative.

c. The next figure in the pattern below has 15 dots.

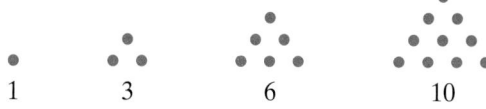

1   3   6   10

The conjecture is correct. The diagram below shows the next
figure in the pattern.

Check Understanding Example 5

5. Is each conjecture correct or incorrect? If it is incorrect,
give a counterexample.

a. The last digit of the product of 5 and a whole number is
either 0 or 5. correct

b. A number and its absolute value are always opposites. Incorrect; 8 and |8|
are not opposites.

c. The next figure in the pattern has 25 dots. correct

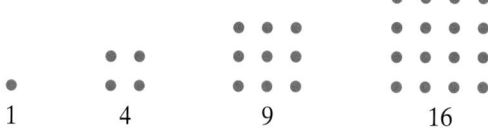

1   4   9   16

Additional Examples:

1. The next figure will have a
shaded circle at the top right.

5c.

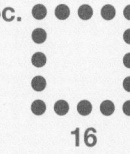

16

1 Use inductive reasoning. Make
a conjecture about the next
figure in the pattern. Then
draw the figure.

See bottom margin.

2 Write a rule for each number
pattern.
a. 0, −4, −8, −12, . . .
Start with 0 and subtract 4
repeatedly.
b. 4, −4, 4, −4, . . .
Alternate 4 and its opposite.
c. 1, 2, 4, 8, 10, . . . Start with 1.
Alternate multiplying by 2
and adding 2.

3 Write a rule for the number
pattern 110, 100, 90, 80, . . .
Find the next two numbers in
the pattern. Start with 110
and subtract 10 repeatedly;
70, 60

4 A child grows an inch for
three years in a row. Is it a
reasonable conjecture that
this child will grow an inch in
the year 2015? No; children
grow at an uneven rate, and
eventually they stop growing.

5 Is each conjecture correct or
incorrect? If it is incorrect, give
a counterexample.
a. Every triangle has three sides
of equal length. incorrect;

b. The opposite of a number
is negative. Incorrect; the
opposite of −2 is 2.
c. The next figure in the
pattern below has 16 dots.

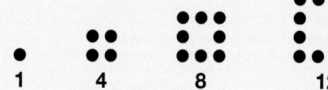

1   4   8   12

Correct; see bottom margin
for figure.

Closure

Ask students to explain how
looking for a pattern can help
them solve a problem.

37

Assignment Guide

1 Objective 1
- Ⓐ Ⓑ **Core** 1–8, 13–17
- Ⓒ **Extension** 21–22

2 Objective 2
- Ⓐ Ⓑ **Core** 9–12, 18–20
- Ⓒ **Extension** 23

Test Prep 24–26
Mixed Review 27–33

EXERCISES

❓ *For more exercises, see* Extra Practice.

Practice and Problem Solving

Ⓐ **Practice by Example**

Visual Patterns Describe the next figure in each pattern. Then draw the figure.

Example 1
(page 35)

1. 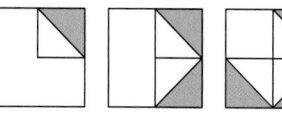 a square with four corners shaded

2. 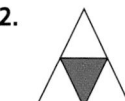 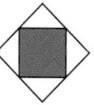 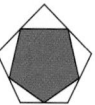  a six-sided figure with a six-sided figure inside it

Examples 2 and 3
(pages 35 and 36)

Write a rule for each pattern. Then find the next two numbers in each pattern. 3–8. See margin.

3. 100, 85, 70, 55, . . .   **4.** 5, 20, 80, 320, . . .   **5.** 2, 7, 12, 17, . . .

6. −10, −4, 2, 8, . . .   **7.** 1, 4, 7, 10, . . .   **8.** 1, 2, 5, 6, 9, . . .

Example 4
(page 36)

9. Mario caught a cold on each of his last three visits with his cousin. Is it reasonable for Mario to conclude that his catching a cold is the result of visiting his cousin? Explain. Answers may vary. Sample: No. Mario's catching a cold could be due to many different reasons.

Example 5
(page 37)

Is each conjecture correct or incorrect? If it is incorrect, give a counterexample.

10. All birds can fly. Incorrect; an ostrich cannot fly.

11. Every square is a rectangle. correct

12. The product of two numbers is never less than either of the numbers. Incorrect; $\frac{1}{2} \cdot \frac{1}{2} = \frac{1}{4}$, which is less than $\frac{1}{2}$.

Ⓑ **Apply Your Skills**

Visual Patterns Describe the next figure in each pattern. Then draw the figure.

13.      an eight-sided figure with bottom right eighth shaded

14. 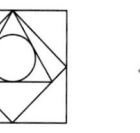 a square inside a circle inside a triangle inside a diamond

15. Start with 1 and add 0.5 repeatedly; 3.5, 4, 4.5
16. Start with −1 and alternate between finding the opposite and the next negative integer. −4, 4, −5
17. Start with 6 and add −2 repeatedly; −2, −4, −6

Write a rule for each pattern. Then find the next three numbers in each pattern. 15–17. See left.

15. 1, 1.5, 2, 2.5, 3, . . .   **16.** −1, 1, −2, 2, −3, 3, . . .   **17.** 6, 4, 2, 0, . . .

38   Chapter 1   Algebraic Expressions and Integers

3. Start with 100 and subtract 15 repeatedly; 40, 25

4. Start with 5 and multiply by 4 repeatedly; 1,280, 5,120

5. Start with 2 and add 5 repeatedly; 22, 27

6. Start with −10 and add 6 repeatedly; 14, 20

7. Start with 1 and add 3 repeatedly; 13, 16

8. Start with 1 and alternately add 1 and 3; 10, 13

21. Start with 1, and then double and add 2, repeatedly; 190, 382, 766

22. Start with 1 and alternately subtract and add consecutive multiples of 3; 10, −11, 13

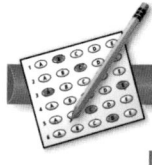 **C** Challenge

23a. Answers may vary. Sample: The unemployment rate will decrease; it has decreased every year shown in the graph.

23b. Answers may vary. Sample: Look up unemployment records for 2001.

Reasoning Is each conjecture correct? If incorrect, give a counterexample.

18. Every clover has three leaves. Incorrect; some have 4.

19. The sum of two numbers is always greater than either of the two numbers. Incorrect; 8 + (−6) is 2, 2 < 8.

20. A whole number is divisible by 3 if the sum of its digits is [GPS] divisible by 3. correct

Write a rule for each pattern. Then find the next three numbers.

21. 1, 4, 10, 22, 46, 94, . . .
See above left.

22. 1, −2, 4, −5, 7, −8, . . .
See above left.

23. a. Writing in Math Use the graph at the right. Write a conjecture about the unemployment rate in 2001. Justify your reasoning.
b. How could you test your conjecture? See left.
See left.

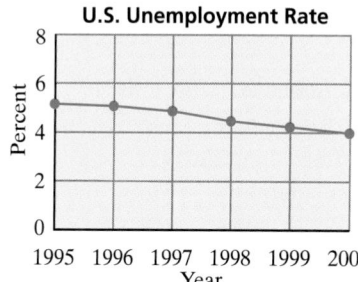

U.S. Unemployment Rate

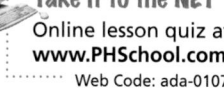 **Test Prep**

Multiple Choice

24. What are the next three numbers in this pattern? 11, 22, 12, 23, . . . C
   A. 13, 23, 14   **B.** 13, 24, 15   **C.** 13, 24, 14   **D.** 32, 43, 33

25. Which best describes the rule for this pattern?
   1, −12, 12, −1, . . . G
   F. subtract 24, then add 13   **G.** subtract 13, then add 24
   H. subtract −24, then add 13   **I.** subtract −13, then add 24

26. Which letter continues this pattern of letters in the alphabet?
   B, E, I, N, ■ C
   A. R   **B.** S   **C.** T   **D.** U

 **Take It to the NET**
Online lesson quiz at
www.PHSchool.com
Web Code: ada-0107

 Mixed Review

Lesson 1-6   **Find each difference.**

27. 1 − 8 −7   **28.** −4 − (−9) 5   **29.** 86 − (−17) 103

Lessons 1-3, 1-5   **Evaluate each expression for x = −1 and y = −3.**

30. x + y −4   **31.** y + x + 2 −2   **32.** 24 + x + y 20

Lesson 1-3 ● **33. Science** The water in a stream flows at the rate of 1,500 gal/h. Write a variable expression for the amount of water that flows in n hours. Evaluate your expression for n = 24.
1,500n; 36,000 gallons

[GPS] Use the Guided Problem Solving worksheet with Exercise 20.

---

4. Assess

 **PowerPoint** **Lesson Quiz 1-7**

Find the next three numbers in each pattern.

1. 1, −1, 2, −2, 3, . . .
   −3, 4, −4

2. 1, 3, 7, 15, 31, . . .
   63, 127, 255

3. −11, −8, −5, −2, . . . 1, 4, 7

Error Prevention!

Exercises 3–8 Remind students that a rule must account for the first number in the pattern.

Alternative Assessment

Have volunteers strike a pattern of handclaps or whistle a pattern of notes. Ask other students to repeat and continue each pattern.

Test Prep

 **Resources**
For additional practice with a variety of test item formats:
• Test Prep, p. 61
• Test-Taking Strategies, p. 56
• Test-Taking Strategies With Transparencies

Reteaching 1-7 *Inductive Reasoning*

The sum of two numbers is always at least as great as either number. Is the statement correct or incorrect? If incorrect, give a counterexample.
Try some examples.

2 + 8 = 10   10 ≥ 8 and 10 ≥ 2
365 + 241 = 606   606 ≥ 365 and 606 ≥ 241

The conjecture seems correct. Try different kinds of numbers. Although the numbers in the second trial are much larger than those in the first, all are whole numbers. Try zero, fractions, and negative numbers.

56 + 0 = 56   56 ≥ 56 and 56 ≥ 0
½ + ¼ = ¾   ¾ ≥ ½ and ¾ ≥ ¼
−4 + 7 = 3   3 ≥ −4 but 3 is not as least as great as 7

The conjecture is incorrect and −4 + 7 = 3 is a counterexample.

Is each conjecture correct or incorrect? If incorrect, give a counterexample.

1. The difference of two numbers is less than or equal to each number.
   Incorrect. 6 − (−4) = 10

2. The sum of two negative numbers is always less than each number.
   Correct.

3. The sum of 5 and any positive integer is divisible by 5.
   Incorrect. 4 + 5 = 9

4. A number is divisible by 10 if its last digit is 0.
   Correct.

5. The sum of a number and its absolute value is always 0.
   Incorrect. 2 + |2| = 4

6. The next number in the pattern 2, 4, 8, . . . is 10.
   Incorrect. The next number is 16.

7. Every even number is divisible by 4.
   Incorrect. 6 is even, but not divisible by 4.

8. The next number in the pattern 5, 3, 1, . . . is −1.
   Correct.

1-8

Lesson Preview

 Check Skills You'll Need

Inductive Reasoning
Lesson 1-7: Example 3;
Exercises 3–8.
Extra Practice, p. 744.

Lesson Resources

 Teaching Resources
Practice, Reteaching, Enrichment

 Reaching All Students
Practice Workbook 1-8
Spanish Practice Workbook 1-8
Guided Problem Solving 1-8

 Presentation Assistant Plus!
Transparencies and PowerPoint™
• Check Skills You'll Need 1-8
• Additional Examples 1-8
• Student Edition Answers 1-8
• Lesson Quiz 1-8
PH Presentation Pro CD-ROM 1-8

 ASSESSMENT *SYSTEM*

Computer Test Generator CD-ROM

 Technology
Resource Pro® CD-ROM
Computer Test Generator CD-ROM
PH Presentation Pro CD-ROM

 www.PHSchool.com
Student Site
• Teacher Web Code: adk-5500
• Self-grading Lesson Quiz
PH SuccessNet Teacher Center
• Lesson Planner
• Resources

Plus **iTEXT**

 1-8 **Problem Solving**

Look for a Pattern

What You'll Learn

OBJECTIVE 1 To find number patterns

...And Why

To use patterns to solve real-world problems involving communication

 Check Skills You'll Need

Write a rule for each pattern. Find the next three numbers.
1–4. See below.
1. 8, 11, 14, 17, . . .

2. 1, 5, 4, 8, 7, . . .

3. 3, 5, 10, 12, 24, . . .

4. 1, 4, 7, 10, . . .

 For help, go to Lesson 1-7.

1. Start with 8 and add 3 repeatedly; 20, 23, 26
2. Start with 1, then alternately add 4 and subtract 1; 11, 10, 14
3. Start with 3, then alternately add 2 and multiply by 2; 26, 52, 54
4. Start with 1, then add 3 repeatedly; 13, 16, 19

 iTEXT Interactive lesson includes instant self-check, tutorials, and activities.

OBJECTIVE 1 Finding Number Patterns

Math Strategies in Action
What do songs on the radio, computer code, and your body's DNA have in common?

All are based on patterns. Radio uses patterns of electromagnetic waves. Computer code consists of patterns of numbers. Your DNA is made up of molecules that repeat in special patterns.

You can solve many types of problems by finding and using patterns. Making predictions from patterns is a form of inductive reasoning.

1 EXAMPLE Real-World Problem Solving

Information News spreads quickly at Riverdell High. Each student who hears a story repeats it 15 minutes later to two students who have not yet heard it, and then tells no one else.

Suppose one student hears some news at 8:00 A.M. How many students will know the news at 9:00 A.M.?

Read and Understand

1. How many students does each student tell? **2 students**

2. How long does the news take to reach the second and third students? **15 min**

Plan and Solve

Make a table to organize the numbers. Then look for a pattern.

3. How many *new* students will hear the news at 8:15 A.M.? **2 students**

4. How many 15-minute periods are there between 8:00 A.M. and 9:00 A.M.? **4 periods**

Ongoing Assessment and Intervention

Before the Lesson
Diagnose prerequisite skills using:
• Check Skills You'll Need

During the Lesson
Monitor progress using:
• Check Understanding
• Additional Examples
• Test Prep

After the Lesson
Assess knowledge using:
• Lesson Quiz
• Computer Test Generator CD-ROM

The pattern is to add the number of new students to the number who already know.

$$1 + 2 = 3 \quad \text{the number who know at 8:15}$$
(One student talks to 2.)

$$3 + 4 = 7 \quad \text{the number who know at 8:30}$$
(Two students talk to 4.)

Make a table and extend the pattern to 9:00.

Time	8:00	8:15	8:30	8:45	9:00
Number of new students told	1	2	4	8	16
Number of students who know	1	$1 + 2 = 3$	$3 + 4 = 7$	$7 + 8 = 15$	$15 + 16 = 31$

By 9:00 A.M., 31 students will know the news.

Look Back and Check

One way to check a solution is to solve the problem by another method. You can use a *tree diagram* to show the pattern visually.

	Time	New Students	Students Who Know
1	8:00	1	1
2	8:15	2	3
4	8:30	4	7
8	8:45	8	15
16	9:00	16	31

5. Describe two ways to find the number of students who will know the news at 9:15 A.M.
Answers may vary. Sample: Extend the table. Extend the diagram.

6. Suppose you want to continue the pattern beyond 9:15. Which would work better, a table or a tree diagram? Explain.
A table; it would be difficult to draw all the branches of the tree.

7. There are 251 students at Riverdell High. By what time will every student know the news? **9:45 A.M.**

✓ Check Understanding

8. Suppose each student who hears the story repeats it in 10 minutes. How many students will know the news at 9:00 A.M.? **127**

2. Teach

Professional Development

Math Background

Look for a Pattern is one of many problem-solving strategies. See page 42 for a list of these strategies.

Teaching Notes

Science Connection
Ask a student who is familiar with computer code or DNA to share his or her knowledge with others in the class about the patterns these examples contain.

Careers
Many occupations use patterns to help solve problems or make predictions. Law enforcement professionals use patterns to help solve crimes. Financial analysts use patterns to make decisions about the economy. Ask students to suggest occupations that use patterns. Have them explain how patterns might be used in each instance.

1 EXAMPLE Error Prevention

Students often make errors in seeing what happens at the beginning of a pattern. Remind them to read carefully and to check their table or tree diagram for reasonableness.

PowerPoint
Additional Example

1 Each student on a committee of five students shakes hands with every other committee member. How many handshakes will there be in all? **10 handshakes**

Closure

Ask: *What are two ways to find the solution to a problem that involves a pattern?* **Answers may vary. Sample: You can make a table or a tree diagram.**

Assignment Guide

▼ **Objective 1**
- **A B Core** 1–7
- **C Extension** 8

Test Prep 9–11
Mixed Review 12–17

Practice 1-8 Look for a Pattern

Solve by looking for a pattern.

1. Each row in a window display of floppy disk cartons contains two more boxes than the row above. The first row has one box.
   a. Complete the table.

Row Number	1	2	3	4	5	6
Boxes in the Row	1	3	5	7	9	11
Total Boxes in the Display	1	4	9	16	25	36

   b. Describe the pattern in the numbers you wrote.
   The total in the display is the row number
   multiplied by itself (the row number squared).

   c. Find the number of rows in a display containing the given number of boxes.
   81 __9__ 144 __12__ 400 __20__

   d. Describe how you can use the number of boxes in the display to calculate the number of rows.
   The number of rows is the square root of the
   number of boxes in the display.

2. A computer multiplied nine 100 times. You can use patterns to find the ones digit of the product.
   $9 \times 9 \times 9 \times 9 \times \cdots \times 9$
   100 times
   a. Find the ones digit when nine is multiplied:
   1 time __9__ 2 times __1__ 3 times __9__ 4 times __1__
   b. Describe the pattern. When 9 is multiplied an even
   number of times the ones' digit is 1. When 9 is
   multiplied an odd number of times the ones' digit
   is 9.
   c. What is the ones digit of the computer's product? __1__

3. Use the method of Exercise 2 to find the ones digit of the product when 4 is multiplied by itself 100 times. __6__

Enrichment 1-8 Changes in Temperature

Two of the most important factors influencing temperature are elevation and latitude. (Latitude is position on the earth's surface measured in degrees north or south of the equator, from 0° to 90°.)

Elevation Rule
For every 300-ft gain in elevation, subtract 1° F.

Latitude Rule
For every 2 degrees of latitude north or south of the equator, subtract 3° F.

For Exercises 1–8, refer to the table.

1. On average, how much warmer is Albuquerque than Portland due to latitude? __12°__
2. On average, how much colder is Albuquerque than Portland due to altitude? __17°__

Location	Latitude	Altitude (ft)
Albuquerque, NM	35°N	5,100
Chicago, IL	42°N	0
Mount Massive, CO	40°N	14,400
Portland, ME	43°N	0

3. Find the net difference. __5°__
4. Which city is colder? By how much? __Albuquerque; 5°F__
5. How much warmer is Mount Massive than Chicago due to latitude? __3°__
6. How much colder is Mount Massive than Chicago due to altitude? __48°__
7. Find the net difference. __45°__
8. Which location is colder? By how much? __Mount Massive; 45°F__
9. Moscow, Russia, has a latitude of 56°N and an altitude of 400 ft. Mexico City, Mexico, has a latitude of 20°N and an altitude of 7,300 ft. Which location is colder? By how much?
   __Moscow, Russia; 31°F__
10. Peking, China, has a latitude of 40°N and an altitude of 150 ft. St. Louis, Missouri, has a latitude of 38°N and an altitude of 450 ft. Which location is colder? By how much?
   __Peking, China; 2°F__

EXERCISES

? For more exercises, see *Extra Practice.*

Practice and Problem Solving

A Practice by Example

Example 1
(page 40)

Look for a Pattern to help you solve each problem.

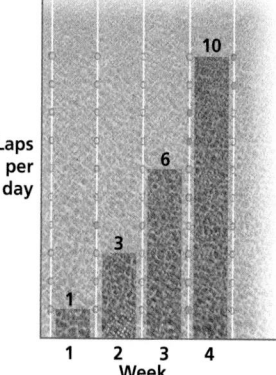

1. **Data Analysis** Caroline is training for a swim meet. The graph shows the number of laps per day she swims each week. If she stays with this training pattern, how many laps per day will Caroline swim in week 8?
   36 laps/day

2. **GPS** Students are to march in a parade. There will be one first grader, two second graders, three third graders, and so on, through the twelfth grade. How many students will march in the parade? **78 students**

3. **Savings** Suppose that every day you save twice as many pennies as you saved the day before. You start by saving one penny on January 1. How much money will you have in all on January 10?
   $10.23

4. An old clock started to lose one minute each day. It was too fragile to fix, but too beloved to stop. How slow was the clock after one year of this? After two years?
   365 min, or 6 h and 5 min; 10 min

B Apply Your Skills

Strategies

- Account for All Possibilities
- Draw a Diagram
- Look for a Pattern
- Make a Model
- Make a Table
- Simplify the Problem
- Simulate the Problem
- Solve by Graphing
- Try, Test, Revise
- Use Multiple Strategies
- Work Backward
- Write an Equation
- Write a Proportion

Solve using any strategy.

5. **Geometry** You can cut a pizza into two pieces with one straight cut. With two cuts you can get four pieces. Three cuts give a maximum of seven pieces. What is the maximum number of pieces with four cuts? With five cuts? **11 pieces; 16 pieces**

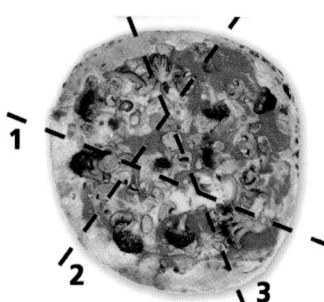

6. a. **Number Sense** Complete. Then look for a pattern.

$2 \cdot 2 = $ ■ 4	$3 \cdot 3 = $ ■ 9
$1 \cdot 3 = $ ■ 3	$2 \cdot 4 = $ ■ 8
Difference = ■ 1	Difference = ■ 1

$4 \cdot 4 = $ ■ 16	$5 \cdot 5 = $ ■ 25	The
$3 \cdot 5 = $ ■ 15	$4 \cdot 6 = $ ■ 24	differences
Difference = ■ 1	Difference = ■ 1	are all 1.

   b. Which is greater, $10 \cdot 12$ or $11 \cdot 11$? What is the difference? **$11 \cdot 11$; 1**
   c. **Reasoning** Suppose you know that $47 \cdot 47 = 2{,}209$. Use this to find $46 \cdot 48$. **2,208**
   d. Suppose you know that $64 \cdot 66 = 4{,}224$. Use this to find $65 \cdot 65$.
   4,225

Use the Guided Problem Solving worksheet with Exercise 2.

7a. $59; $21
7b. 10 people

7. For a buffet dinner, a restaurant charges $10 for one person, $20 for two, $29 for three, $37 for four, $44 for five, and so on.
  a. How much does a buffet dinner for 8 cost? How much does a group of 8 save by eating together rather than separately?
  b. The buffet costs the restaurant $6 per person. How large a group can the restaurant serve without losing money?
  a–b. See left.

 **C** Challenge

8. A woman jogging at 6 mi/h passes a man biking in the opposite direction at 12 mi/h. If they maintain their speeds, how far from each other will they be 10 minutes after passing? **3 mi**

 **Test Prep**

Multiple Choice

9. One edition of *Alice's Adventures in Wonderland* has 352 pages. How many 4s were used in its page numbers? **C**
  A. 38 **B.** 52 **C.** 75 **D.** 88

10. Jayne has 3 quarters, 2 dimes, a nickel, and 2 pennies in her pocket. How many different amounts of money can she make using three of these coins? **I**
  F. 24 **G.** 20 **H.** 17 **I.** 14

Take It to the NET
Online lesson quiz at
www.PHSchool.com
Web Code: ada-0108

11. Assuming one yeast cell "buds" into two cells (the original cell and one new cell) at a rate of once every hour, how many yeast cells will be present from one yeast cell after 8 hours? **B**
  A. 128 **B.** 256 **C.** 512 **D.** 1,024

Mixed Review

Lesson 1-7

Visual Patterns Describe the next figure in each pattern. Then draw the figure.

12. 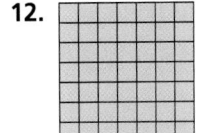 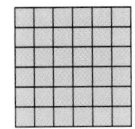 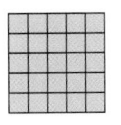   a 4 × 4 square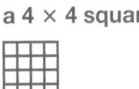

13. 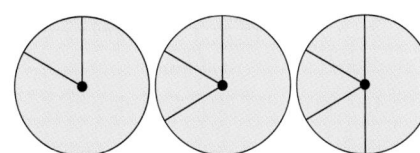   a circle divided into 5 pieces

Lesson 1-5 **14. Weather** At midnight, the temperature was −5°F. By dawn, the temperature had risen 14°. What was the temperature at dawn?
9°F

Lesson 1-3 **Evaluate each expression for $m = 1$ and $n = 4$.**

15. $4m - n$ **0**   **16.** $mn + 13$ **17**   **17.** $4(n + 2) + m$ **25**

1-8 Look for a Pattern **43**

1-9 Multiplying and Dividing Integers

Lesson Preview

 Check Skills You'll Need

Multiplying Whole Numbers
Skills Handbook: p. 759; Example 2;
Exercises 19–23.

Lesson Resources

 Teaching Resources
Practice, Reteaching, Enrichment
Checkpoint Quiz 2

 Reaching All Students
Practice Workbook 1-9
Spanish Practice Workbook 1-9
Reading and Math Literacy 1C
Spanish Reading and Math
  Literacy 1C
Spanish Checkpoint Quiz 2
Guided Problem Solving 1-9
Technology Activities 3

 Presentation Assistant Plus!
Transparencies and PowerPoint™
• Check Skills You'll Need 1-9
• Additional Examples 1-9
• Student Edition Answers 1-9
• Lesson Quiz 1-9
PH Presentation Pro CD-ROM 1-9

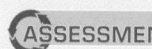 **ASSESSMENT SYSTEM**

Checkpoint Quiz 2
Computer Test Generator CD-ROM

 Technology
Resource Pro® CD-ROM
Computer Test Generator CD-ROM
PH Presentation Pro CD-ROM

 www.PHSchool.com
Student Site
• Teacher Web Code: adk-5500
• Algebra Readiness Puzzles 5, 6
• Self-grading Lesson Quiz
PH SuccessNet Teacher Center
• Lesson Planner
• Resources

 Plus **iTEXT**

44

What You'll Learn

OBJECTIVE 1 To multiply integers using repeated addition, patterns, and rules

OBJECTIVE 2 To divide integers using rules

. . . And Why

To solve real-world problems involving deep-sea exploration and currency

 **Check Skills You'll Need**

Simplify each expression.

1. $5 \cdot 4$ 20 **2.** $3 \cdot 8$ 24

3. $5 \cdot 5$ 25 **4.** $14 \cdot 2$ 28

5. $6 \cdot 5$ 30 **6.** $20 \cdot 7$ 140

For help, go to Skills Handbook, p. 759.

OBJECTIVE 1 Multiplying Integers

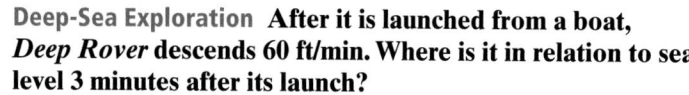

Investigation

Preparing to Multiply Integers

1. Copy and complete the table. The first row is done for you.
See back of book.

Multiplication	Repeated Addition	Sum
$3 \cdot (-5)$	$-5 + (-5) + (-5)$	-15
$5 \cdot (-4)$	■	■ -20
$2 \cdot (-8)$	■	■ -16
$4 \cdot (-10)$	■	■ -40

2. What do you notice about the signs of the sums?
They are all negative.

3. **Inductive Reasoning** What does the pattern suggest about the product of a positive integer and a negative integer?
It is negative.

You can think of multiplication as repeated addition.

1 EXAMPLE **Real-World** 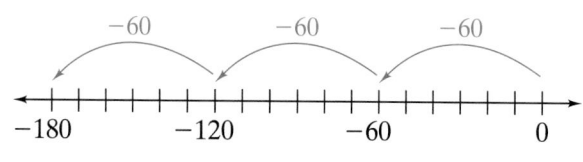 **Problem Solving**

Deep-Sea Exploration **After it is launched from a boat, *Deep Rover* descends 60 ft/min. Where is it in relation to sea level 3 minutes after its launch?**

Use a number line to show repeated addition.

$3(-60) = (-60) + (-60) + (-60) = -180$

Deep Rover is at -180 feet, or 180 feet below sea level.

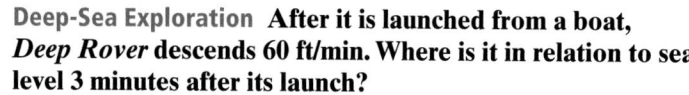 **Check Understanding** Example 1

1. Simplify each product.

a. $2(-6)$ -12 **b.** $4(-3)$ -12 **c.** $7(-2)$ -14

Real-World **Connection**

Scientists explore the deep waters of the Pacific Ocean in *Deep Rover,* a submersible designed for research.

iTEXT Interactive lesson includes instant self-check, tutorials, and activities.

Ongoing Assessment and Intervention

Before the Lesson
Diagnose prerequisite skills using:
• Check Skills You'll Need

During the Lesson
Monitor progress using:
• Check Understanding
• Additional Examples
• Test Prep

After the Lesson
Assess knowledge using:
• Lesson Quiz
• Computer Test Generator CD-ROM
• Chapter Checkpoint 2 (p. 49)

You can use patterns to simplify the product of a negative number and a positive number, or the product of two negative numbers.

2 EXAMPLE Using Patterns to Multiply Integers

Patterns Use a pattern to find each product.

a. $-2(5)$

$2(5) = 10$	**Start with products you know.**
$1(5) = 5$	
$0(5) = 0$	
$-1(5) = -5$	**Continue the pattern.**
$-2(5) = -10$	

b. $-2(-5)$

$2(-5) = -10$
$1(-5) = -5$
$0(-5) = 0$
$-1(-5) = 5$
$-2(-5) = 10$

Writing in Math

Symbols for multiplication:

×	-2×2
·	$-2 \cdot 2$
( )	$-2(3)$
*	$-2 * 3$

✔ **Check Understanding** Example 2

2. **Patterns** Use a pattern to simplify $-3(-4)$. 12

By inductive reasoning, the patterns from Example 2 suggest rules for multiplying integers.

Key Concepts Multiplying Integers

The product of two integers with the same sign is positive.
The product of two integers with different signs is negative.
The product of zero and any integer is zero.

Examples

$3(4) = 12$ $3(-4) = -12$
$-3(-4) = 12$ $-3(4) = -12$
$3(0) = 0$ $-4(0) = 0$

3 EXAMPLE Using Rules to Multiply Integers

Multiply $-3 \cdot 5(-4)$.

$-3 \cdot 5(-4) = -15(-4)$ **Multiply from left to right. The product of a negative integer and a positive integer is negative.**

$= 60$ **Multiply. The product of two negative integers is positive.**

✔ **Check Understanding** Example 3

3. Simplify each product.

a. $-4 \cdot 8(-2)$ 64   **b.** $6(-3)(5)$ −90   **c.** $-7 \cdot (-14) \cdot 0$ 0

👬 Reaching All Students

Below Level Remind students of how two negative words in one phrase can cancel their negative meanings. Ask students for a possible meaning of the statement *That fact is not unknown.* That fact is known.	**Advanced Learners** Have students make conjectures about the sign of a product involving one negative factor, two negative factors, three negative factors, and so on.	**Alternative Method** See note on page 45. **Error Prevention** See note on page 48.

2. Teach

Math Background

The product of two negative integers is positive. This rule often seems counterintuitive. You can use a pattern to suggest that multiplying two negative integers results in a positive answer.

$4(-3) = -12$
$3(-3) = -9$
$2(-3) = -6$
$1(-3) = -3$
$0(-3) = 0$
$-1(-3) = 3$
$-2(-3) = 6$

Teaching Notes

Investigation (Optional)
Tactile Learners Suggest students model the multiplications in the table with tiles.

3 EXAMPLE Alternative Method

Suggest students count the negative signs in the problem. Since the product of every two negative integers is a positive integer, their signs "cancel" each other. Therefore, if there is an even number of negative integers, all negative signs cancel. The product is positive. If there is an odd number of negative integers, there will be one negative sign left. The product is negative. So you can find the product of the absolute values of the numbers first, and then use the number of negative signs to determine the sign of the product.

PowerPoint
Additional Examples

1 A diver is descending from the surface of the water at a rate of 5 ft/s. Write an expression with repeated addition to show how far the diver is from the surface of the water after four seconds. $4(-5) = (-5) + (-5) + (-5) + (-5) = -20$; the diver is 20 feet below the surface of the water.

2 Use a pattern to find each product.
a. $-2(7)$ −14 **b.** $-2(-7)$ 14

3 Multiply $6(-2)(-3)$. 36

45

Additional Examples

④ Use the table in Example 4 to find the average of the differences in the values of a Canadian dollar and a U.S. dollar for 1994–1997.   −27¢

Closure

Ask: *What is the sign of the quotient or product of two integers with the same sign?* It is positive. *What is the sign of the quotient or product of two integers with opposite signs?* It is negative.

OBJECTIVE

▶ 2 | Dividing Integers

The rules for dividing integers are similar to those for multiplying.

| **Key Concepts** | **Dividing Integers** |

The quotient of two integers with the same sign is positive. The quotient of two integers with different signs is negative. Remember that division by zero is undefined.

Examples

$$12 \div 3 = 4 \qquad 12 \div (-3) = -4$$
$$-12 \div (-3) = 4 \qquad -12 \div 3 = -4$$

4 | EXAMPLE | **Real-World 🌐 Problem Solving**

Currency Find the average of the differences in the values of a Canadian dollar and a U.S. dollar for 1994–1998.

Value of Dollars (U.S. Cents)

Year	Canadian Dollar	U.S. Dollar	Difference
1994	73	100	−27
1995	73	100	−27
1996	74	100	−26
1997	72	100	−28
1998	68	100	−32

SOURCES: Bank of Canada; *The World Almanac*

$$\frac{-27 + (-27) + (-26) + (-28) + (-32)}{5} \qquad \text{Write an expression for the average.}$$

$$= \frac{-140}{5} \qquad \text{Use the order of operations. The fraction bar acts as a grouping symbol.}$$

$$= -28 \qquad \text{The quotient of a negative integer and a positive integer is negative.}$$

For 1994–1998, the average difference was −28¢. The Canadian dollar was worth an average of 28¢ less than the U.S. dollar.

✓ Check Understanding Example 4

4. Simplify each quotient.

    a. −32 ÷ 8 −4   **b.** −48 ÷ (−6) 8   **c.** −56 ÷ (−4) 14
    d. Find the average of 4, −3, −5, 2, and −8. −2

EXERCISES

For more exercises, see *Extra Practice*.

Practice and Problem Solving

A Practice by Example

Example 1
(page 44)

1. Write a number sentence for the product shown on the number line.
$5 \cdot (-2) = -10$

Write each sum as a product. Simplify the product.

2. $(-9) + (-9) + (-9) + (-9)$ 4(−9); −36

3. $(-5) + (-5) + (-5) + (-5) + (-5)$ 5(−5); −25

 4. Weather The temperature dropped 5 degrees each hour for 7 h. Use an integer to represent the total change in temperature. −35

Simplify each product.

5. $3(-3)$ −9   **6.** $4(-11)$ −44   **7.** $3(-8)$ −24

8. $5(-10)$ −50   **9.** $6(-3)$ −18   **10.** $2(-15)$ −30

11. $9(-9)$ −81   **12.** $3(-24)$ −72   **13.** $8(-6)$ −48

Examples 2 and 3
(page 45)

14. $-5(-3)$ 15   **15.** $-6 \cdot 10$ −60   **16.** $-10 \cdot 0$ 0

17. $-9(-8)(-5)$ −360   **18.** $0(-12) \cdot 4$ 0   **19.** $8 \cdot 3(-4)$ −96

Example 4
(page 46)

Find each quotient.

20. $24 \div (-24)$ −1   **21.** $18 \div (-1)$ −18   **22.** $-120 \div 12$ −10

23. $56 \div (-8)$ −7   **24.** $-72 \div 12$ −6   **25.** $-100 \div (-10)$ 10

26. $-38 \div (-2)$ 19   **27.** $-72 \div 6$ −12   **28.** $-33 \div 11$ −3

For each group, find the average.

29. temperatures: $-9°C, -12°C, 9°C, 4°C, -2°C$ −2°C

30. football yardage: $10 \text{ yd}, -5 \text{ yd}, 7 \text{ yd}, 9 \text{ yd}, -11 \text{ yd}$ 2 yd

31. golf scores: $-3, 4, 2, 1, -4, -1, 3, -2$ 0

32. bank balances: $\$325, -\$150, \$130, \$200, -\$45$ $92

B Apply Your Skills

33. Positive; the integers have the same sign.
34. Negative; the integers have opposite signs.
35. Negative; the integers have opposite signs.
36. Positive; the first product is negative, so the second is a product of integers with the same sign.

Mental Math Without computing, tell whether each product or quotient is *positive* or *negative*. Explain your reasoning. 33–36. See left.

33. $-6(-20)$ **34.** $7(-83)$ **35.** $39 \div (-3)$ **36.** $-3(8)(-24)$

Name the point on the number line that is the graph of each product.

37. $-2 \cdot 0$ A   **38.** $4(-2)$ D   **39.** $2(-2)$ C   **40.** $|-2| \cdot |-2|$ B

GPS Use the Guided Problem Solving worksheet with Exercise 4.

Assignment Guide

1 **Objective 1**
A **B** **Core** 1–19, 36–40, 56–58
C Extension 63, 66, 67

2 **Objective 2**
A **B** **Core** 20–35, 41–55, 59–60
C Extension 61–62, 64, 65

Test Prep 68–71
Mixed Review 72–79

Practice 1-9 *Multiplying and Dividing Integers*

Use repeated addition, patterns, or rules to find each product or quotient.

1. $23 \cdot 16$ 368   **2.** $8 \cdot 7(-6)$ −336   **3.** $-17 \cdot 3$ −51

4. $-24 \div 4$ −6   **5.** $-65 \div 5$ −13   **6.** $117 \div (-1)$ −117

7. $-30 \div (-6)$ 5   **8.** $-21 \div (-3)$ 7   **9.** $63 \div (-21)$ −3

10. $5(-1)(-9)$ 45   **11.** $-6(-3) \cdot 2$ 36   **12.** $-3 \cdot 7(-2)$ 42

13. $\frac{1,512}{-42}$ −36   **14.** $\frac{-4,875}{-65}$ 75   **15.** $\frac{-15(-3)}{-9}$ −5

Compare. Use >, <, or = to complete each statement.

16. $-7(5)$ < $-6 \cdot (-6)$ **17.** $-20 \cdot (-5)$ = $10 \cdot |-10|$

18. $3(-6)$ = $-3(6)$ **19.** $121 \div (-11)$ < $-45 \div (-6)$

20. $-40 \div 8$ = $40 \div (-8)$ **21.** $-54 \div 9$ > $21 \div (-3)$

For each group, find the average.

22. temperatures: $6°, -15°, -24°, 3°, -25°$ −11°

23. bank balances: $\$52, -\$7, \$20, -\$63, -\$82$ −$16

24. stock price changes: $\$6, -\$6, -\$9, \$1, \$3$ −$1

25. golf scores: $-2, 0, 3, -2, -3, 1, -4$ −1

26. elevations (ft): $-120, 168, -60, -42, -36$ −18 ft

Write a multiplication or division sentence to answer the question.

27. The temperature dropped 4° each hour for 3 hours. What was the total change in temperature?
$3(-4) = -12$; The temperature dropped a total of 12°.

Enrichment 1-9 *Curious Methods of Multiplication*

A. Finger Multiplication

Adding on your fingers is easy. Here is how to *multiply* numbers from 6 to 10 using your fingers.

Example Multiply: $9 \cdot 8$
Solution Imagine the fingers of both hands are numbered from 6 (thumb) to 10 (little finger). Touch finger 9 on one hand to finger 8 on the other hand. Bend any fingers beyond the touching fingers.

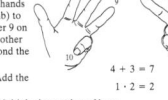

To find the tens' digit of the product: Add the upright fingers.
To find the ones' digit of the product: Multiply the number of bent fingers on one hand times the number of bent fingers on the other hand.
Product: 72

$4 + 3 = 7$
$1 \cdot 2 = 2$

Use your fingers to multiply.

1. $7 \cdot 8$ 56   **2.** $9 \cdot 9$ 81   **3.** $9 \cdot 7$ 63   **4.** $6 \cdot 8$ 48

B. Binary Multiplication

Using only multiplication and division by 2, you can find the product of any two numbers.

Example Multiply: $39(-13)$
Solution Write the factors side by side. On the left side, divide by 2, dropping any remainder. On the right side multiply by 2. Continue until you reach 1 on the left.

39	−13
19	−26
9	−52
4	−104
2	−208
1	−416

List those numbers from the right side that are positioned across from the odd numbers on the left side. Add them.

−13
−26
−52
−416

Product: −507

Find each product using binary multiplication.

5. $22 \cdot 17$ 374   **6.** $45(-25)$ −1,125   **7.** $68(-33)$ −2,244   **8.** $75(-41)$ −3,075

Use repeated addition, patterns, or rules to simplify each product or quotient.

41. $225 \div (-15)$ −15 **42.** $|-2| \cdot (-7)$ −14 **43.** $-59(-79)$ 4,661

44. $243(-88)$ −21,384 **45.** $-200 \div -25$ 8 **46.** $-18(-12)$ 216

47. $38(-2)$ −76 **48.** $1{,}000 \div (-50)$ −20 **49.** $24(-16)(-32)$
12,288

🌐 **50. Investing** The price of one share of a stock fell $3 each day for 12 days.
a. Write an integer to represent the total change in price of a share of the stock. −36
b. The original stock price was $76 per share. What was the price after the drop? $40 per share

Compare. Use >, <, or = to complete each statement.

51. $(-9)(-6)$ ■ $8(-10)$ >   **52.** $5(-2)$ ■ $(-6)(-1)$ <

53. $-10 \div (-2)$ ■ $25 \div (-5)$ >   **54.** $-|-28| \div 7$ ■ $-28 \div (-7)$ <

55. $|-25| \div |-5|$ ■ $|-25 \div (-5)|$ **56.** $-(-15 \div 5)$ ■ $-100 \div (-20)$
=   <

Number Sense Use integer rules and other math facts to answer each question.

57. What integer and −8 have the product −96? 12

58. What integer and 9 have the product −135? −15

59. What integer and −3 have the quotient 9? −27

60. What two integers have a sum of negative ten and a product of negative seventy-five? −15, 5

Ⓒ Challenge

Open-Ended Simplify each pair of expressions. Then write an integer that is between the values of the expressions. 61–64. Answers may vary. Samples are given.

61. $-2 \cdot (-2)$ and $2 \cdot 4$
4 and 8; 7
62. $10 + (-7)$ and $10 \div (-5)$
3 and −2; −1
63. $50 + (-48)$ and $80 \div (-20)$
2 and −4; 1
64. $121 \div (-11)$ and $|-7| - |7|$
−11 and 0; −6

65b. If there are an even number of negative integers, the sign of the product will be positive; otherwise, the sign will be negative.

65. a. Inductive Reasoning Will the sign be positive or negative for the product of three negative integers? Of four negative integers? Of five negative integers? negative; positive; negative
b. **Writing in Math** Use inductive reasoning to write a rule for the sign of the product of more than two negative integers. See left.

66. Negative; the numerator is positive, and the denominator is negative, so the quotient is negative.

66. Reasoning If a and b are positive integers, and x and y are negative integers, what is the sign of $\frac{a + b}{x + y}$? Explain. See left.

🌐 **67. Investing** Jerry owns 20 shares of stock valued at $23 each. One day, the price of the stock rose $2. It fell $1 on each of the next three days. The stock price rose $4 on the next day. What was the average daily gain or loss for a share of the stock over this time period? What was the total value of Jerry's stock at the end of this time period? $.60; $520

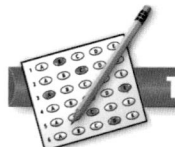

Multiple Choice

68. A scuba diver descended to a depth of 50 feet in 25 seconds. Which integer indicates the average number of feet per second the diver traveled? C
  A. −50   **B.** −25   **C.** −2   **D.** −1

69. Which of the following is the simplest form of $\frac{-1,225}{35}$? F
  F. −35   **G.** −25   **H.** −25   **I.** 35

In Exercises 70 and 71, what is the average for each group of data?

70. bank balances: $200, −$85, $120, $200, $280 C
  A. $97   **B.** $119   **C.** $143   **D.** $177

Take It to the NET
Online lesson quiz at
www.PHSchool.com
Web Code: ada-0109

71. feet above and below sea level:
    135 ft, −56 ft, 92 ft, −29 ft, −88 ft, −60 ft G
  F. −31 ft   **G.** −1 ft   **H.** 19 ft   **I.** 76 ft

Mixed Review

Lesson 1-8

72. Reasoning How many whole numbers from 10 to 200 have exactly two identical digits? 37

Lessons 1-5 and 1-6

Compare. Use >, <, or = to complete each statement.

73. −3 + (−8) ■ 12 − (−6) <

74. −9 + 13 ■ 24 − 30 >

75. |−6| − |12| ■ −8 + |−12| <

Lesson 1-1

Write a variable expression for each word phrase.

76. 50 decreased by a number n **77.** the product of y and 60 60y
50 − n

78. the sum of x and y $x + y$ **79.** the quotient of d divided by 5 $\frac{d}{5}$

✔ **Checkpoint Quiz 2**   **Lessons 1-5 through 1-9**

iTEXT Instant self-check quiz online and on CD-ROM

Simplify each expression.

  1. 3 + (−11) −8   **2.** 12 − (−8) 20   **3.** −9 · 5 −45

  4. −64 ÷ (−8) 8   **5.** |3| · 8 ÷ (−2) −12   **6.** −8(−3)(3) 72

Open-Ended Use integers to complete each equation.
7–9. Answers may vary. Samples are given.
  7. ■ + ■ = −7   **8.** ■ − (−20) = ■   **9.** ■ · ■ = −40
  3 + (−10) = −7   2 − (−20) = 22   8 · (−5) = −40

Patterns Find the next three numbers in each pattern.

  10. −7, −2, 3, 8, . . . 13, 18, 23   **11.** 1, 3, 9, 27, . . . 81, 243, 729

Alternative Assessment

Have each student make a poster displaying the rules for multiplying and dividing integers. Encourage students to include examples and use colors to help explain the rules. If students made posters for adding and subtracting integers, as suggested in the Alternative Assessment in Lesson 1-6, they may want to use the same colors or styles for these posters.

---

4. Assess

PowerPoint Lesson Quiz 1-9

Find each product or quotient.
1. −7(−3) 21
2. −36 ÷ (−9) 4
3. −12 · 2 −24
4. 7(−3) −21
5. −6 · (−2) · (−1) −12

Test Prep

Resources
For additional practice with a variety of test item formats:
• Test Prep, p. 61
• Test-Taking Strategies, p. 56
• Test-Taking Strategies With Transparencies

✔ **Chapter Checkpoint 2**

To check understanding of Lessons 1-5 to 1-9:
Checkpoint Quiz 2 (p. 49)

Teaching Resources
Checkpoint Quiz 2 (also in Prentice Hall Assessment System)

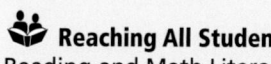
Reaching All Students
Reading and Math Literacy 2C

Spanish versions available.

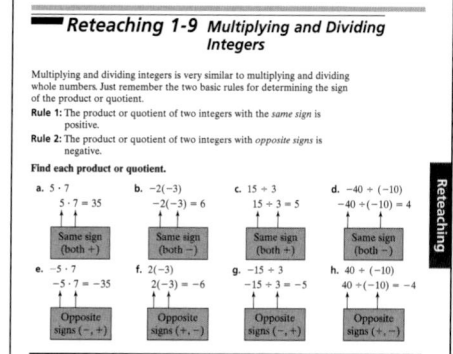

Reteaching 1-9 Multiplying and Dividing Integers

Multiplying and dividing integers is very similar to multiplying and dividing whole numbers. Just remember the two basic rules for determining the sign of the product or quotient.
Rule 1: The product or quotient of two integers with the *same sign* is positive.
Rule 2: The product or quotient of two integers with *opposite signs* is negative.

Find each product or quotient.

Complete the table. The first row has been done for you.

		Same or Opposite Sign?	Sign of Product or Quotient	Product or Quotient
	−5 · 12	Opposite	Negative	−60
1.	−91 ÷ (−13)	Same	Positive	7
2.	6 · 8	Same	Positive	48
3.	72 ÷ −9	Opposite	Negative	−8
4.	−3(−6)	Same	Positive	18
5.	−18 ÷ 2	Opposite	Negative	−9
6.	11 · (−5)	Opposite	Negative	−55
7.	52 ÷ 4	Same	Positive	13
8.	−12(6)	Opposite	Negative	−72

49

1-10

1. Plan

Lesson Preview

 Check Skills You'll Need

Integers and Absolute Value
Lesson 1-4: Example 3;
Exercises 16–27.
Extra Practice, p. 744.

Lesson Resources

Teaching Resources
Practice, Reteaching, Enrichment

Reaching All Students
Practice Workbook 1-10
Spanish Practice Workbook 1-10
Guided Problem Solving 1-10
Hands-On Activities 1

Presentation Assistant Plus!
Transparencies and PowerPoint™
• Check Skills You'll Need 1-10
• Additional Examples 1-10
• Student Edition Answers 1-10
• Lesson Quiz 1-10
• Classroom Aid 2
PH Presentation Pro CD-ROM 1-10

ASSESSMENT SYSTEM

Computer Test Generator CD-ROM

 Technology
Resource Pro® CD-ROM
Computer Test Generator CD-ROM
PH Presentation Pro CD-ROM

 www.PHSchool.com

Student Site
• Teacher Web Code: adk-5500
• Algebra Readiness Puzzles 61, 62
• Self-grading Lesson Quiz
PH SuccessNet Teacher Center
• Lesson Planner
• Resources

Plus **iTEXT**

What You'll Learn

OBJECTIVE 1 To name coordinates and quadrants in the coordinate plane

OBJECTIVE 2 To graph points in the coordinate plane

. . . And Why

To solve real-world problems involving geography

 Check Skills You'll Need

Graph the numbers on a number line.
1–4. See back of book.
1. $-2, 1, -5$

2. $0, 2, -4$

3. $-3, 3, -2$

4. $-1, -5, -8$

 For help, go to Lesson 1-4.

New Vocabulary
• coordinate plane
• x-axis
• y-axis
• quadrants
• origin
• ordered pair
• x-coordinate
• y-coordinate

 Interactive lesson includes instant self-check, tutorials, and activities.

A **coordinate plane** is formed by the intersection of two number lines. The horizontal number line is called the **x-axis** and the vertical number line is called the **y-axis.**

The x- and y-axes divide the coordinate plane into four **quadrants.**

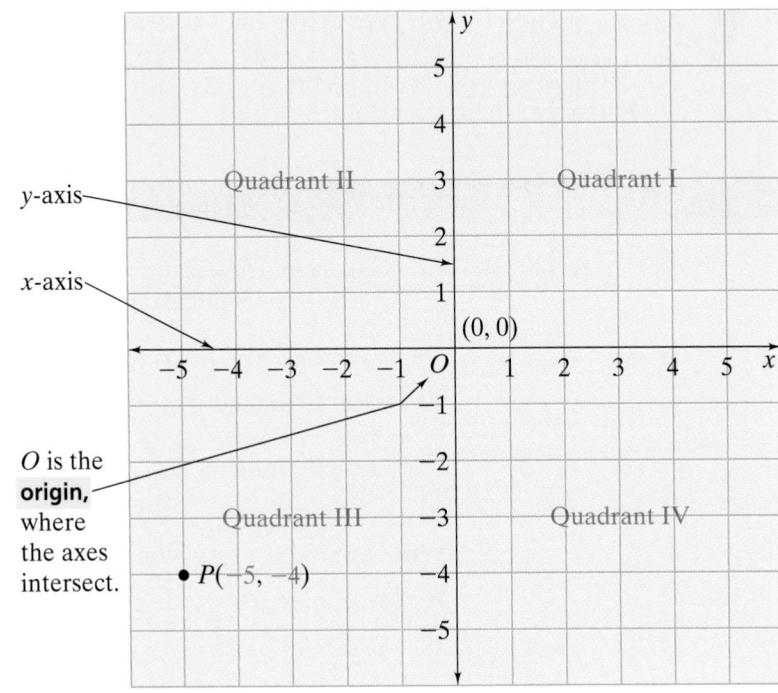

An **ordered pair** gives the coordinates and location of a point. The ordered pair $(-5, -4)$ identifies point P in Quadrant III above.

$$(-5, -4)$$

The **x-coordinate** shows the position right or left of the y-axis.

The **y-coordinate** shows the position above or below the x-axis.

50   **Chapter 1**   Algebraic Expressions and Integers

Ongoing Assessment and Intervention

Before the Lesson
Diagnose prerequisite skills using:
• Check Skills You'll Need

During the Lesson
Monitor progress using:
• Check Understanding
• Additional Examples
• Test Prep

After the Lesson
Assess knowledge using:
• Lesson Quiz
• Computer Test Generator CD-ROM

1 EXAMPLE Naming Coordinates and Quadrants

Write the coordinates of point A. In which quadrant is point A located?

Point A is located 2 units to the left of the y-axis. So the x-coordinate is -2. The point is 1 unit above the x-axis. So the y-coordinate is 1.

The coordinates of point A are $(-2, 1)$. Point A is located in Quadrant II.

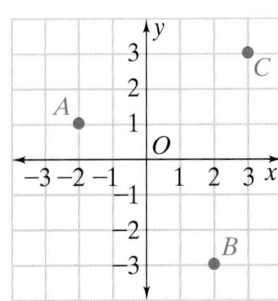

✔ **Check Understanding** Example 1

1. **a.** Use the graph in Example 1. Write the coordinates of B and C. **(2, −3); (3, 3)**
   b. Identify the quadrants in which B and C are located.
   Quadrant IV; Quadrant I

OBJECTIVE

2 Graphing Points

To graph a point $A(x, y)$ in a coordinate plane, you graph the ordered pair (x, y).

2 EXAMPLE Graphing Points

Graph point $R(3, -5)$.

Step 1
Start at the origin.

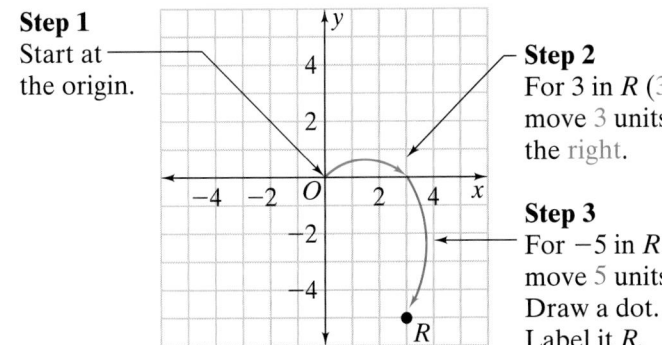

Step 2
For 3 in $R\,(3, -5)$, move 3 units to the right.

Step 3
For -5 in $R\,(3, -5)$, move 5 units down. Draw a dot. Label it R.

✔ **Check Understanding** Example 2

2. **a.** Graph these points on one coordinate plane: $K(3, 1)$, $L(-2, 1)$, and $M(-2, -4)$. **See above right.**
   b. **Geometry** Draw lines to connect points K, L, and M. Describe the figure that results. **See above right; a triangle.**

2a–b.

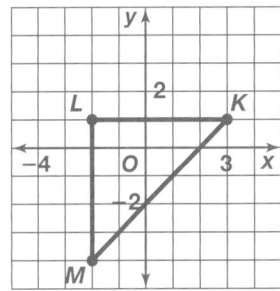

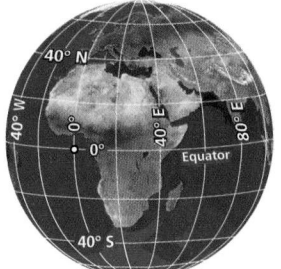

Real-World Connection

Latitude and longitude are measurements in a coordinate system that locates every point on Earth's surface.

👥 Reaching All Students

Below Level Have students look at a map of a city. Point out the letters and numbers around the edge of the map. Have the students find the map coordinates for given places, or find places located at given coordinates.

Advanced Learners Ask: *What figure is formed in the coordinate plane when you connect the points $(-4, -3)$, $(4, -3)$, $(4, 3)$, and $(-4, 3)$ in order?* **a rectangle**

Auditory Learners See note on page 51.
Error Prevention See note on page 53.

---

2. Teach

Professional Development

Math Background

Pierre de Fermat and René Descartes developed the Cartesian coordinate system in the seventeenth century. This system uses two perpendicular number lines to identify the position of any point in a plane. An *ordered pair of numbers* names the position of a point. The pair is called *ordered* because the order of the numbers is crucial. The first number always gives the horizontal distance from zero and the second number always gives the vertical distance from zero.

Teaching Notes

1 EXAMPLE Auditory Learners

A common error is to move vertically with the first coordinate. Have the students practice saying "over and up" or "over and down" as they find coordinates.

PowerPoint

📄 Additional Examples

① Write the coordinates of point G. In which quadrant is point G located?

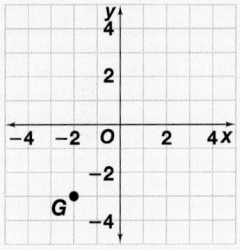

$(-2, -3)$; Quadrant III

② Graph point $M(-3, 3)$.

Closure

Ask: *In which quadrant is $(-3, 5)$?* **Quadrant II** *Give an example of an ordered pair in Quadrant IV.* **Answers may vary. Sample: $(-3, -2)$.**

51

3. Practice

Assignment Guide

1 Objective 1
- **A B** Core 1–12, 29–50, 57–60
- **C** Extension 64–66

2 Objective 2
- **A B** Core 13–28, 51–56, 61–63

Test Prep 67–71
Mixed Review 72–81

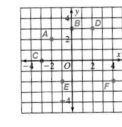

Practice 1-10 The Coordinate Plane

Graph each point.
1. $A(-2,2)$ 2. $B(0,3)$
3. $C(-3,0)$ 4. $D(2,3)$
5. $E(-1,-2)$ 6. $F(4,-2)$

Write the coordinates of each point.
7. A ___(-1, 1)___   8. B ___(4, 3)___
9. C ___(-2, -1)___   10. D ___(0, -1)___

In which quadrant or on what axis does each point fall?
11. A ___II___   12. B ___I___
13. C ___III___   14. D ___y-axis___

Name the point with the given coordinates.
15. $(1,4)$ ___G___   16. $(-3,0)$ ___T___
17. $(5,-1)$ ___K___   18. $(-2,-4)$ ___R___

Complete using *positive, or negative*, or *zero*.
19. In Quadrant II, x is ___negative___ and y is ___positive___.
20. In Quadrant III, x is ___negative___ and y is ___negative___.
21. On the y-axis x is ___zero___.
22. On the x-axis y is ___zero___.

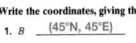

Enrichment 1-10 Latitude and Longitude

Geographers divide the earth into a coordinate grid using *latitude* and *longitude* lines. Latitude lines are parallel to the equator and run from 90°N (the North Pole) to 90°S (the South Pole). Longitude lines are measured east and west of the *prime meridian*, the 0° longitude line which runs through Greenwich, England. Point A in the figure has coordinates (15°S, 45°W).

Write the coordinates, giving the latitude first.
1. B ___(45°N, 45°E)___
2. C ___(15°S, 15°E)___
3. D ___(45°N, 90°W)___
4. E ___(60°S, 0°)___
5. F ___(35°N, 25°W)___   6. South Pole ___(90°S, 0°)___

Graph each point on the coordinate grid above. Write the letter beside the point.
7. $G(75°S, 75°E)$ 8. $H(25°N, 45°E)$ 9. $I(60°S, 90°W)$
10. $J(0°, 30°E)$ 11. $K(75°N, 82\frac{1}{2}°E)$ 12. $L(50°N, 55°W)$
13. How many degrees of latitude separate Halifax, Nova Scotia (45°N, 65°W), and Cordoba, Argentina (32°S, 65°W)? ___77°___
14. How many degrees of longitude separate Baku, U.S.S.R. (41°N, 50°E), and New Haven, CT (41°N, 73°W)? ___123°___
15. One degree of longitude at the equator equals 69.2 mi. How far is it from Quito, Ecuador (0°, 79°W) to Kampala, Uganda (0°, 32\frac{1}{2}°E)? ___7,715.8 miles___
16. Belem, Brazil (0°, 48°W), is located due west of Libreville, Gabon. The distance between the cities is 3944.4 mi. Give the latitude and longitude of Libreville. ___(0°, 9°E)___

EXERCISES

? For more exercises, see *Extra Practice.*

Practice and Problem Solving

A Practice by Example

In which quadrant does each point lie?

Example 1 (page 51)

1. J III   2. V II
3. M IV   4. K I
5. P II   6. Q III

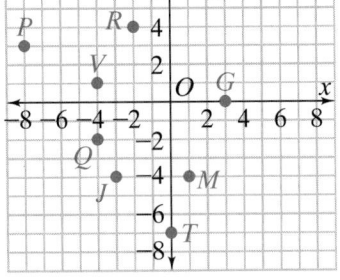

Write the coordinates of each point.
7. T (0, −7)   8. G (3, 0)
9. R (−2, 4)   10. Q (−4, −2)
11. P (−8, 3)   12. M (1, −4)

Example 2 (page 51)

Draw a coordinate plane. Then graph each point. 13–28. See margin.
13. $A(-1,3)$ 14. $B(-4,-1)$ 15. $C(2,5)$ 16. $D(2,-2)$
17. $E(0,6)$ 18. $F(-3,2)$ 19. $G(6,0)$ 20. $H(1,7)$
21. $K(5,-6)$ 22. $L(0,0)$ 23. $M(-5,-2)$ 24. $N(7,0)$
25. $P(-1,-3)$ 26. $Q(1,1)$ 27. $R(0,-4)$ 28. $S(-3,4)$

B Apply Your Skills

29. What ordered pair names the origin? (0, 0)

Name the point with the given coordinates.
30. $(3,2)$ Q   31. $(0,-5)$ F
32. $(2,3)$ M   33. $(-2,-3)$ P

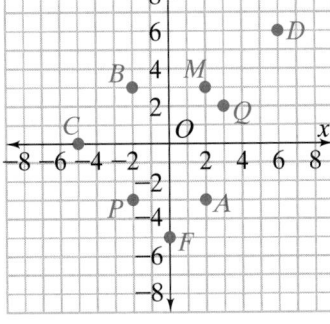

Write the coordinates of each point.
34. A (2, −3)   35. B (−2, 3)
36. C (−5, 0)   37. D (6, 6)

Mental Math Write the coordinates of each point.

38. the point 5 units to the left of the y-axis and 2 units below the x-axis (−5, −2)

39. the point on the y-axis 4 units below the x-axis (0, −4)

40. the point on the x-axis 3 units to the right of the origin (3, 0)

Mental Math In which quadrant does $P(x, y)$ lie?

41. x is positive, y is negative. IV   42. x is positive, y is positive. I

43. x is negative, y is positive. II   44. x is negative, y is negative. III

13–28.
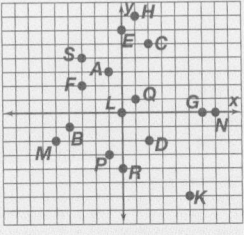

In which quadrant or on which axis does each point lie?

45. $V(13, 25)$ I

46. $W(x, y)$ if $x = 0, y > 0$
y-axis

47. $X(-17, -2)$ III

48. $Z(x, y)$ if $x > 0, y < 0$ IV

49. $B(0, |-2|)$ y-axis

50. $R(x, y)$ if $x < 0, y > 0$ II

Error Prevention!

Exercises 41–44 Suggest that students test a numerical example, for instance, (2, −3) for Exercise 41, to check their answer.

Geometry **Graph and connect the points in the order given. Connect the last point to the first. Name the figure.** 51–54. Graphs. See margin.

51. $(-4, 1), (1, 1), (-3, -1)$
triangle

52. $(2, 2), (2, -1), (-5, -1), (-5, 2)$
rectangle

53. $(-1, 2), (1, 5), (7, 5), (5, 2)$
parallelogram

54. $(2, -4), (7, -1), (4, 4), (-1, 1)$
square

Geometry **$PQRS$ is a square. Find the coordinates of S.**

GPS **55.** $P(-5, 0), Q(0, 5), R(5, 0), S(\blacksquare, \blacksquare)$ (0, −5)

56. $P(-1, 3), Q(4, 3), R(4, -2), S(\blacksquare, \blacksquare)$ (−1, −2)

🌐 **Geography** On a map, coordinates are given in degrees of longitude and latitude. Use the map below for Exercises 57–60.

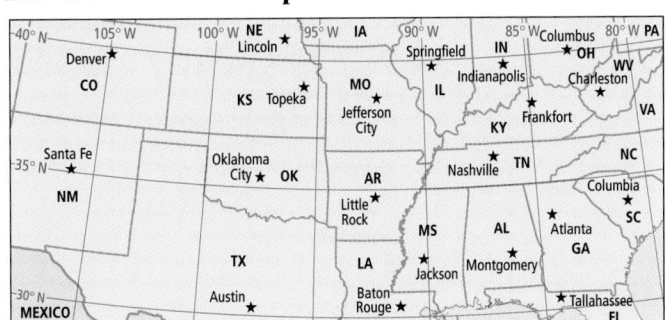

SAMPLE
Little Rock, Arkansas:
Longitude:
   about 92° W
Latitude:
   about 34° N

57. Find the longitude and latitude of Jackson, Mississippi.
about 90° W, 32° N

58. Find the longitude and latitude of Topeka, Kansas.
about 96° W, 39° N

59. What city is located near 85° W, 38° N? Frankfort, Kentucky

60. What city is located near 106° W, 35° N? Santa Fe, New Mexico

Geometry **Use one coordinate plane for Exercises 61–63.**

61. Graph the points $(-2, 1), (-2, 3), (1, 3),$ and $(1, 1)$. Connect them in the order given. Connect the last point to the first.
See above left.

62. Change the coordinates of Exercise 61 as described below. Graph and connect the points for each new set of coordinates. Use a different color for each set.
   a. Multiply each x-coordinate by −1. a–d. See left.
   b. Multiply each y-coordinate by −1.
   c. Multiply each coordinate by −1.
   d. Multiply each coordinate by 2.

63. **Writing in Math** Compare each figure in Exercise 62 to the figure in Exercise 61. Write a short paragraph describing your results.
See margin.

61.
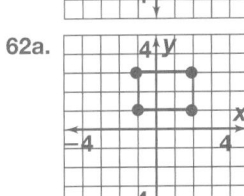

62a.

62b.

62c.

62d.

Geometry Connection
Exercises 55–56 Ask students to recall what they know about a square. four equal sides, four right angles

51.
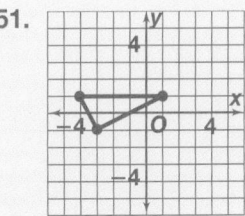

52.
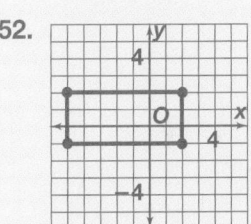

53.
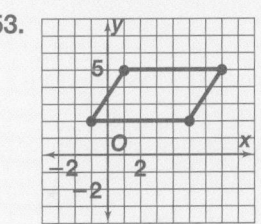

54.
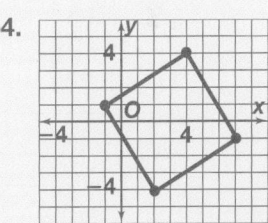

63. **Answers may vary.**
Sample: 62a flips the figure across the y-axis. 62b flips the figure across the x-axis. 62c flips the figure across one axis and then the other. 62d doubles the lengths of the sides.

GPS Use the Guided Problem Solving worksheet with Exercise 55.

 **PowerPoint** Lesson Quiz 1-10

Draw a coordinate grid. Graph each point.

1. $S(2, 3)$

2. $T(2, -3)$

3. $U(-2, 3)$

4. $K(0, -3)$

5. $L(3, 0)$

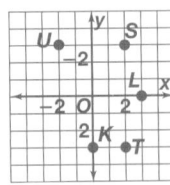

Test Prep

📁 **Resources**

For additional practice with a variety of test item formats:

• Test Prep, p. 61
• Test-Taking Strategies, p. 56
• Test-Taking Strategies With Transparencies

Reteaching 1-10 *The Coordinate Plane*

Write the coordinates of point A.

Point A is 3 units to the right of the y-axis. So the x-coordinate is 3. It is 4 units below the x-axis. So the y-coordinate is −4. The coordinates of point A are (3, −4).

In which quadrant is point A located?

Compare the point to the diagram. Point A is in the fourth quadrant.

Quadrant II (2) | Quadrant I (1)
Quadrant III (3) | Quadrant IV (4)

Write the coordinates of each point.

1. A _(−2, −5)_   **2.** B _(4, 1)_
3. C _(−3, 3)_   **4.** D _(2, −1)_
5. E _(−1, 2)_   **6.** F _(1, −3)_
7. G _(−3, −2)_   **8.** H _(4, 4)_

In which quadrant does each point lie?

9. A ___III___   **10.** B ___I___
11. C ___II___   **12.** D ___IV___
13. E ___II___   **14.** F ___IV___
15. G ___III___   **16.** H ___I___

---

65. Explanations may vary.
Sample:
No; since *a* and *b* describe positions on two number lines, (*a*, *b*) and (*b*, *a*) describe different points (unless *a* = *b*).

C Challenge

Writing in Math

Describe how to graph $Q(4, 23)$ and four other points, each 1 unit from *Q*. **See margin.**

64. Open-Ended Draw a dot-to-dot picture on a coordinate grid. Write the coordinates of the points in order. Exchange coordinates with a classmate and draw the other's picture. **Check students' work.**

65. Reasoning Assume that $a \neq b$. Do (a, b) and (b, a) describe the same point? Explain. **See margin.**

66. Write the coordinates of four points in the coordinate plane that are 3 units from the origin. Graph the points.
$A(3, 0), B(0, 3), C(-3, 0), D(0, -3)$ **See below left for graph.**

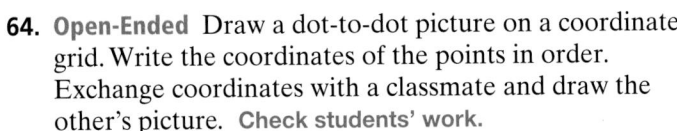

Test Prep

Multiple Choice

66.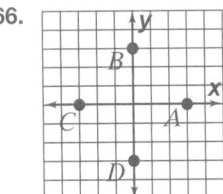

💻 **Take It to the NET**
Online lesson quiz at
www.PHSchool.com
Web Code: ada-0110

67. $P(a, b)$ is in Quadrant III. Which word pair makes the following sentence true?

The value of *a* must be __?__ and the value of *b* must be __?__ **D**

A. positive; positive   **B.** positive; negative
C. negative; positive   **D.** negative; negative

68. $C(x, y)$ is in Quadrant IV. Which ordered pair could be the coordinates of *C*? **I**

F. $(-3, -7)$ **G.** $(0, 2)$ **H.** $(-8, 0)$ **I.** $(5, -6)$

69. To graph point *R*, start at the origin, move 10 units to the right, 4 units down, and 6 units to the left. What are the coordinates of point *R*? **A**

A. $(4, -4)$ **B.** $(10, 2)$ **C.** $(6, 10)$ **D.** $(-4, -6)$

70. $P(a, b)$ is located on the *x*-axis. Which statement is true for all nonzero values of *a* and *b*? **H**

F. $a > b$ **G.** $b > a$ **H.** $|a| > b$ **I.** $|b| > a$

71. $T(a, b)$ is located in Quadrant II. Which statement is *never* true? **A**

A. $a > b$ **B.** $b > a$ **C.** $|a| > b$ **D.** $|b| > a$

Mixed Review

Lesson 1-9   **Find each product or quotient.**

72. $-11 \cdot 11$ **−121**   **73.** $-432 \div 48$ **−9**   **74.** $\frac{0}{-56}$ **0**

Lesson 1-5 🌐 **75. Submarines** A submarine at sea level dives 800 ft and then another 125 ft. Find the submarine's final depth. **−925 ft**

Lesson 1-4   **Write the value of each expression.**

76. $|-8|$ **8**   **77.** $-|-95|$ **−95**   **78.** the opposite of 12 **−12**

79. $|16| + 4$ **20**   **80.** $|-6| - 2$ **4**   **81.** the opposite of −3 **3**

Alternative Assessment

Have students draw a triangle on a coordinate plane so that its vertices have integer coordinates and are in different quadrants. Ask them to label each vertex with its ordered pair. Also, name the quadrant that does not contain a vertex.

Writing in Math. On a coordinate plane, count 4 units right and 23 units up. Draw a dot and label it *Q*. Then draw 4 dots, each 1 unit from *Q* in 4 different directions.

Graphing Ordered Pairs

You can use a graphing calculator to display ordered pairs on a coordinate plane.

EXAMPLE

Graph these ordered pairs: $(-6, 2), (-5, 6), (-4, -1), (-3, -5),$ $(-2, 4), (0, 9), (1, 5), (2, -4), (2, 0), (3, 6), (5, 2), (7, -5), (8, 4)$

Step 1 Enter the ordered pairs into list L_1 for the x-coordinates and list L_2 for the y-coordinates.

Press **LIST**. To clear old entries in L_1, select **L₁**

and press **CLEAR** **ENTER**. (Clear old entries in other columns in a similar way.) Enter all the x-coordinates into list L_1. Enter all y-coordinates into list L_2. Check L_1 and L_2 to make sure the coordinates align as they should.

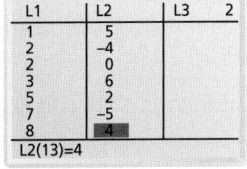

Step 2 In **PLOT,** enter 1 and select **On.** Select the Type as shown below, and check that Xlist and Ylist show L_1 and L_2, respectively.

Step 3 Press **GRAPH**

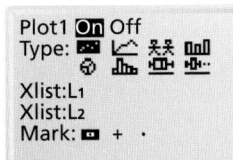

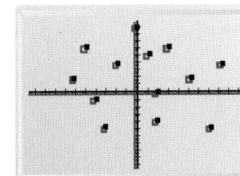

EXERCISES

Graph each group of ordered pairs. 1–4. See margin.

1. $(-5, -1), (-2, 4), (-1, 3), (0, 4), (1, 6), (3, 0), (4, 2), (5, -3)$

2. $(-5, 7), (4, 6), (9, 2), (-2, -8), (0, 3), (-3, -1), (-6, 1), (5, 5),$ $(1, -6), (-1, -3), (3, -2), (-4, 9), (-8, 4), (2, -5), (6, 0), (7, -4)$

Graph the ordered pairs. Adjust the window settings to see all the points.

3. $(5, 2), (6, 5), (8, 1), (11, 3), (12, 8), (14, 10), (15, 6), (17, 2)$

4. $(-10, -5), (-8, -9), (-6, 2), (-5, 8), (7, -3), (9, -6), (10, 4), (12, 9)$

Graph the ordered pairs. Describe the pattern you see. 5–6. See margin for graphs.

5. $(7, 3), (-3, -2), (1, 0), (-5, -3), (9, 4), (3, 1), (5, 2), (-7, -4)$ line

6. $(0, -5), (-2, -3), (4, -5), (0, -1), (2, -3), (-4, -5)$ triangle

4.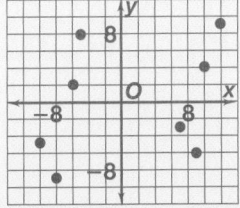

5.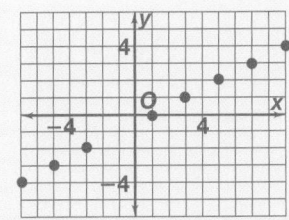

6.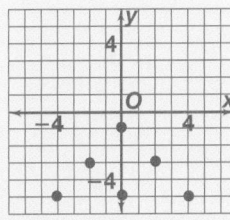

Graphing Ordered Pairs

This Technology extension shows students how to use a graphing calculator to display ordered pairs on a coordinate plane.

Resources

Students may use any graphing calculator available.

Teaching Notes

Error Prevention!

Have students count the number of ordered pairs to make sure they included each pair in their lists. When students have entered the last coordinate, the number in parentheses on the screen should be the same as the number of ordered pairs given in the exercise.

Inclusion

Pair students who have difficulty with eye-hand coordination with partners. Have the student with difficulties instruct his or her partner on what to input.

1.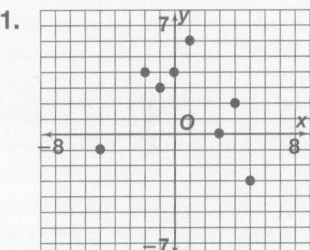

2.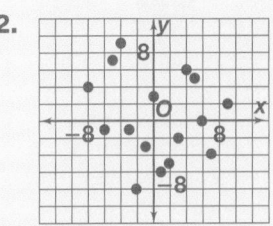

3.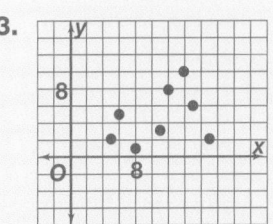

55

 **Test-Taking Strategies**

Writing Gridded Responses

This feature gives students practice in filling in gridded responses. Students need to know the forms of answers that can be gridded and the forms that cannot. They need to know how to change mixed numbers to improper fractions or decimals. They also need to know how to write repeating decimals as improper fractions. This practice is important since a student will not get credit for an answer if it is not gridded correctly.

Resources

A sheet of blank grids is available in the *Test-Taking Strategies With Transparencies* booklet. Give copies of this sheet to students so they can practice filling in the grids.

ASSESSMENT SYSTEM

Test-Taking Strategies With Transparencies
• Transparency 1
• Practice sheet, p. 1

Test-Taking Strategies With Transparencies

Chapter 1: Writing Gridded Responses
Exercises

Mark your answers on the grid for each exercise.

1. A chemist mixes 0.75 mL of water with 0.333 mL of acetic acid and 0.257 mL of citric acid. What is the total number of milliliters in the solution?

2. Find 2.1 + 0.365 − 0.165.
3. 5.32 + 4
4. 7.9 − 0.85
5. 4.8 ÷ 0.12
6. 10 − 4.5
7. 1.5 × 20
8. 4.4 + 0.76 + 0.3
9. 17.3 − 14.88
10. 6.5 − (4.1 + 0.6)
11. $12\frac{1}{4} + \frac{1}{4}$
12. You have $440 in a bank. You add $4 per week to the bank for the next six weeks. What is your balance in dollars at the end of six weeks?
13. A carpenter cuts a 12-m board into 5 equal pieces. To the nearest tenth, how many meters long is each piece?
14. You spent $11.32 on earrings. Each set of earrings cost $2.83. How many sets of earrings did you buy?

Test-Taking Strategies   Pre-Algebra   **1**

Some tests require you to enter a number answer on a grid. You must find the answer and also show it in a form that you can fit on the grid. For example, you can enter an improper fraction on the grid, but not a mixed number.

1 EXAMPLE

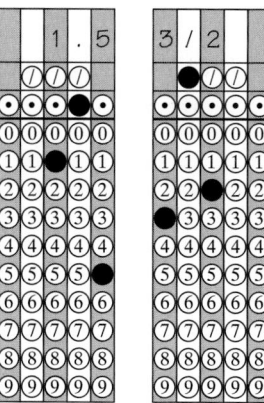

What is the sum of −0.5 and 2?
$$-0.5 + 2 = 1.5, \frac{3}{2}, \text{ or } 1\frac{1}{2}.$$

For the grid, you can use 1.5 or $\frac{3}{2}$, but not $1\frac{1}{2}$. You write the answer in the spaces at the top of the grid and fill in the corresponding bubbles below.

The grids at the right are correct for 1.5 and $\frac{3}{2}$, respectively.

Here are things to remember as you grid your responses:
• You must begin in the left column OR end in the right column.
• You cannot have blanks in the middle of a response.
• Always write a mixed number as an improper fraction.
• You do not have to simplify fractions.

2 EXAMPLE

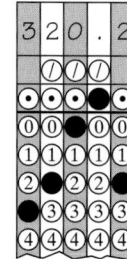

The surface of a lake is 29.8 ft below sea level. What is the elevation in feet of a hilltop that is 350 ft above the surface of the lake?

$(-29.8) + 350$	**Write an expression.**
$\|350\| - \|-29.8\|$	**Find the difference of the absolute values.**
320.2	**Simplify. Since 350 has the greater absolute value, the sum is positive.**

The hilltop is 320.2 feet above sea level. Enter 320.2 on the grid as shown. You do not enter the units.

EXERCISES

Write what you would grid for each answer.

1. Simplify $12 \div [12 - (4 \cdot 2)]$. **3**

2. What is the next number in the pattern 0.4, 0.8, 1.3, 1.9, 2.6, . . . ? **3.4**

3. What is the next number in the pattern $0, \frac{1}{2}, 1, 1\frac{1}{2}, 2, \ldots$? **5/2 or 2.5**

Chapter Review

Vocabulary

absolute value (p. 19)
conjecture (p. 35)
coordinate plane (p. 50)
counterexample (p. 37)
evaluate (p. 14)
inductive reasoning (p. 35)

integers (p. 19)
opposites (p. 19)
order of operations (p. 8)
ordered pair (p. 50)
origin (p. 50)
quadrants (p. 50)

variable (p. 4)
variable expression (p. 4)
x-axis (p. 50)
x-coordinate (p. 50)
y-axis (p. 50)
y-coordinate (p. 50)

Reading Math
Understanding
Vocabulary

Take It to the NET
Online vocabulary quiz
at **www.PHSchool.com**
Web Code: adj-0151

Choose the vocabulary term that correctly completes the sentence.

1. The ordered pair $(0, 0)$ represents the location of the _?_ .
   origin
2. A letter that stands for a number in an expression is a(n) _?_ .
   variable
3. The vertical axis in the coordinate plane is known as the _?_ .
   y-axis
4. The coordinate plane is divided into four _?_ . quadrants
5. All whole numbers and their opposites are _?_ .
   integers
6. In the ordered pair $(-5, 2)$, the number -5 is the _?_ .
   x-coordinate
7. The distance that a number is from zero on a number line is the
   _?_ of the number. absolute value

Skills and Concepts

1-1 Objectives

▼ To identify variables,
numerical expressions,
and variable expressions
(p. 4)

▼ To write variable
expressions for word
phrases (p. 5)

A **variable** is a letter that stands for a number. A **variable expression**
uses variables, numerals, and operation symbols.

Write a variable expression for each word phrase.

8. twenty-five less than x
   $x - 25$
9. the product of n and 3 $3n$
10. ten decreased by t $10 - t$
11. a number x divided by 4 $\frac{x}{4}$
12. a number n increased by 5
    $n + 5$
13. two more than y $y + 2$

1-2 Objectives

▼ To use the order of
operations (p. 8)

▼ To use grouping symbols
(p. 9)

To simplify a numerical expression, follow the **order of operations.**

1. Work inside grouping symbols.

2. Multiply and divide in order from left to right.

3. Add and subtract in order from left to right.

Simplify each expression.

14. $3 \cdot 7 + 6 \div 2$ **24** 15. $(4 + 8) \div 2 \cdot 2$ **12** 16. $9 \cdot 5 - 4(12 \div 6)$ **37**

1-3 Objectives

▼ To evaluate variable expressions (p. 14)

▼ To solve real-world problems involving packaging and shopping (p. 15)

To **evaluate** a variable expression, substitute a number for each variable. Use the order of operations to simplify.

Evaluate each expression.

17. $3x + 4$, for $x = 5$ **19**

18. $15 + 10 \div n$, for $n = 5$ **17**

19. $(y - 6)2$, for $y = 16$ **20**

20. $4(4 + m)$, for $m = 6$ **40**

21. $15t \cdot 10$, for $t = 3$ **450**

22. $z + [15 - (z - 1)]$, for $z = 4$
16

1-4 Objectives

▼ To represent, graph, and order integers (p. 18)

▼ To find opposites and absolute values (p. 19)

Integers are the set of whole numbers and their **opposites.** The **absolute value** of an integer is its distance from zero on a number line. On a number line, the integer farther to the right is the greater integer.

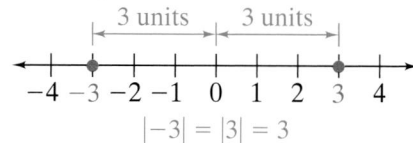

$|-3| = |3| = 3$

Simplify each expression.

23. the opposite of 17 **−17**

24. $|-1{,}000|$ **1,000**

25. the absolute value of negative 9 **9**

26. the opposite of the absolute value of 12 **−12**

Compare. Use >, <, or = to complete each statement.

27. $-7 \ \blacksquare \ -9$
>

28. $0 \ \blacksquare \ -3$
>

29. $-6 \ \blacksquare \ 2$
<

30. $|-5| \ \blacksquare \ |5|$
=

🌐 **31. Water Slides** A slide at a water park is 30 ft high. What integer represents your change in elevation when you go down the slide? **−30**

1-5 and 1-6 Objectives

▼ To use models to add integers (p. 24)

▼ To use rules to add integers (p. 25)

▼ To use models to subtract integers (p. 30)

▼ To use a rule to subtract integers (p. 31)

To add integers with the *same* sign, add their absolute values. The sum has the same sign. To add integers with *different* signs, find the difference of their absolute values. The sum has the sign of the integer with the greater absolute value. To subtract an integer, add its opposite.

Simplify each expression.

32. $8 + (-15)$ **−7**

33. $-9 + 21$ **12**

34. $9 - (-5)$ **14**

35. $14 + (-9) + (-20)$ **−15**

36. $-62 - (-59) - 24$ **−27**

37. $-7 - 4$ **−11**

38. $-4 + 12 + (-3) + (-6)$ **−1**

🌐 **39. Wildlife** An eagle leaves her nest on the side of a cliff. She soars upward 60 ft and then dives 80 ft. What is her change in elevation after leaving the nest? **−20 ft**

1-7 Objectives

▼ To write rules for patterns (p. 35)

▼ To make predictions and test conjectures (p. 36)

Inductive reasoning is making conclusions based on patterns you observe. A conclusion reached by inductive reasoning is a **conjecture.**

Write a rule for each pattern. Find the next three numbers in the pattern.

40. $0, 6, 12, 18, \ldots$
Start with 0 and add 6 repeatedly; 24, 30, 36

41. $-18, -9, 0, 9, \ldots$
Start with -18 and add 9 repeatedly; 18, 27, 36

42. $\frac{1}{2}, 1, 1\frac{1}{2}, 2, \ldots$
Start with $\frac{1}{2}$ and add $\frac{1}{2}$ repeatedly; $2\frac{1}{2}, 3, 3\frac{1}{2}$

1-8 Objectives

▼ To find number patterns using rules (p. 40)

You can use patterns to solve problems.

43. Suppose you plan to save $12 per week. You have already saved $7.50. In how many weeks will you have saved at least $100? 8 weeks

44. A four-line classified ad costs $28 for a week. Each additional line costs $10.50. What is the weekly cost of a 12-line ad? $112

1-9 Objectives

▼ To multiply integers using repeated addition, patterns, and rules (p. 44)

▼ To divide integers using rules (p. 46)

To multiply or divide integers, multiply or divide the absolute values of the integers. If the integers have the same sign, the product or quotient is positive. If the integers have different signs, the product or quotient is negative.

Multiply or divide.

45. $7(-6)$ -42

46. $250 \div (-50)$ -5

47. $(-9)(-8)$ 72

48. $-56 \div (-8)$ 7

49. $-120 \div 40$ -3

50. $-15(11)$ -165

51. $\frac{-64}{8}$ -8

52. $(-5)(-7)$ 35

53. $(-6)(-17)$ 102

1-10 Objectives

▼ To name coordinates and quadrants in the coordinate plane (p. 50)

▼ To graph points in the coordinate plane (p. 51)

A **coordinate plane** is formed by the intersection of two number lines. The **x-axis** and the **y-axis** divide the coordinate plane into four **quadrants.** An **ordered pair** gives the coordinates of a point. The **x-coordinate** shows the position right or left of the y-axis. The **y-coordinate** shows the position above or below the x-axis.

Write the coordinates of each point.

54. A (1, −3)

55. B (−2, 1)

56. C (−3, −3)

57. D (2, 2)

Chapter Test

Write an expression for each phrase.

1. a number n increased by nineteen $n + 19$

2. ten less than negative three $-3 - 10$

3. the product of x and negative five $-5x$

4. 5 more than the opposite of y $-y + 5$

Evaluate each expression for the given values of the variables.

5. $3a + 5$, for $a = -5$ -10

6. $5m + 9 + 7n$, for $m = 8$ and $n = 1$ 56

7. $3|x - y| + x$, for $x = 1$ and $y = 8$ 22

8. $20 - 2(a - b)$, for $a = 3$ and $b = 2$ 18

Simplify each expression.

9. $|-5|$ 5   10. opposite of -9 9

11. opposite of 7 -7 12. $|15|$ 15

Use >, <, or = to complete each sentence.

13. $-6 \blacksquare -5$ <   14. $8 \blacksquare -10$ >

15. $-3 \blacksquare 3$ <   16. $0 \blacksquare -7$ >

Simplify each expression.

17. $15 + (-7)$ 8   18. $-8 - (-12)$ 4

19. $-9(-7)$ 63   20. $54 \div (-6)$ -9

21. $-6 \cdot 48$ -288 22. $\frac{-56}{-7}$ 8

23. $119 - (-24)$ 143   24. $-47 + (-21)$ -68

25. $-83 + 17$ -66 26. $5(-12)(-3)(-1)$ -180

27. $2 \cdot |14 - (-9)|$ 46   28. $8 \cdot 6 \div (2 + 1)$ 16

29. $4 + 7 \cdot 2 + 8$ 26   30. $16 - 2 \cdot (5 + 3)$ 0

In which quadrant or on which axis does each point lie?

31. $(-5, 7)$ II   32. $(0, -4)$ y-axis   33. $(-8, -6)$ III

Write the coordinates of each point.

34. F $(-3, 2)$

35. G $(1, -2)$

36. H $(2, 0)$

37. J $(-2, -2)$

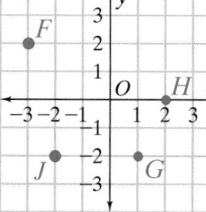

38. A shirt costs $15 and jeans cost $25.
   a. Write an expression for the cost of j jeans and s shirts. $25j + 15s$
   b. Evaluate the expression to find the cost of three pairs of jeans and five shirts. $150
   c. How many pairs of jeans can you buy for $60? 2

39. Which statement is *always* true? D
   A. The absolute value of an integer is equal to the opposite of the integer.
   B. The absolute value of an integer is greater than zero.
   C. An integer is greater than its opposite.
   D. A positive integer is greater than a negative integer.

40. A submarine was 250 m below sea level. It rose 75 m. Use an integer to describe the new depth of the submarine. -175

41. Write a rule for the pattern below. Find the next three numbers in the pattern.
   100, 90, 85, 75, 70, 60, . . . Start with 100 and alternately subtract 10 and 5; 55, 45, 40.

42. You are in an elevator on the seventh floor. You go down 4 floors and then up 8 floors. Then you go down 3 floors and up 9 floors. The elevator goes down again 2 floors, and you get off. According to the pattern, on which floor are you now? 15th floor

43. **Writing in Math** Describe how to order the integers 2, -6, 9, 0, and -13 from least to greatest. Place them on a number line and write them as they appear from left to right.

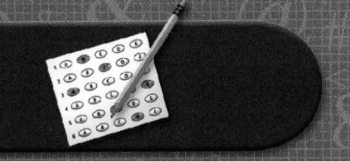
Reading Comprehension Read each passage below. Then answer the questions on the basis of what is *stated* or *implied* in the passage.

Numbers in Nature Numbers appear everywhere in the patterns of nature. For example, the numbers of petals on flowers form patterns. Find some flowers and count their petals. You will find, with few exceptions, the number of petals to be one of 3, 5, 8, 13, 21, 34, and so forth. Also, although all snowflakes are different, each one has 6-fold symmetry. Put 20 pennies on a table and push them as close together as you can. Notice that all the pennies in the middle are surrounded by 6 others. This is an example of 6-fold symmetry.

1. What is true about the pattern for numbers of petals on flowers? **C**
   A. The numbers are all odd.
   B. The increases from one to the next are always the same.
   C. The increases from one to the next suggest a pattern you've seen before.
   D. The number of petals on any flower has to be a number in the pattern.

2. Describe the pattern for the numbers of petals in flowers.
   See below left. Answers may vary.

3. What number would follow 34 in the pattern for the numbers of petals on flowers? **H**
   F. 4th   G. 35   H. 55   I. 68

4. What do patterns in snowflakes and pennies pushed close together have in common?
   Answers may vary. Sample: Both involve 6-fold symmetry.

2. Sample: Start with 3 and 5 and then each term is the sum of the two preceding terms.

Wings or Wheels? The Arctic tern, a small sea bird, is the animal that migrates the longest distance each year. It can fly from a latitude of 84°N in the Arctic to 78°S in the Antarctic, and back. For some terns, this journey may be about 25,000 mi, which is about the distance around Earth at the equator. By contrast, the average number of miles a vehicle in the United States travels each year is about 14,000. Some Arctic terns live 25 years, which means they pile up an impressive number of miles traveled in a lifetime.

5. About how far does an Arctic tern fly in one migration south? **C**
   A. 162 mi   B. 14,000 mi
   C. 12,500 mi   D. 25,000 mi

6. On average, how far does a vehicle in the United States travel each year? **F**
   F. 14,000 mi   G. 14,000 km
   H. 25,000 mi   I. 25,000 km

7. Which travels farther in a year, an Arctic tern in its annual migration or a vehicle that's driven the average number of miles? About how much farther? **An Arctic tern travels farther; 11,000 mi farther**

8. About how far could an Arctic tern fly in its migrations over 25 years? Justify your answer.
   625,000 mi; 25 y times 25,000 mi/y = 625,000 mi in 25 y.

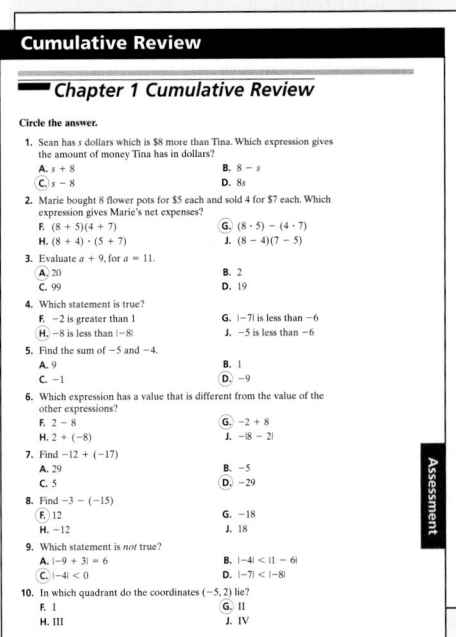

Cumulative Review

Chapter 1 Cumulative Review

Circle the answer.

1. Sean has s dollars which is $8 more than Tina. Which expression gives the amount of money Tina has in dollars?
   A. $s + 8$ B. $8 - s$
   C. $s - 8$ D. $8s$

2. Marie bought 8 flower pots for $5 each and sold 4 for $7 each. Which expression gives Marie's net expenses?
   F. $(8 + 5)(4 + 7)$ G. $(8 \cdot 5) - (4 \cdot 7)$
   H. $(8 + 4) \cdot (5 + 7)$ J. $(8 - 4)(7 - 5)$

3. Evaluate $a + 9$, for $a = 11$.
   A. 20   B. 2
   C. 99   D. 19

4. Which statement is true?
   F. -2 is greater than 1   G. $|-7|$ is less than -6
   H. -8 is less than $|-8|$ J. -5 is less than -6

5. Find the sum of -5 and -4.
   A. 9   B. 1
   C. -1 D. -9

6. Which expression has a value that is different from the value of the other expressions?
   F. $2 - 8$ G. $-2 + 8$
   H. $2 + (-8)$ J. $-|8 - 2|$

7. Find $-12 + (-17)$.
   A. 29   B. -5
   C. 5   D. -29

8. Find $-3 - (-15)$.
   F. 12   G. -18
   H. -12 J. 18

9. Which statement is *not* true?
   A. $|-9 + 3| = 6$ B. $|-4| < |1 - 6|$
   C. $|-4| < 0$ D. $|-7| < |-8|$

10. In which quadrant do the coordinates $(-5, 2)$ lie?
    F. I   G. II
    H. III   J. IV

Assessment

Locating Sunken Ships

In this activity, students apply their knowledge of integers, parts of the coordinate plane, and writing and simplifying expressions.

Activating Prior Knowledge

Have students research what caused famous ships such as the *Titanic* (1912), the *Lusitania* (1915), or the *Andrea Doria* (1956) to sink. Discuss whether a ship could sink in this way today. **Answers may vary. Sample:** The *Titanic* hit an iceberg. The *Lusitania* was torpedoed by a German submarine. The *Andrea Doria* collided with another cruise ship, the *Stockholm.* In a war today, a torpedo could sink a ship.

Teaching Notes

Teaching Tip

Have a volunteer read the introductory paragraph. Ask: *How might the location of a sunken ship affect how it can be studied? What might scientists learn by studying sunken ships?* **Answers may vary. Sample:** If the ship lies too deep for divers to reach, scientists must use submersibles. Scientists can learn about the time period when the ship was used by studying the objects on the ship. They can also learn why the ship sank.

Teaching Tip

Have a volunteer label on the board the *x*-axis, the *y*-axis, and the origin of a coordinate plane. Review with students how to write and simplify an expression to show change.

Teaching Tip

Before students begin the activity, discuss the illustrations and their captions. Instruct students to read through the activity before beginning to work. Have students work individually or in pairs to complete the activity.

62

Locating Sunken Ships

Applying Integers Marine archeologists are scientists who study sunken ships. They use scanning devices to locate objects on the ocean floor. When they find a "hot spot," divers take a closer look. If they find a sunken ship, the divers take underwater photographs and record the ship's latitude and longitude, identifying a specific point on Earth's surface.

Ancient World
This globe includes latitude (lines that run east–west) and longitude (lines that run north–south) rings.

Activity

Which part of Earth's coordinate globe corresponds to the indicated part of a coordinate plane? 1–8. See margin.

1. the *x*-axis   **2.** the *y*-axis   **3.** the origin

Write and simplify an expression to show how the depth of a submersible robot changes.

4. from the *Edmund Fitzgerald* to the *Andrea Doria*

5. from the *Titanic* to the *Atocha*

6. from the water's surface to the *Atocha*

7. Estimation About how many times the depth of the *Atocha* is the depth of the *Andrea Doria*? Write an equation to model this relationship.

8. Research Pick one of the ships discussed here or another sunken ship. What factors led to its sinking? Explain.

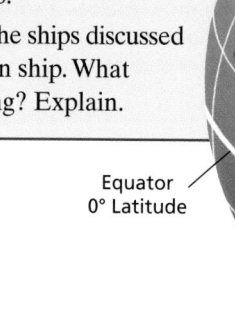
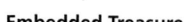

Embedded Treasure
Time and water pressure pushed these coins into a piece of wood.

Prime Meridian
0° Longitude

Titanic
41° N 49° W
−12,600 ft

Edmund Fitzgerald
47° N 85° W
−530 ft

Equator
0° Latitude

Atocha
24° N 82° W
−55 ft

Andrea Doria
40° N 69° W
−240 ft

---

1. **equator**

2. **prime meridian**

3. **the place where the equator crosses the prime meridian**

4. **up 290 ft**

5. **up 12,545 ft**

6. **down 55 ft**

7. **Answers may vary. Sample: $55x = 240$; about 4 times**

8. **Check students' work.**

Sunken World

Scientists explore shipwrecks in submersible vehicles such as Alvin (above) when the ship is too deep for scuba gear (worn by the diver).

Take It to the NET For more information about sunken ships, go to **www.PHSchool.com**.
Web Code: ade-0153

Visual Learners

Have pairs or small groups of students use a globe to locate the sunken ships shown on the map in their book.

Science Connection

Have students research the hunt for the *Titanic.* Ask: *How did new technology lead to finding the sunken ship in 1985? What technology has enabled scientists to study the ship since then?* Answers may vary. Sample: By 1985, new technology for deep-sea exploration included side-scan sonar equipment and unmanned submersibles with special video cameras and lighting. Since the discovery of the *Titanic,* scientists have used manned submersibles and ROVs (Remote Operated Vehicles) to study the wreck.

Put It All Together

Students must be able to extract information from reading passages and maps and construct responses in order to be successful in state and national assessments.

Inclusion

Exercises 1–3 Review with students that the equator is at 0 degrees latitude and the prime meridian is at 0 degrees longitude.

Exercises 4–6 Ask students which sunken ship is at the deepest depth, and which is at the shallowest depth. The *Titanic* is the deepest at −12,600 ft, and the *Atocha* is the shallowest at −55 ft.

Solving One-Step Equations and Inequalities

Chapter at a Glance

2-1
Properties of Numbers
pp. 66–70

Objectives
- ▽ Identifying Properties
- ▽ Using Properties

New Vocabulary
Commutative Properties, Associative Properties, additive identity, multiplicative identity, Identity Properties

NCTM Standards
1, 2, 8, 9, 10

Local Standards

2-2
The Distributive Property
pp. 71–75

Objectives
- ▽ Numerical Expressions
- ▽ Algebraic Expressions

New Vocabulary
Distributive Property

NCTM Standards
1, 2, 6, 8, 9, 10

Local Standards

2-3
Simplifying Variable Expressions
pp. 76–79

Objectives
- ▽ Identifying Parts of a Variable Expression
- ▽ Simplifying Variable Expressions

New Vocabulary
term, constant, like terms, coefficient, simplify a variable expression, deductive reasoning

NCTM Standards
1, 2, 6, 7, 8, 9, 10

Local Standards

✓ **Checkpoint Quiz 1**

2-4
Variables and Equations
pp. 80–83

Objectives
- ▽ Classifying Types of Equations
- ▽ Checking Equations Using Substitution

New Vocabulary
equation, open sentence, solution of an equation

NCTM Standards
1, 2, 6, 8, 9, 10

Local Standards

2-5
Solving Equations by Adding or Subtracting *pp. 86–90*

Objectives
- ▽ Using Subtraction to Solve Equations
- ▽ Using Addition to Solve Equations

New Vocabulary
inverse operations

Materials
algebra tiles

NCTM Standards
1, 2, 4, 6, 8, 9, 10

Local Standards

2-6
Solving Equations by Multiplying or Dividing
pp. 92–95

Objectives
- ▽ Using Division to Solve Equations
- ▽ Using Multiplication to Solve Equations

NCTM Standards
1, 2, 4, 6, 8, 9, 10

Local Standards

2-7 Problem Solving
Try, Test, Revise
pp. 96–99

Objective
- ▽ Try, Test, Revise

NCTM Standards
1, 2, 3, 4, 6, 7, 8, 9, 10

Local Standards

2-8
Inequalities and Their Graphs
pp. 102–105

Objectives
- ▽ Graphing Inequalities
- ▽ Writing Inequalities

NCTM Standards
1, 2, 3, 6, 8, 9, 10

Local Standards

2-9
Solving One-Step Inequalities by Adding or Subtracting *pp. 106–109*

Objectives
- ▽ Using Subtraction to Solve Inequalities
- ▽ Using Addition to Solve Inequalities

NCTM Standards
1, 2, 6, 8, 9, 10

Local Standards

✓ **Checkpoint Quiz 2**

2-10
Solving One-Step Inequalities by Multiplying or Dividing *pp. 110–114*

Objectives
- ▽ Using Division to Solve Inequalities
- ▽ Using Multiplication to Solve Inequalities

NCTM Standards
1, 2, 6, 8, 9, 10

Local Standards

Correlation to Standardized Tests

| Lesson | NAEP | Terra Nova | | | | Local Test |
		CAT/6	CTBS	ITBS	SAT10	
2-1	N5e			■	■	
2-2	N5e					
2-3	A3b		■		■	
2-4	A3a				■	
2-5	A4a, A4b			■	■	
2-6	A4a, A4b			■	■	
2-7				■		
2-8	A4a, A4c				■	
2-9	A4a, A4c					
2-10	A4a, A4c					

NAEP National Assessment of Educational Progress
      N = Number Sense, Properties, and Operations
      M = Measurement
      G = Geometry and Spatial Sense
      D = Data Analysis, Statistics and Probability
      A = Algebra and Functions
CAT/6 California Achievement Test, 6th Ed.
CTBS Comprehensive Test of Basic Skills
ITBS Iowa Test of Basic Skills, Form M
SAT10 Stanford Achievement Test, 10th Ed.

NCTM STANDARDS 2000

1 Number and Operations
2 Algebra
3 Geometry
4 Measurement
5 Data Analysis and Probability
6 Problem Solving
7 Reasoning and Proof
8 Communication
9 Connections
10 Representation

Pacing Options

This chart suggests pacing for only the core lessons and their parts. It is provided as a possible guide. It will help you determine how much time you have in your schedule to cover other components, such as the features, chapter projects, Chapter Review, and Chapter Test.

Day	Traditional 45-minute class periods	Two-Year 45-minute class periods	Block 90-minute class periods
1	2-1 ▼	2-1 ▼	2-1 ▼ ▼
2	2-1 ▼	2-1 ▼	2-2 ▼ ▼
3	2-2 ▼	2-1 ▼	2-3 ▼ ▼ / 2-4 ▼ ▼
4	2-2 ▼	2-2 ▼	2-5 ▼ ▼ / 2-6 ▼ ▼
5	2-3 ▼ ▼	2-2 ▼	2-7 ▼ / 2-8 ▼ ▼
6	2-4 ▼ ▼	2-2 ▼	2-9 ▼ ▼ / 2-10 ▼ ▼
7	2-5 ▼	2-3 ▼	
8	2-5 ▼	2-3 ▼	
9	2-6 ▼ ▼	2-3 ▼	
10	2-7 ▼	2-4 ▼	
11	2-8 ▼ ▼	2-4 ▼	
12	2-9 ▼ ▼	2-5 ▼	
13	2-10 ▼ ▼	2-5 ▼	
14		2-5 ▼	
15		2-6 ▼	
16		2-6 ▼	
17		2-7 ▼	
18		2-7 ▼	
19		2-8 ▼	
20		2-8 ▼	
21		2-9 ▼	
22		2-9 ▼	
23		2-10 ▼	
24		2-10 ▼	

Math Background

Skills Trace

BEFORE Chapter 2

Students probably had some exposure to properties of numbers and to solving one-step equations and inequalities in previous courses.

DURING Chapter 2

Algebraic expressions developed in Chapter 1 are extended to more complex expressions and connected to algebraic equations. Techniques for solving one-step equations and inequalities are developed.

AFTER Chapter 2

Students solve one-step equations and inequalities in Chapters 3 through 6. Chapter 7 introduces two-step equations and inequalities. The techniques for solving equations and inequalities developed in Chapters 2 and 7 are core to the study of algebra.

2-1 2-2 Properties of Numbers

The order of operations states an agreed-upon convention about the order in which you perform operations when evaluating a numerical expression. The properties in these lessons state the various ways an expression can be renamed without changing its value. Generally, you apply these properties first to simplify calculations, and then you use the order of operations as you actually perform the calculations.

Here is a summary of the key properties.

Commutative Property
Of Addition: $a + b = b + a$
Of Multiplication: $ab = ba$

Associative Property
Of Addition: $(a + b) + c = a + (b + c)$
Of Multiplication: $(ab)c = a(bc)$

Notice that each of these properties involves only *one* operation, either addition or multiplication. A third property combines two operations. This property is sometimes called the Distributive Property of Multiplication over Addition. Make sure students

understand the Distributive Property, as it is an important tool that is used quite often in solving equations.

Distributive Property
$a(b + c) = ab + ac$ $(b + c)a = ba + ca$
$ab + ac = a(b + c)$ $ba + ca = (b + c)a$

Be sure students realize that the Distributive Property can be represented in different ways.

The following identity properties define the results of adding 0 and multiplying by 1.

Identity Property
Of Addition: $a + 0 = a$
Of Multiplication: $a \cdot 1 = a$

These identity properties state that adding 0 to a number or multiplying a number by 1 results in a number *identical* to the original number.

2-3 Simplifying Variable Expressions

When plus or minus signs separate an algebraic expression into parts, each part is called a *term.* The expression $3x + 7y + 2x + 8 - 4y$ has 5 terms.

Terms with no variables, such as 8 in this example, are called *constants.* The numerical multipliers of the variables (3, 7, 2, and -4) are called numerical *coefficients.* The terms with identical variables are called *like terms.* When the like terms in this example are combined, the expression simplifies to $5x + 3y + 8$. Now the expression has only three terms. When a term shows a variable with no numerical coefficient, the coefficient is understood to be 1, so x means $1x$.

2-4 Variables and Equations

An *equation* is a mathematical sentence that contains an equal sign (=). An equation with at least one variable is an *open sentence*. An equation can be

always true: $x + x = 2x$ or $4 \cdot 5 = 20$,

always false: $x + 1 = x$ or $2 + 3 = 6$,

or sometimes true: $x - 3 = 2$.

The equation $x - 3 = 2$ is true if $x = 5$ and false if $x =$ any other number.

To solve an equation such as $3x - 2 = 4$ you must find the set of all the values for x that will, when substituted for x, make the

equation true. For linear equations with one variable, such as this example, there will be only one value for x (in this example, $x = 2$).

A true equation remains true if you add, subtract, multiply, or divide (by a nonzero number) *both sides* of the equation by the *same* number.

If $a = b$, then:
$$a + c = b + c$$
$$a - c = b - c$$
$$ca = cb$$
$$a \div c = b \div c \text{ (if } c \neq 0)$$

To keep an equation (or an inequality) in balance, you must perform the same operation with the same number on both sides of the equation.

2-5 2-6 Solving Equations

Linear equations with one variable have only one solution. To find this solution, first simplify by using the properties and the order of operations to rewrite without grouping symbols and to collect like terms. Then, isolate the variable by using *inverse* operations. Addition and subtraction are inverse operations; multiplication and division are inverse operations.

There are two inverse properties:
$$a + (-a) = 0$$
and
$$a \cdot \left(\frac{1}{a}\right) = 1, \text{ (if } a \neq 0)$$

Note that 0 does not have a multiplicative inverse.

Division by zero is undefined. Students are often interested in why division by zero is undefined. The equation $\frac{a}{b} = c$ means that $b \cdot c = a$. For example, $\frac{10}{2} = 5$ means that $2 \cdot 5 = 10$. It follows that $\frac{10}{0} = c$ would mean that $0 \cdot c = 10$, but there is no number c that would make this sentence true.

2-8 Inequalities and Their Graphs

An *inequality* is a mathematical sentence that contains $<$, $\leq$, $>$, or $\geq$. As with an equation, a solution to an inequality containing a variable is a number that, when substituted for the variable, makes the inequality true. Unlike a linear equation, a linear inequality may have more than one number as a solution.

2-9 2-10 Solving One-Step Inequalities

The addition and subtraction properties of equality used to solve equations can be extended to solve inequalities. To multiply or divide each side of an inequality by a negative number, you must *reverse* the direction of the inequality symbol. For example,

$-2 > -3$, but $-1(-2) < -1(-3)$ because $2 < 3$.

If $c < 0$, and $a > b$, then $ac < cb$ and $\frac{a}{c} < \frac{b}{c}$.

Similarly, if $c < 0$, and $a < b$, then $ac > cb$ and $\frac{a}{c} > \frac{b}{c}$.

Additional Professional Development Opportunities

Chapter 2 Math Background notes: pp. 67, 72, 77, 81, 87, 93, 97, 103, 107, 111

Professional Development, Content Facilitator Guide: Pre-Algebra, Chapter 2

SkyLight
Professional Development

Additional resources available from SkyLight Professional Development: On-site courses, workshops, summer institutes. Online courses and chat rooms. Videocassettes and books. Visit www.skylightedu.com.

Ongoing Assessment and Intervention

The *Prentice Hall Pre-Algebra* program provides many options for assessment in the Student Edition, Teacher's Edition, and teaching resources. From these options you may choose instructional materials that are appropriate for your students and support your district's curriculum requirements.

Daily Assessment

 Instant Check System™ in Chapter 2

Allows students to check their own learning before, during, and after each lesson.

Diagnosing Readiness before the chapter (p. 64)

Check Skills You'll Need exercises in each lesson (pp. 66, 71, 76, 80, 86, 92, 96, 102, 106, 110)

Check Understanding questions with each Example (pp. 67, 68, 72, 73, 76, 77, 80, 81, 87, 88, 92, 93, 97, 102, 103, 106, 107, 111, 112)

Checkpoint Quiz (pp. 79, 109)

Formal Assessment

In Chapter 2 and Additional Resources

Assesses student progress throughout the *Pre-Algebra* text and with blackline masters and CD-ROM.

Student Edition

- Chapter 2 Review, with Vocabulary Skills and Concepts Review, pp. 117–119
- Chapter 2 Test, p. 120

Assessment Resources   *Spanish versions available.*

- Checkpoint Quizzes 1 & 2
- Chapter Test, Forms A & B
- Chapter Alternative Assessment

 Computer Test Generator CD-ROM

- Instant Chapter Tests™ — pre-made tests with items that vary every time you print.
- Online Testing allows you to give tests online and receive progress reports.
- Diagnose readiness with questions on prerequisite skills.
- Prepare students by making tests based on standardized test objectives.

Algebra Readiness Tests

- Includes Basic Skills Tests and Concept-Readiness Tests.
- Assess understanding of skills and concepts needed for success in algebra.

Standardized Test Preparation

 Test Prep in Chapter 2

Teaches students strategies and gives them practice with all the test item formats they will encounter on high-stakes tests.

Test Prep exercises in each lesson (pp. 70, 75, 79, 83, 90, 95, 99, 105, 109, 114)

Test-Taking Strategies (p. 116: Writing Short Responses)

Test Prep (p. 121: Cumulative Review)

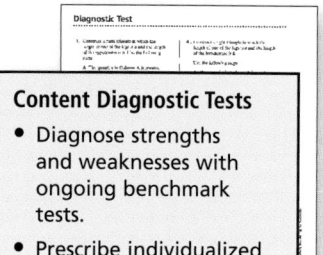

PRENTICE HALL
ASSESSMENT SYSTEM

Provides a three-step approach to preparing students for high-stakes, national, and state exams.

1 Diagnose & Prescribe

Content Diagnostic Tests
- Diagnose strengths and weaknesses with ongoing benchmark tests.
- Prescribe individualized reteaching opportunities.

2 Review & Reteach

Skills and Concepts Review
- Provides reteaching worksheets with instruction and practice for each skill.
- Includes course prerequisite skills.

3 Practice & Assess

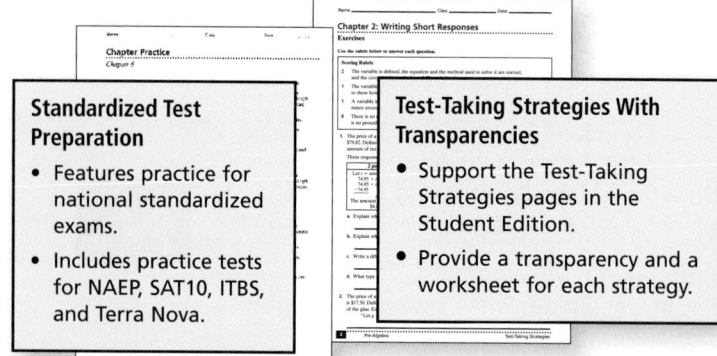

Standardized Test Preparation
- Features practice for national standardized exams.
- Includes practice tests for NAEP, SAT10, ITBS, and Terra Nova.

Test-Taking Strategies With Transparencies
- Support the Test-Taking Strategies pages in the Student Edition.
- Provide a transparency and a worksheet for each strategy.

Reaching All Students

The textbook, the iText, and other technology components provide numerous opportunities to reach students of various ability levels and learning styles. Each Teacher's Edition lesson suggests how you can help all your students be successful and understand the mathematics in Chapter 2.

Below Level

Student Edition
- Diagnosing Readiness*: p. 64
- Check Skills You'll Need*: pp. 66, 71, 76, 80, 86, 92, 96, 102, 106, 110

Reteaching
Chapter 2 Grab & Go™ File: pp. 11–20

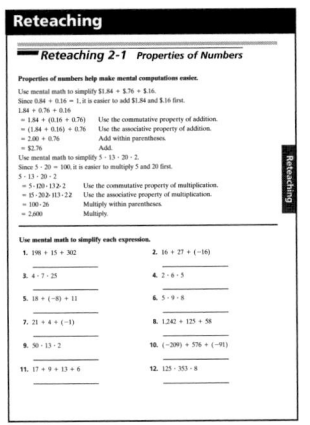

* Can be used with all ability levels to ensure mastery of prerequisite skills.

Advanced Learners

Student Edition
- Challenge exercises: pp. 70, 75, 79, 83, 90, 95, 98, 105, 108, 109, 114

Enrichment
Chapter 2 Grab & Go™ File: pp. 21–30

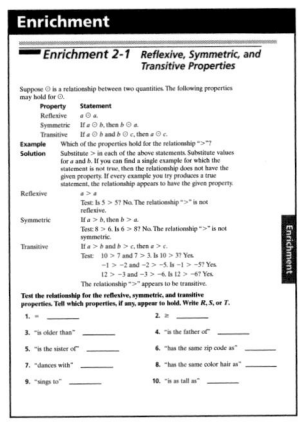

Problem Solving

Student Edition
- Strategies: pp. 96–99
- Real-World Problem Solving: pp. 66, 68, 72, 81, 87, 88, 92, 96, 103, 107, 111

Guided Problem Solving Masters
Chapter 2: pp. 11–20

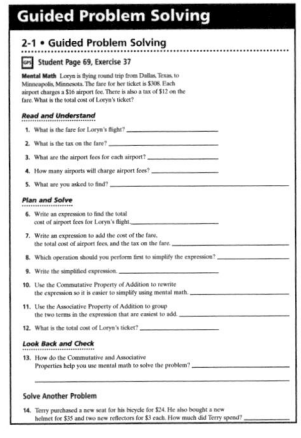

Reading and Math Literacy

Student Edition
- Vocabulary: pp. 65, 117, plus in most lessons
- Reading Math: pp. 73, 89, 91, 93, 103, 117
- Writing in Math: pp. 69, 75, 79, 83, 90, 95, 101, 105, 109, 113, 115, 120
- Illustrated Glossary: pp. 782–826

Reading and Math Literacy Masters
Chapter 2: pp. 5–8

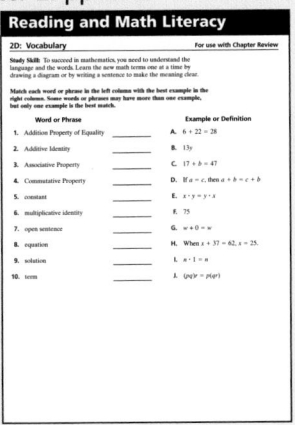

English Learners

Student Edition
- English/Spanish Illustrated Glossary: pp. 782–826

Workbook and Masters
Spanish Practice Workbook: pp. 11–20
Spanish Reading and Math Literacy Masters: pp. 5–8

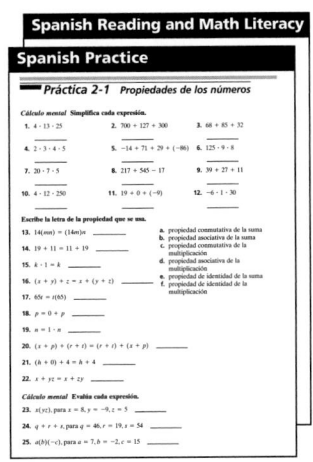

Learning Styles

Student Edition
- Investigation: pp. 71, 84, 110
- Technology: p. 100
- DK Activities: pp. 122–123
- Chapter Project: p. 738

Activity Masters
Hands-On Activities: 2, 3
Technology Activities: 4, 5

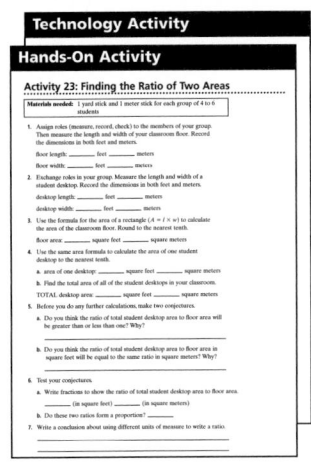

Program Resources

	Resources in Grab & Go™ Files				Resources for Reaching All Students				Spanish Resources			Presentation Assistant Plus! Transparencies				Prentice Hall Presentation Pro CD-ROM
	Practice	Reteach	Enrich	Checkpt Quiz	Reading & Math Literacy	Technology Activities	Hands-On Activities	Guided Problem Solving	Practice	Reading & Math Literacy	Checkpt Quiz	Skills Check	Additional Examples	Answers to Exercises	Lesson Quiz	
2-1	■	■	■		■			■	■	■		■	■	■	■	■
2-2	■	■	■				■	■	■			■	■	■	■	■
2-3	■	■	■	■	■			■	■	■	■	■	■	■	■	■
2-4	■	■	■					■	■			■	■	■	■	■
2-5	■	■	■			■	■	■	■			■	■	■	■	■
2-6	■	■	⊛			■	■	■	■			■	■	■	■	■
2-7	■	■	■					■	■			■	■	■	■	■
2-8	■	■	■			■		■	■			■	■	■	■	■
2-9	■	■	■	■	■			■	■	■	■	■	■	■	■	■
2-10	■	■	■					■	■			■	■	■	■	■
For the Chapter	Chapter Projects, Chapter Tests, Alternative Assessment, Cumulative Review, Cumulative Assessment				**On Web site only:** Home Activities, Algebra Readiness Puzzles, Interdisciplinary Activities				Spanish Chapter Tests, Alternative Assessment, Cumulative Review, Cumulative Assessment			Classroom Aid Transparencies				

Also available for use with the chapter:
- Practice Workbook
- Solution Key
- MathNotes folder
- For additional online and technology resources, see below.
- For teacher support and access to student Web site materials, use Web Code adk-5500.

 **PRENTICE HALL ASSESSMENT SYSTEM**

Program assessment and test preparation, all in one place.
See page 64E.

 Skills Intervention Kit

A *complete* system for the student who is struggling with course-level work

How to Use With Chapter 2

2-1, 2-3, 2-4 Pre-Algebra Basics

 **Online Intervention**

Integrated within the iText, this online intervention system includes diagnostic tests and prescribed remediation, plus reports to track student mastery.

Technology

 iTEXT Online and on CD-ROM

Complete Interactive Student Text online and on CD-ROM—with instant-feedback assessment, tutorial help, dynamic activities, instructional and real-world videos, audio, and additional practice.

 www.PHSchool.com For Students

Use Web Codes for easy access to online activities, chapter projects, self-grading lesson quizzes, chapter tests, vocabulary quizzes, updated data sources, graphing calculator procedures, and more.

PH SuccessNet For Teachers

Online lesson planning with built-in state correlations, all the teaching resources, complete reference library, your own calendar and Teacher Web page, professional development, and more.

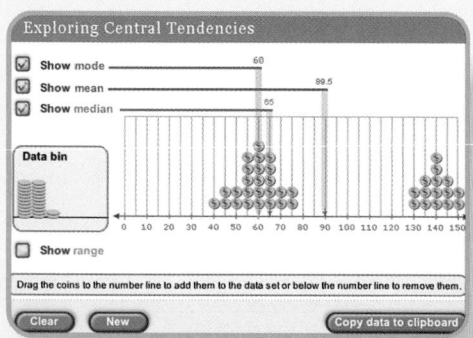

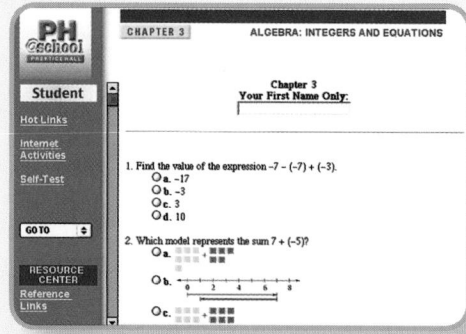

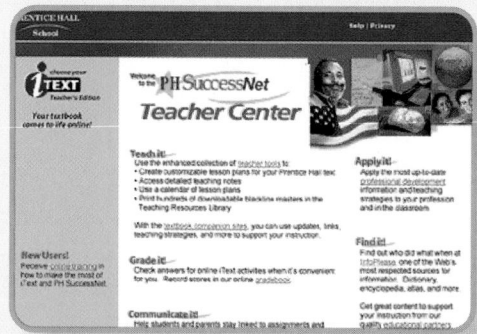

Presentation Assistant Plus!

The Prentice Hall *Presentation Assistant Plus!* provides you with the material you need to teach a lesson from beginning to end. Two easy-to-use formats—Transparencies and CD-ROM—allow you to present a lesson the way you are most comfortable.

 ## Transparencies

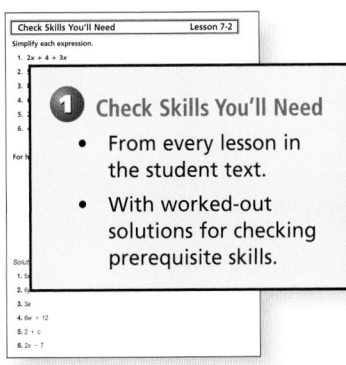

1 Check Skills You'll Need
- From every lesson in the student text.
- With worked-out solutions for checking prerequisite skills.

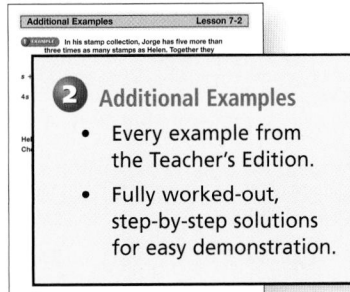

2 Additional Examples
- Every example from the Teacher's Edition.
- Fully worked-out, step-by-step solutions for easy demonstration.

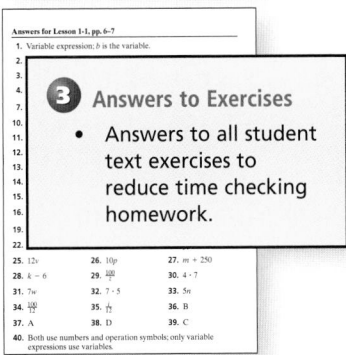

3 Answers to Exercises
- Answers to all student text exercises to reduce time checking homework.

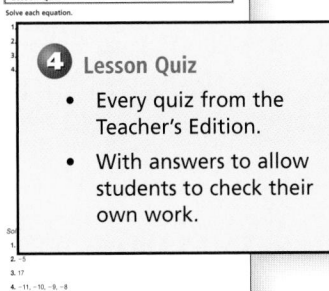

4 Lesson Quiz
- Every quiz from the Teacher's Edition.
- With answers to allow students to check their own work.

 Throughout the Teacher's Edition, this symbol indicates material that is available in the Presentation Assistant Plus!

PowerPoint Prentice Hall Presentation Pro CD-ROM

- Includes all Transparencies as PowerPoint® presentations.
- Conveniently organized by lesson so you can easily **1** Introduce, **2** Teach, **3** Check Homework, and **4** Assess each lesson.
- Animated examples allow step-by-step instruction at your own pace.
- Easy to edit so you can create custom presentations.

Teaching Chapter 2 Using Presentation Assistant Plus!

	1 Introduce	**2 Teach**	**3 Check Homework**	**4 Assess**
	Check Skills You'll Need	Additional Examples	Student Edition Answers	Lesson Quiz
2-1	p. 11	pp. 15–16	✔	p. 11
2-2	p. 12	pp. 17–18	✔	p. 12
2-3	p. 13	p. 19	✔	p. 13
2-4	p. 14	pp. 20–21	✔	p. 14
2-5	p. 15	pp. 22–23	✔	p. 15
2-6	p. 16	pp. 24–25	✔	p. 16
2-7	p. 17	p. 25	✔	p. 17
2-8	p. 18	pp. 26–27	✔	p. 18
2-9	p. 19	pp. 27–28	✔	p. 19
2-10	p. 20	p. 29	✔	p. 20

 ### Prentice Hall Presentation Pro

CD-ROM with dynamic Powerpoint® presentations for every lesson. Helps you introduce and develop concepts, check homework, and assess progress. Part of Presentation Assistant Plus! *(See above.)*

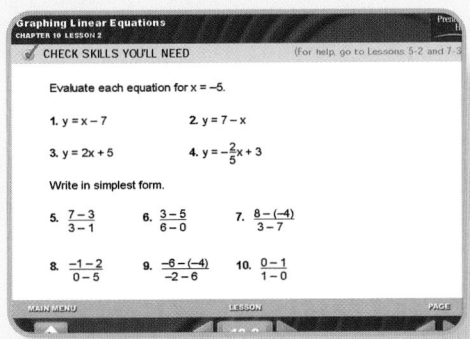

 ### Computer Test Generator

CD-ROM to create practice sheets and tests for course objectives and standardized tests. Includes Instant Chapter Tests™, online testing, and student reports. Part of the PH Assessment System. *(See page 64E.)*

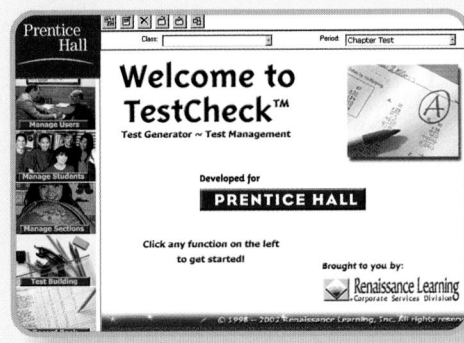

 ### Resource Pro® with Planning Express®

CD-ROM with a lesson planning tool that allows you to import state and local objectives. Includes electronic versions of all the teaching resources.

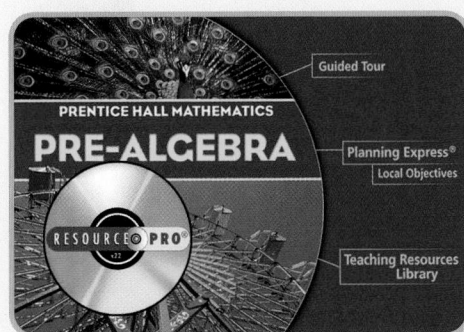

Solving One-Step Equations and Inequalities

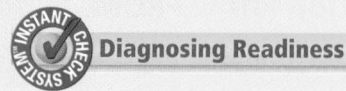
Diagnosing Readiness

Students will find the answers to these exercises in the back of their textbooks.

Prescribing Intervention
For intervention, direct students to:

Related Equations
Pre-course skills.

Comparing Numbers
Lesson 1-5; Example 3;
Exercises 13–21.
Lesson 1-6; Example 3;
Exercises 18–29.
Lesson 1-9; Examples 3 and 4;
Exercises 11–28.
Extra Practice, p. 744.

Order of Operations With Integers
Lesson 1-2: Examples 1–3;
Exercises 1–21.
Extra Practice, p. 744.

Where You've Been

In Chapter 1, you learned:

● How to apply the order of operations to evaluate numerical expressions.

● How to evaluate expressions with variables.

● How to add, subtract, multiply, and divide integers.

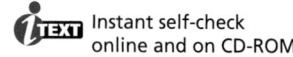 Instant self-check online and on CD-ROM

 **Diagnosing Readiness**   (For help, go to the lesson in green.)

Related Equations (Previous Course)

Complete the related equations.

1. $20 - \blacksquare = 9$ 11 $9 + \blacksquare = 20$ 11   **2.** $-2 + \blacksquare = 3$ 5 $3 - \blacksquare = -2$ 5

3. $20 - \blacksquare = 23$ −3 $23 + \blacksquare = 20$ −3   **4.** $\blacksquare + 12 = -7$ −19 $-7 - \blacksquare = 12$ −19

5. $3 \cdot \blacksquare = 75$ 25 $75 \div \blacksquare = 3$ 25   **6.** $72 \div \blacksquare = 12$ 6 $12 \cdot \blacksquare = 72$ 6

7. $-36 \div \blacksquare = -6$ 6 $-6 \cdot \blacksquare = -36$ 6   **8.** $\blacksquare \cdot (-10) = -70$ 7 $-70 \div \blacksquare = -10$ 7

Comparing Numbers (Lessons 1-5, 1-6, and 1-9)

Compare. Use $>$, $<$, or $=$ to complete each statement.

9. $6 \blacksquare 16$ $<$ **10.** $5 \blacksquare -5$ $>$ **11.** $-52 \blacksquare -21$ $<$

12. $0 \blacksquare -8$ $>$ **13.** $-7 \blacksquare 3$ $<$ **14.** $12 + 3 \blacksquare 19 - 4$ $=$

15. $-2 \cdot 6 \blacksquare 4 \cdot (-3)$ $=$ **16.** $27 \div 9 \blacksquare 6 \cdot 2$ $<$ **17.** $18 - 27 \blacksquare -34 + 12$ $>$

18. $8(-5) \blacksquare 100 - 65$ $<$ **19.** $6 \div (10 - 8) \blacksquare 1 + 5$ $<$ **20.** $3(-2)(-4) \blacksquare 4(-3)(2)$ $>$

Order of Operations With Integers (Lesson 1-2)

Simplify each expression.

21. $5 \cdot 2 + 5 \cdot 3$ 25   **22.** $7(6 - 2)$ 28   **23.** $10 \cdot 3 - 5 \cdot 3$ 15

24. $-(34 + 76)$ −110   **25.** $4(6) + 4(3)$ 36   **26.** $-4(12 - 16)$ 16

27. $7(8) - 10(8)$ −24   **28.** $11 \cdot 9 - 6 \cdot 9$ 45   **29.** $-2 \cdot 3 - 2 \cdot 7$ −20

30. $6 \cdot (-9) - 3(-9)$ −27   **31.** $-5(3) - (-5)(2)$ −5   **32.** $(72 - 81)(5)$ −45

Solving One-Step Equations and Inequalities

Where You're Going

In this chapter, you will learn how to

- Use the Distributive Property.
- Write and solve equations.
- Write, solve, and graph inequalities.
- Solve a problem by Try, Test, Revise.

Real-World Snapshots Applying what you learn, on pages 122–123 you will solve problems about a school fair.

Key Vocabulary

- coefficient (p. 76)
- constant (p. 76)
- deductive reasoning (p. 77)
- equation (p. 80)
- inequality (p. 102)
- inverse operations (p. 86)
- like terms (p. 76)
- open sentence (p. 80)
- simplify a variable expression (p. 76)
- solution of an equation (p. 81)
- solution of an inequality (p. 102)
- term (p. 76)

65

Chapter 2 Overview

Chapter 2 introduces the basic algebraic properties needed to solve equations and inequalities. The Associative, Commutative, and Identity Properties of Addition and Multiplication show how to rewrite expressions. Then students learn to solve one-step equations and inequalities by applying inverse operations and the Addition and Multiplication Properties of Equality. Students will continue to draw upon these skills throughout their study of pre-algebra. Students will also learn to graph inequalities and to identify inequalities by looking at graphs.

Activating Prior Knowledge
Students apply the arithmetic skills they learned in Chapter 1 to solve one-step equations and inequalities. Ask: *What is the difference between a mathematical expression and an equation?* An expression is a mathematical phrase, whereas an equation is a mathematical sentence with an equal sign.

Reading Math
- Reading for Problem Solving, p. 91
- **Vocabulary** A complete list of terms, plus vocabulary exercises, appears in the Chapter Review on p. 117.
- **Illustrated Glossary** Examples for each vocabulary term, plus definitions in both English and Spanish, appear starting on p. 782.

Test-Taking Strategies
Writing Short Responses, p. 116

Real-World Problem Solving
- **Strategy:** Try, Test, Revise, pp. 96–99
- **DK Real-World Snapshots:** Applying Equations, pp. 122–123
- **Chapter Project:** Don't Lose Your Balance, p. 738

www.PHSchool.com
Internet support includes:
- Self-grading Vocabulary and Chapter 2 Tests
- Activity Masters
- Chapter Project support
- Chapter Planner
- Chapter 2 Resources

65

2-1

Lesson Preview

 Check Skills You'll Need

Adding Integers
Lesson 1-5: Example 3;
Exercises 13–21.
Extra Practice, p. 744.

Lesson Resources

 Teaching Resources
Practice, Reteaching, Enrichment

 Reaching All Students
Practice Workbook 2-1
Spanish Practice Workbook 2-1
Reading and Math Literacy 2A
Spanish Reading and Math
  Literacy 2A
Guided Problem Solving 2-1

 Presentation Assistant Plus!
Transparencies and PowerPoint™
• Check Skills You'll Need 2-1
• Additional Examples 2-1
• Student Edition Answers 2-1
• Lesson Quiz 2-1
PH Presentation Pro CD-ROM 2-1

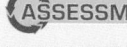 ASSESSMENT SYSTEM

Computer Test Generator CD-ROM

 Technology
Resource Pro® CD-ROM
Computer Test Generator CD-ROM
PH Presentation Pro CD-ROM

 www.PHSchool.com

Student Site
• Teacher Web Code: adk-5500
• Self-grading Lesson Quiz
PH SuccessNet Teacher Center
• Lesson Planner
• Resources

Plus

2-1 Properties of Numbers

What You'll Learn

 To identify properties
of addition and
multiplication

 To use properties to
solve problems

. . . And Why

To solve real-world problems
involving purchases

 Check Skills You'll Need
Simplify.

1. $-18 + (-7)$ -25

2. $32 - (-3)$ 35

3. $(-13) + 6$ -7

4. $2 - 48$ -46

For help, go to Lesson 1-6.

New Vocabulary
• **Commutative Properties**
• **Associative Properties**
• **additive identity**
• **multiplicative identity**
• **Identity Properties**

OBJECTIVE

1 Identifying Properties

The sum of 6 and 4 is the same as the sum of 4 and 6. Similarly, the product of 9 and 5 is the same as the product of 5 and 9. These suggest the following properties.

> **Key Concepts** | **Commutative Properties of Addition and Multiplication**
>
> Changing the order of the values you are adding or multiplying does not change the sum or product.
>
> | Arithmetic | Algebra |
> |---|---|
> | $6 + 4 = 4 + 6$ | $a + b = b + a$ |
> | $9 \cdot 5 = 5 \cdot 9$ | $a \cdot b = b \cdot a$ |

You can also change the grouping of the values before you add or multiply them.

> **Key Concepts** | **Associative Properties of Addition and Multiplication**
>
> Changing the grouping of the values you are adding or multiplying does not change the sum or product.
>
> | Arithmetic | Algebra |
> |---|---|
> | $(2 + 7) + 3 = 2 + (7 + 3)$ | $(a + b) + c = a + (b + c)$ |
> | $(9 \cdot 4)5 = 9(4 \cdot 5)$ | $(ab)c = a(bc)$ |

1 EXAMPLE Real-World Problem Solving

Golf Carlos rented a set of golf clubs for $7 and a golf cart for $12. He paid a greens fee of $23. Find his total cost.

You can use the Associative Property of Addition to find the total cost in two different ways.

$(7 + 12) + 23 = 19 + 23 = 42$ **Add 7 and 12 first.**
$7 + (12 + 23) = 7 + 35 = 42$ **Add 12 and 23 first.**

• Carlos's total cost was $42.

 Interactive lesson
includes instant self-check,
tutorials, and activities.

Ongoing Assessment and Intervention

Before the Lesson
Diagnose prerequisite skills using:
• Check Skills You'll Need

During the Lesson
Monitor progress using:
• Check Understanding
• Additional Examples
• Test Prep

After the Lesson
Assess knowledge using:
• Lesson Quiz
• Computer Test Generator
  CD-ROM

✓ Check Understanding   Example 1

1. You spend $6 for dinner, $8 for a movie, and $4 for popcorn. Find your total cost. Explain which property or properties you used.
$18; see back of book for explanation.

When you add a number and 0, the sum equals the original number. The **additive identity** is 0. When you multiply a number and 1, the product equals the original number. The **multiplicative identity** is 1.

Key Concepts   **Identity Properties of Addition and Multiplication**

The sum of any number and zero is the original number. The product of any number and 1 is the original number.

Arithmetic	Algebra
$12 + 0 = 12; 10 \cdot 1 = 10$	$a + 0 = a; a \cdot 1 = a$

---

2 EXAMPLE   Identifying Properties

Name each property shown.

a. $5 \cdot 7 = 7 \cdot 5$ Commutative Property of Multiplication

b. $c \cdot 1 = c$ Identity Property of Multiplication

c. $7 + a = a + 7$ Commutative Property of Addition

d. $5(xy) = (5x)y$ Associative Property of Multiplication

✓ Check Understanding   Example 2

2. Name each property shown. 2a–c. See right.

a. $3 + 6 = 6 + 3$ b. $8 = 1 \cdot 8$ c. $(3z)m = 3(zm)$

2a. Comm. Prop. of Add.
2b. Ident. Prop. of Mult.
2c. Assoc. Prop. of Mult.

OBJECTIVE

2 Using Properties

You can use properties and mental math to help you find sums.

3 EXAMPLE   Using Mental Math With Addition

Use mental math to simplify $(81 + 6) + 9$.

$(81 + 6) + 9$
$= (6 + 81) + 9$ **Use the Commutative Property of Addition.**
$= 6 + (81 + 9)$ **Use the Associative Property of Addition.**
$= 6 + 90$ **Add within parentheses.**
$= 96$ **Add.**

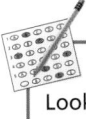

Test-Taking Tip

Look for combinations that equal 10 or a multiple of 10, since they are easier to use in calculating mentally.

2-1 Properties of Numbers   **67**

Professional Development

Math Background

The Commutative and Associative Properties of Addition and Multiplication apply when an expression has a single type of operation, either addition or multiplication. With mixed operations, use the order of operations.

Teaching Notes

1 EXAMPLE English Learners

When you *commute* to school, you change where you are. A Commutative Property of Addition or Multiplication allows you to change where numbers are in an expression involving addition or multiplication. You may *associate* with different groups of people, such as your school friends or your family. The Associative Property of Addition or Multiplication allows you to form different groups of numbers in an expression involving addition or multiplication.

2 EXAMPLE Auditory Learners

Lead students to see that applying an *identity* property results in a number that has the same *identity* as the original number.

PowerPoint

⬛ Additional Examples

❶ Carlos spent $42 on his golf game. He then bought a bottle of water for $2 and a chef's salad for $8. What was the total cost for his golf game and meal? $52

❷ Name each property shown.
a. $17 + x + 3 = 17 + 3 + x$
   Comm. Prop. of Add.
b. $(36 \times 2)10 = 36(2 \times 10)$
   Assoc. Prop. of Mult.
c. $km = km \cdot 1$
   Id. Prop. of Mult.
d. $(103 + 26) + 4 = 103 + (26 + 4)$
   Assoc. Prop. of Add.

❸ Use mental math to simplify $(48 + 7) + 2$. 57

👥 Reaching All Students

Below Level Since the Commutative and Associative Properties are for addition and multiplication only, review with students how to add and multiply integers.	**Advanced Learners** Ask students to explain why zero, the additive identity, is not a multiplicative identity. The product of zero and any number is zero.	**English Learners** See note on page 67. **Inclusion** See note on page 68.

4 Suppose you buy school supplies costing $.45, $.65, and $1.55. Use mental math to find the cost of these supplies. **$2.65**

5 Use mental math to simplify (20 · 13) · 5. **1,300**

4 EXAMPLE Teaching Tip

Ask: *All three numbers end with 5, so any two of them have a sum that ends with "0." Why add 1.65 and 0.35 first?* Their sum is a whole number, which makes adding mentally even easier.

5 EXAMPLE Inclusion

Most students will understand that multiplying by 10 is rather easy. However, students who do not know their multiplication facts may not readily see why you may prefer to multiply 4 and 5 first, instead of 4 and 9. Provide a multiplication chart to help these students find pairs of numbers that are multiples of 10.

Closure

Have students write descriptions of the Commutative, Associative, and Identity properties for either addition or multiplication in their own words. Have them provide an example for each description.

✔ **Check Understanding** Example 3

3. Use mental math to simplify each expression.

   a. $6 + 7 + 14$ **27**   **b.** $8 + 0 + 2 + (-7)$ **3**
   c. $5 + 12 + 18 + 5$ **40**   **d.** $19 + (-30) + 21$ **10**

4 EXAMPLE   Real-World 🌐 Problem Solving

School Supplies **Suppose you buy the school supplies shown at the left. Use mental math to find the cost of the supplies.**

$1.65 + 0.85 + 0.35$

$= 0.85 + 1.65 + 0.35$ **Use the Commutative Property of Addition.**

$= 0.85 + (1.65 + 0.35)$ **Use the Associative Property of Addition.**

$= 0.85 + 2.00$ **Add within parentheses.**

$= 2.85$ **Add.**

● The cost of the school supplies is $2.85.

$.85

$.35

$1.65

? Need Help?

For help with adding decimals, see Skills Handbook, page 764.

✔ **Check Understanding** Example 4

4. Use the supermarket receipt and mental math to find the cost of the groceries. **$6.30**

```
        SOUTH STREET
          MARKET

DATE 08.03.03     THU
1 GALLON MILK   $2.30
BREAD           $1.80
APPLES          $2.20
```

You can also use mental math to help you find products.

5 EXAMPLE   **Using Mental Math With Multiplication**

Use mental math to simplify (4 · 9) · 5.

$(4 \cdot 9) \cdot 5 = (9 \cdot 4) \cdot 5$ **Use the Commutative Property of Multiplication.**

$= 9 \cdot (4 \cdot 5)$ **Use the Associative Property of Multiplication.**

$= 9 \cdot 20$ **Multiply within parentheses.**

● $= 180$ **Multiply.**

✔ **Check Understanding** Example 5

5. Use mental math to simplify each expression.

   a. $25 \cdot (3 \cdot 4)$ **300**   **b.** $3 \cdot 1 \cdot -5 \cdot 8$ **−120**
   c. $2(-8)(-15)$ **240**   **d.** $5 \cdot 9 \cdot 6 \cdot (-2) \cdot (-1)$ **540**

Practice and Problem Solving

 A Practice by Example

Example 1
(page 66)

Use the Associative Property to write two different expressions that you could use to find each sum.

1. Add 1, 3, and 25.
(1 + 3) + 25; 1 + (3 + 25)

2. Add 5, 91, and 11.
(5 + 91) + 11; 5 + (91 + 11)

 **3. Travel** On a road trip, your family spends $120 for gas, $15 for bottled water, and $80 for food. Find your family's total cost. Explain which property or properties you used. $215; see margin for explanation.

Example 2
(page 67)

Name each property shown.

4. 7 + 6 = 6 + 7
Comm. Prop. of Add.

5. 0 + 8 = 8
Ident. Prop. of Add.

6. (6 · 15)2 = 6(15 · 2)
Assoc. Prop. of Mult.

7. (12r)s = 12(rs)
Assoc. Prop. of Mult.

8. 999 · 1 = 999
Ident. Prop. of Mult.

9. ab = ba
Comm. Prop. of Mult.

Example 3
(page 67)

Mental Math Use mental math to simplify each expression.

10. (5 + 23) + 65 93

11. (3 + 62) + 7 72

12. 9 + (14 + 1) 24

13. −8 + 35 + 15 42

14. 31 + 0 + (−2) 29

15. 15 + 13 + (−25) 3

Example 4
(page 68)

16. (0.50 + 34) + 3.50 38

17. (4.55 + 27) + 5.45 37

18. 1.50 + (3.17 + 6.50) 11.17

19. −0.25 + 4.88 + 3.25 7.88

20. 7.02 + 3.40 + 1.98 12.40

21. 8.39 + (−2.00) + 1.61 8

$15.20 Potting Soil

$7.65

$1.35

 22. Gardening Lance has purchased some supplies to start his new garden. Use the prices shown at the left and mental math to find the cost of the supplies. $24.20

Example 5
(page 68)

Mental Math Use mental math to simplify each expression.

23. 6 · 3 · 5
90

24. 5 · 7 · (−2)
−70

25. 25 · 4 · 8
800

26. 8 · 4 · (−10)
−320

B Apply Your Skills

Name each property shown.

27. 8(3 · 2) = (8 · 3)2
Assoc. Prop. of Mult.

28. 5 + 8 = 8 + 5
Comm. Prop. of Add.

29. (6x)y = 6(xy)
Assoc. Prop. of Mult.

30. 6 · 1 = 6
Ident. Prop. of Mult.

31. 999 + 0 = 999
Ident. Prop. of Add.

32. a · 1 = 1 · a
Comm. Prop. of Mult.

Simplify each expression.

33. 25 + 157 + (−75) 107

34. 140 + 17 + (−60) 97

35. 5 · 50 · 20 · (−2) −10,000

36. 125 + 18 + 75 + 162 380

38. Answers may vary. Sample: Combine 3 and 27 first since their sum is 30, a multiple of 10. It is easier to add mentally if you look for numbers whose sum is a multiple of 10.

37. Mental Math Loryn is flying roundtrip from Dallas, Texas, to GPS Minneapolis, Minnesota. The fare for her ticket is $308. Each airport charges a $16 airport fee. There is also a tax of $12 on the fare. What is the total cost of Loryn's ticket? $352

38. Writing in Math Which two numbers would you combine first to simplify 3 + 6 + 27? Explain. See left.

3. Answers may vary. Sample: 120 + 15 + 80
= 120 + (15 + 80)   Assoc. Prop. of Add.
= 120 + (80 + 15)   Comm. Prop. of Add.
= (120 + 80) + 15   Assoc. Prop. of Add.
= 200 + 15   Add within parentheses.
= 215   Add.

GPS Use the Guided Problem Solving worksheet with Exercise 37.

Assignment Guide

1 Objective 1
A B Core 1–9, 27–32
C Extension 43

2 Objective 2
A B Core 10–26, 33–38
C Extension 39–42

Test Prep 44–46
Mixed Review 47–54

Practice 2-1 *Properties of Numbers*

Simplify each expression using mental math.

1. 4 · 13 · 25	2. 700 + 127 + 300	3. 68 + 85 + 32
1,300	1,127	185
4. 2 · 3 · 4 · 5	5. −14 + 71 + 29 + (−86)	6. 125 · 9 · 8
120	0	9,000
7. 20 · 7 · 5	8. 217 + 545 − 17	9. 39 + 27 + 11
700	745	77
10. 4 · 12 · 250	11. 19 + 0 + (−9)	12. −6 · 1 · 30
12,000	10	−180

Write the letter of the property shown.

13. 14(mn) = (14m)n   d
14. 19 + 11 = 11 + 19   a
15. k · 1 = k   f
16. (x + y) + z = x + (y + z)   b
17. 65t = t(65)   c
18. p = 0 + p   e
19. n = 1 · n   f
20. (x + p) + (r + t) = (r + t) + (x + p)   a
21. (h + 0) + 4 = h + 4   e
22. x + yz = x + zy   c

a. commutative property of addition
b. associative property of addition
c. commutative property of multiplication
d. associative property of multiplication
e. additive identity
f. multiplicative identity

Evaluate each expression using mental math.

23. x(yz), for x = 8, y = −9, z = 5   −360
24. q + r + s, for q = 46, r = 19, s = 54   119
25. a(b)(−c), for a = 7, b = −2, c = 15   210

Enrichment 2-1 *Reflexive, Symmetric, and Transitive Properties*

Suppose ⊙ is a relationship between two quantities. The following properties may hold for ⊙.

Property	Statement
Reflexive	a ⊙ a.
Symmetric	If a ⊙ b, then b ⊙ a.
Transitive	If a ⊙ b and b ⊙ c, then a ⊙ c.

Example Which of the properties hold for the relationship ">"?

Solution Substitute > in each of the above statements. Substitute values for a and b. If you can find a single example for which the statement is not true, then the relationship does not have the given property. If every example you try produces a true statement, the relationship appears to have the given property.

Reflexive   a > a
Test: Is 5 > 5? No. The relationship ">" is not reflexive.

Symmetric   If a > b, then b > a.
Test: 8 > 6. Is 6 > 8? No. The relationship ">" is not symmetric.

Transitive   If a > b and b > c, then a > c.
Test: 10 > 7 and 7 > 3. Is 10 > 3? Yes.
−1 > −2 and −2 > −5. Is −1 > −5? Yes.
12 > −3 and −3 > −6. Is 12 > −6? Yes.
The relationship ">" appears to be transitive.

Test the relationship for the reflexive, symmetric, and transitive properties. Tell which properties, if any, appear to hold. Write R, S, or T.

1. =   R, S, T
2. ≥   R, T
3. "is older than"   T
4. "is the father of"   none
5. "is the sister of"   T
6. "has the same zip code as"   R, S, T
7. "dances with"   S
8. "has the same color hair as"   R, S, T
9. "sings to"   R
10. "is as tall as"   R, S, T

Lesson Quiz 2-1

Name each property shown.

1. $d \times 1 = d$ Id. Prop. of Mult.

2. $3 + (2 + 5) = (3 + 2) + 5$
Assoc. Prop. of Add.

3. $f \times g = g \times f$
Comm. Prop. of Mult.

4. $32 + 45 + 102 = 45 + 32 + 102$
Comm. Prop. of Add.

Alternative Assessment

Have students make posters displaying the Commutative, Associative, and Identity Properties of Addition and Multiplication with both arithmetic and algebraic examples.

Test Prep

Resources

For additional practice with a variety of test item formats:
- Test Prep, p. 121
- Test-Taking Strategies, p. 116
- Test-Taking Strategies With Transparencies

Reteaching 2-1 *Properties of Numbers*

Properties of numbers help make mental computations easier.

Use mental math to simplify $1.84 + .76 + .16$.
Since $0.84 + 0.16 = 1$, it is easier to add $1.84 and $.16 first.
$1.84 + 0.76 + 0.16$
$= 1.84 + (0.16 + 0.76)$ Use the commutative property of addition.
$= (1.84 + 0.16) + 0.76$ Use the associative property of addition.
$= 2.00 + 0.76$ Add within parentheses.
$= 2.76 Add.
Use mental math to simplify $5 \cdot 13 \cdot 20 \cdot 2$.
Since $5 \cdot 20 = 100$, it is easier to multiply 5 and 20 first.
$5 \cdot 13 \cdot 20 \cdot 2$
$= 5 \cdot (20 \cdot 13) \cdot 2$ Use the commutative property of multiplication.
$= (5 \cdot 20) \cdot (13 \cdot 2)$ Use the associative property of multiplication.
$= 100 \cdot 26$ Multiply within parentheses.
$= 2,600$ Multiply.

Use mental math to simplify each expression.

1. $198 + 15 + 302$ **2.** $16 + 27 + (-16)$
    515   27
3. $4 \cdot 7 \cdot 25$ **4.** $2 \cdot 6 \cdot 5$
    700   60
5. $18 + (-8) + 11$ **6.** $5 \cdot 9 \cdot 8$
    21   360
7. $21 + 4 + (-1)$ **8.** $1,242 + 125 + 58$
    24   1,425
9. $50 \cdot 13 \cdot 2$ **10.** $(-209) + 576 + (-91)$
    1,300   276
11. $17 + 9 + 13 + 6$ **12.** $125 \cdot 353 \cdot 8$
    45   353,000

Reteaching

C Challenge

Mental Math **Evaluate each expression.**

39. $x(y \cdot z)$, for $x = 4$, $y = 27$, and $z = 5$ 540

40. $t(u)(-v)$, for $t = 3$, $u = 20$, and $v = 8$ −480

41. $a + b + c$, for $a = 14$, $b = 252$, and $c = 26$ 292

42. $d(v)(d)$, for $d = 5$ and $v = 24$ 600

43. No; both $3 \cdot 4$ and $2 \div (-2)$ must be found first by the order of operations.

43. **Reasoning** Can you use $4 + 2 = 6$ as your first step in simplifying $3 \cdot 4 + 2 \div (-2)$? Explain. See left.

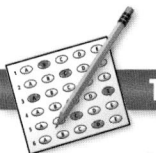

Test Prep

Multiple Choice **44.** Which equation shows the Associative Property of Addition? B
A. $8 + 6 + 7 = 8 + 7 + 6$ **B.** $(10 + 5) + 15 = 10 + (5 + 15)$
C. $9 + 0 + (-1) = 9 + (-1)$ **D.** $(-2) \cdot 1 \cdot 9 = (-2) \cdot 9$

Reading Comprehension Read the passage below before doing Exercises 45 and 46.

A Fair Fare in Alaska

Railroads are a popular means of transportation in Alaska. One scenic train route travels 356 miles from Anchorage to Fairbanks. It includes a stop in Denali Park, where you can see the tallest mountain in the United States, Mount McKinley. A one-way fare for the 12-hour trip is $154 in the summer and $120 in the spring and fall. A one-way fare for the 7.5-hour trip from Anchorage to Denali Park is $102 in the summer, and $84 in the spring and fall. Children's fares are half the fares for adults.

45. Two adults and two children plan to travel round trip from Anchorage to Fairbanks. How much will the trip cost in the summer? I
F. $360   **G.** $462   **H.** $720   **I.** $924

Take It to the NET
Online lesson quiz at
www.PHSchool.com
Web Code: ada-0201

46. Three adults and two children plan to travel round trip from Anchorage to Denali Park. How much will the trip cost in the fall? A
A. $672   **B.** $504   **C.** $336   **D.** $252

Mixed Review

Lesson 1-10 **In which quadrant does the graph of each ordered pair lie?**

47. $(-6, -3)$ **48.** $(8, -1)$ **49.** $(-4, 17)$ **50.** $(-1, 4)$
III   IV   II   II

Lesson 1-9 **51.** **Recreation** Lin worked 4 hours per day for 3 days to build a model bridge. How many hours did she spend on the project? 12 h

Lesson 1-2 **Simplify each expression.**

52. $3 \cdot 5 + 3 \cdot 15$ 60 **53.** $4 \cdot 7 + 4 \cdot 11$ 72 **54.** $5 \cdot 22 - 5 \cdot 2$ 100

The Distributive Property

OBJECTIVE
1 **Numerical Expressions**

OBJECTIVE
1 **Numerical Expressions**

vestigation

Exploring the Distributive Property

You can find the total area of two rectangles by two methods.

1. **Method 1:** Find the area of each rectangle. Then find the sum of the areas. **12; 20; 32**

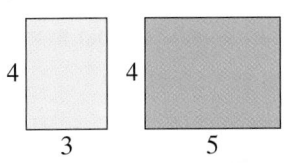

2. **Method 2:** Combine the two rectangles into one large rectangle. Find its length. Find its width. Then find its area.
8; 4; 32

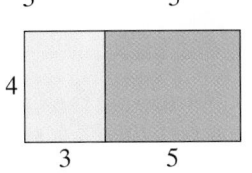

3. On a piece of paper, draw two rectangles with the same width, and lengths different from those above. Label the dimensions. Repeat Method 1 and Method 2 with your pair of rectangles. What do you notice about your results? **Answers may vary. Sample: Suppose you draw rectangles with width 6 and lengths 8 and 3. Method 1: 8 · 6 + 3 · 6 = 48 + 18 = 66. Method 2: (8 + 3)6 = 11 · 6 = 66.**

The Investigation above shows different ways to find the sum of the areas of two rectangles. It suggests the *Distributive Property,* which combines multiplication with addition and subtraction.

Key Concepts — Distributive Property

To multiply a sum or difference, multiply each number within the parentheses by the number outside the parentheses.

Arithmetic	Algebra
$3(2 + 6) = 3(2) + 3(6)$	$a(b + c) = ab + ac$
$(2 + 6)3 = 2(3) + 6(3)$	$(b + c)a = ba + ca$
$6(7 - 4) = 6(7) - 6(4)$	$a(b - c) = ab - ac$
$(7 - 4)6 = 7(6) - 4(6)$	$(b - c)a = ba - ca$

What You'll Learn

OBJECTIVE 1 To use the Distributive Property with numerical expressions

OBJECTIVE 2 To use the Distributive Property with algebraic expressions

. . . And Why

To solve real-world problems involving fundraising

✔ Check Skills You'll Need

Simplify each expression.

1. $3 \cdot 7 - 9$ **12**

2. $(9 - 5)6$ **24**

3. $8 + 2 \cdot 6$ **20**

4. $2(6 - 3)$ **6**

5. $4 \cdot 5 - 4 \cdot 3$ **8**

6. $3 \cdot 2 - 1 \cdot 2$ **4**

 For help, go to Lesson 1-2.

New Vocabulary

• **Distributive Property**

 Interactive lesson includes instant self-check, tutorials, and activities.

1. Plan

Lesson Preview

✔ **Check Skills You'll Need**

Order of Operations
Lesson 1-2: Examples 1 and 2; Exercises 1–12.
Extra Practice, p. 744.

Lesson Resources

📁 **Teaching Resources**
Practice, Reteaching, Enrichment

👥 **Reaching All Students**
Practice Workbook 2-2
Spanish Practice Workbook 2-2
Guided Problem Solving 2-2
Hands-On Activities 3

⏱ **Presentation Assistant Plus!**
Transparencies and PowerPoint™
• Check Skills You'll Need 2-2
• Additional Examples 2-2
• Student Edition Answers 2-2
• Lesson Quiz 2-2
PH Presentation Pro CD-ROM 2-2

ASSESSMENT SYSTEM
Computer Test Generator CD-ROM

💻 **Technology**
Resource Pro® CD-ROM
Computer Test Generator CD-ROM
PH Presentation Pro CD-ROM

💻 **www.PHSchool.com**
Student Site
• Teacher Web Code: adk-5500
• Algebra Readiness Puzzles 7
• Self-grading Lesson Quiz
PH SuccessNet Teacher Center
• Lesson Planner
• Resources

Plus

✔ Ongoing Assessment and Intervention

Before the Lesson
Diagnose prerequisite skills using:
• Check Skills You'll Need

During the Lesson
Monitor progress using:
• Check Understanding
• Additional Examples
• Test Prep

After the Lesson
Assess knowledge using:
• Lesson Quiz
• Computer Test Generator CD-ROM

2. Teach

Math Background

The Distributive Property allows you to evaluate an expression in two ways. With 6(2 + 3), you can either add first and then multiply by 6, or multiply before finding the sum. The multiplier 6 is distributed to both the 2 and the 3.

Teaching Notes

Investigation (Optional)
English Learners Some students may not be familiar with the word *distributive*. Give a student the same number of index cards as there are students in the class. Ask the student to *distribute* one card to each member of the class. Write 4(3 + 5) = 4(3) + 4(5) on the board. Tell students to think of the class as the expression inside the parentheses. Point out that just as the cards are distributed to everyone in the class, the number in front of the parentheses is distributed to every term within the parentheses.

1 EXAMPLE **Visual Learners**

Point out the arrows drawn from the number outside the parentheses to each number inside. Suggest that students may wish to draw these arrows on all their exercises in which they use the Distributive Property.

2 EXAMPLE **Teaching Tip**

Stress that sometimes thinking of one factor as the difference or sum of two numbers can help with mental math, whereas at other times, it may *not* be so helpful. For example, it may not be helpful when multiplying 7(263). Have students give examples of factors that could be rewritten to help with mental math.

3 EXAMPLE **Auditory Learners**

Have a student read aloud a question from *Check Understanding*. Have a partner state the steps for simplifying the expression, using the Distributive Property.

You can use the Distributive Property to multiply mentally.

1 EXAMPLE **Using the Distributive Property I**

Use the Distributive Property to find 20(102) mentally.

$$20(102) = 20(100 + 2)$$ Write 102 as (100 + 2).

$$20(100 + 2) = 20 \cdot 100 + 20 \cdot 2$$ Use the Distributive Property.

$$= 2{,}000 + 40$$ Multiply.

$$= 2{,}040$$ Add.

✔ **Check Understanding**   Example 1

1. Find each product mentally.

   a. (53)50 2,650   **b.** 30 · 104 3,120   **c.** 9 · 199 1,791

2 EXAMPLE   Real-World 🌐 Problem Solving

Fundraising At the Parent-Teacher Association (PTA) Pancake Breakfast, the PTA served 397 people 4 pancakes each. How many pancakes did the PTA serve?

$$(397)4 = (400 - 3)4$$ Write 397 as (400 − 3).

$$= 400 \cdot 4 - 3 \cdot 4$$ Use the Distributive Property.

$$= 1{,}600 - 12$$ Multiply.

$$= 1{,}588$$ Subtract.

● The PTA served 1,588 pancakes.

✔ **Check Understanding**   Example 2

2. Your club sold calendars for $7. Club members sold 204 calendars. How much money did they raise? $1,428

3 EXAMPLE   **Using the Distributive Property II**

Simplify 8(15) − 8(5).

$$8(15) - 8(5) = 8(15 - 5)$$ Use the Distributive Property.

$$= 8(10)$$ Subtract within parentheses.

$$= 80$$ Multiply.

✔ **Check Understanding**   Example 3

3. Simplify each expression.

   a. 7(21) + 7(9)   **b.** 12(52) − 12(62)   **c.** (16)7 − (11)7
   210   −120   35

👥 Reaching All Students

Below Level Have the first student in each row distribute papers to each student in his or her row. Use the word "distribute" when you describe what you want the students to do.	Advanced Learners Challenge students to multiply 3(10,523) mentally. 31,569	English Learners See note on page 72. Auditory Learners See note on page 72.

2 Variable Expressions

You can use algebra tiles to model the Distributive Property with variable expressions.

4 EXAMPLE   Using Tiles to Multiply

Use algebra tiles to multiply $3(2x + 5)$.

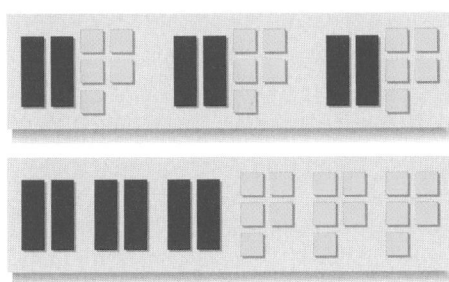

Model three groups of $2x + 5$.

Group like tiles.

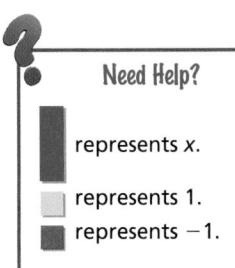

Need Help?

▮ represents x.

▯ represents 1.

▮ represents -1.

So, $3(2x + 5) = 6x + 15$.

✓ **Check Understanding   Example 4**

4. Use algebra tiles to multiply.

    a. $4(2x - 3)$ 8x − 12 **b.** $3(x + 4)$ 3x + 12 **c.** $(3x + 1)2$ 6x + 2

In Example 4, notice that 3 multiplies both $2x$ and 5.
That is, $3(2x + 5) = 3(2x) + 3(5)$.

5 EXAMPLE   Using the Distributive Property III

Multiply.

a. $-5(4x - 3)$

$-5(4x - 3) = -5(4x) - (-5)(3)$ **Use the Distributive Property.**

$= -20x - (-15)$ **Multiply.**

$= -20x + 15$ **Simplify.**

b. $(2x + 5)7$

$(2x + 5)7 = (2x)7 + (5)7$ **Use the Distributive Property.**

$= 14x + 35$ **Multiply.**

Reading Math

When you distribute papers in class, you give some to each classmate. Similarly, when you distribute a number over a sum or difference, you multiply each value within the parentheses by that number.

✓ **Check Understanding   Example 5**

5. Multiply.

    a. $2(7 - 3d)$ **b.** $(6m + 1)(3)$ **c.** $-3(5t - 2)$
        14 − 6d   18m + 3   −15t + 6

2-2   The Distributive Property   **73**

4 EXAMPLE   Tactile Learners
Have students model the multiplication so that they can see that there are three times as many of both types of tiles, variable and unit, than they started with.

5 EXAMPLE   Error Prevention
Remind students that when they use the Distributive Property to multiply an arithmetic or algebraic expression by a negative number, they must apply the rules for multiplying integers.

PowerPoint

Additional Examples

❶ Use the Distributive Property to find 15(110) mentally. **1,650**

❷ Ms. Thomas gave 5 pencils to each of her 37 students. What is the total number of pencils she gave to the students?
185 pencils

❸ Simplify 11(23) + 11(7). **330**

❹ Use algebra tiles to multiply $4(3x - 4)$. **12x − 16**

❺ Multiply.
   a. $-9(2 - 8y)$ **−18 + 72y**
   b. $(5m + 6)11$ **55m + 66**

Closure

Ask students to explain how the Distributive Property and mental math can be helpful in an everyday situation. **Answers may vary. Sample: If you need to multiply an amount close to $1.00 by a number, you can multiply $1.00 by the number and also the difference between $1.00 and the original amount by the number. Then add or subtract the two products.**

3. Practice

Assignment Guide

 **Objective 1**
Ⓐ Ⓑ **Core** 1–15, 30–37
Ⓒ **Extension** 46, 47

Objective 2
Ⓐ Ⓑ **Core** 16–29, 38–45
Ⓒ **Extension** 48–51

Test Prep 52–54
Mixed Review 55–61

Practice 2-2 **The Distributive Property**

Write an expression using parentheses for each model. Then multiply.

1.
$3(4x + 2) = 12x + 6$

2.
$2(5x + 3) = 10x + 6$

Multiply each expression.

3. $6(h - 4)$ $6h - 24$
4. $(p + 3)5$ $5p + 15$
5. $-3(x + 8)$ $-3x - 24$
6. $(4 - y)(-9)$ $-36 + 9y$
7. $2(7n - 11)$ $14n - 22$
8. $-10(-a + 5)$ $10a - 50$

Use the distributive property to simplify.

9. $98 \cdot 7$ $(100 - 2)7 = 700 - 14 = 686$
10. $9 \cdot 28$ $9(30 - 2) = 270 - 18 = 252$
11. $78 \cdot 8$ $(80 - 2)8 = 640 - 16 = 624$
12. $7(2,009)$ $7(2,000 + 9) = 14,000 + 63 = 14,063$
13. $899 \cdot 5$ $(900 - 1)5 = 4,500 - 5 = 4,495$
14. $30 \cdot 105$ $30(100 + 5) = 3,000 + 150 = 3,150$
15. $8 \cdot 5 - 12 \cdot 5$ $(8 - 12)5 = -20$
16. $7 \cdot 10 + 7(-3)$ $7[10 + (-3)] = 49$
17. $-4(3) + (-4)(6)$ $-4(3 + 6) = -36$
18. $6(8) + 6(-2)$ $6[8 + (-2)] = 36$

Solve using mental math.

19. A shipping container holds 144 boxes. How many boxes can be shipped in 4 containers?   576 boxes

---

Enrichment 2-2 **Multiplying Binomials**

A *term* is part of an expression. Terms are separated by addition and subtraction symbols. A *binomial* is an expression with two terms.

Binomials	Not Binomials
$2x + 7$	$12n$ (only one term)
$3x + 4y$	$6 + 5k - 3py$ (three terms)
$-7k - 9$	$-(2g)$ (only one term)

You can multiply binomials using the distributive property.

Complete the following to find the product $(a + b)(c + d)$.
Hint: Think of $a + b$ as a single quantity. Distribute $a + b$ to both c and d.

1. $(a + b)(c + d) = (a + b)(\underline{c}) + (a + b)(\underline{d})$
   $= ac + \underline{bc} + ad + \underline{bd}$

To multiply two binomials, multiply each of the terms in the first binomial by each of the terms in the second binomial.

Example   Find the product: $(3 + k)(m - 4)$
Solution $(3 + k)(m - 4) = (3 + k)m - (3 + k)(4)$
$= 3 \cdot m + k \cdot m - 3 \cdot 4 - k \cdot 4$
$= 3m + km - 12 - 4k$

Find the product.

2. $(h + w)(c + d)$ $hc + wc + hd + wd$
3. $(5 + p)(9 + t)$ $45 + 9p + 5t + pt$
4. $(x + y)(7 - m)$ $7x + 7y - mx - my$
5. $(n - 5)(y - 6)$ $ny - 5y - 6n + 30$

You can use binomials to find the product of two numbers.
$12 \times 8 = (10 + 2)(10 - 2)$
$= 10 \cdot 10 + 2 \cdot 10 - 10 \cdot 2 - 2 \cdot 2$
$= 100 + 20 - 20 - 4$
$= 96$

Find the product by multiplying two binomials.

6. $23 \times 17 = (20 + 3)(20 - 3) =$ $400 + 60 - 60 - 9 = 391$
7. $55 \times 45 = (50 + 5)(50 - 5) =$ $2,500 + 250 - 250 - 25 = 2,475$

EXERCISES

For more exercises, see *Extra Practice*.

Practice and Problem Solving

Ⓐ **Practice by Example**

Examples 1 and 2
(page 72)

Mental Math   **Use the Distributive Property to simplify.**

1. $6(23)$ 138
2. $5(18)$ 90
3. $7(48)$ 336
4. $13(101)$ 1,313
5. $(104)(9)$ 936
6. $6(52)$ 312
7. $8(98)$ 784
8. $(208)4$ 832

9. **Ticket Sales** A theater sold out its evening performances four nights in a row. The theater has 294 seats. How many people attended the theater in the four nights?   **1,176 people**

Example 3
(page 72)

Simplify each expression.

10. $7(3) + 7(5)$ 56
11. $2(9) - 3(9)$ –9
12. $6(4) + 6(8)$ 72
13. $9(3) - 2(3)$ 21
14. $(12)27 - (12)24$ 36
15. $(3)5 + (27)5$ 150

Example 4
(page 73)

Write an expression using parentheses for each model. Then multiply.

16.

$4(x + 2);\ 4x + 8$

17.
$3(3x - 1);\ 9x - 3$

Multiply. Use algebra tiles as needed.

18. $2(t - 5)$ $2t - 10$
19. $(v - 3)4$ $4v - 12$
20. $3(2h - 1)$ $6h - 3$
21. $-2(7z + 3)$ $-14z - 6$

Example 5
(page 73)

Multiply.

22. $7(b - 3)$ $7b - 21$
23. $12(a + 3)$ $12a + 36$
24. $(2 + 3d)5$ $10 + 15d$
25. $-5(m + 6)$ $-5m - 30$
26. $3(5 - 3w)$ $15 - 9w$
27. $-7(t - 4)$ $-7t + 28$
28. $4(b + 5)$ $4b + 20$
29. $(y - 6)2$ $2y - 12$

Ⓑ **Apply Your Skills**

Mental Math   **Use the Distributive Property to simplify.**

30. $5(1,005)$ 5,025
31. $(8) \cdot 11 + (-13) \cdot 11$ –55
32. $13 \cdot (-3) - 7 \cdot (-3)$ –18
33. $-32 \cdot 6 + 29 \cdot 6$ –18
34. $4 \cdot 19 - 4 \cdot (11)$ 32
35. $(-8) \cdot 10 + 3 \cdot (-8)$ –104

Mental Math   **Solve using mental math.**

36. Every day, Lila eats a bowl of cereal that has 193 calories. What is the total number of calories from cereal that Lila eats in a week?   **1,351 calories**
37. The trip from Roberto's house to his aunt's house is 896 miles. How long is the round trip?   **1,792 miles**

GPS Use the Guided Problem Solving worksheet with Exercise 9.

Use the Distributive Property to multiply.

38. $-3(2t + 6)$
$-6t - 18$

39. $-7(-3n + 2)$
$21n - 14$

40. $(4 - t)(-7)$
$-28 + 7t$

41. $-5(-m + 6)$
$5m - 30$

42. $-8(6 - c)$
$-48 + 8c$

43. $(5y + 8)(-3)$
$-15y - 24$

44. Writing in Math Explain how to use the Distributive Property to multiply $6(3r + 4s)$.
Multiply 3r and 4s by 6, then write the sum: 18r + 24s.

45. Error Analysis Suppose your friend wrote $7(2m + t) = 14m + t$. What error did your friend make?
My friend didn't distribute the 7 to the t.

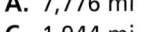 **Challenge**

Mental Math **Use the Distributive Property to simplify.**

46. $(-4)(70) + (-4)(-90)$ 80

47. $3(9) - 3(5) + 3(6)$ 30

Name each property shown.

48. $m[t + (-t)] = mt + m(-t)$
Dist. Prop.

49. $m[t + (-t)] = m(-t + t)$
Comm. Prop. of Add.

50. $m[t + (-t)] = [t + (-t)]m$
Comm. Prop. of Mult.

51. $m + [t + (-t)] = (m + t) + (-t)$
Assoc. Prop. of Add.

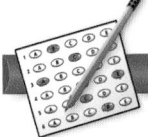

Test Prep

Multiple Choice

52. According to the map, if you drive from Atlanta to Los Angeles (L.A.) and back, how many miles would you travel? **B**
A. 7,776 mi   **B.** 3,888 mi
C. 1,944 mi   **D.** 1,888 mi

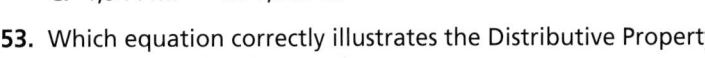

Los Angeles 1,944 miles
L.A.   ATLANTA

53. Which equation correctly illustrates the Distributive Property? **I**
F. $18(100 + 4) = (18 \cdot 100) + 4$
G. $18(100 + 4) = (18 + 100) \cdot (18 + 4)$
H. $18(100 + 4) = (18 + 100) \cdot 4$
I. $18(100 + 4) = (18 \cdot 100) + (18 \cdot 4)$

54. You rent three videos for $2.95 each. What do you pay? **B**
A. $6.95   **B.** $8.85   **C.** $9.00   **D.** $9.15

Take It to the NET
Online lesson quiz at **www.PHSchool.com**
Web Code: ada-0202

Mixed Review

Lesson 2-1

Name the property shown.

55. $3(6 \cdot 2) = 3(2 \cdot 6)$
Comm. Prop. of Mult.

56. $8 = 8 + 0$
Ident. Prop. of Add.

57. $4(8 \cdot 3) = (4 \cdot 8)3$
Assoc. Prop. of Mult.

Lessons 1-5 and 1-6

58. You have $120 in your checking account. In one month, you deposit $30, write a check for $21, withdraw $20, and deposit $45. Find your balance at the end of the month. **$154**

Lesson 1-3

Evaluate each expression.

59. $7 - m$, for $m = 6$
1

60. $6t + 1$, for $t = -2$
-11

61. $c \div 3 - 5$, for $c = 6$
-3

2-2 The Distributive Property **75**

75

2-3

Lesson Preview

✓ **Check Skills You'll Need**

The Distributive Property
Lesson 2-2: Example 5;
Exercises 22–29.
Extra Practice, p. 745.

Lesson Resources

📁 **Teaching Resources**
Practice, Reteaching, Enrichment
Checkpoint Quiz 1

👥 **Reaching All Students**
Practice Workbook 2-3
Spanish Practice Workbook 2-3
Reading and Math Literacy 2B
Spanish Reading and Math
  Literacy 2B
Spanish Checkpoint Quiz 1
Guided Problem Solving 2-3

⏰ **Presentation Assistant Plus!**
Transparencies and PowerPoint™
• Check Skills You'll Need 2-3
• Additional Examples 2-3
• Student Edition Answers 2-3
• Lesson Quiz 2-3
PH Presentation Pro CD-ROM 2-3

ASSESSMENT SYSTEM

Checkpoint Quiz 1
Computer Test Generator CD-ROM

💻 **Technology**
Resource Pro® CD-ROM
Computer Test Generator CD-ROM
PH Presentation Pro CD-ROM

💻 **www.PHSchool.com**
Student Site
• Teacher Web Code: adk-5500
• Algebra Readiness Puzzles 28
• Graphing Calculator, Procedure 1
• Self-grading Lesson Quiz
PH SuccessNet Teacher Center
• Lesson Planner
• Resources

Simplifying Variable Expressions

What You'll Learn

OBJECTIVE 1 To identify parts of a variable expression

OBJECTIVE 2 To simplify expressions

. . . And Why

To extend addition and subtraction skills to include variables

✓ **Check Skills You'll Need**
Simplify each expression.

1. $5(b + 4)$ $5b + 20$

2. $-3(2x + 5)$ $-6x - 15$

3. $4(-8 - 3q)$ $-32 - 12q$

4. $-6(2b - 7)$ $-12b + 42$

🔑 For help, go to Lesson 2-2.

New Vocabulary

• term
• constant
• like terms
• coefficient
• simplify a variable expression
• deductive reasoning

📱 **TEXT** Interactive lesson includes instant self-check, tutorials, and activities.

OBJECTIVE

1 Identifying Parts of a Variable Expression

The diagram shows the possible parts of a variable expression.

A **term** is a number or the product of a number and variable(s).

$$7a + 4a + 3b - 6 \leftarrow \text{A \textbf{constant} is a term that has no variable.}$$
Like terms have identical variables.

A **coefficient** is a number that multiplies a variable.

When you have a variable expression that includes subtraction, you can rewrite the expression using only addition. This will help you find the coefficient(s) and constant(s).

$$5x - 3y + z - 2$$
$$= 5x + (-3y) + z + (-2) \quad \text{Rewrite subtraction as adding opposites.}$$
$$= 5x + (-3y) + 1z + (-2) \quad \text{Identity Property of Multiplication}$$

Rewriting the expression using addition shows that the coefficients are 5, -3, and 1. The constant is -2. Notice that the sign between terms in the original expression determines whether a coefficient or constant is positive or negative.

1 EXAMPLE   Identifying Parts of an Expression

Name the coefficients, the like terms, and the constants in $3m - 2n + n - 4$.

Coefficients: $3, -2, 1$ Like terms: $-2n$ and n Constant: -4

✓ **Check Understanding**   Example 1

1. Name the coefficients, the like terms, and the constants.

a. $6 + 2s + 4s$
2, 4; 2s, 4s; 6

b. $-4x$
−4; none; none

c. $9m + 2r - 2m + r$
9, 2, −2, 1; 9m and −2m, 2r and r; none

OBJECTIVE

2 Simplifying Variable Expressions

You **simplify a variable expression** by replacing it with an equivalent expression that has as few terms as possible. Algebra tiles can help you model this process.

76   Chapter 2   Solving One-Step Equations and Inequalities

✓ **Ongoing Assessment and Intervention**

Before the Lesson	**During the Lesson**	**After the Lesson**
Diagnose prerequisite skills using:	Monitor progress using:	Assess knowledge using:
• Check Skills You'll Need	• Check Understanding	• Lesson Quiz
	• Additional Examples	• Computer Test Generator
	• Test Prep	CD-ROM
		• Chapter Checkpoint 1 (p. 79)

2 EXAMPLE Using Tiles to Simplify

Simplify $2x + 4 + 3x$.

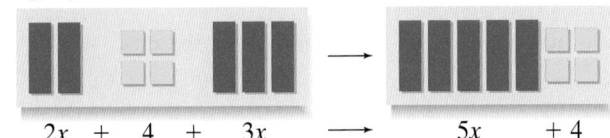

$$2x \quad + \quad 4 \quad + \quad 3x \quad \longrightarrow \quad 5x \quad + 4$$

✓ **Check Understanding** Example 2

2. Use tiles to simplify $3a + 2 + 4a - 1$. **7a + 1**

You can also use the Distributive Property to combine like terms.

3 EXAMPLE Combining Like Terms

Simplify $5y + y$.

$5y + y = 5y + 1y$	Use the Identity Property of Multiplication.
$= (5 + 1)y$	Use the Distributive Property.
$= 6y$	Simplify.

✓ **Check Understanding** Example 3

3. Simplify each expression.

   a. $3b - b$ **2b**   **b.** $-4m - 9m$ **−13m** **c.** $p + 6p - 4p$ **3p**

Deductive reasoning is the process of reasoning logically from given facts to a conclusion. As you use properties, rules, and definitions to justify the steps in a problem, you are using deductive reasoning.

4 EXAMPLE Using Deductive Reasoning

Simplify $4g + 3(3 + g)$. Justify each step.

$4g + 3(3 + g) = 4g + 9 + 3g$	Use the Distributive Property.
$= 4g + 3g + 9$	Use the Commutative Property of Addition.
$= (4 + 3)g + 9$	Use the Distributive Property to combine like terms.
$= 7g + 9$	Simplify.

✓ **Check Understanding** Example 4

4. Simplify each expression. Justify each step.

   a. $6y + 4m - 7y + m$ **−y + 5m**   **b.** $4x + 3 - 2(5 + x)$ **2x − 7**

👥 Reaching All Students

| **Below Level** Discuss the benefits of grouping similar items together, like on supermarket shelves or in your dresser drawers. | **Advanced Learners** Ask: *How can you apply the Commutative and Associative Properties of Addition to an expression that contains subtraction?* Rewrite to show addition of the opposite. | **Tactile Learners** See note on page 77. **Auditory Learners** See note on page 77. |

---

2. Teach

 Professional Development

Math Background

Addition and subtraction signs separate an expression into *terms*. Thus, $2 + x - 8$ has three terms. In contrast, *xyz* is just one term.

Teaching Notes

1 EXAMPLE English Learners

A *constant* constantly has the same value. Each number is a constant.

2 EXAMPLE Tactile Learners

Have students write expressions on a sheet of paper and use scissors to cut out each term, including the operation in front of the term. They can then rearrange the pieces to group like terms and constants.

3 EXAMPLE Error Prevention

Some variable terms have an unwritten coefficient of 1. Have students write a 1 in front of these variables to help remember the value of the coefficient.

4 EXAMPLE Auditory Learners

When combining like terms, students may want to give each variable a name, like grape for *g*. Then they can say, "4 grapes plus 3 grapes equals 7 grapes." This practice will help later when there is more than one variable.

PowerPoint

🖥 Additional Examples

1 Name the coefficients, the like terms, and the constants in $7x + y - 2x - 7$.
7, 1, −2; 7x, −2x; −7

2 Simplify $9 + 4f + 3 + 2f$.
6f + 12

3 Simplify $2b + b - 4$. **3b − 4**

4 Simplify $(7 - 3x)5 + 20x$.
35 + 5x

Closure

Ask students how to simplify an expression containing variable and constant terms. Group all like variable terms together and all constants together. Then combine like terms and constants.

77

3. Practice

Assignment Guide

1 **Objective 1**
Ⓐ Ⓑ Core 1–6, 35

2 **Objective 2**
Ⓐ Ⓑ Core 7–34
Ⓒ Extension 36–41

Test Prep 42–44
Mixed Review 45–49

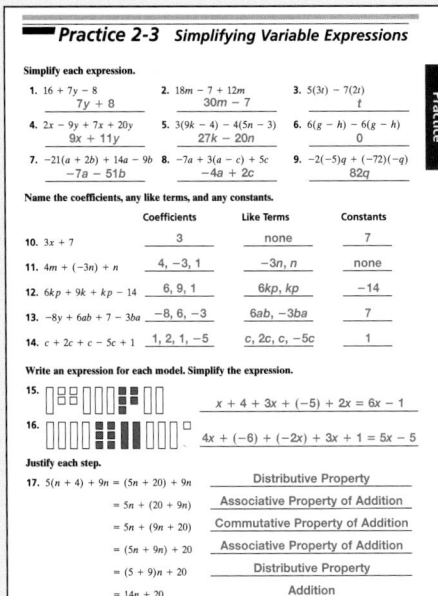

Practice 2-3 *Simplifying Variable Expressions*

Simplify each expression.

1. $16 + 7y - 8$
   $7y + 8$
2. $18m - 7 + 12m$
   $30m - 7$
3. $5(3t) - 7(2t)$
   t
4. $2x - 9y + 7x + 20y$
   $9x + 11y$
5. $3(9k - 4) - 4(5n - 3)$
   $27k - 20n$
6. $6(g - h) - 6(g - h)$
   0
7. $-21(a + 2b) + 14a - 9b$
   $-7a - 51b$
8. $-7a + 3(a - c) + 5c$
   $-4a + 2c$
9. $-2(-5)q + (-72)(-q)$
   $82q$

Name the coefficients, any like terms, and any constants.

	Coefficients	Like Terms	Constants
10. $3x + 7$	3	none	7
11. $4m + (-3n) + n$	4, −3, 1	−3n, n	none
12. $6kp + 9k + kp - 14$	6, 9, 1	6kp, kp	−14
13. $-8y + 6ab + 7 - 3ba$	−8, 6, −3	6ab, −3ba	7
14. $c + 2c + c - 5c + 1$	1, 2, 1, −5	c, 2c, c, −5c	1

Write an expression for each model. Simplify the expression.

15. $x + 4 + 3x + (-5) + 2x = 6x - 1$
16. $4x + (-6) + (-2x) + 3x + 1 = 5x - 5$

Justify each step.

17. $5(n + 4) + 9n = (5n + 20) + 9n$ — Distributive Property
$= 5n + (20 + 9n)$ — Associative Property of Addition
$= 5n + (9n + 20)$ — Commutative Property of Addition
$= (5n + 9n) + 20$ — Associative Property of Addition
$= (5 + 9)n + 20$ — Distributive Property
$= 14n + 20$ — Addition

Enrichment 2-3 *Find the Speed*

In 1976, Captain Elden Joersz set the world aircraft speed record. On July 28, 1976, Captain Joersz flew an SR-71 Blackbird at Beale Air Force Base in California. How fast did Captain Joersz fly?
To find out, simplify each expression. Find the answer in the digital read-out and shade the region containing the answer.

1. $9x + (-5x)$ — $4x$
2. $-7y + 12y$ — $5y$
3. $-17p + 12p - 11p$ — $-16p$
4. $3(2a + 5a)$ — $21a$
5. $4(3f) - 8f$ — $4f$
6. $n(8 + 6 - 19)$ — $-5n$
7. $-2(4x) + 7x$ — $-x$
8. $7(3f - 2g) + 14(g - f)$ — $7f$
9. $-15y + 11y - 9y$ — $-13y$
10. $-3[12p + (-7p)]$ — $-15p$
11. $-2n(5 - 7) + 3(3n)$ — $13n$
12. $6(b - a) + 2(4a - 3b)$ — $2a$
13. $-9(4f - 6f) + (-15f)$ — $3f$
14. $8(5 - n) - 19 + 17n - 21$ — $9n$
15. $8(3x - 2y) + 4[(-3x) + 4y]$ — $12x$
16. $-5p + 3p - 2p - 9p + 7p - 3p$ — $-9p$
17. $-9(7y - 8y) + 12(6y - 7y)$ — $-3y$
18. $8(5a - 4n + 3p) - 4(6p - 8n + 11a)$ — $-4a$

12x		−17y		−3y		−16p	
7a	21a	9p	−5n	5y	9n	10y	−4a
−x		15p		4f		7f	
−15p	−7a	−5x	4x	−10n	2a	−8x	−9p
3f		−5f		−13y		13n	

Answer: __2__ __1__ __9__ __3__ mi/h

Practice and Problem Solving

Ⓐ **Practice by Example**

Name the coefficients, the like terms, and the constants.

Example 1
(page 76)

1. $3x + 5y - 3$
   3, 5; none; −3
2. $2x - 7$
   2; none; −7
3. $4x - 7x + 3x$
   See left.
4. $6xy - 5xy$
   See left.
5. $-3x$
   −3; none; none
6. $a + 2a + 3a - 4a$
   See left.

3. 4, −7, 3; 4x, −7x, 3x; none
4. 6, −5; 6xy, −5xy; none
6. 1, 2, 3, −4; a, 2a, 3a, −4a; none

Example 2
(page 77)

Use tiles to simplify each expression.

7. $x + 2 + 3x + 5 + x + 3 + 2x$
   $7x + 10$

8. $2x + 1 + x - 4 + 4x + 1$
   $7x - 2$

9. $x + 2 + 3x$ $4x + 2$
10. $2x + 1 + 6x - 4$ $8x - 3$

Example 3
(page 77)

Simplify each expression.

11. $12a + a$ $13a$
12. $5a + 8a$ $13a$
13. $-2b + b$ $-b$
14. $7w - w$ $6w$
15. $2r - 5 + 6r$ $8r - 5$
16. $4a - 3 + 5a$ $9a - 3$

Example 4
(page 77)

Simplify each expression. Justify each step.

17. $2g + 3(g + 5)$ $5g + 15$
18. $-3z + 8(z + y)$ $5z + 8y$
19. $4m + 3d - 5m + d$ $-m + 4d$
20. $t - 3 + 2(t + 2)$ $3t + 1$

Ⓑ **Apply Your Skills**

Simplify each expression.

21. $8z + 8y + 3z$
    $11z + 8y$
22. $t - 3t + 2t + 4$ 4
23. $18 + 6(9k - 13)$
    $-60 + 54k$
24. $r + 3 - 6r + r$
    $-4r + 3$
25. $-4(a + 3) - a$
    $-5a - 12$
26. $4m + 3 - 5m + m$
    3
27. $3(g + 5) + 2g$
    $5g + 15$
28. $2b - 6 + 3b - b$
    $4b - 6$
29. $-5 + 3x + 3 + 2$ $3x$
30. $4(w + 2x) + 9(-4w)$
    $-32w + 8x$
31. $3(2n + 4) - 2(3n + 6)$ 0

🌐 **32. Pet Supplies** Juan bought supplies for his new gecko. He bought four plants for p dollars each. He also bought a 10-gallon tank for $10 and a water dish for $3. Write an expression Juan could use to find the total cost of the supplies. $4p + 10 + 3$, or $4p + 13$

[GPS]

33. Error Analysis Your friend simplified $x + y + xy$ to $2xy$. What error did your friend make? **Answers may vary. Sample: my friend added $x + y$ to get xy.**

34. Open-Ended Use the variables r and s to write a variable expression. Evaluate your expression for $r = 2$ and $s = -5$.
Answers may vary. Sample: $3r - 4s + 1$; 27

[GPS] Use the Guided Problem Solving worksheet with Exercise 32.

35. <u>Writing in Math</u> The expression $10bc$ has two variables. Explain why $10bc$ is not two terms. **The variables are not separated by plus or minus signs.**

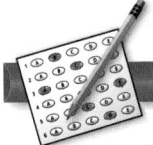

C Challenge   **Simplify each expression. Justify each step.**

36. $12 - 4(-8v + 17)$ $-56 + 32v$ **37.** $6(2x + y) + 2y - 12x$ $8y$

38. $(2t + 4)3 + 6(-5t) - (-8)$
$-24t + 20$

39. $-12(5x) + 3(-7x) - x$
$-82x$

40. $w + 3w + 4(5 + w - 3w)$
$-4w + 20$

41. $18u - 6(9k - 7 - 10u) + 4k$
$78u - 50k + 42$

Test Prep

Multiple Choice

42. Which expression has exactly two like terms? **A**
A. $3t + 1 - t$ **B.** $7 + 2m$ **C.** $8q + 3p$ **D.** $6r + r - 9r$

43. Which expression simplifies to $3x + 4z + 6$? **H**
F. $3(x + 6) + 4z$ **G.** $7(x + z) + 6$
H. $7z + 3(x + 2) - 3z$ **I.** $3 + x + 4 + z + 6$

44. Jaleesa bought three folders for b cents each and two report covers for c cents each. She also bought a binder for \$1.89. Which expression could Jaleesa use to find the total cost? **C**
A. $b + c + 189$ **B.** $3b + 189$
C. $3b + 2c + 189$ **D.** $189 - 2b - 3c$

Take It to the NET
Online lesson quiz at
www.PHSchool.com
Web Code: ada-0203

Mixed Review

Lesson 2-2   **Mental Math Use the Distributive Property to find each product.**

45. $8(102)$ 816   **46.** $54 \cdot 6$ 324   **47.** $19(30)$ 570   **48.** $(41)(9)$ 369

Lesson 1-8   **49. Rock Climbing** A pair of rock climbers start up a 1,000-ft cliff. After one hour, they have gone up 160 ft. After two hours, they have gone up 320 ft. If they continue at this rate, how far up will they have gone after five hours? **800 ft**

✓ Checkpoint Quiz 1   Lessons 2-1 through 2-3

Instant self-check quiz online and on CD-ROM

Name each property shown.

1. $3 \cdot (-6) = -6 \cdot 3$
Comm. Prop. of Mult.

2. $(3a)b = 3(ab)$
Assoc. Prop. of Mult.

3. $17 \cdot 1 = 17$
Ident. Prop. of Mult.

4. $6 + 0 = 0 + 6$
Comm. Prop. of Add.

5. $(3 + 2)(4) = (4)(3 + 2)$
Comm. Prop. of Mult.

6. $4(3 - 2) = 4(3) - 4(2)$
Dist. Prop.

Simplify each expression.

7. $3(a + 2a)$ $9a$ **8.** $9y - 3y + 12y$ $18y$ **9.** $7(2w) + 2(w - 3)$
$16w - 6$

---

4. Assess

PowerPoint Lesson Quiz 2-3

Name coefficients, like terms, and constants.

1. $4f - 2f + 3$ 4, −2; 4f, −2f; 3

2. $z + 2y - 14$ 1, 2; none; −14

Simplify each expression.

3. $3(a + c - 1) - 2c$
   $3a + c - 3$

4. $4(4v) - 4(v - 9)$ $12v + 36$

✓ Chapter Checkpoint 1

To check understanding of Lessons 2-1 to 2-3:

Checkpoint Quiz 1 (p. 79)

📁 **Teaching Resources**
Checkpoint Quiz 1 (also in Prentice Hall Assessment System)

👥 **Reaching All Students**
Reading and Math Literacy 2B

Spanish versions available.

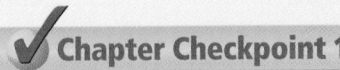

Reteaching 2-3 *Simplifying Variable Expressions*

Simplify $5n + (-n - 4)(-2)$.
$5n + (-n - 4)(-2)$
$= 5n + (-n)(-2) - 4(-2)$ Use the Distributive Property.
$= 5n + 2n + 8$ Multiply. Think of $-4(-2)$ as $+(-4)(-2)$.
$= (5 + 2)n + 8$ Use the Distributive Property to combine like terms.
$= 7n + 8$ Add.

Complete each equation.

1. $9a - 7a + 5$
$= (9 - 7)\underline{\quad a \quad} + 5$
$= \underline{\quad 2 \quad} a + 5$

2. $5k - 4 - 8k$
$= 5k - 8\underline{\quad k \quad} - 4$
$= (5 - 8)\underline{\quad k \quad} - 4$
$= \underline{\quad -3k \quad} - 4$

Simplify each expression.

3. $12a + 4 - 10a$ $2a + 4$
4. $7 + x - 7x$ $7 - 6x$
5. $2(n - 4) + 3$ $2n - 5$
6. $-3(a + 5) + 9$ $-3a - 6$
7. $5(2y + 1) - 7y$ $3y + 5$
8. $2(4 - 3t) - (-3) + 2t$ $11 - 4t$
9. $8c + 5(c - 3)$ $13c - 15$
10. $-2(-4 - 3s)$ $6s + 8$
11. $q(-3) + 3(2 + q)$ 6
12. $(3 + k)(-4) - 5k$ $-9k - 12$
13. $(-3)(1 - 2n) + 2(n + 4)$ $8n + 5$
14. $9p - 3(5p + 2) + 6$ $-6p$

Alternative Assessment

Give students the following list:
Coefficients: $-4, 6, 1$ Variable: w Constants: $2, -3$
Have them construct a variable expression using only items from the list. Then have students simplify the expression.

Test Prep

📁 **Resources**
For additional practice with a variety of test item formats:
• Test Prep, p. 121
• Test-Taking Strategies, p. 116
• Test-Taking Strategies With Transparencies

Variables and Equations

1. Plan

Lesson Preview

✓ **Check Skills You'll Need**

Variables and Expressions
Lesson 1-1: Example 2;
Exercises 7–22.
Extra Practice, p. 744.

Lesson Resources

📁 **Teaching Resources**
Practice, Reteaching, Enrichment

 Reaching All Students
Practice Workbook 2-4
Spanish Practice Workbook 2-4
Guided Problem Solving 2-4

⏱ **Presentation Assistant Plus!**
Transparencies and PowerPoint™
• Check Skills You'll Need 2-4
• Additional Examples 2-4
• Student Edition Answers 2-4
• Lesson Quiz 2-4
PH Presentation Pro CD-ROM 2-4

♲ **ASSESSMENT SYSTEM**

Computer Test Generator CD-ROM

💻 **Technology**
Resource Pro® CD-ROM
Computer Test Generator CD-ROM
PH Presentation Pro CD-ROM

💻 **www.PHSchool.com**

Student Site
• Teacher Web Code: adk-5500
• Algebra Readiness Puzzles 35, 36
• Self-grading Lesson Quiz
PH SuccessNet Teacher Center
• Lesson Planner
• Resources

Plus **TEXT**

What You'll Learn

 OBJECTIVE 1 To classify types of equations

 OBJECTIVE 2 To check equations using substitution

. . . And Why

To check solutions of real-world equations involving weights

✓ **Check Skills You'll Need**

Write a variable expression for each phrase.

1. the sum of x and 46
   $x + 46$
2. four less than g
   $g - 4$
3. t decreased by five
   $t - 5$
4. the quotient of z and 26 $\frac{z}{26}$

 For help, go to Lesson 1-1.

New Vocabulary

• equation
• open sentence
• solution of an equation

Writing in Math

The verb *is* between two quantities suggests writing the equal sign.

**TEXT** Interactive lesson includes instant self-check, tutorials, and activities.

OBJECTIVE

1 Classifying Types of Equations

An **equation** is a mathematical sentence with an equal sign. Here are three of the ways you will see equations in this book.

$9 + 2 = 11$	a numerical expression equal to a numerical expression
$x + 7 = 37$	a variable expression equal to a numerical expression
$a + (-3) = 2a + 5$	a variable expression equal to a variable expression

An equation with a numerical expression equal to another numerical expression is either *true* or *false*. An equation with one or more variables is an **open sentence**.

1 EXAMPLE **Classifying Equations**

State whether each equation is *true*, *false*, or an *open sentence*.

a. $6 + 12 = 18$ true, because $18 = 18$

b. $6 = 4 + 3$ false, because $6 \neq 7$

• c. $6y = -3 + 5y$ an open sentence, because there is a variable

✓ **Check Understanding** **Example 1**

1. State whether each equation is *true*, *false*, or an *open sentence*. Explain.

   a. $9 - 7 = 3$ b. $8 + x = 2$ c. $4 \cdot 5 = 20$
   false; $2 \neq 3$ open; has a variable   true; $20 = 20$

You can write a mathematical word sentence as an equation.

2 EXAMPLE **Writing an Equation**

Write an equation for
Nine times the opposite of five is forty-five.
State whether the equation is *true*, *false*, or an *open sentence*.

Words	nine	times	the opposite of five	is	forty-five
	9	times	-5	is	45
Equation	9	$\cdot$	(-5)	$=$	45

• The equation is false. $9 \cdot (-5) = -45$, and $-45 \neq 45$.

INSTANT CHECK SYSTEM **Ongoing Assessment and Intervention**

Before the Lesson
Diagnose prerequisite skills using:
• Check Skills You'll Need

During the Lesson
Monitor progress using:
• Check Understanding
• Additional Examples
• Test Prep

After the Lesson
Assess knowledge using:
• Lesson Quiz
• Computer Test Generator CD-ROM

2. Write an equation for *Twenty minus x is three.*
Is the equation true, false, or an open sentence? Explain.
$20 - x = 3$; open because there is a variable

2 ▸ **Checking Equations Using Substitution**

A | solution of an equation | is a value for a variable that makes an
equation true. You substitute a number for a variable to determine
whether the number is a solution of the equation.

> **Reading Math**
>
> ≠ shows that two
> values are not equal.
> ≟ asks whether two
> values are equal.

3 EXAMPLE   **Substituting to Check**

Is 30 a solution of the equation $170 + x = 200$?

$$170 + x = 200$$
$$170 + 30 \stackrel{?}{=} 200 \quad \textbf{Substitute 30 for } x.$$
$$200 = 200$$

● Yes, 30 is a solution of the equation.

✔ **Check Understanding**   Example 3

3. Is the given number a solution of the equation?

a. $8 + t = 2t; 1$ no   **b.** $9 - m = 3; 6$ yes

4 EXAMPLE   **Real-World 🌐 Problem Solving**

Scuba Diving A diver's equipment weighs 35 lb. The diver plus
the equipment weighs 165 lb. Can the diver's weight be 200 lb?

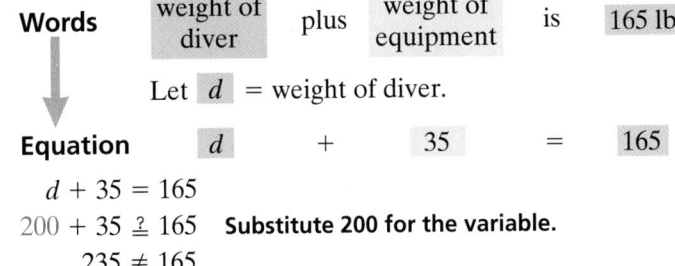

| **Words** | weight of diver | plus | weight of equipment | is | 165 lb |

Let d = weight of diver.

| **Equation** | d | + | 35 | = | 165 |

$$d + 35 = 165$$
$$200 + 35 \stackrel{?}{=} 165 \quad \textbf{Substitute 200 for the variable.}$$
$$235 \neq 165$$

● No, the diver's weight cannot be 200 lb.

✔ **Check Understanding**   Example 4

4. A tent weighs 6 lb. Your backpack and the tent together
weigh 33 lb. Use an equation to find whether the backpack
weighs 27 lb.
$b + 6 = 33; 27 + 6 = 33$; Yes, the backpack weighs 27 lb.

Real-World 🌐 Connection

A scuba tank can hold 63 ft³
of compressed air. It weighs
29 lb when full.

👥 **Reaching All Students**

| **Below Level** Discuss the difference between an expression and an equation. Stress that an equation always contains an equal sign, whereas an expression never does. | **Advanced Learners** Have students find solutions for the following equations:
a. $x = x$ any number
b. $0y = 0$ any number | **Diversity**
See note on page 81.
Error Prevention
See note on page 83. |

---

2. Teach

Math Background

An equation is true, false, or open.
The equation $x + 5 = 8$ is open
because it contains a variable.
Replace x by 3 and the resulting
equation is true. Replace x by any
other value and the resulting
equation is false.

Teaching Notes

4 EXAMPLE Diversity

Some students may not have
realized that a diver's equipment is
so heavy. Have a knowledgeable
student explain how difficult it is
to walk with a scuba tank on
while out of the water. The
difficulty disappears after entering
the water due to buoyancy.

PowerPoint

📺 Additional Examples

1 State whether each equation
is *true*, *false*, or an *open
sentence*. Explain.
   a. $3(b - 8) = 12$ open
   sentence; there is a
   variable
   b. $7 - (-6) = 1$ false; $13 \neq 1$
   c. $-9 + 5 = -4$
   true; $-4 = -4$

2 Write an equation for *Six
times a number added to the
number is the opposite of
forty-two.* State whether the
equation is *true*, *false*, or an
open sentence. Explain.
$6x + x = -42$; open sentence

3 Is 45 a solution of the
equation $120 + x = 75$? no

4 A gift pack must hold 20 lb of
food. Apples weigh 9 lb and
cheese weighs 5 lb. Can the
jar of jam that completes the
package weigh 7 lb? no

Closure

Ask students to explain the
difference between equations that
are true or false and equations
that are open sentences.
Equations that are true or false
contain only numbers. Open
sentences contain a variable.

Assignment Guide

1 Objective 1

ⒶⒷ **Core** 1–11, 23–36

Ⓒ **Extension** 41, 42

2 Objective 2

ⒶⒷ **Core** 12–22, 37–40

Ⓒ **Extension** 43

Test Prep 44–46

Mixed Review 47–53

Practice 2-4 *Variables and Equations*

Is the given number a solution of the equation?

1. $9k = 10 - k; -1$ no
2. $-7r - 15 = -2r; -3$ yes
3. $3g \div (-6) = 5 - g; -10$ no
4. $-3p = 4p + 35; -5$ yes
5. $8 - e = 2e - 16; 8$ yes
6. $5 - 15x = 8 - 16x; 3$ yes
7. $2(x - 2) - 5x = 5(2 - x); 7$ yes
8. $6a + 3 = 3(3a - 2); 4$ no

Is each equation true, false, or an open sentence?

9. $14 = x - 9$ open sentence
10. $8 + 7 = 10$ false
11. $4 - 15 = 22 - 33$ true
12. $5 + x = 90 \div 9 + 4$ open sentence
13. $-7(5 - 9) = 19 - 3(-3)$ true
14. $6(5 - 8) = 2(10 - 1)$ false

Write an equation for each sentence. Is each equation true, false, or an open sentence?

15. One fifth of a number n is equal to -7.
    $\frac{1}{5}n = -7$; open sentence
16. The product of 13 and -7 is -91.
    $13(-7) = -91$; true
17. Fifty-four divided by six equals negative nine.
    $54 \div 6 = -9$; false
18. Seven less than the product of a number z and 3 is equal to 4.
    $3z - 7 = 4$; open sentence

Write an equation. Is the given value a solution?

19. A truck driver drove 468 miles on Tuesday. That was 132 miles farther than she drove on Monday. Let d represent the distance she drove on Monday. Did she drive 600 miles on Monday?
    $d + 132 = 468$; no

Enrichment 2-4 *Keeping Time*

The world's most accurate clocks are those at the U.S. Naval Research Laboratory in Washington, D.C. The clocks, called *masers*, are accurate to 1 second in 1,700,000 years. The masers are keyed to the activity of hydrogen electrons.

To find out how many times a hydrogen electron changes position each second, choose the number that is a solution of each equation. Write the *absolute value* of the solution above the number of the exercise at the bottom of the page.

Example $8 + k = 6$ $k = 3, -2, -4$
Solution $8 + k = 6$; 3 is not a solution
     $8 + (-2) = 6$; -2 is a solution
     $k = -2$
     $|-2| = 2$
You would write 2 in the correct space.

Which of the given values is a solution of the equation?

1. $m + 3 = 2$ -1 $m = -1, 2, -3$
2. $-6k + 8 = 3$ -4 $k = -2, -4, -6$
3. $7 - 3p = 4p - 7$ 2 $p = -1, 2, -3$
4. $-5r + 6 = 6$ 0 $r = -1, 0, 2$
5. $-4x + 2 = -2(x + 3)$ 4 $x = -2, 3, 4$
6. $2n - 13 = -n + 2$ 5 $n = -2, 4, 5$
7. $-12k + 3 = k$ 0 $k = 0, 2, 6$
8. $6t + 24 = 3t + 3$ -7 $t = -7, -2, 5$
9. $5(h - 3) = 35 - 5h$ 5 $h = -3, 2, 5$
10. $-m - 1 = 0$ -1 $m = -1, 0, 2$
11. $8(9 - 2y) = -4y$ 6 $y = -4, 3, 6$
12. $5e + 36 = e$ -9 $e = -12, -9, -4$
13. $17 - 9c = -3(c + 3) + 2$ 4 $c = 2, 3, 4$

Answer: $\frac{1}{1} \frac{4}{2} \frac{2}{3} \frac{0}{4} \frac{4}{5} \frac{5}{6} \frac{0}{7} \frac{7}{8} \frac{5}{9} \frac{1}{10} \frac{6}{11} \frac{9}{12} \frac{4}{13}$
times per second

❓ For more exercises, see *Extra Practice*.

Practice and Problem Solving

Ⓐ **Practice by Example**

Example 1
(page 80)

State whether each equation is *true*, *false*, or an *open sentence*. Explain.

1. $5 + 9 = 14$
   true; $14 = 14$
2. $4x - 8 = 25$
   open; variable
3. $15 = 3 \cdot 5$
   true; $15 = 15$
4. $x - 10 = 22 - x$
   open; variable
5. $6 + 1 = 5 + 3$
   false; $7 \neq 8$
6. $4c - 12 = 20$
   open; variable
7. $20 = 2 \cdot 10$
   true; $20 = 20$
8. $20 + 3x = 42$
   open; variable
9. $3 \cdot 9 = 30$
   false; $27 \neq 30$

Example 2
(page 80)

Write an equation for each sentence. State whether the equation is *true*, *false*, or an *open sentence*. Explain.

11. $25 = v + 15$;
    open; variable

10. Four times the opposite of five equals negative twenty.
    $4(-5) = -20$; true; $-20 = -20$

11. Twenty-five equals a number v plus fifteen.
    See left.

Example 3
(page 81)

Is the given number a solution of the equation?

12. $c + 5 = 3; -2$
    yes
13. $24 = c + 29; -2$
    no
14. $4 + d = 6; 2$
    yes
15. $20 - c = 12; 8$
    yes
16. $8 = a + 3; 10$
    no
17. $3 + 2t = 7; 4$
    no
18. $3 = 12 - a; 6$
    no
19. $2m = m + 6; 4$
    no
20. $5q - 1 = -1; 0$
    yes

Example 4
(page 81)

Write an equation. Is the given value a solution?

🌐 21. **Weight** A veterinarian weighs 140 lb. When she steps on a scale
 while holding a dog, the scale shows 192 lb. Let d represent the weight of the dog. Does the dog weigh 52 lb? $140 + d = 192$; yes

🌐 22. **Income** A family's expenses are $1,200. One parent makes $850. Must the other earn $400 for both incomes to equal expenses?
    $850 + x = 1,200$; no

Ⓑ **Apply Your Skills**

Determine whether each statement is true or false. Explain.

25. True; by definition, an open sentence is one that contains a variable.

23. An equation can be false.
    True; for example $3 + 2 = 7$.
24. $3w - 7$ is an open sentence.
    False; $3w - 7$ is not an equation.
25. An open sentence must contain a variable.
    See left.
26. Some open sentences are true for all variable values.
    True; for example, $x = x$.

State whether each equation is *true*, *false*, or an *open sentence*. Explain.

27. $18 = -3(-6)$
    true; $18 = 18$
28. $-24(-2) = 18(4 + 2)$
    false; $48 \neq 108$
29. $-9 + x = 50 \div 10 + 3$
    open; variable
30. $-2(3 - 8) = 2[-3 - (-8)]$
    true; $10 = 10$
31. $6[-3 - (-5)] = 2(-4 + 10)$
    true; $12 = 12$
32. $4[2 + (-6)] = 2[x - (-12)]$
    open sentence; contains a variable

Write an equation for each sentence. State whether each equation is *true*, *false*, or an *open sentence*. Explain.

33. $(-20)(9) = -11$; false;
    $-180 \neq -11$
34. $15 + n = 50$; open;
    contains a variable

33. The product of negative twenty and nine is negative eleven.
    See left.
34. The sum of fifteen and a number n is fifty.   See left.
35. Forty-eight divided by twelve equals three. $48 \div 12 = 3$; false; $4 \neq 3$

GPS Use the Guided Problem Solving worksheet with Exercise 21.

36. Writing in Math Equations can be true or false. Can an expression be true or false? Explain.
No; an expression is not a sentence.

Is the given number a solution of the equation? Explain.

37. $\frac{c}{2} - 8 = 3(-3); -2$ **38.** $14 = 28 \div x; 14$ no; $14 \neq 2$
yes; $-9 = -9$

39. $-x - 5 = 6; 1$ **40.** $3b \div 18 = 2; 12$
no; $-6 \neq 6$ yes; $2 = 2$

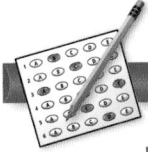 **C** Challenge 🌐 **Language Arts** Some word sentences are similar to equations. **Exercises 41–43 are about word sentences.**
41–43. Answers may vary. See left.

41. **Sample:** London is the capital of England. Water is made of hydrogen and oxygen.

42. **Sample:** Hawaii is in the Atlantic Ocean. Potatoes are a fruit.

43. **Sample:** she has new shoes. It has six legs.

41. The sentence *Abraham Lincoln was an American president* is true. Write two other true sentences.

42. The sentence *Eleanor Roosevelt was an American president* is false. Write two other false sentences.

43. The sentence *He is a professional baseball player* is open. It is not clear to whom the word *he* refers. Write two other open sentences.

Test Prep

Multiple Choice   **44.** Which equation is false? **A**
  A. $3 + (-7) = 10$ **B.** $6 \div 2 = 3$
  C. $8 \cdot 2 - 15 = 1$ **D.** $7w = 3w + 12$

45. Together Mike and Amy weigh 350 pounds. Amy weighs 150 pounds and Mike weighs *m* pounds. Which equation represents this situation? **I**
  F. $m + 350 = 150$ **G.** $m = 350 + 200$
  H. $m - 200 = 150$ **I.** $m = 350 - 150$

Take It to the NET
Online lesson quiz at
www.PHSchool.com
Web Code: ada-0204

46. A recipe calls for 4 c of flour. You have 20 c of flour. Let *r* represent the flour you have left after making the recipe. Which equation represents this situation? **B**
  A. $r - 20 = 4$ **B.** $20 - 4 = r$ **C.** $r - 4 = 16$ **D.** $r - 4 = 20$

Mixed Review

Lesson 2-3   **Simplify each expression.**

47. $6m + 7 - 2m$ **48.** $-8t + 4t - 19$ **49.** $3w + 5k - 4w + k$
$4m + 7$ $-4t - 19$ $6k - w$

Lesson 1-8 🌐 **50. Marathon Training** Larissa ran 15 mi per week before she decided to train for a marathon. The first week of training she ran 17 mi. The second week she ran 19 mi. If she continued her pattern, how far did she run the fifth week? **25 mi**

Lesson 1-3   **Evaluate each expression for *a* = 3 and *b* = 2.**

51. $a - b + 15$ **16**   **52.** $(3b - 2a) \div 4$ **0**   **53.** $3(b + 2) - 4$ **8**

 **Lesson Quiz 2-4**

1. Is $b + 3b - 1 = 15$ true, false, or an open sentence?
open sentence

2. Write an equation for *A number added to seven times the number is the opposite of thirty-two.* Is the equation true, false, or an open sentence?
$7x + x = -32$; **open sentence**

3. Is 25 a solution of the equation $175 - x = 150$?
yes

4. Can you stack eight books that are each 3 in. thick inside a box that is 18 in. tall? **no**

Error Prevention!

Exercises 33–35 Suggest that students copy the sentence and then write the parts of the equation under the corresponding word phrases.

Test Prep

📁 **Resources**
For additional practice with a variety of test item formats:
• Test Prep, p. 121
• Test-Taking Strategies, p. 116
• Test-Taking Strategies With Transparencies

 Reteaching 2-4 *Variables and Equations*

You earned $84 at $6 an hour. Let *h* be the number of hours you worked. Can *h* be 12? Can *h* be 14?
Write an equation.

| Words | Rate of pay · Hours worked = Total pay |
| Let *h* = hours worked. |

Equation   6 · *h* = 84
    $6h = 84$
  $6(12) \stackrel{?}{=} 84$ Substitute 12 for *h*.
    $72 \neq 84$
No, you did not work 12 hours.
  $6(14) \stackrel{?}{=} 84$ Substitute 14 for *h*.
    $84 = 84$
Yes, you worked 14 hours.

Write an equation. Is the given value a solution?

1. You rode 180 miles at 60 miles per hour. Let *t* be the time it took. Can *t* be 4 hours?
  $60t = 180$; No, it did not take 4 hours.

2. Ernie scored 8 more points than Mike scored. Ernie scored 20 points. Let *p* be the number of points Mike scored. Can *p* be 12?
  $20 = p + 8$; Yes, Mike scored 12 points.

3. Each person in your class contributed a quart of punch for the school dance. You divided them into gallon containers and got 5 gallons. Let *q* be the number of quarts you started with. Could *q* be 20? (*Hint:* There are 4 quarts in a gallon.)
  $\frac{q}{4} = 5$; Yes, you started with 20 qts.

4. You typed a 600 word essay in 12 minutes. Let *w* be the number of words you can type in one minute. Can *w* be 60?
  $12w = 600$; No, you cannot type 60 words in one minute.

Alternative Assessment

Have students write number riddles that describe open sentences. For example: *I am a number that adds to seven to equal ten. What am I?* $x + 7 = 10$; $x = 3$. Have students exchange riddles, write the open sentence that each riddle describes, and solve the riddles.

Using Models With Equations

Modeling equations with algebra tiles provides a way to concretely represent the abstract ideas involved in solving equations.

Materials

Algebra tiles

Teaching Notes

Teaching Tip
It is important to realize that the green rectangle, although one unit wide, is of undetermined length in order to represent the variable.

Teaching Tip
Point out that you model the opposite of a unit (or variable) by turning the tile over.

Teaching Tip
Remind students that one or more zero pairs can always be removed from either side of the equation without changing any values.

1.

2.

3.

4.

5.

6.

Investigation **Using Models With Equations**

You can model an equation using algebra tiles. Use a green rectangular tile to represent the variable. Here are two examples.

Equation 1

$$x + 3 = 4$$

Equation 2

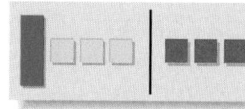

$$x + 3 = -3$$

Model each equation. 1–6. See margin.

1. $x + 3 = 5$
2. $z + 2 = -6$
3. $y + 1 = 4$
4. $-3 = a - 4$
5. $2b + 2 = 8$
6. $3 + 3x = -6$

To solve an equation, get the variable alone on one side of the equal sign. To do this, remove the same number of tiles from each side.

Here's how to solve $x + 3 = 7$.

Model the equation. **Solve by removing 3 tiles from each side.**

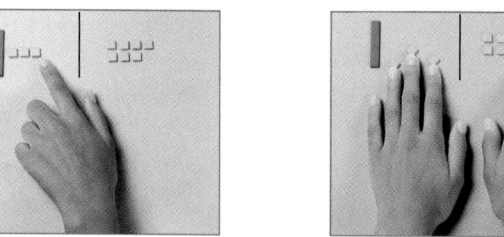 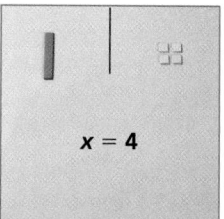

$x = 4$

Check $x + 3 = 7$

$4 + 3 \stackrel{?}{=} 7$ **Replace x with 4.**

$7 = 7$ ✔

Model and solve each equation. Check your result.

7. $x + 3 = 6$ $x = 3$
8. $m + 2 = 8$ $m = 6$
9. $1 = 1 + d$ $d = 0$
10. $-4 + y = -7$ $y = -3$
11. $-1 + p = -5$ $p = -4$
12. $w - 2 = -3$ $w = -1$

Modeling **Write and solve the equation for each model.**

13.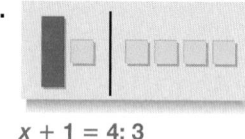

$x + 1 = 4; 3$

14.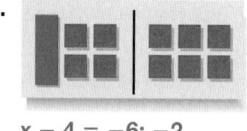

$x - 4 = -6; -2$

15.

$3 = x + 1; 2$

Sometimes you cannot remove the same number of tiles from each side. You may need to add tiles to create zero pairs. Here's how to solve $x + 2 = -4$.

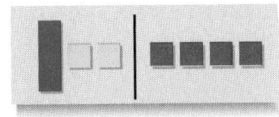 Model the equation.

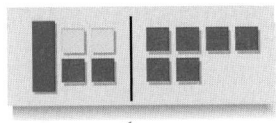 Add -2 to each side.

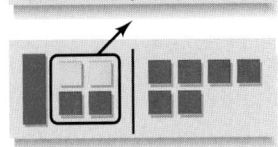 Remove zero pairs.

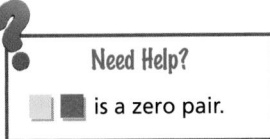

Need Help?

▢ ■ is a zero pair.

 $x = -6$

Check $x + 2 = -4$

$-6 + 2 \stackrel{?}{=} -4$ **Replace x with -6.**

$-4 = -4$ ✔

Model and solve each equation. Check your result.

16. $y + 2 = -2$ $y = -4$ **17.** $x + 5 = 2$ $x = -3$ **18.** $n + 7 = 1$ $n = -6$

19. $-1 = k + 3$ $k = -4$ **20.** $x - 4 = 5$ $x = 9$ **21.** $2 = z - 3$ $z = 5$

Modeling   **Write and solve the equation for each model.**

22.
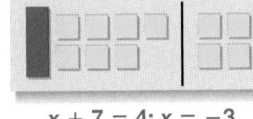
$x + 7 = 4; x = -3$

23.
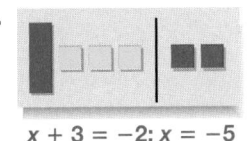
$x + 3 = -2; x = -5$

24.
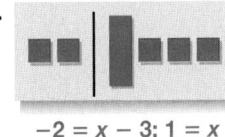
$-2 = x - 3; 1 = x$

25. Open-Ended Write two different equations that have the solution modeled at the right.
Answers may vary. Samples: $x + 1 = 4$; $x - 1 = 2$

26. Number Sense Give an example of an equation model that has the same color unit squares on each side but still requires zero pairs to solve. Explain why zero pairs are needed. **Answers may vary. Sample: The model for $x + 3 = 1$ has positive unit squares on each side. Zero pairs are needed in order to remove 2 of the 3 positive unit tiles on the left side.**

2-5

Lesson Preview

 Check Skills You'll Need

Properties of Numbers
Lesson 2-1: Example 3;
Exercises 10–15.
Extra Practice, p. 745.

Lesson Resources

 Teaching Resources
Practice, Reteaching, Enrichment

 Reaching All Students
Practice Workbook 2-5
Spanish Practice Workbook 2-5
Guided Problem Solving 2-5
Technology Activities 4
Hands-On Activities 2

 Presentation Assistant Plus!
Transparencies and PowerPoint™
• Check Skills You'll Need 2-5
• Additional Examples 2-5
• Student Edition Answers 2-5
• Lesson Quiz 2-5
• Classroom Aid 13
PH Presentation Pro CD-ROM 2-5

 **ASSESSMENT** *SYSTEM*

Computer Test Generator CD-ROM

 Technology
Resource Pro® CD-ROM
Computer Test Generator CD-ROM
PH Presentation Pro CD-ROM

 **www.PHSchool.com**
Student Site
• Teacher Web Code: adk-5500
• Algebra Readiness Puzzles 37, 38
• Graphing Calculator, Procedure 7
• Self-grading Lesson Quiz
PH SuccessNet Teacher Center
• Lesson Planner
• Resources

Plus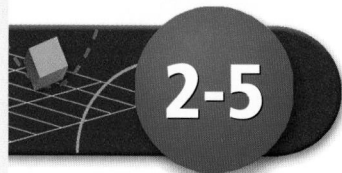

2-5 Solving Equations by Adding or Subtracting

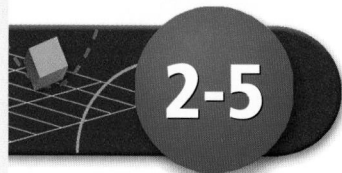
2-5

What You'll Learn

 OBJECTIVE 1 To solve one-step equations using subtraction

OBJECTIVE 2 To solve one-step equations using addition

. . . And Why

To solve real-world problems involving health

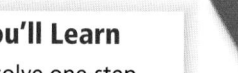 **Check Skills You'll Need**

Simplify each expression.

1. $3 + 4 - 4$ 3

2. $7 + 9 - 7$ 9

3. $8 - 2 + 2$ 8

4. $6 + 2 - 2$ 6

 For help, go to Lesson 2-1.

New Vocabulary

• inverse operations

 Interactive lesson includes instant self-check, tutorials, and activities.

OBJECTIVE

1 Using Subtraction to Solve Equations

Solving an equation is like keeping a barbell balanced. If you add weight to or subtract weight from one side of the bar, you must do the same on the other side.

Subtract 5 lb from each side.

As you can see in the photos, you keep the barbell balanced when you remove the same weight from each side.

In previous math courses, you used related equations like $3 + 5 = 8$ and $8 - 3 = 5$. These equations show that addition and subtraction undo each other.

When you solve an equation, your goal is to get the variable alone on one side of the equation. The value on the other side tells you the solution of the original equation. You use **inverse operations,** which undo each other, to get the variable alone.

> **Key Concepts**   **Subtraction Property of Equality**
>
> You can subtract the same number from each side of an equation.
>
> | Arithmetic | Algebra |
> |:---:|:---:|
> | $10 = 2(5)$ | If $a = b$, |
> | $10 - 5 = 2(5) - 5$ | then $a - c = b - c$. |

After you solve an equation, use your result in the original equation (as shown in Example 1) to check that your solution is correct.

Ongoing Assessment and Intervention

Before the Lesson
Diagnose prerequisite skills using:
• Check Skills You'll Need

During the Lesson
Monitor progress using:
• Check Understanding
• Additional Examples
• Test Prep

After the Lesson
Assess knowledge using:
• Lesson Quiz
• Computer Test Generator CD-ROM

1 EXAMPLE Subtracting to Solve an Equation

Solve $x + 6 = 4$.

Method 1

$x + 6 = 4$
$x + 6 - 6 = 4 - 6$ **Subtract 6 from each side.**
$x = -2$ **Simplify.**

Method 2

$x + 6 = 4$
$\underline{- 6 -6}$
$x = -2$

Check $x + 6 = 4$
$-2 + 6 \stackrel{?}{=} 4$ **Replace *x* with −2.**
$4 = 4 ✓$

✓ Check Understanding   Example 1

1. Solve each equation.

   a. $x + 8 = 3$ **−5**   **b.** $5 = d + 1$ **4**   **c.** $c + (-4) = -5$ **−1**

You can write and solve equations describing real-world situations. To help check, decide whether your solution is correct using the original problem.

2 EXAMPLE   Real-World Problem Solving

Health Fred's target heart rate is 130 beats/min. This is 58 beats/min more than his resting heart rate. Find his resting heart rate.

Words   target rate   is   58   more than   resting rate

          Let   *r*   = resting heart rate.

Equation   130   =   58   +   *r*

$130 = 58 + r$

$130 = r + 58$ **Use the Commutative Property of Addition.**

$130 - 58 = r + 58 - 58$ **Subtract 58 from each side.**

$72 = r$ **Simplify.**

Fred's resting heart rate is 72 beats per minute.

Check The resting heart rate plus 58 beats per minute should be 130 beats per minute.
$72 + 58 = 130 ✓$

Real-World Connection

Here is one method for estimating your target heart-rate range: Begin by subtracting your age from 220. Then multiply the result by 0.6 and 0.8 to find the lower and upper limits of your heart-rate range.

✓ Check Understanding   Example 2

2. Cora measures her heart rate at 123 beats per minute. This is 55 beats per minute more than her resting heart rate *r*. Write and solve an equation to find Cora's resting heart rate.
   123 = r + 55; 68 beats/min

👥 Reaching All Students

Below Level Have students describe what happens when one person on a seesaw gets off. Lead students to see that a seesaw becomes unbalanced when weight is changed on only one side.

Advanced Learners Challenge students to describe how they would solve 8 − *r* − 4 = 25. Sample: First combine 8 and −4. Then subtract 25 from each side. Then add *r* to each side. The result is *r* = −21.

English Learners See note on page 87. **Error Prevention** See note on page 88.

Math Background

To solve an equation having one variable, you undo operations in order to get the variable alone on one side of the equation. You must always do the same thing to both sides of an equation to keep the two sides equal.

Teaching Notes

English Learners
Some students may not understand the meaning of *balance*. Have a student stand with feet heel to toe, one foot in front of the other as if on a balance beam. Have them extend both arms outward to each side with palms up. Place a heavy book in one hand. Ask what the student should do to stay *balanced*. Place something of equal weight in the other hand.

Teaching Tip
Point out that the solution to an equation can show the variable either on the left side or the right side of the equal sign. Show students that the solutions of these equations are the same.

$2x = 10$ $10 = 2x$
$x = 5$ $5 = x$

2 EXAMPLE Alternative Method
Have students use the Commutative Property of Addition as the first step to rewrite 58 + *r* as *r* + 58. This will help students see that 58 is being added to *r*. Regularly remind students that when you use the Commutative Property of Addition, the signs on the terms that switch places remain unchanged. This practice will help when students need to rearrange the terms in expressions such as 13 − *x*.

PowerPoint
📇 Additional Examples

❶ Solve $y + 5 = 13$. **8**

❷ Larissa wants to increase the number of books in her collection to 327 books. She has 250 books now. Find the number of books she needs to buy. **77 books**

87

Additional Examples

3 Solve $c - 23 = -40$. -17

4 Marcy's CD player cost $115 less than her DVD player. Her CD player cost $78. How much did her DVD player cost? $193

3 EXAMPLE **Error Prevention**

Some students may forget to add 12 to the right side of the equation. Have students work with a balance scale to understand that the same operation must be done to both sides of the equation to retain equivalent (balanced) equations. First have them add 12 units to one side of the balance scale only, and then add 12 units to the other side to see the "balance."

4 EXAMPLE **English Learners**

Some students may confuse *less than* with *is less than* and *greater than* with *is greater than*. Have students write these phrases and then circle the word *is* in the two phrases that contain it. Point out that the phrases containing *is* represent inequalities. The other two phrases mean to take away from or add to an amount.

Closure

Ask: *When solving equations, addition and subtraction are known as what type of operation?* inverse operations *Why?* They undo each other. *What other pair of operations are of this type?* multiplication and division *Why?* They undo each other.

When you solve an equation involving subtraction, *add* the same number to each side of the equation.

Key Concepts **Addition Property of Equality**

You can add the same number to each side of an equation.

Arithmetic	Algebra
$8 = 2(4)$	If $a = b$,
$8 + 3 = 2(4) + 3$	then $a + c = b + c$.

3 EXAMPLE **Adding to Solve an Equation**

Solve $b - 12 = -49$.

$$b - 12 = -49$$
$$b - 12 + 12 = -49 + 12 \quad \text{Add 12 to each side.}$$
$$b = -37 \quad \text{Simplify.}$$

✓ Check Understanding Example 3

3. Solve each equation.

a. $y - 5 = 8$ 13 **b.** $p - 30 = 42$ 72 **c.** $98 = x - 14$ 112

4 EXAMPLE **Real-World 🌐 Problem Solving**

Purchasing **Your friend's VCR cost $328 less than her TV. Her VCR cost $179. How much did her TV cost?**

Words | cost of VCR | was | $328 | less than | cost of TV

Let t = the cost of the TV.

Equation | 179 | = | t | − | 328

$$179 = t - 328$$
$$179 + 328 = t - 328 + 328 \quad \text{Add 328 to each side.}$$
$$507 = t \quad \text{Simplify.}$$

● Your friend's TV cost $507.

✓ Check Understanding Example 4

4. A softcover book costs $17 less than its hardcover edition. The softcover costs $5. Write and solve an equation to find the cost h of the hardcover book. $5 = h - 17$; $22

Writing in Math

When you go from words to an equation, the order of the math symbols may be different from the order of the words:

- ten fewer than n ➔ $n - 10$
- eight less than r ➔ $r - 8$
- n times 5 ➔ $5n$

EXERCISES

For more exercises, see *Extra Practice*.

Practice and Problem Solving

A Practice by Example

Solve each equation.

Example 1
(page 87)

1. $a + 8 = 12$ 4
2. $t + (-3) = 8$ 11
3. $3 = n + 4$ -1
4. $d + (-4) = -7$ -3
5. $c + 9 = 37$ 28
6. $q + (-10) = -25$ -15
7. $b + 24 = 19$ -5
8. $65 = n + 24$ 41
9. $40 = w + (-5)$ 45

Example 2
(page 87)

🌐 **10. Astronomy** The average distance from the sun to Jupiter is 778 million km. This distance is 550 million km greater than the average distance from the sun to Mars. Write and solve an equation to find the average distance d that Mars is from the sun. $778 = d + 550$; 228 million km

> **Reading Math**
> For help with reading and solving Exercise 11, see page 91.

🌐 **11. Physics** The speed of sound through steel is 5,200 meters per second (m/s). This is 2,520 m/s faster than the speed of sound through silver. Write and solve an equation to find the speed s of sound through silver. $5,200 = s + 2,520$; 2,680 m/s

Example 3
(page 88)

Solve each equation.

12. $d - 4 = -7$ -3
13. $c - 34 = 20$ 54
14. $a - 4 = -18$ -14
15. $r - 3 = 8$ 11
16. $z - 100 = 100$ 200
17. $5 = d - 1$ 6
18. $40 = g - 20$ 60
19. $34 = c - 19$ 53
20. $-54 = q - 9$ -45

Example 4
(page 88)

🌐 **21. Astronomy** Venus's average distance from the sun is 108 million km. This distance is 42 million km less than the average distance from the sun to Earth. Write and solve an equation to find Earth's average distance d from the sun. $108 = d - 42$; 150 million km

🌐 **22. Languages** In 1996, 487 million people across the world spoke [GPS] English. This was 512 million people fewer than the number who spoke Mandarin Chinese. Write and solve an equation to find the number of people n who spoke Mandarin Chinese.
$487 = n - 512$; 999 million people

B Apply Your Skills

Copy and complete the steps for solving each equation.

23. $35 + b = -90$
     $35 - \blacksquare + b = -90 - \blacksquare$
     $b = \blacksquare$
     35; 35; -125

24. $y - 86 = -322$
     $y - 86 + \blacksquare = -322 + \blacksquare$
     $y = \blacksquare$
     86; 86; -236

Solve each equation.

25. $54 + x = 98$ 44
26. $e - 43 = -45$ -2
27. $47 = 7 + y$ 40
28. $450 = a - 325$ 775
29. $h + 35 = 15$ -20
30. $298 + n = 294$ -4
31. $x - 366 = -415$ -49
32. $89 + y = 112$ 23
33. $-27 = w - 14$ -13

34. Answers may vary. Sample: Gary bought 15 more model cars so that his collection now has 18 cars. How many cars did he have to start with?

34. Open-Ended Write a word problem that can be solved using the equation $x + 15 = 18$.   See left.

2-5 Solving Equations by Adding or Subtracting   **89**

[GPS] Use the Guided Problem Solving worksheet with Exercise 22.

---

3. Practice

Assignment Guide

1 Objective 1
Ⓐ Ⓑ Core 1–11, 24, 25, 27, 29, 30, 32, 34, 36–38, 40
Ⓒ Extension 41, 44–46

2 Objective 2
Ⓐ Ⓑ Core 12–23, 26, 28, 31, 33, 35, 39
Ⓒ Extension 42, 43

Test Prep 47–52
Mixed Review 53–59

Practice 2-5 *Solving Equations by Adding or Subtracting*

Use mental math to solve each equation.

1. $-52 = -52 + k$ $k = 0$
2. $837 = p + 37$ $p = 800$
3. $x - 155 = 15$ $x = 170$
4. $180 = 80 + n$ $n = 100$
5. $2,000 + y = 9,500$ $y = 7,500$
6. $81 = x - 19$ $x = 100$
7. $111 + f = 100$ $f = -11$
8. $w - 6 = -16$ $w = -10$

Solve each equation.

9. $m - 17 = -8$ $m = 9$
10. $k - 55 = 67$ $k = 122$
11. $-44 + n = 36$ $n = 80$
12. $-36 = p - 91$ $p = 55$
13. $x - 255 = 671$ $x = 926$
14. $19 = c - (-12)$ $c = 7$
15. $x + 14 = 21$ $x = 7$
16. $31 = p + 17$ $p = 14$
17. $-19 = k + 9$ $k = -28$
18. $87 + y = 19$ $y = -68$
19. $36 + n = 75$ $n = 39$
20. $-176 = h + (-219)$ $h = 43$
21. $41 + k = 7$ $k = -34$
22. $1,523 + c = 2,766$ $c = 1,243$
23. $-88 + z = 0$ $z = 88$
24. $-33 + (-7) = 29 + m$ $m = -69$
25. $t + (-2) = -66$ $t = -64$
26. $-390 + x = 11 - 67$ $x = 334$

27. The combined enrollment in the three grades at Jefferson Middle School is 977. There are 356 students in the seventh grade and 365 in the eighth grade. Write and solve an equation to find how many students are in the ninth grade.

Equation $356 + 365 + n = 977$

Solution   256 students

Enrichment 2-5 *Two Equations, One Solution*

The equation $x + y = 16$ has many solutions.
  $x = 9, y = 7 \rightarrow x + y = 16$
  $x = 22, y = -6 \rightarrow x + y = 16$
The equations $x - y = 6$ also has many solutions.
  $x = 13, y = 7 \rightarrow x - y = 6$
  $x = 24, y = 18 \rightarrow x - y = 6$
Only one pair of numbers solves *both* equations: $x = 11, y = 5$
  $x + y \stackrel{?}{=} 16$ $x - y \stackrel{?}{=} 6$
  $11 + 5 = 16$ $11 - 5 = 6$

Answer these questions to find the pair of numbers that solves both of the following equations.

   Equation 1: $x + y = 8$ Equation 2: $x - y = 20$

1. Find x in Equation 1 if $y = -4$ 12
   Find x in Equation 2 if $y = -4$ 16
2. Find x in Equation 1 if $y = -5$ 13
   Find x in Equation 2 if $y = -5$ 15
3. Find x in Equation 1 if $y = -6$ 14
   Find x in Equation 2 if $y = -6$ 14

4. Write the pair of numbers that solves both equations.
   $x =$ 14, $y =$ -6

Complete the table to find the pair of numbers that solves both equations.

5. Equation 1: $x + y = -6$ Equation 2: $x - y = -12$

y	1	2	3	4	5
x (Equation 1)	-7	-8	-9	-10	-11
x (Equation 2)	-11	-10	-9	-8	-7

Solution: $x =$ -9, $y =$ 3

 **Lesson Quiz 2-5**

Solve each equation.

1. $y + 8 = 12$ 4

2. $7 + f - 21 = -20$ −6

3. $67 = g - (-36)$ 31

4. Ricky rides his bike 12 miles every day. He stops after 7 miles to rest. How much farther does he have to ride? 5 mi

Alternative Assessment

Write several variable equations on the board, such as $b + 5 = 7$ and $-8 = y - 3$. Have students model and solve the equations using tiles.

Test Prep

A sheet of blank grids is available in the *Test-Taking Strategies With Transparencies* booklet. Give copies of this sheet to students so they can practice filling in the grids.

📁 **Resources**

For additional practice with a variety of test item formats:
• Test Prep, p. 121
• Test-Taking Strategies, p. 116
• Test-Taking Strategies With Transparencies

 **Reteaching 2-5** *Solving Equations by Adding or Subtracting*

Solve $x - 9 = 2$ and $x + 8 = 3$.
Since the 9 is subtracted from x, do the inverse and add 9 to both sides of the equation.
$x - 9 = 2$
$x - 9 + 9 = 2 + 9$
$x = 11$
In $x + 8 = 3$, 8 is added to x. So, subtract 8 from both sides of the equation.
$x + 8 = 3$
$x + 8 - 8 = 3 - 8$
$x = -5$

Solve each equation.

1. $17 + m = 21$ $m = 4$

2. $y - 34 = 43$ $y = 77$

3. $t + 9 = -9$ $t = -18$

4. $15 = z + 6$ $z = 9$

5. $r + 7 = -16$ $r = -23$

6. $68 = p - 41$ $p = 109$

7. $144 + g = 78$ $g = -66$

8. $311 = y - 281$ $y = 592$

9. $-11 + b = -11$ $b = 0$

10. $s + 31 = 14$ $s = -17$

11. $24 = k - 2$ $k = 26$

12. $8 + f = 30$ $f = 22$

13. $37 = z - 3$ $z = 40$

14. $a + 19 = -82$ $a = -101$

15. $18 + n - 7 = 44$ $n = 33$

16. $15 = 7 + h + 14$ $h = -6$

35. This year, the Tigers won six more games than the Panthers. What other fact would you need to know in order to use the equation $p + 6 = 22$ to find the number of games, p, that the Panthers won?
Answers may vary. Sample: This year the Tigers won 22 games in all.

Mental Math Use mental math to solve each equation.

36. $b + 15 = -5$ −20 **37.** $130 = 30 + s$ 100 **38.** $x + 800 = 500$ −300

39. The student subtracted (rather than added) 6 on the right side.

39. Error Analysis A student solved the equation $x - 6 = -6$. His solution was -12. What error did the student make? **See left.**

40. 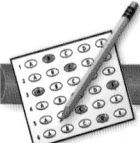 **Writing in Math** To solve $x + 25 = -22$, one student subtracted 25 from each side. Another student added -25 to each side. Will both methods work? Explain.
Yes; subtracting a number gives the same result as adding its opposite.

C Challenge **Solve each equation.**

41. $-45 = x + (-3) + 50$ −92 **42.** $-215 + e + (-43) = -145$ 113

43. $n - 29 - 16 = 246$ 291 **44.** $34 + p + 112 = 78 - 7$ −75

45. $183 + k - 20 = -15$ −178 **46.** $328 = z - 31 + 219$ 140

 **Test Prep**

Gridded Response Solve the equation given by each sentence.

47. Negative six plus y equals eighteen. 24

48. Twelve equals 23 subtracted from n. 35

49. Negative five equals x minus eight. 3

50. The number a plus 5 is 18. 13

51. Negative 8 plus y equals 13. 21

52. Negative seventeen is 32 less than y. 15

💻 **Take It to the NET**
Online lesson quiz at
www.PHSchool.com
Web Code: ada-0205

Mixed Review

Lesson 2-4 **State whether each equation is *true, false,* or an *open sentence.* Explain.**

53. $x + 2 = 4$
open; variable

54. $4 = 6 - 2$
true; $4 = 4$

55. $5 - 3 = 7 - 4$
false; $2 \neq 3$

Lesson 1-8 **56. Patterns** Deric studied 30 min for his first math test. He studied 45 min for the second test, and 60 min for the third test. If he continues this pattern, how long will he study for the fifth test?
90 min

Lesson 1-3 **Evaluate.**

57. $6n$, for $n = 8$ 48 **58.** $\frac{k}{20}$, for $k = 140$ 7 **59.** $50x$, for $x = 8$ 400

Read the exercise below and then follow along with what Tom thinks and writes. Check your understanding by solving the exercise at the bottom of the page.

Physics The speed of sound through steel is 5,200 meters per second (m/s). This is 2,520 m/s faster than the speed of sound through silver. Write and solve an equation to find the speed *s* of sound through silver.

What Tom Thinks

I'll read the problem and write down the important information.

Where to start? Well, it's always helpful to look for a relationship in the problem.

The speed is greater through steel. I will either have to subtract from the speed through steel to get the speed through silver, or add to the speed through silver to get the speed through steel. I'll add.

Since I know the speed through steel, I have to name only one variable.

Now I can write the equation.

I can solve the equation by using the Subtraction Property of Equality.

I have to state what was asked for in the problem.

What Tom Writes

Speed of sound through steel = 5,200 m/s. The speed through steel is 2,520 m/s faster than the speed through silver.

The speed through steel is 2,520 m/s faster than the speed through silver.

Steel speed = silver speed + 2,520

Let s = speed of sound through silver.

$$5,200 = s + 2,520$$

$$5,200 - 2,520 = s + 2,520 - 2,520$$
$$2,680 = s$$

The speed of sound through silver is 2,680 m/s.

EXERCISE

1. Pamela can run the 300-m hurdles in 52.3 s. Elaine takes 2.8 s more than Pamela to make the same run. How long does it take Elaine to run the 300-m hurdles? **55.1 s**

■ **Reading Math**

Reading for Problem Solving

Students must be able to extract important information from word sentences in order to translate the words into math. This feature helps students analyze written material and extract relevant information.

Teaching Notes

English Learners
Be sure students know what *speed of sound* is. You may want to have a student look up the definition in a reference book and read it to the class.

91

Solving Equations by Multiplying or Dividing

Lesson Preview

 Check Skills You'll Need

Dividing Integers
Lesson 1-9: Example 4;
Exercises 20–28.
Extra Practice, p. 744.

Lesson Resources

 Teaching Resources
Practice, Reteaching, Enrichment

 Reaching All Students
Practice Workbook 2-6
Spanish Practice Workbook 2-6
Guided Problem Solving 2-6
Technology Activities 4
Hands-On Activities 2

 Presentation Assistant Plus!
Transparencies and PowerPoint™
• Check Skills You'll Need 2-6
• Additional Examples 2-6
• Student Edition Answers 2-6
• Lesson Quiz 2-6
• Classroom Aid 13
PH Presentation Pro CD-ROM 2-6

ASSESSMENT SYSTEM

Computer Test Generator CD-ROM

 Technology
Resource Pro® CD-ROM
Computer Test Generator CD-ROM
PH Presentation Pro CD-ROM

 www.PHSchool.com
Student Site
• Teacher Web Code: adk-5500
• Updated Data
• Algebra Readiness Puzzles 39, 40
• Self-grading Lesson Quiz
PH SuccessNet Teacher Center
• Lesson Planner
• Resources

Plus

What You'll Learn

 OBJECTIVE 1 To solve one-step equations using division

 OBJECTIVE 2 To solve one-step equations using multiplication

. . . And Why

To solve real-world problems involving population growth

 Check Skills You'll Need

Simplify each quotient.

1. $\frac{18}{18}$ 1   **2.** $\frac{-7}{7}$ −1

3. $\frac{21}{-21}$ −1   **4.** $\frac{-13}{-13}$ 1

For help, go to Lesson 1-9.

OBJECTIVE

1 **Using Division to Solve Equations**

Division and multiplication are inverse operations. You can solve an equation that involves multiplication by using the Division Property of Equality.

 Key Concepts **Division Property of Equality**

If you divide each side of an equation by the same nonzero number, the two sides remain equal.

Arithmetic	Algebra
$6 = 3(2)$	If $a = b$ and $c \neq 0$,
$\frac{6}{3} = \frac{3(2)}{3}$	then $\frac{a}{c} = \frac{b}{c}$.

1 **EXAMPLE** **Real-World** **Problem Solving**

Statistics **The United States population in 1998 was twice the population in 1943. Find the 1943 population in millions.**

Words   1998 population   was   twice   1943 population

Let p = population in 1943.

Equation   270   =   2 · p

$$270 = 2p$$

$$\frac{270}{2} = \frac{2p}{2} \quad \textbf{Divide each side by 2.}$$

$$135 = p \quad \textbf{Simplify.}$$

The United States population in 1943 was 135 million people.

Check Is the answer reasonable? Twice the 1943 population should be the 1998 population. Since $135 \cdot 2 = 270$, the answer is reasonable.

U.S. Population Growth

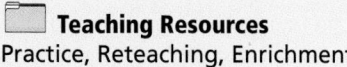 **iTEXT** Interactive lesson includes instant self-check, tutorials, and activities.

 Check Understanding **Example 1**

1. Solve each equation.

a. $4x = 84$ 21   **b.** $91 = 7y$ 13   **c.** $12w = 108$ 9

INSTANT CHECK SYSTEM **Ongoing Assessment and Intervention**

Before the Lesson	**During the Lesson**	**After the Lesson**
Diagnose prerequisite skills using:	Monitor progress using:	Assess knowledge using:
• Check Skills You'll Need	• Check Understanding	• Lesson Quiz
	• Additional Examples	• Computer Test Generator
	• Test Prep	CD-ROM

2 EXAMPLE Dividing to Solve an Equation

Solve $5r = -20$.

$$5r = -20$$

$$\frac{5r}{5} = \frac{-20}{5} \quad \text{Divide each side by 5.}$$

$$r = -4 \quad \text{Simplify.}$$

Check $\qquad 5r = -20$

$$5 \cdot (-4) \stackrel{?}{=} -20 \qquad \text{Replace } r \text{ with } -4.$$

$$-20 = -20 \checkmark$$

✓ Check Understanding   Example 2

2. Solve each equation.

   a. $-3b = 24$ −8   **b.** $96 = -8n$ −12   **c.** $-4d = -56$ 14

OBJECTIVE

2 Using Multiplication to Solve Equations

When you multiply each side of an equation by the same number, the two sides remain equal.

Key Concepts   Multiplication Property of Equality

You can multiply each side of an equation by the same number.

Arithmetic	Algebra
$12 = 3(4)$	If $a = b$,
$12 \cdot 2 = 3(4) \cdot 2$	then $ac = bc$.

---

3 EXAMPLE Multiplying to Solve an Equation

Solve $\frac{x}{-9} = -3$.

$$\frac{x}{-9} = -3$$

$$-9\left(\frac{x}{-9}\right) = -9(-3) \qquad \text{Multiply each side by } -9.$$

$$x = 27 \qquad \text{Simplify.}$$

Reading Math

Read the equation $\frac{x}{-9} = -3$ as "x divided by negative nine equals negative three."

✓ Check Understanding   Example 3

3. Solve each equation.

   a. $\frac{r}{-5} = 10$ −50   **b.** $\frac{s}{6} = 54$ 324   **c.** $-30 = \frac{t}{20}$ −600

👫 Reaching All Students

Below Level Ask students if they have ever shared a cost, perhaps of a meal or a video, among a group of friends. Show students how they can represent the sharing of the cost with an equation.	**Advanced Learners** Multiplication equations have the form $ax = b$. If b is 134, what whole numbers are possible for a and x? 1 and 134, 2 and 67, 134 and 1	**English Learners** See note on page 93. **Auditory Learners** See note on page 93.

---

2. Teach

Math Background

The Division Property of Equality suggests that you can divide each side of an equation by the same *nonzero* number. Divisors are restricted to *nonzero* values because division by *zero* is not defined.

Teaching Notes

1 EXAMPLE English Learners

Point out that *twice* means "two times." When you do something twice, you do it two times.

2 EXAMPLE Error Prevention

Some students may divide by a positive number when they should divide by a negative number, as in the Check Understanding Exercises. Remind students that if you divide a negative number by a positive number, the result is a negative number.

3 EXAMPLE Auditory Learners

Some students try incorrectly to divide to solve problems such as these, especially when the denominator is a factor of the number on the other side of the equation. Suggest to students that when they see a fraction, they think of both words <u>denominator</u> and <u>divide</u>, putting emphasis on the *d*. Suggest they use this to remind them to undo the division.

PowerPoint

Additional Examples

1 288 pens are boxed by the dozen. How many boxes are needed? 24 boxes

2 Solve $-2v = -24$. 12

3 Solve $\frac{x}{8} = -5$. −40

Closure

Ask students how to solve equations involving multiplication and division. Find the number multiplying or dividing the variable. Perform its inverse operation on each side of the equation.

93

3. Practice

Assignment Guide

▼1 Objective 1
- Ⓐ Ⓑ Core 1–20, 29, 30, 34, 35, 37, 40, 41, 43–48
- Ⓒ Extension 52, 56

▼2 Objective 2
- Ⓐ Ⓑ Core 21–28, 31–33, 36, 38, 39, 42, 49, 50
- Ⓒ Extension 51, 53–55

Test Prep 57–60
Mixed Review 61–67

Practice 2-6 *Solving Equations by Multiplying or Dividing*

Solve each equation.

1. $\frac{k}{-5} = -5$ _____ $k = 25$ _____   2. $-3 = \frac{n}{7}$ _____ $n = -21$
3. $\frac{x}{12} = 0$ _____ $x = 0$ _____   4. $-6 = \frac{m}{-2}$ _____ $m = 12$
5. $\frac{y}{-4} = -12$ _____ $y = 48$ _____   6. $\frac{s}{30} = 6$ _____ $s = 180$
7. $\frac{1}{6}z = 0$ _____ $z = 0$ _____   8. $-\frac{m}{55} = 1$ _____ $m = -55$
9. $-3x = 18$ _____ $x = -6$ _____   10. $-56 = 8y$ _____ $y = -7$
11. $8p = -8$ _____ $p = -1$ _____   12. $-4s = -32$ _____ $s = 8$
13. $14h = 42$ _____ $h = 3$ _____   14. $-175 = 25g$ _____ $g = -7$
15. $-42 = 6m$ _____ $m = -7$ _____   16. $-2x = 34$ _____ $x = -17$
17. $\frac{x}{9} = -11$ _____ $x = 99$ _____   18. $216 = 9w$ _____ $w = 24$
19. $-17v = -17$ _____ $v = 1$ _____   20. $-161 = 23t$ _____ $t = -7$
21. $56h = 3,136$ _____ $h = 56$ _____   22. $20 = \frac{e}{-25}$ _____ $e = -500$
23. $4,200 = 30x$ _____ $x = 140$ _____   24. $\frac{y}{-21} = -21$ _____ $y = 441$
25. $\frac{m}{3} = 21$ _____ $m = -63$ _____   26. $4,000 = \frac{x}{-40}$ _____ $x = -160,000$

27. A bamboo tree grew 3 in. per day. Write and solve an equation to find how many days d it took the tree to grow 144 in.
Equation: $3d = 144$ Solution: 48 days

28. Carl drove 561 miles. His car averages 33 miles per gallon of gas. Write and solve an equation to find how much gas g Carl's car used.
Equation: $33g = 561$ Solution: 17 gallons

For what values of y is each equation true?

29. $-5|y| = -25$ _____ $-5, 5$ 30. $\frac{|y|}{2} = 28$ _____ $-56, 56$ 31. $9|y| = 27$ _____ $-3, 3$

Enrichment 2-6 *Analyzing Puzzles*

You can use variable expressions and the distributive property to analyze mathematical puzzles and determine why they work.

Carry out the following directions for three different integers.

1. Choose any integer.	2	−4	17
2. Add 7.	9	3	24
3. Multiply by 3.	27	9	72
4. Subtract the original number.	25	13	55
5. Subtract 11.	14	2	44
6. Divide by 2.	7	1	22
7. Subtract the original number.	5	5	5

8. What unusual result did you obtain? The final result is always 5.

To discover why you obtain this result, choose n as your original number. Since n is a variable, it represents every number that can possibly be chosen.

Write variable expressions for each direction in the puzzle.

9. Add 7 to n. $n + 7$
10. Multiply this quantity by 3 using the distributive property. $3n + 21$
11. Subtract n, the original number. $2n + 21$
12. Subtract 11. $2n + 10$
13. Divide by 2. (Note that you must divide both terms by 2.) $n + 5$
14. Subtract n, the original number. 5

You will obtain this result for every possible value of n.

Write your own mathematical puzzle, trade with a partner, and solve.

15. Check students' work.

EXERCISES

♦ For more exercises, see *Extra Practice*.

Practice and Problem Solving

Ⓐ Practice by Example

Examples 1 and 2
(pages 92 and 93)

Solve each equation.

1. $6x = 96$ **16**   2. $108 = 9x$ **12**   3. $8y = 112$ **14**
4. $45 = 9a$ **5**   5. $5w = 95$ **19**   6. $15c = 90$ **6**
7. $125 = 25d$ **5**   8. $180 = 45s$ **4**   9. $20b = 2,000$ **100**
10. $8x = -48$ **−6**   11. $4a = 28$ **7**   12. $-60 = 12m$ **−5**
13. $-2b = 30$ **−15**   14. $-10d = 100$ **−10**   15. $162 = -18t$ **−9**
16. $-75 = -15x$ **5**   17. $-5x = -115$ **23**   18. $-60y = -360$ **6**

🌐 19. **Earnings** Carol earns \$8/h. How many hours must she work to earn \$288? **36 h**

🌐 20. **Savings** Raul saves \$15 each month. At this rate, how many months will he take to save \$135? **9 months**

Example 3
(page 93)

Solve each equation.

21. $6 = \frac{a}{7}$ **42**   22. $\frac{w}{12} = 2$ **24**   23. $\frac{n}{15} = 7$ **105**   24. $\frac{b}{-6} = 20$ **−120**
25. $-2 = \frac{d}{8}$ **−16**   26. $\frac{v}{3} = -4$ **−12**   27. $-\frac{m}{20} = -2$ **40**   28. $\frac{r}{-5} = -4$ **20**

Ⓑ Apply Your Skills

Solve each equation.

29. $39 = c \cdot 3$ **13**   30. $25x = -125$ **−5**   31. $\frac{v}{3} = 14$ **42**   32. $\frac{m}{-4} = 13$ **−52**
33. $-50 = \frac{n}{-6}$ **300**   34. $72 = 8n$ **9**   35. $22p = 110$ **5**   36. $\frac{r}{-9} = -18$ **162**

37. **Dividing by 0 would result in 4 = 5, which is not a true statement.**

37. **Reasoning** You can divide each side of an equation by the same nonzero value. Explain what would result from the equation $4 \cdot 0 = 5 \cdot 0$ if you could divide each side by zero, and if $\frac{0}{0} = 1$. See left.

Mental Math Is −3 a solution of each equation? Explain.

38. $\frac{b}{-3} = 1$
yes; $\frac{-3}{-3} = 1$

39. $\frac{-18}{k} = -6$
no; $\frac{-18}{-3} \ne -6$

40. $3t = 9$
no; $3(-3) \ne 9$

Write an equation for each sentence. Solve the equation.

41. The product of negative twenty and y is one hundred.
$-20y = 100$; -5

42. The value n divided by ten is one hundred. $\frac{n}{10} = 100$; **1,000**

43. Seven multiplied by k is negative one hundred and sixty-eight.
$7k = -168$; -24

🌐 44. **Buildings** One of the world's tallest office buildings is in Malaysia. The building has 88 stories. The height of the 88 stories is 1,232 ft. What is the height of one story? **14 ft**

 GPS
Use the Guided Problem Solving worksheet with Exercise 44.

---

94   **Chapter 2** Solving One-Step Equations and Inequalities

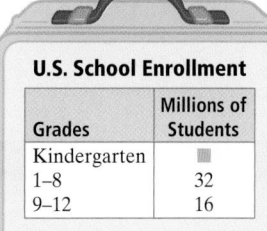

U.S. School Enrollment

Grades	Millions of Students
Kindergarten	■
1–8	32
9–12	16

SOURCE: U.S. Census Bureau.
Go to **www.PHSchool.com** for a
data update. Web Code: adg-2041

45. Use the table at the left. The number of students in grades 1–8 is four times the number of students in kindergarten. Write and solve an equation to find the number of students *s* in kindergarten. **32 = 4s; 8 million students**

46.  **Writing in Math** How are the procedures to solve $3x = 9$ and $x + 3 = 9$ alike? How are they different? **See below left.**

47. Open-Ended Write a question that can be solved using the equation $5x = 45$. **Answers may vary. Sample: Jessie buys 5 games for $45. How much is each game?**

Mental Math Solve each equation.

48. $75m = -7,500$
  −100

49. $\frac{v}{-50} = 300$
  −15,000

50. $3,823 = \frac{s}{100}$
  382,300

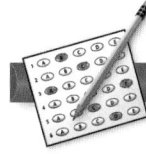 **C Challenge**

For what values of *x* is each equation true?

51. $|x| = 7$ **7, −7**

52. $-3|x| = -9$
  3, −3

53. $\frac{|x|}{3} = 2$ **6, −6**

54. $x - a = b$ **b + a**

55. $a + x = b$ **b − a**

56. $ax = b$ $\frac{b}{a}, a \neq 0$

Test Prep

Multiple Choice

46. You do something to each side of the equation. You divide by 3 in the first equation; you subtract 3 in the second.

Take It to the NET
Online lesson quiz at
www.PHSchool.com
Web Code: ada-0206

In Exercises 57–60, which equation matches the given sentence?

57. Negative six multiplied by *q* equals one hundred eight. **B**
  A. $-6 + q = 108$ **B.** $-6q = 108$
  C. $108q = -6$ **D.** $q = -6 + 108$

58. Thirteen equals the quotient of *x* divided by three. **F**
  F. $13 = \frac{x}{3}$ **G.** $\frac{x}{13}$ **H.** $13 = 3x$ **I.** $\frac{13}{3} = x$

59. Forty-two is the product of some number and 6. **D**
  A. $6(42) = x$ **B.** $\frac{6}{x} = 42$ **C.** $\frac{x}{42} = 6$ **D.** $42 = 6x$

60. Some number divided by eight equals four. **H**
  F. $\frac{8}{x} = 4$ **G.** $\frac{8}{4} = x$ **H.** $\frac{x}{8} = 4$ **I.** $\frac{4}{8} = x$

Mixed Review

Lesson 2-5 **Solve each equation.**

61. $-4 = a + 7$ **62.** $n - 5 = 12$ **63.** $t - (-4) = -15$ **64.** $y + 10 = 12$
  −11 **17** **−19** **2**

Lesson 1-5 ● **65. Hiking** Suppose you start hiking from a point 92 ft below sea level and break for lunch on a hilltop that is 1,673 ft above sea level. What is your change in elevation? **increase of 1,765 ft**

Lesson 1-1 **Write a variable expression for each phrase.**

66. three less than *a* **a − 3** **67.** 7 times a number *n* **7n**

4. Assess

 PowerPoint **Lesson Quiz 2-6**

Solve each equation.

1. $8x = -48$ **−6**

2. $-2x = 18$ **−9**

3. $108 = 9x$ **12**

4. $\frac{v}{-3} = 14$ **−42**

5. $-6 = \frac{n}{4}$ **−24**

Alternative Assessment

Write the following equations on the board:
  $-2m = 6$
  $-3t = -24$
  $\frac{y}{-3} = 6$
  $\frac{x}{-2} = -4$

Have the students explain how they can predict the sign of the solution.

positive ÷ negative = negative
negative ÷ negative = positive
negative × positive = negative
negative × negative = positive

Test Prep

 **Resources**

For additional practice with a variety of test item formats:
• Test Prep, p. 121
• Test-Taking Strategies, p. 116
• Test-Taking Strategies With Transparencies

■■■ *Reteaching 2-6* *Solving Equations by Multiplying or Dividing*

Solve $4x = -32$.
$4x = -32$
$\frac{4x}{4} = \frac{-32}{4}$ Since 4 is multiplied by *x*, divide both sides of the equation by 4.
$x = -8$

Solve $\frac{x}{-5} = -9$.
$\frac{x}{-5} = -9$
$-5\left(\frac{x}{-5}\right) = -5(-9)$ Since *x* is divided by −5, multiply both sides of the equation by −5.
$x = 45$

Solve each equation.

1. $7m = 35$
  $m = 5$

2. $\frac{b}{8} = -3$
  $b = -24$

3. $90 = 10k$
  $k = 9$

4. $1 = \frac{n}{14}$
  $n = 14$

5. $100 = -20n$
  $n = -5$

6. $\frac{p}{15} = 5$
  $p = 75$

7. $-87,654y = 0$
  $y = 0$

8. $\frac{m}{4} = -12$
  $m = -48$

9. $-10a = 10$
  $a = -1$

10. $\frac{z}{-4} = 16$
  $z = -64$

11. $350t = -700$
  $t = -2$

12. $11j = 121$
  $j = 11$

13. $\frac{r}{-7} = 13$
  $r = -91$

14. $-7,650 = 10c$
  $c = -765$

15. $23 = \frac{w}{3}$
  $w = 69$

16. $125 = 25g$
  $g = 5$

2-7

1. Plan

Lesson Preview

 Check Skills You'll Need

Adding Integers
Lesson 1-5: Example 3;
Exercises 13–21.
Extra Practice, p. 744.

Lesson Resources

📁 **Teaching Resources**
Practice, Reteaching, Enrichment

 **Reaching All Students**
Practice Workbook 2-7
Spanish Practice Workbook 2-7
Guided Problem Solving 2-7

⏱ **Presentation Assistant Plus!**
Transparencies and PowerPoint™
• Check Skills You'll Need 2-7
• Additional Examples 2-7
• Student Edition Answers 2-7
• Lesson Quiz 2-7
PH Presentation Pro CD-ROM 2-7

ASSESSMENT SYSTEM

Computer Test Generator CD-ROM

💻 **Technology**
Resource Pro® CD-ROM
Computer Test Generator CD-ROM
PH Presentation Pro CD-ROM

💻 **www.PHSchool.com**

Student Site
• Teacher Web Code: adk-5500
• Algebra Readiness Puzzles 103
• Self-grading Lesson Quiz
PH SuccessNet Teacher Center
• Lesson Planner
• Resources

Plus 🔲**TEXT**

 2-7 **Problem Solving** **Try, Test, Revise**

What You'll Learn

OBJECTIVE 1
To solve a problem using the Try, Test, Revise strategy

. . . And Why

To solve real-world problems involving money

 **Check Skills You'll Need**

Simplify.

1. $158 + 20$ **178**

2. $158 + 30$ **188**

3. $158 + 25$ **183**

4. $158 + 22$ **180**

5. In Exercises 1–4, which result came closest to 181?
   180 (Ex. 4)
   ❓ For help, go to Lesson 1-5.

🔲**TEXT** Interactive lesson includes instant self-check, tutorials, and activities.

OBJECTIVE

1 Try, Test, Revise

Math Strategies in Action Did you know that meteorologists use weather balloons to collect data? They use the temperature, humidity, and other data in mathematical models to bring you the daily weather forecast. As more data become available—from weather balloons and satellites, for example—the models, and therefore the weather reports, become more accurate.

Similarly, in math problems, you can make an initial conjecture. You can test your conjecture. If it is not the right answer, you can use what you learn from your first conjecture to make a better, second conjecture.

Real-World 🌐 Connection

Each day, weather balloons make more than 1,000 measurements of conditions in the upper atmosphere around the world.

1 EXAMPLE **Real-World 🌐 Problem Solving**

Ticket Sales The theater club at school put on a play. For one performance, the club sold 133 tickets and raised $471. Tickets cost $4 for adults and $3 for students. How many student tickets and how many adult tickets did the club sell?

Read and Understand

Look at the given information to make an informed conjecture.

1. How much does each type of ticket cost? **adult $4, student $3**

2. How many tickets did the club sell for the performance?
   133 tickets
3. How much money did the club raise from ticket sales for this performance? **$471**

Plan and Solve

Make a conjecture, and then test it. Use what you learn from your conjecture to make a better, second conjecture.

✓ **Ongoing Assessment and Intervention**

Before the Lesson	**During the Lesson**	**After the Lesson**
Diagnose prerequisite skills using:	Monitor progress using:	Assess knowledge using:
• Check Skills You'll Need	• Check Understanding	• Lesson Quiz
	• Additional Examples	• Computer Test Generator CD-ROM
	• Test Prep	

4. When you make a conjecture for how many adult tickets were sold, how can you use your conjecture to find how many student tickets could have been sold?
Subtract the number of adult tickets from 133
5. By what number do you multiply your conjecture of adult tickets sold to find how much money was made on adult tickets? 4

You can organize conjectures in a table. As a first conjecture, try making about half the tickets adult tickets.

Adult Tickets	Student Tickets	Total Money (in dollars)	
60	$133 - 60 = 73$	$60(4) + 73(3) = 240 + 219$ $= 459$	The total is too low. Increase the number of adult tickets.
80	$133 - 80 = 53$	$80(4) + 53(3) = 320 + 159$ $= 479$	The total is too high. Decrease the number of adult tickets.
70	$133 - 70 = 63$	$70(4) + 63(3) = 280 + 189$ $= 469$	The total is very close. Increase the number of adult tickets.
72	$133 - 72 = 61$	$72(4) + 61(3) = 288 + 183$ $= 471$	The total is correct.

There were 72 adult tickets and 61 student tickets sold.

Look Back and Check

Is it possible to solve the problem in another way? Consider using logical reasoning.

- The less expensive ticket is $3. So the theater club would get $133 \cdot \$3 = \$399$ if all the tickets sold were student tickets.
- $\$471 - \$399 = \$72$. The theater club actually raised $72 more than if they had sold only student tickets.
- Since adult tickets are $1 more than student tickets, there must have been 72 adult tickets sold.
- $133 - 72 = 61$. There were 61 student tickets sold.
- Since $72 \cdot 4 + 61 \cdot 3 = 471$, the solution 72 adult tickets and 61 student tickets is correct.

✓ **Check Understanding**

6. Suppose the club sold the same number of tickets, but raised $452. How many tickets of each type did the theater club sell?
53 adult tickets, 80 student tickets

Professional Development

Math Background

The *Try, Test, Revise* problem-solving strategy is common in the world outside the classroom. Everyone uses this strategy—from an infant just discovering his or her world to a scientist making discoveries that change the world. In this strategy, a *try* is a reasonable trial solution, not merely a random or wild speculation.

Teaching Notes

1 EXAMPLE **Science Connection**
Scientists solve problems and make new discoveries by using a method that is similar to the Try, Test, Revise strategy. This strategy is the *scientific method*. In the first step of the scientific method, you form an assumption, or *hypothesis*. You conduct experiments to test the hypothesis. You revise the hypothesis many times.

English Learners
Help students understand the meaning of *conjecture*. A conjecture is a statement of what might be true. It is then tested and possibly revised to be more accurate. Possibly, it may be shown to be false.

Visual Learners
Have students organize data into tables or charts before trying to find solutions.

PowerPoint
Additional Example

1 During the intermission of the play, the Theater Club sold cups of popcorn and soda. The club sold 79 cups of popcorn and 96 sodas for a total of $271. What was the selling price of a cup of popcorn? Of a soda? popcorn: $1; soda: $2

Closure

Ask students to describe how to use the Try, Test, Revise strategy.

Reaching All Students

Below Level	Advanced Learners	English Learners
Think of a number. Ask students to guess the number. After each guess, tell them whether their number is too high or too low. After several guesses, ask students to explain their strategies.	Have students solve the following: *Two integers have a difference of −11 and a sum of −3. What are the integers?* −7 and 4	See note on page 97. **Visual Learners** See note on page 97.

97

Assignment Guide

Objective 1

Ⓐ Ⓑ Core 1–12

Ⓒ Extension 13, 14

Test Prep 15–17

Mixed Review 18–26

Practice 2-7 Try, Test, Revise

Use the try, test, revise strategy to solve each problem.

1. The length of a rectangle is 9 in. greater than the width. The area is 36 in.² Find the dimensions. **3 in by 12 in**
   Sample guesses are shown.

Width	1	2	3		
Length	10	11	12		
Area	10	22	36		

2. Shari Williams, a basketball player, scored 30 points on 2-point and 3-point goals. She hit 5 more 2-pointers than 3-pointers. How many of each did she score? **4 3-pointers; 9 2-pointers**
   Sample guesses are shown.

3-Pointers	1	2	3	4
2-Pointers	6	7	8	9
Points	15	20	25	30

3. The sums and products of pairs of integers are given. Find each pair of integers.

   a. sum = −12, product = 36 **−6, −6**

   b. sum = −12, product = 35 **−7, −5**

   c. sum = −12, product = 32 **−8, −4**

   d. sum = −12, product = 11 **−11, −1**

   e. sum = −12, product = 0 **−12, 0**

4. Jess had 3 more nickels than dimes for a total of $1.50. How many of each coin did he have? **9 dimes; 12 nickels**

5. A brush cost $2 more than a comb. The brush and a comb together cost $3.78. Find the cost of each. **brush $2.89; comb $.89**

6. The hard-cover edition of a book cost 3 times as much as the paperback edition. Both editions together cost $26.60. Find the cost of each. **paperback $6.65; hardcover $19.95**

Enrichment 2-7 Try, Test, Revise

In many problems, you have used the try, test, revise strategy to find two numbers. Here is a classic problem that involves finding three numbers. Finding three numbers is more complicated than finding two, but you can still do it by using the try, test, revise strategy.

A farmer sold cows for $100 apiece, sheep for $20, and rabbits for $1. The farmer sold 100 animals in all and earned exactly $2,000.

Complete to find the number of each type of animal sold.

1. Let *c* = the number of cows sold, *s* = the number of sheep sold, and *r* = the number of rabbits sold. Write an equation using *c*, *s*, and *r* expressing the total number of animals sold.
   $$c + s + r = 100$$

2. Write a variable expression for:

   a. the amount of money earned on the sale of cows **100c**

   b. the amount of money earned on the sale of sheep **20s**

   c. the amount of money earned on the sale of rabbits **r**

3. Use the above expressions to write an equation expressing the total amount of money the farmer earned.
   $$100c + 20s + r = 2,000$$

4. How do you know that the number of cows is less than 20?
   20 cows would bring in $2,000, but 100 animals were sold.

5. Complete the table.

Number of Cows Sold	14	15	16	17	18	19
Number of Sheep Sold	3	5	6	8	9	2
Number of Rabbits Sold	83	80	78	75	73	79
Amount Earned	$1,543	$1,680	$1,798	$1,935	$2,053	$2,019

6. Find the values in the table which produce earnings closest to $2,000. Adjust them using guess and test until you find the correct answer.

   Number of cows **19** Number of sheep **1** Number of rabbits **80**

EXERCISES

For more exercises, see Extra Practice.

Practice and Problem Solving

Ⓐ **Practice by Example**

Example 1
(page 96)

Use the Try, Test, Revise strategy to solve each problem.

1. **Coin Collections** Bonnie has 16 coins in her pocket worth $1.50. What are two different combinations of coins she could have in her pocket? **Answers may vary.**
   Samples: 14 dimes, 2 nickels; 2 quarters, 6 dimes, 8 nickels

2. **Currency** A cashier's drawer has some $5 bills, some $10 bills, and some $20 bills. There are 15 bills worth a total of $185. How many $5 bills, $10 bills, and $20 bills are there?
   1, 10, and 4, or 3, 7, and 5, or 5, 4, and 6, or 7, 1, and 7

3. The Smiths have two children. The sum of their ages is 23. The product of their ages is 132. How old are the children?
   11 years and 12 years

4. The sum of Mr. and Mrs. Bergen's ages is 100. The difference between their ages is 10. How old are Mr. and Mrs. Bergen?
   45 years and 55 years

Ⓑ **Apply Your Skills**

Solve using any strategy.

5. **Geometry** A rectangular vegetable garden has a length of 5 ft and a width of 8 ft. The length is increased by 2 ft. By how many square feet does the area increase? **16 ft²**

6. Trains leave New York for Boston every 40 min. The first train leaves at 5:20 A.M. What departure time is closest to 12:55 P.M.?
   12:40 P.M.

7. Lovell is 16 years old. Lovell's age is the same as Rafi's age divided by three. How old is Rafi? **48 years**

8. **Number Theory** A number multiplied by itself and then by itself again gives −1,000. What is the number? **−10**

9. **Coin Collections** In a group of quarters and nickels, there are four more nickels than quarters. How many nickels and quarters are there if the coins are worth $2.30? **11 nickels, 7 quarters**
   [GPS]

10. The sum of the page numbers on two facing pages is 245. The product of the numbers is 15,006. What are the page numbers?
    122, 123

11. **Shopping** A student bought some compact discs for $12 each and some books for $5 each. She spent $39 in all on five items. How many of each item did she buy? **2 CDs, 3 books**

12. **Relay Races** Two runners ran as a team in a 5,000-m relay race. The first runner ran 500 m farther than the second runner. How many meters did each run? **2,750 m, 2,250 m**

Ⓒ **Challenge**

13. **Savings** Ron puts three pennies in a jar. His father offers to triple the total amount of money in Ron's jar at the end of each day. How much is in the jar at the end of one week? **$65.61**

14. **Biology** A certain bacteria doubles the number of its cells every 20 min. A scientist puts 50 cells in a culture dish. How many cells will be in the culture dish after 2 h? **3,200 cells**

Strategies

- Account for All Possibilities
- Draw a Diagram
- Look for a Pattern
- Make a Model
- Make a Table
- Simplify the Problem
- Simulate the Problem
- Solve by Graphing
- Try, Test, Revise
- Use Multiple Strategies
- Work Backward
- Write an Equation
- Write a Proportion

---

98 Chapter 2 Solving One-Step Equations and Inequalities

 Use the Guided Problem Solving worksheet with Exercise 9.

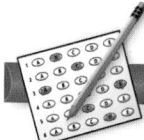

Test Prep

Multiple Choice

15. A photograph is 6 in. × 4 in. If you make a copy of the photograph with double the length and width, what is the area of the copy? **A**
   A. 96 in.^{2} **B.** 48 in.^{2} **C.** 24 in.^{2} **D.** 20 in.^{2}

16. Cara's age is 4 times Laura's age. If Cara is 16, how old is Laura? **F**
   F. 4 years   **G.** 12 years   **H.** 20 years   **I.** 64 years

Take It to the NET
Online lesson quiz at
www.PHSchool.com
Web Code: ada-0207

17. On a recent test, the lowest score was one fourth the highest score. If the lowest score was 25, how much higher was the highest score? **C**
   A. 4   **B.** 25   **C.** 75   **D.** 100

Mixed Review

Lesson 2-6   **Algebra**   **Solve each equation.**

18. $\frac{m}{4} = 52$ **19.** $3x = -18$ **20.** $63 = \frac{t}{-3}$ **21.** $-32 = -16y$
   208   -6   -189   2

Lessons 2-1 and 2-2   **Identify each property shown.**

22. $8 + (6 + 17) = (8 + 6) + 17$ **23.** $1,879 \cdot 1 = 1,879$
   Assoc. Prop. of Add.   Ident. Prop. of Mult.
24. $8(5 - 3) = 8(5) - 8(3)$ **25.** $-1 + 7 - 3 = -1 - 3 + 7$
   Dist. Prop.   Comm. Prop. of Add.

Lesson 1-9 **26. Weather** The sound of thunder travels about one mile in five seconds. Suppose a bolt of lightning strikes 3 mi away. How long does it take for the sound of the thunder to reach you?
about 15 s

Math at Work

Nurse

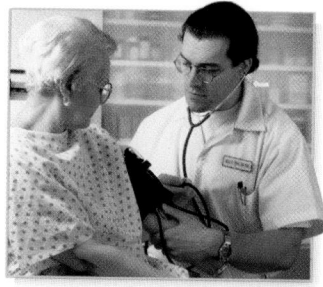

Anyone who has been in a hospital knows that nurses are patients' principal caregivers. Nurses dispense medication, monitor patients' progress, and tend to patients' daily medical needs.

Mathematics is important in a nurse's duties. Nurses compare a patient's blood pressure reading against established norms and make a conclusion about the result. They also solve math problems when they convert one unit of measure of medication to another, and then calculate the total amount of various medications needed for a patient in their care.

 Take It to the NET For more information about nurses, go to **www.PHSchool.com**.
Web Code: adb-2031

---

4. Assess

Lesson Quiz 2-7

Solve using any strategy.

1. A sporting goods store manager ordered twice as many pairs of basketball shoes as tennis shoes. He ordered 96 pairs in all. How many pairs of each did he order? **32 pairs of tennis shoes; 64 pairs of basketball shoes**

2. Manuel wrote a 512-word paper over the weekend. He wrote 180 more words on Sunday than he did on Saturday. How many words did he write on Saturday? **166**

Error Prevention!

Exercises 1–4 After students have completed each exercise, have them reread the problem and make sure each of the solutions fully and correctly answers the original question.

Reteaching 2-7   *Try, Test, Revise*

On vacation, your family spent 4 hours driving 220 miles across a state. Part of the time you drove on a scenic state highway at 40 miles per hour. The rest of the time you drove on an interstate at 60 miles per hour. How long did you drive on each type of highway?

Try 3 hours on the state highway. That leaves 1 hour on the interstate. In 3 hours, at 40 miles per hour, you travel 120 miles. In 1 hour, at 60 miles per hour, you drive 60 miles. That is a total of 180 miles, which is not enough. You must have spent more time on the interstate.

Organize the conjectures in a table.

Hours on State Hwy	Hours on Interstate	Distance on State Hwy	Distance on Interstate	Total Distance
3	1	3(40) = 120	1(60) = 60	120 + 60 = 180
2	2	2(40) = 80	2(60) = 120	80 + 120 = 200
1	3	1(40) = 40	3(60) = 180	40 + 180 = 220

Your family traveled one hour on the state highway and three hours on the interstate highway.

Solve using the try, test, revise strategy. Organize your guesses in the table.

1. The Wolverines scored 42 points in a football game. They scored 2 more field goals (3 points each) than touchdowns (6 points each). How many field goals and touchdowns did they score?
6 field goals and 4 touchdowns

Possible guesses are shown.

Touchdowns	Field Goals	Points From Touchdowns	Points From Field Goals	Total Points
1	3	6	9	15
2	4	12	12	24
3	5	18	15	33
4	6	24	18	42

Reteaching

Alternative Assessment

Ask students to write a description of how they might teach someone else to use the Try, Test, Revise strategy for problem solving.

Test Prep

 **Resources**
For additional practice with a variety of test item formats:
- Test Prep, p. 121
- Test-Taking Strategies, p. 116
- Test-Taking Strategies With Transparencies

Data and Graphs

Computers can make graphing easier. This Technology feature shows students how to use a spreadsheet to create line and bar graphs.

Resources

Students may use any spreadsheet software program to create different types of graphs.

Teaching Notes

A graph often shows relationships between data sets more quickly and effectively than a table of data. Changes such as growth or decline are obvious at a glance, and unusual data stand out more than they would in a list. When one data set represents time, you usually use a line graph. A bar graph effectively uses the lengths of bars to represent data values. The bars may be either horizontal or vertical. If there are no spaces between the bars, the bar graph is also called a *histogram*.

Inclusion

Pair students who have difficulty with eye-hand coordination with partners. Have the student with difficulties give the partner instructions on what to input.

Diversity

Pair students with little or no background in computers or spreadsheet software with experienced students. Have the novice input data while the experienced student serves as a guide.

100

 **Technology**

Sometimes a graph will help you analyze data. You can use a spreadsheet program to create different types of graphs. First, enter the data in a spreadsheet. Then use a graphing tool to draw an appropriate graph.

1 EXAMPLE

The spreadsheet gives the voting-age populations in thousands for two states. Graph the data in the spreadsheet.

	A	B	C
1	Year	Arizona	Georgia
2	1992	2,812	5,006
3	1994	2,923	5,159
4	1996	3,245	5,420
5	1998	3,405	5,620
6	2000	3,764	6,017

Row 3 contains voting-age populations of both states in 1994.

Cell B3 contains the voting-age population of Arizona in 1994.

Column B contains the voting-age population of Arizona.

Choose an appropriate type of graph from your spreadsheet program. Line graphs are often useful to display changes in data over a period of time. Since the data show changes over time for two states, use a double line graph.

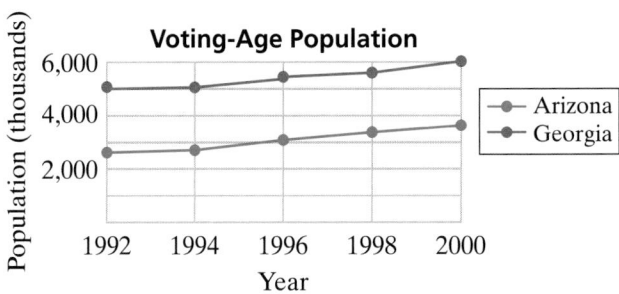

Voting-Age Population

1. Use a spreadsheet to graph the data below. **See margin.**

Average Prices Farmers Received

Year	1990	1991	1992	1993	1994	1995	1996	1997
Price for Turkey (¢/lb)	39.4	38.4	37.7	39.0	40.4	41.6	43.3	39.9
Price for Chicken (¢/lb)	32.6	30.8	31.8	34.0	35.0	34.4	38.1	37.7

SOURCE: U.S. Department of Agriculture.
Go to **www.PHSchool.com** for a data update.
Web Code: adg-2041

Teaching Tip
After entering the data, students should check the choices the program offers for graphic representation. Have them explain the choice they make. Point out that the computer can create a graph even if it's not appropriate for the data.

Error Prevention!

Remind students to be careful to enter data correctly. Check the graph for unexpected results to help make sure there are no mistakes in data entry.

2 EXAMPLE

The spreadsheet gives population data (in thousands) for five states. Graph the data in the spreadsheet.

	A	B	C
1		Age 25 to 34	Age 75 to 84
2	California	5,285	1,229
3	Florida	1,968	958
4	Illinois	1,764	517
5	New York	2,767	825
6	Texas	2,882	638

Bar graphs are often useful in comparing amounts. Since the data in the spreadsheet show populations for two age ranges, use a double bar graph.

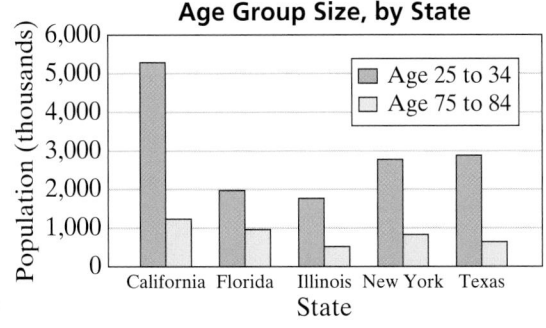

2. a. Use a spreadsheet to make a double bar graph of the postage rate data below. **See margin.**

Postage Rates

Sent from the United States to	First Class 1-oz Letter (¢)	Postcard (¢)
United States	37	23
Canada	60	50
Mexico	60	50
All other countries	80	70

SOURCE: U.S. Postal Service. Go to **www.PHSchool.com** for a data update. Web Code: adg-2041

b. Data Analysis Use the graph you made in part (a). Which bar is tallest? Explain. **bar for 1-oz letters to countries other than U.S., Canada, and Mexico because their postage rate is greater.**

3. Writing in Math Explain when you would use a line graph and when you would use a bar graph to display a data set. **Use a line graph to show change over time. Use a bar graph to compare quantities.**

1. Graphs may vary. Sample:

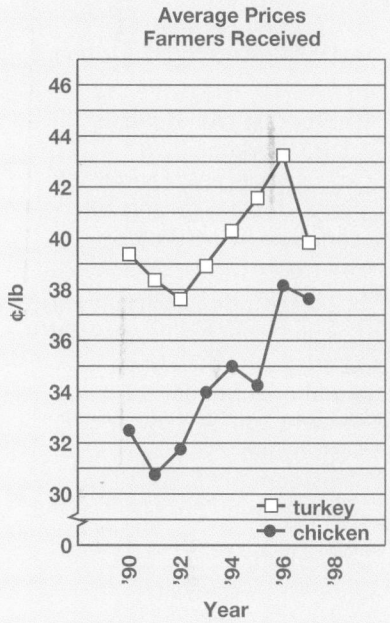

2. Graphs may vary. Sample:

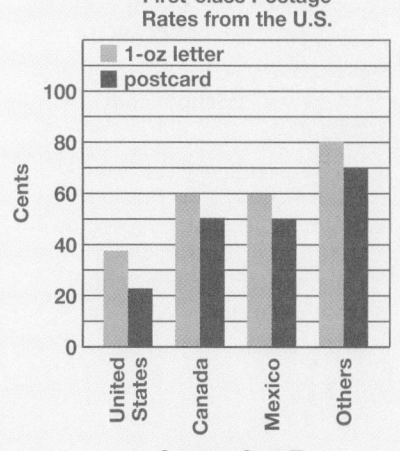

2-8

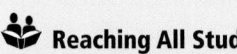

2-8 Inequalities and Their Graphs

2-8

What You'll Learn

OBJECTIVE 1 To graph inequalities

OBJECTIVE 2 To write inequalities

. . . And Why

To solve real-world problems involving nutrition

 Check Skills You'll Need

Graph each set of numbers on a number line. Order the numbers from least to greatest.
For graphs, see below.

1. $-3, 7, -9$ $-9, -3, 7$

2. $-2, -10, -8$ $-10, -8, -2$

3. $0, 3, -5$ $-5, 0, 3$

4. $3, -6, 10$ $-6, 3, 10$

 For help, go to Lesson 1-4.

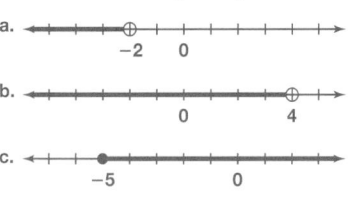

1.
2.
3.
4.

Check Understanding Example 1

a.

b.

c.

d.

 **TEXT** Interactive lesson includes instant self-check, tutorials, and activities.

OBJECTIVE

1 Graphing Inequalities

An **inequality** is a mathematical sentence that contains $>$, $<$, $\geq$, $\leq$, or $\neq$. Some inequalities contain a variable. Any number that makes an inequality true is a **solution of the inequality.** For example, -4 is a solution of $y \geq -5$ because $-4 \geq -5$.

You can graph the solutions of an inequality on a number line.

1 EXAMPLE **Graphing Solutions of Inequalities**

Graph the solutions of each inequality on a number line.

a. $y < 3$

An open dot shows that 3 is *not* a solution.

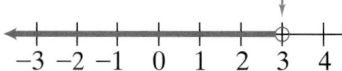

Shade all the points to the left of 3.

b. $x > -1$

An open dot shows that -1 is *not* a solution.

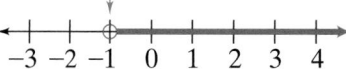

Shade all the points to the right of -1.

c. $a \leq -2$

A closed dot shows that -2 *is* a solution.

Shade all the points to the left of -2.

d. $-6 \leq g$

A closed dot shows that -6 *is* a solution.

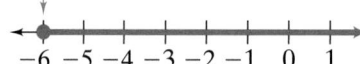

Shade all the points to the right of -6.

 **Check Understanding** Example 1

1. Graph the solutions of each inequality. **1a–d. See left.**
   a. $z < -2$ **b.** $4 > t$ **c.** $a \geq -5$ **d.** $2 \geq c$

Ongoing Assessment and Intervention

Before the Lesson	**During the Lesson**	**After the Lesson**
Diagnose prerequisite skills using:	**Monitor progress using:**	**Assess knowledge using:**
• Check Skills You'll Need	• Check Understanding • Additional Examples • Test Prep	• Lesson Quiz • Computer Test Generator CD-ROM

You can write an inequality for a graph.

2 EXAMPLE Writing Inequalities to Describe Graphs

Write the inequality shown in each graph.

a.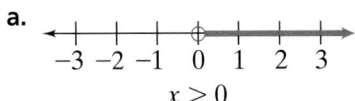
$$x > 0$$

b.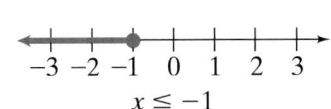
$$x \le -1$$

Reading Math

Read $>$ as "is greater than."

Read $<$ as "is less than."

Read $\ge$ as "is greater than or equal to."

Read $\le$ as "is less than or equal to."

✓ **Check Understanding** Example 2

2. Write an inequality for the graph below. $x \ge 3$

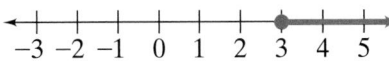

You can write an inequality to describe a real-world situation. Keep in mind that *at most* means "no more than," and hence, "less than or equal to." *At least* means "no less than," and hence, "greater than or equal to."

3 EXAMPLE Real-World Problem Solving

Nutrition Food can be labeled *low sodium* only if it meets the requirement established by the federal government. Use the table to write an inequality for this requirement.

Label	Definition
Sodium-free food	Less than 5 mg per serving
Very low sodium food	At most 35 mg per serving
Low-sodium food	At most 140 mg per serving

Words

a serving of low-sodium food	has at most	140 mg sodium

Let s = number of milligrams of sodium in a serving of low-sodium food.

Inequality s $\le$ 140

✓ **Check Understanding** Example 3

3. Use the table in Example 3. A certain food is labeled *sodium free*. Write an inequality for n, the number of milligrams of sodium in a serving of this sodium-free food. $n < 5$

2-8 Inequalilties and Their Graphs **103**

Reaching All Students

Below Level Have students recall situations in which they've heard phrases like *at least, at most, no more than, as much as, less than,* or *greater than*.	**Advanced Learners** Ask students: *Are there any fractions that are solutions of $x \le 1$? If so, name one.* Yes; Answers may vary. Sample: $\frac{1}{2}, -\frac{1}{2}$.	**English Learners** See note on page 103. **Inclusion** See note on page 103.

2. Teach

Professional Development

Math Background

The equation $x = 1$ has exactly one solution: 1. However, the inequality $x < 1$ has an infinite number of solutions. They are all the numbers less than 1. For example: $\frac{1}{2}$, 0, -0.7, -9, etc. In general, it is impossible to list all the solutions for an inequality.

Teaching Notes

1 EXAMPLE English Learners

Graphs provide a visual way for students with minimal English language skills to communicate their solutions clearly. The circle that is *not* shaded is an *open dot*. The number associated with the open dot is *not* part of the solution. The shaded circle is a *closed dot*. The number associated with the closed dot is part of the solution.

3 EXAMPLE Inclusion

Explain why food and beverage labeling for sodium content is very important for people with certain health problems, like high blood pressure or heart disease.

PowerPoint
Additional Examples

1 Graph the solutions of each inequality on a number line.
a. $x > -2$
b. $w \ge -5$
c. $k \le 4$
d. $y < 6$
1a–d. See back of book.

2 Write the inequality shown in each graph.
a. $x \ge -3$
b. $x < 3$

3 Use the table in Example 3 to write an inequality for a very low-sodium food. $v \le 35$

Closure

Have students explain the use of the open dot and the closed dot in graphing inequalities.
See back of book.

3. Practice

Assignment Guide

▼ **1 Objective 1**
  Ⓐ Ⓑ **Core** 1–12, 33
  Ⓒ **Extension** 37

▼ **2 Objective 2**
  Ⓐ Ⓑ **Core** 13–32, 34–36
  Ⓒ **Extension** 38

Test Prep 39–41
Mixed Review 42–47

Practice 2-8 *Inequalities and Their Graphs*

Write an inequality for each sentence.
1. The total *t* is less than sixteen. $t < 16$
2. A number *h* is not less than 7. $h \geq 7$
3. The price *p* is less than or equal to $25. $p \leq 25$
4. A number *n* is negative. $n < 0$

Write an inequality for each graph.
5. $x \leq -7$
6. $x > -11$
7. $x < 2$
8. $x \geq -3$

Graph the solutions of each inequality on a number line.
9. $x < -2$
10. $y \geq -1$
11. $k > 1$
12. $p \leq 4$

Write an inequality for each situation.
13. Everyone in the class is under 13 years old. Let *x* be the age of a person in the class. $x < 13$
14. The speed limit is 60 miles per hour. Let *s* be the speed of a car driving within the limit. $s \leq 60$
15. You have $4.50 to spend on lunch. Let *c* be the cost of your lunch. $c \leq \$4.50$

Enrichment 2-8 *Conjunctions and Disjunctions*

Two statements connected by the word "and" form a *conjunction*. Two statements connected by the word "or" form a *disjunction*. You can use inequality symbols to write conjunctions and disjunctions.
Conjunction: *x* is greater than 5 *and* *x* is less than 8.
Symbols: $5 < x < 8$
Disjunction: *p* is less than -3 *or* *p* is greater than or equal to 4.
Symbols: $-3 > p$ or $p \geq 4$

Use symbols to write each statement.
1. The number *n* is greater than 7 and it is less than 10.
   $7 < n < 10$
2. *k* is less than -2 or *k* is greater than 0.
   $k < -2$ or $k > 0$
3. *y* is greater than or equal to -6 and less than or equal to 5.
   $-6 \leq y \leq 5$

List the integers that satisfy each statement.
4. $1 < m \leq 6$ 2, 3, 4, 5, 6
5. $13 < e < 15$ 14
6. $p > 6$ and $p \leq 9$ 7, 8, 9
7. $h > -3$ and $h < -4$ none

You can graph conjunctions and disjunctions on a number line.
Statement	Graph
$x < 5$ and $x > 3$	
$p < -2$ or $p \geq 1$	

Graph each statement.
8. $x > 7$ or $x \leq 4$
9. $x > -2$ and $x \leq 3$
10. $x \leq 3$ or $x > 5$
11. $x < 9$ and $x > 6$

EXERCISES

❓ For more exercises, see *Extra Practice*.

Practice and Problem Solving

Ⓐ **Practice by Example**

Example 1
(page 102)

Graph the solutions of each inequality on a number line.
1–12. See margin.
1. $x < 7$ 2. $y > 2$ 3. $a < 3$ 4. $c < 1$
5. $-3 < z$ 6. $x > 1$ 7. $m \leq -4$ 8. $b \geq 6$
9. $4 \leq p$ 10. $a \geq -2$ 11. $j \geq -1$ 12. $-5 < w$

Example 2
(page 103)

Write an inequality for each graph.

13. $x \leq -2$
14. $x \geq 2$
15. $x < 0$
16. $x > -4$

Example 3
(page 103)

Write an inequality for each situation. Use the variable given.

17. Let *t* be truck weight in tons.   18. Let *s* be speed in mi/h.

 $t \leq 3$  $s \leq 25$

27. Use a closed dot for $\geq$ and $\leq$; use an open dot for $>$ and $<$.

Ⓑ **Apply Your Skills**

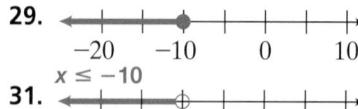

Write an inequality for each sentence. Graph the solutions of each inequality on a number line. 19–26. For graphs, see back of book.

19. *x* is less than 5. $x < 5$
20. *y* is greater than -3. $y > -3$
21. A number *c* is at least 12. $c \geq 12$
22. *r* is not greater than five. $r \leq 5$
23. The total *t* is greater than 7. $t > 7$
24. *p* is not more than 30. $p \leq 30$
25. *b* is less than or equal to 8. $b \leq 8$
26. A number *n* is positive. $n > 0$

27. **Reasoning** Explain how you know whether the endpoint of the graph of an inequality should be a closed dot or an open dot.
See above left.
28. The sign at the amusement park (left) tells you how tall you must be to ride. Write an inequality for this situation. Let *h* be height in feet. $h \geq 4$

Write an inequality for each graph.

Real-World 🌐 Connection

Amusement parks make rules for safety.

29. $x \leq -10$
30. $x > 300$
31. $x < -\frac{1}{2}$
32. $x \leq 1$

---

1.   0 2   7
2.   0 2
3.   0 3
4.   0 1
5. $-5 -4 -3 -2 -1 \ 0 \ 1 \ 2 \ 3 \ 4 \ 5$

6–12. See back of book.

Writing in Math

Explain how an inequality with one variable differs from an equation with one variable. **See margin.**

33. Graphing can show infinitely many solutions.

34. To go to a movie rated PG-13, you have to be 13 years old or older; $a \geq 13$

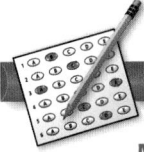
Challenge

33. **Reasoning** Explain why graphing the solutions of an inequality is more efficient than listing all the solutions of the inequality. **See below left.**

34. **Writing in Math** Describe a situation that you could represent with an inequality. Then write the inequality. **See below left.**

35. **Movie Tickets** Write an inequality to describe this situation. A student pays for three movie tickets with a twenty-dollar bill and gets change back. Let t be the cost of a movie ticket. $3t < 20$

36. **Nutrition** High-fiber foods have at least 5 g of fiber per serving. Write an inequality to represent this situation. Let f be the number of grams of fiber per serving of high-fiber food. $f \geq 5$

37. **Compare.** Use $>$ or $<$ to complete each statement.
   a. If $a < b$, then $b \blacksquare a$. $>$
   b. If $x > y$ and $y > z$, then $x \blacksquare z$. $>$

38. **Number Sense** No more than 50 students walked in a walkathon. Let s be the number of students. Determine which numbers are reasonable values for s: $40, 45\frac{1}{2}, 50,$ and 55. **40 and 50**

Test Prep

Multiple Choice

39. Which inequality best represents the following sentence? A number t is greater than or equal to -8. **A**
   A. $-8 \leq t$ **B.** $t > -8$ **C.** $t \leq -8$ **D.** $-8 \geq t$

40. Which graph matches the inequality $x < -4$? **H**
   F.
   G.
   H.
   I.

41. A game-board designer has to design a board that is at least 5 feet wide. Let w be the width of the board. Which inequality describes this situation? **D**
   A. $w < 5$ **B.** $w > 5$ **C.** $w \leq 5$ **D.** $w \geq 5$

Take It to the NET
Online lesson quiz at **www.PHSchool.com**
Web Code: ada-0208

Mixed Review

Lessons 2-5 and 2-6   **Solve each equation.**

42. $x - 5 = 29$ **34**   43. $7y = 35$ **5**   44. $t \div 12 = 6$ **72**

Lesson 2-3   **Simplify each expression.**

45. $6 - 5s + 4s + 3$ **9 − s**   46. $n + (n + 2) + (n + 4)$ **3n + 6**

Lesson 1-1   47. Write a variable expression for the number of weeks in y years. **52y**

Alternative Assessment

Have students write four true numerical inequalities, one for each symbol: $<, \leq, >, \geq$. Instruct them to represent each inequality in three different ways: using words, symbols, and a graph.

GPS Use the Guided Problem Solving worksheet with Exercise 35.

Writing in Math—The solution of an inequality can have many solutions. The solution of an equation usually has one solution.

Error Prevention!

Exercises 1–12 Students may confuse the open and closed dot when graphing. Remind them that when there is a line under the $>$ or $<$, they must fill in the dot.

Test Prep

Resources
For additional practice with a variety of test item formats:
- Test Prep, p. 121
- Test-Taking Strategies, p. 116
- Test-Taking Strategies With Transparencies

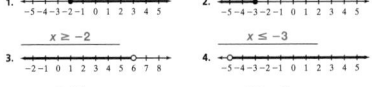
Reteaching 2-8 *Inequalities and Their Graphs*

Write an inequality for each graph.

Lesson Preview

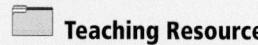 **Check Skills You'll Need**

Solving Equations by Adding or Subtracting
Lesson 2-5: Examples 1 and 3;
Exercises 1–9, 12–20.
Extra Practice, p. 745.

Lesson Resources

 **Teaching Resources**
Practice, Reteaching, Enrichment
Checkpoint Quiz 2

Reaching All Students
Practice Workbook 2-9
Spanish Practice Workbook 2-9
Reading and Math Literacy 2C
Spanish Reading and Math
  Literacy 2C
Spanish Checkpoint Quiz 2
Guided Problem Solving 2-9

Presentation Assistant Plus!
Transparencies and PowerPoint™
• Check Skills You'll Need 2-9
• Additional Examples 2-9
• Student Edition Answers 2-9
• Lesson Quiz 2-9
PH Presentation Pro CD-ROM 2-9

ASSESSMENT *SYSTEM*

Checkpoint Quiz 2
Computer Test Generator CD-ROM

Technology
Resource Pro® CD-ROM
Computer Test Generator CD-ROM
PH Presentation Pro CD-ROM

www.PHSchool.com

Student Site
• Teacher Web Code: adk-5500
• Algebra Readiness Puzzles 55, 56
• Self-grading Lesson Quiz
PH SuccessNet Teacher Center
• Lesson Planner
• Resources

Plus **iTEXT**

What You'll Learn

OBJECTIVE 1 To solve one-step inequalities using subtraction

OBJECTIVE 2 To solve one-step inequalities using addition

...And Why

To solve real-world problems involving computer memory

 **Check Skills You'll Need**

Solve each equation.

1. $m + 7 = 5$ -2

2. $k - 8 = 11$ 19

3. $12 + h = 21$ 9

4. $6 = n - 23$ 29

For help, go to Lesson 2-5.

iTEXT Interactive lesson includes instant self-check, tutorials, and activities.

Solving One-Step Inequalities by Adding or Subtracting

OBJECTIVE

1 Solving Inequalities by Subtracting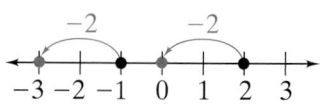

Solving an inequality is similar to solving an equation. You want to get the variable alone on one side of the inequality.

You can see from the number line that if you subtract 2 from each side of the inequality $-1 < 2$, the resulting inequality $-3 < 0$ is still true.

Key Concepts **Subtraction Property of Inequality**

You can subtract the same number from each side of an inequality.

Arithmetic	Algebra
$7 > 4$, so $7 - 3 > 4 - 3$	If $a > b$, then $a - c > b - c$.
$6 < 9$, so $6 - 2 < 9 - 2$	If $a < b$, then $a - c < b - c$.

1 EXAMPLE **Subtracting to Solve an Inequality**

Solve each inequality. Graph the solutions.

a. $n + 8 \geq 19$

$$n + 8 \geq 19$$
$$n + 8 - 8 \geq 19 - 8 \quad \text{Subtract 8 from each side.}$$
$$n \geq 11 \quad \text{Simplify.}$$

b. $-26 > y + 14$

$$-26 > y + 14$$
$$-26 - 14 > y + 14 - 14 \quad \text{Subtract 14 from each side.}$$
$$-40 > y \text{ or } y < -40 \quad \text{Simplify.}$$

 Check Understanding Example 1

1. Solve each inequality. Graph the solutions.
a–c. See back of book for graphs.
a. $m + 3 > 6$ $m > 3$ **b.** $8 + t < 15$ $t < 7$ **c.** $-3 \leq x + 7$
$x \geq -10$

Ongoing Assessment and Intervention

Before the Lesson
Diagnose prerequisite skills using:
• Check Skills You'll Need

During the Lesson
Monitor progress using:
• Check Understanding
• Additional Examples
• Test Prep

After the Lesson
Assess knowledge using:
• Lesson Quiz
• Computer Test Generator
  CD-ROM
• Chapter Checkpoint 2 (p. 109)

2 EXAMPLE Real-World 🌐 Problem Solving

Computers Nearly 32 megabytes (MB) of memory are available for running your computer. If its basic systems require 12 MB, how much memory is available for other programs?

Words	memory for basic systems	plus	memory for other programs	is less than	total memory

Let m = memory available for other programs.

Inequality	12	+	m	<	32

$$12 + m < 32$$
$$12 - 12 + m < 32 - 12 \quad \textbf{Subtract 12 from each side.}$$
$$m < 20 \quad \textbf{Simplify.}$$

• Less than 20 MB of memory is available for other programs.

✓ Check Understanding Example 2

2. An airline lets you check up to 65 lb of luggage. One suitcase weighs 37 lb. How much can another suitcase weigh? **≤ 28 lb**

OBJECTIVE

2 Using Addition to Solve Inequalities

To solve an inequality involving subtraction, use addition.

Key Concepts Addition Property of Inequality

You can add the same number to each side of an inequality.

Arithmetic	Algebra
$7 > 3$, so $7 + 4 > 3 + 4$	If $a > b$, then $a + c > b + c$.
$2 < 5$, so $2 + 6 < 5 + 6$	If $a < b$, then $a + c < b + c$.

Real-World 🌐 Connection

You can increase the memory of a computer by adding more memory chips. These chips have extra memory in multiples of 8 megabytes.

3 EXAMPLE Adding to Solve an Inequality

Solve $n - 15 < 3$.

$$n - 15 < 3$$
$$n - 15 + 15 < 3 + 15 \quad \textbf{Add 15 to each side.}$$
$$n < 18 \quad \textbf{Simplify.}$$

Test-Taking Tip

To check that $n < 18$ is a solution of $n - 15 < 3$, use related equations $n = 18$ and $n - 15 = 3$. Substitute 18 into $n - 15 = 3$ and get $18 - 15 = 3$. The result suggests that you solved correctly.

✓ Check Understanding Example 3

3. Solve each inequality.

a. $m - 13 > 29$ b. $v - 4 \le 7$ c. $t - 5 \ge 11$
   $m > 42$ $v \le 11$ $t \ge 16$

Math Background

The same number can be added to or subtracted from each side of an inequality to get a new inequality with the same solutions as the original.

Teaching Notes

1 EXAMPLE Error Prevention

Point out that to rewrite an inequality in reverse order, you must pay attention to the direction of the inequality symbol. You rewrite $5 > x$ as $x < 5$, changing $>$ to $<$. Have students write an inequality for *Kyle is older than Jaime* in two ways. **Kyle's age > Jaime's age; Jaime's age < Kyle's age**

2 EXAMPLE Diversity

Some students may be unfamiliar with computer terminology. Explain that a *byte* is a unit of computer memory that stores a single character. Explain to students that the prefix *mega* means one million. Ask students to guess what 1 *megabyte* might mean. **one million bytes**

PowerPoint

📖 Additional Examples

1 Solve each inequality. Graph the solutions.
   a. $4 + s < 12$ **$s < 8$**
   b. $-16 \ge y - 14$
   $-2 \ge y$ or $y \le -2$
   See back of book for graphs.

2 Suppose your computer's hard drive has a capacity of 6 gigabytes (GB). The files you have stored on the hard drive occupy at least 2 GB. How much storage space is left for other files? **$s \le 4$; at most 4 GB are left.**

3 Solve $-10 < -13 + q$. **$3 < q$**

👥 Reaching All Students

Below Level Ask: *What do you do to each side of the equation to get the variable alone for $d + 5 = 9$?* **Subtract 5. For $f - 6 = 4$? Add 6.**	**Advanced Learners** Ask: *If you try to list all the solutions for $x > 1$, which number would you list first? Explain.* **Answers may vary. Sample: 2; because it's the first integer greater than 1.**	**Error Prevention** See note on page 107. **Diversity** See note on page 107.	**Closure** Ask students to compare solving *inequalities* involving addition and subtraction with solving *equations* involving addition and subtraction. **See back of book.**

3. Practice

Assignment Guide

1 Objective 1
ⒶⒷ **Core** 1–10, 20, 23, 28, 29, 31–34
Ⓒ **Extension** 35, 37

 **2 Objective 2**
ⒶⒷ **Core** 11–19, 21, 22, 24–27, 30
Ⓒ **Extension** 36

Test Prep 38–40
Mixed Review 41–47

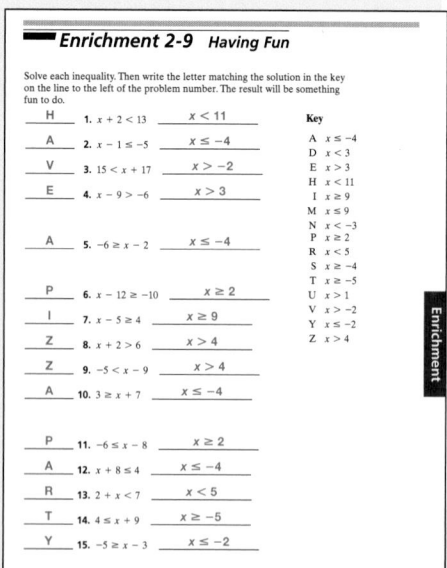

EXERCISES

Practice and Problem Solving

🔍 For more exercises, see *Extra Practice*.

Ⓐ **Practice by Example**

Example 1
(page 106)

Solve each inequality. Graph the solutions.
1–8. See back of book for graphs.

1. $w + 5 < 12$
$w < 7$
2. $2 > 9 + a$
$a < -7$
3. $x + 6 \geq 7$
$x \geq 1$
4. $2 + m \leq 2$
$m \leq 0$

5. $18 \leq 20 + w$
$w \geq -2$
6. $-7 < 5 + x$
$x > -12$
7. $30 \geq t + 45$
$t \leq -15$
8. $p + 22 \geq -10$
$p \geq -32$

Example 2 🌐
(page 107)

9. Transportation The total weight limit for a truck is 100,000 lb. The truck weighs 36,000 lb empty. What is the most that the truck's load can weigh? **64,000 lb**

🌐 **10. Budgeting** You are saving to buy a bicycle that will cost at least
[GPS] $120. Your parents give you $45 toward the bicycle. How much money will you have to save? **≥ $75**

Example 3
(page 107)

Solve each inequality.

11. $x - 5 \geq 6$
$x \geq 11$
12. $n - 12 \leq 3$
$n \leq 15$
13. $r - 4 \leq 3$
$r \leq 7$

14. $x - 7 < 15$
$x < 22$
15. $c - 9 > 5$
$c > 14$
16. $h - 10 \geq 6$
$h \geq 16$

17. $w - 8 < 3$
$w < 11$
18. $12 \geq y - 5$
$y \leq 17$
19. $4 \geq y - 4$
$y \leq 8$

Ⓑ **Apply Your Skills**

What do you do to the first inequality to get the second inequality?

20. $x + 8 \leq 11; x \leq 3$
Subtract 8 from each side.
21. $x - 3 > 9; x > 12$
Add 3 to each side.

Solve each inequality. Graph the solutions.
22–30. See margin for graphs.

22. $x - 8 > -2$
$x > 6$
23. $6 < y + 19$
$y > -13$
24. $3 \leq y - 5$
$y \geq 8$

25. $-8 \geq k - 3$
$k \leq -5$
26. $-3 + y > 4$
$y > 7$
27. $a - 0.5 < 2.5$
$a < 3$

28. $7 + r > 11$
$r > 4$
29. $9 < b + 4$
$b > 5$
30. $u - 3 \geq 9$
$u \geq 12$

Write an inequality for each sentence. Then solve the inequality.

35. Comm. Prop. of Add. Simplify.
Subt. Prop. of Inequality Simplify.
Simplify.

36. Subt. within parentheses. Simplify.
Add. Prop. of Inequality Simplify.

31. Thirteen plus a number n is greater than fifteen.
$13 + n > 15; n > 2$
32. The sum of a number w and 3 is less than or equal to ten.
$w + 3 \leq 10; w \leq 7$

🌐 **33. Shopping** Jim has $87. He spends $6 for socks and at least $32 for shoes. How much does he have left to spend for shirts?
≤ $49

34. A store's dressing room has a limit of 10 garments per customer. If Carol has at least 3 garments below the limit, how many garments does she have in her dressing room? **≤ 7 garments**

Ⓒ **Challenge**

Reasoning Justify each step. 35–36. See above left.

35. $4 + a + 3 > 16$
$4 + 3 + a > 16$
$7 + a > 16$
$7 - 7 + a > 16 - 7$
$a > 9$

36. $m - 2(8 - 5) \leq -9$
$m - 2(3) \leq -9$
$m - 6 \leq -9$
$m - 6 + 6 \leq -9 + 6$
$m \leq -3$

[GPS] Use the Guided Problem Solving worksheet with Exercise 10.

22.
[number line: 0 2 6, open circle at 6]

23.
[number line: −13 0 5, open circle at −13]

24.
[number line: 0 2 8, closed circle at 8]

25–30. See back of book.

Practice 2-9 Solving One-Step Inequalities by Adding or Subtracting

Write an inequality for each sentence. Then solve the inequality.

1. Six less than n is less than −4.
$n - 6 < -4; n < 2$

2. The sum of a number k and five is greater than or equal to two.
$k + 5 \geq 2; k \geq -3$

3. Nine more than a number b is greater than negative three.
$b + 9 > -3; b > -12$

4. You must be at least 48 inches tall to ride an amusement park ride, and your little sister is 39 inches tall. How many inches i must she grow before she may ride the ride?
$39 + i \geq 48; i \geq 9$

5. You need no more than 3,000 calories in a day. You consumed 840 calories at breakfast and 1,150 calories at lunch. How many calories c can you eat for dinner?
$840 + 1,150 + c \leq 3,000; c \leq 1,010$

Solve each inequality. Graph the solutions.

6. $7 + x \geq 9$ $x \geq 2$
7. $-5 \leq x - 6$ $x \geq 1$
8. $0 \geq x + 12$ $x \leq -12$
9. $x - 15 \leq -8$ $x \leq 7$
10. $13 + x \geq 13$ $x \geq 0$
11. $x - 8 > -5$ $x > 3$
12. $4 + x < -2$ $x < -6$
13. $x - 9 > -11$ $x > -2$
14. $x - 6 \leq -1$ $x \leq 5$
15. $-4 + x < -4$ $x < 0$

Enrichment 2-9 Having Fun

Solve each inequality. Then write the letter matching the solution in the key on the line to the left of the problem number. The result will be something fun to do.

			Key
H	1. $x + 2 < 13$	$x < 11$	A $x \leq -4$
A	2. $x - 1 \leq -5$	$x \leq -4$	D $x < 3$
V	3. $15 < x + 17$	$x > -2$	E $x > 3$
E	4. $x - 9 > -6$	$x > 3$	H $x < 11$
			I $x \geq 9$
			M $x \leq 9$
			N $x < -3$
A	5. $-6 \geq x - 2$	$x \leq -4$	P $x \geq 2$
			R $x < 5$
			S $x \geq -4$
P	6. $x - 12 \geq -10$	$x \geq 2$	T $x \geq -5$
I	7. $x - 5 \geq 4$	$x \geq 9$	U $x > 1$
Z	8. $x + 2 > 6$	$x > 4$	V $x > -2$
Z	9. $-5 < x - 9$	$x > 4$	Y $x \leq -2$
A	10. $3 \geq x + 7$	$x \leq -4$	Z $x > 4$
P	11. $-6 \leq x - 8$	$x \geq 2$	
A	12. $x + 8 \leq 4$	$x \leq -4$	
R	13. $2 + x < 7$	$x < 5$	
T	14. $4 \leq x + 9$	$x \geq -5$	
Y	15. $-5 \geq x - 3$	$x \leq -2$	

---

37. Writing in Math Which of the inequalities $m > -2, m < -2$, $-2 < m$, and $-2 > m$ are solutions to $m + 4 > 2$? Explain.
Solving $m + 4 > 2$ gives $m > -2$, which can also be written $-2 < m$.

Test Prep

Multiple Choice

38. If x and y are positive and $x > y$, which is true? **A**

A. $x > \dfrac{x + y}{2}$ **B.** $y > \dfrac{x + y}{2}$ **C.** $x = \dfrac{x + y}{2}$ **D.** $x < \dfrac{x + y}{2}$

For Exercises 39 and 40, use the table at the left. Assume that your computer's basic systems use at least 12 MB of memory.

Computer Memory

Application	Memory Requirement
Word processor	11 MB
Spreadsheet	5 MB
Web browser	9 MB
E-mail	4 MB

39. You want to have your e-mail active while you work on a paper with your word processor. How much memory must your computer have? **H**

F. at most 12 MB **G.** at least 15 MB

H. at least 27 MB **I.** at most 32 MB

40. If you search the Web for data at the same time that you have your e-mail active, how much memory must your computer have? **B**

A. at most 41 MB **B.** at least 25 MB

C. at most 20 MB **D.** at least 15 MB

Take It to the NET
Online lesson quiz at
www.PHSchool.com
Web Code: ada-0209

Mixed Review

Lesson 2-8

Graph the solutions of each inequality. 41–44. See back of book.

41. $x < 2$ **42.** $x \ge -5$ **43.** $y \le 4$ **44.** $m > 0$

Lesson 2-3

Simplify each expression.

45. $4x + 6 - 2x + 6$
$2x + 12$

46. $-4 - 5t + t - 10$
$-4t - 14$

Lesson 1-4

47. Write an integer to represent a debt of \$35. -35

✓ Checkpoint Quiz 2

Lessons 2-4 through 2-9

Instant self-check quiz online and on CD-ROM

State whether the equation is *true*, *false*, or an *open sentence*. Explain.

1. $4 + 15 = 27 - 8$
true; $19 = 19$

2. $-30 = 9w$
open; variable

3. $|9 - 10| = 8 - 9$
false; $1 \ne -1$

Solve each equation or inequality.

4. $y - 3 = -7$
-4

5. $x + 4 = 8$
4

6. $7t = 42$
6

7. $m \div 8 = -4$
-32

8. $-90 = 10f$
-9

9. $9 \le 3 + a$
$a \ge 6$

10. $r - 12 < 7$
$r < 19$

11. $m + 15 > -4$
$m > -19$

12. You have some quarters, dimes, and pennies—eight coins worth \$.77 altogether. How many of each type of coin do you have?
1 quarter, 5 dimes, 2 pennies

---

4. Assess

Solve each inequality.

1. $e + 4 \le 14$ $e \le 10$

2. $-22 \ge g - 6$ $-16 \ge g$

3. A number q plus the opposite of 5 is less than or equal to 0. $q \le 5$

Test Prep

Resources

For additional practice with a variety of test item formats:
• Test Prep, p. 121
• Test-Taking Strategies, p. 116
• Test-Taking Strategies With Transparencies

✓ Chapter Checkpoint 2

To check understanding of Lessons 2-4 to 2-9:

Checkpoint Quiz 2 (p. 109)

Teaching Resources
Checkpoint Quiz 2 (also in Prentice Hall Assessment System)

Reaching All Students
Reading and Math Literacy 2C

Spanish versions available.

Reteaching 2-9 *Solving One-Step Inequalities by Adding or Subtracting*

Write an inequality for the sentence. Then solve the inequality. The sum of a number n and seven is greater than twelve.

Words Sum of a number n and seven is greater than twelve
↓
Inequality n $+$ 7 $>$ 12

To solve, subtract 7 from each side.
$n + 7 > 12$
$n + 7 - 7 > 12 - 7$
$n > 5$
Check: $6 > 5$
Is $6 + 7 > 12$? Yes.

Write an inequality for each sentence. Then solve the inequality.

1. Eight less than a number k is less than 5.
$k - 8 < 5; k < 13$

2. Nine plus a number x is greater than or equal to negative two.
$9 + x \ge -2; x \ge -11$

3. Five subtracted from a number p is less than or equal to negative ten.
$p - 5 \le -10; p \le -5$

4. A number d plus 17 is less than 25.
$d + 17 < 25; d < 8$

5. The sum of a number s and six is greater than negative seven.
$s + 6 > -7; s > -13$

6. Ten subtracted from a number y is less than twenty.
$y - 10 < 20; y < 30$

7. 82 plus a number j is greater than or equal to -28.
$82 + j \ge -28; j \ge -110$

8. A number n minus 9 is less than or equal to -23.
$n - 9 \le -23; n \le -14$

9. Nineteen less than a number h is greater than three.
$h - 19 > 3; h > 22$

Alternative Assessment

Have students work in groups of five to construct and write inequalities. One student chooses a variable or rolls a number cube to determine the first term. The second student chooses a $+$ or $-$ symbol. The third student does whatever the first student did not do, rolls a number cube or chooses a variable, to determine the next term. The fourth student chooses an inequality symbol. The fifth student rolls a number cube to determine the last term. Have students solve the inequality. Then have group members switch roles.

109

2-10

1. Plan

Lesson Preview

✔ **Check Skills You'll Need**

Solving Equations by Multiplying or Dividing
Lesson 2-6: Examples 2 and 3;
Exercises 1–28.
Extra Practice, p. 745.

Lesson Resources

 **Teaching Resources**
Practice, Reteaching, Enrichment

 Reaching All Students
Practice Workbook 2-10
Spanish Practice Workbook 2-10
Guided Problem Solving 2-10

⏱ **Presentation Assistant Plus!**
Transparencies and PowerPoint™
• Check Skills You'll Need 2-10
• Additional Examples 2-10
• Student Edition Answers 2-10
• Lesson Quiz 2-10
PH Presentation Pro CD-ROM 2-10

(**ASSESSMENT** *SYSTEM*)

Computer Test Generator CD-ROM

💻 **Technology**
Resource Pro® CD-ROM
Computer Test Generator CD-ROM
PH Presentation Pro CD-ROM

💻 **www.PHSchool.com**
Student Site
• Teacher Web Code: adk-5500
• Self-grading Lesson Quiz
PH SuccessNet Teacher Center
• Lesson Planner
• Resources

Plus 🔲**TEXT**

Solving One-Step Inequalities by Multiplying or Dividing

What You'll Learn

OBJECTIVE 1 To solve one-step inequalities using division

OBJECTIVE 2 To solve one-step inequalities using multiplication

. . . And Why

To solve real-world problems involving weight limits

✔ **Check Skills You'll Need**

Solve each equation.

1. $6x = 24$ 4

2. $63 = -7v$ -9

3. $\frac{x}{-2} = 10$ -20

4. $\frac{t}{6} = 48$ 288

🔖 For help, go to Lesson 2-6.

🔲**TEXT** Interactive lesson includes instant self-check, tutorials, and activities.

OBJECTIVE
1 **Solving Inequalities Using Division**

Investigation

Solving Inequalities

Explore what happens when you divide each side of an inequality by a number.

1. Simplify each expression at the right. Replace each ▪ with > or <.

$6 \div 3$ ▪ $12 \div 3$	<
$6 \div 2$ ▪ $12 \div 2$	<
$6 \div 1$ ▪ $12 \div 1$	<
$6 \div (-1)$ ▪ $12 \div (-1)$	>
$6 \div (-2)$ ▪ $12 \div (-2)$	>
$6 \div (-3)$ ▪ $12 \div (-3)$	>

2. **Patterns** Does the direction of the inequality symbol stay the same as you divide each side of an inequality by the given numbers? Explain your reasoning. **No; the inequality symbol switches direction when you divide by a negative number.**

You can solve an inequality that involves multiplication by dividing each side of the inequality by a nonzero number.

Key Concepts **Division Properties of Inequality**

If you divide each side of an inequality by a positive number, you leave the inequality symbol unchanged.

Arithmetic

$3 < 6$, so $\frac{3}{3} < \frac{6}{3}$

$8 > 2$, so $\frac{8}{2} > \frac{2}{2}$

Algebra

If $a < b$ and c is positive, then $\frac{a}{c} < \frac{b}{c}$.

If $a > b$ and c is positive, then $\frac{a}{c} > \frac{b}{c}$.

If you divide each side of an inequality by a negative number, *you reverse the inequality symbol.*

Arithmetic

$6 < 12$, so $\frac{6}{-3} > \frac{12}{-3}$

$16 > 8$, so $\frac{16}{-4} < \frac{8}{-4}$

Algebra

If $a < b$ and c is negative, then $\frac{a}{c} > \frac{b}{c}$.

If $a > b$ and c is negative, then $\frac{a}{c} < \frac{b}{c}$.

🔄 **Ongoing Assessment and Intervention**

Before the Lesson
Diagnose prerequisite skills using:
• Check Skills You'll Need

During the Lesson
Monitor progress using:
• Check Understanding
• Additional Examples
• Test Prep

After the Lesson
Assess knowledge using:
• Lesson Quiz
• Computer Test Generator CD-ROM

1 EXAMPLE Real-World Problem Solving

Engineering An elevator can carry up to 2,500 lb. Suppose the weight of an average adult is 150 lb. At most how many average-sized adults can safely ride the elevator at the same time?

Words

| the number of adults | times | 150 lb | is less than or equal to | 2,500 lb |

Let x = the number of adults.

Inequality x ·   150 lb   ≤   2,500

$$150x \leq 2,500$$

$$\frac{150x}{150} \leq \frac{2,500}{150}$$ Divide each side by 150.

$$x \leq 16.\overline{6}$$ Simplify. Round the answer down to find a whole number of people.

At most 16 average adults can safely ride the elevator at one time.

Check Is the answer reasonable? The total weight of 16 average adults is 16(150) = 2,400 lb. This is less than 2,500 lb but so close that another adult could not ride. The answer is reasonable.

✓ Check Understanding   Example 1

1. Solve each inequality.

   a. $4x > 40$ **b.** $-21 > 3m$ **c.** $36 > -9t$

   $x > 10$ $m < -7$ $t > -4$

OBJECTIVE

2 Solving Inequalities Using Multiplication

You can solve inequalities that involve division.

Key Concepts   Multiplication Properties of Inequality

If you multiply each side of an inequality by a positive number, you leave the inequality symbol unchanged.

Arithmetic	**Algebra**
3 < 4, so 3(5) < 4(5)	If $a < b$ and c is positive, then $ac < bc$.
7 > 2, so 7(6) > 2(6)	If $a > b$ and c is positive, then $ac > bc$.

If you multiply each side of an inequality by a negative number, *you reverse the inequality symbol.*

Arithmetic	**Algebra**
6 < 9, so 6(−2) > 9(−2)	If $a < b$ and c is negative, then $ac > bc$.
7 > 5, so 7(−3) < 5(−3)	If $a > b$ and c is negative, then $ac < bc$.

2-10 Solving One-Step Inequalities by Multiplying or Dividing   **111**

👥 Reaching All Students

Below Level If you allow students to use "reverse the inequality," make sure they understand that it means reversing the direction of the inequality symbol.

Advanced Learners Ask students what results if each side of an inequality is multiplied by zero. The value of each side becomes zero and you no longer have an inequality.

Visual Learners See note on page 111.
Error Prevention See note on page 112.

---

2. Teach

Professional Development

Math Background

When you multiply or divide each side of an inequality by a negative number, you must reverse the direction of the inequality symbol. If you don't reverse the direction of the symbol, the resulting inequality does not have the same meaning as the original inequality.

Teaching Notes

Investigation (Optional)
Use a numerical example to help students understand why the direction of an inequality symbol must be reversed when dividing each side of the inequality by a negative number. Draw a number line on the board. Mark 6 and 12. Point out that 6 < 12. Multiply 6 and 12 by −1 to get −6 and −12, graph them on the number line, and point out that −12 < −6.

1 EXAMPLE Visual Learners

Give students a set of one-step inequalities that can be solved by division or multiplication. Have them identify those for which they will have to divide or multiply by a negative number. Suggest that whenever they recognize such an inequality, they circle the inequality symbol to remind them to reverse the direction.

1 EXAMPLE Teaching Tip

Ask students why the answer is not 16.$\overline{6}$ adults and not 17 adults.

The answer cannot be 16.$\overline{6}$ adults because 0.$\overline{6}$ of an adult does not make sense. The answer cannot be 17 adults because 17 is not a solution to $x \leq 16.\overline{6}$.

PowerPoint

Additional Examples

1 1. A 1-ton truck has the ability to haul 1 ton, or 2,000 lb. At most, how many television sets can the truck carry if each TV set weighs 225 lb? **8 television sets**

Real-World Connection

Express elevators can travel as fast as 1,800 ft/min.

STATE INSPECTION CERTIFICATE
Department of Public Safety
Certificate for Use of Elevator

LOCATION: 221 Pat Street
SPEED: 150 ft. per min.
CAPACITY: 2,500 lb.
ISSUED ON: 08/06/03
EXPIRES: 08/06/04

111

Additional Examples

2 Solve.

$\frac{z}{-8} \le -2$ $z \ge 16$

2 EXAMPLE Error Prevention

Students sometimes forget to reverse the inequality symbol because they are involved with the multiplying or dividing of the numbers. Suggest students determine first whether they must change the direction of the inequality symbol. If so, write the new inequality symbol first.

Closure

Have students state the main difference between solving one-step multiplication and division *inequalities* and solving one-step multiplication and division *equations*. **An inequality symbol points in one direction. To solve a one-step multiplication or division inequality might require that you divide or multiply each side of the inequality by a negative number. When you do this, you must also reverse the direction of the inequality symbol.**

2 EXAMPLE   **Multiplying to Solve an Inequality**

Solve $\frac{t}{-4} \ge 7$.

$$\frac{t}{-4} \ge 7$$

$$-4\left(\frac{t}{-4}\right) \le -4(7) \qquad \text{Multiply each side by } -4 \text{ and reverse the inequality symbol.}$$

$$t \le -28 \qquad \text{Simplify.}$$

✓ **Check Understanding**   Example 2

2. Solve each inequality.

   a. $\frac{m}{4} \ge 2$ $m \ge 8$ b. $\frac{t}{-3} < 7$ $t > -21$ c. $5 < \frac{r}{7}$ $r > 35$

More Than One Way

Solve $-3x < 12$.

Roberto's Method

Divide each side by -3 and reverse the direction of the inequality symbol.

$$-3x < 12$$
$$\frac{-3x}{-3} > \frac{12}{-3}$$
$$x > -4$$

Michelle's Method

Rewrite the inequality so the coefficient of the variable is positive.

$$-3x < 12$$
$$-3x + 3x < 12 + 3x$$
$$0 < 12 + 3x$$
$$0 - 12 < 3x + 12 - 12$$
$$-12 < 3x$$
$$\frac{-12}{3} < \frac{3x}{3}$$
$$-4 < x, \text{ or } x > -4$$

Choose a Method

1. Which method would you use to solve this inequality? Explain. **Answers may vary.**
   Sample: Roberto's method; it uses fewer steps.
2. Solve $18 < -6x$ using Roberto's Method or Michelle's Method.
   $x < -3$

112   **Chapter 2** Solving One-Step Equations and Inequalities

Practice and Problem Solving

Assignment Guide

1 Objective 1
Ⓐ Ⓑ Core 1–13, 28,
30–32, 36–40, 43, 45
Ⓒ Extension 46, 47, 49, 50

2 Objective 2
Ⓐ Ⓑ Core 14–27, 29,
33–35, 41, 42, 44
Ⓒ Extension 48

Test Prep 51–54
Mixed Review 55–62

Ⓐ **Practice by Example**

Example 1
(page 111)

Solve each inequality.

1. $3t > 21$
$t > 7$
2. $-2x < 14$
$x > -7$
3. $8 > -4x$
$x > -2$
4. $6m > 24$
$m > 4$
5. $9x \le 27$
$x \le 3$
6. $18 < -2m$
$m < -9$
7. $64 \le -8k$
$k \le -8$
8. $7m > 28$
$m > 4$
9. $3x < 21$
$x < 7$
10. $81 > -9y$
$y > -9$
11. $5f \ge -15$
$f \ge -3$
12. $-3x < 0$
$x > 0$

🌐 **13. Earnings** Paul earns $9 per hour. How many hours must Paul work to earn at least $645? **at least 72 hours**

Example 2
(page 112)

42. $\frac{b}{4} \ge 3$; $b \ge 12$

43. $\frac{v}{-5} < 9$; $v > -45$

Solve each inequality.

14. $\frac{x}{-6} > 3$
$x < -18$
15. $\frac{m}{6} \le -18$
$m \le -108$
16. $\frac{x}{3} \ge 5$
$x \ge 15$
17. $\frac{y}{4} > 3$
$y > 12$
18. $\frac{r}{-4} > 2$
$r < -8$
19. $6 > \frac{q}{-3}$
$q > -18$
20. $20 < \frac{v}{6}$
$v > 120$
21. $\frac{b}{4} \ge 3$
$b \ge 12$
22. $\frac{v}{-5} < 9$
$v > -45$
23. $\frac{x}{4} \le 12$
$x \le 48$
24. $\frac{x}{-3} < 0$
$x > 0$
25. $8 > \frac{h}{10}$
$h < 80$

Ⓑ **Apply Your Skills**

44. Answers may vary. Sample: Multiplying each side by zero can give the inequality $0 < 0$, which is false. Division by zero is not defined.

45. You have to divide by –4 instead of 4. The direction of the inequality sign is different when you solve each inequality.

$3x > -12$
$\frac{3x}{3} < \frac{-12}{3}$
$x < -4$

What happens to the inequality symbol when you do the following to each side of an inequality?

26. subtract a negative number
unchanged
27. multiply by a positive number
unchanged
28. divide by a negative number
reverses
29. multiply by a negative number
reverses

Solve each inequality.

30. $-4x < -16$
$x > 4$
31. $-r \ge 21$
$r \le -21$
32. $\frac{1}{2}x \ge -3$
$x \ge -6$
33. $\frac{b}{3} \ge -31$
$b \ge -93$
34. $-3 \ge \frac{g}{-7}$
$g \ge 21$
35. $3 > \frac{b}{-6}$
$b > -18$
36. $4x > -8$
$x > -2$
37. $-6x \le -24$
$x \ge 4$

🌐 **38. Budgeting** Marnie pays $.06 per kilowatt-hour for electricity. She
[GPS] has budgeted $72 for her electricity. What is the greatest number of kilowatt-hours Marnie can use and stay within her budget?
1,200 kilowatt-hours

39. Error Analysis Your friend solved $3x > -12$ as shown at the left. What error did your friend make? **You reversed the inequality symbol when dividing each side by a positive number.**

Write an inequality for each sentence. Then solve the inequality.

40. The product of negative two and a number a is greater than ten.
$-2a > 10$; $a < -5$
41. A number t multiplied by seven is less than or equal to 21.
$7t \le 21$; $t \le 3$
42. A number b divided by 4 is greater than or equal to 3.
See above left.
43. The quotient of a number v divided by -5 is less than 9.
See above left.
44. Reasoning The rules for multiplying and dividing both sides of an inequality do not mention zero. Discuss why.
See above left.
45. Writing in Math Explain how solving $-4t < 32$ is different from solving $4t < -32$. **See above left.**

Writing in Math

For help with writing an explanation for Exercise 45, see page 115.

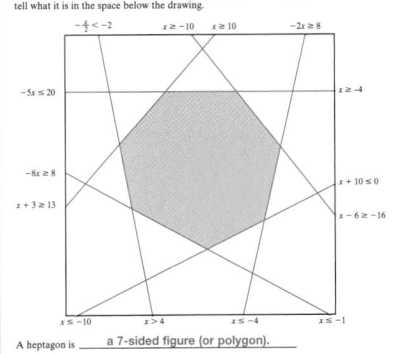
 GPS Use the Guided Problem Solving worksheet with Exercise 38.

Lesson Quiz 2-10

Solve each inequality.

1. $3x \geq -27$ $x \geq -9$

2. $-5w > 15$ $w < -3$

3. $\frac{1}{4}y \leq \frac{1}{2}$ $y \leq 2$

4. $\frac{-x}{5} \leq 0$ $x \geq 0$

5. $4f > -12$ $f > -3$

Alternative Assessment

Have students write a letter to a classmate who was absent. The letter should explain why we must reverse the inequality symbol whenever we multiply or divide each side of an inequality by a negative number.

Test Prep

 **Resources**

For additional practice with a variety of test item formats:
• Test Prep, p. 121
• Test-Taking Strategies, p. 116
• Test-Taking Strategies With Transparencies

Reteaching 2-10 *Solving One-Step Inequalities by Multiplying or Dividing*

Solve $5x < -40$.
$5x < -40$
Since 5 and x are multiplied, use a division property of inequality and divide both sides by 5.
$5x < -40$
$\frac{5x}{5} < \frac{-40}{5}$
$x < -8$

Solve $\frac{x}{-4} \geq 3$.
Since x is divided by -4, use a multiplication property of inequality and multiply both sides by -4.
When you multiply both sides of an inequality by a negative number, you must reverse the direction of the inequality symbol.
$\frac{x}{-4} \geq 3$
$(-4)\frac{x}{-4} \leq (-4)3$
$x \leq -12$

Solve each inequality.
1. $7n \geq 42$ 2. $-3m < 27$
   $n \geq 6$ $m > -9$
3. $\frac{x}{3} > 7$ 4. $\frac{y}{4} \leq 8$
   $x > 21$ $y \leq 32$
5. $\frac{q}{-2} < 5$ 6. $-n \geq 2$
   $q > -10$ $n \leq -2$
7. $27 \leq 3k$ 8. $6 \geq \frac{d}{7}$
   $k \geq 9$ $d \leq 42$
9. $\frac{r}{-9} < 12$ 10. $-13 < \frac{h}{-3}$
   $r > -108$ $h < 39$
11. $-15 \geq -3z$ 12. $2f \leq -27$
   $z \geq 5$ $f \leq -\frac{27}{2}$

Reasoning Justify each step.

46. $2g \geq -18$ Div.
$\frac{2g}{2} \geq \frac{-18}{2}$ Prop. of Ineq.
$g \geq -9$ Simplify.

47. $-7m \leq -28$ Div.
$\frac{-7m}{-7} \geq \frac{-28}{-7}$ Prop. of Ineq.
$m \geq 4$ Simplify.

48. $\frac{a}{3} > 12$ Mult.
$\left(\frac{a}{3}\right)(3) > 12(3)$ Prop. of Ineq.
$a > 36$ Simplify.

49. Answers may vary. Sample: Bill needs at most $15 for the day. How many five-dollar bills does he need?

49. Open-Ended Write a problem that you would solve using the inequality $5m \leq 15$. **See left.**

🌐 **50. Day Care** In Georgia, for every 18 four-year-old children in day care there must be at least one teacher. At one day-care center, 56 four-year-olds are signed up for next year. At least how many teachers must the center have to teach four-year-olds next year?

4 teachers

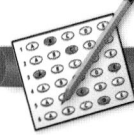

Test Prep

Multiple Choice

51. What is done to $\frac{1}{3}x \leq 18$ to get $x \leq 54$? **A**
  A. Multiply each side by 3.
  B. Divide each side by 3.
  C. Multiply each side by $\frac{1}{3}$.
  D. Multiply each side by $3x$.

52. Which number is a solution of $-2x \leq -4$? **I**
  F. -2 **G.** 0   **H.** 1   **I.** 10

53. Which inequality has the same solutions as $\frac{a}{4} < -20$? **D**
  A. $4d > 80$ **B.** $\frac{m}{-4} < -40$ **C.** $-2r < -40$ **D.** $\frac{z}{-2} > 40$

54. Which inequality best represents the following sentence?
  A number x divided by 7 is greater than -13. **G**
  F. $\frac{7}{x} > -13$ **G.** $\frac{x}{7} > -13$ **H.** $\frac{7}{x} < -13$ **I.** $\frac{x}{7} < -13$

Take It to the NET
Online lesson quiz at
www.PHSchool.com
Web Code: ada-0210

Mixed Review

Lesson 2-9 **Solve each inequality.**

55. $6 + t > 17$ $t > 11$ **56.** $m - 4 \leq 6$ $m \leq 10$

57. $-9 \geq r + 5$ $r \leq -14$ **58.** $11 > v - 12$ $v < 23$

Lessons 2-1 and 2-2 **Name each property shown.**

59. $-12(100 - 3) = -12(100) - (-12)(3)$ **Dist. Prop.**

60. $102 + 34 + 98 = 102 + 98 + 34$ **Comm. Prop. of Add.**

61. $(80 + 321) + 109 = 80 + (321 + 109)$ **Assoc. Prop. of Add.**

Lesson 1-6 🌐 **62. Weather** The high temperature one day in January was $34°F$, and the low temperature was $27°F$. What was the difference between the high and the low temperatures that day? **7°F**

Writing in Math

Writing to Compare

For Use With Page 113, Exercise 45

Sometimes you are asked to compare two or more quantities, methods, or concepts. When you are writing to compare two methods, it is important to explain the similarities and differences.

Writing in Math Explain how solving $-4t < 32$ is different from solving $4t < -32$.

Here is one student's response.

Since the question is to explain how solving the inequalities is different, I will solve each one separately to see what I do differently. Then I will explain the difference.

The first inequality:

$-4t < 32$

$\dfrac{-4t}{-4} < \dfrac{32}{-4}$ **Divide each side of the inequality by -4.**

$t > -8$ **When you divide by a negative number on each side of an inequality, you reverse the inequality symbol.**

The second inequality:

$4t < -32$

$\dfrac{4t}{4} < \dfrac{-32}{4}$ **Divide each side of the inequality by 4.**

$t < -8$ **When you divide by a positive number on each side of an inequality, you keep the inequality symbol as is.**

Now I can explain what is different.

To solve $-4t < 32$, you divide each side by -4, a negative number. You have to reverse the direction of the inequality symbol.

To solve $4t < 32$, you divide each side by 4, a positive number. You leave the direction of the inequality symbol unchanged.

EXERCISES

1. Explain how solving $\dfrac{x}{3} > -6$ is different from solving $\dfrac{x}{-3} > 6$.
   See margin.
2. Explain how finding the value of $4 \cdot 2 + 5$ is different from finding the value of $4(2 + 5)$.
   See margin.

Writing in Math

Writing to Compare

This feature helps students learn to write a comparison of two methods for solving inequalities.

Teaching Notes

Teaching Tip
Some students may want to skip solving the inequalities and go straight to the explanation. Encourage students to always do whatever math is involved first because there may be other differences that are not always obvious.

Error Prevention!

After students solve the inequalities, have them compare the solutions carefully to make sure there is a difference. If there is no difference, they need to check their solution process.

1. When solving $\dfrac{x}{-3} > 6$, you multiply by a negative number. Therefore you must reverse the inequality symbol. You do not have to reverse the inequality symbol when solving $\dfrac{x}{3} > -6$ since you multiply by a positive number.

2. When finding the value of $4 \cdot 2 + 5$, you follow the order of operations and multiply $4 \cdot 2$ first, then add 5. The value is 13. When finding the value of $4(2 + 5)$, you can follow the order of operations and add $2 + 5$ first, then multiply the sum by 4 to get 28. You can also use the Distributive Property and multiply both 2 and 5 by 4, then find the sum of the products to get 28.

Writing Short Responses

To get full test credit for a short-response answer, students need to do more than just show an answer.

Resources

ASSESSMENT SYSTEM

Test-Taking Strategies With Transparencies
• Transparency 2
• Practice sheet, p. 2

Teaching Notes

Explaining steps, justifying answers, showing work, and drawing diagrams will not only earn students more points on tests but will also help them develop better problem-solving skills.

Teaching Tip
Students can sometimes earn one or two points even when they are unable to write an equation to represent a problem. Students can receive partial credit for showing the reasoning they used to find the answer.

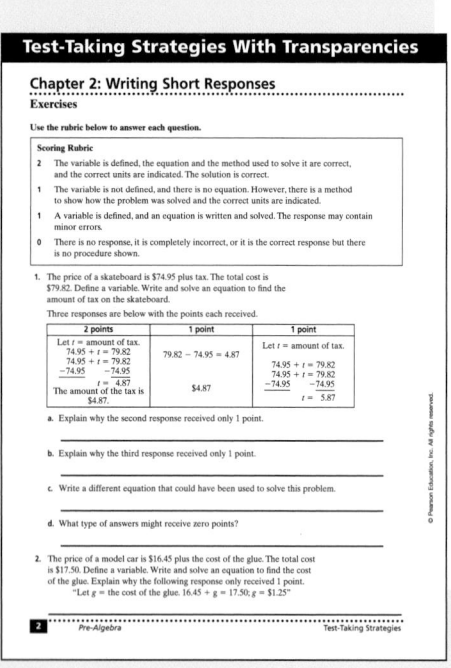

Short-response questions are often worth 2 points. To get full credit you need to give the correct answer and either give a good explanation, justify your thinking, or show your work.

EXAMPLE

Jenna had a coupon for $15 off the price of a graphing calculator. She used it to buy a calculator for $89 before tax. **(a)** Write an equation to find the original price. **(b)** Solve your equation.

Here is a *scoring rubric* to help assess different types of answers.

Scoring Rubric

[2] The original price of the calculator is correct. The equation and the solution are correct with all work shown.

[1] The original price is correct, but no work is shown, OR the original price is incorrect but the work shown has minimal errors.

Here are three responses with the points each received.

2 points	1 point	0 points
x is the original price. $$x - 15 = 89$$ $$x - 15 + 15 = 89 + 15$$ $$x = 104$$ The original price was $104.	x is the original price. $$x + 15 = 89$$ $$x + 15 - 15 = 89 - 15$$ $$x = 74$$ The original price was $74.	The original price was $74.

EXERCISES

Use the scoring rubric to explain the score given for each response. 1–5. See back of book.

1. the 2-point response   **2.** the 1-point response   **3.** the 0-point response

Write and solve an equation to solve each problem. Then score your answer using the scoring rubric above.

4. Your grandfather gives you a share of stock that it is currently worth $62. He tells you that it has increased in value by $17 since he purchased it. How much did he pay for the stock?

5. The height of a multistory building is 135 ft. It has 15 stories. What is the height of each story?

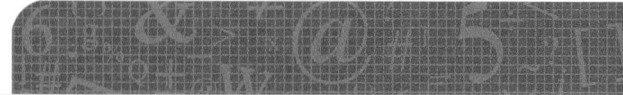

Chapter Review

Vocabulary

additive identity (p. 67)	deductive reasoning (p. 77)	multiplicative identity (p. 67)
Associative Properties of Addition and Multiplication (p. 66)	Distributive Property (p. 71)	open sentence (p. 80)
coefficient (p. 76)	equation (p. 80)	simplify a variable expression (p. 76)
Commutative Properties of Addition and Multiplication (p. 66)	Identity Properties of Addition and Multiplication (p. 67)	solution of an equation (p. 81)
constant (p. 76)	inequality (p. 102)	solution of an inequality (p. 102)
	inverse operations (p. 86)	term (p. 76)
	like terms (p. 76)	

Reading Math
Understanding Vocabulary

For each definition given on the left, write the letter of the word or phrase being defined.

1. a value that makes an equation true **d**
2. a term that has no variable **b**
3. a number or the product of a number and variable(s) **e**
4. the number that multiplies a variable **a**
5. the number zero **c**
6. terms with identical variables **h**
7. an equation with one or more variables **j**
8. a mathematical sentence with an equal sign **f**
9. the number one **g**
10. a mathematical sentence with $>, <, \geq, \leq,$ or $\neq$ **i**

a. coefficient
b. constant
c. additive identity
d. solution of an equation
e. term
f. equation
g. multiplicative identity
h. like terms
i. inequality
j. open sentence

Take It to the NET
Online vocabulary quiz at **www.PHSchool.com**
Web Code: adj-0251

Skills and Concepts

2-1 Objectives

▼ To identify properties of addition and multiplication (p. 66)

▼ To use properties to solve problems (p. 67)

Use the **Commutative Property** to change order. Use the **Associative Property** to change grouping. Adding zero to an expression does not change its value. Multiplying an expression by 1 does not change its value.

Simplify each expression. Justify each step.

11. $58 + 16 + 2 + 4$ **80**   **12.** $4 \cdot 7 \cdot 25 \cdot 1$ **700**   **13.** $125 + 347 + 75$ **547**

14. $(20 \cdot 65) \cdot 5$ **6,500**   **15.** $10 \cdot 15 \cdot 2$ **300**   **16.** $37 + 0 + (5 + 63)$ **105**

2-2 Objectives

▼ To use the Distributive Property with numerical expressions (p. 71)

▼ To use the Distributive Property with algebraic expressions (p. 73)

Use the **Distributive Property** to multiply a number outside parentheses by each term of a sum or difference.

Mental Math Use the Distributive Property to simplify.

17. $9(96)$ 864   **18.** $8(62)$ 496   **19.** $(43)(9)$ 387

Use the Distributive Property to multiply.

20. $4(w + 9)$
$4w + 36$

21. $(2 + 4a)12$
$24 + 48a$

22. $-7(6 - 2m)$
$-42 + 14m$

23. Explain why $5x + 15 = 5(x + 3)$.
You can write 15 as $5 \cdot 3$. $5x + 5 \cdot 3 = 5(x + 3)$ by the Distributive Property.

2-3 Objectives

▼ To identify parts of a variable expression (p. 76)

▼ To simplify expressions (p. 76)

To **simplify** a variable expression, replace it with an equivalent expression with as few terms as possible.

Simplify each expression.

24. $8a + 7 - 11a$ $-3a + 7$ **25.** $3(w + 3) + 4w$ $7w + 9$

26. $6 + x - 4x + 3$ $9 - 3x$ **27.** $19 - 4(5n + 1) - 4n$ $15 - 24n$

28. $10 + 7k - 2(3k + 5)$ k **29.** $-7(2r - 1) + 3(8 - r)$
$-17r + 31$

30. Explain how to determine whether terms are like terms.
They have the same variable or no variable and are separated by addition or subtraction signs.

2-4 Objectives

▼ To classify types of equations (p. 80)

▼ To check equations using substitution (p. 81)

You can write an **equation** to model a situation. An equation with numerical expressions is true or false. An equation with at least one variable is an **open sentence**. A **solution** of an open-sentence equation is a value of a variable that makes the equation true.

Write an equation for each sentence. Is each equation *true, false,* **or an** *open sentence?*

31. Thirty-two plus five equals the product of six and six.
$32 + 5 = 6 \cdot 6$; false

32. A number t divided by seventeen equals the opposite of three.
$\frac{t}{17} = -3$; open

33. The product of four and twenty equals eighty.
$4 \cdot 20 = 80$; true

34. **Culture** The admission price to an art museum increased by $1.75 to $6.50. Let p be the original admission price. Write an equation to model the situation. $p + 1.75 = 6.50$

2-5 and 2-6 Objectives

▼ To solve one-step equations using subtraction (p. 86)

▼ To solve one-step equations using addition (p. 88)

▼ To solve one-step equations using division (p. 92)

▼ To solve one-step equations using multiplication (p. 93)

To solve an equation, use an **inverse operation** and the **properties of equality** to get the variable alone on one side of the equation.

Solve each equation.

35. $6 + y = 17$ **11** **36.** $-2 = a - 10$ **8** **37.** $3x = -15$ **−5**

38. $\frac{m}{9} = 3$ **27** **39.** $\frac{w}{4} = 32$ **128** **40.** $40 = -5b$ **−8**

2-7 Objectives

▼ To solve a problem using the Try, Test, Revise strategy (p. 96)

You can solve some problems by trying an answer. Use each incorrect conjecture to make a better conjecture.

🌐 **41. School Supplies** Marcella and Danilo went to a bookstore. Marcella bought 2 notebooks and 3 pens for $14.50. Danilo bought 1 notebook and 2 pens for $7.50. How much does 1 notebook cost? **$6.50**

2-8 Objectives

▼ To graph inequalities (p. 102)

▼ To write inequalities (p. 103)

To graph an **inequality,** use a number line. Use an open dot for $>$ and $<$. Use a closed dot for $\geq$ and $\leq$.

Graph the solutions of each inequality. **42–45. See margin.**

42. $m > 5$ **43.** $t \geq -2$ **44.** $0 < r$ **45.** $w \leq 6$

Write an inequality for each sentence.

46. The temperature t is less than zero degrees. $t < 0$

47. The height h is greater than twelve feet. $h > 12$

2-9 and 2-10 Objectives

▼ To solve one-step inequalities using subtraction (p. 106)

▼ To solve one-step inequalities using addition (p. 107)

▼ To solve one-step inequalities using division (p. 110)

▼ To solve one-step inequalities using multiplication (p. 111)

To solve a one-step inequality, use inverse operations and the **properties of inequality** to get the variable alone on one side of the inequality. When multiplying or dividing each side of an inequality by a negative number, *reverse* the direction of the inequality symbol.

Solve each inequality.

48. $n - 4 > 10$ $n > 14$

49. $-5 \leq k - 7$ $k \geq 2$

50. $6s \leq 18$ $s \leq 3$

51. $\frac{m}{3} < -2$ $m < -6$

52. $-d > 14$ $d < -14$

53. $\frac{c}{-4} \geq -9$ $c \leq 36$

42.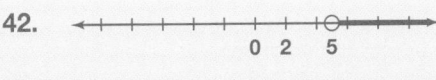

43.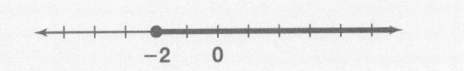

44.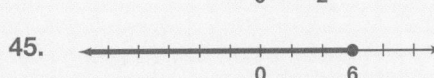

45.

119

Chapter Test

Take It to the NET
Online chapter test at
www.PHSchool.com
Web Code: ada-0252

Resources

Teaching Resources
Ch. 2 Test, Forms A & B
Ch. 2 Alternative Assessment,
Form C

Reaching All Students
Spanish Ch. 2 Test, Forms A & B
Spanish Ch. 2 Alternative
Assessment, Form C

ASSESSMENT SYSTEM

Assessment Resources
• Ch. 2 Test, Forms A & B
• Ch. 2 Alternative Assessment,
  Form C
Computer Test Generator CD-ROM
• Instant Chapter Test™ for Ch. 2

www.PHSchool.com
Student Site
• Self-grading Ch. 2 Test
PH SuccessNet Teacher Center
• Resources

Plus iTEXT

Is each equation *true, false,* **or an** *open sentence?* **Explain.**

1. $24 = 3(-8)$ false; $24 \neq -24$

2. $5x + 28 = 153$ open; variable

3. $18(-7 \div 7) = (-2)(9)$ true; $-18 = -18$

4. $-6 + 15 = (120 \div 20) - (5 - 8)$ true; $9 = 9$

Simplify. Use the Commutative and the Associative Properties.

5. $50 \cdot 38 \cdot 2$ 3,800

6. $45 + 62 + 55$ 162

7. $2 \cdot 27 \cdot 5$ 270

8. $99 + (-7) + 101$ 193

9. Open-Ended Write a number sentence that illustrates the Associative Property of Addition. Answers may vary. Sample: $5 + (3 + 8) = (5 + 3) + 8$

Simplify each expression.

10. $2(x + y) - 2y$ 2x

11. $5a + 2b + 3a - 7b$ 8a − 5b

12. $3(2r - 5) + 8(r + 2)$ 14r + 1

13. $(-2c + 3d)(-5) + 3(-2c) - (-8d)$
4c − 7d

Solve each equation.

14. $k - 23 = 17$ 40

15. $\frac{t}{-5} = 15$ −75

16. $y \div 12 = -3$ −36

17. $7w = -217$ −31

18. $-9 + a = 11$ 20

19. $n - 2 = 13$ 15

20. $120 = 38 + p$ 82

21. $w \cdot (-2) = 14$ −7

22. $r + 6 = 30$ 24

23. $m - 7 = -3$ 4

24. $9t = 18$ 2

25. $-3f = -42$ 14

26. $5 = \frac{s}{-7}$ −35

27. $\frac{h}{12} = 12$ 144

For Exercises 28 and 29, write and solve an equation.

28. Fencing Thirty-six sections of fencing, all the same length, are joined to form a fence 180 m long. How long is each section of fencing? $36\ell = 180$; 5 m

29. Brian bought a used bike for $25 less than its original price. He paid a total of $88 for the bike. What was the original price of the bike? $p - 25 = 88$; $113

30. Writing in Math How are the rules for solving inequalities similar to those for solving equations? How are they different? See below.

Write an inequality for each situation. Graph the solutions. 31–35. See margin for graphs.

31. The total t is greater than 5. $t > 5$

32. The perimeter p is less than 64. $p < 64$

33. The number of passengers p on the bus is no more than 45. $p \leq 45$

34. The number of students s that ran in the road race was not less than 55. $s \geq 55$

35. The number of questions q answered correctly is at most 49. $q \leq 49$

Solve each inequality.

36. $5 \leq x + 1$ $x \geq 4$

37. $\frac{a}{3} > 4$ $a > 12$

38. $y - 6 < 9$ $y < 15$

39. $-2n \leq 10$ $n \geq -5$

40. $3b \geq 3$ $b \geq 1$

41. $\frac{p}{-2} < -5$ $p > 10$

42. $r + 8 > 12$ $r > 4$

43. $j - 7 \leq 24$ $j \leq 31$

44. $h - 5 \geq -16$
$h \geq -11$

45. $8 + b < -3$
$b < -11$

46. $3k \leq -27$ $k \leq -9$

47. $\frac{h}{4} > 16$ $h > 64$

48. $9 < \frac{a}{6}$ $a > 54$

49. $-7z < 21$ $z > -3$

30. The rules are alike except that when you multiply or divide each side of an inequality by a negative number, you must reverse the inequality symbol.

Chapter Test – Form B

Chapter Test – Form A

■ *Chapter 2 Test • Form A*

Circle the letter of the best answer.
1. Which word describes the equation $17 = t - 5$?
   A. true   B. false   C. open   D. not given
2. Which property does $a + 11 = 11 + a$ illustrate?
   A. commutative property of multiplication
   B. commutative property of addition
   C. associative property of multiplication
   D. associative property of addition
3. Which of the following is a solution of the equation $5x + 4 = 14$?
   A. 2   B. −2   C. 3   D. 1
4. Which is *not* equal to $2(x + 5)$?
   A. $2x + 10$ B. $(x + 5)2$ C. $2(5 + x)$ D. $2x + 5$
Simplify. Use the commutative, associative, and distributive properties.
5. $175 + 37 + 25$
   $= 175 + (25 + 37) = (175 + 25) + 37 = 200 + 37 = 237$
6. $50(11 \cdot 2)$
   $= 50(2 \cdot 11) = (50 \cdot 2)11 = 100 \cdot 11 = 1,100$
7. $12(99)$
   $= 12(100 - 1) = 1,200 - 12 = 1,188$
Simplify each expression.
8. $12n + (-3k) + 2n - 5k$ $14n - 8k$
9. $(-3y + 2x)(-2) + y + (-x)$ $7y - 5x$
Solve each equation.
10. $x - 9 = 14$ $x = 23$
11. $b + 14 = 22$ $b = 8$
12. $-5z = -45$ $z = 9$
13. $\frac{m}{7} = 14$ $m = -98$

31.
-6 -4 -2 0 2 4 6 8

32.
-40 0 40 80

33.
-50 -25 0 25 50 75

34.
-50 -25 0 25 50 75

35.
-50 -25 0 25 50 75

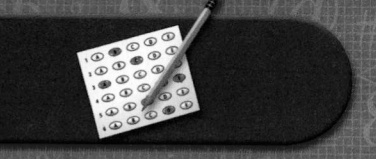

Test Prep

Multiple Choice

Choose the best answer.

1. You make $8.00 per hour. Each week you work n hours. Which expression describes your weekly pay? **D**

   A. $\frac{n}{8}$ **B.** $8 - n$ **C.** $n + 8$ **D.** $8n$

2. Which equation shows the Associative Property of Addition? **G**
   F. $9 + 7 + 8 = 9 + 8 + 7$
   G. $(8 + 3) + 13 = 8 + (3 + 13)$
   H. $12 + (-4) + 0 = 12 + (-4)$
   I. $19 \cdot (-3) \cdot 1 = 19 \cdot (-3)$

3. Mara ordered 5 bags of seed for $7 each and 3 wildflower seed kits for $9 each. She also paid a $13 shipping fee. Which expression shows the total cost? **B**
   A. $5 + 7 + 3 + 9 + 13$
   B. $(5 \cdot 7) + (3 \cdot 9) + 13$
   C. $(5 + 3)16 + 13$
   D. $(5 \cdot 7 + 13) + (3 \cdot 9 + 13)$

4. What is the solution of $r + 43 = -45$? **F**
   F. -88 **G.** -2 **H.** 2 **I.** 88

5. What is the value of $5(n + m)$ for $n = 12$ and $m = 6$? **C**
   A. 30 **B.** 66 **C.** 90 **D.** 810

6. Which integer is *not* a solution of $p + 12 < 16$? **F**
   F. 4 **G.** 3 **H.** -4 **I.** -28

7. Which numbers are in order from least to greatest? **C**
   A. $4, 2, -2, -4$ **B.** $|-3|, |-4|, -5, 6$
   C. $-7, 1, 4, |-12|$ **D.** $-3, 4, -5, 6, -7$

8. What is the value of $-23 + (-12)$? **I**
   F. 35 **G.** 11 **H.** -11 **I.** -35

9. Which symbol makes the statement true? **A**
   $11 - (-4) \ \blacksquare \ -6 - 12$
   A. $>$ **B.** $<$ **C.** $=$ **D.** $\leq$

10. Which product equals $3t - 12$? **G**
    F. $4(t - 3)$ **G.** $3(t - 4)$
    H. $(4 - t)3$ **I.** $(3 - t)4$

11. Which equation is an open sentence? **C**
    A. $8(8 \div 2) = 32$ **B.** $18 = (2 \cdot 7) + 6$
    C. $5x = 3 + 2x$ **D.** $15 - 1 = 52 \div 4$

12. What is the value of $-(2 \cdot 7) + 6 \cdot 2$? **G**
    F. 26 **G.** -2 **H.** -16 **I.** -26

Short Response

Simplify each expression. Show your work.
13–16. See back of book.
13. $3c - 4c + 1$ 14. $6(t + 7) + t$
15. $-5(n + 9) - n$ 16. $8 - 4(s + 2) - s$

Solve each inequality. Show your work.
17–20. See back of book.
17. $24 > b + 17$ 18. $x - 9 < -14$
19. $\frac{r}{13} \geq 3$ 20. $-4s \geq -56$

21. **a.** How are the rules for solving inequalities with addition and subtraction similar to those for solving inequalities with multiplication and division?
    b. In part (a), how are they different?
    a–b. See back of book.

22. Simplify $25 \cdot 7 \cdot 4$. Explain how you can use the Commutative and Associative Properties to multiply mentally. See back of book.

For Exercises 23 and 24, (a) write an expression for total cost and (b) simplify the expression.
23–24. See back of book.
23. Lana bought juice for $3.25 and some fruit for $5.25. She also bought five beach passes for x dollars each.

24. Chung bought 6 brushes for b dollars each, 2 paint tubes for p dollars each, 5 more brushes later in the day, and paper for $12.

Gridded Response

Simplify each expression.
25. $7(58)$ 406 26. $6(92)$ 552 27. $5(1,002)$ 5010

Solve each equation.
28. $b - 7 = 21$ 28 29. $18 + n = 37$ 19
30. $\frac{c}{7} = 8$ 56 31. $-9r = 108$ -12

Chapter 2 Test Prep **121**

Test Prep

Resources

📁 **Teaching Resources**
Cumulative Review

👥 **Reaching All Students**
Spanish Cumulative Review

 ASSESSMENT *SYSTEM*

Test Preparation
• Ch. 2 Test Prep
Assessment Resources
• Cumulative Review
Computer Test Generator CD-ROM
• Test Prep

💻 **www.PHSchool.com**
• Test Prep
• Resources

Plus  TEXT

Cumulative Review

━━ *Chapter 2 Cumulative Review*

Circle the letter of the best answer.

1. You earn d dollars working 40 hours. Which expression describes how much you earn per hour?
   A. $\frac{40}{d}$ **(B.)** $\frac{d}{40}$ **C.** $40d$ **D.** $d + 40$

2. Which equation shows the commutative property of multiplication?
   A. $5 \cdot 0 = 0$ **(B.)** $ab = ba$ **C.** $3 + 2 = 2 + 3$ **D.** $(ab)c = a(bc)$

3. Kara ran 3 miles a day for 5 days and 4 miles a day for 2 days. Which expression shows the total distance she ran?
   A. $3 + 5 + 4 + 2$ **B.** $(3 + 4)5 + 2$
   (C.) $(3 \cdot 5) + (4 \cdot 2)$ **D.** $7 \cdot 5 + 7 \cdot 2$

4. Solve $s + 12 = -8$
   A. 4 **B.** 20 **(C.)** -20 **D.** -4

5. Evaluate $4(a + b)$, for $a = 11$ and $b = 4$.
   A. 32 **B.** 88 **C.** 28 **(D.)** 60

6. Which integer is *not* a solution of $h + 4 < 9$?
   (A.) 6 **B.** 2 **C.** -3 **D.** -5

7. Find $22 + (-8)$.
   A. -30 **B.** -14 **(C.)** 14 **D.** 30

8. Which symbol makes $15 - (-7) \ \underline{\hspace{0.5cm}} \ -2(11)$ a true statement?
   (A.) $>$ **B.** $<$ **C.** $=$ **D.** $+$

9. Which group is in order from least to greatest?
   A. $6, 3, -3, -6$ **B.** $-8, |-8|, 4, 5$
   C. $|-15|, -10, 5, 10$ **(D.)** $-5, -2, |-2|, 7$

Use the distributive property to simplify each expression.
10. $8(106)$ $= 8(100 + 6) = 800 + 48 = 848$
11. $4(98)$ $= 4(100 - 2) = 400 - 8 = 392$

Simplify each expression.
12. $9 - 2x + 9x + 6$ $7x + 15$
13. $5 - 2(m + 3) - m$ $-3m - 1$

Assessment

A Profitable Fair

In this activity, students apply their knowledge of equations to analyze income, cost, and profit for a real-world event.

Activating Prior Knowledge

Ask students what fundraising event their school has organized. Have them find out how much profit the event made. **Answers may vary. Sample: The school book fair made $200 dollars in profit.**

Teaching Notes

Teaching Tip

Have a volunteer read the introductory paragraph. Ask: *What have profits earned from your school fundraising events purchased?* **Answers may vary. Sample: The book fair profits were used to purchase books for the school library.**

Tactile Learners

Use real coins to illustrate income, cost, and profit. Have a student buy 5 pencils at a "fair table" at a cost of one cent each. Have the student sell the pencils for 5 cents each to other students. Explain that the income (25 cents) minus the cost (5 cents) equals the profit (20 cents).

Inclusion

Examine the chart with students. Point out what information is provided and what information is left out in each row and column.

Teaching Tip

Ask students why all the information is provided in the column titled "Last Year." **Answers may vary. Sample: Since last year's fair has already taken place, the information for this column is available.**

122

A Profitable Fair

Applying Equations Many schools hold fairs and other events to raise money for extracurricular activities. To make a profit, you must begin with an idea of what your expenses and your income will be. At your school fair, your student council will rent school tables and sell tickets, hot dogs, and juice. The student council makes plans for this year's fair based on last year's fair.

Activity

Copy the chart. Write and solve equations to fill in the blanks. 1–8. See margin.

1. Find the profit P from renting yard-sale tables.

> **Profit = Income − Cost**

2. Suppose you make the tickets. Find the price T to charge for each ticket to make the planned profit.

Treasurer's Chart

Item	Last Year	This Year	Income	Profit
Tables (yard sale)	45 tables	▪	$35/table = ▪	▪
Tickets	320 sold	▪	▪	$800
Hot dogs (and buns)	200 sold	▪	▪	$280
Juice boxes	200 sold	▪	▪	$100
Total	N/A	N/A	▪	▪

3. You calculate that you will have to pay an average of $.35 per hot dog, bun, and toppings. How much will this cost in all?

4. Juice boxes cost you $.25 each. How much will they cost in all?

5. How much, h, should you charge for each hot dog?

6. How much, j, should you charge for each juice box?

7. You could sell a hot dog and juice box only as a combination. If you do, how much, c, should you charge for each "combo"?

8. Open-Ended How could you improve the Treasurer's Chart?

Clean Machines
Some schools use donated supplies for their fundraising car washes.

122

1. $1,575
2. $2.50
3. $70
4. $50
5. $1.75

6. $.75
7. $2.50
8. Answers may vary. Sample: Change the column labeled *This Year* to *Cost*.

A Little Goes a Long Way

Middle-school students in Maynard, Massachusetts, are collecting 1 million pennies as their school fundraiser.

Painting Faces

Kids of all ages love having their faces painted! But be warned: Small children can't sit still for long, so know what you're going to paint before you begin.

Take It to the NET For more information about school fairs, go to **www.PHSchool.com**.
Web Code: ade-0253

123

Students must be able to use equations in problem solving to calculate missing information in a table and to make decisions in planning real-world events.

Teaching Tip

Before students begin the activity, discuss the illustrations and their captions. Have students read through the activity before beginning to work. Have students work individually or in pairs to complete the activity.

Diversity

Ask students to identify places other than a school that might organize a fundraiser. Brainstorm other situations in which you would need to calculate income, cost, and profit. Answers may vary. Sample: a church or hospital; running a business.

English Learners

Exercise 1 Review the definitions of income, cost, and profit. Answers may vary. Sample: Income is the amount of money received. Cost is the amount that must be paid out for goods or services. Profit is the amount remaining after all costs are paid.

Chapter 3

Decimals and Equations

Chapter at a Glance

Correlation to Standardized Tests

Lesson	NAEP	Terra Nova		ITBS	SAT10	Local Test
		CAT/6	CTBS			
3-1	N2a, N2b, N2c	■		■	■	
3-2	N2a, N2b, N2c	■				
3-3	D2a, D2b	■	■		■	
3-4	A4e	■	■	■		
3-5	A4a, A4b				■	
3-6	A4a, A4b			■	■	
3-7	M2b	■	■	■		
3-8						

NAEP National Assessment of Educational Progress
    N = Number Sense, Properties, and Operations
    M = Measurement
    G = Geometry and Spatial Sense
    D = Data Analysis, Statistics and Probability
    A = Algebra and Functions
CAT/6 California Achievement Test, 6th Ed.
CTBS Comprehensive Test of Basic Skills
ITBS Iowa Test of Basic Skills, Form M
SAT10 Stanford Achievement Test, 10th Ed.

NCTM STANDARDS 2000

1	Number and Operations	6	Problem Solving
2	Algebra	7	Reasoning and Proof
3	Geometry	8	Communication
4	Measurement	9	Connections
5	Data Analysis and Probability	10	Representation

Pacing Options

This chart suggests pacing for only the core lessons and their parts. It is provided as a possible guide. It will help you determine how much time you have in your schedule to cover other components, such as the features, chapter projects, Chapter Review, and Chapter Test.

Day	Traditional 45-minute class periods	Two-Year 45-minute class periods	Block 90-minute class periods
1	3-1 ▼ ▼	3-1 ▼	3-1 ▼ ▼ / 3-2 ▼ ▼
2	3-2 ▼ ▼	3-1 ▼	3-3 ▼ ▼
3	3-3 ▼ ▼	3-1 ▼	3-4 ▼ ▼
4	3-4 ▼ ▼	3-2 ▼	3-5 ▼ ▼ / 3-6 ▼ ▼
5	3-5 ▼ ▼	3-2 ▼	3-7 ▼ ▼
6	3-6 ▼ ▼	3-2 ▼	3-8 ▼
7	3-7 ▼ ▼	3-3 ▼	
8	3-8 ▼	3-3 ▼	
9		3-3 ▼	
10		3-4 ▼	
11		3-4 ▼	
12		3-5 ▼	
13		3-5 ▼	
14		3-5 ▼	
15		3-6 ▼	
16		3-6 ▼	
17		3-6 ▼	
18		3-7 ▼	
19		3-7 ▼	
20		3-8 ▼	
21		3-8 ▼	
22			
23			
24			

Math Background

Skills Trace

BEFORE Chapter 3

The meaning of a decimal was introduced in the early elementary school grades and used in previous courses with the metric system. Previous courses should also have introduced students to solving one-step equations involving decimals.

DURING Chapter 3

This chapter uses decimals to develop the concepts and skills of rounding, estimation, mean, median, and mode. Students connect their work solving equations with whole numbers from Chapter 2 to solving equations with decimals.

AFTER Chapter 3

The remainder of this book uses equations involving decimals. Simple and complex equations with decimals are introduced early in Algebra 1.

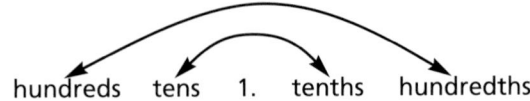

hundreds   tens   1.   tenths   hundredths

The 1 in the first place to the left of the decimal point has no partner to the right of the decimal point. Students may be confused if they think of the decimal point itself as the center, or dividing line, between units and decimal fractions.

Rounding is based on knowing what number is halfway between two numbers for a given place value. For example, if you want to round 3.467 to the nearest tenth, you are asking, "Is 3.467 closer to 3.400 or 3.500?" The point halfway between these is 3.450. Numbers less than the halfway point are replaced with 3.4 when rounding; numbers 3.450 and greater are replaced with 3.5 when rounding. Some people use other rules for rounding the number halfway between (3.450), but the most common rule is to "round up."

Students sometimes mistakenly think that rounding is a kind of "rolling process" beginning at the far right digit. This mistake leads them to round 3.247 to the nearest tenth by first increasing the 4 to a 5 (because of the 7) to get 3.25 and then increasing the 2 to a 3 because of the 5. This results in the wrong conclusion that 3.247 rounds to 3.3 even though it is clearly closer to 3.200 than to 3.300.

3-1 Rounding and Estimating

Working with decimals requires an understanding of how the various decimal places are named. The names for the decimal places 10 (ten) and 0.1 (tenth) differ only by two letters, but ten is 100 times one-tenth. Notice in the place value system (as the following diagram shows) that the ones place (followed by the decimal point) is the center of this system.

3-2 Estimating Decimal Products and Quotients

There are several estimation techniques; however, all of these are based on the idea of replacing numbers with ones that are close and allow a calculation to be done mentally.

There is no one right way to estimate. The kinds of numbers used and the real-world situation in which an estimate is needed often determine which estimation technique makes sense and how close the estimate needs to be to the exact answer.

3-3 Mean, Median, and Mode

In everyday language, the word "average" is ambiguous. In the more precise language of mathematics, you use the mean, the median, or the mode of a set of numbers to represent an "average" value. Finding the mean, median, and mode are all ways to summarize the data. A measure that summarizes a whole set of measurements by representing the approximate center of the distribution is called a *measure of central tendency.*

The most familiar measure of central tendency is the *mean.* When you add a set of grades and divide by how many grades there are, you are finding the mean. The mean is the only measure of central tendency that is dependent upon the exact value of every measurement. A change in any measurement will produce a change in the mean.

Less familiar is the *mode,* which is simply the number that occurs most often.

The *median* is the middle number in a distribution where all the numbers are arranged in order from greatest to least. If there are an even number of data items, the median is the mean of the middle two numbers. The median is often used when incomes or housing prices are given. Mathematicians have other more precise ways of defining the median to reflect repeated numbers, but these are used only in advanced statistical analysis.

3-4 Using Formulas

In this lesson, students substitute values in formulas to solve for one variable. Later they will apply their skills in solving equations to restating a formula in different forms, as shown here.

$$d = rt; \ r = \frac{d}{t}; \ t = \frac{d}{r}$$

3-5, 3-6 Solving One-Step Decimal Equations

In these lessons, students apply to decimal equations what they know about using inverse operations and the properties of equality. Remind students that they are also applying the two inverse properties

$$a + (-a) = 0 \text{ and}$$
$$a \cdot \left(\frac{1}{a}\right) = 1, \ (a \neq 0)$$

as they solve these equations.

3-7 Using the Metric System

The English, or customary, system uses the concept of weight (measured in pounds) while the metric system uses the concept of mass. Mass is the amount of material that can be measured on a balance. Weight is the gravitational force exerted by the given amount of material.

$$\text{weight} = \text{gravitational force}$$

$$\text{weight} = \text{mass} \cdot \text{acceleration due to gravity}$$

Weight depends on mass and gravity. An astronaut who weighs 150 pounds on Earth weighs 25 pounds on the moon, where the gravitational pull is $\frac{1}{6}$ that of Earth. The astronaut is weightless in space, but in all three places has a mass of 68.2 kilograms.

As long as the measurements are made on Earth, a mass of 1 kilogram weighs approximately 2.2 pounds.

Additional Professional Development Opportunities

Chapter 3 Math Background notes:
pp. 128, 133, 138, 144, 149, 153, 157, 165

Professional Development, Content Facilitator Guide: Pre-Algebra, Chapter 3

SkyLight
Professional
Development

Additional resources available from SkyLight Professional Development: On-site courses, workshops, summer institutes. Online courses and chat rooms. Videocassettes and books. Visit www.skylightedu.com.

Ongoing Assessment and Intervention

The *Prentice Hall Pre-Algebra* program provides many options for assessment in the Student Edition, Teacher's Edition, and teaching resources. From these options you may choose instructional materials and that are appropriate for your students and support your district's curriculum requirements.

Daily Assessment

 Instant Check System™ in Chapter 3

Allows students to check their own learning before, during, and after each lesson.

Diagnosing Readiness before the chapter (p. 124)

Check Skills You'll Need exercises in each lesson (pp. 127, 132, 137, 143, 148, 152, 156, 164)

Check Understanding questions with each Example (pp. 127, 128, 129, 132, 133, 138, 139, 143, 144, 148, 149, 152, 153, 156, 157, 158, 165)

Checkpoint Quiz (pp. 146, 161)

Formal Assessment

In Chapter 3 and Additional Resources

Assesses student progress throughout the *Pre-Algebra* text and with blackline masters and CD-ROM.

Student Edition

- Chapter 3 Review, with Vocabulary Skills and Concepts Review, pp. 169–171
- Chapter 3 Test, p. 172

Assessment Resources   *Spanish versions available.*

- Checkpoint Quizzes 1 & 2
- Chapter Test, Forms A & B
- Chapter Alternative Assessment

 Computer Test Generator CD-ROM

- Instant Chapter Tests™ — pre-made tests with items that vary every time you print.
- Online Testing allows you to give tests online and receive progress reports.
- Diagnose readiness with questions on prerequisite skills.
- Prepare students by making tests based on standardized test objectives.

Algebra Readiness Tests

- Includes Basic Skills Tests and Concept-Readiness Tests.
- Assess understanding of skills and concepts needed for success in algebra.

Standardized Test Preparation

 Test Prep in Chapter 3

Teaches students strategies and gives them practice with all the test item formats they will encounter on high-stakes tests.

Test Prep exercises in each lesson (pp. 131, 135, 141, 146, 151, 155, 161, 167)

Test-Taking Strategies (p. 168: Writing Extended Responses)

Test Prep (p. 173: Reading Comprehension)

PRENTICE HALL
ASSESSMENT *SYSTEM*

Provides a three-step approach to preparing students for high-stakes, national, and state exams.

1 Diagnose & Prescribe

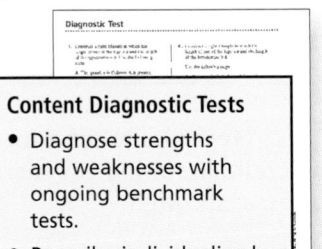

Content Diagnostic Tests

- Diagnose strengths and weaknesses with ongoing benchmark tests.
- Prescribe individualized reteaching opportunities.

2 Review & Reteach

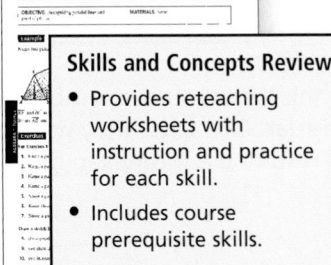

Skills and Concepts Review

- Provides reteaching worksheets with instruction and practice for each skill.
- Includes course prerequisite skills.

3 Practice & Assess

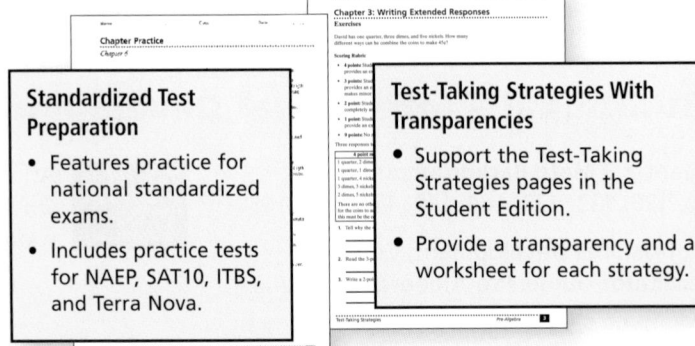

Standardized Test Preparation

- Features practice for national standardized exams.
- Includes practice tests for NAEP, SAT10, ITBS, and Terra Nova.

Test-Taking Strategies With Transparencies

- Support the Test-Taking Strategies pages in the Student Edition.
- Provide a transparency and a worksheet for each strategy.

124E

Reaching All Students

The textbook, the iText, and other technology components provide numerous opportunities to reach students of various ability levels and learning styles. Each Teacher's Edition lesson suggests how you can help all your students be successful and understand the mathematics in Chapter 3.

Below Level

Student Edition
- Diagnosing Readiness*: p. 124
- Check Skills You'll Need*: pp. 127, 132, 137, 143, 148, 152, 156, 164

Reteaching
Chapter 3 Grab & Go™ File: pp. 9–16

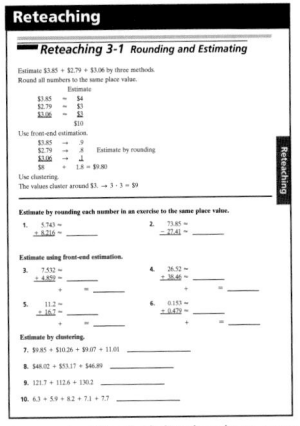

* Can be used with all ability levels to ensure mastery of prerequisite skills.

Advanced Learners

Student Edition
- Challenge exercises: pp. 131, 135, 141, 145, 151, 155, 160, 166
- Extension: p. 162

Enrichment
Chapter 3 Grab & Go™ File: pp. 17–24

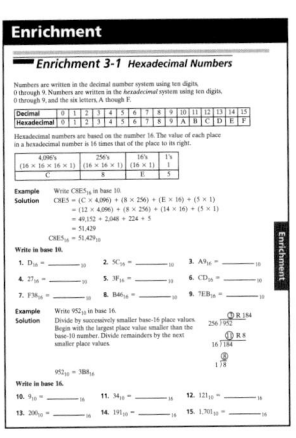

Problem Solving

Student Edition
- Strategies: pp. 164–167
- Real-World Problem Solving: pp. 128, 129, 132, 133, 137, 138, 143, 148, 149, 152, 153, 158, 164

Guided Problem Solving Masters
Chapter 3: pp. 21–28

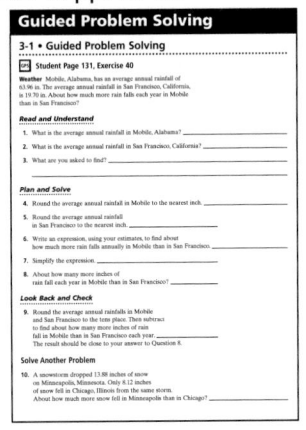

Reading and Math Literacy

Student Edition
- Vocabulary: pp. 125, 169, plus in most lessons
- Reading Math: pp. 128, 134, 136, 139, 144, 157, 160, 166, 169
- Writing in Math: pp. 131, 135, 141, 145, 151, 154, 160, 166, 172
- Illustrated Glossary: pp. 782–826

Reading and Math Literacy Masters
Chapter 3: pp. 9–12

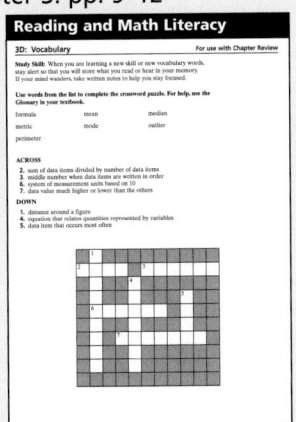

English Learners

Student Edition
- English/Spanish Illustrated Glossary: pp. 782–826

Workbook and Masters
Spanish Practice Workbook: pp. 21–28
Spanish Reading and Math Literacy Masters: pp. 9–12

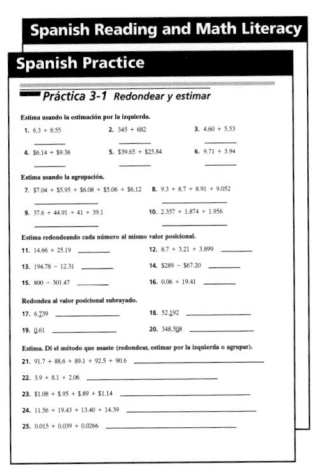

Learning Styles

Student Edition
- Investigation: pp. 126, 127
- Technology: pp. 142, 147
- DK Activities: pp. 174–175
- Chapter Project: p. 739

Activity Masters
Hands-On Activities: 6, 22, 23, 26
Technology Activities: 6

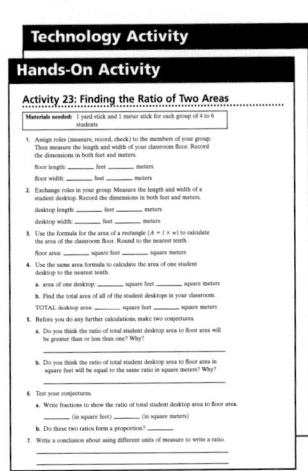

Program Resources

	Resources in Grab & Go™ Files				Resources for Reaching All Students				Spanish Resources			Transparencies				Prentice Hall Presentation Pro CD-ROM
	Practice	Reteach	Enrich	Checkpt Quiz	Reading & Math Literacy	Technology Activities	Hands-On Activities	Guided Problem Solving	Practice	Reading & Math Literacy	Checkpt Quiz	Skills Check	Additional Examples	Answers to Exercises	Lesson Quiz	
3-1	■	■	■		■			■	■	■		■	■	■	■	■
3-2	■	■	■					■	■			■	■	■	■	■
3-3	■	■	■			■		■	■			■	■	■	■	■
3-4	■	■	■	■	■		■	■	■	■	■	■	■	■	■	■
3-5	■	■	■					■	■			■	■	■	■	■
3-6	■	■	■					■	■			■	■	■	■	■
3-7	■	■	■		■		■	■	■	■	■	■	■	■	■	■
3-8	■	■	■					■				■	■	■	■	■
For the Chapter	Chapter Projects, Chapter Tests, Alternative Assessment, Cumulative Review, Cumulative Assessment				**On Web site only:** Home Activities, Algebra Readiness Puzzles, Interdisciplinary Activities				Spanish Chapter Tests, Alternative Assessment, Cumulative Review, Cumulative Assessment			Classroom Aid Transparencies				

Also available for use with the chapter:
- Practice Workbook
- Solution Key
- MathNotes folder
- For additional online and technology resources, see below.
- For teacher support and access to student Web site materials, use Web Code adk-5500.

 **PRENTICE HALL ASSESSMENT SYSTEM**

Program assessment and test preparation, all in one place.

See page 124E.

 Skills Intervention Kit

A *complete* system for the student who is struggling with course-level work

How to Use With Chapter 3

3-1, 3-3	Whole Numbers
3-5, 3-6	Decimals
3-7, 3-8	Measurement

 **Online Intervention**

Integrated within the iText, this online intervention system includes diagnostic tests and prescribed remediation, plus reports to track student mastery.

Technology

 iTEXT Online and on CD-ROM

Complete Interactive Student Text online and on CD-ROM—with instant-feedback assessment, tutorial help, dynamic activities, instructional and real-world videos, audio, and additional practice.

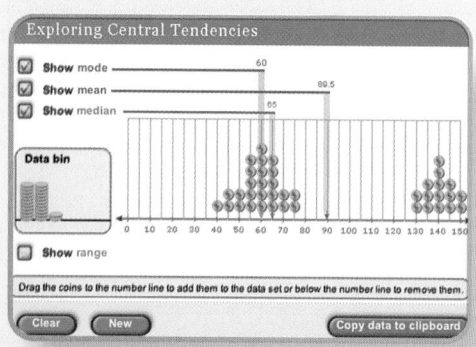

 www.PHSchool.com For Students

Use Web Codes for easy access to online activities, chapter projects, self-grading lesson quizzes, chapter tests, vocabulary quizzes, updated data sources, graphing calculator procedures, and more.

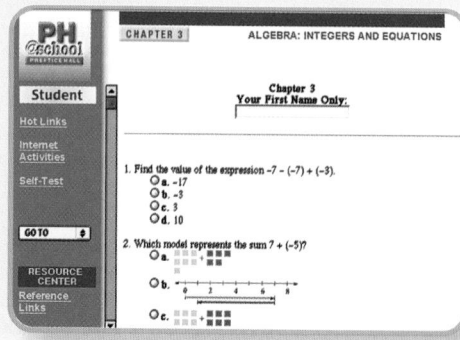

PH SuccessNet For Teachers

Online lesson planning with built-in state correlations, all the teaching resources, complete reference library, your own calendar and Teacher Web page, professional development, and more.

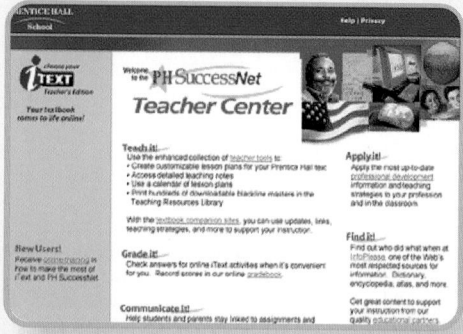

Presentation Assistant Plus!

The Prentice Hall *Presentation Assistant Plus!* provides you with the material you need to teach a lesson from beginning to end. Two easy-to-use formats—Transparencies and CD-ROM—allow you to present a lesson the way you are most comfortable.

Transparencies

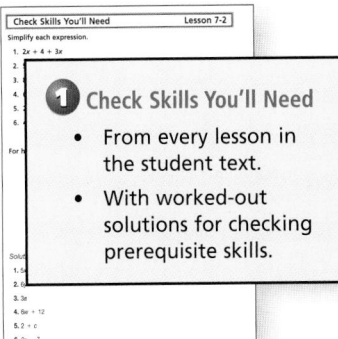

1 Check Skills You'll Need
- From every lesson in the student text.
- With worked-out solutions for checking prerequisite skills.

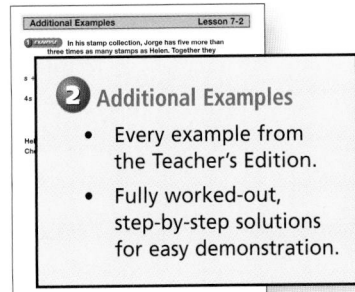

2 Additional Examples
- Every example from the Teacher's Edition.
- Fully worked-out, step-by-step solutions for easy demonstration.

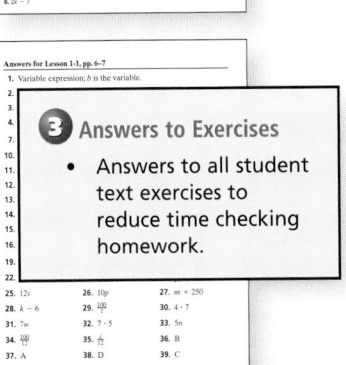

3 Answers to Exercises
- Answers to all student text exercises to reduce time checking homework.

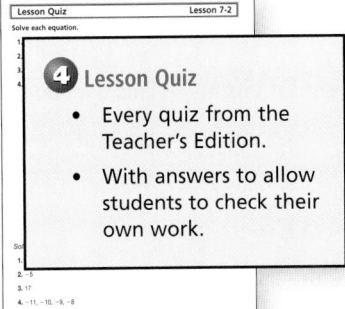

4 Lesson Quiz
- Every quiz from the Teacher's Edition.
- With answers to allow students to check their own work.

 Throughout the Teacher's Edition, this symbol indicates material that is available in the Presentation Assistant Plus!

Prentice Hall Presentation Pro CD-ROM

- Includes all Transparencies as PowerPoint® presentations.
- Conveniently organized by lesson so you can easily **1** Introduce, **2** Teach, **3** Check Homework, and **4** Assess each lesson.
- Animated examples allow step-by-step instruction at your own pace.
- Easy to edit so you can create custom presentations.

Teaching Chapter 3 Using Presentation Assistant Plus!

	1 Introduce Check Skills You'll Need	**2 Teach** Additional Examples	**3 Check Homework** Student Edition Answers	**4 Assess** Lesson Quiz
3-1	p. 21	pp. 30–31	✔	p. 21
3-2	p. 22	pp. 32–33	✔	p. 22
3-3	p. 23	pp. 34–35	✔	p. 23
3-4	p. 24	p. 36	✔	p. 24
3-5	p. 25	pp. 37–38	✔	p. 25
3-6	p. 26	pp. 39–40	✔	p. 26
3-7	p. 27	pp. 40–41	✔	p. 27
3-8	p. 28	p. 42	✔	p. 28

Prentice Hall Presentation Pro

CD-ROM with dynamic Powerpoint® presentations for every lesson. Helps you introduce and develop concepts, check homework, and assess progress. Part of Presentation Assistant Plus! *(See above.)*

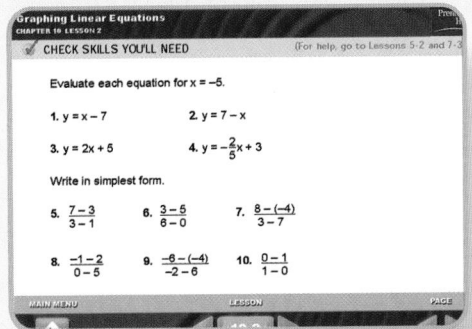

Computer Test Generator

CD-ROM to create practice sheets and tests for course objectives and standardized tests. Includes Instant Chapter Tests™, online testing, and student reports. Part of the PH Assessment System. *(See page 124E.)*

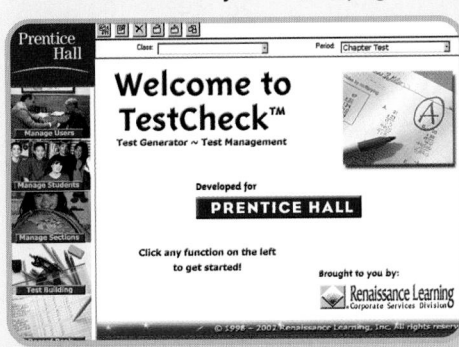

Resource Pro® with Planning Express®

CD-ROM with a lesson planning tool that allows you to import state and local objectives. Includes electronic versions of all the teaching resources.

Decimals and Equations

Diagnosing Readiness

Students will find answers to these exercises in the back of their textbooks.

Prescribing Intervention
For intervention, direct students to:

Rounding Numbers
Skills Handbook: p. 758;
Exercises 1–6.

Comparing and Ordering Decimals
Skills Handbook: p. 762;
Exercises 1–12.

Operations With Decimals
Skills Handbook: p. 764;
Exercises 16–35.
Skills Handbook: p. 765;
Exercises 11–30.
Skills Handbook: p. 769;
Exercises 11–46.

Multiplying and Dividing by Powers of 10
Skills Handbook: p. 768;
Exercises 1–36.

Where You've Been

- In Chapter 1, you learned how to add, subtract, multiply, and divide integers.

- In Chapter 2, you solved equations by adding or subtracting.

- In Chapter 2, you also solved equations by multiplying or dividing.

Diagnosing Readiness

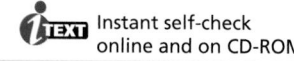 Instant self-check online and on CD-ROM

(For help, go to the Skills Handbook.)

Rounding Numbers (Skills Handbook, p. 758)

Round each number to the nearest ten.

1. 37 40   **2.** 9 10   **3.** 2 0   **4.** 602 600   **5.** 834 830   **6.** 6,009 6,010

Comparing and Ordering Decimals (Skills Handbook, p. 762)

Compare. Use $>$, $<$, or $=$ to complete each statement.

7. 0.96 ■ 1.32 $<$ **8.** 7.641 ■ 7.593 $>$ **9.** 6.3 ■ 6.38 $<$

10. 5.001 ■ 5.02 $<$ **11.** -9.871 ■ -10.3 $>$ **12.** -27.619 ■ -27.7 $>$

Order each group of decimals from least to greatest.

13. 8.35, 8.349, 8.351, 9.25
8.349, 8.35, 8.351, 9.25
14. 0.02, 0.017, 0.201, 0.0201
0.017, 0.02, 0.0201, 0.201
15. $-1.4, -1.04, -1.401, -14.1$
$-14.1, -1.401, -1.4, -1.04$
16. $-2.3, -3.2, -3.19, -2.8$
$-3.2, -3.19, -2.8, -2.3$

Operations With Decimals (Skills Handbook, pp. 764, 765, and 769)

Simplify.

17. 3.4 + 8.09
11.49
18. 8 − 4.93
3.07
19. 0.59 + 3.06
3.65
20. 2.19 − 0.984
1.206
21. (1.001)(6.7)
6.7067
22. 40.02 ÷ 5.8
6.9
23. 10.4 · 5.3
55.12
24. $\dfrac{77.38}{7.3}$ 10.6

Multiplying and Dividing by Powers of 10 (Skills Handbook, p. 768)

Simplify.

25. 9.87 · 10
98.7
26. 5.32 · 100
532
27. 0.3 · 1,000
300
28. 15.407 · 10,000
154,070
29. 0.8 ÷ 10
0.08
30. 8.42 ÷ 100
0.0842
31. 16.1 ÷ 1,000
0.0161
32. 12.09 ÷ 10,000
0.001209

Decimals and Equations

Where You're Going

In this chapter, you will learn how to

- Estimate with decimals.
- Solve equations with decimals.
- Convert metric units of measure.
- Solve a problem by simplifying the problem.

Real-World Snapshots Applying what you learn, on pages 174–175 you will solve problems about price comparisons.

LESSONS

Key Vocabulary

- compatible numbers (p. 133)
- formula (p. 143)
- mean (p. 137)
- measures of central tendency (p. 137)
- median (p. 137)
- mode (p. 137)
- outlier (p. 138)
- perimeter (p. 144)

125

Chapter 3 Overview

Students start their study of decimals and equations with lessons on rounding decimals, and on estimating decimal sums, differences, products, and quotients. In the next lessons, students are introduced to the central tendency measures of mean, median, and mode, and to the use of decimals in formulas. Then students learn to solve one-step equations involving decimals. The chapter concludes as students relate what they've learned to work in the metric system, and to the problem-solving strategy of simplifying a problem.

Activating Prior Knowledge
In Chapter 2, students learned to solve one-step equations and inequalities with whole numbers. Ask: *When you show the steps you take to solve an equation, what should your last step be?* Get the variable alone on one side of the equation.

Reading Math
- Reading a Table, p. 136
- **Vocabulary** A complete list of terms, plus vocabulary exercises, appears in the Chapter Review on p. 169.
- **Illustrated Glossary** Examples for each vocabulary term, plus definitions in both English and Spanish, appear starting on p. 782.

Test-Taking Strategies
Writing Extended Responses, p. 168

Real-World Problem Solving
- **Strategy:** Simplify the Problem, pp. 164–167
- **DK Real-World Snapshots:** Applying Decimals, pp. 174–175
- **Chapter Project:** Currency Events, p. 739

www.PHSchool.com
Internet support includes:
- Self-grading Vocabulary and Chapter 3 Tests
- Activity Masters
- Chapter Project support
- Chapter Planner
- Chapter 3 Resources

Plus

Writing and Comparing Decimals

Students review how to read and write decimals.

Teaching Notes

Inclusion
Reproduce a large version of the place-value chart on poster board to help any student who may have a vision impairment.

Tactile Learners
Organize the students in small groups. Give each group a decimal written in words that contains one less digit than the number of students in the group. Each student chooses one of the digits or the decimal point, and writes the choice on a piece of paper. The groups stand at the front of the classroom and display their decimal. Have each student state his or her place value, and then the student holding the decimal point states the number.

Visual Learners
Exercises 1–4 Suggest that students copy the decimal using different color pencils to represent the different place values.

Auditory Learners
Exercises 5–7 Pair students. Then have the students take turns reading aloud the exercises and writing each as a decimal.

Review | **Writing and Comparing Decimals**

For Use With Lesson 3-1

Each digit in a decimal has both a place and a value. The value of any place is one-tenth the value of the place to its left. A place-value chart like the one at the right can help you read and write decimals.

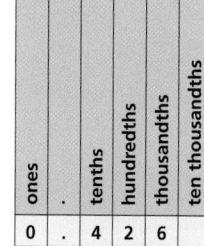

ones	.	tenths	hundredths	thousandths	ten thousandths
0	.	4	2	6	

1 EXAMPLE

a. Express 0.426 using words.

The last digit, 6, is in the thousandths place. So, 0.426 ends with the word *thousandths*.

0.426 is four hundred twenty-six thousandths.

b. Write *two and three hundredths* as a decimal.

And represents the decimal point. The hundredths place is the second place to the right of the decimal point.

Two and three hundredths is 2.03.

You can use decimal squares to model and compare decimals.

2 EXAMPLE

a. Model 0.6.

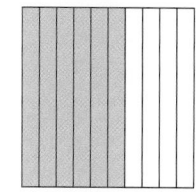

b. Model 0.58.

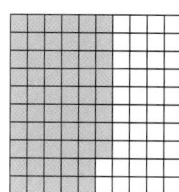

c. Model 1.05.

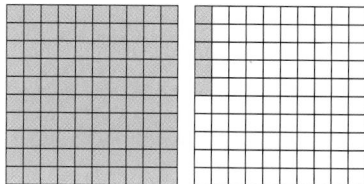

d. Compare 0.6 and 0.58. The models show that 0.6 > 0.58.

EXERCISES

1. twenty-three hundredths
2. six hundred twenty-four thousandths
3. three and eighty-one thousandths
4. fifty-eight and thirty-six hundredths

Express each decimal using words. 1–4. See right.

1. 0.23   **2.** 0.624   **3.** 3.081   **4.** 58.36

Write each as a decimal.

5. three and two tenths
3.2

6. five and forty-one hundredths
5.41

7. fourteen ten-thousandths
0.0014

Model and compare each pair of decimals.

8. 0.2 and 0.12
0.2 > 0.12

9. 0.89 and 0.9
0.89 < 0.9

10. 0.53 and 0.5
0.53 > 0.5

11. 1.35 and 1.4
1.35 < 1.4

Rounding and Estimating

3-1

OBJECTIVE

1 Rounding Decimals

Investigation

Estimating in the Real World

Some real-world problems require only an estimate for an answer. Others require an exact answer. Decide whether each situation needs an estimate or an exact answer. Explain your reasoning.

1–6. Answers may vary. Samples are given.

1. a headline noting the number of people living in China
   Estimate; an exact count of such a large population is not possible.

2. the amount of money a baby sitter charges per hour
   Exact; the baby sitter gets paid an exact rate.

3. the width of a window screen
   Exact; the screen needs to fit.

4. the distance from Earth to the moon
   Estimate; the distance is very large.

5. the hours at soccer practice in one month
   Estimate; your practice times may vary each day.

6. the number of tickets to sell for a play
   Exact; you know how many seats are in the theater.

You can round decimal numbers when you don't need exact values.

1 EXAMPLE   Rounding Decimals

a. Round 4.2683 to the nearest tenth.

tenths place
4.2683
5 or greater
Round up to 3.
4.3

b. Round 4.2683 to the nearest one.

ones place
4.2683
less than 5
Do not change.
4

✓ Check Understanding   Example 1

1. Identify the underlined place. Then round each number to that place. **a–f. See right.**

   a. 38.4̲1   **b.** 0̲.7772   **c.** 7,098.5̲6

   d. 274.94̲34   **e.** 5.0̲25   **f.** 9.85̲1

What You'll Learn

 OBJECTIVE 1 To round decimals

 OBJECTIVE 2 To estimate sums and differences

. . . And Why

To understand and apply appropriate estimation strategies in real-world situations such as grocery shopping

✓ Check Skills You'll Need

Use the number 27.3865. Write the value of the given digit. **1–4. See below.**

1. 2   **2.** 3

3. 8   **4.** 6

 For help, go to Skills Handbook, p. 761.

---

1. 2 tens
2. 3 tenths
3. 8 hundredths
4. 6 thousandths

1a. tenths; 38.4
1b. ones; 1
1c. tenths; 7,098.6
1d. thousandths; 274.943
1e. tenths; 5.0
1f. hundredths; 9.85

 TEXT Interactive lesson includes instant self-check, tutorials, and activities.

Lesson Preview

✓ **Check Skills You'll Need**

Decimals and Place Value
Skills Handbook: p. 761;
Exercises 1–12.

Lesson Resources

📁 **Teaching Resources**
Practice, Reteaching, Enrichment

👥 **Reaching All Students**
Practice Workbook 3-1
Spanish Practice Workbook 3-1
Reading and Math Literacy 3A
Spanish Reading and Math Literacy 3A
Guided Problem Solving 3-1

⏱ **Presentation Assistant Plus!**
Transparencies and PowerPoint™
• Check Skills You'll Need 3-1
• Additional Examples 3-1
• Student Edition Answers 3-1
• Lesson Quiz 3-1
• Classroom Aid 20
PH Presentation Pro CD-ROM 3-1

ASSESSMENT SYSTEM

Computer Test Generator CD-ROM

💻 **Technology**
Resource Pro® CD-ROM
Computer Test Generator CD-ROM
PH Presentation Pro CD-ROM

💻 **www.PHSchool.com**
Student Site
• Teacher Web Code: adk-5500
• Algebra Readiness Puzzles 14
• Self-grading Lesson Quiz
PH SuccessNet Teacher Center
• Lesson Planner
• Resources

Plus **TEXT**

Ongoing Assessment and Intervention

Before the Lesson	**During the Lesson**	**After the Lesson**
Diagnose prerequisite skills using:	Monitor progress using:	Assess knowledge using:
• Check Skills You'll Need	• Check Understanding	• Lesson Quiz
	• Additional Examples	• Computer Test Generator CD-ROM
	• Test Prep	

2. Teach

Professional Development

Math Background

Note the difference between rounding to a decimal place and rounding to a place greater than the ones place. When rounding to a place that is to the left of the ones place, you replace the digits between the rounded place and the decimal point with zeros. When rounding to a place to the right of the decimal point, you drop the digits to the right of the rounded place.

Teaching Notes

Investigation (Optional)
Have students give other examples of situations where estimations seem appropriate.

1 EXAMPLE English Learners

Point out that *th* distinguishes *ten* from *tenth*. The same is true for *hundred* and *hundredth* and so on. It is important to listen and speak carefully for the *th* sound.

2 EXAMPLE Tactile Learners

Students may not recall why you round up if 5, 6, 7, 8, or 9 is to the right of the place to which you are rounding. They may think of 5 as being the middle digit. Have students write each digit, 0–9, on its own index card or piece of paper. Have students line up the cards from least to greatest value. Ask them to count the cards. 10 Then have the students slide the first 5 cards to the left, making two equal groups. Ask: *What are the first five cards?* 0, 1, 2, 3, and 4 *What are the last five cards?* 5, 6, 7, 8, and 9 Explain that the five cards on the left are less in value than the five cards on the right.

3 EXAMPLE Auditory Learners

Have students practice reading decimals aloud, using *and* to indicate the decimal point.

128

OBJECTIVE

2 Estimating Sums and Differences

Reading Math

Read the symbol ≈ as "is approximately equal to."

You can estimate a result before you calculate. Then, if your answer is close to your estimate, you know that it probably is correct.

Write $126 ≈ $130

Read $126 is approximately equal to $130.

One way to estimate is to round all numbers to the same place.

2 EXAMPLE Rounding to Estimate

Estimate to find whether each answer is reasonable.

a. Calculation   Estimate

$$
\begin{array}{rcr}
\$135.95 & \approx & \$140 \\
\$15.90 & \approx & \$20 \\
+ \$24.05 & \approx & + \$20 \\
\hline
\$275.90 & & \$180
\end{array}
$$

b. Calculation   Estimate

$$
\begin{array}{rcr}
464.90 & \approx & 460 \\
- 125.73 & \approx & - 130 \\
\hline
339.17 & & 330
\end{array}
$$

The answer is not close to the estimate. It is *not* reasonable.

The answer is close to the estimate. It is reasonable.

Writing in Math

After you have rounded to a place greater than the ones place, write zeros from that place to the decimal point. Do not write zeros after the decimal point.

✓ **Check Understanding** Example 2

2. Estimate by rounding. Answers may vary. Samples are given.

   a. 355.302 + 204.889
   about 560

   b. 453.56 − 230.07
   about 220

A *front-end estimate* is often closer to the exact sum than an estimate you find by rounding. First add the front-end digits. Round to estimate the sum of the remaining digits. Then combine estimates.

3 EXAMPLE Real-World 🌐 Problem Solving

$1.73

$1.10

$2.71

Grocery Shopping Carrots cost $2.71, peppers cost $1.73, and broccoli costs $1.10. Estimate the total cost of the vegetables.

Add the front-end digits. →

$$
\begin{array}{l}
2.71 \longrightarrow .70 \\
1.73 \longrightarrow .70 \\
+ 1.10 \longrightarrow + .10 \\
\hline
4 \qquad + \qquad 1.50 = 5.50
\end{array}
$$

} Estimate by rounding.

The total cost is about $5.50.

✓ **Check Understanding** Example 3

3. Estimate using front-end estimation.

   a. 6.75 + 2.2 + 9.58
   about 18.6

   b. $1.07 + $2.49 + $7.40
   about $11

128 **Chapter 3** Decimals and Equations

👥 Reaching All Students

Below Level When rounding a number, have students underline the place to which they are going to round and then circle the digit to the right.	**Advanced Learners** Have students find the cost of a gallon of gasoline at ten different places that sell gasoline. Instruct them to estimate the total cost of buying one gallon of gasoline at each place.	**English Learners** See note on page 128. **Tactile Learners** See note on page 128.

You can also use *clustering* to estimate the sum of several numbers that are all close to the same value.

4 EXAMPLE <u>Real-World</u>  <u>Problem Solving</u>

Telephone Service Estimate the total long-distance charge for the months of May, June, July, and August shown at the right.

four months
↓
The values cluster around $15. ⟶ $15 \cdot 4 = 60$

● The total long-distance charge is about $60.00.

✓ **Check Understanding** Example 4

4. Estimate using clustering.

   a. $4.50 + $5.20 + $5.55 **about $15**
   b. 26.7 + 26.2 + 24.52 + 25.25 + 23.9 **about 125**

In this lesson, you have seen several methods for finding a reasonable estimate. Here are two methods used for the same situation.

More Than One Way

Estimate the total cost of four items priced at $4.39, $3.75, $4.96, and $2.40.

Nicole's Method

Round each price to the nearest dollar. Then add.

$4.39 + $3.75 + $4.96 + $2.40
$4   + $4   + $5   + $2   = $15

Eric's Method

Use front-end estimation.

$4.39 ⟶ $.40
3.75 ⟶ .80
4.96 ⟶ 1.00
+ 2.40 ⟶ + .40
———————————————
$13   + $2.60 = $15.60

Choose a Method

1. Which method would you use to estimate the cost of the items? Explain.
See margin.
2. Find the exact cost. Which estimate is nearer the exact cost?
$15.50; Eric's estimate

1. Answers may vary. Sample: Eric's Method; it will probably give an answer closer to the actual cost.

MAY TOTAL **$15.35**

JUNE TOTAL **$16.05**

JULY TOTAL **$14.90**

AUGUST TOTAL **$15.05**

PowerPoint

Additional Examples

1 a. Round 8.7398 to the nearest tenth. **8.7**
   b. Round 8.7398 to the nearest integer. **9**

2 Estimate to find whether each answer is reasonable.
   a. Calculation: $115.67
   reasonable $83.21
             +$59.98
             $258.86
   b. Calculation: $176.48
   not   − 39.34
   reasonable $147.14

3 You are buying some fruit. The bananas cost $1.32, the apples cost $2.19, and the avocados cost $1.63. Use front-end estimation to estimate the total cost of the fruit. **about $5.10**

4 Estimate the total electricity charge: March: $81.75; April: $79.56; May: $80.89.
about $240

Closure

Have students estimate the sum or difference of the following decimal expressions by rounding, front-end estimating, or clustering. Have them explain to a partner how they did each calculation.
24.96 + 33.52 **Estimates may vary. Sample: about 59**
18.5 − 12.3 **Estimates may vary. Sample: about 7**
13.25 + 12.89 + 13.08 **Estimates may vary. Sample: about 39**

3. Practice

Assignment Guide

1 Objective 1
- **A B** Core 1–8
- **C** Extension 41

2 Objective 2
- **A B** Core 9–40
- **C** Extension 42, 43

Test Prep 44–46
Mixed Review 47–55

Practice 3-1 Rounding and Estimating

Estimate using front-end estimation.

1. 6.3 + 8.55   **14.9**
2. 345 + 682   **1,030**
3. 4.60 + 5.53   **10.1**
4. $6.14 + $9.38   **$15.50**
5. $39.65 + $25.84   **$66**
6. 9.71 + 3.94   **13.6**

Estimate by clustering.

7. $7.04 + $5.95 + $6.08 + $5.06 + $6.12   **$30**
8. 9.3 + 8.7 + 8.91 + 9.052   **36**
9. 37.6 + 44.91 + 41 + 39.1   **160**
10. 2.357 + 1.874 + 1.956   **6**

Estimate by rounding each number to the same place value.

11. 14.66 + 25.19   **40**
12. 8.7 + 3.21 + 3.899   **16**
13. 194.78 − 12.31   **180**
14. $289 − $67.20   **$220**
15. 800 − 301.47   **500**
16. 0.06 + 19.41   **19.5**

Round to the underlined place value.

17. 6.2̲39   **6.7**
18. 52.1̲92   **52.2**
19. 0̲.61   **1**
20. 348.5̲08   **348.51**

Estimate. State your method (rounding, front-end, or clustering).

21. 91.7 + 88.6 + 89.1 + 92.5 + 90.6   **450, clustering**
22. 3.9 + 8.1 + 2.06   **14, rounding; 14.1, front-end**
23. $1.08 + $.95 + $.89 + $1.14   **$4, clustering**
24. 11.56 + 19.43 + 13.40 + 14.39   **50, rounding; 58, front-end**
25. 0.015 + 0.039 + 0.0266   **0.09, rounding; 0.081, front-end**

Enrichment 3-1 Hexadecimal Numbers

Numbers are written in the decimal number system using ten digits, 0 through 9. Numbers are written in the *hexadecimal* system using ten digits, 0 through 9, and the six letters, A though F.

Decimal	0	1	2	3	4	5	6	7	8	9	10	11	12	13	14	15
Hexadecimal	0	1	2	3	4	5	6	7	8	9	A	B	C	D	E	F

Hexadecimal numbers are based on the number 16. The value of each place in a hexadecimal number is 16 times that of the place to its right.

4,096's $(16 \times 16 \times 16 \times 1)$	256's $(16 \times 16 \times 1)$	16's (16×1)	1's 1
C	8	E	5

Example Write $C8E5_{16}$ in base 10.
Solution
$C8E5 = (C \times 4,096) + (8 \times 256) + (E \times 16) + (5 \times 1)$
$= (12 \times 4,096) + (8 \times 256) + (14 \times 16) + (5 \times 1)$
$= 49,152 + 2,048 + 224 + 5$
$= 51,429$
$C8E5_{16} = 51,429_{10}$

Write in base 10.

1. $D_{16} =$ **13**$_{10}$
2. $5C_{16} =$ **92**$_{10}$
3. $A9_{16} =$ **169**$_{10}$
4. $27_{16} =$ **39**$_{10}$
5. $5F_{16} =$ **63**$_{10}$
6. $CD_{16} =$ **205**$_{10}$
7. $F38_{16} =$ **3,896**$_{10}$
8. $B46_{16} =$ **2,886**$_{10}$
9. $7EB_{16} =$ **2,027**$_{10}$

Example Write 952_{10} in base 16.
Solution Divide by successively smaller base-16 place values. Begin with the largest place value smaller than the base-10 number. Divide remainders by the next smaller place values.

③ R 184
256) 952
① R 8
16) 184
⑧
1) 8

$952_{10} = 3B8_{16}$

Write in base 16.

10. $9_{10} =$ **9**$_{16}$
11. $34_{10} =$ **22**$_{16}$
12. $121_{10} =$ **79**$_{16}$
13. $200_{10} =$ **C8**$_{16}$
14. $191_{10} =$ **BF**$_{16}$
15. $1,701_{10} =$ **6A5**$_{16}$

EXERCISES

For more exercises, see *Extra Practice*.

Practice and Problem Solving

A Practice by Example
Example 1 (page 127)

1. hundredths; 27.39
2. thousandths; 0.912

Identify the underlined place. Then round each number to that place.

1. 27.38̲56   2. 0.912̲2   3. 1,04̲5.98   4. 74.8̲79
1–2. See left.   ones; 1,046   tenths; 74.9

Round to the underlined place.

5. 345.6̲78 **345.7**
6. 3.14̲159 **3.14**
7. 214̲.76 **215**
8. 2.943̲7 **2.944**

Example 2 (page 128)

Estimate by rounding. 9–14. Answers may vary. Samples are given.

9. $37.99 − $27.32   **about $10**
10. 1.58 + 17.0244   **about 19**
11. 172.98 − 128.301   **about 40**
12. $4.89 + $3.87   **about $9**
13. $16.81 + $11.49   **about $30**
14. $565 − $225   **about $340**

Example 3 (page 128)

Estimate using front-end estimation.

15. $6.04 + $3.45 + $4.43   **about $13.90**
16. $5.92 + $4.07   **about $10**
17. 9.89 + 2.43 + 8.37   **about 20.7**
18. 14.39 + 79.12   **about 93.5**

19. **Fitness** Kim ran 2.76 miles on Monday, 2.34 miles on Tuesday, and 1.97 miles on Wednesday. Use front-end estimation to estimate the total distance Kim ran. **about 7.10 miles**

Example 4 (page 129)

Estimate using clustering. 20–23. Answers may vary. Samples are given.

20. 44.87 + 42.712 + 43.5   **about 129**
21. $9.50 + $8.45 + $9.08   **about $27**
22. $21.37 + $22.99 + $22.15   **about $66.00**
23. 15.4 + 16 + 15.9 + 16.25 + 15.7   **about 80**

24. **Pets** Rico's dog has a litter of four puppies. The puppies weigh 2.33 lb, 2.70 lb, 2.27 lb, and 2.64 lb. Use clustering to estimate the total weight of the puppies. **10 lb**

B Apply Your Skills

Estimate. Use a method of your choice. 25–32. Answers may vary. Samples are given.

25. 8.974 + 2.154   **about 11.1**
26. 102.44 + 48.35   **about 150**
27. 600 − 209.52   **about 400**
28. $38.59 + $15.28   **about $53.90**
29. $50.00 − $28.89   **about $20.00**
30. $412.44 + $72.23   **about $480**
31. 800 + 810.5 + 807.3 + 791.1   **about 3,200**
32. 54.23 + 56.12 + 57.98 + 55.55   **about 224**

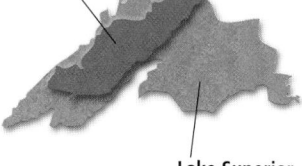

Lake Erie

Lake Superior

33. **Geography** Lake Superior, the largest of the Great Lakes, has an area of about 31,760 mi². Lake Erie, the smallest of the Great Lakes, has an area of about 9,920 mi². About how much larger is Lake Superior than Lake Erie? **about 22,000 mi²**

Estimate. State the method you used.
34–39. Answers may vary. Samples are given.

34. $8.99 + $8.01   **about $17; rounding**
35. 2.3 + 2.3 + 4.56   **about 9.2; front-end**
36. $89.90 − $49.29   **about $40; rounding**
37. 102.54 − 74.75   **about 30; rounding**
38. 20.55 − 1.48   **about 20; rounding**
39. 78.87 + 11.49   **about 90; front-end**

130   Chapter 3   Decimals and Equations

40. Weather Mobile, Alabama, has an average annual rainfall of 63.96 in. The average annual rainfall in San Francisco, California, is 19.70 in. About how much more rain falls each year in Mobile than in San Francisco? **about 44 in.**

C Challenge

41. Answers may vary. Sample: the number of hours you studied last month; the amount you have to pay for a purchase.

42. Answers may vary. Sample: front-end; it gives an estimate of $11.80, so you may not have enough money.

41. Open-Ended Describe a situation in which a rounded answer is appropriate. Describe one in which an exact answer is necessary. **See left.**

42. Writing in Math You have $11.50 to buy two presents. You find one item that costs $7.43. Another item costs $4.41. What estimation strategy will help you decide whether you have enough money to buy both? Explain. **See left.**

43. Error Analysis You used a calculator to find $383.8 - 21.9$. Your estimate was 360, but your display reads 164.8. How could you have gotten 164.8 on your calculator?
You subtracted 219 instead of 21.9.

 **Test Prep**

Multiple Choice

44. Which phrase best completes the statement?
The sum of $12.75 and $7.65 is _?_ . **B**
A. less than $20.00   **B.** greater than $20.00
C. an integer   **D.** greater than $25.00

 **Take It to the NET**
Online lesson quiz at
www.PHSchool.com
Web Code: ada-0301

45. When you estimate $320.18 + 46 + 8.68$ by rounding to tens, what value do you get? **I**
F 370   **G.** 374.9   **H.** 375   **I.** 380

Short Response

46. In 2000, the population of the state of Georgia was about 8.19 million. In 1950, the population was about 3.44 million.
  a. About how much greater was Georgia's population in 2000 than in 1950?
  b. Explain how you found your answer for part (a). **See margin.**

Mixed Review

Lesson 2-10   **Solve each inequality.**

47. $9x \leq 27$ **48.** $4x < 16$ **49.** $-3y \leq 0$ **50.** $-6k > -24$
$x \leq 3$ $x < 4$ $y \geq 0$ $k < 4$

Lesson 2-7   **51. Collections** Ming's model vehicle collection contains 4-wheeled trucks and 2-wheeled bikes. She owns an even number of vehicles, and they have 26 wheels in all. If Ming has a little more than twice as many bikes as trucks, how many of each does she own? **7 bikes; 3 trucks**

Lesson 1-9   **Simplify.**

52. $(-2)(-2)$ **4**   **53.** $4(-3)$ **−12**   **54.** $-8 \div 2$ **−4**   **55.** $6(-5)$ **−30**

3-1   Rounding and Estimating   **131**

46. [2] about 5 million; round 8.19 to 8 and round 3.44 to 3 (in millions). Then subtract 3 from 8.
[1] minor error OR answer only

 Use the Guided Problem Solving worksheet with Exercise 40.

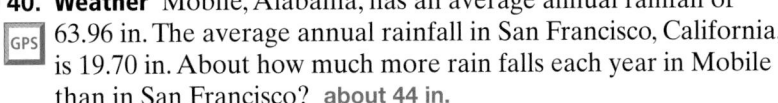 **PowerPoint** Lesson Quiz 3-1

Round to the underlined place.
1. 6.5̲57 **6.6**
2. 3.04̲48 **3.04**
Estimate.
3. $4.95 + $.89 **about $6.00**
4. 4.589 + 5.098 + 5.179
  about 15

Alternative Assessment

Ask students to make a poster containing examples of estimating by rounding, front-end estimation, and clustering.

Test Prep

Resources
For additional practice with a variety of test item formats:
• Test Prep, p. 173
• Test-Taking Strategies, p. 168
• Test-Taking Strategies With Transparencies

Teaching Tip
Exercise 44 Remind students that estimating can help eliminate answer choices and, thus, find the correct choice faster. This can be particularly helpful when a test has a time limit.

 **Reteaching 3-1** *Rounding and Estimating*

Estimate $3.85 + $2.79 + $3.06 by three methods.
Round all numbers to the same place value.
         Estimate
$3.85 ≈ $4
$2.79 ≈ $3
$3.06 ≈ $3
      $10
Use front-end estimation.
$3.85 → .9
$2.79 → .8   Estimate by rounding
$3.06 → .1
$8   +   1.8 = $9.80
Use clustering.
The values cluster around $3. → 3 · 3 = $9

Estimate by rounding each number in an exercise to the same place value.

1.	5.743 ≈ 6	2.	73.85 ≈ 70
	+ 8.216 ≈ + 8		− 27.41 ≈ − 30
	14		40

Estimate using front-end estimation.

3.	7.532 ≈ 0.5	4.	26.52 ≈ 7
	+ 4.859 ≈ 0.9		+ 38.46 ≈ 8
	11 + 1.4 = 12.4		50 + 15 = 65
5.	11.2 ≈ 1	6.	0.153 ≈ 0.05
	+ 16.7 ≈ 7		+ 0.479 ≈ 0.08
	20 + 8 = 28		0.5 + 0.13 = 0.63

Estimate by clustering.
7. $9.85 + $10.26 + $9.07 + 11.01   4 · 10 = $40
8. $48.02 + $53.17 + $46.89   3 · 50 = $150
9. 121.7 + 112.6 + 130.2   3 · 120 = 360
10. 6.3 + 5.9 + 8.2 + 7.1 + 7.7   5 · 7 = 35

131

3-2

1. Plan

Lesson Preview

 Check Skills You'll Need

Rounding
Lesson 3-1: Example 1;
Exercises 1–8.
Extra Practice, p. 746.

Lesson Resources

 **Teaching Resources**
Practice, Reteaching, Enrichment

 **Reaching All Students**
Practice Workbook 3-2
Spanish Practice Workbook 3-2
Guided Problem Solving 3-2

Presentation Assistant Plus!
Transparencies and PowerPoint™
• Check Skills You'll Need 3-2
• Additional Examples 3-2
• Student Edition Answers 3-2
• Lesson Quiz 3-2
PH Presentation Pro CD-ROM 3-2

 **ASSESSMENT SYSTEM**

Computer Test Generator CD-ROM

 Technology
Resource Pro® CD-ROM
Computer Test Generator CD-ROM
PH Presentation Pro CD-ROM

www.PHSchool.com
Student Site
• Teacher Web Code: adk-5500
• Self-grading Lesson Quiz
PH SuccessNet Teacher Center
• Lesson Planner
• Resources

Plus **iTEXT**

3-2

Estimating Decimal Products and Quotients

What You'll Learn

OBJECTIVE 1 To estimate products

OBJECTIVE 2 To estimate quotients

. . . And Why

To determine the reasonableness of answers to real-world problems involving mass

 Check Skills You'll Need

Round to the nearest one.

1. 145.89
   146
2. 199.27
   199
3. 101.06
   101
4. 28.45
   28

❓ For help, go to Lesson 3-1.

New Vocabulary

• compatible numbers

iTEXT Interactive lesson includes instant self-check, tutorials, and activities.

OBJECTIVE

1 Estimating Products

You can use mental math to estimate products and quotients. It is a good idea to estimate answers to check your calculations.

1 EXAMPLE **Estimating the Product**

Estimate 7.65 · 3.2.

$7.65 \approx 8$ $3.2 \approx 3$ **Round to the nearest one.**
         $8 \cdot 3 = 24$ **Multiply.**
$7.65 \cdot 3.2 \approx 24$

✔ **Check Understanding** Example 1

1. Estimate each product.

   a. $4.72 \cdot 1.8$
   about 10
   b. $17.02 \cdot 3.78$
   about 68
   c. $8.25 \cdot 19.8$
   about 160

2 EXAMPLE **Real-World  Problem Solving**

Quilting Arlene bought 6 yd of fabric to make this Lone Star quilt. The fabric cost $6.75/yd. The sales clerk charged Arlene $45.90 before tax. Did the clerk make a mistake? Explain.

$6.75 \approx 7$ **Round to the nearest dollar.**

$7 \cdot 6 = 42$ **Multiply 7 times 6, the number of yards of fabric.**

The sales clerk made a mistake. Since $6.75 < 7$, the actual cost should be less than the estimate. The clerk should have charged Arlene less than $42.00 before tax.

✔ **Check Understanding** Example 2

2. **Photography** You buy 8 rolls of film for your camera. Each roll costs $4.79. Estimate the cost of the film before tax. about $40

Ongoing Assessment and Intervention

Before the Lesson	During the Lesson	After the Lesson
Diagnose prerequisite skills using:	**Monitor progress using:**	**Assess knowledge using:**
• Check Skills You'll Need	• Check Understanding	• Lesson Quiz
	• Additional Examples	• Computer Test Generator
	• Test Prep	CD-ROM

When dividing, remember these names for the parts of a division sentence.

```
        ┌─── dividend
6 ÷ 3 = 2  ◄─── quotient
        └─── divisor
```

When dividing, you can use *compatible numbers* to estimate quotients. **Compatible numbers** are numbers that are easy to divide mentally. When you estimate a quotient, first round the divisor, and then round the dividend to a compatible number.

3 **EXAMPLE** Real-World Problem Solving

Measurement **A bowling ball has a mass of 5.61 kg. Each bowling pin has a mass of 1.57 kg. How many bowling pins are about equal to the bowling ball in mass? Estimate 5.61 ÷ 1.57.**

$1.57 \approx 2$ **Round the divisor.**

$5.61 \approx 6$ **Round the dividend to a multiple of 2 that is close to 5.61.**

$6 \div 2 = 3$ **Divide.**

The mass of three bowling pins is about equal to that of the bowling ball.

✓ **Check Understanding** Example 3

3. Estimate each quotient.

a. $38.9 \div 1.79$
about 20

b. $11.95 \div 2.1$
about 6

c. $82.52 \div 4.25$
about 20

You can estimate to determine the reasonableness of results.

4 **EXAMPLE** **Estimating to Determine Reasonableness**

Number Sense **Is 2.15 a reasonable quotient for 17.931 ÷ 8.34?**

$8.34 \approx 8$ **Round the divisor.**

$17.931 \approx 16$ **Round the dividend to a multiple of 8 that is close to 17.931.**

$16 \div 8 = 2$ **Divide.**

Since 2.15 is close to the estimate 2, it is reasonable.

✓ **Check Understanding** Example 4

4. Use estimation. Is each quotient reasonable? Explain.

a. $1.564 \div 2.3 = 0.68$
b. $26.0454 \div 4.98 = 52.3$
a–b. See back of book.

Real-World Connection

The masses of ten-pin bowling balls range from 3.63 kg to 7.26 kg.

Test-Taking Tip

You can sometimes use estimation to eliminate answer choices on a multiple choice test.

What is $8.19 \div 2.1$?

A. 39   **B.** 4.1
C. 3.9   **D.** 0.41

If you estimate $8 \div 2 \approx 4$, then you know you can eliminate choices A and D.

3-2   Estimating Decimal Products and Quotients   **133**

👥 **Reaching All Students**

Below Level Begin with estimating the products and quotients of two-digit numbers and then build to numbers with more digits, as seems appropriate.	**Advanced Learners** Have students estimate $798.603 \div 0.506$. **Answers may vary. Sample: 1,600**	**Visual Learners** See note on page 133. **English Learners** See note on page 135.

Math Background

Rounding is an important step in estimating products. It complements the use of a calculator, since you can easily make a keystroking error. Estimating the answer first can help you recognize unreasonable answers on your calculator.

Teaching Notes

2 **EXAMPLE** **Visual Learners**

Bring in advertisements with the prices of different items. Have the students estimate the cost of buying several of a particular item.

3 **EXAMPLE** **Science Connection**

Mass is the measure of matter in an object. Weight is the measure of gravitational pull on an object. A person has the same mass whether on Earth or on the moon. However, the person weighs much less on the moon because of the moon's lesser pull of gravity.

PowerPoint
📋 **Additional Examples**

1 Estimate $6.43 \cdot 4.7$. **30**

2 Joshua bought 3 yd of fabric to make a flag. The fabric cost $5.35/yd. The clerk said his total was $14.95 before tax. Did the clerk make a mistake? Explain. **Yes; the total should be more than $3 \cdot 5$.**

3 The cost to ship one yearbook is $3.12. The total cost for a shipment was $62.40. Estimate how many books were in the shipment. **about 20 books**

4 Is 3.29 a reasonable quotient for $31.423 \div 5.94$? Explain. **No; $30 \div 6 = 5$**

Closure

Have students think of situations outside the classroom where it might be practical to estimate.

133

3. Practice

Assignment Guide

▼ **1 Objective 1**
  Ⓐ Ⓑ **Core** 1–8, 19, 22, 24, 26, 28
  Ⓒ **Extension** 33

▼ **2 Objective 2**
  Ⓐ Ⓑ **Core** 9–18, 20, 21, 23, 25, 27, 29, 30
  Ⓒ **Extension** 31, 32, 34

Test Prep 35–38
Mixed Review 39–50

Practice 3-2 *Estimating Decimal Products and Quotients*

Determine whether each product or quotient is reasonable. If it is not reasonable, find a reasonable result.

1. 62.77(29.8) = 187.0546   2. 16.132 ÷ 2.96 = 54.5
   no; 1800   no; 5

3. (47.89)(6.193) = 296.5828   4. 318.274 ÷ 4.07 = 78.2
   yes   yes

5. 2.65(−0.84) = −0.2226   6. −38.6(−1.89) = 7.2954
   no; −2.4   no; 80

7. 6,355 ÷ 775 = 8.2   8. 1,444.14 ÷ 67.8 = 213
   yes   no; 20

9. 1.839(6.3) = 115.857   10. 3.276 ÷ 0.63 = 5.2
   no; 12   yes

Estimate each product or quotient.

11. 8.73 · 6.01 __54__   12. 11.042(4.56) __55__

13. 197.4 · 2.85 __600__   14. 675.1 · 0.051 __35__

15. 479.2(3.2) __1500__   16. 712.9 · 0.41 __280__

17. 11.57 ÷ 3.09 __4__   18. 43.68 ÷ 8.7 __5__

19. 29.5 ÷ 5.1 __6__   20. $41.09 ÷ $6.88 __6__

21. 148.8 ÷ 9.8 __15__   22. $76.77 ÷ $24.19 __3__

23. Apples cost $.89 per lb. Estimate the cost of three 5-lb bags. __$15__

24. You buy 3 dinners that are $6.85 each. Before tax and tip, the total is $25.42. Is this total correct? Explain.
    No; 6.85 ≈ 7; the total should be less than 3 · 7 = $21.

25. You worked 18 hours last week and received $92.70 in your paycheck. Estimate your hourly pay.
    __$5__

Enrichment 3-2 *Scrambled Digits*

The answer to each problem is correct but the digits in each problem are scrambled. Unscramble the digits and write them in the correct order in the empty boxes.

EXERCISES

? For more exercises, see *Extra Practice*.

Practice and Problem Solving

Ⓐ Practice by Example

Estimate each product.

Example 1
(page 132)

1. 4.56 · 7.02
about 35

2. 11.15 · 4.44
about 44

3. 6.3 · 9.2
about 54

4. 24.5 · 4.2
about 100

5. 3.29 · 58
about 180

6. 0.08 · 40.05
about 4

Example 2
(page 132)

Estimate the cost of each purchase.

7. Food Tom bought 6 hamburgers for $2.89 each. about $18

8. Sports Equipment The athletic director bought 5 soccer balls for $12.29 each. about $60

Example 3
(page 133)

Estimate each quotient using compatible numbers.

9. 3.9 ÷ 2.1
about 2

10. 3.86 ÷ 1.95
about 2

11. 19.56 ÷ 0.71
about 30

12. $585 ÷ 11.75
about $50

13. 18.2 ÷ 3.4
about 6

14. 57.1 ÷ 7.2
about 8

15. Unit Pricing Marshall buys a sack of peaches for $5.98. If the peaches weigh 2.77 pounds, about what price per pound did Marshall pay? about $2.00 per pound

Example 4
(page 133)

Use estimation. Is each quotient reasonable? Explain.

16. No; 45.6 is not close to an estimate of 5.
17. No; $67.50 is not close to an estimate of $6.

16. 102.6 ÷ 22.5 = 45.6
16–17. See above left.

17. $32.40 ÷ 4.80 = $67.50

18. Number Sense Explain how you would find a reasonable estimate for 14.90 ÷ 4.56. Answers may vary. Sample: 14.90 is about 15, and 4.56 is about 5, so 14.90 ÷ 4.56 ≈ 15 ÷ 5, or 3.

Ⓑ Apply Your Skills

Estimate each product or quotient.

25. Answers may vary: Samples are given. physical therapist: about $18/h in Dallas, about $16/h in Washington, D.C.; pharmacist: about $20/h in Dallas, about $21/h in Washington, D.C.; nurse: about $15/h in Dallas, about $18/h in Washington, D.C.

19. 193.7 · 1.78
about 380

20. 7.95 ÷ 2.1
about 4

21. 9.392 ÷ 2.9
about 3

22. 876.66 · 39.64
about 36,000

23. $75.45 ÷ 12.48
about $6

24. 16.33 · 3.5
about 64

Data Analysis Use the table below for Exercises 25–27.

Hospital Staff Wages (40-h week)

Occupation	Dallas, TX	Washington, DC
Physical Therapist	$733.20	$655.20
Pharmacist	$793.60	$851.60
Nurse	$606.80	$714.80

SOURCE: *The American Almanac of Jobs and Salaries*

Reading Math

For help with reading and solving Exercise 27, see page 136.

25. Estimate the hourly wage for each staff position. See upper left.

26. Estimate the yearly (52 weeks) salary for each staff position. See margin.

27. How much more per hour does a physical therapist in Dallas, Texas, make than a physical therapist in Washington, D.C.? about $2

26. Answers may vary: Samples are given. physical therapist: about $35,000 in Dallas and $33,000 in Washington D.C.; pharmacist: about $40,000 in Dallas and $43,000 in Washington D.C.; nurse: about $30,000 in Dallas and $35,000 in Washington, D.C.

Use estimation. Is each product or quotient reasonable? Explain.

28. $-46.82(-1.5) = 702.3$
not reasonable; $47 \times 2 = 94$

29. $-71.5071 \div (-11.9) = 6.009$
reasonable; $72 \div 12 = 6$

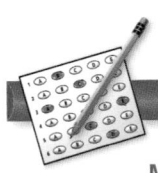 **30. Gas Mileage** Shari is planning a 450-mi car trip. Her car can travel about 39 mi on a gallon of gasoline. Gasoline costs $1.89/gal. About how much will the gas cost for her trip? **about $22**

Challenge — **Estimate each quotient.**

31. $-483.09 \div 7.29$ about -70

32. $-362,400 \div (-4.2)$ about 90,000

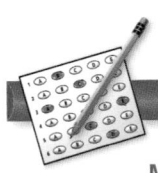 **33. Health** Humans breathe about 15 breaths in a minute. The average breath at rest contains 0.76 liter of air. About how many liters of air will you breathe while at rest for 25 minutes? **about 300 L**

34. You round to $20 \div 4$. Your friend used compatible numbers, $21 \div 3$.

34. Writing in Math You estimate $21.2 \div 3.75$ to be 5. Your friend estimates the quotient to be 7. Explain how the two estimates can be different and yet both be reasonable. **See left.**

Test Prep

Multiple Choice

35. Greta ran the 400-m dash in 49.07 s. If Greta ran at a constant rate, how many meters did she run in one second? **A**
A. between 8 m and 9 m   **B.** between 9 m and 10 m
C. between 10 m and 11 m   **D.** between 11 m and 12 m

36. A shrew, the world's smallest mammal, has a heart rate of 790 beats per minute. About how many times does a shrew's heart beat in 5 minutes? **G**
F. 3,500   **G.** 4,000   **H.** 4,500   **I.** 4,790

Short Response

37. Two people estimate the product $1.99 \cdot 8.5$. **a–b. See margin.**
a. Will they necessarily get the same estimate?
b. Explain your answer.

Take It to the NET
Online lesson quiz at
www.PHSchool.com
Web Code: ada-0302

38. You review your sales slip after buying 4 CDs that cost $14.95 each. Before tax, the total was $77.80. Is this total correct? Explain. **See margin.**

Mixed Review

Lesson 3-1 — **Estimate each sum or difference.**

39. $2.99 + $6.01
about $9

40. $25.90 - $5.79
about $20

41. $12.3 + 12.3 + 14.56$
about 39

42. $1,242.24 - 24.05$
about 1,220

43. $18.95 - 7.48$
about 12

44. $7.47 - $5.50
about $2

Lesson 1-10 — **In which quadrant or on which axis of a coordinate plane does each point lie?**

45. $(2, 4)$ **46.** $(-5, 0)$ **47.** $(8, -6)$ **48.** $(0, 8)$ **49.** $(-5, -3)$
Quadrant I x-axis   Quadrant IV y-axis   Quadrant III

Lesson 1-8 **50. Travel** A bus trip from Sacramento to Los Angeles takes 7 h 40 min. You depart at 11:40 A.M. At what time will you arrive in Los Angeles?
7:20 P.M.

37. [2] No; good explanation. Sample:
$2 \cdot 9 = $18 will give one estimate.
A closer estimate is
$($2 \cdot 8) + ($2 \cdot 0.5) = $16 + $1 = $17.$
[1] No; minor error in explanation.

38. [2] No; $14.95 \times 4 \approx $15 \times 4 = $60.
So, 4 CDs cost about $60. The total, $77.80, is not reasonable.
[1] No; minor error in explanation.

---

4. Assess

English Learners
Exercise 11 Have students read 0.71 as "seventy-one hundredths" rather than "zero point seven one" so they will understand the value of the number.

Alternative Assessment

Ask students to write down the mental steps they use when estimating $22.33 \div 6.83$. **See back of book.**

Test Prep

 Resources
For additional practice with a variety of test item formats:
• Test Prep, p. 173
• Test-Taking Strategies, p. 168
• Test-Taking Strategies With Transparencies

Reteaching 3-2 *Estimating Decimal Products and Quotients*

Estimate $3.14 \div $0.75.
Round 0.75. Since 5 is 5 or greater, add one to the 7, so $0.75 \approx 0.8$.
Round 3.14 to a compatible number, one that is easy to divide by 0.8. Since $8 \cdot 4 = 32$, round 3.14 to 3.2.
Mentally divide $3.2 \div 0.8 = 4$.
Thus $3.14 \div 0.75 \approx $4.

Estimate each quotient using compatible numbers.
Answers may vary. Samples are given.

1. $15.831 \div 7.87 \approx$ _16_ $\div$ _8_ = _2_
2. $163.7 \div 0.46 \approx$ _150_ $\div$ _0.5_ = _300_
3. $-472 \div 78.6 \approx$ _-480_ $\div$ _80_ = _-6_
4. $11.45 \div 3.2 \approx$ _12_ $\div$ _3_ = _4_
5. $549.7 \div 51.4 \approx$ _550_ $\div$ _50_ = _11_
6. $-9.6 \div (-1.854) \approx$ _-10_ $\div$ (_-2_) = _5_
7. $6.39 \div (-0.82) \approx$ _6.4_ $\div$ (_-0.8_) = _-8_
8. $-31.8 \div 0.56 \approx$ _-30_ $\div$ _0.6_ = _-50_
9. $336.4 \div (-4.23) \approx$ _320_ $\div$ (_-4_) = _-80_
10. $82.56 \div 8.72 \approx$ _81_ $\div$ _9_ = _9_
11. $-62.31 \div 14.89 \approx$ _-60_ $\div$ _15_ = _-4_
12. $25.8 \div 6.72 \approx$ _24_ $\div$ _6_ = _4_
13. $131 \div 42.1 \approx$ _120_ $\div$ _40_ = _3_
14. $1.53 \div 0.28 \approx$ _1.5_ $\div$ _0.3_ = _5_
15. $6,243 \div (-75) \approx$ _6,300_ $\div$ (_-70_) = _-90_

Use the Guided Problem Solving worksheet with Exercise 30.

Reading a Table

Information is often summarized and displayed in tables. Students will learn to read a table and extract the needed information or data.

Teaching Notes

Math Tip

Point out to students that it is important to always take the time to read the title of the table and all sections of the table, not just the numbers.

Auditory Learners

Have students bring into class some tables they find in a magazine or newspaper. Pair students and have them take turns reading the tables aloud. Ask volunteers to share their tables with the class.

Reading Math

Reading a Table

For Use With Page 134, Exercise 27

Read the exercise below and then read how the needed data are found in the table. Follow along as the problem is solved. Check your understanding by solving the exercise at the bottom of the page.

Use the table. How much more per hour does a physical therapist in Dallas, Texas, make than a physical therapist in Washington, D.C.?

The title of the table tells you that the table entries are wages for a 40-h week.

Occupations: Look down for physical therapist.

Cities: Look across for Dallas and Washington.

The table tells you that in a 40-h week:

A physical therapist in Dallas makes $733.20.

A physical therapist in Washington makes $655.20.

Hospital Staff Wages (40-h week)

Occupation	Dallas, TX	Washington, DC
Physical Therapist	$733.20	$655.20
Pharmacist	$793.60	$851.60
Nurse	$606.80	$714.80

SOURCE: *The American Almanac of Jobs and Salaries*

Estimate:

A Dallas physical therapist makes about $730 − $650 = $80 more in a 40-h week.

That's about $80 ÷ 40 = $2 more per hour.

Calculate — Method 1

733.20 − 655.20 = 78.00   **Subtract to find the difference in weekly wages.**

78.00 ÷ 40 = 1.95   **Divide to find the difference in hourly wages.**

Calculate — Method 2

733.20 ÷ 40 = 18.33   **Divide to find the Dallas hourly wage.**

655.20 ÷ 40 = 16.38   **Divide to find the Washington hourly wage.**

18.33 − 16.38 = 1.95   **Subtract to find the difference in hourly wages.**

A Dallas physical therapist makes $1.95/h more than one in Washington.

This is close to the estimate of $2/h.

EXERCISES

1. How much less per hour does a nurse in Dallas make than a nurse in Washington? **$2.70**

2. How much more per hour does a pharmacist in Dallas make than a nurse in Dallas? **$4.67**

Mean, Median, and Mode

OBJECTIVE 1 Finding Mean, Median, and Mode

Mean, median, and *mode* are **measures of central tendency** of a collection of data. Consider the data 2, 3, 4, 5, 8, 8, and 12.

The **mean** is the sum of the data values divided by the number of data values.

$$\text{mean} = \frac{2 + 3 + 4 + 5 + 8 + 8 + 12}{7}$$
$$= \frac{42}{7}$$
$$\text{mean} = 6$$

The **median** is the middle number when data values are written in order and there is an odd number of data values. For an even number of data values, the median is the mean of the two middle numbers.

2 3 4 5 8 8 12
        ↑
      median

The **mode** is the data item that occurs most often. There can be one mode, more than one mode, or no mode.

2 3 4 5 8 8 12
              ‿
             mode

1 EXAMPLE Real-World  Problem Solving

Fundraising Six elementary students are participating in a one-week Readathon to raise money for a good cause. Use the graph. Find the (a) mean, (b) median, and (c) mode.

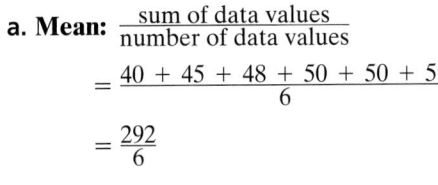

READATHON (PAGES READ)

a. Mean: $\dfrac{\text{sum of data values}}{\text{number of data values}}$

$$= \frac{40 + 45 + 48 + 50 + 50 + 59}{6}$$

$$= \frac{292}{6}$$

$$= 48.666 \ldots$$

Rounded to the nearest tenth, the mean is 48.7.

b. Median: 40 45 48 50 50 59 **Write the data in order.**

$\dfrac{48 + 50}{2} = 49$ **Find the mean of the two middle numbers.**

The median is 49.

c. Mode: Find the data value that occurs most often.
The mode is 50.

What You'll Learn

OBJECTIVE 1
To find mean, median, and mode of a set of data

OBJECTIVE 2
To choose the best measure of central tendency

... And Why

To solve real-world problems involving consumer issues

✓ Check Skills You'll Need

Write the numbers from least to greatest.

1. 8, 6, 4, 9, 3, 5, 6
   3, 4, 5, 6, 6, 8, 9
2. 72, 68, 69, 71, 72
   68, 69, 71, 72, 72
3. 112, 101, 98, 120, 101
   98, 101, 101, 112, 120
4. 3.74, 3, 3.7, 3.3, 37
   3, 3.3, 3.7, 3.74, 37

? For help, go to Skills Handbook, p. 757.

New Vocabulary

• measures of central tendency
• mean • median
• mode • outlier

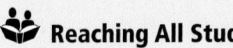 Interactive lesson includes instant self-check, tutorials, and activities.

Lesson Preview

✓ Check Skills You'll Need

Ordering Whole Numbers
Skills Handbook: p. 757;
Exercises 11–14.

Lesson Resources

📁 **Teaching Resources**
Practice, Reteaching, Enrichment

👥 **Reaching All Students**
Practice Workbook 3-3
Spanish Practice Workbook 3-3
Guided Problem Solving 3-3
Technology Activities 6

⏰ **Presentation Assistant Plus!**
Transparencies and PowerPoint™
• Check Skills You'll Need 3-3
• Additional Examples 3-3
• Student Edition Answers 3-3
• Lesson Quiz 3-3
PH Presentation Pro CD-ROM 3-3

ⒶSSESSMENT *SYSTEM*

Computer Test Generator CD-ROM

💻 **Technology**
Resource Pro® CD-ROM
Computer Test Generator CD-ROM
PH Presentation Pro CD-ROM

💻 **www.PHSchool.com**
Student Site
• Teacher Web Code: adk-5500
• Graphing Calculator, Procedure 21
• Self-grading Lesson Quiz
PH SuccessNet Teacher Center
• Lesson Planner
• Resources

Plus 🅸TEXT

3-3 Mean, Median, and Mode **137**

Ongoing Assessment and Intervention

Before the Lesson
Diagnose prerequisite skills using:
• Check Skills You'll Need

During the Lesson
Monitor progress using:
• Check Understanding
• Additional Examples
• Test Prep

After the Lesson
Assess knowledge using:
• Lesson Quiz
• Computer Test Generator CD-ROM

137

Math Background

Finding the mean, median, and mode are all ways to give information about a set of data. A single number that represents the approximate "center" of the distribution of the numbers in a set is called a *measure of central tendency.*

Teaching Notes

1 EXAMPLE Visual Learners

Some students may not understand the importance of ordering data when finding the median. Place an odd number of shoes of various sizes in a line, in random order. Try to have at least 9 shoes. Ask: *Can you tell which shoe is the middle size?* **no** Have students order the shoes from smallest to largest. Ask: *Now can you tell which shoe is the middle size? Explain.* **Yes, the middle-size shoe is in the middle.** Remind students to always arrange the data in order before trying to find the median.

2 EXAMPLE Error Prevention

Point out that if students are asked to find the mode and there is none, then they should not write "0" as an answer. Writing 0 would mean that the number 0 occurs most often.

3 EXAMPLE Geography Connection

Ask if any students have ever visited or lived in Central America. Ask if any of them know why the percentage of land for farming seems low in some of the countries. Have students do research to better understand why some of the countries have more farmland than others.

✓ **Check Understanding** Example 1

1. Find the mean, median, and mode: 2.3 4.3 3.2 2.9 2.7 2.3
   2.95, 2.8, 2.3

2 EXAMPLE Identifying Modes

How many modes, if any, does each have?

a. **$1.50 $2.00 $2.25 $2.40 $3.50 $4.00**
   No values are the same, so there is no mode.

b. **2 3 6 8 8 10 11 12 14 14 18 20**
   Both 8 and 14 appear the same number of times, and most often. There are two modes.

c. **grape, grape, banana, nectarine, strawberry, strawberry, strawberry, orange, watermelon**
   Strawberry appears most often. There is one mode.

✓ **Check Understanding** Example 2

2. Find the number of modes.

   a. 11 9 7 7 8 8 13 11   b. 38.5 55.4 45.3 38.5 68.4
      3 modes   **1 mode**

An **outlier** is a data value that is much greater or less than the other data values. An outlier can affect the mean of a group of data.

3 EXAMPLE Real-World Problem Solving

Approximate Land Areas That Can Be Farmed in Central American Countries

Guatemala 5,000 mi²
Belize 200 mi²
Honduras 6,500 mi²
Nicaragua 4,500 mi²
El Salvador 2,200 mi²
Costa Rica 1,200 mi²
Panama 2,100 mi²

SOURCE: *The New York Times Almanac*

Geography Use the map of Central America at the left.

a. **Which data value is an outlier?**
   The data value for Honduras, 6,500 mi², is an outlier. It is an outlier because it is 1,500 mi² away from the closest data value.

b. **How does the outlier affect the mean?**

   $\dfrac{21,700}{7} = 3,100$ **Find the mean with the outlier.**

   $\dfrac{15,200}{6} \approx 2,500$ **Find the mean without the outlier.**

   $3,100 - 2,500 = 600$

   The outlier raises the mean by about 600 mi².

✓ **Check Understanding** Example 3

3. Find an outlier in each group of data below and tell how it affects the mean. Round to the nearest tenth.

   a. 9 10 12 13 8 9 31 9   b. 1 17.5 18 19.5 16 17.5
      31; raises the mean by 2.6   **1; lowers the mean by 2.8**

Reaching All Students

| **Below Level** Help students remember the difference between *median* and *mode* by associating median with the median on a highway. "Mode" sounds like *most.* It occurs the most often. | **Advanced Learners** Challenge students to write five data items that have the same mean, median, and mode. All data items may not be the same number. | **Visual Learners** See note on page 138. **Error Prevention** See note on page 138. |

2 Choosing the Best Measure

One measure of central tendency may be better than another to describe data. For example, consider the eight hourly wage rates shown at the right. Here are the measures of central tendency.

Mode: $5.50
Mean: $7.50
Median: $6.10

Employees' Hourly Wages	
$5.50	$6.20
$5.50	$6.30
$5.50	$8.00
$6.00	$17.00

The mode is the lowest wage listed. So the mode does not describe the data well.

The mean is above the hourly wage of all but two workers. The mean is influenced by the outlier, $17.

The median is the best measure of central tendency here since it is not influenced by the size of the outlier.

4 EXAMPLE   Identifying the Best Measure

Which measure of central tendency best describes each situation? Explain.

a. the favorite movies of students in the eighth grade

Mode; since the data are not numerical, the mode is the appropriate measure. When determining the most frequently chosen item, or when the data are not numerical, use the mode.

b. the daily high temperatures during a week in July

Mean; since daily high temperatures in July are not likely to have an outlier, mean is the appropriate measure. When the data have no outliers, use the mean.

c. the distances students in your class travel to school

Median; since one student may live much farther from school than the majority of students, the median is the appropriate measure. When an outlier may significantly influence the mean, use the median.

Reading Math

To help you recall that *median* means "middle number," think of the green, grassy median strip in the middle of a divided highway.

✓ Check Understanding   Example 4

4. a. Comparison Shopping Toshio found the following prices for sport shirts:
$20, $26, $27, $28, $21, $42, $18, and $20.
Find the mean, median, and mode for the shirt prices. $25.25, $23.50, $20

b. Reasoning Which measure of central tendency best describes the data? Justify your reasoning.
Answers may vary. Sample: Median; the mode is equal to two of the smaller data values, and the outlier ($42) affects the mean too much.

Assignment Guide

▼ **1** Objective 1
- **A** **B** Core 1–12
- **C** Extension 26, 28

▼ **2** Objective 2
- **A** **B** Core 13–25
- **C** Extension 27

Test Prep 29–32
Mixed Review 33–39

Practice 3-3 *Mean, Median, and Mode*

1. There were 8 judges at a gymnastics competition. Kathleen received these scores for her performance on the uneven parallel bars:
8.9, 8.7, 8.9, 9.2, 8.8, 8.2, 8.9, 8.8

a. Find these statistics: mean __8.8__ median __8.85__ mode __8.9__

b. Which measure of central tendency best describes the data? Explain.
   Answers may vary. Sample: The median; the mean is affected by the outlier, and the mode is next to the highest score.

c. Why do you think that the highest and lowest judge's scores are disregarded in tallying the total score in a gymnastics competition?
   This eliminates scores that are not representative of the majority.

Find the mean, median, and mode. Round to the nearest tenth where necessary. Identify any outliers.

Data	Mean	Median	Mode	Outliers
2. 8, 15, 9, 7, 4, 5, 9, 11	8.5	8.5	9	15
3. 70, 61, 28, 40, 60, 72, 25, 31, 64, 63	51.4	60.5	none	none
4. 4.9, 5.7, 6.0, 5.3, 4.8, 4.9, 5.3, 4.7, 4.9, 5.6, 5.1	5.2	5.1	4.9	none
5. 271, 221, 234, 240, 271, 234, 213, 253, 155	232.4	234	234 & 271	155
6. 0, 2, 3, 3, 3, 4, 4, 5	3	3	3	none

Use the data in the table. Round to the nearest tenth where necessary.

Peak	Height (ft)
Mont Blanc	15,771
Monte Rosa	15,203
Dom	14,911
Liskamm	14,852
Weisshorn	14,780

7. What is the mean height of the five highest European mountains? __15,103.4 ft__

8. What is the median height? __14,911 ft__

9. Is any of the heights an outlier? Explain.
   Mont Blanc is over 500 ft higher than Monte Rosa.

Enrichment 3-3 *More on Mean, Median, and Mode*

Solve. Round to the nearest tenth, if necessary.

1. Leon must have a mean score of 90 on his math quizzes to earn an A. So far, he has received grades of 88, 85, 91, 92, 94, 81, 86, and 98. What grade must he earn on his final quiz? __95__

2. The median of the following set of data is 6: 1, 8, 7, 1, 6, 8, 3, 6. What number from the set of data can you subtract 1 from so that the median of the resulting set will be 5½? __6__

3. There are twelve girls and eight boys in a math class. The girls' mean score on the final exam was 83.5. The boys' mean score was 81.5. What was the mean score for the entire class? Hint: First find the total points scored by all members of the class. __82.7__

4. The mode of the following set of data is 23: 19, 5, 23, x, 17. What is the mean? __17.4__

5. The median of the following set of data is 26: 17, y, 49, 13. Find y. __35__

6. The total weight of all the students in a class is 3,159 lb. The mean weight of the students is 117 lb. How many students are in the class? __27__

7. Ramon, Jake, and Pearl are all less than 50 years old. The age difference between the youngest person and the oldest person is 15. The mode of their ages is 37. What is their mean age? What is their median age? __32, 37__

8. There are five one-digit numbers in a set of data. The mean of the numbers is 3. A mode is 1. The median is 4. What are the numbers? __1, 1, 4, 4, 5__

EXERCISES

🔍 For more exercises, see *Extra Practice*.

Practice and Problem Solving

A Practice by Example
Example 1
(page 137)

Find the mean, median, and mode of each group of data. If an answer is not a whole number, round to the nearest tenth.

1. 47 56 57 63 89 44 56
   58.9, 56, 56

2. 4 5 2 3 2 3 3 3 1 1 3
   2.7, 3, 3

3. 1 2 4 5 5 6 9
   4.6, 5, 5

4. 2.8 3.6 3.8 4.1 2.8 3.7 4.3
   3.6, 3.7, 2.8

 5. **Fitness** Mia's workouts lasted 1.0 h, 1.5 h, 2.25 h, 1.5 h, 2.4 h, and 2.1 h. Find the mean, median, and mode of these times. If the answer is not an integer, round to the nearest tenth.
   1.8 h, 1.8 h, 1.5 h

Example 2
(page 138)

How many modes, if any, does each group of data have?

6. 31 44 44 31 38 **2 modes**

7. 4.3 4.9 4.9 5.2 **1 mode**

8. 64 68 64 65 68 65 72 61
   3 modes

9. Bob, Ana, Ron, Bob, Kay
   1 mode

Example 3
(page 138)

Find the outlier in each group of data and tell how it affects the mean.

10. 37 4 7 3 11 9 13 5
    37; raises mean by about 3.7

11. 126 123 115 125 123
    115; lowers mean by about 1.9

🌐 12. **Grades** Rita's quiz scores are 72, 96, 74, 80, and 79. Find the outlier and tell how it affects Rita's mean quiz score.
    96; raises mean by about 4

Example 4
(page 139)

Which measure of central tendency best describes each situation? Explain. 13–15. See left.

13. Mean; there likely are no outliers.
14. Mode; the data are not numerical.
15. Mean; there likely are no outliers.

13. numbers of apples in 2-lb bags

14. favorite brands of jeans of 14-year-olds

15. ages of students in a fifth-grade classroom

Which measure of central tendency best describes each group of data? Explain. 16–17. See below left.

16. minutes on the Internet
    50 63 59 85 367 48

17. heights of students in inches
    51 45 47 48 50 50 50 52

B Apply Your Skills

16. Median; there is no mode, and the outlier (367) affects the mean too much.
17. Mean, median, or mode since they are all about equal.

For Exercises 18–22, find mean, median, and mode. Which measure of central tendency best describes each group of data? Explain.
18–22. See margin.

18. 3,456 560 435 456

19. 5.6 6.8 1.2 6.5 7.9 6.5

20. 33 76 86 92 86

21. 8 2 4 9 16

 22. resting heart rate in beats per minute: 79 72 80 81 40 72

Which measure of central tendency best describes each situation? Explain.

23. shoe colors in a classroom
    Mode; the data are not numerical.

24. widths of computer screens at a bank
    Mean; there likely are no outliers.

25. numbers of pets owned by classmates
    Median; there could easily be outliers.

GPS Use the Guided Problem Solving worksheet with Exercise 22.

18. 1,226.8; 508, none; median; there is no mode and the outlier (3,456) affects the mean too much.

19. 5.8, 6.5, 6.5; median (or mode); the outlier (1.2) affects the mean too much.

20. 74.6, 86, 86; median (or mode); the outlier (33) affects the mean too much.

21. 7.8, 8, none; mean (or median); there is no mode and the mean and median are nearly the same.

22. 70.7, 75.5, 72; median; the outlier (40) affects the mean too much and the mode is too low.

 **Challenge**

For Exercises 26–28, use the table at the left. Round answers to the nearest tenth.

Fat and Calorie Content
(per 2-tablespoon serving)

Seed or Nut	Fat (g)	Calories
Peanut	8.9	104
Pecan	9.1	90
Pistachio	7.9	92
Pumpkin	7.9	93
Sunflower	8.9	102
Walnut	7.7	80

26. Data Analysis You make a mixture using the same amount of each kind of seed and nut.
  a. What is the mean number of grams of fat in a 2-tablespoon serving of the mixture? **8.4 g**
  b. What is the mean number of calories in a 2-tablespoon serving of the mixture? **93.5 calories**

27. Writing in Math Describe two mixtures that each use a total of 8 tablespoons. Do the two parts of Exercise 26 for your mixtures. **See margin.**

28. Nutrition A mixture of equal amounts of pumpkin seeds, sunflower seeds, and pistachios contains 12 tablespoons in all. How many grams of fat and how many calories does the mixture have? **49.4 g, 574 calories**

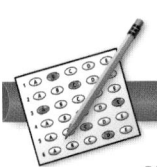

Test Prep

Multiple Choice

29. The average cost of a meal at the Grand Plaza is $20. Which one of the following statements *cannot* be true? **D**
  A. The cost of four meals is greater than $20.
  B. Some meals cost less than $10.
  C. Each meal costs exactly $20.
  D. Each meal costs more than $20.

Take It to the NET
Online lesson quiz at
www.PHSchool.com
Web Code: ada-0303

30. Kayla's first three quiz scores are 90, 85, and 88. Which score on her next quiz will raise Kayla's mean quiz score to 90? **F**
  F. 97   **G.** 95   **H.** 92   **I.** 90

31. Ten out of 20 students score a perfect 100 on a math test. Which of the following describes the score of 100 for the 20 students? **C**
  A. mean   **B.** median   **C.** mode   **D.** outlier

Short Response

32. In a neighborhood with 46 homes, two are more than 6,000 ft² in area, and the rest are less than 2,500 ft² in area.
  a. Would the mean or the median provide a better measure of the typical home size?
  b. Explain your reasoning.
  [2] Median; the two large homes are outliers and distort the mean. **[1]** correctly identifies median, but gives incorrect or no explanation

Mixed Review

Lesson 3-2   **Estimate each product or quotient.**

33. $9.01 ÷ $1.42   **34.** 7.5 · 89.1   **35.** 12.6 · $2.99
     about 6   **about 720**   **about $39.00**

Lesson 2-7 **36. Retail Sales** Karen sells children's hats for $4 and adults' hats for $7. On Saturday, she sold 120 hats, and she collected $720. How many adults' hats did she sell? **80 adults' hats**

Lesson 2-3   **Simplify each expression.**

37. $6x + 8 + 2$ **38.** $5z + 4x + 3z$ **39.** $x - 4t + 2t + 5$
     6x + 10   **4x + 8z**   **x − 2t + 5**

3-3 Mean, Median, and Mode   **141**

27. Two tablespoons each of peanuts, pecans, pistachios, and pumpkin seeds; 8.45 g; 94.75 calories; two tablespoons each of walnuts, sunflower seeds, pumpkin seeds, and pistachios; 8.1 g; 91.75 calories.

---

4. Assess

 **PowerPoint** **Lesson Quiz 3-3**

Which measure of central tendency best describes each situation?

1. numbers of legs on the animals in a zoo **mode**

2. favorite digits (from 0 to 9) of the students in a class **mode**

3. numbers of days-per-student that students are absent from school **median**

4. test scores **mean**

Alternative Assessment

Have students use data sets from their daily lives, like the amounts of time spent over 5 days doing homework, to explain in their own words the differences among the three measures of central tendency.

Test Prep

 Resources

For additional practice with a variety of test item formats:
• Test Prep, p. 173
• Test-Taking Strategies, p. 168
• Test-Taking Strategies With Transparencies

Reteaching 3-3 *Mean, Median, and Mode*

In 1995, eight states had pupil-teacher ratios that were close to the U.S. average of 17.3. Use the table at the right. Find the **a)** mean, **b)** median, and **c)** mode.

State	Pupils per Teacher
Arkansas	17.1
Illinois	17.1
Indiana	17.5
Louisiana	17.0
Mississippi	17.5
New Mexico	17.0
Ohio	17.1
Pennsylvania	17.0

a. Mean: $\frac{\text{sum of data items}}{\text{number of data items}}$
$= \frac{17.1 + 17.1 + 17.5 + 17.0 + 17.5 + 17.0 + 17.1 + 17.0}{8}$
$= \frac{137.3}{8} = 17.1625$
Rounded to the nearest tenth, the mean is 17.2.

b. Median: Write the data in order.
17.0, 17.0, 17.0, 17.1, 17.1, 17.1, 17.5, 17.5
$\frac{17.1 + 17.1}{2} = 17.1$ Find the mean of the two middle numbers. The median is 17.1.

c. Mode: Find the data item that occurs most often.
Both 17.0 and 17.1 occur 3 times. The modes are 17.0 and 17.1.

Find the mean, median, and mode. Round to the nearest tenth where necessary.

	mean	median	mode
1. 14.2 14.7 14.3 14.6	14.5	14.45	none
2. 8 7 3 5 9 2 4 7	5.6	6	7
3. 37 42 51 28 36	38.8	37	none
4. 1.1 1.8 2.6 1.8 1.9 2.6	2.0	1.85	1.8 & 2.6

The world's largest body of freshwater is formed by the Great Lakes of North America. Use the table of depths at the right. Find the following statistics. Round to the nearest tenth where necessary.

Lake	Depth (in ft)
Superior	1,333
Michigan	923
Huron	750
Erie	210
Ontario	802

5. mean: **803.6 ft**

6. median: **802 ft**

7. mode: **none**

Reteaching

141

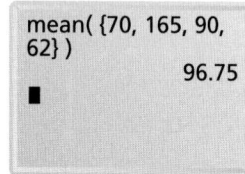

Mean and Median on a Graphing Calculator

Mean and Median on a Graphing Calculator

For Use With Lesson 3-3

This Technology extension shows students how to use a graphing calculator to find the mean and median for a set of data.

Resources

Students may use any graphing calculator

Teaching Notes

Error Prevention!

For a brace, {, students may want to press the parenthesis key without pressing **2nd** first. The calculator will not perform correctly if this is done. Students must see braces in the expression on the calculator screen before pressing **ENTER**.

Teaching Tip

Have students work together to do the Example in the book and the following problem:
Use a calculator to find the mean and median of this set of data:
5.6 ft, 3.2 ft, 8.9 ft, 1.7 ft.
mean: 4.85 ft median: 4.4 ft

You can use a graphing calculator to find means and medians.

EXAMPLE

Find (a) the mean and (b) the median number of acres in Ohio zoos.

Zoos in Ohio

Zoo	Number of Acres	Number of Species
Cincinnati Zoo	70	712
Cleveland Metroparks Zoo	165	599
Columbus Zoo	90	650
Toledo Zoological Gardens	62	633

SOURCE: *The World Almanac*

a. Use the mean function. In **STAT,** select **MATH** and **mean,** then **ENTER**. Enter the data between braces { } using commas. Press **ENTER** to find the mean.

```
mean( {70, 165, 90,
62} )
               96.75
■
```

The mean is about 97 acres.

b. Use the median function. In **STAT,** select **MATH** and **median,** then **ENTER**. Enter the data between braces { } using commas. Press **ENTER** to find the mean.

```
median( {70, 165, 90,
62} )
                  80
■
```

The median is 80 acres.

EXERCISES

Use a calculator to find the mean and median.

1. number of species in Ohio zoos about 649 species; about 642 species

2. 85°F, 79°F, 80°F, 75°F, 82°F 80.2°F; 80°F

3. $3.75, $4.50, $9.25, $4.70, $5.90 $5.62; $4.70

4. 100, 95, 82, 102, 78, 76 about 88.8; 88.5

5. **Miles of Atlantic Coastline by State**

State	DE	FL	GA	ME	MD	MA	NH	NJ	NY	NC	RI	SC	VA
Miles	28	580	100	228	31	192	13	130	127	301	40	187	112

about 159 mi; 127 mi

SOURCE: National Oceanic and Atmospheric Administration, U.S. Dept. of Commerce

6. Investigate entering the data in a list, L_1, and then using L_1 as the data list in parts (a) and (b) of the Example. The function mean(L_1) gives the mean, and median(L_1) gives the median.

142 Technology Mean and Median

Using Formulas

OBJECTIVE

1 Substituting Into Formulas

A **formula** is an equation that shows a relationship between quantities that are represented by variables.

An important formula in math and science is $d = rt$, where d is the distance, r is the rate, or speed, and t is the time spent traveling.

1 EXAMPLE   Real-World Problem Solving

Travel Suppose you travel 162 miles in 3 hours. Use the formula $d = rt$ to find your average speed.

$d = rt$	Write the formula.
$162 = (r)(3)$	Substitute 162 for d and 3 for t.
$\dfrac{162}{3} = \dfrac{3r}{3}$	Divide each side by 3.
$54 = r$	Simplify.

● Your average speed is 54 mi/h.

✓ Check Understanding   Example 1

1. Use the formula $d = rt$. Find d, r, or t.

    a. $d = 273$ mi, $t = 9.75$ h   **b.** $d = 540.75$ in., $r = 10.5$ in./yr
       $r = 28$ mi/h $t = 51.5$ yr

2 EXAMPLE   Real-World Problem Solving

Insects You can estimate the temperature outside using the chirps of a cricket. Use the formula $F = \dfrac{n}{4} + 37$, where n is the number of times a cricket chirps in one minute, and F is the temperature in degrees Fahrenheit. Estimate the temperature when a cricket chirps 100 times in a minute.

$F = \dfrac{n}{4} + 37$	Write the formula.
$F = \dfrac{100}{4} + 37$	Replace n with 100.
$F = 25 + 37$	Divide.
$F = 62$	Add.

● The temperature is about 62°F.

3-4 Using Formulas   **143**

⟲ Ongoing Assessment and Intervention

Before the Lesson
Diagnose prerequisite skills using:
● Check Skills You'll Need

During the Lesson
Monitor progress using:
● Check Understanding
● Additional Examples
● Test Prep

After the Lesson
Assess knowledge using:
● Lesson Quiz
● Computer Test Generator CD-ROM
● Chapter Checkpoint 1 (p. 146)

Professional Development

Math Background

A formula is an open-sentence equation that shows a relationship between variables. You use a formula to relate quantities in the real world. You cannot use a formula to find a value of a variable unless the values of all other variables in the formula are known.

Teaching Notes

2 EXAMPLE Diversity

Be sensitive to some people being extremely uncomfortable about insects. Even photographs of insects may disturb them.

3 EXAMPLE Geometry Connection

Formulas represent many relationships in geometry. Formulas for perimeter, area, and volume are some of the most common.

PowerPoint
Additional Examples

1 Suppose you ride your bike 18 miles in 3 hours. Use the formula $d = rt$ to find your average speed. **6 mi/h**

2 Use the formula $F = \frac{n}{4} + 37$, where n is the number of chirps a cricket makes in one minute, and F is the temperature in degrees Fahrenheit. Estimate the temperature when a cricket chirps 76 times in a minute. **about 56°F**

3 Find the perimeter of a rectangular tabletop with a length of 14.5 in. and width of 8.5 in. Use the formula for the perimeter of a rectangle, $P = 2\ell + 2w$. **46 in.**

Closure

Ask students how you can use a formula to find the perimeter of a rectangle if you know its length and width. **Answers may vary. Sample: Use the formula $P = 2\ell + 2w$. Replace ℓ with the length and w with the width and evaluate.**

✓ **Check Understanding** Example 2

2. Use the formula $F = \frac{n}{4} + 37$ to estimate the temperature in degrees Fahrenheit for each situation.

a. 96 chirps/min
61°F

b. 88 chirps/min
59°F

c. 66 chirps/min
53.5°F

OBJECTIVE

2 **Using a Perimeter Formula**

The **perimeter** of a figure is the distance around the figure. You can find the perimeter of a rectangle by adding the lengths of the four sides, or by using the formula $P = 2\ell + 2w$, where ℓ is the length and w is the width. For rectangles, it does not matter which dimension you choose to be the length or the width.

3 EXAMPLE **Finding Perimeter**

Measurement **Find the perimeter of the room. Use the formula for the perimeter of a rectangle, $P = 2\ell + 2w$.**

> **Reading Math**
> Think of *peRIMeter* as the distance around the "rim" of a figure.

12.5 ft
18.5 ft

$P = 2\ell + 2w$ **Write the formula.**
$P = 2(18.5) + 2(12.5)$ **Replace ℓ with 18.5 and w with 12.5.**
$P = 37 + 25$ **Multiply.**
$P = 62$ **Add.**

● The perimeter of the room is 62 ft.

✓ **Check Understanding** Example 3

3. Find the perimeter of each rectangle.

a.

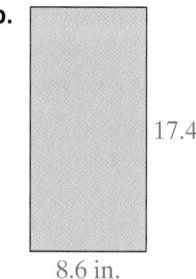
27.3 cm
16.8 cm
88.2 cm

b.

17.4 in.
8.6 in.
52 in.

144 Chapter 3 Decimals and Equations

👥 Reaching All Students

Below Level Review various formulas that students have learned in previous courses.	**Advanced Learners** Challenge students to write three formulas for the perimeter of a rectangle. Answers may vary. Sample: $P = 2\ell + 2w$, $P = \ell + \ell + w + w$, $P = 2(\ell + w)$	**Diversity** See note on page 144. **Error Prevention** See note on page 146.

EXERCISES

 For more exercises, see *Extra Practice.*

Practice and Problem Solving

A **Practice by Example**

Example 1
(page 143)

Use the formula $d = rt$. Find d, r, or t.

1. $r = 38.5$ m/h, $t = 12.5$ h
$d = 481.25$ m

2. $d = 2{,}730$ mi, $t = 9.75$ h
$r = 280$ mi/h

3. $d = 596.39$ cm, $r = 2.3$ cm/s
$t = 259.3$ s

4. $d = 10.2$ ft, $r = 0.5$ ft/h
$t = 20.4$ h

Example 2
(page 143)

Use the formula $F = \frac{n}{4} + 37$ to estimate each temperature.

5. 120 chirps/min 67°F

6. 80 chirps/min 57°F

7. 92 chirps/min 60°F

8. 64 chirps/min 53°F

Example 3
(page 144)

Use the formula $P = 2\ell + 2w$. Find the perimeter of each rectangle.

9.

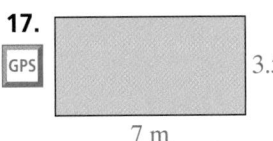

11.2 mm

16.5 mm
55.4 mm

10.

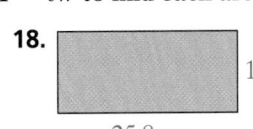

6.2 m

7.3 m
27 m

B **Apply Your Skills**

Given that C is the temperature in degrees Celsius, use the formula $F = 1.8C + 32$ to find each temperature F in degrees Fahrenheit.

11. $C = 58$
136.4°F

12. $C = -4$
24.8°F

13. $C = 72$
161.6°F

14. $C = 56$
132.8°F

15. $C = -89$
−128.2°F

16a. 36°F; 40°F; 80°F
16b. Lower temperatures;
for 10°C, the
estimation formula
gives the correct
Fahrenheit
temperature. The
more the temperature
differs from 10°C, the
greater the difference
between the estimate
and the actual
Fahrenheit
temperatures.

16. a. Estimation You can *estimate* a temperature in degrees Fahrenheit using the formula $F = 2 \cdot C + 30$, where C is the temperature in degrees Celsius (°C). What is the approximate temperature in degrees Fahrenheit when it is 3°C? 5°C? 25°C?

b. Writing in Math Is this formula better for estimating higher temperatures or lower temperatures? Explain.
16a–b. See left.

Geometry Use the formula $P = 2\ell + 2w$. Find the perimeter of each rectangle. Then use the formula $A = \ell w$ to find each area.

17.

3.5 m

7 m
21 m; 24.5 m²

18.

11.2 cm

25.8 cm
74 cm; 288.96 cm²

C **Challenge**

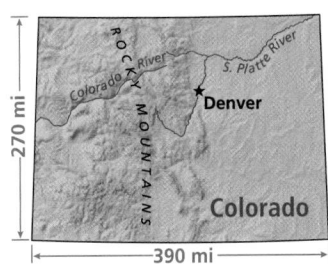

270 mi

390 mi

19. The top surface of a world-record rectangular strawberry shortcake was 175.33 ft long and 48 in. wide. Use the formula for perimeter. Find the approximate perimeter of the cake.
about 358 or 359 ft

20. Find the approximate area of the top of the cake in Exercise 19.
about 700 ft²

21. The state of Colorado is nearly rectangular in shape. Use the formula for area. Find the approximate area of Colorado.
about 100,000 mi²

22. Use the formula for perimeter. Find the approximate perimeter of Colorado. about 1,300 mi

3-4 Using Formulas **145**

GPS Use the Guided Problem Solving worksheet with Exercise 17.

3. Practice

Assignment Guide

1 Objective 1
A **B** Core 1–8, 11–16
C Extension 20, 21

2 Objective 2
A **B** Core 9, 10, 17, 18
C Extension 19, 22

Test Prep 23–27
Mixed Review 28–33

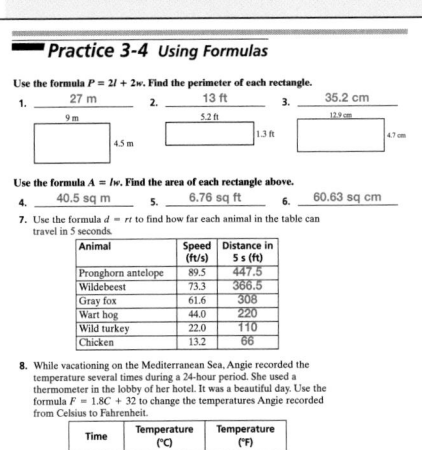

Practice 3-4 *Using Formulas*

Use the formula $P = 2l + 2w$. Find the perimeter of each rectangle.

1. 27 m; 9 m
2. 13 ft; 5.2 ft; 4.5 ft; 1.3 ft
3. 35.2 cm; 12.9 cm; 4.7 cm

Use the formula $A = lw$. Find the area of each rectangle above.

4. 40.5 sq m
5. 6.76 sq ft
6. 60.63 sq cm

7. Use the formula $d = rt$ to find how far each animal in the table can travel in 5 seconds.

Animal	Speed (ft/s)	Distance in 5 s (ft)
Pronghorn antelope	89.5	447.5
Wildebeest	73.3	366.5
Gray fox	61.6	308
Wart hog	44.0	220
Wild turkey	22.0	110
Chicken	13.2	66

8. While vacationing on the Mediterranean Sea, Angie recorded the temperature several times during a 24-hour period. She used a thermometer in the lobby of her hotel. It was a beautiful day. Use the formula $F = 1.8C + 32$ to change the temperatures Angie recorded from Celsius to Fahrenheit.

Time	Temperature (°C)	Temperature (°F)
4:00 A.M.	19	66.2
8:00 A.M.	22	71.6
12:00 P.M.	30	86
4:00 P.M.	28	82.4
8:00 P.M.	24	75.2
12:00 A.M.	20	68

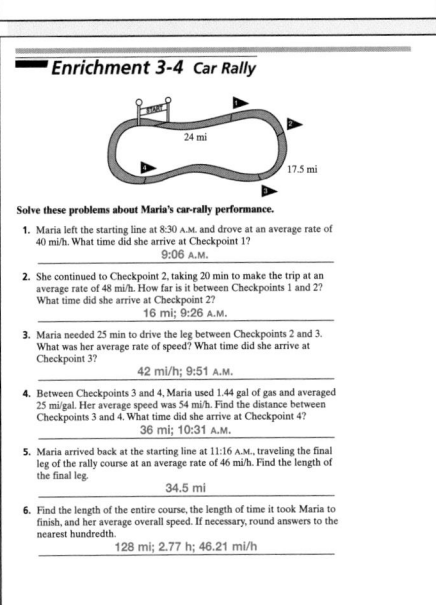

Enrichment 3-4 *Car Rally*

24 mi

17.5 mi

Solve these problems about Maria's car-rally performance.

1. Maria left the starting line at 8:30 A.M. and drove at an average rate of 40 mi/h. What time did she arrive at Checkpoint 1?
9:06 A.M.

2. She continued to Checkpoint 2, taking 20 min to make the trip at an average rate of 48 mi/h. How far is it between Checkpoints 1 and 2? What time did she arrive at Checkpoint 2?
16 mi; 9:26 A.M.

3. Maria needed 25 min to drive the leg between Checkpoints 2 and 3. What was her average rate of speed? What time did she arrive at Checkpoint 3?
42 mi/h; 9:51 A.M.

4. Between Checkpoints 3 and 4, Maria used 1.44 gal of gas and averaged 25 mi/gal. Her average speed was 54 mi/h. Find the distance between Checkpoints 3 and 4. What time did she arrive at Checkpoint 4?
36 mi; 10:31 A.M.

5. Maria arrived back at the starting line at 11:16 A.M., traveling the final leg of the rally course at an average rate of 46 mi/h. Find the length of the final leg.
34.5 mi

6. Find the length of the entire course, the length of time it took Maria to finish, and her average overall speed. If necessary, round answers to the nearest hundredth.
128 mi; 2.77 h; 46.21 mi/h

 **Lesson Quiz 3-4**

Use the formula $P = 4s$ to find the perimeter of a square with side s.

1. $s = 5.6$ m **22.4 m**

2. $s = 9.3$ in. **37.2 in.**

3. Find the side of a square with a perimeter of 164 yd. **41 yd**

Error Prevention!

Exercises 1–4 Have students write the formula first. Then have them rewrite it, carefully substituting values for the variables. This may help prevent hastily substituting the incorrect value for a variable.

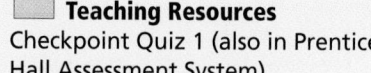 **Chapter Checkpoint 1**

To check understanding of Lessons 3-1 to 3-4:

Checkpoint Quiz 1 (p. 146)

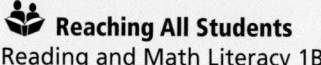 **Teaching Resources**
Checkpoint Quiz 1 (also in Prentice Hall Assessment System)

Reaching All Students
Reading and Math Literacy 1B

Spanish versions available.

Reteaching 3-4 *Using Formulas*

Given that C is the temperature in degrees Celsius, use the formula $F = 1.8C + 32$ to find the temperature F in degrees Fahrenheit. What is the temperature in degrees Fahrenheit for a temperature of 18° in Celsius?

$F = 1.8C + 32$	Write the formula.
$F = 1.8(18) + 32$	Substitute 18 for C.
$F = 32.4 + 32$	Simplify.
$F = 64.4°$	

The temperature is 64.4° Fahrenheit, or 64.4°F.

Find the temperature in degrees Fahrenheit for each temperature in degrees Celsius.

1. $C = 4°$ $F = 1.8(\underline{4}) + 32 = \underline{7.2} + 32 = \underline{39.2°F}$
2. $C = 40°$ $F = 1.8(\underline{40}) + 32 = \underline{72} + 32 = \underline{104°F}$
3. $C = 22°$ $F = 1.8(\underline{22}) + 32 = \underline{39.6} + 32 = \underline{71.6°F}$
4. $C = 35°$ $F = 1.8(\underline{35}) + 32 = \underline{63} + 32 = \underline{95°F}$
5. $C = -6°$ $F = 1.8(\underline{-6}) + 32 = \underline{-10.8} + 32 = \underline{21.2°F}$
6. $C = -24°$ $F = 1.8(\underline{-24}) + 32 = \underline{-43.2} + 32 = \underline{-11.2°F}$

Given that F is the temperature in degrees Fahrenheit, the formula $C = (F - 32)/1.8$ is the temperature C in degrees Celsius. Find the temperature in degrees Celsius for each temperature in degrees Fahrenheit.

7. $F = 68°$ $C = (\underline{68} - 32)/1.8 = \underline{36}/1.8 = \underline{20°C}$
8. $F = 17.6°$ $C = (\underline{17.6} - 32)/1.8 = \underline{-14.4}/1.8 = \underline{-8°C}$
9. $F = 5°$ $C = (\underline{5} - 32)/1.8 = \underline{-27}/1.8 = \underline{-15°C}$
10. $F = 57.2°$ $C = (\underline{57.2} - 32)/1.8 = \underline{25.2}/1.8 = \underline{14°C}$
11. $F = 32°$ $C = (\underline{32} - 32)/1.8 = \underline{0}/1.8 = \underline{0°C}$
12. $F = 212°$ $C = (\underline{212} - 32)/1.8 = \underline{180}/1.8 = \underline{100°C}$

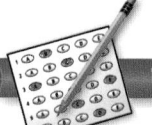 **Test Prep**

Multiple Choice

23. What is the perimeter of a rectangle that measures 32 cm by 11 cm?
A. 352 cm **B.** 86 cm **C.** 54 cm **D.** 43 cm **B**

24. Suppose you travel 320 mi in 5 h. What is your average speed?
F. 58 mi/h **G.** 60 mi/h **H.** 64 mi/h **I.** 75 mi/h **H**

26. **[2]** $P = 2\ell + 2w$, 89.2 m; **[1]** one answer

25. A giant tortoise travels about 0.17 mi/h on land. If a tortoise travels at a constant speed, how far can it travel in 2.5 h? **C**
A. 0.0425 mi **B.** 0.267 mi **C.** 0.425 mi **D.** 4.25 mi

Short Response

 **Take It to the NET**
Online lesson quiz at **www.PHSchool.com**
Web Code: ada-0304

26. A rectangular yard has width w and length ℓ. **(a)** What is a formula for its perimeter, P? **(b)** Find P when w is 16.4 m and ℓ is 28.2 m.
See above left.

27. The pronghorn antelope can run 0.73 mi/min. **(a)** At this speed, how far can this animal travel in 30 seconds? **(b)** In 1.5 minutes?
See back of book.

Mixed Review

Lesson 3-3

Find the mean, median, and mode. Round to the nearest whole number where necessary. Which measure of central tendency best describes the data?

28. 106 min, 123 min, 125 min; median or mode

28. minutes of homework
8 125 154 120 105 125
See left.

29. milliliters per container
250 250 355 355 375 250
306 mL, 303 mL, 250 mL; mean or median

Lesson 2-5 **Solve each equation.**

30. $c + 8 = 41$ **33** **31.** $b + 32 = 19$ **−13** **32.** $98 = n + 42$ **56**

Lesson 1-7 **33. Patterns** Which equation, $n = 2t$ or $t = n \cdot 2$, describes the relationship between the variables in the table? Explain. $n = 2t$; each n value is twice the t value below it.

n	14	16	18	20
t	7	8	9	10

 Checkpoint Quiz 1 **Lessons 3-1 through 3-4**

TEXT Instant self-check quiz online and on CD-ROM

Round each number to the underlined place value.

1. 15.6<u>5</u>71 **2.** 0.89<u>1</u>4 **3.** 7,0<u>2</u>2.56 **4.** 345.<u>6</u>78
15.66 0.891 7,023 345.7

Estimate.
5–8. Answers may vary. Samples are given.

5. $3.7 \cdot 8.06$ **6.** $17.25 + 6.66$ **7.** $8.7 - 9.6$ **8.** $11.7 \div 1.8$
about 32 about 24 about −1 about 6

Find the mean, median, and mode.

9. 47, 56, 58, 63 **10.** 1, 4, 1, 3, 1, 2, 3, 2, 1, 2
56, 57, no mode 2, 2, 1

11. Jennifer drives at an average speed of 54 mi/h. At this rate, how long does it take Jennifer to drive 459 miles? **8.5 h**

Alternative Assessment

Ask students to write a formula that relates a number of nickels, n, to the number of quarters, q, that have the same value. $n = 5q$

Test Prep

 Resources
For additional practice with a variety of test item formats:
• Test Prep, p. 173
• Test-Taking Strategies, p. 168
• Test-Taking Strategies With Transparencies

Technology

Formulas in a Spreadsheet

For Use With Lesson 3-4

You can use a computer spreadsheet to evaluate formulas. Look at the spreadsheet below. In the spreadsheet, the algebraic formula $d = rt$ is evaluated for $r = 50$ mi/h and $t = 3$ h.

The spreadsheet formula "=A2*B2" is used in cell C2 to calculate $d = rt$. The spreadsheet formula means that the value in cell C2 equals the value in cell A2 times the value in cell B2.

	A	B	C
1	r	t	d
2	50	3	150

In spreadsheet formulas the asterisk symbol * means multiply. The slash symbol / means divide.

EXAMPLE

Use a spreadsheet and the formula $P = 2L + 2W$ to find the perimeter P of a rectangle. Evaluate the formula for a length L of 7.8 in. and a width W of 2.6 in.

	A	B	C
1	L	W	P
2	7.8	2.6	20.8

◄—— Use the spreadsheet formula "=2*A2+2*B2."

● The perimeter is about 21 in.

EXERCISES

Use a spreadsheet to find each perimeter.

1. $L = 5.6$ in., $W = 7.9$ in. 27 in.
2. $L = 12.7$ in., $W = 15.6$ in. 56.6 in.
3. $L = 0.2$ in., $W = 1.3$ in. 3 in.

Use a spreadsheet to evaluate the formula $t = d \div r$ for the given values of d and r.

4. $d = 250$ mi, $r = 5$ mi/h 50 h
5. $d = 1{,}400$ mi, $r = 50$ mi/h 28 h
6. $d = 4{,}500$ mi, $r = 250$ mi/h 18 h

Write a spreadsheet formula for each algebraic formula.

7. to find A, using $A = 0.5bh$
=0.5*A2*B2
8. to find P, using $P = 4a$
=4*A2
9. to find y, using $y = mx + b$
=A2*B2+C2

10. a. Open-Ended Use a spreadsheet to evaluate the formula $A = \ell w$. How does the value of A change as you double the value of ℓ while keeping w unchanged? It doubles.
   b. How does the value of A change as you double the values of both ℓ and w? It is multiplied by 4.

Technology

Formulas in a Spreadsheet

This Technology extension shows students you can use a computer spreadsheet to quickly find the value of a variable for many situations that require the same formula.

Resources

Students may use any spreadsheet software.

Teaching Notes

You can use spreadsheet software to help you evaluate the same expression for several different values of its variables. You enter numbers into specified spreadsheet cells. Each column should represent a different variable. Then you enter into another cell the formula using the appropriate cell names as variables. You place the cursor on the bottom right corner of the formula cell and drag down to input the formula into all the cells in the same column.

Error Prevention!

Remind students that the spreadsheet results will be accurate only if the data are entered correctly.

Error Prevention!

When keying a formula into a cell, it must be preceded by an equal sign, and you must press the "Enter" key so the calculation will be done.

Lesson Preview

 Check Skills You'll Need

Adding and Subtracting Decimals
Skills Handbook: p. 764;
Exercises 16–35.

Lesson Resources

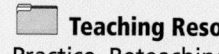 **Teaching Resources**
Practice, Reteaching, Enrichment

 **Reaching All Students**
Practice Workbook 3-5
Spanish Practice Workbook 3-5
Guided Problem Solving 3-5

 **Presentation Assistant Plus!**
Transparencies and PowerPoint™
• Check Skills You'll Need 3-5
• Additional Examples 3-5
• Student Edition Answers 3-5
• Lesson Quiz 3-5
PH Presentation Pro CD-ROM 3-5

Computer Test Generator CD-ROM

 Technology
Resource Pro® CD-ROM
Computer Test Generator CD-ROM
PH Presentation Pro CD-ROM

 **www.PHSchool.com**
Student Site
• Teacher Web Code: adk-5500
• Graphing Calculator, Procedure 7
• Self-grading Lesson Quiz
PH SuccessNet Teacher Center
• Lesson Planner
• Resources

Plus

What You'll Learn

 To solve one-step decimal equations involving addition

 To solve one-step decimal equations involving subtraction

. . . And Why

To solve real-world problems involving astronomy and money management

 Check Skills You'll Need
Simplify.

1. $2.8 + 7.06$ **9.86**

2. $0.65 + 1.8$ **2.45**

3. $4.52 - 2.48$ **2.04**

4. $3.7 - 0.62$ **3.08**

For help, go to Skills Handbook, p. 764.

Interactive lesson includes instant self-check, tutorials, and activities.

OBJECTIVE

1 Using Subtraction to Solve Equations

In Lesson 2-5, you used the Subtraction Property of Equality to solve equations involving integers. You can also use this property to solve equations with decimals. Remember to subtract the same number from each side of the equation.

1 EXAMPLE **Subtracting to Solve an Equation**

Solve $n + 4.5 = -9.7$.

$$n + 4.5 = -9.7$$
$$n + 4.5 - 4.5 = -9.7 - 4.5 \quad \text{Subtract 4.5 from each side.}$$
$$n = -14.2 \quad \text{Simplify.}$$

Check $n + 4.5 = -9.7$
$$-14.2 + 4.5 \stackrel{?}{=} -9.7 \quad \text{Replace } n \text{ with } -14.2.$$
$$-9.7 = -9.7 ✔$$

 Check Understanding Example 1

1. Solve each equation.

   a. $x + 4.9 = 18.8$ **13.9**   b. $14.73 = -24.23 + b$ **38.96**

2 EXAMPLE **Real-World**  **Problem Solving**

Astronomy A communications satellite is circling Earth. Use the diagram below to find the approximate distance from the satellite to the moon.

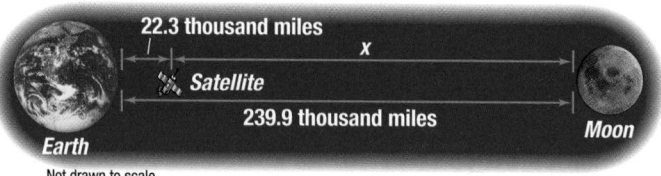

22.3 thousand miles   x
Satellite
239.9 thousand miles
Earth   Moon
Not drawn to scale

$$22.3 + x = 239.9$$
$$22.3 + x - 22.3 = 239.9 - 22.3 \quad \text{Subtract 22.3 from each side.}$$
$$x = 217.6 \quad \text{Simplify.}$$
$$x \approx 218 \quad \text{Round to the nearest one.}$$

The approximate distance from the satellite to the moon is 218 thousand miles.

148 Chapter 3 Decimals and Equations

Ongoing Assessment and Intervention

Before the Lesson
Diagnose prerequisite skills using:
• Check Skills You'll Need

During the Lesson
Monitor progress using:
• Check Understanding
• Additional Examples
• Test Prep

After the Lesson
Assess knowledge using:
• Lesson Quiz
• Computer Test Generator CD-ROM

✓ Check Understanding Example 2

2. **Analyzing Markup** A store's cost plus markup is the price you pay for an item. Suppose a pair of shoes costs a store $35.48. You pay $70. Write and solve an equation to find the store's markup. $35.48 + m = 70$; **$34.52**

OBJECTIVE

2 Using Addition to Solve Equations

You can also use the Addition Property of Equality to solve an equation involving decimals. Remember to add the same number to each side of the equation.

3 EXAMPLE Adding to Solve an Equation

Solve $k - 14.4 = -18.39$.

$$k - 14.4 = -18.39$$
$$k - 14.4 + 14.4 = -18.39 + 14.4 \quad \text{Add 14.4 to each side.}$$
$$k = -3.99 \quad \text{Simplify.}$$

? Need Help?
For help with adding and subtracting decimals, see Skills Handbook, page 764.

✓ Check Understanding Example 3

3. Solve each equation.

   a. $n - 5.85 = 15.25$ **21.1**   b. $-10 = c - 2.6$ **−7.4**

4 EXAMPLE Real-World  Problem Solving

Personal Finance Danzel wrote a check for $76.85. His new account balance is $235.00. What was his previous balance?

| Words | previous balance | minus | check | is | new balance |

Let p = previous balance.

| Equation | p | $-$ | 76.85 | $=$ | 235 |

$$p - 76.85 = 235$$
$$p - 76.85 + 76.85 = 235 + 76.85 \quad \text{Add 76.85 to each side.}$$
$$p = 311.85 \quad \text{Simplify.}$$

Danzel's previous balance was $311.85.

✓ Check Understanding Example 4

4. **Shopping** You spent $14.95 for a new shirt. You now have $12.48. Write and solve an equation to find how much money you had before you bought the shirt. $x - 14.95 = 12.48$; **$27.43**

👥 Reaching All Students

| **Below Level** Review using addition and subtraction to solve one-step equations involving integers (Lesson 2-5). | **Advanced Learners** Challenge students to use mental math to solve the Check Understanding Exercises for Examples 1 and 3. | **Error Prevention** See note on page 149. **Inclusion** See note on page 149. |

2. Teach

Professional Development

Math Background

The Subtraction and Addition Properties of Equality are used to solve equations involving addition and subtraction no matter what type of numbers they contain: integers, decimals, fractions, etc.

Teaching Notes

2 EXAMPLE Error Prevention

Since the subtraction in the solution is written horizontally, some students may subtract incorrectly. Remind students to subtract corresponding place values.

4 EXAMPLE Inclusion

Some students may not see how the word problem was translated into the word equation. Pair these students with ones who understand checking accounts. Have the students who understand checking accounts explain the basics of maintaining a checkbook.

PowerPoint

📖 Additional Examples

1 Solve $6.8 + p = -9.7$. **−16.5**

2 Ping has a board that is 14.5 ft long. She saws off a piece that is 8.75 ft long. Find the length of the piece that is left. **5.75 ft**

3 Solve $-23.34 = q - 16.99$. **−6.35**

4 Alejandro wrote a check for $49.98. His new account balance is $169.45. What was his previous balance? **$219.43**

Closure

Read aloud a decimal equation involving subtraction or addition. Ask students to tell you what to do to get the variable alone on one side of the equation.

149

Assignment Guide

1 Objective 1
Ⓐ Ⓑ **Core** 1–8, 17, 19, 20,
23, 26–28, 31
Ⓒ **Extension** 32, 33

2 Objective 2
Ⓐ Ⓑ **Core** 9–16, 18, 21,
22, 24, 25, 29, 30
Ⓒ **Extension** 34

Test Prep 35–37
Mixed Review 38–43

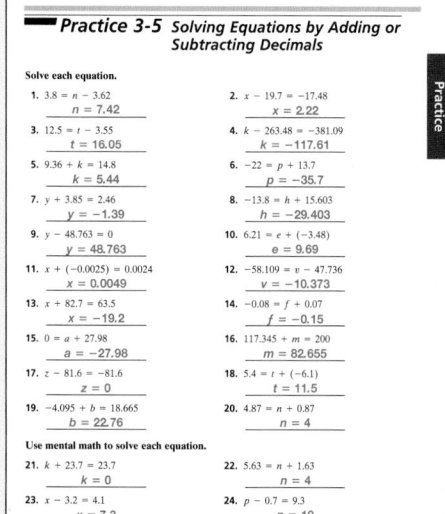

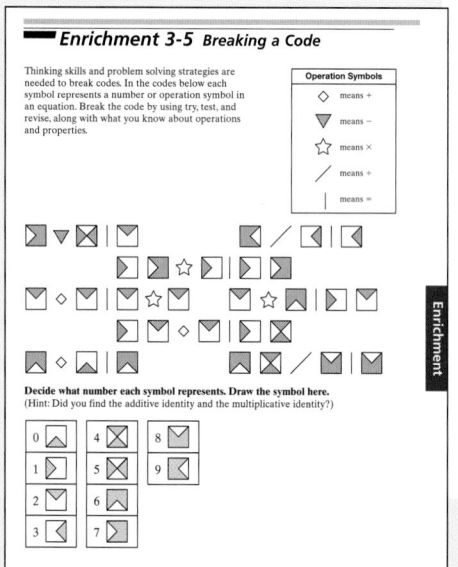

EXERCISES

🔍 For more exercises, see *Extra Practice*.

Practice and Problem Solving

Ⓐ **Practice by Example**

Examples 1 and 2
(page 148)

Solve each equation.

1. $c + 9 = 3.7$ **−5.3**   2. $b + 7.6 = 23$ **15.4**   3. $43.6 = n + 17.5$ **26.1**

4. $6.35 + b = 9.89$ **3.54**   5. $12.13 = n + 1.4$ **10.73**   6. $x + 0.35 = 9.15$ **8.8**

🌐 7. **Astronomy** The planet Mars takes 599.01 days longer than Mercury to orbit the sun. In all, the Mars orbit takes 686.98 days. Write and solve an equation to find how long it takes Mercury to orbit the sun. $s + 599.01 = 686.98$; **87.97 days**

🌐 8. **Car Sales** Julia trades in her small car for a large pickup truck that weighs 1,855.3 lb more than the car. If the truck weighs 4,360.3 lb, what is the weight of the car? $c + 1,855.3 = 4,360.3$; **2,505 lb**

Examples 3 and 4
(page 149)

Solve each equation.

9. $d - 4.9 = 18.8$ **23.7** 10. $c - 19.2 = 24$ **43.2** 11. $-2.5 = q - 1.7$ **−0.8**

12. $-5.6 = y - 8$ **2.4**   13. $4.3 = g - 1$ **5.3**   14. $a - 108.8 = -203$ **−94.2**

🌐 15. **Personal Finance** You spent $13.50 for movie tickets. You now have $26.50. Write and solve an equation to find out how much money you had before buying the tickets. $x - 13.50 = 26.50$; **$40**

16. Rachel wrote a check for $161.15. Her new account balance is $423.28. What was her previous account balance? **$584.43**

Ⓑ **Apply Your Skills**

Complete the steps for each equation. Justify each step.

17. $x + 1.2 = 15$
$x + 1.2 - ∎ = 15 - ∎$ **1.2, 1.2**
$x = ∎$ **13.8**

18. $y - 3.33 = 12.42$
$y - 3.33 + ∎ = 12.42 + ∎$
$y = ∎$
3.33, 3.33; 15.75

🌐 19. **Running** Michael Johnson's world record in the 200-m sprint is 19.32 s. His 400-m world record is 23.86 s slower than his 200-m record. Write and solve an equation to find Johnson's 400-m record. $r - 23.86 = 19.32$; **43.18 s**
GPS

🌐 20. **Biology** A hare travels about 17.83 mi/h faster on land than a giant tortoise. A hare can hop at about 18 mi/h. Write and solve an equation to find how fast a giant tortoise can travel on land. $t + 17.83 = 18$; **0.17 mi/h**

Solve each equation.

21. $4.035 = a - 3.25$ **7.285** 22. $h - (-1.5) = 1.5$ **0**   23. $e + (-7.8) = -6.7$ **1.1**

24. $r - 0.832 = 8.67$ **9.502** 25. $b - (-1.5) = -9$ **−10.5** 26. $-32 = x + (-8.05)$ **−23.95**

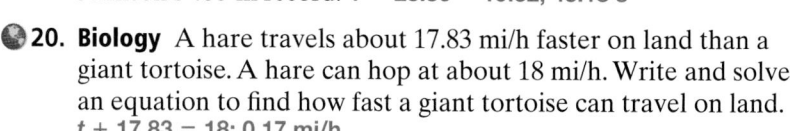

Real-World 🌐 **Connection**

Giant tortoises can weigh up to 500 lb.

Mental Math **Use mental math to solve each equation.**

27. $1.60 = 0.40 + s$ **1.2**   28. $x + 8.8 = 9.9$ **1.1** 29. $5.5 = x - 5.5$ **11**

Use the Guided Problem
Solving worksheet with
Exercise 19.

$$x - 1.6 = -6$$
$$x - 1.6 + 1.6 = -6 - 1.6$$
$$x = -7.6$$

30. Error Analysis A student solved an equation as shown at the left. Explain the student's error. **The student should have added 1.6 to each side.**

31. Writing in Math Explain how you would use the Addition (not Subtraction) Property of Equality to solve $x + 1.8 = -4.7$. **Add −1.8 to each side.**

 **Challenge** **Solve each equation.**

32. $143.587 + x - 22.96 = 156.4$ **33.** $-924.87 - 1{,}237 + b = 86.125$
35.773 **2,247.995**

34. Reasoning Without solving, tell how the solutions of the equations $x + 14 = 15$, $x + 1.4 = 1.5$, and $x + 0.14 = 0.15$ compare. Explain. See below left.

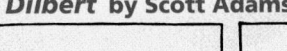 **Test Prep**

Multiple Choice **35.** Which statement describes how to solve $x + 0.042 = 0.826$? **B**
  A. Add 0.042 to each side. **B.** Subtract 0.042 from each side.
  C. Add 0.826 to each side. **D.** Subtract 0.826 from each side.

Reading Comprehension Read the cartoon below before doing Exercises 36 and 37.

34. Explanations may vary. Sample: The solution of the first equation is 10 times the solution of the second equation, which, in turn, is 10 times the solution of the third equation because the numbers in the equations are related in the same way.

Dilbert by Scott Adams

SOURCE: ©1993 United Features Syndicate, Inc.

36. How much money does the clerk owe Dilbert? **$5.25**

37. Dilbert does not want any pennies. What other amount of money could Dilbert have given the cashier? Justify your answer.
  Answers may vary. Sample: $8.14. The change will be $6.25, which can be made with 1 quarter and no pennies.

Take It to the NET
Online lesson quiz at
www.PHSchool.com
Web Code: ada-0305

Mixed Review

Lesson 3-4 Use the formula $A = \ell w$. Find A.

38. $\ell = 23.4$ in., $w = 15.8$ in. **39.** $\ell = 5.5$ cm, $w = 7$ cm
  369.72 in.² **38.5 cm²**

Lesson 2-6 Solve each equation.

40. $6a = 24$ **4** **41.** $-2b = 60$ **−30** **42.** $-81 = 9a$ **−9**

Lesson 2-2 **43.** A large juice costs $.83. A small juice costs $.57. Ida buys one juice each school day. If Ida buys small juices instead of large juices, how much money will she save each week? **$1.30**

 **PowerPoint** **Lesson Quiz 3-5**

Solve each equation.
1. $a + 10 = 7.9$ **−2.1**
2. $-1.01 = c - 9$ **7.99**
3. $s - (-2.6) = 1.6$ **−1**
4. $3.02 + d = 2.91$ **−0.11**
5. $-23.7 = 13.3 + g$ **−37**

Alternative Assessment

Have each student write an equation in which a negative decimal equals a variable plus another decimal, positive or negative. Instruct students to write the solution on another piece of paper. Have students exchange equations, solve, and then compare their solutions with the written solutions.

Test Prep

Resources
For additional practice with a variety of test item formats:
• Test Prep, p. 173
• Test-Taking Strategies, p. 168
• Test-Taking Strategies With Transparencies

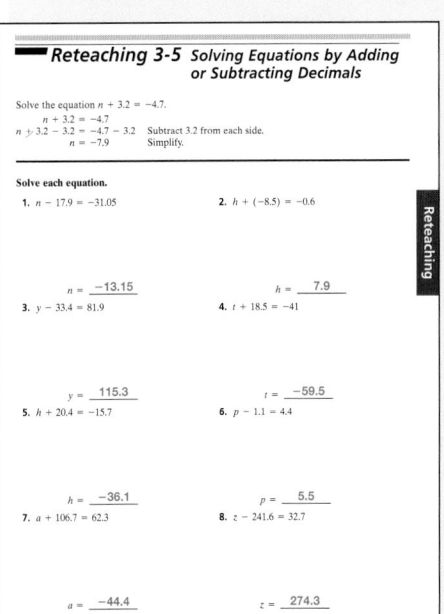

Reteaching 3-5 *Solving Equations by Adding or Subtracting Decimals*

Lesson Preview

 Check Skills You'll Need

Multiplying Decimals
Skills Handbook: p. 765;
Exercises 1–30.

Lesson Resources

 **Teaching Resources**
Practice, Reteaching, Enrichment

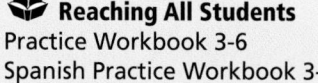 **Reaching All Students**
Practice Workbook 3-6
Spanish Practice Workbook 3-6
Guided Problem Solving 3-6

Presentation Assistant Plus!
Transparencies and PowerPoint™
• Check Skills You'll Need 3-6
• Additional Examples 3-6
• Student Edition Answers 3-6
• Lesson Quiz 3-6
PH Presentation Pro CD-ROM 3-6

 **ASSESSMENT SYSTEM**

Computer Test Generator CD-ROM

Technology
Resource Pro® CD-ROM
Computer Test Generator CD-ROM
PH Presentation Pro CD-ROM

www.PHSchool.com
Student Site
• Teacher Web Code: adk-5500
• Self-grading Lesson Quiz
PH SuccessNet Teacher Center
• Lesson Planner
• Resources

Plus **iTEXT**

 **3-6**

Solving Equations by Multiplying or Dividing Decimals

What You'll Learn

OBJECTIVE 1 To solve one-step decimal equations involving multiplication

OBJECTIVE 2 To solve one-step decimal equations involving division

. . . And Why

To solve real-world problems in oil production

 Check Skills You'll Need

Find each product.

1. 2.6(4.5) **11.7**

2. 3.2(0.15) **0.48**

3. 11.03(0.6) **6.618**

4. 8.003(0.6) **4.8018**

 For help, go to Skills Handbook, p. 765.

Need Help?
For help with dividing decimals, see Skills Handbook, page 769.

iTEXT Interactive lesson includes instant self-check, tutorials, and activities.

OBJECTIVE

1 Using Division to Solve Equations

In Lesson 2-6, you used the Division Property of Equality to solve equations involving integers. You can also use this property to solve equations with decimals. Remember to divide each side of the equation by the same nonzero number.

1 EXAMPLE Dividing to Solve an Equation

Solve $0.9r = -5.4$.

$$0.9r = -5.4$$
$$\frac{0.9r}{0.9} = \frac{-5.4}{0.9} \quad \textbf{Divide each side by 0.9.}$$
$$r = -6 \quad \textbf{Simplify.}$$

Check $\quad 0.9r = -5.4$
$\quad\quad 0.9(-6) \stackrel{?}{=} -5.4 \quad$ **Replace r with -6.**
$\quad\quad\quad -5.4 = -5.4 \checkmark$

 Check Understanding Example 1

1. Solve each equation.

a. $0.8x = -1.6$ 　　**b.** $1.15 = 2.3x$ 　　**c.** $-81.81 = -0.9n$
　　-2 　　　　　　　　0.5 　　　　　　　　90.9

2 EXAMPLE Real-World 🌐 Problem Solving

Petroleum An oil field produces an average of 16.8 thousand barrels of crude oil per day. About how many days will it take to produce 200 thousand barrels?

Words | daily barrel production | times | number of days | equals | 200 thousand barrels

Let d = number of days.

Equation 　　16.8 　　·　　 d 　　=　　 200

$$16.8d = 200$$
$$\frac{16.8d}{16.8} = \frac{200}{16.8} \quad \textbf{Divide each side by 16.8.}$$
$$d = 11.904\ldots \quad \textbf{Simplify.}$$
$$d \approx 12 \quad \textbf{Round to the nearest whole number.}$$

It will take about 12 days to produce 200 thousand barrels.

Ongoing Assessment and Intervention

Before the Lesson
Diagnose prerequisite skills using:
• Check Skills You'll Need

During the Lesson
Monitor progress using:
• Check Understanding
• Additional Examples
• Test Prep

After the Lesson
Assess knowledge using:
• Lesson Quiz
• Computer Test Generator CD-ROM

2. **Postage** You paid $7.70 to mail a package that weighed 5.5 lb. Write and solve an equation to find the cost per pound.
5.5*p* = 7.70; $1.40

OBJECTIVE

2 Using Multiplication to Solve Equations

To solve an equation involving division, multiply each side by the same nonzero number.

3 EXAMPLE Multiplying to Solve an Equation

Solve $\frac{m}{-7.2} = -12.5$.

$$\frac{m}{-7.2} = -12.5$$

$$\frac{m}{-7.2}(-7.2) = -12.5(-7.2) \qquad \text{Multiply each side by } -7.2.$$

$$m = 90 \qquad \text{Simplify.}$$

✔ **Check Understanding** Example 3

3. Solve each equation.

a. $\frac{r}{-6.0} = 0.5$ −3   b. $\frac{s}{2.5} = 5$ 12.5   c. $-80 = \frac{t}{4.5}$ −360

4 EXAMPLE Real-World 🌐 Problem Solving

Batting Averages The 1923 baseball season was one of Babe Ruth's best. He was at bat 522 times and had a batting average of 0.393, rounded to the nearest thousandth. The batting average formula is $a = \frac{h}{n}$, where *a* is the batting average, *h* is the number of hits, and *n* is the number of times at bat. Use the formula to find the number of hits Babe Ruth made.

$$a = \frac{h}{n}$$

$$0.393 = \frac{h}{522} \qquad \text{Replace } a \text{ with 0.393 and } n \text{ with 522.}$$

$$(0.393)(522) = \frac{h}{522}(522) \qquad \text{Multiply each side by 522.}$$

$$h = 205.146 \qquad \text{Simplify.}$$

$$h \approx 205 \qquad \text{Since } h \text{ (hits) represents an integer, round to the nearest integer.}$$

● Babe Ruth made 205 hits.

✔ **Check Understanding** Example 4

4. Suppose your batting average is 0.222. You have batted 54 times. How many hits do you have? 12 hits

Real-World 🌐 Connection

During his professional career, Babe Ruth was at bat 8,399 times and had a batting average of 0.342.

3-6 Solving Equations by Multiplying or Dividing Decimals **153**

👥 Reaching All Students

| **Below Level** Review dividing with decimals. You may wish to assign exercises from page 769 in the Skills Handbook. Stress locating decimal points in the quotients. | **Advanced Learners** Challenge students to write a variable equation in which the variable is multiplied by a three-digit decimal, and is equal to a four-digit decimal. Have them solve the equation. | **Error Prevention** See note on page 153. **Auditory Learners** See note on page 155. |

---

3. Practice

Assignment Guide

▼ **1 Objective 1**

Ⓐ Ⓑ **Core** 1–11, 22–24, 28, 29, 33, 34

Ⓒ **Extension** 35, 36

▼ **2 Objective 2**

Ⓐ Ⓑ **Core** 12–21, 25–27, 30–32

Ⓒ **Extension** 37

Test Prep 38–40
Mixed Review 41–46

Practice 3-6 *Solving Equations by Multiplying or Dividing Decimals*

Use mental math to solve each equation.

1. $0.7h = 4.2$ $h = 6$
2. $\frac{x}{2.5} = -3$ $x = -7.5$
3. $38.7 = -100k$ $k = -0.387$
4. $-45.6e = -4.56$ $e = 0.1$

Solve each equation.

5. $\frac{p}{2.9} = 0.55$ $p = 1.595$
6. $9.1 = \frac{x}{-0.7}$ $x = -6.37$
7. $-6.4 = \frac{y}{8.5}$ $y = -54.4$
8. $\frac{k}{-1.2} = -0.07$ $k = 0.084$
9. $277.4 = \frac{n}{3.5}$ $n = 970.9$
10. $\frac{e}{-0.76} = 2.809$ $e = -2,134.84$
11. $\frac{a}{27} = -32.3$ $a = -872.1$
12. $\frac{p}{-1.52} = -3,600$ $p = 5,472$
13. $-9k = 2.34$ $k = -0.26$
14. $-12.42 = 0.03p$ $p = -414$
15. $-7.2y = 61.2$ $y = -8.5$
16. $-0.1035 = 0.23n$ $n = -0.45$
17. $1.5m = 3.03$ $m = 2.02$
18. $-0.007h = 0.2002$ $h = -28.6$
19. $8.13t = -100.812$ $t = -12.4$
20. $0.546 = 0.42y$ $y = 1.3$

Write an equation for each sentence. Solve for the variable.

21. The opposite of seventy-five hundredths times some number n equals twenty-four thousandths. Find the value of n.
$-0.75n = 0.024$; $n = -0.032$

22. A number n divided by -3.88 equals negative two thousand. Find the value of n.
$\frac{n}{-3.88} = -2,000$; $n = 7,760$

23. Four hundredths times some number n equals thirty-three and four tenths. Find the value of n.
$0.04n = 33.4$; $n = 835$

24. The product of some number n and -0.26 equals 169.39. Find the value of n.
$-0.26n = 169.39$; $n = -651.5$

Enrichment 3-6 *Diving Scores*

Each judge in a diving competition grades every dive from 0 to 10, with 10 representing a perfect dive. High and low scores are thrown out. (If there are duplications of high and low scores, only one of the duplicated scores is thrown out.) The remaining scores are added and their sum is multiplied by the degree of difficulty.

Degrees of Difficulty

Position:	Tuck	Pike	Layout
Forward 1½ somersault	1.4	1.7	2.1
Back double somersault	1.9	2.2	2.5
Reverse dive	1.5	1.7	1.8
Inward 2½ somersault	2.8	—	—
Back 1½ somersault 2½ twist	—	3.1	—

1. A back double somersault in the tuck position is awarded these scores: 6, 5, 7, 7, 8, 6, 7, 6

   a. Which scores should be thrown out?   5 and 8
   b. Find the total score for the dive.   74.1

Complete.

	Dive	Position	Judge's Scores	Diver's Score
2.	Reverse	Layout	6, 8, 6, 8, 7, 7, 6, 6	72
3.	Forward 1½ somersault	Pike	3, 4, 6, 4, 5, 5, 3, 7	45.9
4.	Inward 2½ somersault	Tuck	9, 9, 8, 7, 8, 7, 9, 9	140

5. A diver received scores of 6, 9, 7, 9, 7, 7, 8, and 5 and earned a total score of 136.4. What dive did the diver perform?
Back 1½ somersault 2½ twist

6. To win, a diver needs to score 110 points on her final dive. She thinks she could average 7.5 points from each of the 8 judges. What degree of difficulty should she attempt?
2.5 or greater

EXERCISES

🔎 For more exercises, see *Extra Practice*.

Practice and Problem Solving

Ⓐ **Practice by Example**

Examples 1 and 2 (page 152)

Solve each equation.

1. $0.8s = -6.4$ -8
2. $0.8x = 0.48$ 0.6
3. $-0.5y = -0.73$ 1.46
4. $2x = -4.88$ -2.44
5. $-0.3y = 7.53$ -25.1
6. $2.21 = 1.7w$ 1.3
7. $1.92 = 1.6s$ 1.2
8. $3.2n = 27.52$ 8.6
9. $0.7x = 2.8$ 4

🌐 10. **Manufacturing** A factory produces an average of seven thousand televisions per day. About how many days will it take to produce 63.5 thousand televisions? **9 days**

🌐 11. **Postage** You paid $5.30 to mail a package that weighed 2.5 lb. Write and solve an equation to find the mailing cost per pound.
2.5m = 5.30; $2.12

Examples 3 and 4 (page 153)

Solve each equation.

12. $\frac{n}{2.3} = -4.8$ -11.04
13. $0.97 = \frac{c}{-2}$ -1.94
14. $\frac{h}{7} = -8$ -56
15. $\frac{n}{1.7} = 0.22$ 0.374
16. $\frac{k}{2.01} = 0.04$ 0.0804
17. $120 = \frac{v}{3.8}$ 456
18. $9 = \frac{a}{1.5}$ 13.5
19. $\frac{m}{7.08} = -100$ -708
20. $-200 = \frac{f}{4}$ -800

🌐 21. **Batting Averages** During the 1954 baseball season with the New York Yankees, Yogi Berra was at bat 584 times and had a batting average of 0.307. Use the batting-average formula in Example 4 to find the number of hits Berra made. **179 hits**

Ⓑ **Apply Your Skills**

Solve each equation.

22. $6.4x = 0.2816$ 0.044
23. $-5.1z = -11.73$ 2.3
24. $0.004m = 0.12$ 30
25. $4.5 = m \div (-3.3)$ -14.85
26. $-33.04 = \frac{z}{-0.03}$ 0.9912
27. $-0.45 = x \div 12$ -5.4

28a. Harry multiplied by 4 instead of dividing each side by 4.

28. a. **Error Analysis** Harry found 324.8 as a solution for the equation $4x = 81.2$. What was Harry's error? See left.
   b. **Estimation** How could Harry have used estimation to check whether his answer was reasonable? Answers may vary. Sample: He could have compared his result, 324.8, to the estimate $81.2 \div 4 \approx 20$.

Write an equation for each sentence. Solve for the variable.

29. The product of a number n and -7.3 is 30.66.
$-7.3n = 30.66$; -4.2

30. $\frac{n}{-4.5} = 200.6$; -902.7
30. The quotient of a number n divided by -4.5 equals 200.6. See left.

31. $\frac{n}{-2.35} = 400.9$; -942.115
31. A number n divided by -2.35 equals 400.9. See left.

🌐 32. a. **Batting Averages** Your batting average is 0.244, and you have been at bat 82 times. How many hits do you have? **20 hits**
   b. **Writing in Math** Why is it necessary to round your answer in part (a) to the nearest integer?
You can have only a whole number of hits.

154 Chapter 3 Decimals and Equations

154

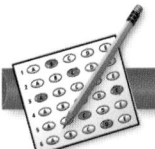 **33. Utilities** Jan pays \$.08 per kilowatt-hour for electricity. Her electric bill is \$59.22. Write and solve an equation to find how many kilowatt-hours of electricity Jan used. **0.08k = 59.22; 740.25 kWh**

34. Number Sense The weight of a record-setting onion was 12.25 lb. An average-sized onion weighs 0.5 lb. About how many average-sized onions have a total weight equal to the record-setting onion? **25 onions**

C Challenge

35. Measurement If you know a length ℓ in meters, you can multiply the length by 3.28 to find the length in feet f.
  a. Write an equation to model this situation. **f = 3.28ℓ**
  b. A tree is 7.5 m tall. Use your equation to find this height in feet. **24.6 ft**
  c. A bookshelf is 6 ft tall. What is this height in meters? **about 1.8 m**
  d. A room is 12 ft long and 15 ft wide. Use your equation and the formula for the area of a rectangle to find the area of the room in square meters. Round to the nearest tenth. **16.7 m²**

36. Reasoning Find values for x and y that satisfy $xy = 0.42$ and $x + y = 1.3$. **x = 0.6, y = 0.7 (or x = 0.7, y = 0.6)**

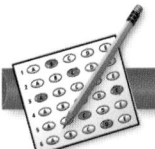 **37. Batting Averages** About how many hits did Babe Ruth have during his professional career? (*Hint*: See page 153.) **about 2,870 hits**

Test Prep

Multiple Choice

38. A group of friends goes out for dinner. The bill is \$36.81. If they share the cost equally and each person's share is about \$7.35, how many people are in the group? **B**
  A. 4   **B.** 5   **C.** 6   **D.** 7

Take It to the NET
Online lesson quiz at
www.PHSchool.com
Web Code: ada-0306

39. Which equation has 3.2 as its solution? **G**
  F. $20x = 6.4$ **G.** $6.4 = 2x$ **H.** $\frac{x}{2} = 6.4$ **I.** $\frac{x}{6.4} = 2$

Short Response

40. A barber gave enough haircuts in one day to earn \$337.50. Each haircut cost \$12.50. **(a)** How many haircuts did the barber give that day? **(b)** Estimate the amount of money the barber can make in a week.
  [2] 12.50n = 337.50; 27 haircuts. Gives a reasonable estimate.
      Sample: 337.50 ≈ 300; 7 · 300 = 2,100; \$2,100 in a week.
  [1] one correct answer

Mixed Review

Lesson 3-5   Solve each equation.

41. $c + 9 = 3.7$ **42.** $-5.6 = y - 8$ **43.** $4.035 = a - 3.25$
    −5.3   **2.4**   **7.285**

Lesson 2-4   Is the given number a solution of the equation? Show why.

44. $20 - c = 12; c = 8$ **45.** $8 = 2a + 3; a = 0$
    yes; 12 = 12   **no; 8 ≠ 3**

Lesson 1-7

46. a. Patterns Multiply $99 \cdot 24$, $99 \cdot 25$, and $99 \cdot 26$. **2,376, 2,475, 2,574**
  b. Describe the pattern you found in part (a). **See left.**
  c. Use the pattern to evaluate $99 \cdot 27$. **2,673**

46b. Answers may vary. Sample: The first pair of digits "increases" by 1; the second pair "decreases" by 1.

3-6   Solving Equations by Multiplying or Dividing Decimals   **155**

---

4. Assess

PowerPoint Lesson Quiz 3-6

Solve each equation.
  1. $9b = -30.6$ **−3.4**
  2. $-10.8 = \frac{p}{-2.5}$ **27**
  3. $2.45 = -0.7k$ **−3.5**
  4. $\frac{t}{3.7} = 240$ **888**
  5. $y \div (-0.3) = 146.7$ **−44.01**

Auditory Learners
Exercises 1–9, 12–20 Students can read the equations in the Exercises quietly to themselves so they can hear the name of the operation in each equation to be undone. For example, suggest students say "0.8 times s" and "n divided by 2.3" to hear "times" and "divided by."

Alternative Assessment

Have students create a chart or diagram. Have it illustrate how to decide which of the four properties of equality to use when solving a one-step equation.

Test Prep

Resources
For additional practice with a variety of test item formats:
• Test Prep, p. 173
• Test-Taking Strategies, p. 168
• Test-Taking Strategies With Transparencies

Reteaching 3-6 Solving Equations by Multiplying or Dividing Decimals

Solve the equations $0.7x = -2.8$ and $\frac{x}{1.5} = 0.2$.
   $0.7x = -2.8$ Write the equation.
   $\frac{0.7x}{0.7} = \frac{-2.8}{0.7}$ Divide each side by 0.7.
   $x = -4$ Simplify.

   $\frac{x}{1.5} = 0.2$ Write the equation.
   $\frac{x}{1.5}(1.5) = 0.2(1.5)$ Multiply each side by 1.5.
   $x = 0.3$ Simplify.

Solve each equation.
  1. $4x = -2.44$ **2.** $1.8x = 5.76$
  3. $\frac{x}{-1.05} = -0.36$ $x = -0.61$ **4.** $\frac{x}{-0.02} = 5.9$ $x = 3.2$
  5. $4.25y = 0.85$ $h = 0.378$ **6.** $\frac{a}{-1.9} = 24.6$ $z = -0.118$
  7. $\frac{y}{8.04} = 1.55$ $y = 0.2$ **8.** $11.32a = -39.62$ $n = -46.74$

 Use the Guided Problem Solving worksheet with Exercise 34.

155

3-7

Using the Metric System

1. Plan

Lesson Preview

 Check Skills You'll Need

Multiplying and Dividing by Powers of Ten
Skills Handbook: p. 768;
Exercises 1–36.

Lesson Resources

 Teaching Resources
Practice, Reteaching, Enrichment
Checkpoint Quiz 2

 Reaching All Students
Practice Workbook 3-7
Spanish Practice Workbook 3-7
Reading and Math Literacy 3B
Spanish Reading and Math
  Literacy 3C
Spanish Checkpoint Quiz 2
Guided Problem Solving 3-7
Hands-On Activities 6, 22, 23

 Presentation Assistant Plus!
Transparencies and PowerPoint™
• Check Skills You'll Need 3-7
• Additional Examples 3-7
• Student Edition Answers 3-7
• Lesson Quiz 3-7
• Classroom Aid 14
PH Presentation Pro CD-ROM 3-7

(**ASSESSMENT SYSTEM**)

Checkpoint Quiz 2
Computer Test Generator CD-ROM

 Technology
Resource Pro® CD-ROM
Computer Test Generator CD-ROM
PH Presentation Pro CD-ROM

 www.PHSchool.com

Student Site
• Teacher Web Code: adk-5500
• Self-grading Lesson Quiz
PH SuccessNet Teacher Center
• Lesson Planner
• Resources

Plus

156

What You'll Learn

 OBJECTIVE 1 To identify appropriate metric measures

 OBJECTIVE 2 To convert metric units

. . . And Why

To solve real-world problems involving metric measures

 Check Skills You'll Need

Find each product or quotient.

1. 5×100 **500**

2. $14.06 \div 1,000$ **0.01406**

3. 0.294×10 **2.94**

4. $0.9 \div 100$ **0.009**

For help, go to Skillls Handbook, p. 768.

iTEXT Interactive lesson includes instant self-check, tutorials, and activities.

OBJECTIVE

1 Identifying Appropriate Metric Measures

Knowing the approximate size of each metric unit of measure will allow you to choose an appropriate unit.

Key Concepts | **Metric Units of Measurement**

	Unit	Reference Example
Length	millimeter (mm)	about the thickness of a dime
	centimeter (cm)	about the width of a thumbnail
	meter (m)	about the distance from a doorknob to the floor
	kilometer (km)	a little more than one half mile
Capacity	milliliter (mL)	about 5 drops of water
	liter (L)	a little more than a quart of milk
Mass	milligram (mg)	about the mass of a speck of sawdust
	gram(g)	about the mass of a paper clip
	kilogram (kg)	about one half the mass of this math book

1 EXAMPLE   **Choosing an Appropriate Unit**

Choose an appropriate metric unit. Explain your choice.

a. height of a classroom chalkboard

Meter; the height of a chalkboard is about twice the distance from the floor to a doorknob.

b. mass of a backpack filled with books

Kilogram; the mass of a backpack filled with books is many times the mass of this textbook.

c. capacity of a birdbath

Liter; several quart bottles of water would fill a birdbath.

Check Understanding   **Example 1**

1. Choose an appropriate metric unit. Explain your choice.
   a–d. See back of book.
   a. length of a broom
   b. the mass of an energy bar
   c. mass of a horse
   d. capacity of a car's gas tank

Ongoing Assessment and Intervention

Before the Lesson
Diagnose prerequisite skills using:
• Check Skills You'll Need

During the Lesson
Monitor progress using:
• Check Understanding
• Additional Examples
• Test Prep

After the Lesson
Assess knowledge using:
• Lesson Quiz
• Computer Test Generator CD-ROM
• Chapter Checkpoint 2 (p. 161)

2 EXAMPLE   Estimating With Metric Units

Estimation Choose a reasonable estimate. Explain your choice.

a. capacity of a juice box: 200 mL or 200 L

200 mL; the juice box holds less than a quart of milk.

b. length of a new pencil: 15 cm or 15 m

15 cm; the length of a pencil would be about 15 widths of a thumbnail.

c. mass of a small tube of toothpaste: 100 g or 100 kg

100 g; the mass is about the same as a box of paper clips.

✓ Check Understanding   Example 2

2. Choose a reasonable estimate. Explain your choice.

    a. distance between two cities: 50 mm or 50 km

    b. amount of liquid that an eyedropper holds: 10 mL or 10 L

    a. 50 km; millimeters are used to measure very small lengths.
    b. 10 mL; the eyedropper holds several drops of water but much less than a quart.

OBJECTIVE

2 Converting Metric Units

The metric system uses a decimal system to relate different units to each other. Look at the metric-units chart below. The units highlighted in yellow are the units most often used. From left to right, each unit is 10 times the size of the unit before it.

	milli-	centi-	deci-	UNIT	deka-	hecto-	kilo-
Length	millimeter (mm)	centimeter (cm)	decimeter (dm)	meter (m)	dekameter (dam)	hectometer (hm)	kilometer (km)
Capacity	milliliter (mL)	centiliter (cL)	deciliter (dL)	liter (L)	dekaliter (daL)	hectoliter (hL)	kiloliter (kL)
Mass	milligram (mg)	centigram (cg)	decigram (dg)	gram (g)	dekagram (dag)	hectogram (hg)	kilogram (kg)

You can convert from one unit to another by multiplying or dividing by 10; 100; 1,000; and so on.

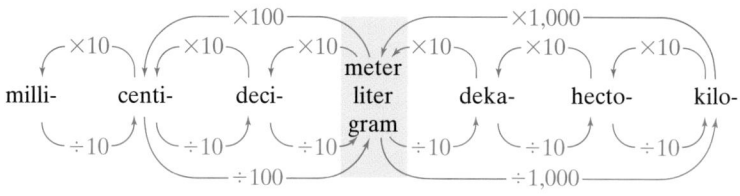

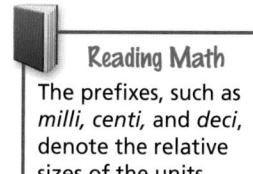

> **Reading Math**
> The prefixes, such as *milli, centi,* and *deci,* denote the relative sizes of the units.

👥 Reaching All Students

Below Level Have students identify different objects in the room that can be measured for length, capacity, and mass. Have them then make the measurements or describe how they could make the measurements.	**Advanced Learners** Have students write paragraphs on the advantages and disadvantages of both the customary system of measurement used in the United States and the metric system.	**Diversity** See note on page 157. **English Learners** See note on page 158.

---

2. Teach

Professional Development

Math Background

Nearly all the countries of the world use the metric system for measurement. The meter is defined as the distance a certain wavelength of light travels in a certain fraction of a second. The kilogram is defined as the mass of a certain platinum-iridium sphere that is kept in France, although some scientists are working to redefine the kilogram as the mass of an exact number of a certain type of atom. A liter is 1,000 cubic centimeters, or 1 cubic decimeter.

Teaching Notes

Tactile Learners

To help students understand different metric lengths, have them use a meter stick and put masking tape one meter long on the floor or wall of the classroom. Write "1 meter" on the tape. Have them use a centimeter ruler to do the same for various other lengths, such as 10 cm and 50 mm.

1 EXAMPLE Diversity

Have students who speak languages other than English share the words for metric units in their languages. Discuss similarities.

PowerPoint
🖥 Additional Examples

① Choose an appropriate metric unit. Explain your choice.
  a. the width of this textbook
  b. the mass of a pair of glasses
  c. the capacity of a thimble

② Choose a reasonable estimate. Explain your choice.
  a. capacity of a drinking glass: 500 L or 500 mL
  b. length of a hair clip: 5 m or 5 cm
  c. mass of a pair of hiking boots: 1 kg or 1 g
  1–2. See back of book.

157

3 Complete each statement.
   a. 7,603 mL = ▇ L **7.603**
   b. 4.57 m = ▇ cm **457**

4 A blue whale caught in 1931 was about 2,900 cm long. What was its length in meters? **about 29 m**

Auditory Learners

Point out the metric prefixes across the top of the chart on page 157. Have students create a mnemonic device to help them remember the names in either order. For example, from right to left(or large to small), "King Henry Danced Usually Down Center Main."

English Learners

Remind students that they may have learned the meanings of metric prefixes in previous math courses. *Kilo-* means thousand. *Centi-* means hundredths. *Milli-* means thousandths.

3 EXAMPLE Alternative Method

Have students write the following letters to represent the metric prefixes and their order from large to small:

   k h dk __ dc c m

The blank in the middle represents the basic unit. Have students think "liter" and place their pencil point on the blank. Then move the pencil to m, the prefix for milliliter, touching and counting each prefix as they go. Tell students to move the decimal point in 4.35 the same number of places, 3, and in the same direction to the right. Let students practice this method with the Check Understanding exercises to see that it works for metric units in general.

Closure

Ask: *How is converting measurements in the metric system different from converting measurements in the customary system?*

158

To convert from one unit to another in the metric system, find the relationship between the two units.

Remember:
- Multiply if you are going from a larger unit to a smaller unit since there will be more of the smaller units.
- Divide if you are going from a smaller unit to a larger unit since there will be fewer of the larger units.

Need Help?

For help with multiplying and dividing decimals by powers of ten, see Skills Handbook, page 768.

3 EXAMPLE **Converting Between Metric Units**

Mental Math Complete each statement.

a. 4.35 L = ▇ mL

   $4.35 \cdot 1{,}000 = 4{,}350$

   To convert liters to milliliters, multiply by 1,000.

   $4.35 \text{ L} = 4{,}350 \text{ mL}$

b. 914 cm = ▇ m

   $914 \div 100 = 9.14$

   To convert centimeters to meters, divide by 100.

   $914 \text{ cm} = 9.14 \text{ m}$

✔ **Check Understanding** Example 3

   3. Complete each statement.

   a. 35 mL = ▇ L   **b.** ▇ g = 250 kg   **c.** ▇ cm = 60 m
       0.035   **250,000**   **6,000**

4 EXAMPLE **Real-World** 🌐 **Problem Solving**

Real-World 🌐 **Connection**

The ancient city of Machu Picchu (c. 1450–1550) is located in Peru's Andes Mountains. It is one of the few major pre-Columbian sites found nearly intact.

Geography The ancient Incan city of Machu Picchu is located in Peru. Its altitude is about 2,300 m above sea level. What is Machu Picchu's altitude in kilometers?

Words	altitude in meters	÷	meters per kilometer	=	altitude in kilometers
Equation	2,300	÷	1,000	=	2.3

● Machu Picchu is about 2.3 km above sea level.

✔ **Check Understanding** Example 4

   4. a. The record for the highest a kite has flown is 3.8 km. Find the height of the kite in meters. **3,800 m**
   b. Number Sense You have a recipe that requires 0.25 L of milk. Your measuring cup is marked only in milliliters. How many milliliters of milk do you need? **250 mL**

In the metric system, you convert from one unit to another by multiplying or dividing by one of 10, 100, 1,000 and so on, according to the unit prefixes involved. In the customary system, there is no standard relationship between units, so you must recall the relationship for each type of measurement.

Ⓐ Practice by Example

Example 1
(page 156)

7. 5 kg; the mass of a dog is much greater than the mass of 5 paper clips.
8. 2,000 mL; 2,000 L is about 2,000 qt and 2,000 mL ≈ 2 qt.
9. 350 g; 350 mg is less than the mass of a paper clip.

Match each quantity with an appropriate metric unit. Explain your choice.

1. length of your thumb **C**
2. mass of a book **F**
3. length of a soccer field **B**
4. amount of water in a fishbowl **E**
5. mass of an eraser **A**
6. amount of fluid in a straw **D**

    A. gram
    B. meter
    C. centimeter
    D. milliliter
    E. liter
    F. kilogram

Example 2
(page 157)

Choose a reasonable estimate. Explain your choice.
7–9. See above left.

7. the mass of a small dog: 5 g or 5 kg
8. amount of liquid you should drink daily: 2,000 mL or 2,000 L
9. the mass of a box of cereal: 350 mg or 350 g

Example 3
(page 158)

Mental Math Complete each statement.

10. 54 m = ■ cm
   5,400
11. ■ L = 234 mL
   0.234
12. 12 g = ■ kg
   0.012
13. ■ m = 3.01 km
   3,010
14. 0.25 m = ■ cm
   25
15. ■ mL = 7.3 L
   7,300
16. 595 g = ■ kg
   0.595
17. 35 m = ■ km
   0.035
18. ■ mg = 0.27 g
   270

Example 4 🌐 (page 158)

19. **Geography** The shortest street in the world is Elgin Street, in Bacup, England. It is 518 cm long. How many meters long is it? **5.18 m**

🌐 20. **Biology** A shrew, the mammal with the fastest metabolism, has a mass of only 0.004 kg. What is its mass in grams? **4 g**

Ⓑ Apply Your Skills

21. Gram; a banana is well under a kilogram, so kilograms are too large.
22. Meter; the depth is less than a kilometer, so kilometers are too large.
23. Centimeter; the length is much less than a meter and much more than a millimeter, so meters are too large and millimeters are too small.
24. Kilogram; a car is very heavy, so grams are too small.

Choose an appropriate metric unit of measure. Explain your choice.

21. mass of a banana
   21–24. See left.
22. depth of Lake Michigan
23. length of a small calculator
24. mass of a car
25. width of a highway
   25–26. See margin.
26. quantity of water in a spoon

27. **Error Analysis** One of the world's largest pearls had a mass of 6,392 g. Camille wrote in her report that the pearl had a mass of 6,392,000 kg. What was her error? **See margin.**

🌐 28. **Model Trains** The world's longest model train has 650 cars and is 0.695 km long. How many meters long is the train? **695 m**

Write the metric unit that makes each statement true.

29. 9.03 m = 9,030 ■
   mm
30. 890 cm = 8.9 ■
   m
31. 130,000 ■ = 1.3 km
   cm

25. Meter; the width is much less than a kilometer and much more than a centimeter, so kilometers are too large and centimeters are too small.
26. Milliliter; a spoon holds much less than a liter, so a liter is too large.
27. Camille multiplied 6,392 g by 1,000, so she changed grams to milligrams. To change grams to kilograms she should have *divided* 6,392 by 1,000 to get 6.392 kg.

Assignment Guide

1 Objective 1
  Ⓐ Ⓑ **Core** 1–9, 21–26, 33–35
  Ⓒ **Extension** 54

2 Objective 2
  Ⓐ Ⓑ **Core** 10–20, 27–32, 36–53
  Ⓒ **Extension** 55

Test Prep 56–60
Mixed Review 61–67

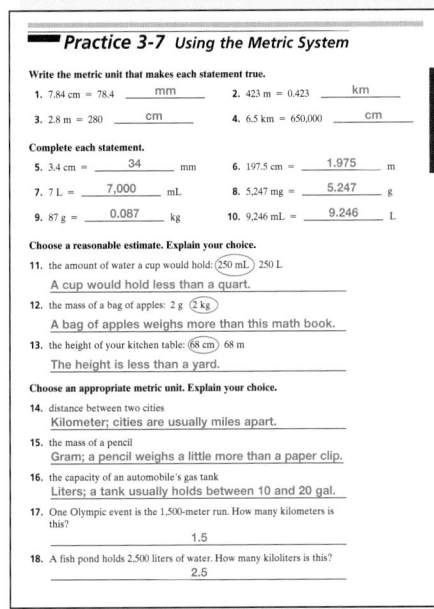

Practice 3-7 *Using the Metric System*

Write the metric unit that makes each statement true.

1. 7.84 cm = 78.4 _mm_
2. 423 m = 0.423 _km_
3. 2.8 m = 280 _cm_
4. 6.5 km = 650,000 _cm_

Complete each statement.

5. 3.4 cm = _34_ mm
6. 197.5 cm = _1.975_ m
7. 7 L = _7,000_ mL
8. 5,247 mg = _5.247_ g
9. 87 g = _0.087_ kg
10. 9,246 mL = _9.246_ L

Choose a reasonable estimate. Explain your choice.

11. the amount of water a cup would hold: (250 mL) 250 L
   A cup would hold less than a quart.
12. the mass of a bag of apples: 2 g (2 kg)
   A bag of apples weighs more than this math book.
13. the height of your kitchen table: (68 cm) 68 m
   The height is less than a yard.

Choose an appropriate metric unit. Explain your choice.

14. distance between two cities
   Kilometer; cities are usually miles apart.
15. the mass of a pencil
   Gram; a pencil weighs a little more than a paper clip.
16. the capacity of an automobile's gas tank
   Liters; a tank usually holds between 10 and 20 gal.
17. One Olympic event is the 1,500-meter run. How many kilometers is this?
   1.5
18. A fish pond holds 2,500 liters of water. How many kiloliters is this?
   2.5

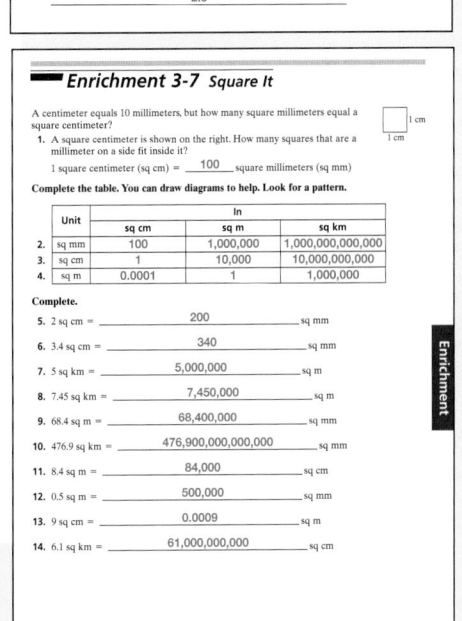

Enrichment 3-7 *Square It*

A centimeter equals 10 millimeters, but how many square millimeters equal a square centimeter?

1. A square centimeter is shown on the right. How many squares that are a millimeter on a side fit inside it?
   1 square centimeter (sq cm) = _100_ square millimeters (sq mm)

Complete the table. You can draw diagrams to help. Look for a pattern.

Unit	In sq cm	In sq mm	In sq km
2. sq mm	100	1,000,000	1,000,000,000,000
3. sq cm	1	10,000	10,000,000,000
4. sq km	0.0001	1	1,000,000

Complete.

5. 2 sq cm = _200_ sq mm
6. 3.4 sq cm = _340_ sq mm
7. 5 sq km = _5,000,000_ sq m
8. 7.45 sq km = _7,450,000_ sq m
9. 68.4 sq m = _68,400,000_ sq mm
10. 476.9 sq km = _476,900,000,000,000_ sq mm
11. 8.4 sq m = _84,000_ sq cm
12. 0.5 sq m = _500,000_ sq mm
13. 9 sq cm = _0.0009_ sq m
14. 6.1 sq km = _61,000,000,000_ sq cm

Error Prevention!

Exercises 47–52 Suggest that students look first for matching types of measurement (length, mass, capacity).

Real-World **Connection**

A hydroelectric power plant at Niagara Falls can produce 2,100,000 kilowatts of electricity.

32. Earth Science The flow of water over Niagara Falls averages 6,008,835,000 mL/s.

   a. On the average, about how many liters of water flow over Niagara Falls each second? **6,008,835 L**

   b. About how many liters flow over the falls in a minute? **360,530,100 L**

Estimation **Choose a reasonable estimate. Explain your choice.**
33–35. Answers may vary. Samples are given.

33. the width of a sidewalk: 150 cm or 150 m
150 cm; 150 m is greater than the length of a football field.

34. the length of 24 city blocks: 2 m or 2 km
2 km; 2 m can be walked in 3 or 4 steps.

35. the mass of a thumbtack: 1 mg or 1 g
1 g; 1 mg is closer to the mass of a speck of sawdust.

Mental Math **Complete each statement.**

36. 90,050 mL = ■ L
90.05

37. ■ m = 875 cm
8.75

38. 620 m = ■ km
0.62

39. 9,120 mg = ■ g
9.12

40. 900 km = ■ m
900,000

41. 5 g = ■ kg
0.005

42. ■ cm = 13 km
1,300,000

43. 301 kg = ■ mg
301,000,000

44. ■ km = 562,300 cm
5.623

45. Nutrition A world-record grapefruit had a mass of 3,068 g. What was its mass in kilograms? **3.068 kg**

46. Zoology A hippopotamus is so large that it has a stomach [GPS] 304.8 cm long, yet it is agile enough to outrun a human. How long is the stomach of a hippopotamus in meters? **3.048 m**

Number Sense **Match each measurement with its equivalent measurement from the table.**

47. 0.015 km E   **48.** 1,500 cm E   **49.** 150,000 mg C

50. 0.15 L F   **51.** 15 L A   **52.** 1,500 g D

A. 15,000 mL	**B.** 150 cm	**C.** 150 g
D. 1.5 kg	**E.** 15 m	**F.** 150 mL
G. 150 kg	**H.** 0.15 mL	**I.** 1,500 mm

53. Marine Biology The blue whale is the largest of all known animals. The largest known blue whale measured 33.58 meters in length.

   a. How many millimeters long was this whale? **33,580 mm**

   b. How many kilometers long was this whale? **0.03358 km**

C Challenge

54. A kilometer is 1,000 meters, a kilogram is 1,000 grams, a milliliter is 0.001 liter, and a milligram is 0.001 gram.

54. Writing in Math The prefix kilo- means "one thousand," and the prefix milli- means "one thousandth." What do the prefixes tell you about kilometer and kilogram, and milliliter and milligram? See left.

55. Physical Fitness You walk about 3 mi/h.

   a. Approximately how many kilometers can you walk in an hour? **5 to 6 km**

   b. How many meters can you walk in an hour? **5,000 to 6,000 m**

GPS Use the Guided Problem Solving worksheet with Exercise 46.

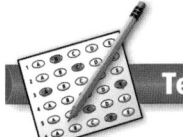

Gridded Reponse

56. The albatross has a wingspan of 3,350 mm, the largest wingspan of any bird. What is the wingspan of an albatross in meters? 3.35

57. What part of a second is a millisecond? 0.001

58. A worm is about 143 mm long. What is the length of the worm in meters? 0.143

59. A pitcher threw a baseball 95 mi/h at a baseball game. Rounded to the nearest tenth, how many feet per second is this? 139.3

Take It to the NET
Online lesson quiz at
www.PHSchool.com
Web Code: ada-0307

60. Sean tries to drink $2\frac{1}{2}$ qt of water every day. How many gallons does he average in a week? 35/8 or 4.375

Lesson 3-6 **61. Knot Tying** Clinton Bailey, Sr., holds the record for knot tying. He tied six different rope knots in 8.1 s. Write and solve an equation to find his average time per knot.
$6t = 8.1$ or $t = \frac{8.1}{6}$; 1.35 s/knot

Lesson 3-2 **Estimate each product or quotient.**

62. $28.134 \div 3.75$
about 7

63. $8,517 \cdot 9.82$
about 90

64. $101.49 \div 9.51$
about 10

Lessons 2-9 and 2-10 **Solve each inequality.**

65. $a - 5 \geq 16$
$a \geq 21$

66. $n + 8 < -7$
$n < -15$

67. $-3r \leq 21$
$r \geq -7$

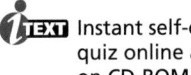

Checkpoint Quiz 2   **Lessons 3-5 through 3-7**

TEXT Instant self-check
quiz online and
on CD-ROM

Solve each equation.

1. $0.5m = 0.125$ 0.25   **2.** $d \div 0.3 = 28.5$ 8.55   **3.** $y - 135.43 = -5.43$
130

4. $12.2 = 4x$ 3.05   **5.** $29.25 = 4.5w$ 6.5   **6.** $k + 870.9 = 1,000.5$
129.6

Choose the most reasonable estimate. Explain your choice.

7. height of a standard house window: 1.5 cm or 1.5 m
1.5 m; 1.5 cm is a little wider than the width of a thumbnail.

8. capacity of a shampoo bottle: 500 mL or 500 L
500 mL; 500 L would be about 500 qt.

Complete each statement.

9. 95 mL = ■ L   0.095

10. ■ cm = 76.5 km   7,650,000

11. ■ km = 675 m   0.675

12. 7.1 kg = ■ g   7,100

 13. Horses The world's smallest horse had a mass of only 9.1 kg. What was the mass of the horse in grams? 9,100 g

---

4. Assess

 **Lesson Quiz 3-7**

Write the metric unit that makes each statement true.
1. 23 kg = 23,000 ■ g
2. 970 cm = 9.7 ■ m
Complete each statement.
3. ■ g = 42 mg   0.042
4. ■ km = 5,000 m   5

✓ **Chapter Checkpoint 2**

To check understanding of
Lessons 3-5 to 3-7:
Checkpoint Quiz 2 (p. 161)

📁 **Teaching Resources**
Checkpoint Quiz 2 (also in Prentice Hall Assessment System)

👥 **Reaching All Students**
Reading and Math Literacy 3C

Spanish versions available.

Reteaching 3-7 *Using the Metric System*

Complete each statement.
a. 2.5 cm = _____ mm
The diagram shows

2.5 cm = __25__ mm.
You know 10 mm = 1 cm.
Since a mm is smaller, it takes more of them to make the same length. This can help you remember to *multiply* by 10.

b. 347 g = _____ kg
You know 1,000 g = 1 kg.
A kilogram is heavier than a gram, so it takes fewer to equal the same weight as 347 g. Thus, divide by 1,000 by moving the decimal point 3 places to the left.

347 g = __0.347__ kg

Complete each statement.

1. 6,900 mL = 6.9 L	**2.** 5.62 cm = 56.2 mm
3. 5,346 m = 5.346 km	**4.** 246 mg = 0.246 g
5. 890 cm = 8.9 m	**6.** 473 cm = 4,730 mm
7. 9.4 L = 9,400 mL	**8.** 29 cg = 0.29 g
9. 2.1 km = 2,100 m	**10.** 1.65 L = 165 cL
11. 37 L = 37,000 mL	**12.** 87.5 g = 0.0875 kg
13. 797 mm = 0.797 m	**14.** 1.75 km = 175,000 cm
15. 3,926 mg = 3.926 g	**16.** 0.71 kL = 710 L
17. 9,836 cm = 0.09836 km	**18.** 17.9 g = 17,900 mg

Alternative Assessment

Have students list their estimates for the lengths, masses, and capacities in metric units of familiar objects in the classroom or around the school.

Test Prep

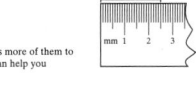 **Resources**
For additional practice with a variety of test item formats:
• Test Prep, p. 173
• Test-Taking Strategies, p. 168
• Test-Taking Strategies With Transparencies

161

Precision and Significant Digits

This Extension shows students how to indicate the precision of a measurement and how to use significant digits.

Teaching Notes

All digits different from zero are significant. Any measurement that is zero is significant. If the weight of a person is given as 102 lb, all the digits are significant. If the weight of an elephant is given as 12,000 lb, whether the last three digits are significant depends on the precision of the measurement.

Error Prevention!

Exercises 6–9 Have students find the less precise measurement and underline or circle the place to which they are to round.

 **Extension** — **Precision and Significant Digits**

For Use With Lesson 3-7

The pin at the right measures about 5 cm. A more precise measurement is 4.5 cm. An even more precise measurement is 46 mm. The smaller the units on the scale of a measuring instrument, the more precise the measurement is.

1 EXAMPLE

Choose the more precise measurement.

a. **5 g or 8 mg**
Since a milligram is a smaller unit of measure than a gram, 8 mg is more precise than 5 g.

b. **2.72 m or 3.5 m**
A hundredth of a meter is a smaller unit of measure than a tenth of a meter. So 2.72 m is more precise than 3.5 m.

A calculation will be only as precise as the least precise measurement used in the calculation. So, round your results to match the precision of the least precise measurement.

2 EXAMPLE

Add the lengths 6.31 m, 5.447 m, and 2.8 m.

$6.31 + 5.447 + 2.8 = 14.557$ **The least precise measurement is 2.8 m. Round the sum to the nearest tenth of a meter.**
Rounded to tenths ≈ 14.6 m

Digits that represent an actual measurement are *significant digits*. Nonzero digits (1–9) are always significant. The rules below will help you decide whether a zero is a significant digit.

Type of Number	Which Zeros Are Significant	Example
decimal numbers between 0 and 1	Zeros to the left of *all* the nonzero digits are not significant. All other zeros are significant.	significant digits 0.006040 not significant digits
positive integers	Zeros to the right of *all* the nonzero digits are not significant (unless specifically known to be). Zeros between nonzero digits are significant.	significant digits 203,400 not significant digits
noninteger decimal numbers greater than 1	All zeros are significant.	significant digits 350.07050

3 EXAMPLE

How many significant digits are in 0.0504 m?

The 5 and the 4 are significant. The zero between them is significant.
● The other zeros are not significant. There are three significant digits.

When you multiply or divide measurements, round your answer to
match the least number of significant digits in the problem.

4 EXAMPLE

A plot for a new house measures 152.6 m by 121 m.
What is the area of the plot? Use significant digits.

┌──────3 significant digits
│
$152.6 \cdot 121 = 18,464.6$ ←——Multiply.

└——— 4 significant digits

● The area is 18,500 m^2. ←—— **Round the area to 3 significant digits.**

EXERCISES

Choose the more precise measurement.

1. 3 m or 5.2 m 5.2 m **2.** 8 mL or 9.5 L 8 mL **3.** 1.89 km or 8.7 cm **4.** 1.9 kg or 1.87 kg
                                                            8.7 cm   1.87 kg

5. Error Analysis Your friend says that 4.35 km is more precise
than 5.2 cm because a hundredths unit is a smaller unit than a
tenths unit. What mistake did your friend make?
Answers may vary. Sample: You ignored the units of length.

Find each sum or difference. Round to the place value of the less
precise measurement.

6. 5.6 g + 8 g 14 g **7.** 8.35 kg + 6.2 kg **8.** 8.2 km − 1.75 km **9.** 9 cm − 2.3 cm
                            14.6 kg   6.5 km   7 cm

Determine the number of significant digits in each measurement.

10. 0.069 m **11.** 100.5 L **12.** 3,400 kL **13.** 5.2100 km
2 significant digits 4 significant digits 2 significant digits 5 significant digits

Find each product or quotient. Use significant digits.

14. 1,234 in. · 31 in. **15.** 0.0702 ft · 227 ft **16.** 16,250 m ÷ 14.5 s **17.** 132.5 cm · 43.2 cm
38,000 in.² 15.9 ft² 1,120 m/s 5,720 cm²

3-8

1. Plan

Lesson Preview

 **Check Skills You'll Need**

Inductive Reasoning
Lesson 1-7: Example 2;
Exercises 3–8.
Extra Practice, p. 744.

Lesson Resources

📁 **Teaching Resources**
Practice, Reteaching, Enrichment

👬 **Reaching All Students**
Practice Workbook 3-8
Spanish Practice Workbook 3-8
Guided Problem Solving 3-8

⏱ **Presentation Assistant Plus!**
Transparencies and PowerPoint™
• Check Skills You'll Need 3-8
• Additional Examples 3-8
• Student Edition Answers 3-8
• Lesson Quiz 3-8
PH Presentation Pro CD-ROM 3-8

ASSESSMENT SYSTEM

Computer Test Generator CD-ROM

💻 **Technology**
Resource Pro® CD-ROM
Computer Test Generator CD-ROM
PH Presentation Pro CD-ROM

💻 **www.PHSchool.com**
Student Site
• Teacher Web Code: adk-5500
• Self-grading Lesson Quiz
PH SuccessNet Teacher Center
• Lesson Planner
• Resources

Plus 📘**TEXT**

 **Problem Solving** **Simplify the Problem**

OBJECTIVE
1 Simplify the Problem

What You'll Learn

OBJECTIVE
1 To solve complex problems by first solving simpler cases

. . . And Why

To solve real-world problems involving motion

 Check Skills You'll Need

Write a rule for each number pattern. Find the next three numbers in the pattern.

1. $0, 6, 12, 18, \ldots$
See below.
2. $-18, -9, 0, 9, \ldots$
See below.
3. $0, 2, 1, 3, 2, 4, 3, \ldots$
See below.
4. $7, 6, 8, 7, 9, 8, 10, \ldots$
See below.

🔍 For help, go to Lesson 1-7.

1. Start with 0 and add 6 repeatedly; 24, 30, 36
2. Start with −18 and add 9 repeatedly; 18, 27, 36
3. Start with 0. Alternately add 2 and subtract 1; 5, 4, 6
4. Start with 7. Alternately subtract 1 and add 2; 9, 11, 10

Math Strategies in Action
Scientists often encounter problems that are very complicated. When they work to develop a new vaccine or develop a new method to fight disease, they usually work on smaller or simpler pieces of the problem first. Sometimes when you solve a problem, it helps to solve other problems that have similar conditions. Here is a well-known problem that shows you how to use this strategy.

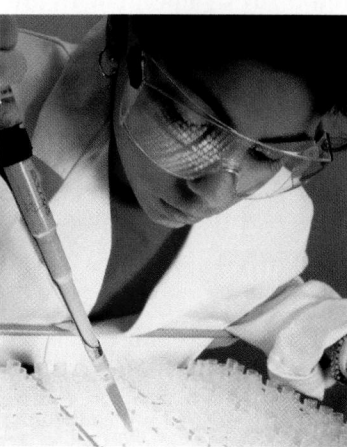

1 EXAMPLE **Real-World 🌐 Problem Solving**

A snail is trying to escape from a well 10 ft deep. The snail can climb 2 ft each day, but each night it slides back 1 ft. How many days will the snail take to climb out of the well?

Read and Understand

A snail needs to climb 10 ft to escape from a well. It can climb 2 ft per day. At night the snail slides back 1 ft.

1. How far up the well will the snail be after the first day and the first night? **1 ft**

2. How far up the well will the snail be after the second day? **3 ft**

3. How far up the well will the snail be after the second day and the second night? **2 ft**

Plan and Solve

At first you might think that the snail progresses 1 ft each day and will therefore take 10 days to escape. This answer is wrong, however, because it leaves out an important part of the problem.

164 Chapter 3 Decimals and Equations

✅ **Ongoing Assessment and Intervention**

Before the Lesson	During the Lesson	After the Lesson
Diagnose prerequisite skills using:	**Monitor progress using:**	**Assess knowledge using:**
• Check Skills You'll Need	• Check Understanding	• Lesson Quiz
	• Additional Examples	• Computer Test Generator
	• Test Prep	CD-ROM

Try to solve a simpler problem. Change the problem to a simpler one based on a 3-ft well, and then try a 4-ft well to see if there is a pattern.

Time	3-ft Well	4-ft Well
Day 1	Up 2 ft from bottom	Up 2 ft from bottom
Night 1	Up 1 ft from bottom	Up 1 ft from bottom
Day 2	Up 3 ft from bottom; OUT!	Up 3 ft from bottom
Night 2		Up 2 ft from bottom
Day 3		Up 4 ft from bottom; OUT!

4. Using the information from the simpler 3-ft-well and 4-ft-well problems, describe the pattern. **The number of days it takes to get out is 1 less than the depth of the well in feet.**
5. How many days will the snail take to escape from the 10-ft well? **9 days**

Look Back and Check

You can check your answer by drawing a diagram.

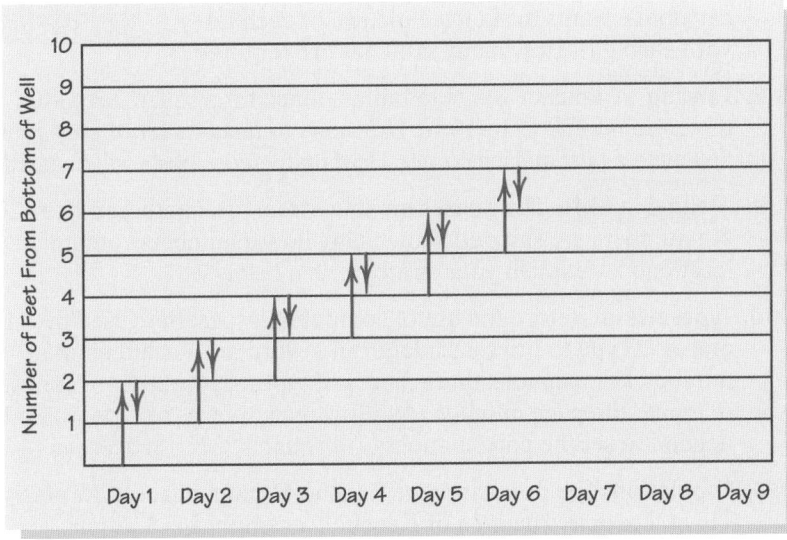

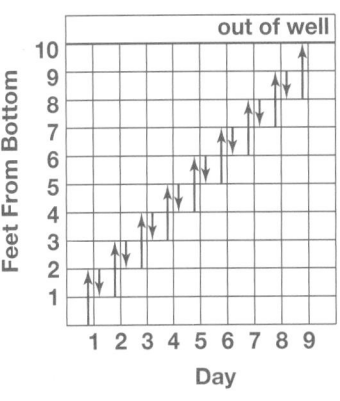

✓ **Check Understanding**

6. Copy and complete the diagram to check your answer. **See right.**

👥 **Reaching All Students**

| **Below Level** Have students think about a big task they need to do. Have them describe a way they might do it, and then ways to simplify the task. | **Advanced Learners** Have students find how many days it would take a snail to climb out of a 25 ft well if the snail can climb 3 ft each day but slides back 1 ft each night. **12 days** | **Tactile Learners** See note on page 165. **Error Prevention** See note on page 167. |

Math Background

You can often solve a difficult math problem by recalling a similar, simpler problem you have solved and using the same method.

Teaching Notes

1 EXAMPLE Tactile Learners

Have a student place a ruler on a desk so that the 10-in. mark aligns with the edge of the desk. Tape the ruler to the desk so it won't slide. Give the student a token to represent the snail. Instruct the student to place the token beside the 0-in. mark on the ruler, then model the snail's movements. When the token (likely) falls off the desk, the snail is out of the well.

PowerPoint

Additional Example

1 Marta gives her sister one penny on the first day of October, two pennies on the second day, and four pennies on the third day. She continues to double the number of pennies each day. On what date will Marta give her sister $10.24 in pennies? **October 11**

Closure

Have students work in groups to solve this problem using any strategy.

Han and Ping each have some horses. Han says, "If you give me one of yours, we will have the same number." Ping replies, "No, you give me one of yours and then I will have twice as many as you do." How many horses do they each have at the beginning? **Han 5, Ping 7** Have students share their strategies for solving this problem.

3. Practice

Assignment Guide

1 Objective 1
- Ⓐ Ⓑ **Core** 1–9
- Ⓒ **Extension** 10–12

Test Prep 13–16
Mixed Review 17–26

Practice 3-8 *Simplify a Problem*

Solve by simplifying the problem.

1. A house-number manufacturer sold numbers to retail stores for $.09 per digit. A hardware store bought enough digits for two of every house number from 1 to 999. How many digits did the store purchase for house numbers:

   a. 1–9 ___18___   b. 10–99 ___360___   c. 100–999 ___5,400___

   d. Find the total cost of the house numbers. ___$520.02___

2. A tic-tac-toe diagram uses 2 vertical lines and 2 horizontal lines to create 9 spaces. How many spaces can you create using:

   a. 1 vertical line and 1 horizontal line ___4___

   b. 2 vertical lines and 1 horizontal line ___6___

   c. 3 vertical lines and 3 horizontal lines ___16___

   d. 4 vertical lines and 5 horizontal lines ___30___

   e. 17 vertical lines and 29 horizontal lines ___540___

3. Each side of each triangle in the figure has length 1 cm. The perimeter (the distance around) the first triangle is 3 cm. Find the perimeter of the figure formed by connecting:

   a. 2 triangles ___4 cm___   b. 3 triangles ___5 cm___

   c. 4 triangles ___6 cm___   d. 50 triangles ___52 cm___

Solve using any strategy.

4. At the inauguration, the President was honored with a 21-gun salute. The report from each gunshot lasted 1 s. Four seconds elapsed between shots. How long did the salute last? ___101 s___

5. Bernie began building a model airplane on day 7 of his summer vacation and finished building it on day 65. He worked on the plane each day. How many days did it take? ___59 days___

Enrichment 3-8 *Stranded in the Desert*

0.1 mi. 0.1 mi. 0.2 mi.   0.4 mi.   0.8 mi.

A party of explorers is stranded in the desert at ⊠. Water supplies, 10 in all, have previously been buried at increasingly greater distances from the party's camp, as shown on the map. In order to gauge how long the party can survive, the leader must calculate the difficulty of retrieving the water from the supplies.

1. Write a rule that the leader can use to calculate the distances between water supplies.
   ___Each distance is twice the previous distance.___

2. Find the round-trip distances from camp to:
   supply 1 ___0.2 mi___   supply 2 ___0.4 mi___   supply 3 ___0.8 mi___
   supply 4 ___1.6 mi___   supply 5 ___3.2 mi___   supply 6 ___6.4 mi___

3. Because of their weakened condition, water-retrieval parties can travel at a rate of only 0.2 mi/h. Find the round-trip times from camp to:
   supply 1 ___1 h___   supply 2 ___2 h___   supply 3 ___4 h___
   supply 4 ___8 h___   supply 5 ___16 h___   supply 6 ___32 h___

4. The leader wished to calculate the total amount of time the party would spend retrieving water from all 10 supplies. Find the time needed to retrieve the indicated supplies.
   the first 1 ___1 h___   the first 2 ___3 h___   the first 3 ___7 h___
   the first 4 ___15 h___   the first 5 ___31 h___   the first 6 ___63 h___

5. The leader stumbled onto a simple method for calculating total water-retrieval times.
   Complete: (2) − 1 = ___1___
   (2 × 2) − 1 = ___3___
   (2 × 2 × 2) − 1 = ___7___
   (2 × 2 × 2 × 2) − 1 = ___15___

6. Use the leader's method to calculate the total amount of time the party will need to retrieve all 10 water supplies.
   ___1,023 h___

EXERCISES

 For more exercises, see *Extra Practice.*

Practice and Problem Solving

Ⓐ **Practice by Example**

Solve by simplifying each problem.

Example 1
(page 164)

1. You decide to number the 58 pages in your journal from 1 to 58. How many digits do you have to write? **107 digits**

🌎 2. **Sports** In a tennis tournament, each athlete plays one match against each of the other athletes. There are 12 athletes scheduled to play in the tournament. How many matches will be played? **66 matches**

3. **Geometry** What is the total number of triangles in the figure at the right? **13 triangles**

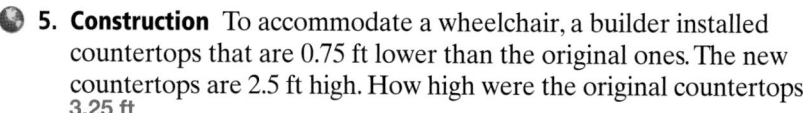

Ⓑ **Apply Your Skills**

Solve using any strategy.

4. The school store buys pencils for $.20 each. It sells the pencils for $.25 each. How much profit does the store make if it sells five dozen pencils? **$3.00**   [GPS]

🌎 5. **Construction** To accommodate a wheelchair, a builder installed countertops that are 0.75 ft lower than the original ones. The new countertops are 2.5 ft high. How high were the original countertops? **3.25 ft**

6. What is the total number of squares in the figure at the right? **55 squares**

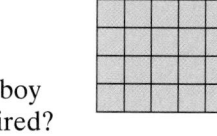

7. There are 10 girls and 8 boys at a party. A cartoonist wants to sketch a picture of each boy with each girl. How many sketches are required? **80 sketches**

🌎 8. **Fencing** A rancher wants to build a fence for a square lot with dimensions of 50 yd by 50 yd. He wants to install a fence post every 5 yd with a post at each corner. How many fence posts will he need? **40 fence posts**

9. **Writing in Math** The houses on your street are numbered 1 to 120. No numbers are skipped. How many house numbers contain at least one 5? Explain your strategy. **See below left.**

Strategies

- Account for All Possibilities
- Draw a Diagram
- Look for a Pattern
- Make a Model
- Make a Table
- Simplify the Problem
- Simulate the Problem
- Solve by Graphing
- Try, Test, Revise
- Use Multiple Strategies
- Work Backward
- Write an Equation
- Write a Proportion

Ⓒ **Challenge**

9. **21 house numbers; Explanations may vary. Sample:** There is 1 single-digit number that has a 5. The two-digit numbers have 9 numbers that end in 5, and there are 9 other numbers in the 50s. From 100 to 120, there are 2 numbers that have a 5. In all, there are 1 + 9 + 9 + 2 = 21 numbers that contain at least one digit 5.

🌎 10. **Typesetting** Before the use of computers, typesetters used metal pieces of type to print each letter in a word and each digit in a number. For example, three pieces of type—1, 4, and 8—were used to create the page number 148. How many pieces of type would be needed to set the page numbers 1 through 476? **1,320 pieces**

🌎 11. **Population** The population of Rancho Cucamonga, California, is 117,000 people. The area of Rancho Cucamonga is 37.8 mi². Find the population density—the number of people per square mile. Show your work. **about 3,095 people/mi²; 117,000 ÷ 37.8 ≈ 3,095**

12. You are hiking with three friends. You pass a group of six hikers going the other way. Each person in one group greets each person in the other group. How many greetings are there? Explain. **24; Answers may vary. Sample: If you were hiking by yourself, you would greet 6 people. 4 hikers × 6 greetings per hiker = 24 greetings.**

166 Chapter 3 Decimals and Equations

 Use the Guided Problem Solving worksheet with Exercise 4.

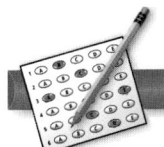
Multiple Choice

What is the solution of each equation?

13. $x - 8 = -4.8$ **C**

    A. -12.8 **B.** -3.2 **C.** 3.2 **D.** 12.8

Take It to the NET
Online lesson quiz at
www.PHSchool.com
Web Code: ada-0308

14. $8 + c = -2.3$ **F**

    F. -10.3 **G.** -5.7 **H.** 5.7 **I.** 10.3

15. $7.53 = -0.3y$ **D**

    A. 25.1 **B.** 2.26 **C.** -2.26 **D.** -25.1

Short Response

16. A corral is ringed by 60 ft of fencing with posts every 4 ft. How many fence posts are there? Show your work. **See back of book.**

Mixed Review

Lesson 3-7   **Measurement**   **Complete each statement.**

17. $27 \text{ cm} = \blacksquare \text{ m}$
0.27

18. $5,200 \text{ km} = \blacksquare \text{ m}$
5,200,000

19. $2,000 \text{ mg} = \blacksquare \text{ g}$
2

20. $0.5 \text{ L} = \blacksquare \text{ mL}$
500

21. $3 \text{ m} = \blacksquare \text{ cm}$
300

22. $6 \text{ kg} = \blacksquare \text{ mg}$
6,000,000

Lesson 3-3   **23. Test Scores** Your test scores so far this semester are 100, 90, 82, 96, and 78. You have one more 100-point test to take. After you complete the last test, what is your highest possible average? **91**

Lesson 3-1   **Estimate using front-end estimation.**

24. $\$9.54 + \$1.25$
about $10.80

25. $\$6.72 + \$5.28$
about $12

26. $\$12.19 + \$5.66$
about $17.90

Math at Work
Woodworker

Woodworkers cut, shape, assemble, and finish wood to create tables, chairs, and other types of furniture. To create these items, woodworkers must plan and carry out many individual steps in sequence.

Machines used in professional woodworking shops cut and shape wood with great precision. The most sophisticated machines are controlled by computer programs. Woodworkers can enhance their skills by taking mathematics and computer courses that develop their ability to think three-dimensionally.

Take It to the NET For more information about woodworkers, go to **www.PHSchool.com**.
Web Code: adb-2031

3-8 Simplify the Problem   **167**

---

4. Assess

PowerPoint Lesson Quiz 3-8

Solve using any strategy.

1. On Monday, Jon reads page 45 of his book and continues to read until he finishes page 89. How many pages does he read on Monday?
$89 - 45 + 1$, or 45 pages

2. Marion put one penny in a bank. Each day after that she put in the bank double the number of pennies from the previous day until the bank was full. If the bank was full on the 8th day, when was the bank only half-full? **7th day**

Error Prevention!

Exercise 6 It is easy to get confused with counting the squares unless you follow an organized process. For example, first identify and count all the one-by-one squares. Then identify and count (in an organized manner) all the two-by-two squares, and so on. You may find it helpful to use grid paper and colored pencils.

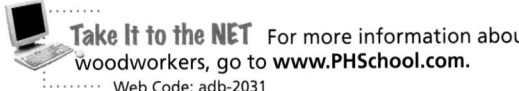

Reteaching 3-8 *Simplify a Problem*

You have 12 meters of ribbon to cut into half-meter pieces. How many cuts do you need to make?
Simplify the problem. Suppose you only had 3 meters of ribbon. Use a diagram.

Although you will get 6 pieces of ribbon (2 · 3), you need to make only 5 cuts.
With 12 meters of ribbon, you would get 24 pieces with 23 cuts.

Solve by simplifying the problem.

1. A plumber charges $25 to weld two pipes together. Pipe comes in 4-foot pieces and you need one piece 60 feet long. How much will it cost to have enough 4-foot pieces welded together? Fill in the table first.

Length of Pipe	Number of Welds
8	1
12	2
16	3
20	4
60	14

$350

2. How many digits are used to number the pages of a 425-page book? Fill in the table first.

Page Number	Number of Pages	Digits
1–9	9	9
10–99	90	180
100–425	326	978

Total digits: 1,167

3. You are serving fruit in small bowls at a luncheon. You decide to place one slice of melon and a spoonful of one type of berry in each bowl. You have three types of melon and four types of berries available. How many different combinations of melon and berries can you make?

12

Alternative Assessment

Have each student select one of the exercises from this lesson and write a paragraph explaining the problem-solving strategy he or she used to solve the exercise.

Test Prep

Resources

For additional practice with a variety of test item formats:
- Test Prep, p. 173
- Test-Taking Strategies, p. 168
- Test-Taking Strategies With Transparencies

Writing Extended Reponses

This feature helps students understand how answers to extended response questions are evaluated. Knowing this will encourage students to write better solutions.

Resources

ASSESSMENT SYSTEM

Test-Taking Strategies With Transparencies
• Transparency 3
• Practice Sheet, p. 3

Teaching Notes

You may want to write a generic four-point rubric based on the Example. Have students solve several problems prior to introducing this feature. Then, when you teach this feature, have them examine their solutions and give themselves 0 to 4 points for each, based on the rubric. If they award fewer than four points, have them rewrite the solution so that they feel it is worth four points. Ask volunteers to share their solutions with the class. Students may begin to understand why showing work is a beneficial test-taking strategy.

Test-Taking Strategies With Transparencies

Chapter 3: Writing Extended Responses

Exercises

David has one quarter, three dimes, and five nickels. How many different ways can he combine the coins to make 45¢?

Scoring Rubric

• **4 points:** Student correctly answers question in a complete sentence, provides an explanation, and shows all possible combinations.

• **3 points:** Student answers question in a complete sentence, provides an explanation, and shows possible combinations, but makes minor calculation errors.

• **2 point:** Student provides an incorrect explanation and does not completely answer the question.

• **1 point:** Student incorrectly answers the question and does not provide an explanation.

• **0 points:** No response or answer is completely incorrect.

Three responses to the question are shown below.

4 point response	3 point response	1 point response
1 quarter, 2 dimes	1 quarter, 2 dimes	1 quarter, 2 dimes
1 quarter, 1 dime, 2 nickels	1 quarter, 1 dime, 2 nickels	
1 quarter, 4 nickels	1 quarter, 3 nickels	1 quarter, 1 dime, 2 nickels
3 dimes, 3 nickels	3 dimes, 3 nickels	
2 dimes, 5 nickels	2 dimes, 5 nickels	1 quarter, 4 nickels
There are no other possible ways for the coins to add up to 45¢ so this must be the complete answer.	These are the only combinations that add up to 45¢.	2 dimes, 5 nickels

1. Tell why the 4-point response received the points it did.

2. Read the 3-point response. What error did the student make?

3. Write a 2-point response that has an incorrect explanation.

Test-Taking Strategies   Pre-Algebra   3

An extended-response question can be worth as many as four points. It often has multiple parts. To get full credit, you need to answer each part and show all of your work or justify your thinking.

EXAMPLE

To get a 90 for this grading period, Jerilyn needs a test average of 94.5. She had a 93.2 average on her first three tests and scored 97 on the fourth test. **(a)** Explain in words how to find the next score she needs. **(b)** Write an equation to find the fifth test score. **(c)** Solve your equation.

Here are three responses with the points each received.

4 points	3 points	1 point
There are 5 tests. For a test average of 94.5, the sum of the test scores must be 5 times 94.5, or 472.5 points.	There are 5 tests. For a test average of 94.5, the sum of the test scores must be 5 times 94.5, or 472.5 points.	Let g = grade on fifth test.
Let g = grade on fifth test.	Let g = grade on fifth test.	$93.2 + 97 + g = 90$
$3(93.2) + 97 + g = 472.5$	$3(93.2) + 97 + g = 472.5$	$190.2 + g = 90$
$376.6 + g = 472.5$	$276.9 + 97 + g = 472.5$	$g = 90 - 190.2$
$g = 472.5 - 376.6$	$373.9 + g = 472.5$	$g = 100.2$
$g = 95.9$	$g = 472.5 - 373.9$	
Jerilyn must score 95.9 or higher on her fifth test.	$g = 98.6$	
	Jerilyn must score 98.6.	

The 4-point response shows the work and gives a written answer to the problem. Note that it identifies the variable before writing the equation. The 3-point response contains a computational error, but the student completed all parts. The 1-point response shows an incorrect equation, and it does not explain the process.

EXERCISES

Use the Example above to do each exercise.

1. **Error Analysis** What is the error in the 3-point response? $3(93.2) = 279.6$, not 276.9.
2. Write a possible 2-point response for the problem. Explain why it is worth 2 points. See right.

2. Let g = the grade of the fifth test.
$376.6 + g = 472.5$
$376.6 - 376.6 + g = 472.5 - 376.6$
$g = 95.9$
This is a 2-point response because the computation is correct, but there is no explanation.

Chapter Review

Resources

Student Edition
Extra Practice, Ch. 3, p. 746
English/Spanish Glossary, p. 782
Table of Symbols, p. 777

Reaching All Students
Reading and Math Literacy 3D
Spanish Reading and Math
  Literacy 3D

ASSESSMENT SYSTEM

Test Prep
• Chapter 3 practice in test
  formats

www.PHSchool.com

Student Site
• Self-grading vocabulary test
PH SuccessNet Teacher Center
• Resources

Plus iTEXT

Vocabulary

compatible numbers (p. 133)   **mean** (p. 137)   **median** (p. 137)   **outlier** (p. 138)
formula (p. 143)   **measures of central tendency** (p. 137)   **mode** (p. 137)   **perimeter** (p. 144)

Reading Math
Understanding Vocabulary

Choose the vocabulary word that completes each sentence.

1. The sum of a group of data items divided by the number of data items is the _?_. **mean**

2. Numbers that are easy to divide are called _?_.
   compatible numbers

3. The data item that occurs most often in a group is the _?_. **mode**

4. A data item that is much greater or much less than the rest of the data items in a group is a(n) _?_. **outlier**

5. When an odd number of data items are written in order, the middle item is the _?_. **median**

6. An equation that shows a relationship between quantities that are represented by variables is a(n) _?_. **formula**

Take It to the NET
Online vocabulary quiz at **www.PHSchool.com**
Web Code: adj-0351

7. Numbers that describe groups of data items are called _?_.
   measures of central tendency

8. The distance around a figure is the _?_. **perimeter**

Skills and Concepts

3-1 Objectives

▼ To round decimals (p. 127)

▼ To estimate sums and differences (p. 128)

19. Answers may vary. Sample: You use rounding when only a rough answer is needed and the numbers are not clustered. You use front-end estimation when you need a better estimate of a sum. You use clustering when there are 3 or more numbers and there is one number that they are all close to.

You can estimate the sum of decimals by rounding, front-end estimating, or clustering.

You can estimate the difference of decimals by rounding.

Estimate each sum or difference. State which method you used.
9–18. Answers may vary. Samples are given.

9. $3.14 + 6.952$
   about 10; front-end
10. $10.2538 - 6.095$
    about 4; rounding
11. $14.451 + 9.736$
    about 24; rounding
12. $14.27 - 4.268$
    about 10; rounding
13. $20.681 + 19.39 + 20.56$
    about 60; clustering
14. $12.814 - 6.3791$
    about 7; rounding
15. $9.0426 + 2.7182$
    about 11.7; front-end
16. $21.9384 - 15.639$
    about 6; rounding
17. $6.257 + 6.129 + 6.34$
    about 18; clustering
18. $19.83 - 14.268$
    about 6; rounding

19. Explain when you would use each estimation method named above to estimate a sum of decimals. Use examples. **See left.**

🌐 20. **Weather** Last year Lake Jones rose to 672.42 feet during the spring floods. This year Lake Jones rose to 711.36 feet. About how much higher did the lake rise this year? **about 40 feet**

3-2 Objectives

▼ To estimate products (p. 132)

▼ To estimate quotients (p. 133)

You can estimate a product by rounding. You can estimate a quotient of two decimals by using **compatible numbers.**

Estimate each product or quotient.

21. 8.15(6.04)
about 48

22. 19.28 ÷ 5.439
about 4

23. 1.9 · 4.92
about 10

24. 25.1 ÷ 4.87
about 5

25. 12.497 · 0.894
about 12

26. 59.3581 ÷ 11.5304
about 5

27. 3.59(−2.3291)
about −8

28. −17.45 ÷ 3.059
about −6

29. (−2.0936)(−5.6892)
about 12

3-3 Objectives

▼ To find mean, median, and mode of a set of data (p. 137)

▼ To choose the best measure of central tendency (p. 139)

You can use a **measure of central tendency** to describe a collection of data. The **mean** is the sum of the data items divided by the number of data items. The **median** is the middle value or the mean of the two middle values when the data are written in order. The **mode** is the data item that occurs most often. An **outlier** is a data item that is much greater or much less than the rest of the data items.

Find the mean, median, and mode. When an answer is not an integer, round to the nearest tenth. Identify any outliers.

30. 2, 3, 6, 2, 8, 9, 5, 10, 4, 5
5.4, 5, 2 and 5; no outliers

31. 16.1, 16.3, 15.9, 16.2, 16.3, 16.3, 15.8
16.1, 16.2, 16.3; no outliers

32. 32, 35, 31, 57, 33, 30, 34
36, 33, none; outlier: 57

33. 0.1, 7.9, 0.2, 0.3, 0.1, 0.2, 0.1, 0.1, 0.3
1.0, 0.2, 0.1; outlier: 7.9

Which measure of central tendency best describes each situation? Explain. 34–36. Answers may vary. Samples are given.

34. the favorite radio stations of teenagers in your neighborhood
Mode; the data are not numerical.

35. the numbers of videos owned by students in your class
Median; there could easily be outliers.

36. the prices of 8-oz containers of yogurt at six local grocery stores
Mean; there likely are no outliers.

3-4 Objectives

▼ To substitute into formulas (p. 143)

▼ To use the formula for the perimeter of a rectangle (p. 144)

A **formula** is an equation that shows a relationship between quantities that are represented by variables. You can use formulas to find such things as **perimeter,** area, and distance.

Evaluate each formula for the values given.

37. distance: $d = rt$
when $r = 35$ mi/h and
$t = 2$ h
70 mi

38. area of a rectangle: $A = \ell w$
when $\ell = 16$ mm and
$w = 24$ mm
384 mm^2

39. Circumference: $C = 2\pi r$
when $r = 6$ in. Use 3.14 for π.
37.68 in.

40. perimeter of a square: $P = 4s$
when $s = 13$ cm
52 cm

3-5 and 3-6 Objectives

▼ To solve one-step decimal equations involving subtraction (p. 148)

▼ To solve one-step decimal equations involving addition (p. 149)

▼ To solve one-step decimal equations involving division (p. 152)

▼ To solve one-step decimal equations involving multiplication (p. 153)

To solve a one-step equation, use an inverse operation and a property of equality to get the variable alone on one side of the equation.

Solve each equation.

41. $n + 3.8 = 10.9$
7.1

42. $y - 6.72 = 2.53$
9.25

43. $h + 0.67 = -1.34$
−2.01

44. $t - 2.7 = 23.5$
26.2

45. $12.9 + x = 3.8$
−9.1

46. $5.7 = b - 4.9$
10.6

47. $6.3m = 15.75$
2.5

48. $a \div 4.9 = 8.33$
40.817

49. $v \cdot 7.1 = 80.23$
11.3

50. $c \div 12.5 = 77.5$
968.75

51. $-5.7z = 110.58$
−19.4

52. $d \div 4.75 = -38.95$
−185.0125

🌐 **53. Finance** On Monday a stock is worth $3.20 per share. By Friday the stock is worth $2.64 per share.
   a. Write an equation to model the change in price. $3.2 + x = 2.64$
   b. Solve the equation to find the amount by which the price changed. −$.56

3-7 Objectives

▼ To identify appropriate metric measures (p. 156)

▼ To convert metric units (p. 157)

54. Meter; a kilometer is too large unless you use fractional parts of a kilometer; centimeters are too small.

55. Kilogram; a bicycle is heavy, so grams are too small.

56. Milliliter; a liter is about the same as a quart, so liters are too large.

The **metric system** of measurement uses a decimal system to relate units to one another. To measure, you must choose an appropriate unit of measure.

Choose an appropriate metric unit of measure. Explain each choice.

54. height of a building
See left.

55. mass of a bicycle
See left.

56. amount of milk in a glass
See left.

Mental Math Complete each statement.

57. $0.85 \text{ m} = \blacksquare \text{ cm}$
85

58. $160 \text{ mL} = \blacksquare \text{ L}$
0.16

59. $2.3 \text{ m} = \blacksquare \text{ cm}$
230

60. $1.6 \text{ kg} = \blacksquare \text{ g}$
1,600

61. $0.62 \text{ L} = \blacksquare \text{ mL}$
620

62. $80 \text{ g} = \blacksquare \text{ kg}$
0.08

63. Explain why centimeters would be an inappropriate unit to measure the height of a mature oak tree.
A mature oak tree would be a number of meters tall. Centimeters is too small a unit.

3-8 Objectives

▼ To solve complex problems by first solving simpler cases (p. 164)

When a problem is complicated, you can solve related simpler problems to better understand the problem.

64. Reasoning A school's lockers are numbered 1 to 100. One hundred students enter the school one at a time. The first student opens the lockers. The second student closes the even-numbered lockers. The third student either closes or opens every third locker. The remaining students continue the pattern. After all the students have passed the lockers, which lockers are open?
1, 4, 9, 16, 25, 36, 49, 64, 81, 100

Resources

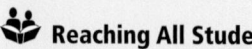

Chapter Test – Form B

Chapter Test – Form A

Chapter 3 Test • Form A

Circle the letter of the best answer.
1. Which of the following is the best estimate of 7.78 + 12.003?
   A. 17   B. 18   C. 19   D. 20
2. Which of the following is the best estimate of 8.79 − 2.49?
   F. 5   G. 6   H. 6.3   J. 7
3. Which of the following is the best estimate of 4.2 · 10.85?
   A. 40   B. 44   C. 50   D. 55
4. Which of the following is the best estimate of 31.8 ÷ 5.9?
   F. 5   G. 6   H. 7   J. 8
5. Which of the following is the most appropriate metric unit to measure your mass?
   A. mg   B. g   C. kg   D. L
6. Which of the following is the most appropriate metric unit to measure the length of you fingers?
   F. mm   G. km   H. m   J. cm
7. A set of data has a mean of 25 and an outlier of 4. You find the mean without the outlier. Which of the following best describes your new mean?
   A. The new mean is the same as the original mean.
   B. The new mean is the same as the median.
   C. The new mean is greater than the original mean.
   D. The new mean is less than the original mean.

Solve each equation.
8. y − 4.7 = 12.52   y = 17.22
9. 2.97 = x + 1.6   x = 1.37
10. n/13 = 0.24   n = 3.6
11. −3.5z = 2.31   z = −0.66

Chapter 3

Chapter Test

Take It to the NET
Online chapter test at
www.PHSchool.com
Web Code: ada-0352

Estimate each value.

1. 6.43 − 4.079
   about 2.3
2. 2.06 + 3.91
   about 6
3. 5.97 − 1.674
   about 4.3
4. 6.025 + 0.35
   about 6.4
5. 8.54 + 2.3
   about 10.8
6. 6.25 · 9.87
   about 60
7. 12.89 ÷ 3.04
   about 4
8. 1.76 · 3.93
   about 8
9. 4.96 ÷ 2.49
   about 2
10. 3.2 · 14.69
   about 45

Find the mean, median, and mode. When an answer is not an integer, round to the nearest tenth. Identify any outliers.

11. 11, 12, 9, 13, 10, 12, 11, 14, 12
    11.6, 12, 12; no outlier
12. 5.3, 5.6, 5.2, 5.0, 5.4, 5.6, 5.1, 5.0
    5.3, 5.25, 5.0 and 5.6; no outliers
13. 10.6, 9.8, 11.6, 29.1, 3.4, 11.4, 12.7
    12.7, 11.4, no mode; outliers: 3.4 and 29.1
14. 8.7, 8.5, 8.7, 8.5, 8.6, 8.5, 8.7, 8.6
    8.6, 8.6, 8.5 and 8.7; no outliers

Evaluate each formula for the given values.

15. area of a rectangle: $A = \ell w$
    when $\ell = 3.8$ in. and $w = 1.5$ in. 5.7 in.²

16. perimeter of a square: $P = 4s$
    when $s = 4.7$ cm 18.8 cm

17. perimeter of a rectangle: $P = 2\ell + 2w$
    when $\ell = 2.9$ m and $w = 6.05$ m 17.9 m

Solve each equation.

18. $x + 7.8 = 12.5$ 4.7

19. $n - 5.9 = 0.5$ 6.4

20. $4.1 + c = -1.2$ −5.3

21. $d - 6.3 = 11$ 17.3

22. $-9.7 + h = 10.3$ 20

23. $m \div 2.7 = 14.58$ 39.366

24. $h \cdot 4.7 = 30.55$ 6.5

25. $b \div (-7.8) = -79.56$ 620.568

26. $-3.4t = 30.94$ −9.1

Write an appropriate metric unit of measure for each quantity.

27. the height of a truck meter

28. the capacity of a standard shampoo bottle
    milliliter

29. the mass of a pineapple kilogram

30. the width of a paperback book centimeter

Complete.

31. 4.5 m = ■ cm
    450
32. 68 mL = ■ L
    0.068
33. 90 kg = ■ g
    90,000
34. 6,700 cm = ■ m
    67
35. 4 L = ■ mL
    4,000
36. 50.2 g = ■ kg
    0.0502

For Exercises 37 and 38, write an equation, and then solve.

37. **Shopping** You have a $20 bill. You buy gloves for $6.50. How much money do you now have? 6.50 + m = 20; $13.50

38. **Reptiles** The fastest speed recorded for a reptile on land is 9.7 m/s for a spiny-tailed iguana. At this rate, how far could a spiny-tailed iguana travel in 12 s?
    d = 9.7(12); 116.4 m

39. **Geography** Madrid and Barcelona are cities in Spain. The distance between them is 636,000 m. What is this in kilometers?
    636 km

40. You have an 18-ft metal pipe. How many cuts must you make to cut the pipe into 2-ft-long pieces? 8 cuts

41. **Data Analysis** Which measure of central tendency best describes the weights of the dogs in one neighborhood? B

    15 lb, 20 lb, 18 lb, 27 lb, 15 lb, 70 lb

    A. mean   B. median
    C. mode   D. all of the above

42. **Writing in Math** Explain how the outlier in the data set affects the mean.

    3, 2, 6, 3, 5, 4, 15, 4, 3
    The outlier 15 raises the mean by 1.25.

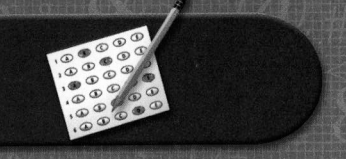

Test Prep

READING COMPREHENSION

Reading Comprehension Read the passages below. Then answer the questions on the basis of what is stated or implied in each passage.

> **Milk and Calcium** Doctors and dieticians agree that calcium is an important part of good nutrition as calcium helps to build and maintain strong bones. The recommended daily intake of calcium for adults is 1,000 mg. The National Academy of Sciences recommends that people from 9 to 18 years of age get at least 1,300 mg of calcium per day. Milk, perhaps the best-known source for calcium, has 300 mg of calcium per cup.

1. Which is true about *n*, the number of milligrams of calcium recommended daily for an adult? **C**
   A. $n > 1,000$ **B.** $n < 1,000$
   C. $n = 1,000$ **D.** $n = 10,000$

2. Which is true about *c*, the number of milligrams of calcium recommended daily for people ages 9 to 18? **I**
   F. $c = 1,000$ **G.** $c > 1,300$
   H. $c < 1,300$ **I.** $c \geq 1,300$

3. How many more milligrams of calcium per day does a young person need than an adult? **A**
   A. 300 mg   **B.** 1,000 mg
   C. 1,300 mg   **D.** 10,000 mg

4. How many full cups of milk does 14-year-old Janet have to drink if she is going to get her daily-recommended amount of calcium from milk? **5 cups**

> **Other Sources of Calcium** Although one slice of cheese pizza supplies 220 milligrams of calcium, dairy products are not the only source of calcium. For example, $\frac{3}{4}$ cup of a certain brand of cereal supplies 330 mg of calcium, 1 cup of broccoli supplies 90 mg of calcium, and 3 oz of canned salmon with bones supplies 180 mg of calcium. You can get 300 mg from one cup of calcium-fortified orange juice. However, it is important to know that exercising can do as much to help you build strong bones as calcium in your diet.

5. Which of these foods has the most calcium per portion? **G**
   F. cheese pizza   **G.** cereal
   H. broccoli   **I.** salmon

6. How many cups of broccoli give you 45 mg of calcium? **B**
   A. 0.25 cup   **B.** 0.5 cup
   C. 1 cup   **D.** 2 cups

7. How many cups of orange juice would supply exactly 1,000 mg of calcium? $3\frac{1}{3}$ **c**

8. How else can you build strong bones besides getting enough calcium from food?
   exercising

9. From the items in the passage, plan what you could eat that would give you exactly 1,300 mg of calcium in a day. Make a list to show your one-day diet. **Answers may vary.**
   Sample: 1 slice of cheese pizza; 1 cup of orange juice; 1 cup of broccoli; $\frac{3}{4}$ cup of cereal; and 6 oz of salmon.

Chapter 3 Test Prep   **173**

Real-World Snapshots

What's $10 Worth?

In this activity, students analyze information from two tables and apply their knowledge of math processes using decimals to solve problems involving the value of money.

Activating Prior Knowledge

Ask students to brainstorm a list of items that have increased in price during their lifetime. Do they remember a price that decreased? **Answers may vary. Sample: tickets to movies and sports events, pizza, video rentals, clothing, school lunch; prices go down during store sales and when fast-food restaurants have a special for a limited time.**

Teaching Notes

Teaching Tip

Have a volunteer read the introductory paragraph. Ask: *As prices go up, what else must increase so that people will be able to afford to pay more for necessities?* **Answers may vary. Sample: the amount of money people earn**

Tactile Learners

Use real money to show students that the equivalent of a one-dollar bill is 4 quarters, 10 dimes, 20 nickels, or 100 pennies. Have students determine different combinations of dimes, nickels, and pennies that equal 2 quarters. **Answers may vary. Sample: 5 dimes; 10 nickels; 50 pennies; 4 dimes, 1 nickel, and 5 pennies; 2 dimes, 5 nickels, and 5 pennies**

Inclusion

Examine the two tables with students. Point out that in both tables, the amount of money increases from the second column to the third column. Discuss the generalization that prices and income rise over time.

Real-World Snapshots

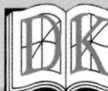

What's $10 Worth?

Applying Decimals If you shop with an older adult, you may have heard the statement, "Ten dollars isn't worth what it used to be!" Of course, $10 is always worth ten $1 bills, or 40 quarters, or 100 dimes. That doesn't change. What does change is the price of items. For example, a stamp for a letter cost $.03 back in 1950. The 2002 cost of a stamp, $.37, is more than twelve times that price. Back in 1950, you could buy 333 first-class stamps with a $10 bill. Today, that same $10 bill will get you only 27 stamps!

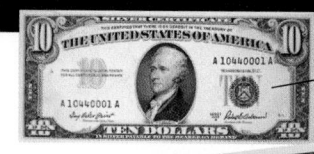

A $10 bill in 1950 looked like this.
A $10 bill today looks like this.

$10 Bills

Federal Reserve Notes began circulating in 1913. The design remained virtually unchanged until May 2000.

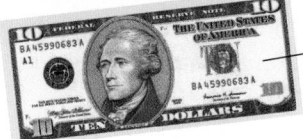

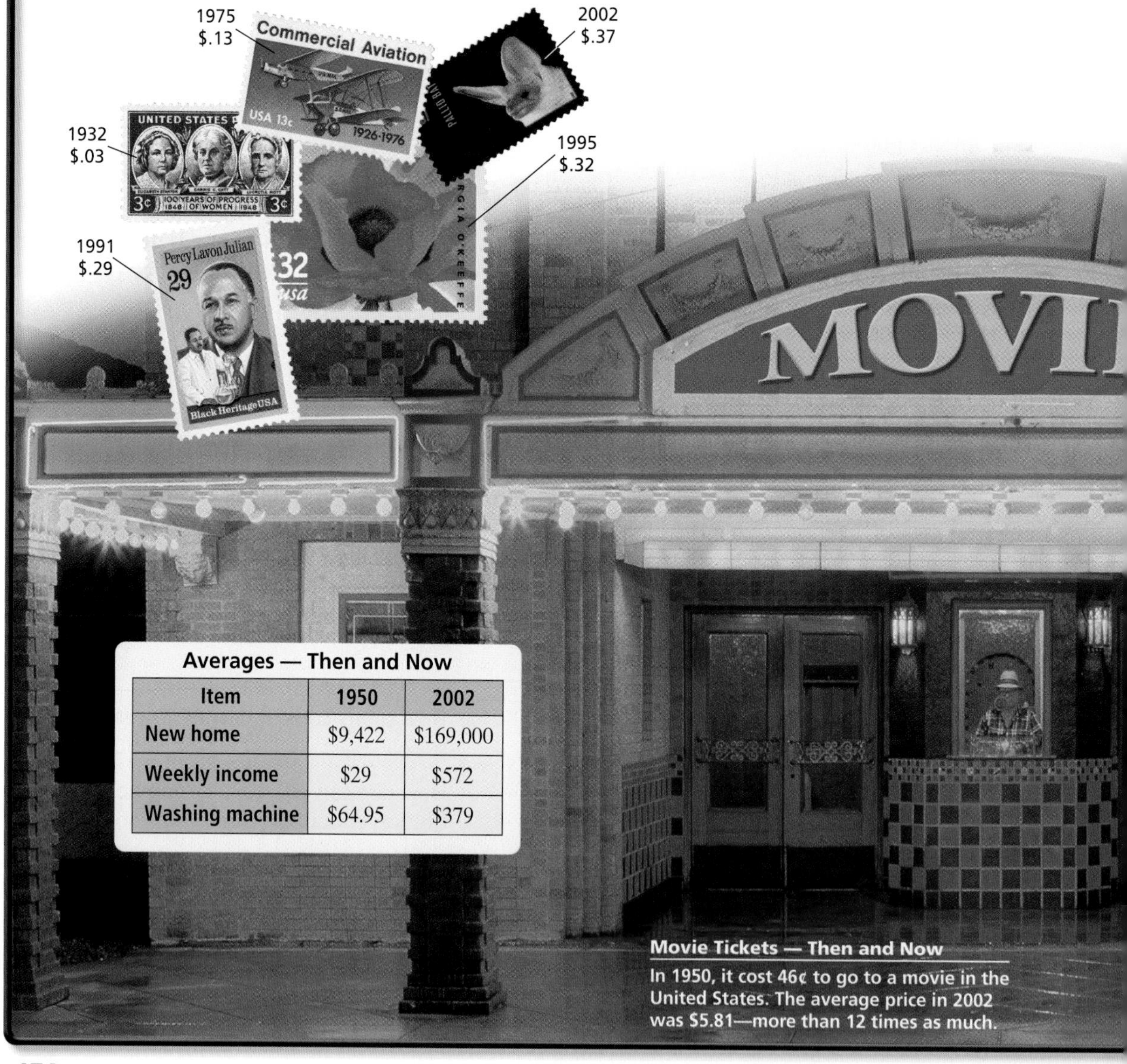
1975
$.13
Commercial Aviation
2002
$.37
1932
$.03
1995
$.32
1991
$.29
Percy Lavon Julian
Black Heritage USA
MOVI

Averages — Then and Now

Item	1950	2002
New home	$9,422	$169,000
Weekly income	$29	$572
Washing machine	$64.95	$379

Movie Tickets — Then and Now

In 1950, it cost 46¢ to go to a movie in the United States. The average price in 2002 was $5.81—more than 12 times as much.

Full Service

In the 1950s, gas-station attendants pumped your gas, checked your oil, and washed your windshield. Mechanics were ready to help if something was wrong with your car.

Activity

Shopping List
2 loaves bread
1 lb coffee
2 gal milk
1 dozen muffins
2 bars soap
1 lb steak
3 cans tuna

Suppose you have a $10 bill. 1–4. See margin.

1. How many pounds of steak could you buy in 1950? In 2002?

2. **a.** How many gallons of gas could you buy in 1950?
   b. How much would that same gas have cost you in 2002?

3. Compare the prices of milk.
   a. What fraction of the 2002 price is the 1950 price?
   b. How many times the 1950 price is the 2002 price?

4. Suppose you earn the average weekly income and you buy the items on the shopping list.
   a. What is your total cost in 1950? In 2002?
   b. What part of your weekly income is this in 1950? In 2002?
   c. <u>Writing in Math</u> In which year is the average worker better off, 1950 or 2002? Explain.

Prices of Common Items

Item	Cost in 1950	Cost in 2002
Bread (1 loaf)	$.18	$1.49
Coffee (1 lb)	$.93	$3.29
Cookies (12-oz package)	$.39	$2.59
Gas (1 gal)	$.20	$1.35
Milk (1 gal)	$.92	$3.05
Muffins (6)	$.24	$2.89
Soap (2 bars)	$.29	$1.79
Steak (1 lb)	$.77	$3.89
Tuna (1 large can)	$.25	$1.39

Take It to the NET For more information about the 1950s, go to **www.PHSchool.com**.
Web Code: ade-0353

175

Put It All Together

Students must be able to calculate with decimals and interpret multiple tables in problem solving to compare the value of money over time.

Teaching Tip

Before students begin the activity, discuss the illustrations and their captions. Students should read through the activity before beginning to work. Have students work individually or in pairs to complete the activity.

Diversity

Have students interview an adult member of their family about the price of a gallon of gas, a first-class stamp, a gallon of milk, and a candy bar when the adult was the student's age. Answers may vary. Sample: (1975) gallon of gas: $.57; stamp: $.10; gallon of milk: $1.57; candy bar: $.25

Visual Learners

Have students visit a local supermarket, find the current cost of each item in the table, and create a third column titled "Today" with their data.

1. about 13 lb; about 2.6 lb

2a. 50 gal
   b. $67.50

3a. about $\frac{1}{3}$
   b. about 3 times

4a. $5.42; $28
   b. about 0.20; about 0.05

c. Answers may vary. Sample: The cost of groceries is a smaller part of the 2002 worker's income. In this case, the 2002 worker is better off.

Factors, Fractions, and Exponents

Chapter at a Glance

4-1

Divisibility and Factors

pp. 178–181

Objectives

▼ Using Divisibility Tests

▼ Finding Factors

New Vocabulary
divisible, factor

NCTM Standards
1, 2, 6, 8, 9

Local Standards

4-2

Exponents

pp. 182–185

Objectives

▼ Using Exponents

▼ Using the Order of Operations With Exponents

New Vocabulary
exponents, power, base

NCTM Standards
1, 2, 6, 8, 10

Local Standards

4-3

Prime Factorization and Greatest Common Factor

pp. 186–190

Objectives

▼ Finding Prime Factorizations

▼ Finding the Greatest Common Factor

New Vocabulary
prime number, composite number, prime factorization, greatest common factor (GCF)

NCTM Standards
1, 2, 6, 8, 9

Local Standards

4-4

Simplifying Fractions

pp. 192–195

Objectives

▼ Finding Equivalent Fractions

▼ Writing Fractions in Simplest Form

New Vocabulary
equivalent fractions, simplest form

NCTM Standards
1, 2, 6, 8, 9, 10

Local Standards

✔ **Checkpoint Quiz 1**

4-5 Problem Solving

Account for All Possibilities

pp. 197–200

Objective

▼ Finding All Possibilities

NCTM Standards
1, 2, 5, 6, 7, 8, 9, 10

Local Standards

4-6

Rational Numbers

pp. 201–204

Objectives

▼ Identifying and Graphing Rational Numbers

▼ Evaluating Fractions Containing Variables

New Vocabulary
rational number

NCTM Standards
1, 2, 6, 8, 9, 10

Local Standards

4-7

Exponents and Multiplication

pp. 205–208

Objectives

▼ Multiplying Powers With the Same Base

▼ Finding a Power of a Power

NCTM Standards
1, 2, 6, 8, 9, 10

Local Standards

4-8

Exponents and Division

pp. 210–214

Objectives

▼ Dividing Expressions Containing Exponents

▼ Simplifying Expressions With Integer Exponents

NCTM Standards
1, 2, 6, 8, 9, 10

Local Standards

✔ **Checkpoint Quiz 2**

4-9

Scientific Notation

pp. 215–220

Objectives

▼ Writing and Evaluating Scientific Notation

▼ Calculating With Scientific Notation

New Vocabulary
scientific notation, standard notation

NCTM Standards
1, 2, 4, 6, 8, 9, 10

Local Standards

Correlation to Standardized Tests

Lesson	NAEP	Terra Nova		ITBS	SAT10	Local Test
		CAT/6	CTBS			
4-1	N5b, N5d	■	■		■	
4-2		■	■	■		
4-3	N5b, N5c	■	■	■	■	
4-4	N3a, N3b					
4-5	A3b					
4-6	N1b, A3b				■	
4-7	A3b	■	■			
4-8	A3b	■				
4-9	N1f				■	

NAEP National Assessment of Educational Progress
  N = Number Sense, Properties, and Operations
  M = Measurement
  G = Geometry and Spatial Sense
  D = Data Analysis, Statistics and Probability
  A = Algebra and Functions
CAT/6 California Achievement Test, 6th Ed.
CTBS Comprehensive Test of Basic Skills
ITBS Iowa Test of Basic Skills, Form M
SAT10 Stanford Achievement Test, 10th Ed.

NCTM STANDARDS 2000

1 Number and Operations
2 Algebra
3 Geometry
4 Measurement
5 Data Analysis and Probability
6 Problem Solving
7 Reasoning and Proof
8 Communication
9 Connections
10 Representation

Pacing Options

This chart suggests pacing for only the core lessons and their parts. It is provided as a possible guide. It will help you determine how much time you have in your schedule to cover other components, such as the features, chapter projects, Chapter Review, and Chapter Test.

Day	Traditional 45-minute class periods	Two-Year 45-minute class periods	Block 90-minute class periods
1	4-1 ▽ ▽	4-1 ▽	4-1 ▽ ▽ / 4-2 ▽ ▽
2	4-2 ▽ ▽	4-1 ▽	4-3 ▽ ▽ / 4-4 ▽ ▽
3	4-3 ▽ ▽	4-2 ▽	4-5 ▽ / 4-6 ▽ ▽
4	4-4 ▽ ▽	4-2 ▽	4-7 ▽ ▽ / 4-8 ▽
5	4-5 ▽	4-3 ▽	4-8 ▽ / 4-9 ▽ ▽
6	4-6 ▽ ▽	4-3 ▽	
7	4-7 ▽ ▽	4-3 ▽	
8	4-8 ▽ ▽	4-4 ▽	
9	4-9 ▽	4-4 ▽	
10	4-9 ▽	4-4 ▽	
11		4-5 ▽	
12		4-5 ▽	
13		4-6 ▽	
14		4-6 ▽	
15		4-7 ▽	
16		4-7 ▽	
17		4-7 ▽	
18		4-8 ▽	
19		4-8 ▽	
20		4-8 ▽	
21		4-9 ▽	
22		4-9 ▽	
23		4-9 ▽	

Math Background

Skills Trace

> ### BEFORE Chapter 4
> Students encountered factors, divisibility, positive exponents, prime factorization, and greatest common factor in previous courses.
>
> ### DURING Chapter 4
> This chapter reviews the number theory topics mentioned in the BEFORE comments, and simplest form fractions. Fractions are then identified with the set of rational numbers. Exponents are extended to negative exponents and used in scientific notation.
>
> ### AFTER Chapter 4
> The number theory topics and simplest form fractions are used primarily in Chapters 5 and 6. Rational numbers and exponents are used throughout the remainder of this book, and they are used from the beginning of the Algebra 1 course.

4-1 Divisibility and Factors

There are several concepts that have similar names or alternate names that lead to confusion for many students. Consider $12 \div 3$. We can say these things:

12 is divisible by 3 because 3 divides 12 without a remainder.
3 is a divisor of 12.
3 is a factor of 12.
12 is a multiple of 3.

In general the positive integer divisors of a number are called the *factors* of that number. The factors of 12 are 12, 6, 4, 3, 2, and 1.

The *fundamental theorem of arithmetic* states that every integer greater than one can be expressed as a product of prime factors in one and only one way (except for the order in which the factors may be listed). This means that writing 12 as $2 \cdot 2 \cdot 3$ is a unique way of expressing 12.

4-2 Exponents

For the expression 3^4, remember that 3 is called the *base* and 4 is the *exponent*. Students may find it useful to think of an exponent as saying "write the base as a factor as many times as the exponent indicates." You can interpret 3^4 as saying "write the number 3 four times and multiply" so that $3^4 = 3 \cdot 3 \cdot 3 \cdot 3$, or 81.

An exponent applies only to the base to which it is attached, so $-3^4 = -(3^4)$, or -81, while $(-3)^4 = (-3) \cdot (-3) \cdot (-3) \cdot (-3)$, or 81.

4-3 Prime Factorization and Greatest Common Factor

Integers that are not prime numbers, that is, integers that have a factor other than 1 and the number itself, are called *composite* numbers. The integer 1 is neither prime nor composite.

The *greatest common factor* is the largest factor common to a given set of integers. For example, the numbers 48, 60, and 96 have the factors 1, 2, 3, 4, 6, and 12 in common, but 12 is the greatest common factor of 48, 60, and 96.

4-4 Simplifying Fractions

Equivalent fractions are fractions that name the same amount. Since 4 and 9 have no common factors, $\frac{4}{9}$ cannot be expressed in simpler form.

A fraction is in *simplest form* when the numerator and denominator have no factors in common other than 1. When the numerator and denominator have no common factor other than 1, we say they are *relatively prime.*

You can write a fraction such as $\frac{x}{y}$ in simplest form by finding the greatest common factor for x and y. For example, $\frac{6}{10} = \frac{2 \cdot 3}{2 \cdot 5}$ can be written as $\frac{2}{2} \cdot \frac{3}{5}$ because $\frac{ac}{bd} = \frac{a}{b} \cdot \frac{c}{d}$ ($b, d \neq 0$), or $1 \cdot \frac{3}{5}$ because $\frac{a}{a} = 1 (a \neq 0)$, and finally as $\frac{3}{5}$ because $1a = a$.

A shorter form of this same reasoning is expressed in the *cancellation law for fractions,* which simply says $\frac{ac}{bc} = \frac{a}{b}$ ($b, c \neq 0$).

 **4-6** **Rational Numbers**

A *rational number* is a number that can be written as the quotient of two integers, where the second integer does not equal zero. Notice that the word *rational* contains the word *ratio*.

Any decimal that ends, such as 3.567 or 0.00011, can be written as a ratio of integers: $\frac{3,567}{1,000}$ or $\frac{11}{100,000}$.

Any decimal that repeats a set of digits, such as $0.333\overline{3}$ (where the bar over the 3 indicates that the 3 repeats forever) or $2.456456\overline{456}$, can be written as a ratio of integers.

For example, set

$$x = 2.456456\overline{456}$$

$$1,000x = 2,456.456\overline{456}$$

$$\underline{-\ x = \qquad 2.456456} \text{ gives}$$

$$999x = 2,454 \qquad\qquad \text{so}$$

$$x = \frac{2,454}{999}, \text{ which is clearly a rational number.}$$

You can use a similar procedure for any decimal that repeats a set of digits by multiplying by a power of 10 that has the same number of zeros as there are digits in the repeating set.

However, an unending decimal that has a pattern without a repeating set of digits, such as 1.02002000200002000002 . . . , is not rational, even though you can always predict the next digit.

Similarly, a decimal such as π that goes on forever without repeating or forming a pattern is also irrational. Some students may have been incorrectly taught that π is equal to $\frac{22}{7}$, and so they may mistakenly think that π is rational. The fraction $\frac{22}{7}$ is only an approximation of the value of π. The number π is an irrational number.

 4-7 **Exponents and Multiplication**
4-8 **and Division**

Students can easily remember when to add exponents and when to multiply them if they take a moment to write an example in expanded form.

$a^2 \cdot a^3$ means $(a \cdot a) \cdot (a \cdot a \cdot a)$, which is clearly a^5.

However, $(a^2)^3$ means $a^2 \cdot a^2 \cdot a^2$ or

$a \cdot a \cdot a \cdot a \cdot a \cdot a$, which is a^6.

Students can also remember the rules for division with exponents if they write the problem in expanded form.

$$\frac{a^3}{a^2} \cdot \frac{a \cdot a \cdot a}{a \cdot a} = a$$

Therefore, $\frac{a^3}{a^2} = a^{3-2}$, or a^1.

4-9 **Scientific Notation**

A number is written in scientific notation when it is written as

a number greater than or equal to 1 and less than 10

multiplied by

a power of 10.

When a number is written in scientific notation, a zero or positive exponent on 10 indicates that the number is greater than 1. A negative exponent on 10 indicates that the number is less than 1.

For example:
The weight of Earth in tons is 6.6×10^{21}.
The diameter of a hydrogen atom in cm is 1.016×10^{-8}.

In standard notation, these numbers are 6,600,000,000,000,000,000,000 and 0.00000001016.

The exponent on 10 tells you to make the first part of the number larger or smaller by that many decimal places in order to write the standard notation.

Additional Professional Development Opportunities

Chapter 4 Math Background notes:
pp. 179, 183, 187, 193, 198, 202, 206, 211, 216

Professional Development, Content Facilitator Guide: Pre-Algebra, Chapter 4

Additional resources available from SkyLight Professional Development: On-site courses, workshops, summer institutes. Online courses and chat rooms. Videocassettes and books. Visit www.skylightedu.com.

Ongoing Assessment and Intervention

The *Prentice Hall Pre-Algebra* program provides many options for assessment in the Student Edition, Teacher's Edition, and teaching resources. From these options you may choose instructional materials that are appropriate for your students and support your district's curriculum requirements.

Daily Assessment

Instant Check System™ in Chapter 4

Allows students to check their own learning before, during, and after each lesson.

Diagnosing Readiness before the chapter (p. 176)

Check Skills You'll Need exercises in each lesson (pp. 178, 182, 186, 192, 197, 201, 205, 210, 215)

Check Understanding questions with each Example (pp. 178, 179, 182, 183, 186, 187, 188, 192, 193, 198, 201, 202, 205, 206, 210, 211, 212, 216, 217, 218)

Checkpoint Quiz (pp. 195, 214)

Formal Assessment

In Chapter 4 and Additional Resources

Assesses student progress throughout the *Pre-Algebra* text and with blackline masters and CD-ROM.

Student Edition

• Chapter 4 Review, with Vocabulary Skills and Concepts Review, pp. 223–225

• Chapter 4 Test, p. 226

Assessment Resources *Spanish versions available.*

• Checkpoint Quizzes 1 & 2

• Chapter Test, Forms A & B

• Chapter Alternative Assessment

Computer Test Generator CD-ROM

• Instant Chapter Tests™ — pre-made tests with items that vary every time you print.

• Online Testing allows you to give tests online and receive progress reports.

• Diagnose readiness with questions on prerequisite skills.

• Prepare students by making tests based on standardized test objectives.

Algebra Readiness Tests

• Includes Basic Skills Tests and Concept-Readiness Tests.

• Assess understanding of skills and concepts needed for success in algebra.

Standardized Test Preparation

Test Prep in Chapter 4

Teaches students strategies and gives them practice with all the test item formats they will encounter on high-stakes tests.

Test Prep exercises in each lesson (pp. 181, 185, 190, 195, 200, 204, 208, 214, 220)

Test-Taking Strategies (p. 222: Reading-Comprehension Questions)

Test Prep (p. 227: Cumulative Review)

Provides a three-step approach to preparing students for high-stakes, national, and state exams.

① Diagnose & Prescribe

② Review & Reteach

Content Diagnostic Tests

• Diagnose strengths and weaknesses with ongoing benchmark tests.

• Prescribe individualized reteaching opportunities.

Skills and Concepts Review

• Provides reteaching worksheets with instruction and practice for each skill.

• Includes course prerequisite skills.

③ Practice & Assess

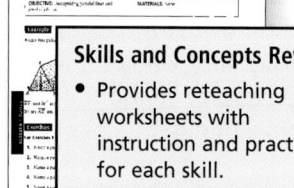

Standardized Test Preparation

• Features practice for national standardized exams.

• Includes practice tests for NAEP, SAT10, ITBS, and Terra Nova.

Test-Taking Strategies With Transparencies

• Support the Test-Taking Strategies pages in the Student Edition.

• Provide a transparency and a worksheet for each strategy.

Reaching All Students

The textbook, the iText, and other technology components provide numerous opportunities to reach students of various ability levels and learning styles. Each Teacher's Edition lesson suggests how you can help all your students be successful and understand the mathematics in Chapter 4.

Below Level

Student Edition
- Diagnosing Readiness*: p. 176
- Check Skills You'll Need*: pp. 178, 182, 186, 192, 197, 201, 205, 210, 215

Reteaching
Chapter 4 Grab & Go™ File: pp. 10–18

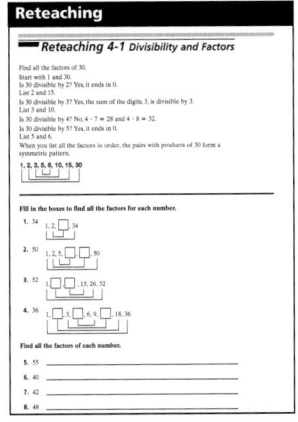

* Can be used with all ability levels to ensure mastery of prerequisite skills.

Advanced Learners

Student Edition
- Challenge exercises: pp. 181, 185, 190, 194, 195, 200, 204, 207, 213, 220
- Extension: p. 191

Enrichment
Chapter 4 Grab & Go™ File: pp. 19–27

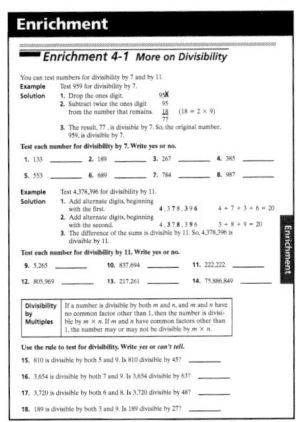

Problem Solving

Student Edition
- Strategies: pp. 197–200
- Real-World Problem Solving: pp. 179, 183, 193, 197, 202, 216, 218

Guided Problem Solving Masters
Chapter 4: pp. 29–37

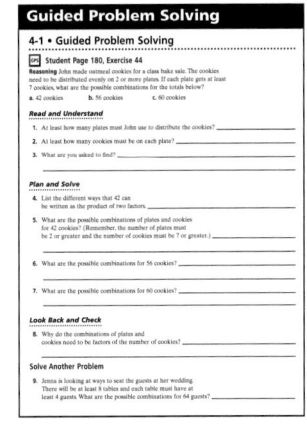

Reading and Math Literacy

Student Edition
- Vocabulary: pp. 177, 223, plus in most lessons
- Reading Math: pp. 183, 192, 194, 196, 206, 223
- Writing in Math: pp. 180, 185, 190, 194, 203, 207, 213, 219, 226
- Illustrated Glossary: pp. 782–826

Reading and Math Literacy Masters
Chapter 4: pp. 13–16

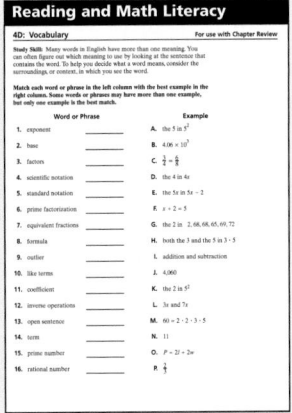

English Learners

Student Edition
- English/Spanish Illustrated Glossary: pp. 782–826

Workbook and Masters
Spanish Practice Workbook: pp. 29–37
Spanish Reading and Math Literacy Masters: pp. 13–16

Learning Styles

Student Edition
- Investigation: pp. 186, 215
- Technology: pp. 209, 221
- DK Activities: p. 228
- Chapter Project: p. 739

Activity Masters
Hands-On Activities: 4, 5, 6
Technology Activities: 7

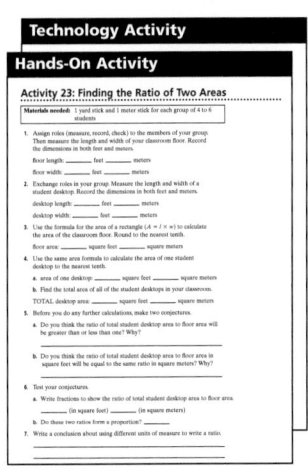

Program Resources

	Resources in Grab & Go™ Files				Resources for Reaching All Students				Spanish Resources			Presentation Assistant Plus! Transparencies				Prentice Hall Presentation Pro CD-ROM
	Practice	Reteach	Enrich	Checkpt Quiz	Reading & Math Literacy	Technology Activities	Hands-On Activities	Guided Problem Solving	Practice	Reading & Math Literacy	Checkpt Quiz	Skills Check	Additional Examples	Answers to Exercises	Lesson Quiz	
4-1	■	■	■		■		■	■	■	■		■	■	■	■	■
4-2	■	■	■					■	■			■	■	■	■	■
4-3	■	■	■				■	■	■			■	■	■	■	■
4-4	■	■	■	■	■			■	■	■	■	■	■	■	■	■
4-5	■	■	■					■	■			■	■	■	■	■
4-6	■	■	■					■	■			■	■	■	■	■
4-7	■	■	■			■		■	■			■	■	■	■	■
4-8	■	■	■		■		■	■	■			■	■	■	■	■
4-9	■	■	■					■	■			■	■	■	■	■
For the Chapter	Chapter Projects, Chapter Tests, Alternative Assessment, Cumulative Review, Cumulative Assessment				On Web site only: Home Activities, Algebra Readiness Puzzles, Interdisciplinary Activities				Spanish Chapter Tests, Alternative Assessment, Cumulative Review, Cumulative Assessment			Classroom Aid Transparencies				

Also available for use with the chapter:
- Practice Workbook
- Solution Key
- MathNotes folder
- For additional online and technology resources, see below.
- For teacher support and access to student Web site materials, use Web Code adk-5500.

PRENTICE HALL ASSESSMENT SYSTEM

Program assessment and test preparation, all in one place.
See page 176E.

Skills Intervention Kit

A *complete* system for the student who is struggling with course-level work

How to Use With Chapter 4

4-1, 4-3	Whole Numbers
4-4	Fractions
4-5	Pre-Algebra Basics
4-6, 4-9	Number Theory and Fraction Concepts

Online Intervention

Integrated within the iText, this online intervention system includes diagnostic tests and prescribed remediation, plus reports to track student mastery.

Technology

iTEXT Online and on CD-ROM

Complete Interactive Student Text online and on CD-ROM—with instant-feedback assessment, tutorial help, dynamic activities, instructional and real-world videos, audio, and additional practice.

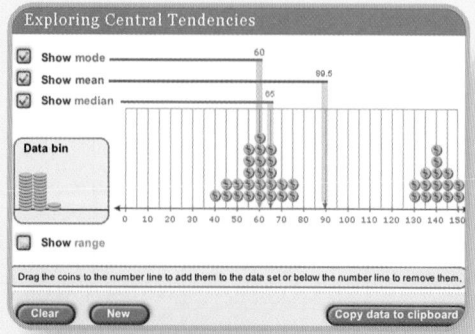

www.PHSchool.com For Students

Use Web Codes for easy access to online activities, chapter projects, self-grading lesson quizzes, chapter tests, vocabulary quizzes, updated data sources, graphing calculator procedures, and more.

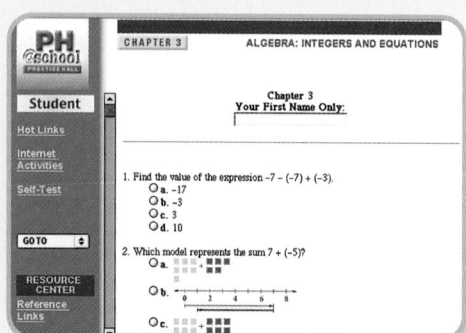

PH SuccessNet For Teachers

Online lesson planning with built-in state correlations, all the teaching resources, complete reference library, your own calendar and Teacher Web page, professional development, and more.

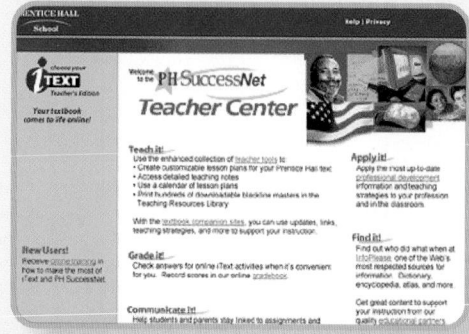

Presentation Assistant Plus!

The Prentice Hall *Presentation Assistant Plus!* provides you with the material you need to teach a lesson from beginning to end. Two easy-to-use formats—Transparencies and CD-ROM—allow you to present a lesson the way you are most comfortable.

 ## Transparencies

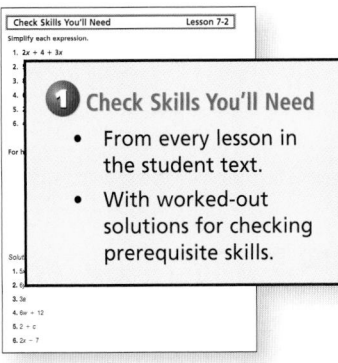

1 Check Skills You'll Need
- From every lesson in the student text.
- With worked-out solutions for checking prerequisite skills.

2 Additional Examples
- Every example from the Teacher's Edition.
- Fully worked-out, step-by-step solutions for easy demonstration.

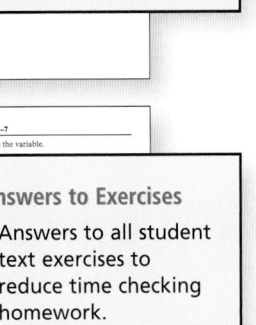

3 Answers to Exercises
- Answers to all student text exercises to reduce time checking homework.

4 Lesson Quiz
- Every quiz from the Teacher's Edition.
- With answers to allow students to check their own work.

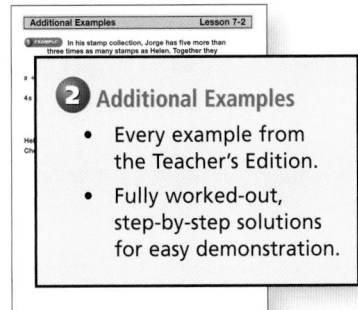 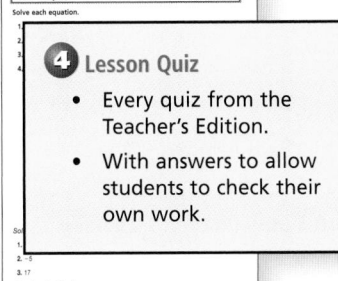

 **PowerPoint** Throughout the Teacher's Edition, this symbol indicates material that is available in the Presentation Assistant Plus!

PowerPoint Prentice Hall Presentation Pro CD-ROM

- Includes all Transparencies as PowerPoint® presentations.
- Conveniently organized by lesson so you can easily ❶ Introduce, ❷ Teach, ❸ Check Homework, and ❹ Assess each lesson.
- Animated examples allow step-by-step instruction at your own pace.
- Easy to edit so you can create custom presentations.

Teaching Chapter 4 Using Presentation Assistant Plus!

	❶ Introduce	❷ Teach	❸ Check Homework	❹ Assess
	Check Skills You'll Need	Additional Examples	Student Edition Answers	Lesson Quiz
4-1	p. 29	p. 43	✔	p. 29
4-2	p. 30	p. 44	✔	p. 30
4-3	p. 31	pp. 45–46	✔	p. 31
4-4	p. 32	pp. 46–47	✔	p. 32
4-5	p. 33	p. 48	✔	p. 33
4-6	p. 34	p. 49	✔	p. 34
4-7	p. 35	p. 50	✔	p. 35
4-8	p. 36	pp. 51–52	✔	p. 36
4-9	p. 37	pp. 53–55	✔	p. 37

 ### Prentice Hall Presentation Pro

CD-ROM with dynamic Powerpoint® presentations for every lesson. Helps you introduce and develop concepts, check homework, and assess progress. Part of Presentation Assistant Plus! *(See above.)*

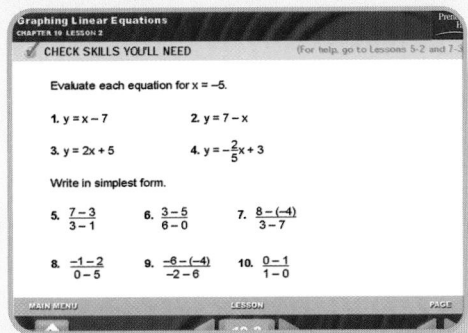

 ### Computer Test Generator

CD-ROM to create practice sheets and tests for course objectives and standardized tests. Includes Instant Chapter Tests™, online testing, and student reports. Part of the PH Assessment System. *(See page 176E.)*

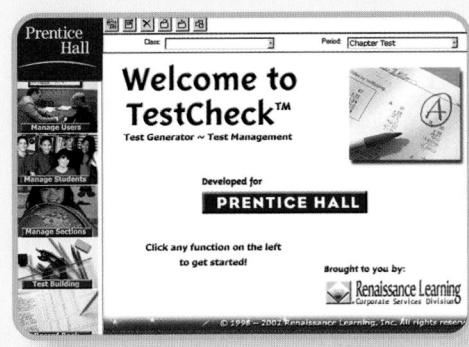

 ### Resource Pro® with Planning Express®

CD-ROM with a lesson planning tool that allows you to import state and local objectives. Includes electronic versions of all the teaching resources.

176H

Chapter 4

Factors, Fractions, and Exponents

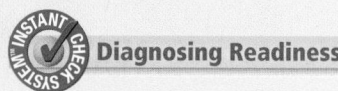
Diagnosing Readiness

Students will find answers to these exercises in the back of their textbooks.

Prescribing Intervention
For intervention, direct students to:

Multiplying Three or More Factors
Lesson 1–9: Example 1;
Exercises 17–19.
Extra Practice, p. 747

Recalling Multiplication Facts
Previous course.

Dividing Whole Numbers
Skills Handbook: p. 760;
Exercises 1–50.

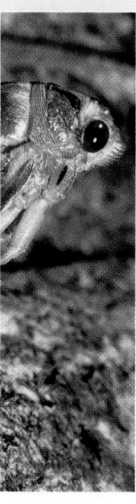

Where You've Been

- In Chapter 1, you learned how to add, subtract, multiply, and divide integers.

- In Chapter 2, you solved equations by adding, subtracting, multiplying, and dividing.

- In Chapter 3, you estimated solutions and solved equations with decimals.

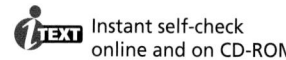
Instant self-check
online and on CD-ROM

Diagnosing Readiness   (For help, go to the lesson in green.)

Multiplying Three or More Factors (Lesson 1-9)

Find each product.

1. $12 \cdot 12 \cdot 12$ 1,728   **2.** $(-4)(-4)(-4)$ –64   **3.** $9 \cdot 9 \cdot 9 \cdot 9$ 6,561

4. $5 \cdot 5 \cdot 5 \cdot 5 \cdot 5 \cdot 5$ 15,625   **5.** $8 \cdot 8 \cdot 8$ 512   **6.** $(-2)(-2)(-2)(-2)(-2)(-2)$ 64

Recalling Multiplication Facts (Previous Course)

Write two numbers that, when multiplied, result in each product.
Answers may vary. Samples are given.

7. 12 2, 6   **8.** 45 9, 5   **9.** 18 3, 6   **10.** 63 9, 7   **11.** 24 6, 4

12. 50 2, 25   **13.** 32 16, 2   **14.** 81 9, 9   **15.** 54 6, 9   **16.** 60 6, 10

17. 28 4, 7   **18.** 56 7, 8   **19.** 44 4, 11   **20.** 36 9, 4   **21.** 72 8, 9

Dividing Whole Numbers (Skills Handbook, p. 760)

Find each quotient.

22. $720 \div 8$ 90   **23.** $7,200 \div 8$ 900   **24.** $6\overline{)132}$ 22

25. $3\overline{)147}$ 49   **26.** $\frac{189}{9}$ 21   **27.** $\frac{450}{10}$ 45

28. $424 \div 2$ 212   **29.** $700 \div 5$ 140   **30.** $92 \div 4$ 23

31. $5\overline{)135}$ 27   **32.** $\frac{273}{3}$ 91   **33.** $10\overline{)1,300}$ 130

Factors, Fractions, and Exponents

Where You're Going

In this chapter, you will learn how to

● Simplify expressions with exponents.

● Simplify fractions.

● Write and calculate in scientific notation.

● Solve problems by accounting for all possibilities.

Real-World Snapshots Applying what you learn, on pages 228–229 you will solve problems about cicada emergence cycles.

Key Vocabulary

- base (p. 182)
- composite number (p. 186)
- divisible (p. 178)
- equivalent fractions (p. 192)
- exponents (p. 182)
- factor (p. 179)
- greatest common factor (GCF) (p. 187)
- power (p. 182)
- prime factorization (p. 187)
- prime number (p. 186)
- rational number (p. 201)
- scientific notation (p. 215)
- simplest form (p. 192)
- standard notation (p. 216)

177

Chapter 4 Overview

In this chapter, students will use divisibility rules to find factors. They will apply these rules to find prime factorizations and the greatest common factor, and to simplify fractions. Students will also study exponents. They will learn how to add, subtract, multiply, and divide expressions containing powers with the same base. They will also recognize rational numbers, and simplify rational numbers that contain powers.

Activating Prior Knowledge

In Chapter 3, students worked with decimals, including solving equations with decimals. Ask: *What is another way to represent a number given as a decimal?* **as a fraction**

Reading Math
- Reading for Problem Solving, p. 196
- **Vocabulary** A complete list of terms, plus vocabulary exercises, appears in the Chapter Review on p. 223.
- **Illustrated Glossary** Examples for each vocabulary term, plus definitions in both English and Spanish, appear starting on p. 782.

Test-Taking Strategies
Reading-Comprehension Questions, p. 222

Real-World Problem Solving
- **Strategy:** Account for All Possibilities, pp. 197–200
- **DK Real-World Snapshots:** Applying Factors and Multiples, pp. 228–229
- **Chapter Project:** Time After Time, p. 739

www.PHSchool.com
Internet support includes:
- Self-grading Vocabulary and Chapter 4 Tests
- Activity Masters
- Chapter Project support
- Chapter Planner
- Chapter 4 Resources

Plus

4-1

Divisibility and Factors

What You'll Learn

OBJECTIVE 1 To use divisibility tests

OBJECTIVE 2 To find factors

. . . And Why

To solve real-world problems involving arrangements

 Check Skills You'll Need

Find each quotient.
See below.
1. 480 ÷ 3 **2.** 365 ÷ 5

3. 459 ÷ 9 **4.** 288 ÷ 6

5. $\frac{354}{2}$ **6.** $\frac{354}{3}$

❓ For help, go to Skills Handbook, p. 760.

New Vocabulary

• divisible
• factor

1. 160
2. 73
3. 51
4. 48
5. 177
6. 118

1a. Yes; 160 ends in 0.
1b. No; 56 does not end in 0.
1c. No; 53 does not end in 0, 2, 4, 6, or 8.
1d. Yes; 1,118 ends in 8.

 Interactive lesson includes instant self-check, tutorials, and activities.

One integer is **divisible** by another if the remainder is 0 when you divide. Because $18 \div 3 = 6$, 18 is divisible by 3. You can test for divisibility using mental math.

Key Concepts | Divisibility Rules for 2, 5, and 10

An integer is divisible by
• 2 if it ends in 0, 2, 4, 6, or 8.
• 5 if it ends in 0 or 5.
• 10 if it ends in 0.

Even numbers end in 0, 2, 4, 6, or 8 and are divisible by 2.
Odd numbers end in 1, 3, 5, 7, or 9 and are not divisible by 2.

1 EXAMPLE Divisibility by 2, 5, and 10

Is the first number divisible by the second? Explain.

a. 567 by 2   No; 567 does not end in 0, 2, 4, 6, or 8.

b. 1,015 by 5   Yes; 1,015 ends in 5.

c. 111,120 by 10   Yes; 111,120 ends in 0.

✓ **Check Understanding** Example 1

1. Is the first number divisible by the second? Explain. a–d. See left.

   a. 160 by 5   **b.** 56 by 10   **c.** 53 by 2   **d.** 1,118 by 2

To see a pattern for divisibility by 3 and 9, compare the answers to the questions asked in this table.

Number	Sum of digits	Is the sum divisible by		Is the number divisible by	
		3?	9?	3?	9?
282	2 + 8 + 2 = 12	Yes	No	Yes	No
468	4 + 6 + 8 = 18	Yes	Yes	Yes	Yes
215	2 + 1 + 5 = 8	No	No	No	No
1,017	1 + 0 + 1 + 7 = 9	Yes	Yes	Yes	Yes

 Ongoing Assessment and Intervention

Before the Lesson
Diagnose prerequisite skills using:
• Check Skills You'll Need

During the Lesson
Monitor progress using:
• Check Understanding
• Additional Examples
• Test Prep

After the Lesson
Assess knowledge using:
• Lesson Quiz
• Computer Test Generator CD-ROM

The pattern in the table suggests the following rules for divisibility by 3 and 9.

2 EXAMPLE   Divisibility by 3 and 9

Is the first number divisible by the second? Explain.

a. 567 by 3   Yes; $5 + 6 + 7 = 18$. 18 is divisible by 3.

b. 1,015 by 9   No; $1 + 0 + 1 + 5 = 7$. 7 is not divisible by 9.

✓ **Check Understanding**   Example 2

2. Is the first number divisible by the second? Explain. **See right.**

   a. 64 by 9   **b.** 472 by 3   **c.** 174 by 3   **d.** 43,542 by 9

2a. No; the sum of the digits, 10, is not divisible by 9.
2b. No; the sum of the digits, 13, is not divisible by 3.
2c. Yes; the sum of the digits, 12, is divisible by 3.
2d. Yes; the sum of the digits, 18, is divisible by 9.

OBJECTIVE

2 Finding Factors

You can form the three rectangles at the right with 12 squares. Each rectangle has an area of 12 square units. Their dimensions, 1, 2, 3, 4, 6, and 12, are the *factors* of 12. One integer is a **factor** of another nonzero integer if it divides that integer with remainder zero.

3 x 4

2 x 6

1 x 12

3 EXAMPLE   Real-World 🌐 **Problem Solving**

Concerts There are 20 students singing at a school concert. Each row of singers must have the same number of students. If there are at least 5 students in each row, what are all the possible arrangements?

   $1 \cdot 20$, $2 \cdot 10$, $4 \cdot 5$ **Find the factors of 20.**

There can be 1 row of 20 students, 2 rows of 10 students, or 4 rows of 5 students.

✓ **Check Understanding**   Example 3

3. List the positive factors of each integer. **See right.**

   a. 10   **b.** 21   **c.** 24   **d.** 31

   e. What are the possible arrangements for Example 3 if there are 36 students singing at the concert?

3a. 1, 2, 5, 10
3b. 1, 3, 7, 21
3c. 1, 2, 3, 4, 6, 8, 12, 24
3d. 1, 31
3e. 1 row of 36 students, 2 rows of 18 students, 3 rows of 12 students, 4 rows of 9 students, or 6 rows of 6 students

Reaching All Students

Below Level Ask students to recall forming groups of 3 or 4 students and having students left over. Relate this to dividing by 3 or 4. Point out that when this happens, the number of students is not divisible by 3 or 4.

Advanced Learners Ask students to explain why an integer that is divisible by 6 is also divisible by 2 and 3. Both 2 and 3 are factors of 6, so they are also factors of the integer that is divisible by 6.

Tactile Learners See note on page 179.
Error Prevention See note on page 181.

---

2. Teach

Professional Development

Math Background

The product of two integers is an integer, and both integers are factors of the product. Moreover, both integers divide the product, and the product is said to be divisible by each integer.

Teaching Notes

Tactile Learners
Have students use tiles to model divisibility. Give each student 20 tiles. Instruct them to arrange the tiles into 2 equal groups, 5 equal groups, and then 10 equal groups. Finally, have them arrange the tiles into 3 equal groups. Ask: *Why are tiles left over?*
20 is not divisible by 3.

3 EXAMPLE **Alternative Method**
Once you find one factor, find its corresponding factor. This eliminates the need to test the corresponding factor.

PowerPoint
Additional Examples

Is the first number divisible by the second? Explain.
1 a. 1,028 by 2 Yes; 1,028 ends in 8.
   b. 572 by 5 No; 572 does not end in 0 or 5.
   c. 275 by 10 No; 275 does not end in 0.
2 a. 1,028 by 3 No; 11 is not divisible by 3.
   b. 522 by 9 Yes; 9 is divisible by 9.

3 Ms. Washington's class is having a class photo taken. Each row must have the same number of students. There are 35 students in the class. How can Ms. Washington arrange the students in rows if there must be at least 5 students, but no more than 10 students, in each row? There can be 5 rows of 7 students, or 7 rows of 5 students.

Closure

Call out numbers and ask students to list the positive factors of each one. Start with 15, 28, 48, and 53.

179

Assignment Guide

1 Objective 1
  A B **Core** 1–16, 22–30, 39–43
  C **Extension** 45–48

2 Objective 2
  A B **Core** 17–21, 31–38, 44
  C **Extension** 49

Test Prep 50–53
Mixed Review 54–58

Practice 4-1 *Divisibility and Factors*

List all the factors of each number.

1. 12   1, 2, 3, 4, 6, 12
2. 45   1, 3, 5, 9, 15, 45
3. 41   1, 41
4. 54   1, 2, 3, 6, 9, 18, 27, 54
5. 48   1, 2, 3, 4, 6, 8, 12, 16, 24, 48
6. 100   1, 2, 4, 5, 10, 20, 25, 50, 100
7. 117   1, 3, 9, 13, 39, 117

Test whether each number is divisible by 2, 3, 5, 9, and 10.

8. 215   5   9. 432   2, 3, 9
10. 770   2, 5, 10   11. 1,011   3
12. 975   3, 5   13. 2,070   2, 3, 5, 9, 10
14. 3,707 none   15. 5,715   3, 5, 9

Write the missing digit to make each number divisible by 9.

16. 7 [1] 1   17. 2,2 [3] 2   18. 88. [8] 12

19. There are four different digits which, when inserted in the blank space in the number 4☐5, make the number divisible by 3. Write them.
0, 3, 6, 9

20. There are two different digits which, when inserted in the blank space in the number 7,16☐, make the number divisible by 5. Write them.
0, 5

21. There are five different digits which, when inserted in the blank space in the number 99,99☐, make the number divisible by 2. Write them.
0, 2, 4, 6, 8

Enrichment 4-1 *More on Divisibility*

You can test numbers for divisibility by 7 and 11.
Example   Test 959 for divisibility by 7.
Solution 1. Drop the ones digit.   95☒
              2. Subtract twice the ones digit   95
                 from the number that remains.   18   (18 = 2 × 9)
                                                    77
              3. The result, 77, is divisible by 7. So, the original number, 959, is divisible by 7.

Test each number for divisibility by 7. Write yes or no.

1. 133   yes   2. 189   yes   3. 267   no   4. 385   yes
5. 553   yes   6. 689   no   7. 784   yes   8. 987   yes

Example   Test 4,378,396 for divisibility by 11.
Solution 1. Add alternate digits, beginning
                 with the first.   4,378,396   4 + 7 + 3 + 6 = 20
              2. Add alternate digits, beginning
                 with the second.   4,378,396   3 + 8 + 9 = 20
              3. The difference of the sums is divisible by 11. So, 4,378,396 is divisible by 11.

Test each number for divisibility by 11. Write yes or no.

9. 5,265   no   10. 837,694   yes   11. 222,222   yes
12. 805,969 no   13. 217,261   yes   14. 75,886,849   no

Divisibility by Multiples	If a number is divisible by both *m* and *n*, and *m* and *n* have no common factor other than 1, then the number is divisible by *m* × *n*. If *m* and *n* have common factors other than 1, the number may or may not be divisible by *m* × *n*.

Use the rule to test for divisibility. Write *yes* or *can't tell*.

15. 810 is divisible by both 5 and 9. Is 810 divisible by 45?   yes
16. 3,654 is divisible by both 7 and 9. Is 3,654 divisible by 63?   yes
17. 3,720 is divisible by both 6 and 8. Is 3,720 divisible by 48?   can't tell
18. 189 is divisible by both 3 and 9. Is 189 divisible by 27?   can't tell

---

EXERCISES

? For more exercises, see *Extra Practice*.

Practice and Problem Solving

A Practice by Example

Example 1
(page 178)

Example 2
(page 179)

Is the first number divisible by the second? Explain. 1–16. See margin.

1. 20 by 10   2. 37 by 2   3. 45 by 5   4. 240 by 2
5. 60 by 5   6. 123 by 2   7. 1,468 by 2   8. 2,005 by 10
9. 78 by 9   10. 69 by 3   11. 108 by 9   12. 258 by 3
13. 3,694 by 9   14. 5,751 by 9   15. 123 by 3   16. 456 by 3

Example 3
(page 179)

List the positive factors of each integer.

17. 4 1, 2, 4   18. 8 1, 2, 4, 8   19. 23 1, 23   20. 75 1, 3, 5, 15, 25, 75

 21. **Drill Team** There are 32 students in the school drill team performance. Each row of team members must have the same number of students. If there are at least 8 students in each row, what are all the possible arrangements?
1 row of 32; 2 rows of 16; 4 rows of 8

B Apply Your Skills

22. 3; 1 + 1 + 1 = 3; 3 is divisible by 3.
24. 2, 3, 9; the number ends in 8; 2 + 8 + 8 = 18; 18 is divisible by 3 and 9.
25. 2, 3, 5, 10; the number ends in 0; 3 + 0 + 0 = 3; 3 is divisible by 3.
26. 2; the number ends in 2.
27. 3, 9; 8 + 9 + 1 = 18; 18 is divisible by 3 and 9.
28. 5; the number ends in 5.
29. 2; the number ends in 4.

30c. An integer is divisible by 6 if it is an even number and the sum of its digits is divisible by 3.

31. 1 · 25, 5 · 5
32. 1 · 28, 2 · 14, 4 · 7
33. 1 · 32, 2 · 16, 4 · 8
34. 1 · 35, 5 · 7
35. 1 · 37
36. 1 · 50, 2 · 25, 5 · 10
37. 1 · 53
38. 1 · 72, 2 · 36, 3 · 24, 4 · 18, 6 · 12, 8 · 9

State whether each number is divisible by 2, 3, 5, 9, 10, or none. Explain. Some numbers may have more than one divisor.
22, 24–29. See left.

22. 111   23. 131 none   24. 288   25. 300
26. 52   27. 891   28. 4,805   29. 437,684

30. a. Which of the following numbers are divisible by both 2 and 3?
      10   66   898   4,710   975 66 and 4,710
   b. Which of the numbers above are divisible by 6? 66 and 4,710
   c. Using your results, write a divisibility rule for 6. See below left.

Show all possible ways that each integer can be written as the product of two positive factors. See below left.

31. 25   32. 28   33. 32   34. 35
35. 37   36. 50   37. 53   38. 72

Write the missing digit to make each number divisible by 9.

39. 22 ■,034 7   40. 3 ■,817 8   41. 2,03 ■,371 2   42. 1 ■,111 5

43. **Writing in Math** If a number is divisible by 9, is it also divisible by 3? Explain how you reached your conclusion. **Explanations may vary. Sample: Yes; a number divisible by 9 has 3 as a factor.**

44. **Reasoning** John made oatmeal cookies for a class bake sale. The cookies need to be distributed equally on 2 or more plates. If each plate gets at least 7 cookies, what are the possible combinations for the totals below? See back of book.
    a. 42 cookies   b. 56 cookies
    c. 60 cookies   d. 144 cookies

180   Chapter 4   Factors, Fractions, and Exponents

GPS Use the Guided Problem Solving worksheet with Exercise 44.

1. yes; ends in 0
2. no; does not end in 0, 2, 4, 6, or 8
3. yes; ends in 5
4. yes; ends in 0
5. yes; ends in 0
6. no; does not end in 0, 2, 4, 6, or 8
7. yes; ends in 8
8. no; does not end in 0
9. no; sum of digits is not divisible by 9
10. yes; sum of digits is divisible by 3
11. yes; sum of digits is divisible by 9
12. yes; sum of digits is divisible by 3

13–16. See back of book.

C Challenge

45. a. Copy and complete the table.

Number	Last two digits	Are last two digits divisible by 4?	Is the number divisible by 4?
136	36	Yes	Yes
1,268	68	Yes	Yes
314	14	No	No
1,078	▦ 78	▦ No	▦ No
696	▦ 96	▦ Yes	▦ Yes

b. Reasoning Write a divisibility rule for 4.
An integer is divisible by 4 if its last 2 digits are divisible by 4.

Open-Ended **Write three numbers greater than 20 that match each description.**

46. Divisible by 5, but not divisible by 10
Answers may vary. Sample: 25, 35, 45

47. Divisible by 3, but not divisible by 5, 9, or 10
Answers may vary. Sample: 21, 24, 33

48. Divisible by 2, 3, 5, and 10, but not divisible by 9
Answers may vary. Sample: 30, 60, 120

49. Reasoning If a is divisible by 2, what can you conclude about $a + 1$? Justify your answer.

Answers may vary. Sample: $a + 1$ is not divisible by 2.
Dividing by 2 will leave a remainder of 1.

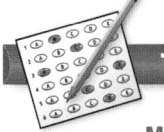

Test Prep

Multiple Choice

50. Which list shows all the positive factors of 15? **D**
A. 1, 15   **B.** 1, 3, 15   **C.** 1, 5, 15   **D.** 1, 3, 5, 15

51. Which list shows all the positive factors of 17? **F**
F. 1, 17   **G.** 1, 7, 17   **H.** 1, 2, 7, 17   **I.** 1, 2, 8, 17

52. Which number is NOT a factor of 438? **C**
A. 2   **B.** 3   **C.** 5   **D.** 6

Take It to the NET
Online lesson quiz at
www.PHSchool.com
Web Code: ada-0401

Short Response

53. a. What three positive numbers less than 100 are divisible by 2, 3, and 5?
b. Justify your answer.

[2] 30, 60, and 90; each number ends in zero and has digits with a sum divisible by 3.
[1] Correct answer; no justification is given.

Mixed Review

Lesson 3-7   **Complete each statement.**

54. 24 ▦ = 24,000 mg g   **55.** 18.2 km = 1,820,000 ▦ cm

Lesson 2-9 🌐 **56. Grocery Shopping** You have $5 to spend at the grocery store. You need $2.89 for a gallon of milk. Write and solve an inequality to show how much money m you can spend on a box of cereal.
$m + 2.89 \leq 5.00; m \leq 2.11$

Lesson 1-3   **Evaluate.**

57. $3y + 3$, for $y = 8$ **27**   **58.** $4(2 + a)$, for $a = 10$ **48**

181

Lesson Preview

 Check Skills You'll Need

Multiplying Integers
Lesson 1-9: Example 3;
Exercises 14–19.
Extra Practice, p. 744.

Lesson Resources

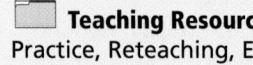 **Teaching Resources**
Practice, Reteaching, Enrichment

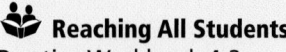 **Reaching All Students**
Practice Workbook 4-2
Spanish Practice Workbook 4-2
Guided Problem Solving 4-2

 **Presentation Assistant Plus!**
Transparencies and PowerPoint™
• Check Skills You'll Need 4-2
• Additional Examples 4-2
• Student Edition Answers 4-2
• Lesson Quiz 4-2
• Classroom Aid 17
PH Presentation Pro CD-ROM 4-2

ASSESSMENT SYSTEM

Computer Test Generator CD-ROM

 Technology
Resource Pro® CD-ROM
Computer Test Generator CD-ROM
PH Presentation Pro CD-ROM

 www.PHSchool.com
Student Site
• Teacher Web Code: adk-5500
• Algebra Readiness Puzzles 10, 11
• Graphing Calculator, Procedure 1
• Self-grading Lesson Quiz
PH SuccessNet Teacher Center
• Lesson Planner
• Resources

Plus

Exponents

What You'll Learn

OBJECTIVE 1 To use exponents

OBJECTIVE 2 To use the order of operations with exponents

. . . And Why
To solve real-world problems involving magnification

 Check Skills You'll Need

Find each product.

1. $3 \cdot 3 \cdot 3 \cdot 3$ 81

2. $-12 \cdot (-12)$ 144

3. $(-4)(-4)(-4)$ −64

4. $10 \cdot 10 \cdot 10 \cdot 10$ 10,000

 For help, go to Lesson 1-9.

New Vocabulary

• exponents
• power
• base

OBJECTIVE 1 **Using Exponents**

You can use **exponents** to show repeated multiplication.

$$\text{base} \rightarrow 2^{\overset{\text{exponent}}{\underset{\text{power}}{6}}} = 2 \cdot 2 \cdot 2 \cdot 2 \cdot 2 \cdot 2 = 64 \leftarrow \text{the value of the expression}$$

The base 2 is used as a factor 6 times.

A **power** has two parts, a **base** and an exponent. The expression 2^6 is read as "two to the sixth power."

Power	Verbal Expression	Value
12^1	*Twelve to the first power*	12
6^2	*Six to the second power, or six squared*	$6 \cdot 6 = 36$
$(0.2)^3$	*Two tenths to the third power, or two tenths cubed*	$(0.2)(0.2)(0.2) = 0.008$
-7^4	*The opposite of the quantity seven to the fourth power*	$-(7 \cdot 7 \cdot 7 \cdot 7) = -2,401$
$(-8)^5$	*Negative eight to the fifth power*	$(-8)(-8)(-8)(-8)(-8) = -32,768$

---

1 EXAMPLE   **Using an Exponent**

Write the expression using an exponent.

a. $(-5)(-5)(-5)$

$\quad (-5)^3$ Include the negative sign within parentheses.

b. $-2 \cdot a \cdot b \cdot a \cdot a$

$\quad -2 \cdot a \cdot a \cdot a \cdot b$ Rewrite the expression using the Commutative and Associative Properties.

$\quad -2a^3b$ Write $a \cdot a \cdot a$ using exponents.

 Check Understanding   Example 1

1. Write using exponents.

   a. $6 \cdot 6 \cdot 6$ 6^3 **b.** $4 \cdot y \cdot x \cdot y$ $4xy^2$ **c.** $(-3)(-3)(-3)(-3)$ $(-3)^4$

iTEXT Interactive lesson includes instant self-check, tutorials, and activities.

Ongoing Assessment and Intervention

Before the Lesson
Diagnose prerequisite skills using:
• Check Skills You'll Need

During the Lesson
Monitor progress using:
• Check Understanding
• Additional Examples
• Test Prep

After the Lesson
Assess knowledge using:
• Lesson Quiz
• Computer Test Generator CD-ROM

2 **EXAMPLE** <u>Real-World</u> <u>Problem Solving</u>

Science A microscope can magnify a specimen 10^3 times.
How many times is that?

$10^3 = 10 \cdot 10 \cdot 10$ **The exponent indicates that the base 10 is used as a factor 3 times.**

$= 1,000$ **Multiply.**

● The microscope can magnify the specimen 1,000 times.

✓ **Check Understanding**   **Example 2**

   2. a. Simplify 7^2.   49   **b.** Evaluate $-a^4$ and $(-a)^4$, for $a = 2$.
                                                  -16, 16

OBJECTIVE

2 **Using the Order of Operations With Exponents**

You can extend the order of operations to include exponents.

Key Concepts   Order of Operations
1. Work inside grouping symbols.
2. Simplify any terms with exponents.
3. Multiply and divide in order from left to right.
4. Add and subtract in order from left to right.

3 **EXAMPLE**   **Using the Order of Operations**

a. Simplify $4(3 + 2)^2$.

$4(3 + 2)^2 = 4(5)^2$ **Work within parentheses first.**

$= 4 \cdot 25$ **Simplify 5^2.**

$= 100$ **Multiply.**

b. Evaluate $-2x^3 + 4y$, for $x = -2$ and $y = 3$.

$-2x^3 + 4y = -2(-2)^3 + 4(3)$ **Replace x with -2 and y with 3.**

$= -2(-8) + 4(3)$ **Simplify $(-2)^3$.**

$= 16 + 12$ **Multiply from left to right.**

$= 28$ **Add.**

✓ **Check Understanding**   **Example 3**

   3. a. Simplify $2 \cdot 5^2 + 4 \cdot (-3)^3$. -58
      b. Evaluate $3a^2 + 6$, for $a = -5$.   81

A

B

C

Real-World **Connection**

Human blood cells are shown here magnified (A) 10^2 times, (B) 10^3 times, and (C) 10^4 times.

Reading Math

The expression $4(3 + 2)^2$ is read as "four times the square of the quantity three plus two."

Math Background

An *exponent* is a number that is placed to the upper right of another number or expression, called the *base*. If an exponent has as its base an expression involving addition or subtraction, the whole expression must be written inside parentheses. Otherwise, the exponent has only the number next to it as its base.

Teaching Notes

English Learners
To help students understand why we read x^2 as *x squared*, show them a square with dimensions marked as *x* and explain that you multiply the two equal dimensions to find the area. Write x^2 on the square. To help students understand why we read x^3 as *x cubed*, repeat the activity using a cube accordingly.

3 **EXAMPLE** **Inclusion**

Some students with visual impairment may have difficulty distinguishing exponents from bases. For example, they may see $4(3 + 2)^2$ as $4(3 + 2)2$. Suggest these students align the edge of a ruler with the bottom edge of an exponential expression to show the alignment of the numbers.

PowerPoint

Additional Examples

1 Write using exponents.
   a. $(-11)(-11)(-11)(-11)$
      $(-11)^4$
   b. $-5 \cdot x \cdot x \cdot y \cdot y \cdot x$ $-5x^3 y^2$

2 Suppose a certain star is 10^4 light-years from Earth. How many light-years is that?
10,000 light-years

3 **a.** Simplify $3(1 + 4)^3$.   375
   b. Evaluate $7(w + 3)^3 + z$,
      for $w = -5$ and $z = 6$. -50

Closure

Ask students to write a numerical expression with exponents and then explain how to simplify it.
Check students' explanation.

 Reaching All Students

Below Level Help students connect finding the area of a square with side x and the expression x^2. Area is found by multiplying the length x by the width x, or $x \cdot x$. This expression equals x^2.	**Advanced Learners** Ask students to find a geometric representation for x^3 and explain their reasoning. Volume of a cube; all three dimensions of a cube are equal and are multiplied to find the volume.	**English Learners** See note on page 183. **Inclusion** See note on page 183.

183

3. Practice

Assignment Guide

1 Objective 1
- Ⓐ Ⓑ **Core** 1–13, 24–33, 40–42
- Ⓒ **Extension** 44–48, 50

2 Objective 2
- Ⓐ Ⓑ **Core** 14–23, 34–39, 43
- Ⓒ **Extension** 49

Test Prep 51–54
Mixed Review 55–66

Practice 4-2 Exponents

Evaluate each expression.

1. m^4, for $m = 5$ ___625___
2. $(5a)^3$, for $a = -1$ ___-125___
3. $-(2p)^2$, for $p = 7$ ___-196___
4. $-n^6$, for $n = 2$ ___-64___
5. b^b, for $b = -1$ ___1___
6. $(e - 2)^3$, for $e = 11$ ___729___
7. $(6 + h^2)^2$, for $h = 3$ ___225___
8. $x^2 + 3x - 7$, for $x = -4$ ___-3___
9. $y^3 - 2y^2 + 3y - 4$, for $y = 5$ ___86___

Write using exponents.

10. $3 \cdot 3 \cdot 3 \cdot 3$ ___3^4___
11. $k \cdot k \cdot k \cdot k \cdot k$ ___k^5___
12. $(-9)(-9)(-9)m \cdot m \cdot m$ ___$(-9)^3m^3$___
13. $g \cdot g \cdot g \cdot g \cdot h$ ___g^4h___
14. $7 \cdot a \cdot a \cdot b \cdot b$ ___$7a^2b^3$___
15. $-8 \cdot m \cdot n \cdot 2 \cdot m \cdot m$ ___$-16m^3n^2$___
16. $d \cdot (-3) \cdot e \cdot e \cdot d \cdot (-3) \cdot e$ ___$(-3)^2d^2e^3$___

Simplify each expression.

17. $(-2)^3$ and -2^3 ___-8 ; -8___
18. 0^{12} ___0___
19. 2^8 and 4^4 ___256; 256___
20. $-5^2 + 4 \cdot 2^3$ ___7___
21. $3(8 - 6)^2$ ___12___
22. $-6^2 + 2 \cdot 3^2$ ___-18___
23. $(-2)(-5)^2(3)$ ___-150___
24. $24 + (11 - 3)^2 \div 4$ ___40___
25. $(17 - 3)^2 \div (4^2 - 3^2)$ ___28___
26. $(5 + 10)^2 \div 5^2$ ___9___
27. $4^3 \div (2^5 - 4^2)$ ___4___
28. $(-1)^5 \cdot (2^4 - 13)^2$ ___-9___

Enrichment 4-2 Exponent Patterns

Complete the patterns. Then use your results to make the indicated predictions.

1. $5^1 =$ ___5___
   $5^2 =$ ___25___
   $5^3 =$ ___125___
   Predict:
   the tens digit of 5^{74} ___2___
2. $6^1 =$ ___6___
   $6^2 =$ ___36___
   $6^3 =$ ___216___
   Predict:
   the ones digit of 6^{113} ___6___
3. $4^1 =$ ___4___
   $4^2 =$ ___16___
   $4^3 =$ ___64___
   $4^4 =$ ___256___
   Predict:
   the ones digit of 4^{29} ___4___
   the ones digit of 4^{82} ___6___
4. $9^1 =$ ___9___
   $9^2 =$ ___81___
   $9^3 =$ ___729___
   $9^4 =$ ___6,561___
   Predict:
   the ones digit of 9^{114} ___1___
   the ones digit of 9^{223} ___9___
5. $2^1 =$ ___2___
   $2^2 =$ ___4___
   $2^3 =$ ___8___
   $2^4 =$ ___16___
   $2^5 =$ ___32___
   $2^6 =$ ___64___
   $2^7 =$ ___128___
   $2^8 =$ ___256___
   Predict:
   the ones digit of 2^{84} ___6___
   the ones digit of 2^{43} ___8___
6. $1^2 =$ ___1___
   $11^2 =$ ___121___
   $111^2 =$ ___12,321___
   $1,111^2 =$ ___1,234,321___
   Predict:
   $11,111^2$ ___123,454,321___
   $111,111^2$ ___12,345,654,321___
7. Study the pattern of the ones digits in the powers of 3 and the powers of 7. Then predict the ones digit of each number.
   a. 3^{50} ___9___
   b. 7^{101} ___7___
   c. 3^{81} ___3___
   d. 7^{44} ___1___

Practice and Problem Solving

Ⓐ **Practice by Example**

Example 1
(page 182)

Write using exponents. See left.

1. $8 \cdot 8 \cdot 8$
2. $r \cdot r \cdot r \cdot r \cdot s \cdot s$
3. $-7 \cdot a \cdot a \cdot b$
4. $5 \cdot 5 \cdot a \cdot a$
5. $9 \cdot 9 \cdot 9 \cdot 9 \cdot 9$
6. $(-5)(-5)(-5)(-5)$

See left:
1. 8^3
2. r^4s^2
3. $-7a^2b$
4. $25a^2$
5. 9^5
6. $(-5)^4$

Example 2
(page 183)

Simplify.

7. 10^4 ___10,000___
8. 4^3 ___64___
9. 2^6 ___64___
10. $(-4)^3$ ___-64___
11. -4^3 ___-64___
12. $(-6)^3$ ___-216___

13. **Science** An electron microscope can magnify a specimen about 10^6 times. How many times is that? **1,000,000**

Example 3
(page 183)

Simplify.

14. $3(4 + 2)^2$ **108**
15. $49 - (4 \cdot 2)^2$ **-15**
16. $-3^2 + 5 \cdot 2^3$ **31**
17. $2(9 - 4)^2$ **50**
18. $25 - (3 \cdot 2)^2$ **-11**
19. $2 \cdot (-2)^4 + 10^1$ **42**

Evaluate.

20. $3a^2 - 2$, for $a = 5$ **73**
21. $c^3 + 4$, for $c = -6$ **-212**
22. $-4y^2 + y^3$, for $y = 3$ **-9**
23. $2m^2 + n$, for $m = -3$ and $n = 4$ **22**

Ⓑ **Apply Your Skills**

Write using exponents.

24. $-5 \cdot x \cdot x \cdot 3 \cdot y$ **$-15x^2y$**
25. d cubed d^3
26. $-2 \cdot a \cdot (-4) \cdot b \cdot b$ **$8ab^2$**

27. **Error Analysis** A student gives ab^3 as an answer when asked to write the expression $ab \cdot ab \cdot ab$ using exponents. What is the student's error? **The student didn't multiply $a \cdot a \cdot a$.**

Simplify.

28. -1^8 and $(-1)^8$ **-1 and 1**
29. -2^4 and $(-2)^4$ **See left.**
30. $15 + (4 + 6)^2 \div 5$ **35**
31. $(-4)(-6)^2$ **(2) -288**
32. $(4 + 8)^2 \div 4^2$ **9**
33. $(12 - 3)^2 \div (2^2 - 1^2)$ **27**

29. **-16 and 16**

Evaluate each expression.

34. $-6m^2$, for $m = 2$ **-24**
35. $5k^2$, for $k = 1.2$ **7.2**
36. $8 - x^3$, for $x = -2$ **16**
37. $3(2m + 5)^2$, for $m = 2$ **243**
38. $4(2y - 3)^2$, for $y = 5$ **196**
39. $y^2 + 2y + 5$, for $y = -6$ **29**

40. **a.** Copy and complete the table at the left.
    b. For what value(s) of n is each sentence true?
    $4^n = n^4$ **2, 4** $4^n < n^4$ **3** $4^n > n^4$ **1**

n	$4n$	4^n	n^4
1	▨ 4	▨ 4	▨ 1
2	▨ 8	▨ 16	▨ 16
3	▨ 12	▨ 64	▨ 81
4	▨ 16	▨ 256	▨ 256

41. **Reasoning** Does $-a^2 = (-a)^2$ for any values of a? Explain.
    Yes; $-a^2 = (-a)^2$ only when $a = 0$.

42. **Mental Math** Given that $2^{10} = 1,024$, find 2^{11} mentally. **2,048**

184 Chapter 4 Factors, Fractions, and Exponents

 Use the Guided Problem Solving worksheet with Exercise 27.

43. Read the word phrase that follows:
the square of a, increased by the sum of twice a and 3.
a. Write a variable expression for the word phrase. $a^2 + 2a + 3$
b. Evaluate the expression for $a = 7$. **66**

 **Challenge**

Geometry Exercises 44–48 involve cubes made from smaller cubes, like the one at the left. Suppose such a cube has edges of length 5 cm.

44. What is the area of a face? **45.** What is the volume? **125 cm³**
25 cm²

What is the length of an edge of a cube that has the following measurement?

46. face area of 64 in.² **8 in.** **47.** a volume of 64 in.³ **4 in.**

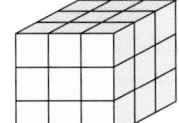

Edge length $s = 3$ in.
Area of Face $= s^2$
$= 9$ in.²
Volume $= s^3$
$= 27$ in.³

48. **Language Arts** Why do you think *squared* and *cubed* are used to indicate the second power and the third power?
See back of book.

49. **Reasoning** Describe all pairs of values of x and y for which $5x^2y = 5xy^2$. Justify your answer. **See back of book.**

50. **Writing in Math** Evaluate $(-1)^m$ for $m = 2, 4,$ and 6. Then evaluate $(-1)^m$ for $m = 1, 3,$ and 5. Write a conjecture about the sign of an even power of a negative number. Then write a conjecture about the sign of an odd power of a negative number.
An even power of a negative number is positive. An odd power of a negative number is negative.

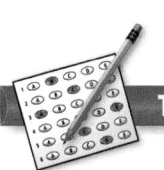

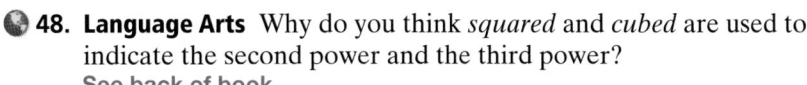 **Test Prep**

Multiple Choice

51. What is the value of $(0.5)^2$? **B**
A. 0.1 **B.** 0.25 **C.** 1.0 **D.** 25

Take It to the NET
Online lesson quiz at
www.PHSchool.com
Web Code: ada-0402

52. What is the value of xy^2 for $x = 3$ and $y = 4$? **I**
F. 12 **G.** 24 **H.** 36 **I.** 48

53. Which expression equals 1? **D**
A. -1^2 **B.** $(-1)^3$ **C.** $-(-1)^2$ **D.** $|-1|^3$

Short Response

54. Is $a^3 \geq a$ for all integer values of a? Explain and give an example.
See back of book.

Mixed Review

Lesson 4-1

State whether each number is divisible by 2, 3, 5, 9, 10, or none.

55. 36 **2, 3, 9** **56.** 135 **3, 5, 9** **57.** 171 **3, 9** **58.** 190 **2, 5, 10**

59. 253 **none** **60.** 123 **3** **61.** 117 **3, 9** **62.** 30 **2, 3, 5, 10**

Lesson 3-3

63. a. Sara's grades are 79, 82, 75, 86, and 93. What is the mean? **83**
b. What is the median? **82**

Lesson 2-3

Simplify each expression.

64. $3x - 2y + x$ **65.** $w + 8 - 4w - 15$ **66.** $9a + 2(a - 5) + 3$
4x − 2y **−3w − 7** **11a − 7**

4. Assess

 **Lesson Quiz 4-2**

Write using exponents.
1. $x \cdot y \cdot z \cdot x \cdot z$ x^2yz^2
2. $a \cdot b \cdot b \cdot b$ **3** $3ab^3$
3. Simplify $5(2 + 4)^2$. **180**
4. Evaluate $(g^3 - 7)^2 \cdot 5 + 4$, for $g = 3$. **2,004**

Error Prevention!

Exercises 10–12, 28, and 29
Remind students that a negative sign is part of the base only if the base is indicated using parentheses. If there are no parentheses, then the base is only the number or variable that the exponent is next to.

Test Prep

 **Resources**
For additional practice with a variety of test item formats:
• Test Prep, p. 227
• Test-Taking Strategies, p. 222
• Test-Taking Strategies With Transparencies

Reteaching 4-2 Exponents

Evaluate $(-x)^2$, $-x^2$, and $2(x - 4)^2 + 1$ when $x = 9$.

Substitute 9 for x in $(-x)^2$.
$(-9)^2 = (-9)(-9) = 81$

Substitute 9 for x in $-x^2$.
$-9^2 = -(9 \cdot 9) = -81$

Substitute 9 for x in $2(x - 4)^2 + 1$.
$2(x - 4)^2 + 1 = 2(9 - 4)^2 + 1$ Substitute 9 for x.
$= 2(5)^2 + 1$ Work within parentheses first.
$= 2(25) + 1$ Simplify $(5)^2$.
$= 50 + 1$ Multiply.
$= 51$ Add.

Evaluate each expression.

1. $(-a)^2$, for $a = 10$ $(-\underline{10})^2 = \underline{100}$
2. $-a^2$, for $a = 10$ $-\underline{10}^2 = \underline{-100}$
3. a^2, for $a = -10$ $\underline{-10}^2 = \underline{100}$
4. $-a^2$, for $a = -10$ $-(\underline{-10})^2 = \underline{-100}$
5. $-3m^2$, for $m = 5$ $-3(\underline{5})^2 = -3(\underline{25}) = \underline{-75}$
6. $2n^2 - 4$, for $n = 3$ $2(\underline{3})^2 - 4 = 2(\underline{9}) - 4$
  $= (\underline{18}) - 4 = \underline{14}$
7. $5(2h - 4)^2$, for $h = 4$ $5(2 \cdot \underline{4} - 4)^2 = 5(\underline{8} - 4)^2$
  $= 5(\underline{4})^2 = 5(\underline{16}) = \underline{80}$
8. xy^2, for $x = 7, y = 2$ $(\underline{7})(\underline{2})^2 = (\underline{7})(\underline{4})$
  $= \underline{28}$

Reteaching

Alternative Assessment

Have students work in groups of four. Give each group a set of dominoes, removing all dominoes having zero dots in either half. Instruct the students to place the dominoes facedown. Have students take turns selecting dominoes. The student selecting a domino designates one number as the base and the other as its exponent. All group members simplify the expression and compare answers. This can be repeated with students choosing more than one domino and constructing an expression to simplify.

1. Plan

Lesson Preview

 Check Skills You'll Need

Divisibility and Factors
Lesson 4-1: Example 3;
Exercises 17–20.
Extra Practice, p. 747.

Lesson Resources

 Teaching Resources
Practice, Reteaching, Enrichment

Reaching All Students
Practice Workbook 4-3
Spanish Practice Workbook 4-3
Guided Problem Solving 4-3
Hands-On Activities 4

 Presentation Assistant Plus!
Transparencies and PowerPoint™
• Check Skills You'll Need 4-3
• Additional Examples 4-3
• Student Edition Answers 4-3
• Lesson Quiz 4-3
• Classroom Aid 16
PH Presentation Pro CD-ROM 4-3

ASSESSMENT SYSTEM

Computer Test Generator CD-ROM

 Technology
Resource Pro® CD-ROM
Computer Test Generator CD-ROM
PH Presentation Pro CD-ROM

 www.PHSchool.com
Student Site
• Teacher Web Code: adk-5500
• Algebra Readiness Puzzles 12
• Self-grading Lesson Quiz
PH SuccessNet Teacher Center
• Lesson Planner
• Resources

Plus

 **4-3**

Prime Factorization and Greatest Common Factor

What You'll Learn

OBJECTIVE 1 To find the prime factorization of a number

OBJECTIVE 2 To find the greatest common factor (GCF) of two or more numbers

. . . And Why

To solve real-world problems involving organization

 Check Skills You'll Need

List the positive factors of each number.
See below.
1. 15 **2.** 35 **3.** 7
4. 20 **5.** 100 **6.** 121

 For help, go to Lesson 4-1.

New Vocabulary

• prime number
• composite number
• prime factorization
• greatest common factor (GCF)

1. 1, 3, 5, 15
2. 1, 5, 7, 35
3. 1, 7
4. 1, 2, 4, 5, 10, 20
5. 1, 2, 4, 5, 10, 20, 25, 50, 100
6. 1, 11, 121

 iTEXT Interactive lesson includes instant self-check, tutorials, and activities.

OBJECTIVE

1 **Finding Prime Factorizations**

 **Investigation**

Exploring Prime Numbers

The diagram shows the only rectangle you can make with integer side lengths and an area of 5 square units. Work with a partner. Find the number of rectangles you can make with each number of unit squares: 2, 3, 4, 5, 6, 7, 8, 9, and 10.

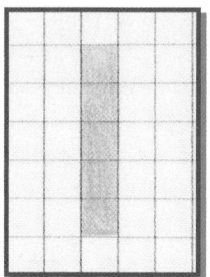

1. For which numbers of squares is only one rectangle possible? **2, 3, 5, 7**

2. For which numbers of squares is more than one rectangle possible? **4, 6, 8, 9, 10**

3. List the dimensions of the rectangles you can make with each of the following numbers of unit squares: 13, 15, 17, 19, and 21. **1 by 13; 1 by 15, 3 by 5; 1 by 17; 1 by 19; 1 by 21, 3 by 7**

A **prime number** is an integer greater than 1 with exactly two positive factors, 1 and the number itself. The numbers 2, 3, 5, and 7 are prime numbers.

A **composite number** is an integer greater than 1 with more than two positive factors. The numbers 4, 6, 8, 9, and 10 are composite numbers. The number 1 is neither prime nor composite.

1 EXAMPLE **Prime or Composite?**

State whether each number is *prime* or *composite*. Explain.

a. 23 Prime; it has only two factors, 1 and 23.

b. 129 Composite; it has more than two factors, 1, 3, 43, and 129.

 Check Understanding Example 1

1. Which numbers from 10 to 20 are prime? **11, 13, 17, 19** Which are composite? **10, 12, 14, 15, 16, 18, 20**

186 Chapter 4 Factors, Fractions, and Exponents

Ongoing Assessment and Intervention

Before the Lesson	During the Lesson	After the Lesson
Diagnose prerequisite skills using:	**Monitor progress using:**	**Assess knowledge using:**
• Check Skills You'll Need	• Check Understanding	• Lesson Quiz
	• Additional Examples	• Computer Test Generator CD-ROM
	• Test Prep	

Writing a composite number as a product of its prime factors shows the **prime factorization** of the number. You can use a *factor tree* to find prime factorizations. Write the final factors in increasing order from left to right. Use exponents to indicate repeated factors.

Test-Taking Tip
To check whether a number is prime, look for prime factors in order, starting with 2. When you get to a prime whose square is greater than the original number, you can stop. For 23, check 2 and 3. Then stop at 5, since $5^2 > 23$. Since 2, 3, and 5 are not factors of 23, 23 is prime.

2 EXAMPLE **Writing the Prime Factorization**

Use a factor tree to write the prime factorization of 825.

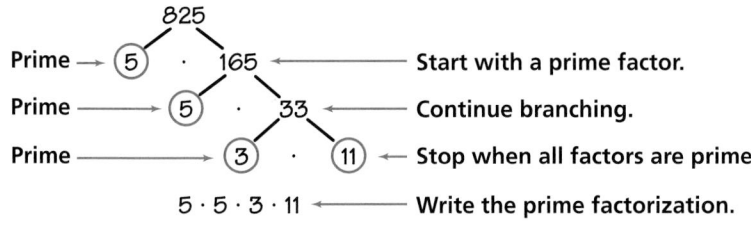

Prime → ⑤ · 165 ← Start with a prime factor.

Prime → ⑤ · 33 ← Continue branching.

Prime → ③ · ⑪ ← Stop when all factors are prime.

5 · 5 · 3 · 11 ← Write the prime factorization.

• $825 = 3 \cdot 5^2 \cdot 11$ **Use exponents to write the prime factorization.**

✓ **Check Understanding** Example 2

2. Write the prime factorization of each number.

a. 72 $2^3 \cdot 3^2$ **b.** 121 11^2 **c.** 225 $3^2 \cdot 5^2$ **d.** 236 $2^2 \cdot 59$

OBJECTIVE

2 **Finding the Greatest Common Factor**

Factors that are the same for two or more numbers or expressions are *common factors*. The greatest of these common factors is called the **greatest common factor (GCF).** You can use prime factorization to find the GCF of two or more numbers or expressions. If there are no prime factors and variable factors in common, the GCF is 1.

3 EXAMPLE **Finding the GCF**

Find the GCF of each pair of numbers or expressions.

a. 40 and 60

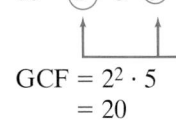

$40 = 2^3 \cdot 5$
$60 = 2^2 \cdot 3 \cdot 5$

Write the prime factorizations.

Find the common factors. Use the lesser power of the common factors.

$GCF = 2^2 \cdot 5$
$= 20$

The GCF of 40 and 60 is 20.

b. $6a^3b$ and $4a^2b$

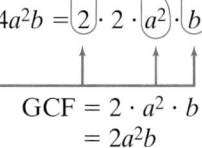

$6a^3b = 2 \cdot 3 \cdot a^3 \cdot b$
$4a^2b = 2 \cdot 2 \cdot a^2 \cdot b$

$GCF = 2 \cdot a^2 \cdot b$
$= 2a^2b$

The GCF of $6a^3b$ and $4a^2b$ is $2a^2b$.

4-3 Prime Factorization and Greatest Common Factor **187**

Reaching All Students

| **Below Level** Students may find it helpful to make a list of all prime numbers less than 100. 2, 3, 5, 7, 11, 13, 17, 19, 23, 29, 31, 37, 41, 43, 47, 53, 59, 61, 67, 71, 73, 79, 83, 89, 97 | **Advanced Learners** Ask students whether 822,367,941 is prime. Explain. The number is not prime because the sum of the digits, 42, is divisible by 3. | **Visual Learners** See note on page 187. **Tactile Learners** See note on page 188. |

2. Teach

Professional Development

Math Background

Every prime number has exactly two factors and every composite number has at least three factors. The numbers 2 and 3 have exactly two factors. The number 4, for example, has factors of 1, 2, and 4.

Teaching Notes

Investigation (Optional)
Visual Learners
Suggest students use graph paper to draw rectangles with the given numbers of unit squares.

1 EXAMPLE **History Connection**

It is not known when prime numbers were first recognized. The Greek mathematicians Euclid and Eratosthenes studied them as early as 300 B.C.

2 EXAMPLE **Error Prevention**

Remind students that the prime factorization of a number must contain only prime numbers. Even though 5 · 165 is a factorization of 825, it is not a prime factorization since 165 is not prime.

3 EXAMPLE **Auditory Learners**

When students see "GCF," have them say "greatest common factor" instead of "GCF" to reinforce the meaning of GCF.

PowerPoint
Additional Examples

❶ State whether each number is *prime* or *composite*. Explain.
   a. 46 Composite; 46 has more than two factors.
   b. 13 Prime; 13 has exactly two factors.

❷ Use a factor tree to write the prime factorization of 273.
   3 · 7 · 13

❸ Find the GCF of each pair of numbers or expressions.
   a. 24 and 30 6
   b. $36ab^2$ and $81b$ $9b$

✓ **Check Understanding**   Example 3

3. Use prime factorizations to find each GCF.

   a. $8, 20$ 4   **b.** $12, 87$ 3   **c.** $12r^3, 8r$ 4r   **d.** $15m^2n, 45m$ 15m

You can find the GCF of two or more numbers or expressions by listing factors or by using prime factorizations.

More Than One Way

A parade organizer wants each of three marching bands to have the same number of band members in each row. The bands have 48, 32, and 56 band members. What is the greatest number of band members possible for each row?

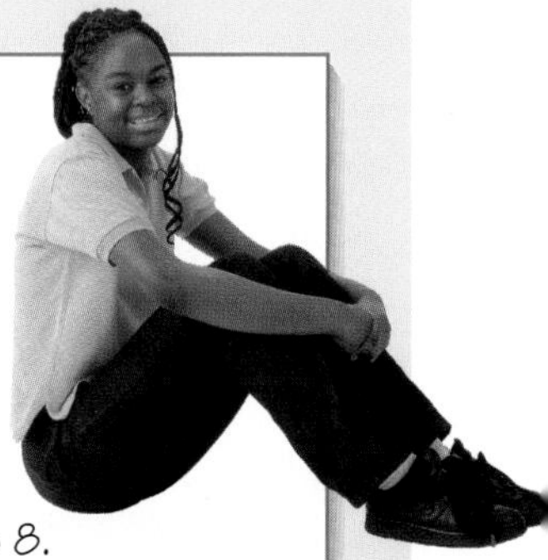

Jasmine's Method

List the factors of each number. Then find the greatest factor the numbers have in common.

48: 1, 2, 3, 4, 6, 8, 12, 16, 24, 48
32: 1, 2, 4, 8, 16, 32
56: 1, 2, 4, 7, 8, 14, 28, 56

The GCF of 48, 32, and 56 is 8. The greatest possible number of band members in each row is 8.

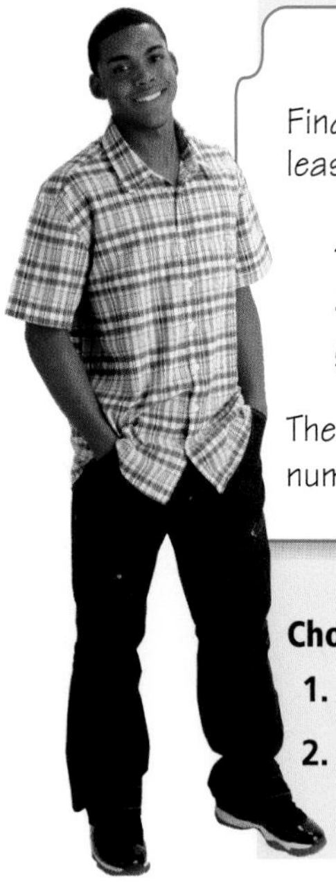

Daryl's Method

Find the prime factorization of each number. Then find the least power of all common prime factors.

48: $2^4 \cdot 3$
32: 2^5
56: $2^3 \cdot 7$

The GCF of 48, 32, and 56 is 2^3, or 8. The greatest possible number of band members in each row is 8.

Choose a Method

1. Which method do you prefer to find the GCF? Explain why.
See margin.
2. Which method would you use to find the GCF of 4, 8, and 24? Of 54, 27, and 36? Explain why.

Answers may vary. Sample: Jasmine's Method; the lists are very short for 4, 8, and 24; Daryl's Method; factors may be missed for 54, 27, and 36.

For more exercises, see *Extra Practice*.

3. Practice

Practice and Problem Solving

A Practice by Example

Example 1
(page 186)

State whether each number is prime or composite. Explain.
1–8. See below left.

1. 27   **2.** 19   **3.** 31   **4.** 38

5. 45   **6.** 53   **7.** 87   **8.** 93

Example 2
(page 187)

Write the prime factorization of each number.

9. 8   **10.** 49   **11.** 34   **12.** 42
2^3 7^2 $2 \cdot 17$ $2 \cdot 3 \cdot 7$

13. 360   **14.** 115   **15.** 186   **16.** 621
$2^3 \cdot 3^2 \cdot 5$ $5 \cdot 23$ $2 \cdot 3 \cdot 31$ $3^3 \cdot 23$

Example 3
(page 187)

Use prime factorization to find each GCF.

17. 10, 45 5   **18.** 14, 21 7   **19.** 25, 100 25   **20.** 57, 84 3

21. $14c^2, 35c$ **22.** $3y^2, 24y^3$ **23.** $18c^3, 24c^3$ **24.** $6m^3n, 8mn^2$
$7c$ $3y^2$ $6c^3$ $2mn$

B Apply Your Skills

Is each number prime, composite, or neither? For each composite number, write the prime factorization.

25. 17 prime   **26.** 1 neither   **27.** 49   **28.** 522
                                                       See below left.   See below left.

1. Composite; it has more than two factors, 1, 3, 9, and 27.

2. Prime; it has only two factors, 1 and 19.

3. Prime; it has only two factors, 1 and 31.

4. Composite; it has more than two factors, 1, 2, 19, and 38.

5. Composite; it has more than two factors, 1, 3, 5, 9, 15, and 45.

6. Prime; it has only two factors, 1 and 53.

7. Composite; it has more than two factors, 1, 3, 29, and 87.

8. Composite; it has more than two factors, 1, 3, 31, and 93.

27. composite; 7^2
28. composite; $2 \cdot 3^2 \cdot 29$

29. Organization A math teacher and a science teacher combine their first-period classes for a group activity. The math class has 24 students and the science class has 16 students. The teachers need to divide the students into groups of the same size. Each group must have the same number of math students. Find the greatest number of groups possible. **8 groups**

Find each GCF.

30. 6, 8, 12 2   **31.** 42, 65 1   **32.** 54, 144 18   **33.** 8, 16, 20 4

34. 12, 18, 21 3   **35.** 143, 169 13   **36.** z, z^2 z   **37.** $180a^2, 210a$ 30a

38. x^2y, xy^2 **39.** a^3b, a^2b^2 **40.** c^3df^2, c^2d^2f **41.** a^2b, b^2c, ac^2
xy a^2b c^2df 1

42. Reasoning Find the integers that fit the following conditions:
- They are between 44 and 53.
- The sums of their digits are prime.
- They have more than three factors. **50, 52**

43. Open-Ended The GCF of 36 and x is 6. What are two possible values for x? **Answers may vary. Sample: 6, 30**

44. Seating Arrangements Organizers for a high school graduation have set up chairs in two sections. They put 126 chairs for graduates in the front section and 588 chairs for guests in the back section. If all rows have the same number of chairs, what is the greatest number of chairs possible for a row? **42 chairs**

4-3 Prime Factorization and Greatest Common Factor   **189**

Assignment Guide

1 Objective 1
A B Core 1–16, 25–28, 42
C Extension 45–48, 57

2 Objective 2
A B Core 17–24, 29–41, 43, 44
C Extension 49–56

Test Prep 58–62
Mixed Review 63–71

Practice 4-3 *Prime Factorization and Greatest Common Factor*

Find each GCF.

1. 8, 12   4   2. 36, 54   18
3. 63, 81   9   4. 69, 92   23
5. 15, 28   1   6. 21, 35   7
7. 30m, 36n   6   8. $75x^3y^2, 100xy$ 25xy
9. 15, 24, 30   3   10. 48, 80, 128   16
11. $36hk^3, 60k^2m, 84k^4n$ $12k^2$ 12. $2mn, 4m^2n^2$ 2mn

Is each number prime, composite, or neither? For each composite, write the prime factorization.

13. 75   composite; $3 \cdot 5^2$ 14. 152   composite; $2^3 \cdot 19$
15. 432   composite; $2^4 \cdot 3^3$ 16. 588   composite; $2^2 \cdot 3 \cdot 7^2$
17. 160   composite; $2^5 \cdot 5$ 18. 108   composite; $2^2 \cdot 3^3$
19. 19   prime   20. 143   composite; $11 \cdot 13$
21. 531   composite; $3^2 \cdot 59$ 22. 369   composite; $3^2 \cdot 41$
23. 83   prime   24. 137   prime

25. The numbers 3, 5, and 7 are factors of *n*. Find four other factors of *n* besides 1.   15, 35, 21, 105

26. For which expressions is the GCF $8x$?
A. $2xy$ and $4x^2$ **B.** $16x^2$ and $24xy$ C. $8x^3$ and $4x$ D. $24x^2$ and $48x^3$

Practice

Enrichment 4-3 *Number of Factors*

1. Find the factors of 23.   1, 23
2. Find the factors of 24.   1, 2, 3, 4, 6, 8, 12, 24

As the above examples show, two numbers may have greatly different numbers of factors, even though the numbers are nearly equal.

3. How many factors does 23 have?   2
4. How many factors does 24 have?   8

You can use prime factorizations to find out how many factors a number has.

Example   How many factors does 40 have?
Solution   1. Write the prime factorization. $40 = 2^3 \cdot 5^1$
          2. Take each exponent and add 1. $3 + 1 = 4$
                                    $1 + 1 = 2$
          3. Multiply the sums. $4 \times 2 = 8$
            40 has 8 factors.

Complete the table. The first one is done for you.

Number	Prime Factorization	Number of Factors	Factors
6	$2 \cdot 3$	4	1, 2, 3, 6
5. 44	$2^2 \cdot 11$	6	1, 2, 4, 11, 22, 44
6. 91	$7 \cdot 13$	4	1, 7, 13, 91
7. 125	5^3	4	1, 5, 25, 125
8. 54	$2 \cdot 3^3$	8	1, 2, 3, 6, 9, 18, 27, 54
9. 664	$2^3 \cdot 83$	8	1, 2, 4, 8, 83, 166, 332, 664
10. 369	$3^2 \cdot 41$	6	1, 3, 9, 41, 123, 369
11. 475	$5^2 \cdot 19$	6	1, 5, 19, 25, 95, 475
12. 222	$2 \cdot 3 \cdot 37$	8	1, 2, 3, 6, 37, 74, 111, 222

Enrichment

GPS Use the Guided Problem Solving worksheet with Exercise 29.

Tell whether each number is *prime* or *composite*.

1. 123   **2.** 47
composite   prime

Write the prime factorization for each number.

3. 64   **4.** 45
2^6 $3^2 \cdot 5$

Find the GCF for each pair.

5. 80 and 120 40

6. $62b^3c^2d$ and $31b^2c^3d$
$31b^2c^2d$

Test Prep

Resources
For additional practice with a variety of test item formats:
- Test Prep, p. 227
- Test-Taking Strategies, p. 222
- Test-Taking Strategies With Transparencies

Reteaching 4-3 *Prime Factorization and Greatest Common Factor*

Find the GCF of 36 and 54.

$36 = 2^2 \cdot 3^2 = 2 \cdot 2 \cdot 3 \cdot 3$ write the prime factorization
$54 = 2 \cdot 3^3 = 2 \cdot 3 \cdot 3 \cdot 3$

find the common factors

GCF $= 2 \cdot 3 \cdot 3 = 2 \cdot 3^2 = 18$
Notice 2 is the lesser power of 2^2 and 2, and 3^2 is the lesser power of 3^2 and 3^3.

Find the GCF.

1. $50 = 2 \cdot 5^2$ 2. $75 = 3 \cdot 5^2$
$35 = 5 \cdot 7$ $30 = 2 \cdot 3 \cdot 5$
GCF $= 5$ GCF $= 3 \cdot 5 = 15$

3. $48 = 2^4 \cdot 3$ 4. $45 = 3^2 \cdot 5$
$60 = 2^2 \cdot 3 \cdot 5$ $72 = 2^3 \cdot 3^2$
GCF $= 2^2 \cdot 3 = 12$ GCF $= 3^2 = 9$

5. $98 = 2 \cdot 7^2$ 6. $24 = 2^3 \cdot 3$
$42 = 2 \cdot 3 \cdot 7$ $80 = 2^4 \cdot 5$
GCF $= 2 \cdot 7 = 14$ GCF $= 2^3 = 8$

7. $315 = 3^2 \cdot 5 \cdot 7$ 8. $156 = 2^2 \cdot 3 \cdot 13$
$360 = 2^3 \cdot 3^2 \cdot 5$ $208 = 2^4 \cdot 13$
GCF $= 3^2 \cdot 5 = 45$ GCF $= 2^2 \cdot 13 = 52$

C Challenge

Is each number prime, composite, or neither? For each composite number, write the prime factorization. 45–48. See left.

45. composite; $11 \cdot 23$
46. composite; $3^2 \cdot 5^2 \cdot 7$
47. composite; $17 \cdot 59$
48. prime

45. 253   **46.** 1,575   **47.** 1,003   **48.** 283

Two numbers are *relatively prime* if their GCF is 1. Are the numbers in each pair below relatively prime? Explain. 49–56. See left.

49. Yes; the GCF is 1.
50. No; the GCF is 3.
51. No; the GCF is 13.
52. Yes; the GCF is 1.
53. No; the GCF is 13.
54. Yes; the GCF is 1.
55. Yes; the GCF is 1.
56. No; the GCF is 6.

SAMPLE   8, 17   Yes, 8 and 17 are relatively prime. The GCF is 1.
         7, 35   No, 7 and 35 are not relatively prime. The GCF is 7.

49. 3, 20   **50.** 9, 42   **51.** 13, 52   **52.** 24, 47

53. 52, 65   **54.** 63, 74   **55.** 15, 22   **56.** 42, 72

57. <u>Writing in Math</u> Explain how to find the prime factorization of 50.
See margin.

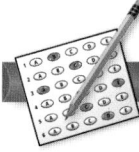

Test Prep

Multiple Choice   In Exercises 58 and 59, what is the GCF of each given pair?

58. $27x^2y^3$ and $46x^2y$ **C**
   A. $3x^2y$ **B.** x^2y^2 **C.** x^2y **D.** $9x^2y$

59. $25b^2c$ and $42bc$ **G**
   F. bc^2 **G.** bc **H.** b^2c **I.** b^2c^2

Take It to the NET
Online lesson quiz at
www.PHSchool.com
Web Code: ada-0403

60. For which pair is the GCF 12? **B**
   A. 3, 4   **B.** $24x^2$, 36y   **C.** 12xy, 24y   **D.** 3x, 12x

61. Simon is covering a wall with equal-sized tiles that cannot be cut into smaller pieces. The wall is 66 inches high by 72 inches wide. What is the area of the largest square tile that Simon can use? **H**
   F. 9 in.^{2} **G.** 16 in.^{2} **H.** 36 in.^{2} **I.** 64 in.^{2}

Extended Response   **62. a.** Is the product of two prime numbers also prime?
   b. Justify your answer.   **c.** Give an example.   See back of book.

Mixed Review

Lesson 4-2   **Evaluate for $x = 2$ and $y = 5$.**

63. x^2y 20   **64.** xy^2 50   **65.** $x^2 + y^2$ 29 **66.** $x^4 - y$ 11

Lesson 3-6   **Solve each equation.**

67. $3x = 5.4$ 1.8   **68.** $-0.5a = 4.35$ -8.7

69. $4.32 = 1.6y$ 2.7   **70.** $-8m = -74.4$ 9.3

Lesson 2-7 🌐 **71. Bookstore** A store manager ordered three times as many books as magazines. She ordered a total of 108 books and magazines. How many books did she order? **81 books**

Alternative Assessment

Group students in pairs. Have each student write down a number less than 200. Partners then exchange numbers and find the prime factorization for each number. Then have the partners work together to find the GCF of their numbers.

57.   Answers may vary. Sample: Divide 50 by the prime factor 5, and then divide the quotient, 10, by the prime factor 5 in a factor tree. Write the prime factorization $2 \cdot 5^2$.

 **Extension**

Venn Diagrams

For Use With Lesson 4-3

In a *Venn diagram* you use circles to represent collections of objects. The *intersection*, or overlap, of two circles indicates what is common to both collections.

1 EXAMPLE

School coaches plan to send notices to all students playing fall or winter sports. How many notices do they need to send?

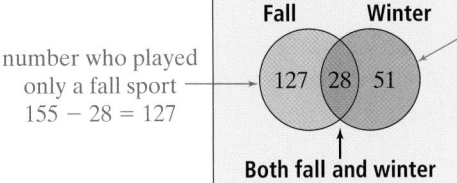

Students in Sports

Season	Students
Fall	155
Winter	79
Both fall and winter	28

number who played only a fall sport
$155 - 28 = 127$

number who played only a winter sport
$79 - 28 = 51$

Add all three numbers to find the number of notices needed.

$127 + 28 + 51 = 206$

● The coaches need to send 206 notices.

You can use a Venn diagram to find the GCF of two numbers.

2 EXAMPLE

Find the GCF of 30 and 84.

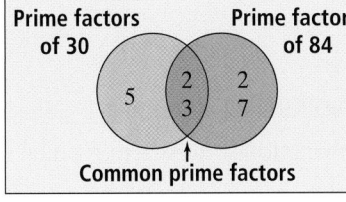

Include the common prime factors of 30 and 84 in the intersection.

The GCF is the product of the factors in the intersection.

● The GCF is $2 \cdot 3$, or 6.

EXERCISES

1. In a class of 38 students, 32 are wearing jeans, 21 are wearing T-shirts, and 15 are wearing both. How many students are wearing jeans and something other than a T-shirt? **17 students**

Draw a Venn diagram to find the GCF of each pair of numbers. 2–5. Check students' diagrams.

2. 24, 56 **8**
3. 35, 49 **7**
4. 36, 84 **12**
5. 72, 108 **36**

Venn Diagrams

This Extension shows how to use a Venn diagram to clarify relationships.

Teaching Notes

Venn diagrams are geometric figures used to illustrate sets and set relations. The sizes and shapes of the diagrams do not matter. Sometimes you use rectangles to represent the universal, or entire, set, as is done in Examples 1 and 2 (all students in Example 1; all whole numbers in Example 2). You may use circles to represent subsets of the universal set. The section formed by overlapping circles represents data that are common to the sets represented by the circles.

Tactile Learners

Make two large overlapping sections on the floor using colored chalk or masking tape. Have one section represent students who are wearing rings. Have the other section represent students who are wearing watches. Instruct students to stand in the circles according to what they are wearing (watches or rings). Students wearing both a watch and a ring should stand in the intersection of the two sections. You may want to form a universal space for students not wearing watches or rings. To involve all class members, try this technique with other collections of objects or numbers.

1 EXAMPLE Teaching Tip

Have students work in groups to conduct simple polls or surveys. Have them display the data gathered using Venn diagrams. Ask a volunteer from each group to explain his or her diagram to the class.

2 EXAMPLE Error Prevention

Have students check the answer by multiplying the GCF by the remaining prime factors of each number. Check to see whether each product is equal to the original number.

191

4-4

Lesson Preview

 Check Skills You'll Need

Greatest Common Factor
Lesson 4-3: Example 3;
Exercises 17–24.
Extra Practice, p. 747.

Lesson Resources

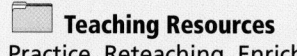 **Teaching Resources**
Practice, Reteaching, Enrichment
Checkpoint Quiz 1

 **Reaching All Students**
Practice Workbook 4-4
Spanish Practice Workbook 4-4
Reading and Math Literacy 4B
Spanish Reading and Math
  Literacy 4B
Spanish Checkpoint Quiz 1
Guided Problem Solving 4-4
Hands-On Activities 6

 Presentation Assistant Plus!
Transparencies and PowerPoint™
• Check Skills You'll Need 4-4
• Additional Examples 4-4
• Student Edition Answers 4-4
• Lesson Quiz 4-4
PH Presentation Pro CD-ROM 4-4

 ASSESSMENT SYSTEM

Checkpoint Quiz 1
Computer Test Generator CD-ROM

 **Technology**
Resource Pro® CD-ROM
Computer Test Generator CD-ROM
PH Presentation Pro CD-ROM

 **www.PHSchool.com**
Student Site
• Teacher Web Code: adk-5500
• Self-grading Lesson Quiz
PH SuccessNet Teacher Center
• Lesson Planner
• Resources

Plus **iTEXT**

192

4-4 Simplifying Fractions

What You'll Learn

OBJECTIVE 1 To find equivalent fractions

OBJECTIVE 2 To write fractions in simplest form

. . . And Why

To solve real-world problems involving statistics

 Check Skills You'll Need

Find each GCF.

1. $14, 21$ **7**   **2.** $48, 60$ **12**

3. $5mn, 15m^2n$ **5mn**

4. $63r^2, 48s^3$ **3**

💡 For help, go to Lesson 4-3.

New Vocabulary

• equivalent fractions
• simplest form

Reading Math

Most fraction names are made by adding *th* or *ths* to the denominator. You read $\frac{1}{4}$ as "one fourth," $\frac{2}{5}$ as "two fifths," and $\frac{8}{10}$ as "eight tenths." Halves and thirds are two exceptions.

iTEXT Interactive lesson includes instant self-check, tutorials, and activities.

OBJECTIVE

1 Finding Equivalent Fractions

Each fraction model below represents one whole. The blue model is divided into four equal parts. The orange model is divided into twelve equal parts.

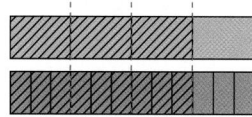

$\frac{3}{4}$ of the model is shaded.

$\frac{9}{12}$ of the model is shaded.

$$\frac{3}{4} = \frac{3 \cdot 3}{4 \cdot 3} = \frac{9}{12}$$

The fraction models show that $\frac{3}{4} = \frac{9}{12}$. The fractions $\frac{3}{4}$ and $\frac{9}{12}$ are **equivalent fractions** because they describe the same part of a whole.

You can find equivalent fractions by multiplying or dividing the numerator and denominator by the same nonzero factor.

1 EXAMPLE **Finding an Equivalent Fraction**

Find two fractions equivalent to $\frac{4}{12}$.

a. $\frac{4}{12} = \frac{4 \cdot 3}{12 \cdot 3}$ **b.** $\frac{4}{12} = \frac{4 \div 4}{12 \div 4}$

$= \frac{12}{36}$ $= \frac{1}{3}$

The fractions $\frac{12}{36}$ and $\frac{1}{3}$ are both equivalent to $\frac{4}{12}$.

✔ **Check Understanding** **Example 1** 1a–c. Answers may vary. Samples are given.

1. Find two fractions equivalent to each fraction.

a. $\frac{5}{15}$ $\frac{1}{3}, \frac{10}{30}$ **b.** $\frac{10}{12}$ $\frac{5}{6}, \frac{20}{24}$ **c.** $\frac{14}{20}$ $\frac{7}{10}, \frac{28}{40}$

OBJECTIVE

2 Writing Fractions in Simplest Form

A fraction is in **simplest form** when the numerator and the denominator have no common factors other than 1. You can use the GCF to write a fraction in simplest form.

Ongoing Assessment and Intervention

Before the Lesson
Diagnose prerequisite skills using:
• Check Skills You'll Need

During the Lesson
Monitor progress using:
• Check Understanding
• Additional Examples
• Test Prep

After the Lesson
Assess knowledge using:
• Lesson Quiz
• Computer Test Generator CD-ROM
• Chapter Checkpoint 1 (p. 195)

2 EXAMPLE   Real-World Problem Solving

Statistics You survey your friends about their favorite sandwich and find that 8 out of 12, or $\frac{8}{12}$, prefer peanut butter. Write this fraction in simplest form.

The GCF of 8 and 12 is 4.

$$\frac{8}{12} = \frac{8 \div 4}{12 \div 4}$$ **Divide the numerator and denominator by the GCF, 4.**

$$= \frac{2}{3}$$ **Simplify.**

● The favorite sandwich of $\frac{2}{3}$ of your friends is peanut butter.

✓ Check Understanding Example 2

2. Write each fraction in simplest form.

  a. $\frac{6}{8}$ $\frac{3}{4}$ **b.** $\frac{9}{12}$ $\frac{3}{4}$ **c.** $\frac{28}{35}$ $\frac{4}{5}$

You can often simplify a fraction that contains a variable. In this book, you may assume that no expression for a denominator equals zero.

3 EXAMPLE   Simplifying a Fraction

Write in simplest form.

a. $\dfrac{y}{xy}$

$$\frac{y}{xy} = \frac{y^1}{x y_1}$$ **Divide the numerator and denominator by the common factor, *y*.**

$$= \frac{1}{x}$$ **Simplify.**

b. $\dfrac{3ab^2}{12ac}$

$$\frac{3ab^2}{12ac} = \frac{3 \cdot a \cdot b \cdot b}{2 \cdot 2 \cdot 3 \cdot a \cdot c}$$ **Write as a product of prime factors.**

$$= \frac{3^1 \cdot a^1 \cdot b \cdot b}{2 \cdot 2 \cdot {}_1 3 \cdot {}_1 a \cdot c}$$ **Divide the numerator and denominator by the common factors.**

$$= \frac{b \cdot b}{2 \cdot 2 \cdot c}$$ **Simplify.**

$$= \frac{b \cdot b}{4 \cdot c}$$

$$= \frac{b^2}{4c}$$

✓ Check Understanding Example 3

3. Write in simplest form.

  a. $\dfrac{b}{abc}$ $\frac{1}{ac}$ **b.** $\dfrac{2mn}{6m}$ $\frac{n}{3}$ **c.** $\dfrac{24x^2y}{8xy}$ $3x$

Real-World Connection

The average American child will eat 1,500 peanut butter and jelly sandwiches by the time she or he graduates from high school.

Test-Taking Tip

You will see the directions *write in lowest terms* on some tests. This is another way of saying "write in simplest form."

4-4 Simplifying Fractions **193**

👥 Reaching All Students

Below Level Ask students what fractions of a dollar are represented by a quarter and a half dollar. $\frac{1}{4}$; $\frac{1}{2}$ Point out that the names of these coins come from their values as related to a dollar.

Advanced Learners Ask: *If the numerator of a fraction is a prime number, is the fraction in simplest form? Explain.* Not necessarily; the prime number may be a factor of the denominator.

Tactile Learners See note on page 193.
English Learners See note on page 193.

---

2. Teach

Professional Development

Math Background

When you multiply both numerator and denominator of a fraction by the same nonzero number, you get a fraction that is equivalent to the original fraction. Equivalent fractions represent equal values. They name the same point on a number line.

Teaching Notes

Tactile Learners
Have students cut several paper plates into equal sections (2, 3, 4, 6, and 8 sections). Label the sections with the appropriate fractions. Have students compare to find combinations of sections that are equivalent, such as 1 section from the plate cut into halves and 2 sections of the plate cut into fourths. Have them write the relationship, $\frac{1}{2} = \frac{2}{4}$.

English Learners
Point out the Reading Math note in the margin of the textbook. Tell students that $\frac{1}{2}$ is read as "one half," not "one twoth," and $\frac{1}{3}$ is read as "one third," not "one threeth."

PowerPoint
📥 Additional Examples

1 Find two fractions equivalent to $\frac{18}{21}$. Answers may vary. Sample: $\frac{6}{7}$ and $\frac{36}{42}$.

2 You learn that 21 out of the 28 students in a class, or $\frac{21}{28}$, buy their lunches in the cafeteria. Write this fraction in simplest form. $\frac{3}{4}$

3 Write in simplest form.
  a. $\dfrac{p}{2p}$ $\frac{1}{2}$
  b. $\dfrac{14q^2rs^3}{8qrs^2}$ $\frac{7qs}{4}$

Closure

Ask students to explain why it is useful to write fractions in simplest form. Then have them explain how to write a fraction in simplest form. Simplest form is often simplest to use. You write a fraction in simplest form by dividing both the numerator and the denominator by their GCF.

193

EXERCISES

For more exercises, see *Extra Practice*.

Practice and Problem Solving

Assignment Guide

1 Objective 1
  Ⓐ Ⓑ Core 1–6, 22–27, 41

2 Objective 2
  Ⓐ Ⓑ Core 7–21, 28–40, 42
  Ⓒ Extension 43–46

Test Prep 47–50
Mixed Review 51–58

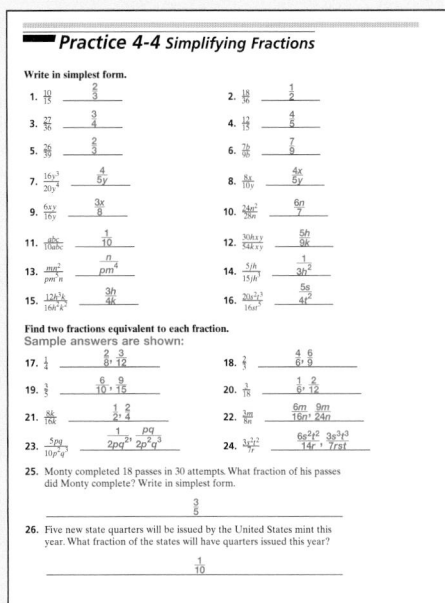

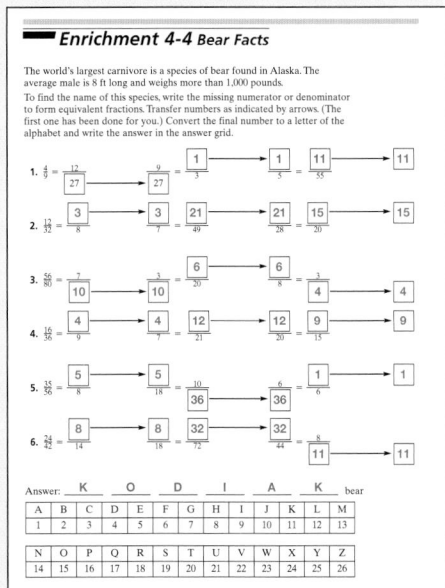

Ⓐ Practice by Example

Example 1 (page 192)

1–6. Answers may vary. Samples are given.

Find two fractions equivalent to each fraction.

1. $\frac{2}{8}$ $\frac{1}{4}, \frac{4}{16}$
2. $\frac{8}{10}$ $\frac{4}{5}, \frac{16}{20}$
3. $\frac{3}{9}$ $\frac{1}{3}, \frac{2}{6}$
4. $\frac{8}{36}$ $\frac{2}{9}, \frac{16}{72}$
5. $\frac{6}{18}$ $\frac{1}{3}, \frac{12}{36}$
6. $\frac{20}{22}$ $\frac{10}{11}, \frac{40}{44}$

Example 2 (page 193)

Write each fraction in simplest form.

7. $\frac{3}{9}$ $\frac{1}{3}$
8. $\frac{4}{10}$ $\frac{2}{5}$
9. $\frac{12}{48}$ $\frac{1}{4}$
10. $\frac{2}{10}$ $\frac{1}{5}$
11. $\frac{4}{12}$ $\frac{1}{3}$
12. $\frac{6}{15}$ $\frac{2}{5}$

🌐 **13. Health** Doctors suggest that most people need about 8 h of sleep each night to stay healthy. What fraction of the day is this? Write your answer in simplest form. $\frac{1}{3}$

Example 3 (page 193)

Write in simplest form.

14. $\frac{2x}{3x}$ $\frac{2}{3}$
15. $\frac{4km^2}{12k}$ $\frac{m^2}{3}$
16. $\frac{b}{bc}$ $\frac{1}{c}$
17. $\frac{24x}{16}$ $\frac{3x}{2}$
18. $\frac{8pr}{12p}$ $\frac{2r}{3}$
19. $\frac{14a^2}{24a}$ $\frac{7a}{12}$
20. $\frac{4bc}{16b}$ $\frac{c}{4}$
21. $\frac{40ab^2}{5ab}$ $8b$

Ⓑ Apply Your Skills

22–27. Answers may vary. Samples are given.

Find two fractions equivalent to each fraction.

22. $\frac{4}{8}$ $\frac{1}{2}, \frac{2}{4}$
23. $\frac{4}{10}$ $\frac{2}{5}, \frac{8}{20}$
24. $\frac{5}{20}$ $\frac{1}{4}, \frac{2}{8}$
25. $\frac{10}{16}$ $\frac{5}{8}, \frac{20}{32}$
26. $\frac{18}{20}$ $\frac{9}{10}, \frac{36}{40}$
27. $\frac{25}{100}$ $\frac{1}{4}, \frac{2}{8}$

Write in simplest form.

28. $\frac{8}{14}$ $\frac{4}{7}$
29. $\frac{18}{32}$ $\frac{9}{16}$
30. $\frac{20}{30}$ $\frac{2}{3}$
31. $\frac{12}{16}$ $\frac{3}{4}$
32. $\frac{15^3}{15^2}$ 15
33. $\frac{56pq}{7pq}$ 8
34. $\frac{5c^2d}{15c}$ $\frac{cd}{3}$
35. $\frac{4r^3st}{36st^2}$ $\frac{r^3}{9t}$
36. $\frac{5t}{10t^2}$ $\frac{1}{2t}$
37. $\frac{x^2y}{3yz}$ $\frac{x^2}{3z}$
38. $\frac{12gh}{8g^2h^2}$ $\frac{3}{2gh}$
39. $\frac{6m^2n^2}{9mn^2}$ $\frac{2m}{3}$

Reading Math

For help with reading and solving Exercise 40, see page 196.

41. Answers may vary.

Sample: $\frac{6x}{10}, \frac{3xy}{5y}$

Ⓒ Challenge

40. Error Analysis A student claims $\frac{65}{91}$ is in simplest form. Do you agree? Explain. No; the GCF of 65 and 91 is 13. The fraction can be simplified to $\frac{5}{7}$.

41. Open-Ended Write two fractions whose simplest form is $\frac{3x}{5}$. See left.

42. Writing in Math Does $\frac{1}{2}$ of one pizza represent the same amount as $\frac{1}{2}$ of another pizza? Justify your answer. Answers may vary. Sample: Yes, as long as the pizzas are the same size and weight.

Data Analysis The table shows the number of personal computers (PCs) and households with Internet access in the United States. For Exercises 43–45, write each fraction in simplest form.

PC and On-Line Households in the U.S. (millions)

Households	1997	1998
Total households	100	101
Households with PCs	44	48
Households with Internet access	21	27

SOURCE: *The Wall Street Journal Almanac 1999*

43. In 1997, what fraction of U.S. households had PCs? $\frac{11}{25}$

44. In 1997, what fraction of U.S. households with PCs had Internet access? (Assume that a household with Internet access had a PC.) $\frac{21}{44}$

45. a. In 1998, what fraction of U.S. households with PCs had Internet access? (*Hint:* See Exercise 44.) $\frac{9}{16}$

b. Was the fraction greater in 1997 or 1998? Explain. 1998; $\frac{9}{16}$ is greater than $\frac{1}{2}$, $\frac{21}{44}$ is less than $\frac{1}{2}$.

194 Chapter 4 Factors, Fractions, and Exponents

GPS Use the Guided Problem Solving worksheet with Exercise 13.

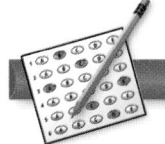

46. Write the numerator and denominator of $\frac{24}{32}$ as products of prime factors. Then use the prime factors to write $\frac{24}{32}$ in simplest form.

$$\frac{2 \cdot 2 \cdot 2 \cdot 3}{2 \cdot 2 \cdot 2 \cdot 2 \cdot 2} = \frac{3}{2 \cdot 2} = \frac{3}{4}$$

Test Prep

Multiple Choice

47. Which fraction is equivalent to $\frac{15}{30}$? **A**

   A. $\frac{2}{4}$ **B.** $\frac{3}{5}$ **C.** $\frac{3}{4}$ **D.** $\frac{5}{6}$

48. What is the simplest form for $\frac{14}{42}$? **F**

   F. $\frac{1}{3}$ **G.** $\frac{7}{21}$ **H.** $\frac{2}{6}$ **I.** $\frac{2}{3}$

> **Take It to the NET**
> Online lesson quiz at
> **www.PHSchool.com**
> Web Code: ada-0404

49. What is the simplest form for $\frac{6m}{15m}$? **D**

   A. $\frac{2m}{15m}$ **B.** $\frac{3m}{5m}$ **C.** $\frac{3}{5}$ **D.** $\frac{2}{5}$

Short Response

50. a. Is $\frac{ab}{5}$ equivalent to $\frac{15a^2b}{75a}$?   **b.** Justify your answer.

   [2] Yes; $\frac{ab}{5} \cdot \frac{15a}{15a} = \frac{15a^2b}{75a}$ [1] Yes; no work shown.

Mixed Review

Lesson 4-3   **Find the GCF for each pair.**

51. $10, 12$ **2**   **52.** $28, 60$ **4**   **53.** $14a, 21a$ **7a**   **54.** $24x^2, 40x^3$ **$8x^2$**

Lesson 3-5   **Solve each equation.**

55. $y + 3.23 = 5.85$ **56.** $b - 2.13 = 9.9$ **57.** $12.8 + z = 6.47$
    2.62   12.03   −6.33

Lesson 3-2 **58. Oil Spills** A damaged oil tanker spilled 34.7 million gallons of crude oil over 4 days. On the average, about how many gallons did the tanker spill each day? **9 million gallons**

 Checkpoint Quiz 1   **Lessons 4-1 through 4-4**

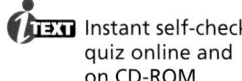 Instant self-check quiz online and on CD-ROM

State whether each number is divisible by 2, 3, 5, 9, 10, or none.

1. 30   **2.** 54 **2, 3, 9**   **3.** 48 **2, 3**   **4.** 161 **none**   **5.** 2,583
   2, 3, 5, 10   **3, 9**

Evaluate each expression.

6. x^2, for $x = 8$ **64**   **7.** a^3, for $a = 5$ **125**   **8.** $-2z^2$, for $z = -3$
                                                                −18

Write in simplest form.

9. $\frac{8}{16}$ $\frac{1}{2}$ **10.** $\frac{14}{21}$ $\frac{2}{3}$ **11.** $\frac{16}{28}$ $\frac{4}{7}$ **12.** $\frac{3a}{12a}$ $\frac{1}{4}$ **13.** $\frac{2xy}{x}$ **2y**

14. Open-Ended Write two expressions whose GCF is $5a^2$.
   Answers may vary. Samples: $5a^2$, $10a^2$; $25a^3b$, $30a^2$

 Lesson Quiz 4-4

Find two fractions equivalent to each fraction.

1. $\frac{11}{16}$ Sample answer: $\frac{22}{32}$ and $\frac{33}{48}$

2. $\frac{7}{21}$ Sample answer: $\frac{1}{3}$ and $\frac{10}{30}$

Write in simplest form.

3. $\frac{13}{52}$ $\frac{1}{4}$

4. $\frac{wx^4y^8}{w^2x^3y}$ $\frac{xy^7}{w}$

✓ Chapter Checkpoint 1

To check understanding of Lessons 4-1 to 4-4:

Checkpoint Quiz 1 (p. 195)

📁 **Teaching Resources**
Checkpoint Quiz 1 (also in Prentice Hall Assessment System)

👥 **Reaching All Students**
Reading and Math Literacy 4B

Spanish versions available.

Reteaching 4-4 Simplifying Fractions

Alternative Assessment

Have students create a diagram that models the fact that the fraction $\frac{6}{8}$ and its simplest form are equivalent.

Test Prep

📁 **Resources**
For additional practice with a variety of test item formats:
• Test Prep, p. 227
• Test-Taking Strategies, p. 222
• Test-Taking Strategies With Transparencies

Reading for Problem Solving

Students read through a problem and follow the thinking of another student before solving a similar type of problem.

Teaching Notes

Students become better problem solvers if they can explain their own thinking about how they solved a problem. Suggest that students pair together after they have solved a problem to explain their thinking to each other, and see if they understand and agree with the other's thinking and answers.

Error Prevention!

Remind students to always check their answers and the steps involved in finding the answers.

Visual Learners

Exercises 1–5 Give each pair of students a transparency and a marker. Ask them to write their solutions to the Exercises. They should divide the transparency into two columns: write what they think on the left and the solution on the right (similar to the Example). Ask student pairs to volunteer to show their solutions on the overhead projector. Allow for class discussion of the various solutions.

Reading Math

Reading for Problem Solving

For Use With Page 194, Exercise 40

Read the exercise below and then follow along with what Tina thinks and writes. Check your understanding by solving the exercises at the bottom of the page.

Error Analysis A student claims $\frac{65}{91}$ is in simplest form. Do you agree? Explain.

What Tina Thinks and Writes

Do I agree?	The wording of the problem suggests that the student is wrong. I'll write:
	No.
	Now I have to "Explain."
What does simplest form mean for a fraction?	The numerator and denominator can have no common factor other than 1.
65 ends in 5, so 65 has 5 as a factor. Is 5 also a factor of 91?	No! 91 does not end in 5. 5 is not a factor of 91.
Are there other possibilities for common factors?	Since 5 is a factor of 65. There has to be another factor. $65 = 5 \cdot 13$
Is 13 a factor of 91?	$91 = 7 \cdot 13$. A ha! I'll finish:

No.
$$\frac{65}{91} = \frac{5 \cdot \overset{1}{\cancel{13}}}{7 \cdot \underset{1}{\cancel{13}}} = \frac{5}{7}$$
$\frac{5}{7}$ is the simplest form for the fraction.

I'm done!

EXERCISES

Use what you know about factors to decide whether each fraction is in simplest form. If not, simplify.

1. $\frac{17}{51}$ $\frac{1}{3}$

2. $\frac{39}{91}$ $\frac{3}{7}$

3. $\frac{51}{57}$ $\frac{17}{19}$

4. $\frac{57}{76}$ $\frac{3}{4}$

5. $\frac{57}{87}$ $\frac{19}{29}$

Account for All Possibilities

OBJECTIVE

 1 Account for All Possibilities

Math Strategies in Action Have you ever lost something that you just couldn't find anywhere? Don't you usually discover that you didn't check *every* place you could, even when you thought you had?

"Has anyone seen the remote?"

Even for a situation like losing a TV remote control, making a list of places to search might help.

In some problems, you need to count the possibilities. To solve these problems, you need to be sure that you have found every possibility. Organized lists and diagrams help you keep track of the possibilities as you find them.

---

1 EXAMPLE Real-World Problem Solving

Photography Mandy, Jim, Keisha, Darren, Lin, Chris, and Jen are friends. They want to take pictures of themselves with two people in each picture. How many pictures do they need to take?

Read and Understand

1. What do you need to find? the number of pictures that must be taken

2. How many people are there in all? 7 people

3. How many people will be in each photograph? 2 people

 TEXT Interactive lesson includes instant self-check, tutorials, and activities.

What You'll Learn

OBJECTIVE 1 To find all possibilities when you solve a problem

. . . And Why

To solve real-world problems involving photography

✔ **Check Skills You'll Need**

**Compare.
Use > or < to complete each statement.**

1. $3 \ \blacksquare\ 0$ >

2. $-16 \ \blacksquare\ -25$ >

3. $0 \ \blacksquare\ 1$ <

4. $-30 \ \blacksquare\ -20$ <

❓ For help, go to Skills Handbook, p. 775.

---

1. Plan

Lesson Preview

✔ **Check Skills You'll Need**

Working With Integers
Skills Handbook: p. 775;
Exercises 9–33.

Lesson Resources

 **Teaching Resources**
Practice, Reteaching, Enrichment

Reaching All Students
Practice Workbook 4-5
Spanish Practice Workbook 4-5
Guided Problem Solving 4-5

 Presentation Assistant Plus!
Transparencies and PowerPoint™
• Check Skills You'll Need 4-5
• Additional Examples 4-5
• Student Edition Answers 4-5
• Lesson Quiz 4-5
PH Presentation Pro CD-ROM 4-5

ASSESSMENT SYSTEM

Computer Test Generator CD-ROM

 Technology
Resource Pro® CD-ROM
Computer Test Generator CD-ROM
PH Presentation Pro CD-ROM

www.PHSchool.com
Student Site
• Teacher Web Code: adk-5500
• Self-grading Lesson Quiz
PH SuccessNet Teacher Center
• Lesson Planner
• Resources

Plus **TEXT**

Ongoing Assessment and Intervention

Before the Lesson	During the Lesson	After the Lesson
Diagnose prerequisite skills using:	**Monitor progress using:**	**Assess knowledge using:**
• Check Skills You'll Need	• Check Understanding	• Lesson Quiz
	• Additional Examples	• Computer Test Generator CD-ROM
	• Test Prep	

Math Background

One way to account for all possibilities is to organize problem data into carefully constructed lists or diagrams. If you do not draw diagrams neatly or construct lists systematically, it is easy to miss one of the possibilities, or to include a possibility more than once.

Teaching Notes

Statistics Connection

The collection, manipulation, analysis, and classification of data are parts of a branch of mathematics called *statistics*.

1 EXAMPLE Error Prevention

Students may count one pair of friends twice. Mandy and Jim form a pair, but students may also count the pair Jim and Mandy. Point out that order does not matter in this problem. Ask why.

Tactile Learners

Have students work together in groups of seven to model the Example. Give each group more than twenty-one pieces of twine, each 3 ft long. Ask students to form a "diagram of pairs" using themselves and the twine. Each should share a piece of twine with each of the other members of the group. Only two students may hold any one piece of twine.

PowerPoint
Additional Example

Aaron, Chris, Maria, Sonia, and Ling are on a class committee. They want to choose two members to present their conclusions to the class. How many different groups of two members can they form?
10 groups

Closure

Ask students for two methods that can help solve problems about the numbers of ways that events can happen.
See back of book.

198

Plan and Solve

To make sure that you account for every pair of friends, make an organized list.

First pair Mandy with each of her six friends. Next, pair Jim with each of the five friends left. Since Mandy and Jim have already been paired, you don't need to count them again.

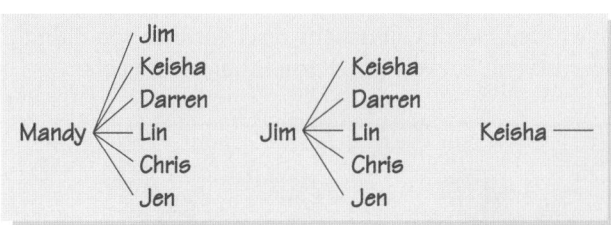

4.

Keisha ⟨ Darren, Lin, Chris, Jen

Darren ⟨ Lin, Chris, Jen

Lin ⟨ Chris, Jen

Chris —— Jen

4. Copy and complete the list of paired friends. **See left.**

5. What pattern do you see? Sample: Each successive list has one fewer person to pair with.

6. How many pictures do they need to take? **21 pictures**

Look Back and Check

Another way to solve this problem is to use a diagram. Draw line segments to show all possible pairs of friends.

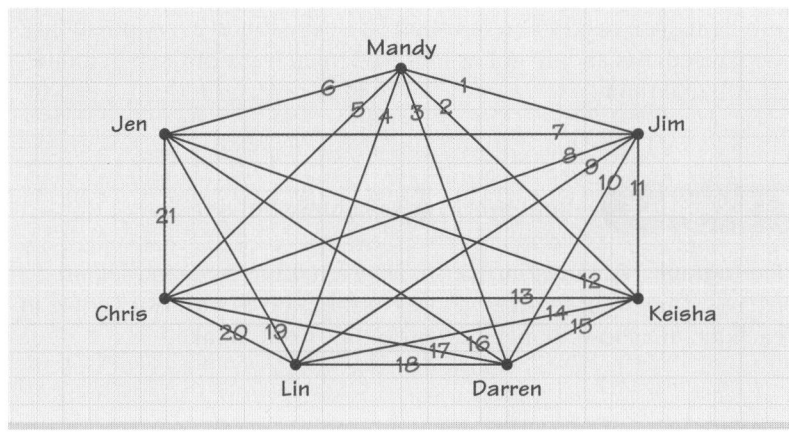

There are 21 line segments. This shows there are 21 pairs of friends.

✓ Check Understanding

7. Suppose Mandy and nine friends pair up for pictures. Use the pattern suggested above and find how many pictures there will be. **45 pictures**

👥 Reaching All Students

Below Level Ask volunteers to describe how they organize data they need for some daily activities. Class schedules, assignment lists, and shopping lists are good examples.	**Advanced Learners** Challenge students to write a formula that gives the number of pictures to be taken when there are *n* friends in the group and two friends are in each picture. $\frac{n(n-1)}{2}$	**Tactile Learners** See note on page 198. **Visual Learners** See note on page 199.

EXERCISES

For more exercises, see Extra Practice.

Practice and Problem Solving

A Practice by Example

Example 1
(page 197)

Solve each problem by accounting for all possibilities.

1. A sandwich shop serves turkey, ham, tuna, chicken, and egg salad sandwiches. You can have any sandwich using white, wheat, or rye bread. Suppose you eat there every day. For how many days can you order a sandwich that is different from any you have ordered before? The start of an organized list is shown above. Copy and complete the list to solve the problem.
15 days; see margin for diagram.

turkey
ham
white — tuna
chicken
egg salad

turkey
wheat — ham

Strategies

- Account for All Possibilities
- Draw a Diagram
- Look for a Pattern
- Make a Model
- Make a Table
- Simplify the Problem
- Simulate the Problem
- Solve by Graphing
- Try, Test, Revise
- Use Multiple Strategies
- Work Backward
- Write an Equation
- Write a Proportion

2. You throw three darts at the board shown at the right. If each dart hits the board, what possible point totals can you score? **30, 24, 21, 18, 15, 12, 9, 6, 3**

3. **GPS** You have pepperoni, mushrooms, onions, and green peppers. How many different pizzas can you make by using one, two, three, or four of the toppings?
15 pizzas

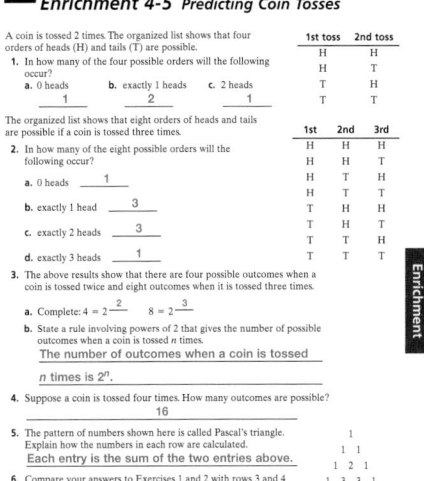

A dart landing on the board scores 1, 4, or 10 points.

4. **Elections** Four candidates run for president of the student council. Three other candidates run for vice-president. In how many different ways can the two offices be filled? **12 ways**

B Apply Your Skills

5. **Patterns** Eight people are at a party. Everyone shakes hands once with everyone else. How many handshakes are there altogether? **28 handshakes**

6. **Geometry** You have 24 feet of fence to make a rectangular garden. Each side will measure a whole number of feet. How many different-sized rectangular gardens can you make?
6 gardens

Solve using any strategy.

7. **Patterns** The bottom row of a stack of blocks contains 11 blocks. The row above it contains 9 blocks. The next higher row contains 7 blocks. The rows continue in this pattern, and the top row contains a single block. How many blocks does the stack contain in all? **36 blocks**

1.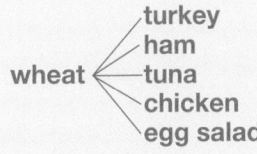

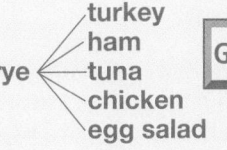

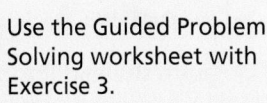

GPS Use the Guided Problem Solving worksheet with Exercise 3.

---

3. Practice

Assignment Guide

1 Objective 1
A B Core 1–7
C Extension 8–12

Test Prep 13–16
Mixed Review 17–24

Visual Learners
Exercise 7 Have students draw models systematically for this problem and look for a pattern.

Practice 4-5 _Account for All Possibilities_

Solve each problem by accounting for all possibilities.

1. A baseball team has 4 pitchers and 3 catchers. How many different pitcher-catcher combinations are possible? One way to solve this problem is to make a list like the one started below. Finish the list.
12

P1-C1	P2-C1
P1-C2	P2-C2
P1-C3	P2-C3
P3-C1	P4-C1
P3-C2	P4-C2
P3-C3	P4-C3

2. The baseball team has 2 first basemen, 3 second basemen, and 2 third basemen. How many combinations of the three positions are possible?
12

3. A quarter is tossed 3 times. In how many different orders can heads and tails be tossed?
8

4. A quarter is tossed 4 times. In how many different orders can heads and tails be tossed?
16

5. Curtains are manufactured in 3 different styles and 5 different colors.
a. How many different style-color combinations are possible?
15

b. The curtains are produced in 2 different fabrics. How many different style-color-fabric combinations are possible?
30

Enrichment 4-5 _Predicting Coin Tosses_

A coin is tossed 2 times. The organized list shows that four orders of heads (H) and tails (T) are possible.

1. In how many of the four possible orders will the following occur?
a. 0 heads   b. exactly 1 heads   c. 2 heads
1   **2**   **1**

1st toss	2nd toss
H	H
H	T
T	H
T	T

The organized list shows that eight orders of heads and tails are possible if a coin is tossed three times.

2. In how many of the eight possible orders will the following occur?
a. 0 heads **1**
b. exactly 1 head **3**
c. exactly 2 heads **3**
d. exactly 3 heads **1**

1st	2nd	3rd
H	H	H
H	H	T
H	T	H
H	T	T
T	H	H
T	H	T
T	T	H
T	T	T

3. The above results show that there are four possible outcomes when a coin is tossed twice and eight outcomes when it is tossed three times.
a. Complete: $4 = 2^{2}$ $8 = 2^{3}$
b. State a rule involving powers of 2 that gives the number of possible outcomes when a coin is tossed n times.
The number of outcomes when a coin is tossed n times is 2^n.

4. Suppose a coin is tossed four times. How many outcomes are possible?
16

5. The pattern of numbers shown here is called Pascal's triangle. Explain how the numbers in each row are calculated.
Each entry is the sum of the two entries above.

6. Compare your answers to Exercises 1 and 2 with rows 3 and 4 of Pascal's triangle. What do you notice?
They are the same.

```
            1
          1   1
        1   2   1
      1   3   3   1
    1   4   6   4   1
  1   5  10  10   5   1
1   6  15  20  15   6   1
```

7. When a coin is tossed 4 times in how many of the outcomes does exactly 2 heads occur?
6

Lesson Quiz 4-5

1. Twelve people are at a party. Each person greets each of the other persons exactly once. How many greetings will there be in all? **66**

2. How many different pairs of classmates can you choose from six classmates?
15 pairs

3. Each small box is a square. What is the number of different squares shown?

17

Test Prep

📁 Resources
For additional practice with a variety of test item formats:
- Test Prep, p. 227
- Test-Taking Strategies, p. 222
- Test-Taking Strategies With Transparencies

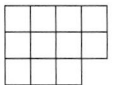

Reteaching 4-5 Account for All Possibilities

A taco shop serves beef, chicken, or bean burritos. You can have any burrito on a corn or a flour tortilla and with or without hot sauce. How many different burritos does the shop serve? The different burritos are listed in the table at the right. To be sure all possibilities are counted, all the beef burritos are listed first. Within those, the two types of beef burritos on a corn tortilla are listed first. The pattern is continued with chicken and then bean burritos.

Filling	Tortilla	Hot Sauce
beef	corn	yes
beef	corn	no
beef	flour	yes
beef	flour	no
chicken	corn	yes
chicken	corn	no
chicken	flour	yes
chicken	flour	no
bean	corn	yes
bean	corn	no
bean	flour	yes
bean	flour	no

Solve each problem by accounting for all possibilities.

1. Kara and Karl love steak, fried chicken, hamburgers, mashed potatoes, and french fries. They like green beans and peas. How many different meals including a meat, potatoes, and a green vegetable can they make from these choices? List all possibilities to find the number of different meals.
12 meals

Meat	Potato	Vegetable
steak	mashed	beans
steak	mashed	peas
steak	fries	beans
steak	fries	peas
chicken	mashed	beans
chicken	mashed	peas
chicken	fries	beans
chicken	fries	peas
hamburger	mashed	beans
hamburger	mashed	peas
hamburger	fries	beans
hamburger	fries	peas

2. You are interested in four different extracurricular activities: jazz band, soccer, debate, and theater. You have time in your schedule for only two activities. How many different combinations of two activities can you pick from the four choices?
6

C Challenge 🌐 8. **Routes** Copy the diagram at the left. Using the paths shown, Jill can walk to Trisha's house in many different ways. Draw each route that is four blocks long. How can you be sure that you have found all possible routes? **Answers may vary. Sample: Draw line segments for all 4-block routes. For sketch, see back of book.**

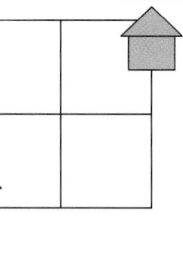

Trisha

Jill

🌐 9. **Seating Arrangements** Ana, Brian, Carla, David, and Eric are friends. They go to a movie, but cannot find five seats together. They have to split up into a group of three and a group of two. How many different ways can the friends organize themselves into these two groups? **10 different ways**

10. You have one penny, one nickel, one dime, and one quarter. How many different amounts of money can you make using one or more of these coins? **15 amounts**

🌐 11. **Softball** There are seven softball teams in a league. Each team plays each of the other teams twice. What is the total number of games played? **42 games**

12. **Geometry** How many different rectangles are there with an area of 36 cm^2 if the side lengths of each, in centimeters, are whole numbers? **5 rectangles**

Test Prep

Multiple Choice

13. Which list shows all the positive factors of 32? **B**
    A. 1, 2, 3, 8, 16, 32   **B.** 1, 2, 4, 8, 16, 32
    C. 1, 2, 3, 4, 8, 16, 32   **D.** 1, 2, 4, 6, 8, 16, 32

14. What is the value of $(0.3)^2$? **I**
    F. 0.6   **G.** 0.9   **H.** 0.06   **I.** 0.09

15. What is the GCF of $24x^2y^3$ and $32x^3y$? **D**
    A. $4xy$ **B.** $4x^2y$ **C.** $8xy$ **D.** $8x^2y$

🖥 Take It to the NET
Online lesson quiz at
www.PHSchool.com
Web Code: ada-0405

16. Which fraction is the simplest form of $\frac{45}{60}$? **G**
    F. $\frac{2}{3}$ **G.** $\frac{3}{4}$ **H.** $\frac{15}{20}$ **I.** $\frac{5}{6}$

Mixed Review

21. Start with 10; **Lesson 4-4** add 10 repeatedly.

22. Start with 8; subtract 3 repeatedly. **Lesson 1-7**

23. Start with 2; multiply by 3 repeatedly.

Write in simplest form.

17. $\frac{6}{12}$ $\frac{1}{2}$ 18. $\frac{10}{40}$ $\frac{1}{4}$ 19. $\frac{6a^2}{15}$ $\frac{2a^2}{5}$ 20. $\frac{14a^3}{28a^2}$ $\frac{a}{2}$

Write a rule for each pattern.

21. 10, 20, 30, . . .
    See left.
22. 8, 5, 2, −1, . . .
    See left.
23. 2, 6, 18, 54, . . .
    See left.

Lesson 1-2

24. Elki has read the first 60 pages of a book. When he has read 35 more pages, he will have read half the book. How many pages are in the book? **190 pages**

Alternative Assessment

Organize students into groups of 4 or 5. Assign each group a different exercise from the lesson. Instruct each group to model all possibilities of their assigned exercise, either with concrete objects or drawings. If a group needs more members to accomplish its goal, there may be other groups who need fewer members.

1. Plan

OBJECTIVE

1 Identifying and Graphing Rational Numbers

A **rational number** is any number you can write as a quotient $\frac{a}{b}$ of two integers, where b is not zero. The diagram below shows relationships among rational numbers.

Notice that all integers are rational numbers. This is true because you can write any integer a as $\frac{a}{1}$.

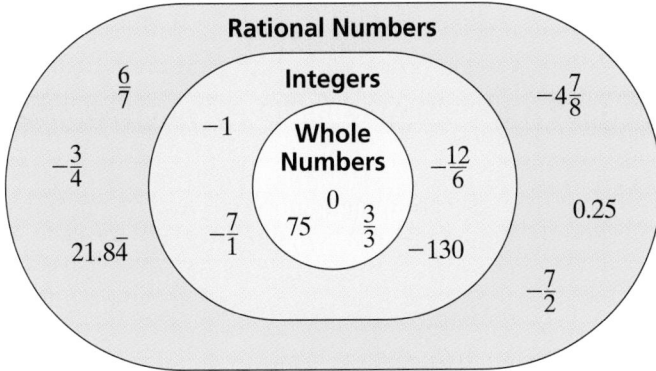

Here are three ways you can write a negative rational number.

$$-\frac{7}{9} = \frac{-7}{9} = \frac{7}{-9}$$

For each rational number, there is an unlimited number of equivalent fractions.

1 EXAMPLE Writing Equivalent Fractions

Write two lists of fractions equivalent to $\frac{1}{2}$.

$\frac{1}{2} = \frac{2}{4} = \frac{3}{6} = \cdots$ **Numerators and denominators are positive.**

$\frac{1}{2} = \frac{-1}{-2} = \frac{-2}{-4} = \cdots$ **Numerators and denominators are negative.**

✓ Check Understanding Example 1

1a–d. Answers may vary. Samples are given.

1. Write three fractions equivalent to each fraction.

a. $\frac{1}{3}$ b. $-\frac{4}{5}$ c. $\frac{5}{8}$ d. $-\frac{1}{2}$

$\frac{2}{6}, \frac{-2}{-6}, \frac{-1}{-3}$ $-\frac{8}{10}, \frac{-4}{5}, \frac{4}{-5}$ $\frac{10}{16}, \frac{-10}{-16}, \frac{-5}{-8}$ $\frac{-2}{4}, \frac{-1}{2}, \frac{1}{-2}$

What You'll Learn

 OBJECTIVE 1 To identify and graph rational numbers

 OBJECTIVE 2 To evaluate fractions containing variables

. . . And Why

To solve real-world problems involving rates

✓ Check Skills You'll Need

Write in simplest form.

1. $\frac{2}{10}$ $\frac{1}{5}$ **2.** $\frac{14}{21}$ $\frac{2}{3}$

3. $\frac{28}{35}$ $\frac{4}{5}$ **4.** $\frac{6}{8}$ $\frac{3}{4}$

❓ For help, go to Lesson 4-4.

New Vocabulary

• rational number

Need Help?

The quotient of two integers with the same sign is positive.

ⓘTEXT Interactive lesson includes instant self-check, tutorials, and activities.

1. Plan

Lesson Preview

✓ **Check Skills You'll Need**

Simplifying Fractions
Lesson 4-4: Example 2;
Exercises 7–12.
Extra Practice, p. 747

Lesson Resources

 Teaching Resources
Practice, Reteaching, Enrichment

 Reaching All Students
Practice Workbook 4-6
Spanish Practice Workbook 4-6
Guided Problem Solving 4-6

⏲ **Presentation Assistant Plus!**
Transparencies and PowerPoint™
• Check Skills You'll Need 4-6
• Additional Examples 4-6
• Student Edition Answers 4-6
• Lesson Quiz 4-6
PH Presentation Pro CD-ROM 4-6

 ASSESSMENT SYSTEM

Computer Test Generator CD-ROM

 Technology
Resource Pro® CD-ROM
Computer Test Generator CD-ROM
PH Presentation Pro CD-ROM

 www.PHSchool.com
Student Site
• Teacher Web Code: adk-5500
• Algebra Readiness Puzzles 15
• Graphing Calculator, Procedure 2
• Self-grading Lesson Quiz
PH SuccessNet Teacher Center
• Lesson Planner
• Resources

Plus ⓘTEXT

🔄 Ongoing Assessment and Intervention

Before the Lesson
Diagnose prerequisite skills using:
• Check Skills You'll Need

During the Lesson
Monitor progress using:
• Check Understanding
• Additional Examples
• Test Prep

After the Lesson
Assess knowledge using:
• Lesson Quiz
• Computer Test Generator CD-ROM

2. Teach

Professional
Development

Math Background

Any rational number can be written as a ratio. See Lesson 5-2 for another form for rational numbers.

Teaching Notes

English Learners

Students may be puzzled by the use of *rational* in a math context. Point out that any *rati*onal number can be written as a *ratio*.

2 EXAMPLE Tactile Learners

Use masking tape to make a long number line on the floor. Use tick marks on the tape to indicate integers, naming one of them zero. Distribute index cards with rational numbers written on them. Instruct students to stand at the places on the number line that correspond to their rational numbers.

3 EXAMPLE Error Prevention

Remind students that the fraction bar is a grouping symbol, so they must simplify the numerator and denominator before dividing.

PowerPoint

Additional Examples

❶ Write two lists of fractions equivalent to $\frac{2}{3}$.

❷ Graph each rational number on a number line.
a. $-\frac{3}{4}$ b. 0.5 c. 0 d. $\frac{1}{3}$
1–2. See back of book.

❸ A fast sports car can accelerate from a stop to 90 ft/s in 5 seconds. What is its acceleration in feet per second per second (ft/s²)? Use the formula $a = \frac{f-i}{t}$, where a is acceleration, f is final speed, i is initial speed, and t is time.
18 ft/s²

Closure

Ask students to give examples of several equivalent forms of one rational number. **Answers may vary. Sample:** $\frac{1}{2}, \frac{-1}{-2}, \frac{5}{10}, \frac{-5}{-10}$

202

You can graph rational numbers on a number line.

2 EXAMPLE Graphing a Rational Number

Graph each rational number on a number line.

a. $\frac{1}{2}$ b. $-\frac{8}{10}$ c. 1 d. -0.2

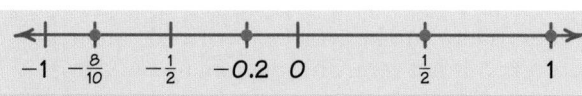

✓ **Check Understanding** Example 2

2. Graph each rational number on a number line. **See back of book.**

a. $-\frac{1}{2}$ b. $-\frac{4}{10}$ c. -2 d. 0.9

OBJECTIVE

2 Evaluating Fractions Containing Variables

Recall that a fraction bar is a grouping symbol, so you first simplify the numerator and the denominator. Then, simplify the fraction.

Simplify the numerator. ⟶ $\dfrac{1+9+2}{2-5} = \dfrac{12}{-3} = -4$ ⟵ simplest form
Simplify the denominator. ⟶

To simplify a fraction with variables, first substitute for the variables.

3 EXAMPLE Real-World Problem Solving

Science The speed of a car changes from 37 ft/s to 102 ft/s in five seconds. What is its acceleration in feet per second per second (ft/s²)? Use the formula $a = \dfrac{f-i}{t}$ where a is acceleration, f is final speed, i is initial speed, and t is time.

$a = \dfrac{f-i}{t}$ Use the acceleration formula.

$= \dfrac{102-37}{5}$ Substitute for the variables.

$= \dfrac{65}{5}$ Subtract.

$= 13$ Write in simplest form.

Real-World Connection

The world's fastest car, the *Thrust SSC,* can go from 0 ft/s to 1,119 ft/s in thirty seconds.

The car's acceleration is 13 ft/s².

✓ **Check Understanding** Example 3

3. Evaluate for $a = 6$ and $b = -5$. Write in simplest form.

a. $\dfrac{a+b}{-3}$ $-\frac{1}{3}$ b. $\dfrac{7-b}{3a}$ $\frac{2}{3}$ c. $\dfrac{a+9}{b}$ -3

202 Chapter 4 Factors, Fractions, and Exponents

👥 Reaching All Students

Below Level Ask students to list positive and negative numbers that are not integers. Ask if they can think of other forms for each number they list.	Advanced Learners Ask: *How many fractions equivalent to $\frac{2}{7}$ can be found?* infinitely many	English Learners See note on page 202. Tactile Learners See note on page 202.

EXERCISES

Practice and Problem Solving

For more exercises, see *Extra Practice*.

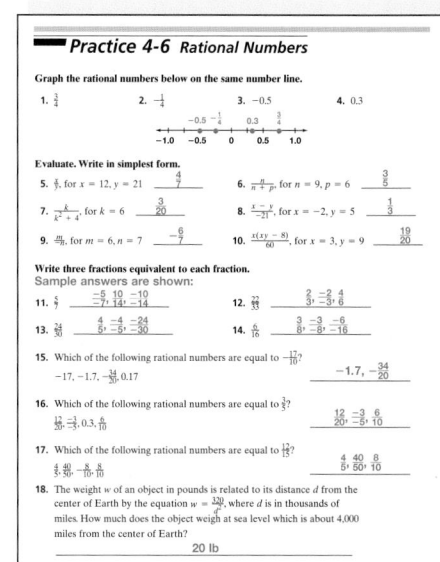

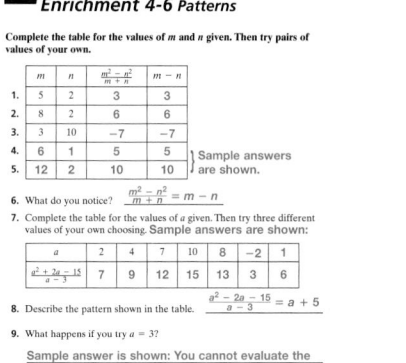

A Practice by Example

Example 1
(page 201)

Show the next three fractions equivalent to $\frac{1}{2}$ in each list.

1. $\frac{1}{2}, \frac{2}{4}, \frac{3}{6}, \cdots$ $\frac{4}{8}, \frac{5}{10}, \frac{6}{12}$

2. $\frac{1}{2}, \frac{-1}{-2}, \frac{-3}{-6}, \cdots$ $\frac{-5}{-10}, \frac{-7}{-14}, \frac{-9}{-18}$

Write three fractions equivalent to each fraction. 3–8. Answers may vary. See below left.

3. $\frac{1}{6}$ **4.** $\frac{3}{5}$ **5.** $-\frac{5}{9}$ **6.** $-\frac{4}{4}$ **7.** $-\frac{2}{3}$ **8.** $\frac{4}{7}$

Example 2
(page 202)

Graph each rational number on a number line. 9–14. See margin.

9. $\frac{1}{10}$ **10.** $-\frac{3}{5}$ **11.** 2   **12.** -0.3 **13.** -0.75 **14.** $\frac{2}{3}$

Example 3
(page 202)

Evaluate for $a = -4$ and $b = -6$. Write in simplest form.
16–20. See below left.

15. $\frac{a}{b}$ $\frac{2}{3}$ **16.** $\frac{a + 9}{b}$ **17.** $\frac{b + a}{3a}$ **18.** $\frac{2a + b}{20}$ **19.** $\frac{b + 7}{2a}$ **20.** $\frac{b - a}{3b}$

21. Boat Races The speed of a racing boat changes from 0 ft/s to 264 ft/s in six seconds. What is the acceleration of the boat in ft/s²? Use the acceleration formula given in Example 3. **44 ft/s²**

B Apply Your Skills

Write three fractions equivalent to each fraction. 22–27. Answers may vary. See below left.

22. $\frac{2}{8}$ **23.** $-\frac{2}{5}$ **24.** $\frac{4}{12}$ **25.** $-\frac{12}{27}$ **26.** $\frac{7}{11}$ **27.** $-\frac{5}{13}$

Write a rational number that is between each pair of numbers.
28–30. Answers may vary. Samples are given.

28. $0, -1\frac{-2}{8}$ **29.** $0.9, 1.1\frac{8}{8}$ **30.** $\frac{-1}{5}, \frac{-4}{5}$ -0.5

Evaluate. Write in simplest form.

31. $\frac{y}{-x}$, for $x = 5$ and $y = -4$ $\frac{4}{5}$ **32.** $\frac{-2y}{x^2}$, for $x = 9$ and $y = 3$ $-\frac{2}{27}$

33. $\frac{m}{n}$, for $m = -2$ and $n = 8$ $-\frac{1}{4}$ **34.** $\frac{m - n}{-12}$, for $m = -3$ and $n = 6$ $\frac{3}{4}$

35. $\frac{6b - 16}{3c}$, for $b = 8$ and $c = 12$ $\frac{8}{9}$ **36.** $\frac{3m - 11}{n}$, for $m = 7$ and $n = 14$ $\frac{5}{7}$

37. Which of the following rational numbers are equivalent to $-\frac{4}{5}$?
$\frac{4}{-5}, \frac{-12}{15}, -\frac{16}{20}, \frac{-4}{-5}, \frac{4}{-5}, \frac{-12}{15}, -\frac{16}{20}$

38. a. Open-Ended Write two rational numbers between 0 and $\frac{1}{2}$.

   b. How many other rational numbers are between 0 and $\frac{1}{2}$? Explain.
a–b. See back of book.

39. Reasoning What are three fractions equivalent to $\frac{a}{b}$? Explain.
See back of book.

40. Science The formula $s = \frac{1,600}{d^2}$ gives the strength s of a radio signal at a distance d miles from the transmitter. What is the strength at 5 mi? Write your answer in simplest form. **64**

41. Writing in Math Explain why a whole number is an integer and an integer is a rational number. **See back of book.**

42. If the *Thrust SSC* (see page 202) can go from 0 ft/s to 1,119 ft/s in 30 s, what is its acceleration in feet per second per second? **37.3 ft/s²**

4-6 Rational Numbers **203**

(left margin answers)

3. $\frac{2}{12}, \frac{-2}{-12}, \frac{-1}{-6}$

4. $\frac{6}{10}, \frac{-6}{-10}, \frac{-3}{-5}$

5. $-\frac{10}{18}, \frac{-5}{9}, \frac{5}{-9}$

6. $-\frac{1}{1}, -\frac{2}{2}, -\frac{3}{3}$

7. $\frac{-4}{6}, \frac{-2}{3}, \frac{2}{-3}$

8. $\frac{8}{14}, \frac{-8}{-14}, \frac{-4}{-7}$

16. $-\frac{5}{6}$

17. $\frac{5}{6}$

18. $-\frac{7}{10}$

19. $-\frac{1}{8}$

20. $\frac{1}{9}$

22. $\frac{1}{4}, \frac{-1}{-4}, \frac{-2}{-8}$

23. $-\frac{4}{10}, \frac{-2}{5}, \frac{2}{-5}$

24. $\frac{1}{3}, \frac{-1}{-3}, \frac{-4}{-12}$

25. $-\frac{4}{9}, \frac{-12}{27}, \frac{12}{-27}$

26. $\frac{14}{22}, \frac{-14}{-22}, \frac{-7}{-11}$

27. $\frac{-10}{26}, \frac{-5}{13}, \frac{10}{-26}$

9–14.

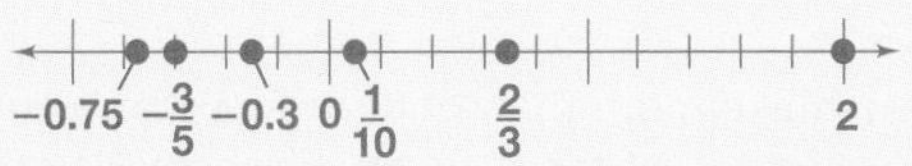

$-0.75 \quad -\frac{3}{5} \quad -0.3 \quad 0 \quad \frac{1}{10} \quad \frac{2}{3} \quad 2$

GPS Use the Guided Problem Solving worksheet with Exercise 40.

3. Practice

Assignment Guide

1 Objective 1
  A B **Core** 1–14, 22–30, 37–39, 41
  C **Extension** 43–48

2 Objective 2
  A B **Core** 15–21, 31–36, 40, 42
  C **Extension** 49–51

Test Prep 52–55
Mixed Review 56–64

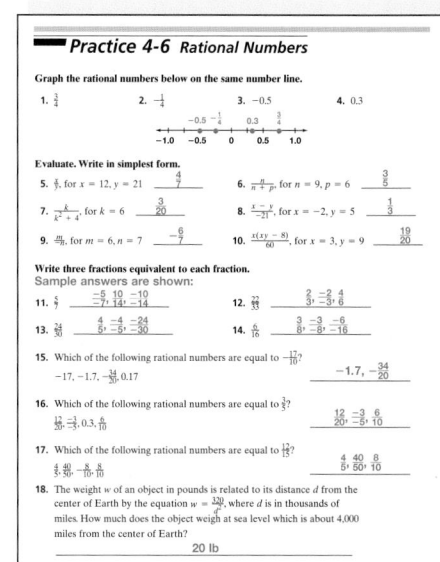

Practice 4-6 Rational Numbers

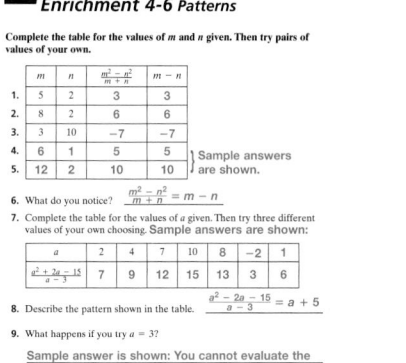

Enrichment 4-6 Patterns

203

Lesson Quiz 4-6

Write three fractions equivalent to the given fraction.

1. $\frac{5}{6}$ Sample: $\frac{-5}{-6}, \frac{10}{12}, \frac{15}{18}$

Graph each rational number on a number line.

2. a. $\frac{1}{4}$ **b.** $-\frac{1}{2}$ **c.** 1.5 **d.** 0.4

3. A car can accelerate from 0 to 70 ft/s in 5 s. What is the acceleration of the car in feet per second per second (ft/s²)? **14 ft/s²**

Error Prevention!

Exercise 37 Remind students that for the fraction to be negative, only the numerator or the denominator of the fractions given can be negative, not both.

Test Prep

Resources
For additional practice with a variety of test item formats:
- Test Prep, p. 227
- Test-Taking Strategies, p. 222
- Test-Taking Strategies With Transparencies

Reteaching 4-6 Rational Numbers

C Challenge

Write the opposite and the absolute value of each number.

SAMPLE Find the opposite and the absolute value of $-\frac{3}{5}$.

Opposite:

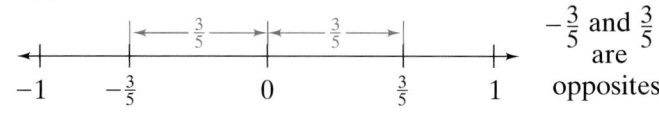

$-\frac{3}{5}$ and $\frac{3}{5}$ are opposites.

Absolute value:

$\left|-\frac{3}{5}\right| = \frac{3}{5}$

48. $\frac{a}{b}, \left|-\frac{a}{b}\right|$ or $\left|\frac{a}{b}\right|$

43. $\frac{2}{3}$ $-\frac{2}{3}, \frac{2}{3}$ **44.** $-\frac{5}{6}$ $\frac{5}{6}, \frac{5}{6}$ **45.** $\frac{-4}{5}$ $\frac{4}{5}, \frac{4}{5}$ **46.** $\frac{2}{-7}$ $\frac{2}{7}, \frac{2}{7}$ **47.** $\frac{-3}{-5}$ $-\frac{3}{5}, \frac{3}{5}$ **48.** $-\frac{a}{b}$
See left.

Reasoning Tell whether each statement is true for all positive integers a and b. If the statement is not always true, give a counterexample.

49. $\frac{a^2}{b} > \frac{a}{b}$ **50.** $\frac{3a}{3b} = \frac{a}{b}$ **51.** $\frac{a^2}{b^2} > \frac{a}{b}$
See margin.   **always true**   **See margin.**

Test Prep

Multiple Choice

52. Which three fractions are equivalent to $\frac{3}{4}$? **C**
A. $\frac{6}{8}, \frac{9}{16}, \frac{-6}{-8}$ **B.** $\frac{-3}{4}, \frac{12}{16}, \frac{15}{20}$ **C.** $\frac{6}{8}, \frac{-3}{-4}, \frac{9}{12}$ **D.** $\frac{15}{20}, \frac{12}{16}, \frac{-6}{8}$

53. What is the simplest form of $\frac{y(xy-7)}{10}$ when $x = 6$ and $y = 2$? **H**
F. 3 **G.** $\frac{30}{10}$ **H.** 1 **I.** $\frac{10}{10}$

54. Which pair of numbers is between -3 and -2? **A**
A. $-2\frac{1}{2}, -2\frac{1}{3}$ **B.** $-3\frac{1}{2}, -3\frac{1}{3}$ **C.** $-2, -\pi$ **D.** $-2\frac{1}{2}, -3$

Take It to the NET
Online lesson quiz at
www.PHSchool.com
Web Code: ada-0406

Short Response

55. Is $\frac{a^2}{b^2} > \frac{a}{b}$ true for all negative integers a and b? Explain.
[2] No; for $a = b = -1$, both expressions equal 1.
[1] No; incorrect or no explanation.

Mixed Review

Lesson 4-5
56. Patterns Lucia has 4 pairs of slacks, 5 shirts, and 2 sweaters. How many different three-piece outfits can she make?
40 three-piece outfits

Lesson 1-9
Multiply or divide.
57. $-7 \cdot 4$ **58.** $19(-5)$ **59.** $-124 \div (-4)$ **60.** $-204 \div 6$
-28 -95 31 -34

Lesson 1-4
Write the integer represented by each point on the number line.
61. A -1 **62.** B 1
63. C -4 **64.** D -2

Alternative Assessment

Mark a set of index cards prior to class. Write one rational number on a card and an equivalent form for that number on another card, until you have enough cards to give one to each student in the class. Shuffle the cards and distribute them to the class. If there are an odd number of students in the

class, make more than one card with an equivalent form for one of the rational numbers. Have each student find the classmate with the "match" for his or her card.

49. Not always true; **51.** Not always true;
for $a = 1, \frac{1^2}{1} = \frac{1}{1}$ for $a = 1 = b, \frac{1^2}{1^2} = \frac{1}{1}$

Exponents and Multiplication

OBJECTIVE

1 Multiplying Powers With the Same Base

In Lesson 4-2, you learned how to use exponents to indicate repeated multiplication. What happens when you multiply two powers with the same base, such as 7^2 and 7^3?

$$7^2 \cdot 7^3 = (7 \cdot 7) \cdot (7 \cdot 7 \cdot 7) = 7^5$$

Notice that $7^2 \cdot 7^3 = 7^5 = 7^{2+3}$. In general, when you multiply powers with the same base, you can add the exponents.

Key Concepts Multiplying Powers With the Same Base

To multiply numbers or variables with the same base, add the exponents.

Arithmetic	Algebra
$2^3 \cdot 2^4 = 2^{3+4} = 2^7$	$a^m \cdot a^n = a^{m+n}$, for positive integers m and n.

You *simplify* an expression by doing as many of the indicated operations as possible.

1 EXAMPLE Multiplying Powers

Simplify each expression.

a. $3 \cdot 3^3$

$3^1 \cdot 3^3 = 3^{1+3}$ **Add the exponents of powers with the same base.**

$= 3^4$

$= 81$ **Simplify.**

b. $a^5 \cdot a \cdot b^2$

$a^5 \cdot a^1 \cdot b^2 = a^{5+1}b^2$ **Add the exponents of powers with the same base.**

$= a^6b^2$ **Simplify.**

✓ **Check Understanding** Example 1

1. Simplify each expression.

a. $2^2 \cdot 2^3$ 32   **b.** $m^5 \cdot m^7$ m^{12} **c.** $x^2 \cdot x^3 \cdot y \cdot y^4$ x^5y^5

What You'll Learn

 OBJECTIVE 1 To multiply powers with the same base

 OBJECTIVE 2 To find a power of a power

... And Why

To learn the rules for operating with exponents

✓ **Check Skills You'll Need**

Write using exponents.

1. $k \cdot k \cdot k \cdot k$ k^4

2. $m \cdot n \cdot m \cdot n$ m^2n^2

3. $2 \cdot 2 \cdot 2 \cdot 2$ 2^4

4. $5 \cdot 5 \cdot 5$ 5^3

 For help, go to Lesson 4-2.

 **Need Help?**

Recall that $3 = 3^1$ and $a = a^1$ because a base with exponent 1 is equal to the base itself.

TEXT Interactive lesson includes instant self-check, tutorials, and activities.

Lesson Preview

✓ **Check Skills You'll Need**

Exponents
Lesson 4-2: Example 1;
Exercises 1–6.
Extra Practice, p. 747.

Lesson Resources

📁 **Teaching Resources**
Practice, Reteaching, Enrichment

 Reaching All Students
Practice Workbook 4-7
Spanish Practice Workbook 4-7
Guided Problem Solving 4-7
Technology Activities 7

⏱ **Presentation Assistant Plus!**
Transparencies and PowerPoint™
• Check Skills You'll Need 4-7
• Additional Examples 4-7
• Student Edition Answers 4-7
• Lesson Quiz 4-7
PH Presentation Pro CD-ROM 4-7

ASSESSMENT SYSTEM

Computer Test Generator CD-ROM

 Technology
Resource Pro® CD-ROM
Computer Test Generator CD-ROM
PH Presentation Pro CD-ROM

💻 **www.PHSchool.com**
Student Site
• Teacher Web Code: adk-5500
• Self-grading Lesson Quiz
PH SuccessNet Teacher Center
• Lesson Planner
• Resources

Plus **TEXT**

 Ongoing Assessment and Intervention

Before the Lesson
Diagnose prerequisite skills using:
• Check Skills You'll Need

During the Lesson
Monitor progress using:
• Check Understanding
• Additional Examples
• Test Prep

After the Lesson
Assess knowledge using:
• Lesson Quiz
• Computer Test Generator CD-ROM

Math Background

To discover the rules of exponents, write out all the factors of $5^3 \cdot 5^2$ and $(5^3)^2$. You find that to multiply powers having the same base, you add exponents. To raise a power to a power, you multiply exponents.

Teaching Notes

Error Prevention!

When simplifying $2^3 \cdot 2^4$, students may multiply the 2's and get 4^7. Have them find the values of 2^7, 4^7, and $2^3 \cdot 2^4$, and compare.

Auditory Learners

Direct students' attention to the title of Objective 2. Have students say *power of a power*, stressing the word *of*. Ask: *What operation does "of" signify?* multiplication Suggest students use this as a way to remember to multiply the exponents to find the power of a power.

3 EXAMPLE Visual Learners

Have students come to the board and write out all of the factors for each problem. Seeing all of the factors may reinforce the rule for finding a power of a power.

PowerPoint

Additional Examples

Simplify each expression.

1. **a.** $5^2 \cdot 5^3$ 3,125
   b. $x^5 \cdot x^7 \cdot y^2 \cdot y$ $x^{12}y^3$

2. $3a^3 \cdot -5a^4$ $-15a^7$

3. **a.** $(2^3)^3$ 512   **b.** $(g^5)^4$ g^{20}

Closure

Have students explain how to evaluate products of powers with the same base, and a power of a power. To evaluate products of powers with the same base, first add the exponents. To evaluate a power of a power, first multiply the exponents.

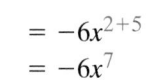

Test-Taking Tip

When in doubt, write it out! If you are unsure about the rules for multiplying powers, write the powers out. For instance, write $x^2 \cdot x^5$ as $(x \cdot x) \cdot (x \cdot x \cdot x \cdot x \cdot x)$. This simplifies to x^7.

---

2 EXAMPLE Using the Commutative Property

Simplify $-2x^2 \cdot 3x^5$.

$$-2x^2 \cdot 3x^5 = -2 \cdot 3 \cdot x^2 \cdot x^5 \quad \text{Use the Commutative Property of Multiplication.}$$
$$= -6x^{2+5} \quad \text{Add the exponents.}$$
$$= -6x^7 \quad \text{Simplify.}$$

✓ **Check Understanding** Example 2

2. Simplify each expression.
   a. $6a^3 \cdot 3a$ $18a^4$ **b.** $-5c^2 \cdot -3c^7$ $15c^9$ **c.** $4x^2 \cdot 3x^4$ $12x^6$

OBJECTIVE

2 Finding a Power of a Power

You can find the power of a power by using the rule of Multiplying Powers With the Same Base.

$$(7^2)^3 = (7^2) \cdot (7^2) \cdot (7^2) \quad \text{Use } 7^2 \text{ as a base 3 times.}$$
$$= 7^{2+2+2} \quad \text{When multiplying powers with the same base, add the exponents.}$$
$$= 7^6 \quad \text{Simplify.}$$

Notice that $(7^2)^3 = 7^6 = 7^{2 \cdot 3}$. You can raise a power to a power by multiplying the exponents.

Key Concepts Finding a Power of a Power

To find a power of a power, multiply the exponents.

Arithmetic	Algebra
$(2^3)^4 = 2^{3 \cdot 4} = 2^{12}$	$(a^m)^n = a^{m \cdot n}$, for positive integers m and n.

Reading Math

You read $(3^2)^3$ as "three squared to the third power." You read $(a^6)^2$ as "a to the sixth power squared."

---

3 EXAMPLE Simplifying Powers of Powers

Simplify each expression.

a. $(3^2)^3$

$$(3^2)^3 = (3)^{2 \cdot 3} \quad \longleftarrow \text{Multiply the exponents.} \longrightarrow$$
$$= (3)^6 \quad \longleftarrow \text{Simplify the exponent.} \longrightarrow$$
$$= 729 \quad \longleftarrow \text{Simplify.}$$

b. $(a^6)^2$

$$(a^6)^2 = a^{6 \cdot 2}$$
$$= a^{12}$$

✓ **Check Understanding** Example 3

3. Simplify each expression.
   a. $(2^4)^2$ 256   **b.** $(c^5)^4$ c^{20} **c.** $(m^3)^2$ m^6

206 Chapter 4 Factors, Fractions, and Exponents

👥 Reaching All Students

Below Level Write $6^2 \cdot 6^3$ on the board. Have students write $(6 \cdot 6) \cdot (6 \cdot 6 \cdot 6) = 6^5$. Repeat this process with several examples. Ask students what the rule seems to be for multiplying powers with the same base.	**Advanced Learners** Challenge students to predict how to handle exponents when dividing powers with the same base. They may want to experiment with examples. You subtract the exponents.	**Auditory Learners** See note on page 206. **Visual Learners** See note on page 206.

Practice and Problem Solving

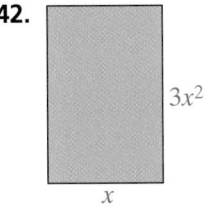 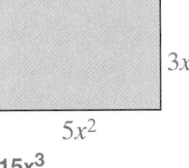 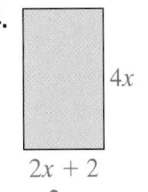

3. Practice

Assignment Guide

1 Objective 1
Ⓐ Ⓑ Core 1–18, 28–33, 38, 39
Ⓒ Extension 42–44

2 Objective 2
Ⓐ Ⓑ Core 19–27, 34–37
Ⓒ Extension 40, 41

Test Prep 45–48
Mixed Review 49–55

Ⓐ **Practice by Example**

Example 1
(page 205)

Example 2
(page 206)

Example 3
(page 206)

Simplify each expression.

1. $4^2 \cdot 4$ 64

2. $a^2 \cdot a^5$ a^7

3. $x^4 \cdot y \cdot x^5 \cdot y$ $x^9 y^2$

4. $10^2 \cdot 10^5$ 10,000,000

5. $2^2 \cdot 2^5$ 128

6. $x^4 \cdot x^4$ x^8

7. $m^{50} \cdot m^2$ m^{52}

8. $(3)^2 \cdot (2)^3 \cdot 2 \cdot 3$ 432

9. $x \cdot y \cdot y \cdot x^5 \cdot y^3$ $x^6 y^5$

10. $7b^3 \cdot 4b^4$ $28b^7$

11. $-9c^2 \cdot -2c^8$ $18c^{10}$

12. $5x^3 \cdot 2x^6$ $10x^9$

13. $4y^7 \cdot 6y^4$ $24y^{11}$

14. $-2a^2 \cdot -2a^2$ $4a^4$

15. $9b^2 \cdot -4b^2$ $-36b^4$

16. $-7x^6 \cdot -5x^8$ $35x^{14}$

17. $-5d^5 \cdot 6d^2$ $-30d^7$

18. $4b^4 \cdot 12b^7$ $48b^{11}$

19. $(10^3)^2$ 1,000,000

20. $(x^3)^4$ x^{12}

21. $(m^6)^4$ m^{24}

22. $(2^2)^3$ 64

23. $(3^2)^4$ 6,561

24. $(c^2)^8$ c^{16}

25. $(x^5)^7$ x^{35}

26. $(0^5)^8$ 0

27. $(g^8)^{12}$ g^{96}

Ⓑ **Apply Your Skills**

Complete each equation.

28. $8^2 \cdot 8^{\blacksquare} = 8^9$ 7

29. $c^{\blacksquare} \cdot c^4 = c^{11}$ 7

30. $(9^{\blacksquare})^4 = 9^{16}$ 4

31. $5^6 \cdot 5^{\blacksquare} = 5^{14}$ 8

32. $x^{\blacksquare} \cdot x^{12} = x^{15}$ 3

33. $(a^{\blacksquare})^9 = a^{27}$ 3

Compare. Use >, <, or = to complete each statement.

34. $25^2 \blacksquare (5^2)^2$ =

35. $(2^7)^7 \blacksquare (2^{25})^2$ <

36. $(4^3 \cdot 4^2)^3 \blacksquare 4^9$ >

37. Answers may vary.
Sample: 2^{20}, $(2^2)^{10}$,
$(2^4)^5$, $2^2 \cdot 2^{18}$

37. Open-Ended A megabyte is 2^{20} bytes. Use exponents to write 2^{20} in four different ways. **See left.**

38. <u>Writing in Math</u> Explain why $x^8 \cdot x^2$ has the same value

GPS as $x^5 \cdot x^5$. Both $x^8 \cdot x^2$ and $x^5 \cdot x^5$ are equivalent to x^{10}.

39. Error Analysis Marcos thinks that $x^4 + x^4$ simplifies to $2x^4$. Doug thinks that $x^4 + x^4$ simplifies to x^8. Which result is correct? Explain. $2x^4$; the two terms are being added, not multiplied.

Ⓒ **Challenge**

40. Reasoning Does $-(2^3)^2$ have the same value as $(-2^3)^2$? Justify your answer. No; $-(2^3)^2$ is -64, but $(-2^3)^2$ is 64.

41. Reasoning Which of 2^{30} or 2^{16} is twice the value of 2^{15}? Explain.
2^{16}; $2^{16} = 2^{1+15} = 2 \cdot 2^{15}$

Geometry Find the area of each rectangle.

42.
$3x^2$
x
$3x^3$

43.
$3x$
$5x^2$
$15x^3$

44.
$4x$
$2x + 2$
$8x^2 + 8x$

GPS Use the Guided Problem Solving worksheet with Exercise 38.

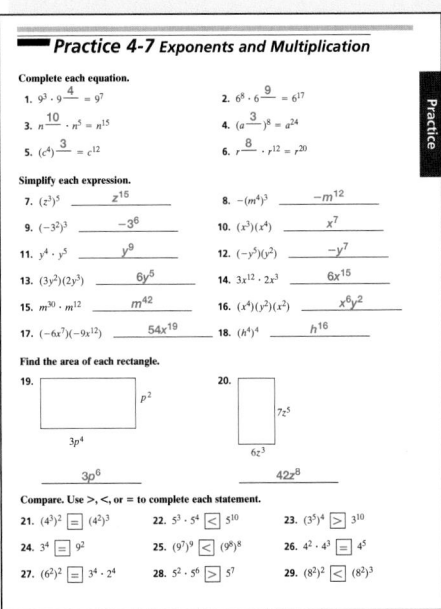

Practice 4-7 Exponents and Multiplication

Complete each equation.

1. $9^3 \cdot 9^{\underline{4}} = 9^7$
2. $6^8 \cdot 6^{\underline{9}} = 6^{17}$
3. $n^{\underline{10}} \cdot n^5 = n^{15}$
4. $(a^{\underline{3}})^8 = a^{24}$
5. $(c^4)^{\underline{3}} = c^{12}$
6. $r^{\underline{8}} \cdot r^{12} = r^{20}$

Simplify each expression.

7. $(z^3)^5$ z^{15}
8. $-(m^4)^3$ $-m^{12}$
9. $(-3^2)^3$ -3^6
10. $(x^3)(x^4)$ x^7
11. $y^4 \cdot y^5$ y^9
12. $(-y^5)(y^2)$ $-y^7$
13. $(3y^2)(2y^3)$ $6y^5$
14. $3x^{12} \cdot 2x^3$ $6x^{15}$
15. $m^{30} \cdot m^{12}$ m^{42}
16. $(x^4)(y^2)(x^2)$ x^6y^2
17. $(-6x^7)(-9x^{12})$ $54x^{19}$
18. $(h^4)^4$ h^{16}

Find the area of each rectangle.

19.
p^2
$3p^4$
$3p^6$

20.
$7z^5$
$6z^3$
$42z^8$

Compare. Use >, <, or = to complete each statement.

21. $(4^3)^2 \boxed{=} (4^2)^3$
22. $5^3 \cdot 5^4 \boxed{<} 5^{10}$
23. $(3^5)^4 \boxed{>} 3^{10}$
24. $3^4 \boxed{=} 9^2$
25. $(9^7)^9 \boxed{<} (9^8)^8$
26. $4^2 \cdot 4^3 \boxed{=} 4^5$
27. $(6^2)^2 \boxed{=} 3^4 \cdot 2^4$
28. $5^2 \cdot 5^6 \boxed{>} 5^7$
29. $(8^2)^2 \boxed{<} (8^2)^3$

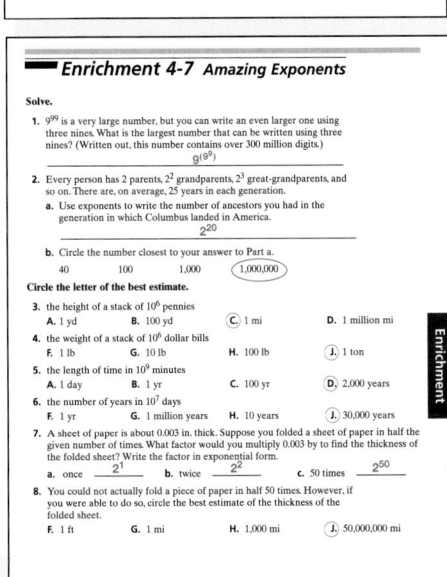

Enrichment 4-7 Amazing Exponents

Solve.

1. 9^{99} is a very large number, but you can write an even larger one using three nines. What is the largest number that can be written using three nines? (Written out, this number contains over 300 million digits.)
$9^{(9^9)}$

2. Every person has 2 parents, 2^2 grandparents, 2^3 great-grandparents, and so on. There are, on average, 25 years in each generation.
   a. Use exponents to write the number of ancestors you had in the generation in which Columbus landed in America.
   2^{20}
   b. Circle the number closest to your answer to Part a.
   40   100   1,000   ⟨1,000,000⟩

Circle the letter of the best estimate.

3. the height of a stack of 10^6 pennies
   A. 1 yd   B. 100 yd   Ⓒ 1 mi   D. 1 million mi
4. the weight of a stack of 10^6 dollar bills
   F. 1 lb   G. 10 lb   H. 100 lb   Ⓙ 1 ton
5. the length of time in 10^9 minutes
   A. 1 day   B. 1 yr   C. 100 yr   Ⓓ 2,000 years
6. the number of years in 10^7 days
   F. 1 yr   G. 1 million years   H. 10 years   Ⓙ 30,000 years
7. A sheet of paper is about 0.003 in. thick. Suppose you folded a sheet of paper in half the given number of times. What factor would you multiply 0.003 by to find the thickness of the folded sheet? Write the factor in exponential form.
   a. once 2^1 b. twice 2^2 c. 50 times 2^{50}
8. You could not actually fold a piece of paper in half 50 times. However, if you were able to do so, circle the best estimate of the thickness of the folded sheet.
   F. 1 ft   G. 1 mi   H. 1,000 mi   Ⓙ 50,000,000 mi

Test Prep

Multiple Choice

45. $(x^2)(y^5)(x) = \underline{\ ?\ }$ C
   A. x^2y B. x^2y^5 C. x^3y^5 D. x^7y

**Take It to the NET**
Online lesson quiz at **www.PHSchool.com**
Web Code: ada-0407

46. What is the simplest form for $a^{10} \cdot a \cdot a^2$?   H
   F. $a^{10} \cdot a^3$ G. a^{12} H. a^{13} I. a^{20}

47. $(9^5)^5 = \underline{\ ?\ }$ C
   A. 9^1 B. 9^{10} C. 9^{25} D. 9^{55}

Short Response

48. a. Find four expressions equivalent to 2^{13}.
   b. Explain why each is equivalent to 2^{13} for part (a). See margin.

Mixed Review

Lesson 4-6   **Evaluate. Write in simplest form.**

49. $\dfrac{mn}{m-6}$, for $m = 4$ and $n = 2$ -4

50. $\dfrac{g+gh}{h-g}$, for $g = -3$ and $h = -5$ -6

Lesson 2-8   **Graph the solutions of each inequality on a number line.**
51–54. See margin.
51. $x < -3$ 52. $a > 0$ 53. $y \le -4$ 54. $b > -2$

Lesson 1-2 55. **Party Planning** The Scotts are getting ready for a barbeque. They buy 8 lb of hamburger at $1.50/lb and 10 lb of chicken at $1.25/lb. Write and simplify an expression that shows the total cost.
$8(1.50) + 10(1.25)$; $24.50

Math at Work

····························· **Geophysicist**

A geophysicist studies Earth's surface, including the history of Earth's crust and rock formations. Geophysicists search for oil, natural gas, minerals, and underground water. They also work to solve environmental problems. They study what makes up Earth's interior, as well as its magnetic, electrical, and gravitational forces. They often study earthquakes and volcanoes.

Geophysicists use physics and mathematics in their studies. Much of their work involves measurement. They use instruments to track sound waves, gravity, energy waves, and magnetic fields. Exponents appear in the data that geophysicists gather because they often work with very large numbers.

**Take It to the NET** For more information about geophysicists, go to **www.PHSchool.com**.
Web Code: adb-2031

48. [2] Correct expressions and explanation(s). Sample:
$2 \cdot 2^{12} = 2^{1+12} = 2^{13}$
$2^3 \cdot 2^{10} = 2^{3+10} = 2^{13}$
$2^6 \cdot 2^7 = 2^{6+7} = 2^{13}$
$2^9 \cdot 2^4 = 2^{9+4} = 2^{13}$
[1] Correct expressions without explanation.

51.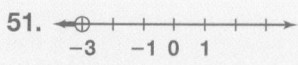
   -3 $-1\ 0\ 1$

52.
   -2 0 2

53.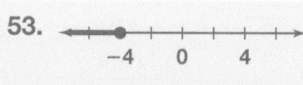
   -4 0 4

54.
   -2 0 2

Evaluating Expressions With Graphing Calculators

For Use With Lesson 4-7

Evaluating Expressions With Graphing Calculators

This Technology exploration explains how a student can use a graphing calculator to evaluate expressions.

Resources

Students may use any type of graphing calculator.

Teaching Notes

Remind students that the designs of graphing calculators can differ, so each student should follow the instructions and steps specific to his or her calculator.

Inclusion
Pair a student who does not have good vision with another student who states the steps aloud while pressing the keys.

1 EXAMPLE Error Prevention
Remind students that the key used to enter a negative number may be different from the key used to subtract numbers.

You can use a graphing calculator to evaluate an expression.

1 EXAMPLE

Use a graphing calculator to evaluate $-4x^2 + x - 2$ for $x = 6$.

Step 1 First store the value 6 to the variable x.
Press 6 STO▶ x ENTER.

Step 2 Enter $-4x^2 + x - 2$. Press ENTER.

```
6→X
              6
-4X²+X-2
           -140
■
```

To evaluate the expression in Example 1 for another value of x, start by storing that value to x. Press **ENTRY** *twice* to recall the expression $-4x^2 + x - 2$ from memory. Then press ENTER again. Repeat to evaluate the expression for another value of x.

2 EXAMPLE

Use a graphing calculator to evaluate $3c^3 + 5d - 6$ for $c = -2$ and $d = 7$.

You can evaluate an expression with more than one variable by following Step 1 twice to store the value of each variable separately. Then follow the directions in Step 2 to enter and evaluate the expression.

```
-2→C
             -2
7→D
              7
3C^3+5D-6
              5
■
```

To evaluate the expression for other values of the variables, first store the new values. Press **ENTRY** until the expression appears on the calculator screen. Then press ENTER again to evaluate the expression.

EXERCISES

Use a graphing calculator. Evaluate each expression for the given values of the variable(s). Round to the nearest hundredth where necessary.

1. $x^2 - 3x + 8$
   a. $x = 2$ 6   **b.** $x = -3$ 26   **c.** $x = 4.2$ 13.04

2. $y^6 + y$
   a. $y = -5$ 15,620   **b.** $y = 3$ 732   **c.** $y = 1.5$ 12.89

3. $-4c^2 + 34b - 42$
   a. $c = -12; b = 3$ −516   **b.** $c = 2; b = 4$ 78   **c.** $c = 5.1; b = 4$ −10.04

4. Evaluate $6x^3 - 2x$ for whole number values of x from 1 to 10. 4; 44; 156; 376; 740; 1,284; 2,044; 3,056; 4,356; 5,980

Exponents and Division

1. Plan

Lesson Preview

 Check Skills You'll Need

Simplifying Fractions
Lesson 4-4: Example 3;
Exercises 14–21.
Extra Practice, p. 747.

Lesson Resources

 Teaching Resources
Practice, Reteaching, Enrichment
Checkpoint Quiz 2

 Reaching All Students
Practice Workbook 4-8
Spanish Practice Workbook 4-8
Reading and Math Literacy 4C
Spanish Reading and Math
  Literacy 4C
Spanish Checkpoint Quiz 2
Guided Problem Solving 4-8
Technology Activities 7

 Presentation Assistant Plus!
Transparencies and PowerPoint™
• Check Skills You'll Need 4-8
• Additional Examples 4-8
• Student Edition Answers 4-8
• Lesson Quiz 4-8
PH Presentation Pro CD-ROM 4-8

 ASSESSMENT SYSTEM

Checkpoint Quiz 2
Computer Test Generator CD-ROM

 Technology
Resource Pro® CD-ROM
Computer Test Generator CD-ROM
PH Presentation Pro CD-ROM

 www.PHSchool.com

Student Site
• Teacher Web Code: adk-5500
• Algebra Readiness Puzzles 30
• Self-grading Lesson Quiz
PH SuccessNet Teacher Center
• Lesson Planner
• Resources

Plus

210

What You'll Learn

 OBJECTIVE 1
To divide expressions
containing exponents

 OBJECTIVE 2
To simplify
expressions with
integer exponents

... And Why

To solve real-world problems
involving science

 Check Skills You'll Need

Write in simplest form.

1. $\dfrac{x^2}{x}$ x

2. $\dfrac{y}{y^2}$ $\dfrac{1}{y}$

3. $\dfrac{6xy}{9y}$ $\dfrac{2x}{3}$

4. $\dfrac{4ab^2}{16b}$ $\dfrac{ab}{4}$

 For help, go to Lesson 4-4.

OBJECTIVE

1 Dividing Expressions Containing Exponents

In Lesson 4-7, you learned that you add exponents to multiply powers with the same base. To divide powers with the same base, you subtract exponents. Here's why.

$$\frac{7^8}{7^3} = \frac{7 \cdot 7 \cdot 7 \cdot 7 \cdot 7 \cdot 7 \cdot 7 \cdot 7}{7 \cdot 7 \cdot 7}$$ **Expand the numerator and denominator.**

$$= \frac{7^1 \cdot 7^1 \cdot 7^1 \cdot 7 \cdot 7 \cdot 7 \cdot 7 \cdot 7}{{}_17 \cdot {}_17 \cdot {}_17}$$ **Divide common factors.**

$$= 7^5$$

Notice that $\frac{7^8}{7^3} = 7^5 = 7^{8-3}$. This suggests the following rule.

> **Key Concepts**   **Dividing Powers With the Same Base**
>
> To divide numbers or variables *with the same nonzero base*, subtract the exponents.
>
> **Arithmetic**
> $$\frac{4^5}{4^2} = 4^{5-2} = 4^3$$
>
> **Algebra**
> $$\frac{a^m}{a^n} = a^{m-n}, \text{for } a \neq 0 \text{ and positive integers } m \text{ and } n.$$

---

1 EXAMPLE   **Dividing a Power by a Power**

Simplify each expression.

a. $\dfrac{3^8}{3^5}$ b. $\dfrac{a^4}{a^2}$

$\dfrac{3^8}{3^5} = 3^{8-5}$ ⟵ **Subtract the exponents.** ⟶ $\dfrac{a^4}{a^2} = a^{4-2}$

$= 3^3$ ⟵ **Simplify the exponent.** ⟶ $= a^2$

$= 27$ ⟵ **Simplify.**

 Check Understanding   Example 1

1. Simplify each expression.

a. $\dfrac{10^7}{10^4}$ 1,000   b. $\dfrac{x^{25}}{x^{18}}$ x^7 c. $\dfrac{12m^5}{3m}$ $4m^4$

TEXT Interactive lesson
includes instant self-check,
tutorials, and activities.

210   **Chapter 4** Factors, Fractions, and Exponents

Ongoing Assessment and Intervention

Before the Lesson
Diagnose prerequisite skills using:
• Check Skills You'll Need

During the Lesson
Monitor progress using:
• Check Understanding
• Additional Examples
• Test Prep

After the Lesson
Assess knowledge using:
• Lesson Quiz
• Computer Test Generator
  CD-ROM
• Chapter Checkpoint 2 (p. 214)

2 Simplifying Expressions With Integer Exponents

What happens when you divide powers with the same base and get zero as an exponent? Consider $\frac{3^4}{3^4}$.

$$\frac{3^4}{3^4} = 3^{4-4} = 3^0 \qquad\qquad \frac{3^4}{3^4} = \frac{3^1 \cdot 3^1 \cdot 3^1 \cdot 3^1}{{}_1 3 \cdot {}_1 3 \cdot {}_1 3 \cdot {}_1 3} = \frac{1}{1} = 1$$

Notice that $\frac{3^4}{3^4} = 3^0$ and $\frac{3^4}{3^4} = 1$. This suggests the following rule.

Key Concepts — Zero as an Exponent

Arithmetic	Algebra
$3^0 = 1$	$a^0 = 1$, for $a \neq 0$.

2 EXAMPLE Simplifying When Zero Is an Exponent

Simplify each expression.

a. $\dfrac{(-8)^2}{(-8)^2}$

$\dfrac{(-8)^2}{(-8)^2} = (-8)^{2-2}$ **Subtract the exponents.**

$= (-8)^0$ **Simplify.**

$= 1$

b. $\dfrac{6b^3}{18b^3}$

$\dfrac{6b^3}{18b^3} = \frac{1}{3}b^0$ **Subtract the exponents. Simplify $\frac{6}{18}$.**

$= \frac{1}{3} \cdot 1$ **Simplify b^0.**

$= \frac{1}{3}$ **Multiply.**

✓ **Check Understanding** Example 2

2. Simplify each expression.

a. 43^0 1   b. $\dfrac{5^2 x^6}{5x^6}$ 5   c. $\dfrac{x^5 y^6}{x^5 y^3}$ y^3 d. $5x^0$ 5

What happens when you divide powers with the same base and get a negative exponent? Consider $\frac{3^2}{3^4}$.

$$\frac{3^2}{3^4} = 3^{2-4} = 3^{-2} \qquad\qquad \frac{3^2}{3^4} = \frac{3^1 \cdot 3^1}{{}_1 3 \cdot {}_1 3 \cdot 3 \cdot 3} = \frac{1}{3^2}$$

These results suggest the rule at the top of page 212.

Reaching All Students

Below Level Review using exponents in Lesson 4-2 and simplifying fractions with variables having exponents in Lesson 4-4.

Advanced Learners Ask: *The expressions x and −x represent opposites. Are x^1 and x^{-1} opposites? Explain.* No; opposites have a sum of zero. The sum of x^1 and x^{-1} is $x^1 + x^{-1}$.

Diversity See note on page 211. **Visual Learners** See note on page 211.

2. Teach

Math Background

The properties of exponents are given in terms of positive integer exponents. Negative and zero exponents are defined to maintain consistency with these properties.

Teaching Notes

Diversity
Some students have a difficult time remembering rules. To help these students remember how to divide powers, have them work through several examples the long way. Expand the numerator and denominator, and then divide common factors. Relate the results to the results of using the rule.

1 EXAMPLE Tactile Learners
Select a group of thirteen students. Give each student a card with the number 3 written on it. Make a fraction bar on the floor with masking tape. Have eight of the selected students stand in the numerator and five stand in the denominator. Simplify the expression by removing one pair of students at a time (one from the numerator and one from the denominator).

Alternative Method
Another way to help students with the notation of zero as an exponent is to use the following pattern.
$10^3 = 1{,}000$
$10^2 = 100$
$10^1 = 10$
$10^0 = 1$

2 EXAMPLE Visual Learners
Suggest students compare the numerator and denominator carefully before they begin simplifying an expression. Whenever numerator and denominator factors are the same, then their quotient is equal to 1. Have students draw a mark through any numerator and denominator factors whose quotients are equal to 1.

211

Key Concepts Negative Exponents

Arithmetic	Algebra
$3^{-2} = \frac{1}{3^2}$	$a^{-n} = \frac{1}{a^n}$, for $a \neq 0$.

A hummingbird has a mass of about 10^{-2} kg, or $\frac{1}{10^2}$ kg. To simplify 10^{-2}, you write $\frac{1}{100}$ or 0.01. So the hummingbird has a mass of 0.01 kg. To simplify an expression such as x^{-2}, you write it as $\frac{1}{x^2}$, using no negative exponents.

3 EXAMPLE Using Positive Exponents

Simplify each expression.

a. $\frac{5^6}{5^8}$

b. $\frac{m^2}{m^5}$

$$\frac{5^6}{5^8} = 5^{6-8} \quad \longleftarrow \textbf{Subtract the exponents.} \longrightarrow \quad \frac{m^2}{m^5} = m^{2-5}$$

$$= 5^{-2} \qquad\qquad\qquad\qquad\qquad\qquad\qquad\qquad = m^{-3}$$

$$= \frac{1}{5^2} \quad \longleftarrow \textbf{Write with a positive exponent.} \longrightarrow \quad = \frac{1}{m^3}$$

$$= \frac{1}{25} \quad \longleftarrow \textbf{Simplify.}$$

✓ Check Understanding Example 3

3. Simplify each expression.

a. $\frac{4^5}{4^7}$ $\frac{1}{16}$

b. $\frac{a^4}{a^6}$ $\frac{1}{a^2}$

c. $\frac{3y^8}{9y^{12}}$ $\frac{1}{3y^4}$

You can also write an expression such as $\frac{1}{x^2}$ so that there is no fraction bar.

4 EXAMPLE Using Negative Exponents

Write $\frac{x^2y^3}{x^3y}$ without a fraction bar.

$$\frac{x^2y^3}{x^3y} = x^{2-3}y^{3-1} \qquad \textbf{Use the Rule for Dividing Powers With the Same Base.}$$

$$= x^{-1}y^2 \qquad \textbf{Subtract the exponents.}$$

✓ Check Understanding Example 4

4. Write each expression without a fraction bar.

a. $\frac{b^3}{b^9}$ b^{-6}

b. $\frac{m^3n^2}{m^6n^8}$ $m^{-3}n^{-6}$

c. $\frac{xy^5}{x^5y^3}$ $x^{-4}y^2$

212 Chapter 4 Factors, Fractions, and Exponents

EXERCISES

Practice and Problem Solving

 For more exercises, see *Extra Practice*.

 **Practice by Example**

Simplify each expression.

Example 1
(page 210)

1. $\frac{2^5}{2^2}$ 8

2. $\frac{h^6}{h^2}$ h^4

3. $\frac{10y^7}{6y^2}$ $\frac{5y^5}{3}$

4. $\frac{10b^8}{2b^6}$ $5b^2$

5. $\frac{6^2}{6^1}$ 6

6. $\frac{11^5}{11^3}$ 121

7. $\frac{x^7}{x^3}$ x^4

8. $\frac{a^{27}}{a^{19}}$ a^8

Example 2
(page 211)

9. $\frac{18x^{20}}{18x^{20}}$ 1

10. $(-4)^0$ 1

11. $\frac{w^8z^{15}}{w^8z^8}$ z^7

12. 3^0 1

13. $\frac{b^3c^2}{b^3c}$ c

14. $\frac{(-2)^4}{(-2)^4}$ 1

15. $2b^0$ 2

16. $\frac{2y^3}{8y^3}$ $\frac{1}{4}$

Example 3
(page 212)

17. $\frac{7^3}{7^5}$ $\frac{1}{49}$

18. $\frac{m^2}{m^6}$ $\frac{1}{m^4}$

19. $\frac{4a^3}{20a^6}$ $\frac{1}{5a^3}$

20. $\frac{100m^{100}}{200m^{200}}$ $\frac{1}{2m^{100}}$

21. $\frac{b^5}{b^8}$ $\frac{1}{b^3}$

22. $\frac{3m}{15m^3}$ $\frac{1}{5m^2}$

23. $\frac{6^7}{6^{11}}$ $\frac{1}{1,296}$

24. $\frac{a^2}{a^7}$ $\frac{1}{a^5}$

Example 4
(page 212)

Write each expression without a fraction bar.

25. $\frac{y^4}{y^7}$ y^{-3}

26. $\frac{a^2b^4}{a^8b^2}$ $a^{-6}b^2$

27. $\frac{m^5n^6}{m^7n^8}$ $m^{-2}n^{-2}$

28. $\frac{xy^2}{x^4y^9}$ $x^{-3}y^{-7}$

 Apply Your Skills

Complete each equation.

29. $\frac{x^6}{x^\blacksquare} = x^4$ 2

30. $\frac{14x^5}{7x^3} = 2x^\blacksquare$ 2

31. $\frac{10^5}{10^\blacksquare} = 1$ 5

32. $\frac{1}{a^3} = a^\blacksquare$ −3

33. $\frac{y^\blacksquare}{y^9} = y^{-4}$ 5

34. $\frac{1}{-27} = (-3)^\blacksquare$ −3

Real-World **Connection**

The photo shows damage from the Loma Prieta, California, earthquake of October 17, 1989.

37. Answers may vary.
Sample: $\frac{1}{5^7}, \frac{5}{5^8}, \frac{x}{5^7x}$

35. Earthquakes The *magnitude* of an earthquake is a measure of the amount of energy released. An earthquake of magnitude 6 releases about 30 times as much energy as an earthquake of magnitude 5. The magnitude of the 1989 earthquake in Loma Prieta, California, was about 7. The magnitude of the 1933 earthquake in Sanriku, Japan, was about 9. Simplify $\frac{30^9}{30^7}$ to find how many times as much energy was released in the Sanriku earthquake. **900 times as much**

36. Error Analysis A student wrote that $-5^0 = 1$. What was the student's error? **The student thought that the base was −5.**

37. Open-Ended Write three different quotients that equal 5^{-7}. See below left.

38. Writing in Math Is -3^{-2} positive or negative? Justify your answer. **Negative; $-3^{-2} = -\frac{1}{3^2} = -\frac{1}{9}$**

Write each expression without a fraction bar.

39. $\frac{x^3}{x^5}$ x^{-2}

40. $\frac{a^9b^3}{a^7b^8}$ a^2b^{-5}

41. $\frac{m^9n^3}{m^2n^{10}}$ m^7n^{-7}

42. $\frac{b^{14}c^2}{b^9c^{11}}$ b^5c^{-9}

 Challenge

Simplify each expression.

43. $\frac{5x^2}{10x^{-5}}$ $\frac{x^7}{2}$

44. $\frac{5b^{-7}}{5b^{-2}}$ $\frac{1}{b^5}$

45. $\frac{4^2 + 6^2}{2^2}$ 13

46. $\frac{r^{-5}}{s^{-2}}$ $\frac{s^2}{r^5}$

 4-8 Exponents and Division **213**

 GPS Use the Guided Problem Solving worksheet with Exercise 35.

3. Practice

Assignment Guide

1 Objective 1
Ⓐ Ⓑ **Core** 1–8, 31, 35
Ⓒ **Extension** 45

2 Objective 2
Ⓐ Ⓑ **Core** 9–30, 32–34, 36–42
Ⓒ **Extension** 43, 44, 46

Test Prep 47–50
Mixed Review 51–57

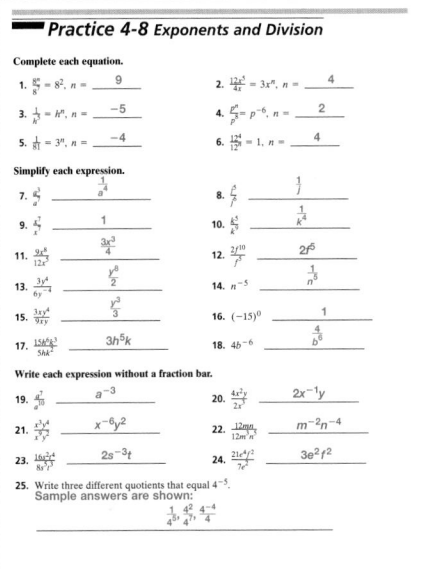

Practice 4-8 Exponents and Division

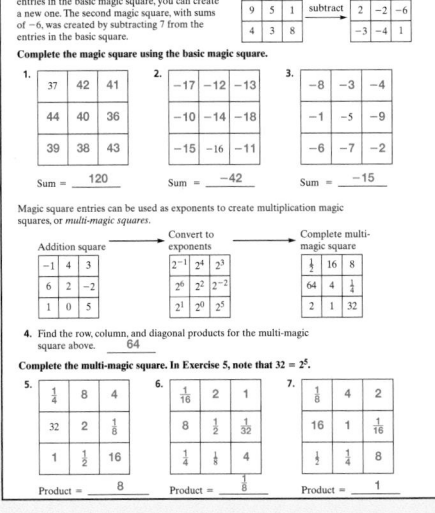

Enrichment 4-8 Multi-Magic Squares

PowerPoint Lesson Quiz 4-8

Simplify each expression.

1. $\frac{7^5}{7^3}$ 49

2. $\frac{-15b^5c^3}{60b^3c^2}$ $-\frac{1}{4}b^2c$

3. Write $\frac{6n^{14}}{3n^{24}}$ without a
fraction bar. $2n^{-10}$

Test Prep

 **Resources**

For additional practice with a
variety of test item formats:
- Test Prep, p. 227
- Test-Taking Strategies, p. 222
- Test-Taking Strategies With
  Transparencies

 **Chapter Checkpoint 2**

To check understanding of
Lessons 4-5 to 4-8

Checkpoint Quiz 2 (p. 214)

 **Teaching Resources**

Checkpoint Quiz 2 (also in
Prentice Hall Assessment System)

 **Reaching All Students**

Reading and Math Literacy 4C

Spanish versions available.

Reteaching 4-8 Exponents and Division

Simplify $\frac{a^3}{a^3}$ and $\frac{m^2}{m^6}$.

To divide variables with the same non-zero base, you subtract the exponents.

$\frac{a^3}{a^3} = a^{3-3}$ Subtract the exponents.

$= a^0$ Simplify the exponent.

However, $\frac{a^3}{a^3} = 1$ as long as a is not zero, just like $\frac{2}{2} = 1$, $\frac{9}{9} = 1$, and so on.

So $\frac{a^3}{a^3} = 1$ and $a^0 = 1$.

$\frac{m^2}{m^6} = m^{2-6}$ Subtract the exponents.

$= m^{-4}$ Simplify the exponent.

However, $\frac{m^2}{m^6} = \frac{m \cdot m}{m \cdot m \cdot m \cdot m \cdot m \cdot m} = \frac{1}{m^4}$

So, $\frac{m^2}{m^6} = \frac{1}{m^4}$ and $m^{-4} = \frac{1}{m^4}$.

The *simplified* form of $\frac{a^3}{a^3}$ is 1, and the *simplified* form of $\frac{m^2}{m^6}$ is $\frac{1}{m^4}$.

Simplify each expression.

1. $\frac{7^8}{7^2}$ 7^6

2. $\frac{x^5}{x}$ x^4

3. 5^0 1

4. n^{-3} $\frac{1}{n^3}$

5. $x^{-2}y^4$ $\frac{y^4}{x^2}$

6. $6a^{-3}$ $\frac{6}{a^3}$

7. $(-4)^0$ 1

8. $\frac{b^2}{b^8}$ $\frac{1}{b^6}$

9. $\frac{y^2}{y^3}$ $\frac{1}{y}$

10. $7s^{-5}t^{-3}$ $\frac{7}{s^5t^3}$

11. $\frac{3^{18}}{3^3}$ 3^{15}

12. $(-729)^0$ 1

13. $\frac{z^7}{z^4}$ $\frac{1}{z^{27}}$

14. $4c^3f^{-2}$ $\frac{4c^3}{f^2}$

Reteaching

214

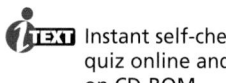 **Test Prep**

Multiple Choice

47. What is a simpler form of $\frac{x^5y^4}{x^2y^9}$? **D**

   A. $\frac{x^5}{y^3}$ **B.** $\frac{y^5}{x^3}$ **C.** x^3y^5 **D.** $\frac{x^3}{y^5}$

Take It to the NET
Online lesson quiz at
www.PHSchool.com
Web Code: ada-0408

48. What is a simpler form of $\frac{12a^{35}}{36a^{50}}$? **H**

   F. $\frac{1^{85}}{3^a}$ **G.** $\frac{1}{3a^{85}}$ **H.** $\frac{1}{3a^{15}}$ **I.** $\frac{1}{3}a^{15}$

49. Which expression is equal to $\frac{42a^6b^7}{7a^3b^3}$? **B**

   A. $6a^3b^{-4}$ **B.** $6a^3b^4$ **C.** $6a^{-3}b^4$ **D.** $6a^{-3}b^{-4}$

Short Response

50. a. Is 5^{-3} a negative number?   **b.** Explain your answer.

[2] No; $5^{-3} = \frac{1}{5^3} = \frac{1}{125}$, which is positive.

[1] Correct answer with no explanation.

Mixed Review

Lesson 4-7   **Simplify each expression.**

51. $5^2 \cdot 5$ 125   **52.** $x^7 \cdot x^2$ x^9 **53.** $2a^9 \cdot 8a^7$ $16a^{16}$

Lesson 3-1   **Estimate using front-end estimation.**

54. $5.68 + 3.24$ **55.** $17.86 + 2.321$ **56.** $20.2 + 5.8$
    about 8.9   about 20.2   about 26.0

Lesson 2-7   **57. Number Sense** The sum of three consecutive integers is 264.
What are the three integers? 87, 88, 89

Checkpoint Quiz 2   Lessons 4-5 through 4-8

iTEXT Instant self-check
quiz online and
on CD-ROM

Write three fractions equivalent to each given fraction. 1–5. See margin.

1. $\frac{3}{12}$ **2.** $\frac{12}{36}$ **3.** $\frac{49}{70}$ **4.** $\frac{18}{28}$ **5.** $\frac{4}{5}$

Evaluate for $a = 4$ and $b = -6$. Write in simplest form.

6. $\frac{a}{2b}$ $-\frac{1}{3}$ **7.** $\frac{b+a}{a}$ $-\frac{1}{2}$ **8.** $\frac{a-b}{15}$ $\frac{2}{3}$ **9.** $\frac{b-a}{a^2}$ $-\frac{5}{8}$ **10.** $\frac{3a+b}{24}$ $\frac{1}{4}$

Graph the rational numbers below on the same number line.

11. -0.8 **12.** $\frac{1}{2}$ **13.** 0.6 **14.** $-\frac{2}{10}$ **15.** $\frac{9}{10}$
11–15. See margin.

Simplify each expression.

16. $2^3 \cdot 2^4$ **17.** $(x^5)^{10}$ x^{50} **18.** $\frac{18a^4}{3a^2}$ $6a^2$ **19.** $\frac{x^3}{x^8}$ $\frac{1}{x^5}$ **20.** $\frac{a^3b^5}{9a^9b^5}$ $\frac{1}{a^6}$
128

21. If 12 of 16 students vote to do a project, what fraction of the
students is this? Write the fraction in simplest form. $\frac{3}{4}$

Alternative Assessment

Have students work in groups to develop a board
game in which the players, in order to advance,
have to simplify expressions with exponents.

Checkpoint Quiz 2

1. $\frac{1}{4}, \frac{-1}{-4}, \frac{2}{8}$ **2.** $\frac{1}{3}, \frac{-1}{-3}, \frac{2}{6}$ **3.** $\frac{7}{10}, \frac{-7}{-10}, \frac{14}{20}$

4. $\frac{9}{14}, \frac{-9}{-14}, \frac{-18}{-28}$ **5.** $\frac{8}{10}, \frac{-8}{-10}, \frac{-4}{-5}$

11–15.

```
   ←──┼──●──┼──┼──●──┼──┼──●─●─┼●─┼→
     -1    ↑   -2/10  0      1/2  ↑ 1
         -0.8                0.6  9/10
```

Scientific Notation

Writing and Evaluating Scientific Notation

Investigation

Exploring Scientific Notation

1. Copy and complete the chart below.

5×10^4	$= 5 \times 10,000$	$= 50,000$
5×10^3	$= 5 \times 1,000$	$= \blacksquare\ 5,000$
5×10^2	$= 5 \times \blacksquare\ 100$	$= \blacksquare\ 500$
5×10^1	$= 5 \times \blacksquare\ 10$	$= \blacksquare\ 50$
5×10^0	$= 5 \times \blacksquare\ 1$	$= \blacksquare\ 5$
5×10^{-1}	$= 5 \times \frac{1}{10}$	$= 5 \times 0.1$ $= 0.5$
5×10^{-2}	$= 5 \times \blacksquare\ \frac{1}{100}$	$= 5 \times 0.01$ $= 0.05$
5×10^{-3}	$= 5 \times \blacksquare\ \frac{1}{1,000}$	$= 5 \times \blacksquare^{0.001}\ = 0.005$
5×10^{-4}	$= 5 \times \blacksquare\ \frac{1}{10,000}$	$= 5 \times \blacksquare^{0.0001}\ = \blacksquare\ 0.0005$

2. **Patterns** Describe any related patterns that you see in your chart. **See below.**

3. **a.** Based on the patterns you see, simplify 5×10^7. **50,000,000**
   b. Simplify 5×10^{-6}. **0.000005**

   2. **Answers may vary. Sample: As the exponent of 10 decreases by 1, the denominator becomes 10 times as great.**

Scientific notation provides a way to write numbers using powers of 10. You write a number in scientific notation as the product of two factors.

Second factor is a power of 10.

$$7,500,000,000,000 = 7.5 \times 10^{12}$$

First factor is greater than or equal to 1, but less than 10.

Scientific notation lets you know the size of a number without having to count digits. For example, if the exponent of 10 is 6, the number is in the millions. If the exponent is 9, the number is in the billions.

What You'll Learn

 To write and evaluate numbers in scientific notation

 To calculate with scientific notation

... And Why

To solve real-world problems involving weight and mass

✓ Check Skills You'll Need

Write each expression with a single exponent.

1. $10^3 \cdot 10^5$ 10^8

2. $10^7 \cdot 10^9$ 10^{16}

3. $10^5 \cdot 10^{-3}$ 10^2

4. $10^{-6} \cdot 10^3$ 10^{-3}

 For help, go to Lesson 4-7.

New Vocabulary

• scientific notation
• standard notation

Need Help?

For help with multiplying by powers of ten, see Skills Handbook, page 768.

iTEXT Interactive lesson includes instant self-check, tutorials, and activities.

Lesson Preview

✓ **Check Skills You'll Need**

Exponents and Multiplication
Lesson 4-7: Example 1;
Exercises 1–9.
Extra Practice, p. 747.

Lesson Resources

 **Teaching Resources**
Practice, Reteaching, Enrichment

 **Reaching All Students**
Practice Workbook 4-9
Spanish Practice Workbook 4-9
Guided Problem Solving 4-9

Presentation Assistant Plus!
Transparencies and PowerPoint™
• Check Skills You'll Need 4-9
• Additional Examples 4-9
• Student Edition Answers 4-9
• Lesson Quiz 4-9
PH Presentation Pro CD-ROM 4-9

ASSESSMENT SYSTEM

Computer Test Generator CD-ROM

 Technology
Resource Pro® CD-ROM
Computer Test Generator CD-ROM
PH Presentation Pro CD-ROM

 www.PHSchool.com
Student Site
• Teacher Web Code: adk-5500
• Algebra Readiness Puzzles 13
• Graphing Calculator, Procedure 18
• Self-grading Lesson Quiz
PH SuccessNet Teacher Center
• Lesson Planner
• Resources

Plus **iTEXT**

 ## Ongoing Assessment and Intervention

Before the Lesson
Diagnose prerequisite skills using:
• Check Skills You'll Need

During the Lesson
Monitor progress using:
• Check Understanding
• Additional Examples
• Test Prep

After the Lesson
Assess knowledge using:
• Lesson Quiz
• Computer Test Generator CD-ROM

Math Background

Professional Development

Scientific notation provides a short form for very large and very small numbers. In scientific notation, $347{,}100{,}000{,}000$ is 3.471×10^{11}. Scientific notation often uses the multiplication symbol $\times$ to avoid confusion with the decimal point in the first factor. The exponent with 10 shows the number of places you move the decimal point. A positive exponent indicates that the number is greater than or equal to 1. A negative exponent indicates that the number is less than 1.

Teaching Notes

Investigation (Optional)
Have students work together. Ask them to write a rule that relates the exponent in scientific notation to the number of places and direction they move the decimal point.

Science Connection
As the name suggests, the sciences commonly use scientific notation. They often deal with numbers so large or small that it is inconvenient to write them in the standard form. Such numbers can also be very difficult to read. Compare, for example, the two forms for the mass of a single hydrogen atom: 1.7×10^{-24} g, or $0.000\,000\,000\,000\,000\,000\,000\,0017$ g.

1 EXAMPLE Tactile Learners
Have students write 4,200,000 with large spaces between digits, and place a token at the end of the number to represent a decimal point. Instruct students to move the token as shown in the diagram below, one "move" for each decimal place. Count the number of moves. Write this number as the exponent of 10.

4200000.

10^6

Real-World Connection
The total weight of the Statue of Liberty is about 450,000 lb.

---

1 EXAMPLE   Real-World Problem Solving

About 4,200,000 people visit the Statue of Liberty every year. Write this number in scientific notation.

4,200,000	Move the decimal point to get a decimal greater than 1 but less than 10.
6 places	
4.2	Drop the zeros after the 2.
4.2×10^6	You moved the decimal point 6 places. The number is large. Use 6 as the exponent of 10.

✓ Check Understanding   Example 1

1. Write each number in scientific notation.

   a. 54,500,000
      5.45×10^7
   b. 723,000
      7.23×10^5
   c. 602,000,000,000
      6.02×10^{11}

In scientific notation, you use a negative exponent to write a number between 0 and 1.

2 EXAMPLE   Writing in Scientific Notation

Write 0.000079 in scientific notation.

0.000079	Move the decimal point to get a decimal greater than 1 but less than 10.
5 places	
7.9	Drop the zeros before the 7.
7.9×10^{-5}	You moved the decimal point 5 places. The number is small. Use -5 as the exponent of 10.

✓ Check Understanding   Example 2

2. Write each number in scientific notation.

   a. 0.00021
      2.1×10^{-4}
   b. 0.00000005
      5×10^{-8}
   c. 0.0000000000803
      8.03×10^{-11}

You can change expressions from scientific notation to **standard notation** by simplifying the product of the two factors.

3 EXAMPLE   Writing in Standard Notation

Write each number in standard notation.

a. 8.9×10^5 b. 2.71×10^{-6}

| 8.90000 | Write zeros while moving the decimal point. | 000002.71 |
| 890,000 | Rewrite in standard notation. | 0.00000271 |

👥 Reaching All Students

| **Below Level** List powers of ten greater than or equal to 1 in both exponential and standard form. Have students compare the exponent with the number of zeros in standard form. They are the same number. | **Advanced Learners** Tell students that a *googol* is 1 followed by 100 zeros. A *googolplex* is 1 followed by a googol of zeros. Ask: *How would you write a googolplex in scientific notation?* $1 \times 10^{\text{googol}}$ or $1.0 \times 10^{10^{100}}$ | **Tactile Learners** See note on page 216. **Diversity** See note on page 220. |

✓ Check Understanding   Example 3

3. Write each number in standard notation.

a. 3.21×10^7 **b.** 5.9×10^{-8} **c.** 1.006×10^{10}
   32,100,000   0.000000059   10,060,000,000

For a number to be in scientific notation, the digit in front of the decimal must be 1 or between 1 and 10.

4 EXAMPLE   Changing to Scientific Notation

Write each number in scientific notation.

a. 0.37×10^{10}

$0.37 \times 10^{10} = 3.7 \times 10^{-1} \times 10^{10}$ **Write 0.37 as 3.7×10^{-1}.**
$\quad\quad\quad\quad = 3.7 \times 10^9$ **Add the exponents.**

b. 453.1×10^8

$453.1 \times 10^8 = 4.531 \times 10^2 \times 10^8$ **Write 453.1 as 4.531×10^2.**
$\quad\quad\quad\quad = 4.531 \times 10^{10}$ **Add the exponents.**

✓ Check Understanding   Example 4

4. Write each number in scientific notation.

a. 16×10^5 **b.** 0.203×10^6 **c.** $7,243 \times 10^{12}$
   1.6×10^6 2.03×10^5 7.243×10^{15}

You can compare and order numbers using scientific notation. First compare the powers of 10, and then compare the decimals.

5 EXAMPLE   Comparing and Ordering Numbers

Order 0.064×10^8, 312×10^2, and 0.58×10^7 from least to greatest.

Write each number in scientific notation.

0.064×10^8 312×10^2 0.58×10^7
$\quad\downarrow$ $\quad\downarrow$ $\quad\downarrow$
6.4×10^6 3.12×10^4 5.8×10^6

Order the powers of 10. Arrange the decimals with the same power of 10 in order.

3.12×10^4 5.8×10^6 6.4×10^6

Write the original numbers in order.

$312 \times 10^2, 0.58 \times 10^7, 0.064 \times 10^8$

✓ Check Understanding   Example 5

5. Order from least to greatest. **5a.** $18.3 \times 10^6, 0.098 \times 10^9, 526 \times 10^7$
5b. $0.22 \times 10^{-10}, 8 \times 10^{-9}, 14.7 \times 10^{-7}$

a. $526 \times 10^7, 18.3 \times 10^6, 0.098 \times 10^9$
b. $8 \times 10^{-9}, 14.7 \times 10^{-7}, 0.22 \times 10^{-10}$

4-9 Scientific Notation   **217**

---

2 EXAMPLE   Error Prevention

To relate scientific and standard notations, you have to know how to "go both ways"—from standard to scientific and from scientific to standard. The method of moving the decimal point so that the number of moves matches the exponent works well. The key is to remember that positive exponents relate to very large values and negative exponents relate to values close to zero.

4 EXAMPLE   Alternative Method

Point out that to preserve the value of a product, if you increase the value of one factor, you must decrease the value of the other factor. Students can apply this rule to manipulating forms into scientific notation. Consider 0.37×10^{10}. If you increase the value of 0.37 to 3.7, then you must decrease the value of 10^{10} to 10^9 to leave the product unchanged.

PowerPoint
Additional Examples

1 About 6,300,000 people visited the Eiffel Tower in the year 2000. Write this number in scientific notation. 6.3×10^6

2 Write 0.00037 in scientific notation. 3.7×10^{-4}

3 Write each number in standard notation.
a. 3.6×10^4 36,000
b. 7.2×10^{-3} 0.0072

4 Write each number in scientific notation.
a. 0.107×10^{12} 1.07×10^{11}
b. 515.2×10^{-4} 5.152×10^{-2}

5 Order 0.035×10^4, 710×10^{-1}, and 0.69×10^2 from least to greatest.
$0.69 \times 10^2, 710 \times 10^{-1}, 0.035 \times 10^4$

OBJECTIVE
2 Calculating With Scientific Notation

You can multiply numbers in scientific notation using the rule for Multiplying Powers with the Same Base.

6 EXAMPLE **Multiplying With Scientific Notation**

Multiply 3×10^{-7} and 9×10^3. Express the result in scientific notation.

$(3 \times 10^{-7})(9 \times 10^3) = 3 \times 9 \times 10^{-7} \times 10^3$	Use the Commutative Property of Multiplication.
$= 27 \times 10^{-7} \times 10^3$	Multiply 3 and 9.
$= 27 \times 10^{-4}$	Add the exponents.
$= 2.7 \times 10^1 \times 10^{-4}$	Write 27 as 2.7×10^1.
$= 2.7 \times 10^{-3}$	Add the exponents.

 **Check Understanding** Example 6

6. Multiply. Express each result in scientific notation.

   a. $(4 \times 10^4)(6 \times 10^6)$ **b.** $(7.1 \times 10^{-8})(8 \times 10^4)$
     2.4×10^{11} 5.68×10^{-3}

7 EXAMPLE 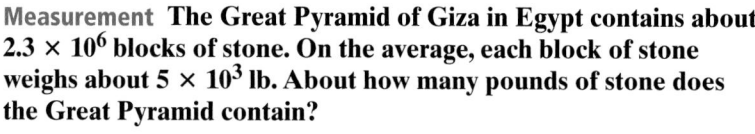 Real-World Problem Solving

Measurement **The Great Pyramid of Giza in Egypt contains about 2.3×10^6 blocks of stone. On the average, each block of stone weighs about 5×10^3 lb. About how many pounds of stone does the Great Pyramid contain?**

$(2.3 \times 10^6)(5 \times 10^3)$	Multiply number of blocks by weight of each.
$= 2.3 \times 5 \times 10^6 \times 10^3$	Use the Commutative Property of Multiplication.
$= 11.5 \times 10^6 \times 10^3$	Multiply 2.3 and 5.
$= 11.5 \times 10^9$	Add the exponents.
$= 1.15 \times 10^1 \times 10^9$	Write 11.5 as 1.15×10^1.
$= 1.15 \times 10^{10}$	Add the exponents.

The Great Pyramid contains about 1.15×10^{10} lb of stone.

Check Understanding Example 7

7. **Chemistry** A hydrogen atom has a mass of 1.67×10^{-27} kg. What is the mass of 6×10^3 hydrogen atoms? Express the result in scientific notation. **1.002×10^{-23} kg**

Real-World Connection

In ancient times, the Great Pyramid of Giza was plundered inside and out. Outside, most of the casing of smooth, white limestone was removed. The height of the pyramid is now about 30 ft less than the original height.

EXERCISES

Practice and Problem Solving

 For more exercises, see *Extra Practice*.

A **Practice by Example**

Examples 1 and 2
(page 216)

In Exercises 1–7, write each number in scientific notation.

1. 8,900,000,000
8.9×10^9

2. 555,900,000
5.559×10^8

3. 0.000631
6.31×10^{-4}

4. 0.000006 6×10^{-6}

5. 0.209 2.09×10^{-1}

6. 0.00409 4.09×10^{-3}

 7. Solar System Pluto is about 5 billion km from the sun. 5×10^9 km

Example 3
(page 216)

Write each number in standard notation.

8. 5.94×10^7
59,400,000

9. 2.104×10^{-8}
0.00000002104

10. 1.2×10^5
120,000

11. 7.2×10^{-4}
0.00072

12. 2.75×10^8
275,000,000

13. 6.0502×10^{-3}
0.0060502

Example 4
(page 217)

Write each number in scientific notation.

14. 0.09×10^{12} 9×10^{10}

15. 0.72×10^{-4} 7.2×10^{-5}

16. 52.8×10^9 5.28×10^{10}

17. $3,508 \times 10^{-7}$ 3.508×10^{-4}

Example 5
(page 217)

Order from least to greatest.

18. $16 \times 10^9, 2.3 \times 10^{12}, 0.065 \times 10^{11}$ $0.065 \times 10^{11}, 16 \times 10^9, 2.3 \times 10^{12}$

19. $253 \times 10^{-9}, 3.7 \times 10^{-8}, 12.9 \times 10^{-7}$ $3.7 \times 10^{-8}, 253 \times 10^{-9}, 12.9 \times 10^{-7}$

20. $65 \times 10^4, 432 \times 10^3, 2.996 \times 10^4$ $2.996 \times 10^4, 432 \times 10^3, 65 \times 10^4$

Example 6
(page 218)

Multiply. Express each result in scientific notation.

21. $(5 \times 10^6)(6 \times 10^2)$
3×10^9

22. $(4.3 \times 10^3)(2 \times 10^{-8})$ 8.6×10^{-5}

23. $(9 \times 10^{-3})(7 \times 10^8)$
6.3×10^6

24. $(3 \times 10^2)(2 \times 10^2)$ 6×10^4

Example 7
(page 218)

 25. Zoology An ant weighs about 2×10^{-5} lb. There are about 10^{15}

GPS ants on Earth. How many pounds of ants are on Earth?
2×10^{10} lb

B **Apply Your Skills**

In Exercises 26–30, write each number in standard notation.

26. 9×10^2
900

27. 8.43×10^6
8,430,000

28. 6.02×10^{-7}
0.000000602

29. Astronomy One light year is 5.88×10^{12} mi. 5,880,000,000,000 mi

30. Zoology The most venomous scorpion delivers 9×10^{-6} oz of venom per bite. 0.000009 oz

33a–b. Answers may vary.
Samples are given.
Move the decimal
point 4 places to the
right and write 4.3 ×
10^{-4}.
Write 523.4 × 10^5 =
5.234 × 10^2 × 10^5 =
5.234 × 10^7.

Order from least to greatest.

31. $10^9, 10^{-8}, 10^5, 10^{-6}, 10^0$ $10^{-8}, 10^{-6}, 10^0, 10^5, 10^9$

32. $55.8 \times 10^{-5}, 782 \times 10^{-8}, 9.1 \times 10^{-5}, 1,009 \times 10^2, 0.8 \times 10^{-4}$
$782 \times 10^{-8}, 0.8 \times 10^{-4}, 9.1 \times 10^{-5}, 55.8 \times 10^{-5}, 1,009 \times 10^2$

33. **Writing in Math** Explain how to write each number in scientific notation. **See left.**

a. 0.00043

b. 523.4×10^5

3. Practice

Assignment Guide

1 **Objective 1**
A **B** **Core** 1–20, 26–33

2 **Objective 2**
A **B** **Core** 21–25
C **Extension** 34, 35

Test Prep 36–39
Mixed Review 40–47

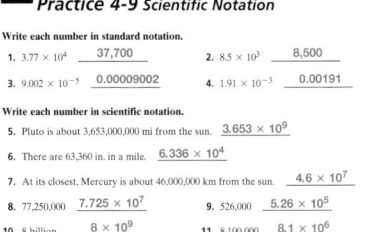

Practice 4-9 *Scientific Notation*

Write each number in standard notation.

1. 3.77×10^4 ___37,700___

2. 8.5×10^3 ___8,500___

3. 9.002×10^{-5} ___0.00009002___

4. 1.91×10^{-3} ___0.00191___

Write each number in scientific notation.

5. Pluto is about 3,653,000,000 mi from the sun. ___3.653×10^9___

6. There are 63,360 in. in a mile. ___6.336×10^4___

7. At its closest, Mercury is about 46,000,000 km from the sun. ___4.6×10^7___

8. 77,250,000 ___7.725×10^7___

9. 526,000 ___5.26×10^5___

10. 8 billion ___8×10^9___

11. 8,100,000 ___8.1×10^6___

12. 0.00000073 ___7.3×10^{-7}___

13. 0.000903 ___9.03×10^{-4}___

Multiply. Express each result in scientific notation.

14. $(2 \times 10^5)(3 \times 10^2)$
___6×10^7___

15. $(1.5 \times 10^5)(4 \times 10^9)$
___6×10^{14}___

16. $(6 \times 10^{-4})(1.2 \times 10^{-3})$
___7.2×10^{-7}___

17. $(5 \times 10^3)(1.7 \times 10^{-5})$
___8.5×10^{-2}___

Order from least to greatest.

18. $72 \times 10^5, 6.9 \times 10^6, 23 \times 10^5$
___$23 \times 10^5, 6.9 \times 10^6, 72 \times 10^5$___

19. $19 \times 10^{-3}, 2.5 \times 10^{-4}, 1.89 \times 10^{-4}$
___$1.89 \times 10^{-4}, 2.5 \times 10^{-4}, 19 \times 10^{-3}$___

20. An ounce is 0.00003125 tons. Write this number in scientific notation.
___3.125×10^{-5}___

21. A century is 3,153,600,000 seconds. Write this number in scientific notation.
___3.1536×10^9___

Enrichment 4-9 *Star Travel*

Solve. Write your answers in scientific notation unless otherwise directed.

1. An unmanned spacecraft sets out to explore the moon, Jupiter, and Alpha Centauri, the closest star in our galaxy. A typical rocket travels about 20,000 mi/h. Write this number in scientific notation.
___2×10^4 mi/h___

2. The trip to the moon will take about 12 h. Use your answer to Exercise 1 and the formula $d = rt$ to find the distance to the moon in scientific notation.
___2.4×10^5 mi___

3. The trip from the moon to Jupiter will take about 24,000 h.
a. Write the number of hours in scientific notation.
___2.4×10^4 h___
b. Find the distance from the moon to Jupiter.
___4.8×10^8 mi___
c. Write the number of days the journey will take in standard notation.
(1 day = 24h)
___1,000 days___

4. From Earth, the trip to Alpha Centauri will take about 1.25×10^9 h. Find the distance to Alpha Centauri.
___2.5×10^{13} mi___

5. The most distant star in the Milky Way is about 2.5×10^4 times as far from Earth as Alpha Centauri. Find the distance to this star.
___6.25×10^{17} mi___

GPS Use the Guided Problem
Solving worksheet with
Exercise 25.

Lesson Quiz 4-9

Write each number in scientific notation.

1. 5,400,000 5.4×10^6

2. 0.0000867 8.67×10^{-5}

Write each number in standard notation.

3. 3.45×10^6 3,450,000

4. 1.99×10^{-5} 0.0000199

5. Order 7.2×10^5, 7.2×10^6, 7.02×10^6, and 7.1×10^{-6} from least to greatest.
7.1×10^{-6}, 7.2×10^5, 7.02×10^6, 7.2×10^6

6. Multiply 14×10^6 and 4×10^{-4}. Express the result in scientific notation.
5.6×10^3

Diversity

Exercise 38 If there are any students in the class from another country, have them determine the approximate distance from your community to the capital of their native country (in both miles and kilometers). Have the class express the distance in scientific notation.

Reteaching 4-9 *Scientific Notation*

Write each number in scientific notation, then multiply: (8,600,000)(0.0042).

8.6 is between 1 and 10

8,600,000. = 8.6×10^6

6 places to the left

4.2 is between 1 and 10

0.0042 = 4.2×10^{-3}

3 places to the right

$(8.6 \times 10^6)(4.2 \times 10^{-3}) = 8.6 \times 4.2 \times 10^6 \times 10^{-3}$ Use the commutative property of multiplication.

$= 36.12 \times 10^6 \times 10^{-3}$ Multiply 8.6 and 4.2.

$= 36.12 \times 10^3$ Add the exponents.

$= 3.612 \times 10^1 \times 10^3$ Write 36.12 as 3.612×10^1.

$= 3.612 \times 10^4$ Add the exponents.

Write each number in scientific notation.

1. 745 million 7.45×10^8 2. 0.00034 3.4×10^{-4}

3. 888,200,000 8.882×10^8 4. 5,700 5.7×10^3

Multiply. Write your result using scientific notation.

5. $(1.6 \times 10^6)(3.7 \times 10^4)$ 5.92×10^{10}

6. $(3 \times 10^{-4})(2 \times 10^{-5})$ 6×10^{-9}

7. $72,000 \times 143,000$ 1.0296×10^{10}

8. $(2.3 \times 10^{-2})(1.5 \times 10^4)$ 3.45×10^2

C Challenge   **Solve. Write each result in scientific notation.**

34. Statistics The population density of India is about 8.33×10^2 people per square mile. The area of India is $1.2 \times 10^6 \, \text{mi}^2$. What is the approximate population of India? 9.996×10^8 **people**

35. Health Care In the year 2005, the population of the United States is expected to be about 296 million. Health expenditures will be about \$7,350 per person. In total, about how much will the United States spend on health care in 2005? **about \$2.18 $\times 10^{12}$**

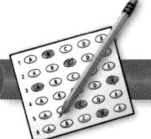

Test Prep

Multiple Choice

36. What is 55,000 in scientific notation?   **D**
A. 5.5×10^{-4} **B.** 55×10^3 **C.** 0.55×10^4 **D.** 5.5×10^4

37. What is 2×10^{-4} in standard notation?   **H**
F. 8,000   **G.** 0.0008   **H.** 0.0002   **I.** 2,000

Reading Comprehension   Read the passage before doing Exercises 38 and 39.

One Giant Leap

On July 20, 1969, Neil Armstrong and Edwin "Buzz" Aldrin, Jr., were first to set foot on the moon. With his first step, Armstrong announced over the radio, "That's one small step for a man, one giant leap for mankind."

The moon is about 380,000 km from Earth. The footsteps the astronauts left on the moon will probably be visible for at least 10 million years.

 **Take It to the NET**
Online lesson quiz at **www.PHSchool.com**
Web Code: ada-0409

38. What is the distance in meters from Earth to the moon? Use scientific notation. 3.8×10^8 **m**

39. How many 0.5-meter footsteps would it take to walk from Earth to the moon? Use scientific notation. 7.6×10^8 **footsteps**

Mixed Review

Lesson 4-8   **Simplify each expression.**

40. $\dfrac{10^7}{10^9}$ $\dfrac{1}{100}$ **41.** $\dfrac{x^3 y}{xy}$ x^2 **42.** $\dfrac{15b^2}{10b^5}$ $\dfrac{3}{2b^3}$ **43.** $\dfrac{9m^7}{3m^5 n}$ $\dfrac{3m^2}{n}$

Lesson 3-4   **Algebra** **Use the formula $d = rt$. Find d, r, or t.**

44. $r = 46.2$ m/h, $t = 2.75$ h
127.05 m

45. $d = 4.68$ ft, $t = 5.2$ h
0.9 ft/h

46. $d = 988$ cm, $r = 6.5$ cm/s
152 s

Lesson 1-8   **47. Patterns** A clock strikes a chime once at one o'clock, twice at two o'clock, and so on. In a twelve-hour period, what is the total number of chimes the clock strikes? **78 chimes**

Alternative Assessment

Have a contest between groups of students to see which group can find the smallest living organism listed in a reference source. Have students record in scientific notation the weights and lengths of the organisms they find.

Test Prep

 **Resources**

For additional practice with a variety of test item formats:
• Test Prep, p. 227
• Test-Taking Strategies, p. 222
• Test-Taking Strategies With Transparencies

When you enter a number with more digits than a calculator can display, the calculator translates the number into scientific notation. "E11" in the output below means "$\times 10^{11}$."

112,345,678,999 ENTER ⟶ *1.12345679E11*   The display shows the number rounded.

You can use a calculator to calculate with numbers in scientific notation.

1 EXAMPLE

Use a calculator to find
$(9.8 \times 10^5)(4.56 \times 10^4)$.

9.8E5*4.56E4
4.4688E10

Use
EE 5 to enter E5 and
EE 4 to enter E4.

• The product is 4.4688×10^{10}.

2 EXAMPLE

Use a calculator to find
$3.9 \times 10^{-7} + 4.7 \times 10^{-8}$.

3.9E-7+4.7E-8
4.37E-7

Use (−) for
negative exponents.

• The sum is 4.37×10^{-7}.

EXERCISES

Use a calculator to simplify. Write each result in scientific notation.
1–12. See right.

1. $1.5 \times 10^{11} - 2.4 \times 10^8$

2. $6.97 \times 10^5 + 4.8 \times 10^{10}$

3. $(1.02 \times 10^9)(1.98 \times 10^7)$

4. $(5.1 \times 10^3) \div (3.64 \times 10^{10})$

5. $(2.8 \times 10^{13})(3.335 \times 10^{10})$

6. $9.807 \times 10^7 + 7.08 \times 10^{10}$

7. $7.1 \times 10^{-5} - 9.1 \times 10^{-6}$

8. $3.5 \times 10^{-6} + 6.76 \times 10^{-4}$

9. $(2.43 \times 10^{-3})(4.9 \times 10^{-10})$

10. $(1.08 \times 10^4) \div (7.3 \times 10^{-7})$

11. $(5.01 \times 10^{-3})(8.5 \times 10^{-8})$

12. $1.99 \times 10^{-5} - 3.81 \times 10^{-4}$

1. 1.4976×10^{11}
2. 4.8000697×10^{10}
3. 2.0196×10^{16}
4. $1.401098901 \times 10^{-7}$
5. 9.338×10^{23}
6. 7.089807×10^{10}
7. 6.19×10^{-5}
8. 6.795×10^{-4}
9. 1.1907×10^{-12}
10. $1.479452055 \times 10^{10}$
11. 4.2585×10^{-10}
12. -3.611×10^{-4}

Technology

Scientific Notation With Calculators

This Technology extension explains how a graphing calculator uses scientific notation to show large and small numbers.

Resources

Students may use any type of calculator that will perform operations with numbers in scientific notation.

Teaching Notes

Teaching Tip
To demonstrate how a large number is displayed on a calculator, have the students enter 12,345,678,901. Then press the equal (or ENTER) key. Some calculators will display the number as 1.2345678901E10 or $1.23456789 \times 10^{10}$.

1 EXAMPLE Error Prevention

Have students check the digits in the display of the calculator before pressing an operation or Enter key.

2 EXAMPLE Error Prevention

If students get an error message, have them check to make sure they pressed the negative key, not the minus key.

Reading-Comprehension Questions

This feature helps students learn to read written material and understand the needed information. They read a passage, and then answer questions about what is stated or implied in the passage.

Resources

Test-Taking Strategies With Transparencies
• Transparency 4
• Practice sheet, p. 4

Teaching Notes

Visual Learners
Display a poster depicting the planets in our solar system. Have students draw the planets used in the Example on a piece of paper and write the given facts next to each planet. Students may repeat this procedure for the Exercises.

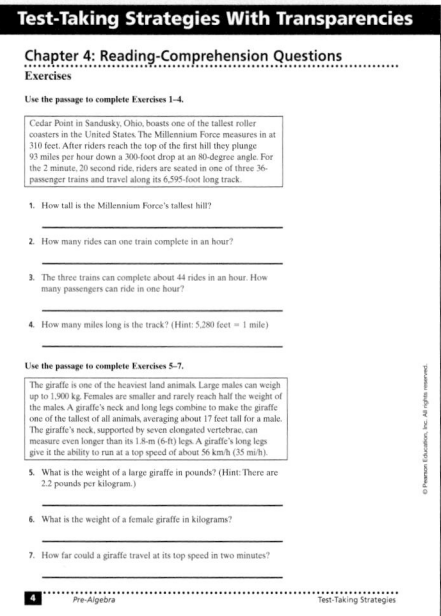

Reading-comprehension questions require that you read and understand information given to you in print in order to use mathematics to solve the problem.

EXAMPLE

Read the passage below. Then answer the questions based on what is stated or implied in the passage.

> **Solar System Masses** The sun is the largest object in our solar system. It contains approximately 98% of the total solar-system mass. The interior of the sun can hold over 1.3 million Earths. The mass of Earth is 5.98×10^{24} kg. The sun is approximately 330,000 times the mass of Earth.

What is the mass of the sun?

You read, "The sun is approximately 330,000 times the mass of Earth."

$$
\begin{aligned}
\text{Mass of sun} &\approx 330{,}000 \times \text{mass of Earth.} \\
M &\approx 330{,}000 \times 5.98 \times 10^{24} \\
&\approx 3.3 \times 10^{5} \times 5.98 \times 10^{24} \\
&\approx 19.734 \times 10^{29} \\
&\approx 1.97 \times 10^{30}
\end{aligned}
$$

The mass of the sun is about 1.97×10^{30} kg.

EXERCISES

Read the passage below. Then answer the questions based on what is stated or implied in the passage.

> **Planet Distances** The diameter of Jupiter is 142,800 km. Saturn is almost as big with a diameter of 120,000 km. Earth, by comparison, has a diameter of only 12,756 km. Jupiter's mass is 318 times the mass of Earth. Saturn's mass is only 95 times the mass of Earth.

1. Put the planets named in the above passage in order from smallest to largest, based on their diameters. **Earth, Saturn, Jupiter**

2. The mass of Jupiter is about how many times the mass of Saturn? **about 3 times**

3. The diameter of Jupiter is about how many times the diameter of Saturn? **about 1.2 times**

4. What could you conclude about Saturn from this passage? **Answers may vary. Sample: Although Saturn is almost as big as Jupiter, it has a lot less mass.**

222 Test-Taking Strategies Reading Comprehension

Chapter Review

Vocabulary

base (p. 182)
composite number (p. 186)
divisible (p. 178)
equivalent fractions (p. 192)
exponents (p. 182)

factor (p. 179)
greatest common
  factor (GCF) (p. 187)
power (p. 182)
prime factorization (p. 187)

prime number (p. 186)
rational number (p. 201)
scientific notation (p. 215)
simplest form (p. 192)
standard notation (p. 216)

Reading Math
Understanding
Vocabulary

Choose the vocabulary term that correctly completes each sentence.

1. One integer is a _?_ of another integer if it divides that integer with remainder zero. factor

2. A fraction is in _?_ when the numerator and denominator have no factors in common other than 1. simplest form

3. A number that you can write as the quotient $\frac{a}{b}$ of two integers, where b is not zero, is a _?_. rational number

4. You can write numbers using powers of 10 in a shorthand way called _?_. scientific notation

5. You can show repeated multiplication with _?_. exponents

6. If a positive integer greater than 1 has exactly two factors, 1 and the integer itself, the integer is a _?_. prime number

Take It to the NET
Online vocabulary quiz
at www.PHSchool.com
Web Code: adj-0451

Skills and Concepts

4-1 Objectives

▼ To use divisibility tests
(p. 178)

▼ To find factors (p. 179)

One integer is **divisible** by another if the remainder is zero when you divide. Divisibility tests help you find factors. One integer is a **factor** of another integer if it divides that integer with remainder zero.

List the positive factors of each number. 7–12. See margin.

7. 12 **8.** 30 **9.** 42 **10.** 72 **11.** 111 **12.** 252

4-2 Objectives

▼ To use exponents
(p. 182)

▼ To use the order of
operations with
exponents (p.183)

To simplify an expression that has an **exponent,** remember that the **base** is the number used as a factor. The exponent shows the number of times the base is used as a factor.

Simplify each expression.

13. 2^3 8

14. $3(10 - 7)^2$ 27

15. $28 + (1 + 5)^2 \cdot 4$ 172

16. -5^2 -25

Resources

Student Edition
Extra Practice, Ch. 4, p. 747
English/Spanish Glossary, p. 782
Table of Symbols, p. 777

 Reaching All Students
Reading and Math Literacy 4D
Spanish Reading and Math
  Literacy 4D

 ASSESSMENT *SYSTEM*

Test Preparation
• Chapter 4 practice in test
  formats

 www.PHSchool.com
Student Site
• Self-grading vocabulary test
PH SuccessNet Teacher Center
• Resources

Plus

Spanish Reading and Math Literacy

Reading and Math Literacy

4D: Vocabulary   For use with Chapter Review

Study Skill: Many words in English have more than one meaning. You can often figure out which meaning to use by looking at the sentence that contains the word. To help you decide what a word means, consider the surroundings, or context, in which you see the word.

Match each word or phrase in the left column with the best example in the right column. Some words or phrases may have more than one example, but only one example is the best match.

	Word or Phrase			Example
1.	exponent	K	A.	the 5 in 5^2
2.	base	A	B.	4.06×10^3
3.	factors	H	C.	$\frac{3}{4} = \frac{6}{8}$
4.	scientific notation	B	D.	the 4 in $4x$
5.	standard notation	J	E.	the $5x$ in $5x - 2$
6.	prime factorization	M	F.	$x + 2 = 5$
7.	equivalent fractions	C	G.	the 2 in 2, 68, 65, 69, 72
8.	formula	O	H.	both the 3 and the 5 in $3 \cdot 5$
9.	outlier	G	I.	addition and subtraction
10.	like terms	L	J.	4,060
11.	coefficient	D	K.	the 2 in 5^2
12.	inverse operations	I	L.	$3x$ and $7x$
13.	open sentence	F	M.	$60 = 2 \cdot 2 \cdot 3 \cdot 5$
14.	term	E	N.	11
15.	prime number	N	O.	$P = 2l + 2w$
16.	rational number	P	P.	$\frac{2}{3}$

---

7. 1, 2, 3, 4, 6, 12
8. 1, 2, 3, 5, 6, 10, 15, 30
9. 1, 2, 3, 6, 7, 14, 21, 42
10. 1, 2, 3, 4, 6, 8, 9, 12, 18, 24, 36, 72
11. 1, 3, 37, 111
12. 1, 2, 3, 4, 6, 7, 9, 12, 14, 18, 21, 28, 36, 42,
    63, 84, 126, 252

223

Evaluate each expression.

17. x^2, for $x = 11$ 121   **18.** $7m^2 - 5$, for $m = 3$ 58

19. $(2a + 1)^2$, for $a = -4$ 49   **20.** b^2, for $b = -4$ 16

4-3 Objectives

▼ To find the prime factorization of a number (p. 186)

▼ To find the greatest common factor (GCF) of two or more numbers (p. 187)

A **prime number** is an integer greater than 1 with exactly two positive factors, 1 and itself. An integer greater than 1 with more than two factors is a **composite number**. The **prime factorization** of a composite number is the product of its prime factors.

The **greatest common factor (GCF)** of two or more numbers or expressions is the greatest factor that the numbers or expressions have in common. You can list factors or use prime factorization to find the GCF of two or more numbers or expressions.

Is each number *prime, composite,* or *neither*? For each composite number, write the prime factorization. Use exponents where possible.
21–25. See margin.

21. 13   **22.** 20   **23.** 73   **24.** 110   **25.** 87

Find the GCF.

26. 16, 60 4   **27.** 36, 81, 27 9   **28.** 15, 17, 30 1

29. $3x^2y, 9x^2$ $3x^2$ **30.** $8a^2b, 14ab^2$ 2ab   **31.** $3cd^4, 12c^3d, 6c^2d^2$ 3cd

32. Reasoning Why is the GCF of two or more positive integers never greater than the least of the numbers?
No factor of a positive integer is greater than the integer.

4-4 Objectives

▼ To find equivalent fractions (p. 192)

▼ To write fractions in simplest form (p. 192)

Equivalent fractions describe the same part of a whole. A fraction is in **simplest form** when the numerator and the denominator have no common factors other than 1. You can use the GCF of the numerator and denominator to write a fraction in simplest form.

Write in simplest form.

33. $\frac{3}{15}$ $\frac{1}{5}$ **34.** $\frac{10}{20}$ $\frac{1}{2}$ **35.** $\frac{16}{52}$ $\frac{4}{13}$ **36.** $\frac{28}{40}$ $\frac{7}{10}$ **37.** $\frac{21}{33}$ $\frac{7}{11}$ **38.** $\frac{9}{54}$ $\frac{1}{6}$

39. $\frac{xy}{y}$ x **40.** $\frac{25m}{5m}$ 5 **41.** $\frac{2y}{8y}$ $\frac{1}{4}$ **42.** $\frac{2c}{5c}$ $\frac{2}{5}$ **43.** $\frac{9x^2}{27x}$ $\frac{x}{3}$ **44.** $\frac{36bc}{9c}$ 4b

---

4-5 Objectives

▼ To find all possibilities when you solve a problem (p. 197)

To account for all possibilities in a word problem, make an organized list or a diagram to keep track of possibilities as you find them.

🌐 **45. School** Mike, Don, Tameka, and Rosa sit in the four desks in the last row of desks. Each day they sit in a different order. How many days can they do this before they repeat a seating pattern?
24 days

21. prime
22. composite; $2^2 \cdot 5$
23. prime
24. composite; $2 \cdot 5 \cdot 11$
25. composite; $3 \cdot 29$

4-6 Objectives

▼ To identify and graph rational numbers (p. 201)

▼ To evaluate fractions containing variables (p. 202)

A **rational number** is any number you can write as a quotient $\frac{a}{b}$ of two integers, where b is not zero.

Graph the rational numbers below on the same number line. 46–49.
See margin.

46. 2   **47.** -0.6 **48.** $-\frac{5}{10}$ **49.** $\frac{2}{10}$

Evaluate each expression for $a = -5$ and $b = -2$. Write in simplest form.

50. $\frac{b}{a}$ $\frac{2}{5}$ **51.** $\frac{a+b}{4b}$ $\frac{7}{8}$ **52.** $\frac{b-a}{a-b}$ -1 **53.** $\frac{b^2}{a}$ $-\frac{4}{5}$

4-7 and 4-8 Objectives

▼ To multiply powers with the same base (p. 205)

▼ To find a power of a power (p. 206)

▼ To divide expressions containing exponents (p. 210)

▼ To simplify expressions with integer exponents (p. 211)

To multiply numbers or variables with the same base, add the exponents. To raise a power to a power, multiply the exponents. To divide numbers or variables with the same nonzero base, subtract the exponents.

Simplify each expression.

54. $2^4 \cdot 2^3$ 128 **55.** $7a^4 \cdot 3a^2$ $21a^6$ **56.** $b \cdot c^2 \cdot b^6 \cdot c^2$ b^7c^4 **57.** $(x^3)^5$ x^{15}

58. $(y^4)^5$ y^{20} **59.** $\frac{4^8}{4^2}$ $4,096$ **60.** $\frac{b^2}{b^4}$ $\frac{1}{b^2}$ **61.** $\frac{28xy^7}{32xy^{12}}$ $\frac{7}{8y^5}$

4-9 Objectives

▼ To write and evaluate numbers in scientific notation (p. 215)

▼ To calculate with scientific notation (p. 218)

66. 800,000,000,000
67. 0.0000032
68. 11,190,000
69. 0.000000000005

Scientific notation provides a way to write numbers as the product of two factors, a power of 10 and a decimal greater than or equal to 1, but less than 10. To multiply numbers in scientific notation, multiply the decimals, multiply the powers of ten, and then put the result into scientific notation.

Write each number in scientific notation.

62. 2,000,000
2×10^6

63. 458,000,000
4.58×10^8

64. 0.0000007
7×10^{-7}

65. 0.0000000059
5.9×10^{-9}

Write each number in standard notation. 66–69. See left.

66. 8×10^{11} **67.** 3.2×10^{-6} **68.** 1.119×10^7 **69.** 5×10^{-12}

Order from least to greatest.

70. $3,644 \times 10^9, 12 \times 10^{11}, 4.3 \times 10^{10}$ $4.3 \times 10^{10}, 12 \times 10^{11}, 3,644 \times 10^9$

71. $58 \times 10^{-10}, 8 \times 10^{-10}, 716 \times 10^{-10}$ $8 \times 10^{-10}, 58 \times 10^{-10}, 716 \times 10^{-10}$

Multiply. Express each result in scientific notation.

72. $(4 \times 10^9)(6 \times 10^6)$
2.4×10^{16}

73. $(5 \times 10^7)(3.6 \times 10^3)$
1.8×10^{11}

46–49.

225

Chapter Test – Form B

Chapter Test – Form A

Chapter 4 Test • Form A

Circle the letter of the best answer.
1. Evaluate 3^5.
   A. 15   B. 125   C. 243   D. 81
2. Evaluate $8 - 3^2$.
   F. −25   G. 25   H. 1   J. −1
3. Evaluate cd^2 for $c = 3$ and $d = −1$.
   A. −3   B. 3   C. −9   D. 9
4. Simplify $y^3 \cdot y^2 \cdot y^4$.
   F. y^9 G. y^{24} H. $24y^4$ J. $2y^7$
5. Simplify $\frac{h^2}{h^6}$.
   A. h^2 B. $\frac{8}{8}h$ C. h^5 D. $\frac{1}{h^3}$
6. Simplify $(x^5)^2$.
   F. x^{10} G. x^7 H. $2x^5$ J. x^{25}
7. Simplify $\frac{5x^3y^4}{15xy^6}$.
   A. $3x^2y^2$ B. $\frac{x^2}{3y}$ C. $\frac{x^2}{3y}$ D. $3x^3y^2$
8. Express 207,500 in scientific notation.
   F. 2.75×10^5 G. 2.075×10^6 H. 2.075×10^5 J. 2.75×10^6
9. Express 7.02×10^{-5} in standard notation.
   A. 702,000   B. 70,200   C. 0.00000702   D. 0.0000702
10. 38,220 is *not* divisible by which of the following?
   F. 2   G. 3   H. 5   J. 9
11. In which of the following are the numbers in order from least to greatest?
   A. $5 \times 10^{-4}, 40 \times 10^{-5}, 0.6 \times 10^{-3}$ B. $7.2 \times 10^{-6}, 6.8 \times 10^{-5}, 73 \times 10^{-6}$
   C. $4.2 \times 10^{-3}, 45 \times 10^{-4}, 0.32 \times 10^{-2}$ D. $9.8 \times 10^{-2}, 8.4 \times 10^{-3}, 85 \times 10^{-2}$

Write your answer.
12. List all the factors of 110.   1, 2, 5, 10, 11, 22 , 55, 110

Is each number prime or composite? For each composite number, write the prime factorization.
13. 63   composite; $3^2 \cdot 7$ 14. 23   prime

Find each GCF.
15. 18, 35   1   16. $4x^2y^3, 6xy^2$ $2xy^2$

Chapter **4**

Chapter Test

Take It to the NET
Online chapter test at
www.PHSchool.com
Web Code: ada-0452

State whether each number is divisible by 2, 3, 5, 9, or 10.

1. 36   2, 3, 9   2. 100   2, 5, 10   3. 270   2, 3, 5, 9, 10
4. 84   2, 3   5. 555   3, 5   6. 49   none

List all the factors of each number. See margin.

7. 16   8. 30   9. 41
10. 23   11. 55   12. 64

Simplify each expression.

13. 5^3 125   14. $2^0 \cdot 2^3$ 8   15. $3^2 + 3^3$ 36
16. $4^2 \cdot 1^3$ 16   17. $(−9)^2$ 81   18. $(7 − 6)^4$ 1
19. $−2(3 + 2)^2$ −50   20. $−6^2 + 6$ −30

21. **Writing in Math**   A number written in scientific notation is doubled. Must the exponent of the power of 10 change? Explain.   See margin.

Evaluate for $a = −2$ and $b = 3$.

22. $(a \cdot b)^2$ 36   23. a^2b 12   24. $b^3 \cdot b^0$ 27
25. $(a + b)^5$ 1   26. $b^2 − a$ 11   27. $2(a^2 + b^3)$ 62

Is each number *prime* or *composite*? For each composite number, write the prime factorization.   28–33. See margin.

28. 24   29. 17   30. 42
31. 54   32. 72   33. 100

Find each GCF.

34. 56, 96   8   35. 36, 60   12   36. 14, 25   1
37. $15x, 24x^2$ 3x   38. $14a^2b^3, 21ab^2$ $7ab^2$

Simplify.

39. $\frac{4}{16}$ $\frac{1}{4}$ 40. $\frac{44}{52}$ $\frac{11}{13}$ 41. $\frac{15}{63}$ $\frac{5}{21}$
42. $\frac{a^3}{a^2}$ a 43. $\frac{5b^4}{b}$ $5b^3$ 44. $\frac{8m^4n^2}{40mn}$ $\frac{m^3n}{5}$

Graph the numbers on the same number line.
45–48. See back of book.

45. $\frac{1}{10}$ 46. $−0.3$ 47. $−\frac{1}{2}$ 48. 1

49. A car manufacturer offers exterior colors of white, blue, red, black, and silver. The manufacturer offers interior colors of black and silver. How many different color combinations are there?
   10 color combinations

Evaluate for $x = 4$ and $y = −3$. Write in simplest form.

50. $\frac{2y}{x^2}$ $−\frac{3}{8}$ 51. $\frac{xy}{5x}$ $−\frac{3}{5}$ 52. $\frac{(x + y)^3}{x}$ $\frac{1}{4}$
53. $\frac{x + 3y}{10}$ $−\frac{1}{2}$ 54. $\frac{y^2 − x}{5}$ 1   55. $\frac{x − y}{x + y}$ 7

Simplify each expression.

56. $a^4 \cdot a$ a^5 57. $(y^3)^6$ y^{18} 58. $x^3 \cdot x^6 \cdot y^2$ x^9y^2
59. $(a^3)^2$ a^6 60. $6b^7 \cdot 5b^2$ $30b^9$ 61. $\frac{98}{9^2}$ 531,441
62. $\frac{6a^7}{15a^3}$ $\frac{2a^4}{5}$ 63. $\frac{b^8}{b^{11}}$ $\frac{1}{b^3}$ 64. $\frac{2x^2y^5}{8x^3y^5}$ $\frac{1}{4x}$

Write each number in scientific notation.

65. 43,000,000 4.3×10^7 66. 6,000,000,000 6×10^9
67. 0.0000032 3.2×10^{-6} 68. 0.00000000099 9.9×10^{-10}

Write each number in standard notation.
69–72. See margin.
69. 5×10^5 70. 3.812×10^{-7}
71. 9.3×10^8 72. 1.02×10^{-9}

Order from least to greatest.

73. $3 \times 10^{10}, 742 \times 10^7, 0.006 \times 10^{12}$
   $0.006 \times 10^{12}, 742 \times 10^7, 3 \times 10^{10}$
74. $85 \times 10^{-7}, 2 \times 10^{-5}, 0.9 \times 10^{-8}$
   $0.9 \times 10^{-8}, 85 \times 10^{-7}, 2 \times 10^{-5}$

Multiply. Express each result in scientific notation.

75. $(3 \times 10^{10})(7 \times 10^8)$ 2.1×10^{19}
76. $(8.3 \times 10^6)(3 \times 10^5)$ 2.49×10^{12}

7. 1, 2, 4, 8, 16
8. 1, 2, 3, 5, 6, 10, 15, 30
9. 1, 41
10. 1, 23
11. 1, 5, 11, 55
12. 1, 2, 4, 8, 16, 32, 64
21. Answers may vary. Sample: No, but if the

decimal between 1 and 10 is at least 5, doubling the original number will increase the exponent of 10 by 1.

28. composite; $2^3 \cdot 3$
29. prime
30. composite; $2 \cdot 3 \cdot 7$
31. composite; $2 \cdot 3^3$
32. composite; $2^3 \cdot 3^2$
33. composite; $2^2 \cdot 5^2$
69. 500,000
70. 0.0000003812
71. 930,000,000
72. 0.00000000102

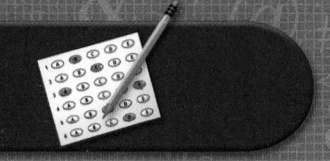

Test Prep

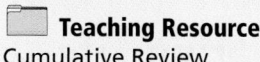 **Test Prep**

Multiple Choice

Choose the best answer.

1. Which expression is equivalent to $\frac{x^3y^7}{x^5y^2}$? **A**
   A. $x^{-2}y^5$ B. x^2y^5
   C. $x^{-2}y^{-5}$ D. x^2y^{-5}

2. What is the simplest form of $(4c - 5c) + (7 - 2)$? **G**
   F. $c + 5$ G. $-c + 5$
   H. $9c + 5$ I. $c - 5$

3. Which integer is *not* a solution of $25 + t < 19$? **D**
   A. -43 B. -7
   C. -8 D. -6

4. Which sentence is true? **H**
   F. $16 \geq 2 \cdot 9$
   G. $-36 - 10 = 4(5)$
   H. $5[-6 - (-2)] = 2 \cdot (-5)2$
   I. $32 - (-4 \cdot 6) \leq 54$

5. Which number is divisible by both 3 and 9? **C**
   A. 24,000   B. 36,089
   C. 45,288   D. 95,500

6. Which expression is equivalent to $-8 \cdot n \cdot n \cdot n \cdot 4 \cdot t$? **F**
   F. $-32n^3t$ G. $-8n^3 + 4t$
   H. $-32 \cdot 3n \cdot t$ I. $-32nt^3$

7. Which expression is the GCF of $24x^3$ and $64x$? **D**
   A. $1,536x^4$ B. $4x^4$
   C. $40x^2$ D. $8x$

8. Which expression is equivalent to x^{12}? **I**
   F. $x^6 + x^6$ G. $(x^4)^8$
   H. $x^2 \cdot x^6$ I. $x^6 \cdot x^6$

9. Which symbol makes $7^2 \cdot 7^5 \ \blacksquare \ (7^5)^2$ true? **B**
   A. $>$ B. $<$
   C. $=$ D. $\geq$

10. What is the simplest form of $x^5 \cdot y \cdot x^5 \cdot y$? **I**
    F. $(x^{25})(2y)$ G. x^5y^2
    H. $2x^5y$ I. $x^{10}y^2$

11. What is the simplest form of $\frac{w^{12}y^{15}z}{w^9y^7}$? **A**
    A. w^3y^8z B. $w^{21}y^{22}z$
    C. $\frac{w^{21}y^{22}z}{wz}$ D. $\frac{w^3y^8z}{wz}$

12. What is the prime factorization of 90? **F**
    F. $2 \cdot 3^2 \cdot 5$ G. $2 \cdot 5 \cdot 9$
    H. $3 \cdot 3 \cdot 5^2$ I. $2 \cdot 45$

13. Which number is divisible by 2, 3, and 5? **C**
    A. 70   B. 105   C. 120   D. 235

Gridded Response

14. Simplify 2^{-3}. **1/8**

15. Evaluate $\frac{3m - 12}{n}$, for $m = 8$ and $n = 4$. **3**

16. Simplify $2(11 + 7 \cdot 2)$. **50**

17. Evaluate $-a^2 + 4$ for $a = -1$. **3**

18. Simplify $8 + (-8) - (-8)$. **8**

Short Response   19–21. See back of book.

19. **a.** The product of -6.2 and a number k is -70.68. Write an equation to find k.
    b. Solve for k.

20. What is the GCF of 45 and 54? Explain.

21. **a.** Write a variable expression for the length of the red segment.
    b. What is the segment length if $a = 7$?

Extended Response   See back of book.

22. The store sells erasers for $.05, $.10, and $.15. In how many ways can you spend $.20 to buy erasers? Explain your answer using a table.

Resources

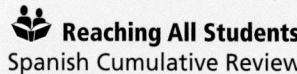 **Teaching Resources**
Cumulative Review

 **Reaching All Students**
Spanish Cumulative Review

ASSESSMENT SYSTEM

Test Preparation
• Ch. 4 Test Prep
Assessment Resources
• Cumulative Review
Computer Test Generator CD-ROM
• Test Prep

www.PHSchool.com
• Test Prep
• Resources

Plus **TEXT**

Cumulative Review

Chapter 4 Cumulative Review

Circle the letter of the best answer.

1. Simplify $-3 + 2 \cdot 4 - 2$.
   A. -2 B. 3   C. 1   D. -6
2. What is the opposite of 19?
   F. -1 G. $\frac{1}{19}$ H. 19   J. -19
3. Simplify $5 + (-4) + (-5)$.
   A. -4 B. 14   C. -14 D. -10
4. Simplify $-2y - (3k - 2y) + 3k$.
   F. 0   G. $4y - 6k$ H. $4y$ J. $6k - 4y$
5. Which integer is *not* a solution of $36 + x > 14$?
   A. 5   B. -20 C. -22 D. -16
6. Which number is divisible by both 3 and 2?
   F. 68,211   G. 45,305   H. 28,000   J. 58,404
7. Which expression is equivalent to $-6 \cdot m \cdot m \cdot n \cdot 3 \cdot m$?
   A. $-6m^3 + 3n$ B. $-18m^3n$ C. $-18mn$ D. $-18 \cdot 3m \cdot n$
8. Which expression is the GCF of $12x^3$ and $32xy$?
   F. $93x^3y$ G. $96x^4y$ H. $4x$ J. $4xy$
9. Which is equivalent to $\frac{m^4n^3}{m^6n}$?
   A. m^2n^3 B. $m^{-2}n^3$ C. m^2n^{-3} D. $m^{-2}n^{-3}$
10. Evaluate $\frac{4m - 5}{n}$ for $m = 5, n = 25$.
    F. 5   G. 3   H. $\frac{4}{3}$ J. $\frac{3}{5}$
11. Simplify $x^6 \cdot y^2 \cdot x^3 \cdot y$.
    A. x^3y B. x^2y C. x^9y^3 D. $x^{18}y^2$
12. Simplify $\frac{w^{10}y^{12}z}{w^6z^5}$.
    F. $\frac{w^4y^{12}}{z^4}$ G. $\frac{w^{16}y^{12}}{z^5}$ H. $w^{16}y^{12}z^6$ J. $w^4y^{12}z^4$
13. Simplify 5^{-2}.
    A. -10 B. 25   C. -25 D. $\frac{1}{25}$
14. Which is true?
    F. $14 > 9 \cdot 3$ G. $-26 - 12 = 38$
    H. $4[-5 + (-2)] = (-2)6$ J. $50 - (-3 \cdot 5) \geq 55$

Item	1	2	3	4	5	6	7	8	9	10	11	12	13	14	15	16	17	18	19	20	21	22
Lesson	4-8	2-3	2-9	2-10	4-1	4-7	4-3	4-7	4-7	4-7	4-8	4-3	4-3	4-8	4-4	1-2	4-2	1-6	3-6	4-3	1-4	3-6

Comparing Life Cycles

In this activity, students apply knowledge of factors and multiples, incorporating information from two tables about the life cycles of different kinds of cicadas.

Activating Prior Knowledge

Ask students to discuss the stages of growth and development of some familiar living things such as people, dogs and cats, and flowers. **Answers may vary. Sample: People begin as infants, grow through toddler and child stages, become teenagers, and finally reach adulthood. Puppies and kittens grow into adult dogs and cats. Flowers begin as seeds, grow into seedlings, and then blossom.**

Teaching Notes

Diversity

Have a volunteer read the introductory paragraphs. Ask: *Have you ever heard the sound of singing cicadas, and if so, where were you at the time?* **Answers may vary. Sample: Since cicadas live in the eastern part of North America, only students who have been in this part of the country should have heard the cicada's song.**

English Learners

Explain that *life cycle* refers to the stages of growth and development that occur in a particular organism. Define *habitat* as the environment in which an organism normally lives.

Teaching Tip

Before students begin the activity, discuss the illustrations and their captions. Have students read through the exercises before beginning to work.

228

Comparing Life Cycles

Applying Factors and Multiples All living things go through stages of growth and development marked by changes in how they look. Few animals, however, have a life cycle as unusual as the periodic cicadas (sih-CAY-duhs) of North America.

Some of these insects spend 13 or 17 years living underground and feeding on roots. Then, within a matter of days, thousands of them emerge above ground. These large groups of periodic cicadas are called broods. They molt into winged adults but live for only a few more weeks.

Periodic Cicada
An adult cicada perches on a branch to dry its wings.

Cicada Song
A male cicada "sings" using a special membrane on its abdomen called a *tymbal.* Cicada songs continue from dawn until dusk.

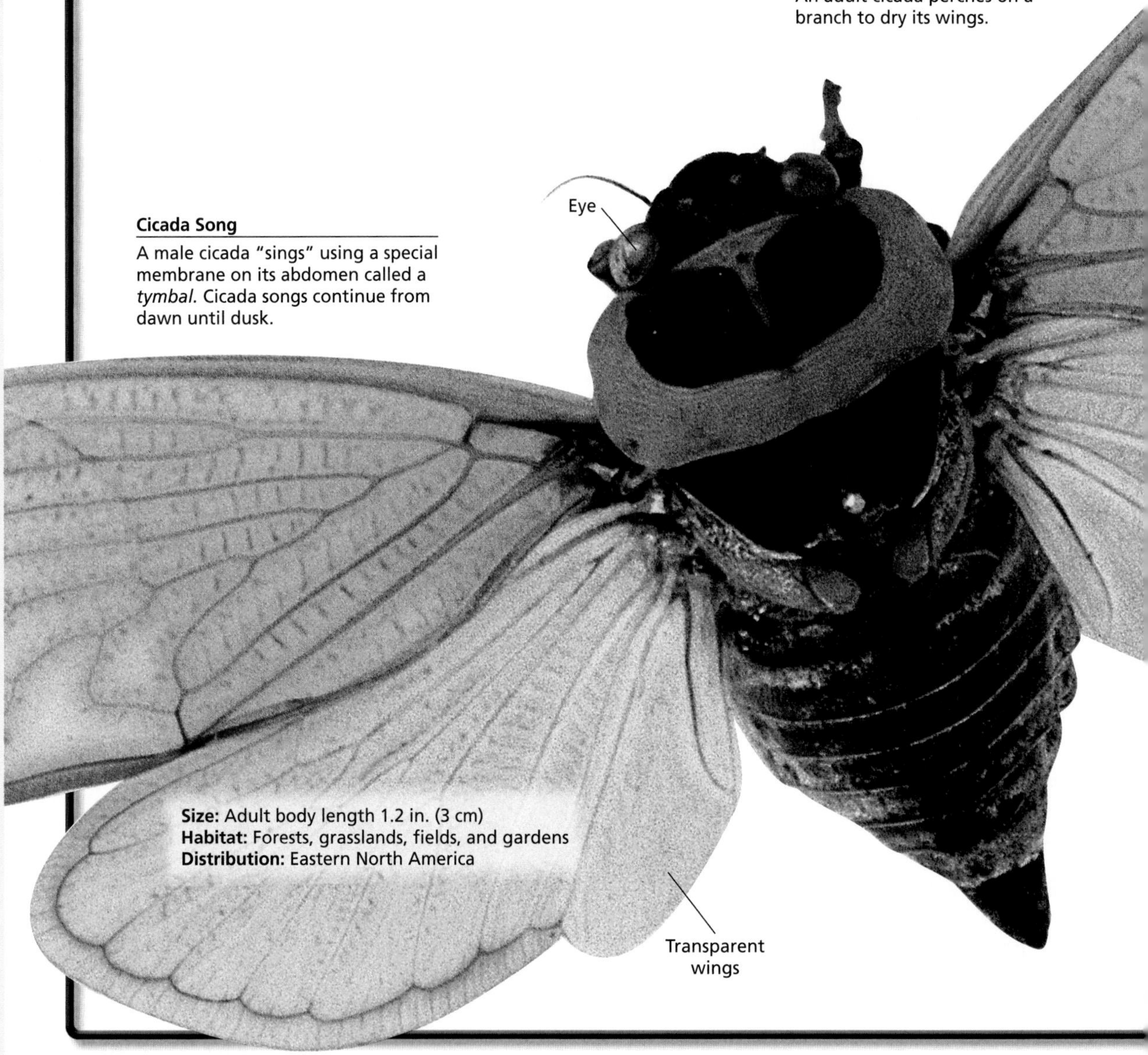

Eye

Size: Adult body length 1.2 in. (3 cm)
Habitat: Forests, grasslands, fields, and gardens
Distribution: Eastern North America

Transparent wings

228

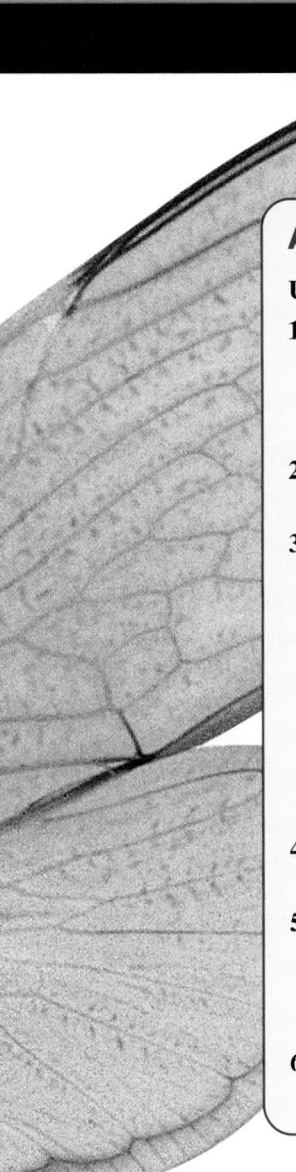

Activity

Use the information in the tables. 1–6. See margin.

1. **a.** When was the last time brood IV emerged?
   b. When will brood IV emerge next?
   c. How many times will brood IV emerge during this century?

2. How many times did brood XXII emerge during the last century?

3. In 1998, a 17-year brood and a 13-year brood both emerged in Missouri.
   a. How many years will pass before they emerge together again?
   b. What year will it be?
   c. **Reasoning** Suppose these two broods are the only cicadas that emerge in Missouri. Before 1998, how many years had passed without adult cicadas in Missouri? Explain.

4. Brood VII and brood XXII recently emerged in the same year. How many years earlier did they also emerge together?

5. Some cicadas are called "dog-day" cicadas. These cicadas have cycles of 2 to 5 years. Suppose broods of 3-year, 4-year, and 5-year cicadas emerged in 2005. In what year would all three broods next emerge together? Explain.

6. Suppose a 17-year cicada emerges, molts, and dies after 4 weeks. What percent of its life has the cicada spent as an adult?

17-Year Cicadas

Brood	Year Seen
III	1997
IV	1998
VII	2001

13-Year Cicadas

Brood	Year Seen
XIX	1998
XXII	2001
XXIII	2002

Gathering Insects
Students taking a class on entomology collect and study insects.

Take It to the NET For more information about cicadas, go to **www.PHSchool.com**.
Web Code: ade-0453

229

1a. 1998
   b. 2015
   c. 5 times

2. 7 times

3a. 221 years
   b. 2219
   c. 13 years; The 13-year brood emerged 13 years before 1998.

4. 221 years

5. 2065; the least common multiple of 3, 4, and 5 is 60

6. about 0.5%

Operations With Fractions

Chapter at a Glance

5-1

Comparing and Ordering Fractions

pp. 232–236

Objectives

▼ Finding the Least Common Multiple

② Comparing Fractions

New Vocabulary
multiple, least common multiple (LCM), least common denominator (LCD)

NCTM Standards

1, 2, 6, 8, 9, 10

Local Standards

5-2

Fractions and Decimals

pp. 237–241

Objectives

▼ Writing Fractions as Decimals

② Writing Decimals as Fractions

New Vocabulary
terminating decimal, repeating decimal

NCTM Standards
1, 6, 7, 8, 9, 10

Local Standards

5-3

Adding and Subtracting Fractions

pp. 243–247

Objectives

▼ Adding and Subtracting Fractions

② Adding and Subtracting Mixed Numbers

NCTM Standards
1, 2, 6, 8, 9, 10

Local Standards

✓ **Checkpoint Quiz 1**

5-4

Multiplying and Dividing Fractions

pp. 248–252

Objectives

▼ Multiplying Rational Numbers

② Dividing Rational Numbers

New Vocabulary
reciprocals

Materials
folding paper

NCTM Standards
1, 2, 6, 7, 8, 9, 10

Local Standards

5-5

Using Customary Units of Measurement

pp. 253–257

Objectives

▼ Identifying Appropriate Customary Units

② Converting Customary Units

New Vocabulary
dimensional analysis

NCTM Standards
1, 4, 6, 8, 9, 10

Local Standards

5-6 [Problem Solving]

Work Backward

pp. 259–262

Objective

▼ Working Backward to Solve Problems

NCTM Standards
1, 2, 4, 6, 8, 9, 10

Local Standards

5-7

Solving Equations by Adding or Subtracting Fractions

pp. 264–267

Objectives

▼ Using Subtraction to Solve Equations

② Using Addition to Solve Equations

NCTM Standards
1, 2, 6, 8, 9, 10

Local Standards

5-8

Solving Equations by Multiplying Fractions

pp. 268–272

Objectives

▼ Using Multiplication to Solve Equations

② Solving Equations With Mixed Numbers

NCTM Standards
1, 2, 6, 8, 9, 10

Local Standards

✓ **Checkpoint Quiz 2**

5-9

Powers of Products and Quotients

pp. 274–277

Objectives

▼ Finding Powers of Products

② Finding Powers of Quotients

NCTM Standards
1, 2, 6, 8, 9, 10

Local Standards

Correlation to Standardized Tests

Lesson	NAEP	Terra Nova CAT/6	Terra Nova CTBS	ITBS	SAT10	Local Test
5-1	N1d, N1i	■			■	
5-2	N1e	■	■		■	
5-3	N3a	■	■	■	■	
5-4	N3a	■	■	■	■	
5-5	M2a, M2b		■	■	■	
5-6	M2a		■			
5-7	N3g					
5-8	A4a					
5-9	A3b					

NAEP National Assessment of Educational Progress
    N = Number Sense, Properties, and Operations
    M = Measurement
    G = Geometry and Spatial Sense
    D = Data Analysis, Statistics and Probability
    A = Algebra and Functions

CAT/6 California Achievement Test, 6th Ed.
CTBS Comprehensive Test of Basic Skills
ITBS Iowa Test of Basic Skills, Form M
SAT10 Stanford Achievement Test, 10th Ed.

NCTM STANDARDS 2000

1	Number and Operations	6	Problem Solving
2	Algebra	7	Reasoning and Proof
3	Geometry	8	Communication
4	Measurement	9	Connection
5	Data Analysis and Probability	10	Representation

Pacing Options

This chart suggests pacing for only the core lessons and their parts. It is provided as a possible guide. It will help you determine how much time you have in your schedule to cover other components, such as the features, chapter projects, Chapter Review, and Chapter Test.

Day	Traditional 45-minute class periods	Two-Year 45-minute class periods	Block 90-minute class periods
1	5-1 ▽	5-1 ▽	5-1 ▽ ▽
2	5-1 ▽	5-1 ▽	5-2 ▽ ▽
3	5-2 ▽	5-1 ▽	5-3 ▽ ▽
4	5-2 ▽	5-1 ▽	5-4 ▽ ▽
5	5-3 ▽ ▽	5-2 ▽	5-5 ▽ ▽ / 5-6 ▽
6	5-4 ▽	5-2 ▽	5-7 ▽ ▽ / 5-8 ▽
7	5-4 ▽	5-2 ▽	5-8 ▽ / 5-9 ▽ ▽
8	5-5 ▽ ▽	5-2 ▽	
9	5-6 ▽	5-3 ▽	
10	5-7 ▽ ▽	5-3 ▽	
11	5-8 ▽ ▽	5-3 ▽	
12	5-9 ▽ ▽	5-3 ▽	
13		5-4 ▽	
14		5-4 ▽	
15		5-4 ▽	
16		5-4 ▽	
17		5-5 ▽	
18		5-5 ▽	
19		5-6 ▽	
20		5-7 ▽	
21		5-7 ▽	
22		5-8 ▽	
23		5-8 ▽	
24		5-9 ▽ ▽	

Math Background

Skills Trace

BEFORE Chapter 5

Chapter 4 develops number theory ideas needed for this chapter, such as greatest common factor. Previous courses have taught operations with fractions.

DURING Chapter 5

This chapter extends operations with fractions to operations and solving equations with rational numbers, particularly negative fractions and mixed numbers.

AFTER Chapter 5

Operations and equations with rational numbers are used throughout this course. These are reviewed in Algebra 1 and then extended to more complex equations.

5-1 Comparing and Ordering Fractions

The most frequently used method for comparing two fractions is to find a common denominator. Usually you use the least common denominator, which is the same as the least common multiple of the denominators.

When you compare rational numbers like $-\frac{3}{8}$ and $-\frac{5}{16}$, you need to think about the relative sizes of negative numbers and use what you know about fractions and integers. Again, the most frequently used procedure is to find a common denominator, in this case 16. So $-\frac{3}{8} = -\frac{6}{16}$, which you can then compare to $-\frac{5}{16}$. Then you can compare the rational numbers in the same way you compare integers. Since $-6 < -5$, $-\frac{3}{8} < -\frac{5}{16}$.

5-2 Fractions and Decimals

Any fraction that is the ratio of two integers can be converted to a decimal by dividing the numerator by the denominator. If

this division reaches a point where there is no remainder, the decimal is called a *terminating decimal*. You can always write a terminating decimal as the ratio of two integers.

5-3 Adding and Subtracting Fractions

While most students probably know how to write two fractions with a common denominator, the following algorithm is a purely algebraic explanation of how to find a common denominator and then add two fractions.

$$\frac{a}{b} + \frac{c}{d}$$
$$\frac{a}{b} \cdot \frac{d}{d} + \frac{c}{d} \cdot \frac{b}{b}$$
$$\frac{ad}{bd} + \frac{bc}{bd}$$
$$\frac{ad + bc}{bd}$$

This algorithm also works with negative fractions or when subtracting fractions. However, when working with negative fractions, you also need to apply rules for operations with integers.

Students may gain an understanding of the process of adding or subtracting fractions using the lowest common denominators by writing out prime factors.

$$\frac{3}{4} + \frac{1}{6} = \frac{3}{2^2} + \frac{1}{2 \cdot 3}$$
$$= \frac{3 \cdot 3}{2^2 \cdot 3} + \frac{1 \cdot 2}{2 \cdot 3 \cdot 2}$$
$$= \frac{9}{2^2 \cdot 3} + \frac{2}{2^2 \cdot 3}$$
$$= \frac{11}{2^2 \cdot 3}$$
$$= \frac{11}{12}$$

5-4 Multiplying and Dividing Fractions

The rules for multiplying fractions are very straightforward. The rules for dividing fractions may be a little strange to students at first, but once they've gotten used to the idea of multiplying by the reciprocal, the concept is also straightforward. You may wish to review the rules for multiplying and dividing integers as you must apply the same rules to multiply and divide positive and negative fractions.

5-5 Using Customary Units of Measurement

The United States *customary system* of measurement (sometimes called the English system of measure) is based on the customary yard as a standard. The standard U.S. yard is defined to be $\frac{3,600}{3,937}$ of the standard meter.

You use systems of measurement to measure length, weight, mass, volume, temperature, and time. The *accuracy* of a measurement tells how correctly you make the measurement. An accurate scale gives the same reading every time and is adjusted to match standard weights.

The *precision* of a measurement tells how closely, or finely, you make the measurement. The precision tells you the smallest unit you used with the measuring device. Bathroom scales, for example, are much less precise than the scales used in a laboratory.

The *greatest possible error* in a measurement is related to the precision you use; the greatest possible error is one-half the unit you choose.

5-6 Work Backward

Quite often, you encounter mathematics problems for which you must find an unknown quantity, while given several other quantities. When you are given some quantities in a problem, it is often useful to work backward from the known quantities to find the unknown quantity.

Students may already know how to work backward, but they may not realize it. Identifying this skill will help students apply it in problem-solving situations.

5-7 Solving Equations by Adding or Subtracting Fractions

You have already learned to solve one-step equations with integers, and the basic procedures for solving equations by adding or subtracting fractions are the same. However, you must also apply the rules for adding and subtracting fractions when solving equations with fractions. Also, you must use the rules for adding and subtracting integers when you are working with positive and negative fractions.

5-8 Solving Equations by Multiplying Fractions

Solving equations by multiplying by fractions is very similar to solving equations by multiplying by integers, a process with which you are already familiar. However, you must remember to multiply each side of an equation by the *reciprocal* of the coefficient of the variable. You must also apply the rules for multiplying integers when working with positive and negative fractions.

5-9 Powers of Products and Quotients

To raise a product to a power, you raise each factor to the power. So, $(ab)^m = a^m b^m$. This means that $(2 \cdot 3)^2 = 2^2 \cdot 3^2$, or $4(9)$, which is 36. Notice that there is no similar rule for raising a sum to a power. For example, $(2 + 3)^2 \neq 2^2 + 3^2$.

Additional Professional Development Opportunities

Chapter 5 Math Background notes:
pp. 233, 238, 244, 249, 254, 260, 265, 269, 275

Additional resources available from SkyLight Professional Development: On-site courses, workshops, summer institutes. Online courses and chat rooms. Videocassettes and books. Visit www.skylightedu.com.

Professional Development, Content Facilitator Guide: Pre-Algebra, Chapter 5

# Ongoing Assessment and Intervention

The *Prentice Hall Pre-Algebra* program provides many options for assessment in the Student Edition, Teacher's Edition, and teaching resources. From these options you may choose instructional materials that are appropriate for your students and support your district's curriculum requirements.

Daily Assessment

Instant Check System™ in Chapter 5

Allows students to check their own learning before, during, and after each lesson.

Diagnosing Readiness before the chapter (p. 230)

Check Skills You'll Need exercises in each lesson (pp. 232, 237, 243, 248, 253, 259, 264, 268, 274)

Check Understanding questions with each Example (pp. 232, 233, 234, 237, 238, 239, 243, 244, 245, 248, 249, 250, 253, 254, 260, 264, 265, 268, 269, 274, 275)

Checkpoint Quiz (pp. 247, 272)

Formal Assessment

In Chapter 5 and Additional Resources

Assesses student progress throughout the *Pre-Algebra* text and with blackline masters and CD-ROM.

Student Edition

- Chapter 5 Review, with Vocabulary Skills and Concepts Review, pp. 279–281
- Chapter 5 Test, p. 282

Assessment Resources   *Spanish versions available.*

- Checkpoint Quizzes 1 & 2
- Chapter Test, Forms A & B
- Chapter Alternative Assessment

Computer Test Generator CD-ROM

- Instant Chapter Tests™ — pre-made tests with items that vary every time you print.
- Online Testing allows you to give tests online and receive progress reports.
- Diagnose readiness with questions on prerequisite skills.
- Prepare students by making tests based on standardized test objectives.

Algebra Readiness Tests

- Includes Basic Skills Tests and Concept-Readiness Tests.
- Assess understanding of skills and concepts needed for success in algebra.

Standardized Test Preparation

Test Prep in Chapter 5

Teaches students strategies and gives them practice with all the test item formats they will encounter on high-stakes tests.

Test Prep exercises in each lesson (pp. 236, 241, 247, 252, 257, 262, 267, 271, 277)

Test-Taking Strategies (p. 278: Answering the Question Asked)

Test Prep (p. 283: Reading Comprehension)

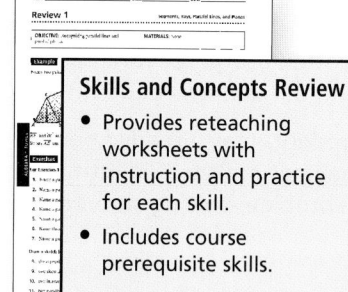

PRENTICE HALL
ASSESSMENT *SYSTEM*

Provides a three-step approach to preparing students for high-stakes, national, and state exams.

1 Diagnose & Prescribe

Content Diagnostic Tests
- Diagnose strengths and weaknesses with ongoing benchmark tests.
- Prescribe individualized reteaching opportunities.

2 Review & Reteach

Skills and Concepts Review
- Provides reteaching worksheets with instruction and practice for each skill.
- Includes course prerequisite skills.

3 Practice & Assess

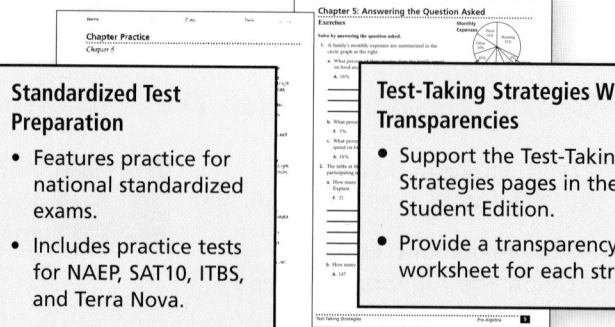

Standardized Test Preparation
- Features practice for national standardized exams.
- Includes practice tests for NAEP, SAT10, ITBS, and Terra Nova.

Test-Taking Strategies With Transparencies
- Support the Test-Taking Strategies pages in the Student Edition.
- Provide a transparency and a worksheet for each strategy.

Reaching All Students

The textbook, the iText, and other technology components provide numerous opportunities to reach students of various ability levels and learning styles. Each Teacher's Edition lesson suggests how you can help all your students be successful and understand the mathematics in Chapter 5.

Below Level

Student Edition
- Diagnosing Readiness*: p. 230
- Check Skills You'll Need*: pp. 232, 237, 243, 248, 253, 259, 264, 268, 274

Reteaching
Chapter 5 Grab & Go™ File: pp. 10–18

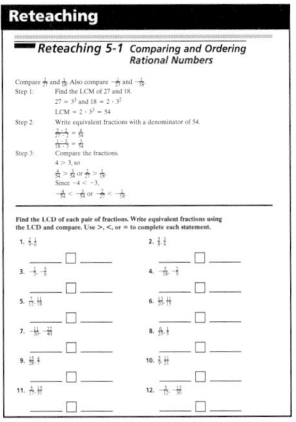

* Can be used with all ability levels to ensure mastery of prerequisite skills.

Advanced Learners

Student Edition
- Challenge exercises: pp. 236, 241, 246, 252, 257, 262, 266, 267, 271, 276, 277
- Extension: p. 258

Enrichment
Chapter 5 Grab & Go™ File: pp. 19–27

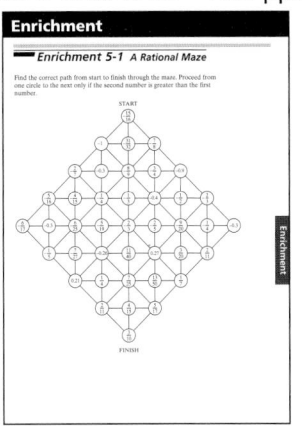

Problem Solving

Student Edition
- Strategies: pp. 259–262
- Real-World Problem Solving: pp. 232, 234, 237, 244, 249, 254, 259, 264, 269, 275

Guided Problem Solving Masters
Chapter 5: pp. 38–46

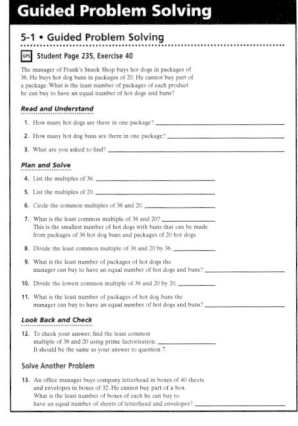

Reading and Math Literacy

Student Edition
- Vocabulary: pp. 231, 279, plus in most lessons
- Reading Math: pp. 234, 250, 261, 263, 275, 279
- Writing in Math: pp. 236, 241, 246, 252, 256, 258, 261, 267, 270, 273, 276, 282
- Illustrated Glossary: pp. 782–826

Reading and Math Literacy Masters
Chapter 5: pp. 17–20

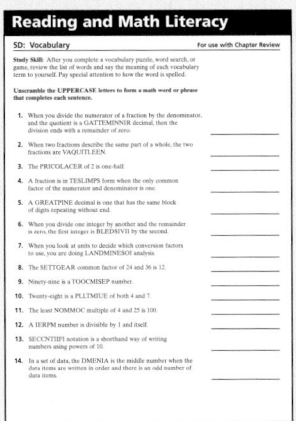

English Learners

Student Edition
- English/Spanish Illustrated Glossary: pp. 782–826

Workbook and Masters
Spanish Practice Workbook: pp. 38–46
Spanish Reading and Math Literacy Masters: pp. 17–20

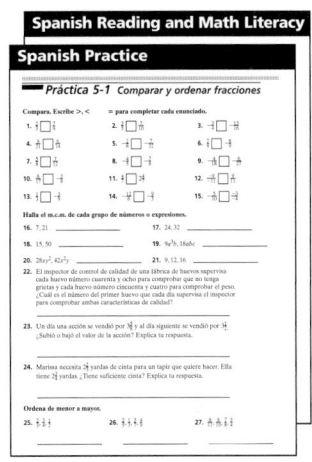

Learning Styles

Student Edition
- Investigation: pp. 243, 248
- DK Activities: pp. 284–285
- Chapter Project: p. 740

Activity Masters
Hands-On Activities: 6, 7, 8, 9, 10, 11, 12, 13, 22, 23
Technology Activities: 8, 9, 10

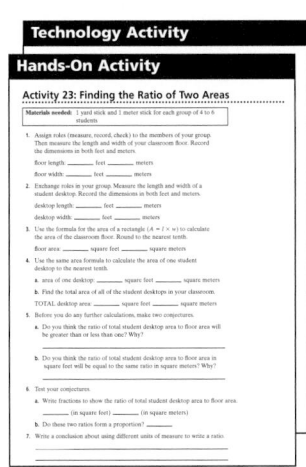

Program Resources

	Resources in Grab & Go™ Files				Resources for Reaching All Students				Spanish Resources			Transparencies				Presentation Assistant Plus!
	Practice	Reteach	Enrich	Checkpt Quiz	Reading & Math Literacy	Technology Activities	Hands-On Activities	Guided Problem Solving	Practice	Reading & Math Literacy	Checkpt Quiz	Skills Check	Additional Examples	Answers to Exercises	Lesson Quiz	Prentice Hall Presentation Pro CD-ROM
5-1	■	■	■		■			■	■	■		■	■	■	■	■
5-2	■	■	■			■	■	■	■			■	■	■	■	■
5-3	■	■	■	■	■	■	■	■	■	■	■	■	■	■	■	■
5-4	■	■	■			■	■	■	■			■	■	■	■	■
5-5	■	■	■				■	■	■			■	■	■	■	■
5-6	■	■	■				■	■	■			■	■	■	■	■
5-7	■	■	■				■	■	■			■	■	■	■	■
5-8	■	■	■	■	■		■	■	■		■	■	■	■	■	■
5-9	■	■	■					■	■			■	■	■	■	■
For the Chapter	Chapter Projects, Chapter Tests, Alternative Assessment, Cumulative Review, Cumulative Assessment				**On Web site only:** Home Activities, Algebra Readiness Puzzles, Interdisciplinary Activities				Spanish Chapter Tests, Alternative Assessment, Cumulative Review, Cumulative Assessment			Classroom Aid Transparencies				

Also available for use with the chapter:
- Practice Workbook
- Solution Key
- MathNotes folder
- For additional online and technology resources, see below.
- For teacher support and access to student Web site materials, use Web Code adk-5500.

 **PRENTICE HALL ASSESSMENT SYSTEM**

Program assessment and test preparation, all in one place.

See page 230E.

 Skills Intervention Kit

A *complete* system for the student who is struggling with course-level work

How to Use With Chapter 5

5-1, 5-3, 5-4	Fraction Concepts
5-2	Decimals
5-5	Measurement
5-6	Fraction Operations
5-7, 5-8, 5-9	Pre-Algebra Basics

 **Online Intervention**

Integrated within the iText, this online intervention system includes diagnostic tests and prescribed remediation, plus reports to track student mastery.

 # Technology

 iTEXT Online and on CD-ROM

Complete Interactive Student Text online and on CD-ROM—with instant-feedback assessment, tutorial help, dynamic activities, instructional and real-world videos, audio, and additional practice.

 www.PHSchool.com For Students

Use Web Codes for easy access to online activities, chapter projects, self-grading lesson quizzes, chapter tests, vocabulary quizzes, updated data sources, graphing calculator procedures, and more.

PH SuccessNet For Teachers

Online lesson planning with built-in state correlations, all the teaching resources, complete reference library, your own calendar and Teacher Web page, professional development, and more.

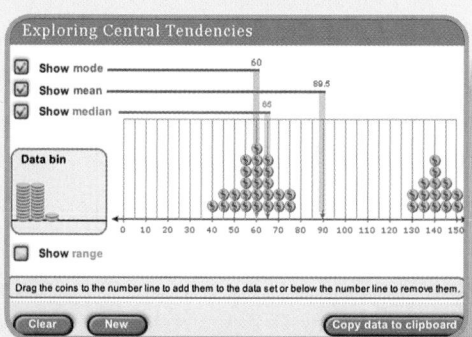

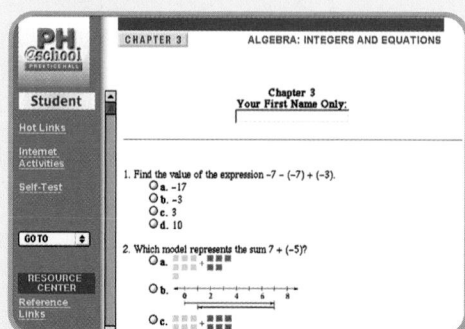

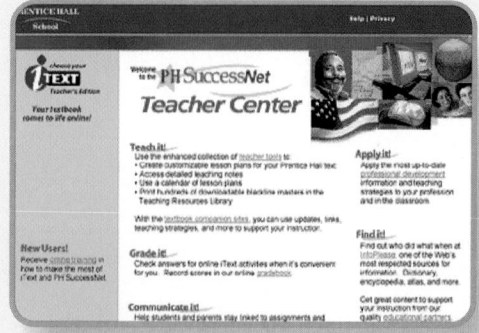

Presentation Assistant Plus!

The Prentice Hall *Presentation Assistant Plus!* provides you with the material you need to teach a lesson from beginning to end. Two easy-to-use formats—Transparencies and CD-ROM—allow you to present a lesson the way you are most comfortable.

Transparencies

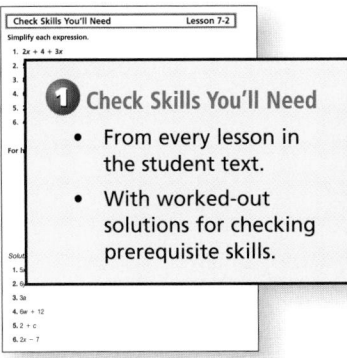

1 Check Skills You'll Need
- From every lesson in the student text.
- With worked-out solutions for checking prerequisite skills.

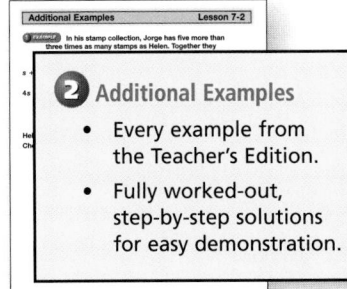

2 Additional Examples
- Every example from the Teacher's Edition.
- Fully worked-out, step-by-step solutions for easy demonstration.

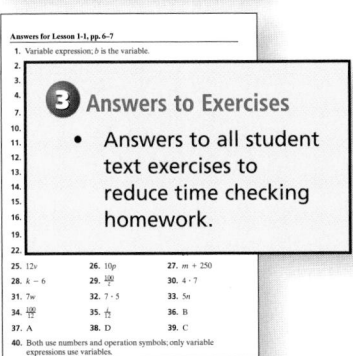

3 Answers to Exercises
- Answers to all student text exercises to reduce time checking homework.

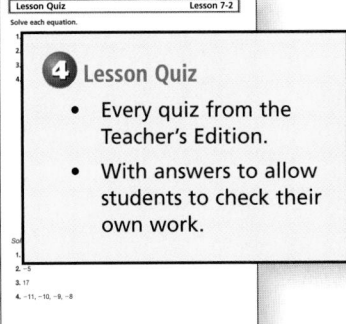

4 Lesson Quiz
- Every quiz from the Teacher's Edition.
- With answers to allow students to check their own work.

 Throughout the Teacher's Edition, this symbol indicates material that is available in the Presentation Assistant Plus!

PowerPoint **Prentice Hall Presentation Pro CD-ROM**

- Includes all Transparencies as PowerPoint® presentations.
- Conveniently organized by lesson so you can easily ❶ Introduce, ❷ Teach, ❸ Check Homework, and ❹ Assess each lesson.
- Animated examples allow step-by-step instruction at your own pace.
- Easy to edit so you can create custom presentations.

Teaching Chapter 5 Using Presentation Assistant Plus!

	❶ Introduce	❷ Teach	❸ Check Homework	❹ Assess
	Check Skills You'll Need	Additional Examples	Student Edition Answers	Lesson Quiz
5-1	p. 38	pp. 56–58	✔	p. 38
5-2	p. 39	pp. 59–60	✔	p. 39
5-3	p. 40	pp. 61–62	✔	p. 40
5-4	p. 41	pp. 63–64	✔	p. 41
5-5	p. 42	p. 65	✔	p. 42
5-6	p. 43	p. 66	✔	p. 43
5-7	p. 44	pp. 67–68	✔	p. 44
5-8	p. 45	pp. 69–70	✔	p. 45
5-9	p. 46	p. 71	✔	p. 46

 Prentice Hall Presentation Pro

CD-ROM with dynamic Powerpoint® presentations for every lesson. Helps you introduce and develop concepts, check homework, and assess progress. Part of Presentation Assistant Plus! *(See above.)*

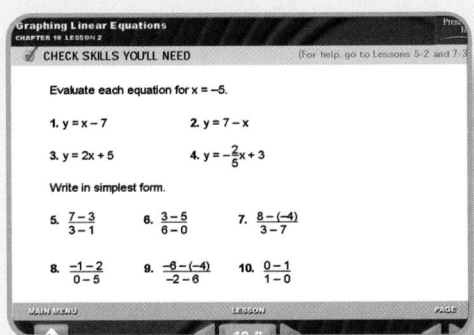

 Computer Test Generator

CD-ROM to create practice sheets and tests for course objectives and standardized tests. Includes Instant Chapter Tests™, online testing, and student reports. Part of the PH Assessment System. *(See page 230E.)*

 Resource Pro® with Planning Express®

CD-ROM with a lesson planning tool that allows you to import state and local objectives. Includes electronic versions of all the teaching resources.

Operations With Fractions

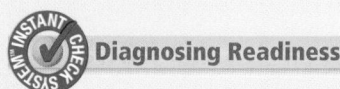
Diagnosing Readiness

Students will find the answers to these exercises in the back of their textbooks.

Prescribing Intervention
For intervention, direct students to:

Solving Equations
Lesson 3-5: Examples 1, 3;
Exercises 1–6, 9–14.
Lesson 3-6: Examples 1, 3;
Exercises 1–9, 12–20.
Extra Practice, p. 746.

Finding the Greatest Common Factor
Lesson 4-3: Example 3;
Exercises 17–24.
Extra Practice, p. 747.

Reading and Writing Fractions
Lesson 4-4: Example 1;
Exercises 1–6.
Extra Practice, p. 747.

Writing Fractions and Decimals
Lesson 4-4: Example 2;
Exercises 7–12.
Extra Practice, p. 747.

Where You've Been

- In Chapter 1, you learned how to add, subtract, multiply, and divide integers.

- In Chapter 2, you solved equations by adding, subtracting, multiplying, and dividing.

- In Chapter 4, you investigated exponents.

 Instant self-check online and on CD-ROM

Diagnosing Readiness   (For help, go to the lesson in green.)

Solving Equations (Lessons 3-5 and 3-6)

Solve each equation.

1. $x + 1.8 = 3$ 1.2   **2.** $n - 41 = 19$ 60   **3.** $a \div (-3) = 15$ −45   **4.** $-19 = p + 21$ −40

5. $6t = 9$ 1.5   **6.** $40 = z - 34$ 74   **7.** $8d = 64$ 8   **8.** $-0.89 = \frac{x}{2}$ −1.78

Finding the Greatest Common Factor (Lesson 4-3)

Find the GCF of each group of numbers.

9. $3, 15$ 3   **10.** $16, 20$ 4   **11.** $12, 36$ 12   **12.** $11, 30$ 1   **13.** $30, 40, 210$ 10

14. $45, 80$ 5   **15.** $27, 72$ 9   **16.** $15, 121$ 1   **17.** $30, 500$ 10 **18.** $14, 28, 84$ 14

Reading and Writing Fractions (Lesson 4-4)

Write two equivalent fractions to describe each model. **19–21. Answers may vary. Sample answers are given.**

19. 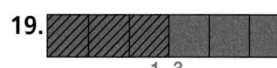   **20.** 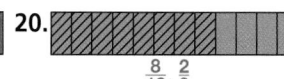   **21.**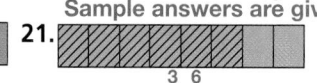
$\frac{1}{2}, \frac{3}{6}$ $\frac{8}{12}, \frac{2}{3}$ $\frac{3}{4}, \frac{6}{8}$

Writing Fractions and Decimals (Lesson 4-6)

Write each fraction in simplest form.

22. $\frac{10}{12}$ $\frac{5}{6}$ **23.** $\frac{8}{20}$ $\frac{2}{5}$ **24.** $-\frac{32}{16}$ −2 **25.** $\frac{25}{100}$ $\frac{1}{4}$ **26.** $-\frac{120}{125}$ $-\frac{24}{25}$ **27.** $\frac{15}{45}$ $\frac{1}{3}$

28. $\frac{-20}{-75}$ $\frac{4}{15}$ **29.** $\frac{16}{124}$ $\frac{4}{31}$ **30.** $-\frac{18}{81}$ $-\frac{2}{9}$ **31.** $-\frac{10}{65}$ $-\frac{2}{13}$ **32.** $\frac{14}{84}$ $\frac{1}{6}$ **33.** $\frac{55}{77}$ $\frac{5}{7}$

Divide. Write each quotient as a decimal.

34. $27 \div 5$ **35.** $6 \div 10$ **36.** $10 \div 16$ **37.** $9 \div 12$ **38.** $15 \div 40$

5.4   0.6   0.625   0.75   0.375

Operations With Fractions

Where You're Going

In this chapter, you will learn how to

● Perform operations with fractions.

● Solve equations with fractions.

● Find powers of products and quotients.

● Solve problems by working backward.

 **Real-World Snapshots** Applying what you learn, on pages 284–285 you will solve problems about quiltmaking.

Key Vocabulary

- dimensional analysis (p. 254)
- least common denominator (LCD) (p. 234)
- least common multiple (LCM) (p. 232)
- multiple (p. 232)
- reciprocals (p. 250)
- repeating decimal (p. 238)
- terminating decimal (p. 237)

231

Chapter 5 Overview

In this chapter, students build on their basic knowledge of fractions to compare and order fractions, and then to perform operations with fractions. They apply these skills to solve equations by adding, subtracting, and multiplying fractions. They also apply the multiplication of fractions to convert customary units of measure. Students relate the values of fractions to the values of decimals, by converting fractions to decimals. Students use concepts from Chapter 4 to find powers of products and quotients.

Activating Prior Knowledge

Students apply skills learned in Chapter 2 for solving one-step equations. Ask: *How do you solve a one-step equation?* You decide on an inverse operation to get the variable alone on one side of the equation, and then you apply the Addition, Subtraction, Multiplication, or Division Property of Equality.

Reading Math

- Reading for Problem Solving, p. 263
- **Vocabulary** A complete list of terms, plus vocabulary exercises, appears in the Chapter Review on p. 279.
- **Illustrated Glossary** Examples for each vocabulary term, plus definitions in both English and Spanish, appear starting on p. 782.

Test-Taking Strategies

Answering the Question Asked, p. 278

Real-World Problem Solving

Strategy: Work Backward, pp. 259–262

DK Real-World Snapshots: Applying Fractions, pp. 284–285

Chapter Project: If the Shoe Fits, p. 740

www.PHSchool.com

Internet support includes:
- Self-grading Vocabulary and Chapter 5 Tests
- Activity Masters
- Chapter Project support
- Chapter Planner
- Chapter 5 Resources

Plus

Lesson Preview

 Check Skills You'll Need

Prime Factorization
Lesson 4-3: Example 2;
Exercises 9–16.
Extra Practice, p. 747.

Lesson Resources

📁 **Teaching Resources**
Practice, Reteaching, Enrichment

👥 **Reaching All Students**
Practice Workbook 5-1
Spanish Practice Workbook 5-1
Reading and Math Literacy 5A
Spanish Reading and Math
 Literacy 5A
Guided Problem Solving 5-1

⏱ **Presentation Assistant Plus!**
Transparencies and PowerPoint™
• Check Skills You'll Need 5-1
• Additional Examples 5-1
• Student Edition Answers 5-1
• Lesson Quiz 5-1
PH Presentation Pro CD-ROM 5-1

ASSESSMENT SYSTEM

Computer Test Generator CD-ROM

💻 **Technology**
Resource Pro® CD-ROM
Computer Test Generator CD-ROM
PH Presentation Pro CD-ROM

💻 **www.PHSchool.com**
Student Site
• Teacher Web Code: adk-5500
• Self-grading Lesson Quiz
PH SuccessNet Teacher Center
• Lesson Planner
• Resources

Plus 📕**TEXT**

Comparing and Ordering Fractions

What You'll Learn

 OBJECTIVE 1 To find the least common multiple

 OBJECTIVE 2 To compare fractions

. . . And Why

To solve real-world problems involving team records

 **Check Skills You'll Need**

Write the prime factorization of each number.
1–6. See below.
1. 20   **2.** 125   **3.** 45

4. 186   **5.** 621   **6.** 1,575

📌 For help, go to Lesson 4-3.

New Vocabulary
• multiple
• least common multiple (LCM)
• least common denominator (LCD)

1. $2^2 \cdot 5$
2. 5^3
3. $3^2 \cdot 5$
4. $2 \cdot 3 \cdot 31$
5. $3^3 \cdot 23$
6. $3^2 \cdot 5^2 \cdot 7$

📕**TEXT** Interactive lesson includes instant self-check, tutorials, and activities.

OBJECTIVE

1 Finding the Least Common Multiple

A **multiple** of a number is the product of that number and any nonzero whole number.

Multiples of 4: 4, 8, ⑫, 16, 20, ㉔, 28, 32, ㊱, . . .

Multiples of 6: 6, ⑫, 18, ㉔, 30, ㊱, 42, . . .

The numbers 12, 24, and 36 are *common multiples* of 4 and 6. The common multiple 12 is their **least common multiple (LCM)**.

1 EXAMPLE   <u>Real-World</u> 🌐 <u>Problem Solving</u>

Sports Today, both the school baseball and school soccer teams had games. The baseball team plays every 6 days. The soccer team plays every 5 days. When will both teams have games on the same day again?

  6, 12, 18, 24, ㉚, 36, . . .   List the multiples of 6.

  5, 10, 15, 20, 25, ㉚, . . .   List the multiples of 5.

● The LCM is 30. In 30 days both teams will have games again.

✓**Check Understanding** Example 1

 1. Find the LCM.

   a. 3, 4   12   **b.** 4, 5   20   **c.** 3, 4, 5   60

You can also use prime factorization to find the LCM.

2 EXAMPLE   **Using Prime Factorization**

 Find the LCM of 12 and 40.

   $12 = 2^2 \cdot ③$ ⎫
   $40 = ②^3 \cdot ⑤$ ⎬ Write the prime factorizations.
   $\mathrm{LCM} = 2^3 \cdot 3 \cdot 5$ Use the greatest power of each factor.
     $= 120$ Multiply.

● The LCM of 12 and 40 is 120.

INSTANT CHECK SYSTEM ✓ **Ongoing Assessment and Intervention**

Before the Lesson
Diagnose prerequisite skills using:
• Check Skills You'll Need

During the Lesson
Monitor progress using:
• Check Understanding
• Additional Examples
• Test Prep

After the Lesson
Assess knowledge using:
• Lesson Quiz
• Computer Test Generator CD-ROM

2. Use prime factorization to find the LCM.

   a. 6, 16 **48**   **b.** 9, 15 **45**   **c.** 12, 15, 18 **180**

You can find the LCM of a variable expression.

3 EXAMPLE   **Finding the LCM of Variable Expressions**

Find the LCM of $6a^2$ and $18a^3$.

$$\left.\begin{array}{l} 6a^2 = \enclose{circle}{2} \cdot 3 \cdot a^2 \\ 18a^3 = 2 \cdot \enclose{circle}{3^2} \cdot \enclose{circle}{a^3} \end{array}\right\}$$ **Write the prime factorizations.**

$\text{LCM} = 2 \cdot 3^2 \cdot a^3$ **Use the greatest power of each factor.**

$\qquad\quad = 18a^3$ **Multiply.**

The LCM of $6a^2$ and $18a^3$ is $18a^3$.

Check Understanding Example 3

3. Find the LCM.

   a. $12x, 15xy$ **60xy**   **b.** $8m^2, 14m^4$ **56m⁴**   **c.** $25y^2, 15x$ **75xy²**

OBJECTIVE

2   Comparing Fractions

You can use a number line to compare fractions.

4 EXAMPLE   **Using a Number Line**

Graph and compare the fractions in each pair.

  a. $\dfrac{9}{11}, \dfrac{6}{11}$ **b.** $-\dfrac{1}{2}, -\dfrac{1}{10}$

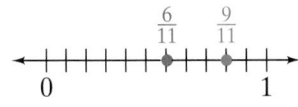

$\dfrac{9}{11}$ is on the right, so $\dfrac{9}{11} > \dfrac{6}{11}$. $-\dfrac{1}{2}$ is on the left, so $-\dfrac{1}{2} < \dfrac{1}{10}$.

Check Understanding Example 4

4. Use a number line to compare the fractions in each pair.

  a. $\dfrac{4}{9}, \dfrac{2}{9}$ $\dfrac{4}{9} > \dfrac{2}{9}$ **b.** $-\dfrac{4}{9}, -\dfrac{2}{9}$ $-\dfrac{4}{9} < -\dfrac{2}{9}$ **c.** $-\dfrac{4}{9}, \dfrac{2}{9}$ $-\dfrac{4}{9} < \dfrac{2}{9}$

👥 Reaching All Students

Below Level Have students count by 2's and then by 5's. Point out that they are naming multiples of 2 and 5.	**Advanced Learners** Ask: *What is a rule that always gives you the LCM of two prime numbers?* The LCM of two prime numbers is the product of the two numbers.	**Visual Learners** See note on page 233. **English Learners** See note on page 234.

---

2. Teach

Professional Development

Math Background

There are two common ways to find the least common multiple (LCM) of two numbers. You can list the multiples of each number until you find a common multiple. Or, you can write the prime factorization of each number and use the greatest power of each prime factor. Listing the multiples may be easiest for lesser numbers whereas prime factorization may be best for greater ones.

Teaching Notes

1 EXAMPLE   **Visual Learners**

Students may not see why finding the LCM helps in the situation in Example 1. Mark a day on a calendar. Tell students that this is the day that both teams played. From that day, mark each sixth day with a "B" and each fifth day with an "S." Stop when the two letters are written on the same day. Ask a volunteer to count the number of days from the first date to the day where the letters coincide. Point out that the number of days counted is the same as the LCM in the Example.

2 EXAMPLE   **Error Prevention**

Since the prime factorization of 12 is $2^2 \cdot 3$ and the prime factorization of 40 is $2^3 \cdot 5$, students may incorrectly think that the LCM is the product of all factors, $2^5 \cdot 3 \cdot 5 = 480$. Stress that although 480 is a common multiple of 12 and 40, it is *not* the *least* common multiple.

4 EXAMPLE   **Tactile Learners**

Let students use fraction models to model and compare the fractions. Remind them to watch the signs when modeling. When both fractions are negative, then the model with the greater size is less than the other. When only one of the fractions is positive, that fraction is greater.

Reading Math

The LCD is sometimes called the *lowest common denominator.*

When fractions have different denominators, rewrite the fractions with a common denominator. Then compare the numerators. The **least common denominator (LCD)** of two or more fractions is the LCM of the denominators.

5 EXAMPLE   Real-World ● Problem Solving

Academic Competitions The math team won $\frac{5}{8}$ of its competitions and the debate team won $\frac{7}{10}$ of its competitions. Which team won the greater fraction of competitions?

Step 1 Find the LCM of 8 and 10.

$$8 = 2^3 \text{ and } 10 = 2 \cdot 5$$
$$\text{LCM} = 2^3 \cdot 5 = 40$$

Step 2 Write equivalent fractions with a denominator of 40.

$$\frac{5 \cdot 5}{8 \cdot 5} = \frac{25}{40}$$
$$\frac{7 \cdot 4}{10 \cdot 4} = \frac{28}{40}$$

Step 3 Compare the fractions.

$$\frac{25}{40} < \frac{28}{40}, \text{ so } \frac{5}{8} < \frac{7}{10}.$$

● The debate team won the greater fraction of competitions.

Real-World ● Connection

High school debate teams can have as few as 8 debates and as many as 20 debates in a school year.

✓ **Check Understanding**   Example 5

5. Compare the fractions in each pair.

a. $\frac{6}{7}, \frac{4}{5}$ $\frac{6}{7} > \frac{4}{5}$ **b.** $\frac{2}{3}, \frac{3}{4}$ $\frac{2}{3} < \frac{3}{4}$ **c.** $-\frac{3}{4}, -\frac{7}{10}$ $-\frac{3}{4} < -\frac{7}{10}$

6 EXAMPLE   Ordering Fractions

Order $\frac{1}{2}, \frac{3}{4}$, and $\frac{2}{5}$ from least to greatest.

$$
\left.
\begin{array}{l}
\frac{1}{2} = \frac{1 \cdot 10}{2 \cdot 10} = \frac{10}{20} \\[4pt]
\frac{3}{4} = \frac{3 \cdot 5}{4 \cdot 5} = \frac{15}{20} \\[4pt]
\frac{2}{5} = \frac{2 \cdot 4}{5 \cdot 4} = \frac{8}{20}
\end{array}
\right\}
$$

The LCM of 2, 4, and 5 is 20.
Use 20 as the common denominator.

$$\frac{8}{20} < \frac{10}{20} < \frac{15}{20}, \text{ so } \frac{2}{5} < \frac{1}{2} < \frac{3}{4}.$$

✓ **Check Understanding**   Example 6

6. Order from least to greatest.

a. $\frac{2}{3}, \frac{1}{6}, \frac{5}{12}$ $\frac{1}{6} < \frac{5}{12} < \frac{2}{3}$ **b.** $\frac{3}{10}, \frac{1}{5}, \frac{1}{2}, \frac{7}{12}$ $\frac{1}{5} < \frac{3}{10} < \frac{1}{2} < \frac{7}{12}$

EXERCISES

 For more exercises, see *Extra Practice*.

Practice and Problem Solving

 Practice by Example

Example 1
(page 232)

Find the LCM of each pair by listing multiples.

1. 10, 45 90   **2.** 6, 9 18   **3.** 12, 20 60   **4.** 5, 9 45

5. 10, 36 180   **6.** 7, 12 84   **7.** 5, 6 30   **8.** 5, 6, 7 210

9. Schedules Both the football and volleyball teams have games today. The football team plays every 7 days. The volleyball team plays every 3 days. When will both teams have games on the same day again? **in 21 days**

Examples 2 and 3
(page 232 and 233)

Find the LCM.

10. 20, 36
 180
11. 15, 27
 135
12. 8, 14, 20
 280
13. 5, 12, 15
 60

14. $12x, 40y$
 $120xy$
15. $8x, 25y$
 $200xy$
16. $2b^2, 6c^3$
 $6b^2c^3$
17. $6a^3, 8a$
 $24a^3$

Example 4
(page 233)

Graph and compare the fractions in each pair. 18–21. See margin.

18. $\frac{4}{5}, \frac{2}{5}$ **19.** $-\frac{2}{3}, -\frac{1}{3}$ **20.** $\frac{5}{8}, -\frac{5}{8}$ **21.** $\frac{11}{12}, \frac{7}{12}$

Example 5
(page 234)

Compare the fractions in each pair.

22. $\frac{5}{6} \blacksquare \frac{3}{4}$ >   **23.** $\frac{6}{8} \blacksquare \frac{7}{9}$ <   **24.** $\frac{1}{6} \blacksquare \frac{1}{8}$ >   **25.** $-\frac{5}{18} \blacksquare -\frac{1}{3}$ >

26. Track and Field At the track meet, Maria placed first in $\frac{4}{5}$ of her events and Carla placed first in $\frac{2}{3}$ of her events. Who placed first in the greater fraction of events? **Maria**

27. $\frac{3}{9} < \frac{5}{9} < \frac{7}{9}$

28. $\frac{1}{4} < \frac{1}{3} < \frac{1}{2}$

29. $\frac{2}{7} < \frac{2}{5} < \frac{2}{3}$

30. $\frac{1}{3} < \frac{3}{8} < \frac{2}{5} < \frac{2}{4}$

Example 6
(page 234)

Order from least to greatest. 27–30. See left.

27. $\frac{7}{9}, \frac{3}{9}, \frac{5}{9}$ **28.** $\frac{1}{2}, \frac{1}{3}, \frac{1}{4}$ **29.** $\frac{2}{5}, \frac{2}{3}, \frac{2}{7}$ **30.** $\frac{2}{5}, \frac{3}{8}, \frac{1}{3}, \frac{2}{4}$

 Apply Your Skills

Mental Math Compare. Use >, <, or = to complete each statement.

31. $-\frac{3}{19} \blacksquare \frac{1}{200}$ <   **32.** $\frac{-1}{-3} \blacksquare \frac{1}{3}$ =   **33.** $\frac{9}{11} \blacksquare \frac{7}{11}$ >   **34.** $\frac{-2}{-7} \blacksquare \frac{4}{14}$ =

35. $\frac{8}{8} \blacksquare \frac{3}{3}$ =   **36.** $\frac{2}{10} \blacksquare \frac{2}{100}$ >   **37.** $\frac{2}{5} \blacksquare 3\frac{2}{5}$ <   **38.** $\frac{-4}{-17} \blacksquare -\frac{5}{2}$ >

39. Measurement You need $\frac{5}{8}$ yd of fabric for a craft project. You find a piece marked $\frac{2}{3}$ yd. Is the piece long enough? Explain. **Yes; $\frac{2}{3} > \frac{5}{8}$.**

41. 1,800

42. 60

43. $120x$

44. $280a^4b^2$

45. $72xy$

46. $36b^3c^2$

47. $20g^2j^4$

48. $30x^3y^2$

40. The manager of Frank's Snack Shop buys hot dogs in packages of 36. He buys hot dog buns in packages of 20. He cannot buy part of a package. What is the least number of packages of each product he can buy to have an equal number of hot dogs and buns?
5 packages of hot dogs and 9 packages of buns

Find the LCM. 41–48. See left.

41. 45, 120, 150   **42.** 2, 5, 12, 15   **43.** $12x, 40$ **44.** $7ab, 8a^3b^2, 10a^4$

45. $8x, 18xy$ **46.** $9b^3, 12bc^2$ **47.** $4g^2, 10j^4$ **48.** $2x^3, 5y^2, 15xy^2$

Assignment Guide

1 Objective 1
Ⓐ Ⓑ **Core** 1–17, 40–48
Ⓒ **Extension** 58

2 Objective 2
Ⓐ Ⓑ **Core** 18–39, 49–57
Ⓒ **Extension** 59

Test Prep 60–63
Mixed Review 64–72

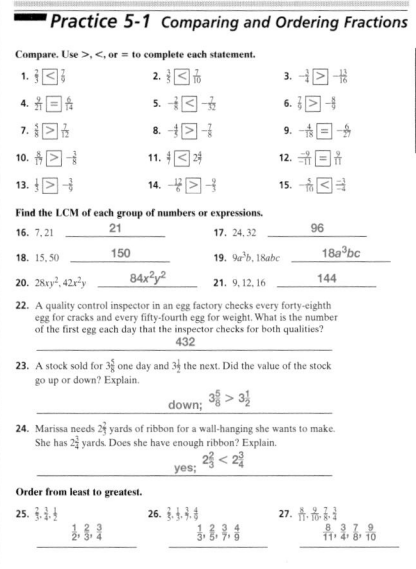

18.

$\frac{4}{5} > \frac{2}{5}$

19.

$-\frac{2}{3} < -\frac{1}{3}$

20–21. See back of book.

GPS Use the Guided Problem Solving worksheet with Exercise 40.

Teaching Tip
Exercises 31–38 Students may not understand how to do these mental math exercises without performing any operations on paper. Suggest visualizing the approximate positions of the fractions on a number line. Also, if only one fraction is negative, it is always the lesser fraction.

Test Prep

Resources
For additional practice with a variety of test item formats:
• Test Prep, p. 283
• Test-Taking Strategies, p. 278
• Test-Taking Strategies With Transparencies

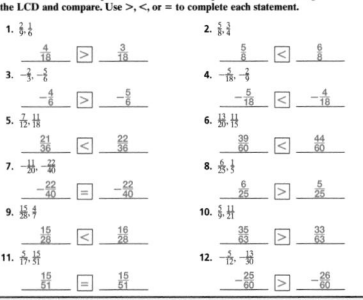

Reteaching 5-1 Comparing and Ordering Rational Numbers

Compare $\frac{2}{27}$ and $\frac{1}{18}$. Also compare $-\frac{2}{27}$ and $-\frac{1}{18}$.

Step 1: Find the LCM of 27 and 18.
$27 = 3^3$ and $18 = 2 \cdot 3^2$
$LCM = 2 \cdot 3^3 = 54$

Step 2: Write equivalent fractions with a denominator of 54.
$\frac{2}{27} \cdot \frac{2}{2} = \frac{4}{54}$
$\frac{1}{18} \cdot \frac{3}{3} = \frac{3}{54}$

Step 3: Compare the fractions.
$4 > 3$, so
$\frac{4}{54} > \frac{3}{54}$ or $\frac{2}{27} > \frac{1}{18}$.
Since $-4 < -3$,
$-\frac{4}{54} < -\frac{3}{54}$ or $-\frac{2}{27} < -\frac{1}{18}$.

Find the LCD of each pair of fractions. Write equivalent fractions using the LCD and compare. Use >, <, or = to complete each statement.

(Worked exercises 1–12 with fraction comparisons)

Compare. Use >, <, or = to complete each statement.

49. $\frac{7}{14}$ ■ $\frac{3}{6}$ **=**   50. $-\frac{7}{9}$ ■ $-\frac{2}{3}$ **<**   51. $\frac{8}{5}$ ■ $\frac{3}{2}$ **>**   52. $-\frac{19}{24}$ ■ $-\frac{5}{6}$ **>**

53. $-\frac{3}{8}$ ■ $-\frac{6}{16}$ **=**   54. $\frac{10}{11}$ ■ $\frac{4}{5}$ **>**   55. $\frac{1}{2}$ ■ $\frac{2}{4}$ **=**   56. $-\frac{7}{12}$ ■ $-\frac{28}{48}$ **=**

57. **Writing in Math** Jeremy and Fran want to compare $\frac{5}{8}$ to $\frac{9}{12}$. Jeremy writes equivalent fractions with a denominator of 96. Fran writes equivalent fractions with a denominator of 24. Which method would you prefer? Explain. **See margin.**

C Challenge

58. **Geometry** You have tiles that measure 4 in. by 5 in. What is the smallest square region you can cover without cutting or overlapping the tiles? Explain. **20 in. by 20 in. The length of the sides of the square must be a multiple of 4 and 5. The LCM of 4 and 5 is 20.**

59. **Servings** Suppose you and your brother shared two 12-in. pizzas, a mushroom pizza cut into 8 slices and a cheese pizza cut into 6 slices. If you ate 5 slices of the mushroom pizza, and your brother ate 3 slices of the cheese pizza, who ate more pizza? **you**

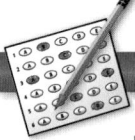

Test Prep

Multiple Choice

60. What is the LCM of 2, 3, 4, and 5? **B**
A. 30   B. 60   C. 90   D. 120

61. What is the GCF of $6a^3b$ and $4a^2b$? **H**
F. a^2b G. a^5b^2 H. $2a^2b$ I. $4a^5b^2$

Take It to the NET
Online lesson quiz at
www.PHSchool.com
Web Code: ada-0501

62. Salt shakers come in boxes of 30 and pepper shakers come in boxes of 24. How many whole boxes of each must you buy to get an equal number of salt and pepper shakers? **A**
A. 4 salt, 5 pepper   B. 5 salt, 4 pepper
C. 24 salt, 30 pepper   D. 30 salt, 24 pepper

Short Response

63. Are the numbers in order from least to greatest: $\frac{5}{8}$, $\frac{7}{16}$, $\frac{11}{20}$? Explain.
[2] No; the LCD is 80. $\frac{35}{80} < \frac{44}{80} < \frac{50}{80}$, so $\frac{7}{16} < \frac{11}{20} < \frac{5}{8}$.
[1] minor error OR answer only

Mixed Review

Lesson 4-9   **Write in scientific notation.**

64. 5,000,000   65. 0.001394   66. 8,900,000   67. 0.000005
5×10^6 1.394×10^{-3} 8.9×10^6 5×10^{-6}

Lesson 4-3   **Find each GCF.**

68. 24, 42 **6**   69. 16, 52 **4**   70. $25c, 55c^2$ **5c**   71. $90xy, 45x^2$ **45x**

Lesson 2-5 72. **History** The first modern Olympics took place in 1896 in Athens, Greece. One hundred years later, 197 nations took part in the Olympics in Atlanta, Georgia. This was 184 more nations than at the first Olympics. Solve the equation $x + 184 = 197$ to find the number of nations at the first Olympics. **13 nations**

Alternative Assessment

Have students write a paragraph that explains how they can use the LCD to help them compare or order fractions. Ask them to include an example of ordering fractions.

57. Answers may vary. Sample: I would prefer Fran's method. The LCD of $\frac{5}{8}$ and $\frac{9}{12}$ is 24. It would be easier to work with smaller numbers.

Fractions and Decimals

OBJECTIVE

1 Writing Fractions as Decimals

You can write a fraction as a decimal by dividing the numerator by the denominator. When the division ends with a remainder of zero, the quotient is called a **terminating decimal.**

$$\frac{5}{8} \text{ or } 5 \div 8 \longrightarrow \begin{array}{r} 0.625 \\ 8\overline{)5.000} \\ -4\,8 \\ \hline 20 \\ -16 \\ \hline 40 \\ -40 \\ \hline 0 \end{array}$$ ← quotient

← remainder

The division process for $5 \div 8$ ends with a remainder of zero. So 0.625 is a terminating decimal.

1 EXAMPLE Real-World 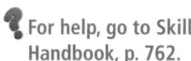 Problem Solving

Consumer Issues A customer at a delicatessen asks for $\frac{3}{4}$ lb of potato salad. The scale reads 0.75. Is the customer getting the amount of potato salad she requested? Explain.

$$\frac{3}{4} = 3 \div 4 = 0.75$$

Since $\frac{3}{4} = 0.75$, the customer is getting the right amount
● of potato salad.

✓ Check Understanding Example 1

1. Write each fraction or mixed number as a decimal.

a. $\frac{1}{4}$ 0.25   **b.** $1\frac{7}{8}$ 1.875

c. $3\frac{3}{10}$ 3.3   **d.** $\frac{3}{5}$ 0.6

What You'll Learn

OBJECTIVE 1 To write fractions as decimals

OBJECTIVE 2 To write terminating and repeating decimals as fractions

. . . And Why

To solve real-world problems involving buying food

✓ Check Skills You'll Need

Write the decimals in order from least to greatest.
1–3. See below.
1. 2.41, 0.241, 24.1, 12.4

2. 1.030, 13.03, 1.300, 1.003

3. 0.1, 0.01, −0.1, −0.01

 For help, go to Skills Handbook, p. 762.

New Vocabulary

• terminating decimal

• repeating decimal

1. 0.241, 2.41, 12.4, 24.1
2. 1.003, 1.030, 1.300, 13.03
3. −0.1, −0.01, 0.01, 0.1

 TEXT Interactive lesson includes instant self-check, tutorials, and activities.

Lesson Preview

✓ Check Skills You'll Need

Ordering Decimals
Skills Handbook: p. 762;
Exercises 13–20.

Lesson Resources

 Teaching Resources
Practice, Reteaching, Enrichment

Reaching All Students
Practice Workbook 5-2
Spanish Practice Workbook 5-2
Guided Problem Solving 5-2
Technology Activities 8
Hands-On Activities 9

Presentation Assistant Plus!
Transparencies and PowerPoint™
• Check Skills You'll Need 5-2
• Additional Examples 5-2
• Student Edition Answers 5-2
• Lesson Quiz 5-2
PH Presentation Pro CD-ROM 5-2

ASSESSMENT SYSTEM

Computer Test Generator CD-ROM

 Technology
Resource Pro® CD-ROM
Computer Test Generator CD
PH Presentation Pro CD-ROM

www.PHSchool.com
Student Site
• Teacher Web Code: adk-5500
• Self-grading Lesson Quiz
PH SuccessNet Teacher Center
• Lesson Planner
• Resources

Plus **TEXT**

Ongoing Assessment and Intervention

Before the Lesson
Diagnose prerequisite skills using:
• Check Skills You'll Need

During the Lesson
Monitor progress using:
• Check Understanding
• Additional Examples
• Test Prep

After the Lesson
Assess knowledge using:
• Lesson Quiz
• Computer Test Generator CD-ROM

Professional Development

Math Background

A rational number is any number you can write as a ratio $\frac{a}{b}$ of two integers a and b, where $b \neq 0$. Both terminating and repeating decimals can be written as the ratio of two integers. Decimals that are neither terminating nor repeating are irrational numbers and cannot be written as the ratio of two integers.

Teaching Notes

1 EXAMPLE Error Prevention

When dividing to write $\frac{3}{4}$ as a decimal, many students may begin with $3\overline{)4}$. Review the correct way to write this expression, $4\overline{)3}$. Ask students to suggest methods for remembering the correct placement of the divisor and the dividend.

2 EXAMPLE Auditory Learners

Students may write $\frac{2}{3}$ as 0.23, moving the numerator and denominator to the right of the decimal point instead of dividing. Remind students that the fraction bar indicates the division they must do to write a fraction as a decimal. Encourage them to say quietly to themselves "2 divided by 3" or "15 divided by 11" instead of reading the fractions as "two thirds" or "fifteen elevenths." Encourage students to use this method whenever they convert fractions to decimals.

3 EXAMPLE Alternative Method

Ask: *How can you use mental math to order the fractions?* Answers may vary. Sample: First compare the negative numbers. 0.2 is less than one-half and $\frac{3}{5}$ is greater than one-half. However, since these are negative numbers, $-\frac{3}{5}$ is less than -0.2. Then compare the positive numbers. $\frac{1}{4}$ is less than 1.1. So the list is $-\frac{3}{5}, -0.2, \frac{1}{4}, 1.1$.

Calculator Hint

Enter 2 ÷ 3 into your calculator. Then check whether the last digit in the display is 6 or 7 to see how your calculator rounds.

2a. $0.\overline{7}$; repeating; 7
2b. $0.9\overline{54}$; repeating; 54
2c. 1.375; terminating
2d. $0.\overline{72}$; repeating; 72

In a **repeating decimal,** the same block of digits repeats infinitely many times. The block of digits that repeats can be one digit or more than one digit.

2 EXAMPLE Writing a Repeating Decimal

Write each fraction as a decimal. State the block of digits that repeats.

a. $\frac{2}{3}$　　　　　　　　　　　　　　　**b.** $\frac{15}{11}$

$2 \div 3 = 0.66666\ldots$ ←Divide.→ $15 \div 11 = 1.36363\ldots$

$= 0.\overline{6}$ ← Place a bar over the block of digits that repeats. → $= 1.\overline{36}$

$\frac{2}{3} = 0.\overline{6}$; the digit that repeats is 6.

$\frac{15}{11} = 1.\overline{36}$; the block of digits that repeats is 36.

✓ Check Understanding　Example 2

2. Write each fraction as a decimal. State whether the decimal is *terminating* or *repeating*. If the decimal repeats, state the block of digits that repeats. **See left.**

a. $\frac{7}{9}$　　　**b.** $\frac{21}{22}$　　　**c.** $\frac{11}{8}$　　　**d.** $\frac{8}{11}$

When you compare and order decimals and fractions, it may be helpful to first write the fractions as decimals.

3 EXAMPLE Ordering Fractions and Decimals

Write the numbers in order, from least to greatest.

$$\frac{1}{4}, -0.2, -\frac{3}{5}, 1.1$$

$\left.\begin{array}{l} 1 \div 4 = 0.25 \\ -3 \div 5 = -0.6 \end{array}\right\}$ Change the fractions to decimals.

$-0.6 < -0.2 < 0.25 < 1.1$　　Compare the decimals.

From least to greatest, the numbers are $-\frac{3}{5}, -0.2, \frac{1}{4}$, and 1.1.

✓ Check Understanding　Example 3

3. Order from least to greatest.

a. $0.2, \frac{4}{5}, \frac{7}{10}, 0.5$　　　　　　　**b.** $-\frac{1}{8}, -0.75, -\frac{1}{4}, -0.375$

$\quad 0.2, 0.5, \frac{7}{10}, \frac{4}{5}$　　　　　　　　　　$-0.75, -0.375, -\frac{1}{4}, -\frac{1}{8}$

Reaching All Students

Below Level Ask students to name measurements that they've seen expressed in both fraction and decimal forms. **Answers may vary. Sample: weights of produce, lengths of objects, amounts of rain**	**Advanced Learners** Have students use mental math to find three fractions that are repeating decimals when expressed in decimal form.	**Auditory Learners** See note on page 238. **English Learners** See note on page 239.

Reading a decimal correctly provides a way to write a fraction.

Decimal	Read	Fraction
0.43	"forty-three hundredths"	$\frac{43}{100}$

If a decimal is greater than 1, you can write it as a mixed number.

4 EXAMPLE Writing a Decimal as a Fraction

Write 1.12 as a mixed number in simplest form.

$1.12 = 1\frac{12}{100}$ **Keep the whole number 1. Write twelve hundredths as a fraction.**

$= 1\frac{12 \div 4}{100 \div 4}$ **Divide the numerator and denominator of the fraction by the GCF, 4.**

$1.12 = 1\frac{3}{25}$ **Simplify.**

✓ Check Understanding Example 4

4. Write as a fraction or a mixed number in simplest form.

   a. 1.75 $1\frac{3}{4}$ **b.** 2.32 $2\frac{8}{25}$ **c.** 0.65 $\frac{13}{20}$

You can use algebra to write a repeating decimal as a fraction.

5 EXAMPLE Writing a Repeating Decimal as a Fraction

Write the repeating decimal $0.\overline{72}$ as a fraction in simplest form.

$n = 0.\overline{72}$ **Let the variable n equal the decimal.**

$100n = 72.\overline{72}$ **Multiply each side by 10^2, or 100.**

$\begin{array}{r} 100n = 72.\overline{72} \\ -n = -0.\overline{72} \\ \hline 99n = 72 \end{array}$ **The Subtraction Property of Equality lets you subtract the same value from each side of the equation.**

$\frac{99n}{99} = \frac{72}{99}$ **Divide each side by 99.**

$n = \frac{72 \div 9}{99 \div 9}$ **Divide the numerator and denominator by the GCF, 9.**

$= \frac{8}{11}$ **Simplify.**

As a fraction in simplest form, $0.\overline{72} = \frac{8}{11}$.

✓ Check Understanding Example 5

5. Write each decimal as a fraction in simplest form.

   a. $0.\overline{7}$ $\frac{7}{9}$ **b.** $0.\overline{54}$ $\frac{6}{11}$ **c.** $0.\overline{213}$ $\frac{71}{333}$

Need Help?

Properties of Equality allow you to change both sides of an equation in the same way.

---

4 EXAMPLE English Learners

Be sure students understand the correct way to read decimals that are greater than 1. You say "and" for the decimal point. For example, you read 1.12 as "one and twelve hundredths," *not* as "one point twelve." Naming the place value may also help when writing a decimal as a fraction.

Economics Connection

In 1997, the Board of Directors of the New York Stock Exchange voted to begin trading stocks in decimal prices rather than fractions. Previously, a stock that was valued at $65.25 per share was priced on the Exchange as $65\frac{1}{4}$. The smallest fraction of a dollar allowed for trade was $\frac{1}{8}$. The year 2000 was chosen as the starting date for the decimal pricing.

PowerPoint

Additional Examples

1 The fuel tank of Scott's new lawn mower holds $\frac{1}{2}$ gal of gasoline. Scott poured 0.4 gal into the tank. Did Scott fill the tank? no

2 Write each fraction as a decimal. State the block of digits that repeats.
   a. $\frac{5}{6}$ $0.8\overline{3}$; 3
   b. $\frac{7}{11}$ $0.\overline{63}$; 63

3 Write the numbers in order, from least to greatest.
   $-0.8, \frac{3}{12}, -\frac{5}{4}, 0.125$
   $-\frac{5}{4}, -0.8, 0.125, \frac{3}{12}$

4 Write 1.72 as a mixed number in simplest form. $1\frac{18}{25}$

5 Write $0.\overline{18}$ as a fraction in simplest form. $\frac{2}{11}$

Closure

Have students explain how to write fractions as decimals and how to write terminating and repeating decimals as fractions.

Assignment Guide

1 Objective 1
- **Ⓐ Ⓑ Core** 1–15, 28–38, 43
- **Ⓒ Extension** 50

2 Objective 2
- **Ⓐ Ⓑ Core** 16–27, 39–42, 44
- **Ⓒ Extension** 45–49, 51

Test Prep 52–54
Mixed Review 55–63

Practice 5-2 *Fractions and Decimals*

Write as a fraction or mixed number in simplest form.
1. 0.4 — $\frac{2}{5}$ 2. 0.75 — $\frac{3}{4}$ 3. 0.16 — $\frac{4}{25}$
4. 2.34 — $2\frac{17}{50}$ 5. 0.09 — $\frac{9}{100}$ 6. 8.8 — $8\frac{4}{5}$

Write each fraction or mixed number as a decimal.
7. $\frac{17}{20}$ — 0.85   8. $\frac{7}{8}$ — 0.875   9. $-\frac{9}{16}$ — −0.5625
10. $3\frac{1}{8}$ — 3.125   11. $6\frac{5}{32}$ — 6.28125   12. $2\frac{87}{125}$ — 2.696
13. $\frac{13}{25}$ — 0.52   14. $4\frac{31}{50}$ — 4.62   15. $-\frac{7}{12}$ — −0.58$\overline{3}$
16. $\frac{4}{9}$ — 0.$\overline{4}$ 17. $\frac{5}{18}$ — 0.2$\overline{7}$ 18. $\frac{15}{11}$ — 1.$\overline{36}$

Order from least to greatest.
19. $0.4, \frac{3}{10}, \frac{1}{2}, \frac{3}{10}$ — $\frac{3}{10}, 0.4, \frac{1}{2}, \frac{3}{10}$
20. $-\frac{3}{8}, -\frac{3}{4}, -0.38, -0.6$ — $-\frac{3}{4}, -0.6, -0.38, -\frac{3}{8}$
21. $\frac{1}{5}, -\frac{1}{5}, 0.2, \frac{2}{5}$ — $-\frac{1}{5}, 0.2, \frac{1}{5}, \frac{2}{5}$

22. Write an improper fraction with the greatest possible value using each of the digits 5, 7, and 9 once. Write this as a mixed number and as a decimal.
$\frac{97}{5} = 19\frac{2}{5} = 19.4$

Write each decimal as a fraction or mixed number in simplest form.
23. $10.0\overline{7}$ — $10\frac{7}{90}$ 24. 3.44 — $3\frac{11}{25}$ 25. $-4.\overline{27}$ — $-4\frac{3}{11}$
26. 0.09 — $\frac{9}{100}$ 27. 0.375 — $\frac{3}{8}$ 28. $0.2\overline{43}$ — $\frac{241}{990}$

Compare. Use <, >, or = to complete each statement.
29. $\frac{5}{6}$ ⊡ 0.8 — >   30. $\frac{7}{11}$ ⊡ 0.65 — <   31. $4.\overline{2}$ ⊡ $4\frac{2}{9}$ — =
32. $-\frac{3}{11}$ ⊡ −0.25 — <   33. $0.\overline{80}$ ⊡ $\frac{80}{99}$ — =   34. -0.43 ⊡ $-\frac{7}{16}$ — >

Enrichment 5-2 *Nines in the Denominator*

Recall that you can indicate repeating digits in a decimal by writing a bar over the repeating digits.
Example $\frac{1}{3} = 0.33333\ldots$ Shorthand: $\frac{1}{3} = 0.\overline{3}$
Example $\frac{51}{110} = 0.4636363\ldots$ Shorthand: $\frac{51}{110} = 0.4\overline{63}$
Use your calculator to do the following exercises.

Write as a decimal, using a bar.
1. $\frac{17}{18}$ — $0.9\overline{4}$ 2. $\frac{3}{11}$ — $0.\overline{27}$ 3. $\frac{14}{55}$ — $0.2\overline{54}$
4. $\frac{8}{33}$ — $0.\overline{24}$ 5. $\frac{66}{133}$ — $0.4\overline{9}$ 6. $\frac{7,067}{990}$ — 7.138

When only nines appear in a denominator, you can predict the decimal equivalent of a fraction.

Write as a decimal.
7. $\frac{4}{9}$ — $0.\overline{4}$ 8. $\frac{7}{9}$ — $0.\overline{7}$ 9. $\frac{2}{9}$ — $0.\overline{2}$ 10. $\frac{5}{9}$ — $0.\overline{5}$
11. Predict the decimal equivalent of $\frac{8}{9}$. — $0.\overline{8}$
12. Find the answer using your calculator. — $0.\overline{8}$

Write as a decimal.
13. $\frac{37}{99}$ — $0.\overline{37}$ 14. $\frac{82}{99}$ — $0.\overline{82}$ 15. $\frac{5}{99}$ — $0.\overline{05}$ 16. $\frac{61}{99}$ — $0.\overline{61}$
17. Predict the decimal equivalent of $\frac{47}{99}$. — $0.\overline{47}$
18. Find the answer using your calculator. — $0.\overline{47}$

Write as a decimal.
19. $\frac{571}{999}$ — $0.\overline{571}$ 20. $\frac{7}{999}$ — $0.\overline{007}$ 21. $\frac{365}{999}$ — $0.\overline{365}$ 22. $\frac{998}{999}$ — $0.\overline{998}$
23. Predict the decimal equivalent of $\frac{135}{999}$. — $0.\overline{135}$
24. Find the answer using your calculator. — $0.\overline{135}$
25. Predict the decimal equivalent of $\frac{8,705}{99,999}$. — $0.\overline{08705}$

EXERCISES

🔍 For more exercises, see *Extra Practice*.

Practice and Problem Solving

Ⓐ Practice by Example

Example 1
(page 237)

Write each fraction or mixed number as a decimal.

1. $\frac{7}{25}$ 0.28   2. $\frac{3}{5}$ 0.6   3. $1\frac{9}{20}$ 1.45   4. $6\frac{1}{4}$ 6.25

🌐 5. **Remodeling** Randy and Becky measure a carpet. Becky says the carpet's length is $10\frac{5}{16}$ ft. Randy writes "10.3125 ft." Did Randy write the correct measurement? Explain.
Yes; $\frac{5}{16} = 5 \div 16 = 0.3125$, so $10\frac{5}{16} = 10.3125$.

Example 2
(page 238)

6. −0.625; terminating
7. −0.1$\overline{6}$; repeating; 6
8. 0.$\overline{2}$; repeating; 2
9. 0.$\overline{81}$; repeating; 81

Write each fraction as a decimal. State whether the decimal is *terminating* or *repeating*. If the decimal repeats, state the block of digits that repeats. **6–9. See left.**

6. $-\frac{5}{8}$ 7. $-\frac{1}{6}$ 8. $\frac{2}{9}$ 9. $\frac{9}{11}$

Example 3
(page 238)

12. $-0.75, -0.625, -\frac{1}{4}, -\frac{1}{8}$
13. $0.06, \frac{2}{5}, \frac{6}{5}, \frac{3}{2}$
14. $-0.87, -\frac{8}{10}, -0.77, -\frac{7}{10}$
15. $\frac{22}{11}, 2.01, 2.1, \frac{22}{10}$

Order from least to greatest.

10. $1.2, \frac{3}{5}, -0.5, \frac{9}{10}$ — $-0.5, \frac{3}{5}, \frac{9}{10}, 1.2$ 11. $\frac{1}{2}, \frac{3}{2}, \frac{5}{2}, 0.3$ — $0.3, \frac{1}{2}, \frac{3}{2}, \frac{5}{2}$

12. $-\frac{1}{4}, -\frac{1}{8}, -0.75, -0.625$ 13. $\frac{3}{2}, \frac{2}{5}, \frac{6}{5}, 0.06$

14. $-\frac{7}{10}, -\frac{8}{10}, -0.77, -0.87$ 15. $2.1, \frac{22}{10}, 2.01, \frac{22}{11}$

12–15. See left.

Examples 4 and 5
(page 239)

Write each decimal as a fraction or a mixed number in simplest form.

16. 2.25 $2\frac{1}{4}$ 17. 3.4 $3\frac{2}{5}$ 18. 0.08 $\frac{2}{25}$ 19. 7.15 $7\frac{3}{20}$

20. 2.48 $2\frac{12}{25}$ 21. 6.37 $6\frac{37}{100}$ 22. 5.36 $5\frac{9}{25}$ 23. 2.55 $2\frac{11}{20}$

24. $0.\overline{5}$ $\frac{5}{9}$ 25. $0.\overline{126}$ $\frac{14}{111}$ 26. $0.\overline{27}$ $\frac{3}{11}$ 27. $-0.\overline{3}$ $-\frac{1}{3}$

Ⓑ Apply Your Skills

Mental Math Compare. Use >, <, or = to complete each statement.

28. $\frac{1}{2}$ ▮ 1.2 <   29. $\frac{7}{8}$ ▮ 0.875 =   30. $\frac{3}{5}$ ▮ 0.25 >   31. $\frac{1}{8}$ ▮ 0.375 <

32. **Number Sense** A carpenter has a bolt with diameter $\frac{5}{32}$ in. Will the bolt fit in a hole made by a drill bit with diameter 0.2 in.? Explain.
GPS   Yes; the bolt has diameter 0.15625 in., which is less than 0.2 in.

Write each fraction or mixed number as a decimal.

33. $5\frac{3}{8}$ 34. $2\frac{5}{16}$ 35. $\frac{1}{25}$ 36. $3\frac{4}{5}$ 37. $-\frac{31}{100}$ 38. $\frac{7}{11}$
5.375   2.3125   0.04   3.8   −0.31   0.$\overline{63}$

Write as a fraction or a mixed number in simplest form.

39. 0.35 $\frac{7}{20}$ 40. 6.8 $6\frac{4}{5}$ 41. −3.9 $-3\frac{9}{10}$ 42. $10.\overline{105}$ $10\frac{35}{333}$

43. Batting averages are usually expressed as decimals. Sarah got 32 hits in 112 times at bat. Lizzie got 26 hits in 86 times at bat.
    a. **Data Analysis** Find their batting averages, to the nearest thousandth. Sarah: 0.286; Lizzie: 0.302
    b. **Probability** Based on their batting averages, who is more likely to get a hit? Explain. Lizzie; 0.302 > 0.286

 Use the Guided Problem Solving worksheet with Exercise 32.

44. Number Sense Copy and complete this table of some commonly used fractions and decimals. Write the fractions in simplest form.

Fraction	▦ $\frac{1}{8}$	▦ $\frac{1}{4}$	$\frac{3}{8}$	$\frac{1}{2}$	▦ $\frac{5}{8}$	$\frac{3}{4}$	$\frac{7}{8}$
Decimal	0.125	0.25	▦ 0.375	▦ 0.5	0.625	▦ 0.75	▦ 0.875

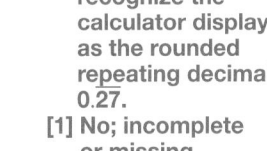 **C** Challenge **Write as a fraction or a mixed number in simplest form.**

47. $\frac{272,727}{1,000,000}$

49. No; there is no block of digits that repeats.

54. [2] No; Lucia should recognize the calculator display as the rounded repeating decimal 0.27. [1] No; incomplete or missing explanation.

45. $0.0\overline{6}$ $\frac{1}{15}$ **46.** $0.1\overline{83}$ $\frac{91}{495}$ **47.** 0.272727 **48.** $1.1\overline{9}$ $1\frac{1}{5}$
                                                                    See left.

49. <u>Writing in Math</u> Is 3.010010001... a repeating decimal? Explain.
See left.
50. Number Sense The number of digits that repeat in a repeating decimal is called the *period* of the decimal. The period of $0.\overline{3}$ is 1.
 a. Write $\frac{5}{7}, \frac{4}{13}$, and $\frac{7}{15}$ as decimals. $0.\overline{714285}, 0.\overline{307692}, 0.4\overline{6}$
 b. What is the period of each decimal you wrote in part (a)? 6, 6, 1

51. Reasoning Seth had just finished a division problem on his calculator when the telephone rang. He got distracted. When he looked back at the calculator, all he could see was the display 0.04040404. What might have been the division problem? Explain.
$4 \div 99$ since $0.0\overline{4} = \frac{4}{99}$

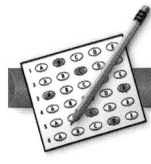 **Test Prep**

Multiple Choice

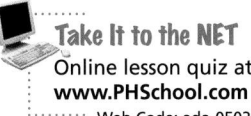
Take It to the NET
Online lesson quiz at
www.PHSchool.com
Web Code: ada-0502

Short Response

52. Which decimal is the closest approximation to $\frac{2}{3}$? D
 A. 0.230   **B.** 0.233   **C.** 0.600   **D.** 0.667

53. A clerk puts slices of cheese on a scale until it reads 1.625 lb. What is this amount as a mixed number? H
 F. $1\frac{1}{6}$ lb   **G.** $1\frac{1}{4}$ lb   **H.** $1\frac{5}{8}$ lb   **I.** $1\frac{6}{25}$ lb

54. Lucia's math teacher asks her to write $\frac{3}{11}$ as a decimal. She enters $3 \div 11$ on her calculator. The calculator displays 0.2727273. **(a)** Is this the answer Lucia should record? **(b)** Explain your response.
See above left.

Mixed Review

55. $-\frac{5}{6}, -\frac{1}{3}, \frac{1}{6}, \frac{2}{3}$ Lesson 5-1
56. $\frac{1}{8}, \frac{1}{5}, \frac{3}{8}, \frac{3}{5}, \frac{5}{8}$
57. $-\frac{6}{7}, -\frac{4}{7}, -\frac{3}{14}, -\frac{1}{14}$

Lesson 4-9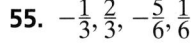

Order the fractions in each group from least to greatest.

55. $-\frac{1}{3}, \frac{2}{3}, -\frac{5}{6}, \frac{1}{6}$ **56.** $\frac{5}{8}, \frac{3}{8}, \frac{1}{5}, \frac{3}{5}, \frac{1}{8}$ **57.** $-\frac{4}{7}, -\frac{1}{14}, -\frac{3}{14}, -\frac{6}{7}$

55–57. See left.

58. Geography Lake Mead, located between Arizona and Nevada, has a capacity of 34,850,000,000 m³. Write this number in scientific notation. 3.485×10^{10}

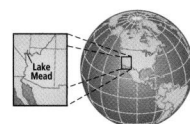
Lake Mead

Previous Course

Change each number to an improper fraction.

59. $3\frac{2}{3}$ $\frac{11}{3}$ **60.** $1\frac{5}{6}$ $\frac{11}{6}$ **61.** $10\frac{3}{7}$ $\frac{73}{7}$ **62.** $7\frac{5}{8}$ $\frac{61}{8}$ **63.** $4\frac{7}{10}$ $\frac{47}{10}$

5-2 Fractions and Decimals **241**

Estimating With Fractions and Mixed Numbers

Review

Estimating With Fractions and Mixed Numbers

For Use With Lesson 5-3

This review shows students how to round to estimate calculations involving fractions and mixed numbers. Comparing an estimate to the final answer can help you find errors.

Teaching Notes

Check to see which operation (addition, subtraction, multiplication, division) you will use before you start to estimate.

Auditory Learners

Have student partners explain to each other the reasoning behind their estimates.

Careers

Estimating answers is important on the job, where many people use calculators to help them find solutions to problems. Have students think of different job situations in which they would use estimating. Also, have students tell about people they know who use estimating in their job work.

You can round to estimate sums and differences involving fractions and mixed numbers. In one method, you round the fraction or the fraction part of a mixed number to $0, \frac{1}{2}$, or 1.

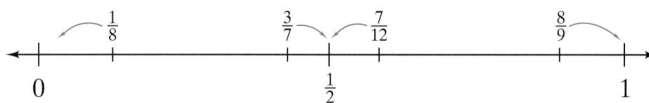

Round to 0 when the numerator is less than half of the denominator.

Round to $\frac{1}{2}$ when the numerator is about half the denominator.

Round to 1 when the numerator and denominator are almost equal.

1 EXAMPLE

a. Estimate $\frac{5}{6} + \frac{5}{12}$.

$$\frac{5}{6} \approx 1$$
$$+ \frac{5}{12} \approx + \frac{1}{2}$$
$$\overline{1\frac{1}{2}}$$

←—— **Round each fraction.** ——→

←—— **Add or subtract.** ——→

b. Estimate $\frac{9}{20} - \frac{1}{5}$.

$$\frac{9}{20} \approx \frac{1}{2}$$
$$- \frac{1}{5} \approx - 0$$
$$\overline{\frac{1}{2}}$$

You can get reasonable estimates when multiplying by first rounding to the nearest whole number. For division, use compatible numbers.

2 EXAMPLE

a. Estimate $4\frac{1}{8} \cdot 1\frac{9}{10}$.

$$4\frac{1}{8} \cdot 1\frac{9}{10}$$

If the fractional part is greater than $\frac{1}{2}$, round up.

↓   ↓

$4 \cdot 2 = 8$ **Multiply.**

b. Estimate $16\frac{1}{5} \div 2\frac{3}{4}$.

$$16\frac{1}{5} \div 2\frac{3}{4}$$

$2\frac{3}{4}$ rounds to 3. A number compatible with 3 and close to $16\frac{1}{5}$ is 15.

↓   ↓

$15 \div 3 = 5$ **Divide.**

EXERCISES

Estimate the value of each expression. 1–8. Answers may vary. Sample answers are given.

1. $\frac{2}{3} + \frac{7}{8}$ 2

2. $5\frac{1}{12} - 2\frac{7}{9}$ 2

3. $\frac{1}{5} + 5\frac{5}{8}$ 6

4. $4\frac{11}{24} - \frac{7}{12}$ 4

5. $\frac{11}{12} \cdot 4$ 4

6. $6\frac{8}{9} \div 1\frac{1}{5}$ 7

7. $10\frac{1}{10} \div 4\frac{7}{8}$ 2

8. $2\frac{4}{5} \cdot 5$ 15

Adding and Subtracting Fractions

OBJECTIVE

1 Adding and Subtracting Fractions

Investigation

Using Models to Add Fractions

Use the models to answer each question below.

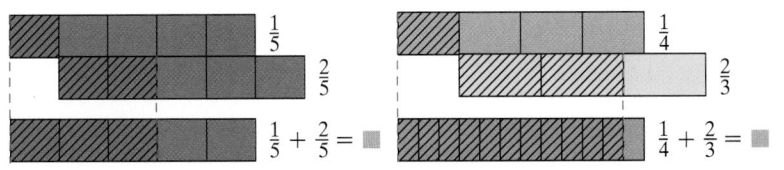

$\frac{1}{5}$

$\frac{2}{5}$

$\frac{1}{5} + \frac{2}{5} = \blacksquare$

$\frac{1}{4}$

$\frac{2}{3}$

$\frac{1}{4} + \frac{2}{3} = \blacksquare$

1. a. Refer to the model for $\frac{1}{5} + \frac{2}{5}$. What fraction does $\frac{1}{5} + \frac{2}{5}$ equal? $\frac{3}{5}$

  b. Reasoning The sum of any two fractions can be written as a fraction. Write a conjecture about how to find the numerator and denominator of such a sum.
See below right.

2. a. Refer to the model for $\frac{1}{4} + \frac{2}{3}$. What fraction does $\frac{1}{4} + \frac{2}{3}$ equal? $\frac{11}{12}$

  b. Can you add the numerators to find the sum? Explain.

  c. Can you add the denominators to find the sum? Explain.
2b–c. See below right.

In the model for $\frac{1}{5} + \frac{2}{5}$ above, you can see that the sum (or difference) of fractions with the same denominator is the sum (or difference) of the numerators. The denominators do not change.

1 **EXAMPLE** **Simplifying With Like Denominators**

Find each sum or difference. Simplify if possible.

a. $\frac{1}{8} + \frac{3}{8}$

$\frac{1}{8} + \frac{3}{8} = \frac{1+3}{8}$ Add or subtract the numerators.

$= \frac{4}{8} = \frac{1}{2}$ Simplify.

b. $\frac{9}{x} - \frac{7}{x}$

$\frac{9}{x} - \frac{7}{x} = \frac{9-7}{x}$

$= \frac{2}{x}$

✓ **Check Understanding** Example 1

1. Find each sum or difference. Simplify if possible.

  a. $\frac{3}{7} + \frac{1}{7}$ $\frac{4}{7}$ **b.** $\frac{2}{k} + \frac{3}{k}$ $\frac{5}{k}$ **c.** $\frac{7}{10} - \frac{3}{10}$ $\frac{2}{5}$ **d.** $\frac{11}{y} + \left(-\frac{5}{y}\right)$ $\frac{6}{y}$

What You'll Learn

OBJECTIVE
1 To add and subtract fractions

OBJECTIVE
2 To add and subtract mixed numbers

. . . And Why

To solve real-world problems involving cooking

✓ **Check Skills You'll Need**

Find the LCM of each group of numbers or expressions.

1. 4, 8 8   **2.** 9, 18 18

3. $2n, 5$ $10n$ **4.** 3, 6, 9 18

5. 8, 5, 4 40   **6.** $10, n$ $10n$

❓ For help, go to Lesson 5-1.

1b. Add the numerators of the two fractions.

2b. No; $1 + 2 = 3$, but the correct numerator is 11.

2c. No; $4 + 3 = 7$, but the correct denominator is 12.

🅣 **iTEXT** Interactive lesson includes instant self-check, tutorials, and activities.

Lesson Preview

✓ **Check Skills You'll Need**

Finding the Least Common Multiple
Lesson 5-1: Example 1;
Exercises 1–8.
Extra Practice, p. 748.

Lesson Resources

📁 **Teaching Resources**
Practice, Reteaching, Enrichment
Checkpoint Quiz 1

👥 **Reaching All Students**
Practice Workbook 5-3
Spanish Practice Workbook 5-3
Reading and Math Literacy 5A
Spanish Reading and Math Literacy 5B
Spanish Checkpoint Quiz 5
Guided Problem Solving 5-3
Technology Activities 9, 10
Hands-On Activities 7, 8

⏱ **Presentation Assistant Plus!**
Transparencies and PowerPoint™
• Check Skills You'll Need 5-3
• Additional Examples 5-3
• Student Edition Answers 5-3
• Lesson Quiz 5-3
PH Presentation Pro CD-ROM 5-3

🅐**SSESSMENT** *SYSTEM*

Checkpoint Quiz 1
Computer Test Generator CD-ROM

💻 **Technology**
Resource Pro® CD-ROM
Computer Test Generator CD-ROM
PH Presentation Pro CD-ROM

💻 **www.PHSchool.com**
PH SuccessNet Student Site
• Teacher Web Code: adk-5500
• Algebra Readiness Puzzles 16, 17
• Graphing Calculator, Procedures 1, 7
• Self-grading Lesson Quiz
PH SuccessNet Teacher Center
• Lesson Planner
• Resources

INSTANT CHECK SYSTEM **Ongoing Assessment and Intervention**

Before the Lesson
Diagnose prerequisite skills using:
• Check Skills You'll Need

During the Lesson
Monitor progress using:
• Check Understanding
• Additional Examples
• Test Prep

After the Lesson
Assess knowledge using:
• Lesson Quiz
• Computer Test Generator CD-ROM
• Chapter Checkpoint 1 (p. 247)

2. Teach

Math Background

To add or subtract fractions with unlike denominators, you first rewrite the fractions with a common denominator. It is often practical to use the LCD because the resulting numerators have the least possible values, so are easiest to add. Also, the result often is already in simplest form.

Teaching Notes

Investigation (Optional)
Help students follow the transition from the model procedure provided to the mathematical procedure. Both allow you to find the sum of fractions with unlike denominators. Encourage students to refer back to the model if necessary.

Tactile Learners
Show students how to use fraction models to help them add or subtract fractions.

1 EXAMPLE Auditory Learners

Students sometimes try to add or subtract the denominators. Since like denominators represent parts of a whole that are the same size, have students say, "1 part plus 3 parts equals 4 parts." Students may use this method any time they are adding or subtracting fractions with like denominators.

1 EXAMPLE Teaching Tip

Point out that in Example 1b, x cannot equal 0: Ask students to explain why. Division by zero is undefined.

2 EXAMPLE Alternative Method

After students add or subtract fractions that do not contain variables, suggest that they check their work by using a calculator to convert the fractions to decimals and perform the operation again. Then use the calculator to also convert their fraction answer to a decimal and compare the results.

Before you can add or subtract fractions with unlike denominators, first write the fractions with a common denominator. The method shown here for addition works with subtraction also.

$$\text{Arithmetic} \quad \frac{2}{3} + \frac{1}{5} \qquad\qquad \text{Algebra} \quad \frac{a}{b} + \frac{c}{d}$$

$$\frac{2}{3} \cdot \frac{5}{5} + \frac{1}{5} \cdot \frac{3}{3} \qquad\qquad \frac{a}{b} \cdot \frac{d}{d} + \frac{c}{d} \cdot \frac{b}{b}$$

$$\frac{10}{15} + \frac{3}{15} \qquad\qquad\qquad \frac{ad}{bd} + \frac{bc}{bd}$$

$$\frac{13}{15} \qquad\qquad\qquad\qquad \frac{ad + bc}{bd}$$

2 EXAMPLE Simplifying With Unlike Denominators

Simplify each difference.

a. $\dfrac{1}{8} - \dfrac{5}{6}$

$$\frac{1}{8} - \frac{5}{6} = \frac{1 \cdot 6 - 8 \cdot 5}{8 \cdot 6}$$
$$= \frac{6 - 40}{48}$$
$$= \frac{-34}{48} = -\frac{17}{24}$$

Need Help?
If either the numerator or denominator is negative, or if the negative sign is in front of the fraction, then the entire fraction is negative. $\dfrac{-17}{24} = -\dfrac{17}{24}$

Rewrite using a common denominator.

Use the Order of Operations to simplify.

Simplify.

b. $\dfrac{1}{8} - \dfrac{5x}{6}$

$$\frac{1}{8} - \frac{5x}{6} = \frac{1 \cdot 6 - 8 \cdot 5x}{8 \cdot 6}$$
$$= \frac{6 - 40x}{48}$$

✓ Check Understanding   Example 2

2. Simplify each sum or difference.

a. $\dfrac{2}{3} - \dfrac{1}{5}$ $\dfrac{7}{15}$

b. $-\dfrac{7}{8} + \dfrac{3}{4}$ $-\dfrac{1}{8}$

c. $\dfrac{3}{7} - \dfrac{2}{m}$ $\dfrac{3m - 14}{7m}$

Real-World 🌐 **Connection**

Mt. Shasta, in northern California, is 14,162 ft high. You can hike the Avalanche Gulch route from Bunny Flat for 6 mi and climb 7,000 ft.

OBJECTIVE

2 Adding and Subtracting Mixed Numbers

Before you add or subtract mixed numbers, write the mixed numbers as improper fractions.

3 EXAMPLE   Real-World 🌐 Problem Solving

Hiking Suppose you hiked $2\frac{2}{3}$ mi near Mt. Shasta and then another $1\frac{3}{4}$ mi to your campsite. How far did you hike in all?

$$2\frac{2}{3} + 1\frac{3}{4} = \frac{8}{3} + \frac{7}{4} \qquad \text{Write mixed numbers as improper fractions.}$$
$$= \frac{8 \cdot 4 + 3 \cdot 7}{3 \cdot 4} \qquad \text{Rewrite using a common denominator.}$$
$$= \frac{32 + 21}{12} \qquad \text{Use the Order of Operations to simplify.}$$
$$= \frac{53}{12} = 4\frac{5}{12} \qquad \text{Write as a mixed number.}$$

You hiked $4\frac{5}{12}$ mi in all.

🌱 Reaching All Students

Below Level Review adding and subtracting numbers on a number line. Students may find help in Lesson 1-5.	**Advanced Learners** Challenge students to visually represent a fraction problem. For example, students use slices of pizza as fractions of a whole pizza that can be added and subtracted.	**Tactile Learners** See note on page 244. **Auditory Learners** See note on page 244.

3. Find each sum or difference. Simplify if possible.

   a. $5\frac{3}{4} + \frac{7}{8}$ $6\frac{5}{8}$ b. $5\frac{2}{3} - 3\frac{1}{6}$ $2\frac{1}{2}$ c. $2\frac{3}{8} + \frac{7}{8}$ $3\frac{1}{4}$

   d. A recipe for punch calls for $1\frac{1}{2}$ qt of orange juice, $1\frac{1}{4}$ qt of ginger ale, and $\frac{3}{4}$ qt of cranberry juice. How many quarts of punch will the recipe make? $3\frac{1}{2}$ qt

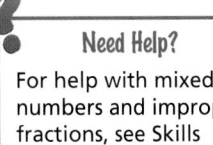

Need Help?

For help with mixed numbers and improper fractions, see Skills Handbook, page 772.

You can subtract mixed numbers in more than one way.

More Than One Way

You are making banana bread for a bake sale, using the recipe at the right. You have $1\frac{3}{4}$ c of sugar left in a bag of sugar. How much more sugar do you need?

Banana Bread

5 ripe bananas	$3\frac{1}{2}$ cups flour
4 eggs	2 tsp baking soda
1 cup shortening	1 tsp salt
$2\frac{1}{2}$ cups sugar	$1\frac{1}{2}$ cups chopped walnuts, optional
3 tsp vanilla	

Tina's Method

You write both mixed numbers as improper fractions.

$$2\frac{1}{2} - 1\frac{3}{4} = \frac{5}{2} - \frac{7}{4}$$
$$= \frac{5 \cdot 4 - 2 \cdot 7}{2 \cdot 4}$$
$$= \frac{20 - 14}{8}$$
$$= \frac{\cancel{6}^3}{\cancel{8}_4} = \frac{3}{4}$$

You need $\frac{3}{4}$ c more sugar.

Kevin's Method

You write $2\frac{1}{2}$ as $2\frac{2}{4}$, and then rewrite it as $1\frac{6}{4}$ before subtracting.

$$2\frac{1}{2} - 1\frac{3}{4} = 2\frac{2}{4} - 1\frac{3}{4}$$
$$= 1\frac{6}{4} - 1\frac{3}{4}$$
$$= \frac{3}{4}$$

You need $\frac{3}{4}$ c more sugar.

Choose a Method 1–2. Answers may vary. See right for sample answers.

1. For the problem above, which method do you prefer? Explain.

2. Which method would you use to find $2\frac{4}{7} - 1\frac{9}{14}$? Which method would you use to find $-1\frac{1}{2} - 1\frac{3}{4}$? Explain your choices.

More Than One Way

1. Tina's Method; writing both mixed numbers as improper fractions is easier than renaming $2\frac{1}{2}$ as $1\frac{6}{4}$.

2. Tina's method because writing both mixed numbers as improper fractions is easier than renaming $2\frac{4}{7}$; Kevin's method because I need only to find common denominators and then use addition.

Assignment Guide

1 Objective 1
   Ⓐ Ⓑ Core 1–12, 28,
   30–32, 34
   Ⓒ Extension 36–38

2 Objective 2
   Ⓐ Ⓑ Core 13–27, 29,
   33, 35
   Ⓒ Extension 39

Test Prep 40–44
Mixed Review 45–50

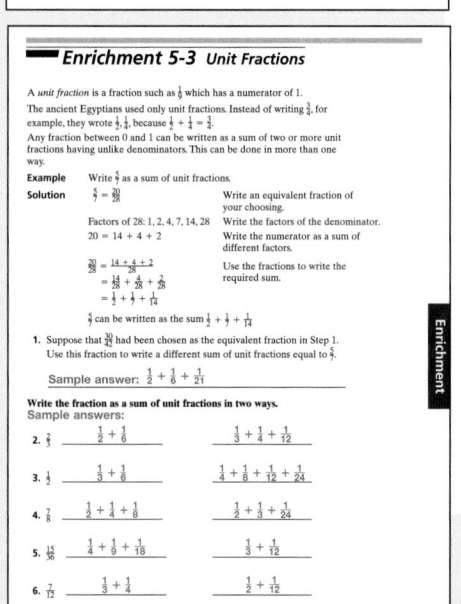

EXERCISES   ❓ **For more exercises, see *Extra Practice*.**

Practice and Problem Solving

Ⓐ Practice by Example

Example 1
(page 243)

Find each sum or difference. Simplify if possible.

1. $\frac{3}{16} + \frac{7}{16}$ $\frac{5}{8}$ 2. $\frac{6}{z} + \left(-\frac{2}{z}\right)$ $\frac{4}{z}$ 3. $\frac{15}{q} - \frac{8}{q}$ $\frac{7}{q}$ 4. $\frac{5}{11} + \frac{4}{11}$ $\frac{9}{11}$

5. $\frac{11}{12} - \frac{7}{12}$ $\frac{1}{3}$ 6. $\frac{7}{8} + \frac{5}{8}$ $1\frac{1}{2}$ 7. $\frac{3}{10} - \frac{7}{10}$ $-\frac{2}{5}$ 8. $\frac{2}{x} + \frac{3}{x}$ $\frac{5}{x}$

Example 2
(page 244)

Simplify each sum or difference.

9. $\frac{3}{4} - \frac{2}{3}$ $\frac{1}{12}$ 10. $\frac{12}{20} - \frac{1}{4}$ $\frac{7}{20}$ 11. $-\frac{3}{10} - \frac{5}{100}$ $-\frac{7}{20}$ 12. $\frac{6}{x} - \frac{2}{5}$ $\frac{30 - 2x}{5x}$

Example 3
(page 244)

Find each sum or difference. Simplify if possible.

13. $3\frac{3}{4} + 2\frac{1}{4}$ 6   14. $\frac{4}{16} + 1\frac{3}{8}$ $1\frac{5}{8}$ 15. $10\frac{1}{8} + 3\frac{3}{4}$ 16. $3\frac{5}{8} + 2\frac{7}{12}$ $6\frac{5}{24}$

15. $13\frac{7}{8}$

See left.

17. $1\frac{5}{9} - 1\frac{2}{9}$ $\frac{1}{3}$ 18. $5\frac{3}{4} - 2\frac{1}{8}$ $3\frac{5}{8}$ 19. $1\frac{17}{18} - \frac{7}{9}$ $1\frac{1}{6}$ 20. $1\frac{7}{8} - 2\frac{3}{4}$ $-\frac{7}{8}$

🌐 **21. Homework** Kim works on Social Studies homework for $2\frac{2}{5}$ h. Then she works on Math homework for $1\frac{1}{4}$ h. How many hours total does Kim spend doing homework? $3\frac{13}{20}$ h

Ⓑ Apply Your Skills

22–25. Answers may vary.
Estimation **Estimate each sum or difference.** Samples are given.

22. $2\frac{1}{3} + 7\frac{1}{8}$ 9   23. $25\frac{5}{18} - 9\frac{11}{17}$ 15   24. $15\frac{3}{4} + 31\frac{1}{2}$ 48   25. $-4\frac{7}{8} + 15\frac{1}{10}$ 10

26. **Writing in Math** Describe why estimating a sum or difference before adding or subtracting is useful.   See left.

26. A good way to check your work is to see whether your answer is close to your estimate.

🌐 **27. Crafts** A doll artist cuts a piece of lace $8\frac{5}{8}$ in. long from a piece $10\frac{1}{2}$ in. long. How many inches of lace are left? $1\frac{7}{8}$ in.

Find each sum or difference.

29. $\frac{30 - 3n}{10n}$

28. $\frac{12}{15} + \frac{1}{2}$ $1\frac{3}{10}$ 29. $\frac{3}{n} - \frac{3}{10}$ 30. $\frac{7}{10} + \frac{2d}{3}$ 31. $\frac{5}{6} + \frac{7}{9}$ $1\frac{11}{18}$

See left. $\frac{21 + 20d}{30}$

Mental Math **Find each sum.**

32. $\frac{3}{4} + \frac{3}{8} + \frac{1}{4}$ $1\frac{3}{8}$ 33. $2\frac{5}{7} + 1\frac{2}{5} + 3\frac{2}{7}$ $7\frac{2}{5}$ 34. $\frac{2}{7} + \frac{x}{2} + \left(-\frac{2}{7}\right)$ $\frac{x}{2}$

🌐 **35. Weather** There were three snowstorms last winter. The storms [GPS] dropped $3\frac{1}{2}$ in., $6\frac{1}{2}$ in., and $10\frac{3}{4}$ in. of snow. What was the combined snowfall of the three storms? $20\frac{3}{4}$ in.

Ⓒ Challenge

Use prime factors to find the LCD. Then simplify each expression.

36. $\frac{7}{24} - \frac{15}{90}$ $\frac{1}{8}$ 37. $\frac{-5}{66} + \frac{-7}{99} - \frac{29}{198}$ 38. $\frac{2}{28} + \frac{1}{49}$ $\frac{9}{98}$

🌐 **39. Collections** Dora and Paul have a collection of x marbles. Dora has $\frac{x}{3}$ marbles. What fraction of the marbles does Paul have? $\frac{2x}{3}$

[GPS] Use the Guided Problem Solving worksheet with Exercise 35.

Practice 5-3 *Adding and Subtracting Fractions*

Find each sum or difference.

1. $\frac{2}{3} + \frac{1}{6}$ $\frac{5}{6}$ 2. $\frac{5}{8} - \frac{1}{4}$ $\frac{3}{8}$

3. $2 - \frac{4}{9}$ $1\frac{5}{9}$ 4. $1\frac{1}{2} - 2\frac{4}{5}$ $-1\frac{3}{10}$

5. $\frac{1}{4} - \frac{1}{3}$ $-\frac{1}{12}$ 6. $5\frac{1}{6} + 3\frac{5}{12}$ $9\frac{7}{24}$

7. $\frac{x}{5} + \frac{x}{3}$ $\frac{8x}{15}$ 8. $\frac{3}{4} + \left(-\frac{2}{3}\right)$ $\frac{7a}{30}$

9. $\frac{7}{12} - \frac{1}{3}$ $\frac{1}{3}$ 10. $3\frac{1}{2} + 2\frac{3}{8}$ $5\frac{3}{8}$

11. $1\frac{3}{8} - 1\frac{1}{3}$ $\frac{1}{2}$ 12. $\frac{3}{5y} + \frac{1}{5y}$ $\frac{4}{5y}$

13. $\frac{x}{16} + \frac{3}{4}$ $1\frac{5}{16}$ 14. $2\frac{7}{10} - 3\frac{9}{20}$ $-\frac{13}{20}$

15. $3\frac{1}{2} + 2\frac{3}{4}$ $6\frac{7}{12}$ 16. $-1\frac{3}{4} + \left(-2\frac{1}{4}\right)$ $-3\frac{11}{12}$

Find each sum using mental math.

17. $3\frac{3}{8} + 2\frac{1}{8} + 1\frac{3}{8}$ $6\frac{7}{8}$ 18. $6\frac{7}{12} + 4\frac{5}{12}$ 11

19. $8\frac{5}{16} + 2\frac{4}{16} + 4\frac{7}{16}$ $14\frac{15}{16}$ 20. $7\frac{9}{10} + 3\frac{3}{10}$ $11\frac{1}{5}$

Estimate each sum or difference.

21. $13\frac{3}{4} - 2\frac{9}{10}$ 11   22. $18\frac{8}{9} + 11\frac{4}{9}$ 30

23. $23\frac{4}{13} + 32\frac{7}{8}$ 56   24. $26\frac{9}{10} + 72\frac{4}{5}$ 100

Use prime factors to simplify each expression.

25. $\frac{7}{30} - \frac{22}{75}$ $-\frac{23}{150}$ 26. $\frac{3}{14} + \frac{17}{63}$ $\frac{61}{126}$

27. $\frac{x}{42} + \frac{x}{12}$ $\frac{15}{28}$ 28. $2\frac{5}{6} - 2\frac{5}{22}$ $\frac{20}{33}$

29. $4\frac{4}{15} + 2\frac{4}{39}$ $6\frac{24}{65}$ 30. $3\frac{5}{9} - 2\frac{11}{12}$ $\frac{23}{36}$

Enrichment 5-3 *Unit Fractions*

A *unit fraction* is a fraction such as $\frac{1}{5}$ which has a numerator of 1. The ancient Egyptians used only unit fractions. Instead of writing $\frac{3}{4}$, for example, they wrote $\frac{1}{2}, \frac{1}{4}$, because $\frac{1}{2} + \frac{1}{4} = \frac{3}{4}$.
Any fraction between 0 and 1 can be written as a sum of two or more unit fractions having unlike denominators. This can be done in more than one way.

Example   Write $\frac{5}{7}$ as a sum of unit fractions.
Solution $\frac{5}{7} = \frac{20}{28}$ Write an equivalent fraction of your choosing.
    Factors of 28: 1, 2, 4, 7, 14, 28   Write the factors of the denominator.
    $20 = 14 + 4 + 2$ Write the numerator as a sum of different factors.
    $\frac{20}{28} = \frac{14 + 4 + 2}{28}$ Use the fractions to write the required sum.
    $= \frac{14}{28} + \frac{4}{28} + \frac{2}{28}$
    $= \frac{1}{2} + \frac{1}{7} + \frac{1}{14}$
$\frac{5}{7}$ can be written as the sum $\frac{1}{2} + \frac{1}{7} + \frac{1}{14}$.

1. Suppose that $\frac{30}{42}$ had been chosen as the equivalent fraction in Step 1. Use this fraction to write a different sum of unit fractions equal to $\frac{5}{7}$.

   Sample answer: $\frac{1}{2} + \frac{1}{6} + \frac{1}{21}$

Write the fraction as a sum of unit fractions in two ways.
Sample answers:

2. $\frac{2}{3}$ $\frac{1}{2} + \frac{1}{6}$ $\frac{1}{3} + \frac{1}{4} + \frac{1}{12}$

3. $\frac{1}{2}$ $\frac{1}{3} + \frac{1}{6}$ $\frac{1}{4} + \frac{1}{8} + \frac{1}{12} + \frac{1}{24}$

4. $\frac{7}{8}$ $\frac{1}{2} + \frac{1}{4} + \frac{1}{8}$ $\frac{1}{2} + \frac{1}{3} + \frac{1}{24}$

5. $\frac{13}{36}$ $\frac{1}{4} + \frac{1}{9} + \frac{1}{18}$ $\frac{1}{3} + \frac{1}{12}$

6. $\frac{7}{12}$ $\frac{1}{3} + \frac{1}{4}$ $\frac{1}{2} + \frac{1}{12}$

Test Prep

Multiple Choice

40. Which sum or difference is greater than 0? **D**

    A. $-\frac{7}{8} + \frac{3}{4}$ **B.** $-\frac{7}{8} - \frac{3}{4}$ **C.** $-\frac{7}{8} + \left(-\frac{3}{4}\right)$ **D.** $\frac{7}{8} + \left(-\frac{3}{4}\right)$

41. Sue is fishing. She catches a bass weighing $5\frac{1}{4}$ lb. Then she catches three more weighing $3\frac{1}{2}$ lb, $1\frac{3}{4}$ lb, and 2 lb. She releases the smallest fish. What is the total weight of the fish Sue keeps? **H**

    F. $8\frac{3}{4}$ lb   **G.** $9\frac{1}{4}$ lb   **H.** $10\frac{3}{4}$ lb   **I.** $12\frac{1}{2}$ lb

42. Which expression is equal to $\frac{1}{3} + \frac{1}{6}$? **B**

    A. $\frac{1}{2} + \frac{2}{4}$ **B.** $\frac{1}{4} + \frac{2}{8}$ **C.** $\frac{1}{5} + \frac{2}{10}$ **D.** $\frac{1}{7} + \frac{2}{14}$

Short Response

43. In 2003, first-class postage in the United States costs 37¢ for 1 oz. Your letter weighs $\frac{3}{4}$ oz. **(a)** Do you need extra postage to include a newspaper clipping that weighs $\frac{3}{8}$ oz? **(b)** Explain.
See back of book.

Take It to the NET
Online lesson quiz at
www.PHSchool.com
Web Code: ada-0503

44. José and Letty plan to ride their bicycles at least eight miles. They ride for $5\frac{3}{8}$ miles and stop for a break. Then they ride for another $2\frac{5}{7}$ miles. **(a)** Do they meet their goal? **(b)** Explain your answer.
See back of book.

Mixed Review

Lesson 5-2   **Order from least to greatest.**

45. $\frac{5}{8}, \frac{4}{7}, \frac{3}{6}$ $\frac{3}{6}, \frac{4}{7}, \frac{5}{8}$ **46.** $\frac{2}{3}, 0.6, 0.66$ **47.** $\frac{10}{9}, \frac{9}{10}, -\frac{9}{10}, -\frac{10}{9}$

                                            0.6, 0.66, $\frac{2}{3}$ $-\frac{10}{9}, -\frac{9}{10}, \frac{9}{10}, \frac{10}{9}$

Lesson 4-7   **Simplify each expression.**

48. $x \cdot x^2$ x^3 **49.** $(x^3)^4$ x^{12}

Lesson 3-3   **50. Data Analysis** Use the data at the right. Find the mean, median, and mode of the annual salaries. Which statistic would you use to encourage someone to take a job at Company A?
$34,600, $26,000, $22,000; mean

10 Salaries at Company A	
$26,000	$62,000
$30,000	$22,000
$22,000	$26,000
$50,000	$21,000
$22,000	$65,000

Checkpoint Quiz 1   Lessons 5-1 through 5-3

Instant self-check quiz online and on CD-ROM

Compare. Use >, <, or = to complete each statement.

1. $\frac{2}{3} \blacksquare \frac{2}{5}$ **2.** $2\frac{2}{3} \blacksquare 2\frac{4}{6}$ **3.** $-\frac{1}{5} \blacksquare -\frac{1}{8}$ **4.** $-1.65 \blacksquare -1\frac{5}{8}$

   >   =   <   <

Write each fraction or mixed number as a decimal and each decimal as a fraction in simplest form.

5. $\frac{51}{100}$ **6.** 0.012 **7.** $1\frac{1}{4}$ **8.** $0.\overline{3}$ **9.** $\frac{5}{6}$ **10.** $0.\overline{51}$

   0.51 $\frac{3}{250}$ 1.25 $\frac{1}{3}$ $0.8\overline{3}$ $\frac{17}{33}$

Find each sum or difference. Simplify if possible. 11–14. See left.

11. $\frac{6}{13} + \frac{5}{13}$ **12.** $\frac{11}{12} - \frac{7}{9}$ **13.** $1\frac{3}{5} + 2\frac{7}{8}$ **14.** $4\frac{1}{7} - 3\frac{10}{21}$

11. $\frac{11}{13}$

12. $\frac{5}{36}$

13. $4\frac{19}{40}$

14. $\frac{2}{3}$

5-3 Adding and Subtracting Fractions   **247**

Alternative Assessment

Pass out recipes to groups of three or four students. Be sure the ingredient lists are long enough to use numerous fractional measurements. Have them identify and then add the recipe measurements in like units. For example, add measurements in cups or add measurements in teaspoons.

Test Prep

Resources
For additional practice with a variety of test item formats:
• Test Prep, p. 283
• Test-Taking Strategies, p. 278
• Test-Taking Strategies With Transparencies

5-4

1. Plan

Lesson Preview

✓ **Check Skills You'll Need**

Mixed Numbers and Improper Fractions
Skills Handbook: p. 772;
Exercises 25–42.

Lesson Resources

📁 **Teaching Resources**
Practice, Reteaching, Enrichment

👥 **Reaching All Students**
Practice Workbook 5-4
Spanish Practice Workbook 5-4
Guided Problem Solving 5-4
Technology Activities 10
Hands-On Activities 10, 11, 12, 13

⏰ **Presentation Assistant Plus!**
Transparencies and PowerPoint™
• Check Skills You'll Need 5-4
• Additional Examples 5-4
• Student Edition Answers 5-4
• Lesson Quiz 5-4
• Classroom Aid 21
PH Presentation Pro CD-ROM 5-4

ASSESSMENT SYSTEM

Computer Test Generator CD-ROM

💻 **Technology**
Resource Pro® CD-ROM
Computer Test Generator CD-ROM
PH Presentation Pro CD-ROM

💻 **www.PHSchool.com**
Student Site
• Teacher Web Code: adk-5500
• Algebra Readiness
  Puzzles 18, 19
• Self-grading Lesson Quiz
PH SuccessNet Teacher Center
• Lesson Planner
• Resources

Plus 📄TEXT

5-4 Multiplying and Dividing Fractions

OBJECTIVE

1 Multiplying Rational Numbers

What You'll Learn

OBJECTIVE 1 To multiply fractions

OBJECTIVE 2 To divide fractions

. . . And Why

To solve real-world problems involving area

✓ **Check Skills You'll Need**

Write each mixed number as a fraction.
1–6. See below.
1. $2\frac{1}{3}$ 2. $3\frac{3}{10}$ 3. $1\frac{4}{9}$

4. $4\frac{4}{5}$ 5. $7\frac{7}{8}$ 6. $5\frac{1}{7}$

❓ For help, go to Skills Handbook, p. 772.

New Vocabulary

• reciprocals

1. $\frac{7}{3}$
2. $\frac{33}{10}$
3. $\frac{13}{9}$
4. $\frac{24}{5}$
5. $\frac{63}{8}$
6. $\frac{36}{7}$

📄TEXT Interactive lesson includes instant self-check, tutorials, and activities.

In**vestigation**

Modeling Multiplication of Fractions

Use paper folding to find $\frac{2}{3}$ of $\frac{1}{4}$, or $\frac{2}{3} \cdot \frac{1}{4}$.

1. Fold a sheet of paper into fourths as shown. Shade $\frac{1}{4}$ of it.

2. Now unfold the paper and fold it into thirds as shown in the second picture. Shade $\frac{2}{3}$ of it.

3. **a.** Count the small rectangles. **12**
   b. How many did you shade twice? **2**
   c. What fraction of the small rectangles is this? $\frac{2}{12}$, or $\frac{1}{6}$

4. Use your model to complete:
   $\frac{2}{3} \cdot \frac{1}{4} =$ ▦ $\frac{2}{12}$, or $\frac{1}{6}$

5. **Modeling** Use paper folding and shading to find $\frac{3}{4} \cdot \frac{1}{2}$. $\frac{3}{8}$

To multiply fractions, first multiply their numerators and multiply their denominators. Then write the result in simplest form.

1 EXAMPLE **Multiplying Fractions**

Find $\frac{3}{7} \cdot \frac{4}{5}$. Simplify if possible.

$\frac{3}{7} \cdot \frac{4}{5} = \frac{3 \cdot 4}{7 \cdot 5}$ ⟵ Multiply the numerators.
⟵ Multiply the denominators.

$= \frac{12}{35}$ Simplify.

✓ **Check Understanding** Example 1

1. Find each product. Simplify if possible.
   a. $\frac{2}{5}\left(\frac{1}{3}\right)$ $\frac{2}{15}$ **b.** $-\frac{5}{6} \cdot \frac{2}{3}$ $-\frac{5}{9}$ **c.** $\frac{7}{8} \cdot \frac{5}{9}$ $\frac{35}{72}$ **d.** $-\frac{1}{4}\left(-\frac{3}{8}\right)$ $\frac{3}{32}$

INSTANT CHECK SYSTEM 📋 **Ongoing Assessment and Intervention**

Before the Lesson
Diagnose prerequisite skills using:
• Check Skills You'll Need

During the Lesson
Monitor progress using:
• Check Understanding
• Additional Examples
• Test Prep

After the Lesson
Assess knowledge using:
• Lesson Quiz
• Computer Test Generator CD-ROM

When a numerator and a denominator have common factors, you can simplify before multiplying.

② EXAMPLE **Simplifying Before Multiplying**

a. Find $\frac{9}{15} \cdot \frac{5}{9}$.

$$\frac{9}{15} \cdot \frac{5}{9} = \frac{\overset{1}{\cancel{9}}}{\underset{3}{\cancel{15}}} \cdot \frac{\overset{1}{\cancel{5}}}{\underset{1}{\cancel{9}}}$$ Divide the common factors.

$$= \frac{1}{3}$$ Multiply.

b. Find $\frac{y}{4} \cdot \frac{8}{11}$.

$$\frac{y}{4} \cdot \frac{8}{11} = \frac{y}{\underset{1}{\cancel{4}}} \cdot \frac{\overset{2}{\cancel{8}}}{11}$$ Divide the common factors.

$$= \frac{2y}{11}$$ Multiply.

✓ **Check Understanding** Example 2

2. Find each product. Simplify if possible.

   a. $\frac{2}{3} \cdot \frac{6}{7}$ $\frac{4}{7}$ b. $-\frac{5}{15} \cdot \frac{21}{25}$ $-\frac{7}{25}$ c. $\frac{2x}{9} \cdot \frac{3}{4}$ $\frac{x}{6}$

To multiply mixed numbers, first write them as improper fractions. Then simplify before multiplying, if possible.

③ EXAMPLE **Real-World 🌐 Problem Solving**

Geometry Central Park in New York City is a rectangle. It is approximately $2\frac{1}{2}$ mi long and $\frac{1}{2}$ mi wide. What is the area of Central Park?

$A = 2\frac{1}{2} \cdot \frac{1}{2}$ Area of a rectangle = length · width.

$= \frac{5}{2} \cdot \frac{1}{2}$ Write $2\frac{1}{2}$ as an improper fraction, $\frac{5}{2}$.

$= \frac{5}{4}$ Multiply.

$= 1\frac{1}{4}$ Write as a mixed number.

The area of Central Park is about $1\frac{1}{4}$ mi².

✓ **Check Understanding** Example 3

3. Find each product. Simplify if possible.

   a. $3\frac{3}{4} \cdot \frac{2}{5}$ $1\frac{1}{2}$ b. $\frac{2}{3} \cdot 1\frac{2}{7}$ $\frac{6}{7}$ c. $\left(-2\frac{5}{6}\right) \cdot 1\frac{3}{5}$ $-4\frac{8}{15}$

Real-World 🌐 Connection

Central Park is a rectangle. The angle of the photo makes two sides appear to be not parallel.

👥 **Reaching All Students**

Below Level Some students may need help understanding reciprocals. Write several fractions on the board and have students write the reciprocal for each. Show the correct answers so they can check theirs.

Advanced Learners Ask students how to divide a fraction by an integer. Write the reciprocal of the integer, then multiply.

Inclusion See note on page 249.

Tactile Learners See note on page 250.

---

2. Teach

Professional Development

Math Background

When subtracting integers, you make two changes to the expression. You *add* the *opposite* of the second integer. When you divide fractions, you also make two changes. You *multiply* by the *reciprocal* of the second fraction, or divisor. Point out that in both cases you are performing two actions that, in effect, offset each other so that the value of the expression remains unchanged.

Teaching Notes

Investigation (Optional)
Explain to students that while arithmetic is exact, folding paper is not. This paper model only approximates the product.

② EXAMPLE **Inclusion**
Some students may not be able to determine the common factors mentally. Suggest that they write the prime factors of each numerator and denominator and then strike through each numerator-denominator pair of common prime factors.
For Example 2(a):

$$\frac{3 \cdot 3}{3 \cdot 5} \cdot \frac{5}{3 \cdot 3}$$

Some students may see that when the same number is in the numerator of one fraction and the denominator of the other, such as 9 in this example, they can strike through them as common factors without finding the prime factorization first. However, students may have more success if they use the same method for all fraction products.

③ EXAMPLE **Geometry Connection**

You may also use the area formula $A = bh$, where b is the length of the base, and h is the height, or altitude, to that base, to find the area of a rectangle. Some formulas for area involve multiplication with fractions. The formula for the area of a triangle is $A = \frac{1}{2}bh$.

249

2 Dividing Rational Numbers

Asking "What is $2 \div \frac{1}{2}$?" is the same as asking "How many halves are in two wholes?" As the oranges show, there are four halves in two wholes.

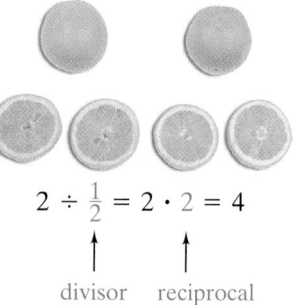

Numbers like $\frac{1}{2}$ and 2 (or $\frac{2}{1}$) are **reciprocals** because their product is 1. To divide fractions, rewrite the division as a related multiplication in which you multiply by the reciprocal of the divisor.

$$2 \div \frac{1}{2} = 2 \cdot 2 = 4$$

divisor   reciprocal

Reading Math
Reciprocals are also called *multiplicative inverses*.

4 EXAMPLE Dividing Fractions

a. Find $\frac{2}{9} \div \frac{2}{5}$.

$\frac{2}{9} \div \frac{2}{5} = \frac{2}{9} \cdot \frac{5}{2}$ **Multiply by the reciprocal of the divisor.**

$= \frac{2^1}{9} \cdot \frac{5}{2_1}$ **Divide the common factors.**

$= \frac{5}{9}$ **Simplify.**

b. Find $\frac{x}{3} \div \frac{x}{4}$.

$\frac{x}{3} \div \frac{x}{4} = \frac{x}{3} \cdot \frac{4}{x}$

$= \frac{x^1}{3} \cdot \frac{4}{1x}$

$= \frac{4}{3} = 1\frac{1}{3}$

✓ **Check Understanding**   Example 4

4. Find each quotient. Simplify if possible.

   a. $-\frac{1}{4} \div \frac{1}{2}$ $-\frac{1}{2}$ b. $\frac{5a}{8} \div \frac{2}{3}$ $\frac{15a}{16}$ c. $\frac{3b}{7} \div \frac{6}{7}$ $\frac{b}{2}$

To divide mixed numbers, change the mixed numbers to improper fractions before multiplying by the reciprocal of the divisor.

5 EXAMPLE Dividing Mixed Numbers

Find $1\frac{3}{4} \div \left(-2\frac{5}{8}\right)$.

$1\frac{3}{4} \div \left(-2\frac{5}{8}\right) = \frac{7}{4} \div \left(-\frac{21}{8}\right)$ **Change to improper fractions.**

$= \frac{7}{4} \cdot \left(-\frac{8}{21}\right)$ **Multiply by $-\frac{8}{21}$, the reciprocal of $-\frac{21}{8}$.**

$= \frac{{}^1 7}{{}_1 4} \cdot -\frac{{}^2 8}{{}_3 21} = -\frac{2}{3}$ **Divide the common factors. Simplify.**

✓ **Check Understanding**   Example 5

5. Find each quotient. Simplify if possible.

   a. $1\frac{1}{3} \div \frac{5}{6}$ $1\frac{3}{5}$ b. $-1\frac{3}{5} \div 1\frac{1}{5}$ $-1\frac{1}{3}$ c. $12\frac{1}{2} \div 1\frac{2}{3}$ $7\frac{1}{2}$

EXERCISES

 For more exercises, see *Extra Practice*.

Practice and Problem Solving

Assignment Guide

1 Objective 1
- **Ⓐ Ⓑ** Core 1–13, 30–38, 47, 49, 51, 53
- **Ⓒ** Extension 62

2 Objective 2
- **Ⓐ Ⓑ** Core 14–29, 39–46, 48, 50, 52, 54–58
- **Ⓒ** Extension 59–61

Test Prep 63–66
Mixed Review 67–78

Ⓐ Practice by Example

Find each product. Simplify if possible.

Examples 1 and 2 (pages 248 and 249)

1. $\frac{2}{3} \cdot \frac{1}{5}$ $\frac{2}{15}$ **2.** $-\frac{1}{2}\left(\frac{3}{8}\right)$ $-\frac{3}{16}$ **3.** $-\frac{4}{7} \cdot -\frac{3}{5}$ $\frac{12}{35}$ **4.** $\left(-\frac{2}{3}\right)\left(\frac{11}{13}\right)$ $-\frac{22}{39}$

5. $\left(-\frac{7}{8}\right)\left(-\frac{4}{5}\right)$ $\frac{7}{10}$ **6.** $\frac{12y}{25} \cdot \frac{5}{6}$ $\frac{2y}{5}$ **7.** $\frac{9}{10} \cdot \frac{15x}{3}$ $\frac{9x}{2}$ **8.** $\frac{5}{9}\left(\frac{9}{10}\right)$ $\frac{1}{2}$

Example 3 (page 249)

9. $5\frac{7}{8} \cdot \frac{6}{7}$ $5\frac{1}{28}$ **10.** $2\frac{3}{4} \cdot 1\frac{1}{5}$ $3\frac{3}{10}$ **11.** $-1\frac{2}{5} \cdot 2\frac{2}{7}$ $-3\frac{1}{5}$ **12.** $-3\frac{2}{5} \cdot -1\frac{2}{3}$ $5\frac{2}{3}$

🌐 13. Homework Jim spends $\frac{3}{4}$ of an hour on homework. His older sister Gina spends $1\frac{2}{3}$ times as much on her homework as Jim spends on his. How much time does Gina spend doing her homework? $1\frac{1}{4}$ hours

Example 4 (page 250)

Find each quotient. Simplify if possible.

14. $\frac{1}{2} \div \frac{1}{3}$ $1\frac{1}{2}$ **15.** $\frac{5}{8} \div \frac{3}{4}$ $\frac{5}{6}$ **16.** $-\frac{3}{4} \div \frac{1}{3}$ $-2\frac{1}{4}$ **17.** $\frac{11}{12} \div \left(-\frac{7}{8}\right)$ $-1\frac{1}{21}$

18. $\frac{3}{4} \div \frac{8}{9}$ $\frac{27}{32}$ **19.** $\frac{3}{4} \div \frac{1}{2}$ $1\frac{1}{2}$ **20.** $\frac{2t}{5} \div \frac{2}{5}$ t **21.** $\frac{1}{x} \div \frac{3}{x}$ $\frac{1}{3}$

Example 5 (page 250)

22. $12\frac{2}{3} \div \frac{3}{4}$ $16\frac{8}{9}$ **23.** $1\frac{3}{8} \div 2\frac{1}{16}$ $\frac{2}{3}$ **24.** $-1\frac{7}{9} \div \frac{8}{9}$ -2 **25.** $-3\frac{2}{3} \div \left(-2\frac{4}{9}\right)$ $1\frac{1}{2}$

26. $3\frac{1}{2} \div \frac{4}{21}$ $18\frac{3}{8}$ **27.** $7\frac{2}{3} \div 1\frac{5}{6}$ $4\frac{2}{11}$ **28.** $6\frac{3}{4} \div \frac{9}{10}$ $7\frac{1}{2}$ **29.** $1\frac{4}{5} \div \left(-1\frac{1}{2}\right)$ $-1\frac{1}{5}$

Ⓑ Apply Your Skills

Find each product. Simplify if possible.

30. $\frac{6x}{7} \cdot \frac{1}{3}$ $\frac{2x}{7}$ **31.** $-\frac{2}{3} \cdot \frac{9}{10}$ $-\frac{3}{5}$ **32.** $\frac{8}{9} \cdot \frac{15}{28}$ $\frac{10}{21}$ **33.** $-1\frac{1}{4} \cdot 6\frac{2}{3}$ $-8\frac{1}{3}$

34. $\frac{4}{t} \cdot \frac{3t}{8}$ $1\frac{1}{2}$ **35.** $\frac{4a}{9} \cdot \frac{3}{10}$ $\frac{2a}{15}$ **36.** $1\frac{3}{5} \cdot \left(-2\frac{1}{2}\right)$ -4 **37.** $\left(-\frac{7}{12}\right)\left(-\frac{5}{6}\right)$ $\frac{35}{72}$

38. Number Sense One granola bar weighs $1\frac{1}{2}$ oz. What is the weight of six granola bars? **9 oz**

Find each quotient. Simplify if possible.

39. $-\frac{1}{2} \div \frac{2}{3}$ $-\frac{3}{4}$ **40.** $\frac{10}{13} \div \frac{15}{26}$ $1\frac{1}{3}$ **41.** $-\frac{5}{6} \div \frac{4}{9}$ $-1\frac{7}{8}$ **42.** $\frac{4}{9x} \div \frac{2}{3x}$ $\frac{2}{3}$

43. $\frac{2}{5} \div \frac{15}{16}$ $\frac{32}{75}$ **44.** $-\frac{6n}{7} \div \frac{n}{3}$ $-2\frac{4}{7}$ **45.** $\frac{2}{9} \div \frac{w}{3}$ $\frac{2}{3w}$ **46.** $\frac{3}{8} \div \frac{6}{32}$ 2

Mental Math **Simplify each expression.**

47. $\frac{1}{2} \cdot \frac{2}{5}$ $\frac{1}{5}$ **48.** $\frac{1}{2} \div \frac{2}{5}$ $1\frac{1}{4}$ **49.** $10 \cdot \frac{1}{4}$ $2\frac{1}{2}$ **50.** $10 \div \frac{1}{4}$ 40

51. $\frac{5}{8} \cdot \frac{3}{5}$ $\frac{3}{8}$ **52.** $\frac{5}{8} \div \frac{3}{5}$ $1\frac{1}{24}$ **53.** $\frac{3}{7} \cdot \frac{12}{21}$ $\frac{12}{49}$ **54.** $\frac{3}{7} \div \frac{12}{21}$ $\frac{3}{4}$

🌐 55. Construction A cable television crew has to install cable along a road $1\frac{1}{2}$ mi long. The crew takes a day to install each $\frac{1}{4}$ mi of cable. How many days will the installation take? **6 days**

56. a. Write an expression for the following: The product of $\frac{1}{2}a$ and 3 is decreased by the quotient $a \div (-4)$. $3\left(\frac{1}{2}a\right) - \frac{a}{-4}$

     b. Evaluate your expression for $a = 3$. $5\frac{1}{4}$

---

3. Practice

Practice 5-4 *Multiplying and Dividing Fractions*

Find each quotient.

1. $\frac{1}{2} \div \frac{5}{8}$ $\frac{4}{5}$ 2. $-\frac{5}{24} \div \frac{7}{12}$ $-\frac{5}{14}$

3. $\frac{3}{8} \div \frac{6}{7}$ $\frac{7}{16}$ 4. $\frac{15}{19} \div \frac{15}{19}$ 1

5. $8 \div \frac{4}{5}$ 10 6. $6\frac{1}{4} \div 2\frac{1}{2}$ $2\frac{1}{2}$

7. $5\frac{2}{8} \div 1\frac{1}{6}$ $4\frac{1}{2}$ 8. $2\frac{1}{2} \div \frac{7}{10}$ $3\frac{4}{7}$

9. $\frac{5}{32} \div \frac{9}{7}$ $\frac{2}{8}$ 10. $1\frac{3}{5} \div \left(-2\frac{2}{5}\right)$ $-\frac{2}{3}$

Find each product.

11. $\frac{6}{7} \cdot \frac{1}{5}$ $\frac{6}{35}$ 12. $\frac{5}{9} \cdot \frac{3}{5}$ $\frac{1}{3}$

13. $\frac{7}{9} \cdot \frac{6}{13}$ $\frac{14}{39}$ 14. $\frac{5}{6} \cdot \left(-1\frac{9}{10}\right)$ $-1\frac{7}{12}$

15. $-4\frac{5}{9}\left(-5\frac{1}{3}\right)$ $24\frac{1}{9}$ 16. $2\frac{5}{8}\left(-\frac{2}{3}\right)$ $-1\frac{2}{3}$

17. $4\frac{7}{8} \cdot 6$ $29\frac{1}{4}$ 18. $\frac{3}{4} \cdot \frac{3}{10}$ $\frac{9}{14}$

19. $\frac{9}{10} \cdot \frac{5}{12}$ $\frac{3}{8}$ 20. $\frac{9}{16} \cdot \frac{13}{17}$ $\frac{27}{68}$

21. You are making cookies for a bake sale. The recipe calls for $2\frac{3}{4}$ cups of flour. How much flour will you need if you triple the recipe? $8\frac{1}{4}$ cups

22. It took you 1 hour to read $1\frac{3}{8}$ chapters of a novel. At this rate, how many chapters can you read in three hours? $4\frac{1}{8}$ chapters

23. A teacher wants to tape sheets of paper together to make a science banner. He wants the banner to be $127\frac{1}{2}$ inches long, and each sheet of paper is $8\frac{1}{2}$ inches wide. How many sheets of paper will he need? 15 sheets

---

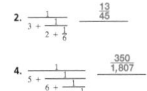

Enrichment 5-4 *Continued Fractions*

The fraction at the right is a continued fraction. A *continued fraction* consists of a series of fractions, each with 1 in the numerator and a sum in the denominator. $\frac{1}{3 + \frac{1}{4 + \frac{1}{5}}}$

To simplify a continued fraction, start at the bottom right and work upwards.

$\frac{1}{3 + \frac{1}{4 + \frac{1}{5}}} = \frac{1}{3 + \frac{1}{4\frac{1}{5}}} = \frac{1}{3 + \frac{5}{21}} = \frac{1}{3\frac{5}{21}} = \frac{21}{68}$

Simplify.

1. $\frac{1}{1 + \frac{1}{1 + \frac{1}{2}}}$ $\frac{3}{5}$ 2. $\frac{1}{3 + \frac{1}{2 + \frac{1}{6}}}$ $\frac{13}{45}$

3. $\frac{1}{2 + \frac{1}{2 + \frac{1}{2 + \frac{1}{2}}}}$ $\frac{12}{29}$ 4. $\frac{1}{5 + \frac{1}{6 + \frac{1}{7 + \frac{1}{8}}}}$ $\frac{350}{1,807}$

Example Write $\frac{21}{46}$ as a continued fraction.

Solution

$\frac{46}{21} = 2$ R 4   Divide the denominator by the numerator. Write the quotient as a whole number plus the remainder.

$\frac{21}{4} = 5$ R 1   Divide the previous denominator by the remainder.

$\frac{4}{1} = 4$ R 0   Repeat, following the pattern, until the remainder is zero.

$\frac{21}{46} = \frac{1}{2 + \frac{1}{5 + \frac{1}{4}}}$ Write the continued fraction using the quotients from the pattern.

Write as a continued fraction.

5. $\frac{6}{31}$ $\frac{1}{5 + \frac{1}{6}}$ 6. $\frac{5}{41}$ $\frac{1}{8 + \frac{1}{5}}$ 7. $\frac{7}{31}$ $\frac{1}{4 + \frac{1}{2 + \frac{1}{3}}}$ 8. $\frac{9}{41}$ $\frac{1}{6 + \frac{1}{2 + \frac{1}{5}}}$

Error Prevention!

Exercises 14–29, 39–46 Remind students to rewrite division as multiplication by the reciprocal of the divisor *before* they divide common factors to simplify.

Alternative Assessment

Organize the class into groups of three or four. Give each group a recipe. Have the group write "half recipes" and "$3\frac{1}{3}$ recipes."

Test Prep

 **Resources**

For additional practice with a variety of test item formats:
- Test Prep, p. 283
- Test-Taking Strategies, p. 278
- Test-Taking Strategies With Transparencies

Reteaching 5-4 *Multiplying and Dividing Fractions*

Find $3\frac{2}{3} \cdot 1\frac{4}{5}$.
$3\frac{2}{3} \cdot 1\frac{4}{5} = \frac{11}{3} \cdot \frac{9}{5}$ Change to improper fractions.
$= \frac{11}{3} \cdot \frac{9}{5}$ Divide the common factors.
$= \frac{33}{5} = 6\frac{3}{5}$ Simplify.

Find $-1\frac{1}{2} \cdot 2\frac{1}{4}$.
$-1\frac{1}{2} \cdot 2\frac{1}{4} = -\frac{3}{2} \div \frac{9}{4}$ Change to improper fractions.
$= -\frac{3}{2} \cdot \frac{4}{9}$ Multiply by the reciprocal.
$= -\frac{3}{2} \cdot \frac{4}{9}$ Divide the common factors.
$= -\frac{2}{3}$ Simplify.

Check your sign with the original problem. A negative times a positive has a negative product.

Find each product.

1. $\frac{2}{3} \cdot \frac{1}{2} =$ _____ $\frac{1}{3}$

2. $2\frac{1}{2} \cdot (-1\frac{1}{15}) =$ _____ $-2\frac{2}{3}$

3. $-3\frac{2}{3} \cdot 2\frac{5}{6} =$ _____ $-10\frac{1}{3}$

4. $5\frac{1}{3} \cdot 4\frac{1}{2} =$ _____ 24

Find each quotient.

5. $-\frac{6}{11} \div \frac{4}{11} =$ _____ $-1\frac{1}{2}$

6. $1\frac{1}{6} \div 2\frac{1}{3} =$ _____ $\frac{1}{2}$

7. $-4\frac{1}{3} \div (-1\frac{5}{8}) =$ _____ $2\frac{2}{3}$

8. $-6\frac{1}{6} \div \frac{7}{3} =$ _____ $-2\frac{5}{8}$

C Challenge

59. Answers may vary. Sample: You change mixed numbers to improper fractions so that you can use the rules for multiplying and dividing fractions.

Test Prep

Multiple Choice

Short Response

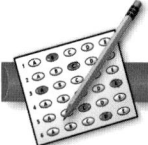 **Take It to the NET**
Online lesson quiz at
www.PHSchool.com
Web Code: ada-0504

---

57. A cheetah can run as fast as 64 mi/h. At that speed, how far could a cheetah run in $\frac{1}{16}$ h? $\frac{1}{30}$ h? **4 mi; $2\frac{2}{15}$ mi**

58. You are hiking along a trail that is $13\frac{1}{2}$ mi long. You plan to rest every $2\frac{1}{4}$ mi. How many rest stops will you make? **5 rest stops**

59. **Writing in Math** Why must you change mixed numbers to improper fractions before multiplying or dividing them? See left.

60. **a. Patterns** Find each quotient: $\frac{1}{2} \div 2$, $\frac{1}{2} \div 3$, $\frac{1}{2} \div 4$, and $\frac{1}{2} \div 5$.
    b. Explain what happens to the quotients as the divisor increases in value. 60a. $\frac{1}{4}$, $\frac{1}{6}$, $\frac{1}{8}$, $\frac{1}{10}$ 60b. The quotients decrease.

61. **Reasoning** Write a multiplication equation and a division equation that you could use to show the result of cutting four melons into eight equal slices each. See margin.

62. **Open-Ended** Find two fractions greater than $\frac{1}{2}$ with a product less than $\frac{1}{2}$. **Answers may vary. Sample: $\frac{2}{3}$, $\frac{4}{7}$**

63. Which quotient does NOT equal 1? **D**
    A. $2\frac{3}{4} \div \frac{11}{4}$ B. $\frac{3}{8} \div 0.375$ C. $\frac{7}{8} \div \frac{7}{8}$ D. $-1\frac{2}{3} \div \left(-\frac{3}{5}\right)$

64. Which expression simplifies to $\frac{x}{3}$? **H**
    F. $\frac{5x}{36}\left(\frac{5}{12}\right)$ G. $\frac{x}{6}\left(2\frac{2}{5}\right)$ H. $\frac{5x}{36}\left(2\frac{2}{5}\right)$ I. $\frac{36}{5x}\left(2\frac{2}{5}\right)$

65. **a.** A family wants to travel 300 miles. They drive at an average speed of 65 mi/h for $3\frac{1}{2}$ hours. Have they driven far enough?
    b. Explain your answer for part (a). See margin.

66. Natasha's bedroom floor is $10\frac{1}{2}$ ft by $14\frac{3}{4}$ ft. She buys 160 ft^2 of carpet. Does she have enough carpet to cover the floor? Explain.
    [2] Yes; $10\frac{1}{2}$ ft $\cdot$ $14\frac{3}{4}$ ft $= 154\frac{7}{8}$ $\text{ft}^2 < 160$ ft^2.
    [1] minor error OR answer only

Mixed Review

Lesson 5-3 **Add or subtract.**

67. $\frac{4}{5} + \frac{6}{7}$ $1\frac{23}{35}$ 68. $\frac{10}{13} - \frac{25}{26}$ $-\frac{5}{26}$ 69. $-\frac{3}{10} + \frac{3}{5}$ $\frac{3}{10}$ 70. $\frac{16}{21} - \frac{5}{7}$ $\frac{1}{21}$

Lesson 4-4 **Simplify each fraction.**

71. $\frac{10}{12}$ $\frac{5}{6}$ 72. $\frac{24}{40}$ $\frac{3}{5}$ 73. $\frac{45}{10}$ $4\frac{1}{2}$ 74. $\frac{12}{50}$ $\frac{6}{25}$ 75. $\frac{34}{51}$ $\frac{2}{3}$ 76. $\frac{105}{135}$ $\frac{7}{9}$

Lesson 2-7 77. Hal's age is three times Ida's age. In 8 years Hal will be twice as old as Ida. How old is Hal? **24 years old**

78. **Personal Finance** You spent $\frac{1}{4}$ of your money on lunch. After lunch, you gave half of what you had left to a friend, and then you spent $3 on a book. You have $4.50 left. How much money did you have before lunch? **$20**

 Use the Guided Problem Solving worksheet with Exercise 58.

61. Answers may vary. Sample:
    $4 \cdot 8 = 32$; $4 \div \frac{1}{8} = 32$

65. [2] No; $65 \cdot 3\frac{1}{2} = 227\frac{1}{2}$, which is less than 300 miles.
    [1] minor error OR answer only

Using Customary Units of Measurement

OBJECTIVE 1 — Identifying Appropriate Units of Measure

Most people in the United States use the *customary system* of measurement.

Customary Units of Measure

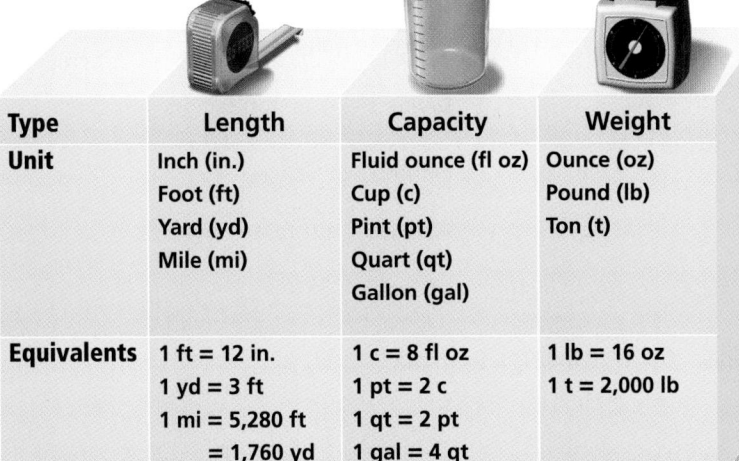

Type	Length	Capacity	Weight
Unit	Inch (in.) Foot (ft) Yard (yd) Mile (mi)	Fluid ounce (fl oz) Cup (c) Pint (pt) Quart (qt) Gallon (gal)	Ounce (oz) Pound (lb) Ton (t)
Equivalents	1 ft = 12 in. 1 yd = 3 ft 1 mi = 5,280 ft = 1,760 yd	1 c = 8 fl oz 1 pt = 2 c 1 qt = 2 pt 1 gal = 4 qt	1 lb = 16 oz 1 t = 2,000 lb

In order to measure an object, you should choose an appropriate unit of measure.

1 EXAMPLE — Choosing a Unit of Measure

Choose an appropriate unit of measure. Explain your choice.

a. weight of a truck — Measure its weight in tons because a truck is very heavy.

b. length of a hallway rug — Measure its length in feet or yards because the length is too great to measure in inches.

✓ Check Understanding — Example 1

1. Choose an appropriate unit of measure. Explain.
1a–d. Explanations may vary. See samples at the right.
- **a.** length of a swimming pool
- **b.** weight of a baby
- **c.** length of a pencil
- **d.** capacity of an eyedropper

1a. Feet or yards; inches are too small and miles are too large.
1b. Pounds; the weight is too great to measure in ounces.
1c. Inches; the length is too small to measure in feet.
1d. Fluid ounces; the capacity of a cup is too large.

 Interactive lesson includes instant self-check, tutorials, and activities.

What You'll Learn

 OBJECTIVE 1 To identify appropriate customary units

 OBJECTIVE 2 To convert customary units

. . . And Why

To solve real-world problems involving consumer issues

✓ Check Skills You'll Need

Find each product.

1. $4 \cdot \frac{1}{12}$ $\frac{1}{3}$ **2.** $3\frac{1}{4} \cdot \frac{16}{1}$ 52

3. $1\frac{1}{4} \cdot \frac{8}{1}$ 10   **4.** $4\frac{1}{2} \cdot \frac{1}{3}$ $1\frac{1}{2}$

 For help, go to Lesson 5-4.

New Vocabulary

- dimensional analysis

---

1. Plan

Lesson Preview

✓ **Check Skills You'll Need**

Multiplying Fractions
Lesson 5-4: Example 3;
Exercises 9–12.
Extra Practice, p. 748.

Lesson Resources

 Teaching Resources
Practice, Reteaching, Enrichment

 Reaching All Students
Practice Workbook 5-5
Spanish Practice Workbook 5-5
Guided Problem Solving 5-5
Hands-On Activities 6, 22, 23

 Presentation Assistant Plus!
Transparencies and PowerPoint™
- Check Skills You'll Need 5-5
- Additional Examples 5-5
- Student Edition Answers 5-5
- Classroom Aid 14
- Lesson Quiz 5-5
PH Presentation Pro CD-ROM 5-5

ASSESSMENT SYSTEM

Computer Test Generator CD-ROM

 Technology
Resource Pro® CD-ROM
Computer Test Generator CD-ROM
PH Presentation Pro CD-ROM

 www.PHSchool.com
Student Site
- Teacher Web Code: adk-5500
- Graphing Calculator, Procedure 2
- Self-grading Lesson Quiz
PH SuccessNet Teacher Center
- Lesson Planner
- Resources

Plus

Ongoing Assessment and Intervention

Before the Lesson
Diagnose prerequisite skills using:
- Check Skills You'll Need

During the Lesson
Monitor progress using:
- Check Understanding
- Additional Examples
- Test Prep

After the Lesson
Assess knowledge using:
- Lesson Quiz
- Computer Test Generator CD-ROM

2. Teach

Professional Development

Math Background

Note the difference between the metric system (Lesson 3-7) and the customary system. To convert units in the metric system, you multiply or divide by powers of 10. To convert units in the customary system, you multiply or divide by 3, 8, 12, 16, or some other number, depending upon the units.

Teaching Notes

Tactile Learners
As you discuss customary units, have students examine some tools used to measure length, capacity, and weight.

③ EXAMPLE English Learners
The abbreviation *lb* may be difficult for students to associate with *pound*. Ask if they are familiar with the symbol for the constellation Libra, a set of balance scales. The abbreviation *lb* comes from the Latin word *libra*, which means "a scale used to measure weight."

PowerPoint
Additional Examples

① Choose an appropriate unit of measure. Explain your choice.
a. weight of a hummingbird
   ounces
b. length of a soccer field
   yards

② Use dimensional analysis to convert 68 fluid ounces to cups. $8\frac{1}{2}$ c

③ Fred's fruit stand sells homemade lemonade in $6\frac{1}{2}$-pint bottles for $1.99. Jill's fruit stand sells homemade lemonade in $3\frac{1}{2}$-qt containers for the same price. At which stand do you get more lemonade for your money?
Jill's stand

Closure

Have students convert the measurements of different items around the classroom to various units of measure.

254

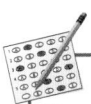

Test-Taking Tip
You can work faster during tests if you memorize common conversions.

You can use *conversion factors* to change from one unit of measure to another in a process called **dimensional analysis**. You use equivalent units to write a conversion factor. For example, $\frac{12 \text{ in.}}{1 \text{ ft}} = 1$, so you can use $\frac{12 \text{ in.}}{1 \text{ ft}}$ to convert from feet to inches.

② EXAMPLE Using Dimensional Analysis

Use dimensional analysis to convert 10 quarts to gallons.

$$10 \text{ qt} = \frac{10 \text{ qt}}{1} \cdot \frac{1 \text{ gal}}{4 \text{ qt}}$$
Use a conversion factor that changes quarts to gallons.

$$= \frac{^5 10 \text{ qt} \cdot 1 \text{ gal}}{_2 4 \text{ qt}}$$
Divide the common factors and units.

$$= \frac{5}{2} \text{ gal}$$
Simplify.

$$= 2\frac{1}{2} \text{ gal}$$
Write as a mixed number.

● There are $2\frac{1}{2}$ gal in 10 qt.

✓ Check Understanding Example 2
2. Complete each equation.
   a. 14 oz = ■ lb $\frac{7}{8}$ b. 14 in. = ■ ft $1\frac{1}{6}$ c. 14 pt = ■ qt 7

Converting units can help you make comparisons.

③ EXAMPLE Real-World ● Problem Solving

Consumer Issues At Store A, a $4\frac{1}{4}$-lb bag of cashew nuts costs $15.99. Store B charges the same price for a 76-oz bag of cashews. Which store gives you more for your money?

$$4\frac{1}{4} \text{ lb} = \frac{17}{4} \text{ lb} \cdot \frac{16 \text{ oz}}{1 \text{ lb}}$$
Use a conversion factor that changes pounds to ounces.

$$= \frac{17}{_1 4} \text{ lb} \cdot \frac{^4 16 \text{ oz}}{1 \text{ lb}}$$
Divide the common factors and units.

$$= 68 \text{ oz}$$
Multiply.

● Since 76 oz > 68 oz, Store B gives you more for your money.

✓ Check Understanding Example 3
3. Complete each equation.
   a. $3\frac{1}{2}$ lb = ■ oz 56   b. $3\frac{1}{2}$ yd = ■ ft $10\frac{1}{2}$ c. $3\frac{1}{2}$ pt = ■ c 7

👥 Reaching All Students

| **Below Level** Bring several items to class with different units of measure on their labels. Discuss the different units. For example, show a label with fluid ounces. Ask students why fluid ounces are used for that product. | **Advanced Learners** Have students research the origins of customary units of measure. For example, an inch originally represented the width of a thumb. | **English Learners** See note on page 254. **Auditory Learners** See note on page 256. |

For more exercises, see *Extra Practice*.

Practice and Problem Solving

 Practice by Example

Example 1
(page 253)

Choose an appropriate unit of measure. Explain your choice.
1–4. See below left.
1. weight of a paper clip
2. volume of a baby bottle
3. distance to Australia
4. length of a sports field

Example 2
(page 254)

Use dimensional analysis to complete each equation.

5. 3 qt = ▨ gal $\frac{3}{4}$
6. 3 gal = ▨ qt   12
7. 1,000 lb = ▨ t $\frac{1}{2}$
8. 1,000 oz = ▨ lb $62\frac{1}{2}$
9. 18 in. = ▨ ft $1\frac{1}{2}$
10. 18 ft = ▨ in.   216

Explanations may vary.
Samples are given.
1. Ounces; it is closest to the weight of a paper clip.
2. Fluid ounces; baby bottles are usually marked in fluid ounces.
3. Miles; distances to continents would be measured in miles.
4. Yards or feet; miles are too large and inches are too small.

Number Sense **Match each measurement from the first group with an equivalent amount from the second group.**

11. 15 mi   G
12. 15 t   A
13. 15 in.   C
14. 15 fl oz   F
15. 15 c   D
16. 15 lb   B
17. 15 pt   E

A. 30,000 lb
B. $\frac{3}{400}$ t
C. $1\frac{1}{4}$ ft
D. $7\frac{1}{2}$ pt
E. $7\frac{1}{2}$ qt
F. $1\frac{7}{8}$ c
G. 79,200 ft

Example 3
(page 254)

Complete each equation.

18. $\frac{1}{2}$ yd = ▨ ft $1\frac{1}{2}$
19. $\frac{1}{2}$ mi = ▨ ft   2,640
20. $10\frac{1}{2}$ lb = ▨ oz   168
21. $6\frac{1}{2}$ ft = ▨ in.   78
22. $7\frac{1}{2}$ c = ▨ fl oz   60
23. $6\frac{1}{4}$ gal = ▨ qt   25
24. $\frac{3}{4}$ lb = ▨ oz   12
25. $3\frac{1}{2}$ qt = ▨ pt   7
26. $1\frac{1}{3}$ yd = ▨ in.   48
27. $\frac{1}{5}$ t = ▨ lb   400
28. 7 pt = ▨ c   14
29. $5\frac{1}{2}$ mi = ▨ ft   29,040

 **30. Track and Field** Julia clears $9\frac{1}{2}$ ft in the pole vault. Maya clears 112 in. Which vaulter clears the greater height?   Julia

 Apply Your Skills

Estimation **Match each indicated measurement with a possible value.**

31. height of a 7-year-old   C
32. weight of a bag of apples   B
33. width of your palm   F
34. amount of water in a vase   D
35. weight of a peach   E
36. amount of juice in a child's cup   A

A. 4 fl oz
B. 4 lb
C. 4 ft
D. 4 c
E. 4 oz
F. 4 in.

Assignment Guide

1 Objective 1
Ⓐ Ⓑ **Core** 1–4, 31–36, 38–47, 50–55

2 Objective 2
Ⓐ Ⓑ **Core** 5–30, 37, 48, 49, 56–69
Ⓒ **Extension** 70–75

Test Prep 76–84
Mixed Review 85–92

Practice 5-5 *Using Customary Units of Measurement*

Use estimation, mental math, or paper and pencil to convert from one unit to the other.

1. 2 gal 2 qt = __10__ qt
2. 3 yd = __9__ ft
3. 1 ft 8 in. = __20__ in.
4. $\frac{3}{5}$ t = __1200__ lb
5. 30 in. = __$2\frac{1}{2}$__ ft
6. 20 fl oz = __$2\frac{1}{2}$__ c
7. 20 oz = __$1\frac{1}{4}$__ lb
8. $2\frac{1}{2}$ pt = __5__ c
9. $1\frac{1}{8}$ lb = __18__ oz
10. 7920 ft = __$1\frac{1}{2}$__ mi

Is each measurement reasonable? If not, give a reasonable measurement.

11. A glass of milk holds about 8 pt.
    A glass of milk holds about 8 fl oz.
12. A newborn baby weighs about $7\frac{1}{2}$ oz.
    A newborn weighs about $7\frac{1}{2}$ lb.
13. A phonebook is $\frac{3}{4}$ ft wide.
    Reasonable

Choose an appropriate unit of measure. Explain your choice.

14. weight of a whale
    ton; A whale is very heavy.
15. sugar in a cookie recipe
    cup; Cookies have about a cup of sugar.
16. length of a mouse
    inch; A mouse is small.

Should each item be measured by *length, weight,* or *capacity*?

17. amount of soup in a can   18. height of a can
    capacity   length
19. heaviness of a can   20. diameter of a can
    weight   length

Enrichment 5-5 *American Trees*

American Forests maintains a national Register of Big Trees. The organization lists the "National Champion" tree of each species, which is the largest known tree of that kind by total mass. The table lists ten National Champion trees that American Forests has selected as noteworthy.

1. Complete the table.

Tree Type	Girth 4.5 ft from ground		Height		Location
	Inches	Feet	Feet	Yards	
American Beech	279	$23\frac{1}{4}$	115	$38\frac{1}{3}$	Harwood, MD
Black Willow	400	$33\frac{1}{3}$	76	$25\frac{1}{3}$	Grand Traverse County, MI
Coast Douglas-Fir	438	$36\frac{1}{2}$	329	$109\frac{2}{3}$	Coos County, OR
Coast Redwood	867	$72\frac{1}{4}$	313	$104\frac{1}{3}$	Prairie Creek, CA
Giant Sequoia	998	$83\frac{1}{6}$	275	$91\frac{2}{3}$	Sequoia National Park, CA
Loblolly Pine	188	$15\frac{2}{3}$	148	$49\frac{1}{3}$	Warren, AZ
Pinyon Pine	213	$17\frac{3}{4}$	69	23	Cuba, NM
Sugar Maple	233	$19\frac{5}{12}$	87	29	Kingston, NM
Sugar Pine	442	$36\frac{5}{6}$	232	$77\frac{1}{3}$	Dorrington, CA
White Oak	374	$31\frac{1}{6}$	79	$26\frac{1}{3}$	Wye Mills State Park, MD

National Champion Trees

2. Which units were most appropriate for measuring the girth and the height of these giant trees? Explain.
   Sample answer: The larger units are more appropriate, but the people at American Forests probably wanted to avoid fractions.

Auditory Learners
Exercises 35, 36 Remind students that ounces and fluid ounces are not the same. The *fluid* in fluid ounces is a reminder that the fluid ounce is a unit of liquid capacity. The ounce is a unit of weight.

37. Hiking You are hiking a 2-mi-long trail. You pass by a sign showing that you have hiked 1,000 ft. How many feet are left? **9,560 ft**

Is each item likely to be measured by *length, weight,* or *volume*?

38. a hair ribbon **length**

39. a package of meat **weight**

40. a bottle of juice **volume**

41. a bag of oranges **weight**

42. a zipper **length**

43. the contents of an eyedropper **volume**

Choose an appropriate unit of measure. Explain your choice.
44–47. See below left.

44. volume of a cooking pot

45. weight of a medium-sized fish

46. weight of a sheet of paper

47. volume of a swimming pool

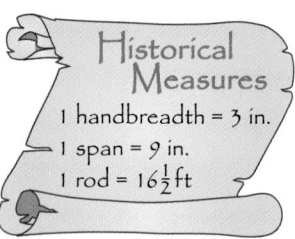

Historical Measures

1 handbreadth = 3 in.
1 span = 9 in.
1 rod = $16\frac{1}{2}$ ft

44–47. Explanations may vary. Samples are given.
44. Quarts; ounces are too small and gallons are too large.
45. Pounds or ounces; tons are too large.
46. Ounces; a piece of paper is very light.
47. Gallons; quarts or ounces are too small.
48b. Answers may vary. Sample: Suppose the length of a room is 16 ft. This is 64 handbreadths, $21\frac{1}{3}$ spans, and $0.\overline{96}$ rod.
48c. Answers may vary. Sample: Spans; handbreadths are too small and rods are too large.

48. History People once measured lengths in *handbreadths, spans,* and *rods.*
   a. How many are there: handbreadths in 1 span? handbreadths in 1 rod? spans in 1 rod? **3 handbreadths; 66 handbreadths; 22 spans**
   b. Open-Ended Measure the length of an object. Give the length in *handbreadths, spans,* and *rods.* **48b–c. See below left.**
   c. Writing in Math Consider the measurements you made in part (b). Which unit of measure is the most appropriate for the item you chose? Explain.

49. a. Geography The Mississippi River is about 19,747,200 ft long. What is a better unit of measure? Find the length of the Mississippi using the better unit of measure. **mile; about 3,740 mi**
   b. Choose an historical measure from Exercise 48. Find the length of the Mississippi in that unit. **rod; about 1,196,800 rods**

Estimation Is each measurement reasonable? If not, give a reasonable measurement.

50. A textbook weighs 2 oz. **no; 2 lb**

51. The street is 25 ft wide. **yes**

52. You drink about 10 gal of liquid per day. **no; 10 c**

53. A sewing needle is about 2 ft long. **no; 2 in.**

54. A car is 12 yd long. **no; 12 ft**

55. A shoe weighs 1 t. **no; 1 lb**

56. Reasoning A student converted 8 cups to pints. His answer was 16 pints. Use dimensional analysis to determine whether the student's answer is reasonable. **$8 \text{ c} \cdot \frac{1 \text{ pt}}{2 \text{ c}} = 4 \text{ pt}$; the student's answer is not reasonable.**

Use estimation, mental math, or paper and pencil to complete each statement.

57. 28 in. = ■ ft **$2\frac{1}{3}$** **58.** 5 c = ■ pt **$2\frac{1}{2}$** **59.** 5 t = ■ lb **10,000**

60. 2,640 ft = ■ mi **$\frac{1}{2}$** **61.** 3,000 lb = ■ t **$1\frac{1}{2}$** **62.** 13 pt = ■ qt **$6\frac{1}{2}$**

63. 70 fl oz = ■ c **$8\frac{3}{4}$** **64.** 1 ft 9 in. = ■ in. **21** **65.** 18 qt = ■ gal **$4\frac{1}{2}$**

66. 3 gal = ■ qt **12** **67.** 50 oz = ■ lb **$3\frac{1}{8}$** **68.** 20 c = ■ qt **5**

Use the Guided Problem Solving worksheet with Exercise 37.

69. Error Analysis Suzanne claims a quarter-pound hamburger is heavier than a 6-oz hamburger. Explain why she is incorrect.
A quarter pound is $\frac{1}{4}$ of 16 oz, or 4 oz, and 4 oz < 6 oz.

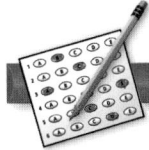

C **Challenge** **Complete each equation.**

70. $2\frac{1}{4}$ yd = $6\frac{3}{4}$ ▨ ft   **71.** 6 qt = $1\frac{1}{2}$ ▨ gal   **72.** 100 lb = $\frac{1}{20}$ ▨ t

73. 6 c = 48 ▨ fl oz   **74.** $1\frac{1}{2}$ pt = ▨ qt $\frac{3}{4}$ **75.** $4\frac{1}{4}$ ft = ▨ in. 51

Test Prep

Gridded Response   Complete each equation.

Take It to the NET
Online lesson quiz at
www.PHSchool.com
Web Code: ada-0505

76. 9 lb 2 oz = ▨ oz   **77.** 4 ft = ▨ in. 48   **78.** 3 yd 2 ft = ▨ ft 11
146
79. 12 pt = ▨ c 24   **80.** 8 oz = ▨ lb 1/2   **81.** 7 ft = ▨ yd 7/3
82. $4\frac{1}{2}$ c = ▨ pt 9/4   **83.** $1\frac{1}{2}$ gal = ▨ qt 6   **84.** $2\frac{1}{2}$ yd = ▨ in. 90

Mixed Review

Lesson 5-4   **Multiply or divide.**

85. $\frac{9}{11} \div 2\frac{7}{11}$ $\frac{9}{29}$ **86.** $1\frac{5}{7} \cdot 1\frac{1}{2}$ $2\frac{4}{7}$ **87.** $\frac{9}{10} \div \frac{3}{4}$ $1\frac{1}{5}$ **88.** $2\frac{2}{5} \cdot 3\frac{2}{3}$ $8\frac{4}{5}$

Lesson 2-3   **Simplify each expression.**

89. $3x + (-2x) + 3y$ **90.** $10 - 3t - 4t$ **91.** $2y - 5y$ $-3y$
$x + 3y$ $10 - 7t$

Lesson 1-7 🌐 **92. Softball** In a single-elimination softball tournament, each team plays until it loses. Eight teams are playing in a single-elimination tournament. How many games must be played? **7 games**

Math at Work

─────────────────────────── **Technical Artist**

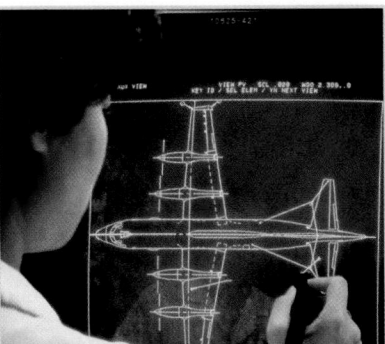

Technical artists prepare the drawings used by manufacturing and construction workers. The drawings give visual guidelines and technical details of products, buildings, and structures. Technical artists specify dimensions and materials to be used in the building process, and state procedures and processes to be followed. Many technical artists use computer-aided design (CAD) systems to prepare plans. Since they draw technical plans to scale, fractions and operations with fractions are an important part of their work.

 **Take It to the NET** For more information about technical artists, go to **www.PHSchool.com**.
Web Code: adb-2031

5-5 Using Customary Units of Measurement   **257**

Alternative Assessment

Have students work in groups of three or four to make posters that describe customary measurements and conversions. Posters might include a table of measurements similar to the one that starts this

lesson. Photos or drawings of items with their measurements given in two different units would be useful. Magazines and newspapers are good sources for such images.

4. Assess

 **Lesson Quiz 5-5**

Choose an appropriate unit of measure. Explain your choice.

1. weight of a dog **Pounds;** dogs are too heavy to measure in ounces and too light to measure in tons.

2. length of a football field **Yards;** it is too long to measure in feet or inches and too short to measure in miles.

3. Use dimensional analysis to convert $1\frac{1}{2}$ mi to ft. **7,920 ft**

Error Prevention!

Exercises 76, 78 Some students may rewrite 9 lb 2 oz as 92 oz or 9.2 oz. All they need to do is change pounds to ounces, and then add the original 2 ounces. The same potential error, and resolution, applies to other "mixed" measurements, such as 3 yd 2 ft.

Test Prep

📁 **Resources**
For additional practice with a variety of test item formats:
• Test Prep, p. 283
• Test-Taking Strategies, p. 278
• Test-Taking Strategies With Transparencies

───────────────────────────

Reteaching 5-5 *Using Customary Units*

Use dimensional analysis to convert 36 ounces to pounds.

36 oz = $\frac{36 \text{ oz}}{1} \cdot \frac{1 \text{ lb}}{16 \text{ oz}}$ Multiply by a fraction that is equal to one and compares pounds to ounces.

= $\frac{36 \text{ oz}}{1} \cdot \frac{1 \text{ lb}}{16 \text{ oz}}$ Divide the common factors and units.

= $\frac{9}{4}$ lb = $2\frac{1}{4}$ lb   Simplify.

There are $2\frac{1}{4}$ lb in 36 oz.

Convert from one unit to the other.

1. 12 fl oz = $1\frac{1}{2}$ c   **2.** 42 in = $3\frac{1}{2}$ ft

3. 6,600 ft = $1\frac{1}{4}$ mi   **4.** 5,000 lb = $2\frac{1}{2}$ t

5. $3\frac{1}{8}$ c = 25 fl oz   **6.** $2\frac{3}{8}$ lb = 38 oz

7. 2 gal 2 qt = 10 qt   **8.** 1 yd 2 ft = 5 ft

9. 2 ton 800 lb = 4,800 lb **10.** 15 qt = $3\frac{3}{4}$ gal

11. 23 pt = $2\frac{7}{8}$ gal   **12.** 81 in. = $2\frac{1}{4}$ yd

257

Greatest Possible Error

This Extension shows students how to find the greatest possible error for a measurement. The greatest possible error in a measurement is one half of the unit used for measuring. Point out that a "unit used for measuring" could be a "$\frac{1}{2}$ ft" or "$\frac{1}{8}$ in."

Teaching Notes

A measurement value is an approximation of the exact measure. The accuracy of a measurement increases when you use more precise measuring instruments, but you cannot correctly claim that any measurement you make is exact.

Tactile Learners

To demonstrate that measurements are approximate, cut a length of paper that is between $17\frac{1}{2}$ and $18\frac{1}{2}$ in. Have five students measure the length of your piece of paper with different instruments (various 12-inch rulers and yardsticks, for example). Do not tell them how precise to be.

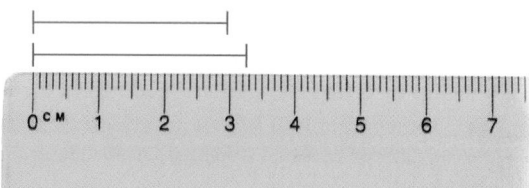

Extension — Greatest Possible Error

For Use With Lesson 5-5

Measurement is not exact. To the nearest centimeter, each segment at the right measures 3 cm.

When a measurement is rounded to the nearest centimeter, it can vary from the actual length by as much as one half centimeter. The *greatest possible error* of a measurement is half the unit used for measuring.

EXAMPLE

Find the greatest possible error for each measurement.

a. $1\frac{1}{2}$ in.   The measurement is to the nearest $\frac{1}{2}$ in.

Since $\frac{1}{2} \cdot \frac{1}{2} = \frac{1}{4}$, the greatest possible error is $\frac{1}{4}$ in.

b. 15.6 L   The measurement is to the nearest tenth of a liter.

Since $\frac{1}{2} \cdot 0.1 = 0.05$, the greatest possible error is 0.05 L.

c. 3.004 mm   The measurement is to the nearest 0.001 mm.

Since $\frac{1}{2} \cdot 0.001 = 0.0005$, the greatest possible error is 0.0005 mm.

EXERCISES

Find the greatest possible error for each measurement.

1. 45.98 mg 0.005 mg   **2.** $12\frac{1}{4}$ in. $\frac{1}{8}$ in.   **3.** 54.4 cm 0.05 cm   **4.** $1\frac{3}{4}$ c $\frac{1}{8}$ c

5. 3 ft $\frac{1}{2}$ ft   **6.** 9 g $\frac{1}{2}$ g   **7.** 12.3 L 0.05 L   **8.** 15.575 mm 0.0005 mm

9. $24\frac{1}{2}$ yd $\frac{1}{4}$ yd   **10.** 512 m 0.5 m   **11.** $10\frac{1}{8}$ oz $\frac{1}{16}$ oz   **12.** $3\frac{1}{16}$ in. $\frac{1}{32}$ in.

13. Geometry A rectangle measures 12 cm by 10.5 cm. What is the greatest possible error for each measurement? 0.5 cm, 0.05 cm

14. Carpentry A carpenter is cutting a table leg that is $2\frac{1}{4}$ ft long.

   a. What is the greatest possible error? $\frac{1}{8}$ ft

   b. Writing in Math Is the greatest possible error acceptable in this situation? Explain. See right.

14b. No; if one or more legs were off by $\frac{1}{8}$ ft (1.5 in.), the table would not be level, so the greatest possible error is not acceptable in this case.

Work Backward

OBJECTIVE

1 Work Backward

Math Strategies in Action The Longleat hedge maze in England was designed in 1975. The hedges are so high you can't see over them unless you stand on one of the wooden staircases placed throughout the maze. Once you find the center of the maze in its 1.7 miles of pathways, you have to remember the path you followed and work backward to get out.

Visitors to the Longleat hedge maze often take 90 min to reach the center.

Working backward from known information will sometimes help you solve a problem.

1 EXAMPLE   Real-World Problem Solving

Time You are planning to go to a baseball game that starts at 1:00 P.M. You want to arrive half an hour early. Your walk to the train station is about 10 minutes long. The train ride to the city takes $\frac{3}{4}$ of an hour. After you arrive in the city, you will need to walk for about 10 more minutes to get to the stadium. What time should you plan to leave?

Read and Understand

Think about the information you are given.

1. What do you want to find? the time you should leave home

2. What is your arrival time? 12:30 P.M.

3. How much time will you spend walking to the train? 10 min

4. How much time will you spend on the train? $\frac{3}{4}$ h

5. How much time will you spend walking from the train? 10 min

---

Lesson Preview

✔ **Check Skills You'll Need**

Fractions and Decimals
Lesson 5-2: Example 3;
Exercises 10–15.
Extra Practice, p. 748.

Lesson Resources

📁 **Teaching Resources**
Practice, Reteaching, Enrichment

👥 **Reaching All Students**
Practice Workbook 5-6
Spanish Practice Workbook 5-6
Guided Problem Solving 5-6

⏰ **Presentation Assistant Plus!**
Transparencies and PowerPoint™
• Check Skills You'll Need 5-6
• Additional Examples 5-6
• Student Edition Answers 5-6
• Lesson Quiz 5-6
PH Presentation Pro CD-ROM 5-6

ASSESSMENT SYSTEM
Computer Test Generator CD-ROM

💻 **Technology**
Resource Pro® CD-ROM
Computer Test Generator CD-ROM
PH Presentation Pro CD-ROM

💻 **www.PHSchool.com**
Student Site
• Teacher Web Code: adk-5500
• Self-grading Lesson Quiz
PH SuccessNet Teacher Center
• Lesson Planner
• Resources

Plus

What You'll Learn

OBJECTIVE 1 To solve problems by working backward

...And Why

To solve real-world problems involving time

✔ **Check Skills You'll Need**

Order the fractions from least to greatest.

1. $\frac{1}{2}, \frac{1}{3}, \frac{1}{4}, \frac{1}{5}, \frac{1}{10}$

2. $\frac{7}{3}, \frac{5}{3}, \frac{13}{3}, \frac{3}{3}$

3. $\frac{3}{7}, \frac{3}{5}, \frac{3}{13}, \frac{3}{3}$

4. $-\frac{3}{7}, -\frac{3}{5}, -\frac{3}{13}, -\frac{3}{3}$

1–4. See below.

❓ For help, go to Lesson 5-2.

1. $\frac{1}{10}, \frac{1}{5}, \frac{1}{4}, \frac{1}{3}, \frac{1}{2}$

2. $\frac{3}{3}, \frac{5}{3}, \frac{7}{3}, \frac{13}{3}$

3. $\frac{3}{13}, \frac{3}{7}, \frac{3}{5}, \frac{3}{3}$

4. $-\frac{3}{3}, -\frac{3}{5}, -\frac{3}{7}, -\frac{3}{13}$

 TEXT Interactive lesson includes instant self-check, tutorials, and activities.

ⓥ Ongoing Assessment and Intervention

Before the Lesson	**During the Lesson**	**After the Lesson**
Diagnose prerequisite skills using:	Monitor progress using:	Assess knowledge using:
• Check Skills You'll Need	• Check Understanding	• Lesson Quiz
	• Additional Examples	• Computer Test Generator
	• Test Prep	CD-ROM

Math Background

In some problem-solving situations, it may be helpful to work backward. These situations often involve a time of day or a known end result of a process. To solve these problems, begin with the final result and work backward to the beginning.

Teaching Notes

1 EXAMPLE **Error Prevention**

Students may choose the incorrect operation or rush into calculations before they visualize the problem. For example, you add sections of travel time to find how long a trip will take, but you subtract that travel time from the arrival time to find the desired departure time. Encourage students to determine which operations to use *before* they begin calculations. When finished, they should make sure their answers are reasonable.

PowerPoint
Additional Example

1 Your flight leaves the airport at 10:00 A.M. You must arrive 2 hours early to check your luggage. The drive to the airport takes about 90 minutes. A stop for breakfast takes about 30 minutes. It will take about 15 minutes to park and get to the terminal. At what time should you leave home?
5:45 A.M.

Closure

Have students give examples of how they use the work backward problem-solving strategy in their lives. Deciding what time to wake up in the morning is a common example. The time they choose to wake up depends on when school starts, how long it takes to travel to school, and how long it takes to get ready.

260

Plan and Solve

You know that the series of events must end at 1:00 P.M. Work backward to find when the events must begin.

Move the hands of a clock to find your departure time.

6. Write the starting time for each event. See below each clock.

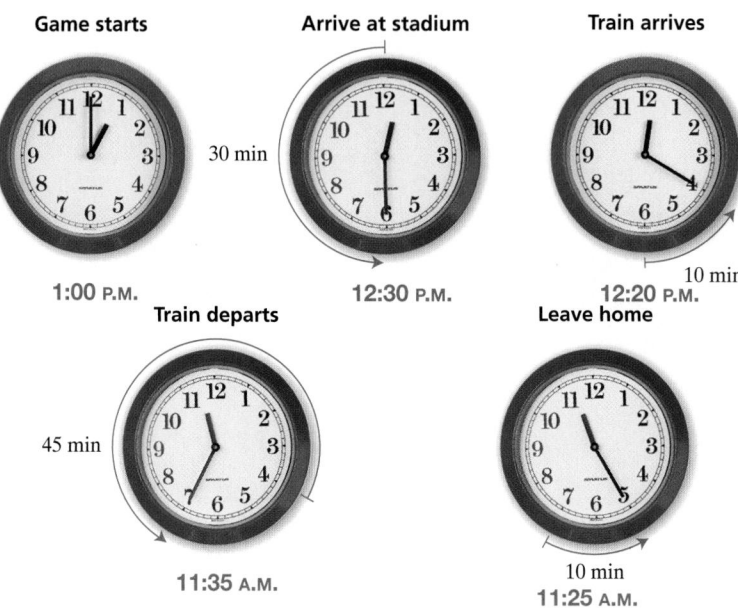

Game starts
1:00 P.M.

30 min

Arrive at stadium
12:30 P.M.

Train arrives
10 min
12:20 P.M.

Train departs
45 min
11:35 A.M.

Leave home
10 min
11:25 A.M.

You should leave home at 11:25 A.M.

Look Back and Check

Check the departure time. Find the total time needed.

$$10 \text{ min} + 45 \text{ min} + 10 \text{ min} + 30 \text{ min} = 95 \text{ min}$$

Add 95 minutes to your departure time.

$$\begin{array}{r} 11\text{:}\ 25 \\ +\ 0\text{:}\ 95 \\ \hline 11\text{:}120 \end{array} \quad \textbf{120 min = 2 h}$$

11:120 = 2 hours after 11:00, or 1:00 P.M.

Since the game starts at 1 P.M., your departure time is correct.

✓ Check Understanding

7. Suppose you must be home by 6:00 P.M. If the return trip takes the same amount of time, how long can the game run in order for you to be at home on time? 3 h 55 min

260 Chapter 5 Operations With Fractions

 ## Reaching All Students

Below Level Some students may not understand what is meant by the phrase *work backward*. Have students briefly describe the last five things they've done, starting with the most recent thing first.	**Advanced Learners** Ask: *I'm thinking of a number. When you divide my number by 2, add 5, multiply by 3, and then subtract 14, you get 169. What is my number?* 112	**Error Prevention** See note on page 260. **Auditory Learners** See note on page 262.

EXERCISES

For more exercises, see *Extra Practice*.

Practice and Problem Solving

A Practice by Example

Work backward to solve each problem.

Example 1
(page 259)

1. Lawn Care Eduardo wants to finish mowing lawns at 3:00 P.M. on Saturday. It takes $1\frac{1}{2}$ h to mow the first lawn and twice as long to mow the lawn next door. The lawn across the street takes $1\frac{1}{2}$ h to mow. Eduardo plans to take a $\frac{1}{2}$-h break between the second and third lawns. What time should he plan to start mowing? **8:30 A.M.**

2. Travel Siobhan's family is planning a trip to the Grand Canyon. It will take 5 h of driving along with three $\frac{1}{2}$-h stops. They want to arrive at 3:30 P.M. What time should they plan to leave? **9:00 A.M.**

3. Transportation Korin is going to a movie. The movie begins at 1:00 P.M. She has a 15-minute walk to the bus from her home and a 5-minute walk from the bus to the movie. The bus ride takes 38 min. What is the latest bus she can take to make the movie? **the 12:15 P.M. bus**

BUS DEPARTURE TIMES

10:10 A.M.	12:05 P.M.
10:30 A.M.	12:15 P.M.
11:00 A.M.	12:25 P.M.
11:35 A.M.	12:40 P.M.

Strategies

- Account for All Possibilities
- Draw a Diagram
- Look for a Pattern
- Make a Model
- Make a Table
- Simplify the Problem
- Simulate the Problem
- Solve by Graphing
- Try, Test, Revise
- Use Multiple Strategies
- Work Backward
- Write an Equation
- Write a Proportion

Solve using any strategy.

4. Pump A can fill 5 identical tanks in 60 min.
Pump B can fill 3 tanks that same size in 60 min.
 a. How long does it take pump A to fill one tank? **12 min**
 b. How long does it take pump B to fill one tank? **20 min**
 c. How long does it take pumps A and B together to fill one tank? **$7\frac{1}{2}$ min**

B Apply Your Skills

5. You have two nickels, three dimes, and a quarter. Using at least one of each coin, how many different amounts of money can you make? Explain. **6 different amounts; $.40, $.45, $.50, $.55, $.60, $.65**

6. Geometry Zach's rectangular garden measures 12 ft by 10 ft. He puts a stake in each corner and one every 2 ft along each side. How many stakes are there in all? **22 stakes**

Reading Math

For help with reading and describing the pattern in Exercise 8, see page 263.

7. You spent half of your money at the amusement park and had $15 left. How much money did you have originally? **$30**

8. Describe the pattern of the numbers below. Then find the next three numbers in the pattern. **Start with $\frac{2}{3}$ and add $\frac{3}{4}$ repeatedly;** $3\frac{2}{3}, 4\frac{5}{12}, 5\frac{1}{6}$
$\frac{2}{3}, 1\frac{5}{12}, 2\frac{1}{6}, 2\frac{11}{12}, \blacksquare, \blacksquare, \blacksquare, \ldots$

 Use the Guided Problem Solving worksheet with Exercise 7.

Assignment Guide

1 Objective 1
  A B Core 1–8
  C Extension 9, 10

Test Prep 11–14
Mixed Review 15–27

Practice 5-6 *Work Backward*

Work backward to solve each problem.

1. Manuel's term paper is due on March 31. He began doing research on March 1. He intends to continue doing research for 3 times as long as he has done already. Then he will spend a week writing the paper and the remaining 3 days typing. What day is it? (Assume he will finish typing on March 30.)
March 5

2. A disc jockey must allow time for 24 minutes of commercials every hour, along with 4 minutes for news, 3 minutes for weather, and 2 minutes for public-service announcements. If each record lasts an average of 3 minutes, how many records per hour can the DJ play?
9 records per hour

3. Margaret is reading the 713-page novel *War and Peace*. When she has read twice as many pages as she has read already, she will be 119 pages from the end. What page is she on now?
page 198

4. On Monday the low temperature at the South Pole dropped 9°F from Sunday's low. On Tuesday it fell another 7°, then rose 13° on Wednesday and 17° more on Thursday. Friday it dropped 8° to −50°F. What was Sunday's low temperature?
−56°F

5. Each problem lists the operations performed on n to produce the given result. Find n.
 a. Multiply by 3, add 4, divide by 5, subtract 6; result, −1.
  $n = \underline{7}$
 b. Add 2, divide by 3, subtract 4, multiply by 5; result, 35.
  $n = \underline{31}$
 c. Multiply by 2, add 7, divide by 17; result, 1.
  $n = \underline{5}$
 d. Divide by 3, add 9, multiply by 2, subtract 12; result, 4.
  $n = \underline{-3}$
 e. Subtract 2, divide by 5, add 7, multiply by 3; result, 30.
  $n = \underline{17}$

Enrichment 5-6 *The Nomograph*

Addition and subtraction problems can be checked by working backwards.

7	11	15 6
+4	−4	−9 +9
11	7	6 15

You can use a nomograph to add and subtract fractions and to check solutions to addition and subtraction problems.

Example Add $\frac{5}{16} + \frac{3}{4}$.

Solution Place one end of a straight edge at $\frac{5}{16}$ on scale ①. Place the other end at $\frac{3}{4}$ on scale ③. Read the sum where the straightedge crosses scale ②: $1\frac{1}{16}$
$\frac{5}{16} + \frac{3}{4} = 1\frac{1}{16}$

Add or subtract using the nomograph.

1. $\frac{15}{16} + \frac{1}{2}$ $1\frac{7}{16}$ 2. $\frac{3}{4} + \frac{7}{8}$ $1\frac{5}{8}$
3. $\frac{13}{16} - \frac{5}{8}$ $\frac{3}{16}$ 4. $1\frac{1}{16} - \frac{3}{4}$ $\frac{7}{16}$
5. $\frac{5}{8} - \frac{7}{16}$ $\frac{3}{16}$ 6. $\frac{1}{2} + \frac{7}{8}$ $1\frac{3}{8}$

7. Between what two numbers on scale ② can you find each fraction?
 a. $1\frac{7}{32}$ $\frac{5}{16}$ and $\frac{3}{8}$
 b. $1\frac{11}{16}$ $1\frac{1}{2}$ and $1\frac{9}{16}$
 c. $1\frac{31}{32}$ $1\frac{15}{16}$ and 2
 d. $\frac{27}{32}$ $\frac{13}{16}$ and $\frac{7}{8}$

Add or subtract using the nomograph.

8. $\frac{3}{4} + \frac{11}{32}$ $1\frac{3}{32}$ 9. $\frac{15}{16} - \frac{5}{32}$ $\frac{5}{32}$
10. $\frac{1}{4} + \frac{7}{32}$ $\frac{15}{32}$ 11. $\frac{21}{32} - \frac{1}{2}$ $\frac{9}{32}$
12. $\frac{11}{16} + \frac{19}{32}$ $\frac{5}{32}$ 13. $\frac{5}{32} - \frac{1}{8}$ $\frac{1}{32}$

PowerPoint Lesson Quiz 5-6

Solve by working backward.

1. Jason has a total of 212 sheep. Last spring, 52 lambs were born, but 9 died. How many sheep did he have before the lambs were born? **169 sheep**

2. The bus picks up Tom every morning at 7:20 A.M. Tom walks his dog every morning before school for 36 minutes. It takes him 25 minutes to get ready for school and 7 minutes to walk to the bus stop. At what time does Tom need to wake up in order to get to the bus stop on time? **6:12 A.M.**

Auditory Learners

Exercises 1–10 Remind students to use the same problem solving steps—Read and Understand, Plan and Solve, Look Back and Check—that they used to solve the Example. Have students state the name of each step aloud as they solve the problems.

Reteaching 5-6 **Work Backward**

Jody, Karl, and Kara want to buy a pizza. Jody said she can pay half the cost. Karl said he can pay $\frac{1}{3}$ of what was left after Jody paid half. Kara said she could pay the remaining $4. How much does the pizza cost?

Work backward.

Kara will pay $4. This is $\frac{2}{3}$ of what is left after Jody pays half, since Karl pays $\frac{1}{3}$ and $1 - \frac{1}{3} = \frac{2}{3}$. Let h equal half the cost of the pizza.

$\frac{2}{3}h = 4$

Use the Try, Test, Revise strategy to find $h = 6$.

Thus, Jody pays $6 and Karl pays $\frac{1}{3} \cdot 6 = 2.

The pizza costs $6 + 2 + 4 = $12.

1. Steven, Lisa, and Mark want to buy a pizza. Steven said he could pay twice as much as Lisa. Mark said he could pay the remaining $3, which is $1 less than Lisa's share. How much does the pizza cost?

a. How much is Mark paying? ___$3___
b. How much is Lisa paying? ___$4___
c. How much is Steven paying? ___$8___
d. How much does the pizza cost? ___$15___

2. On Wednesday, Olga's parents said she owed them too much money to borrow any more. On Thursday, she paid her parents $15 she had earned babysitting. On Friday, she borrowed $5 to go to a movie. On Saturday, she paid them the $12 she earned babysitting. Then her debt was down to $22. How much did she owe on Wednesday? ___$44___

3. Yuki, Mollie, Brandon, and Anna share an apple pie for dessert. Brandon eats half the amount Mollie eats. Yuki eats four times as much pie as Brandon. Mollie eats $\frac{1}{4}$ of the pie. How much does Anna eat? ___$\frac{1}{8}$ of the pie___

Reteaching

 **Challenge**

9. Answers may vary.

Sample: $\frac{1}{2} + \frac{1}{3} = \frac{5}{6}, \frac{1}{3} + \frac{1}{6} = \frac{1}{2},$
$\frac{3}{1} + \frac{2}{1} = \frac{5}{1}, \frac{1}{2} + \frac{3}{6} = \frac{1}{1}$

9. Number Sense Use the equation at the right. Choose from the numbers 1, 2, 3, 5, and 6, and make four different true equations. **See left.**

$\frac{\blacksquare}{\blacksquare} + \frac{\blacksquare}{\blacksquare} = \frac{\blacksquare}{\blacksquare}$

10. Several freshmen tried out for the school track team.

After Round 1, $\frac{1}{2}$ of the freshmen were eliminated.

After Round 2, $\frac{1}{3}$ of those remaining were eliminated.

After Round 3, $\frac{1}{4}$ of those remaining were eliminated.

After Round 4, $\frac{1}{5}$ of those remaining were eliminated.

After Round 5, $\frac{1}{6}$ of those remaining were eliminated.

The 10 freshmen who remained made it onto the track team. How many freshmen originally tried out? **60 freshmen**

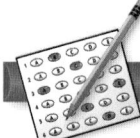

Test Prep

Multiple Choice

11. You spent $\frac{1}{2}$ of your money at the theater and $\frac{1}{4}$ at an arcade. You have $17.50 left. How much money did you have originally? **A**
A. $70 **B.** $35 **C.** $17.50 **D.** $13.12

Take It to the NET
Online lesson quiz at
www.PHSchool.com
Web Code: ada-0506

12. Angela is twice as old as Brent. Brent is $2\frac{1}{2}$ times as old as Casey. Casey is 5 years old. How old is Angela? **H**
F. 5 years **G.** 10 years **H.** 25 years **I.** 50 years

13. What is the next number in this pattern?
$\frac{3}{4}, 1\frac{1}{2}, 2\frac{1}{4}, 3, \ldots$ **C**
A. $3\frac{1}{4}$ **B.** $3\frac{1}{2}$ **C.** $3\frac{3}{4}$ **D.** 4

Short Response

14. The odometer on Melissa's bike reads 813 miles. When she let Joan borrow the bike last week, it read 799 miles. Joan rode the bike 1 mile to school every day and then back home. **(a)** Did Joan ride the bike anywhere else? **(b)** Explain your answer.
[2] Yes; Joan rode 10 miles to school and back in one week, and the odometer shows that she rode a total of 14 miles.
[1] answer only with missing or incorrect explanation

Mixed Review

Lessons 5-4 and 1-9

Simplify each expression.

15. $\frac{1}{3} \div \frac{5}{6}$ **$\frac{2}{5}$**   **16.** $1\frac{2}{3} \div 1\frac{1}{9}$ **$1\frac{1}{2}$**   **17.** $\frac{2}{5} \cdot (-20)$ **-8**

18. $\frac{4}{9} \cdot \frac{5}{12}$ **$\frac{5}{27}$**   **19.** $\frac{3}{4} \div 8$ **$\frac{3}{32}$**   **20.** $-\frac{1}{6} \cdot (-12)$ **2**

21. $-8 \cdot 5$ **-40**   **22.** $2 \cdot 3 \cdot (-4) \cdot 5$ **-120**   **23.** $-1(-1)$ **1**

24. $-56 \div 8$ **-7**   **25.** $100 \div (-2)$ **-50**   **26.** $-100 \div (-10)$ **10**

Lesson 3-2

27. Estimation You want to buy three shirts for $15.95 each. Estimate the total cost of the shirts. **about $48**

Alternative Assessment

Ask students to write a word problem that uses their school-morning routines. They should include the amounts of time needed to complete the different parts of the routine. Have them exchange problems and solve them by working backward.

Test Prep

 Resources

For additional practice with a variety of test item formats:
• Test Prep, p. 283
• Test-Taking Strategies, p. 278
• Test-Taking Tips Strategies With Transparencies

Read the problem below. Then follow along with what Greg thinks as he solves the problem. Check your understanding with the exercise at the bottom of the page.

Describe the pattern of the numbers below. Then find the next three numbers in the pattern.

$\frac{2}{3}, 1\frac{5}{12}, 2\frac{1}{6}, 2\frac{11}{12}, \blacksquare, \blacksquare, \blacksquare, \ldots$

What Greg Thinks

I must find what kind of pattern this is so that I can describe it. I'll check the differences between terms.

The differences are the same, $\frac{3}{4}$. I can describe the pattern.

Now I have to find the next three numbers. A fraction calculator would help, but I'll do it longhand.

First I have to find $2\frac{11}{12} + \frac{3}{4}$.

Next, $3\frac{2}{3} + \frac{3}{4}$.

Finally, $4\frac{5}{12} + \frac{3}{4}$.

I'm done!

What Greg Writes

$1\frac{5}{12} - \frac{2}{3} = \frac{17}{12} - \frac{2}{3} = \frac{17}{12} - \frac{8}{12} = \frac{9}{12}$, or $\frac{3}{4}$

$2\frac{1}{6} - 1\frac{5}{12} = \frac{13}{6} - \frac{17}{12} = \frac{26}{12} - \frac{17}{12} = \frac{9}{12}$, or $\frac{3}{4}$

$2\frac{11}{12} - 2\frac{1}{6} = 2\frac{11}{12} - 2\frac{2}{12} = \frac{9}{12}$, or $\frac{3}{4}$

Start with $\frac{2}{3}$ and add $\frac{3}{4}$ repeatedly.

$2\frac{11}{12} + \frac{3}{4} = 2\frac{11}{12} + \frac{9}{12}$
$= 2\frac{20}{12} = 3\frac{8}{12} = 3\frac{2}{3}$

$3\frac{2}{3} + \frac{3}{4} = \frac{11}{3} + \frac{3}{4}$
$= \frac{44}{12} + \frac{9}{12} = \frac{53}{12} = 4\frac{5}{12}$

$4\frac{5}{12} + \frac{3}{4} = 4\frac{5}{12} + \frac{9}{12}$
$= 4\frac{14}{12} = 5\frac{2}{12} = 5\frac{1}{6}$

The next three numbers are $3\frac{2}{3}, 4\frac{5}{12}$, and $5\frac{1}{6}$.

EXERCISE

1. Describe the pattern of the numbers below. Then find the next three numbers in the pattern.

$1\frac{3}{4}, 3, 4\frac{1}{4}, 5\frac{1}{2}, \blacksquare, \blacksquare, \blacksquare, \ldots$ Start with $1\frac{3}{4}$ and add $1\frac{1}{4}$ repeatedly; $6\frac{3}{4}, 8, 9\frac{1}{4}$.

Reading Math

Reading for Problem Solving

Students read and analyze someone else's thinking about a solution of a patterning problem before solving a similar problem.

Teaching Notes

Error Prevention!

Suggest that students always leave ample room between the steps on their papers by skipping at least one line between each step.

Exercise

Have students work independently on a similar problem. Then have volunteers share each step involved in solving the problem. You can write on the overhead as they describe the steps. Allow for discussion about other ways of thinking and solving the problem.

1. Plan

Lesson Preview

 Check Skills You'll Need

Adding and Subtracting Fractions
Lesson 5-3: Example 3;
Exercises 13–20.
Extra Practice, p. 748.

Lesson Resources

 Teaching Resources
Practice, Reteaching, Enrichment

Reaching All Students
Practice Workbook 5-7
Spanish Practice Workbook 5-7
Guided Problem Solving 5-7
Hands-On Activities 8

Presentation Assistant Plus!
Transparencies and PowerPoint™
• Check Skills You'll Need 5-7
• Additional Examples 5-7
• Student Edition Answers 5-7
• Lesson Quiz 5-7
PH Presentation Pro CD-ROM 5-7

 ASSESSMENT SYSTEM

Computer Test Generator CD-ROM

 Technology
Resource Pro® CD-ROM
Computer Test Generator CD-ROM
PH Presentation Pro CD-ROM

 www.PHSchool.com
Student Site
• Teacher Web Code: adk-5500
• Self-grading Lesson Quiz
PH SuccessNet Teacher Center
• Lesson Planner
• Resources

Plus

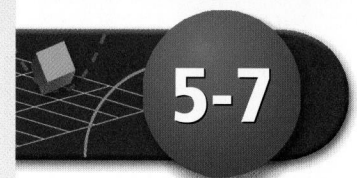 **5-7**

Solving Equations by Adding or Subtracting Fractions

What You'll Learn

OBJECTIVE 1 To solve equations by subtracting fractions

OBJECTIVE 2 To solve equations by adding fractions

. . . And Why
To solve real-world problems involving recycling

 Check Skills You'll Need

Find each sum or difference.

1. $1\frac{3}{4} - 2\frac{7}{8}$ $-1\frac{1}{8}$

2. $3\frac{5}{8} + 4\frac{7}{12}$ $8\frac{5}{24}$

3. $5\frac{3}{4} - 3\frac{1}{8}$ $2\frac{5}{8}$

4. $-4\frac{1}{6} - 3\frac{2}{9}$ $-7\frac{7}{18}$

 For help, go to Lesson 5-3.

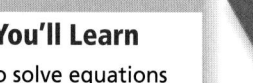 **OBJECTIVE**

1 Using Subtraction to Solve Equations

You solve equations with fractions the same way you solve equations with integers and decimals, by using inverse operations and the Properties of Equality.

1 EXAMPLE   Real-World Problem Solving

Recycling In 1999, the average household in the United States recycled about $\frac{1}{4}$ of its solid waste. The Environmental Protection Agency (EPA) has set a goal of recycling about $\frac{1}{3}$ of solid waste. By how much would the average U.S. household need to increase its recycling to meet the EPA goal?

Words   fraction U.S. households recycle   plus   the increase   is   EPA goal

Let n = the increase.

Equation $\frac{1}{4}$ + n = $\frac{1}{3}$

$$\frac{1}{4} + n = \frac{1}{3}$$

$$\frac{1}{4} - \frac{1}{4} + n = \frac{1}{3} - \frac{1}{4} \qquad \text{Subtract } \tfrac{1}{4} \text{ from each side.}$$

$$n = \frac{4 \cdot 1 - 3 \cdot 1}{3 \cdot 4} \qquad \text{Use 3 · 4 as the common denominator.}$$

$$n = \frac{4 - 3}{12} \qquad \text{Use the Order of Operations.}$$

$$n = \frac{1}{12} \qquad \text{Simplify.}$$

To meet the EPA goal, the average U.S. household needs to recycle $\frac{1}{12}$ more of its waste.

Check Is the answer reasonable? The present fraction of solid waste that is recycled plus the increase must equal the goal. Since $\frac{1}{4} + \frac{1}{12} = \frac{3}{12} + \frac{1}{12} = \frac{4}{12} = \frac{1}{3}$, the answer is reasonable.

 Check Understanding   Example 1

1. Solve and check each equation.

  a. $y + \frac{8}{9} = \frac{5}{9}$ $-\frac{1}{3}$ **b.** $\frac{2}{3} = u + \frac{3}{5}$ $\frac{1}{15}$ **c.** $c + \frac{3}{10} = \frac{11}{15}$ $\frac{13}{30}$

 TEXT Interactive lesson includes instant self-check, tutorials, and activities.

264   Chapter 5   Operations With Fractions

Ongoing Assessment and Intervention

Before the Lesson	**During the Lesson**	**After the Lesson**
Diagnose prerequisite skills using:	Monitor progress using:	Assess knowledge using:
• Check Skills You'll Need	• Check Understanding	• Lesson Quiz
	• Additional Examples	• Computer Test Generator CD-ROM
	• Test Prep	

You can use addition to solve an equation involving subtraction.

2 EXAMPLE **Adding a Fraction to Solve an Equation**

Solve $n - \frac{3}{4} = -\frac{5}{8}$.

$$n - \frac{3}{4} = -\frac{5}{8}$$

$$n - \frac{3}{4} + \frac{3}{4} = -\frac{5}{8} + \frac{3}{4}$$ Add $\frac{3}{4}$ to each side.

$$n = \frac{-5 \cdot 4 + 8 \cdot 3}{8 \cdot 4}$$ Use $8 \cdot 4$ as the common denominator.

$$n = \frac{-20 + 24}{32}$$ Use the Order of Operations.

$$n = \frac{4^1}{32_8} = \frac{1}{8}$$ Divide the common factors and simplify.

? Need Help?
To review the Order of Operations, see page 183.

✓ **Check Understanding** Example 2

2. Solve and check each equation.

   a. $a - \frac{3}{5} = \frac{1}{5}$ $\frac{4}{5}$

   b. $\frac{6}{7} = x - \frac{2}{7}$ $1\frac{1}{7}$

You can use the same methods to solve equations with mixed numbers.

3 EXAMPLE **Using a Mixed Number to Solve an Equation**

Solve $p - 1\frac{3}{5} = 2\frac{1}{4}$.

$$p - 1\frac{3}{5} = 2\frac{1}{4}$$

$$p - 1\frac{3}{5} + 1\frac{3}{5} = 2\frac{1}{4} + 1\frac{3}{5}$$ Add $1\frac{3}{5}$ to each side.

$$p = \frac{9}{4} + \frac{8}{5}$$ Write mixed numbers as improper fractions.

$$p = \frac{9 \cdot 5 + 4 \cdot 8}{4 \cdot 5}$$ Use $4 \cdot 5$ as the common denominator.

$$p = \frac{45 + 32}{20}$$ Use the Order of Operations.

$$p = \frac{77}{20} = 3\frac{17}{20}$$ Simplify. Write as a mixed number.

✓ **Check Understanding** Example 3

3. Solve and check each equation.

   a. $c - 2\frac{1}{6} = 5\frac{1}{4}$ $7\frac{5}{12}$

   b. $3\frac{7}{18} = z + 1\frac{1}{3}$ $2\frac{1}{18}$

5-7 Solving Equations by Adding or Subtracting Fractions **265**

👥 Reaching All Students

Below Level Have students review the process for solving $3 + x = 7$. Point out that they will use the same process to solve equations involving fractions.

Advanced Learners Ask: *When you solve equations containing fractions, will the value of the variable always be a fraction? Explain.* No; in the equation $x - \frac{1}{3} = \frac{2}{3}$, $x = 1$.

Diversity See note on page 265.
Auditory Learners See note on page 267.

2. Teach

Professional Development

Math Background

You use inverse operations and the Addition and Subtraction Properties of Equality to solve equations involving subtraction or addition of fractions. You often must find the LCD of the fractions to complete the solution.

Teaching Notes

1 EXAMPLE Diversity

Students who live in small towns may not have access to recycling programs or facilities. Have students research the variety of ways people around the world recycle their waste products. Discuss how students can recycle at home and buy recycled products.

2 EXAMPLE Alternative Method

Some students may prefer to rewrite the fractions with common denominators, particularly the LCD, before adding (or subtracting) the same amount to (from) each side.

3 EXAMPLE Alternative Method

Ask students for another way to add the mixed numbers. You can add the whole numbers and fractions separately.

PowerPoint

Additional Examples

1 One school recycles about $\frac{1}{3}$ of its waste paper. The student council set a goal of recycling $\frac{3}{4}$ of the school's waste paper by the end of the year. By how much does the school need to increase its paper recycling to reach the goal? $\frac{5}{12}$ more

2 Solve $x - \frac{2}{3} = \frac{1}{9}$. $\frac{7}{9}$

3 Solve $q - 6\frac{1}{2} = -1\frac{3}{5}$. $4\frac{9}{10}$

Closure

Have students explain how to solve equations involving addition or subtraction of fractions. Use inverse operations to solve the equations, and find the LCDs to add or subtract the fractions.

265

Assignment Guide

1 Objective 1
  Ⓐ Ⓑ Core 1–7, 20–22, 25, 27–32
  Ⓒ Extension 35

2 Objective 2
  Ⓐ Ⓑ Core 8–19, 23, 24, 26, 33, 34
  Ⓒ Extension 36–39

Test Prep 40–43
Mixed Review 44–54

Practice 5-7 *Solving Equations by Adding or Subtracting Fractions*

Solve each equation.

1. $m - \left(-\frac{7}{10}\right) = -1\frac{1}{5}$ $-1\frac{9}{10}$
2. $k - \frac{1}{4} = -\frac{2}{3}$ $1\frac{3}{20}$
3. $x - \frac{5}{6} = \frac{1}{10}$ $\frac{14}{15}$
4. $t - \left(-3\frac{1}{6}\right) = 7\frac{2}{3}$ $4\frac{1}{2}$
5. $x + \frac{5}{8} = \frac{7}{8}$ $\frac{1}{4}$
6. $k + \frac{1}{3} = 1\frac{2}{5}$ $\frac{4}{5}$
7. $4 = \frac{4}{9} + y$ $3\frac{5}{9}$
8. $h + \left(-\frac{5}{6}\right) = -\frac{7}{12}$ $\frac{5}{24}$
9. $n + \frac{2}{3} = \frac{1}{9}$ $-\frac{5}{9}$
10. $e - \frac{11}{16} = -\frac{7}{8}$ $-\frac{3}{16}$
11. $w - 14\frac{1}{12} = -2\frac{3}{4}$ $11\frac{1}{3}$
12. $v + \left(-4\frac{5}{6}\right) = 2\frac{1}{3}$ $7\frac{1}{6}$
13. $a - 9\frac{1}{2} = -3\frac{7}{8}$ $5\frac{5}{8}$
14. $f + |-3\frac{1}{2}| = 18$ $14\frac{1}{2}$
15. $z + \left(-3\frac{2}{5}\right) = -4\frac{1}{10}$ $-\frac{7}{10}$
16. $x - \frac{7}{15} = \frac{1}{60}$ $\frac{7}{12}$
17. $h - \left(-6\frac{1}{4}\right) = 14\frac{1}{4}$ $7\frac{3}{4}$
18. $p - 5\frac{3}{8} = -\frac{11}{14}$ $4\frac{11}{14}$

Solve each equation using mental math.

19. $x + \frac{1}{7} = \frac{4}{7}$ $\frac{2}{7}$
20. $k - \frac{6}{9} = -\frac{1}{9}$ $\frac{7}{9}$
21. $a + \frac{1}{6} = \frac{5}{6}$ $\frac{2}{3}$
22. $g - \frac{4}{9} = -\frac{2}{9}$ $\frac{2}{9}$

Write an equation to solve each problem.

23. Pete's papaya tree grew $3\frac{7}{12}$ ft during the year. If its height at the end of the year was $21\frac{1}{6}$ ft, what was its height at the beginning of the year?

$h + 3\frac{7}{12} = 21\frac{1}{6}; h = 17\frac{7}{12}$ ft

24. Lee is $1\frac{3}{4}$ ft taller than Jay. If Lee is $6\frac{1}{4}$ ft tall, how tall is Jay?

$h + 1\frac{3}{4} = 6\frac{1}{4}; h = 4\frac{1}{2}$ ft

EXERCISES

For more exercises, see *Extra Practice*.

Practice and Problem Solving

Ⓐ **Practice by Example**

Example 1 (page 264)

20–22. Explanations may vary. Samples are given.

20. Zero; $2\frac{9}{11} - 2\frac{9}{11} = 0$.

21. Negative; $\frac{9}{10} > \frac{1}{2}$, so $\frac{1}{2} - \frac{9}{10} < 0$.

22. Positive; $4\frac{1}{5} < 5\frac{1}{2}$, so $5\frac{1}{2} - 4\frac{1}{5} > 0$.

Example 2 (page 265)

Example 3 (page 265)

Ⓑ **Apply Your Skills**

Solve and check each equation.

1. $b + \frac{4}{5} = \frac{9}{10}$ $\frac{1}{10}$
2. $g + \frac{9}{10} = \frac{7}{10}$ $-\frac{1}{5}$
3. $m + \frac{3}{4} = \frac{1}{4}$ $-\frac{1}{2}$
4. $a + \frac{3}{5} = \frac{4}{5}$ $\frac{1}{5}$
5. $\frac{5}{16} = c + \frac{3}{16}$ $\frac{1}{8}$
6. $t + \frac{1}{4} = \frac{5}{9}$ $\frac{11}{36}$

7. **Reading** Jarrel's goal is to be half finished with the book he is reading by Friday. By Wednesday he has read $\frac{1}{3}$ of the book. How much more does he need to read to meet his goal? $\frac{1}{6}$ of the book

Solve and check each equation.

8. $a - \frac{1}{8} = \frac{5}{8}$ $\frac{3}{4}$
9. $t - \frac{2}{3} = \frac{4}{9}$ $1\frac{1}{9}$
10. $c - \frac{9}{10} = \frac{1}{3}$ $1\frac{7}{30}$
11. $\frac{1}{2} = n - \frac{5}{8}$ $1\frac{1}{8}$
12. $a - \frac{5}{8} = \frac{7}{12}$ $1\frac{5}{24}$
13. $3 = j - \frac{5}{8}$ $3\frac{5}{8}$
14. $x + 1\frac{1}{4} = 4\frac{3}{4}$ $3\frac{1}{2}$
15. $5\frac{1}{4} = w + 2\frac{1}{2}$ $2\frac{3}{4}$
16. $10\frac{1}{2} = x + 1\frac{1}{2}$ 9
17. $z + 7\frac{5}{9} = 7\frac{5}{9}$ 0
18. $c - 2\frac{1}{12} = 3\frac{1}{12}$ $5\frac{1}{6}$
19. $y + 4\frac{7}{8} = 2$ $-2\frac{7}{8}$

Number Sense Without solving each equation, state whether *x* is *positive*, *negative*, or *zero*. Justify your response. 20–22. See above left.

20. $x + 2\frac{9}{11} = 2\frac{9}{11}$
21. $x + \frac{9}{10} = \frac{1}{2}$
22. $x + 4\frac{1}{5} = 5\frac{1}{2}$

23. **Growth** At the beginning of the school year, Jamie's height was $62\frac{1}{2}$ inches. During the school year she grew $1\frac{3}{4}$ inches, $\frac{1}{8}$ inch more than she grew the previous year.
    a. What was Jamie's height at the end of the school year? $64\frac{1}{4}$ in.
    b. How tall was Jamie at the start of the previous school year? $60\frac{7}{8}$ in.

Solve and check each equation.

24. $p - 3\frac{2}{3} = 1\frac{1}{3}$ 5
25. $1\frac{3}{8} = b + 2\frac{1}{6}$ $-\frac{19}{24}$
26. $y - 4\frac{7}{8} = \frac{3}{4}$ $5\frac{5}{8}$
27. $k + 2\frac{1}{9} = 1\frac{1}{3}$ $-\frac{7}{9}$
28. $f + 4\frac{5}{12} = 5\frac{3}{8}$ $\frac{23}{24}$
29. $g + 8\frac{4}{9} = 3\frac{1}{6}$ $-5\frac{5}{18}$
30. $h + 2\frac{1}{2} = 5\frac{7}{10}$ $3\frac{1}{5}$
31. $6\frac{1}{4} = a + \frac{5}{8}$ $5\frac{5}{8}$
32. $2\frac{1}{16} = d + 5\frac{7}{16}$ $-3\frac{3}{8}$

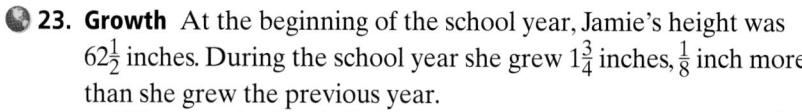

Real-World 🌐 **Connection**

The average weight of an Alaskan Coho salmon is about $7\frac{9}{10}$ lb.

33. **Seafood** A restaurant chef needs $8\frac{1}{2}$ lb of salmon. To get a good [GPS] price, he buys more than he needs. He ends up with $4\frac{7}{8}$ lb too much. How much salmon did he buy? $13\frac{3}{8}$ lb

34. **Carpentry** A carpenter used $3\frac{3}{16}$ lb of nails for a job. After the job was over, the remaining nails weighed $1\frac{1}{16}$ lb. How many pounds of nails did the carpenter have at the beginning of the job? $4\frac{1}{4}$ lb

Ⓒ **Challenge**

Solve and check each equation.

35. $x + \frac{2}{3} - \frac{1}{3} = 3\frac{1}{3}$ 3
36. $x - \frac{3}{4} + \frac{1}{6} = 1\frac{5}{12}$ 2
37. $x - 2\frac{2}{5} + 3\frac{1}{10} = \frac{3}{5}$ $-\frac{1}{10}$

[GPS] Use the Guided Problem Solving worksheet with Exercise 33.

38. Answers may vary.
Sample: Your house
plant grows $\frac{1}{2}$ in. in the
month after you buy it.
If it is 7 in. tall now, how
tall was the plant when
you bought it? $x = 6\frac{1}{2}$ in.

38. **Writing in Math** Write a problem that you could solve with the equation $x + \frac{1}{2} = 7$. Solve your problem. **See left.**

39. **Environment** During a recent wet spell, the water level in Jasper's Pond rose $2\frac{3}{4}$ in. The depth of the pond was then 10 ft 3 in. What was the depth of the water in the pond before the wet spell? **10 ft $\frac{1}{4}$ in.**

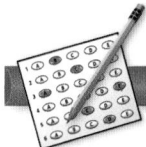

Test Prep

Multiple Choice

40. A tree is $10\frac{1}{2}$ ft tall. Which equation can you use to find the height of the tree before last spring's growth of 8 in.? **A**

   A. $t + \frac{8}{12} = 10\frac{1}{2}$ **B.** $t - \frac{8}{12} = 10\frac{1}{2}$

   C. $t + 10\frac{1}{2} = \frac{8}{12}$ **D.** $t - 10\frac{1}{2} = \frac{8}{12}$

41. What is the value of d in the equation $d + \frac{3}{4} = 4\frac{5}{8}$? **G**

   F. $3\frac{1}{2}$ **G.** $3\frac{7}{8}$ **H.** $4\frac{1}{4}$ **I.** $5\frac{3}{8}$

42. What is the value of c in $1\frac{1}{4} - c = \frac{3}{8}$? **C**

   A. $-1\frac{5}{8}$ **B.** $-\frac{7}{8}$ **C.** $\frac{7}{8}$ **D.** $1\frac{5}{8}$

Extended Response

43. Below is a student's work for solving the equation $x - (-\frac{1}{2}) = 3$.

   a. What is the student's error?
   b. What likely caused the error?
   c. What is the correct value of x?
   d. How did the error affect the value of x? **See margin.**

   $$x - (-\tfrac{1}{2}) = 3$$
   $$x - (-\tfrac{1}{2}) + \tfrac{1}{2} = 3 + \tfrac{1}{2}$$
   $$x = 3\tfrac{1}{2}$$

Take It to the NET
Online lesson quiz at
www.PHSchool.com
Web Code: ada-0507

Mixed Review

Lesson 5-5 **Complete each statement.**

44. $2\frac{2}{3}$ ft $= 32$ ■ in.   45. $1\frac{1}{2}$ ■ $= 12$ fl oz **c**   46. 9 pt $= 4\frac{1}{2}$ ■ qt

47. $\frac{1}{2}$ ■ $= \frac{1}{4}$ qt **pt**   48. 750 lb $= \frac{3}{8}$ ■ **t**   49. $1\frac{2}{3}$ ■ $= 5$ ft **yd**

Lesson 5-4 50. a. **Jobs** Your job is to paint $\frac{1}{4}$ of the lockers in the school. Your friend agrees to share the job equally with you. What fraction of the lockers will each of you paint? $\frac{1}{8}$

   b. If the job of painting all of the lockers in the school pays $1,100, how much will you earn? **$137.50**

Lesson 3-6 **Solve each equation.**

51. $3.5t = 8.75$ **2.5**   52. $\frac{b}{4} = -38$ **-152**

53. $y \div 7.5 = -3.75$ **-28.125**   54. $1.7x = 8.5$ **5**

5-7 Solving Equations by Adding or Subtracting Fractions **267**

43. **[4]a.** The student added $\frac{1}{2}$ to each side instead of $-\frac{1}{2}$.
   b. The student didn't add to each side the number that is subtracted on the left side.
   c. The correct value of x is $2\frac{1}{2}$.
   d. The student's value of x was too large.
   [3] correct answers for a, c, and d
   [2] correct answers for a and c
   [1] correct answers for a or c

5-8

1. Plan

Lesson Preview

 Check Skills You'll Need

Multiplying Fractions
Lesson 5-4: Example 3;
Exercises 9–13.
Extra Practice, p. 748.

Lesson Resources

 Teaching Resources
Practice, Reteaching, Enrichment
Checkpoint Quiz 2

 Reaching All Students
Practice Workbook 5-8
Spanish Practice Workbook 5-8
Reading and Math Literacy 5C
Spanish Reading and Math
  Literacy 5C
Spanish Checkpoint Quiz 2
Guided Problem Solving 5-8
Hands-On Activities 10

 Presentation Assistant Plus!
Transparencies and PowerPoint™
• Check Skills You'll Need 5-8
• Additional Examples 5-8
• Student Edition Answers 5-8
• Lesson Quiz 5-8
PH Presentation Pro CD-ROM 5-8

(ASSESSMENT *SYSTEM*)

Checkpoint Quiz 2
Computer Test Generator CD-ROM

 Technology
Resource Pro® CD-ROM
Computer Test Generator CD-ROM
PH Presentation Pro CD-ROM

 www.PHSchool.com

Student Site
• Teacher Web Code: adk-5500
• Algebra Readiness Puzzles 41, 42
• Self-grading Lesson Quiz
PH SuccessNet Teacher Center
• Lesson Planner
• Resources

Plus

268

Solving Equations by Multiplying Fractions

What You'll Learn

OBJECTIVE 1 To solve equations by multiplying fractions

OBJECTIVE 2 To solve equations by multiplying mixed numbers

. . . And Why

To solve real-world problems involving carpentry

 Check Skills You'll Need

Find each product.

1. $\frac{4}{7} \cdot \frac{5}{8}$ $\frac{5}{14}$

2. $\frac{9}{10} \cdot \left(-\frac{5}{3}\right)$ $-1\frac{1}{2}$

3. $-1\frac{1}{4} \cdot \left(-\frac{5}{1}\right)$ $6\frac{1}{4}$

4. $4\frac{1}{2} \cdot \frac{2}{3}$ 3

For help, go to Lesson 5-4.

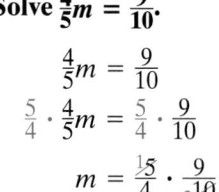

Need Help?
To review reciprocals, see page 250.

TEXT Interactive lesson includes instant self-check, tutorials, and activities.

OBJECTIVE

1 Using Multiplication to Solve Equations

You know how to undo multiplication by dividing each side of an equation by the same number. You can also multiply each side of an equation by the same fraction to undo multiplication.

1 EXAMPLE **Multiplying by a Reciprocal**

Solve $5a = \frac{1}{7}$.

$$5a = \frac{1}{7}$$

$$\frac{1}{5} \cdot (5a) = \frac{1}{5} \cdot \frac{1}{7} \quad \text{Multiply each side by } \frac{1}{5}, \text{ the reciprocal of 5.}$$

$$a = \frac{1}{35} \quad \text{Simplify.}$$

Check Understanding Example 1

1. Solve each equation.

a. $8x = \frac{5}{7}$ $\frac{5}{56}$ **b.** $2y = \frac{7}{9}$ $\frac{7}{18}$ **c.** $3a = \frac{4}{5}$ $\frac{4}{15}$

When a numerator and a denominator have common factors, you can divide the common factors to help you multiply.

2 EXAMPLE **Simplifying Before Multiplying**

Solve $\frac{4}{5}m = \frac{9}{10}$.

$$\frac{4}{5}m = \frac{9}{10}$$

$$\frac{5}{4} \cdot \frac{4}{5}m = \frac{5}{4} \cdot \frac{9}{10} \quad \text{Multiply each side by } \frac{5}{4}, \text{ the reciprocal of } \frac{4}{5}.$$

$$m = \frac{\cancel{5}}{4} \cdot \frac{9}{\cancel{10}_{2}} \quad \text{Divide common factors.}$$

$$m = \frac{9}{8} \quad \text{Simplify.}$$

$$m = 1\frac{1}{8} \quad \text{Write as a mixed number.}$$

Check Understanding Example 2

2. Solve each equation.

a. $\frac{2}{9}t = \frac{5}{6}$ $3\frac{3}{4}$ **b.** $\frac{3}{4}s = \frac{8}{9}$ $1\frac{5}{27}$ **c.** $\frac{5}{4} = \frac{5}{4}d$ 1

 Ongoing Assessment and Intervention

Before the Lesson	**During the Lesson**	**After the Lesson**
Diagnose prerequisite skills using:	Monitor progress using:	Assess knowledge using:
• Check Skills You'll Need	• Check Understanding	• Lesson Quiz
	• Additional Examples	• Computer Test Generator
	• Test Prep	CD-ROM
		• Chapter Checkpoint 2 (p. 272)

3 **EXAMPLE** **Multiplying by the Negative Reciprocal**

Solve $-\frac{14}{25}k = \frac{8}{15}$.

$$-\frac{14}{25}k = \frac{8}{15}$$

$$-\frac{25}{14}\left(-\frac{14}{25}k\right) = -\frac{25}{14}\left(\frac{8}{15}\right)$$ Multiply each side by $-\frac{25}{14}$, the reciprocal of $-\frac{14}{25}$.

$$k = -\frac{\overset{5}{25} \cdot \overset{4}{8}}{\underset{7}{14} \cdot \underset{3}{15}} = -\frac{20}{21}$$ Divide common factors and simplify.

Need Help?
Remember, the reciprocal of a negative fraction is also negative.

✓ **Check Understanding** Example 3

3. Solve each equation.

   a. $-\frac{6}{7}r = \frac{3}{4}$ $-\frac{7}{8}$ b. $-\frac{10}{13}b = -\frac{2}{3}$ $\frac{13}{15}$ c. $-6n = \frac{3}{7}$ $-\frac{1}{14}$

OBJECTIVE

2 **Solving Equations With Mixed Numbers**

Change mixed numbers to improper fractions before multiplying.

4 **EXAMPLE** **Real-World** 🌐 **Problem Solving**

Carpentry Your teacher needs a shelf to hold a set of textbooks each $1\frac{5}{8}$ in. wide. How many books will fit on a 26-in.-long shelf?

Words

| width of each book | times | the number of books | is | width of bookself |

Let n = the number of books.

Equation $1\frac{5}{8}$ · n =   26

$$1\frac{5}{8} \cdot n = 26$$

$$\frac{13}{8}n = 26$$ Write $1\frac{5}{8}$ as $\frac{13}{8}$.

$$\frac{8}{13} \cdot \frac{13}{8}n = \frac{8}{13} \cdot 26$$ Multiply each side by $\frac{8}{13}$, the reciprocal of $\frac{13}{8}$.

$$n = \frac{8 \cdot \overset{2}{26}}{\underset{1}{13} \cdot 1} = 16$$ Divide common factors and simplify.

Your teacher can fit 16 books on the shelf.

✓ **Check Understanding** Example 4

4. Solve each equation.

   a. $3\frac{1}{2}n = 28$ 8   b. $-\frac{7}{20} = 1\frac{1}{6}r$ $-\frac{3}{10}$ c. $-2\frac{3}{4}h = -12\frac{1}{2}$ $4\frac{6}{11}$

5-8 Solving Equations by Multiplying Fractions **269**

👥 **Reaching All Students**

| **Below Level** Review reciprocals (Lesson 5-4). Students will use reciprocals in this lesson to solve equations by multiplying fractions. | **Advanced Learners** Ask students to solve $3\frac{1}{2}x = 23\frac{5}{8}$ and give the result in decimal form. 6.75 | **Inclusion** See note on page 269. **Auditory Learners** See note on page 271. |

2. Teach

Professional Development

Math Background

When a variable in an equation is multiplied by a fraction, you divide each side of the equation by that fraction to solve the equation. Therefore, to solve an equation where the variable is multiplied by a fraction, you multiply each side of the equation by the reciprocal of that fraction.

Teaching Notes

1 **EXAMPLE** **Teaching Tip**

Remind students that a whole number is written as a fraction by writing the whole number over 1. Therefore, the reciprocal of a whole number is written as 1 over the whole number.

3 **EXAMPLE** **Error Prevention**

In the second line of the solution students may incorrectly drop the negative sign with the reciprocal. Remind students that the reciprocal of a negative number must be negative.

4 **EXAMPLE** **Inclusion**

Some below-level students may not remember to write the mixed number as an improper fraction and may just find the reciprocal of the fraction part. Suggest that students circle the whole mixed number as a reminder.

PowerPoint

💻 **Additional Examples**

1 Solve $7y = \frac{1}{3}$. $\frac{1}{21}$

2 Solve $\frac{2}{5}w = \frac{13}{15}$. $2\frac{1}{6}$

3 Solve $-\frac{20}{27}c = \frac{4}{9}$. $-\frac{3}{5}$

4 How many $2\frac{1}{2}$-t trucks can you place on a rail car that has a carrying capacity of 15 t? 6

Closure

Have students explain how to solve an equation that involves multiplying the variable by a fraction. Multiply each side of the equation by the reciprocal of that fraction.

269

3. Practice

Assignment Guide

1 Objective 1
Ⓐ Ⓑ **Core** 1–20, 30–32, 36–39, 44–49
Ⓒ **Extension** 51–54, 56

 **Objective 2**
Ⓐ Ⓑ **Core** 21–29, 33–35, 40–43, 50
Ⓒ **Extension** 55

Test Prep 57–62
Mixed Review 63–72

EXERCISES

For more exercises, see *Extra Practice*.

Practice and Problem Solving

Ⓐ **Practice by Example**

Examples 1–3
(pages 268 and 269)

Solve each equation.

1. $6p = \frac{5}{8}$ $\frac{5}{48}$
2. $5x = \frac{2}{3}$ $\frac{2}{15}$
3. $2k = \frac{5}{6}$ $\frac{5}{12}$
4. $7z = \frac{3}{8}$ $\frac{3}{56}$

5. $2y = \frac{1}{3}$ $\frac{1}{6}$
6. $3b = \frac{4}{7}$ $\frac{4}{21}$
7. $7c = \frac{3}{4}$ $\frac{3}{28}$
8. $9y = \frac{5}{7}$ $\frac{5}{63}$

9. $\frac{2}{3}d = \frac{5}{8}$ $\frac{15}{16}$
10. $\frac{5}{8} = \frac{5}{8}k$ 1
11. $\frac{5}{9} = \frac{1}{8}h$ $4\frac{4}{9}$
12. $\frac{1}{7}x = \frac{4}{7}$ 4

13. $\frac{3}{4}d = \frac{3}{8}$ $\frac{1}{2}$
14. $\frac{10}{27} = \frac{5}{9}t$ $\frac{2}{3}$
15. $\frac{2}{7}a = \frac{5}{8}$ $2\frac{3}{16}$
16. $\frac{1}{9}p = \frac{5}{6}$ $7\frac{1}{2}$

17. $-\frac{2}{3}t = -2$ 3
18. $-5s = \frac{5}{7}$ $-\frac{1}{7}$
19. $\frac{8}{9} = -6d$ $-\frac{4}{27}$
20. $\frac{2}{3}x = -8$ -12

Example 4 🌐
(page 269)

21. Construction A sheet of plywood is $\frac{3}{4}$ in. thick. Write and solve an equation to find how many sheets of plywood are in a stack 9 in. high. $\frac{3}{4}s = 9$; 12 sheets

Solve each equation. 25–29. See margin.

22. $3 = 1\frac{1}{2}b$ 2
23. $2\frac{1}{2}x = \frac{2}{5}$ $\frac{4}{25}$
24. $2\frac{1}{3}m = \frac{7}{12}$ $\frac{1}{4}$
25. $-1\frac{6}{7}g = -\frac{13}{15}$

26. $\frac{1}{15} = -1\frac{1}{10}t$
27. $2\frac{1}{8}k = 7$
28. $1\frac{1}{2}n = 3\frac{4}{9}$
29. $-9\frac{1}{3} = -1\frac{1}{4}t$

Ⓑ **Apply Your Skills**

Real-World 🌐 Connection

A native of China and Japan, kudzu was brought to the United States in 1876. Left alone, it grows over trees, telephone poles, and abandoned houses and cars.

Number Sense Without solving each equation, state whether x is positive, negative, or zero. Justify your response. 30–33. See margin.

30. $17x = -\frac{11}{30}$
31. $\frac{1}{57}x = 2$
32. $\frac{4}{13}x = 0$
33. $-6\frac{1}{2}x = 0$

34. Boat Building Tomás calculates that he will need 86 hours to build a boat. He can work on the boat $8\frac{3}{5}$ hours per week. How many weeks will it take Tomás to build the boat? **10 weeks**

35. Biology In ideal conditions, the kudzu plant can grow at least $1\frac{3}{20}$ ft [GPS] per week. At this rate, how many weeks would it take a kudzu plant to grow 23 ft? **20 weeks**

Solve each equation.

36. $-\frac{5}{7}x = \frac{9}{10}$ $-1\frac{13}{50}$
37. $\frac{9}{13} = -\frac{6}{11}s$ $-1\frac{7}{26}$
38. $-3b = \frac{2}{3}$ $-\frac{2}{9}$

39. $-\frac{12}{13} = -\frac{1}{4}w$ $3\frac{9}{13}$
40. $3\frac{1}{9}a = \frac{3}{7}$ $\frac{27}{196}$
41. $2\frac{3}{4} = -6\frac{3}{5}y$ $-\frac{5}{12}$

42. $1\frac{1}{2}m = 1\frac{3}{4}$ $1\frac{1}{6}$
43. $3\frac{3}{5}p = -4\frac{4}{9}$ $-1\frac{19}{81}$
44. $\frac{1}{8}d = \frac{1}{4}$ 2

45. $\frac{1}{3}y = 2$ 6
46. $\frac{3}{7}x = 1$ $2\frac{1}{3}$
47. $\frac{7}{8}z = 3\frac{1}{2}$ 4

Writing in Math

For help with writing to explain the error in Exercise 49, see page 273.

48. Astronomy The Chandra satellite telescope views X-rays in space. It orbits as much as 87,000 miles above Earth. This is about $\frac{1}{3}$ of the distance to the moon. About how far away is the moon? **261,000 mi**

49. Error Analysis A student solved the equation $-\frac{7}{10}h = 5\frac{3}{5}$ and found the solution 8. Describe and correct the student's error. The student multiplied each side by $\frac{10}{7}$ and lost track of the negative sign.

270 Chapter 5 Operations With Fractions

[GPS] Use the Guided Problem Solving worksheet with Exercise 35.

25. $\frac{7}{15}$ **26.** $-\frac{2}{33}$ **27.** $3\frac{5}{17}$ **28.** $2\frac{8}{27}$ **29.** $7\frac{7}{15}$
30. Negative; a negative product means the two factors have opposite signs.

31. Positive; a positive product means the two factors have the same sign.
32. Zero; a zero product means one of the two factors must be zero.
33. Zero; a zero product means one of the two factors must be zero.

Practice 5-8 Solving Equations by Multiplying Fractions

Solve each equation.

1. $\frac{3}{4}x = \frac{9}{16}$ $x = \frac{3}{4}$
2. $-\frac{1}{3}p = \frac{1}{4}$ $p = -\frac{3}{4}$
3. $-\frac{2}{5}k = \frac{1}{2}$ $k = -1\frac{1}{4}$
4. $\frac{1}{8}h = \frac{1}{10}$ $h = \frac{4}{5}$
5. $2\frac{2}{3}e = \frac{1}{13}$ $e = \frac{1}{48}$
6. $-1\frac{2}{3}m = 6$ $m = -4\frac{2}{3}$
7. $-\frac{1}{2}p = \frac{1}{18}$ $p = -\frac{2}{9}$
8. $\frac{11}{12}w = -1$ $w = 1\frac{1}{11}$
9. $-\frac{3}{4}x = 0$ $x = 0$
10. $\frac{2}{3}m = 2\frac{2}{9}$ $m = 3\frac{1}{3}$
11. $5c = \frac{2}{3}$ $c = \frac{2}{15}$
12. $-8k = \frac{4}{5}$ $k = -\frac{1}{10}$
13. $\frac{4}{7}y = 4$ $y = 7$
14. $2\frac{1}{4}f = \frac{6}{5}$ $f = \frac{8}{15}$
15. $\frac{10}{11}n = \frac{2}{11}$ $n = \frac{1}{5}$
16. $\frac{7}{8}c = \frac{7}{6}$ $c = 1\frac{1}{3}$

Solve each equation using mental math.

17. $7d = 42$ $d = 6$
18. $\frac{1}{4}y = 5$ $y = 20$
19. $-3h = \frac{3}{8}$ $h = -\frac{1}{8}$
20. $\frac{1}{3}k = -\frac{1}{3}$ $k = -1\frac{2}{3}$

Write an equation to solve each problem.

21. It takes Nancy $1\frac{2}{3}$ min to read 1 page in her social studies book. It took her $22\frac{1}{2}$ min to complete her reading assignment. How long was the assignment? Let m represent the number of pages she read.
$1\frac{2}{3}m = 22\frac{1}{2}$; $m = 13\frac{1}{2}$ pages

22. It takes Gary three hours to drive to Boston. If the trip is 156 miles, what is Gary's average number of miles per hour? Let x represent the miles per hour.
$3x = 156$; $x = 52$ mi/h

Enrichment 5-8 Musical Notes

In music notation, the duration of a note (the length of time it is intended to last) is indicated by its shape.

- ○ = whole
- ♩ = half note
- ♩ = quarter note
- ♪ = eighth note
- ♬ = sixteenth note
- ♬ = thirty-second note

The durations of notes are determined relative to one another.

Example The duration of the half note is 1 second. Find the durations of the other notes.

Solution $\frac{1}{2} = \frac{1}{2} \cdot 1$ s $= \frac{1}{2}$ s
○ = $2 \cdot 1$ s $= 2$ s

At the beginning of a piece of music, the composer indicates with a symbol the number of one type of note to be played in one minute.

♩ = 180: Play 180 quarter notes in 60 s
Duration of quarter note = $\frac{60}{180} = \frac{1}{3}$ s.

Write the fractional duration of each note, in seconds, in the spaces to the right. Let ♪ = 120.

1. $\frac{1}{2}$ s $\frac{1}{2}$ s 1 s 2 s
2. $\frac{1}{4}$ s $\frac{1}{4}$ s $\frac{1}{8}$ s $\frac{1}{8}$ s $\frac{1}{8}$ s $\frac{1}{8}$ s 1 s 2 s
3. Suppose that ♩ = 80 appeared at the beginning of the music in Exercises 1 and 2.
   a. Find the duration of a quarter note. $\frac{3}{4}$ s
   b. Find the duration of the music in Exercise 1. 3 s

Placing a dot after a note increases its duration by one-half.

Example Let duration of ♩ = $\frac{1}{5}$ s.
Solution Duration of ♩. = $\frac{1}{5} + (\frac{1}{2} \cdot \frac{1}{5}) = \frac{1}{5} + \frac{1}{10} = \frac{3}{10}$ s.

4. ♪ = 240. Find the duration of the note in seconds.
   ♪ $\frac{1}{4}$ s   ♩ $\frac{1}{2}$ s   ♪. $\frac{3}{8}$ s
   ♩. $1\frac{1}{2}$ s   ♬. $\frac{3}{32}$ s   ♩. $\frac{3}{4}$ s

270

Auditory Learners
Exercises 1–20 Have one student read an equation aloud. Have his or her partner say the reciprocal fraction needed to solve the equation.

50. <u>Writing in Math</u> Describe how you would solve and check the equation $\frac{2}{3}x = 3$. **See back of book.**

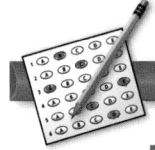 **Challenge** **Solve each equation.**

51. $-\frac{3}{4}x + \frac{1}{4}x = -6$ **52.** $\frac{5}{8}x - 6\frac{3}{8}x = 1\frac{1}{2}$ **53.** $\frac{-5}{-7}x + \left(-\frac{1}{5}x\right) = -\frac{3}{5}$
   12 $-\frac{6}{23}$ $-1\frac{1}{6}$

54. **Reasoning** By what would you multiply each side of the equation $ax = 27$ to solve for x? By what would you multiply each side of the equation $\frac{1}{a}x = 27$ to solve for x? $\frac{1}{a}$; a

55. **Marine Biology** A sailfish can swim about $11\frac{1}{3}$ mi in 10 min. About how many miles can a sailfish swim per minute? At that speed, about how many feet does a sailfish swim in one second? $1\frac{2}{15}$ mi; 100 ft

56. **Aviation** A small airplane coming in for a landing descends $\frac{5}{66}$ mi/min. About how long does it take to descend 4,000 ft? (*Hint:* 1 mi = 5,280 ft) **10 min**

Test Prep

Multiple Choice

57. Which equation has a solution greater than 1? **C**
   A. $-5x = \frac{5}{8}$ **B.** $-\frac{5}{8}x = 5$ **C.** $\frac{5}{8}x = 5$ **D.** $5x = \frac{5}{8}$

58. What is the value of h in the equation $2\frac{1}{2} + h = -1\frac{3}{8}$? **F**
   F. $-3\frac{7}{8}$ **G.** $-1\frac{1}{8}$ **H.** $1\frac{1}{8}$ **I.** $3\frac{7}{8}$

59. The Jones family uses an average of 1 quart of milk each day. At this rate how many days will it take the family to use $5\frac{1}{2}$ gallons of milk? **D**
   A. $19\frac{1}{2}$ **B.** 20 **C.** $21\frac{1}{2}$ **D.** 22

60. A single copy of a book is $2\frac{3}{4}$ in. thick. A shipping box will hold a stack of books up to $16\frac{1}{2}$ in. tall. How many copies of the book can you stack in the box? **F**
   F. 6 **G.** 8 **H.** 32 **I.** 45

Reading Comprehension   Read the passage below before doing Exercises 61 and 62.

Paper Recycling on the Rise During the 1990s, recycling in the United States steadily increased. In 1996, people in the United States recycled about nine twentieths of their paper waste. This amounted to 42.3 million tons of paper, or about 295 lb/person. Only one year earlier, Americans recycled just over two fifths of their paper waste, a total of about 32.7 million tons of paper.

 **Take It to the NET**
Online lesson quiz at
www.PHSchool.com
Web Code: ada-0508

61. How much paper waste did Americans produce in 1995? about 81.75 million tons

62. How much paper waste did Americans produce in 1996? about 94 million tons

5-8 Solving Equations by Multiplying Fractions **271**

Mixed Review

Lesson 5-7 **Solve each equation.**

63. $j + \frac{3}{4} = \frac{7}{8}$ $\frac{1}{8}$
64. $\frac{4}{5} = y - \frac{3}{5}$ $1\frac{2}{5}$
65. $6\frac{1}{2} = m + 2\frac{7}{8}$ $3\frac{5}{8}$

Lesson 5-3 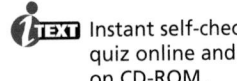 **66. Snacks** One bag of popcorn holds $1\frac{5}{8}$ oz. Another holds $1\frac{3}{4}$ oz.
   a. Which bag holds more popcorn? the $1\frac{3}{4}$-oz bag
   b. How much more? $\frac{1}{8}$ oz
   c. How much popcorn can the two bags hold in all? $3\frac{3}{8}$ oz

Lessons 4-7 and 4-8 **Simplify each expression.**

67. $3r \cdot r^4$ $3r^5$
68. $\frac{6x^3}{2x}$ $3x^2$
69. $10s^2 \cdot 10s^3$ $100s^5$
70. $\frac{20a^5}{4a^2}$ $5a^3$
71. $x^3 \cdot x^{10}$ x^{13}
72. $q^5 \cdot 3q$ $3q^6$

✓ **Checkpoint Quiz 2**   **Lessons 5-4 through 5-8**

iTEXT Instant self-check quiz online and on CD-ROM

Multiply or divide.

1. $\frac{2}{3}(21)$ 14
2. $\frac{4}{5} \cdot \frac{5}{8}$ $\frac{1}{2}$
3. $-\frac{4}{9}\left(\frac{1}{3}\right)$ $-\frac{4}{27}$
4. $\frac{2}{5} \div \frac{3}{10}$ $1\frac{1}{3}$
5. $-\frac{3}{4} \div \frac{3}{8}$ -2
6. $8\frac{1}{2} \div \frac{1}{4}$ 34

Complete each statement.

7. ■ t = 4,500 lb $2\frac{1}{4}$
8. $2\frac{1}{2}$ yd = ■ in. 90
9. 24 oz = ■ lb $1\frac{1}{2}$
10. ■ mi = 1,760 ft $\frac{1}{3}$

Solve each equation.

11. $y + \frac{2}{5} = \frac{3}{5}$ $\frac{1}{5}$
12. $t - \frac{3}{4} = \frac{7}{8}$ $1\frac{5}{8}$
13. $x - 4\frac{1}{2} = 6\frac{3}{4}$ $11\frac{1}{4}$
14. $4t = \frac{24}{35}$ $\frac{6}{35}$
15. $\frac{5}{7}y = \frac{1}{3}$ $\frac{7}{15}$
16. $5\frac{1}{3} + v = -12$ $-17\frac{1}{3}$
17. $-\frac{8}{9}g = \frac{3}{5}$ $-\frac{27}{40}$
18. $\frac{9}{10} = \frac{1}{4}w$ $3\frac{3}{5}$
19. $1\frac{1}{2}d = \frac{5}{22}$ $\frac{5}{33}$

20. A jetliner is cruising at an altitude of 31,680 ft. What is the altitude in miles? **6 miles**

21. A car is travelling $\frac{11}{12}$ miles per minute. What is the speed of the car in miles per hour? **55 mi/h**

22. You spend $\frac{1}{3}$ of your money on lunch. Your friend then pays back a loan of $2.50. Later, you spend $4 on a movie ticket and $1.25 for a snack. You have $5.25 left. How much money did you have before lunch? **$12**

23. **Open-Ended** Describe an object you might measure using the customary system of measurement. Choose a unit of measure and estimate the measurement of the object using that unit.
   Answers may vary. Sample: a desktop can be measured in inches; 48 inches.

272 Chapter 5 Operations With Fractions

Alternative Assessment

Ask students to write a jingle or mnemonic device to help them remember the equation-solving procedure that involves multiplying by the reciprocal.

Writing in Math

Writing to Explain

For Use With Page 270, Exercise 49

In this book, there are many exercises that ask you to explain your work. One type of exercise that asks for an explanation is Error Analysis. For an Error Analysis exercise, you often need to do three things:

- Identify the error.
- Explain the error.
- Show a correct solution.

You do not have to do them in the above order, however. Often, showing a correct solution first will help you find and understand the error.

EXAMPLE

Error Analysis A student solved the equation $-\frac{7}{10}h = 5\frac{3}{5}$ and found the solution 8. Describe and correct the student's error.

- Show a correct solution.

$$-\frac{7}{10}h = 5\frac{3}{5}$$

$$-\frac{7}{10}h = \frac{28}{5}$$

$$\left(-\frac{\cancel{10}^{1}}{\cancel{7}_{1}}\right)\left(-\frac{\cancel{7}^{1}}{\cancel{10}_{1}}h\right) = \frac{\cancel{28}^{4}}{\cancel{5}_{1}}\left(-\frac{\cancel{10}^{2}}{\cancel{7}_{1}}\right)$$

$$h = -8$$

- Identify the error.
  The student lost the negative sign.
- Explain the error.
  You can only make a good guess as to the cause of the error.

  The student multiplied each side by $\frac{10}{7}$ and lost track of the negative sign.

EXERCISES   1. The student multiplied by $-\frac{7}{8}$ instead of multiplying by the reciprocal, $-\frac{8}{7}$; $h = -4$

1. **Error Analysis** A student solved the equation $-\frac{7}{8}h = 3\frac{1}{2}$ and found
   the solution $-3\frac{1}{16}$. Describe and correct the student's error.
   See above.
2. Explain why 0 is a solution and the only solution of $2x = 3x$.
   Any other number for x will yield a false equation.
   $2(0) = 3(0)$.

Writing in Math

Writing to Explain

Students read through a problem and learn to analyze for errors. Then they write an explanation of the error.

Teaching Notes

Have students work independently to analyze an incorrect solution. Then have students work in pairs to explain and discuss their error analyses with each other. If there is a disagreement between partners, have them each explain their thinking to the class. Then classmates can help by asking questions and offering their own analyses.

Teaching Tip

For the Exercise, suggest that students first solve the equation, showing and justifying each step. This will help them see where the error occurred.

Powers of Products and Quotients

Lesson Preview

✓ Check Skills You'll Need

Exponents and Multiplication
Lesson 4-9: Example 3;
Exercises 19–27.
Extra Practice, p. 747.

Lesson Resources

📁 **Teaching Resources**
Practice, Reteaching, Enrichment

👥 **Reaching All Students**
Practice Workbook 5-9
Spanish Practice Workbook 5-9
Guided Problem Solving 5-9

⏰ **Presentation Assistant Plus!**
Transparencies and PowerPoint™
• Check Skills You'll Need 5-9
• Additional Examples 5-9
• Student Edition Answers 5-9
• Lesson Quiz 5-9
PH Presentation Pro CD-ROM 5-9

ASSESSMENT SYSTEM

Computer Test Generator CD-ROM

💻 **Technology**
Resource Pro® CD-ROM
Computer Test Generator CD-ROM
PH Presentation Pro CD-ROM

💻 **www.PHSchool.com**

Student Site
• Teacher Web Code: adk-5500
• Self-grading Lesson Quiz
PH SuccessNet Teacher Center
• Lesson Planner
• Resources

Plus 📖**TEXT**

What You'll Learn

OBJECTIVE 1 To find powers of products

OBJECTIVE 2 To find powers of quotients

. . . And Why

To solve real-world problems involving area

✓ Check Skills You'll Need

Simplify each expression.

1. $(2^2)^3$ 2. $(3^2)^2$ 3. $(1^5)^4$

4. $(x^3)^6$ 5. $(b^2)^5$ 6. $(a^7)^4$
1–6. See below.

💡 For help, go to Lesson 4-7.

1. 64   2. 81   3. 1

4. x^{18} 5. b^{10} 6. a^{28}

OBJECTIVE

1 Finding Powers of Products

You can use the Commutative and Associative Properties of Multiplication to find a pattern in products raised to a power.

$$(4 \cdot 2)^3 = (4 \cdot 2) \cdot (4 \cdot 2) \cdot (4 \cdot 2) \quad \text{Write the factors.}$$

$$= 4 \cdot 4 \cdot 4 \cdot 2 \cdot 2 \cdot 2 \quad \text{Use the Commutative Property to arrange the factors.}$$

$$= (4 \cdot 4 \cdot 4) \cdot (2 \cdot 2 \cdot 2) \quad \text{Use the Associative Property to group the factors.}$$

$$= 4^3 \cdot 2^3 \quad \text{Write the powers.}$$

This result suggests a rule for simplifying products raised to a power.

> **Key Concepts** — **Rule for Raising a Product to a Power**
>
> To raise a product to a power, raise each factor to the power.
>
> | Arithmetic | Algebra |
> |---|---|
> | $(5 \cdot 3)^4 = 5^4 \cdot 3^4$ | $(ab)^m = a^m b^m$, for any positive integer m |

To simplify an expression, you should eliminate as many parentheses as possible.

? Need Help?

Rule for Raising a Power to a Power:
$(a^m)^n = a^{m \cdot n}$

1 EXAMPLE — Simplifying a Power of a Product

Simplify $(4x^2)^3$.

$$(4x^2)^3 = 4^3 \cdot (x^2)^3 \quad \text{Raise each factor to the third power.}$$

$$= 4^3 \cdot x^{2 \cdot 3} \quad \text{Use the Rule for Raising a Power to a Power.}$$

$$= 4^3 \cdot x^6 \quad \text{Multiply exponents.}$$

$$= 64x^6 \quad \text{Simplify.}$$

✓ Check Understanding   Example 1

1. Simplify each expression.

   a. $(2(3))^3$ **216**   b. $(2p)^4$ **$16p^4$**   c. $(xy^2)^5$ **x^5y^{10}**   d. $(5x^3)^2$ **$25x^6$**

📖**TEXT** Interactive lesson includes instant self-check, tutorials, and activities.

✓ Ongoing Assessment and Intervention

Before the Lesson
Diagnose prerequisite skills using:
• Check Skills You'll Need

During the Lesson
Monitor progress using:
• Check Understanding
• Additional Examples
• Test Prep

After the Lesson
Assess knowledge using:
• Lesson Quiz
• Computer Test Generator CD-ROM

The location of a negative sign affects the value of an expression.

2 EXAMPLE **Working With a Negative Sign**

a. Simplify $(-5x)^2$.
$$(-5x)^2 = (-5)^2(x)^2$$
$$= 25x^2$$

b. Simplify $-(5x)^2$.
$$-(5x)^2 = (-1)(5x)^2$$
$$= (-1)(5)^2(x)^2$$
$$= -25x^2$$

✓ **Check Understanding** **Example 2**

2. Simplify each expression.
   a. $(-2y)^4$ $16y^4$ b. $-(2y)^4$ $-16y^4$ c. $(-5a^2b)^3$ $-125a^6b^3$

OBJECTIVE

2 **Finding Powers of Quotients**

You can use repeated multiplication to write a power of a quotient.
$$\left(\frac{4}{5}\right)^3 = \left(\frac{4}{5}\right)\left(\frac{4}{5}\right)\left(\frac{4}{5}\right) = \frac{4 \cdot 4 \cdot 4}{5 \cdot 5 \cdot 5} = \frac{4^3}{5^3}$$

Key Concepts **Raising a Quotient to a Power**

To raise a quotient to a power, raise both the numerator and denominator to the power.

Arithmetic	Algebra
$\left(\frac{2}{3}\right)^4 = \frac{2^4}{3^4}$	$\left(\frac{a}{b}\right)^m = \frac{a^m}{b^m}$, for $b \neq 0$
	and any positive integer m

Reading Math

You read $\left(\frac{2}{3}\right)^4$ as "two thirds to the fourth power." You read $\frac{2}{3^4}$ as "two divided by three to the fourth power."

3 EXAMPLE **Real-World** **Problem Solving**

Geometry **Find the area of the square tile.**

$A = s^2$ s = length of a side

$= \left(\frac{3}{b}\right)^2$

$= \frac{3^2}{b^2} = \frac{9}{b^2}$

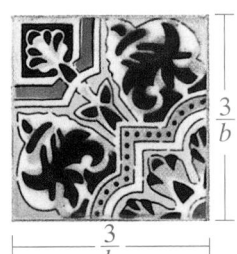

The area of the tile is $\frac{9}{b^2}$ square units.

✓ **Check Understanding** **Example 3**

3. Simplify each expression.
   a. $\left(\frac{1}{2}\right)^3$ $\frac{1}{8}$ b. $\left(-\frac{2}{3}\right)^4$ $\frac{16}{81}$ c. $\left(\frac{2x^2}{3}\right)^3$ $\frac{8x^6}{27}$

5-9 Powers of Products and Quotients **275**

👥 **Reaching All Students**

Below Level Have students review the meaning of the exponent 3 by writing each of a^3, $(2a)^3$, and $(2a^2)^3$ as the product of three factors. Help them see that the last expression can also be written as $2^3 a^6$.

Advanced Learners Have students simplify $\left(\frac{1}{6}d\frac{5}{c^2}\right)^3$. $\frac{125d^3}{216c^6}$

Visual Learners
See note on page 275.
Error Prevention
See note on page 275.

275

Assignment Guide

▼ Objective 1
Ⓐ Ⓑ **Core** 1–21, 32–34, 38, 40–48
Ⓒ **Extension** 57–60

▼ Objective 2
Ⓐ Ⓑ **Core** 22–31, 35–37, 39, 49–56
Ⓒ **Extension** 61–63

Test Prep 64–68
Mixed Review 69–81

Practice 5-9 *Powers of Products and Quotients*

Simplify each expression.

1. $\left(\frac{5}{6}\right)^2$ $\frac{25}{36}$ 2. $\left(-\frac{4}{9}\right)^2$ $\frac{16}{81}$

3. $\left(\frac{x^2}{5}\right)^3$ $\frac{x^6}{125}$ 4. $(2x)^3$ $8x^3$

5. $(-3y^2)^2$ $9y^4$ 6. $(5ab^2)^3$ $125a^3b^6$

7. $(12mn)^2$ $144m^2n^2$ 8. $(-10xy^3)^3$ $-1,000x^3y^9$

9. $(9qrs^4)^3$ $729q^3r^3s^{12}$ 10. $\left(\frac{2x}{9y}\right)^2$ $\frac{4x^2}{81y^2}$

11. $-(a^2b^2)^3$ $-a^6b^6$ 12. $(2a^3b^2)^4$ $16a^{12}b^8$

13. $\left(\frac{2x}{y}\right)^2$ $\frac{4x^2}{y^2}$ 14. $\left(-\frac{3a}{8y}\right)^2$ $\frac{9x^2}{64y^2}$

15. $\left(\frac{3z^2}{x}\right)^3$ $\frac{27y^6}{x^3}$ 16. $\left(\frac{2x^2}{xy}\right)^5$ $\frac{32x^5}{y^{10}}$

Evaluate for $a = 2$, $b = -1$, and $c = \frac{1}{3}$.

17. $(a^2)^3$ 64 18. $2b^3$ -2 19. $(-9c^2)^3$ -1

20. $(a^2b)^2$ 16 21. $(ac)^2$ $\frac{4}{9}$ 22. $(b^3)^7$ -1

Complete each equation.

23. $(3b^{\boxed{5}})^2 = 9b^{10}$ 24. $(m^2n^{\boxed{4}})^2 = m^8n^4$

25. $(xy^{\boxed{3}})^2 = x^2y^6$ 26. $\left(\frac{3z^{\boxed{2}}}{r}\right)^2 = \frac{9z^4}{r^2}$

27. Write an expression for the area of a square with a side of length $4a^2$. Simplify your expression. $(4a^2)^2 = 16a^4$

28. Write an expression for the volume of a cube with a side of length $3z^5$. Simplify your expression. $(3z^5)^3 = 27z^{15}$

Enrichment 5-9 *More Exponent Patterns*

1. a. Simplify 4^3. 64
   b. Simplify 2^6. 64
   c. What do you notice? $4^3 = 2^6$

2. a. Simplify 9^4. $6{,}561$
   b. Simplify 3^8. $6{,}561$
   c. What do you notice? $9^4 = 3^8$

3. Substitute 2^2 for 4 in 4^3 and simplify to show why the pattern in Exercise 1 holds. $4^3 = (2^2)^3 = 2^6$

4. Substitute 3^2 for 9 in 9^4 and simplify to show why the pattern in Exercise 2 holds. $9^4 = (3^2)^4 = 3^8$

You can use this relationship to simplify expressions like $5^4 \cdot 25^3$:
$5^4 \cdot 25^3 = 5^4 \cdot (5^2)^3 = 5^4 \cdot 5^6 = 5^{10}$

Simplify each expression.

5. $2^5 \cdot 4^3$ 2^{11} 6. $3^4 \cdot 9^3$ 3^{10}

7. $8^2 \cdot 2^6$ 2^{12} 8. $36^2 \cdot 6^3$ 6^7

9. $81^2 \cdot 3^5$ 3^{13} 10. $4^3 \cdot 16^2 \cdot 2^4$ 2^{18}

11. $32^2 \cdot 16^3$ 2^{22} 12. $125^2 \cdot 5^4$ 5^{10}

13. $16^4 \cdot 2^7 \cdot 4^3$ 2^{29} 14. $27^4 \cdot 3^6$ 3^{18}

15. $49^5 \cdot 7^3$ 7^{13} 16. $100^5 \cdot 10^7$ 10^{17}

17. $81^6 \cdot 3^5 \cdot 27^4$ 3^{41} 18. $4^7 \cdot 32^3 \cdot 16^5$ 2^{49}

EXERCISES

? For more exercises, see *Extra Practice.*

Practice and Problem Solving

Ⓐ **Practice by Example**

Simplify each expression.

Example 1
(page 274)

1. $(3(2))^2$ 36 2. $(3j)^3$ $27j^3$ 3. $(rs^3)^4$ r^4s^{12} 4. $(7t^2)^3$ $343t^6$

5. $(4a^5)^2$ $16a^{10}$ 6. $(2c^2)^5$ $32c^{10}$ 7. $(2x^2)^3$ $8x^6$ 8. $(a^2b^4)^3$ a^6b^{12}

9. $(2a^5)^3$ $8a^{15}$ 10. $(c^3)^2$ c^6 11. $(2b)^3$ $8b^3$ 12. $(ac^2)^2$ a^2c^4

Example 2
(page 275)

13. $(-10x^3)^4$ See left.   14. $-(xy)^2$ $-x^2y^2$ 15. $(-5b)^3$ $-125b^3$ 16. $-(3x)^2$ $-9x^2$

13. $10{,}000x^{12}$

17. $(-5c^3)^2$ $25c^6$ 18. $-(x^2y^2)^2$ $-x^4y^4$ 19. $(-3a^4b)^3$ $-27a^{12}b^3$ 20. $-(m^2 \cdot n)^4$ $-m^8n^4$

21. The side length of a square tablecloth is $5s^2$ cm.
   a. Find the area of the tablecloth. $25s^4$ cm^2
   b. Will the tablecloth completely cover a square tabletop with area $20s^4$ cm^2? Explain.   Yes; the area of the tablecloth is $25s^4$ cm^2 which is greater than $20s^4$ cm^2.

Example 3
(page 275)

Simplify each expression. 22–31. See margin.

22. $\left(\frac{2}{5}\right)^2$ 23. $\left(-\frac{2}{5}\right)^3$ 24. $\left(\frac{4}{7y}\right)^2$ 25. $\left(\frac{3x^2}{10}\right)^4$ 26. $\left(\frac{4}{9}\right)^2$

27. $\left(-\frac{3}{7}\right)^2$ 28. $\left(-\frac{m}{b^3}\right)^6$ 29. $\left(\frac{1}{3x^2}\right)^4$ 30. $\left(-\frac{3}{4}\right)^3$ 31. $\left(\frac{3t^2}{5}\right)^2$

Ⓑ **Apply Your Skills**

Number Sense Complete each equation.

32. $(5 \cdot 2)^{\blacksquare} = 25 \cdot 4$ 2 33. $(a^2)^{\blacksquare} = a^2$ 1 34. $(4m)^{\blacksquare} = 256m^4$ 4

35. $\left(-\frac{1}{2}\right)^{\blacksquare} = -\frac{1}{8}$ 3 36. $\left(\frac{b^{\blacksquare}}{5}\right)^2 = \frac{b^{10}}{25}$ 5 37. $\left(\frac{3}{7}\right)^{\blacksquare} = \frac{27}{343}$ 3

Evaluate for $a = -1$, $b = 3$, and $c = \frac{1}{2}$.

38. $(-b^2)^2$ 81 39. $\left(\frac{a}{b}\right)^3$ $-\frac{1}{27}$ 40. $(4c^2)^2$ 1 41. $(a^2b)^2$ 9

42. **Geometry** Find the area of a square with side length $4c$ units. $16c^2$ units^2

🌐 43. **Furniture** A table has sides that measure $3x^2$ ft. Write an
   GPS   expression for the area of the tabletop. Simplify your expression. $(3x^2)^2 = 9x^4$ ft^2

44. **Writing in Math** Explain why $(-xy)^2 = (xy)^2$.   Answers may vary. Sample: The square of a number and the square of its opposite are the same.

Simplify each expression. 45–56. See left.

45. $(3 \cdot 4)^3$ 46. $(-2 \cdot 5)^2$ 47. $(3 \cdot 5)^2$ 48. $(2ab^3)^2$

49. $\left(-\frac{5}{8}\right)^3$ 50. $\left(-\frac{2}{x^3}\right)^5$ 51. $\left(\frac{2c}{7d}\right)^2$ 52. $\left(-\frac{3a}{b^2}\right)^3$

53. $\left(-\frac{2x}{7y}\right)^2$ 54. $\left(\frac{2c}{d^2}\right)^4$ 55. $\left(-\frac{xy}{2xy^4}\right)^5$ 56. $\left(\frac{x^3}{2y^4}\right)^5$

Left margin answers:

45. $1{,}728$
46. 100
47. 225
48. $4a^2b^6$
49. $-\frac{125}{512}$
50. $-\frac{32}{x^{15}}$
51. $\frac{4c^2}{49d^2}$
52. $-\frac{27a^3}{b^6}$
53. $\frac{4x^2}{49y^2}$
54. $\frac{16c^4}{d^8}$
55. $-\frac{1}{32y^{15}}$
56. $\frac{x^{15}}{32y^{20}}$

Ⓒ **Challenge**

Number Sense Complete each equation.

57. $(2b^{\blacksquare})^2 = 4b^8$ 4 58. $(4 \cdot (-7))^{\blacksquare} = 64 \cdot (-343)$ 3

59. $(gh^2)^{\blacksquare} = g^3h^{\blacksquare}$ $3; 6$ 60. $3(4c^3)^{\blacksquare} = \blacksquare c^{12}$ $4; 768$

276 Chapter 5 Operations With Fractions

GPS   Use the Guided Problem Solving worksheet with Exercise 43.

22. $\frac{4}{25}$ 23. $-\frac{8}{125}$ 24. $\frac{16}{49y^2}$ 25. $\frac{81x^8}{10{,}000}$ 26. $\frac{16}{81}$

27. $\frac{9}{49}$ 28. $\frac{m^6}{b^{18}}$ 29. $\frac{1}{81x^8}$ 30. $-\frac{27}{64}$ 31. $\frac{9t^4}{25}$

Geometry Use the formula $V = s^3$, where s is the length of a side, to find the volume of each cube.

61.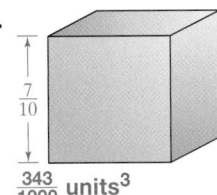
$\frac{343}{1000}$ units³

62.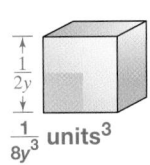
$\frac{1}{8y^3}$ units³

63.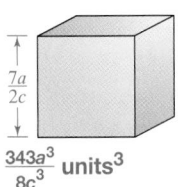
$\frac{343a^3}{8c^3}$ units³

Test Prep

Multiple Choice

64. Which expression does NOT simplify to a^{36}? **B**
   A. $(a^2)^{18}$ **B.** $(a^3)^6$ **C.** $(a^6)^6$ **D.** $(a^9)^4$

65. Which equation is FALSE? **H**

   F. $\left|-\frac{1}{7}\right| = \left|\frac{1}{7}\right|$ **G.** $\left(\frac{3}{9}\right)^3 = \frac{3^3}{9^3}$

   H. $\left(-6 \cdot \frac{2}{3}\right)^2 = 6 \cdot \left(\frac{2}{3}\right)^2$ **I.** $\left(\frac{2}{5}\right)^3 = \frac{8}{125}$

66. What is the simplest form of $(2x^3)^4$? **D**
   A. $8x^7$ **B.** $8x^{12}$ **C.** $16x^7$ **D.** $16x^{12}$

Short Response

67. Does $(3y)^7$ equal $3y^7$? Explain. See margin.

68. The side length of a square rug is $7b$ ft.   **(a)** Will the rug cover a square floor with area $56b^2$ ft²?   **(b)** Explain your reasoning.
   [2] No; the area of the square rug is $(7b)(7b) = 49b^2$ ft². The floor has a larger area of $56b^2$ ft², so the rug will not cover the floor.
   [1] correct answer with incomplete or incorrect explanation

Mixed Review

Lesson 5-8   **Solve each equation.**

69. $\frac{2}{7}h = \frac{7}{8}$ $3\frac{1}{16}$ **70.** $7c = 1\frac{5}{9}$ $\frac{2}{9}$ **71.** $\frac{5}{8} = \frac{10}{12}x$ $\frac{3}{4}$ **72.** $10\frac{3}{4} = -5\frac{1}{2}y$
$-1\frac{21}{22}$

Lesson 3-5 73. **Gardening** Delia bought three shrubs for $5.99, $12.99, and $x. She paid a total of $34.97 for the shrubs. How much did the third shrub cost? $15.99

Lesson 1-10   **Use the coordinate plane at the right. Write the coordinates of each point named below.**

74. A $(-2, 4)$ **75.** C $(4, 2)$

76. F $(0, -4)$ **77.** D $(4, 0)$

Write the name of each point with the given coordinates.

78. $(4, -2)$ E **79.** $(-4, 0)$ H

80. $(0, 4)$ B **81.** $(-2, -4)$ G

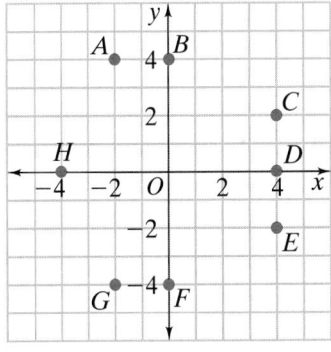

67. **[2]** No; to raise a product to a power, raise *each* factor to the power.
   [1] answer only with incomplete or incorrect explanation

277

---

4. Assess

 Lesson Quiz 5-9

Simplify each expression.

1. $(12x^2yz)^2$ $144x^4y^2z^2$
2. $(-4ab^3)^3$ $-64a^3b^9$
3. $-(-2g^2h)^8$ $-256g^{16}h^8$
4. $\left(\frac{u^3}{6}\right)^2$ $\frac{u^6}{36}$
5. $\left(\frac{3q^8r^6}{s^7}\right)^5$ $\frac{243q^{40}r^{30}}{s^{35}}$

Error Prevention!

Exercises 45–56 Suggest that students first decide on the sign of each answer.

Alternative Assessment

Have each student create a poster that shows how to find the powers of products and quotients. Suggest that they not use words but instead use as many drawings and symbols as they can think of. Display everyone's poster.

Test Prep

 Resources
For additional practice with a variety of test item formats:
• Test Prep, p. 283
• Test-Taking Strategies, p. 278
• Test-Taking Strategies With Transparencies

Reteaching 5-9 *Powers of Products and Quotients*

Simplify $\left(\frac{x^3}{-y^2}\right)^5$.

$\left(\frac{x^3}{-y^2}\right)^5 = \frac{(x^3)^5}{(-y^2)^5}$ Raise both the numerator and the denominator to the power of 5.

$= \frac{x^{15}}{(-1)^5(y^2)^5}$ Multiply exponents in the numerator. Raise each factor to the power of 5 in the denominator.

$= \frac{-x^{15}}{y^{10}}$ Multiply exponents and simplify.

Simplify each expression.

1. $(2 \cdot 5)^4$ 10,000
2. $(-3 \cdot 2)^3$ -216
3. $(4x)^2$ $16x^2$
4. $(a^2b)^5$ $a^{10}b^5$
5. $(3ab^3)^2$ $9a^2b^6$
6. $-(5m^2n^3)^3$ $-125m^6n^9$
7. $\left(\frac{2}{3}\right)^2$ $\frac{4}{81}$
8. $\left(-\frac{7}{8}\right)^2$ $\frac{49}{64}$
9. $\left(-\frac{3}{10}\right)^3$ $-\frac{27}{1,000}$
10. $\left(\frac{4}{x}\right)^2$ $\frac{16}{x^8}$
11. $\left(\frac{3x}{5}\right)^3$ $\frac{27x^3}{125}$
12. $\left(-\frac{x^5}{b}\right)^4$ $\frac{a^8}{b^{20}}$
13. $\left(\frac{4xy^2}{2z}\right)^5$ $\frac{x^5y^{10}}{32z^{15}}$
14. $\left(\frac{-1}{2n}\right)^4$ $\frac{1}{16n^{12}}$
15. $\left(\frac{-2x^3}{3r}\right)^2$ $\frac{4r^6s^2}{9r^4}$
16. $\left(\frac{-3}{a^2bc}\right)^3$ $-\frac{27}{a^6b^3c^8}$
17. $(p^4q^3r^2)^3$ $p^{12}q^9r^6$
18. $\left(\frac{x^2yz^3}{2}\right)^4$ $\frac{x^8y^4z^{12}}{16}$
19. $\left(\frac{5}{7k}\right)^2$ $\frac{25}{49k^2}$
20. $\left(\frac{a^4}{4b}\right)^3$ $\frac{a^{12}}{64b^3}$

Answering the Question Asked

This feature helps students learn to determine the question being asked. Being able to identify the question asked is an important skill that will help students choose the appropriate answers on test items.

Resources

Test-Taking Strategies With Transparencies
• Transparency 5
• Practice sheet, p. 5

Teaching Notes

Auditory Learners
Have students work in pairs. Have one student read the example aloud and the other student determine the question asked in his or her own words. Switch roles and repeat this procedure for the exercise.

Teaching Tip
Suggest that students, after solving the problem, read the question again to check whether the solution does actually answer the question.

Test-Taking Strategies With Transparencies

Chapter 5: Answering the Question Asked
Exercises

Solve by answering the question asked.

1. A family's monthly expenses are summarized in the circle graph at the right.

   a. What percent of their income does the family spend on food *and* housing? Explain.
      A. 16%   B. 32%   C. 48%   D. 50%

   b. What percent of their income does the family save?
      F. 5%   G. 6%   H. 8%   I. 9%

   c. What percent of their income does the family *not* spend on food, clothing or housing?
      A. 16%   B. 22%   C. 38%   D. 46%

2. The table at the right shows the favorite sport of boys participating in various sports at a high school.

   a. How many boys chose a sport other than football? Explain.
      F. 21   G. 34   H. 62   I. 85

   b. How many boys chose basketball *or* football?
      A. 147   B. 96   C. 62   D. 34

Sport	Boys Choosing
Baseball	21
Basketball	34
Football	62
Track	16
Wrestling	14

Test-Taking Strategies   Pre-Algebra   5

On a test item, be sure to answer the question that is asked. Some answer choices are there to "catch" those who read the question carelessly, or those who think carelessly about what they are to find.

1 EXAMPLE

What is the LCM of $4b^2$ and $6b^3$?

A. $2b^2$ **B.** $12b^2$ **C.** $12b^3$ **D.** $24b^3$

You are looking for the LCM, or *least common multiple*.

Choice A is the GCF, or greatest common factor, of $4b^2$ and $6b^3$.

Choice B shows the LCM of 4 and 6, but not of b^2 and b^3.

Choice D shows a common multiple of 4 and 6, but not one that's *least*.

● Choice C is the answer to the question asked.

2 EXAMPLE

Stan needed 6 lb of potatoes for the school picnic. He bought potatoes in 3-lb bags for $1.89 per bag. Zorn bought 10 lb of potatoes to make potato salad for the picnic. He paid $2.59 per 5-lb bag. How much more did Zorn pay for potatoes than Stan?

F. $.70   **G.** $1.40   **H.** $5.18   **I.** $8.96

Choice F is how much more Zorn paid *per bag* of potatoes.

Choice H is how much Zorn paid for 10 lb of potatoes.

Choice I is how much Zorn and Stan paid in all for potatoes.

● Choice G is the answer to the question asked.

EXERCISES

Answer the question asked. Then pick one other answer choice and tell why you might have (incorrectly) selected it as the answer.

1. What is the LCM of $4a$ and $10a^2$? C; A is the GCF
   A. $2a$ **B.** $4a$ **C.** $20a^2$ **D.** $30a^2$

2. Dante, a landscaper, purchased three trees. The first was $38.99. A second was $54.99. His total bill before tax was $152.98. How much more did he pay for the third tree than for the second one? I; G is the cost of the third tree
   F. $93.98   **G.** $59   **H.** $16   **I.** $4.01

Chapter Review

Vocabulary

dimensional analysis (p. 254)
least common denominator (LCD) (p. 234)

least common multiple (LCM) (p. 232)
multiple (p. 232)

reciprocals (p. 250)
repeating decimal (p. 238)
terminating decimal (p. 237)

Reading Math
Understanding Vocabulary

Match each word or phrase with its definition.

1. For $\frac{5}{6}$ and $\frac{4}{9}$, this is equal to 18. **f**

2. The pair of fractions $-\frac{13}{45}$ and $-\frac{45}{13}$ are these. **c**

3. For 5, 6, and 12, this is equal to 60. **a**

4. You can convert the fraction $\frac{1}{9}$ to one of these. **b**

5. For 7, one of these is 35. **g**

6. This tells you to multiply 8 ft by $\frac{12 \text{ in.}}{1 \text{ ft}}$ to find the number of inches in 8 ft. **d**

7. You can convert the fraction $\frac{4}{5}$ to one of these. **e**

a. least common multiple (LCM)

b. repeating decimal

c. reciprocals

d. dimensional analysis

e. terminating decimal

f. least common denominator (LCD)

g. multiple

Take It to the NET
Online vocabulary quiz
at www.PHSchool.com
Web Code: adj-0551

Skills and Concepts

5-1 Objectives

▼ To find the least common multiple (p. 232)

▼ To compare fractions (p. 233)

A **multiple** of a number is the product of that number and any nonzero whole number.

A *common multiple* of any group of numbers is a number that is a multiple of all the numbers. The common multiple with the least value is the **least common multiple (LCM)** of the numbers.

To compare fractions, use the LCM as the **least common denominator (LCD)** and write equivalent fractions.

Find the LCM of each group of numbers or expressions.

8. 12, 18   **36**
9. $8m^2, 14m$ **$56m^2$**
10. 3, 5, 7   **105**
11. $6x, 15y$ **$30xy$**

Compare. Use >, <, or = to complete each statement.

12. $\frac{5}{9}$ ▧ $\frac{5}{11}$ **>**
13. $\frac{2}{3}$ ▧ $\frac{3}{4}$ **<**
14. $-\frac{4}{5}$ ▧ $-\frac{7}{8}$ **>**
15. $\frac{1}{3}$ ▧ $\frac{4}{12}$ **=**

5-2 Objectives

▼ To write fractions as decimals (p. 237)

▼ To write terminating and repeating decimals as fractions (p. 239)

To write a fraction as a decimal, divide the numerator by the denominator. If the division has a remainder of zero, the decimal is a **terminating decimal.** If the division produces a repeating block of digits, the decimal is a **repeating decimal.** The repeating part of the decimal is written with an overbar.

Reading a decimal correctly provides one way to write it as a fraction. To write a repeating decimal as a fraction, use algebra to eliminate the repeating part.

Write each fraction as a decimal.

16. $\frac{3}{5}$ 0.6 **17.** $\frac{1}{6}$ $0.1\overline{6}$ **18.** $\frac{5}{8}$ 0.625 **19.** $\frac{3}{10}$ 0.3 **20.** $\frac{7}{100}$ 0.07

Write each decimal as a fraction or mixed number.

21. 0.25 $\frac{1}{4}$ **22.** $0.8\overline{3}$ $\frac{5}{6}$ **23.** 5.6 $5\frac{3}{5}$ **24.** $2.\overline{04}$ $2\frac{4}{99}$

5-3 Objectives

▼ To add and subtract fractions (p. 243)

▼ To add and subtract mixed numbers (p. 244)

To add or subtract fractions and mixed numbers, write them with a common denominator. Then you can add or subtract the numerators. Change a mixed number to an improper fraction before adding or subtracting.

Add or subtract.

25. $2\frac{1}{3} + \frac{3}{4}$ $3\frac{1}{12}$ **26.** $16\frac{4}{5} - 9\frac{2}{3}$ $7\frac{2}{15}$ **27.** $\frac{6}{x} + \frac{3}{5}$ $\frac{30 + 3x}{5x}$ **28.** $1\frac{1}{2} - \frac{5}{8}$ $\frac{7}{8}$

29. An upholsterer cuts a piece of cording $1\frac{2}{3}$ ft long from a piece $2\frac{1}{4}$ ft long. How much cording is left?
$\frac{7}{12}$ ft, or 7 in.

5-4 Objectives

▼ To multiply fractions (p. 248)

▼ To divide fractions (p. 250)

To multiply fractions, multiply their numerators and their denominators. To divide fractions, multiply the first fraction by the **reciprocal** of the second fraction.

To multiply or divide mixed numbers, write them as improper fractions before multiplying or dividing.

Find each product or quotient.

30. $\frac{1}{4} \cdot \frac{7}{10}$ $\frac{7}{40}$ **31.** $-\frac{2}{3} \div \frac{5}{6}$ $-\frac{4}{5}$ **32.** $1\frac{3}{5} \cdot \frac{3}{4}$ $1\frac{1}{5}$ **33.** $9\frac{3}{4} \div 2\frac{3}{5}$ $3\frac{3}{4}$ **34.** $\frac{3x}{5} \div \frac{6x}{5}$ $\frac{1}{2}$

5-5 Objectives

▼ To identify appropriate customary units (p. 253)

▼ To convert customary units (p. 254)

To convert units of measure in the customary system of measurement, use **dimensional analysis.**

Complete each statement.

35. 30 in. = ■ ft $2\frac{1}{2}$ **36.** ■ lb = 54 oz $3\frac{3}{8}$ **37.** 20 yd = ■ ft   60

38. ■ fl oz = $1\frac{1}{2}$ pt   24   **39.** 12 gal = ■ pt   96   **40.** $2\frac{3}{4}$ t = ■ lb   5,500

5-6 Objectives

▼ To solve problems by working backward (p. 259)

To solve some problems, you have to work backward.

41. Your family is planning a 4-h car trip. Along the way, you are planning to make three $\frac{1}{2}$-h stops. At what time should you leave home to arrive at the destination by 8:00 P.M.?   **2:30 P.M.**

42. Buses bound for Los Angeles leave the station every hour from 6:00 A.M. to 8:00 P.M. How many buses is that in one day?
15 buses

43. You sell used CDs at a local flea market. It costs $15 to rent a booth for the day. You spend $8 on lunch, and you make $140 selling CDs. If you have $162.50 at the end of the day, how much money did you have at the start of the day?   **$45.50**

5-7 and 5-8 Objectives

▼ To solve equations by subtracting fractions (p. 264)

▼ To solve equations by adding fractions (p. 265)

▼ To solve equations by multiplying fractions (p. 268)

▼ To solve equations by multiplying mixed numbers (p. 269)

To solve equations with fractions, use inverse operations to undo addition or subtraction. You can undo multiplication by multiplying each side of the equation by the same fraction, usually a reciprocal of a fraction in the equation.

Solve each equation.

44. $\frac{1}{8} + x = 2\frac{1}{2}$ $2\frac{3}{8}$ **45.** $x - \frac{1}{3} = \frac{4}{5}$ $1\frac{2}{15}$ **46.** $x + 4\frac{2}{3} = 6$ $1\frac{1}{3}$

47. $6x = \frac{1}{9}$ $\frac{1}{54}$ **48.** $-\frac{3}{4}x = \frac{2}{7}$ $-\frac{8}{21}$ **49.** $2\frac{2}{5}x = \frac{8}{15}$ $\frac{2}{9}$

5-9 Objectives

▼ To find powers of products (p. 274)

▼ To find powers of quotients (p. 275)

To raise a product to a power, raise each factor to the power. To raise a quotient to a power, raise both the numerator and the denominator to the power.

Simplify each expression.

50. $(2d)^4$ $16d^4$ **51.** $(-3(2))^2$ 36   **52.** $(a^2b)^5$ $a^{10}b^5$

53. $\left(-\frac{1}{2}\right)^3$ $-\frac{1}{8}$ **54.** $\left(\frac{x}{3}\right)^2$ $\frac{x^2}{9}$ **55.** $\left(\frac{2a}{c^2}\right)^4$ $\frac{16a^4}{c^8}$

Chapter Test

Take It to the NET
Online chapter test at
www.PHSchool.com
Web Code: ada-0552

Resources

Teaching Resources
Ch. 5 Test, Forms A & B
Ch. 5 Alternative Assessment,
Form C

Reaching All Students
Spanish Ch. 5 Test, Forms A & B
Spanish Ch. 5 Alternative
Assessment, Form C

Assessment Resources
• Ch. 5 Test, Forms A & B
• Ch. 5 Alternative Assessment,
Form C
Computer Test Generator CD-ROM
• Instant Chapter Test™ for Ch. 5

www.PHSchool.com
Student Site
• Self-grading Ch. 5 Test
PH SuccessNet Teacher Center
• Resources

Find the LCM of each pair.

1. $24, 36$ **72** **2.** $50, 100$ **100**

3. $3x, 2y$ **6xy** **4.** $16, 20$ **80**

Compare. Use >, <, or = to complete each statement.

5. $\frac{7}{8} \blacksquare \frac{7}{9}$ **>**   **6.** $\frac{2}{3} \blacksquare \frac{10}{15}$ **=**

7. $\frac{7}{10} \blacksquare 0.71$ **<**   **8.** $2\frac{3}{5} \blacksquare 2\frac{2}{3}$ **<**

9. $-0.87 \blacksquare -\frac{7}{8}$ **>**   **10.** $\frac{3}{4} \blacksquare \frac{14}{20}$ **>**

Order from least to greatest.

11. $0.5, \frac{1}{10}, 0, -\frac{1}{4}$ **12.** $-\frac{3}{5}, -0.\overline{6}, \frac{1}{6}, \frac{2}{3}$
$-\frac{1}{4}, 0, \frac{1}{10}, 0.5$ $-0.\overline{6}, -\frac{3}{5}, \frac{1}{6}, \frac{2}{3}$

Write each decimal as a fraction.

13. 0.4 $\frac{2}{5}$ **14.** $0.\overline{7}$ $\frac{7}{9}$ **15.** $12.\overline{36}$ $12\frac{4}{11}$

16. 5.2 $5\frac{1}{5}$ **17.** 0.002 $\frac{1}{500}$ **18.** $7.\overline{1}$ $7\frac{1}{9}$

Write each fraction as a decimal.

19. $\frac{4}{15}$ $0.2\overline{6}$ **20.** $-\frac{2}{3}$ $-0.\overline{6}$ **21.** $\frac{3}{8}$ 0.375

22. $\frac{1}{2}$ 0.5 **23.** $\frac{6}{7}$ $0.\overline{857142}$ **24.** $\frac{5}{9}$ $0.\overline{5}$

Add or subtract.

25. $\frac{1}{8} + \frac{3}{4}$ $\frac{7}{8}$ **26.** $\frac{2}{3} - \frac{1}{9}$ $\frac{5}{9}$

27. $-\frac{1}{6x} + \frac{1}{4}$ $\frac{-2+3x}{12x}$ **28.** $11\frac{5}{6} - 5\frac{3}{8}$ $6\frac{11}{24}$

29. $\frac{2}{3} - \left(-\frac{8y}{9}\right)$ $\frac{6+8y}{9}$ **30.** $2\frac{1}{5} - \frac{3}{4}$ $1\frac{9}{20}$

Multiply or divide.

31. $\frac{3}{5} \cdot \frac{1}{2}$ $\frac{3}{10}$ **32.** $-\frac{3}{4} \cdot \frac{5}{8}$ $-\frac{15}{32}$

33. $\frac{5}{8x} \div \frac{7}{16}$ $\frac{10}{7x}$ **34.** $\frac{4}{m} \div \frac{5m}{9}$ $\frac{36}{5m^2}$

35. $3\frac{3}{4} \cdot 2\frac{4}{5}$ $10\frac{1}{2}$ **36.** $-1\frac{1}{3} \div \left(-\frac{5}{9}\right)$ $2\frac{2}{5}$

59. Answers may vary. Sample: Mark cuts $1\frac{1}{4}$ ft from a piece of rope. If he has 5 ft of rope left, how long was the rope originally?

Complete each equation.

37. $10 \text{ yd} = \blacksquare \text{ ft}$ **30**   **38.** $20 \text{ oz} = \blacksquare \text{ lb}$ $1\frac{1}{4}$

39. $\blacksquare \text{ lb} = 1\frac{3}{4} \text{ t}$ **3,500**   **40.** $6 \text{ pt} = \blacksquare \text{ qt}$ **3**

41. $3\frac{1}{2} \text{ qt} = \blacksquare \text{ c}$ **14**   **42.** $\blacksquare \text{ in.} = 1\frac{3}{4} \text{ yd}$ **63**

Solve each equation.

43. $m - \frac{2}{3} = \frac{1}{4}$ $\frac{11}{12}$ **44.** $h + \frac{3}{5} = \frac{9}{10}$ $\frac{3}{10}$

45. $x - \frac{5}{6} = -\frac{5}{6}$ **0**   **46.** $\frac{3}{5}a = 9$ **15**

47. $n + \frac{7}{8} = \frac{1}{3}$ $-\frac{13}{24}$ **48.** $2\frac{1}{2}n = 3\frac{3}{4}$ $1\frac{1}{2}$

49. $-5b = 3\frac{1}{3}$ $-\frac{2}{3}$ **50.** $\frac{3}{8}y = -15$ **−40**

Simplify each expression.

51. $(3(4))^2$ **144**   **52.** $(2a)^3$ $8a^3$ **53.** $\left(\frac{3}{4}\right)^3$ $\frac{27}{64}$

54. $(3x^2)^3$ $27x^6$ **55.** $-(2x^2y)^4$ $-16x^8y^4$ **56.** $\left(\frac{2y}{5x}\right)^3$ $\frac{8y^3}{125x^3}$

Solve.

57. **Number Sense** Suppose you take a number, subtract 8, multiply by 7, add 10, and divide by 5. The result is 9. What is the original number? **13**

58. You spend $\frac{3}{4}$ of your money on clothes and have \$21 left. How much did you have before you bought the clothes? **$84**

59. **Writing in Math** Write a word problem for the equation $x - 1\frac{1}{4} = 5$.
See below left.

60. Two packages each weigh $1\frac{7}{8}$ lb. How much do they weigh altogether? $3\frac{3}{4}$ **lb**

61. You rode your bicycle a mile and a half to school. Then you rode to a friend's house. Altogether you rode $2\frac{1}{10}$ miles. Write and solve an equation to find how far it is from school to your friend's house.
$1\frac{1}{2} + x = 2\frac{1}{10};$ $\frac{3}{5}$ mi

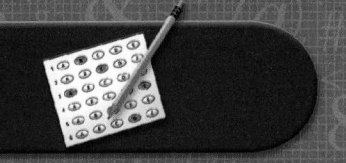

Test Prep

READING COMPREHENSION

Students must be able to extract information from reading passages, answer multiple-choice questions, and construct responses in order to be successful in current state and national assessments.

Resources

 **Teaching Resources**
Cumulative Review

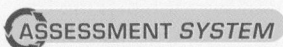 **Reaching All Students**
Spanish Cumulative Review

ASSESSMENT SYSTEM

Test Preparation
• Ch. 5 Test Prep
Assessment Resources
• Cumulative Review
Computer Test Generator CD-ROM
• Test Prep

 www.PHSchool.com
• Test Prep
• Resources

Plus

Reading Comprehension Read each passage below. Then answer the questions on the basis of what is *stated* or *implied* in the passage.

Patterns in the Sky The planet Mercury revolves around the sun about every 87.98 days and turns on its own axis about once every 58.65 (Earth) days. The planet Jupiter revolves around the sun about every 4,329.63 days. It rotates on its axis about once every 0.41 day.

Jupiter has 17 moons, among which four are Ganymede, Io, Castillo, and Europa. These satellites orbit Jupiter about once every 7.16, 1.77, 16.69, and 3.55 days, respectively.

1. How long does it take Castillo to orbit Jupiter? **C**
   A. 7.16 days
   B. 1.77 days
   C. 16.69 days
   D. 3.55 days

2. Which of Jupiter's moons travels the fastest? **G**
   F. Ganymede
   G. Io
   H. Castillo
   I. Europa

3. How many full rotations on its axis does Jupiter complete in 7 days? **17**

4. Is the rotation of Mercury exactly 58.65 days? Explain. **No; the passage uses the word "about."**

5. What is a word that means "turns on its own axis"? **rotates**

Bike Helmets Currently, 19 states and the District of Columbia require bike helmets for people who are under age 16. Even in the states that have no state law requiring helmets, there may be laws in specific counties and cities. Where such laws are in force, a typical fine for each offense is $50. According to the Consumer Product Safety Commission (CPSC), wearing a helmet can reduce the risk of head injury by 85%. The CPSC standard, which all bike helmets must meet, requires a helmet to protect the wearer against an impact on a flat surface at 14 miles per hour and on an irregular surface (such as rocks and curbs) at 11 mph. Recommended youth helmets range in price from $30 to $45.

6. How many states do NOT currently require bike helmets for people under age 16? **B**
   A. 50   B. 31   C. 20   D. 19

7. Which inequality best represents the price range p of a recommended youth helmet? **I**
   F. $p < \$45$
   G. $\$30 < p < \$45$
   H. $p > \$30$
   I. $\$30 \leq p \leq \$45$

8. About how much more than the price of a helmet is a fine for not wearing a helmet? **A**
   A. $10   B. $30   C. $45   D. $50

9. What does *mph* stand for? **miles per hour**

10. At what ages do the bike helmet laws of these states no longer apply?
    16 years and up

Chapter 5 Test Prep **283**

Quilt Tales

In this activity, students work with information from a diagram and a table and apply their knowledge of fractions, measurement, and geometric shapes.

Activating Prior Knowledge

Ask students if they know anyone who makes quilts. Have students think about why the making of a quilt requires careful planning and measurement. Invite students to think of other crafts and hobbies that also require planning and measuring to achieve good results. **Answers may vary. Sample: Students may or may not know someone who quilts. In order to make a beautiful quilt, you need to decide in advance what the overall size and design will be, and then measure and cut out the fabric pieces to create that design. Other hobbies that might require planning and measuring include gardening, furniture-making, knitting, sewing, and baking.**

Teaching Notes

Teaching Tip

Have a volunteer read the introductory paragraph. Ask: *Why might quilting have been more popular in historical times than it is today?* **Answers may vary. Sample: It was done by hand and required many hours to complete. Today, fewer women have the skills and time to devote to the task, and today it is easier to get warm blankets and quilts from stores.**

Tactile Learners

Give students several different colored papers that have been cut into $1\frac{1}{2}$-inch-wide strips. Have pairs of students cut the strips, create one Log Cabin quilt block as shown in the text diagram, and tape it together. Then students can mount their blocks on a poster board to create a class quilt.

284

Quilt Tales

Applying Fractions Quilts are more than simple bed coverings. To historians, quilts are artifacts of the past. Fabrics and dyes provide information about the textile industry. Designs tell stories of life in America. The "Log Cabin" is a traditional quilt block. The red square in the center represents the chimney in the cabin. The strips around the red square symbolize the logs of the cabin. By rotating the blocks, a quilter can make various patterns appear in a quilt.

Log Cabin quilt, made around 1865

284

Activity

Use the pattern and the chart to answer the questions.

1. After you sew them together, the fabric pieces in a Log Cabin quilt are $1\frac{1}{2}$ in. wide. Copy and complete the table for one finished Log Cabin block. **1–5. See margin.**

One Log Cabin Block

Piece Number	Finished Dimensions (length × width)
1	$1\frac{1}{2}$ in. × $1\frac{1}{2}$ in.
2	3 in. × $1\frac{1}{2}$ in.
3	■
4	■
5	■
6	■
7	■

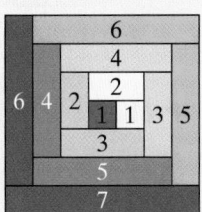

Pattern for One Log Cabin Block

2. A seam allowance is the fabric that overlaps when you sew two pieces of fabric together. In quilting, the seam allowance is $\frac{1}{4}$ in., which means that you make a seam $\frac{1}{4}$ in. from the edge of the fabric. Expand your table to include the original dimensions of each of the pieces.

3. a. What are the dimensions of one Log Cabin block?
b. What are the dimensions of a Log Cabin quilt with four blocks? With nine blocks?

4. Fabric stores sell fabric in multiples of $\frac{1}{8}$ yd. The minimum amount of fabric you can buy is $\frac{1}{8}$ yd, which is a piece of fabric that measures $4\frac{1}{2}$ in. × 44 in. Suppose you decide to make all six blue pieces from the same fabric. How much fabric should you buy for nine blocks?

5. Suppose you have $5\frac{1}{2}$ yards of fabric left over from another quilt. You decide to make all six yellow pieces from this remnant. How much of the remnant will be left after you make a Log Cabin quilt with four blocks?

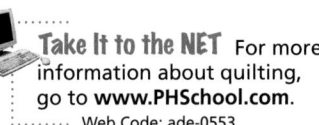
Take It to the NET For more information about quilting, go to **www.PHSchool.com**.
Web Code: ade-0553

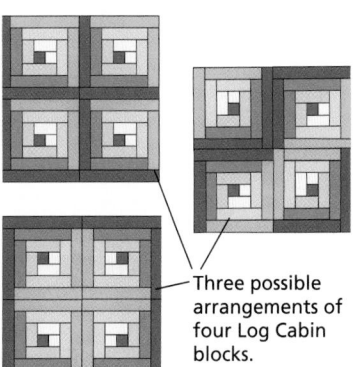

Three possible arrangements of four Log Cabin blocks.

Log Cabin Variations

Some Log Cabin quilts have center squares in colors other than red. When a Log Cabin quilt with black center squares hung on a clothesline, it meant the house was a stop on the Freedom Trail.

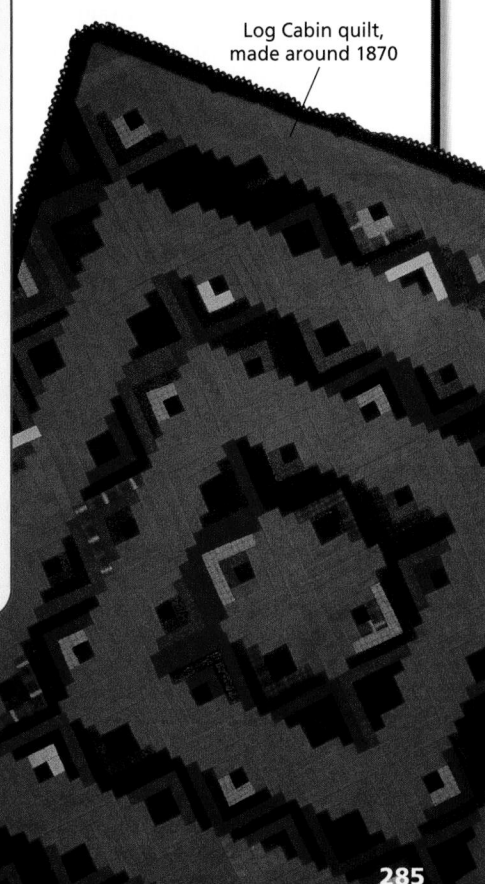

Log Cabin quilt, made around 1870

285

Put It All Together

Students must be able to extract information from a reading passage and a diagram in order to complete tables of measurement using fractions.

Teaching Tip

Before students begin the activity, discuss the illustrations and their captions. Have students work in pairs or small groups to complete the activity. Students should read through the activity before beginning to work.

Visual Learners

Help students use graph paper to draw fabric with dimensions described in Exercises 2, 3, and 4. Each square on the graph paper can equal one inch, or a fractional part of an inch. Work with students to create an appropriate key.

Connection to Art

Have students create their own block pattern for a quilt. They should measure strips and choose colors to form a block. They can rotate the block to form a design.

Connection to Literature

Ask students to find in a library and bring to class a book that tells about quilts. Volunteers can share illustrations or read aloud a part of the story that describes a quilt or the making of a quilt. Book titles may include: *The Log Cabin Quilt* by Ellen Howard, *The Dream Quilt* by Amy Zerner, *The Boy and the Quilt* by Shirley Kurtz, *Sam Johnson and the Blue Ribbon Quilt* by Lisa Campbell Ernst, *Bess's Log Cabin Quilt* by D. Anne Love, *The Quilter's Apprentice* by Jennifer Chiaverini, and *How to Make an American Quilt* by Whitney Otto

1. $4\frac{1}{2}$ in. × $1\frac{1}{2}$ in., 6 in. × $1\frac{1}{2}$ in., $7\frac{1}{2}$ in. × $1\frac{1}{2}$ in., 9 in. × $1\frac{1}{2}$ in., $10\frac{1}{2}$ in. × $1\frac{1}{2}$ in.

2. 2 in. × 2 in., $3\frac{1}{2}$ in. × 2 in., 5 in. × 2 in., $6\frac{1}{2}$ in. × 2 in., 8 in. × 2 in., $9\frac{1}{2}$ in. × 2 in., 11 in. × 2 in.

3a. $10\frac{1}{2}$ in. × $10\frac{1}{2}$ in.
  b. 21 in. × 21 in.; $31\frac{1}{2}$ in. × $31\frac{1}{2}$ in.
4. $\frac{1}{2}$ yd
5. $5\frac{1}{4}$ yd

Ratios, Proportions, and Percents

Chapter at a Glance

6-1
Ratios and Unit Rates
pp. 288–291

Objectives
- ▽ Writing and Simplifying Ratios
- ▽ Finding Rates and Unit Rates

New Vocabulary
ratio, rate, unit rate

NCTM Standards
1, 4, 6, 7, 8, 9, 10

Local Standards

6-2
Proportions
pp. 294–298

Objectives
- ▽ Solving Proportions
- ▽ Using Proportions to Solve Problems

New Vocabulary
proportion, cross products

NCTM Standards
1, 2, 4, 6, 7, 8, 9, 10

Local Standards

6-3
Similar Figures and Scale Drawings
pp. 299–303

Objectives
- ▽ Using Similar Figures
- ▽ Using Scale Drawings

New Vocabulary
similar figures, indirect measurement, scale drawing

NCTM Standards
1, 4, 6, 8, 9, 10

Local Standards

6-4
Probability
pp. 305–309

Objectives
- ▽ Finding Probability
- ▽ Finding Odds

New Vocabulary
outcomes, event, probability, impossible event, certain event, complement, odds

NCTM Standards
5, 6, 8, 9

Local Standards

✓ Checkpoint Quiz 1

6-5
Fractions, Decimals, and Percents
pp. 310–314

Objectives
- ▽ Writing Percents as Fractions and Decimals
- ▽ Writing Decimals and Fractions as Percents

New Vocabulary
percent

NCTM Standards
1, 8, 9

Local Standards

6-6
Proportions and Percents
pp. 315–319

Objectives
- ▽ Finding Part of a Whole and Percent
- ▽ Finding a Whole Amount

NCTM Standards
1, 6, 8, 9, 10

Local Standards

6-7
Percents and Equations
pp. 320–323

Objectives
- ▽ Writing and Solving Percent Equations
- ▽ Using Equations to Solve Percent Problems

New Vocabulary
commission

NCTM Standards
1, 2, 6, 8, 9, 10

Local Standards

6-8
Percent of Change
pp. 325–328

Objectives
- ▽ Finding Percent of Increase
- ▽ Finding Percent of Decrease

New Vocabulary
percent of change

NCTM Standards
1, 2, 6, 7, 8, 9, 10

Local Standards

6-9
Markup and Discount
pp. 329–332

Objectives
- ▽ Finding Markups
- ▽ Finding Discounts

New Vocabulary
markup, discount

NCTM Standards
1, 2, 6, 8, 9, 10

Local Standards

✓ Checkpoint Quiz 2

6-10   Problem Solving
Make a Table
pp. 334–337

Objective
- ▽ Making Tables to Solve Problems

NCTM Standards
1, 2, 6, 8, 9, 10

Local Standards

Correlation to Standardized Tests

| Lesson | NAEP | Terra Nova | | | | Local Test |
		CAT/6	CTBS	ITBS	SAT10	
6-1	N4a, N4b				■	
6-2	N4c			■	■	
6-3	G2e, G2f, M2f	■	■		■	
6-4	D4a, D4b				■	
6-5	N1e		■	■		
6-6	N4d	■	■			
6-7	N4d					
6-8	N4d					
6-9	N4d					
6-10	N4d					

NAEP National Assessment of Educational Progress
  N = Number Sense, Properties, and Operations
  M = Measurement
  G = Geometry and Spatial Sense
  D = Data Analysis, Statistics and Probability
  A = Algebra and Functions

CAT/6 California Achievement Test, 6th Ed.
CTBS Comprehensive Test of Basic Skills
ITBS Iowa Test of Basic Skills, Form M
SAT10 Stanford Achievement Test, 10th Ed.

NCTM STANDARDS 2000

1	Number and Operations	6	Problem Solving
2	Algebra	7	Reasoning and Proof
3	Geometry	8	Communication
4	Measurement	9	Connections
5	Data Analysis and Probability	10	Representation

Pacing Options

This chart suggests pacing for only the core lessons and their parts. It is provided as a possible guide. It will help you determine how much time you have in your schedule to cover other components, such as the features, chapter projects, Chapter Review, and Chapter Test.

Day	Traditional 45-minute class periods	Two-Year 45-minute class periods	Block 90-minute class periods
1	6-1 ▼ ▼	6-1 ▼	6-1 ▼ ▼ / 6-2 ▼ ▼
2	6-2 ▼ ▼	6-1 ▼	6-3 ▼ ▼
3	6-3 ▼ ▼	6-1 ▼	6-4 ▼ ▼
4	6-3 ▼ ▼	6-1 ▼	6-5 ▼ ▼ / 6-6 ▼ ▼
5	6-4 ▼	6-2 ▼	6-7 ▼ ▼ / 6-8 ▼ ▼
6	6-5 ▼ ▼	6-2 ▼	6-9 ▼ ▼ / 6-10 ▼
7	6-6 ▼	6-3 ▼	
8	6-6 ▼	6-3 ▼	
9	6-7 ▼ ▼	6-3 ▼	
10	6-8 ▼ ▼	6-4 ▼	
11	6-9 ▼ ▼	6-4 ▼	
12	6-10 ▼	6-4 ▼	
13		6-5 ▼	
14		6-5 ▼	
15		6-6 ▼	
16		6-6 ▼	
17		6-6 ▼	
18		6-7 ▼	
19		6-7 ▼	
20		6-8 ▼	
21		6-8 ▼	
22		6-9 ▼	
23		6-9 ▼	
24		6-10 ▼	
25		6-10 ▼	

Math Background

Skills Trace

BEFORE Chapter 6
Students should have encountered the concepts and skills in this chapter in previous courses.

DURING Chapter 6
This chapter reviews and extends ideas related to ratios, proportions, and percents.

AFTER Chapter 6
Most of the remaining chapters in Pre-Algebra use ratios and proportional reasoning. These ideas are core in Algebra 1 in developing ideas of slope and change for linear equations.

6-1 6-2 Ratios, Unit Rates, and Proportions

You can solve a proportion that contains a variable by using the fact that in a proportion the *cross products* are equal. In the following statement the cross products are ad and bc.

$\frac{a}{b} = \frac{c}{d}$ means that $ad = bc$. For example, you can solve $\frac{x}{2} = \frac{2}{3}$ by writing the equation with the cross products, $3x = 4$, and then dividing both sides by 3 to get $x = 1\frac{1}{3}$.

The following proof shows why cross products are equal.

$\frac{a}{b} = \frac{c}{d}$	Given.
$bd \cdot \frac{a}{b} = bd \cdot \frac{c}{d}$	Multiplication Property of Equality
$\frac{bda}{b} = \frac{bdc}{d}$	multiplication of fractions
$\frac{bad}{b} = \frac{dbc}{d}$	Commutative Property of Multiplication
$\frac{b}{b} \cdot ad = \frac{d}{d} \cdot bc$	multiplication of fractions
$1 \cdot ad = 1 \cdot bc$	$\frac{n}{n} = 1$
$ad = bc$	$1 \cdot n = n$

6-3 Similar Figures and Scale Drawings

In Lesson 6-2, students learned how to solve proportions. In this lesson, students apply solving proportions to solving problems involving similar figures and scale drawings.

In similar figures, the corresponding angles have equal measures and the corresponding sides are proportional. In the similar triangles below, for example, $\frac{AC}{EG} = \frac{AB}{EF}$.

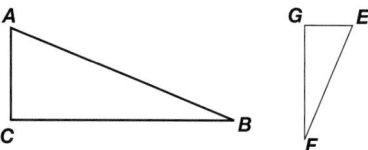

Examples of scale drawings with which students may be familiar are blueprints and maps. Model airplanes and model cars are real examples of similar figures.

6-4 Probability

A ratio that expresses the chance or likelihood that a certain event will occur is called the *probability* of that event. Theoretical probability is a number that estimates how often an event will occur. Experimental probability, instead of being an estimate, reports how often an event actually did occur.

The probability of an event is always between 0 and 1. If an event is certain to happen, the probability of that event is 1. If an event is impossible, then the probability of that event is 0.

The probability of an event is not a very good predictor of what will happen in a small number of cases. The laws of probability predict only what will happen when you survey a very large number of events.

The probability of A, as long as all possible outcomes are equally likely, is given by

$$P(A) = \frac{\text{number of outcomes of event } A}{\text{number of possible outcomes}}$$

The probability that A does not occur is $P(\text{not } A) = 1 - P(A)$. The event A and the event (not A) are *complements*. The sum of $P(A)$ and $P(\text{not } A)$ is always 1.

The probability ratio on the preceding page compares the number of favorable outcomes with the number of all possible outcomes. Another ratio, called the *odds in favor* of an event, compares the number of favorable outcomes with the number of unfavorable outcomes.

$$\text{odds in favor} = \frac{\text{number of favorable outcomes}}{\text{number of unfavorable outcomes}}$$

The *odds against* an event is the ratio of the number of unfavorable outcomes to the number of favorable outcomes.

$$\text{odds against} = \frac{\text{number of unfavorable outcomes}}{\text{number of favorable outcomes}}$$

6-5 6-6 Fractions, Decimals, Percents, and Proportions

A ratio that compares a number with 100 is called a *percent*. The word *percent* comes from the Latin phrase *per centum*, meaning "divided by one hundred." Recall that one dollar is 100 cents; 5 cents is 5 per hundred, or 5%, of one dollar.

Because percent is a way of expressing a fraction in terms of hundredths, you can change the form of a number among percent, fraction, or decimal. For example,

- $27\% = \frac{27}{100}$, which is 0.27 as a decimal.
- $0.349 = \frac{34.9}{100}$, or 34.9%.
- $\frac{4}{7}$, when divided, is approximately 0.571, or 57.1%.
- $1\frac{1}{4} = \frac{5}{4}$. Multiplying $\frac{5}{4}$ by $\frac{25}{25}$ gives $\frac{125}{100}$, or 125%.

A percent greater than 100% converts into an improper fraction or a decimal number greater than 1.

Another way to see why dividing 4 by 7 leads to a decimal for $\frac{4}{7}$ is to think of $\frac{4}{7}$ in the proportion $\frac{4}{7} = \frac{x}{1}$. Dividing the numerator and denominator in $\frac{4}{7}$ by 7, you get

$$\frac{4}{7} \approx \frac{0.571}{1}$$
$$= \frac{0.571}{1} \cdot \frac{100}{100}$$
$$= \frac{57.1}{100}, \text{ or } 57.1\%.$$

6-7 Percents and Equations

The equation method for solving a percent problem is equivalent to the proportion method of Lesson 6-6.

Find the percent.	**Find the part.**	**Find the whole.**
What percent of 40 is 6?	What is 15% of 40?	6 is 15% of what?

The proportion

$$\frac{n}{100} = \frac{6}{40} \qquad \frac{15}{100} = \frac{n}{40} \qquad \frac{15}{100} = \frac{6}{n}$$

becomes the equation

$$\frac{n}{100} \cdot 40 = 6 \qquad n = \frac{15}{100} \cdot 40 \qquad 6 = \frac{15}{100} \cdot n$$

or

$$n(\%) \cdot 40 = 6. \qquad n = 0.15 \cdot 40. \qquad 6 = 0.15 \cdot n.$$

6-8 6-9 Percent of Change, Markup, and Discount

When a store sells an item, it adds an amount called *markup* to the store's cost. In the case of prices, the percent of increase is called the *percent of markup*.

$$\% \text{ of markup} = \frac{\text{amount of markup}}{\text{store's cost}}$$

When a store puts an item on sale, the amount subtracted from the original price is the *discount*. The percent of decrease is the *percent of discount*.

$$\% \text{ of discount} = \frac{\text{amount of discount}}{\text{original price}}$$

Note that
    sale price = regular price − discount.
This means that
    sale price + discount = regular price,
or that the sale price plus the discount equals the "whole."

Thus, if the discount is *n*% of the regular price, then the sale price must be 100% − *n*% of the regular price. For a 20% discount, you can calculate the sale price as 80% of the regular price.

Additional Professional Development Opportunities

Chapter 6 Math Background notes:
pp. 289, 295, 300, 306, 311, 316, 321, 326, 330, 335

Professional Development, Content Facilitator Guide: Pre-Algebra, Chapter 6

Additional resources available from SkyLight Professional Development: On-site courses, workshops, summer institutes. Online courses and chat rooms. Videocassettes and books. Visit www.skylightedu.com.

Ongoing Assessment and Intervention

The *Prentice Hall Pre-Algebra* program provides many options for assessment in the Student Edition, Teacher's Edition, and teaching resources. From these options you may choose instructional materials that are appropriate for your students and support your district's curriculum requirements.

Daily Assessment

 Instant Check System™ in Chapter 6

Allows students to check their own learning before, during, and after each lesson.

Diagnosing Readiness before the chapter (p. 286)

Check Skills You'll Need exercises in each lesson (pp. 288, 294, 299, 305, 310, 315, 320, 325, 329, 334)

Check Understanding questions with each Example (pp. 288, 289, 295, 299, 300, 306, 307, 310, 311, 315, 316, 317, 320, 321, 325, 326, 329, 330, 335)

Checkpoint Quiz (pp. 309, 332)

Formal Assessment

In Chapter 6 and Additional Resources

Assesses student progress throughout the *Pre-Algebra* text and with blackline masters and CD-ROM.

Student Edition
- Chapter 6 Review, with Vocabulary Skills and Concepts Review, pp. 339–341
- Chapter 6 Test, p. 342

Assessment Resources   *Spanish versions available.*
- Checkpoint Quizzes 1 & 2
- Chapter Test, Forms A & B
- Chapter Alternative Assessment

 Computer Test Generator CD-ROM
- Instant Chapter Tests™ — pre-made tests with items that vary every time you print.
- Online Testing allows you to give tests online and receive progress reports.
- Diagnose readiness with questions on prerequisite skills.
- Prepare students by making tests based on standardized test objectives.

Algebra Readiness Tests
- Includes Basic Skills Tests and Concept-Readiness Tests.
- Assess understanding of skills and concepts needed for success in algebra.

Standardized Test Preparation

 Test Prep in Chapter 6

Teaches students strategies and gives them practice with all the test item formats they will encounter on high-stakes tests.

Test Prep exercises in each lesson (pp. 291, 298, 303, 309, 314, 319, 323, 328, 332, 337)

Test-Taking Strategies (p. 338: Using Estimation)

Test Prep (p. 343: Cumulative Review)

PRENTICE HALL ASSESSMENT SYSTEM

Provides a three-step approach to preparing students for high-stakes, national, and state exams.

1 Diagnose & Prescribe

Content Diagnostic Tests
- Diagnose strengths and weaknesses with ongoing benchmark tests.
- Prescribe individualized reteaching opportunities.

2 Review & Reteach

Skills and Concepts Review
- Provides reteaching worksheets with instruction and practice for each skill.
- Includes course prerequisite skills.

3 Practice & Assess

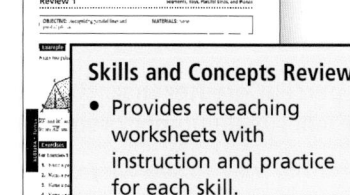

Standardized Test Preparation
- Features practice for national standardized exams.
- Includes practice tests for NAEP, SAT10, ITBS, and Terra Nova.

Test-Taking Strategies With Transparencies
- Support the Test-Taking Strategies pages in the Student Edition.
- Provide a transparency and a worksheet for each strategy.

Reaching All Students

The textbook, the iText, and other technology components provide numerous opportunities to reach students of various ability levels and learning styles. Each Teacher's Edition lesson suggests how you can help all your students be successful and understand the mathematics in Chapter 6.

Below Level

Student Edition
- Diagnosing Readiness*: p. 286
- Check Skills You'll Need*: pp. 288, 294, 299, 305, 310, 315, 320, 325, 329, 334

Reteaching
Chapter 6 Grab & Go™ File: pp. 11–20

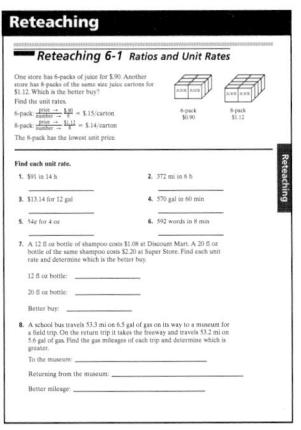

* Can be used with all ability levels to ensure mastery of prerequisite skills.

Advanced Learners

Student Edition
- Challenge exercises: pp. 290, 291, 297, 298, 303, 308, 309, 314, 319, 323, 327, 328, 332, 336
- Extension: p. 292

Enrichment
Chapter 6 Grab & Go™ File: pp. 21–30

Problem Solving

Student Edition
- Strategies: pp. 334–337
- Real-World Problem Solving: pp. 288, 289, 295, 300, 306, 307, 311, 317, 321, 326, 329, 334

Guided Problem Solving Masters
Chapter 6: pp. 47–56

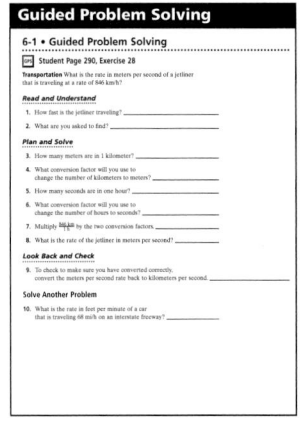

Reading and Math Literacy

Student Edition
- Vocabulary: pp. 287, 339, plus in most lessons
- Reading Math: pp. 288, 294, 306, 307, 310, 320, 324, 330, 339
- Writing in Math: pp. 290, 293, 297, 303, 309, 313, 319, 328, 331, 342
- Illustrated Glossary: pp. 782–826

Reading and Math Literacy Masters
Chapter 6: pp. 21–24

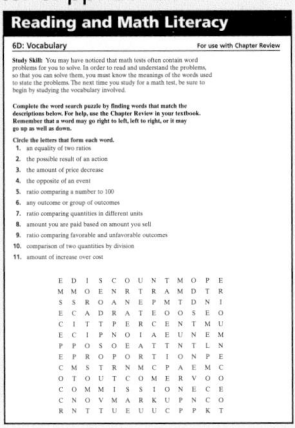

English Learners

Student Edition
- English/Spanish Illustrated Glossary: pp. 782–826

Workbook and Masters
Spanish Practice Workbook: pp. 47–56
Spanish Reading and Math Literacy Masters: pp. 21–24

Learning Styles

Student Edition
- Investigation: pp. 305, 325
- Technology: p. 304, 333
- DK Activities: pp. 344–345
- Chapter Project: p. 740

Activity Masters
Hands-On Activities: 14, 15, 16, 23
Technology Activities: 11, 12

Program Resources

Presentation Assistant Plus!

	Resources in Grab & Go™ Files				Resources for Reaching All Students				Spanish Resources			Transparencies				Prentice Hall Presentation Pro CD-ROM
	Practice	Reteach	Enrich	Checkpt Quiz	Reading & Math Literacy	Technology Activities	Hands-On Activities	Guided Problem Solving	Practice	Reading & Math Literacy	Checkpt Quiz	Skills Check	Additional Examples	Answers to Exercises	Lesson Quiz	
6-1	■	■	■		■		■	■	■	■		■	■	■	■	■
6-2	■	■	■			■		■	■	■		■	■	■	■	■
6-3	■	■	■				■	■	■	■		■	■	■	■	■
6-4	■	■	■	■	■		■	■	■	■	■	■	■	■	■	■
6-5	■	■	■			■	■	■	■			■	■	■	■	■
6-6	■	■	■			■	■	■	■			■	■	■	■	■
6-7	■	■	■			■	■	■	■			■	■	■	■	■
6-8	■	■	■			■	■	■	■			■	■	■	■	■
6-9	■	■	■	■	■		■	■	■	■	■	■	■	■	■	■
6-10	■	■				■	■	■	■			■	■	■	■	■
For the Chapter	Chapter Projects, Chapter Tests, Alternative Assessment, Cumulative Review, Cumulative Assessment				**On Web site only:** Home Activities, Algebra Readiness Puzzles, Interdisciplinary Activities				Spanish Chapter Tests, Alternative Assessment, Cumulative Review, Cumulative Assessment			Classroom Aid Transparencies				

Also available for use with the chapter:
- Practice Workbook
- Solution Key
- MathNotes folder
- For additional online and technology resources, see below.
- For teacher support and access to student Web site materials, use Web Code adk-5500.

PRENTICE HALL ASSESSMENT SYSTEM

Program assessment and test preparation, all in one place.

See page 286E.

Skills Intervention Kit

A *complete* system for the student who is struggling with course-level work

How to Use With Chapter 6

6-1, 6-4	Fraction Concepts
6-2	Pre-Algebra Basics
6-3, 6-6, 6-10	Ratio, Proportion, and Percent
6-5	Decimals

Online Intervention

Integrated within the iText, this online intervention system includes diagnostic tests and prescribed remediation, plus reports to track student mastery.

Technology

iTEXT Online and on CD-ROM

Complete Interactive Student Text online and on CD-ROM—with instant-feedback assessment, tutorial help, dynamic activities, instructional and real-world videos, audio, and additional practice.

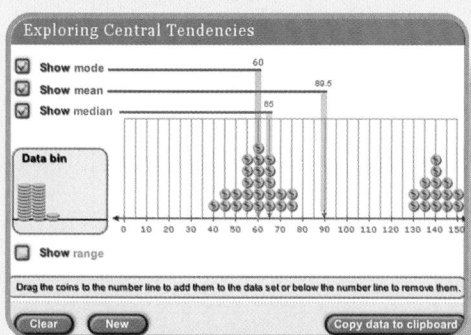

www.PHSchool.com
For Students

Use Web Codes for easy access to online activities, chapter projects, self-grading lesson quizzes, chapter tests, vocabulary quizzes, updated data sources, graphing calculator procedures, and more.

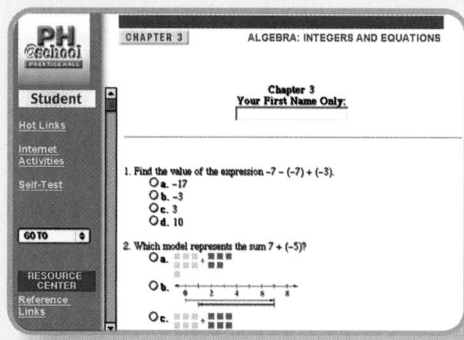

PH SuccessNet
For Teachers

Online lesson planning with built-in state correlations, all the teaching resources, complete reference library, your own calendar and Teacher Web page, professional development, and more.

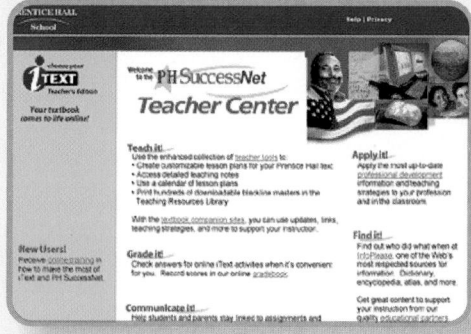

Presentation Assistant Plus!

The Prentice Hall *Presentation Assistant Plus!* provides you with the material you need to teach a lesson from beginning to end. Two easy-to-use formats—Transparencies and CD-ROM—allow you to present a lesson the way you are most comfortable.

Transparencies

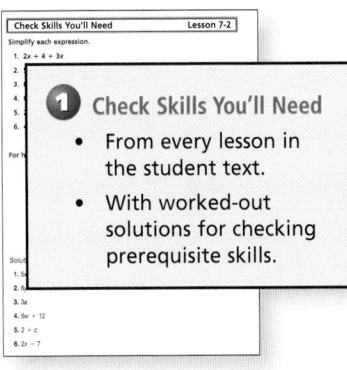

1 Check Skills You'll Need
- From every lesson in the student text.
- With worked-out solutions for checking prerequisite skills.

2 Additional Examples
- Every example from the Teacher's Edition.
- Fully worked-out, step-by-step solutions for easy demonstration.

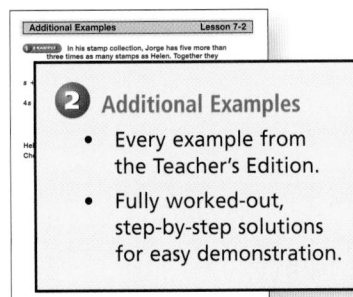

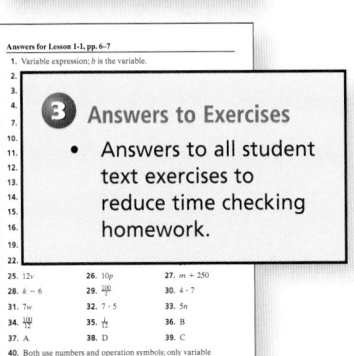

3 Answers to Exercises
- Answers to all student text exercises to reduce time checking homework.

4 Lesson Quiz
- Every quiz from the Teacher's Edition.
- With answers to allow students to check their own work.

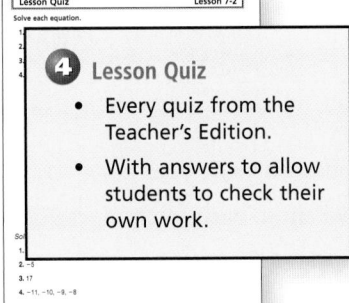

 Throughout the Teacher's Edition, this symbol indicates material that is available in the Presentation Assistant Plus!

PowerPoint Prentice Hall Presentation Pro CD-ROM

- Includes all Transparencies as PowerPoint® presentations.
- Conveniently organized by lesson so you can easily ❶ Introduce, ❷ Teach, ❸ Check Homework, and ❹ Assess each lesson.
- Animated examples allow step-by-step instruction at your own pace.
- Easy to edit so you can create custom presentations.

Teaching Chapter 6 Using Presentation Assistant Plus!

	❶ Introduce	❷ Teach	❸ Check Homework	❹ Assess
	Check Skills You'll Need	Additional Examples	Student Edition Answers	Lesson Quiz
6-1	p. 47	pp. 72–73	✔	p. 47
6-2	p. 48	pp. 73–74	✔	p. 48
6-3	p. 49	pp. 75–76	✔	p. 49
6-4	p. 50	p. 77	✔	p. 50
6-5	p. 51	pp. 78–79	✔	p. 51
6-6	p. 52	pp. 80–81	✔	p. 52
6-7	p. 53	pp. 82–83	✔	p. 53
6-8	p. 54	p. 84	✔	p. 54
6-9	p. 55	p. 85	✔	p. 55
6-10	p. 56	p. 86	✔	p. 57

Prentice Hall Presentation Pro

CD-ROM with dynamic Powerpoint® presentations for every lesson. Helps you introduce and develop concepts, check homework, and assess progress. Part of Presentation Assistant Plus! *(See above.)*

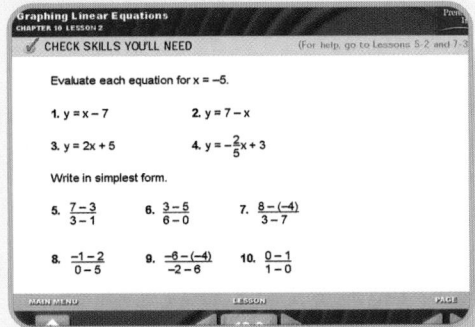

Computer Test Generator

CD-ROM to create practice sheets and tests for course objectives and standardized tests. Includes Instant Chapter Tests™, online testing, and student reports. Part of the PH Assessment System. *(See page 286E.)*

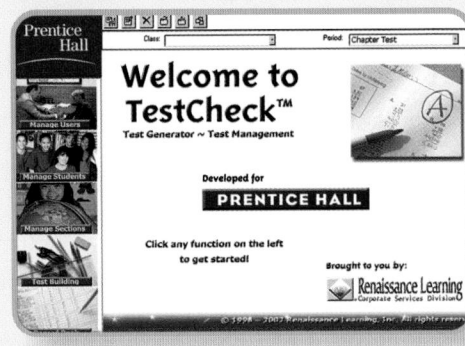

Resource Pro® with Planning Express®

CD-ROM with a lesson planning tool that allows you to import state and local objectives. Includes electronic versions of all the teaching resources.

Chapter 6

Ratios, Proportions, and Percents

Diagnosing Readiness

Students will find the answers to these exercises in the back of their textbooks.

Prescribing Intervention
For intervention, direct students to:

Solving Equations by Multiplying or Dividing
Lesson 2-6: Example 2;
Exercises 1–18.
Extra Practice, p. 745.

Lesson 3-6: Example 1;
Exercises 1–9.
Extra Practice, p. 746.

Lesson 5-8: Example 2;
Exercises 9–16.
Extra Practice, p. 748.

Simplifying Fractions
Lesson 4-4: Examples 1 and 2;
Exercises 1–12.
Extra Practice, p. 747.

Writing Fractions and Decimals
Lesson 5-2: Examples 1 and 4;
Exercises 1–4, 16–23.

Where You've Been

- In Chapter 2, you solved equations by adding, subtracting, multiplying, and dividing.

- In Chapter 4, you investigated exponents.

- In Chapter 5, you learned how to work with fractions.

 Instant self-check
online and on CD-ROM

Diagnosing Readiness　　　　(For help, go to the lesson in green.)

Solving Equations by Multiplying or Dividing (Lessons 2-6, 3-6, and 5-8)

Solve each equation.

1. $3x = 48$ **16**

2. $94.5 = 7r$ **13.5**

3. $\frac{3}{7}t = \frac{3}{8}$ **$\frac{7}{8}$**

4. $0.5y = 1.25$ **2.5**

5. $\frac{4}{5}x = 1$ **$1\frac{1}{4}$**

6. $38.5 = 1.4m$ **27.5**

Simplifying Fractions (Lesson 4-4)

Find two fractions equivalent to each fraction.

7–13. Answers may vary. Samples are given.

7. $\frac{1}{4}$ **$\frac{2}{8}, \frac{4}{16}$**

8. $\frac{4}{10}$ **$\frac{2}{5}, \frac{8}{20}$**

9. $\frac{6}{14}$ **$\frac{3}{7}, \frac{12}{28}$**

10. $\frac{2}{9}$ **$\frac{4}{18}, \frac{6}{27}$**

11. $\frac{3}{8}$ **$\frac{6}{16}, \frac{9}{24}$**

12. $\frac{5}{6}$ **$\frac{10}{12}, \frac{15}{18}$**

Write each fraction in simplest form.

13. $\frac{2}{8}$ **$\frac{1}{4}$**

14. $\frac{6}{24}$ **$\frac{1}{4}$**

15. $\frac{12}{15}$ **$\frac{4}{5}$**

16. $\frac{6}{16}$ **$\frac{3}{8}$**

17. $\frac{18}{42}$ **$\frac{3}{7}$**

18. $\frac{25}{200}$ **$\frac{1}{8}$**

19. $\frac{80}{96}$ **$\frac{5}{6}$**

20. $\frac{40}{1,000}$ **$\frac{1}{25}$**

Writing Fractions and Decimals (Lesson 5-2)

Write each fraction as a decimal. Write each decimal as a fraction or a mixed number in simplest form.

21. $\frac{7}{20}$ **0.35**

22. 0.06 **$\frac{3}{50}$**

23. $\frac{30}{8}$ **3.75**

24. 0.35 **$\frac{7}{20}$**

25. 0.875 **$\frac{7}{8}$**

26. $3\frac{3}{5}$ **3.6**

27. 1.07 **$1\frac{7}{100}$**

28. $\frac{12}{18}$ **$0.\overline{6}$**

29. $11\frac{1}{9}$ **$11.\overline{1}$**

30. $0.\overline{3}$ **$\frac{1}{3}$**

31. $\frac{100}{16}$ **6.25**

32. 3.98 **$3\frac{49}{50}$**

Ratios, Proportions, and Percents

Where You're Going

In this chapter, you will learn how to

● Find and use ratios and unit rates.

● Write and solve proportions.

● Find and use percents.

● Solve a problem by making a table.

Real-World Snapshots Applying what you learn, on pages 344–345 you will solve problems about stock trading.

LESSONS

Key Vocabulary

- certain event (p. 306)
- commission (p. 321)
- complement (p. 306)
- cross products (p. 294)
- discount (p. 329)
- event (p. 305)
- impossible event (p. 306)
- indirect measurement (p. 300)
- markup (p. 329)
- odds (p. 307)
- outcomes (p. 305)
- percent (p. 310)
- percent of change (p. 325)
- probability (p. 305)
- proportion (p. 294)
- rate (p. 289)
- ratio (p. 288)
- scale drawing (p. 300)
- similar figures (p. 299)
- unit rate (p. 289)

Chapter 6 Overview

Chapter 6 begins with students learning the definitions and uses of *ratios*, *rates*, and *unit rates*, including proportions involving similar figures and scale drawings. Students use their knowledge of ratios to find probabilities and odds. They learn that a percent can be written as a ratio in fraction form with 100 as the denominator, and as a decimal. Students solve percent problems with proportions and then with equations. They use what they learn about percents to find percents of change, markup, and discount.

Activating Prior Knowledge

In Chapter 4 students learned to simplify fractions using the GCF. Ask: *How do you find the GCF?* To find the GCF of two numbers, you write the prime factorization of each number. Then find the common factors. Multiply the lesser powers of the common factors.

📖 Reading Math

- Reading Percent Problems, p. 324
- **Vocabulary** A complete list of terms, plus vocabulary exercises, appears in the Chapter Review on p. 339.
- **Illustrated Glossary** Examples for each vocabulary term, plus definitions in both English and Spanish, appear starting on p. 782.

📝 Test-Taking Strategies

Using Estimation, p. 338

🌐 Real-World Problem Solving

- **Strategy:** Make a Table, pp. 334–337
- **DK Real-World Snapshots:** Applying Percents, pp. 344–345
- **Chapter Project:** String Band, p. 740

💻 www.PHSchool.com

Internet support includes:
- Self-grading Vocabulary and Chapter 6 Tests
- Activity Masters
- Chapter Project support
- Chapter Planner
- Chapter 6 Resources

Plus

Lesson Preview

Check Skills You'll Need

Simplifying Fractions
Lesson 4-4: Example 2;
Exercises 7–12.
Extra Practice, p. 747.

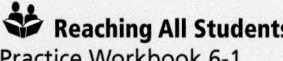
Lesson Resources

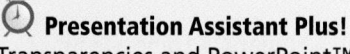
Teaching Resources
Practice, Reteaching, Enrichment

Reaching All Students
Practice Workbook 6-1
Spanish Practice Workbook 6-1
Reading and Math Literacy 6A
Spanish Reading and Math
  Literacy 6A
Guided Problem Solving 6-1
Hands-On Activities 23

Presentation Assistant Plus!
Transparencies and PowerPoint™
• Check Skills You'll Need 6-1
• Additional Examples 6-1
• Student Edition Answers 6-1
• Lesson Quiz 6-1
• Classroom Aid 1
PH Presentation Pro CD-ROM 6-1

ASSESSMENT SYSTEM

Computer Test Generator CD-ROM

Technology
Resource Pro® CD-ROM
Computer Test Generator CD-ROM
PH Presentation Pro CD-ROM

www.PHSchool.com

Student Site
• Teacher Web Code: adk-5500
• Self-grading Lesson Quiz
PH SuccessNet Teacher Center
• Lesson Planner
• Resources

Plus

288

What You'll Learn

OBJECTIVE 1 To write and simplify ratios

OBJECTIVE 2 To find rates and unit rates

. . . And Why

To solve real-world problems involving unit prices, gas mileage, and speed

Check Skills You'll Need

Write in simplest form.

1. $\frac{30}{35}$ $\frac{6}{7}$ 2. $\frac{24}{40}$ $\frac{3}{5}$

3. $\frac{54}{60}$ $\frac{9}{10}$ 4. $\frac{12}{15}$ $\frac{4}{5}$

5. $\frac{14}{42}$ $\frac{1}{3}$ 6. $\frac{40}{24}$ $\frac{5}{3}$, or $1\frac{2}{3}$

For help, go to Lesson 4-4.

New Vocabulary

• ratio
• rate
• unit rate

Reading Math
Regardless of how you write the ratio, you read 10 to 15, 10 : 15 and $\frac{10}{15}$ as "ten to fifteen."

iTEXT Interactive lesson includes instant self-check, tutorials, and activities.

OBJECTIVE 1 Writing Ratios

Statistics In the United States, about 10 out of every 15 people eligible to vote are registered to vote. The numbers 10 and 15 form a *ratio*.

Key Concepts   Ratio

A **ratio** is a comparison of two quantities by division. You can write a ratio in different ways.

Arithmetic	Algebra
10 to 15 10 : 15 $\frac{10}{15}$	a to b $a : b$ $\frac{a}{b}$, for $b \neq 0$

1 EXAMPLE   Real-World Problem Solving

Surveys A survey asked students whether they had after-school jobs. Write each ratio as a fraction in simplest form.

After-School Jobs

Response	Number
Have a Job	40
Don't Have a Job	60
Total	100

a. students with jobs to students without jobs

$\dfrac{\text{students with jobs}}{\text{students without jobs}} = \dfrac{40}{60}$

$= \dfrac{2}{3}$

b. students without jobs to all students surveyed

$\dfrac{\text{students without jobs}}{\text{all students surveyed}} = \dfrac{60}{100}$

$= \dfrac{3}{5}$

Check Understanding   Example 1

1. Write each ratio as a fraction in simplest form.

a. students with jobs to all students surveyed $\frac{2}{5}$

b. students without jobs to students with jobs $\frac{3}{2}$

Ongoing Assessment and Intervention

Before the Lesson
Diagnose prerequisite skills using:
• Check Skills You'll Need

During the Lesson
Monitor progress using:
• Check Understanding
• Additional Examples
• Test Prep

After the Lesson
Assess knowledge using:
• Lesson Quiz
• Computer Test Generator CD-ROM

A **rate** is a ratio that compares quantities in different units.
A **unit rate** is a rate that has a denominator of 1. Examples of
unit rates include unit prices, gas mileage, and speed.

2 EXAMPLE   Real-World  Problem Solving

Unit Prices The table shows prices for different sizes of the same
dish detergent. Which size has the lowest unit price?

Regular: $\dfrac{\text{price}}{\text{volume}} \rightarrow \dfrac{\$1.20}{12 \text{ fl oz}} = \$.10/\text{fl oz}$

Family: $\dfrac{\text{price}}{\text{volume}} \rightarrow \dfrac{\$2.24}{28 \text{ fl oz}} = \$.08/\text{fl oz}$ **Find the unit prices.**

Economy: $\dfrac{\text{price}}{\text{volume}} \rightarrow \dfrac{\$3.60}{40 \text{ fl oz}} = \$.09/\text{fl oz}$

● The family size has the lowest unit price.

Dish Detergent Prices

Size	Volume (fl oz)	Price
Regular	12	$1.20
Family	28	$2.24
Economy	40	$3.60

✔ **Check Understanding** Example 2

2. Find each unit rate.

 a. Two liters of spring water cost $1.98. **$.99/L**
 b. A car goes 425 mi on 12.5 gal of gas. **34 mi/gal**

You can use dimensional analysis to choose conversion factors for
converting rates.

3 EXAMPLE   Converting a Rate

Convert 10 mi/h to feet per minute.

$10 \text{ mi/h} = \dfrac{10 \text{ mi}}{1 \text{ h}} \cdot \dfrac{5{,}280 \text{ ft}}{1 \text{ mi}} \cdot \dfrac{1 \text{ h}}{60 \text{ min}}$

Use conversion factors that convert miles to feet and hours to minutes.

$= \dfrac{^{1}10 \text{ mi}}{1 \text{ h}} \cdot \dfrac{^{880}5{,}280 \text{ ft}}{1 \text{ mi}} \cdot \dfrac{1 \text{ h}}{60 \text{ min}}_{6\ 1}$

Divide the common factors and units.

$= \dfrac{880 \text{ ft}}{\text{min}}$

Simplify.

● 10 mi/h equals 880 ft/min.

✔ **Check Understanding** Example 3

3. Complete each statement.

 a. 3.5 qt/min = ■ gal/h **52.5**   **b.** 12 cm/s = ■ m/h **432**

Reaching All Students

Below Level Discuss with students
rates they hear all the time, but may
not realize are ratios: for example,
miles per hour, minutes per day, and
miles per gallon. Ask: *What word is
said in all these ratios?* **per**

Advanced Learners Have students
find out how many *miles per gallon*
their favorite cars get. Have
students compare their findings to
determine which of their cars have
the best and worst gas mileage.

Auditory Learners
See note on page 289.
Error Prevention
See note on page 291.

2. Teach

Professional Development

Math Background

A *ratio* compares two quantities
by division. For example, a team
that has 3 wins and 5 losses has
a $\frac{3}{5}$ win-loss ratio. The order of
the numbers in a ratio is very
important. The first number in
the ratio always represents the
quantity that is named first in
describing the ratio. The ratios 3:5
and 5:3 are not equivalent.

Teaching Notes

1 EXAMPLE **Auditory Learners**
Reading ratios aloud helps
students write the numbers in the
same order that they say the
words. Suggest that they say
"students with jobs" as they write
40, say "over," and then say
"students without jobs" as they
write 60.

PowerPoint
Additional Examples

1 Use the table in Example 1.
Write each ratio as a fraction
in simplest form.
 a. all students surveyed to
students without jobs $\frac{5}{3}$
 b. all students surveyed to
students with jobs $\frac{5}{2}$

2 The table shows prices for
different packages of index
cards. Which size has the
lowest unit price? **50-card**

Card Prices

Size	Price
100	$2.70
50	$1.30
25	$.75

3 Convert 30 gal/min to
cups/second. **8 c/s**

Closure

Ask students: *What are ratios,
rates, and unit rates?* A ratio
compares two quantities by
division. A rate is a ratio that
compares two quantities that have
different units. A unit rate
has a denominator of 1.

289

3. Practice

Assignment Guide

1 Objective 1
- **A** **B** Core 1–12, 23–26, 30, 31
- **C** Extension 32

2 Objective 2
- **A** **B** Core 13–22, 27–29
- **C** Extension 33

Test Prep 34–38
Mixed Review 39–45

Practice 6-1 *Ratios and Unit Rates*

Find each unit rate.

1. 78 mi on 3 gal   26 mi/gal
2. $52.50 in 7 h $7.50/h
3. 416 mi in 8 h   52 mi/h
4. 9 bull's eyes in 117 throws   13 throws/bull's eye

Write each ratio as a fraction in simplest form.

5. 7th-grade boys to 8th-grade boys $\frac{13}{15}$
6. 7th-grade girls to 7th-grade boys $\frac{17}{13}$
7. 7th graders to 8th graders $\frac{15}{13}$

	Boys	Girls
7th Grade	26	34
8th Grade	30	22

8. boys to girls $\frac{1}{1}$
9. girls to all students $\frac{1}{2}$

Write three different ratios for each model.

10. $\frac{3}{4}, \frac{3}{7}, \frac{4}{7}$
11. $\frac{3}{2}, \frac{3}{5}, \frac{2}{5}$
12. $\frac{2}{4}, \frac{2}{6}, \frac{4}{6}$

Write each ratio as a fraction is simplest form.

13. 7:12 $\frac{7}{12}$
14. 3 is to 6 $\frac{1}{2}$
15. 10:45 $\frac{2}{9}$
16. 32 out of 40 $\frac{4}{5}$
17. 36 is to 60 $\frac{3}{5}$
18. 13 out of 14 $\frac{13}{14}$
19. 9 out of 21 $\frac{3}{7}$
20. 45:63 $\frac{5}{7}$
21. 24 is to 18 $\frac{4}{3}$
22. 15 out of 60 $\frac{1}{4}$

Enrichment 6-1 *Sampling*

A sample is a small group chosen to represent a large group. For example, public opinion surveys of small samples of the population are assumed to represent the entire population. Using proportions, the results from the small group can be applied to the large one.

A toothpaste manufacturer conducted a survey of consumers to find their preferences in toothpaste. The results are shown in the table at the right.

Toothpaste Survey	
Brand	Number Preferring
Delightful	138
New Shine	23
Peppy	184
Other	115

1. How many people were surveyed?   460
2. Calculate the following ratios. Write all ratios as fractions in simplest form.
   a. the number of people who prefer Delightful to the total number of people surveyed $\frac{3}{10}$
   b. the number of people who prefer Shine to the total $\frac{1}{20}$
   c. the number of people who prefer Peppy to the total $\frac{2}{5}$
   d. the number of people who prefer other to the total $\frac{1}{4}$
3. The number of toothpaste users in one state is 8,464,000.
   a. If the survey results represent an accurate sample, how many people in that state can be expected to prefer New Shine?   423,200 people
   b. How many people can be expected to prefer Peppy?   3,385,600 people

Results of a poll of Alphaville are shown in the table at the right.

4. How many people were surveyed?   168
5. Calculate the following ratios. Write all ratios as fractions in simplest form.

Do You Favor Widening Smith Road to 6 Lanes?	
Yes	56
No	70
Not sure	42

   a. the number of people in favor to the total number of people surveyed $\frac{1}{3}$
   b. the number of people against to the total $\frac{5}{12}$
   c. the number of people who are not sure to the total $\frac{1}{4}$
6. How many of the people polled who are not sure must vote yes in order for yes to win, assuming the rest of those not sure vote no?   29
7. What is the ratio of the number who need to vote yes to the total who were not sure? $\frac{29}{42}$

EXERCISES

Practice and Problem Solving

For more exercises, see *Extra Practice.*

A Practice by Example

Example 1
(page 288)

Write each ratio as a fraction in simplest form.

1. $9:27$ $\frac{1}{3}$
2. 12 to 8 $\frac{3}{2}$
3. 2 to 18 $\frac{1}{9}$
4. $6:50$ $\frac{3}{25}$
5. $\frac{1,000}{10,000}$ $\frac{1}{10}$
6. $3:8$ $\frac{3}{8}$
7. 7 to 9 $\frac{7}{9}$
8. 8 out of 11 $\frac{8}{11}$

9. 3 out of 12 people live in a rural area. $\frac{1}{4}$

10. 98 homes in 100 have a TV. $\frac{49}{50}$

11. 70 homes out of 125 have a personal computer. $\frac{14}{25}$

12. In one class, there are 6 girls for every 10 boys. $\frac{3}{5}$

Example 2
(page 289)

Find each unit rate.

13. A skydiver falls 144 ft in 3 s.   48 ft/s
14. A pump moves 42 gal in 7 min.   6 gal/min
15. A car travels 676 mi in 13 h.   52 mi/h
16. 20 c of water evaporate in 5 d.   4 c/d

Example 3
(page 289)

Complete each statement.

17. 720 m/day = ▦ m/min $\frac{1}{2}$
18. 1.5 gal/min = ▦ qt/h   360
19. 32 yd/min = ▦ in./s   19.2
20. 0.85 km/s = ▦ m/min   51,000
21. 80 mi/h = ▦ ft/s $117\frac{1}{3}$
22. 20 fl oz/min = ▦ qt/day   900

B Apply Your Skills

Write each ratio as a fraction in simplest form.

23. 36 to 48 $\frac{3}{4}$
24. 60 to 24 $\frac{5}{2}$
25. $16:12$ $\frac{4}{3}$
26. $15:27$ $\frac{5}{9}$

27. **Cycling** Anna and Julia each take a bicycle trip. Anna rides 20 miles in $1\frac{1}{3}$ hours. Julia rides 246 miles in 16 hours. Which rider has the slower unit rate? By how much?   Anna; $\frac{3}{8}$ mi/h

29. Answers may vary.
Sample:
$\frac{100 \text{ ft}}{1 \text{ min}} \cdot \frac{12 \text{ in.}}{1 \text{ ft}} \cdot \frac{1 \text{ min}}{60 \text{ s}}$
shows that 100 ÷ 5, not 100 · 5, gives inches per second.

28. **Transportation** What is the rate in meters per second of a jetliner that is traveling at a rate of 846 km/h?   235 m/s
GPS

29. **Error Analysis** A student converts 100 ft/min to 500 in./s. Use dimensional analysis to explain why the student's result is not reasonable.   See left.

Boys in Two Classes

Class	Number of Boys	Number of Students
A	6	30
B	4	24

Use the table at the left for Exercises 30 and 31.

30. For each class, write the ratio of the number of boys to the total number of students.   class A: $\frac{6}{30}$ or $\frac{1}{5}$; class B: $\frac{4}{24}$ or $\frac{1}{6}$

31. Which class has the greater ratio of boys to students?   class A

C Challenge

32. **Writing in Math** A student claims that a ratio remains unchanged if 1 is added to both the numerator and the denominator of the fraction. Does $\frac{a}{b}$ equal $\frac{a+1}{b+1}$? Write an explanation, and give an example or a counterexample.   Answers may vary. Sample: Usually not; adding 1 to both the numerator and the denominator leaves the ratio unchanged only when $a = b$; $\frac{1}{1} = \frac{1+1}{1+1}$, but $\frac{1}{2} \neq \frac{1+1}{2+1}$, or $\frac{2}{3}$.

290 Chapter 6   Ratios, Proportions, and Percents

 GPS   Use the Guided Problem Solving worksheet with Exercise 28.

33. Science Density is the ratio of a substance's mass to its volume. A volume of 20 cubic centimeters of gold has a mass of 386 grams. Express the density of gold as a unit rate. 19.3 g/cm^3

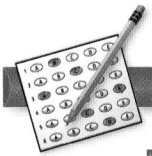

Test Prep

Multiple Choice

34. A 50-lb bag of Glossy Coat Horse Feed costs $23.50. A 25-lb bag costs $15.50. How much money per pound would you save by buying the bag with the lower unit price? **A**

A. $.15   **B.** $.32   **C.** $.47   **D.** $.62

35. Karla and her dad were nailing up plywood. They started at 10:00. Karla drove 30 nails in 10 min, the time it took her dad to drive 50 nails. At that rate for each, when did they finish driving 392 nails in all? **I**

F. 10:30   **G.** 10:39   **H.** 10:45   **I.** 10:49

Reading Comprehension   Read the passage below before doing Exercises 36–38.

A Sappy Story

Connecticut has more than 100 farms that produce maple syrup. Sugarers collect sap and boil it down to syrup. In a good year, one small sugarer in Connecticut averages 301 gallons of sap weekly from 200 trees. The sap boils down to just seven gallons of syrup. The syrup sells for $4.50 per half pint or $44 per gallon.

36. Write the ratio of sap to syrup in simplest form. 43 to 1

37. Find the unit prices for syrup sold by the half pint and syrup sold by the gallon. Which has the lower unit price?
$9/pint or $72/gal, $44/gal; syrup sold by the gallon

Take It to the NET
Online lesson quiz at
www.PHSchool.com
Web Code: ada-0601

38. If the sugarer sells the syrup by the half pint, how much income will there be for 10 weeks of sugaring in a good year? $5,040

Mixed Review

Lesson 5-9   **Simplify each expression.**

39. $(-3 \cdot 4)^3$ $-1{,}728$ **40.** $(2x^2y)^4$ $16x^8y^4$ **41.** $\left(-\dfrac{ab^3}{a^2b}\right)^3$ $-\dfrac{b^6}{a^3}$

Lesson 5-2   **Compare. Use >, <, or = to complete each statement.**

42. $\dfrac{7}{8} \blacksquare \dfrac{14}{24}$ >   **43.** $\dfrac{4}{12} \blacksquare \dfrac{10}{30}$ =   **44.** $\dfrac{13}{20} \blacksquare 0.6$ >

Lesson 2-1   **45. Vacation** Three friends shared the driving on a long trip. Marla drove 7 mi more than Guido. Guido drove five times as far as Juanita did. Juanita drove 112 mi. How long was the trip? 1,239 mi

Alternative Assessment

Have students write and simplify ratios using information gathered from the classroom: pencils to pens, students who play a musical instrument to those who do not, and so forth.

---

4. Assess

 **PowerPoint** Lesson Quiz 6-1

Write each ratio as a fraction in simplest form.

1. 4 out of 20 students ride the bus to school. $\frac{1}{5}$

2. 8 out of 10 students buy lunch. $\frac{4}{5}$

Find each unit rate.

3. You pay $4.50 for 2 gallons of orange juice. $2.25/gal

4. You pay $21.60 for a 20-lb bag of dog food. $1.08/lb

5. Convert 15 yd/min to inches/second. 9 in./s

Error Prevention!

Exercises 24, 25 Students may mistakenly rewrite a simplified ratio as a mixed number. For example, they may rewrite the ratio $\frac{5}{2}$ as $2\frac{1}{2}$. Help them see that a ratio is easy to understand when written as a fraction, but *not* when written as a mixed number.

Test Prep

Resources
For additional practice with a variety of test item formats:
• Test Prep, p. 343
• Test-Taking Strategies, p. 338
• Test-Taking Strategies With Transparencies

Reteaching 6-1 **Ratios and Unit Rates**

One store has 6-packs of juice for $.90. Another store has 8-packs of the same size juice cartons for $1.12. Which is the better buy?
Find the unit rates.

6-pack: $\frac{\text{price}}{\text{number}} \to \frac{\$.90}{6} = \$.15/\text{carton}$

8-pack: $\frac{\text{price}}{\text{number}} \to \frac{\$1.12}{8} = \$.14/\text{carton}$

The 8-pack has the lowest unit price.

6-pack $0.90   8-pack $1.12

Find each unit rate.

1. $91 in 14 h   **2.** 372 mi in 6 h
$6.50/h   62 mi/h

3. $13.14 for 12 gal   **4.** 570 gal in 60 min
$1.095/gal   9.5 gal/min

5. 54¢ for 4 oz   **6.** 592 words in 8 min
13.5¢/oz   74 words/min

7. A 12 fl oz bottle of shampoo costs $1.08 at Discount Mart. A 20 fl oz bottle of the same shampoo costs $2.20 at Super Store. Find each unit rate and determine which is the better buy.

12 fl oz bottle: $.09/ fl oz

20 fl oz bottle: $.11/fl oz

Better buy: 12 fl oz bottle

8. A school bus travels 53.3 mi on 6.5 gal of gas on its way to a museum for a field trip. On the return trip it takes the freeway and travels 53.2 mi on 5.6 gal of gas. Find the gas mileages of each trip and determine which is greater.

To the museum: 8.2 mi/gal

Returning from the museum: 9.5 mi/gal

Better mileage: returning from the museum

Reteaching

Converting Between Measurement Systems

This Extension shows students how to use a conversion factor, which is similar to a unit rate, to convert measurements from one system to another. You may wish to review *dimensional analysis* in Lesson 5-5.

Teaching Note

A conversion factor is a ratio of units that has a value of 1 in either the numerator (for example, $\frac{1 \text{ yd}}{36 \text{ in.}}$), or the denominator $\left(\frac{36 \text{ in.}}{1 \text{ yd}}\right)$. A conversion factor may have units from different systems $\left(\frac{0.914 \text{ m}}{1 \text{ yd}}\right)$.

1 EXAMPLE **Error Prevention**

Students may write conversion factors incorrectly. Remind them that a unit they are trying to eliminate must appear in the numerator of one ratio and in the denominator of another ratio.

Converting Between Measurement Systems

For Use With Lesson 6-1

You can use conversion factors (dimensional analysis) to convert a unit of measure from one system to another. For example, since 1 mi ≈ 1.61 km, you can use $\frac{1 \text{ mi}}{1.61 \text{ km}}$ and $\frac{1.61 \text{ km}}{1 \text{ mi}}$ as conversion factors.

The table shows some useful conversion factors.

Customary Units and Metric Units	Conversion Factors
1 in. = 2.54 cm	$\frac{1 \text{ in.}}{2.54 \text{ cm}}$ or $\frac{2.54 \text{ cm}}{1 \text{ in.}}$
1 mi ≈ 1.61 km	$\frac{1 \text{ mi}}{1.61 \text{ km}}$ or $\frac{1.61 \text{ km}}{1 \text{ mi}}$
1.06 qt ≈ 1 L	$\frac{1.06 \text{ qt}}{1 \text{ L}}$ or $\frac{1 \text{ L}}{1.06 \text{ qt}}$
1 oz ≈ 28.4 g	$\frac{1 \text{ oz}}{28.4 \text{ g}}$ or $\frac{28.4 \text{ g}}{1 \text{ oz}}$
2.20 lb ≈ 1 kg	$\frac{2.20 \text{ lb}}{1 \text{ kg}}$ or $\frac{1 \text{ kg}}{2.20 \text{ lb}}$

In general, a conversion between systems results in an approximate measurement.

1 EXAMPLE

The longest track event at the Olympics is the 50-km walk. How long is the race in miles?

$50 \text{ km} \approx 50 \text{ km} \cdot \dfrac{1 \text{ mi}}{1.61 \text{ km}}$ — Use a conversion factor that changes kilometers to miles.

$= 50 \text{ km} \cdot \dfrac{1 \text{ mi}}{1.61 \text{ km}}$ — Divide the common units.

$= \dfrac{50 \text{ mi}}{1.61}$ — Multiply.

$\approx 31 \text{ mi}$ — Divide.

● The 50-km walk is about 31 mi long.

You can round within a conversion factor to get compatible numbers.

2 EXAMPLE

About how many ounces are in 60 grams?

$60 \text{ g} \approx 60 \text{ g} \cdot \dfrac{1 \text{ oz}}{28.4 \text{ g}}$ — Use the conversion factor that changes grams to ounces.

$\approx 60 \text{ g} \cdot \dfrac{1 \text{ oz}}{30 \text{ g}}$ — Round within the conversion factor to a number compatible with 60.

$= 60^2 \text{g} \cdot \dfrac{1 \text{ oz}}{_1 30 \text{ g}}$ — Divide the common factors and units.

$= 2 \text{ oz}$ — Simplify.

● There are about 2 ounces in 60 grams.

Sometimes you may need to use two or more conversion factors.

3 EXAMPLE

A punch recipe calls for a gallon of sparkling water. How many 2-L bottles should you buy?

$1 \text{ gal} \approx 1 \text{ gal} \cdot \dfrac{4 \text{ qt}}{1 \text{ gal}} \cdot \dfrac{1 \text{ L}}{1.06 \text{ qt}}$ **Use conversion factors that change gallons to quarts and quarts to liters.**

$= 1 \cancel{\text{ gal}} \cdot \dfrac{4 \cancel{\text{ qt}}}{1 \cancel{\text{ gal}}} \cdot \dfrac{1 \text{ L}}{1.06 \cancel{\text{ qt}}}$ **Divide the common units.**

$= \dfrac{4 \text{ L}}{1.06}$ **Multiply.**

$\approx 3.8 \text{ L}$ **Divide.**

Now find the number of bottles you need for 3.8 L.

$\dfrac{3.8}{2} = 1.9$ **Divide by 2, since there are 2 L per bottle.**

You need about 1.9 bottles. You should buy two bottles.

EXERCISES

Convert. Where necessary, round to the nearest tenth.

1. $8 \text{ in.} \approx \blacksquare \text{ cm}$ 20.3
2. $16 \text{ cm} \approx \blacksquare \text{ in.}$ 6.3
3. $\blacksquare \text{ mi} \approx 20 \text{ km}$ 12.4
4. $\blacksquare \text{ km} \approx 100 \text{ mi}$ 161
5. $\blacksquare \text{ L} \approx 50 \text{ qt}$ 47.2
6. $\blacksquare \text{ g} \approx 15 \text{ oz}$ 426
7. $15 \text{ L} \approx \blacksquare \text{ qt}$ 15.9
8. $\blacksquare \text{ lb} \approx 14 \text{ kg}$ 30.8
9. $44 \text{ lb} \approx \blacksquare \text{ kg}$ 20
10. $100 \text{ oz} \approx \blacksquare \text{ kg}$ 2.8
11. $\blacksquare \text{ L} \approx 212 \text{ pt}$ 100
12. $500 \text{ g} \approx \blacksquare \text{ lb}$ 1.1
13. $1,000 \text{ mm} \approx \blacksquare \text{ in.}$ 39.4
14. $\blacksquare \text{ gal} \approx 20 \text{ L}$ 5.3
15. $\blacksquare \text{ km/h} \approx 10 \text{ mi/h}$ 16.1

16. **Home Economics** A recipe calls for 8 oz of figs. The figs come in packages of 100 g. How many packages should you buy? **3 packages**

17. **Writing in Math** Explain how you would estimate the number of kilometers in 19 miles. **Answers may vary. Sample: estimate the product of 1.61 and 19 as 1.5 × 20, or 30 km.**

18. In Exercise 15, you may have found that 10 mi/h ≈ 16.1 km/h. Also, 10 mi/h = 880 ft/min (Example 3, p. 289). Convert both 16.1 km/h and 880 ft/min to meters per second and compare. **Both ≈ 4.47 m/s**

19. Restate Exercise 27 on page 290 in equivalent metric units and solve. **See margin.**

20. In Exercise 28 on page 290, you convert 846 km/h to meters per second. Convert 846 km/h to miles per hour and then to feet per second. **about 525 mi/h; about 770 ft/s**

19. Anna rides about 32.2 km in $1\frac{1}{3}$ h. Julia rides about 396 km in 16 h. Which rider has the slower unit rate? By how much? **Anna; about 0.6 km/h**

Error Prevention!

Students may think that the unit of measure with the greater number is the larger unit of measure. This may cause confusion when they check to see if their answers are reasonable. Have students draw a segment that is 1 in. long. Then have them draw a segment that is 1 cm long. Ask: *Which unit is smaller?* **centimeter** Direct their attention to the part of the table comparing inches and centimeters. *Which number is greater, 1 or 2.54?* **2.54** Lead students to see that it takes more of a smaller unit to equal a larger unit. Therefore, the unit in a conversion factor with the greater number is the smaller unit of measure.

Auditory Learners
Have students develop a mnemonic device to help them remember the concept in the Error Prevention above.

Lesson Preview

 Check Skills You'll Need

Solving Equations by Dividing
Lesson 2-6: Example 2;
Exercises 1–18.
Extra Practice, p. 745.

Lesson Resources

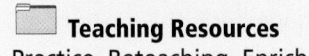 **Teaching Resources**
Practice, Reteaching, Enrichment

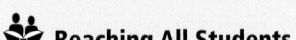 **Reaching All Students**
Practice Workbook 6-2
Spanish Practice Workbook 6-2
Guided Problem Solving 6-2
Technology Activities 11

 **Presentation Assistant Plus!**
Transparencies and PowerPoint™
• Check Skills You'll Need 6-2
• Additional Examples 6-2
• Student Edition Answers 6-2
• Lesson Quiz 6-2
PH Presentation Pro CD-ROM 6-2

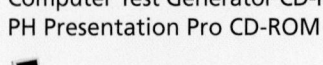 **ASSESSMENT SYSTEM**

Computer Test Generator CD-ROM

 **Technology**
Resource Pro® CD-ROM
Computer Test Generator CD-ROM
PH Presentation Pro CD-ROM

www.PHSchool.com

Student Site
• Teacher Web Code: adk-5500
• Algebra Readiness Puzzles 20, 21
• Self-grading Lesson Quiz
PH SuccessNet Teacher Center
• Lesson Planner
• Resources

Plus **iTEXT**

294

 **6-2**

Proportions

What You'll Learn

OBJECTIVE 1 To solve proportions

OBJECTIVE 2 To use proportions to solve problems

. . . And Why

To solve real-world problems involving science

 Check Skills You'll Need

Solve each equation.

1. $4x = 52$ **2.** $3y = 18$
    13   6
3. $5b = 75$ **4.** $7k = 21$
    15   3

 For help, go to Lesson 2-6.

New Vocabulary
• proportion
• cross products

Reading Math

Read the proportion $\frac{6}{9} = \frac{8}{12}$ as "the ratio 6 to 9 equals the ratio 8 to 12," or as "6 is to 9 as 8 is to 12."

iTEXT Interactive lesson includes instant self-check, tutorials, and activities.

OBJECTIVE

1   Solving Proportions

A **proportion** is an equality of two ratios—for example, $\frac{6}{9} = \frac{8}{12}$. You can use the Multiplication Property of Equality to show an important property of all proportions.

$$\text{If } \frac{a}{b} = \frac{c}{d}$$

$$\text{then } \frac{a}{b} \cdot bd = \frac{c}{d} \cdot bd \quad \text{\textbf{Multiplication Property of Equality}}$$

$$\frac{ab^1 d}{{}_1 b} = \frac{cbd^1}{{}_1 d} \qquad \frac{b}{b} = 1 \text{ and } \frac{d}{d} = 1$$

$$\text{and } ad = cb, \text{ or } ad = bc.$$

The products ad and bc are called the **cross products** of the proportion $\frac{a}{b} = \frac{c}{d}$.

Key Concepts   **Cross Products**

In a proportion, the cross products are equal.

Arithmetic	Algebra
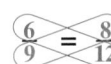	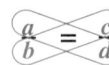
$6 \cdot 12 = 9 \cdot 8 = 72$	$ad = bc$

To solve a proportion that contains a variable, you find the value that makes the equation true.

1 EXAMPLE   **Multiplying to Solve a Proportion**

Solve $\frac{x}{9} = \frac{4}{6}$.

Method 1 Multiplication Property of Equality

$$\frac{x}{9} = \frac{4}{6}$$

$$\frac{x}{9} \cdot 9 = \frac{4}{6} \cdot 9$$

$$x = \frac{36}{6}$$

$$x = 6$$

Method 2 Cross products

$$\frac{x}{9} = \frac{4}{6}$$

$$x \cdot 6 = 9 \cdot 4$$

$$6x = 36$$

$$\frac{6x}{6} = \frac{36}{6}$$

$$x = 6$$

Ongoing Assessment and Intervention

Before the Lesson	**During the Lesson**	**After the Lesson**
Diagnose prerequisite skills using:	Monitor progress using:	Assess knowledge using:
• Check Skills You'll Need	• Check Understanding	• Lesson Quiz
	• Additional Examples	• Computer Test Generator
	• Test Prep	CD-ROM

✔ **Check Understanding** Example 1

1. Solve each proportion.

a. $\frac{h}{9} = \frac{2}{3}$ 6   **b.** $\frac{4}{5} = \frac{t}{55}$ 44   **c.** $\frac{22}{d} = \frac{6}{21}$ 77

Two ratios form a proportion if their cross products are equal.

2 EXAMPLE   Testing for a Proportion

Do the ratios $\frac{4}{6}$ and $\frac{10}{14}$ form a proportion? Explain.

$\frac{4}{6} \overset{?}{=} \frac{10}{14}$ **Test by writing as a proportion.**

$4 \cdot 14 \overset{?}{=} 6 \cdot 10$ **Write cross products.**

$56 \neq 60$ **Simplify.**

● The ratios do not form a proportion. Cross products are not equal.

✔ **Check Understanding** Example 2

2. Tell whether the two ratios form a proportion. Explain.

a. $\frac{6}{9}, \frac{4}{6}$ **b.** $\frac{15}{20}, \frac{5}{7}$ **c.** $\frac{7}{12}, \frac{17.5}{30}$
yes, cross products   no, cross products   yes, cross products
equal   not equal   equal

OBJECTIVE

2 Using Proportions to Solve Problems

You can write and solve proportions for many real-world problems.

3 EXAMPLE   Real-World 🌐 Problem Solving

Navigation One hundred nautical miles equals about 115 standard, or statute, miles. To the nearest mile, how far in statute miles is 156 nautical miles?

Let d = distance in statute miles.

$\underset{\text{distance in statute miles} \,\rightarrow}{\overset{\text{distance in nautical miles} \,\rightarrow}{}} \dfrac{100}{115} = \dfrac{156}{d} \overset{\leftarrow \text{ distance in nautical miles}}{\underset{\leftarrow \text{ distance in statute miles}}{}}$

$100d = 115(156)$ **Write cross products.**

$d = \dfrac{115(156)}{100}$ **Divide each side by 100.**

$d \approx 179$ **A calculator may be useful.**

● 156 nautical miles is about 179 statute miles.

✔ **Check Understanding** Example 3

3. To the nearest mile, how far in nautical miles is 100 statute miles?
87 nautical miles

Real-World 🌐 Connection

Sailors and astronauts measure distances in *nautical miles.* This photo of the Great Lakes was taken from the space shuttle at an altitude of 156 nautical miles.

Math Background

A mathematical sentence that states that two ratios are equal is a *proportion*. Like any mathematical sentence, a proportion may be true $\left(\frac{3}{4} = \frac{6}{8}\right)$, false $\left(\frac{3}{4} = \frac{4}{3}\right)$, or open $\left(\frac{3}{4} = \frac{x}{8}\right)$.

Teaching Notes

1 EXAMPLE Alternative Method

Point out to students that when using Method 2, they are always multiplying the two constants that align diagonally, and then dividing by the constant that aligns diagonally with the variable.

2 EXAMPLE Visual Learners

Suggest that students draw two lines, forming an X that looks like a multiplication sign, to indicate the correct cross-product multiplication: $\frac{4}{6} ✕ \frac{10}{14}$

3 EXAMPLE History Connection

Sailors call the unit rate of one nautical mile per hour a *knot*. This came from a time when sailors used a knotted rope to measure how fast they were sailing. So, 10 knots is 10 nautical miles per hour.

PowerPoint

📲 Additional Examples

1 Solve $\frac{2}{7} = \frac{y}{14}$. 4

2 Do the ratios $\frac{3}{5}$ and $\frac{21}{35}$ form a proportion? Explain. Yes; the cross products are equal.

3 One hundred rods is about 275 fathoms. About how many fathoms is 25 rods? 68.75 fathoms

Closure

Define proportion. Then explain how to solve for a variable in a proportion. A proportion is a statement that two ratios are equal. You multiply cross products and then solve for the variable.

👥 Reaching All Students

Below Level Ask a volunteer to explain how to use ratios to make orange juice from concentrate. If they must use more than one can of concentrate, a *proportion* could be used to determine the amount of water.	**Advanced Learners** Have students research to find the ratios of men to women enrolled at 10 different colleges. Have them use cross products to determine whether any of the ratios can form a proportion.	**Visual Learners** See note on page 295. **Error Prevention** See note on page 297.

Assignment Guide

1 Objective 1
  Ⓐ Ⓑ Core 1–20, 24–31,
    34–49, 55–59
  Ⓒ Extension 65–68

2 Objective 2
  Ⓐ Ⓑ Core 21–23, 32, 33,
    50–54, 60
  Ⓒ Extension 61–64

Test Prep 69–72
Mixed Review 73–80

■ Practice 6-2 *Proportions*

Write a proportion for each phrase. Then solve. When necessary, round to the nearest hundredth.

1. 420 ft² painted in 36 min; f ft² painted in 30 min

$$\frac{420}{36} = \frac{f}{30}, f = 350 \text{ ft}^2$$

2. 75 points scored in 6 games; p points scored in 4 games

$$\frac{75}{6} = \frac{p}{4}, p = 50 \text{ pts}$$

3. 6 apples for $1.00; 15 apples for d dollars

$$\frac{6}{1.00} = \frac{15}{d}, d = \$2.50$$

Tell whether each pair of ratios forms a proportion.

4. $\frac{3}{4}$ and $\frac{9}{12}$ proportion
5. $\frac{25}{40}$ and $\frac{5}{8}$ proportion
6. $\frac{8}{12}$ and $\frac{14}{21}$ proportion
7. $\frac{13}{15}$ and $\frac{4}{5}$ not a proportion
8. $\frac{3}{4}$ and $\frac{5}{6}$ not a proportion
9. $\frac{21}{14}$ and $\frac{18}{12}$ proportion

Solve each proportion. Where necessary, round to the nearest tenth.

10. $\frac{5}{7} = \frac{x}{35}$ x = 25
11. $\frac{15}{16} = \frac{n}{18}$ n = 17
12. $\frac{4}{5} = \frac{h}{35}$ h = 28
13. $\frac{11}{7} = \frac{f}{70}$ f = 110
14. $\frac{29}{40} = \frac{m}{120}$ m = 75
15. $\frac{39}{6} = \frac{j}{7}$ j = 102.9
16. $\frac{4}{13} = \frac{r}{17}$ r = 11.5
17. $\frac{77}{54} = \frac{x}{13}$ x = 19.9

18. At Discount Copy, 12 copies cost $0.66. Melissa needs 56 copies. How much should they cost?

    $3.08

19. You estimate that you can do 12 math problems in 45 min. How long should it take you to do 20 math problems?

    75 min

■ Enrichment 6-2 *More on Proportions*

Consider the proportion $\frac{3}{5} = \frac{9}{15}$. If the ratio of the numerators is set equal to the ratio of the denominators, another true proportion results: $\frac{3}{9} = \frac{5}{15}$.

1. Write a true proportion. Then write the proportion that results when you set the ratio of the numerators equal to the ratio of the denominators. Is this proportion true or false?
Sample answers:

$$\frac{4}{5} = \frac{8}{10} \qquad \frac{4}{8} = \frac{5}{10} \qquad \text{true}$$

2. If $\frac{A}{B} = \frac{C}{D}$, then it appears that $\frac{A}{C} = \frac{B}{D}$.   true

Consider the true proportion $\frac{21}{12} = \frac{56}{32}$. Answer true or false.

3. $\frac{21}{56} = \frac{12}{32}$ true

4. If $\frac{A}{B} = \frac{C}{D}$, then it appears that $\frac{B}{A} = \frac{D}{C}$.   true

Consider the true proportion $\frac{6}{8} = \frac{3}{4}$. Answer true or false.

5. $\frac{6}{3} = \frac{1}{8}$ false

6. If $\frac{A}{B} = \frac{C}{D}$, then it appears that $\frac{A}{C} = \frac{B}{D}$.   false

Consider the true proportion $\frac{3}{8} = \frac{9}{24}$. Answer true or false.

7. $\frac{3+8}{8} = \frac{9+24}{24}$ true
8. $\frac{3-8}{8} = \frac{9-24}{24}$ true

9. If $\frac{A}{B} = \frac{C}{D}$, then it appears that $\frac{A+B}{B} = \frac{C+D}{D}$, and $\frac{A-B}{B} = \frac{C-D}{D}$.

Use the proportion you wrote in Exercise 1 to explore this theorem.

If $\frac{A}{B} = \frac{C}{D}$, then $\frac{A \pm B}{B} = \frac{C \pm D}{D}$. Sample answers are shown.

10. Test the theorem. Write three new proportions.

$$\frac{9}{-1} = \frac{18}{-2} \qquad \frac{5}{-1} = \frac{15}{-3} \qquad \frac{15}{-1} = \frac{30}{-2}$$

11. Does the theorem appear to be true?   yes

EXERCISES

❓ For more exercises, see *Extra Practice*.

Practice and Problem Solving

Ⓐ Practice by Example

Example 1
(page 294)

Solve each proportion.

1. $\frac{2}{v} = \frac{1}{8}$ 16
2. $\frac{z}{42} = \frac{25}{70}$ 15
3. $\frac{4}{h} = \frac{8}{10}$ 5
4. $\frac{4}{16} = \frac{s}{8}$ 2
5. $\frac{4}{11} = \frac{x}{22}$ 8
6. $\frac{2}{9} = \frac{r}{36}$ 8
7. $\frac{12}{n} = \frac{2}{12}$ 72
8. $\frac{1}{15} = \frac{3}{p}$ 45
9. $\frac{4}{15} = \frac{a}{75}$ 20
10. $\frac{3}{4} = \frac{21}{b}$ 28
11. $\frac{13}{c} = \frac{39}{60}$ 20
12. $\frac{3}{6} = \frac{7}{d}$ 14

Example 2
(page 295)

Tell whether the two ratios form a proportion. Explain.

13. $\frac{2}{3}$ and $\frac{10}{20}$
14. $\frac{25}{80}$ and $\frac{5}{16}$
15. $\frac{4}{7}$ and $\frac{20}{25}$
16. $\frac{2}{3}$ and $\frac{10}{16}$
17. $\frac{3}{4}$ and $\frac{12}{15}$
18. $\frac{3}{8}$ and $\frac{21}{56}$
19. $\frac{9}{24}$ and $\frac{15}{40}$
20. $\frac{20}{32}$ and $\frac{12}{20}$

13–20. See margin.

Example 3 🌐
(page 295)

21. **Photocopies** At the Copy Shoppe, 18 copies cost $1.08. At that rate, how much will 40 copies cost? $2.40

22. Three tea bags are needed to make a gallon of iced tea. How many tea bags are needed to make four gallons?   12 tea bags

🌐 23. **Purchasing** Three posters cost $9.60. At that rate, how many posters can you buy for $48?   15 posters

Ⓑ Apply Your Skills

24. yes, cross products equal

25. no, cross products not equal

26. yes, cross products equal

27. no, cross products not equal

33. Answers may vary. Sample: the lengths in the proportion, 3 ft and 15 in., have different units. They should use the same unit.

Tell whether the two ratios form a proportion. Explain.

24. $\frac{3.9}{5.4}$ and $\frac{13}{18}$
25. $\frac{54}{60}$ and $\frac{118}{110}$
26. $\frac{27}{72}$ and $\frac{48}{128}$
27. $\frac{144}{120}$ and $\frac{75}{145}$

24–27. See left.

Mental Math Solve by mental math.

28. $\frac{1}{6} = \frac{a}{72}$ 12
29. $\frac{120}{24} = \frac{y}{2}$ 10
30. $\frac{10}{v} = \frac{3}{1.5}$ 5
31. $\frac{n}{12} = \frac{12}{2}$ 72

🌐 32. **Exchange Rates** On a recent day, the exchange rate for U.S. dollars to European euros was 0.89 dollar per euro. On that day, about how many euros would you get for 25 dollars?   28 euros

33. **Error Analysis** Fancy ribbon costs $3 for 15 in. Your friend wants to find the cost of 3 ft of ribbon. He uses the proportion $\frac{3}{15} = \frac{x}{3}$ and gets an answer of $.60. Explain your friend's error.
   See left.

Solve each proportion. Where necessary, round to the nearest tenth.

34. $\frac{4}{3} = \frac{b}{21}$ 28
35. $\frac{6}{25} = \frac{e}{80}$ 19.2
36. $\frac{4}{9} = \frac{f}{15}$ 6.7
37. $\frac{3}{8} = \frac{50}{g}$ 133.3
38. $\frac{24}{17} = \frac{109}{h}$ 77.2
39. $\frac{7}{9} = \frac{j}{22.5}$ 17.5
40. $\frac{6}{13} = \frac{7.8}{m}$ 16.9
41. $\frac{20}{27} = \frac{1.1}{n}$ 1.5

Estimation Estimate the solution of each proportion.

42. $\frac{11}{a} = \frac{9}{17}$ 22
43. $\frac{w}{20} = \frac{6}{23}$ 5
44. $\frac{3}{2} = \frac{29}{d}$ 20
45. $\frac{20}{3.9} = \frac{s}{6}$ 30
46. $\frac{1.5}{p} = \frac{2.1}{4.1}$ 3
47. $\frac{f}{4} = \frac{12}{49}$ 1
48. $\frac{60}{g} = \frac{24.1}{8.1}$ 20
49. $\frac{9}{4.4} = \frac{x}{19}$ 38

---

13. no, cross products not equal
14. yes, cross products equal
15. no, cross products not equal
16. no, cross products not equal
17. no, cross products not equal

18. yes, cross products equal
19. yes, cross products equal
20. no, cross products not equal

50. At the rate shown in the cartoon, how much would five potatoes cost? **$36.67**

REAL LIFE ADVENTURES by Gary Wise and Lance Aldrich

Potatoes $27⁹⁹/lb.
Potatoes 3 for $22
Onions $32⁹⁹/lb.
Cabbage $15⁰⁰ea.
Green Beans $17⁹⁹/lb.

If the people who own the shops at the airport owned other things.

51. Quality Control A microchip inspector found three defective chips in a batch containing 750 chips. At that rate, how many defective chips would there be in 10,000 chips?
40 defective chips

GPS

52. Reasoning If $\frac{a}{b} = \frac{c}{d}$, will $\frac{a}{c} = \frac{b}{d}$? Assume that $b \neq 0$, $c \neq 0$, and $d \neq 0$. Explain your reasoning. **See left.**

52. Yes; multiply each side by $\frac{b}{c}$.

53. Geometry A rectangle that is 20 cm long and 28 cm wide is the same shape as one that is 9 cm long and z cm wide. Find z. **12.6 cm**

54. Baseball Your team scores 4 runs in the first three innings of a 9-inning baseball game. If it continues at that rate, how many runs will it score in the game? **12 runs**

Write a proportion for each situation. Then solve.

55. 3 oz for $1.65; 5 oz for x dollars $\frac{3}{1.65} = \frac{5}{x}$; **$2.75**

56. 20 lb for $27.50; 12 lb for x dollars $\frac{20}{27.50} = \frac{12}{x}$; **$16.50**

57. 25 yd in $2\frac{1}{2}$ s; 100 yd in x seconds $\frac{25}{2.5} = \frac{100}{x}$; **10 s**

58. 3 miles in 2.8 minutes; 33.3 miles in x minutes $\frac{3}{2.8} = \frac{33.3}{x}$; **31.08 min**

59. $3\frac{1}{2}$ pounds in 4 cubic inches; x pound in 1 cubic inch $\frac{3}{4} = \frac{x}{1}$; **0.875 lb**

60. Writing in Math A truck driver estimates that it will take him 12 h to drive 1,160 km. After 5 h, he has driven 484 km. Is he on schedule? Explain. **Answers may vary. Sample: Yes; $\frac{1,160}{12} = \frac{d}{5}$ so $d \approx 483$, very close to the driver's 484 km.**

C Challenge   **For Exercises 61–64, use the table.**

61. How many times does an adult's heart beat in 270 s? **360 times**

62. In how many seconds will a newborn's heart beat 35 times? **15 s**

63. In how many seconds will a 12-year-old's heart beat 17 times? **12 s**

64. In 45 s, how many more times does a newborn's heart beat than a 6-year-old's heart? **30 more times**

Human Heart Rates

Age (years)	Beats per Minute
newborn	140
1	120
6	100
10	90
12	85
adult	80

Use the Guided Problem Solving worksheet with Exercise 51.

Test Prep

Resources

For additional practice with a variety of test item formats:
• Test Prep, p. 343
• Test-Taking Strategies, p. 338
• Test-Taking Strategies With Transparencies

Reteaching 6-2 *Proportions*

Solve $\frac{4}{6} = \frac{10}{x}$

Method 1: Multiplication Property of Equality

Method 2: cross products

Write a proportion for each situation. Then solve.

65. 5 km in 18 min 36 s; 8 km in v minutes $\frac{5}{18\frac{36}{60}} = \frac{8}{v}$; 29.76 min

66. 96 oz for $2; y pounds for $10 $\frac{6}{2} = \frac{y}{10}$; 30 lb

67. 4 oz for $1.85; 1 lb for t dollars $\frac{4}{1.85} = \frac{16}{t}$; $7.40

68. $5.76 for 2 lb 4 oz; c dollars for 1 pound $\frac{5.76}{2.25} = \frac{c}{1}$; $2.56

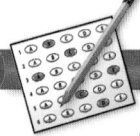

Test Prep

Multiple Choice

69. Four ounces of orange juice contain 50 calories. About how many calories are in 14 ounces of orange juice? C
  A. 1 cal **B.** 14 cal **C.** 175 cal **D.** 700 cal

70. A lion's heart beats 12 times in 16 s. How many times does a lion's heart beat in 60 s? H
  F. 24 **G.** 32 **H.** 45 **I.** 192

71. An artist makes purple paint by mixing red and blue paint in the ratio of 2 parts red to 3 parts blue. What is the ratio of red paint to purple paint? D
  A. 3 : 2 **B.** 3 : 5 **C.** 2 : 3 **D.** 2 : 5

Extended Response

72. On Monday, the ratio of Tara's pocket money to her brother Seth's pocket money was $\frac{3}{1}$. On Tuesday, Tara gave $5 to Seth. Then Tara had twice as much money as Seth. Let $3x$ equal the amount Tara had on Monday and x equal the amount Seth had on Monday.
  a. Write two ratios that each compare the amount of money Tara had on Tuesday to the amount Seth had on Tuesday. Use the ratios to write a proportion.
  b. Solve for x.
  c. Find the amount of money each person had on Monday.
  a–c. See back of book.

Take It to the NET
Online lesson quiz at
www.PHSchool.com
Web Code: ada-0602

Mixed Review

Lesson 6-1 **Write each ratio as a fraction in simplest form.**

73. ten per thousand $\frac{1}{100}$ **74.** 30 to 55 $\frac{6}{11}$ **75.** 125 : 70 $\frac{25}{14}$

Lesson 5-6 **76. Personal Finance** On Saturday afternoon, a student bought two music tapes for $8.95 each and a sweater for $24.95. She received $20 for mowing a lawn. On Saturday night, she had $45.12. How much money did the student have on Saturday morning? $67.97

Lessons 1-3 and 5-3 **Tell whether each equation is true or false.**

77. $\left| -2\frac{1}{4} \right| - \left| 2\frac{1}{4} \right| = 0$ true **78.** $\left| -2\frac{1}{4} \right| + \left| 2\frac{1}{4} \right| = 0$ false

79. $-\left| -\frac{9}{4} \right| + \left| 2\frac{1}{4} \right| = 0$ true **80.** $\left| -\frac{9}{4} \right| - \left| 2\frac{1}{4} \right| = 0$ true

298 Chapter 6 Ratios, Proportions, and Percents

Alternative Assessment

Group students in pairs. Have one student roll a number cube three times, and then use those numbers and a variable to write a proportion. Have both partners solve the proportion and compare answers. Repeat, with students taking turns writing the proportion.

OBJECTIVE 1 — Using Similar Figures

Similar figures have the same shape, but not necessarily the same size. Similar figures have *corresponding angles* and *corresponding sides*.

The symbol ~ means *is similar to*. At the right, $\triangle ABC \sim \triangle XYZ$.

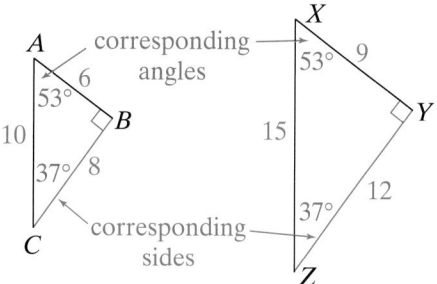

Key Concepts — Similar Figures

Similar figures have two properties.

- The corresponding angles have equal measures.
- The lengths of corresponding sides are in proportion.

1 EXAMPLE — Using Similar Figures

Parallelogram $ABCD \sim$ parallelogram $EFGH$. Find the value of x.

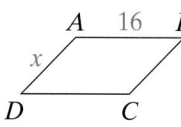 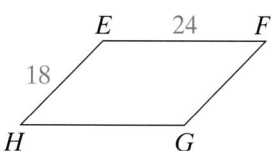

Write a proportion for corresponding sides.

Side *DA* corresponds to side *HE*.	$\dfrac{x}{18} = \dfrac{16}{24}$	Side *AB* corresponds to side *EF*.
	$x \cdot 24 = 18 \cdot 16$	Write cross products.
	$\dfrac{24x}{24} = \dfrac{18 \cdot 16}{24}$	Divide each side by 24.
	$x = 12$	Simplify.

✓ Check Understanding — Example 1

1. Parallelogram *KLMN* is similar to parallelogram *ABCD* in Example 1. Find the value of *y*. Round to the nearest tenth. **15.8**

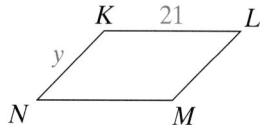

What You'll Learn

OBJECTIVE 1 To solve problems that involve similar figures

OBJECTIVE 2 To solve problems that involve scale drawings

. . . And Why

To solve real-world problems involving maps

✓ Check Skills You'll Need

Solve each proportion. Round to the nearest tenth where necessary.

1. $\dfrac{2}{3} = \dfrac{f}{21}$ **2.** $\dfrac{3}{8} = \dfrac{50}{p}$
   14   133.3

3. $\dfrac{9}{4} = \dfrac{15}{p}$ **4.** $\dfrac{16}{3} = \dfrac{19}{g}$
   6.7   3.6

❓ For help, go to Lesson 6-2.

New Vocabulary

- similar figures
- indirect measurement
- scale drawing

💻 **iTEXT** Interactive lesson includes instant self-check, tutorials, and activities.

6-3

1. Plan

Lesson Preview

✓ **Check Skills You'll Need**

Proportions
Lesson 6-2: Example 1; Exercises 1–12.
Extra Practice, p. 749.

Lesson Resources

📁 **Teaching Resources**
Practice, Reteaching, Enrichment

👥 **Reaching All Students**
Practice Workbook 6-3
Spanish Practice Workbook 6-3
Guided Problem Solving 6-3
Hands-On Activities 15, 16

⏱ **Presentation Assistant Plus!**
Transparencies and PowerPoint™
- Check Skills You'll Need 6-3
- Additional Examples 6-3
- Student Edition Answers 6-3
- Lesson Quiz 6-3
PH Presentation Pro CD-ROM 6-3

ASSESSMENT SYSTEM

Computer Test Generator CD-ROM

💻 **Technology**
Resource Pro® CD-ROM
Computer Test Generator CD-ROM
PH Presentation Pro CD-ROM

💻 **www.PHSchool.com**
Student Site
- Teacher Web Code: adk-5500
- Self-grading Lesson Quiz
PH SuccessNet Teacher Center
- Lesson Planner
- Resources

Plus **iTEXT**

✓ Ongoing Assessment and Intervention

Before the Lesson	During the Lesson	After the Lesson
Diagnose prerequisite skills using:	**Monitor progress using:**	**Assess knowledge using:**
• Check Skills You'll Need	• Check Understanding	• Lesson Quiz
	• Additional Examples	• Computer Test Generator CD-ROM
	• Test Prep	

Math Background

Not only are the corresponding sides of similar figures in proportion, but all other segments, such as medians and altitudes, are also in proportion.

Teaching Notes

1 EXAMPLE Teaching Tip

Make sure students understand how corresponding letters in a similarity statement indicate corresponding parts. For example, in parallelogram *ABCD* ~ parallelogram *EFGH*, the sides named by *A* and *B*, and *E* and *F*, correspond.

2 EXAMPLE Visual Learners

Help students keep track of corresponding sides. Have students sketch the triangles on paper. Then have them use three pencils of different colors to mark the corresponding sides of the triangles.

PowerPoint
Additional Examples

1 Trapezoid *ABCD* ~ trapezoid *EFGH*. Find the value of *k*. **4**

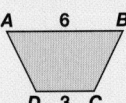

2 A flagpole casts a shadow 5 ft long. At the same time, a yardstick casts a shadow 1.5 ft long. How tall is the flagpole? **10 ft**

3 A map scale is 1 in. : 24 mi. About how far is it between two cities that are 3 in. apart on the map? **about 72 mi**

Closure

Ask: *How can you identify similar figures?* Similar figures have the same shape, but not necessarily the same size. *How can you find the lengths of all parts of similar figures when you know the lengths of some corresponding parts?* Write and solve proportions.

300

You can use similar figures to compute distances that are difficult to measure directly. Such a process is called **indirect measurement.**

2 EXAMPLE Real-World Problem Solving

Indirect Measurement A tree casts a shadow 10 ft long. A 5-ft woman casts a shadow 4 ft long. The triangle shown for the woman and her shadow is similar to the triangle shown for the tree and its shadow. How tall is the tree?

$\frac{4}{10} = \frac{5}{x}$ Corresponding sides of similar triangles are in proportion.

$4x = 10 \cdot 5$ Write cross products.

$\frac{4x}{4} = \frac{10 \cdot 5}{4}$ Divide each side by 4.

$x = 12.5$ Simplify.

● The tree is 12.5 ft tall.

✓ Check Understanding Example 2

2. **Indirect Measurement** A building 70 ft high casts a 150-ft shadow. A nearby flagpole casts a 60-ft shadow. Draw a diagram. Use similar triangles to find the height of the flagpole. **See back of book.**

OBJECTIVE

2 Using Scale Drawings

A **scale drawing** is an enlarged or reduced drawing that is similar to an actual object or place. The ratio of a distance in the drawing to the corresponding actual distance is the *scale* of the drawing.

3 EXAMPLE Real-World Problem Solving

Maps The scale of the map is 1 in. : 40 mi. About how far from Atlanta is Athens?

Map distance = $1\frac{1}{2}$ in., or 1.5 in.   Measure the map distance.

$\frac{\text{map (in.)}}{\text{actual (mi)}} \rightarrow \frac{1}{40} = \frac{1.5}{d} \leftarrow \frac{\text{map (in.)}}{\text{actual (mi)}}$ Write a proportion.

$1 \cdot d = 40 \cdot 1.5$ Write cross products.

$d = 60$ Simplify.

● Athens is about 60 mi from Atlanta.

✓ Check Understanding Example 3

3. **Maps** The distance from Atlanta to Macon is about 75 mi. What is the approximate map distance between these two cities? $1\frac{7}{8}$ **in.**

Reaching All Students

Below Level Ask if anyone has ever built a model of a boat, airplane, car, or building. Ask a volunteer to explain the relationship between the model and its original figure.

Advanced Learners Ask: *When making indirect measurements as in Example 2, why is it important to measure shadows at the same time?* Positions of the sun at different times affect the lengths of shadows.

Visual Learners See note on page 300.
Error Prevention See note on page 302.

EXERCISES

❓ For more exercises, see *Extra Practice*.

Practice and Problem Solving

A **Practice by Example**

Example 1
(page 299)

Trapezoid *EFGH* ~ trapezoid *MNOP*. Find the indicated value.

1. *x* 2⅖ ft
2. *y* 2½ ft
3. *z* 3⅓ ft

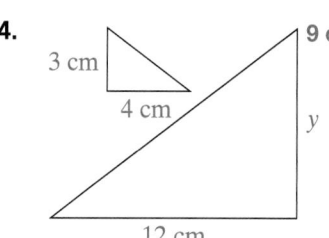
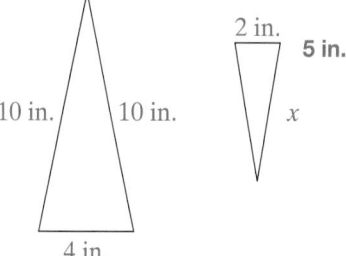

The triangles in each pair are similar. Find the missing length. Round to the nearest tenth where necessary.

4.

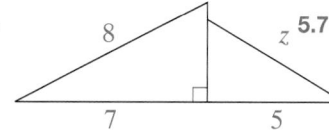

3 cm, 4 cm, 9 cm, 12 cm, *y*

5.

2 in., 5 in., 10 in., 10 in., *x*, 4 in.

6.

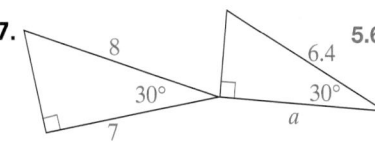

8, *z* 5.7, 7, 5

7.

8, 5.6, 6.4, 30°, 30°, *a*, 7

Example 2
(page 300)

8. **Indirect Measurement** A tree casts a shadow 8 ft long. A 6-ft man casts a shadow 4 ft long. The triangle formed by the tree and its shadow is similar to the triangle formed by the man and his shadow. How tall is the tree? **12 ft**

🌐 9. **Projection** An image on a slide is similar to its projected image. A slide is 35 mm wide and 21 mm high. Its projected image is 85 cm wide. To the nearest centimeter, how high is the image? **51 cm**

Example 3
(page 300)

The scale of a map is 1 cm : 12 km. Find the actual distance for each map distance.

10. 1.5 cm **18 km**
11. 12 cm **144 km**
12. 4.25 cm **51 km**
13. 8.3 cm **99.6 km**

🌐 14. **Maps** Duane is drawing a map with a scale of 1 in. : 3 mi. He knows that the distance from Center Point to Comfort is 9 miles. How far apart should Duane locate the two towns on his map? **3 in.**

The scale of a drawing is 1 in. : 25 yd. Find the length on the drawing for each actual length.

15. 100 yd **4 in.**
16. 375 yd **15 in.**
17. 512.5 yd **20.5 in.**
18. 20 yd **0.8 or ⅘ in.**

19. **Indirect Measurement** Jacques has a scale drawing of his bedroom with a scale of 1 cm : 0.4 m. On the drawing, the front window is 3 cm from the door. What is the actual distance in the room? **1.2 m**

GPS Use the Guided Problem Solving worksheet with Exercise 9.

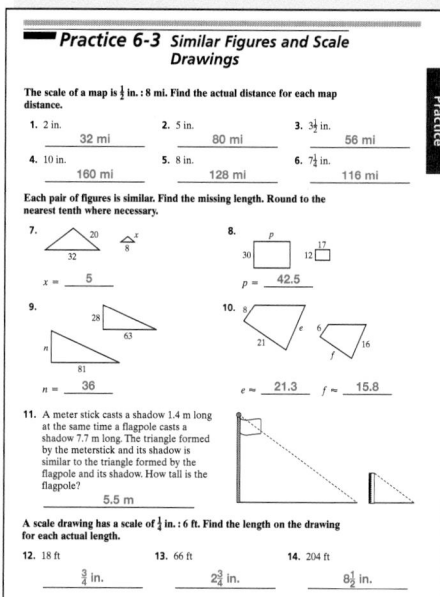

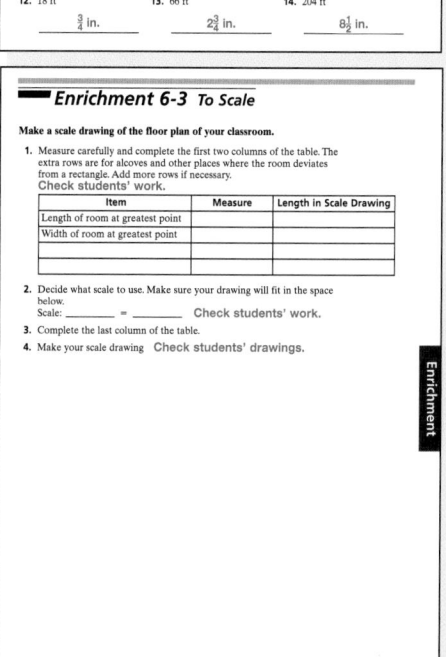

Error Prevention!

Exercises 4–7 Suggest students draw the figures with the same orientations so the corresponding parts will be easier to identify.

20. A scale drawing has a scale of 1 in. : 10 ft. What is the distance on the drawing for an actual distance of 20 ft? Of 45 ft? **2 in.; 4.5 in.**

B **Apply Your Skills**

The scale of a map is 2 cm : 15 km. Find the actual distance for each map distance.

21. 6 cm
45 km

22. 2.1 cm
15.75 km

23. 10 mm
7.5 km

24. 17.4 cm
130.5 km

The length of each piece in a model railroad built on the HO scale is $\frac{1}{87}$ of the actual length. Another popular model is the N scale, for which the scale is $\frac{1}{160}$.

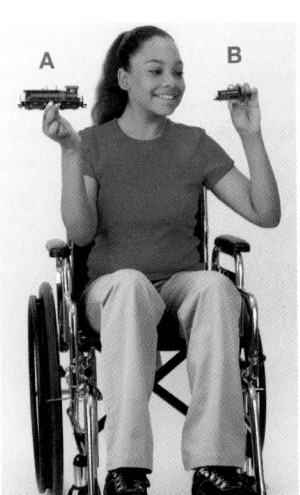

25. The student in the photograph is holding HO and N models of the same locomotive. Which type of model is labeled A? Which type of model is labeled B? **HO model; N model**

26. Each car on a full-size passenger train is 80 ft long. What is the length in inches of a model passenger car in the HO scale? In the N scale? **about 11 in.; 6 in.**

27. A diesel locomotive is 60 ft long. What is the length in inches of a model of the locomotive in the N scale? **4.5 in.**

28. In the O scale, a length is $\frac{1}{48}$ the actual length. An O-scale locomotive is 1.05 ft long. How long is the actual locomotive?
50.4 ft

A scale drawing has a scale of $\frac{1}{2}$ in. : 10 ft. Find the length on the drawing for each actual length.

29. 40 ft **2 in.**   **30.** 5 ft $\frac{1}{4}$ in.   **31.** 35 ft $1\frac{3}{4}$ in.   **32.** $3\frac{1}{2}$ ft $\frac{7}{40}$ in.

36. Answers may vary.
Sample: You cannot assume that map distances are proportional to actual distances.

33. Open-Ended Give some examples of similar figures you find in everyday life. **Answers may vary. Sample: Some figures in board games model actual figures.**

The cities of Jackson, Mississippi, and Carson City, Nevada, are 1,750 mi apart.

34. Geography A map of the United States has a scale of 1 in. : 250 mi. How far apart are the cities on the map? **7 in.**

35. On another map, the cities are 5 in. apart. What is the scale?
1 in. : 350 mi

36. Reasoning A note at the bottom of a map says "not to scale." Explain why that is important information. **See above left.**

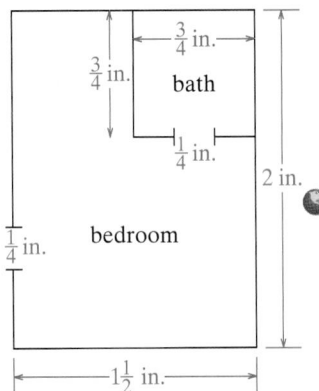

A 2-in. length in the scale drawing at the left represents an actual length of 20 ft.

37. Architecture What is the scale of the drawing? **1 in. : 10 ft**

38. What are the actual dimensions of the bath? **7.5 ft by 7.5 ft**

39. Find the actual width of the doorways that lead into the bedroom and the bathroom. **2.5 ft**

40. Find the actual area of the bedroom. **243.75 ft²**

41. Yes; the narrow section in the drawing is $\frac{3}{4}$ in. by $\frac{3}{4}$ in., representing a space 7.5 ft by 7.5 ft.

41. Can a bed 6 ft long and 3 ft wide fit into the narrow section of the bedroom? Justify your answer. **See above.**

 Challenge  **42. Architecture** The length of a room is 16 ft. The scale of a blueprint is $\frac{1}{2}$ in. : 1 ft. Find the room's length in the blueprint. **8 in.**

43. In a square, all angles have equal measures and the ratios of the lengths of corresponding sides are all equal. All circles are similar. Explanations may vary. Sample: Circles have no angles and only one measurement that can vary.

43. Writing in Math Explain why all squares are similar. For what other shape can you say that all figures are similar? Explain. **See left.**

44. A boxcar on a freight train is 40 ft long. A model boxcar is 3 in. long. In which scale, HO, N, or O was the model built? (*Hint:* See Exercises 25–28.) **N scale**

45. You are building a display shelf for your model train. You have 12 cars. Each car is 1.2 ft long. You want 1.2 in. of space between cars. How long must the shelf be? **$15\frac{1}{2}$ ft**

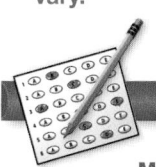

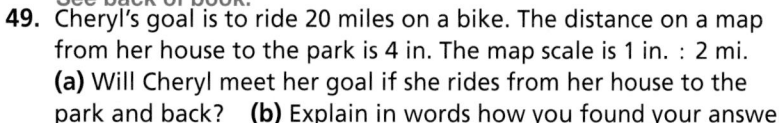

Test Prep

Multiple Choice

46. The scale for a drawing of a garage is 1.5 in. : 12 ft. If one side of the garage is 40 ft, how long would that side be in the drawing? **A**
A. 5 in.   **B.** 0.45 ft   **C.** 5 ft   **D.** 320 in.

47. The scale of a dollhouse is 1 in. : 2 ft. Which is *most likely* to be the measurement of the height of the dollhouse's front door? **F**
F. $3\frac{1}{2}$ in.   **G.** $3\frac{1}{2}$ ft   **H.** 14 in.   **I.** 14 ft

Short Response

48. To plan a rectangular mural 90 ft long and 75 ft wide, you want to make a drawing with a scale of 1 in. : 9 ft. Can you fit the drawing on a piece of paper that is $8\frac{1}{2}$ in. by 11 in.? Explain. **See back of book.**

49. Cheryl's goal is to ride 20 miles on a bike. The distance on a map from her house to the park is 4 in. The map scale is 1 in. : 2 mi.
(a) Will Cheryl meet her goal if she rides from her house to the park and back?   **(b)** Explain in words how you found your answer.

[2] No; the round trip distance by the scale is 16 miles, and Cheryl wants to ride 20 miles. [1] correct answer; incomplete or no explanation

 **Take It to the NET**
Online lesson quiz at
www.PHSchool.com
Web Code: ada-0603

Mixed Review

Lesson 6-2   **Solve each proportion.**

50. $\frac{x}{5} = \frac{32}{80}$ **2**   **51.** $\frac{3}{8} = \frac{r}{15}$ **$5\frac{5}{8}$**   **52.** $\frac{40}{w} = \frac{50}{3}$ **$2\frac{2}{5}$**   **53.** $\frac{24}{16} = \frac{204}{c}$ **136**

Lesson 6-1  **54. Gas Mileage** A car travels 264 mi on 12 gal of gas. Find the unit rate in miles per gallon. **22 mi/gal**

Lesson 5-2   **Write each fraction as a decimal.**

55. $\frac{3}{8}$ **0.375**   **56.** $\frac{4}{9}$ **$0.\overline{4}$**   **57.** $\frac{7}{16}$ **0.4375**   **58.** $\frac{5}{12}$ **$0.41\overline{6}$**

Lesson 3-3   **Find the mean (to nearest tenth), median, and mode.**

59. 12, 10, 11, 7, 9, 8, 10, 5
9, 9.5, 10

60. 4.5, 3.2, 6.3, 5.2, 5, 4.8, 6, 3.9
4.9, 4.9, no mode

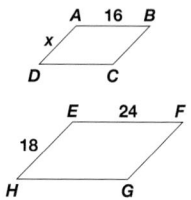

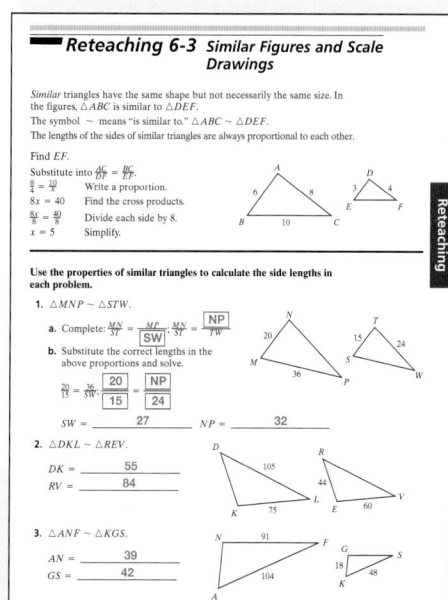
Alternative Assessment

Have students make a scale drawing of something in the classroom. Have them include a key showing the scale as well as the steps and calculations they used to determine the various dimensions.

303

Technology

Dilations

This Technology extension shows students one way to use geometry software to make a scale drawing.

Resources

Any geometry software

Teaching Notes

Teaching Tip
Make sure the students know that the center of a dilation must be a point.

Teaching Tip
Some students may draw a special triangle, such as isosceles. Suggest that they draw a triangle with no sides equal so it is easier to see what happens in the dilation.

Diversity
Students may not have much computer experience and may have trouble following the software instructions. Have these students work with a partner who has computer experience. Have the pair take turns following the steps and helping each other draw the figure in the example.

Teaching Tip
Some students may have had the pupils of their eyes dilated by an optometrist. Have them describe the procedure. Point out that a mathematical dilation can be an enlargement *or* a reduction.

You can use geometry software to make a scale drawing, or *dilation*, of a figure. First choose the Dilate command. Then choose a center of dilation and a scale, which is also known as a *scale factor*.

EXAMPLE

Draw a triangle. Then draw a dilation with scale factor 3.

Use geometry software. Draw $\triangle ABC$. Draw point D on one side of the triangle. Choose D as the center of a dilation with scale factor 3.

The result is an image like the one at the right. Each side of the dilation is 3 times as long as the corresponding side of $\triangle ABC$.

If you move point D, the dilation also will move. If instead you move A, B, or C, the dilation will change as $\triangle ABC$ changes.

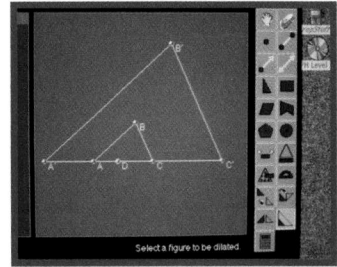

EXERCISES

Use geometry software to draw $\triangle PQR$.

1. **a.** Draw a point S *outside* $\triangle PQR$. Draw a dilation of $\triangle PQR$ with center S and scale factor 2.5. Label the dilation $\triangle XYZ$. $\triangle XYZ$ is similar to $\triangle PQR$. Angle X corresponds to angle P, angle Y corresponds to angle Q, and angle Z corresponds to angle R.

   b. Compare the location of $\triangle XYZ$ to the location of $\triangle PQR$. Does the dilation lie inside the original triangle? Outside the triangle? Do the triangles overlap?

   c. Now move S to be *inside* $\triangle PQR$. Once again, compare the locations of the two triangles. How did moving the center of dilation change the relative locations of the triangles?

   1a. Check students' work.

   1b. No; the dilation could lie outside or it could overlap the original triangle.

   1c. $\triangle PQR$ lies inside $\triangle XYZ$. Check students' work.

2. Change the location of point S so that $\triangle PQR$ and $\triangle XYZ$ have the given number of points in common. Print an example of each case.

   a. 0   **b.** 1   **c.** 2   **d.** more than 2   2a–d. Check students' work.

3. With S inside $\triangle PQR$, change the scale factor to 0.5. Describe the relative locations of the two triangles. $\triangle XYZ$ lies inside $\triangle PQR$.

4. **a.** Keep the scale factor of the dilation at 0.5. Use the Area tool to find the area of $\triangle PQR$. Use the Area tool again to find the area of $\triangle XYZ$. Write a ratio to compare the areas.   area $\triangle PQR$: area $\triangle XYZ = 4 : 1$

   b. Move P, Q, or R to see how the area of $\triangle XYZ$ changes as the area of $\triangle PQR$ changes. Does the ratio of the areas change? No

   c. **Reasoning** What do your results suggest about the areas of similar triangles that have a scale factor of 0.5?   They have the ratio 4 : 1 or 1 : 4.

Investigation

Exploring Probability

Many board games involve rolling two number cubes and then adding the numbers on the cubes. Are certain sums more likely than others? The table shows the possible rolls and their sums.

Sums of 2 Number Cubes

	1	2	3	4	5	6
1	2	3	4	5	6	7
2	3	4	5	6	7	8
3	4	5	6	7	8	9
4	5	6	7	8	9	10
5	6	7	8	9	10	11
6	7	8	9	10	11	12

1. Copy and complete the table.

2. What is the number of times each sum appears in the table? *See below.*

3. Which sum appears most frequently? **7**

4. There is a total of 36 sums in the table. Use your answer to Question 3 to write the ratio
$$\frac{\text{number of times the most frequent sum appears}}{\text{total number of sums}}.$$ $\frac{6}{36}$, or $\frac{1}{6}$

2. 2(1), 3(2), 4(3), 5(4), 6(5), 7(6), 8(5), 9(4), 10(3), 11(2), 12(1)

Outcomes are the possible results of an action. There are six outcomes for rolling a single number cube: 1, 2, 3, 4, 5, and 6.

An **event** is any outcome or group of outcomes. The outcomes are called *favorable outcomes.* In rolling two number cubes, for example, rolling a sum of 4 is an event corresponding to the three favorable outcomes shown here.

Three outcomes result in the event *a sum of 4.*

The outcomes for rolling two number cubes are *random* and therefore *equally likely* to occur. When outcomes are equally likely, you can use a ratio to find the *probability of an event.*

probability of an event $= P(\text{event}) = \dfrac{\text{number of favorable outcomes}}{\text{number of possible outcomes}}$

What You'll Learn

OBJECTIVE 1 To find probability

OBJECTIVE 2 To find odds

. . . And Why

To solve real-world problems involving the likelihood of events

✔ Check Skills You'll Need

Simplify. 1–4. See below.

1. $1 - \dfrac{3}{8}$ **2.** $1 - \dfrac{17}{20}$

3. $1 - \dfrac{6}{11}$ **4.** $1 - \dfrac{1}{12}$

For help, go to Lesson 5-3.

New Vocabulary

- outcomes
- event
- probability
- impossible event
- certain event
- complement
- odds

1. $\frac{5}{8}$
2. $\frac{3}{20}$
3. $\frac{5}{11}$
4. $\frac{11}{12}$

Interactive lesson includes instant self-check, tutorials, and activities.

305

Professional Development

Math Background

Theoretical probability describes the likelihood of an event occurring when all possible outcomes are known and all the outcomes are equally likely to occur. The probability of an event is a number between 0 and 1, with probability 0 meaning that the event will not occur and probability 1 meaning that the event must occur. When such a number is determined by experience (such as your toast landing buttered side down 8 out of 10 times when dropped — establishing a probability of this happening as $\frac{8}{10}$), the probability is called an *experimental probability*.

Teaching Notes

Investigation (Optional)
Ask students to hypothesize about why some people consider 7 to be a "lucky" number in rolling two number cubes. **7 is the sum that appears most frequently.** Ask: *Which sums appear the least number of times?* **2 and 12** *What should be the ratio of the appearances of a sum of 2 or of 12 to the appearances of all possible sums?* $\frac{1}{36}$

English Learners
Some students may think that *favorable outcomes* are only those that they want to occur. Point out that the term *favorable outcome* refers to the event you are specifically studying, whether it is good or bad. For example, if you calculate the probability that a skier will get a broken leg, the term *favorable outcome* stands for a broken leg.

2 EXAMPLE **Error Prevention**

Have students check their answer in Check Understanding by finding P(2). Then have them add this to P(not 2). The sum will equal 1 if the probabilities have been calculated properly.

306

Reading Math
You can read the probability $\frac{3}{6}$ as "three in six" or "three out of six."

Test-Taking Tip
On a multiple-choice test item, you can eliminate any answer choice showing a probability greater than 1 because a probability cannot be greater than 1.

---

1 EXAMPLE **Finding Probability**

Find *P*(rolling an even number) with one number cube.

$\dfrac{\text{number of favorable outcomes}}{\text{number of possible outcomes}} = \dfrac{3}{6}$ ← 3 even-number outcomes
← 6 possible outcomes

● *P*(rolling an even number) = $\frac{3}{6}$, or $\frac{1}{2}$.

✓ **Check Understanding** Example 1

1. Find each probability for one roll of a number cube.

   a. *P*(odd number) $\frac{3}{6}$, or $\frac{1}{2}$ **b.** *P*(2) $\frac{1}{6}$ **c.** *P*(5 or 6) $\frac{2}{6}$, or $\frac{1}{3}$

All probabilities range from 0 to 1.

Probability

less likely   more likely

0 — Impossible event

0.5 — Equally likely as unlikely

1 — Certain event

The **complement** of an event is the opposite of that event. The events *no rain* and *rain* are complements of each other. The probability of an event plus the probability of its complement always equals 1.

2 EXAMPLE **Real-World 🌐 Problem Solving**

Vital Statistics In the United States, the probability that a child is a twin is 2 in 90, or $\frac{2}{90}$. Find *P*(not a twin).

$P(\text{twin}) + P(\text{not a twin}) = 1$ — **Write an equation.**

$\frac{2}{90} + P(\text{not a twin}) = 1$ — **Substitute.**

$\frac{2}{90} - \frac{2}{90} + P(\text{not a twin}) = 1 - \frac{2}{90}$ — **Subtract $\frac{2}{90}$ from each side.**

$P(\text{not a twin}) = \frac{88}{90} = \frac{44}{45}$ — **Simplify.**

● The probability that a child is not a twin is $\frac{44}{45}$.

✓ **Check Understanding** Example 2

2. **a.** When you roll a number cube, what is *P*(not 2)? $\frac{5}{6}$
   b. **Reasoning** What is the complement of an impossible event? a certain event

306 Chapter 6 Ratios, Proportions, and Percents

🌿 Reaching All Students

Below Level Ask a volunteer to choose one counter from a bag containing 40 red counters and 60 blue counters. Ask students what the chance is of choosing a blue counter. **60 out of 100, or 60%**	**Advanced Learners** Ask students what strategies they could use to estimate the probability of an event occurring. **Answers may vary. Sample: Find the results of previous similar situations or conditions.**	**English Learners** See note on page 306. **Inclusion** See note on page 307.

2 Finding Odds

You can think of probability as a ratio of $\frac{part}{whole}$. You can also use a $\frac{part}{part}$ ratio, called **odds,** to describe the likelihood of an event.

$$\text{odds in favor of an event} = \frac{\text{number of } favorable \text{ outcomes}}{\text{number of } unfavorable \text{ outcomes}}$$

$$\text{odds against an event} = \frac{\text{number of } unfavorable \text{ outcomes}}{\text{number of } favorable \text{ outcomes}}$$

3 EXAMPLE Real-World 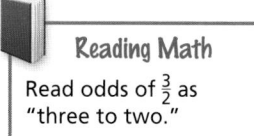 Problem Solving

Coins The reverse sides of five quarters are shown below. If you select one of these quarters at random, what are the odds in favor of it showing at least one human figure on its reverse side?

odds in favor $= \frac{3}{2}$ ← 3 have a human figure.
← 2 do not.

The odds are $\frac{3}{2}$, or 3 to 2, in favor.

> **Reading Math**
> Read odds of $\frac{3}{2}$ as "three to two."

✓ Check Understanding Example 3

3. You choose a quarter at random from the five above.

   a. What are the odds in favor of it showing a horse? **1 to 4**
   b. What are the odds against it showing a horse? **4 to 1**
   c. Consider the event that the quarter shows the outline of a state.
      i. What are the odds in favor of the event? **2 to 3**
      ii. What are the odds against the event? **3 to 2**

English Learners
Point out that the *complement* of an event "*completes* the probability" since the probability of an event and its complement add to 1. This association may help students spell the word correctly and distinguish it from *compliment,* which means to express admiration.

Teaching Tip
Point out to students that the definitions for mathematical probability (page 305) and odds given here apply only when the outcomes occur at random and are equally likely.

3 EXAMPLE Inclusion

For learners who have vision difficulties, enlarge pictures of the quarters or have quarters available that they may inspect, so that they may follow the Example.

PowerPoint

Additional Examples

❶ Find *P*(rolling a prime number) with one number cube. $\frac{1}{2}$

❷ The probability that a child is an identical twin is 4 in 1,000. Find *P*(not an identical twin). $\frac{249}{250}$

❸ You have five different coins in your pocket: a penny, a nickel, a dime, a quarter, and a half-dollar. You pull out one coin at random. What are the odds in favor of the coin being worth less than ten cents? $\frac{2}{3}$

Closure

Have students explain how to find the *probability* of an event. Compare the number of favorable outcomes to the number of possible outcomes. Then have them explain the *complement* of an event. The complement of an event is the opposite of that event. Ask them to give an example of two events that are complements. Answers may vary. Sample: Rolling a 3 on a number cube and rolling a number other than 3 (not three) on a number cube

Assignment Guide

1 Objective 1
  Ⓐ Ⓑ Core 1–13, 17–24
  Ⓒ Extension 33, 34

2 Objective 2
  Ⓐ Ⓑ Core 14–16, 25–32
  Ⓒ Extension 35

Test Prep 36–39
Mixed Review 40–48

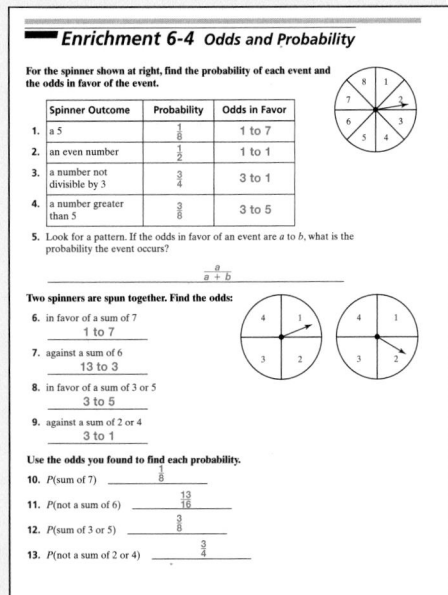

EXERCISES

For more exercises, see *Extra Practice*.

Practice and Problem Solving

Ⓐ **Practice by Example**

Examples 1 and 2
(page 306)

Find each probability for one roll of a number cube.

1. $P(3)$ $\frac{1}{6}$
2. $P(3 \text{ or } 4)$ $\frac{2}{6}$, or $\frac{1}{3}$
3. $P(1, 2, \text{ or } 3)$ $\frac{3}{6}$, or $\frac{1}{2}$

4. $P(\text{not } 2, 3, \text{ or } 6)$ $\frac{3}{6}$, or $\frac{1}{2}$
5. $P(\text{not } 1, 3, 4, \text{ or } 5)$ $\frac{2}{6}$, or $\frac{1}{3}$
6. $P(\text{less than } 4)$ $\frac{3}{6}$, or $\frac{1}{2}$

Find each probability for selecting a letter at random from the word ARKANSAS.

7. $P(A)$ $\frac{3}{8}$
8. $P(R)$ $\frac{1}{8}$
9. $P(S)$ $\frac{2}{8}$, or $\frac{1}{4}$

10. $P(K \text{ or } N)$ $\frac{2}{8}$, or $\frac{1}{4}$
11. $P(\text{vowel})$ $\frac{3}{8}$
12. $P(\text{consonant})$ $\frac{5}{8}$

13. A box of crayons contains one crayon of each of the following colors: red, orange, yellow, green, blue, purple, black, white, pink.
  a. What is the probability of NOT choosing a 6-letter color? $\frac{2}{3}$
  b. What is the complement of choosing green? **not choosing green**

Example 3
(page 307)

14. Suppose you choose a letter at random from the word ARITHMETIC. What are the odds in favor of selecting a vowel? What are the odds against selecting a vowel?
2 to 3; 3 to 2

A teacher chooses a student at random from a class of 10 boys and 15 girls. Find the odds in favor of, and the odds against, each event.

15. choosing a girl **3 to 2; 2 to 3**
16. choosing a boy **2 to 3; 3 to 2**

Ⓑ **Apply Your Skills**

Find each probability for one roll of a number cube.

17. $P(7)$ **0**
18. $P(\text{less than } 3)$ $\frac{2}{6}$, or $\frac{1}{3}$
19. $P(\text{greater than } 2)$ $\frac{4}{6}$, or $\frac{2}{3}$

Find each probability for choosing a letter at random from the word MATHEMATICS.

20. $P(K)$ **0**
21. $P(M, A, \text{ or } T)$ $\frac{6}{11}$
22. $P(\text{vowel})$ $\frac{4}{11}$
23. $P(\text{consonant})$ $\frac{7}{11}$

Lola's Socks

Color	Number of Socks
Pink	6
White	4
Green	3
Purple	2

24. Reasoning The table at the left describes the loose socks in Lola's drawer. One morning Lola pulls a sock from the drawer without looking. It is white. She pulls out another sock without looking. Find the probability that it also is white. $\frac{3}{14}$

You have a set of 36 flash cards numbered from 1 to 36. A card is chosen at random. Find the odds in favor of, and the odds against, each selection.

25. even number **1 to 1; 1 to 1**
26. greater than 20 **4 to 5; 5 to 4**
27. multiple of 3 **1 to 2; 2 to 1**
28. prime number **11 to 25; 25 to 11**
29. multiple of 2 *or* 3 **2 to 1; 1 to 2**
30. multiple of 2 *and* 3 **1 to 5; 5 to 1**
31. It has only one digit. **1 to 3; 3 to 1**
32. It has more than one digit. **3 to 1; 1 to 3**

Ⓒ **Challenge**

33. Open-Ended Give an example of an event for which the probability equals 1. Justify your answer.
Answers may vary. Sample: getting a number less than 7 on one roll of a number cube; all the numbers on a number cube are less than 7.

 Use the Guided Problem Solving worksheet with Exercise 24.

34. Error Analysis Your friend is tossing a coin. He says that heads and tails are equally likely outcomes, so the probability of getting heads is $\frac{50}{50}$. Explain your friend's error. **The friend found odds rather than probability.**

35. 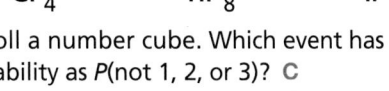 Explain how you can use odds to find probability. Include an example. **See back of book.**

Take It to the NET
Online lesson quiz at
www.PHSchool.com
Web Code: ada-0604

Multiple Choice

36. You draw a name at random from a hat holding the names of 6 girls and 8 boys. What are the odds in favor of choosing a boy? **B**
A. 3 to 4   **B.** 4 to 3   **C.** 3 to 7   **D.** 4 to 7

37. Refer to the spinner. What is the probability of the complement of *stopping on either red or yellow*? **G**
F. $\frac{1}{8}$ **G.** $\frac{1}{4}$ **H.** $\frac{3}{8}$ **I.** $\frac{3}{4}$

38. Suppose you roll a number cube. Which event has the same probability as P(not 1, 2, or 3)? **C**
A. 3 or 4   **B.** less than 5   **C.** not odd   **D.** more than 4

Short Response

39. a. Can a probability be greater than 1?
b. Explain your answer. **See back of book.**

Mixed Review

Lesson 6-3

The scale of a map is 3 in. : 20 mi. Find the actual distance for each map distance.

40. 6 in. **40 mi**   **41.** 1 in. **6$\frac{2}{3}$ mi**   **42.** 4.2 in. **28 mi** **43.** 10$\frac{1}{2}$ in. **70 mi**

Lesson 5-2

Write each decimal as a fraction or mixed number in simplest form.

44. 0.25 **$\frac{1}{4}$**   **45.** 0.$\overline{6}$ **$\frac{2}{3}$**   **46.** 0.8125 **$\frac{13}{16}$**   **47.** 5.15 **5$\frac{3}{20}$**

Lesson 2-6 ⊕ **48. Ticket Sales** Students paid $855 for tickets to a dance. Each ticket cost $5. Write and solve an equation to find the number of tickets the students purchased. **5x = 855; 171 tickets**

✓ Checkpoint Quiz 1   Lessons 6-1 through 6-4

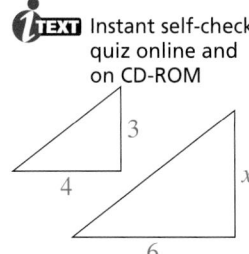

iTEXT Instant self-check quiz online and on CD-ROM

Write each phrase as a unit rate.

1. 20 mi in 5 h **4 mi/h**   **2.** 42 gal in 7 min **6 gal/min**   **3.** a fall of 144 ft in 3 s **48 ft/s**

4. Geometry The figures (left) are similar. Find the missing length. **4.5**

5. A person blinks 112 times in 4 min. At that rate, how many times does the person blink in 1.5 min? **42 times**

6. Suppose you roll a number cube. What is P(2 or 3)? **$\frac{2}{6}$, or $\frac{1}{3}$**

Alternative Assessment

Have students work in pairs. Have one student list an event and then find the probability of that event. Have the partner list the complement of the event and the probability of the complement occurring. Repeat with students switching roles.

Test Prep

📁 **Resources**
For additional practice with a variety of test item formats:
• Test Prep, p. 343
• Test-Taking Strategies, p. 338
• Test-Taking Strategies With Transparencies

---

4. Assess

Find each probability.

1. A letter is selected at random from the letters A, E, I, O, and U. Find the probability that the letter is an A. **$\frac{1}{5}$**

2. In one class, Ms. Lang has 8 boys and 12 girls. She needs to choose one student to help pass out papers. What are the odds that a girl is chosen? **$\frac{3}{2}$**

3. When rolling a number cube, what is P(6)? What is P(not 6)? **$\frac{1}{6}$; $\frac{5}{6}$**

✓ Chapter Checkpoint 1

To check understanding of Lessons 6-1 to 6-4:
Checkpoint Quiz 1 (p. 309)

📁 **Teaching Resources**
Checkpoint Quiz 1 (also in Prentice Hall Assessment System)

👥 **Reaching All Students**
Reading and Math Literacy 6B

Spanish versions available.

■■■ *Reteaching 6-4* **Probability**

Suppose you select a letter at random from the words MIDDLE SCHOOL. Find P(L) and P(not L).
First determine the number of possible outcomes. There are 12 letters in the two words, so there are 12 possible outcomes when you select a letter at random. Next determine the number of favorable outcomes for P(L). There are two L's.

Thus, $P(L) = \frac{\text{number of favorable outcomes}}{\text{number of possible outcomes}} = \frac{2}{12} = \frac{1}{6}$

You can find P(not L) several ways. Since there are 12 possible outcomes and 2 are L, 12 − 2 = 10 are not L.

Thus, $P(\text{not L}) = \frac{\text{number of favorable outcomes}}{\text{number of possible outcomes}} = \frac{10}{12} = \frac{5}{6}$
Also $P(\text{not L}) = 1 - P(L)$
$= 1 - \frac{1}{6} = \frac{5}{6}$

A drawer contains 6 red socks, 4 blue socks, and 14 white socks. A sock is pulled from the drawer at random. Find the probability for each case.

1. P(red) ___ $\frac{1}{4}$ **2.** P(blue) ___ $\frac{1}{6}$

3. P(red or white) ___ $\frac{5}{6}$ **4.** P(red, white, or blue) ___ 1

5. P(not red) ___ $\frac{3}{4}$ **6.** P(green) ___ 0

Suppose you spin a spinner that is equally likely to land on any one of the numbers from 1 to 20. Find the probability for each event.

7. P(17) ___ $\frac{1}{20}$ **8.** P(an odd number) ___ $\frac{1}{2}$

9. P(a number divisible by 5) ___ $\frac{1}{5}$ **10.** P(26) ___ 0

11. P(a number with a 1 in it) ___ $\frac{11}{20}$ **12.** P(a prime number) ___ $\frac{2}{5}$

13. P(a number less than 6) ___ $\frac{1}{4}$ **14.** P(a number) ___ 1

15. P(a number that is not less than 17) ___ $\frac{1}{5}$ **16.** P(a number divisible by 3 or 4) ___ $\frac{1}{2}$

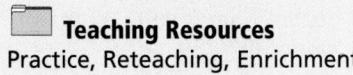

 **6-5**

Fractions, Decimals, and Percents

OBJECTIVE

 1   Writing Percents as Fractions and Decimals

A **percent** is a ratio that compares a number to 100. Therefore, you can write a percent as a fraction with a denominator of 100.

1   EXAMPLE   Writing a Percent as a Fraction

Write each percent as a fraction or a mixed number.

a. 5%

$\frac{5}{100}$ ← Write as a fraction with a denominator of 100. → $\frac{125}{100}$

$\frac{1}{20}$ ← Simplify. → $\frac{5}{4}$

Write as a mixed number. → $1\frac{1}{4}$

b. 125%

✓ **Check Understanding**   Example 1

1. Write each percent as a fraction or mixed number in simplest form.

   a. 58% $\frac{29}{50}$ **b.** 72% $\frac{18}{25}$ **c.** 144% $1\frac{11}{25}$

To write a percent as a decimal, write the percent as a fraction with a denominator of 100. Then divide to convert the fraction to a decimal.

2   EXAMPLE   Writing a Percent as a Decimal

Write 9.7% as a decimal.

$9.7\% = \frac{9.7}{100}$ Write as a fraction with a denominator of 100.

$= 0.09.7$ Divide by moving the decimal point left two places. You may need to write one or more zeros.

$= 0.097$

✓ **Check Understanding**   Example 2

2. Write each percent as a decimal.

   a. 16% 0.16   **b.** 62.5% 0.625   **c.** 120% 1.2

   d. **Biology** About 45% of the people in the United States have type O blood. Write this percent as a decimal and as a fraction in simplest form. 0.45, $\frac{9}{20}$

310   Chapter 6   Ratios, Proportions, and Percents

Reading Math

Percent means "per hundred." The root *cent* shows up in many other words, such as centimeter, century, and centipede. In money, a cent is $\frac{1}{100}$ of a dollar, or $.01.

iTEXT Interactive lesson includes instant self-check, tutorials, and activities.

Writing Decimals and Fractions as Percents

To write a decimal as a percent, rewrite the decimal as a fraction with a denominator of 100. Then write the fraction as a percent.

Another way to change a decimal to a percent is to move the decimal point two places to the right and add a percent sign.

Need Help?
For help on writing decimals as fractions, see Lesson 5-2.

3 EXAMPLE Writing a Decimal as a Percent

Write 0.333 as a percent.

| **Method 1** | **Method 2** |
| Rewrite as a fraction. | Move the decimal point. |

$$0.333 = \frac{333}{1,000}$$

$$= \frac{333 \div 10}{1,000 \div 10}$$

$$= \frac{33.3}{100}$$

$$= 33.3\%$$

$0.333 = 33.3\%$

✓ Check Understanding Example 3

3. Write each decimal as a percent.

   a. 0.4 40%   **b.** 0.023 2.3%   **c.** 1.75 175%

To write a fraction as a percent, divide the numerator by the denominator. Then convert the decimal quotient to a percent.

4 EXAMPLE Real-World  Problem Solving

Pets Five out of sixteen families in the United States own dogs. **What percent of families own dogs?**

$\frac{5}{16}$ **Write a fraction.**

0.3125   **Divide the numerator by the denominator.**

31.25%   **Write as a percent.**

About 31% of families own dogs.

✓ Check Understanding Example 4

4. Three out of eleven families in the United States own cats. To the nearest percent, what percent of families own cats? 27%

Real-World  Connection
There are about 55 million dogs and 61 million cats in the United States.

👥 Reaching All Students

| **Below Level** Bring in newspaper ads and have students look for sale prices expressed as *percent savings* or *percent off*. Help them calculate the savings. | **Advanced Learners** Ask students to imagine they were given $50 as a gift. Ask: *Will you have enough money to buy a $75 jacket that is on sale for 20% off?* no 25% off? no 40% off? yes | **Visual Learners** See note on page 311. **Error Prevention** See note on page 311. |

2. Teach

Professional Development

Math Background

The word *percent* comes from the Latin phrase *per centum*, meaning *by the hundred* or *per 100*. *Per* suggests division. Since 28% means 28 per 100, you can also write 28% as $28 \div 100$, $\frac{28}{100}$, or as 0.28. Reverse this order: Since 0.28 equals $\frac{28}{100}$, you can write 0.28 as $28 \div 100$, 28 per 100, or 28%.

Teaching Notes

1 EXAMPLE Visual Learners

Ask students for possible ways in which they could use the percent sign, %, to help remind them that percent means part of 100. For example, they can think of the parts of the percent sign, %, as the parts of "100" rearranged.

2 EXAMPLE Error Prevention

Remind students to not show the percent sign when they express the percent as a decimal.

PowerPoint
Additional Examples

1 Write each percent as a fraction or a mixed number.
   a. 30% $\frac{3}{10}$
   b. 175% $1\frac{3}{4}$

2 Express 7.3% as a decimal.
0.073

3 Express 0.412 as a percent.
41.2%

4 Four out of seven members of the chess club are boys. What percent of the chess club members are boys? about 57%

Closure

Ask students to explain how percents, fractions, and decimals can be interchanged. A percent is a ratio that compares a number to 100. For example, 30% can be rewritten as the fraction $\frac{30}{100}$, or $\frac{3}{10}$. This can be rewritten as the decimal 0.3.

311

Assignment Guide

▼1 Objective 1
- Ⓐ Ⓑ **Core** 1–21, 59–71, 75
- Ⓒ **Extension** 76, 78–80

▼2 Objective 2
- Ⓐ Ⓑ **Core** 22–58, 72–74
- Ⓒ **Extension** 77

Test Prep 81–85
Mixed Review 86–94

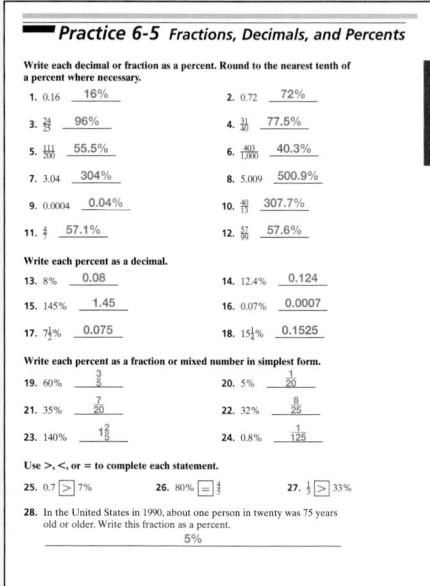

Practice 6-5 *Fractions, Decimals, and Percents*

Write each decimal or fraction as a percent. Round to the nearest tenth of a percent where necessary.

1. 0.16 ___16%___   2. 0.72 ___72%___
3. 24/25 ___96%___   4. 31/40 ___77.5%___
5. 111/200 ___55.5%___   6. 403/1,000 ___40.3%___
7. 3.04 ___304%___   8. 5.009 ___500.9%___
9. 0.0004 ___0.04%___   10. 40/13 ___307.7%___
11. 4/7 ___57.1%___   12. 57/99 ___57.6%___

Write each percent as a decimal.
13. 8% ___0.08___   14. 12.4% ___0.124___
15. 145% ___1.45___   16. 0.07% ___0.0007___
17. 7½% ___0.075___   18. 15¼% ___0.1525___

Write each percent as a fraction or mixed number in simplest form.
19. 60% __3/5__   20. 5% __1/20__
21. 35% __7/20__   22. 32% __8/25__
23. 140% __1 2/5__   24. 0.8% __1/125__

Use >, <, or = to complete each statement.
25. 0.7 [>] 7%   26. 80% [=] 4/5   27. 1/3 [>] 33%

28. In the United States in 1990, about one person in twenty was 75 years old or older. Write this fraction as a percent.
_____5%_____

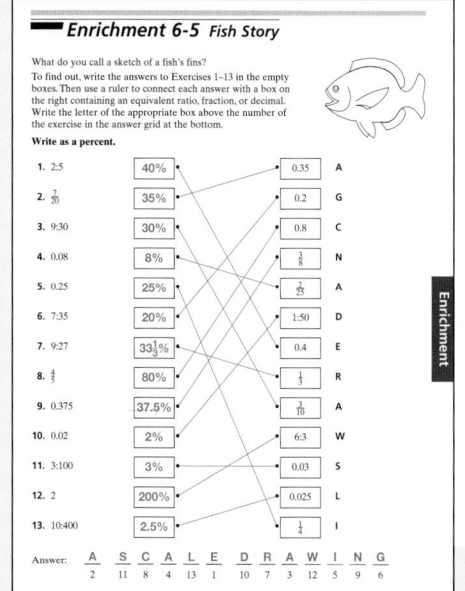

Enrichment 6-5 *Fish Story*

What do you call a sketch of a fish's fins?
To find out, write the answers to Exercises 1–13 in the empty boxes. Then use a ruler to connect each answer with a box on the right containing an equivalent ratio, fraction, or decimal. Write the letter of the appropriate box above the number of the exercise in the answer grid at the bottom.

Write as a percent.

1. 2:5	40%	0.35	A
2. 7/20	35%	0.2	G
3. 9:30	30%	0.8	C
4. 0.08	8%	3/8	N
5. 0.25	25%	1:50	A
6. 7:35	20%	0.4	D
7. 9:27	33⅓%	1/5	E
8. 4/5	80%	1/4	R
9. 0.375	37.5%	3/10	A
10. 0.02	2%	6:3	W
11. 3:100	3%	0.03	S
12. 2	200%	0.025	L
13. 10:400	2.5%	¼	I

Answer: A S C A L E D R A W I N G
           2 11 8 4 13 1 10 7 3 12 5 9 6

EXERCISES

❓ For more exercises, see *Extra Practice*.

Practice and Problem Solving

Ⓐ Practice by Example

Example 1 (page 310)

Write each percent as a fraction or mixed number in simplest form.

1. 40% $\frac{2}{5}$ 2. 28% $\frac{7}{25}$ 3. 39% $\frac{39}{100}$ 4. 55% $\frac{11}{20}$ 5. 20% $\frac{1}{5}$

6. 6% $\frac{3}{50}$ 7. 98% $\frac{49}{50}$ 8. 315% $3\frac{3}{20}$ 9. 220% $2\frac{1}{5}$ 10. 102% $1\frac{1}{50}$

Example 2 (page 310)

Write each percent as a decimal.

11. 36% — 0.36   12. 4.4% — 0.044   13. 1% — 0.01   14. 6.3% — 0.063   15. 133% — 1.33

16. 79.7% — 0.797   17. 350% — 3.5   18. 52% — 0.52   19. 31.4% — 0.314   20. 0.03% — 0.0003

🌐 **21. Education** In 2000, women made up 40% of freshmen studying computer science at a certain university. Write this percent as a decimal and as a fraction in simplest form. 0.4; $\frac{2}{5}$

Example 3 (page 311)

Write each decimal as a percent.

22. 1.68 — 168%   23. 0.36 — 36%   24. 0.70 — 70%   25. 0.002 — 0.2%   26. 0.06 — 6%

27. 1.88 — 188%   28. 2.59 — 259%   29. 1.11 — 111%   30. 0.156 — 15.6%   31. 0.043 — 4.3%

Example 4 (page 311)

Write each fraction as a percent. Round to the nearest tenth of a percent where necessary.

32. $\frac{23}{100}$ 23%   33. $\frac{1}{4}$ 25%   34. $\frac{11}{20}$ 55%   35. $\frac{3}{5}$ 60%   36. $\frac{5}{8}$ 62.5%

37. $\frac{4}{19}$ 21.1%   38. $\frac{1}{6}$ 16.7%   39. $\frac{7}{20}$ 35%   40. $\frac{2}{9}$ 22.2%   41. $\frac{7}{18}$ 38.9%

🌐 **42. Populations** In the United States, about one person in eight lives in California. To the nearest percent, what percent of people in the United States live in California? 13%

🌐 **43. Homework** Ron has read 14 pages of his 22-page reading assignment. To the nearest percent, what percent of the assignment has Ron read? 64%

Ⓑ Apply Your Skills

Write each fraction as a percent. Round to the nearest tenth of a percent where necessary.

44. $\frac{8}{13}$ 61.5%   45. $\frac{5}{6}$ 83.3%   46. $\frac{111}{100}$ 111%   47. $\frac{9}{2}$ 450%   48. $\frac{12}{5}$ 240%

Estimation **About what percent of each flag is red?** See left.

49–50. Answers may vary. Samples are given.

49.
Tennessee
about 80%

50.
North Carolina
about 30%

Error Prevention!

Exercises 66–70 Remind students to convert one side so they can compare two fractions, two decimals, or two percents.

Probability Find each probability for one roll of a number cube. Write the probability as a percent. Round to the nearest tenth of a percent where necessary.

51. $P(6)$
16.7%

52. $P(\text{even})$
50%

53. $P(1 \text{ or } 2)$
33.3%

54. $P(\text{not } 1)$
83.3%

Copy and complete the table.

	Fraction	Decimal	Percent
55.	$\frac{4}{5}$	■ 0.8	■ 80%
56.	■ $\frac{1}{10}$	0.10	■ 10%
57.	■ $\frac{1}{2}$	0.5	■ 50%
58.	$\frac{3}{4}$	■ 0.75	■ 75%
59.	■ $\frac{67}{100}$	■ 0.67	67%
60.	■ $\frac{1}{4}$	■ 0.25	25%

Real-World Connection

Each year, about 45 million Americans go camping.

Reasoning For Exercises 61–64, does each sentence make sense? Explain.

61. About 17% of Americans go camping. That means about 83% do not go camping. **Yes; 100% − 17% = 83%**

62. A student correctly answered 200% of the items on a test. **No; it is not possible to answer more items than are on the test.**

63. Today a runner ran 150% of the distance she ran yesterday.
Yes; the runner ran $1\frac{1}{2}$ times as far as she ran yesterday.

64. On a test, a student missed 12 items and correctly answered 96% of all items. **Yes; the test had 300 items and the student answered 288 of them correctly.**

Compare. Use >, <, or = to complete each statement.

65. 0.05% ■ 50% **<**

66. $\frac{7}{12}$ ■ 60% **<**

67. 0.0325 ■ 32.5% **<**

68. $\frac{7}{8}$ ■ 68% **>**

69. 0.1756 ■ 176% **<**

70. $\frac{140}{130}$ ■ 104% **>**

71. $\frac{1}{10,000}$

72. Yes; $\frac{32}{45} = 71.\overline{1}\%$, and
$71.\overline{1}\% > 70\%$.

71. Maps A map has a scale of 0.01%. Write the scale as a fraction.
See left.

72. Jeanette answered 32 questions correctly on a 45-question test. The passing grade was 70%. Did Jeanette pass? Justify your answer.
See left.

73. Scale Drawings A scale drawing has a scale of 1 : 12. Write the scale as a percent. **8.$\overline{3}$%**

74. Answers may vary. Sample: Move the decimal point two places to the right and add a percent sign.
0.25 = 25%,
1.35 = 135%

74. **Writing in Math** Explain how to write a decimal as a percent. Give examples. **See left.**

75. a. Test Grades On his last math assignment, Kyle answered 5% of the questions incorrectly, or 1 question. How many questions did Kyle answer correctly? **19 questions**

b. On the same test, Diana answered 16 questions correctly. What percent of the questions did she not answer correctly? **20%**

6-5 Fractions, Decimals, and Percents **313**

 Use the Guided Problem Solving worksheet with Exercise 72.

Write each percent as a fraction or mixed number, and as a decimal.

1. 325% $\frac{13}{4}$, or $3\frac{1}{4}$; 3.25

2. 1.1% $\frac{11}{1,000}$; 0.011

Write each as a percent.

3. 2.01 **201%**

4. $\frac{3}{5}$ **60%**

5. Six out of fifteen students own skateboards. What percent of students own skateboards? **40%**

Test Prep

📁 **Resources**

For additional practice with a variety of test item formats:

• Test Prep, p. 343
• Test-Taking Strategies, p. 338
• Test-Taking Strategies With Transparencies

Reteaching 6-5 *Fractions, Decimals, and Percents*

Write $\frac{7}{8}$ as a percent and 64% as a fraction in lowest terms.

Divide 7 ÷ 8.

64% means 64 parts per 100.

$\frac{0.875}{8\,)7.000}$

64% = $\frac{64}{100}$

$\frac{6\,4}{60}$

$= \frac{2^4}{2^2 \cdot 5^2}$

$\frac{56}{40}$

$= \frac{2^4}{5^2}$

$\frac{40}{}$

$= \frac{16}{25}$

$\frac{7}{8} = 0.875$

Thus 64% = $\frac{16}{25}$.

0.875 = 87.5%

Thus $\frac{7}{8}$ = 87.5%.

Write each fraction as a percent.

1. $\frac{7}{10}$ ___70%___   2. $\frac{3}{5}$ ___60%___

3. $\frac{11}{20}$ ___55%___   4. $\frac{17}{25}$ ___68%___

5. $\frac{1}{5}$ ___20%___   6. $\frac{39}{100}$ ___39%___

7. $\frac{1}{20}$ ___5%___   8. $\frac{13}{50}$ ___26%___

9. $\frac{5}{8}$ ___62.5%___   10. $\frac{3}{16}$ ___18.75%___

Write each percent as a fraction in simplest terms.

11. 15% ___$\frac{3}{20}$___   12. 12.5% ___$\frac{1}{8}$___

13. 76% ___$\frac{19}{25}$___   14. 14% ___$\frac{7}{50}$___

15. 60% ___$\frac{3}{5}$___   16. 97% ___$\frac{97}{100}$___

17. 25% ___$\frac{1}{4}$___   18. 30% ___$\frac{3}{10}$___

19. 82% ___$\frac{41}{50}$___   20. 68.75% ___$\frac{11}{16}$___

C Challenge

76. Answers may vary. Sample: There is a 20% chance of snow tomorrow. 20% = $\frac{20}{100}$ = $\frac{1}{5}$; 0.20

84. [2] 39.2%; 0.392 = $\frac{392}{1,000}$ = $\frac{392 \div 10}{1,000 \div 10}$ = $\frac{39.2}{100}$ = 39.2%

[1] minor error OR answer only

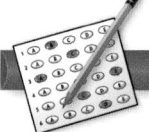

💻 **Take It to the NET**

Online lesson quiz at **www.PHSchool.com**

Web Code: ada-0605

---

76. Open-Ended Use a percent to describe an everyday event. Then write the percent as a fraction and as a decimal. **See left.**

77. Reasoning Explain why 0.25 is different from 0.25%. Explanations may vary. Sample: 0.25 is 25% and 0.25% is 0.0025.

A crowd filled the 8,000 seats in a stadium. There were 1,400 children and 4,800 men present. Write a ratio and a percent to describe how many seats were filled by each group.

78. men $\frac{3}{5}$, 60%   **79.** children $\frac{7}{40}$, 17.5%   **80.** women $\frac{9}{40}$, 22.5%

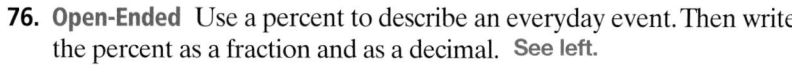

Test Prep

Multiple Choice

81. What is 0.2% written as a decimal? **A**

A. 0.002   B. 0.2   C. 2   D. 20

82. If 12% of an iceberg is above water, what fraction is in the water? **H**

F. $\frac{3}{25}$ G. $\frac{12}{88}$ H. $\frac{22}{25}$ I. $7\frac{1}{3}$

83. In a basketball free-throw contest, four players take the same number of free throws. Player A makes 33 of 40 free throws. Player B makes $\frac{3}{4}$ of his free throws, Player C makes 85% of her free throws, and Player D makes $\frac{4}{5}$ of his free throws. Which player makes the greatest number of free throws? **C**

A. Player A   B. Player B   C. Player C   D. Player D

Short Response

84. A baseball player's batting average is the ratio of the number of hits to the number of times at bat.

a. If Julienne's batting average is .392, what percent of her times at bat are hits?

b. For part (a), explain your answer.
See above left.

85. A weather reporter predicts that at least 20% of the 11 counties in her area will get rain this weekend.

a. If two counties get rain, is the reporter's prediction correct?

b. Explain your answer. [2] No; 20% = 0.20, $\frac{2}{11}$ = 0.$\overline{18}$, and 0.$\overline{18}$ < 0.20. [1] minor error OR answer only

Mixed Review

Lesson 6-4

Find each probability for choosing a letter at random from the word PROBABLE.

86. $P(\text{B})$ **87.** $P(\text{vowel})$ $\frac{3}{8}$ **88.** $P(\text{R})$ $\frac{1}{8}$ **89.** $P(\text{not L or R})$ $\frac{6}{8}$, or $\frac{3}{4}$
$\frac{2}{8}$, or $\frac{1}{4}$

Lesson 3-6

Solve each equation.

90. $0.85x = 39.95$ **47**   **91.** $4.8y = -0.84$ **-0.175**

92. $100 = \frac{a}{13.2}$ **1,320**   **93.** $\frac{b}{-25} = 1.8$ **-45**

Lesson 1-9 🌐 **94. Test Scores** The average of three test scores is 85. One test score is 90. Another is 72. What is the third? **93**

---

314 Chapter 6 Ratios, Proportions, and Percents

Alternative Assessment

Make three sets of index cards using enough cards for each student to receive one. For the first set, write a different fraction on each card. For the second set, write the decimal equivalent for each fraction. For the third set, write the percentage equivalent for each fraction. Shuffle the cards and give one to each student. Have students hold up their cards and then find other students holding up cards with equivalent values. Collect the cards, shuffle them, and repeat the activity.

Proportions and Percents

OBJECTIVE
1 Finding Part of a Whole

You can solve a percent problem by writing and solving a proportion.

A model can help you write a proportion. This model shows that 30 is 75% of 40.

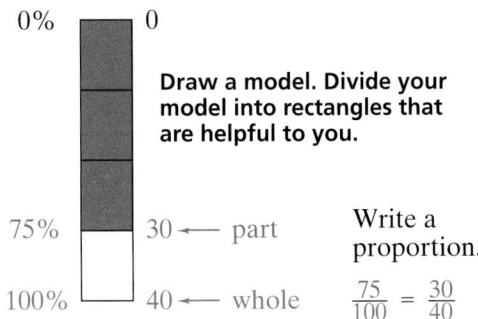

Draw a model. Divide your model into rectangles that are helpful to you.

0% ⟶ 0
75% ⟶ 30 ⟵ part
100% ⟶ 40 ⟵ whole

Write a proportion.

$$\frac{75}{100} = \frac{30}{40}$$

1 EXAMPLE Finding Part of a Whole

Find 65% of 245.

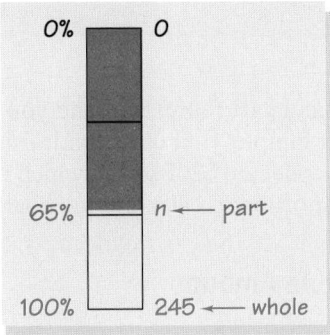

0% ⟶ 0
65% ⟶ n ⟵ part
100% ⟶ 245 ⟵ whole

$\frac{65}{100} = \frac{n}{245}$ **Write a proportion.**

$65(245) = 100n$ **Write cross products.**

$\frac{65(245)}{100} = \frac{100n}{100}$ **Divide each side by 100.**

$159.25 = n$ **Simplify.**

● 65% of 245 is 159.25.

✓ Check Understanding Example 1

1. Draw a model and write a proportion. Then solve.

   a. 25% of 124 is ■.   **b.** 43% of 230 is ■.   **c.** 12.5% of 80 is ■.
   a–c. See back of book.

 Interactive lesson includes instant self-check, tutorials, and activities.

What You'll Learn

 OBJECTIVE 1 To find a part of a whole and a percent

 OBJECTIVE 2 To find a whole amount

. . . And Why

To solve real-world problems involving business data

✓ Check Skills You'll Need

Solve each proportion.

1. $\frac{25}{100} = \frac{x}{28}$ 7

2. $\frac{98.9}{x} = \frac{43}{100}$ 230

3. $\frac{52}{100} = \frac{13}{x}$ 25

4. $\frac{x}{100} = \frac{27}{150}$ 18

 For help, go to Lesson 6-2.

Lesson Preview

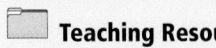 **Check Skills You'll Need**

Proportions
Lesson 6-2: Example 1;
Exercises 1–12.
Extra Practice, p. 749.

Lesson Resources

📁 **Teaching Resources**
Practice, Reteaching, Enrichment

👥 **Reaching All Students**
Practice Workbook 6-6
Spanish Practice Workbook 6-6
Guided Problem Solving 6-6
Technology Activities 12

⏱ **Presentation Assistant Plus!**
Transparencies and PowerPoint™
• Check Skills You'll Need 6-6
• Additional Examples 6-6
• Student Edition Answers 6-6
• Lesson Quiz 6-6
PH Presentation Pro CD-ROM 6-6

ASSESSMENT SYSTEM

Computer Test Generator CD-ROM

💻 **Technology**
Resource Pro® CD-ROM
Computer Test Generator CD-ROM
PH Presentation Pro CD-ROM

💻 **www.PHSchool.com**
Student Site
• Teacher Web Code: adk-5500
• Self-grading Lesson Quiz
PH SuccessNet Teacher Center
• Lesson Planner
• Resources

Plus

✓ Ongoing Assessment and Intervention

Before the Lesson	During the Lesson	After the Lesson
Diagnose prerequisite skills using:	Monitor progress using:	Assess knowledge using:
• Check Skills You'll Need	• Check Understanding	• Lesson Quiz
	• Additional Examples	• Computer Test Generator CD-ROM
	• Test Prep	

315

Professional Development

Math Background

In general, a percent problem has a part over its whole equal to a part of 100 over 100. 35% means 35 equal parts out of 100 total parts. To find 35% of 623, set up a proportion as follows: 35 is to 100 as the part of 623 is to the whole amount of 623: $\frac{35}{100} = \frac{x}{623}$. Then solve for x. **218.05**

Teaching Notes

Inclusion

Some below-level students may have difficulty remembering where to place the different parts of a percent proportion. Have students refer to the table at the bottom of page 317. Write the following on the board:

$$\frac{n}{100} = \frac{\text{part}}{\text{whole}}$$

Since 100% refers to one whole item or amount, 100 and "whole" are in corresponding places in the percent proportion.

1 EXAMPLE Visual Learners

Point out that the number that follows *percent of* in a percent problem is almost always the "whole." This is the denominator of one fraction in the percent proportion. Have students point to *of*, and then write the number after it in the denominator first. Then fill in the rest of the proportion.

2 EXAMPLE Auditory Learners

Repeating the phrase "part over whole" several times may help some students remember where to place the numbers in the percent proportion.

---

2 EXAMPLE Finding a Percent

What percent of 60 is 52? Round to the nearest tenth of a percent.

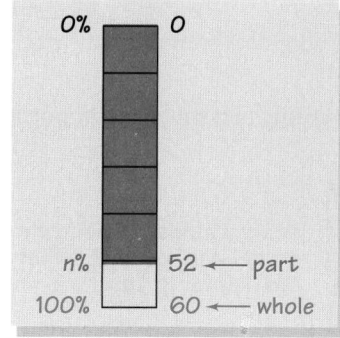

$\frac{n}{100} = \frac{52}{60}$ Write a proportion.

$60n = 100(52)$ Write cross products.

$\frac{60n}{60} = \frac{100(52)}{60}$ Divide each side by 60.

$n = 86.\overline{6}$ Simplify.

≈ 86.7 Round.

● 52 is approximately 86.7% of 60.

✓ Check Understanding Example 2

2. Round to the nearest tenth.

  a. What percent of 250 is 138?   **b.** 14 is what percent of 15?
      55.2%   93.3%

OBJECTIVE

2 Finding a Whole Amount

Sometimes you know the percent that a part represents, and you want to find the whole amount. For example, your class fundraising committee might announce, "We've collected $207 so far, which is 46% of our goal!" You can use a proportion to calculate the goal.

3 EXAMPLE Finding the Whole Amount

207 is 46% of what number?

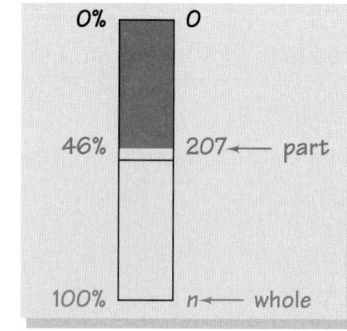

$\frac{46}{100} = \frac{207}{n}$ Write a proportion.

$46n = 100(207)$ Write cross products.

$\frac{46n}{46} = \frac{100(207)}{46}$ Divide each side by 46.

$n = 450$ Simplify.

● 207 is 46% of 450.

316   Chapter 6   Ratios, Proportions, and Percents

👥 Reaching All Students

| Below Level Help students relate test or daily grades to a percent. For example, a test grade of 82 on a test scaled to 100 means you answered 82% of the questions correctly. | Advanced Learners Ask: *Is a percent of a number always less than the number? Explain.* No; a student may run 1 mile one day and run 150% of that distance, 1.5 miles, the next day. | Inclusion See note on page 316. Diversity See note on page 317. |

✔ **Check Understanding** Example 3

3. Round to the nearest tenth.

   a. 19 is 75% of what number? b. 310 is 99% of what number?
      25.3   313.1

④ EXAMPLE Real-World 🌐 Problem Solving

Theaters In 2000, the number of drive-in movie screens in the United States was about 78% of the number in 1990. About how many drive-in screens were there in 1990?

Drive-In Movies

Year	Number of Screens
1990	■
1995	847
2000	717

SOURCE: Motion Picture Association of America

$\frac{78}{100} = \frac{717}{n}$ Write a proportion.

$78n = 100(717)$ Write cross products.

$\frac{78n}{78} = \frac{100(717)}{78}$ Divide each side by 78.

$n \approx 919$ Round to the nearest whole number.

There were about 919 drive-in screens in 1990.

Check Is the answer reasonable? The original problem says that the number of screens in 2000 was 78% of the number in 1990. Check by estimating:

78% of 919 ≈ 0.8 × 900 = 720, which is close to 717, the number for 2000. So the answer is reasonable.

✔ **Check Understanding** Example 4

4. Refer to the table in Example 4. In 2000, the number of drive-in movie screens was about 20.1% of the number in 1980. Find the number of drive-in screens in 1980. **about 3,567 screens**

Here is a summary of how to use proportions to solve percent problems.

Key Concepts	**Percents and Proportions**	
Finding the Percent	**Finding the Part**	**Finding the Whole**
What percent of 40 is 6?	What number is 15% of 40?	6 is 15% of what number?
$\frac{n}{100} = \frac{6}{40} \begin{matrix}\leftarrow \text{part} \\ \leftarrow \text{whole}\end{matrix}$	$\frac{15}{100} = \frac{n}{40} \begin{matrix}\leftarrow \text{part} \\ \leftarrow \text{whole}\end{matrix}$	$\frac{15}{100} = \frac{6}{n} \begin{matrix}\leftarrow \text{part} \\ \leftarrow \text{whole}\end{matrix}$

④ EXAMPLE Diversity
Many students may not have seen or heard of drive-in movie theaters. Ask a volunteer to explain what they are. Have another student do research to find out when they were popular and what happened to most of them.

PowerPoint
Additional Examples

① Find 23% of 158. **36.34**

② What percent of 34 is 28? Round to the nearest tenth of a percent. **about 82.4%**

③ 216 is 72% of what number? **300**

④ A tile floor has 90 blue tiles, which is 15% of all the tiles in the floor. How many tiles are in the floor in all? **600**

Closure

Ask: *How can you use a proportion to find the part or the whole in a percent problem?* Write the percent over 100 as one ratio. Then write the part over the whole in the other ratio. Use cross products and solve for the missing term.

Assignment Guide

▼ 1 **Objective 1**
Ⓐ Ⓑ **Core** 1–16, 25, 27, 28 30, 32
Ⓒ **Extension** 36, 38–41

▼ 2 **Objective 2**
Ⓐ Ⓑ **Core** 17–24, 26, 29, 31, 33–35
Ⓒ **Extension** 37, 42

Test Prep 43–46
Mixed Review 47–53

Practice 6-6 *Proportions and Percents*

Write a proportion. Then solve. Where necessary, round to the nearest tenth or tenth of a percent.

1. $62\frac{1}{2}\%$ of t is 35. What is t? ___56___

2. 38% of n is 33.44. What is n? ___88___

3. 120% of y is 42. What is y? ___35___

4. 300% of m is 600. What is m? ___200___

5. 1.5% of h is 12. What is h? ___800___

6. What percent of 40 is 12? ___30%___

7. What percent of 48 is 18? ___37.5%___

8. What percent is 54 of 60? ___90%___

9. What percent is 39 of 50? ___78%___

10. Find 80% of 25. ___20___

11. Find 150% of 74. ___111___

12. Find 44% of 375. ___165___

13. Find 65% of 180. ___117___

14. The Eagles won 70% of the 40 games that they played. How many games did they win? ___28 games___

15. Thirty-five of 40 students surveyed said that they favored recycling. What percent of those surveyed favored recycling? ___87.5%___

16. Candidate Carson received 2,310 votes, 55% of the total. How many total votes were cast? ___4,200 votes___

Enrichment 6-6 *Opinion Survey*

A survey of recreation preferences was conducted. The table lists the results by gender and age categories.

Respondent Summary	
Male	160
Female	240
Under 20	80
20–39	152
40–59	140
60 and over	28

1. How many people were polled? ___400___

2. What percent of those polled were:
   female? ___60%___
   aged 40–59? ___35%___
   aged 60 and over? ___7%___

3. Which group listed in the table contains 38% of those polled? ___age 20–39___

4. Seventy-five percent of the males polled said that they participate in a sport. How many males participate in a sport? ___120 males___

5. Thirty females said that tennis is their favorite sport. What percent of all females prefer tennis to other sports? ___12.5%___

6. In a more extensive poll, 768 of the females questioned (or 12%) said that they prefer tennis. How many females were questioned in the larger survey? ___6,400 females___

7. Twenty-five percent of those 40 and over who were questioned named bowling as their favorite sport. Twelve were in the 60 and over category. How many were in the 40–59 category? ___30 respondents___

8. Twenty-eight of those under 20 named basketball as their favorite sport.
   a. What percent in this category prefer basketball? ___35%___
   b. Of those in this category who do not prefer basketball, 26.9% (to the nearest tenth of a percent) prefer baseball. How many named baseball as their favorite sport? ___14 respondents___

EXERCISES

For more exercises, see Extra Practice.

Practice and Problem Solving

Ⓐ **Practice by Example**

Example 1 (page 315)

For Exercises 1–22, write and solve a proportion. Where necessary, round to the nearest tenth.

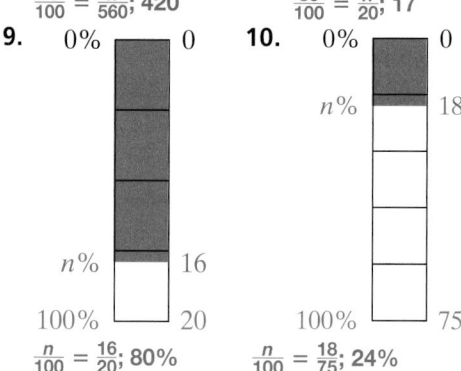

1. $\frac{75}{100} = \frac{n}{560}$; **420**

2. $\frac{85}{100} = \frac{n}{20}$; **17**

3. 80% of 20 is ■. **16**

4. 40% of 60 is ■. **24**

5. 53% of 70 is ■. **37.1**

6. 18% of 150 is ■. **27**

7. 16% of 75 is ■. **12**

8. 92% of 625 is ■. **575**

Example 2 (page 316)

9. $\frac{n}{100} = \frac{16}{20}$; **80%**

10. $\frac{n}{100} = \frac{18}{75}$; **24%**

11. ■% of 40 is 30. **75**

12. ■% of 20 is 4. **20**

13. ■% of 25 is 13. **52**

14. 75 is ■% of 250. **30**

15. ■% of 92 is 17. **18.5**

16. ■% of 80 is 14. **17.5**

Example 3 (page 316)

17. 8 is 25% of ■. **32**

18. 14 is 35% of ■. **40**

19. 31 is 49% of ■. **63.3**

20. 45 is 93% of ■. **48.4**

21. 1 is 2% of ■. **50**

22. 6 is 98% of ■. **6.1**

Example 4 (page 317)

🌐 23. **Population** In 1950, the population of Alaska was about 128,535. That was about 20.5% of the population of Alaska in the year 2000. About how many people lived in Alaska in the year 2000? **627,000 people**

🌐 24. **Banking** At the beginning of the summer Jeri had $480 in her savings account. That was only 15% of the amount in her savings account at the end of the summer. How much money did Jeri have in her account at the end of the summer? **$3,200**

Ⓑ **Apply Your Skills**

Write and solve a proportion. Where necessary, round to the nearest whole amount.

25. Find 300% of 50. **150**

26. 250% of ■ is 50. **20**

27. Find 60% of 15. **9**

28. 40,571 is ■% of 76,550. **53**

29. 35% of ■ is 52.5. **150**

30. 121.8 is ■% of 105. **116**

🌐 31. **Purchasing** A bicycle cost $250 last year. The same bike costs $200 this year. What percent of last year's cost is this year's cost? **80%**

318 Chapter 6 Ratios, Proportions, and Percents

35. You should have used the ratio $\frac{26}{n}$, comparing class enrollment, 26 (or 5%), to school enrollment, n (or 100%).

State	Sales Tax
Georgia	7%
Kansas	4.9%
Pennsylvania	6%
South Carolina	5%

4. Assess

32. Sales Tax The table shows sales tax rates for different states. For each state, find the following amount on a $15,000 car.
  a. the amount of sales tax   **b.** the car's total cost
  a–b. See margin.

33. Profit You invested some money and made a profit of $55. Your profit was 11% of your investment. How much did you invest?
$500

34. Nineteen members, or 38%, of the ski club are going on a ski trip. Find the total number of members in the club. **50 members**

35. Error Analysis Your class has 26 students, which represents 5% of your school's enrollment. Your friend uses the proportion $\frac{5}{100} = \frac{n}{26}$ to find the number of students in your school. Explain your friend's error.
See p. 318 margin.

C Challenge

41. Pacs; $\frac{1}{3} = 33.3\%$. Since $33.3 > 30$, $\frac{1}{3}$ is the greater discount rate.

42. Explanations may vary. Sample: Yes; for *a*% of *b*, solve $\frac{a}{100} = \frac{n}{b}$ to get $n = \frac{ab}{100}$. For *b*% of *a*, solve $\frac{b}{100} = \frac{n}{a}$ to get $n = \frac{ab}{100}$.

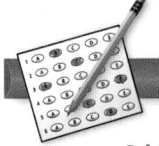

Write and solve a proportion. Where necessary, round to the nearest tenth.

36. Find $33\frac{1}{3}\%$ of 54. **18**

37. $12\frac{1}{2}\%$ of ■ is 6. **48**

38. ■% of 36,500 is 912.5. **2.5**

39. What is $\frac{5}{4}\%$ of 145? **1.8**

40. Open-Ended Write and solve a word problem involving percents.
See below.

41. Writing in Math At Pics, all posters are 30% off. At Pacs, all posters are marked $\frac{1}{3}$ off. Which is the greater discount rate? Explain.
See above left.

42. Reasoning Do *a*% of *b* and *b*% of *a* represent the same amount? Justify your answer. See left.

40. Answers may vary. Sample: Suppose 12% of the species at a zoo can fly. If there are 350 species at the zoo, how many species can fly? 42 species

Test Prep

Gridded Response

43. 42 is 60% of what number? **70**

44. 1.25 is what percent of 25? **5**

45. What number is 30% of 75? **22.5**

46. A student pole-vaulted 5 ft yesterday. Today she vaulted 20% higher. How many feet higher did she vault today? **1**

Take It to the NET
Online lesson quiz at
www.PHSchool.com
Web Code: ada-0606

Mixed Review

Lesson 6-5   **Write each number as a percent.**

47. 0.08 **8%**   **48.** 0.523 **52.3%** **49.** $\frac{7}{12}$ **58.$\overline{3}$%**   **50.** 4.56 **456%**

Lesson 4-9   **Order from least to greatest.**

51. $10^3, 10^{-2}, 10^{-1}, 10^0$ $10^{-2}, 10^{-1}, 10^0, 10^3$

52. $2.3 \times 10^4, 2.03 \times 10^5, 2.03 \times 10^4, 2.4 \times 10^3$
$2.4 \times 10^3, 2.03 \times 10^4, 2.3 \times 10^4, 2.03 \times 10^5$

Lesson 1-1 **53. Family** Peter has four cousins. Paul has *c* cousins fewer than Peter. Write an expression for the number of Paul's cousins. $4 - c$

Solve.

1. Find 47% of 2,400. 1,128

2. What percent of 700 is 1,498? 214%

3. 6 is 3% of what number? 200

4. Water covers about 361,736,000 km^2, or about 70.8% of Earth's surface. What is the approximate surface area of Earth?
about 511,000,000 km^2

Test Prep

📁 **Resources**
For additional practice with a variety of test item formats:
• Test Prep, p. 343
• Test-Taking Strategies, p. 338
• Test-Taking Strategies With Transparencies

■ *Reteaching 6-6* Proportions and Percents

What percent of 98 is 24.5?
You can solve percent problems by writing and solving a proportion.
Any percent problem of the form *x*% of *a* is *b* can be written as:

$\frac{x}{100} = \frac{b}{a}$

so $\frac{x}{100} = \frac{24.5}{98}$ Write a proportion.
$98x = 2,450$ Write cross products.
$\frac{98x}{98} = \frac{2,450}{98}$ Divide each side by 98.
$x = 25$ Simplify.
24.5 is 25% of 98.

Write a proportion. Then solve. Where necessary, round to the nearest tenth or tenth of a percent.

1. What percent of 75 is 60? 80%	**2.** What percent of 68 is 51? 75%
3. What percent is 17 of 25? 68%	**4.** What percent of 51 is 65? 127.5%
5. What percent of 144 is 126? 87.5%	**6.** What percent of 95 is 25? 26.3%
7. Find 24% of 120. 28.8	**8.** Find 75% of 76. 57
9. Find 260% of 30. 78	**10.** Find $27\frac{1}{2}$% of 96. 26.4
11. Find 38% of 32. 12.2	**12.** Find 17% of 85. 14.5
13. 40% of *x* is 28. What is *x*? 70	**14.** 9% of *k* is 27. What is *k*? 300
15. 75% of *p* is 12. What is *p*? 16	**16.** 0.9% of *h* is 276. What is *h*? 30,666.7
17. 13% of *r* is 209. What is *r*? 1,607.7	**18.** 68% of *j* is 44. What is *j*? 64.7

32a. Georgia: $1,050;
  Kansas: $735;
  Pennsylvania: $900;
  South Carolina: $750
 b. Georgia: $16,050;
  Kansas: $15,735;
  Pennsylvania: $15,900;
  South Carolina: $15,750

Alternative Assessment

Ask students to fold a piece of paper into three sections. Have them copy the headings from the table at the bottom of page 317: *Finding the Percent, Finding the Part, Finding the Whole,* one at the top of each section of the paper. Have them create their own percent questions and write

 Use the Guided Problem Solving worksheet with Exercise 33.

corresponding proportions, like those in the table. Then have them solve each proportion to answer each question.

319

6-7

Lesson Preview

 Check Skills You'll Need

Fractions, Decimals, and Percents
Lesson 6-5: Example 2;
Exercises 11–20.
Extra Practice, p. 749.

Lesson Resources

 Teaching Resources
Practice, Reteaching, Enrichment

 Reaching All Students
Practice Workbook 6-7
Spanish Practice Workbook 6-7
Guided Problem Solving 6-7
Technology Activities 12

 Presentation Assistant Plus!
Transparencies and PowerPoint™
• Check Skills You'll Need 6-7
• Additional Examples 6-7
• Student Edition Answers 6-7
• Lesson Quiz 6-7
PH Presentation Pro CD-ROM 6-7

ASSESSMENT SYSTEM

Computer Test Generator CD-ROM

 Technology
Resource Pro® CD-ROM
Computer Test Generator CD-ROM
PH Presentation Pro CD-ROM

 www.PHSchool.com
Student Site
• Teacher Web Code: adk-5500
• Updated Data
• Self-grading Lesson Quiz
PH SuccessNet Teacher Center
• Lesson Planner
• Resources

Plus

320

6-7 Percents and Equations

What You'll Learn

 To write and solve percent equations

 To use equations in solving percent problems

. . . And Why

To solve real-world problems involving earnings and surveys

 **Check Skills You'll Need**

Write each percent as a decimal.

1. 48%
0.48
2. 5%
0.05
3. 23.8%
0.238
4. 72.25%
0.7225
5. 136%
1.36
6. 178.5%
1.785

For help, go to Lesson 6-5.

New Vocabulary

• commission

 OBJECTIVE

1 Writing and Solving Percent Equations

You can solve a percent problem by writing and solving an equation. When you use a percent in an equation, write it as a decimal.

Key Concepts	**Percent Equations**	
Finding the Percent	**Finding the Part**	**Finding the Whole**
What percent of 40 is 6?	What is 15% of 40?	6 is 15% of what?
$n \cdot 40 = 6$	$n = 0.15 \cdot 40$	$6 = 0.15 \cdot n$

1 EXAMPLE Solving a Percent Equation

What is 85% of 62?

$n = 0.85 \cdot 62$ Write an equation. Write the percent as a decimal.
$n = 52.7$ Simplify.

● 85% of 62 is 52.7.

✓ **Check Understanding**   Example 1

1. Write and solve an equation.

a. 0.96 is what percent of 10?
$0.96 = n \cdot 10; 9.6\%$
b. 19.2 is 32% of what?
$19.2 = 0.32 \cdot n; 60$

You can also write and solve equations having percents greater than 100%.

2 EXAMPLE Percents Greater Than 100%

What percent of 48 is 54?

$n \cdot 48 = 54$ Write an equation.
$\dfrac{48n}{48} = \dfrac{54}{48}$ Divide each side by 48.
$n = 1.125$ Simplify.
$= 112.5\%$ Change the decimal to a percent.

● 54 is 112.5% of 48.

✓ **Check Understanding**   Example 2

2. Write and solve an equation. a–b. See left.

a. What is 145.5% of 20?
b. 380 is 125% of what number?

Reading Math

For help with reading and solving percent equations, see page 324.

2a. $n = 1.455 \cdot 20; 29.1$

2b. $380 = 1.25n; 304$

 Interactive lesson includes instant self-check, tutorials, and activities.

320   Chapter 6   Ratios, Proportions, and Percents

INSTANT CHECK SYSTEM **Ongoing Assessment and Intervention**

Before the Lesson Diagnose prerequisite skills using:	**During the Lesson** Monitor progress using:	**After the Lesson** Assess knowledge using:
• Check Skills You'll Need	• Check Understanding • Additional Examples • Test Prep	• Lesson Quiz • Computer Test Generator CD-ROM

OBJECTIVE 2
Using Equations to Solve Percent Problems

Some sales jobs pay an amount based on how much you sell. This amount is called a **commission.**

3 EXAMPLE Real-World Problem Solving

Commission A real-estate agent makes a 4.5% commission on property she sells. How much commission does she make on the sale of a house for $132,500?

Words	amount of commission	is	4.5%	of	$132,500

Let c = amount of commission.

Equation	c	=	0.045	·	132,500

$c = 0.045 \cdot 132{,}500$
  $= 5{,}962.50$

● The agent's commission is $5,962.50.

✓ Check Understanding Example 3

3. **Royalties** A singer receives a 5% royalty on each CD sale. To the nearest cent, find his royalty for a CD that sells for $16.99.
   $.85

4 EXAMPLE Real-World Problem Solving

Surveys The graph shows the results of a survey. There were 1,023 people who answered yes. How many people were surveyed?

Words	1,023	is	93%	of	number surveyed

Let n = number surveyed.

Equation	1,023	=	0.93	·	n

$0.93n = 1{,}023$
$\dfrac{0.93n}{0.93} = \dfrac{1{,}023}{0.93}$
$n = 1{,}100$

● 1,100 people were surveyed.

Responses to the question "Do you feel good about your life overall?"

✓ Check Understanding Example 4

4. In a survey, 922 people, or about 68.6%, preferred smooth peanut butter to chunky. How many people were surveyed? **1,344 people**

6-7 Percents and Equations **321**

👥 Reaching All Students

Below Level Have students take turns being a waiter and a customer. The waiter gives the customer a bill, and the customer estimates tips of 10%, 15%, and 18%. The waiter then checks the customer's estimate.	**Advanced Learners** One number is increased 5%. Another number is increased 60%. Is the 60% increase greater? Explain. No; a large percent of a small amount can be less than a small percent of a large amount.	**Error Prevention** See note on page 321. **English Learners** See note on page 323.

---

2. Teach

Math Background

When writing an equation to solve a percent problem, you can often translate the words almost directly into the equation: "What percent of 120 is 18?" becomes $x \cdot 120 = 18$. In mathematics, the word *of* often suggests *multiply*. And *is* often means *equals*.

Teaching Notes

Alternative Method
Explain to students that if you know the part, it is always divided by the other amount you know, whether it is the percent or the whole. If you do not know the part, then you multiply the two parts you know, the percent and the whole.

2 EXAMPLE Error Prevention

Help students recognize that in this example, the part is greater than the whole. This means the percent is greater than 100%.

📽 Additional Examples

❶ What is 35% of 84? **29.4**

❷ What percent of 26 is 65? **250%**

❸ A car salesman makes a 6.5% commission on each car he sells. How much does he make on the sale of a car for $35,000? **$2,275**

❹ During a telephone survey, 414 people, or 46% of those called, said that they were watching station RFGT at the time of the call. How many people were called? **900 people**

Closure

Have students write the three types of percent equations using n for the unknown and the following symbols and words: %, ·, =, part, and whole.
% · whole = part
(or n · whole = part)
% · n = part
% · whole = n

321

Assignment Guide

▼ 1 **Objective 1**

Ⓐ Ⓑ **Core** 1–16, 21–28, 31–36

▼ 2 **Objective 2**

Ⓐ Ⓑ **Core** 17–20, 29, 30

Ⓒ **Extension** 37–39

Test Prep 40–43
Mixed Review 44–50

Practice 6-7 *Percents and Equations*

Write and solve an equation. Where necessary, round to the nearest tenth or tenth of a percent.

1. What percent of 25 is 17? **68%**
2. What percent of 10 is 8? **125%**
3. What percent is 63 of 84? **75%**
4. What percent is 3 of 600? **0.5%**
5. Find 45% of 60. **27**
6. Find 325% of 52. **169**
7. Find $66\frac{2}{3}$% of 87. **58**
8. Find 1% of 3,620. **36.2**
9. $62\frac{1}{2}$% of x is 5. What is x? **8**
10. 300% of k is 42. What is k? **14**
11. $33\frac{1}{3}$% of p is 19. What is p? **57**
12. 70% of c is 49. What is c? **70**
13. 15% of n is 1,050. What is n? **7,000**
14. 38% of y is 494. What is y? **1,300**
15. A camera regularly priced at $295 was placed on sale at $236. What percent of the regular price was the sale price? **80%**
16. Nine hundred thirty-six students, 65% of the entire student body, attended the football game. Find the size of the student body. **1,440 students**

Enrichment 6-7 *Estimating Percent*

You can use compatible numbers to estimate percents mentally.

Example Of the 88 members of the school orchestra, 68.2% practice at least 1 hour a day. Mentally estimate the numbers of players who practice at least 1 hour.

Solution
1. Choose a simple fraction close to the given percent. $\frac{2}{3} = 66\frac{2}{3}$%
2. Choose an appropriate base close to the given base. Ninety is close to 88 and is divisible by 3.
3. Solve mentally. Think: $\frac{2}{3} \times 90 = 60$
   About 60 members practice at least 1 hour per day.

1. To use this method, you must know some basic percent-fraction equivalents. Complete the table of equivalents.

Percent-Fraction Equivalents

10%	$12\frac{1}{2}$%	20%	25%	30%	$33\frac{1}{3}$%	40%	50%	60%	70%	75%	80%	$83\frac{1}{3}$%	90%
$\frac{1}{10}$	$\frac{1}{8}$	$\frac{1}{5}$	$\frac{1}{4}$	$\frac{3}{10}$	$\frac{1}{3}$	$\frac{2}{5}$	$\frac{1}{2}$	$\frac{3}{5}$	$\frac{7}{10}$	$\frac{3}{4}$	$\frac{4}{5}$	$\frac{5}{6}$	$\frac{9}{10}$

Estimate each percent mentally.

2. 41.7% of 26 **10**
3. 73.9% of 43.1 **33**
4. $82\frac{1}{2}$% of 37 **30**
5. 59% of 198 **120**
6. 34% of 61 **20**
7. 48.7% of 498.7 **250**
8. 91% of 68.7 **63**
9. 11.7% of 7,977 **1,000**
10. The sizes of the four sections of the school orchestra are given. Estimate how many of the 88 members are in each.

string, 48.9% **44**   woodwind, 17% **15**

brass, 23.9% **22**   percussion, 10.2% **9**

11. Of the 26 eighth graders in the orchestra, 15 play stringed instruments. Estimate the percent who play strings. **60%**

EXERCISES

? For more exercises, see *Extra Practice.*

Practice and Problem Solving

Ⓐ **Practice by Example**

Write an equation and solve.

Example 1
(page 320)

1. Find 30% of 30.
$n = 0.3 \cdot 30$; 9
2. What percent of 40 is 25?
$25 = n \cdot 40$; 62.5%
3. 120 is 15% of what number?
$120 = 0.15 \cdot n$; 800
4. What percent of 20 is 11?
$n \cdot 20 = 11$; 55%
5. Find 56% of 75.
$n = 0.56 \cdot 75$; 42
6. 85% of z is 106,250. What is z?
$0.85 \cdot z = 106{,}250$; 125,000
7. What percent of 25 is 17?
$n \cdot 25 = 17$; 68%
8. Find 75% of 840.
$0.75 \cdot 840 = n$; 630

Example 2
(page 320)

9. Find 150% of 90.
$n = 1.5 \cdot 90$; 135
10. 300% of a is 297. What is a?
$3.00 \cdot a = 297$; 99
11. What percent of 4 is 9?
$n \cdot 4 = 9$; 225%
12. Find 500% of 12.
$n = 5 \cdot 12$; 60
13. What percent of 150 is 96?
$n \cdot 150 = 96$; 64%
14. 3.5% of d is 0.105. What is d?
$0.035 \cdot d = 0.105$; 3
15. What percent of 1 is 4.7?
$n \cdot 1 = 4.7$; 470%
16. Find 15% of 150.
$n = 0.15 \cdot 150$; 22.5

Example 3 🌐
(page 321)

17. **Royalties** Julius writes novels and receives 12% of the price for each book sold. To the nearest cent, find the royalty Julius receives for a book price of $7.99. **$.96**

🌐 18. **Sports** An agent makes 16% commission on an athlete's signing bonus. If the bonus is $26,000, what is the agent's commission? **$4,160**

Example 4
(page 321)

For Exercises 19 and 20, the table gives information about videocassette recorders (VCRs) in the United States.

19. The number of households with VCRs in 1995 was about 93% of the number with VCRs in 1998. About how many households had VCRs in 1998?
about 83 million households
20. The number of households with VCRs in 1990 was about 87.5% of the number with VCRs in 1993. About how many households had VCRs in 1993?
about 72 million households

Households With VCRs

Year	Households (millions)
1980	1
1985	18
1990	63
1995	77
1998	■

SOURCE: Statistical Abstract of the United States. Go to **www.PHSchool.com** for a data update. Web Code: adg-2041

Ⓑ **Apply Your Skills**

Write and solve an equation. Where necessary, round to the nearest tenth or tenth of a percent.

21. Find 225% of 3.6.
$n = 2.25 \cdot 3.6$; 8.1
22. What percent of 45 is 24?
$n \cdot 45 = 24$; 53.3%
23. Find 5.5% of 44.
$n = 0.055 \cdot 44$; 2.4
24. 24% of w is 3.6. What is w?
$0.24 \cdot w = 3.6$; 15
25. What percent of 8 is 20?
$n \cdot 8 = 20$; 250%
26. 9.2% of b is 27.6. What is b?
$0.092 \cdot b = 27.6$; 300
27. 135% of t is 63. What is t?
$1.35 \cdot t = 63$; 46.7
28. What is 264% of 12?
$n = 2.64 \cdot 12$; 31.7

🌐 29. **Commission** A salesperson receives 5.4% commission. On one
 sale, she received $6.48. What was the amount of the sale? **$120**

30. **Reasoning** Describe a situation in which you would use a percent greater than 100%. **Answers may vary. Sample: A toy company makes 125% of profit it expected for the year.**

GPS Use the Guided Problem Solving worksheet with Exercise 29.

37. False; 18 is not less than 10% of 63. It is about 29% of 63.

Mental Math Use mental math.

31. What percent of 60 is 30? 50%

32. 100% of t is 100. What is t? 100

33. Find 5% of 10. **0.5**

34. What percent of 55 is 11? 20%

35. 50% of g is 24. What is g? **48**

36. Find 15% of 12. **1.8**

C Challenge

Writing in Math

Which approach do you prefer to use in solving percent problems—the approach you learned in this lesson, or the one you learned in Lesson 6-6? Explain.

See back of book.

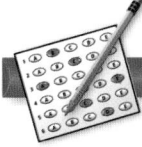

For Exercises 37 and 38, use the table on page 322. Is each statement true or false? Explain.

37. Reasoning The number of households with VCRs in 1985 was less than 10% of the number of households with VCRs in 1990. See above left.

38. The number of households with VCRs in 1985 was more than 1,000% of the number in 1980.
True; 18 is more than 1,000% of 1.

39. Polly got a 20% discount on a computer that regularly cost x dollars. She paid sales tax of 5%. Later she sold the computer for 70% of what she paid for it. Write an expression for the amount Polly received for the computer. **0.588x**

Test Prep

Multiple Choice

40. About what percent of 92 is 63? **B**
A. 63% **B.** 68% **C.** 92% **D.** 146%

Take It to the NET
Online lesson quiz at
www.PHSchool.com
Web Code: ada-0607

41. Seventy students voted for Tim, 25% voted for Li, and the other 40% voted for Mae. How many students voted in the election? **F**
F. 200 **G.** 135 **H.** 100 **I.** 70

42. What is 158% of 35? **D**
A. 12.64 **B.** 20.3 **C.** 42.6 **D.** 55.3

Short Response

43. Chan's team won 70% of the 20 games it played. Latisha's team played 15 games and won 80% of them.
a. Whose team won the greater number of games?
b. For part (a), explain your answer. See margin.

Mixed Review

Lesson 6-6 **Write a proportion. Then solve.**

44. ▇% of 360 is 45.
$\frac{n}{100} = \frac{45}{360}$; 12.5

45. 35% of 60 is ▇.
$\frac{35}{100} = \frac{n}{60}$; 21

46. 45 is 1.5% of ▇.
$\frac{1.5}{100} = \frac{45}{n}$; 3,000

Lesson 5-8 🌐 **47. Creative Writing** Ernest started writing a story on a Friday. He worked on the story for $\frac{1}{2}$ h each day. He took 7 h to finish it. On what day did Ernest finish his story? **Thursday**

Lesson 4-7 **Simplify each expression.**

48. $10^2 \cdot 10^4$
1,000,000

49. $9y^4 \cdot y^5$
$9y^9$

50. $(x^3)^7$
x^{21}

6-7 Percents and Equations **323**

43. [2] Chan's team; 80% of 15 is 12. 70% of 20 is 14, which is greater than 12.
[1] minor error OR answer only

Test Prep

📁 **Resources**
For additional practice with a variety of test item formats:
• Test Prep, p. 343
• Test-Taking Strategies, p. 338
• Test-Taking Strategies With Transparencies

---

4. Assess

 **Lesson Quiz 6-7**

Solve.

1. What is 9% of 30? **2.7**

2. What is 25% of 312? **78**

3. What percent of 9 is 3?
$33\frac{1}{3}$%

4. What percent of 3 is 9?
300%

5. A car dealer makes an 8% commission on each car she sells. How much does she make on a $40,000 sale?
$3,200

6. During a telephone survey, 320 people, or 25% of those called, said they were listening to the same station at the time of the call. How many people were called?
1,280 people

English Learners
Exercises 18 and 29 Ask volunteers to explain what they know about commissions, including a definition, and mention some jobs that pay commission, such as selling cars or real estate.

Alternative Assessment

Have students write a percent problem in words and then show at least two different ways to solve it.

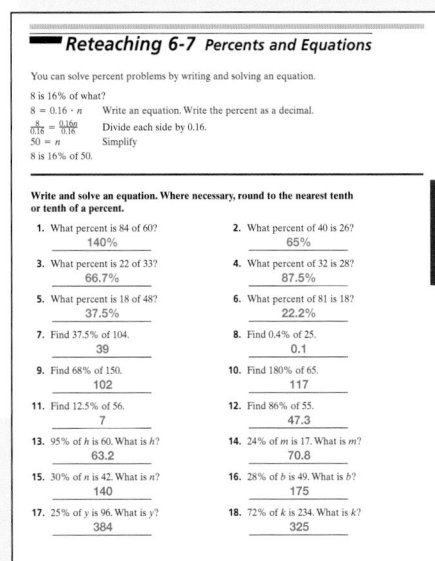

Reteaching 6-7 Percents and Equations

323

Reading Percent Problems

Students read through a word problem and translate it into an equation in order to solve the problem.

Teaching Notes

As you go over the Example with students, have them tell you the words in the problem that translate into mathematical symbols. Ask students for the word that indicates *multiplication*. **times** Ask students for the word that indicates *equals*. **is** Ask students for the word that is replaced with a variable when translating into an equation. **what**

Error Prevention!

Suggest that students put their answer into the percent sentence after solving a problem to see whether the answer makes sense.

Reading Math — Reading Percent Problems

For Use With Page 320, Key Concepts

To go from words to an equation, you first have to recognize a word equation. This requires that you recognize the variable, all operations, and the relationship. Percent problems can have various word equations, but each is equivalent to one of the three types in this table.

Key Concepts | **Percent Equations**

Finding the Percent	Finding the Part	Finding the Whole
What percent of 40 is 6?	What is 15% of 40?	6 is 15% of what?
$n \cdot 40 = 6$	$n = 0.15 \cdot 40$	$6 = 0.15 \cdot n$

EXAMPLE

Six of 40 students wear at least one ring. What percent is this?

What percent of 40 is 6?   **Recognize the percent equation.**

n of 40 is 6   *What percent* **is what you must find. Let a variable, *n*, represent this value.**

n $\cdot$ 40 is 6   **The word *of* suggests multiplication.**

n $\cdot$ 40 = 6   **The word *is* suggests equality.**

Now you have a math equation that you can solve.

$$\frac{n \cdot 40}{40} = \frac{6}{40}$$ **Divide each side by 40.**

$$n = 0.15$$ **Simplify.**

$$n = 15\%$$ **Write as a percent.**

1. What percent of 21 is 7? 33.33%
2. 18 is 30% of what? 60
3. What is 20% of 50? 10
4. What percent of 6 is 40? 667%
5. 60 is 80% of what? 75 entries

EXERCISES

Restate, if necessary, the question to match a type of question in the table. Then solve.
1–5. See above right.

1. Seven is what percent of 21?

2. Eighteen is thirty percent of what number?

3. How much is twenty percent of 50?

4. What percent of 6 is 40?

5. Sixty runners, or 80% of all entries, finished the course. How many entries were there?

6. Thirty students are in Ms. Payne's history class. Ninety percent of the students brought signed permission forms for a field trip. How many students brought permission forms?
   What is 90% of 30?; 27 students

Percent of Change

OBJECTIVE

1 Finding Percent of Increase

Exploring Percent of Change

1. Find the change in population from 1980 to 1990 for each state. **See below.**

2. Which state had the greater change in population? **California**

Populations of Two States

State	1980	1990
California	23,668,000	29,786,000
Nevada	800,000	1,202,000

3. Write the ratio $\frac{\text{change in population}}{\text{1980 population}}$ for each state. Then write each ratio as a percent. **See below.**

4. Compare the two percents. Which state had the greater population change in terms of percent? **Nevada**

1. California 6,118,000; Nevada 402,000

3. California: $\frac{6,118,000}{23,668,000} \approx 25.8\%$; Nevada: $\frac{402,000}{800,000} \approx 50.3\%$

The percent a quantity increases or decreases from its original amount is the **percent of change.**

$$\text{percent of change} = \frac{\text{amount of change}}{\text{original amount}}$$

1 EXAMPLE Finding Percent of Increase

Find the percent of increase from 4 to 7.5.

amount of increase = $7.5 - 4 = 3.5$

percent of increase = $\frac{\text{amount of increase}}{\text{original amount}}$

$= \frac{3.5}{4}$

$= 0.875 = 87.5\%$

The percent of increase from 4 to 7.5 is 87.5%.

✔ Check Understanding Example 1

1. Find each percent of increase.

   a. from 100 to 114
   14%

   b. from 2.0 to 3.2
   60%

   c. from 4,000 to 8,500
   112.5%

What You'll Learn

OBJECTIVE 1 To find percent of increase

OBJECTIVE 2 To find percent of decrease

. . . And Why

To solve real-world problems involving environmental management

✔ Check Skills You'll Need

Write each decimal as a percent.

1. 0.46 **46%**   2. 2.47 **247%**

3. 0.03 **3%**   4. 5.236
                   523.6%

 For help, go to Lesson 6-5.

New Vocabulary

• percent of change

 Interactive lesson includes instant self-check, tutorials, and activities.

Lesson Preview

✔ **Check Skills You'll Need**

Fractions, Decimals, and Percents
Lesson 6-5: Example 3;
Exercises 22–31.
Extra Practice, p. 749.

Lesson Resources

 Teaching Resources
Practice, Reteaching, Enrichment

Reaching All Students
Practice Workbook 6-8
Spanish Practice Workbook 6-8
Guided Problem Solving 6-8
Technology Activities 12
Hands-On Activities 14

Presentation Assistant Plus!
Transparencies and PowerPoint™
• Check Skills You'll Need 6-8
• Additional Examples 6-8
• Student Edition Answers 6-8
• Lesson Quiz 6-8
PH Presentation Pro CD-ROM 6-8

ASSESSMENT SYSTEM

Computer Test Generator CD-ROM

 Technology
Resource Pro® CD-ROM
Computer Test Generator CD-ROM
PH Presentation Pro CD-ROM

www.PHSchool.com
Student Site
• Teacher Web Code: adk-5500
• Updated Data
• Graphing Calculator, Procedure 2
• Self-grading Lesson Quiz
PH SuccessNet Teacher Center
• Lesson Planner
• Resources

Plus iTEXT

Ongoing Assessment and Intervention

Before the Lesson
Diagnose prerequisite skills using:
• Check Skills You'll Need

During the Lesson
Monitor progress using:
• Check Understanding
• Additional Examples
• Test Prep

After the Lesson
Assess knowledge using:
• Lesson Quiz
• Computer Test Generator CD-ROM

2. Teach

Professional Development

Math Background

A large percent of change may not necessarily mean a large amount of actual change. When 4 is increased to 6 by adding 2, the percent of change is 50%. However, when 400 is increased to 500 by adding 100, the percent of change is only 25%.

Teaching Notes

Investigation (Optional)
Students may have difficulty understanding how Nevada can have a greater percent of change than California. Refer to the Math Background above and remind students that percent of change is a comparison of the change to the original amount.

2 EXAMPLE Teaching Tip

Point out that when the amount of increase is greater than the original amount, the percent of increase is more than 100%.

3 EXAMPLE Visual Learners

Students may choose the incorrect number for the original amount, since the lesser number is the original amount in percent of increase. In percent of change problems have students look for the word *from*. The original amount often follows *from*.

PowerPoint
Additional Examples

1 Find the percent of increase from 8 to 9.6. **20%**

2 In a given year, Hillsboro had a total of 7.5 in. of rain by March 1 and a total of 22.5 in. by July 1. Find the percent of increase from 7.5 to 22.5. **200%**

3 Find the percent of decrease from 1,250 to 1,120. **10.4%**

Closure

Have students distinguish between finding percent and finding percent of change. To find percent, you divide the part by the whole. To find percent of change, you divide the amount of change by the original amount.

326

---

2 EXAMPLE Real-World 🌐 Problem Solving

Waste Management
The annual production of municipal solid waste in the United States has more than doubled since 1960. Find the percent of increase from 1960 to 1990.

amount of increase
$$= 205 - 88 = 117$$

percent of increase

$$= \frac{\text{amount of increase}}{\text{original amount}}$$

$$= \frac{117}{88}$$

$$= 1.32\overline{954} \approx 133\%$$

Municipal Solid Waste

88 million tons — 1960
121 million tons — 1970
152 million tons — 1980
205 million tons — 1990
232 million tons — 2000

SOURCE: Environmental Protection Agency.
Go to **www.PHSchool.com** for a data update.
Web Code: adg-2041

• The percent of increase from 1960 to 1990 was about 133%.

✔ Check Understanding Example 2

2. **Waste Management** Find the percent of increase in solid-waste production from 1970 to 1980. Round to the nearest percent. **26%**

OBJECTIVE
2 Finding Percent of Decrease

You also can find percent of decrease.

3 EXAMPLE Finding Percent of Decrease

Find the percent of decrease from 1,500 to 1,416.

amount of decrease $= 1,500 - 1,416 = 84$

percent of decrease $= \dfrac{\text{amount of decrease}}{\text{original amount}}$

$$= \frac{84}{1,500}$$

$$= 0.056 = 5.6\%$$

• The percent of decrease is 5.6%.

✔ Check Understanding Example 3

3. Find each percent of decrease. Where necessary, round to the nearest tenth of a percent.

   a. from 9.6 to 4.8   **b.** from 202 to 192   **c.** from 854.5 to 60.6
   50%   5.0%   92.9%

326 **Chapter 6** Ratios, Proportions, and Percents

👥 Reaching All Students

| Below Level Emphasize to students that percent of change is always a percent of the *original* amount and never a percent of the *new* amount. | Advanced Learners Point out that percents of increase can be greater than 100. Ask: *Can percents of decrease be greater than 100? Explain.* No; amounts of decrease cannot be greater than the whole. | Visual Learners See note on page 326. Error Prevention See note on page 328. |

Practice and Problem Solving

Assignment Guide

Objective 1
Ⓐ Ⓑ **Core** 1–10, 24–26, 28, 29, 31, 33, 34, 36
Ⓒ **Extension** 39, 40

Objective 2
Ⓐ Ⓑ **Core** 11–23, 27, 30, 32, 35, 37, 38
Ⓒ **Extension** 41

Test Prep 42–46
Mixed Review 47–53

 Practice by Example

Examples 1 and 2 (pages 325, 326)

Find each percent of increase.

1. from 30 to 39 **30%** **2.** from 50 to 66 **32%** **3.** from 4 to 4.5 **12.5%**

4. from 48 to 60 **25%** **5.** from 32 to 76 **137.5%** **6.** from 5 to 5.5 **10%**

7. from 55 to 176 **220%** **8.** from 38 to 95 **150%** **9.** from 2.5 to 3 **20%**

🌐 **10. Life Spans** In the United States in the 20th century, average life expectancy increased from about 47 years to about 77 years. Find the percent of increase to the nearest percent. **64%**

Example 3 (page 326)

Find each percent of decrease. Where necessary, round to the nearest tenth of a percent.

11. from 60 to 48 **20%** **12.** from 180 to 54 **70%** **13.** from 180 to 108 **40%**

14. from 280 to 126 **55%** **15.** from 240 to 90 **62.5%** **16.** from 42 to 35 **16.7%**

17. from 64 to 24 **62.5%** **18.** from 6.5 to 4.8 **26.2%** **19.** from 7.4 to 2.4 **67.6%**

20. A computer that cost $1,099 last year costs $999 this year. **9.1%**

21. A racing bicycle that cost $1,500 new costs $845 used. **43.7%**

Ⓑ **Apply Your Skills**

Find each percent of change. Tell whether the change is an increase or a decrease. Where necessary, round to the nearest tenth of a percent.

22. from 96 to 78 **18.8% decrease** **23.** from 90 to 75 **16.7% decrease** **24.** from 80 to 95 **18.8% increase**

25. from 45 to 105 **133.3% increase** **26.** from 27 to 72 **166.7% increase** **27.** from 120 to 95 **20.8% decrease**

28. from 87 to 108 **24.1% increase** **29.** from 59 to 127 **115.3% increase** **30.** from 77 to 13 **83.1% decrease**

31. Error Analysis Eva's first step in finding the percent of change from 7 to 8 was to write $\frac{8-7}{8} = \frac{1}{8}$. Explain Eva's error.
Eva should compare 8 − 7 to 7, not 8.

🌐 **32. Economics** The average cost of a gallon of gasoline was $1.29 in 1997 and $1.12 in 1998. Find the percent of decrease. **about 13.2%**
GPS

Mental Math **Use mental math to find each percent of change. Tell whether the change is an increase or a decrease.**

33. from 25 to 30 **20% increase** **34.** from 40 to 45 **12.5% increase** **35.** from 50 to 45 **10% decrease**

36. from 100 to 101.1 **1.1% increase** **37.** from 40 to 20 **50% decrease** **38.** from 15 to 12 **20% decrease**

Ⓒ **Challenge**

39. The population of Growtown increased from 10,000 to 13,000 in one year. In the same year, the population of Slowtown decreased from 30,000 to 24,000. **a–b. See left.**
a. Find each town's percent of increase or decrease in population.
b. If each town maintains the same rate of change, within how many years will the population of Growtown exceed that of Slowtown?

39. a. Growtown
30% increase;
Slowtown
20% decrease
b. 3 years

 Use the Guided Problem Solving worksheet with Exercise 32.

Practice 6-8 *Percent of Change*

Find each percent of change. Round to the nearest tenth of a percent. Tell whether the change is an increase or a decrease.

1. 24 to 21 **12.5%; decrease** **2.** 64 to 80 **25%; increase**

3. 100 to 113 **13%; increase** **4.** 50 to 41 **18%; decrease**

5. 63 to 105 **66.7%; increase** **6.** 42 to 168 **300%; increase**

7. 80 to 24 **70%; decrease** **8.** 200 to 158 **21%; decrease**

9. 56 to 71 **26.8%; increase** **10.** 127 to 84 **33.9%; decrease**

11. 20 to 24 **20%; increase** **12.** 44 to 22 **50%; decrease**

13. 16 to 12 **25%; decrease** **14.** 10 to 100 **900%; increase**

15. 20 to 40 **100%; increase** **16.** 10 to 50 **400%; increase**

17. 12 to 16 **33.3%; increase** **18.** 80 to 100 **25%; increase**

19. 69 to 117 **69.6%; increase** **20.** 19 to 9 **52.6%; decrease**

21. 95 to 145 **52.6%; increase** **22.** 88 to 26 **70.5%; decrease**

23. Mark weighed 110 pounds last year. He weighs 119 pounds this year. What is the percent of increase in his weight, to the nearest tenth of a percent? **8.2%**

24. Susan had $140 in her savings account last month. She added $20 this month and earned $.50 interest. What is the percent of increase in the amount in her savings account to the nearest tenth of a percent? **14.6%**

25. The population density of California was 151.4 people per square mile in 1980. By 1990 it had increased to 190.8 people per square mile. Find the percent increase to the nearest percent. **26%**

Enrichment 6-8 *Consumer Price Index and Inflation*

Each month, the United States Bureau of Labor Statistics publishes cost-of-living figures called the Consumer Price Index (CPI). The CPI measures how the prices of goods and services change over time. Current prices are given relative to 1982–1984 prices, which are arbitrarily set at 100.

Example The CPI for dairy products in 1996 was 142.1. Find the 1996 cost of a quart of milk which cost $.80 in 1983.

Solution Cost = $\frac{CPI}{100}$ × 1983 price
= $\frac{142.1}{100}$ × 0.8
≈ 1.14
The cost of a quart of milk in 1996 was about $1.14

The table shows the Consumer Price Index for several items in 1990 and 1996. Use the table to find the 1996 cost for each of the following.

Item	1990 CPI	1996 CPI
Footwear	117.4	126.6
Gasoline	101.0	105.9
Cereals and bakery products	140.0	174.0

1. A pair of shoes that cost $35 in 1983. **$44.31**

2. A donut that cost $.20 in 1983. **$.35**

3. A gallon of gasoline that cost $.95 in 1983. **$1.01**

Inflation measures the increase in prices. You can find inflation by calculating the percent of increase in the CPI.

Example The CPI for public transportation rose from 142.6 in 1990 to 181.9 in 1996. Find the inflation in the cost of public transportation for the period.

Solution 181.9 − 142.6 = 39.3
39.3 ÷ 142.6 ≈ 0.276
Inflation was about 27.6% for this period.

Find the inflation from 1990 to 1996 to the nearest tenth of a percent.

4. on cost of footwear **7.8%**

5. on cost of gasoline **4.9%**

6. on cost of cereal **24.3%**

327

Error Prevention!

Exercises 1–9 Some students may have difficulty writing the ratio correctly. Have students first write the formula as $\% = \frac{\text{inc.}}{\text{orig.}}$. Then substitute the numbers into the formula and solve.

Test Prep

 **Resources**

For additional practice with a variety of test item formats:
- Test Prep, p. 343
- Test-Taking Strategies, p. 338
- Test-Taking Strategies With Transparencies

Reteaching 6-8 Percent of Change

Find the percent of decrease from 85 to 60.

Find the amount of decrease.
$85 - 60 = 25$
percent of decrease = $\frac{\text{amount of decrease}}{\text{original amount}}$
$= \frac{25}{85}$
$\approx 0.294 = 29.4\%$
The percent of decrease is about 29.4%

Find each percent of increase. Where necessary, round to the nearest tenth of a percent.

1. 40 is increased to 45. **12.5%**
2. 33 is increased to 55. **66.7%**
3. 15 is increased to 34. **126.7%**
4. 11 is increased to 88. **700%**
5. 72 is increased to 117. **62.5%**
6. 28 is increased to 49. **75%**
7. 35 is increased to 49. **40%**
8. 48 is increased to 132. **175%**

Find each percent of decrease. Where necessary, round to the nearest tenth of a percent.

9. 60 is decreased to 15. **75%**
10. 56 is decreased to 35. **37.5%**
11. 140 is decreased to 77. **45%**
12. 96 is decreased to 64. **33.3%**
13. 99 is decreased to 69. **30.3%**
14. 50 is decreased to 44. **12%**
15. 83 is decreased to 0. **100%**
16. 475 is decreased to 152. **68%**

Real-World Connection

Ganesh was the first elephant born at the Cincinnati Zoo.

40. **Zoology** Ganesh weighed 213 lb at birth, 300 lb at one month, and 1,061 lb at one year. Find each percent of increase of weight. Round to the nearest percent.
    a. from birth to one month **41%**
    b. from one month to one year **254%**
    c. from birth to one year **398%**
    d. **Writing in Math** Explain why the sum of the percent increase from birth to one month and from one month to one year does not equal the percent increase from birth to one year. **See below left.**

41. a. **Reasoning** 100 is increased by 10%. The result is decreased by 10%. Is the final result 100? Explain. **See below.**
    b. Compare the final result in part (a) to 100, the original number. Find the percent of change. **1% decrease**

    41a. No; the decrease is 10% of a greater amount.

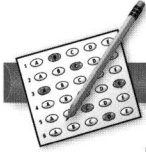

Test Prep

Multiple Choice

40d. The percents were not based on the same original amount.

42. The price of an item is $5.99. With sales tax, you pay $6.35. About what percent of the price of the item is the sales tax? **D**
    A. 3%   B. 4%   C. 5%   D. 6%

43. Kayla was 36 in. tall at age 3. Today, at age 5, she is 42 in. tall. To the nearest percent, what is the percent of change in Kayla's height? **I**
    F. 2%   G. 8%   H. 14%   I. 17%

Take It to the NET
Online lesson quiz at
www.PHSchool.com
Web Code: ada-0608

44. A share of stock sold for $32.13 yesterday. Today, it is selling for $30.08. What is the approximate percent decline in the stock price? **B**
    A. 5%   B. 6%   C. 7%   D. 8%

45. What is the percent of change from 148 to 37? **H**
    F. 3%   G. 25%   H. 75%   I. 111%

Extended Response

46. 200 is decreased by 5%. The result is increased by 5%. What is the final result? Explain why the result is less than 200. Show your work. **See back of book.**

Mixed Review

Lesson 6-7 47. **Astronomy** The Space Surveillance Center in Colorado tracks about 8,500 objects in orbit around Earth. All but about 500 objects are junk from past space missions. What percent are junk? Round to the nearest percent. **94%**

Lesson 5-3 **Find each sum or difference.**

48. $5\frac{3}{4} - 2\frac{5}{8}$ $3\frac{1}{8}$
49. $-4\frac{1}{3} + 2\frac{1}{2}$ $-1\frac{5}{6}$
50. $-6\frac{1}{3} - 6\frac{1}{3}$ $-12\frac{2}{3}$

Lesson 4-2 **Evaluate each expression.**

51. $3x^2$ for $x = -5$ **75**
52. $[(3 + 12)4]^2$ **3,600**
53. $(7 + 4y)^2$ for $y = -2$ **1**

Alternative Assessment

Have the class look at advertisements from a newspaper that give original and reduced prices for items like clothes, cars, or furniture. Ask volunteers to explain how to find the percents of decrease in the prices of selected items. Then have each student find the percent of decrease for each item discussed.

Markup and Discount 6-9

Lesson Preview

 Check Skills You'll Need

Percents and Equations
Lesson 6-7: Example 1;
Exercises 1–8.
Extra Practice, p. 749.

Lesson Resources

 **Teaching Resources**
Practice, Reteaching, Enrichment
Checkpoint Quiz 2

 **Reaching All Students**
Practice Workbook 6-9
Spanish Practice Workbook 6-9
Reading and Math Literacy 6C
Spanish Reading and Math
  Literacy 6C
Spanish Checkpoint Quiz 2
Guided Problem Solving 6-9
Technology Activities 12
Hands-On Activities 14

Presentation Assistant Plus!
Transparencies and PowerPoint™
• Check Skills You'll Need 6-9
• Additional Examples 6-9
• Student Edition Answers 6-9
• Lesson Quiz 6-9
PH Presentation Pro CD-ROM 6-9

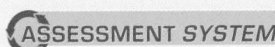 ASSESSMENT SYSTEM

Checkpoint Quiz 2
Computer Test Generator CD-ROM

 Technology
Resource Pro® CD-ROM
Computer Test Generator CD-ROM
PH Presentation Pro CD-ROM

 www.PHSchool.com
Student Site
• Teacher Web Code: adk-5500
• Algebra Readiness Puzzles 23
• Self-grading Lesson Quiz
PH SuccessNet Teacher Center
• Lesson Planner
• Resources

Plus

1 **Finding Markups**

To make a profit, stores charge more for merchandise than they pay for it. The amount of increase is called the **markup.** The percent of increase is the *percent of markup*.

1 EXAMPLE <u>Real-World</u> <u>Problem Solving</u>

Music Sales **A music store's percent of markup is 67%.
A CD costs the store $10.15. Find the markup.**

markup = percent of markup · store's cost

= 0.67 · 10.15

≈ 6.80 **Simplify. Round to the nearest cent.**

The markup is $6.80.

✓ **Check Understanding** Example 1

1. A clothing store pays $56 for a jacket. The store's percent of markup is 75%. Find the markup for the jacket. **$42**

The store's cost plus the markup equals the *selling price*.

2 EXAMPLE <u>Real-World</u>  <u>Problem Solving</u>

Retailing **A computer store pays $6 for a computer mouse.
The percent of markup is 75%. Find the mouse's selling price.**

0.75 · 6 = 4.50 **Multiply to find the markup.**

6.00 + 4.50 = 10.50 **Cost + markup = selling price.**

The selling price is $10.50.

✓ **Check Understanding** Example 2

2. A $5 cap has a 70% markup. Find the selling price. **$8.50**

2 **Finding Discounts**

When an item goes on sale, the amount of the price decrease is the **discount.** The percent of decrease is the *percent of discount*.
Sale price = regular price − discount.

What You'll Learn

1 To find markups

2 To find discounts

. . . And Why

To solve real-world problems involving price markups and discounts

✓ **Check Skills You'll Need**

**Write an equation
and solve. Round to
hundredths as needed.**

1. What is 75% of $82?
  $61.50
2. What is 42% of $170?
  $71.40
3. What is 5.5% of $24?
  $1.32
4. What is 80% of
  $15.99? **$12.79**

For help, go to Lesson 6-7.

New Vocabulary

• markup
• discount

iTEXT Interactive lesson includes instant self-check, tutorials, and activities.

Ongoing Assessment and Intervention

Before the Lesson
Diagnose prerequisite skills using:
• Check Skills You'll Need

During the Lesson
Monitor progress using:
• Check Understanding
• Additional Examples
• Test Prep

After the Lesson
Assess knowledge using:
• Lesson Quiz
• Computer Test Generator CD-ROM
• Chapter Checkpoint 2 (p. 332)

Math Background

One example of percent of increase is the percent of *markup* that stores use to establish the selling price for merchandise. In Lesson 6-8, percent of change is defined as $\frac{\text{amount of change}}{\text{original amount}}$.

You can define percent of markup as $\frac{\text{markup (or amount of change)}}{\text{original cost (to the store)}}$.

Teaching Notes

1 EXAMPLE Error Prevention

Help students distinguish between *markup* (the actual increase in the amount) and *percent of markup* (the ratio of the increase to the original cost).

3 EXAMPLE English Learners

Help students distinguish between the *sale price* and the *selling price*. The *sale price* is equal to the *selling price* minus the discount. It is the price you pay when you buy an item "on sale."

PowerPoint

Additional Examples

1 A grocery store has a 20% markup on a can of soup. The can of soup costs the store $1.25. Find the markup. **$.25**

2 A bookstore pays $4.50 for a novel. The percent of markup is 45%. Find the novel's selling price. **$6.53**

3 A camera that regularly sells for $210 is on sale for 30% off. Find the discount. **$63**

Closure

Ask: *How do you find a selling price when you know the cost and the percent of markup?* You use the percent of markup to find the markup. Then add the markup to the cost. *How do you find a sale price when you know the original price and the percent of discount?* You use the percent of discount to find the discount. Then subtract the discount from the original price.

330

Reading Math

20% *off* means a discount of 20%.

---

3 EXAMPLE Finding Discount

Recreation Athletic shoes that regularly sell for $85.99 are on sale for 20% off. Find the discount.

discount = percent of discount · regular price

$= 0.20 \cdot 85.99$

≈ 17.20 **Simplify. Round to the nearest cent.**

● The discount is $17.20.

✓ **Check Understanding** Example 3

3. Pants priced at $21.99 are marked 15% off. Find the discount.
$3.30

Here are two ways to use percent of discount to find a sale price.

More Than One Way

A video game that regularly sells for $39.95 is on sale for 20% off. What is the sale price?

Eric's Method

Find the discount. Then find the sale price.

discount = percent of discount · regular price

$= 0.20 \cdot 39.95$

$= 7.99$

sale price = regular price − discount

$= 39.95 − 7.99$

$= 31.96$

The sale price is $31.96.

Michelle's Method

Find the sale price directly. The sale price equals 100% of the regular price minus 20% of the regular price.

sale price $= (100\% − 20\%) \cdot$ regular price

$= 80\% \cdot$ regular price

$= 0.80(39.95)$

$= 31.96$

The sale price is $31.96.

Choose a Method

1. Which method do you prefer? Explain. **See back of book.**

2. Find the sale price if the percent of discount is 25%. Round to the nearest cent. **$29.96**

 Reaching All Students

| **Below Level** Some students may have participated in a fundraising sale for an organization. Ask them whether the organization made a profit on the sale. | **Advanced Learners** Have each student find the manufacturer's suggested retail price (MSRP) of a favorite car. Then find an actual price and calculate the percent of decrease or increase from the MSRP. | **Error Prevention** See note on page 330. **English Learners** See note on page 330. |

EXERCISES

For more exercises, see Extra Practice.

Practice and Problem Solving

3. Practice

A Practice by Example

Example 1
(page 329)

For Exercises 1–5, find each markup.

1. cost: $1.50
percent of markup: 70% **$1.05**

2. cost: $38
percent of markup: 58% **$22.04**

3. cost: $111.00
percent of markup: 50% **$55.50**

4. cost: $18
percent of markup: 35% **$6.30**

🌐 **5. Beach Gear** A beach store pays $11.40 for each beach umbrella.
The store's percent of markup is 75%. **$8.55**

Example 2
(page 329)

For Exercises 6–10, find each selling price.

6. cost: $6
percent of markup: 75% **$10.50**

7. cost: $2.66
percent of markup: 50% **$3.99**

8. cost: $149.99
percent of markup: 100%
$299.98

9. cost: $67.20
percent of markup: 10% **$73.92**

🌐 **10. Clothing** A clothing store pays $15 for a shirt. The percent of
markup is 85%. **$27.75**

Example 3
(page 330)

For Exercises 11–15, find each discount and sale price.

11. regular price: $100
percent of discount: 27%
$27; $73

12. regular price: $24.50
percent of discount: 20%
$4.90; $19.60

13. regular price: $700
percent of discount: 30%
$210; $490

14. regular price: $8.49
percent of discount: 5%
$.42; $8.07

🌐 **15. Footwear** Boots, regularly $125, are on sale for 30% off.
$37.50; $87.50

B Apply Your Skills

Find each selling price. Where necessary, round to the nearest cent.

16. regular price: $180
percent of discount: 40% **$108**

17. regular price: $14.99
percent of discount: 15%
$12.74

18. cost: $9.99
percent of markup: 60% **$15.98**

19. cost: $15
percent of markup: 15% **$17.25**

20a. Find 10% of $11 to get
the discount and
subtract the result
from $11; or find 90%
of $11.

🌐 **20. Shopping** An $11 shirt is on sale for 10% off.   See left.
a. Describe two different methods of finding the sale price.
b. Use one of the methods to find the sale price. **$9.90**

🌐 **21. Video Sales** Store A is selling a video for 20% off the store's
[GPS] regular price of $25.95. Store B is selling the same video for 30%
off the store's regular price of $29.50. Which store's sale price is
lower? How much lower is it? **Store B; $.11**

22. The sweater at
Store A; its sale price
of $17.50 is less than
the sale price of $18
at Store B.

22. Writing in Math Identical sweaters are on sale in two
different stores. The sale price in Store A is 30% off the regular
price of $25. The sale price in Store B is 40% off the regular price
of $30. Which sweater is the better buy? Explain. **See left.**

6-9 Markup and Discount **331**

 Use the Guided Problem
Solving worksheet with
Exercise 21.

Assignment Guide

1 Objective 1
Ⓐ Ⓑ Core 1–10, 18, 19
Ⓒ Extension 24, 25

2 Objective 2
Ⓐ Ⓑ Core 11–17, 20–22
Ⓒ Extension 23

Test Prep 26–28
Mixed Review 29–35

Practice 6-9 Markup and Discount

Find each sale price. Round to the nearest cent where necessary.

	Regular Price	Percent of Discount	Sale Price
1.	$46	25%	$34.50
2.	$35.45	15%	$30.13
3.	$174	40%	$104.40
4.	$1.40	30%	$.98
5.	$87	50%	$43.50
6.	$675	20%	$540.00

Find each selling price. Round to the nearest cent where necessary.

	Cost	Percent Markup	Selling Price
7.	$5.50	75%	$9.63
8.	$25	50%	$37.50
9.	$170	85%	$314.50
10.	$159.99	70%	$271.98
11.	$12.65	90%	$24.04
12.	$739	20%	$886.80

13. A company buys a sweater for $14 and marks it up 90%. It later
discounts the sweater 25%.
a. Find the selling price of the sweater after markup.
$26.60
b. How much was the discount?
$6.65
c. Find the sale price after the discount.
$19.95
d. The company's profit on the sweater can be found by subtracting the
final selling price minus the cost. What was the company's profit on
the sweater?
$5.95
e. The profit was what percent of the cost?
42.5%

Enrichment 6-9 Markdown

The Shirt Shack is having a 25% markdown sale the first week of the month.
This means that the sale price is 25% less than the original price. In the
middle of the month Shirt Shack marked down the sale shirts another 15%.

1. Is a markdown of 25% followed by another markdown of 15% the same
as a single markdown of 40%? Explain.
Sample answer: No; a single markdown of 40% is
better because it is taken off the total price.

2. For question 1, which do you think is the better buy and why?
Sample answer is given in question 1.

3. What is the sale price of a $25 shirt first marked down 25% and then
marked down another 15% (to the nearest cent)?
$15.94

4. What is the sale price of a $25 shirt marked down 40%?
$15

5. Compare your answer to question 1 and 2 with your results for
questions 3 and 4. How would you now answer questions 1 and 2?
The single markdown is a better buy. By taking 15%
off the already reduced price, you are taking 15%
off a lesser amount.

6. Successive markdowns on a $25 shirt of 25% and then 15% are equal to
a single markdown of what percent? Explain how you would solve the
problem using a calculator. Then solve.
$1 - (0.75 \times 0.85) = 0.3625$
It is equal to a single markdown of 36.25%

7. The Shirt Shack is giving a 50% markdown on sweatshirts. Terrific Tops
has marked the same sweatshirt down three times: 25%, 20%, and 15%.
If the shirt originally sold for $35, which store has the better buy? What
was the final price at each store?
The final price at Shirt Shack is $17.50. The final
price at Terrific Tops is $17.85. Shirt Shack has the
better buy.

Solve.

1. The school store has a 65% markup on each stapler. Each stapler costs the store $2.10. Find the markup. **$1.37**

2. A clothes store pays $40 for a skirt. The percent of markup is 25%. Find the skirt's selling price. **$50**

3. A pair of shoes that regularly sells for $94.99 is on sale for 30% off. What is the sale price? **$66.49**

✓ **Chapter Checkpoint 2**

To check understanding of Lessons 6-5 to 6-9:

Checkpoint Quiz 2 (p. 332)

📁 **Teaching Resources**
Checkpoint Quiz 2 (also in Prentice Hall Assessment System)

👥 **Reaching All Students**
Reading and Math Literacy 6C

Spanish versions available.

Reteaching 6-9 Markup and Discount

A store pays $8 for a basketball. The markup is 60%. Later, they discount the basketball 25%. Find the original selling price and the sale price of the basketball.

Method 1	**Method 2**
The markup is 60% of the cost. Find 60% of $8. 0.6(8) = $4.80 Store's cost + markup = selling price 8 + 4.80 = $12.80 The original selling price is $12.80.	The selling price equals 100% of the cost plus 60% (the markup) of the cost, or 160%. Find 160% of $8. 1.60(8) = $12.80 The original selling price is $12.80.
The discount is 25% of the original selling price. Find 25% of $12.80. 0.25(12.80) = 3.20 original price − discount = sale price 12.80 − 3.20 = 9.60 The sale price is $9.60	The sale price is 100% of the original price minus 25% of the original price, or 75%. Find 75% of $12.80. 0.75(12.80) = $9.60 The sale price is $9.60

Complete each table. Where necessary, round to the nearest cent.

	Cost	Markup	Selling Price
1.	$17	50%	$25.50
2.	$48	70%	$81.60
3.	$110	85%	$203.50
4.	$87	65%	$143.55
5.	$335	35%	$452.25

	Original Selling Price	Discount	Sale Price
6.	$19	25%	$14.25
7.	$136	15%	$115.60
8.	$849	30%	$594.30
9.	$29.99	40%	$17.99
10.	$2.59	35%	$1.68

C Challenge

23. No; the sale price (before sales tax) is about $21.

23. Estimation Suppose you want to buy three books that cost $6.95, $9.95, and $10.95. The bookstore is having a $\frac{1}{4}$-off sale. Your state charges sales tax of 5% of an item's final price. You have $20. Do you have enough money? Justify your answer. **See left.**

24. Reasoning A store buys an item for $x and sells it for $y. Write expressions for the markup and the percent of markup. $y - x$, $\frac{y-x}{x}(100)$

25. Shoes cost a store $56.40. The markup is 17%. Find the selling price by two different methods. **$65.99; check students' methods.**

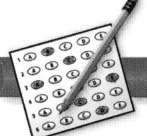

Test Prep

Multiple Choice

Take It to the NET
Online lesson quiz at
www.PHSchool.com
Web Code: ada-0609

26. A $59.50 coat is on sale for $36.50. About how much is the percent of discount? **B**
A. 37% **B.** 39% **C.** 61% **D.** 63%

27. Michael buys a new lawn mower with a 20% discount coupon. The regular price is $359.99. How much is the discounted price? **H**
F. $20.00 **G.** $72.00 **H.** $287.99 **I.** $339.99

Short Response

28. Store A advertises a printer at "15% off its regular price of $79.95." Store B next door advertises the same printer at "20% off of $83.95." **(a)** Which printer would you buy? **(b)** Explain your answer. **See back of book.**

⬤ **Mixed Review**

Lesson 6-8 **Find each percent of decrease. Round to the nearest tenth.**

29. from 90 to 70 **22.2%** **30.** from 44.4 to 14.8 **66.7%** **31.** from 1,750 to 1,125 **35.7%**

Lesson 5-3 🌐 **32. Recipes** A bread recipe calls for $6\frac{1}{2}$ cups of flour. You have $4\frac{3}{4}$ cups. How much more flour do you need? **$1\frac{3}{4}$ c**

Lesson 1-10 **Draw a coordinate plane. Graph each point.** **See back of book.**

33. $A(1,0)$ **34.** $B(-2,3)$ **35.** $C(-1,2)$

✓ **Checkpoint Quiz 2** **Lessons 6-5 through 6-9**

📱 **TEXT** Instant self-check quiz online and on CD-ROM

Compare. Use >, <, or = to complete each statement.

1. $\frac{14}{25}$ ▮ 56% **=** **2.** 1.1% ▮ 0.11 **<** **3.** $\frac{3}{11}$ ▮ 27% **>**

Write and solve an equation.

4. Find 33% of 120. $0.33 \cdot 120 = n$; 39.6

5. Find 125% of 42. $1.25 \cdot 42 = n$; 52.5

6. What percent of 5.6 is 1.4? $n \cdot 5.6 = 1.4$; 25%

7. 15% of q is 9.75. What is q? $0.15 \cdot q = 9.75$; 65

8. A car originally priced at $12,000 is sold at a 20% discount. Find the sale price. **$9,600**

Alternative Assessment

Write various dollar amounts on five index cards, and percents between 5% and 90% on five other cards. Have students draw one card from each set. Use the values to calculate markup and selling price, and discount and sale price.

Test Prep

Resources

For additional practice with a variety of test item formats:
• Test Prep, p. 343
• Test-Taking Strategies, p. 338
• Test-Taking Strategies With Transparencies

 **Technology**

Making a Table

For Use With Lesson 6-10

You can use the **TABLE** feature of a graphing calculator to show values that result from repeated operations.

EXAMPLE

The population of a town increases at the rate of 0.5% each year. Today the town's population is about 5,000. About what will the population be next year? in 5 years?

TABLE lets you show the first two columns of the following table for population $P = 5,000$. In the table, note that after each year, the population is 1.005 times the population at the start of the year.

Year	Population Start of Year	Population End of Year
0	P	$P(1.005)$
1	$P(1.005)$	$P(1.005)^2$
2	$P(1.005)^2$	$P(1.005)^3$
3	$P(1.005)^3$	$P(1.005)^4$
4	$P(1.005)^4$	$P(1.005)^5$
⋮	⋮	⋮

Press **Y=** . Enter $Y_1 = 5000(1.005)$^X.

In **TBLSET,** set TblStart $= 0$ and ΔTbl $= 1$.

Press **TABLE,** to view the first two columns of the table.

X	Y1
0	5000
1	5025
2	5050.1
3	5075.4
4	5100.8
5	5126.3
6	5151.9

X = 5

The table shows that after 1 year, the population will be 5,025. After 5 years, the population will be 5,126.

You can use a table like the one above as you work the Lesson 6-10 Example. Be sure to compare your table with the table on page 335.

EXERCISES

1. Find the population of the town above after 10 years. **5,256**

2. In what year will the population exceed 5,500? **year 20**

3. Suppose the growth rate of the town is 0.6%. What will its population be at the end of 1 year? 5 years? 10 years? In what year will its population exceed 5,500? **5,030; 5,152; 5,308; year 16**

4. A nearby town has population 6,000 and a growth rate of 0.5%. What will its population be at the ends of 1, 5, and 10 years? **6,030; 6,152; 6,307**

 **Technology**

This Technology investigation shows how a student can use a graphing calculator to make a table.

Resources

Students may use any type of graphing calculator.

Teaching Notes

Auditory Learners
Encourage students to say the steps quietly aloud as they press the keys.

Visual Learners
Reproduce the face of a calculator on a transparency. Use the transparency to demonstrate the keys used as you cover the Example in class.

Error Prevention!

Have students work each exercise and then compare tables with a partner. If the tables differ, have students try to determine why. Remind students to check whether their equations are correct. If students cannot find their error, have them compare with another classmate's work or check with you.

Teaching Tip
Students may want to use a graphing calculator to complete the table on page 335 of Lesson 6-10.

6-10

1. Plan

Lesson Preview

 Check Skills You'll Need

Look for a Pattern
Lesson 1-8: Example 1;
Exercises 1–4.
Extra Practice, p. 744.

Lesson Resources

 **Teaching Resources**
Practice, Reteaching, Enrichment

 **Reaching All Students**
Practice Workbook 6-10
Spanish Practice Workbook 6-10
Guided Problem Solving 6-10

Presentation Assistant Plus!
Transparencies and PowerPoint™
• Check Skills You'll Need 6-10
• Additional Examples 6-10
• Student Edition Answers 6-10
• Lesson Quiz 6-10
PH Presentation Pro CD-ROM 6-10

ASSESSMENT SYSTEM

Computer Test Generator CD-ROM

 Technology
Resource Pro® CD-ROM
Computer Test Generator CD-ROM
PH Presentation Pro CD-ROM

 www.PHSchool.com
Student Site
• Teacher Web Code: adk-5500
• Algebra Readiness
  Puzzles 31, 104
• Self-grading Lesson Quiz
PH SuccessNet Teacher Center
• Lesson Planner
• Resources

Plus **iTEXT**

What You'll Learn

OBJECTIVE 1 To solve problems by making a table

...And Why

To solve real-world problems involving population estimates

 Check Skills You'll Need

Solve.

1. For two weeks, you double the amount of money you save each day. You save $.01 the first day. How much money will you have at the end of the two weeks?
   $163.83

For help, go to Lesson 1-8.

OBJECTIVE

1 Make a Table

Math Strategies in Action
Have you ever watched a baseball game at a field that doesn't have a scoreboard? It's hard to keep track of the score!

A scoreboard is a type of table. You can use tables to organize information. Tables are particularly helpful in solving problems that require several steps.

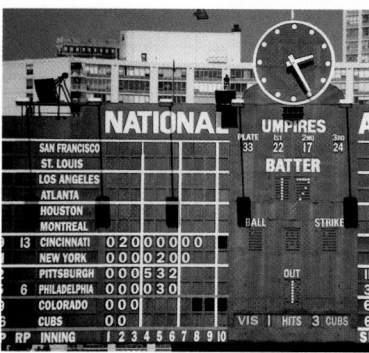

---

1 EXAMPLE **Real-World** **Problem Solving**

Population Growth At the beginning of the year 2000, the population of the United States was about 273.5 million. The rate of population growth was about 0.85% per year. If that rate continues, what will the population be at the beginning of 2010?

Read and Understand

Read the problem carefully.

1. What information are you asked to find?
   the population at the beginning of 2010
2. What information will you need to use to solve the problem?
   the population in 2000 and the growth rate

Plan and Solve

Decide on a strategy. You can use the percent of increase to predict the population increase for each year from 2000 to 2010. You can make a table to organize your predictions for each year.

3. How can you find the increase in population from the beginning of 2000 to the end of that year?
   Answers may vary. Sample: Multiply 273.5 million by 0.0085.
4. How can you find the population at the beginning of 2001?
   Answers may vary. Sample: Add the population increase during 2000 to the population at the beginning of 2000.

334 Chapter 6 Ratios, Proportions, and Percents

Ongoing Assessment and Intervention

Before the Lesson	**During the Lesson**	**After the Lesson**
Diagnose prerequisite skills using:	Monitor progress using:	Assess knowledge using:
• Check Skills You'll Need	• Check Understanding	• Lesson Quiz
	• Additional Examples	• Computer Test Generator
	• Test Prep	CD-ROM

5. The percent of increase is the same each year. Does that mean that the increase in population also will be the same each year? Explain your reasoning. **No; each year the increase is the same percent of an increasing population.**

Copy and complete the table below.

6. Find the numbers for Column 4 by multiplying the numbers in Columns 2 and 3. Round to the nearest tenth of a million. **See table.**

7. Find the numbers for Column 5 (and, hence, the next Column 2 entries) by adding the numbers in Columns 2 and 4. **See table.**

1	2	3	4	5
Year	Population at Beginning of Year (millions)	Rate of Increase (0.85%)	Increase in Population (millions)	Population at End of Year (millions)
2000	273.5	0.0085	2.3	275.8
2001	275.8	0.0085	2.3	278.1
2002	278.1	0.0085	2.4	280.5
2003	280.5	0.0085	2.4	282.9
2004	282.9	0.0085	2.4	285.3
2005	285.3	0.0085	2.4	287.7
2006	287.7	0.0085	2.4	290.1
2007	290.1	0.0085	■2.5	■ 292.6
2008	■ 292.6	0.0085	■2.5	■ 295.1
2009	■ 295.1	0.0085	■2.5	■ 297.6
2010	■ 297.6			

8. Sometimes the number in Column 4 changes from one year to the next, and sometimes it does not change. Explain. **See right.**

9. What is your prediction for population at the beginning of 2010? **297.6 million people**

Answers may vary. Sample: It changes when the increase rounds to the next greatest tenth of a million.

Look Back and Check

10. Your friend says that she knows a quicker way to find the answer. Simply multiply 273.5 · 0.0085 · 10 to find the increase for the ten-year period 2000 to 2010. Do you agree with your friend's approach? Explain your reasoning. **Answers may vary. Sample: No; the increase is slightly greater each year. Your friend's answer will be low.**

✓ **Check Understanding**

11. Suppose the annual percent of increase in population is 0.9%. At that rate, what will the population be at the beginning of 2010? **about 299 million people**

Professional Development

Math Background

You can use a table to help solve problems that describe recurring relationships. Information can easily be compared when displayed in such an organized manner.

Teaching Note

English Learners
Help students understand the meaning of *population* by relating it to the word *people*.

Error Prevention!

Students may interpret one year's population growth as the increase for all 10 years. Emphasize that *"0.85% per year"* means that an increase has to be computed and then added each year. One result (which provides a partial check of your work) is that the amount of increase itself must increase each year.

Alternative Method
You may want to have students solve the example problem using a computer spreadsheet.

PowerPoint

Additional Examples

1 Martin had 100 trees in his orchard the first year. Each year after that he increased the number of trees in his orchard by 10%, rounded to the nearest whole number. How many trees did he have in his orchard in the sixth year? **161 trees**

Closure

Ask: *How might a table help you solve a problem?* **A table allows you to see information clearly organized.**

👣 Reaching All Students

Below Level Ask students to name some real-world situations that use charts and tables. **Answers may vary. Samples: sports statistics, weather forecasts, and menus in restaurants**	**Advanced Learners** Ask: *Sam visits Joe every 4 days and Tim visits Joe every 6 days. If they both visited yesterday, when will Sam and Tim both visit Joe again on the same day?* **in 11 days**	**English Learners** See note on page 335. **Error Prevention** See note on page 335.

335

3. Practice

Assignment Guide

1 Objective 1
A B Core 1–10
C Extension 11–12

Test Prep 13–16
Mixed Review 17–23

Practice 6-10 *Make a Table*

Make a table to solve each problem.

1. A car was worth $12,500 in 1998. Its value depreciates, or decreases, 15% per year. Find its value in 2002.

Year	1998	1999	2000	2001	2002
Car's Value	$12,500	$10,625	$9,031.25	$7,676.56	$6,525.08

2. Marcus spent $105 on 6 items at a sale. Videotapes were on sale for $15 each and music CD's were on sale for $20 each. How many of each item did Marcus buy?

Number of Videotapes	1	2	3	4	5
Number of CD's	5	4	3	2	1
Total Cost	$115	$110	$105	$100	$95

Marcus bought 3 videotapes and 3 CD's.

3. Karina likes to mix either apple, orange, or grape juice with either lemon-lime soft drink or sparkling water to make a fizz. How many different fizzes can she make?

6 fizzes

4. How many ways can you have 25 cents in change?
13 ways

5. The deer population of a state park has increased 8% a year for the last 4 years. If there are 308 deer in the park this year, find how large the population was 4 years ago by completing the table.

Year		1	2	3	4
Deer Population	226	244	264	285	308

6. How many different sandwiches can you make from 3 types of bread, 2 types of cheese, and 2 types of meat? Assume that only one type of each item is used per sandwich.

12 different sandwiches

7. A bus leaves a station at 8:00 A.M. and averages 30 mi/h. Another bus leaves the same station following the same route two hours after the first and averages 50 mi/h. When will the second bus catch up with the first bus?

1:00 P.M.

Enrichment 6-10 *Loan Interest*

You borrow $12,000 to buy a car. You are charged 9% interest. Your payments are $300 a month. How much do you owe at the end of a year? Interest can be found with the formula $I = Prt$ where I is the interest you pay, P is the principal or money you owe, r is the interest rate, and t is the time. Interest rates are usually given as a percent that is charged per year.

1. Find the interest charged on a $12,000 loan at 9% for 1 year.
$1,080

2. Add the interest to the $12,000 and then subtract your payments for one year. Using this method, how much would you owe at the end of a year?
$9,480

Because this method is easy to understand, many loan companies use it to compute a loan balance. However, this method charges the borrower interest on the whole $12,000 for that year, even after some of the loan is paid off. The table shows a more appropriate way to compute a loan balance. The interest is computed each month on the "declining balance." In the interest formula, $t = \frac{1}{12}$ of a year.

3. Complete the table. The first two months are done for you.

Month	Beginning Balance	Interest	Ending Balance
1	$12,000	$90	$11,790
2	$11,790	$88.43	$11,578.43
3	$11,578.43	$86.84	$11,365.27
4	$11,365.27	$85.24	$11,150.51
5	$11,150.51	$83.63	$10,934.14
6	$10,934.14	$82.01	$10,716.15
7	$10,716.15	$80.37	$10,496.52
8	$10,496.52	$78.72	$10,275.24
9	$10,275.24	$77.06	$10,052.30
10	$10,052.30	$75.39	$9,827.69
11	$9,827.69	$73.71	$9,601.40
12	$9,601.40	$72.01	$9,373.41

4. How much more do you owe at the end of one year with the straight method than with the declining balance method?
$106.59

EXERCISES
For more exercises, see *Extra Practice.*

Practice and Problem Solving

A Practice by Example

Make a table to solve each problem.

Example 1
(page 334)

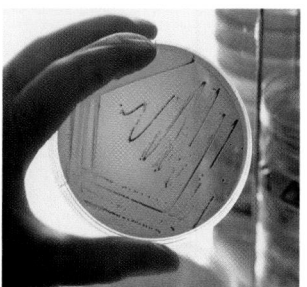

Real-World Connection

Microbe cultures grow on agar gel in petri dishes.

1. **Population** The population of a town increases at the rate of 1% each year. Today the town's population is 8,500. What will the population be in five years? **about 8,934 people**

2. **Biology** A microbe population increases 100% every 10 min. If you start with 1 microbe, how many will you have at the end of 1 h? **64 microbes**

3. Cher has forgotten the combination to her locker. She knows it consists of four numbers—3, 5, 7, and 9—but she can't recall the order. She decides to try every possible order until she gets the right one. How many possible orders are there? **24 orders**

4. **Banking** At the beginning of the year 2000, Bob put $100 in a savings account. The bank pays Bob 5% interest on his total savings at the end of each year including all interest added to the account. Assume the interest rate continues and Bob does not deposit any additional money in the account. How much will he have in his savings account, to the nearest cent, after 5 interest payments? **$127.63**

B Apply Your Skills

Strategies

- Account for All Possibilities
- Draw a Diagram
- Look for a Pattern
- Make a Model
- Make a Table
- Simplify the Problem
- Simulate the Problem
- Solve by Graphing
- Try, Test, Revise
- Use Multiple Strategies
- Work Backward
- Write an Equation
- Write a Proportion

C Challenge

Use any strategy to solve each problem.

5. Paco has four pairs of jeans and four T-shirts. How many outfits of a T-shirt and a pair of jeans can Paco make? **16 outfits**

6. **Geometry** The length of a rectangle is twice the width. The perimeter of the rectangle is 42 cm. Find the length and width.
length = 14 cm, width = 7 cm

7. **Number Sense** The difference of two numbers is 18. The sum of the two numbers is 34. What are the two numbers? **8 and 26**

8. **Capacity** You fill a container $\frac{3}{4}$ full of water. The amount of water now in the container is 6 quarts. How much can the container hold? **8 qt**

9. **Ticket Sales** A family went to the movies. Tickets cost $4 for each child and $6 for each adult. The total admission charge for the family was $26. List all the possible numbers of adults and children in the family. **1 adult, 5 children; 3 adults, 2 children**

10. **Number Sense** A number n is multiplied by $\frac{5}{8}$. The product is subtracted from $\frac{2}{3}$. The result is $\frac{7}{12}$. What is n? **$\frac{2}{15}$**

11. **Geometry** The height of a triangle is half the length of its base. The area of the triangle is 12.25 cm^2. Find the height. **3.5 cm**

12. **Water Resources** Water for irrigation is measured in *acre-feet*. One acre-foot is the volume of water that would cover one acre of land to a depth of one foot. How many acre-feet of water would it take to cover 600 acres to a depth of one inch?
50 acre-feet

336 Chapter 6 Ratios, Proportions, and Percents

Use the Guided Problem Solving worksheet with Exercise 9.

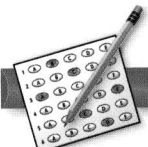

Test Prep

Multiple Choice

13. What is the percent of increase from 1.32 to 1.44, rounded to the nearest percent? **B**

A. 8% **B.** 9% **C.** 12% **D.** 15%

Take It to the NET
Online lesson quiz at
www.PHSchool.com
Web Code: ada-0610

14. A store pays $50.00 for a coat. Its markup is 25%. Later, it puts the coat on sale at 20% off. What is the sale price of the coat? **G**

F. $40.00 **G.** $50.00 **H.** $52.50 **I.** $62.50

15. The width of a rectangle is half the length. The perimeter of the rectangle is 54 in. What is the length of the rectangle? **C**

A. 6 in. **B.** 9 in. **C.** 18 in. **D.** 36 in.

Short Response

16. You must give a customer $.40 in change.
a. In how many ways can you do this without using pennies?
b. For part (a), make a table. See margin.

Mixed Review

Lesson 6-9 **Find each sale price.**

17. regular price: $39
percent of discount: 30%
$27.30

18. regular price: $159.95
percent of discount: 20%
$127.96

Lesson 6-4 **19. Probability** What is the probability that a digit selected at random from the number 364,892 is a multiple of 3? $\frac{1}{2}$

Lesson 4-4 **Write in simplest form.**

20. $\frac{16}{36}$ $\frac{4}{9}$ **21.** $\frac{10x}{65x}$ $\frac{2}{13}$ **22.** $\frac{8ab}{2bc}$ $\frac{4a}{c}$ **23.** $\frac{12x^2y}{9xy^2}$ $\frac{4x}{3y}$

Math at Work

Caterer

Caterers provide food for parties, weddings, and other events. They plan the menu, buy the ingredients, cook the food, and provide the waitstaff. Some will even arrange for music and seating. For each event, a caterer determines the cost per guest.

The catering business requires a thorough knowledge of ratios, proportions, and percents.

Take It to the NET For more information about caterers, go to **www.PHSchool.com**.
Web Code: adb-2031

6-10 Make a Table **337**

16. [2] 7 ways;

Quarters	Dimes	Nickels
1	1	1
1	0	3
0	4	0
0	3	2
0	2	4
0	1	6
0	0	8

[1] correct answer with incomplete table or no table

337

Using Estimation

This feature helps students understand the use of estimation to help determine the correct answer choice. This strategy can save time. Often, choices can be eliminated without doing lengthy calculations.

Resources

Test-Taking Strategies With Transparencies
• Transparency 6
• Practice sheet, p. 6

Teaching Notes

Teaching Tip
Encourage students to estimate even if they intend to calculate the answer. If they get in the habit of doing this, they may catch their own errors when they get answers that are not close to their estimated answers.

Test-Taking Strategies With Transparencies

Chapter 6: Using Estimation

Exercises

Estimate each answer.

1. Ted collects rare gold coins. He bought one coin in his collection for $32.85. Five years later, the card was worth $54.79. What was the percent of increase in the value of the coin?
   A. 21.94%   B. 40%   C. 50%   D. 66⅔ %

2. Georgianne wants to leave a 20% tip for her $45 haircut. How much should she tip her hairdresser?
   F. $54   G. $9   H. $7   I. $5

3. In a recent school election, 76% of the students voted for the winning candidate for student council treasurer. If 392 students voted, how many voted for the winning candidate?
   A. 325   B. 300   C. 275   D. 250

4. Which is the best estimate for 28% of 621?
   F. 280   G. 200   H. 195   I. 180

5. A basketball player made 88% of 48 free-throw attempts in one season. About how many free-throws did the player successfully make during the season?
   A. 45   B. 35   C. 32   D. 9

6. Which is the best estimate for the selling price of a video game if the percent of markup is 24% and the store's cost is $38.99?
   F. $40   G. $50   H. $60   I. $80

7. Which percent is closest to 7/90?
   A. 78%   B. 40%   C. 25%   D. 8%

8. Jiroko deposits $3,046 into a savings account that earns 6.85% simple interest. Approximately how much money will be in the account at the end of 3 years?
   F. $6,320   G. $3,640   H. $3,230   I. $3,000

9. On the first day of a new release, a video store rented out 72% of its 89 copies of the movie. Approximately how many copies did the video store rent?
   A. 45   B. 57   C. 63   D. 72

10. Which is the best estimate for the final cost of a CD that costs $12.99 if the tax rate is 5.25%?
    F. $13.65   G. $14.00   H. $15.00   I. $15.45

6   Pre-Algebra   Test-Taking Strategies

Estimation may help you find an answer, check an answer, or eliminate answer choices. If, however, an incorrect choice is very close to the correct choice, you will still have to find the exact answer.

● EXAMPLE

A coat regularly priced at $89.95 is on sale at 40% off. What is the sale price of the coat?

A. $35.98   **B.** $49.95   **C.** $53.97   **D.** $54.03

$89.95 \approx \$90$

40% is less than half. The discount will be less than $45, which is half of $90. So, the sale price will be more than $45.

This eliminates choice A.

$40\% \text{ of } 90 = 0.4 \cdot 90$

$= 36$

$90 - 36 = 54$, so the sale price is about $54. This eliminates choice B.

Choices C and D are both very close to $54, so you have to compute to find the answer is choice C.

EXERCISES

In Exercises 1–3, which answer choices can you eliminate by using estimation? Explain. See right.

1. A store pays $8.50 for a case of scented candles. The store's percent of markup is 110%. What price will the store charge for the case of candles?
   A. $9.35   **B.** $16.15   **C.** $17.85   **D.** $18.15

2. A store is having a sale. Laverne looks at a $79.80 necklace that is on sale for $59.85. What is the percent of discount?
   F. 20%   **G.** 25%   **H.** $33\frac{1}{3}$%   **I.** 40%

3. An entomologist noted that in the past five years in the local forest preserve, the population of bees decreased by 35%. In her study, she recorded that the number of active hives five years ago was 35. If the number of active hives decreased at the same rate as the bee population, how many hives are there today?
   A. 17 hives   **B.** 19 hives   **C.** 21 hives   **D.** 23 hives

4. For Exercise 3, explain how you can use estimation in two different ways to help you with the answer choices. See right.

1–3. Answers may vary. Check students' work. Correct choices are as follows: 1. C; 2. G; 3. D.

4. Answers may vary. Sample: Subtract $\frac{1}{3}$ of 36 from 36. Compute $\frac{2}{3}$ of 36.

Chapter Review

Vocabulary

certain event (p. 306)
commission (p. 321)
complement (p. 306)
cross products (p. 294)
discount (p. 329)
event (p. 305)
impossible event (p. 306)

indirect measurement (p. 300)
markup (p. 329)
odds (p. 307)
outcomes (p. 305)
percent (p. 310)
percent of change (p. 325)
probability (p. 305)

proportion (p. 294)
rate (p. 289)
ratio (p. 288)
scale drawing (p. 300)
similar figures (p. 299)
unit rate (p. 289)

Reading Math
Understanding
Vocabulary

Match the vocabulary terms with their descriptions.

1. a comparison of two quantities by division c

2. a ratio that compares a number to 100 b

3. the amount charged for an item above the cost a

4. the amount of a price decrease d

5. a ratio that compares quantities in different units g

6. a rate that has a denominator of 1 e

7. two equal ratios f

a. markup
b. percent
c. ratio
d. discount
e. unit rate
f. proportion
g. rate

Take It to the NET
Online vocabulary quiz
at **www.PHSchool.com**
Web Code: adj-0651

Skills and Concepts

6-1 Objectives

▼ To write and
simplify ratios
(p. 288)

▼ To find rates and
unit rates
(p. 289)

A **ratio** is a comparison of two quantities by division. A **rate** is a ratio that compares quantities in different units. A **unit rate** is a rate that has a denominator of 1.

Write each ratio as a fraction in simplest form.

8. $9 : 24$ $\frac{3}{8}$ **9.** $20 : 35$ $\frac{4}{7}$ **10.** $15 : 20$ $\frac{3}{4}$ **11.** $100 : 130$ $\frac{10}{13}$

Write each ratio as a unit rate.

12. 150 mi in 3 h
50 mi/h

13. \$9.45 for 5 lb
\$1.89/lb

14. 270 words in 3 min
90 words/min

6-2 Objectives

▼ To solve proportions
(p. 294)

▼ To use proportions to
solve problems (p. 295)

A **proportion** is an equality of ratios. To solve a proportion, write the cross products, and then solve.

Solve. Round to the nearest tenth where necessary.

15. $\frac{5}{6} = \frac{n}{42}$ 35   **16.** $\frac{53}{2} = \frac{18}{x}$ 0.7   **17.** $\frac{15}{a} = \frac{30}{98}$ 49   **18.** $\frac{m}{150} = \frac{21}{25}$ 126

Resources

Student Edition
Extra Practice, Ch. 6, p. 749
English/Spanish Glossary, p. 782
Table of Symbols, p. 777

 Reaching All Students
Reading and Math Literacy 6D
Spanish Reading and Math
Literacy 6D

ASSESSMENT *SYSTEM*

Test Preparation
• Chapter 6 practice in test
formats

 **www.PHSchool.com**

Student Site
• Self-grading vocabulary test
PH SuccessNet Teacher Center
• Resources

Plus **iTEXT**

Spanish Reading and Math Literacy

Reading and Math Literacy

6D: Vocabulary   For use with Chapter Review

Study Skill: You may have noticed that math tests often contain word problems for you to solve. In order to read and understand the problems, so that you can solve them, you must know the meanings of the words used to state the problems. The next time you study for a math test, be sure to begin by studying the vocabulary involved.

Complete the word search puzzle by finding words that match the descriptions below. For help, use the Chapter Review in your textbook. Remember that a word may go right to left, left to right, or it may go up as well as down.

Circle the letters that form each word.

1. an equality of two ratios
2. the possible result of an action
3. the amount of price decrease
4. the opposite of an event
5. ratio comparing a number to 100
6. any outcome or group of outcomes
7. ratio comparing quantities in different units
8. amount you are paid based on amount you sell
9. ratio comparing favorable and unfavorable outcomes
10. comparison of two quantities by division
11. amount of increase over cost

```
E  D I S C O U N T  M  O  P E
M M O E N R T R A M  D  T  R I
S  S R O A N E P M T  D  N  I O
E  C A D R A T E O O S E  U
C  I  T  P E R C E N T  M  U
E  C I  P N O I A E U N  E  M
P  P O  S O E A T T N T   E
E  P R O P O R T I O N  P  M E
C  M S T R N M C P A E  E  C O
O  T O U T C O M E R  V  O  E
C O M M I S S I O N  E  C  E
C  N O V M A R K U P N  C  O
R  N T T U E U U C P  P  K  T
```

340

6-3 Objectives

▼ To solve problems that involve similar figures (p. 299)

▼ To solve problems that involve scale drawings (p. 300)

Similar figures have the same shape, but not necessarily the same size. In similar figures, the corresponding angles have equal measures and the corresponding sides are proportional.

A **scale drawing** is an enlarged or reduced drawing of an object.

The figures in each pair are similar. Find x.

19.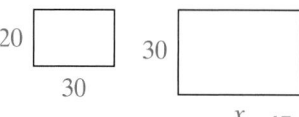

20.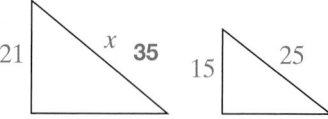

21. A map has a scale of 1 cm : 75 km. What is the distance on the map for an actual distance of 37.5 km? **0.5 cm**

6-4 Objectives

▼ To find probability (p. 305)

▼ To find odds (p. 307)

Outcomes are the possible results of an action. An **event** is any outcome or group of outcomes. When outcomes are equally likely, you can use formulas to find the **probability** of an event and the **odds** in favor of an event.

$$\text{probability} = \frac{\text{number of favorable outcomes}}{\text{number of possible outcomes}}$$

$$\text{odds} = \frac{\text{number of favorable outcomes}}{\text{number of unfavorable outcomes}}$$

Suppose you select a letter at random from the letters in the word EXPONENT. Find the probability of each event. Then find the odds in favor of the event.

22. selecting P
$\frac{1}{8}$; 1 to 7

23. selecting N
$\frac{2}{8}$, or $\frac{1}{4}$; 1 to 3

24. selecting a vowel
$\frac{3}{8}$; 3 to 5

6-5 Objectives

▼ To write percents as fractions and decimals (p. 310)

▼ To write decimals and fractions as percents (p. 311)

A **percent** is a ratio that compares a number to 100.

Write each percent as a fraction in simplest form and as a decimal.

25. 24% $\frac{6}{25}$; 0.24 **26.** 72% $\frac{18}{25}$; 0.72 **27.** 8% $\frac{2}{25}$; 0.08 **28.** 0.5% $\frac{1}{200}$; 0.005

Write each number as a percent. Round to the nearest tenth of a percent.

29. 0.3 30% **30.** 0.33 33% **31.** $\frac{1}{3}$ 33.3% **32.** 0.35 35%

33. $\frac{16}{18}$ 88.9% **34.** 0.021 2.1% **35.** $\frac{120}{50}$ 240% **36.** 0.0064 0.6%

6-6 and 6-7 Objectives

▼ To find a part of a whole and a percent (p. 315)

▼ To find a whole amount (p. 316)

▼ To write and solve percent equations (p. 320)

▼ To use equations in solving percent problems (p. 321)

Solve percent problems by using a proportion or an equation.

Write and solve a proportion.

37. Find 15% of 48. $\frac{15}{100} = \frac{n}{48}$; 7.2

38. 20% of x is 30. What is x?
See below.

39. What percent of 300 is 90?
$\frac{n}{100} = \frac{90}{300}$; 30%

40. 125% of y is 100. What is y?
$\frac{125}{100} = \frac{100}{y}$; 80

Write and solve an equation.

41. 35% of a is 70. What is a?
$0.35 \cdot a = 70$; 200

42. Find 68% of 300.
$n = 0.68 \cdot 300$; 204

43. What percent of 180 is 9?
$n \cdot 180 = 9$; 5%

44. What percent of 56 is 3.5?
$n \cdot 56 = 3.5$; 6.25%

38. $\frac{20}{100} = \frac{30}{x}$; 150

6-8 and 6-9 Objectives

▼ To find percent of increase (p. 325)

▼ To find percent of decrease (p. 326)

▼ To find find markups (p. 329)

▼ To find discounts (p. 329)

A **percent of change** is the percent by which a quantity increases or decreases from its original amount.

$$\text{percent of change} = \frac{\text{amount of change}}{\text{original amount}}$$

Markup is a real-world application of percent of increase. **Discount** is a real-world application of percent of decrease.

Find each percent of change. Tell whether the change is an increase or a decrease.

45. 120 to 90
25% decrease

46. 148 to 37
75% decrease

47. 285 to 342
20% increase

48. 1,000 to 250
75% decrease

49. A cap that cost a retailer $5 was marked up by 75%. Find the selling price. $8.75

50. Peaches that are usually priced at $2/lb are on sale for 15% off. Find the sale price. $1.70/lb

6-10 Objectives

▼ To solve problems by making a table (p. 334)

Make a table to organize information or to solve problems that have several steps.

51. Alicia bikes 25% of a 100-mi trip on the first day. She bikes $\frac{1}{3}$ of the remaining distance on the second day. On the third day, she bikes 40% of the remaining distance. Make a table to find the number of miles left in Alicia's trip. 30 mi

52. Describe how you could use a table together with another problem-solving strategy that you have studied. Justify your answer with an example. Check students' work.

341 Chapter 6 Chapter Review

Chapter 6

Chapter Test

Find each unit rate.

1. A car travels 84 mi on 3 gal of gas. **28 mi/gal**

2. A car travels 220 mi in 4 h. **55 mi/h**

Write = or ≠ to complete each statement.

3. $\frac{7}{8}$ ■ $\frac{40}{42}$ **≠**   4. $\frac{3}{5}$ ■ $\frac{45}{75}$ **=**

5. $\frac{12}{18}$ ■ $\frac{18}{12}$ **≠**   6. $\frac{5}{9}$ ■ $\frac{25}{81}$ **≠**

Solve each proportion.

7. $\frac{x}{8} = \frac{90}{120}$ **6**   8. $\frac{0.8}{90} = \frac{5.6}{y}$ **630**

Write a proportion to describe each situation. Then solve.

9. Three cans of dog food sell for 99¢. Find the cost of 15 cans. $\frac{3}{0.99} = \frac{15}{x}$; **$4.95**

10. A photo that measures 5 in. by 7 in. is enlarged to 7.5 in. by b in. $\frac{5}{7.5} = \frac{7}{b}$; **10.5 in.**

11. A student reads 45 pages in 2 h and x pages in 3 h. $\frac{45}{2} = \frac{x}{3}$; **67.5 pages**

For Exercises 12–14, use the drawing below. The length of the kitchen in the drawing is $1\frac{1}{4}$ in. The actual length is 20 ft.

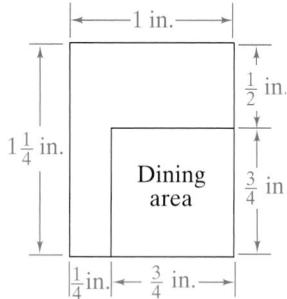

12. What is the scale of the drawing?
   1 in. : 16 ft
13. What is the actual width of the kitchen?
   16 ft
14. What are the actual length and width of the dining area? **12 ft, 12 ft**

Find each probability for one roll of a number cube.

15. $P(1)$ $\frac{1}{6}$ 16. $P(1 \text{ or } 2)$ $\frac{2}{6}$, or $\frac{1}{3}$

17. $P(\text{not 2 or 6})$ $\frac{4}{6}$, or $\frac{2}{3}$ 18. $P(\text{greater than 1})$ $\frac{5}{6}$

Write each decimal as a percent.

19. 0.37 **37%** 20. 0.005 **0.5%** 21. 1.02 **102%**

Write each fraction as a percent.

22. $\frac{5}{8}$ **62.5%**   23. $\frac{7}{16}$ **43.75%** 24. $\frac{5}{4}$ **125%**

Solve.

25. What percent of 400 is 20? **5%**

26. Find 45% of 12. **5.4**

27. 20% of c is 24. What is c? **120**

28. What percent of 3 is 15? **500%**

29. Find 125% of 50. **62.5**

30. 60% of y is 75. What is y? **125**

Find each percent of change. Tell whether the change is an increase or a decrease. Round to the nearest tenth of a percent.

31. from 60 to 36 **40% decrease**   32. from 18 to 24 **33.3% increase**
33. from 15 to 25 **66.7% increase**   34. from 85 to 50 **41.2% decrease**
35. from 8.8 to 30 **240.9% increase**   36. from 1.2 to 0.2 **83.3% decrease**

37. A salesperson made a $128 commission selling merchandise. His commission rate was 5%. Find the dollar amount of his sales. **$2,560**

38. A bicycle that usually sells for $230 is on sale for 15% off. Find the sale price. **$195.50**

39. **Writing in Math** Explain the difference between a markup and a discount. **See below.**

40. In how many ways can you make $.35 in change without using pennies? **6 ways**

39. Answers may vary. Sample: A markup is an amount added to get a selling price. A discount is an amount subtracted from the regular selling price.

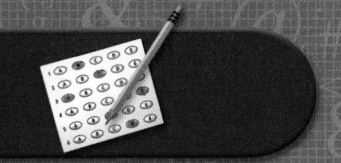
Multiple Choice

1. What is 56,500,000,000 written in scientific notation? **C**
 A. $5.65 \cdot 10^8$ B. $56.5 \cdot 10^{10}$
 C. $5.65 \cdot 10^{10}$ D. $565 \cdot 10^9$

2. What is x when $\frac{2}{3}x = 2\frac{2}{9}$? **H**
 F. $\frac{3}{10}$ G. $2\frac{5}{8}$ H. $3\frac{1}{3}$ I. $7\frac{2}{3}$

3. What is the correct symbol? **A**
$$\left|2\frac{4}{5}\right| \ \blacksquare \ \left|-\frac{9}{4}\right|$$
 A. >   B. <   C. =   D. ≤

4. What is the unit rate for a ball moving 252 ft in 4 s? **G**
 F. 252 : 4   G. 63 ft/s
 H. 252 ft/s   I. 1,008 ft/s

5. What percent of 63 is 41? **B**
 A. about 82%   B. about 65%
 C. about 41%   D. about 0.65%

6. Which equation has −4 as a solution? **H**
 F. $9z = 36$ G. $-\frac{36}{z} = -9$
 H. $z + 9 = 5$ I. $z - 9 = -5$

7. Which has the lowest unit price? **B**
 A. 10 oz for $.30
 B. $.56 for 20 oz
 C. 30 oz for $.87
 D. $1.16 for 40 oz

Gridded Response

8. Evaluate $6x - 9$ for $x = 11$. **57**

9. Simplify $(-1)^8 \cdot (-2)^0$. **1**

10. Solve $y + 0.5 = 3$. **2.5**

11. Find 40% of 40. **16**

Write each fraction as a decimal.

12. $\frac{42}{50}$ 0.84   **13.** $\frac{16}{20}$ 0.8   **14.** $\frac{33}{55}$ 0.6

15. $\frac{6}{80}$ 0.075   **16.** $\frac{524}{200}$ 2.62   **17.** $\frac{45}{1,000}$ 0.045

31. [2] $\frac{80}{x} = \frac{180}{270}$; 120
 [1] correct proportion OR answer only

Find each probability for one roll of a number cube.

18. P(5 or 6) 2/6, or 1/3 **19.** P(less than 4) 3/6, or 1/2

The scale on a map is 1 in. = 5 mi. Find the actual distance in miles for each map distance.

20. 5.5 in. 27.5   **21.** 12 in. 60   **22.** 9.75 in. 48.75

Solve each proportion.

23. $\frac{5}{8} = \frac{15}{n}$ 24   **24.** $\frac{28}{x} = \frac{14}{2.5}$ 5

25. $\frac{n}{9} = \frac{40}{12}$ 30   **26.** $\frac{6}{21} = \frac{s}{70}$ 20

Write each ratio as a fraction in simplest form.

27. 20 : 45 4/9   **28.** 8 : 96 1/12

29. 30 : 36 5/6   **30.** 120 : 80 3/2

Short Response

31. For the similar figures, **(a)** write a proportion to solve for x. **(b)** Find x. See below left.

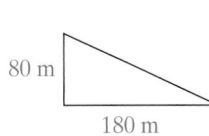

80 m x

180 m   270 m

In Exercises 32 and 33, (a) find the sale price. Round to the nearest cent where necessary. (b) Explain your answer.

32. regular price: $58
 percent of discount: 45% See back of book.

33. regular price: $15.98
 percent of discount: 80% See back of book.

Extended Response

34. Which is the better buy: **(a)** Brand A with a regular price of $15.98 and a 30% discount, or Brand B with a regular price of $18.50 and a 40% discount? **(b)** How much do you save with the better buy? **(c)** Show your work. See back of book.

Item	1	2	3	4	5	6	7	8	9	10	11	12	13	14	15	16
Lesson	4-7	5-4	1-3	6-1	6-7	2-5	6-1	1-3	2-5	3-5	6-7	6-5	6-5	6-5	6-5	6-5

Item	17	18	19	20	21	22	23	24	25	26	27	28	29	30	31	32	33	34
Lesson	6-5	6-4	6-4	6-3	6-3	6-3	6-2	6-2	6-2	6-2	6-1	6-1	6-1	6-1	6-3	6-9	6-9	6-9

Calculating Change

Applying Percents When you buy a company's stock, you buy a small piece of the company. The amount you have to pay for a stock varies from day to day or even minute to minute. You can make money by selling the stock for more than you paid for it. You can lose money by selling it for less than you paid for it.

Wall Street
Since 1870, when continuous stock trading began at the New York Stock Exchange, the ringing of a bell signals the beginning (9:30 A.M. EST) and ending (4:00 P.M. EST) of trading each day.

Activity

1. Copy the table. Add another column for the percent of change in price from Monday to Friday. Indicate whether the percent of change is an increase or a decrease. **1–4. See margin.**

2. Suppose you and a friend buy stock on Monday and sell it on Friday. You buy 50 shares of Pat's Pastas and 25 shares of Leaping Lizards. Your friend buys 35 shares of Map Makers Plus and 25 shares of Wondermarts. Who made the better investment, you or your friend? Justify your answer.

3. Suppose you had $500 to invest on Monday.
   a. Which stock(s) would you buy on Monday, and how many shares of the stock(s) would you buy? Explain.
   b. You sell all your shares on Friday. How much money did you make?

4. a. **Research** Find the price of a stock in the newspaper or online. Find the price at least one day later.
   b. **Writing in Math** Would you invest in the company? Explain.

Seven Stocks

Company	Price per Share on Monday	Price per Share on Friday
All-Star Adventures	$6.25	$5.75
Fun Foods, Inc.	$28.00	$26.60
Leaping Lizards	$19.50	$23.40
Map Makers Plus	$13.00	$14.95
Nature's Nest	$3.80	$4.20
Pat's Pastas	$5.65	$4.45
Wondermarts	$34.00	$32.75

344

T	APOG	POS	AAPL	FDX	AWK	SRR	TWP
.0s4.00	6s14.5	3s19.14	8s50.35	5s22.40	5s30.6	2s35.58	24s15.06

POS is the name of the stock.

$19.14 is the last traded price of the stock.

3s means 300 shares sold.

Stock Trader

A stock trader places orders or buys and sells securities or commodities. A successful trader is very interested in numbers and in investing and understands economic trends.

Stock Certificates

Most securities transactions today are done without stock certificates, although some people like to have the actual certificate in their possession.

Stock Market Floor

Runners at the Chicago Mercantile Exchange wear yellow jackets for visibility. They take orders to buy and sell stocks into and out of the trading areas.

Take It to the NET For more information about the stock market, go to **www.PHSchool.com**.
Web Code: ade-0653

345

Put It All Together

Students must be able to extract information from a reading passage and a table and use this data to calculate percentage and value change in order to analyze and compare stock investments.

Teaching Tip

Before students begin the activity, discuss the illustrations and their captions. Have students work individually or in pairs to complete the activity. Students should read through the activity before beginning to work.

Inclusion

Exercise 3 Work with students to help them choose which stocks and how many shares they will buy with their money. Direct their attention to comparing the price per share of each stock on Monday and Friday. Point out that investors in real-world situations do not know what the end price will be when they buy stock.

Connection to Economics

Have students choose one company that interests them and follow its stock price in the newspaper or online for one week. Ask them to report back to the class about whether the stock went up or down that week. Answers may vary. Sample: If the stock's closing price is higher on Friday than it was on Monday, the stock went up.

Solving Equations and Inequalities

Chapter at a Glance

7-1

Solving Two-Step Equations

pp. 348–351

Objectives

▼ Using Properties to Solve Two-Step Equations

▼ Solving Problems With Two-Step Equations

NCTM Standards
1, 2, 6, 8, 9, 10

Local Standards

7-2

Solving Multi-Step Equations

pp. 352–356

Objectives

▼ Combining Like Terms

▼ Using the Distributive Property

New Vocabulary
consecutive integers

Materials
algebra tiles

NCTM Standards
1, 2, 6, 8, 9, 10

Local Standards

7-3

Multi-Step Equations With Fractions and Decimals *pp. 357–361*

Objectives

▼ Solving Multi-Step Equations With Fractions

▼ Solving Multi-Step Equations With Decimals

NCTM Standards
1, 2, 6, 8, 9, 10

Local Standards

7-4 · Problem Solving

Write an Equation

pp. 362–365

Objective

▼ Writing Equations to Solve Problems

NCTM Standards
1, 2, 6, 8, 9, 10

Local Standards

✓ **Checkpoint Quiz 1**

7-5

Solving Equations With Variables on Both Sides

pp. 367–371

Objectives

▼ Solving Equations With Variables on Both Sides

▼ Using Equations With Variables on Both Sides

NCTM Standards
1, 2, 6, 8, 9, 10

Local Standards

7-6

Solving Two-Step Inequalities

pp. 373–376

Objectives

▼ Solving Two-Step Inequalities

▼ Using Two-Step Inequalities

NCTM Standards
1, 2, 6, 8, 9, 10

Local Standards

7-7

Transforming Formulas

pp. 378–381

Objectives

▼ Solving Formulas for a Given Variable

▼ Using Formulas to Solve Problems

NCTM Standards
1, 2, 3, 4, 6, 8, 9, 10

Local Standards

✓ **Checkpoint Quiz 2**

7-8

Simple and Compound Interest

pp. 382–386

Objectives

▼ Solving Simple-Interest Problems

▼ Solving Compound-Interest Problems

New Vocabulary
principal, interest, interest rate, simple interest, compound interest, balance

NCTM Standards
1, 2, 6, 8, 9, 10

Local Standards

Correlation to Standardized Tests

Lesson	NAEP	Terra Nova CAT/6	CTBS	ITBS	SAT10	Local Test
7-1	A4a, A4c				■	
7-2	A4a, A4c			■	■	
7-3	A4c			■		
7-4	A4c	■		■	■	
7-5	A4a, A4c					
7-6	A4a, A4c					
7-7	A4e					
7-8	A4c	■				

NAEP National Assessment of Educational Progress
  N = Number Sense, Properties, and Operations
  M = Measurement
  G = Geometry and Spatial Sense
  D = Data Analysis, Statistics and Probability
  A = Algebra and Functions

CAT/6 California Achievement Test, 6th Ed.
CTBS Comprehensive Test of Basic Skills
ITBS Iowa Test of Basic Skills, Form M
SAT10 Stanford Achievement Test, 10th Ed.

NCTM STANDARDS 2000

1	Number and Operations	6	Problem Solving
2	Algebra	7	Reasoning and Proof
3	Geometry	8	Communication
4	Measurement	9	Connections
5	Data Analysis and Probability	10	Representation

Pacing Options

This chart suggests pacing for only the core lessons and their parts. It is provided as a possible guide. It will help you determine how much time you have in your schedule to cover other components, such as the features, chapter projects, Chapter Review, and Chapter Test.

Day	Traditional 45-minute class periods	Two-Year 45-minute class periods	Block 90-minute class periods
1	7-1	7-1	7-1 / 7-2
2	7-2	7-1	7-3
3	7-2	7-1	7-4 / 7-5
4	7-3	7-2	7-5 / 7-6
5	7-3	7-2	7-7 / 7-8
6	7-4	7-2	
7	7-5	7-2	
8	7-6	7-3	
9	7-7	7-3	
10	7-8	7-3	
11	7-8	7-3	
12		7-4	
13		7-4	
14		7-5	
15		7-5	
16		7-5	
17		7-6	
18		7-6	
19		7-6	
20		7-7	
21		7-7	
22		7-7	
23		7-8	
24		7-8	

Math Background

Skills Trace

BEFORE Chapter 7

Chapter 2 develops techniques for solving one-step equations and inequalities with whole numbers, which are then used in Chapter 3 (decimals), Chapter 5 (fractions), and Chapter 6 (proportions).

DURING Chapter 7

Chapter 7 extends techniques for solving one-step equations to two-step equations and inequalities.

AFTER Chapter 7

A single, early chapter in Algebra 1 will review and extend one-step and two-step equations.

7-1 Solving Two-Step Equations

You can use algebra tiles to provide a model for the process of solving two-step equations. A set of algebra tiles consists of three kinds of tiles. The smallest tile represents a unit; it measures 1 by 1. The green "x-tile" measures 1 unit by x. Notice that the length (x) of this tile is not exactly a certain number of units. This is because the length of the tile represents an unknown value.

You will meet the third tile in Chapter 13. It measures x by x and represents x^2.

For all the tiles, the red tile represents a negative quantity. You can use algebra tiles to make a concrete model of an equation such as $3x - 5 = 1$.

There is more than one way to solve equations like $3x - 5 = 1$. However, a typical first step is to get the variable alone on one side of the equal sign by using the Addition or Subtraction Property of Equality; add or subtract the same quantity on each side.

$$3x - 5 = 1$$
$$3x - 5 + 5 = 1 + 5$$
$$3x = 6$$

As a second step, you use division to undo the multiplication.
$$\frac{3x}{3} = \frac{6}{3}, \text{ so } x = 2.$$
To model with algebra tiles, divide both sides into 3 groups of tiles, modeling $x = 2$.

7-2 7-3 Solving Multi-Step Equations

When solving a multi-step equation, combine like terms to simplify the expression on each side of the equation as a first step. You may also need to use the Distributive Property to simplify the equation.

When you perform the same operation (other than multiplying by zero) on each side of an equation, the result is an *equivalent equation.* This means that the solution of the resulting equation is the same as the solution of the original equation.

When an equation has a fraction as the coefficient of the variable, for example, $\frac{2}{3}(x + 5) = 6$, you may choose to first simplify by multiplying each side of the equation by the reciprocal of the coefficient.

$$\frac{2}{3}(x + 5) = 6$$
$$\frac{3}{2} \cdot \frac{2}{3}(x + 5) = 6 \cdot \frac{3}{2}$$
$$x + 5 = 9$$
$$x = 4$$

When an equation has decimal coefficients, you can either calculate with the decimals or multiply on each side by the power of ten that will enable you to rewrite all the decimals as integers, as shown here.

$$0.4x = 0.6$$
$$10(0.4x) = 10(0.6)$$
$$4x = 6$$
$$x = 1.5$$

7-4 Write an Equation

Emphasize finding a key relationship and expressing it as a word equation. You may point out words that *might* suggest certain operations, but always talk about the quantities and how they are related to each other. This approach emphasizes the structure of word problems, not the rote translation of words to symbols.

To collect terms when an equation has the variable on both sides, you apply the same procedures as before. For example, using the Distributive Property and the Commutative Property of Addition,

$$14 - 2(x - 1) = 3x + 4 - 2x$$

becomes

$$14 - 2x + 2 = 3x - 2x + 4.$$

Collecting terms and constants on each side gives
$$-2x + 16 = x + 4.$$

You can collect the terms with variables on either the right or left side of the equation. In $-2x + 16 = x + 4$, the variable on the right side (x) has a positive coefficient (1), and the variable on the left side has a negative coefficient (-2), so you might choose to collect the x terms on the right side and the constants on the left side, as shown in the following:
$$-2x + 16 = x + 4$$
$$-2x + 16 + 2x - 4 = x + 4 + 2x - 4$$
$$12 = 3x$$

Then divide each side by 3 to get $4 = x$, or $x = 4$.

To solve an inequality, you can take the same steps as for solving an equation, with one important difference. When you multiply or divide by a negative number, you must *reverse* the direction of the inequality symbol.

$$14 - 2(x - 1) > 3x + 4 - 2x$$
$$14 - 2x + 2 > 3x - 2x + 4$$
$$-2x + 16 > x + 4$$
$$-2x + 16 - x - 16 > x + 4 - x - 16$$
$$-3x > -12$$
$$\frac{-3x}{-3} < \frac{-12}{-3}$$
$$x < 4$$

You may wish to change the form of a formula so the variable whose value you are seeking is alone on the left side of the equation. For example, if you are using $d = rt$ to find d (distance), you would use the formula in the given form. However, if you are finding r (rate) or t (time), another version of the formula may be more useful. The proof that follows shows this transformation.

$d = rt$	given
$\frac{d}{t} = \frac{rt}{t}$	Division Property of Equality
$\frac{d}{t} = r \cdot \frac{t}{t}$	multiplication of fractions
$\frac{d}{t} = r \cdot 1$	$\frac{t}{t} = 1$
$\frac{d}{t} = r$, or $r = \frac{d}{t}$	1 is the identity for multiplication.

A similar transformation leads to $t = \frac{d}{r}$.

The complete formula for compound interest follows.

$$B = p(1 + \frac{r}{n})^{nt}$$

where B is the final balance accumulated,
p is the principal amount invested,
r is the rate per year written as a decimal,
t is the time in years, and
n the number of interest periods per year, which tells how many times per year the interest is compounded.

Note that if the interest is compounded yearly, then $n = 1$, and the formula simplifies to $B = p(1 + r)^t$.

Additional Professional Development Opportunities

Chapter 7 Math Background notes:
pp. 349, 353, 358, 363, 368, 374, 379, 383

Professional Development, Content Facilitator Guide: Pre-Algebra, Chapter 7

Additional resources available from SkyLight Professional Development: On-site courses, workshops, summer institutes. Online courses and chat rooms. Videocassettes and books. Visit www.skylightedu.com.

Ongoing Assessment and Intervention

The *Prentice Hall Pre-Algebra* program provides many options for assessment in the Student Edition, Teacher's Edition, and teaching resources. From these options you may choose instructional materials and that are appropriate for your students and support your district's curriculum requirements.

Daily Assessment

 Instant Check System™ in Chapter 7

Allows students to check their own learning before, during, and after each lesson.

Diagnosing Readiness before the chapter (p. 346)

Check Skills You'll Need exercises in each lesson (pp. 348, 352, 357, 362, 367, 373, 378, 382)

Check Understanding questions with each Example (pp. 349, 353, 354, 357, 358, 363, 367, 368, 373, 374, 378, 379, 383, 384)

Checkpoint Quiz (pp. 365, 381)

Standardized Test Preparation

 Test Prep in Chapter 7

Teaches students strategies and gives them practice with all the test item formats they will encounter on high-stakes tests.

Test Prep exercises in each lesson (pp. 351, 356, 361, 365, 370, 376, 381, 386)

Test-Taking Strategies (p. 388: Eliminating Answers)

Test Prep (p. 393: Reading Comprehension)

Formal Assessment

In Chapter 7 and Additional Resources

Assesses student progress throughout the *Pre-Algebra* text and with blackline masters and CD-ROM.

Student Edition

- Chapter 7 Review, with Vocabulary Skills and Concepts Review, pp. 389–391
- Chapter 7 Test, p. 392

Assessment Resources   *Spanish versions available.*

- Checkpoint Quizzes 1 & 2
- Chapter Test, Forms A & B
- Chapter Alternative Assessment

 Computer Test Generator CD-ROM

- Instant Chapter Tests™ — pre-made tests with items that vary every time you print.
- Online Testing allows you to give tests online and receive progress reports.
- Diagnose readiness with questions on prerequisite skills.
- Prepare students by making tests based on standardized test objectives.

Algebra Readiness Tests

- Includes Basic Skills Tests and Concept-Readiness Tests.
- Assess understanding of skills and concepts needed for success in algebra.

Provides a three-step approach to preparing students for high-stakes, national, and state exams.

① Diagnose & Prescribe   **② Review & Reteach**

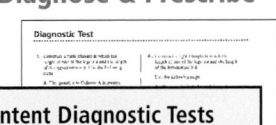

Content Diagnostic Tests

- Diagnose strengths and weaknesses with ongoing benchmark tests.
- Prescribe individualized reteaching opportunities.

Skills and Concepts Review

- Provides reteaching worksheets with instruction and practice for each skill.
- Includes course prerequisite skills.

③ Practice & Assess

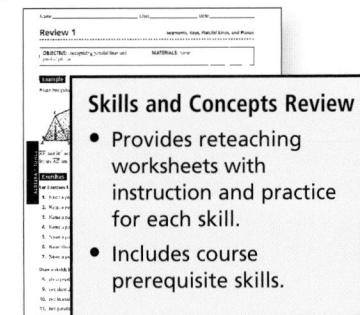

Standardized Test Preparation

- Features practice for national standardized exams.
- Includes practice tests for NAEP, SAT10, ITBS, and Terra Nova.

Test-Taking Strategies With Transparencies

- Support the Test-Taking Strategies pages in the Student Edition.
- Provide a transparency and a worksheet for each strategy.

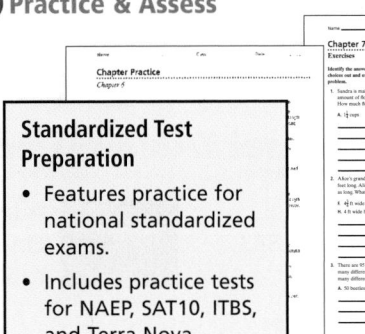

Reaching All Students

The textbook, the iText, and other technology components provide numerous opportunities to reach students of various ability levels and learning styles. Each Teacher's Edition lesson suggests how you can help all your students be successful and understand the mathematics in Chapter 7.

Below Level

Student Edition
- Diagnosing Readiness*: p. 346
- Check Skills You'll Need*: pp. 348, 352, 357, 362, 367, 373, 378, 382

Reteaching
Chapter 7 Grab & Go™ File: pp. 9–16

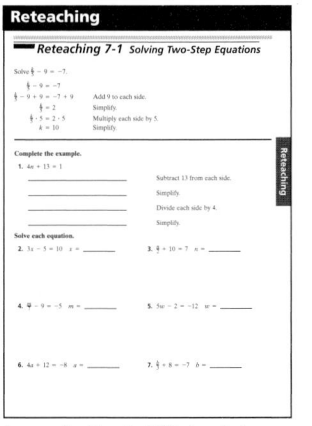

* Can be used with all ability levels to ensure mastery of prerequisite skills.

Advanced Learners

Student Edition
- Challenge exercises: pp. 351, 356, 361, 364, 370, 376, 380, 386
- Extension: p. 377

Enrichment
Chapter 7 Grab & Go™ File: pp. 17–24

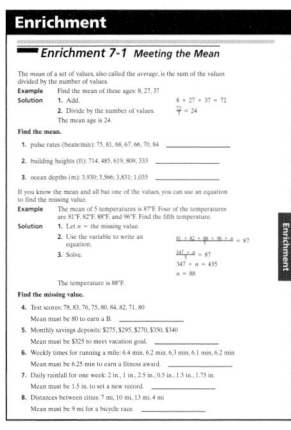

Problem Solving

Student Edition
- Strategies: pp. 362–365
- Real-World Problem Solving: pp. 349, 352, 358, 362, 368, 374, 379, 382, 383, 384

Guided Problem Solving Masters
Chapter 7: pp. 57–64

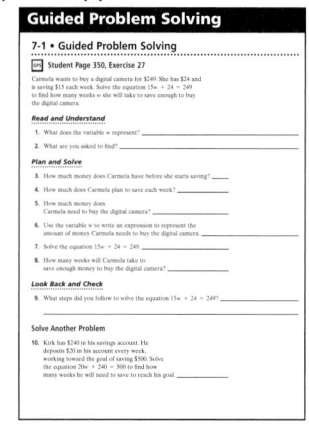

Reading and Math Literacy

Student Edition
- Vocabulary: pp. 347, 389, plus in most lessons
- Reading Math: pp. 349, 353, 364, 366, 374, 389
- Writing in Math: pp. 351, 355, 360, 370, 376, 377, 380, 385, 392
- Illustrated Glossary: pp. 782–826

Reading and Math Literacy Masters
Chapter 7: pp. 25–28

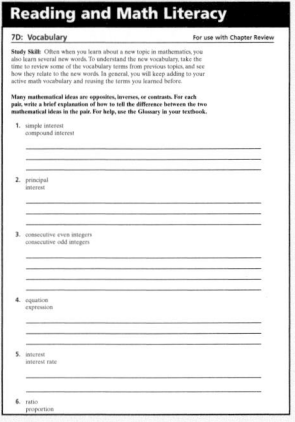

English Learners

Student Edition
- English/Spanish Illustrated Glossary: pp. 782–826

Workbook and Masters
Spanish Practice Workbook: pp. 57–64
Spanish Reading and Math Literacy Masters: pp. 25–28

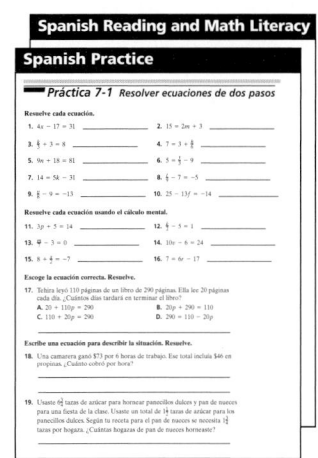

Learning Styles

Student Edition
- Investigation: pp. 352, 367
- Technology: pp. 372, 387
- DK Activities: pp. 394–395
- Chapter Project: p. 741

Activity Masters
Hands-On Activities: 35
Technology Activities: 13

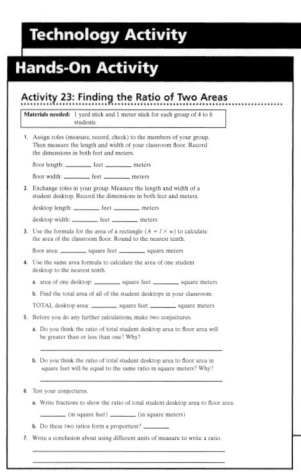

Program Resources

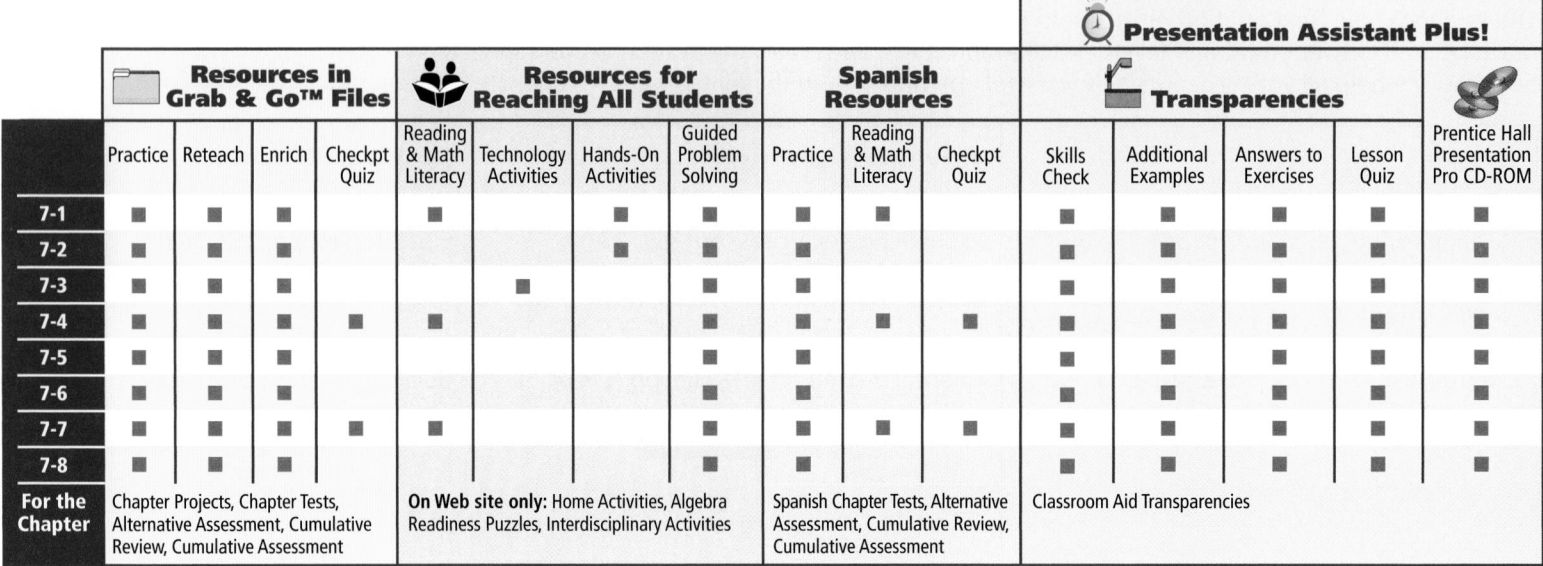

	Resources in Grab & Go™ Files				Resources for Reaching All Students				Spanish Resources			Presentation Assistant Plus! Transparencies				Prentice Hall Presentation Pro CD-ROM
	Practice	Reteach	Enrich	Checkpt Quiz	Reading & Math Literacy	Technology Activities	Hands-On Activities	Guided Problem Solving	Practice	Reading & Math Literacy	Checkpt Quiz	Skills Check	Additional Examples	Answers to Exercises	Lesson Quiz	
7-1	■	■	■		■		■	■	■	■		■	■	■	■	■
7-2	■	■	■				■	■	■			■	■	■	■	■
7-3	■	■	■			■		■	■			■	■	■	■	■
7-4	■	■	■	■	■			■	■	■	■	■	■	■	■	■
7-5	■	■	■					■	■			■	■	■	■	■
7-6	■	■	■					■	■			■	■	■	■	■
7-7	■	■	■	■	■			■	■	■	■	■	■	■	■	■
7-8	■	■	■					■	■			■	■	■	■	■
For the Chapter	Chapter Projects, Chapter Tests, Alternative Assessment, Cumulative Review, Cumulative Assessment				On Web site only: Home Activities, Algebra Readiness Puzzles, Interdisciplinary Activities				Spanish Chapter Tests, Alternative Assessment, Cumulative Review, Cumulative Assessment			Classroom Aid Transparencies				

Also available for use with the chapter:
- Practice Workbook
- Solution Key
- MathNotes folder
- For additional online and technology resources, see below.
- For teacher support and access to student Web site materials, use Web Code adk-5500.

PRENTICE HALL ASSESSMENT SYSTEM

Program assessment and test preparation, all in one place.
See page 346E.

Skills Intervention Kit

A *complete* system for the student who is struggling with course-level work

How to Use With Chapter 7

7-1 Pre-Algebra Basics
7-8 Ratio, Proportion, Percent

Online Intervention

Integrated within the iText, this online intervention system includes diagnostic tests and prescribed remediation, plus reports to track student mastery.

Technology

 Online and on CD-ROM

Complete Interactive Student Text online and on CD-ROM—with instant-feedback assessment, tutorial help, dynamic activities, instructional and real-world videos, audio, and additional practice.

 www.PHSchool.com
For Students

Use Web Codes for easy access to online activities, chapter projects, self-grading lesson quizzes, chapter tests, vocabulary quizzes, updated data sources, graphing calculator procedures, and more.

PH SuccessNet
For Teachers

Online lesson planning with built-in state correlations, all the teaching resources, complete reference library, your own calendar and Teacher Web page, professional development, and more.

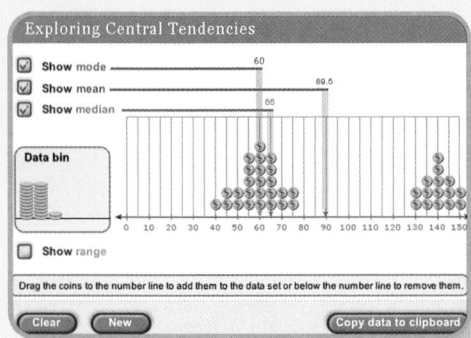

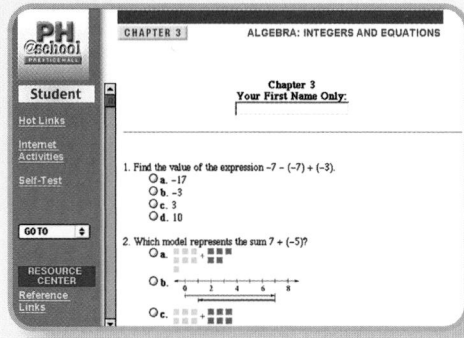

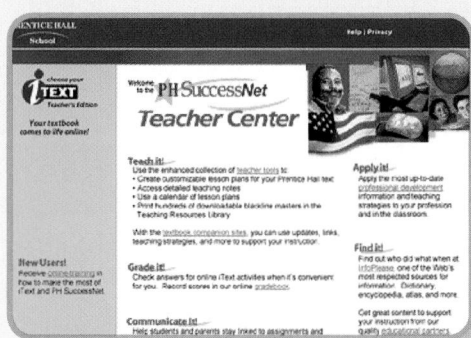

Presentation Assistant Plus!

The Prentice Hall *Presentation Assistant Plus!* provides you with the material you need to teach a lesson from beginning to end. Two easy-to-use formats—Transparencies and CD-ROM—allow you to present a lesson the way you are most comfortable.

Transparencies

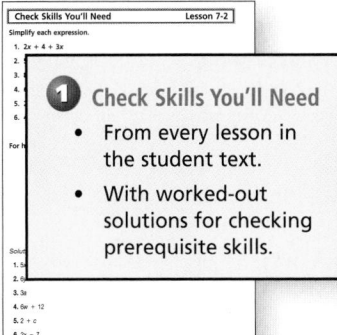

1 Check Skills You'll Need
- From every lesson in the student text.
- With worked-out solutions for checking prerequisite skills.

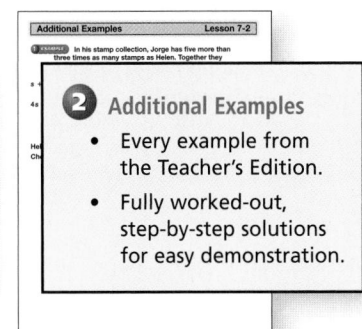

2 Additional Examples
- Every example from the Teacher's Edition.
- Fully worked-out, step-by-step solutions for easy demonstration.

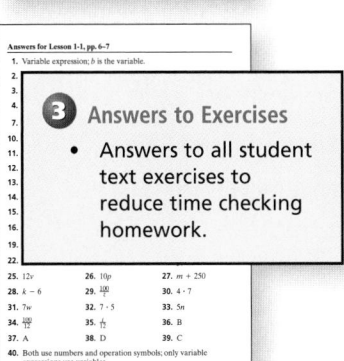

3 Answers to Exercises
- Answers to all student text exercises to reduce time checking homework.

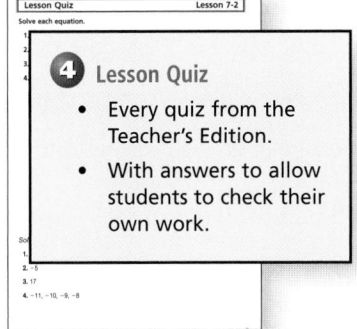

4 Lesson Quiz
- Every quiz from the Teacher's Edition.
- With answers to allow students to check their own work.

 Throughout the Teacher's Edition, this symbol indicates material that is available in the Presentation Assistant Plus!

PowerPoint Prentice Hall Presentation Pro CD-ROM

- Includes all Transparencies as PowerPoint® presentations.
- Conveniently organized by lesson so you can easily **1** Introduce, **2** Teach, **3** Check Homework, and **4** Assess each lesson.
- Animated examples allow step-by-step instruction at your own pace.
- Easy to edit so you can create custom presentations.

Teaching Chapter 7 Using Presentation Assistant Plus!

	1 Introduce Check Skills You'll Need	**2 Teach** Additional Examples	**3 Check Homework** Student Edition Answers	**4 Assess** Lesson Quiz
7-1	p. 58	pp. 87–88	✔	p. 58
7-2	p. 59	pp. 88–90	✔	p. 59
7-3	p. 60	pp. 91–92	✔	p. 60
7-4	p. 61	p. 92	✔	p. 61
7-5	p. 62	pp. 93–94	✔	p. 62
7-6	p. 63	pp. 95–96	✔	p. 63
7-7	p. 64	pp. 97–98	✔	p. 64
7-8	p. 65	pp. 99–100	✔	p. 65

Prentice Hall Presentation Pro

CD-ROM with dynamic Powerpoint® presentations for every lesson. Helps you introduce and develop concepts, check homework, and assess progress. Part of Presentation Assistant Plus! *(See above.)*

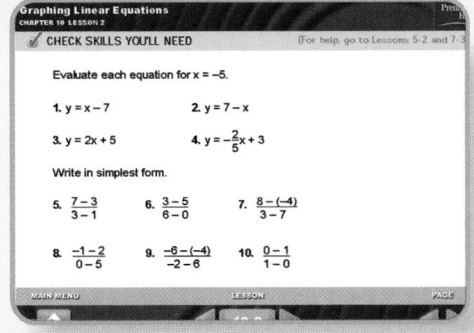

Computer Test Generator

CD-ROM to create practice sheets and tests for course objectives and standardized tests. Includes Instant Chapter Tests™, online testing, and student reports. Part of the PH Assessment System. *(See page 346E.)*

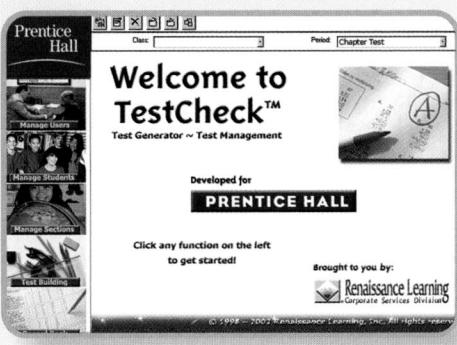

Resource Pro® with Planning Express®

CD-ROM with a lesson planning tool that allows you to import state and local objectives. Includes electronic versions of all the teaching resources.

Solving Equations and Inequalities

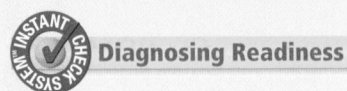

Diagnosing Readiness

Students will find the answers to these exercises in the back of their textbooks.

Prescribing Intervention
For intervention, direct students to:

Writing Variable Expressions
Lesson 1-1: Example 2;
Exercises 7–22.
Extra Practice p. 744.

Simplifying Expressions
Lesson 2-3: Examples 3–4;
Exercises 11–19.
Extra Practice, p. 745.

Solving Equations
Lesson 2-5: Examples 1 and 3;
Exercises 1–9, 12–20.
Lesson 2-6: Examples 2 and 3;
Exercises 1–28.
Extra Practice, p. 745.

Solving Inequalities
Lesson 2-9: Examples 1 and 3;
Exercises 1–8, 11–19.
Lesson 2-10: Examples 1 and 2;
Exercises 1–25.
Extra Practice, p. 745.

Where You've Been

- In Chapter 2, you learned how to simplify variable expressions and to solve one-step equations and inequalities by adding, subtracting, multiplying, or dividing.

- In Chapter 3, you learned how to solve equations by adding, subtracting, multiplying, or dividing decimals.

- In Chapter 5, you learned how to solve equations by adding, subtracting, or multiplying fractions.

 Instant self-check online and on CD-ROM

Diagnosing Readiness   (For help, go to the lesson in green.)

Writing Variable Expressions (Lesson 1-1)

Write a variable expression for each situation.

1. three more than p points $p + 3$ **2.** six fewer than q questions $q - 6$

3. the number of months in y years   **4.** the value in cents of d dimes $10d$
   $12y$

5. twice as many as b baskets $2b$ **6.** eight fewer than n nickels $n - 8$

Simplifying Expressions (Lesson 2-3)

Simplify each expression.

7. $3n + n$ $4n$ **8.** $5b + 10 - 8b$ **9.** $12c + 9 + 7c + 4$ $19c + 13$
                         $-3b + 10$
10. $3x + 2y - 7y - 10x$ **11.** $2(a + 3)$ $2a + 6$ **12.** $5(m - 7) + 4m$ $9m - 35$
   $-7x - 5y$

Solving Equations (Lessons 2-5, 2-6)

Solve each equation.

13. $a - 3 = 8$ 11 **14.** $-9 = 12 + x$ **15.** $\frac{m}{7} = -14$ -98 **16.** $-10 = -2b$ 5
                            -21
17. $y \div 2 = 4$ 8 **18.** $6.8 = c - 2.2$ **19.** $\frac{x}{-4} = 8$ -32 **20.** $-40 = 5a$ -8
                            9

Solving Inequalities (Lessons 2-9, 2-10)

Solve and graph each inequality.   21–28. For graphs, see margin.

21. $c + 6 \geq 7$ **22.** $y - 8 < -6$ **23.** $5b < 20$ $b < 4$ **24.** $-3x < 0$ $x > 0$
   $c \geq 1$ $y < 2$
25. $12 \leq x + 18$ **26.** $-\frac{x}{3} \geq -5$ **27.** $b - 15 \leq 4$ **28.** $\frac{m}{4} \geq 20$ $m \geq 80$
   $x \geq -6$ $x \leq 15$ $b \leq 19$

21. ◄─┼─┼─┼─●─┼─┼─► $-1\ 0\ 1$

22. ◄─┼─┼─┼─⊕─┼─► $-2\ \ 0\ \ 2$

23. ◄─┼─┼─┼─┼─⊕─► $-4\ -2\ \ 0\ \ 2\ \ 4$

24. ◄─┼─┼─⊕─┼─┼─► $-1\ 0\ 1$

25. ◄─●─┼─┼─┼─┼─► $-6\ \ -2\ 0\ 2$

26. ◄─┼─┼─┼─●─► $-10\ \ 0\ \ 10\ 15$

27. ◄─┼─┼─┼─┼─●─► $-10\ \ 0\ \ 10\ 19$

28. ◄─┼─┼─┼─┼─●─► $-40\ \ 0\ \ 40\ 80$

Solving Equations and Inequalities

Where You're Going

In this chapter, you will learn how to

● Write and solve multi-step equations.

● Write and solve two-step inequalities.

● Find simple interest and compound interest.

● Solve problems by writing equations.

Real-World Snapshots Applying what you learn, on pages 394–395 you will solve problems about cellular telephones.

LESSONS

Key Vocabulary

- balance (p. 383)
- compound inequality (p. 377)
- compound interest (p. 383)
- consecutive integers (p. 353)
- interest (p. 382)
- interest rate (p. 382)
- principal (p. 382)
- simple interest (p. 382)

347

Chapter 7 Overview

In this chapter, students will use mathematical properties to solve two-step equations, multi-step equations, and two-step inequalities. The multi-step equations include fractions and decimals, and equations with variables on both sides of the equal sign. Students will use the Problem-Solving Strategy *Write an Equation,* and then solve the equations they write. They will use the same mathematical properties and skills to transform formulas. Then they use formulas to find simple and compound interest.

Activating Prior Knowledge
Students build upon the skills they learned in Chapter 2 for solving single-step equations and inequalities in order to solve two-step and other multi-step equations and inequalities. Ask: *What is the goal when solving an equation?* The goal is to find values of the variable that make the equation true.

 Reading Math
● Reading for Problem Solving, p. 366.
● **Vocabulary** A complete list of terms, plus vocabulary exercises, appears in the Chapter Review, p. 389.
● **Illustrated Glossary** Examples for each vocabulary term, plus definitions in both English and Spanish, appear starting on p. 782.

Test-Taking Strategies
Eliminating Answers, p. 388

Real-World Problem Solving
● **Strategy:** Write an Equation, pp. 362–365
● **DK Real-World Snapshots:** Applying Equations, pp. 394–395
● **Chapter Project:** The Intensity of Density, p. 741

 **www.PHSchool.com**
Internet support includes:
● Self-grading Vocabulary and Chapter 7 Tests
● Activity Masters
● Chapter Project support
● Chapter Planner
● Chapter 7 Resources

Plus **iTEXT**

7-1

1. Plan

Lesson Preview

 Check Skills You'll Need

Solving Equations
Lesson 2-5: Examples 2 and 3;
Exercises 1–9, 12–20.
Extra Practice, p. 745.

Lesson Resources

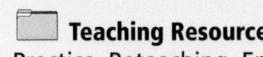

📁 **Teaching Resources**
Practice, Reteaching, Enrichment

👥 **Reaching All Students**
Practice Workbook 7-1
Spanish Practice Workbook 7-1
Reading and Math Literacy 7A
Spanish Reading and Math
  Literacy 7A
Guided Problem Solving 7-1
Hands-On Activities 35

⏰ **Presentation Assistant Plus!**
Transparencies and PowerPoint™
• Check Skills You'll Need 7-1
• Additional Examples 7-1
• Student Edition Answers 7-1
• Lesson Quiz 7-1
• Classroom Aid 13
PH Presentation Pro CD-ROM 7-1

ASSESSMENT *SYSTEM*

Computer Test Generator CD-ROM

💻 **Technology**
Resource Pro® CD-ROM
Computer Test Generator CD-ROM
PH Presentation Pro CD-ROM

💻 **www.PHSchool.com**
Student Site
• Teacher Web Code: adk-5500
• Algebra Readiness Puzzles 43, 44
• Graphing Calculator, Procedure 7
• Self-grading Lesson Quiz
PH SuccessNet Teacher Center
• Lesson Planner
• Resources

Plus

348

Solving Two-Step Equations

What You'll Learn

OBJECTIVE 1 To solve two-step equations

OBJECTIVE 2 To use two-step equations to solve problems

. . . And Why
To solve problems involving savings

 **Check Skills You'll Need**
Solve each equation.

1. $9 + k = 17$ **8**

2. $d - 10 = 1$ **11**

3. $y - 5 = -4$ **1**

4. $x + 16 = 4$ **−12**

5. $b + 6 = -4$ **−10**

📖 For help, go to Lesson 2-5.

Algebra tiles can help you understand the algebra behind solving the equation $2x + 1 = 5$.

$2x + 1 = 5$  **Model the equation.**

$2x + 1 - 1 = 5 - 1$
$2x = 4$ 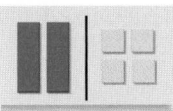 **Remove 1 tile from each side.**

$\frac{2x}{2} = \frac{4}{2}$  **Divide each side into two equal groups.**

$x = 2$  **Simplify.**

To solve a two-step equation, first undo addition or subtraction. Then undo multiplication or division.

1 EXAMPLE **Undoing an Operation**

Solve $3n - 6 = 15$.

$$3n - 6 = 15$$
$$3n - 6 + 6 = 15 + 6 \quad \text{Add 6 to each side.}$$
$$3n = 21 \quad \text{Simplify.}$$
$$\frac{3n}{3} = \frac{21}{3} \quad \text{Divide each side by 3.}$$
$$n = 7 \quad \text{Simplify.}$$

Check
$$3n - 6 = 15$$
$$3(7) - 6 \stackrel{?}{=} 15 \quad \text{Replace } n \text{ with 7.}$$
$$21 - 6 \stackrel{?}{=} 15 \quad \text{Multiply.}$$
$$15 = 15 \checkmark \quad \text{Simplify.}$$

 TEXT Interactive lesson includes instant self-check, tutorials, and activities.

Ongoing Assessment and Intervention

Before the Lesson
Diagnose prerequisite skills using:
• Check Skills You'll Need

During the Lesson
Monitor progress using:
• Check Understanding
• Additional Examples
• Test Prep

After the Lesson
Assess knowledge using:
• Lesson Quiz
• Computer Test Generator
  CD-ROM

✓ **Check Understanding** Example 1

1. Solve each equation.

    a. $15x + 3 = 48$ **3**
    b. $\frac{t}{4} - 10 = -6$ **16**

    c. $\frac{b}{3} + 13 = 11$ **−6**
    d. $9g + 11 = 2$ **−1**

---

2 EXAMPLE **Negative Coefficients**

Solve $5 - x = 17$.

$$5 - x = 17$$
$$-5 + 5 - x = -5 + 17 \quad \textbf{Add −5 to each side.}$$
$$0 - x = 12 \quad \textbf{Simplify.}$$
$$-x = 12 \quad \textbf{0 − x = −x}$$
$$-1(-x) = -1(12) \quad \textbf{Multiply each side by −1.}$$
$$x = -12 \quad \textbf{Simplify.}$$

> **Reading Math**
> Read "$0 - x = -x$" as "Zero minus *x* equals the opposite of *x*."

✓ **Check Understanding** Example 2

2. Solve each equation.

    a. $-a + 6 = 8$ **−2**
    b. $-9 - \frac{y}{7} = -12$ **21**
    c. $13 - 6f = 31$ **−3**

OBJECTIVE

2 **Solving Problems With Two-Step Equations**

You can use two-step equations to model real-world situations.

3 EXAMPLE **Real-World**  **Problem Solving**

Travel Planning Lynne wants to save $900 to go to Puerto Rico. She saves $45 each week and now has $180. To find how many more weeks *w* it will take to have $900, solve $180 + 45w = 900$.

$$180 + 45w = 900$$
$$180 + 45w - 180 = 900 - 180 \quad \textbf{Subtract 180 from each side.}$$
$$45w = 720 \quad \textbf{Simplify.}$$
$$\frac{45w}{45} = \frac{720}{45} \quad \textbf{Divide each side by 45.}$$
$$w = 16 \quad \textbf{Simplify.}$$

It will take Lynne 16 more weeks to have $900.

✓ **Check Understanding** Example 3

3. Jacob bought four begonias in 6-in. pots and a $19 fern at a fundraiser. He spent a total of $63. Solve the equation $4p + 19 = 63$ to find the price *p* of each begonia. **$11**

Real-World  **Connection**

If you fly to San Juan, Puerto Rico, it could cost you $186 to leave from New York, New York, $590 to leave from San Francisco, California, $914 to leave from Reno, Nevada, or $1,392 to leave from Dallas, Texas.

7-1 Solving Two-Step Equations **349**

Reaching All Students

Below Level Discuss with students any processes that are done with several steps in sequence, such as putting on socks and shoes or making a sandwich.

Advanced Learners Ask: *Solve $3x + 4 = 10$ by dividing first. Explain why it would be easier to subtract first.* $\frac{3x+4}{3} = \frac{10}{3}, x + \frac{4}{3} = \frac{10}{3}, x = \frac{6}{3},$ or 2; you do not have to work with fractions.

Alternative Method See note on page 349. **Error Prevention** See note on page 351.

---

2. Teach

 Professional Development

Math Background

To solve two-step equations, you first undo addition or subtraction, and then you undo multiplication or division.

Teaching Notes

1 EXAMPLE **Teaching Tip**

Some students may try to solve two-step equations by multiplying or dividing first, as in the order of operations. Since you use the *opposite* (inverse) operations to undo operations, you perform these operations in the *opposite* order from the order of operations. First you undo addition or subtraction; then you undo multiplication or division.

2 EXAMPLE **Alternative Method**

Suggest to students that they read $-x = 12$ as "the *opposite* of *x* equals 12." Ask: *If the opposite of x equals 12, what must x be?* the opposite of 12, or −12

3 EXAMPLE **Teaching Tip**

Ask students to explain why the equation is $180 + 45w = 900$ instead of $45w = 900$. Lynne already has saved $180 toward the $900 total.

PowerPoint

Additional Examples

1 Solve $5v - 12 = 8$. **4**

2 Solve $7 - 3b = 1$. **2**

3 You borrow $350 to buy a bicycle. You agree to pay $100 the first week, and then $25 each week until the balance is paid off. To find how many weeks *w* it will take you to pay for the bicycle, solve $100 + 25w = 350$. **10 weeks**

Closure

Ask students to explain how to solve two-step equations. In two-step equations you have to undo two operations. First undo the addition or subtraction, then undo the multiplication or division.

349

Assignment Guide

1 Objective 1
Ⓐ Ⓑ Core 1–12, 15–20, 23–25, 28–33

2 Objective 2
Ⓐ Ⓑ Core 13, 14, 21, 22, 26, 27

Ⓒ Extension 34

Test Prep 35–38
Mixed Review 39–43

Practice 7-1 *Solving Two-Step Equations*

Solve each equation.

1. $4x - 17 = 31$ $x = 12$
2. $15 = 2m + 3$ $m = 6$
3. $\frac{k}{5} + 3 = 8$ $k = 15$
4. $7 = 3 + \frac{h}{6}$ $h = 24$
5. $9n + 18 = 81$ $n = 7$
6. $5 = \frac{y}{7} - 9$ $y = 42$
7. $14 = 5k - 31$ $k = 9$
8. $\frac{t}{6} - 7 = -5$ $t = 18$
9. $\frac{v}{8} - 9 = -13$ $v = -32$
10. $25 - 13f = -14$ $f = 3$

Solve each equation using mental math.

11. $3p + 5 = 14$ $p = 3$
12. $\frac{k}{6} - 5 = 1$ $k = 12$
13. $\frac{m}{7} - 3 = 0$ $m = 21$
14. $10v - 6 = 24$ $v = 3$
15. $8 + \frac{x}{5} = -7$ $x = -30$
16. $7 = 6r - 17$ $r = 4$

Choose the correct equation. Solve.

17. Tehira has read 110 pages of a 290-page book. She reads 20 pages each day. How many days will it take to finish?
   A. $20 + 110p = 290$
   B. $20p + 290 = 110$
   Ⓒ $110 + 20p = 290$
   D. $290 = 110 - 20p$
   $p = 9$; it will take her 9 days.

Write an equation to describe the situation. Solve.

18. A waitress earned $73 for 6 hours of work. The total included $46 in tips. What was her hourly wage?
   $6w + 46 = 73$
   $w = 4.5$; she earned $4.50 an hour.

19. You used $6\frac{3}{4}$ c of sugar while baking muffins and nutbread for a class party. You used a total of $1\frac{1}{2}$ c of sugar for the muffins. Your nutbread recipe calls for $1\frac{3}{4}$ c of sugar per loaf. How many loaves of nutbread did you make?
   $b \cdot 1\frac{3}{4} + 1\frac{1}{2} = 6\frac{3}{4}$
   $b = 3$; you made 3 batches of nutbread.

Enrichment 7-1 *Meeting the Mean*

The *mean* of a set of values, also called the *average*, is the sum of the values divided by the number of values.

Example Find the mean of these ages: 8, 27, 37
Solution
1. Add. $8 + 27 + 37 = 72$
2. Divide by the number of values. $\frac{72}{3} = 24$
The mean age is 24.

Find the mean.

1. pulse rates (beats/min): 75, 81, 68, 67, 66, 70, 84   73 beats/min
2. building heights (ft): 714, 485, 619, 809, 333   592 ft
3. ocean depths (m): 3,930; 3,566; 3,831; 1,035   3,090.5 m

If you know the mean and all but one of the values, you can use an equation to find the missing value.

Example The mean of 5 temperatures is 87°F. Four of the temperatures are 81°F, 82°F, 88°F, and 96°F. Find the fifth temperature.
Solution
1. Let n = the missing value.
2. Use the variable to write an equation. $\frac{81 + 82 + 88 + 96 + n}{5} = 87$
3. Solve. $\frac{347 + n}{5} = 87$
  $347 + n = 435$
  $n = 88$
The temperature is 88°F.

Find the missing value.

4. Test scores: 78, 83, 76, 75, 80, 84, 82, 71, 80
   Mean must be 80 to earn a B.   91
5. Monthly savings deposits: $275, $295, $270, $350, $340
   Mean must be $325 to meet vacation goal. $420
6. Weekly times for running a mile: 6.4 min, 6.2 min, 6.3 min, 6.1 min, 6.2 min
   Mean must be 6.25 min to earn a fitness award.   6.3 min
7. Daily rainfall for one week: 2 in., 1 in., 2.5 in., 0.5 in., 1.5 in., 1.75 in.
   Mean must be 1.5 in. to set a new record.   1.25 in.
8. Distances between cities: 7 mi, 10 mi, 13 mi, 4 mi
   Mean must be 9 mi for a bicycle race.   11 mi

EXERCISES

For more exercises, see *Extra Practice*.

Practice and Problem Solving

Ⓐ **Practice by Example**

State the first step in solving each equation.

Example 1
(page 348)

1. $2b + 9 = 3$
   Subtract 9 from each side.
2. $\frac{a}{3} - 4 = 9$
   Add 4 to each side.
3. $4b - 6 = -18$
   Add 6 to each side.

Solve each equation.

4. $2d - 8 = -10$ –1
5. $9x - 15 = 39$ 6
6. $\frac{x}{3} + 2 = 0$ –6

Example 2
(page 349)

7. $12 - 11a = 45$ –3
8. $-8c + 1 = -3$ $\frac{1}{2}$
9. $5 = -\frac{x}{3} + 10$ 15
10. $18 = -a + 2$ –16
11. $4 - \frac{m}{5} = 18$ –70
12. $-75 - k = -95$ 20

Example 3
(page 349)

13. **Finance** Jose bought a new computer that cost $1,200. He paid $400 down and will pay $50 per week until the balance is paid off. Solve the equation $400 + 50w = 1,200$ to find the number of weeks it will take Jose to pay off the computer.   16 weeks

14. Thomas, Ardell, and Nichole baked muffins, which they shared equally. Nichole ate a muffin on the way home. She then had 14 muffins left. Solve the equation $\frac{m}{3} - 1 = 14$ to find the number of muffins m that Thomas, Ardell, and Nichole baked.   45 muffins

Ⓑ **Apply Your Skills**

Solve and check each equation.

15. $15 = -11b + 4$ –1
16. $-35 = 4h + 1$ –9
17. $10 = 3 + \frac{b}{2}$ 14
18. $12y - 6 = 138$ 12
19. $2x + 3 = 15$ 6
20. $-6t + (-4) = 14$ –3

21. You bought a CD for $16.95 and eight blank videotapes. The total cost was $52.55 before the sales tax was added. Solve the equation $8t + 16.95 = 52.55$ to find the cost of each blank videotape. $4.45

22. **Savings** You had $235 in your savings account nine weeks ago. You withdrew the same amount each week for eight weeks. Your balance was then $75. Solve the equation $235 - 8m = 75$ to find how much money m you withdrew each week. $20

Mental Math **Solve each equation.**

23. $\frac{n}{6} + 2 = -8$ –60
24. $4a - 1 = 27$ 7
25. $\frac{k}{5} + 3 = 6$ 15

26. **Construction** A building contractor buys 525 metal bars. Because he is buying more than 500 bars, the wholesaler gives him a discount of $420. The total price is $3,780. Solve the equation $525b - 420 = 3,780$ to find the cost of each metal bar. $8

27. Carmela wants to buy a digital camera for $249. She has $24 and is saving $15 each week. Solve the equation $15w + 24 = 249$ to find how many weeks w it will take Carmela to save enough to buy the digital camera.   15 weeks

GPS Use the Guided Problem Solving worksheet with Exercise 27.

28. The student divided by 4 instead of multiplying by 4.

28. Error Analysis A student solved the equation $\frac{x}{4} + 5 = 1$ without showing all the work. The student's solution is incorrect. What error did the student make?
See below left.

$$\frac{x}{4} + 5 = 1$$
$$\frac{x}{4} = -4$$
$$x = -1$$

29. Writing in Math Explain how the processes of solving $\frac{x}{4} - 2 = 8$ and $\frac{x}{4} = 8$ are different.
The first problem requires an initial step of adding 2 to each side.

Solve and check each equation.

30. $1.5x + 1.2 = 5.7$ **3**

31. $-1.7 = 2.2b - 6.1$ **2**

32. $3c - 3.2 = 4.6$ **2.6**

33. $\frac{y}{4} + 4.7 = 8.2$ **14**

C Challenge **34. Nutrition** A soccer player wants to eat no more than 700 calories at a meal that includes a Reuben sandwich and pickles. The sandwich has 464 calories, and the pickles have 7 calories each.
  a. Solve the equation $464 + 7f = 700$ to find the number of pickles the soccer player can eat. **at most 33 pickles**
  b. Suppose the soccer player drinks a 200-calorie sports drink with the meal. Solve the equation $664 + 7f = 700$ to find the number of pickles the soccer player can eat now. **5 pickles**

Test Prep

Multiple Choice

35. What is the solution of $\frac{x}{6} - 8 = 7$? **D**
  A. -6 **B.** 6 **C.** 15 **D.** 90

36. What is the solution of $-11 = 4h - 3$? **G**
  F. -5 **G.** -2 **H.** -1.25 **I.** 1

37. Which is the best estimate for the solution of $29x + 59.2 = 239$? **C**
  A. 4 **B.** 5 **C.** 6 **D.** 7

Take It to the NET
Online lesson quiz at
www.PHSchool.com
Web Code: ada-0701

Short Response

38. At a carnival, Bret buys game tokens for $.25 each. He spends $7.50 for food and $14 in all. How many tokens did he buy?
  a. Write an equation to model this situation.
  b. Solve your equation and answer the question. **See back of book.**

Mixed Review

Lesson 6-9 **Find each percent of markup.**

39. wholesale price: $34
  selling price: $42.50 **25%**

40. wholesale price: $45.95
  selling price: $82.71 **80%**

Lesson 6-4 **41. Probability** A student is chosen at random from a class of 20 boys and 15 girls. Find the odds that a girl is chosen. **3 to 4**

Lesson 2-3 **Simplify each expression.**

42. $a + 3b + 9a$ **$10a + 3b$**

43. $2(c + 4) - 5c$ **$-3c + 8$**

1. Plan

Lesson Preview

 Check Skills You'll Need

Simplifying Variable Expressions
Lesson 2-3: Example 4;
Exercises 17–20.
Extra Practice, p. 745.

Lesson Resources

 Teaching Resources
Practice, Reteaching, Enrichment

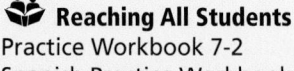 **Reaching All Students**
Practice Workbook 7-2
Spanish Practice Workbook 7-2
Guided Problem Solving 7-2
Hands-On Activities 35

 Presentation Assistant Plus!
Transparencies and Power Point™
• Check Skills You'll Need 7-2
• Additional Examples 7-2
• Student Edition Answers 7-2
• Lesson Quiz 7-2
• Classroom Aid 13
PH Presentation Pro CD-ROM 7-2

ASSESSMENT SYSTEM

Computer Test Generator CD-ROM

 Technology
Resource Pro® CD-ROM
Computer Test Generator CD-ROM
PH Presentation Pro CD-ROM

 www.PHSchool.com
Student Site
• Teacher Web Code: adk-5500
• Algebra Readiness Puzzles 45, 46
• Self-grading Lesson Quiz
PH SuccessNet Teacher Center
• Lesson Planner
• Resources

Plus

What You'll Learn

OBJECTIVE 1 To combine like terms to simplify an equation

OBJECTIVE 2 To use the Distributive Property to simplify an equation

. . . And Why

To solve problems involving consecutive integers

 Check Skills You'll Need

Simplify each expression.

1. $2x + 4 + 3x$
   $5x + 4$
2. $5y + y$
   $6y$
3. $8a - 5a$
   $3a$
4. $2 - 4c + 5c$
   $2 + c$
5. $4x + 3 - 2(5 + x)$
   $2x - 7$

For help, go to Lesson 2-3.

New Vocabulary

• consecutive integers

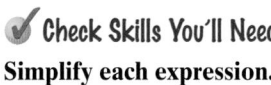 **TEXT** Interactive lesson includes instant self-check, tutorials, and activities.

OBJECTIVE

 **1** Combining Like Terms

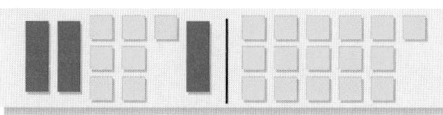 **In**vestigation

Simplifying Equations

The tiles below model the equation $2x + 7 + x = 16$

1. How does this equation differ from others you have seen?
   There are two variable terms instead of one.
2. **a.** Group the tiles so that all the x tiles are together. This is the same as combining like terms. Write an equation to represent the tiles once the x tiles are grouped together.
   b. Solve your equation. Check your solution. $3x + 7 = 16$
   3

Combine like terms to simplify an equation before you solve it.

1 **EXAMPLE**   **Real-World** **Problem Solving**

Model Airplanes Jake and Suki collect model airplanes. Suki has **four fewer than twice as many model airplanes as Jake. Together they have 14 models. Solve the equation $m + 2m - 4 = 14$. Find the number of models each person has.**

$$m + 2m - 4 = 14$$
$$3m - 4 = 14 \qquad \text{Combine like terms.}$$
$$3m - 4 + 4 = 14 + 4 \qquad \text{Add 4 to each side.}$$
$$3m = 18 \qquad \text{Simplify.}$$
$$\frac{3m}{3} = \frac{18}{3} \qquad \text{Divide each side by 3.}$$
$$m = 6 \qquad \text{Simplify.}$$

Jake has 6 models. Suki has $2(6) - 4 = 8$ models.

Check Is the solution reasonable? Jake and Suki have a total of 14 models. Since $6 + 8 = 14$, the solution is reasonable.

INSTANT CHECK SYSTEM

Ongoing Assessment and Intervention

Before the Lesson	**During the Lesson**	**After the Lesson**
Diagnose prerequisite skills using:	**Monitor progress using:**	**Assess knowledge using:**
• Check Skills You'll Need	• Check Understanding	• Lesson Quiz
	• Additional Examples	• Computer Test Generator
	• Test Prep	CD-ROM

 **Check Understanding** Example 1

1. **Basketball Scores** One basketball team defeated another by 13 points. The total number of points scored by both teams was 171. Solve the equation $p + p - 13 = 171$ to find the number of points p scored by the winning team. **92 points**

When you count by 1s from any integer, you are counting **consecutive integers.**

two consecutive integers
$$\overbrace{120, 121}$$

three consecutive integers
$$\overbrace{-5, -4, -3}$$

Reading Math
The definition of *consecutive* is "following one another in uninterrupted intervals."

2 EXAMPLE **Finding Consecutive Integers**

Number Sense **The sum of three consecutive integers is 96. Find the integers.**

Words | sum of three consecutive integers | is | 96

Let n = the least integer.
Then $n + 1$ = the second integer,
and $n + 2$ = the third integer.

Equation | $n + n + 1 + n + 2$ | = | 96

$n + (n + 1) + (n + 2) = 96$

$(n + n + n) + (1 + 2) = 96$ **Use the Commutative and Associative Properties of Addition to group like terms.**

$3n + 3 = 96$ **Combine like terms.**

$3n + 3 - 3 = 96 - 3$ **Subtract 3 from each side.**

$3n = 93$ **Simplify.**

$\dfrac{3n}{3} = \dfrac{93}{3}$ **Divide each side by 3.**

$n = 31$ **Simplify.**

If $n = 31$, then $n + 1 = 32$, and $n + 2 = 33$.
The three integers are 31, 32, and 33.

● **Check** Is the solution reasonable? Yes, because $31 + 32 + 33 = 96$.

Check Understanding Example 2

2. **a. Number Sense** Find four consecutive integers with a sum of 358. **88, 89, 90, 91**
   b. For *consecutive even integers*, the first is n, and the second is $n + 2$. Find two consecutive even integers with a sum of 66. **32, 34**

Test-Taking Tip
Always read problems carefully. It is easy to not see words such as *even* in *consecutive even integers* if you are reading too quickly.

🌱 Reaching All Students

Below Level Ask students what they would do first to solve $2 + 7 = x + 4$. Point out that adding the numbers on the left side of the equation is called *combining like terms.*

Advanced Learners Ask why n and $n + 2$ can represent consecutive odd integers as well as consecutive even integers. Consecutive odd integers are 2 units apart as are consecutive even integers.

English Learners See note on page 353.
Visual Learners See note on page 354.

---

2. Teach

Professional Development

Math Background

You can apply the Distributive Property to remove parentheses from an equation. Then combine all like terms on each side of the equal sign. Undo addition and/or subtraction, and then undo multiplication and/or division, as you did in simpler two-step equations.

Teaching Notes

Investigation (Optional)
When students model the equations with tiles, they can see that the x tiles can be rearranged so that they are grouped together. Help students connect the model and the algebraic steps: grouping the x tiles together is the same as adding the coefficients of the variable x.

1 EXAMPLE **Tactile Learners**
Provide tiles so students can model the equation and check their solution.

2 EXAMPLE **English Learners**
Make sure that students understand that *consecutive* means "one after the other." Have students give examples of consecutive objects (such as desks in a row), consecutive events (such as the signing of the Declaration of Independence, adoption of the U.S. Constitution), and consecutive dates (such as Dec. 31, Jan. 1), etc. Then ask for examples of consecutive whole numbers and consecutive integers.

PowerPoint

📖 Additional Examples

1 In his stamp collection, Jorge has five more than three times as many stamps as Helen. Together they have 41 stamps. Solve the equation $s + 3s + 5 = 41$. Find the number of stamps each one has. **Helen has 9 stamps and Jorge has 32 stamps.**

2 The sum of three consecutive integers is 42. Find the integers. **13, 14, 15**

353

3 Solve each equation.
a. $4(2q - 7) = -4$ **3**
b. $44 = -5(r - 4) - r$ **−4**

3 **EXAMPLE** Error Prevention

There are some common errors that students may make when they use the Distributive Property to solve an equation such as Example 3b. They may forget to distribute -3 to *all* terms inside the parentheses, or they may distribute the -3 to the term outside the parentheses on the right. Students may also multiply one or both terms by 3 instead of -3, thus resulting in one or both terms with wrong signs. Encourage students to check their use of the Distributive Property before moving on to solving the equation.

3 **EXAMPLE** Visual Learners

In Example 3b instruct students to circle the term (-3, not just 3) in front of the parentheses. Then draw an arrow from the circled term to each of the terms inside the parentheses.

Closure

Ask students to describe a process for solving $5(x - 2) - 7 = 38$ without using numbers in their description. **First use the Distributive Property to remove the parentheses. Next combine like terms. Then undo the subtraction before undoing the multiplication.**

Need Help?

The Distributive Property:

$5(a + 4) = 5a + 20$

$3(6b - 2) = 18b - 6$

OBJECTIVE

2 Using the Distributive Property

Sometimes you may need to use the Distributive Property when you solve a multi-step equation.

3 **EXAMPLE** Using the Distributive Property

Solve each equation.

a. $2(5x - 3) = 14$

$\begin{aligned}
2(5x - 3) &= 14 \\
10x - 6 &= 14 &&\text{Use the Distributive Property.} \\
10x - 6 + 6 &= 14 + 6 &&\text{Add 6 to each side.} \\
10x &= 20 &&\text{Simplify.} \\
\frac{10x}{10} &= \frac{20}{10} &&\text{Divide each side by 10.} \\
x &= 2 &&\text{Simplify.}
\end{aligned}$

b. $38 = -3(4y + 2) + y$

$\begin{aligned}
38 &= -3(4y + 2) + y \\
38 &= -12y - 6 + y &&\text{Use the Distributive Property.} \\
38 &= -12y + y - 6 &&\text{Use the Commutative and Associative Properties of Addition to group like terms.} \\
38 &= -11y - 6 &&\text{Combine like terms.} \\
38 + 6 &= -11y - 6 + 6 &&\text{Add 6 to each side.} \\
44 &= -11y &&\text{Simplify.} \\
\frac{44}{-11} &= \frac{-11y}{-11} &&\text{Divide each side by −11.} \\
-4 &= y &&\text{Simplify.}
\end{aligned}$

✓ **Check Understanding** Example 3

3. Solve each equation.

    a. $-3(m - 6) = 4$ $4\frac{2}{3}$ **b.** $3(x + 12) - x = 8$ -14

Key Concepts	Steps for Solving a Multi-Step Equation
Step 1	Use the Distributive Property, if necessary.
Step 2	Combine like terms.
Step 3	Undo addition or subtraction.
Step 4	Undo multiplication or division.

EXERCISES

 For more exercises, see *Extra Practice*.

Practice and Problem Solving

3. Practice

A Practice by Example

Solve each equation.

Example 1
(page 352)

1. $8a + 4a = 144$
12

2. $9x - 2x = -42$
−6

3. $5b + 11 - 2b = 50$
13

4. $4a + 1 - a = 19$
6

5. $18 = b - 7b$
−3

6. $4d + 2d - 3d = 27$
9

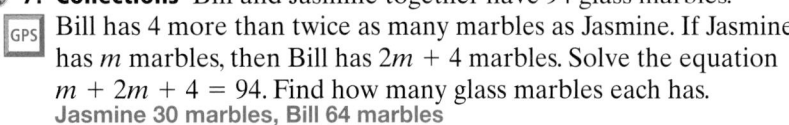 **7. Collections** Bill and Jasmine together have 94 glass marbles. Bill has 4 more than twice as many marbles as Jasmine. If Jasmine has m marbles, then Bill has $2m + 4$ marbles. Solve the equation $m + 2m + 4 = 94$. Find how many glass marbles each has.
Jasmine 30 marbles, Bill 64 marbles

Example 2
(page 353)

Number Sense Find the integers.

8. The sum of two consecutive integers is 131.
65, 66

9. The sum of three consecutive even integers is 60.
18, 20, 22

Example 3
(page 354)

Solve each equation.

10. $3(n - 2) = 36$ 14

11. $4(y - 1) = 36$ 10

12. $2(8 + n) = 22$ 3

13. $-2(a + 3) - a = 0$ −2

14. $3(2x + 1) + x = -39$ −6

15. $m + 4(2m - 3) = -3$ 1

B Apply Your Skills

Solve and check each equation.

16. $5x - x = -12$ −3

17. $-6 = a + a + 4$ −5

26. The student subtracted 5 from the right side of the equation instead of adding 5.

18. $-9 - b + 8b = -23$ −2

19. $36 = y - 5y - 12$ −12

20. $-3(2y + 7) = -18$ $-\frac{1}{2}$

21. $16 = 2(x - 1) - x$ 18

22. $21 = 2(4a + 2)$ $2\frac{1}{8}$

23. $8 - 3(x - 4) = 4$ $5\frac{1}{3}$

Number Sense Find the integers.

24. The sum of four consecutive integers is −22.
−7, −6, −5, −4

25. The sum of five consecutive integers is −65.
−15, −14, −13, −12, −11

26. Error Analysis A student solved the equation $7x - 5 - 5x = 15$ and found $x = 5$. What might be the student's error? See above left.

 **27. Construction** A carpenter is building a fence around a swimming pool. One side of the pool is next to the house and does not need fencing. The carpenter has 120 feet of fencing and plans to use it all. Solve the equation $w + 76 + w = 120$ to find the unknown dimension of the enclosed rectangular area. 22 ft

29. First, use the Distributive Property and combine like terms. Next, subtract 8 from each side. Finally, divide each side by 12.

28. Number Sense Two numbers are w and $3w - 5$. Their sum is 23. Solve the equation $w + 3w - 5 = 23$ to find the numbers. 7, 16

29. Writing in Math Explain how to solve $3(9 + 4a) - 19 = 32$.
See left.

 Use the Guided Problem Solving worksheet with Exercise 7.

Assignment Guide

 **Objective 1**
A B Core 1–9, 16–19, 24–28, 30
C Extension 35, 36

 **Objective 2**
A B Core 10–15, 20–23, 29, 31, 32
C Extension 33, 34

Test Prep 37–40
Mixed Review 41–47

Practice 7-2 Solving Multi-Step Equations

Solve and check each equation.

1. $\frac{p}{6} - 7 = -2$
p = 15

2. $2(n - 7) + 3 = 9$
n = 10

3. $0 = 5(k + 9)$
k = −9

4. $4h + 7h - 16 = 6$
h = 2

5. $3(2n - 7) = 9$
n = 5

6. $-27 = 8x - 5x$
x = −9

7. $4p + 5 - 7p = -1$
p = 2

8. $7 - y + 5y = 9$
y = $\frac{1}{2}$

9. $8e + 3(5 - e) = 10$
e = −1

10. $-37 = 3x + 11 - 7x$
x = 12

11. $9 - 3(n - 5) = 30$
n = −2

12. $\frac{1}{6}(y + 42) - 15 = -3$
y = 30

Write and solve an equation for each situation.

13. Find three consecutive integers whose sum is 51.
$n + (n + 1) + (n + 2) = 51$
16, 17, 18

14. Find three consecutive integers whose sum is −15.
$n + (n + 1) + (n + 2) = -15$
−6, −5, −4

15. Find four consecutive integers whose sum is 30.
$n + (n + 1) + (n + 2) + (n + 3) = 30$
6, 7, 8, 9

16. Jack's overtime wage is $3 per hour more than his regular hourly wage. He worked for 5 hours at his regular wage and 4 hours at the overtime wage. He earned $66. Find his regular wage.
$5h + 4(h + 3) = 66$; $6/h

Enrichment 7-2 Solving Number Problems

You can use two-step equations to solve problems involving odd and even numbers and multiples of whole numbers.

The sum of three consecutive odd numbers is 99. Answer these questions to learn a method for finding the numbers.

1. Let n be the first number. Write an expression for each of the other two numbers in terms of n.
$n + 2, n + 4$

2. Write and solve an equation to find the three numbers.
$n + (n + 2) + (n + 4) = 99$; $3n + 6 = 99$;
$n = 31$; 31, 33, 35

Find the numbers described.

3. three consecutive odd numbers with a sum of 261
85, 87, 89

4. two consecutive even numbers with a sum of 894
446, 448

5. an odd number which when multiplied by 4 and added to the next odd number produces a sum of 177
35

Use the same principle to solve problems involving multiples of whole numbers.

6. m is a multiple of 6. Write the next two multiples of 6 in terms of m.
$m + 6, m + 12$

Write and solve an equation for each situation.

7. The sum of three consecutive multiples of 5 is 90. Find the numbers.
$n + (n + 5) + (n + 10) = 90$; 25, 30, 35

8. The sum of four consecutive multiples of 7 is 378. Find the numbers.
$n + (n + 7) + (n + 14) + (n + 21) = 378$; 84, 91, 98, 105

9. The sum of three times a multiple of 4 and the next two multiples of 4 is 272. Find the numbers.
$3m + (m + 4) + (m + 8) = 272$; 52, 56, 60

4. Assess

PowerPoint **Lesson Quiz 7-2**

Solve each equation.

1. $b + 2b - 11 = 88$ **33**

2. $6(2n - 5) = -90$ **−5**

3. $3(x + 6) + x = 86$ **17**

4. Find four consecutive integers whose sum is −38.
−11, −10, −9, −8

Geometry Connection
Exercises 31, 32 Remind students if necessary, that the formula for the area A of a rectangle is $A = \ell w$ where ℓ is the length and w is the width.

Exercises 33, 34 Remind students that dividing by a number is the same as multiplying by its reciprocal.

Test Prep

Resources
For additional practice with a variety of test item formats:
• Test Prep, p. 393
• Test-Taking Strategies, p. 388
• Test-Taking Strategies With Transparencies

Reteaching 7-2 *Solving Multi-Step Equations*

Solve $6 - 2(x + 5) = 8$

$6 - 2(x + 5) = 8$

$6 - 2x - 10 = 8$ Distribute.

$-2x - 4 = 8$ Simplify. Think of $6 - 2x$ as $6 + (-2x)$. Then subtract $6 - 10$.

$-2x - 4 + 4 = 8 + 4$ Add 4 to each side.

$-2x = 12$ Simplify.

$\frac{-2x}{-2} = \frac{12}{-2}$ Divide each side by −2.

$x = -6$ Simplify.

Solve each equation.

1. $3(a - 4) = 9$

$\underline{3a - 12 = 9}$ Distribute.

$\underline{3a - 12 + 12 = 9 + 12}$ Add 12 to each side.

$\underline{3a = 21}$ Simplify.

$\underline{\frac{3a}{3} = \frac{21}{3}}$ Divide each side by 3.

$\underline{a = 7}$ Simplify.

Solve each equation.

2. $n + 5n = 30$ $n = \underline{5}$ **3.** $y - 4y = 33$ $y = \underline{-11}$

4. $12 = 4(b - 2)$ $b = \underline{5}$ **5.** $-3(k - 4) = -6$ $k = \underline{6}$

6. $m - 3m + 3 = 11$ $m = \underline{-4}$ **7.** $2(x - 9) + 5 = 1$ $x = \underline{7}$

356

---

30. Birdhouses Together, Donal, Yolanda, and Iris made 27 birdhouses for a school fair. Yolanda made n birdhouses. Donal made one more birdhouse than Yolanda, and Iris made one more than Donal. Solve the equation $n + (n + 1) + (n + 1 + 1) = 27$. Find the number of birdhouses each one made.
8, 9, and 10 birdhouses

Geometry For each rectangle, the area is 20 cm². Find the value of x.

31.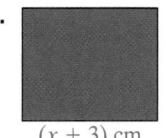
2
4 cm
$(x + 3)$ cm

32. 3
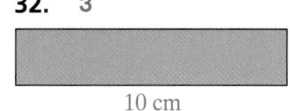
$(2x - 4)$ cm
10 cm

C Challenge

Solve and check each equation.

33. $\frac{1}{3}[2(x - 8) + 1] = 19$ **36**   **34.** $3 = \frac{1}{4}(m - 4) + \frac{1}{4}m$ **8**

Number Sense Find the integers.

35. The sum of four consecutive odd integers is −72.
−21, −19, −17, −15

36. The sum of five consecutive even integers is 0.
−4, −2, 0, 2, 4

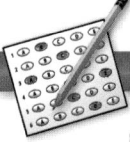

Test Prep

Multiple Choice

37. $3(2x + 5) = \underline{\ ?\ }$. **D**
A. $5x + 5$ **B.** $6x + 5$ **C.** $6x + 8$ **D.** $6x + 15$

38. A rectangle has base 5 cm and height $(x + 2)$ cm. Its area is 20 cm². What is the value of x? **F**
F. 2   **G.** 3.6   **H.** 4.4   **I.** 6

Take It to the NET
Online lesson quiz at
www.PHSchool.com
Web Code: ada-0702

39. What is the solution of $-2(b - 4) = 12$? **B**
A. −4   **B.** −2   **C.** 2   **D.** 4

Short Response

40. Three consecutive integers have a sum of 63. **See margin.**
a. Write an equation to model this situation. Then solve.
b. Show your work for part (a).

Mixed Review

Lesson 7-1

Solve each equation.

41. $10a - 32 = -28$ $\frac{2}{5}$ **42.** $5 - 2d = 15$ **−5**   **43.** $\frac{c}{4} - 7 = 5$ **48**

Lesson 5-8

44. $\frac{7}{10}a = \frac{3}{5}$ $\frac{6}{7}$ **45.** $\frac{2}{7}x = \frac{5}{8}$ $2\frac{3}{16}$ **46.** $-2\frac{3}{4} = 6\frac{3}{5}b$ $-\frac{5}{12}$

Lesson 5-5

47. Measurement If you take $\frac{2}{3}$ c of flour from a bowl containing $2\frac{1}{2}$ c of flour, how much flour is left in the bowl? $1\frac{5}{6}$ c

356   Chapter 7   Solving Equations and Inequalities

Alternative Assessment

Ask each student to write a multi-step equation on an index card. Then write the steps of the solution on separate index cards. Instruct students to shuffle the cards and exchange their sets of cards with each other. Each student is to arrange the index cards in the appropriate order to show how to solve the equation.

40. [2] $n + (n + 1) + (n + 2) = 63$
$3n + 3 = 63$
$3n + 3 - 3 = 63 - 3$
$3n = 60$
$\frac{3n}{3} = \frac{60}{3}$
$n = 20$
The numbers are 20, 21, and 22.
[1] minor error OR answers only

Multi-Step Equations With Fractions and Decimals

Lesson Preview

 Check Skills You'll Need

Solving Two-Step Equations
Lesson 7-1: Examples 1 and 2;
Exercises 1–12.
Extra Practice, p. 750.

Lesson Resources

 Teaching Resources
Practice, Reteaching, Enrichment

 Reaching All Students
Practice Workbook 7-3
Spanish Practice Workbook 7-3
Guided Problem Solving 7-3
Technology Activities 13

Presentation Assistant Plus!
Transparencies and PowerPoint™
• Check Skills You'll Need 7-3
• Additional Examples 7-3
• Student Edition Answers 7-3
• Lesson Quiz 7-3
PH Presentation Pro CD-ROM 7-3

 ASSESSMENT *SYSTEM*

Computer Test Generator CD-ROM

 Technology
Resource Pro® CD-ROM
Computer Test Generator CD-ROM
PH Presentation Pro CD-ROM

 www.PHSchool.com

Student Site
• Teacher Web Code: adk-5500
• Algebra Readiness Puzzles 47
• Self-grading Lesson Quiz
PH SuccessNet Teacher Center
• Lesson Planner
• Resources

Plus **i**TEXT

OBJECTIVE
1 Solving Multi-Step Equations With Fractions

Remember, when the coefficient of a variable in an equation is a fraction, you can use the reciprocal to solve the equation.

$$\frac{4}{5}x = 12$$

$$\frac{5}{4} \cdot \frac{4}{5}x = \frac{5}{4} \cdot 12 \qquad \textbf{Multiply each side by } \frac{5}{4}, \textbf{ because } \frac{5}{4} \cdot \frac{4}{5} = 1.$$

$$x = 15$$

When you have a multi-step equation and the coefficient of the variable is a fraction, gather the variables on one side of the equation and the constants on the other before multiplying by the reciprocal.

1 EXAMPLE Using the Reciprocal

Solve $\frac{2}{3}n - 6 = 22$.

$$\frac{2}{3}n - 6 = 22$$

$$\frac{2}{3}n - 6 + 6 = 22 + 6 \qquad \textbf{Add 6 to each side.}$$

$$\frac{2}{3}n = 28 \qquad \textbf{Simplify.}$$

$$\frac{3}{2} \cdot \frac{2}{3}n = \frac{3}{2} \cdot 28 \qquad \textbf{Multiply each side by } \frac{3}{2}, \textbf{ the reciprocal of } \frac{2}{3}.$$

$$n = \frac{3 \cdot 28^{14}}{{}_{1}2} \qquad \textbf{Divide common factors.}$$

$$n = 42 \qquad \textbf{Simplify.}$$

Check $\quad \frac{2}{3}n - 6 = 22$

$$\frac{2}{3}(42) - 6 \stackrel{?}{=} 22 \qquad \textbf{Replace } n \textbf{ with 42.}$$

$$\frac{2 \cdot 42^{14}}{{}_{1}3} - 6 \stackrel{?}{=} 22 \qquad \textbf{Divide common factors.}$$

$$28 - 6 \stackrel{?}{=} 22 \qquad \textbf{Multiply.}$$

$$22 = 22 ✓$$

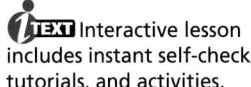 **Check Understanding** Example 1

1. Solve each equation.
   a. $-\frac{7}{10}k + 14 = -21$ **50**   b. $\frac{2}{3}(m - 6) = 3$ **$10\frac{1}{2}$**

What You'll Learn

 OBJECTIVE **1**
To solve multi-step equations with fractions

 OBJECTIVE **2**
To solve multi-step equations with decimals

. . . And Why

To solve problems involving cost of phone service

 **Check Skills You'll Need**

Solve each equation.

1. $2n + 53 = 47$ **−3**

2. $4m - 37 = -28$ **$2\frac{1}{4}$**

3. $-26x - 4 = 100$ **−4**

4. $-3a + 15 = 13$ **$\frac{2}{3}$**

❓ For help, go to Lesson 7-1.

Need Help?

For more help with fractions and reciprocals, see pages 250, 268, and Skills Handbook page 774.

iTEXT Interactive lesson includes instant self-check, tutorials, and activities.

Ongoing Assessment and Intervention

Before the Lesson
Diagnose prerequisite skills using:
• Check Skills You'll Need

During the Lesson
Monitor progress using:
• Check Understanding
• Additional Examples
• Test Prep

After the Lesson
Assess knowledge using:
• Lesson Quiz
• Computer Test Generator CD-ROM

Professional Development

Math Background

To clear a fraction from an equation, you essentially "get rid" of the denominator by making it 1. You do this by multiplying both sides of the equation by the denominator. When a fraction is the coefficient of the variable, you can multiply by the reciprocal of the fraction. This actually combines two steps: multiplying to eliminate the denominator and dividing by what would be the resulting coefficient.

Teaching Notes

1 EXAMPLE Inclusion

Many students have difficulty performing operations with fractions. Review multiplication of reciprocals. Ask why the product of $\frac{3}{2}$ and $\frac{2}{3}$ is 1.

Their product is $\frac{6}{6}$, which equals 1.

2 EXAMPLE Error Prevention

Students may forget to multiply the 2 by 20. Stress to students that when using the Distributive Property every term must be multiplied by the LCM. Suggest they write the LCM beside each term before multiplying.

2 EXAMPLE Teaching Tip

Remind students that the LCM of the denominators of two or more fractions is called the least common denominator (LCD).

You can use the Multiplication Property of Equality to simplify the solving of an equation involving fractions. Use the LCM of the denominators to clear the equation of fractions.

2 EXAMPLE Using the LCM

Solve $\frac{2}{5}x + 2 = \frac{3}{4}$.

$$\frac{2}{5}x + 2 = \frac{3}{4}$$

$$20\left(\frac{2}{5}x + 2\right) = 20\left(\frac{3}{4}\right) \quad \text{Multiply each side by 20, the LCM of 5 and 4.}$$

$$20 \cdot \frac{2}{5}x + 20 \cdot 2 = 20\left(\frac{3}{4}\right) \quad \text{Use the Distributive Property.}$$

$$8x + 40 = 15 \quad \text{Simplify.}$$

$$8x + 40 - 40 = 15 - 40 \quad \text{Subtract 40 from each side.}$$

$$8x = -25 \quad \text{Simplify.}$$

$$\frac{8x}{8} = \frac{-25}{8} \quad \text{Divide each side by 8.}$$

$$x = -3\frac{1}{8} \quad \text{Simplify.}$$

✓ Check Understanding Example 2

2. Solve each equation.

  a. $-\frac{7}{12} + y = \frac{1}{6}$ $\frac{3}{4}$ **b.** $\frac{1}{3}b - 1 = \frac{5}{6}$ $5\frac{1}{2}$

OBJECTIVE

2 Solving Multi-Step Equations With Decimals

You can use the properties of equality to solve equations with decimals.

3 EXAMPLE Real-World 🌐 Problem Solving

Cell Phones Suppose your cell phone plan is $20 per month plus $.15 per minute. Your bill is $37.25. Use the equation $20 + 0.15x = 37.25$ to find the number of minutes on your bill.

$$20 + 0.15x = 37.25$$

$$20 - 20 + 0.15x = 37.25 - 20 \quad \text{Subtract 20 from each side.}$$

$$0.15x = 17.25 \quad \text{Simplify.}$$

$$\frac{0.15x}{0.15} = \frac{17.25}{0.15} \quad \text{Divide each side by 0.15.}$$

$$x = 115 \quad \text{Simplify.}$$

There are 115 minutes on your bill.

✓ Check Understanding Example 3

3. Solve each equation.

  a. $1.5x - 3.6 = 2.4$ **4** **b.** $1.06p - 3 = 0.71$ **3.5**

👥 Reaching All Students

| **Below Level** Review multiplication of fractions with students. Be sure to include simplifying the product. | **Advanced Learners** Have students solve the equation in *More Than One Way* by first writing each decimal as a fraction. Ask: *By what number should you multiply each side to eliminate the fractions?* **1,000** | **Inclusion** See note on page 358. **Error Prevention** See note on page 358. |

Need Help?

For help with finding the least common multiple (LCM), see Lesson 5-1.

You can solve multi-step equations containing decimals by calculating with the decimals or by multiplying by a power of 10 to clear the equation of decimals.

More Than One Way

Telephone Services For local telephone service, the McNeils pay **$9.95/month plus $.035/min for local calls. Last month, they paid $12.75 for local service. To find the minutes *m* of local calls, solve the equation $0.035m + 9.95 = 12.75$.**

Nicole's Method

I can work with decimals as I have before.

$$0.035m + 9.95 = 12.75$$
$$0.035m + 9.95 - 9.95 = 12.75 - 9.95$$
$$0.035m = 2.8$$
$$\frac{0.035m}{0.035} = \frac{2.8}{0.035}$$
$$m = 80$$

The McNeils made 80 min of local calls.

Daryl's Method

Use multiplication to clear the decimals. Use the decimals with the greatest number of decimal places to decide what power of 10 to use.

$$0.035m + 9.95 = 12.75$$
$$1,000(0.035m + 9.95) = 1,000(12.75)$$
$$35m + 9,950 = 12,750$$
$$35m + 9,950 - 9,950 = 12,750 - 9,950$$
$$35m = 2,800$$
$$\frac{35m}{35} = \frac{2,800}{35}$$
$$m = 80$$

The McNeils made 80 min of local calls.

Choose a Method 1–2. See right.

1. Which method would you use to find the number of minutes? Explain.

2. In Daryl's Method, why was each side of the equation multiplied by 1,000?

1. Answers may vary.
   Sample: Daryl's method;
   it is easier to work with
   whole numbers than
   with decimals.
2. to clear the equation of
   decimals

PowerPoint
Additional Examples

❶ Solve $\frac{3}{4}p - 7 = 11$. **24**

❷ Solve $\frac{1}{2}y + 3 = \frac{2}{3}$. **$-4\frac{2}{3}$**

❸ Suppose your cell phone plan is $30 per month plus $.05 per minute. Your bill is $36.75. Use the equation $30 + 0.05x = 36.75$ to find the number of minutes on your bill.
   135 minutes

Closure

Ask: *What is a good first step when you solve an equation containing fractions or decimals?*
Multiply each term by the LCM of the denominators to eliminate any fractions, or multiply each term by a power of 10 to eliminate all decimals.

3. Practice

Assignment Guide

 **Objective 1**
Ⓐ Ⓑ **Core** 1–12, 20, 21, 23, 24, 27, 28, 30, 34, 35
Ⓒ **Extension** 38

Objective 2
Ⓐ Ⓑ **Core** 13–19, 22, 25, 26, 29, 31–33
Ⓒ **Extension** 36, 37

Test Prep 39–43
Mixed Review 44–50

Practice 7-3 **Multi-Step Equations With Fractions and Decimals**

Solve and check each equation.

1. $0.7n - 1.5 + 7.3n = 14.5$ 2. $18p - 45 = 0$
   $n = 2$ $p = 2.5$
3. $16.3k + 19.2 + 7.5k = -64.1$ 4. $h + 3h + 4h = 100$
   $k = -3.5$ $h = 12\frac{1}{2}$
5. $40 - 5n = -2$ 6. $14 = \frac{2}{3}(9y - 15)$
   $n = 8.4$ $y = 4$
7. $\frac{2}{3}y - 6 = 2$ 8. $1.2m + 7.5m + 2.1 = 63$
   $y = 12$ $m = 7$
9. $\frac{7}{8}h - \frac{5}{8} = 2$ 10. $93.96 = 4.7p + 8.7p - 2.6p$
   $h = 3$ $p = 8.7$
11. $9w - 16.3 = 5.3$ 12. $88.1 - 2.3f = 72.46$
    $w = 2.4$ $f = 6.8$
13. $-15.3 = -7.5k + 55.2$ 14. $26e + 891 = -71$
    $k = 9.4$ $e = -37$
15. $2.3(x + 1.4) = -9.66$ 16. $(x - 17.7) + 19.6 = 27.8$
    $x = -5.6$ $x = 25.9$

Write an equation to describe each situation. Solve.

17. Jolene bought three blouses at one price and 2 blouses priced $3 below the others. The total cost was $91.50. Find the prices of the blouses.
    $3x + 2(x - 3) = 91.50;$ $19.50 and $16.50
18. A car rented for $29 per day plus $.08 per mile. Julia paid $46.12 for a one-day rental. How far did she drive?
    $29 + 0.08m = 46.12;$ $m = 214$ miles

By what number would you multiply each equation to clear denominators or decimals? Do not solve.

19. $\frac{1}{3}z + \frac{1}{6} = 5\frac{1}{6}$ 20. $3.7 + 2.75k = 27.35$
    6   100

Enrichment 7-3 **Simplifying Equations With Fractions**

You can use a shortcut to solve equations containing fractions.
Example Solve $\frac{2}{3}x - \frac{7}{6} = \frac{2}{3}$

First, use the normal method to solve. Complete.

1. $\frac{2}{3}x - \frac{7}{6} + \boxed{\frac{7}{6}} = \frac{2}{3} + \boxed{\frac{7}{6}}$
2. $\frac{2}{3}x = \boxed{\frac{20}{6}}$
3. $\frac{2}{3}x \cdot \boxed{\frac{3}{2}} = \boxed{\frac{20}{6}} \cdot \boxed{\frac{3}{2}}$
4. $x = \boxed{7}$

To use the shortcut, first find the LCM of all the denominators appearing in the equation.

5. LCM of 3, 6, and 2 = ____ 6
6. Multiply both sides of the equation by the LCM.
   $\boxed{6}\left(\frac{2}{3}x - \frac{7}{6}\right) = \boxed{6} \cdot \frac{2}{3}$
7. Apply the distributive property.
   $\boxed{6}\left(\frac{2}{3}x\right) - \boxed{6}\left(\frac{7}{6}\right) = \boxed{21}$
8. Multiply. $\boxed{4x} - \boxed{7} = \boxed{21}$
9. Solve. $x = \boxed{7}$

Solve using the shortcut.

10. $\frac{3}{4}k - \frac{7}{10} = \frac{1}{2}$ $k = $ ____ 2   11. $\frac{1}{3}m + \frac{1}{6} = \frac{4}{9}$ $m = $ ____ $\frac{5}{6}$
12. $\frac{5}{8}y - \frac{1}{2} = \frac{3}{4}$ $y = $ ____ 2   13. $\frac{5}{9}n - \frac{3}{14} = \frac{1}{2}$ $n = $ ____ 1
14. $\frac{5}{8}h + \frac{7}{12} = \frac{3}{4}$ $h = $ ____ $\frac{4}{9}$ 15. $\frac{11}{12}e - \frac{7}{10} = \frac{2}{3}$ $e = $ ____ 3

EXERCISES

🔖 For more exercises, see *Extra Practice*.

Practice and Problem Solving

Ⓐ **Practice by Example**

State the first step in solving each equation. Do not solve. 1–3. See left.

Example 1
(page 357)
1. Subtract 3 from each side or multiply each side by 4.
2. Subtract 2 from each side or multiply each side by 5.
3. Multiply each side by 2.

Example 2 (page 358)

1. $\frac{1}{4}x + 3 = 2$ 2. $-\frac{1}{5}y + 2 = -3$ 3. $\frac{1}{2}(n - 8) = 6$

Solve each equation.

4. $\frac{5}{8}c - 8 = 12$ 32   5. $-8 + \frac{3}{5}g = -2$ 10   6. $\frac{3}{4}(b + 8) = 15$ 12

Mental Math By what number would you multiply each equation to get an equation without denominators? Do not solve.

7. $\frac{1}{2}h - 1 = \frac{3}{8}$ 8   8. $\frac{1}{5}y + 3 = \frac{2}{3}$ 15   9. $\frac{7}{10}c - 10 = \frac{2}{5}$ 10

Solve each equation.

10. $\frac{1}{4}c + 2 = \frac{3}{4}$ -5 11. $8 - \frac{w}{10} = \frac{3}{5}$ 74   12. $\frac{2}{3}(a - 3) = \frac{1}{3}$ $3\frac{1}{2}$

Example 3
(page 358)

13. $0.7c - 10 = 0.5$ 15   14. $1.2n + 3.4 = 10$ 5.5

15. $-0.8k - 3.1 = -8.3$ 6.5   16. $0.4b + 9.2 = 10$ 2

17. $0.9x + 2.3x = -6.4$ -2 18. $-2d + 4.3 = 10.7$ -3.2

🌎 19. **Art** Dwayne is taking a drawing class. The drawing pencils cost $.97 apiece and a sketchbook costs $5.95. Dwayne spent a total of $11.77. Solve the equation $0.97n + 5.95 = 11.77$ to find the number n of pencils he bought. **6 pencils**

Ⓑ **Apply Your Skills**

Solve and check each equation.

20. $\frac{5}{8}(p - 4) = 2$ $7\frac{1}{5}$ 21. $p + \frac{1}{3}p = \frac{2}{3}$ $\frac{1}{2}$ 22. $0.07x + 9.95 = 12.47$
                                                                                                      36
23. $-\frac{3}{4}y + \frac{1}{4} = \frac{1}{2}$ $-\frac{1}{3}$ 24. $\frac{x}{4} - \frac{3x}{2} = -\frac{1}{2}$ $\frac{2}{5}$ 25. $2.4b + 5.6 = -11.2$
                                                                                                                            -7
26. $4x + 2 = -28.4$ -7.6 27. $-\frac{1}{12}\frac{1}{3}(x - 9) = -1$ 28. $\frac{2}{7}k - \frac{1}{14}k = -3$ -14
29. $0.4(a + 2) = 2$ 3   30. $\frac{1}{2}(x - 1) = \frac{1}{2}$ 2   31. $1.2c + 2.6c = 4.56$ 1.2

🌎 32. **White-Water Rafting** Six friends hire a raft and guide to go white-water rafting in Colorado. Each person also buys a souvenir photo of the trip for $25.75. The total each person pays is $90.30. To find the cost c of the raft and guide, solve the equation $\frac{c}{6} + 25.75 = 90.30$. **$387.30**

33. **Writing in Math** At a 15%-off sale, a customer pays $11.01 for a video. Explain how to solve the equation $p - 0.15p = 11.01$ to find the original price p of the video. Answers may vary. Sample: First, combine like terms. Then divide each side by 0.85.

Real-World 🌎 **Connection**

White-water rafting trips can be as short as two hours or as long as several days.

🌎 34. **Sales** A pair of athletic shoes is on sale for $\frac{1}{4}$ off the original cost. The sale price is $49.95. Solve the equation $c - \frac{1}{4}c = 49.95$ to find the original cost c of the shoes. **$66.60**

GPS Use the Guided Problem Solving worksheet with Exercise 34.

35. Geometry Use the rectangle at the right.
  a. Find the value of x if the area is 15 square units. **4**
  b. Find the value of x if the perimeter is 24 units. **12**

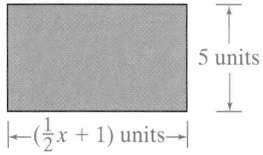

5 units

$\leftarrow (\frac{1}{2}x + 1)$ units$\rightarrow$

 **Challenge** **Solve and check each equation.**

36. $12p + 7 = -15 + 6.5p$ **−4**   **37.** $5(t - 0.4) = -6t$ $\frac{2}{11}$

38a. $\dfrac{65 + 80 + 78 + 92 + s}{5}$

38b. $\dfrac{65 + 80 + 78 + 92 + s}{5} = 80$

38. a. A student has grades of 65, 80, 78, and 92 on four tests. Use s to represent the student's grade on the next test. Write an expression for the average of the five tests. **a–b. See left.**
  b. The student wants to have an average of 80 after the fifth test. Use the expression you wrote in part (a) to write an equation.
  c. Solve the equation to find the grade the student must earn on the fifth test to have an average of 80 for the class. **85**

 **Test Prep**

Gridded Response

39. What is the solution of $\frac{1}{2}(4a - 16) = 5$? **13/2 or 6.5**

40. What is the solution of $7.1 = 3.8h + 5.2$? **0.5**

41. Last season, you scored 48 points in basketball. This is 6 fewer than twice the number of points Gene scored. How many points did Gene score? **27**

42. A cable television company charges $24.95 a month for basic service and $6.95 a month for each premium channel. If your monthly bill is $45.80, how many premium channels are you receiving? **3**

 **Take It to the NET**
Online lesson quiz at
www.PHSchool.com
Web Code: ada-0703

43. A photograph is 4 in. wide and 5 in. long. You want to enlarge it to triple its dimensions. How many times the area of the original will the area of the enlargement be? **9**

Mixed Review

Lesson 7-2   **Solve each equation.**

44. $-9 = 3(y + 4)$ **−7**   **45.** $x + 7 - 3x = 7$ **0**   **46.** $5(t - 8) = 10$ **10**

Lesson 6-2 **47. Commuting** Mrs. Milton travels 60 mi round-trip to work. She works five days a week. Her car gets about 25 mi/gal of gasoline. About how many gallons of gasoline does Mrs. Milton's car use during her weekly commute? **12 gal**

Lesson 4-2   **Write using exponents.**

48. $4 \cdot 4 \cdot 4$ 4^3 **49.** $c \cdot c \cdot c \cdot c \cdot d$ c^4d **50.** $9 \cdot a \cdot a \cdot 2$ $18a^2$

4. Assess

 PowerPoint **Lesson Quiz 7-3**

Solve each equation.

1. $\frac{1}{6}d + 13 = 20$ **42**

2. $\frac{3}{5}(s - 8) = 9$ **23**

3. $5 + \frac{2c}{4} = 14$ **18**

4. $0.07x + 0.03 = 0.38$ **5**

5. $0.015w - 1.85 = 1.615$ **231**

Test Prep

A sheet of blank grids is available in the *Test-Taking Strategies With Transparencies* booklet. Give copies of this sheet to students so they can practice filling in the grids.

 **Resources**

For additional practice with a variety of test item formats:
• Test Prep, p. 393
• Test-Taking Strategies, p. 388
• Test-Taking Strategies With Transparencies

Error Prevention!

Exercise 43 If a problem is geometric and the test is not timed, suggest students draw diagrams to help verify their answer.

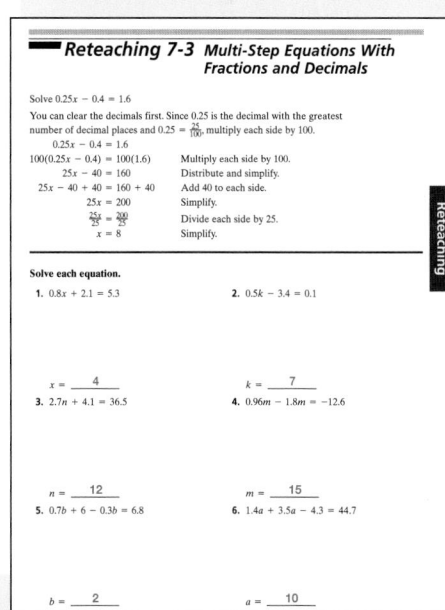

Alternative Assessment

Have students demonstrate different methods for solving the equation $0.7y - 0.3 = 1.1$. Let volunteers explain their methods to the class.

1. Plan

Lesson Preview

 Check Skills You'll Need

Variables and Equations
Lesson 2-4: Example 4;
Exercises 21 and 22.
Extra Practice, p. 745.

Lesson Resources

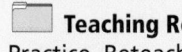 **Teaching Resources**
Practice, Reteaching, Enrichment
Checkpoint Quiz 1

 Reaching All Students
Practice Workbook 7-4
Spanish Practice Workbook 7-4
Reading and Math Literacy 7B
Spanish Reading and Math
  Literacy 7B
Spanish Checkpoint Quiz 1
Guided Problem Solving 7-4

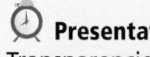 **Presentation Assistant Plus!**
Transparencies and Power Point™
• Check Skills You'll Need 7-4
• Additional Examples 7-4
• Student Edition Answers 7-4
• Lesson Quiz 7-4
PH Presentation Pro CD-ROM 7-4

 **ASSESSMENT SYSTEM**

Checkpoint Quiz 1
Computer Test Generator CD-ROM

 Technology
Resource Pro® CD-ROM
Computer Test Generator CD-ROM
PH Presentation Pro CD-ROM

 www.PHSchool.com
Student Site
• Teacher Web Code: adk-5500
• Algebra Readiness Puzzles 48
• Self-grading Lesson Quiz
PH SuccessNet Teacher Center
• Lesson Planner
• Resources

Plus **iTEXT**

7-4 Problem Solving

Write an Equation

 What You'll Learn

OBJECTIVE **1** To write an equation to solve a problem

. . . And Why

To solve problems about renting moving vans

 Check Skills You'll Need

Write an equation to represent each situation.

1. Pierre bought a puppy for $48. This is $21 less than the original price. What was the original price of the puppy?
   $p - 21 = 48$
2. A tent weighs 6 lb. Together, your backpack and the tent weigh 33 lb. How much does your backpack weigh?
   $b + 6 = 33$
3. A veterinarian weighs 140 lb. She steps on a scale while holding a large dog. The scale shows 192 lb. What is the weight of the dog?
   $140 + d = 192$

? For help, go to Lesson 2-4.

OBJECTIVE

1 Write an Equation

Math Strategies in Action You probably recognize Albert Einstein's famous formula, $E = mc^2$. Many scientists write and use equations and formulas every day. Banks use equations to calculate interest and loan information. Statisticians use equations to find sports and population statistics. Doctors use equations to calculate correct doses of medicines.

You have written one-step equations for word problems. Now you will extend your skills to more complex situations.

1 EXAMPLE **Real-World** 🌐 **Problem Solving**

Moving Vans A moving van rents for $29.95 a day plus $.12/mi. Ms. Smith's bill for a two-day rental was $70.46. How many miles did she drive?

Read and Understand

1. What is the goal of this problem? to find how many miles Ms. Smith drove
2. For how long did Ms. Smith rent the van? 2 days
3. What does the van cost without mileage? $29.95 per day
4. What is the mileage charge? $.12/mi

Ongoing Assessment and Intervention

Before the Lesson
Diagnose prerequisite skills using:
• Check Skills You'll Need

During the Lesson
Monitor progress using:
• Check Understanding
• Additional Examples
• Test Prep

After the Lesson
Assess knowledge using:
• Lesson Quiz
• Computer Test Generator CD-ROM
• Chapter Checkpoint 1 (p. 365)

Plan and Solve

Write an equation.

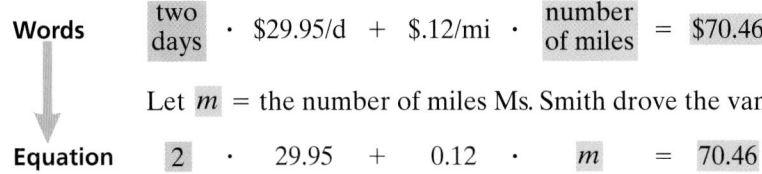

| Words | two days · $29.95/d + $.12/mi · number of miles = $70.46 |

Let m = the number of miles Ms. Smith drove the van.

| Equation | 2 · 29.95 + 0.12 · m = 70.46 |

Solve the equation.

$$2 \cdot 29.95 + 0.12 \cdot m = 70.46$$

$59.9 + 0.12m = 70.46$	**Multiply 2 and 29.95.**
$59.9 - 59.9 + 0.12m = 70.46 - 59.9$	**Subtract 59.9 from each side.**
$0.12m = 10.56$	**Simplify.**
$\dfrac{0.12m}{0.12} = \dfrac{10.56}{0.12}$	**Divide each side by 0.12.**
$m = 88$	**Simplify.**

Ms. Smith drove the van 88 mi.

Look Back and Check

5. A student suggested that another way to solve the gas mileage problem was to use the strategy *Try, Test, Revise*. Suppose that Ms. Smith's bill for the two-day rental was $76.34. How many miles did she drive the van?

   a. Copy and complete the table below to keep track of your trials.

Miles	Cost	High/Low?
75	$2 \cdot 29.95 + 75 \cdot 0.12 = \blacksquare$ 68.90	low
100	$2 \cdot 29.95 + \blacksquare \cdot 0.12 = \blacksquare$ 100 71.90	$\blacksquare$ low

   b. Extend the table to find the solution to the problem. **137 miles**
   c. Check your solution by writing and solving an equation. **Answers may vary. Sample:**

   $$2 \cdot 29.95 + 0.12m = 76.34$$
   $$59.9 + 0.12m = 76.34$$
   $$59.9 - 59.9 + 0.12m = 76.34 - 59.9$$
   $$0.12m = 16.44$$
   $$m = \frac{16.44}{0.12}$$
   $$m = 137$$

✓ **Check Understanding**

6. **Reasoning** Which method do you prefer for solving this type of problem? Explain. **Answers may vary. Sample: Write and solve an equation because it is faster.**
7. Mr. Jones rented the same van for three days. His bill was $104.49. How many miles did he drive? **122 mi**

Math Background

When you write the words to suggest an equation, you are stating a relationship in a clear and unambiguous way. You are also organizing what you know and what you want to find into a mathematical sentence. Represent what you want to find with a variable.

Teaching Notes

Diversity

Families of some students have never moved. Let students whose families have moved describe all the activities (packing, etc.), and how long it may take to perform each activity. Ask for volunteers to call five different moving companies to find their van rental costs.

Error Prevention!

Suggest that students always try to write the words and the equation so that corresponding parts align with each other. This helps them see how the words in a problem and the parts of an equation are related.

PowerPoint

Additional Example

1. A moving van rents for $29.95 a day plus $.12 a mile. Mr. Reynolds's bill was $137.80 and he drove the van 150 mi. For how many days did he have the van? **4 days**

Closure

Ask students: *What problem-solving strategy is used in this lesson?* **Write an Equation**

🧑‍🤝‍🧑 Reaching All Students

| **Below Level** Have students read word problems and list the words or phrases that suggest math operations. Some of these key words are *is* (=), *less than* (−), and *sum* (+). | **Advanced Learners** Give students a variable equation, or have them pick one from the Checkpoint exercises on page 365. Have students write a word problem that can be solved by using the given equation. | **Diversity** See note on page 363. **Error Prevention** See note on page 363. |

3. Practice

Assignment Guide

1 Objective 1
- **A B** Core 1–9
- **C** Extension 10, 11

Test Prep 12–15
Mixed Review 16–22

Practice 7-4 *Write an Equation*

Write an equation. Then solve.

1. Bill purchased 4 pens for $3.32, including $.16 sales tax. Find the cost of 1 pen.

   $4p + 0.16 = 3.32$

   $p = 0.79$; one pen costs $.79.

2. Arnold had $1.70 in dimes and quarters. He had 3 more dimes than quarters. How many of each coin did he have?

   $0.10(n + 3) + 0.25n = \$1.70$

   $n = 4$; Arnold had 7 dimes and 4 quarters.

3. A baby weighed 3.2 kg at birth. She gained 0.17 kg per week. How old was she when she weighed 5.75 kg?

   $3.2 + 0.17w = 5.75$

   $w = 15$; she was 15 weeks old.

4. In the parking lot at a truck stop there were 6 more cars than 18-wheel trucks. There were 134 wheels in the parking lot. How many cars and trucks were there?

   $4(v + 6) + 18v = 134$

   $v = 5$; there were 11 cars and 5 trucks.

5. The product of 6 and 3 more than k is 48.

   $6(k + 3) = 48$

   $k = 5$

6. A bottle and a cap together cost $1.10. The bottle costs $1 more than the cap. How much does each cost?

   $c + (c + 1) = 1.10$

   $c = 0.05$; the bottle costs $1.05 and the cap cost $.05

7. The perimeter of a rectangular garden is 40 ft. The width is 2 ft more than one half the length. Find the length and width.

   $2\left(2 + \frac{1}{2}l + l\right) = 40$

   $l = 12$; the length is 12 and the width is 8.

Enrichment 7-4 *Work Problems*

You can use equations to solve work problems.
Marie can clean a garage in 3 h. Megan can clean it in 4 h. How long would it take them to clean the garage if they worked together?
The key to solving work problems is to look at what happens in 1 h.

Words	Amount Marie does in 1 h	+	Amount Megan does in 1 h	=	Amount they do together in 1 h
Equation	$\frac{1}{3}$	+	$\frac{1}{4}$	=	$\frac{1}{t}$

$\frac{7}{12} = \frac{1}{t}$ Add the fractions.

$7t = 12$ Find the cross product.

$t = \frac{12}{7}$ or $1\frac{5}{7}$ Solve.

Cleaning the garage will take them $1\frac{5}{7}$ h if they work together.

Write an equation. Then solve.

1. Marjorie can wash the car in 2 h. Brad can wash it in 4 h. How long will the job take if they work together?

   $\frac{1}{2} + \frac{1}{4} = \frac{1}{h}$; $h = 1\frac{1}{3}$ h

2. Joe can wax the gym in 3 h. Steve can wax it in 2 h. How long will the job take if they work together?

   $\frac{1}{3} + \frac{1}{2} = \frac{1}{h}$; $h = 1\frac{1}{5}$ h

3. Jessie can paint a barn in 8 h. Jerome needs 10 h to do the same job. How long will it take them working together?

   $\frac{1}{8} + \frac{1}{10} = \frac{1}{h}$; $h = 4\frac{4}{9}$ h

4. Lucy can mow the golf course in 6 h. Stan needs 8 h to do the same job, and Yolanda needs 12 h. How long will it take them to mow the course if they work together?

   $\frac{1}{6} + \frac{1}{8} + \frac{1}{12} = \frac{1}{h}$; $h = 2\frac{2}{3}$ h

5. A swimming pool has 3 drains. One can drain the pool in 5 h, one can drain it in 8 h, and one can drain it in 10 h. How long would it take to drain the pool if all three were open at once?

   $\frac{1}{5} + \frac{1}{8} + \frac{1}{10} = \frac{1}{h}$; $h = 2\frac{6}{17}$ h

---

EXERCISES

?For more exercises, see *Extra Practice.*

Practice and Problem Solving

A Practice by Example

Example 1
(page 362)

Reading Math
For help with reading and solving Exercise 4, see page 366.

Use the *Write an Equation* strategy to solve each problem.

1. The sale price of a sweater is $48. The price is 20% less than the original price. What was the original price? **$60**

2. **Budgeting** Elena has $240 in the bank. She withdraws $15 each week to pay for piano lessons. How many lessons can she afford with her savings? **16 lessons**

3. **Geometry** The perimeter of a rectangle is 64 cm. The length is 4 cm less than twice the width. Find the length and width.
20 cm by 12 cm

4. Wendy bought a drill at a 10%-off sale. The sale price was $75.60. Find the original price p. **$84**

B Apply Your Skills

Solve using any strategy.

Strategies

- Account for All Possibilities
- Draw a Diagram
- Look for a Pattern
- Make a Model
- Make a Table
- Simplify the Problem
- Simulate the Problem
- Solve by Graphing
- Try, Test, Revise
- Use Multiple Strategies
- Work Backward
- Write an Equation
- Write a Proportion

5. Lamar's summer job is mowing lawns for a landscaper. His pay is $7.50/h. Lamar also makes $11.25/h for any time over 40 h that he works in one week. He worked 40 h last week plus n overtime hours and made $339.38. How many overtime hours did he work? **3.5 h**

6. **Number Sense** Find two whole numbers with a sum of 15 and a product of 54. **9 and 6**

7. **Farming** A farmer is building a square pen 21 ft on each side. He puts one post at each corner and one post every 3 ft in between. How many posts will he use? **28 posts**

8. It takes 8 painters 6 hours to paint the walls of a gymnasium.
   a. How many person-hours does this job require? **48 h**
   b. How many hours will 12 painters take to paint the gymnasium? **4 h**

9. Cathy has a collection of dimes and quarters. The number of dimes equals the number of quarters. She has a total of $2.80. How many of each coin does Cathy have? (*Hint:* Let n = the number of dimes. Since each dime has a value of 10¢, the value of n dimes is $10n$. Since the number of quarters is also n, the value of n quarters is $25n$. Also change the value of $2.80 to its value in cents.)
8 quarters and 8 dimes

C Challenge

10. **Physics** The weight of an object on Venus is about $\frac{9}{10}$ of its weight on Earth. The weight of an object on Jupiter is about $\frac{13}{5}$ times its weight on Earth.
    a. If a rock weighs 23 lb on Venus, how much would it weigh on Earth? **$25\frac{5}{9}$ lb**
    b. If the same rock were on Jupiter, how much would it weigh?
    $66\frac{4}{9}$ lb

11. **Collections** Jackson, Petra, and Tyrone went to the beach and collected seashells over the weekend. Jackson collected s seashells. Petra and Tyrone each collected 13 fewer than twice the number of seashells Jackson collected. At the end of the weekend, they had 94 seashells. How many seashells did each person collect?
Jackson: 24 seashells; Petra and Tyrone: 35 seashells apiece

GPS Use the Guided Problem Solving worksheet with Exercise 5.

Multiple Choice

12. What is the solution of $49.95 + 0.6m + 9 = 93.23$ rounded to the nearest whole number? **B**

   A. 20   **B.** 57   **C.** 72   **D.** 155

13. What is the solution of $d + 3.95 + 0.25d = 7.70$? **I**

   F. 6   **G.** 5   **H.** 4   **I.** 3

Take It to the NET
Online lesson quiz at
www.PHSchool.com
Web Code: ada-0704

14. A car salesman makes a weekly salary of $260 plus 3% of the amount of sales he makes that week. Which equation could be used to find the amount of sales if one week's pay was $1,520? **C**

   A. $1,520 = 260 - 0.03x$ **B.** $260 = 1,520 + 0.3x$

   C. $1,520 = 260 + 0.03x$ **D.** $260 = 1,520 - 0.3x$

Short Response

15. The perimeter of a rectangle is 15 ft. The height of the rectangle is 3 more than twice its base. **(a)** Write an equation to model this situation. **(b)** Solve the equation and find the height.
See back of book.

Mixed Review

Lesson 7-3   **Solve each equation.**

16. $\frac{3}{5}k + \frac{1}{5}k = 4$ **5**   **17.** $1.4x + 8.8 = 92.8$ **60**

Lesson 6-5   **Write each percent as a fraction in simplest form and as a decimal.**

18. 52% $\frac{13}{25}$, 0.52 **19.** 20.5%   **20.** 0.5%   **21.** 205%
             $\frac{41}{200}$, 0.205 $\frac{1}{200}$, 0.005 $\frac{41}{20}$ or $2\frac{1}{20}$, 2.05

Lesson 6-1   **22.** You can buy 12 pencils for $.80. At this rate, how much will you pay for 27 pencils? **$1.80**

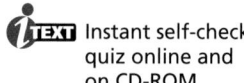
Checkpoint Quiz 1   Lessons 7-1 through 7-4

TEXT Instant self-check quiz online and on CD-ROM

Solve each equation.

1. $12n + 60 = 300$ **20** **2.** $5y - 9 - 3y = 131$ **1** **3.** $-44 = 3x + 10$ **−18**

4. $\frac{a}{4} - \frac{3}{4} = \frac{1}{4}$ **4**   **5.** $\frac{4}{7}x - 3 = 13$ **28**   **6.** $-\frac{x}{6} - 8 = 0$ **−48**

7. $0.6x + 1.9x = 5$ **2**   **8.** $10(5 + m) = 63$ **1.3** **9.** $2c + 4 + 3c = -26$ **−6**

10. $\frac{1}{5}(x + 10) = 2$ **0**   **11.** $7(2y - 1) = 7$ **1**   **12.** $3a + 9 = 27$ **6**

Write an equation for each situation. Then solve.

13. Gloria bought a suit at a 25%-off sale. The sale price was $82.50. Find the original price. $p - 0.25p = 82.50$; $110

14. **Number Sense** Three consecutive integers have a sum of 132. Find the integers. $n + (n + 1) + (n + 2) = 132$; 43, 44, 45

Alternative Assessment

Suggest that each student change the wording and/or numbers in one of the exercises to reflect a situation from their own life. Then, in small groups, have them solve their problems and explain the solutions.

Test Prep

📁 **Resources**
For additional practice with a variety of test item formats:
- Test Prep, p. 393
- Test-Taking Strategies, p. 388
- Test-Taking Strategies With Transparencies

Reading for Problem Solving

This feature encourages students to read carefully, and state what they know and what they are being asked to find. Then students write an equation in words. Writing a word equation makes it easier to write the symbolic equation.

Teaching Notes

Error Prevention!

Some students may benefit from an explanation why $p - 0.1p = 0.9p$. Review the Distributive Property.

$$p - 0.1p = 1p - 0.1p$$
$$= (1 - 0.1)p$$
$$= 0.9p$$

Teaching Tip

Have students do the Exercise and then share their strategies and answers with partners. Some students may use the Try, Test, Revise strategy and others may write an equation. Discuss the advantages of writing and solving an equation with the class.

Read through the problem below. Then follow along with what Elena thinks as she solves the problem. Check your understanding with the exercise at the bottom of the page.

Wendy bought a drill at a 10%-off sale. The sale price was $75.60. Find the original price p.

What Elena Thinks

What information is given in the problem? I'll write it down.

What am I trying to find out? I'll write out the question.

I know that 10% off means that you subtract 10% of the original price from the original price. I'll write this as an equation in words.

I'll use a variable for the original price. And I'll write 10% as the decimal 0.1.

I can write p as $1p$ so that I can subtract like terms. Then I will simplify.

To finish solving the equation, I divide both sides by 0.9.

Is $84.00 a reasonable answer? 10% of 84 is about 8, and $84 - 8$ is 76. This is close to $75.60. Yes, my answer is reasonable.

What Elena Writes

A drill was on sale for 10% off. The sale price was $75.60.

What was the original price?

Original price minus 10% of the original price is the sale price, $75.60.

$$p - 0.1p = 75.60$$

$$1p - 0.1p = 75.60$$
$$0.9p = 75.60$$

$$\frac{0.9}{0.9}p = \frac{75.60}{0.9}$$
$$p = 84$$

The original price of the drill was $84.00.

EXERCISE

1. Tanya got a 5% raise at her job at the video store. She now makes $6.51 per hour. How much did she make per hour before the raise? $6.20

Solving Equations With Variables on Both Sides

OBJECTIVE

1 Solving Equations With Variables on Both Sides

Using Models to Solve Equations

Work in pairs.

1. Write an equation for the model at the right.
   $5x - 8 = 3x$

2. a. You must do the same thing to each side of the model. What can you do to get green tiles on only one side?
   b. Show what the model will look like when green tiles are on only one side. Write the new equation. 2a–b. See below right.
   c. Solve your new equation. 4

To solve an equation with a variable on both sides, use addition or subtraction to collect the variable on one side of the equation.

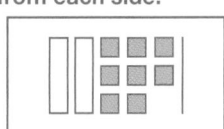

1 EXAMPLE   Collecting the Variable on One Side

Solve $9a + 2 = 4a - 18$.

$9a + 2 = 4a - 18$	
$9a - 4a + 2 = 4a - 4a - 18$	Subtract $4a$ from each side.
$5a + 2 = -18$	Combine like terms.
$5a + 2 - 2 = -18 - 2$	Subtract 2 from each side.
$5a = -20$	Simplify.
$\dfrac{5a}{5} = \dfrac{-20}{5}$	Divide each side by 5.
$a = -4$	Simplify.

Check	$9a + 2 = 4a - 18$	
	$9(-4) + 2 \stackrel{?}{=} 4(-4) - 18$	Substitute -4 for a.
	$-36 + 2 \stackrel{?}{=} -16 - 18$	Multiply.
	$-34 = -34$ ✓	

✓ Check Understanding   Example 1

1. Solve and check each equation.

   a. $4x + 4 = 2x + 36$ 16   b. $-15 + 6b = -8b + 13$ 2

2a. Remove 3 green tiles from each side.

2b.

$2x - 8 = 0$

 TEXT Interactive lesson includes instant self-check, tutorials, and activities.

Math Background

When you solve an equation with variables on both sides, one goal is to get the variable terms on one side of the equation. You do this using inverse operations in the same way you use inverse operations to get constant terms on one side of an equation.

Teaching Notes

Investigation (Optional)

Remind students that a green tile in the model represents *one* of the variable, such as x, and a red tile represents the number -1.

1 EXAMPLE Error Prevention

Encourage students to get the variable term with the lesser coefficient on the side with the variable term that has the greater coefficient. This results in a new variable term with a positive coefficient.

2 EXAMPLE English Learners

Have students describe the phrase *steady rate* by giving examples or demonstrating what is or is not a steady rate.

PowerPoint
Additional Examples

❶ Solve $4c + 3 = 15 - 2c$. **2**

❷ Steve types at a rate of 15 words/min and Jenny types at a rate of 20 words/min. Steve and Jenny are both typing the same document, and Steve starts 5 min before Jenny. How long will it take Jenny to catch up with Steve? **15 min**

Closure

Ask: *How is solving an equation with the variable appearing twice on the same side of the equal sign different from solving an equation with the variable appearing on both sides of the equal sign?* In the first situation given, you combine terms using the operation shown. In the latter situation, you combine terms using inverse operations.

368

You may need to use the Distributive Property to simplify one or both sides of an equation before you can get the variable alone on one side.

2 EXAMPLE Real-World Problem Solving

Bicycling Beth leaves home on her bicycle, riding at a steady rate of 8 mi/h. Her brother Ted leaves home on his bicycle half an hour later, following Beth's route. He rides at a steady rate of 12 mi/h. How long after Beth leaves home will Ted catch up?

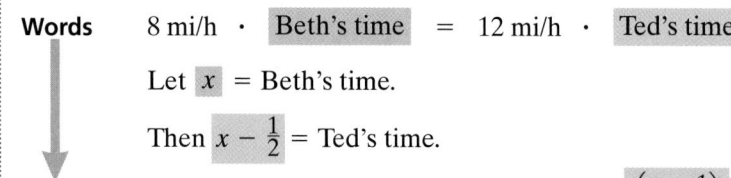

Real-World Connection

An estimated 80.6 million people in the United States ride bicycles. About 14.5% of the nation's bicycle riders live in California.

distance Beth travels = distance Ted travels

Words   8 mi/h $\cdot$ Beth's time $=$ 12 mi/h $\cdot$ Ted's time

Let x = Beth's time.

Then $x - \frac{1}{2}$ = Ted's time.

Equation   8 $\cdot$ x $=$ 12 $\cdot$ $\left(x - \frac{1}{2}\right)$

$$8x = 12\left(x - \frac{1}{2}\right)$$

$8x = 12x - 6$ **Use the Distributive Property.**

$8x - 12x = 12x - 12x - 6$ **Subtract 12x from each side.**

$-4x = -6$ **Combine like terms.**

$\frac{-4x}{-4} = \frac{-6}{-4}$ **Divide each side by −4.**

$x = \frac{6}{4}$, or $1\frac{1}{2}$ **Simplify.**

Ted will catch up with Beth $1\frac{1}{2}$ h after she leaves home.

Check Test the result.

At 8 mi/h, Beth will ride 12 mi in $1\frac{1}{2}$ h.

Ted's time is $\frac{1}{2}$ h less than Beth's. He rides for 1 h.

At 12 mi/h, he travels 12 mi in all.

Since Beth and Ted each travel 12 mi, the answer checks.

✓ Check Understanding Example 2

2. **Travel Time** Car A leaves Eastown traveling at a steady rate of 50 mi/h. Car B leaves Eastown 1 h later following Car A. It travels at a steady rate of 60 mi/h. How long after Car A leaves Eastown will Car B catch up? **6 h**

Reaching All Students

| **Below Level** Review how to use the Distributive Property to simplify expressions involving parentheses. | **Advanced Learners** Ask students how they might get the variable on one side for the equation $3b + 4 + 2b = 8 - 7b + 4b$. **Sample: Combine like terms on each side and then undo addition and subtraction.** | **English Learners** See note on page 368. **Inclusion** See note on page 371. |

EXERCISES

3. Practice

❓ For more exercises, see *Extra Practice*.

Practice and Problem Solving

Assignment Guide

1 Objective 1
Ⓐ Ⓑ **Core** 1–10, 18–23, 29
Ⓒ **Extension** 30–32

2 Objective 2
Ⓐ Ⓑ **Core** 11–17, 24–28
Ⓒ **Extension** 33, 34

Test Prep 35–40
Mixed Review 41–49

Ⓐ **Practice by Example**

Copy and complete the steps to each equation.

Example 1
(page 367)

1. $-2a + 7 = a - 8$
$-2a + 7 - a = a - 8 - \blacksquare\ a$
$-3a\ \blacksquare + 7 = -8$
$-3a\ \blacksquare + 7 - 7 = -8 - 7$
$-3a\ \blacksquare = -15$
$\dfrac{-3a}{-3}\ \blacksquare = \dfrac{-15}{-3}$
$a = \blacksquare\ 5$

2. $2x + 16 = -x - 5$
$2x + 16 + \blacksquare\ ^x= -x - 5 + \blacksquare\ x$
$3x\ \blacksquare + 16 = -5$
$3x + 16 - \blacksquare\ ^{16}= -5 - \blacksquare\ 16$
$3x\ \blacksquare = -21$
$\dfrac{3x\ \blacksquare}{3} = \dfrac{-21}{3}$
$x = \blacksquare\ -7$

Solve each equation.

3. $3y - 20 = 8y$ $\ -4$

4. $x - 7 = 2x - 6$ $\ -1$

5. $5x + 8 = 7x$ $\ 4$

6. $3a = a + 22$ $\ 11$

7. $2a + 6 = -a - 8$ $\ -4\frac{2}{3}$

8. $4w + 8 = 6w - 4$ $\ 6$

9. $q + q + q = q + 6$ $\ 3$

10. $b + b + 18 = 4b$ $\ 9$

Example 2
(page 368)

11. $2(x - 4) = 3x$ $\ -8$

12. $7a = 2(a - 10)$ $\ -4$

13. $5(n - 3) = 2n - 6$ $\ 3$

14. $4(8 - y) = 2y + 16$ $\ 2\frac{2}{3}$

15. $2n = 4(n - 8)$ $\ 16$

16. $3(y + 7) = 10y$ $\ 3$

🌐 **17. Aviation** A jet leaves an airport traveling at a steady rate of 600 km/h. Another jet leaves the same airport $\frac{3}{4}$ h later traveling at 800 km/h in the same direction. How long will it take the second jet to overtake the first? **3 h**

Ⓑ **Apply Your Skills**

Solve each equation.

18. $\frac{1}{2}(4d - 2) = d + 5$ $\ 6$

19. $20.6 + 2.1x = -8.2x$ $\ -2$

20. $-2(y + 6) = y + 3 + 2y$ $\ -3$

21. $6(g + 3) = -2(g + 31)$ $\ -10$

22. $7a - 4 + 2a = 3a - 2$ $\ \frac{1}{3}$

23. $3(2y - 0.3) = 19.4 - y$ $\ 2.9$

24. Open-Ended Write a problem that you can represent with an equation with variables on both sides. Write and solve the equation. **See margin.**

Write an equation for each situation. Then solve.

25. Number Sense If a number n is subtracted from 18, the result is four less than n. What is the value of n? $\ 18 - n = n - 4;\ 11$

🌐 **26. Cell Phones** A cellular phone company charges a $27.95 monthly
[GPS] fee and $.12/min for local calls. Another company charges $12.95 a month and $.32/min for local calls. For what number of minutes of local calls are the costs of the plans the same?
$27.95 + 0.12m = 12.95 + 0.32m;\ 75$ min

24. Answers may vary. Sample: Company A rents a stereo for $50 plus $5 per month. Company B rents the same stereo for $30 plus $10 per month. For how many months can you rent from either company and pay the same price?
$50 + 5x = 30 + 10x;\ x = 4$ **months**

[GPS] **Use the Guided Problem Solving worksheet with Exercise 26.**

■ Practice 7-5 *Solving Equations With Variables on Both Sides*

Solve each equation.

1. $3k + 16 = 5k$
$k = 8$

2. $5e = 3e + 36$
$e = 18$

3. $n + 4n - 22 = 7n$
$n = -11$

4. $2(x - 7) = 3x$
$x = -14$

5. $8h - 10h = 3h + 25$
$h = -5$

6. $7n + 6n - 5 = 4n + 4$
$n = 1$

7. $11(p - 3) = 5(p + 3)$
$p = 8$

8. $9(m + 2) = -6(m + 7)$
$m = -4$

9. $y + 2(y - 5) = 2y + 2$
$y = 12$

10. $-9x + 7 = 3x + 19$
$x = -1$

11. $k + 9 = 6(k - 11)$
$k = 15$

12. $-6(4 - t) = 12t$
$t = -4$

13. $2(x + 7) = 5(x - 7)$
$x = 16\frac{1}{3}$

14. $5m + 9 = 3(m - 5) + 7$
$m = -\frac{17}{2}$

15. $5x + 7 = 6x$
$x = 7$

16. $k + 12 = 3k$
$k = 6$

17. $8m = 5m + 12$
$m = 4$

18. $3p - 9 = 4p$
$p = -9$

Write an equation for each situation. Solve.

19. The difference when 7 less than a number is subtracted from twice the number is 12. What is the number?
$2n - (n - 7) = 12$
$n = 5$

20. Four less than three times a number is three more than two times a number. What is the number?
$3n - 4 = 2n + 3$
$n = 7$

■ Enrichment 7-5 *Equations With Two Variables*

An equation containing one variable has only one solution.
Equation: $3x + 6 = 21$
Solution: $x = 5$
An equation containing two variables may have many solutions. The table lists four solutions of the equation $2x + y = 30$. For example, $x = 1$ and $y = 28$ is a solution of the equation because $2(1) + (28) = 30$.

x	y
1	28
2	26
3	24
4	22

1. Find three more solutions of the equation $2x + y = 30$.
Sample answers are shown.
$x = \underline{5}$, $y = \underline{20}$, $x = \underline{6}$, $y = \underline{18}$, $x = \underline{7}$, $y = \underline{16}$

Complete each table for the given equation and values of x.

2. $x - y = 12$

x	y
15	3
14	2
10	-2
8	-4

3. $x + y = 4$

x	y
-1	5
2	2
5	-1
6	-2

4. $3x + y = 19$

x	y
3	10
4	7
5	4
7	-2

5. $5x - y = 11$

x	y
4	9
3	4
0	-11
-1	-16

6. $2x - 3y = 16$

x	y
17	6
14	4
11	2
5	-2

7. $3x + 2y = 13$

x	y
1	5
3	2
5	-1
7	-4

Find an equation with the solutions given in the table.

8.

x	y
8	3
6	5
4	7
2	9
11	0

Equation: $x + y = 11$

9.

x	y
20	6
16	2
14	0
9	-5
7	-7

Equation: $x - y = 14$

10.

x	y
1	24
2	22
3	20
4	18
5	16

Equation: $2x + y = 26$

369

Error Prevention!

Exercises 11–16 Remind students that parentheses suggest they use the Distributive Property to simplify an expression before undoing operations.

$$8x + 36 = 4(7 - x)$$
$$8x + 36 = 28 - 4x$$
$$4x + 36 = 28$$
$$4x = -8$$
$$x = -2$$

27. The student subtracted $4x$ from the left side of the equation instead of adding $4x$; $x = -\frac{2}{3}$

 **Challenge**

29. First use the Distributive Property on the left side. Next, get the variable on the left side only by subtracting a from each side. Then add 15 to each side. Finally, divide each side by 9.

27. Error Analysis The student who solved the equation at the left made an error. Find the error. State the correct solution. See below left.

28. Boating A group of campers and one group leader left a campsite in a canoe traveling at a steady 8 km/h. One hour later, the other group leader left the campsite in a motorboat with all of the supplies. The motorboat followed the canoe at a steady 20 km/h. How long after the canoe left the campsite did the motorboat overtake it? $1\frac{2}{3}$ h

29. Writing in Math Describe the steps you would use to solve the equation $5(2a - 3) = 20 + a$. See below left.

Solve each equation.

30. $9 - (2k - 3) = k$ 4

31. $2\left(2a + \frac{1}{2}\right) = 3\left(a - \frac{2}{3}\right)$ -3

32. Mental Math Is the solution to $5b = 2b - 42 - 3b$ positive or negative? Explain. See margin.

33. Video Rental A video store offers two types of rental cards. Each rental card is good for six months. The gold rental card costs $25 plus $1.75/rental. The silver rental card costs $10 plus $3.25/rental. Explain why someone would prefer one card over the other. See below left.

34. Reasoning To solve $\frac{2}{3}b = 10 - b$, you can first (a) multiply each side by $\frac{3}{2}$, (b) multiply each side by 3, or (c) add b to each side. Which first step do you prefer? Why? What is the solution? See margin.

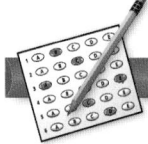

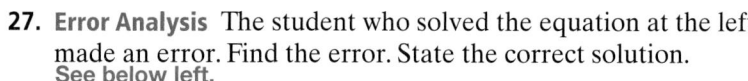 **Test Prep**

Reading Comprehension

Read the passage below before doing Exercises 35 and 36.

33. A renter of a few movies would prefer the silver card (less expensive for fewer than 10 videos). A renter of many movies would prefer the gold card (less expensive for more than 10 videos).

An Algebraic Riddle

Diophantus was a Greek mathematician who lived in the third century. He was one of the first mathematicians to use algebraic symbols.

Most of what is known about Diophantus's life comes from an algebraic riddle from around the early sixth century. The riddle states, "Diophantus's youth lasted one sixth of his life. He grew a beard after one twelfth more. After one seventh more of his life he married. Five years later he and his wife had a son. The son lived exactly one half as long as his father, and Diophantus died four years after his son. All of this adds up to the years Diophantus lived." The riddle, the "facts" of which may or may not be true, results in the following equation:

$$\frac{1}{6}a + \frac{1}{12}a + \frac{1}{7}a + 5 + \frac{1}{2}a + 4 = a$$

where a is Diophantus's age at the time of his death.

35. How many years did Diophantus live? 84 years

36. How old was Diophantus when he married? 33 years

32. Negative; explanations may vary. Sample: When the variable is on only one side of the equation, its coefficient is positive while the constant on the other side of the equation is negative.

34. Answers may vary. Sample: (c) add b to each side. You then have $\frac{5}{3}b = 10$, which is a one-step equation; 6.

37. To which expression does $3(a + 2b) - 3a$ simplify? **D**
  A. $-6a + 6b$ **B.** $3a + 6b$ **C.** $2b$ **D.** $6b$

38. What is the solution of $6(k - 2) = 3k - 6$? **G**
  F. -6 **G.** 2 **H.** $-\frac{4}{3}$ **I.** $\frac{2}{3}$

39. What is the solution of $2(2x + 3) = -3(x + 5)$? **C**
  A. -7 **B.** $-\frac{21}{5}$ **C.** -3 **D.** $\frac{9}{7}$

Take It to the NET
Online lesson quiz at
www.PHSchool.com
Web Code: ada-0705

40. The Garners rented a moving van for $59.95 plus $.50/mi. Before returning the van, they filled the gas tank, which cost $21.50. The total cost for renting the van, including gas, was $199.45. To the nearest mile, how many miles did the Garners drive the van? **H**
  F. 519 mi **G.** 279 mi **H.** 236 mi **I.** 70 mi

Mixed Review

Lesson 6-9 **Find the price after each discount or markup.**

41. $15; 25% discount **$11.25**   **42.** $88; 32% markup **$116.16**

43. $24; 72% markup **$41.28**   **44.** $110; 75% discount **$27.50**

Lesson 2-10 **Solve and graph each inequality.** 45–48. For graphs, see margin.

45. $-4x < 32$ **46.** $\frac{a}{-9} \geq -3$ **47.** $-12 < 3y$ **48.** $12 \leq -2y$
  $x > -8$ $a \leq 27$ $y > -4$ $y \leq -6$

Lesson 1-8 **49. Collections** In a collection of dimes and quarters, there are seven more quarters than there are dimes. How many dimes and quarters are there if the collection is worth $3.50?
5 dimes, 12 quarters

Math at Work

······················· **City Planner**

City planners, also called urban planners or regional planners, determine the best use of a community's land and resources for homes, businesses, and recreation. They also work on community problems such as traffic congestion and air pollution. They study the effects of proposed changes in a community, such as the addition of a bus line or a new highway. Planners use mathematical analysis to evaluate different courses of action and to predict the impact of each course on a community.

Take It to the NET For more information about city planners, go to **www.PHSchool.com**
Web Code: adb-2031

7-5 Solving Equations With Variables on Both Sides **371**

45.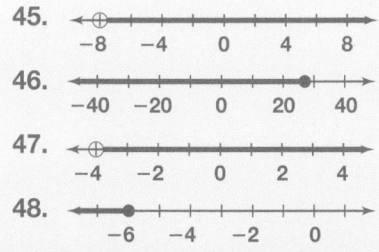
  -8 -4 0 4 8

46.
  -40 -20 0 20 40

47.
  -4 -2 0 2 4

48.
  -6 -4 -2 0

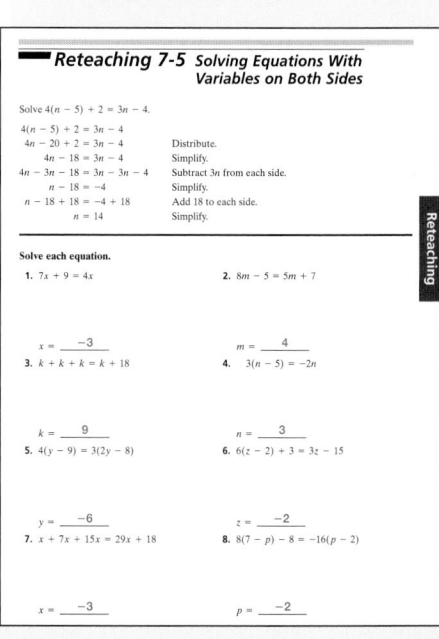

Alternative Assessment

Group students in pairs. One student models an equation with variables on both sides using algebra tiles. The partner solves the equation. Students change roles.

371

Using Tables to Solve Equations

This Technology extension shows students how to use the TABLE feature of a graphing calculator to solve one-variable equations.

Resources

Students may use any graphing calculator.

Teaching Notes

Teaching Tip
Students may wonder what ΔTbl means. The delta symbol, Δ, means change. The number you enter for ΔTbl = is the amount of change you want from one x term to the next x term in the table.

Inclusion
The numbers in the table on the calculator screen may be difficult for some students to read. First remind students that they can darken or lighten the background to change the contrast of the screen by pressing repeatedly
2nd and either the up or down arrow key. If this is not helpful, have a volunteer read the numbers in the table from a few rows above the answer through a few rows below the answer so that any student who cannot read the screen can fill in a table of his or her own.

1 EXAMPLE **Teaching Tip**

Students may not understand why the solution is 8. Explain that when x is 8, the value of both expressions is 17. Therefore, you have found the number that makes the left side of the equation equal to the right side of the equation.

You can use tables on a graphing calculator to solve one-variable equations.

1 EXAMPLE

Solve $x + 9 = 3x - 7$.

Press Y= and enter

$Y_1 = x + 9$
$Y_2 = 3x - 7$

In **TBLSET**, set TBLStart = 0 and ΔTbl = 1.

In **TABLE**, compare the Y_1 and Y_2 values. $Y_1 = Y_2 = 17$ for X = 8.

● The solution of $x + 9 = 3x - 7$ is 8.

X	Y_1	Y_2
3	12	2
4	13	5
5	14	8
6	15	11
7	16	14
8	17	17
9	18	20

X=8

2 EXAMPLE

Solve $x + 3 = 3x - 4$.

Enter $Y_1 = x + 3$
$Y_2 = 3x - 4$

In **TABLE**, compare the Y_1 and Y_2 values. Y_1 values are greater than Y_2 values until X changes from 3 to 4. This suggests that $Y_1 = Y_2$ somewhere between 3 and 4.

In **TBLSET**, set TblStart = 3 and ΔTbl = 0.1.

In **TABLE**, compare the Y_1 and Y_2 values. $Y_1 = Y_2 = 6.5$ for X = 3.5.

● The solution of $x + 3 = 3x - 4$ is 3.5.

X	Y_1	Y_2
3	6	5
3.1	6.1	5.3
3.2	6.2	5.6
3.3	6.3	5.9
3.4	6.4	6.2
3.5	6.5	6.5
3.6	6.6	6.8

X=3.5

EXERCISES

Solve each equation. Round to the nearest tenth where necessary.

1. $p - 5 = 7$ **12**

2. $3x = 21$ **7**

3. $2y + 5 = 14$ **4.5**

4. $2x + x + 3 = 15$ **4**

5. $7m - 3m - 6 = 6$ **3**

6. $15 = -3(2q - 1)$ **−2**

7. $6x - 2 = x + 13$ **3**

8. $3y + 12 = 5y - 3$ **7.5**

9. $2n - 5 = 8n + 7$ **−2**

10. $6a - 9 = -a + 30$ **5.6**

11. $72 - 8c = 32 + 6c$ **2.9**

12. $-2b - 13 = 4b - 10$ **−0.5**

13. Use graphing calculator tables to solve the equation $4(x - 2) = -3(x - 6)$. Find the solution to as many places as possible until "table breakdown" occurs. Then solve the equation using pencil and paper. Compare your two results. **3.7143**

Solving Two-Step Inequalities

Lesson Preview

✓ **Check Skills You'll Need**

Solving One-Step Inequalities
Lesson 2-9: Examples 1 and 3;
Exercises 1–8, 11–19.
Extra Practice, p. 745.

Lesson Resources

📁 **Teaching Resources**
Practice, Reteaching, Enrichment

👥 **Reaching All Students**
Practice Workbook 7-6
Spanish Practice Workbook 7-6
Guided Problem Solving 7-6

⏱ **Presentation Assistant Plus!**
Transparencies and PowerPoint™
• Check Skills You'll Need 7-6
• Additional Examples 7-6
• Student Edition Answers 7-6
• Lesson Quiz 7-6
• Classroom Aid 6
PH Presentation Pro CD-ROM 7-6

(**ASSESSMENT SYSTEM**)

Computer Test Generator CD-ROM

💻 **Technology**
Resource Pro® CD-ROM
Computer Test Generator CD-ROM
PH Presentation Pro CD-ROM

💻 **www.PHSchool.com**
Student Site
• Teacher Web Code: adk-5500
• Algebra Readiness Puzzles 57, 58
• Self-grading Lesson Quiz
PH SuccessNet Teacher Center
• Lesson Planner
• Resources

Plus 📗TEXT

OBJECTIVE

1 Solving Two-Step Inequalities

You solve two-step inequalities and equations using similar steps.

1 EXAMPLE Undoing Operations

Solve and graph $2y - 3 \leq -5$.

$$2y - 3 \leq -5$$
$$2y - 3 + 3 \leq -5 + 3 \qquad \text{Add 3 to each side.}$$
$$2y \leq -2 \qquad \text{Simplify.}$$
$$\frac{2y}{2} \leq \frac{-2}{2} \qquad \text{Divide each side by 2.}$$
$$y \leq -1 \qquad \text{Simplify.}$$

✓ **Check Understanding** Example 1

1. Solve and graph each inequality. **a–c. For graphs, see back of book.**

  a. $5a - 9 > 11$ **b.** $-10 \geq \frac{1}{2}x - 6$ **c.** $17 + \frac{1}{2}c < 14$
  $a > 4$ $x \leq -8$ $c < -6$

Remember to reverse the direction of the inequality symbol when you multiply or divide by a negative number.

2 EXAMPLE Reversing the Inequality Symbol

Solve $-9 > -\frac{1}{3}x + 6$.

$$-9 > -\frac{1}{3}x + 6$$
$$-9 - 6 > -\frac{1}{3}x + 6 - 6 \qquad \text{Subtract 6 from each side.}$$
$$-15 > -\frac{1}{3}x \qquad \text{Simplify.}$$
$$-3(-15) < -3\left(-\frac{1}{3}x\right) \qquad \text{Multiply each side by } -3. \text{ Reverse the direction of the inequality symbol.}$$
$$45 < x, \text{ or } x > 45 \qquad \text{Simplify.}$$

✓ **Check Understanding** Example 2

2. Solve and graph each inequality. **a–c. For graphs, see back of book.**

  a. $-2m + 4 \leq 34$ **b.** $6 - x > 3$ **c.** $8.3 < -0.5b - 2.7$
  $m \geq -15$ $x < 3$ $b < -22$

What You'll Learn

OBJECTIVE 1 To solve two-step inequalities

OBJECTIVE 2 To use two-step inequalities to solve problems

. . . And Why

To solve problems involving camping and jobs

✓ **Check Skills You'll Need**

Solve each inequality. Graph the solutions.
1–4. See back of book.
1. $w + 4 \geq -5$

2. $7 < z - 3$

3. $4 > a + 6$

4. $x - 5 \leq -6$

❓ For help, go to Lesson 2-9.

❓ **Need Help?**

If $a > b$ and $c > 0$, then $ac > bc$.

If $a > b$ and $c < 0$, then $ac < bc$.

📗TEXT Interactive lesson includes instant self-check, tutorials, and activities.

✓ Ongoing Assessment and Intervention

Before the Lesson
Diagnose prerequisite skills using:
• Check Skills You'll Need

During the Lesson
Monitor progress using:
• Check Understanding
• Additional Examples
• Test Prep

After the Lesson
Assess knowledge using:
• Lesson Quiz
• Computer Test Generator CD-ROM

2. Teach

Math Background

You solve two-step inequalities in almost the same way as you solve two-step equations except that when you multiply or divide each side of an inequality by a negative number you must also reverse the inequality symbol.

Teaching Notes

1 EXAMPLE Visual Learners

Students may forget when to use a closed circle in the graph of an inequality. Tell them that if they see the extra line under the inequality symbol (≤ or ≥) then they do the extra work of filling in the circle. If there is no extra line, there is no extra work.

2 EXAMPLE Error Prevention

A common mistake in solving inequalities is to not reverse the inequality symbol when necessary. Encourage students to circle the inequality symbol if the coefficient of the variable term is negative.

3 EXAMPLE English Learners

Help students make a table of examples to relate <, >, ≤, and ≥ to *at least, at most, greatest possible, least possible, greater than,* and *less than.*

PowerPoint
Additional Examples

1 Solve and graph $7g + 11 > 67$.
$g > 8$

```
+--+--+--+--+--+--○--+--+--+--+--+
  2  3  4  5  6  7  8  9 10 11 12
```

2 Solve $6 \leq -\frac{2}{3}r - 6$. $-18 \geq r$, or $r \leq -18$

3 Dale has $25 to spend at a carnival. If the admission to the carnival is $4 and the rides cost $1.50 each, what is the greatest number of rides Dale can go on? 14 rides

Closure

Ask: *How is solving two-step inequalities different from solving two-step equations?*
See Math Background above.

374

Now that you know how to solve two-step inequalities, you can use them to solve real-world problems.

3 EXAMPLE   Real-World Problem Solving

Hiking **An expedition leader estimates that a group of hikers can carry less than 550 lb of food and equipment. The group must carry 336 lb of equipment as well as 25 lb of food for each climber. What is the greatest possible number of people in the expedition?**

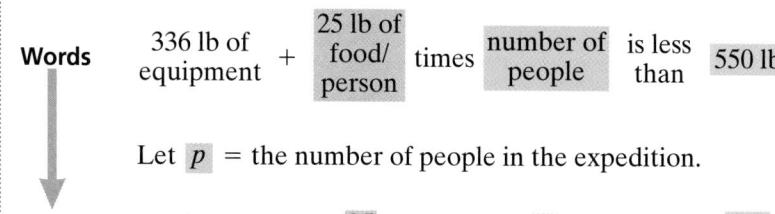

Real-World Connection

A pint of water weighs 1 lb. You need about a gallon of water per person per day.

Words

| 336 lb of equipment | + | 25 lb of food/ person | times | number of people | is less than | 550 lb |

Let p = the number of people in the expedition.

Inequality $336 + 25 \cdot p < 550$

Solve the inequality.

$$336 + 25p < 550$$

$336 + 25p - 336 < 550 - 336$ **Subtract 336 from each side.**

$$25p < 214$$ **Simplify.**

$$\frac{25p}{25} < \frac{214}{25}$$ **Divide each side by 25.**

$$p < 8.56$$ **Simplify.**

The greatest possible number of people in the expedition is 8.

Reading Math

Since $p < 8.56$, the "greatest number of people" must be the greatest whole number less than 8.56.

Check Is the answer reasonable? The original problem states that the total of the equipment plus 25 lb of food per person is less than 550 lb. Since $336 + 25(8) = 536$, the equipment plus the food is less than 550 lb. The answer is reasonable.

✓ Check Understanding   Example 3

3. Commissions A stereo salesperson earns a salary of $1,200 per month, plus a commission of 4% of sales. The salesperson wants to maintain a monthly income of at least $1,500. How much must the salesperson sell each month? ≥ $7,500

👥 Reaching All Students

| **Below Level** Review the one difference between solving equations and inequalities. Refer to Lesson 2-10, where students solved inequalities in which the variable terms have negative coefficients. | **Advanced Learners** Ask: *When might the answer to a stated problem involving inequalities be different from the solution of the inequality?* Sample: when the "real" solution is a single number | **English Learners** See note on page 374. **Auditory Learners** See note on page 376. |

Practice and Problem Solving

 For more exercises, see *Extra Practice*.

3. Practice

Assignment Guide

▼ **Objective 1**
Ⓐ Ⓑ **Core** 1–14, 17–22

▼ **Objective 2**
Ⓐ Ⓑ **Core** 15, 16, 23–27
Ⓒ **Extension** 28, 29

Test Prep 30–33
Mixed Review 34–40

Ⓐ **Practice by Example**

Example 1
(page 373)

Tell what you can do to the first inequality in order to get the second. Be sure to list *all* steps.

1. $4x - 2 \leq 6; x \leq 2$ See left.   **2.** $\frac{1}{2}a - 1 < 3; a < 8$ See left.

1. Add 2 to each side, simplify, divide each side by 4, and simplify.
2. Add 1 to each side, simplify, multiply each side by 2, and simplify.

Solve and graph each inequality. 3–14. For graphs, see margin.

3. $10 + 4a < -6$
$a < -4$

4. $2m + 8 > 0$
$m > -4$

5. $6 + 3y > 5$
$y > -\frac{1}{3}$

6. $4x - 9 > -7$
$x > \frac{1}{2}$

7. $\frac{1}{3}a - 4 \geq -1$
$a \geq 9$

8. $4 + 7a \geq 32$
$a \geq 4$

Example 2
(page 373)

9. $-2x - 1 < 11$
$x > -6$

10. $-\frac{b}{7} + 7 \leq 6$
$b \geq 7$

11. $2.1 - 0.6y \geq 0.9$
$y \leq 2$

12. $10 \leq -8x - 6$
$x \leq -2$

13. $-5y + 3 \geq 28$
$y \leq -5$

14. $-21 - 3m < 0$
$m > -7$

Example 3 🌐 **15. Travel** On a trip from Louisiana to Florida, your family wants to
(page 374)   travel at least 420 miles in 8 hours of driving. Write and solve an
inequality to find what your average speed must be.
$8t \geq 420; t \geq 52.5$; at least 52.5 mi/h

16. Number Sense You divide a number x by -3. Then you subtract 1 from the quotient. The result is at most 5. Write and solve an inequality to find all possible solutions. $\frac{x}{-3} - 1 \leq 5; x \geq -18$

Ⓑ **Apply Your Skills**

Solve each inequality.

17. $-\frac{1}{9}c + 13 \geq 5$
$c \leq 72$

18. $\frac{x}{3} + 11 < 31$
$x < 60$

19. $6y - 10 - y > 14$
$y > 4\frac{4}{5}$

20. $-\frac{x}{6} - 2 < 4$
$x > -36$

21. $\frac{1}{2}c - \frac{1}{4} < -\frac{3}{4}$
$c < -1$

22. $-4(2a + 7) \leq -12$
$a \geq -2$

Write an inequality for each situation. Then solve.

Photo Price List

Size	Price
3 in. x 5 in.	$.40
4 in. x 6 in.	$.45
5 in. x 7 in.	$1.95
8 in. x 10 in.	$4.95
8 in. x 12 in.	$6.45
11 in. x 14 in.	$7.00
16 in. x 20 in.	$13.95
20 in. x 30 in.	$16.95

🌐 **23. Photography** Maureen is ordering photographic reprints and
enlargements. She can spend at most $11. She wants to order an
11-in. × 14-in. enlargement and some 3-in. × 5-in. reprints. How
many reprints can she order using the price list at the left?
at most 10

24. You want to spend at most $10 for a taxi ride. Before you go
[GPS] anywhere, the taxi driver sets the meter at the initial charge of
$2. The meter then adds $1.25 for every mile driven. If you plan
on a $1 tip, what is the farthest you can go? **5.6 mi**

🌐 **25. Test Scores** Students in a math class need an average of at least
90 points to earn an A. One student's test scores are 88, 91, and
85. What must the student score on the next test to earn an A?
96 or above

26. Error Analysis A student
solved and graphed the
inequality $-12x + 40 > 4$.
What error did the
student make? See left.

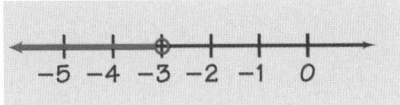

26. The student simplified
$\frac{-36}{-12}$ to -3 instead of 3.

[GPS] Use the Guided Problem Solving worksheet with Exercise 24.

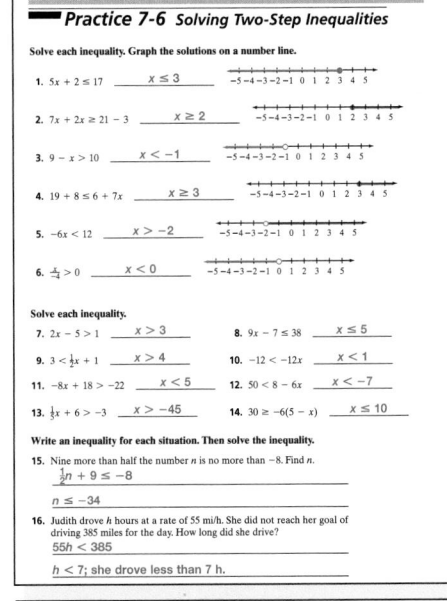

Practice 7-6 *Solving Two-Step Inequalities*

Solve each inequality. Graph the solutions on a number line.

1. $5x + 2 \leq 17$ $x \leq 3$
2. $7x + 2x \geq 21 - 3$ $x \geq 2$
3. $9 - x > 10$ $x < -1$
4. $19 + 8 \leq 6 + 7x$ $x \geq 3$
5. $-6x < 12$ $x > -2$
6. $\frac{4}{4} > 0$ $x < 0$

Solve each inequality.

7. $2x - 5 > 1$ $x > 3$
8. $9x - 7 \leq 38$ $x \leq 5$
9. $3 < \frac{1}{2}x + 1$ $x > 4$
10. $-12 < -12x$ $x < 1$
11. $-8x + 18 > -22$ $x < 5$
12. $50 < 8 - 6x$ $x < -7$
13. $\frac{1}{5}x + 6 > -3$ $x > -45$
14. $30 \geq -6(5 - x)$ $x \leq 10$

Write an inequality for each situation. Then solve the inequality.

15. Nine more than half the number n is no more than -8. Find n.
$\frac{1}{2}n + 9 \leq -8$
$n \leq -34$

16. Judith drove h hours at a rate of 55 mi/h. She did not reach her goal of driving 385 miles for the day. How long did she drive?
$55h < 385$
$h < 7$; she drove less than 7 h.

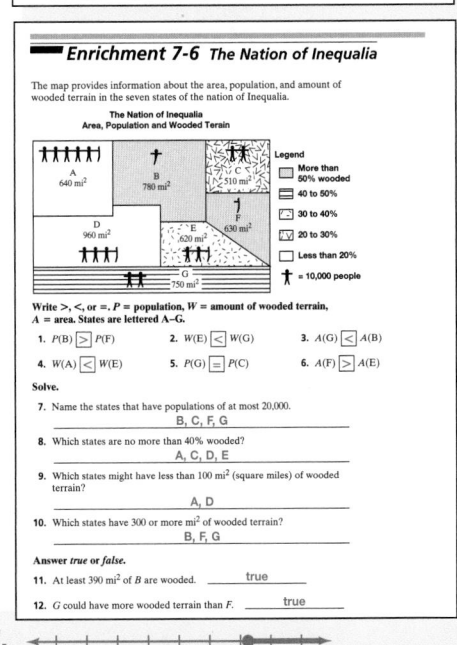

Enrichment 7-6 *The Nation of Inequalia*

The map provides information about the area, population, and amount of wooded terrain in the seven states of the nation of Inequalia.

Write $>$, $<$, or $=$. P = population, W = amount of wooded terrain, A = area. States are lettered A–G.

1. $P(B) > P(F)$
2. $W(E) < W(G)$
3. $A(G) < A(B)$
4. $W(A) < W(E)$
5. $P(G) = P(C)$
6. $A(F) > A(E)$

Solve.

7. Name the states that have populations of at most 20,000.
B, C, F, G
8. Which states are no more than 40% wooded?
A, C, D, E
9. Which states might have less than 100 mi² (square miles) of wooded terrain?
A, D
10. Which states have 300 or more mi² of wooded terrain?
B, F, G

Answer *true* or *false.*

11. At least 390 mi² of B are wooded. true
12. G could have more wooded terrain than F. true

Margin graphs

3.
-5 -4 -3 -2 -1 0 1 2 3 4 5

4.
-4 -2 0 2

5.
-2 0 2 ; $-\frac{1}{3}$

6.
-2 0 $\frac{1}{2}$ 2

7.
-4 0 4 9

8.
-2 -1 0 1 2 3 4 5 6 7 8

9–14. See back of book.

Lesson Quiz 7-6

Solve each inequality.

1. $14 > 4d - 10$ $d < 6$

2. $-\frac{k}{3} + 8 \le 7$ $k \ge 3$

3. $32 - 12g < 176$ $g > -12$

4. $8 + 5a \ge 23$ $a \ge 3$

Auditory Learners
Exercise 12 Suggest students write the solution to the inequality so that the variable is on the left side of the inequality symbol. Then, if the inequality symbol is *less than*, its graph points to the *left*. If the symbol is *greater than*, then its graph points to the *right*.

Test Prep

📁 **Resources**
For additional practice with a variety of test item formats:
• Test Prep, p. 393
• Test-Taking Strategies, p. 388
• Test-Taking Strategies With Transparencies

Reteaching 7-6 *Solving Two-Step Inequalities*

Solve and graph $2x + 9 > 5$.

$2x + 9 > 5$
$2x + 9 - 9 > 5 - 9$ Subtract 9 from each side.
$2x > -4$ Simplify.
$\frac{2x}{2} > \frac{-4}{2}$ Divide each side by 2.
$x > -2$ Simplify.

Since $x > -2$, -2 is not a solution. Use an open circle at -2. Then shade everything to the right of -2.

Solve each inequality. Graph the solutions on a number line.

1. $8 + 3x \le 2$ _____ $x \le -2$ **2.** $\frac{x}{5} - 3 > -4$ _____ $x > -5$

3. $15 - 5k \ge 0$ _____ $k \le 3$ **4.** $9 + 2y < 7$ _____ $y < -1$

5. $\frac{x}{4} + 12 > 10$ _____ $x > -4$ **6.** $6r - 5 \ge -23$ _____ $t \ge -3$

---

27. **Writing in Math** A friend was absent from class today. Write a letter to your friend telling how to solve two-step inequalities. **See left.**

27. Letter excerpt: First undo addition and subtraction, and then undo division and multiplication. Remember to reverse the inequality sign when multiplying or dividing by a negative number.

C Challenge 🌐 **28. Borrowing** Corey's parents agree to loan Corey $182 to help pay for the school's spring music trip to Florida. Corey agrees to monthly payback amounts of $2, $4, $6, $8, and so on. How long will it take Corey to pay back the $182? **13 months**

🌐 **29. Sightseeing** You and a friend want to spend at most $20 each on a horse-carriage sightseeing ride. There is an initial charge of $5 and then $2.50 for each quarter-mile driven. You plan on giving a $6 tip. For how many miles can you ride in the carriage? **at most $2\frac{3}{4}$ mi**

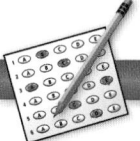

Test Prep

Multiple Choice **30.** Which sign correctly completes
$43(2) - (-3)$ ▇ $-58 + (-4)12$? **D**
A. $\le$ **B.** $<$ **C.** $=$ **D.** $>$

31. Which graph shows the solution of $-15 < -2x - 7$? **H**

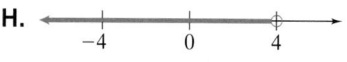 

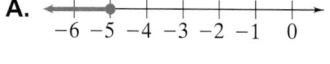 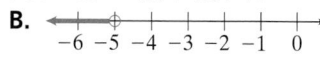

💻 **Take It to the NET**
Online lesson quiz at
www.PHSchool.com
Web Code: ada-0706

32. Which graph shows the solution of $-15 \ge 7x + 20$? **A**

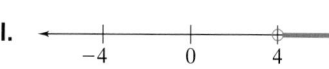

Extended Response **33.** The perimeter of a triangle is at most 32 cm. One side is 11 cm long. The other two sides are the same length. **(a)** What are the possible lengths of the two congruent sides? **(b)** Draw a diagram and show your work. **(c)** Explain your process. **See back of book.**

Mixed Review

Lesson 7-2 **Solve each equation.**

34. $a - 81 = 9a + 7$ **−11**   **35.** $8x - 15 + 4x = 5x + 6$ **3**

Lesson 6-6 🌐 **36. Sales Tax** A stereo costs $262.99. The sales tax rate is 5%. What is the total cost of the stereo? **$276.14**

Lesson 3-4 **Use the distance formula, $d = rt$. Find each missing value.**

37. $r = 45$ mi/h, $t = 3.25$ h
146.25 mi
38. $d = 351$ mi, $r = 54$ mi/h
6.5 h
39. $d = 12$ cm, $t = 0.25$ h
48 cm/h
40. $d = 147.825$ mi, $t = 2.25$ h
65.7 mi/h

Alternative Assessment

Instruct students to draw graphs of inequalities. Students exchange graphs and each writes a two-step inequality for which the graph shows the solution.

Extension

Compound Inequalities

For Use With Lesson 7-6

A **compound inequality** is a statement in which two inequalities are joined by the word *and* or the word *or*.

$x > 4$ and $x \le 6$

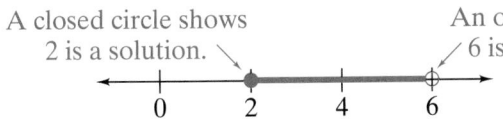

$x \le -2$ or $x > 3$

A solution of a compound inequality joined by *and* is any number that makes both inqualities true.

A solution of a compound inequality joined by *or* is any number that makes either inequality true.

EXAMPLE

Graph each compound inequality on a number line.

a. $2 \le x$ and $x < 6$

A closed circle shows 2 is a solution.

An open circle shows 6 is not a solution.

$2 \le x$ and $x < 6$

b. $z > 4$ or $z \le 1$

closed circle   open circle

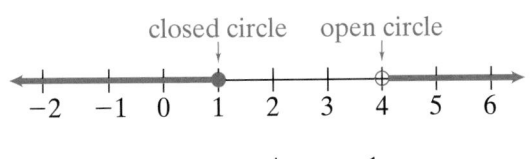

$z > 4$ or $z \le 1$

EXERCISES

Graph each compound inequality. 1–9. See right.

1. $x \ge 0$ and $x \le 7$

2. $z < -2$ and $z \ge -4$

3. $5 > a$ and $a \ge -6$

4. $b < -1$ or $b > 4$

5. $c < 2$ or $c > 3.5$

6. $y \ge 1$ or $y < -3$

7. $x \le 4$ and $x \ge 3$

8. $n \le -5$ or $n > 0$

9. $3 > m$ and $m > -3$

10. <u>Writing in Math</u> Explain why there are no solutions of the compound inequality $x > 2$ and $x \le 2$.
Answers may vary. Sample: There is no number that is both less than or equal to 2 and greater than 2.

1.

2.

3. −6   5

4. −1

5. 3.5

6. −3   1

7. 3

8. −5

9. −3   3

Extension

Compound Inequalities

This Extension shows students how to solve and graph compound inequalities. It explains the difference between a pair of inequalities joined with the word *and* and a pair of inequalities joined with the word *or*.

Teaching Notes

Error Prevention!

Students may not realize how important it is to pay close attention to the word that joins the inequalities. Stress the importance of this by graphing a second compound inequality for each part of the Example. For part (a), draw the graph for the inequality with *or* in place of *and*. Point out that every number is either ≥ 2 or < 6. For part (b), draw the graph for the inequality with *and* in place of *or*. Point out that no number can be both > 4 and ≤ 1.

English Learners

Some students may have difficulty distinguishing the difference between the meanings of *and* and *or*. Ask for all students who are wearing blue *and* red to stand. Then ask for all students who are wearing blue *or* red to stand.

Auditory Learners

A quick "check" is that a graph that looks like a pair of oars shows the solutions of an "or" inequality.

Extension Compound Inequalities **377**

7-7 Transforming Formulas

 Check Skills You'll Need

Using Formulas
Lesson 3-4: Example 1;
Exercises 1–4.
Extra Practice, p. 746

Lesson Resources

 Teaching Resources
Practice, Reteaching, Enrichment
Checkpoint Quiz 2

 Reaching All Students
Practice Workbook 7-7
Spanish Practice Workbook 7-7
Reading and Math Literacy 7C
Spanish Reading and Math
 Literacy 7C
Spanish Checkpoint Quiz 2
Guided Problem Solving 7-7

 Presentation Assistant Plus!
Transparencies and PowerPoint™
• Check Skills You'll Need 7-7
• Additional Examples 7-7
• Student Edition Answers 7-7
• Lesson Quiz 7-7
PH Presentation Pro CD-ROM 7-7

 **ASSESSMENT SYSTEM**

Checkpoint Quiz 2
Computer Test Generator CD-ROM

 Technology
Resource Pro® CD-ROM
Computer Test Generator CD-ROM
PH Presentation Pro CD-ROM

 www.PHSchool.com
Student Site
• Teacher Web Code: adk-5500
• Algebra Readiness Puzzles 49
• Graphing Calculator, Procedure 2
• Self-grading Lesson Quiz
PH SuccessNet Teacher Center
• Lesson Planner
• Resources

 Plus **TEXT**

378

What You'll Learn

 OBJECTIVE 1 To solve a formula for a given variable

 OBJECTIVE 2 To use formulas to solve problems

... And Why

To find travel times in real-world situations

✓ **Check Skills You'll Need**

Use each formula for the values given.

1. Use the formula $d = rt$ to find d when $r = 80$ km/h and $t = 4$ h. **320 km**

2. Use the formula $P = 2\ell + 2w$ to find P when $\ell = 9$ m and $w = 7$ m. **32 m**

3. Use the formula $A = \frac{1}{2}bh$ to find A when $b = 12$ ft and $h = 8$ ft. **48 ft²**

? For help, go to Lesson 3-4.

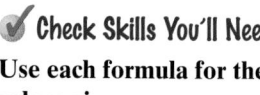 **TEXT** Interactive lesson includes instant self-check, tutorials, and activities.

OBJECTIVE

1 Solving Formulas for a Given Variable

Remember that a formula shows the relationship between two or more quantities. You can use the properties of equality to transform a formula to represent one quantity in terms of another.

1 EXAMPLE **Transforming in One Step**

Solve the area formula $A = \ell w$ for ℓ.

$$A = \ell w$$

$$\frac{A}{w} = \frac{\ell w}{w} \qquad \text{Divide each side by } w.$$

$$\frac{A}{w} = \ell, \text{ or } \ell = \frac{A}{w} \qquad \text{Simplify.}$$

✓ **Check Understanding** Example 1

1. Solve for the variable indicated in red.

a. $p = s - c$ **b.** $h = \frac{k}{j}$ **c.** $I = prt$

$s = p + c$ $k = hj$ $p = \frac{I}{rt}$

Sometimes you need to use more than one step.

2 EXAMPLE **Using More Than One Step**

Solve the perimeter formula $P = 2\ell + 2w$ for ℓ.

$$P = 2\ell + 2w$$

$$P - 2w = 2\ell + 2w - 2w \qquad \text{Subtract } 2w \text{ from each side.}$$

$$P - 2w = 2\ell \qquad \text{Simplify.}$$

$$\frac{1}{2}(P - 2w) = \frac{1}{2}(2\ell) \qquad \text{Multiply each side by } \frac{1}{2}.$$

$$\frac{1}{2}P - w = \ell \qquad \text{Use the Distributive Property and simplify.}$$

✓ **Check Understanding** Example 2

2. Solve for the variable indicated in red.

a. $5a + 7 = b$ **b.** $P = 2\ell + 2w$ **c.** $y = \frac{x}{3} + 8$

$a = \frac{1}{5}b - \frac{7}{5}$ $w = \frac{1}{2}P - \ell$ $x = 3(y - 8)$

378 Chapter 7 Solving Equations and Inequalities

Before the Lesson	During the Lesson	After the Lesson
Diagnose prerequisite skills using:	**Monitor progress using:**	**Assess knowledge using:**
• Check Skills You'll Need	• Check Understanding • Additional Examples • Test Prep	• Lesson Quiz • Computer Test Generator CD-ROM • Chapter Checkpoint 2 (p. 381)

You can transform formulas to solve real-world problems.

3 EXAMPLE <u>Real-World Problem Solving</u>

Travel **You plan a 425-mi trip to Bryce Canyon National Park. You estimate you will average 50 mi/h. To find about how long the trip will take, solve the distance formula $d = rt$ for t. Then substitute to find the time.**

$$d = rt$$

$$\frac{d}{r} = \frac{rt}{r}$$ **Divide each side by r.**

$$\frac{d}{r} = t, \text{ or } t = \frac{d}{r}$$ **Simplify.**

$$t = \frac{425}{50} = 8.5$$ **Replace d with 425 and r with 50. Simplify.**

● It will take you about 8.5 h to complete the trip.

✔ **Check Understanding**   **Example 3**

   3. Solve the distance formula in Example 3 for r. $r = \frac{d}{t}$

4 EXAMPLE <u>Real-World Problem Solving</u>

Temperature **An exchange student in your class wants to know the Celsius equivalent of 77°F. First solve the formula $F = \frac{9}{5}C + 32$ for C. Then substitute to find the temperature.**

$$F = \frac{9}{5}C + 32$$

$$F - 32 = \frac{9}{5}C + 32 - 32$$ **Subtract 32 from each side.**

$$F - 32 = \frac{9}{5}C$$ **Simplify.**

$$\frac{5}{9}(F - 32) = \frac{5}{9} \cdot \frac{9}{5}C$$ **Multiply each side by $\frac{5}{9}$.**

$$\frac{5}{9}(F - 32) = C, \text{ or } C = \frac{5}{9}(F - 32)$$ **Simplify and rewrite.**

$$C = \frac{5}{9}(77 - 32) = 25$$ **Replace F with 77. Simplify.**

● 77°F is 25°C.

✔ **Check Understanding**   **Example 4**

   4. Solve the batting average formula, $a = \frac{h}{n}$, for h. Find the number of hits h a batter needs in 40 times at bat n to have an average of 0.275. $h = an$; 11 hits

Real-World Connection

Wind and water, rushing along stone plateaus, erode the stone and create shapes called "fins" and "hoodoos" in Bryce Canyon, Utah. Each year, more than 1.5 million people visit the national park.

7-7   Transforming Formulas   **379**

Reaching All Students

| **Below Level** Have students review the meanings of the variables in the various formulas used in this lesson. Knowing the meanings will help students understand the formulas when they solve for variables. | **Advanced Learners** Have students use $d = rt$ to show how much time may be saved by driving 70 mi/h instead of 60 mi/h on a 30-mi trip. **about 4 min** | **Alternative Method** See note on page 379. **Error Prevention** See note on page 380. |

Math Background

You transform a formula to solve for one of its variables in terms of the others. You can use a transformed formula repeatedly to evaluate the variable.

Teaching Notes

1 EXAMPLE **Geometry Connection**

Geometry problems often use specific letters consistently to represent certain measures, such as A for area, ℓ for length, w for width, and P for perimeter.

2 EXAMPLE **Alternative Method**

Show students how to use the Distributive Property to first rewrite $P = 2\ell + 2w$ as $P = 2(\ell + w)$. Then divide each side by 2 and subtract w. The result is $\frac{P}{2} - w = \ell$, which is equivalent to $\ell = \frac{1}{2}P - w$.

PowerPoint
Additional Examples

1 Solve the circumference formula $C = 2\pi r$ for r. $r = \frac{C}{2\pi}$

2 Solve the perimeter formula $P = 2\ell + 2w$ for w. $w = \frac{1}{2}P - \ell$

3 You plan a 600-mile trip to New York City. You estimate your trip will take about 10 hours. To estimate your average speed, solve the distance formula $d = rt$ for r. Then substitute to find the average speed. **about 60 mi/h**

4 The high temperature one day in San Diego was 32°C. Solve $C = \frac{5}{9}(F - 32)$ for F. Then substitute to find the temperature in degrees Fahrenheit. **89.6°F**

Closure

Ask: *What is meant by "solving a formula for a given variable"?* expressing one variable in terms of the others used in the formula

Assignment Guide

▼ **Objective 1**
  Ⓐ Ⓑ **Core** 1–8, 11–13

▼ **Objective 2**
  Ⓐ Ⓑ **Core** 9, 10, 14, 15
  Ⓒ **Extension** 16

Test Prep 17–21
Mixed Review 22–27

Error Prevention!

Exercise 16 To help avoid "getting lost" during the solution, suggest students circle the v in each step.

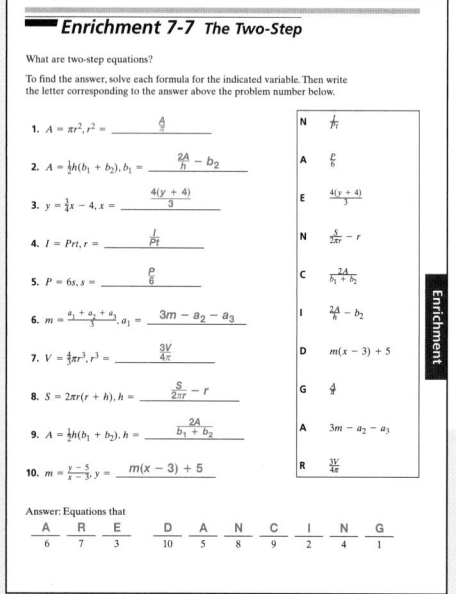

EXERCISES

Practice and Problem Solving

For more exercises, see *Extra Practice*.

Ⓐ **Practice by Example**

Examples 1 and 2
(page 378)

Complete the steps to solve each equation for the variable indicated in red.

1. $a = 6c + 3$

$a - \blacksquare = 6c + 3 - 3 \quad 3$

$a - \blacksquare = 6c \quad 3$

$\dfrac{a - 3}{\blacksquare} = \dfrac{6c}{\blacksquare} \quad 6, 6$

$\dfrac{a - 3}{\blacksquare} = \blacksquare \quad 6, c$

2. $g = \dfrac{h}{j}$

$\blacksquare g = j\left(\dfrac{h}{j}\right) \quad j$

$jg = \blacksquare \quad h$

$\dfrac{jg}{\blacksquare} = \dfrac{h}{g} \quad g$

$\blacksquare = \dfrac{h}{g} \quad j$

Solve for the variable indicated in red.

3. $V = \ell wh \quad w = \dfrac{V}{\ell h}$

4. $P = 4s \quad s = \dfrac{P}{4}$

5. $q = \dfrac{p}{d} \quad p = qd$

6. $r = 2s - 8 \quad s = \frac{1}{2}r + 4$

7. $\frac{2}{3}m - 5 = n \quad m = \frac{3}{2}n + \frac{15}{2}$

8. $m = \dfrac{a + b}{2} \quad a = 2m - b$

Examples 3 and 4
(page 379)

🌐 **9. Commissions** LaTanya sells business suits and gets a 4% commission on her sales. Last week, she received a paycheck that included $196 in commissions. Solve the formula $C = 0.04s$ for s, where C is the amount of commission and s is the amount of sales. Substitute to find LaTanya's sales. **$4,900**

🌐 **10. Renting** You have $12.00 to rent a pair of in-line skates. They rent for $3.00 plus $1.50 per hour. To determine the maximum length of time you can rent the in-line skates, solve the formula $C = 3 + 1.5h$ for h. Then substitute 12 for C. **6 h**

Ⓑ **Apply Your Skills**

Solve for the variable indicated in red.

11. $V = \frac{1}{2}\pi r^2 h \quad h = \dfrac{2V}{\pi r^2}$

12. $d^2 = \frac{3}{2}h \quad h = \frac{2}{3}d^2$

13. $A = \frac{1}{2}(a + b)h \quad h = \dfrac{2A}{a + b}$

🌐 **14. a. Construction** Bricklayers use the formula $N = 7LH$ to estimate the number N of bricks needed in a wall. L is the length of the wall and H is the height. Solve the formula for H. $H = \dfrac{N}{7L}$

  b. If 1,134 bricks are used to build a wall that is 18 ft long, how high is the wall? **9 ft**

15. Writing in Math A formula for the perimeter of a rectangle is $P = 2(b + h)$. Explain how you would find the height of the rectangle if you knew the perimeter and the base. **Answers may vary. Sample: Solve the equation for h and substitute the known values.**

Ⓒ **Challenge** 🌐 **16. a. Economics** Joe uses the formula $p = wh + 1.5wv$ to figure his weekly pay. In the formula, p is the weekly pay, w is the hourly wage, h is the number of regular hours, and v is the number of overtime hours. Solve the formula for v. $v = \dfrac{p}{1.5w} - \dfrac{h}{1.5}$

  b. Joe's hourly wage is $6.24/h. If he earned $282.36 last week working 40 regular hours plus overtime, how many hours overtime did he work? **3.5 h**

 Use the Guided Problem Solving worksheet with Exercise 14.

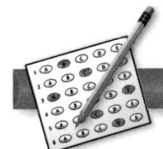

Test Prep

Multiple Choice   For Exercises 17–19, what is the correct result when you solve for the variable indicated in red?

17. $z = xy$ **A**

    A. $x = \frac{z}{y}$ **B.** $x = \frac{y}{z}$ **C.** $x = yz$ **D.** $y = xz$

18. $r = 2s - 8$ **H**

    F. $s = \frac{r+2}{8}$ **G.** $s = r + 4$ **H.** $s = \frac{r+8}{2}$ **I.** $s = 2r + 16$

19. $\frac{2}{3}m - 5 = n$ **B**

    A. $m = \frac{2}{3}(n + 5)$ **B.** $m = \frac{3}{2}(n + 5)$

    C. $m = \frac{3}{2}n + 5$ **D.** $m = \frac{2}{3}n + 5$

20. Use the batting average formula, $a = \frac{h}{n}$. What is the number of hits h for $a = 0.245$ and $n = 25$?   **H**

    F. 98   **G.** 7   **H.** 6   **I.** 0

Extended Response   **21.** Solve $A = \frac{1}{2}(a + b)h$ twice, once for b and once for h. Explain your process for each solution. Then compare the two processes, stating similarities and differences.   See back of book.

Take It to the NET
Online lesson quiz at
www.PHSchool.com
Web Code: ada-0707

Mixed Review

Lesson 7-5   **Solve each inequality.**

22. $3x - 12 > -6$ **23.** $17 \le -4a + 5$ **24.** $-\frac{b}{2} + 9 < -3$

    $x > 2$ $a \le -3$ $b > 24$

Lesson 7-1 🌐 **25. Budgeting** Audrey wants to buy a dress for $54. She has $6 already and plans to save $8 each week. In how many weeks will she be able to buy the dress?   **6 weeks**

Lesson 6-7   **Write and solve an equation. Where necessary, round to the nearest tenth or tenth of a percent.**

26. What percent of 20 is 15?   **75%**   **27.** 80% of what is 25?   **31.3**

Checkpoint Quiz 2   Lessons 7-5 through 7-7

TEXT   Instant self-check quiz online and on CD-ROM

Solve each equation or inequality.

1. $-8a - 6 = 10$ **−2**   **2.** $9b + 42 = -12$ **−6**   **3.** $2c + 6 + 7c = 8$ $\frac{2}{9}$

4. $18y = 12y + 24$ **4**   **5.** $2x + 5 = 9x - 16$ **3**   **6.** $12(m - 4) = 3m - 3$ **5**

7. $15 - 10y < 24$ **8.** $23 > -\frac{x}{2} - 5$ **9.** $1.8x - 3.4 > 5.6$

    $y > -\frac{9}{10}$ $x > -56$ $x > 5$

Solve for the variable indicated in red.

10. $s = g + h$ **11.** $3r + 4 = k$ **12.** $I = prt$

    $h = s - g$ $r = \frac{1}{3}k - \frac{4}{3}$ $t = \frac{I}{pr}$

7-7   Transforming Formulas   **381**

4. Assess

PowerPoint   **Lesson Quiz 7-7**

Solve for the given variable.

1. Solve the area formula $A = \frac{1}{2}bh$ for b. $b = \frac{2A}{h}$

2. Solve the averaging formula $a = \frac{b+c}{2}$ for c.

    $c = 2a - b$

3. The speed v of a satellite as it orbits Earth may be found using the formula $v^2 = \frac{Gm}{r}$. Solve this formula for m, the mass of Earth. $m = \frac{v^2 r}{G}$

✓ **Chapter Checkpoint 2**

To check understanding of Lessons 7-5 to 7-7:
Checkpoint Quiz 2 (p. 381)

📁 **Teaching Resources**
Checkpoint Quiz 2 (also in Prentice Hall Assessment System)

👥 **Reaching All Students**
Reading and Math Literacy 7C

Spanish versions available.

Reteaching 7-7 *Transforming Formulas*

Solve the surface area formula $s = 2\pi r^2 + 2\pi rh$ for h.

    $s = 2\pi r^2 + 2\pi rh$

    $s - 2\pi r^2 = 2\pi r^2 - 2\pi r^2 + 2\pi rh$ Subtract $2\pi r^2$ from each side.

    $s - 2\pi r^2 = 2\pi rh$ Simplify.

    $\frac{s - 2\pi r^2}{2\pi r} = \frac{2\pi rh}{2\pi r}$ Divide each side by $2\pi r$.

    $\frac{s - 2\pi r^2}{2\pi r} = h$ Simplify.

Solve for the indicated variable.

1. $y = mx + b$, for x **2.** $y = mx + b$, for m

    $x = \frac{y - b}{m}$ $m = \frac{y - b}{x}$

3. $p = 6s$, for s **4.** $A = \frac{1}{2}h(B + b)$, for h

    $s = \frac{p}{6}$ $h = \frac{2A}{B + b}$

5. $I = Prt$, for P **6.** $y = \frac{2}{3}x - 5$, for x

    $P = \frac{I}{rt}$ $x = \frac{3(y + 5)}{2}$

7. $t = 0.05p$, for p **8.** $V = lwh$, for w

    $p = \frac{t}{0.05}$ $w = \frac{V}{lh}$

9. $k = \frac{1}{2}mv^2$, for m **10.** $W = p(V - L)$, for V

    $m = \frac{2k}{v^2}$ $V = \frac{W + pL}{p}$

11. $F = \frac{Gm_1 m_2}{r^2}$, for G **12.** $W = p(V - L)$, for L

    $G = \frac{Fr^2}{m_1 m_2}$ $L = \frac{pV - W}{p}$

13. $V = \frac{h}{3}v - \frac{E}{V}$, for e **14.** $mv = (m + M)u$, for m

    $e = \frac{hv - E}{V}$ $m = \frac{Mu}{v - u}$

Alternative Assessment

Ask students to bring formulas from other classes such as health or science. Have them share these with the class and demonstrate how to transform these formulas.

Test Prep

📁 **Resources**
For additional practice with a variety of test item formats:
- Test Prep, p. 393
- Test-Taking Strategies, p. 388
- Test-Taking Strategies With Transparencies

Simple and Compound Interest

Lesson Preview

 Check Skills You'll Need

Proportions and Percents
Lesson 6-6: Example 1;
Exercises 1-8.
Extra Practice, p. 749.

Lesson Resources

 Teaching Resources
Practice, Reteaching, Enrichment

 Reaching All Students
Practice Workbook 7-8
Spanish Practice Workbook 7-8
Guided Problem Solving 7-8

 Presentation Assistant Plus!
Transparencies and PowerPoint™
• Check Skills You'll Need 7-8
• Additional Examples 7-8
• Student Edition Answers 7-8
• Lesson Quiz 7-8
PH Presentation Pro CD-ROM 7-8

 ASSESSMENT *SYSTEM*

Computer Test Generator CD-ROM

 Technology
Resource Pro® CD-ROM
Computer Test Generator CD-ROM
PH Presentation Pro CD-ROM

 www.PHSchool.com
Student Site
• Teacher Web Code: adk-5500
• Graphing Calculator,
  Procedure 19, 27
• Self-grading Lesson Quiz
PH SuccessNet Teacher Center
• Lesson Planner
• Resources

Plus

What You'll Learn

OBJECTIVE 1 To solve simple-interest problems

OBJECTIVE 2 To solve compound-interest problems

. . . And Why

To find interest paid on investments using simple and compound interest

 Check Skills You'll Need

Find each amount.

1. 6% of $400 $24

2. 55% of $2,000 $1,100

3. 4.5% of $700 $31.50

4. $5\frac{1}{2}$% of $325 $17.88

 For help, go to Lesson 6-6.

New Vocabulary
• principal
• interest
• interest rate
• simple interest
• compound interest
• balance

 Interactive lesson includes instant self-check, tutorials, and activities.

OBJECTIVE

1 Simple Interest

When you first deposit money in a savings account, your deposit is called **principal.** The bank takes the money and invests it. In return, the bank pays you **interest** based on the **interest rate. Simple interest** is interest paid only on the principal.

Key Concepts **Simple-Interest Formula**

$$I = prt,$$
where I is the interest, p is the principal,
r is the interest rate per year, and t is the time in years.

1 EXAMPLE **Real-World Problem Solving**

Savings Suppose you deposit $400 in a savings account. The interest rate is 5% per year.

a. Find the simple interest earned in six years. Find the total of principal plus interest.

$I = prt$	**Use the simple-interest formula.**
$I = 400 \cdot 0.05 \cdot 6$	**Replace p with 400, r with 0.05, and t with 6.**
$I = 120$	**Simplify.**
total $= 400 + 120 = 520$	**Find the total.**

The account will earn $120 in six years. The total of principal plus interest will be $520.

b. Find the interest earned in three months. Find the total of principal plus interest.

$t = \frac{3}{12} = \frac{1}{4} = 0.25$	**Write the months as part of a year.**
$I = prt$	**Use the simple-interest formula.**
$I = 400 \cdot 0.05 \cdot 0.25$	**Replace p with 400, r with 0.05, and t with 0.25.**
$I = 5$	**Simplify.**
total $= 400 + 5 = 405$	**Find the total.**

The account will earn $5 in three months. The total of principal plus interest will be $405.

Ongoing Assessment and Intervention

Before the Lesson
Diagnose prerequisite skills using:
• Check Skills You'll Need

During the Lesson
Monitor progress using:
• Check Understanding
• Additional Examples
• Test Prep

After the Lesson
Assess knowledge using:
• Lesson Quiz
• Computer Test Generator CD-ROM

Check Understanding Example 1

1. Find the simple interest.

a. principal = $250
interest rate = 4%
time = 3 years $30

b. principal = $250
interest rate = 3.5%
time = 6 months $4.38

OBJECTIVE

2 **Compound Interest**

When a bank pays interest on the principal and on the interest an account has earned, the bank is paying **compound interest.** The principal plus the interest is the **balance,** which becomes the principal on which the bank figures the next interest payment.

2 **EXAMPLE** **Real-World** **Problem Solving**

Banking **You deposit $400 in an account that earns 5% interest compounded annually (once per year). What is the balance in your account after 4 years? In your last calculation, round to the nearest cent.**

Principal at Beginning of Year	Interest	Balance
Year 1: $400.00	$400.00 \cdot 0.05 = 20.00$	$400 + 20 = 420.00$
Year 2: $420.00	$420.00 \cdot 0.05 = 21.00$	$420 + 21 = 441.00$
Year 3: $441.00	$441.00 \cdot 0.05 = 22.05$	$441 + 22.05 = 463.05$
Year 4: $463.05	$463.05 \cdot 0.05$ $= 23.1525$	$463.05 + 23.1525$ ≈ 486.20

● After four years, the balance is $486.20.

 Check Understanding Example 2

2. Make a table and find the balance. The interest is compounded annually. **a–b. See right.**

a. principal = $500
interest rate = 3%
time = 2 years

b. principal = $625
interest rate = 2%
time = 4 years

You can find a balance using compound interest in one step with the compound interest formula and a calculator. An *interest period* is the length of time over which interest is calculated. The interest period can be a year or less than a year.

2a.

Bal. at Yr Start	Interest	Bal. at Yr End
$500.00	$15.00	$515.00
$515.00	$15.45	$530.45

2b.

Bal. at Yr Start	Interest	Bal. at Yr End
$625.00	$12.50	$637.50
$637.50	$12.75	$650.25
$650.25	$13.01	$663.26
$663.26	$13.27	$676.53

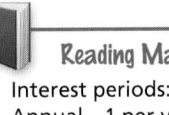

Reading Math

Interest periods:
Annual—1 per year
Semiannual—2 per year
Quarterly—4 per year
Monthly—12 per year
Daily—360 per year
(not 365)

Math Background

The rate for simple interest is the *annual* percentage rate (APR), or the percent used to calculate interest that is paid in one year. In simple interest calculations using the formula $I = prt$, t can represent a fraction of a year. In the compound interest formula $B = p(1 + r)^n$, r is the interest rate for each interest period, and n is the number of interest periods. You find r by dividing the annual interest rate by the number of interest periods in one year.

Teaching Notes

1 **EXAMPLE** **Diversity**

When discussing savings accounts, be sensitive to the fact that some families may not have savings accounts. Some students may not know how such accounts work.

2 **EXAMPLE** **Economics Connection**

A bank pays interest on your savings as a fee for letting the bank use your money. It uses your money for loans on which it charges interest. A bank collects interest on loans at a higher rate than it pays its savings customers. This difference forms a part of the bank's profit.

 Reaching All Students

Below Level Discuss saving money in an account where your money earns interest, and borrowing money where you have to pay interest. Ask for advantages of saving in a bank account over saving money at home.	**Advanced Learners** Ask students to compute the balances of $1,000 at 10% compounded annually and compounded semiannually for 5 years. Have them compare and explain the results.	**Diversity** See note on page 383. **Error Prevention** See note on page 384.

Encourage students to check whether the number of interest periods they use for their formula matches the problem. Students may forget to multiply the number of years by the number of interest periods in a year. Students also may forget to divide the rate (which is an annual rate) by the number of interest periods in a year. Point out that if the interest period is not annual, students must both multiply one quantity and divide another by the number of interest periods in a year.

3 **EXAMPLE** Alternative Method

You may wish to have students use spreadsheet software and the formulas in this lesson to create a spreadsheet that calculates simple and compound interest. Encourage students to use the formulas from the textbook rather than using pre-programmed formulas in the spreadsheet software. Have students share and explain their spreadsheets.

PowerPoint

📃 Additional Examples

❶ Suppose you deposit $1,000 in a savings account that earns 6% per year.
  a. Find the interest earned in two years. Find the total of principal plus interest.
  $120; $1,120
  b. Find the interest earned in six months. Find the total of principal plus interest.
  $30; $1,030

❷ You deposit $400 in an account that earns 5% interest compounded annually (once per year). The balance after the first four years is $486.20. What is the balance in your account after another 4 years, a total of 8 years? Round to the nearest cent.
  $590.98

❸ Find the balance on a deposit of $2,500 that earns 3% interest compounded semiannually for 4 years.
  $2,816.23

384

Calculator Hint
Remember to use the parentheses on your calculator when evaluating the compound-interest formula.

Key Concepts | **Compound-Interest Formula**

$$B = p(1 + r)^n,$$
where B is the final balance, p is the principal, r is the interest rate for each interest period, and n is the number of interest periods.

You can use this formula to solve Example 2.

$B = p(1 + r)^n$

$B = 400(1 + 0.05)^4$ — **Replace p with 400, r with 0.05, and n with 4.**

$B \approx 486.20$ — **Use a calculator. Round to the nearest cent.**

The balance is $486.20. Using the formula means there are fewer calculations and fewer chances for mistakes.

When interest is compounded semiannually (twice per year), you must *divide* the interest rate by the number of interest periods, which is 2.

$$\frac{6\% \text{ annual}}{\text{interest rate}} \div \frac{2 \text{ interest}}{\text{periods}} = \frac{3\% \text{ semiannual}}{\text{interest rate}}$$

To find the number of payment periods, *multiply* the number of years by the number of interest periods per year.

3 **EXAMPLE** Real-World 🌐 Problem Solving

Investing **Find the balance on a deposit of $1,000 that earns 6% interest compounded semiannually for 5 years.**

The interest rate r for compounding semiannually is $0.06 \div 2$, or 0.03. The number of payment periods n is 5 years $\times$ 2 interest periods per year, or 10.

$B = p(1 + r)^n$ — **Use the compound-interest formula.**

$B = 1{,}000(1 + 0.03)^{10}$ — **Replace p with 1,000, r with 0.03, and n with 10.**

$B \approx 1{,}343.92$ — **Use a calculator. Round to the nearest cent.**

The balance is $1,343.92.

✔ Check Understanding Example 3

3. Find the balance for each account.
  Amount deposited: $900, annual interest: 2%, time: 3 years

  a. compounding annually   **b.** compounding semiannually
  $955.09 $955.37

Closure

Ask students to compare simple interest and compound interest. Simple interest is the product of the principal amount, the annual interest rate, and the time in years. Compound interest is paid on both the principal and the previously earned interest.

Practice and Problem Solving

For more exercises, see Extra Practice.

 A Practice by Example

Find the simple interest. Then find the total of principal plus interest.

Example 1
(page 382)

1. principal = $200
interest rate = 7%
time = 2 years **$28; $228**

2. principal = $870
interest rate = 6%
time = 9 months **$39.15; $909.15**

Example 2
(page 383)

Complete each table. Compound the interest annually. In your last calculation, round to the nearest cent.

3. $3,000 at 4% for 3 years

Principal at Start of Year	Interest	Balance
Year 1: $3,000	▪	▪
Year 2: ▪	▪	▪
Year 3: ▪	▪	▪

See margin.

4. $10,000 at 6% for 3 years

Principal at Start of Year	Interest	Balance
Year 1: $10,000	▪	▪
Year 2: ▪	▪	▪
Year 3: ▪	▪	▪

See margin.

Example 3
(page 384)

Find each balance.

5. $495 at 8% compounded annually for 2 years **$577.37**

6. $1,280 at 13% compounded annually for 3 years **$1,846.91**

7. $2,000 at 5% compounded semiannually for 2 years **$2,207.63**

8. $15,600 at 10% compounded semiannually for 3 years **$20,905.49**

 B Apply Your Skills

9. Savings You deposit $600 in a savings account for 3 years. The account pays 8% annual interest compounded quarterly.

GPS

a. What is the quarterly interest rate? **2%**

b. What is the number of payment periods? **12 periods**

c. Find the final balance in the account. **$760.95**

Find each balance.

10. $3,000 at 14% compounded annually for 4 years **$5,066.88**

11. $500 at a simple-interest rate of 3% for 4 years **$560**

12. $35 at a simple-interest rate of 2.5% for 1 year **$35.88**

13. $8,900 at 9% compounded semiannually for 5 years **$13,821.43**

14. $54,500 at 3% compounded semiannually for 9 years **$71,250.06**

15. $900 at a simple-interest rate of 8% for 3 months **$918**

17. Answers may vary.
Sample: $10,000 at 6%;
$13,000; $13,382.26

18. Answers may vary.
Sample: Simple interest is computed only on the original principal. Compound interest is computed on both the principal and the interest.

16. Mental Math Calculate the amount of simple-interest on $9,000 deposited at an interest rate of 5% for 2 years. **$900**

17. Open-Ended Choose an amount of money to be invested and an interest rate. Find the value of the investment after 5 years if the interest is simple interest; if the interest is compounded annually. See left.

18. Writing in Math Explain the difference between simple interest and compound interest. See left.

3.
	$120.00	$3,120.00
$3,120.00	$124.80	$3,244.80
$3,244.80	$129.79	$3,374.59

4.
	$600.00	$10,600.00
$10,600.00	$636.00	$11,236.00
$11,236.00	$674.16	$11,910.16

GPS **Use the Guided Problem Solving worksheet with Exercise 9.**

Assignment Guide

1 Objective 1
A B Core 1, 2, 11, 12, 15, 16

2 Objective 2
A B Core 3–10, 13, 14, 17, 18
C Extension 19, 20

Test Prep 21–25
Mixed Review 26–32

Practice 7-8 *Simple and Compound Interest*

Find each balance.

	Principal	Interest rate	Compounded	Time (years)	Balance
1.	$400	7%	annually	3	$490.02
2.	$8,000	5%	annually	9	$12,410.63
3.	$1,200	4%	semi-annually	2	$1,298.92
4.	$50,000	6%	semi-annually	6	$71,288.04

Find the simple interest.

5. $900 deposited at an interest rate of 3% for 5 years
_____ $135 _____

6. $1,348 deposited at an interest rate of 2.5% for 18 months
_____ $50.55 _____

Complete each table. Compound the interest annually.

7. $5,000 at 6% for 4 years.

Principal at beginning of year	Interest	Balance
Year 1: $5,000	$300	$5,300
Year 2: $5,300	$318	$5,618
Year 3: $5,618	$337.08	$5,955.08
Year 4: $5,955.08	$357.30	$6,312.38

8. $7,200 at 3% for 4 years

Principal at beginning of year	Interest	Balance
Year 1: $7,200	$216	$7,416
Year 2: $7,416	$222.48	$7,638.48
Year 3: $7,638.48	$229.15	$7,867.63
Year 4: $7,867.63	$236.03	$8,103.66

Enrichment 7-8 *Compounding Interest*

Do you earn more interest when it is compounded more often than when it is compounded less often?

Find the balance and interest on a deposit of $2,000, earning 4% interest, after 3 years, for each compounding period.

1. annually
balance: _____ $2,249.73 _____ interest: _____ $249.73 _____

2. semi-annually
balance: _____ $2,252.32 _____ interest: _____ $252.32 _____

The interest rate *r* for compounding quarterly (four times a year) is 0.04 ÷ 4 = 0.01. The number of payment periods *n* is 4 per year × 3 years, or 12.

3. quarterly
balance: _____ $2,253.65 _____ interest: _____ $253.65 _____

4. Which compounding period earned the most interest?
_____ quarterly _____

Find the balance and interest on a deposit of $500, earning 6% interest, after 4 years, for each compounding period.

5. annually
balance: _____ $631.24 _____ interest: _____ $131.24 _____

6. semi-annually
balance: _____ $633.39 _____ interest: _____ $133.39 _____

7. quarterly
balance: _____ $634.49 _____ interest: _____ $134.49 _____

8. bi-monthly
balance: _____ $634.87 _____ interest: _____ $134.87 _____

9. monthly
balance: _____ $635.24 _____ interest: _____ $135.24 _____

10. Which compounding period earned the most interest?
_____ monthly _____

11. What do you notice about how the amount of interest increases each time interest is compounded twice as often?
There is a smaller increase each time.

Find the simple interest and the balance.

1. $1,200 at 5.5% for 2 years
$132; $1,332

2. $2,500 at 8% for 6 months
$100; $2,600

3. Find the balance on a deposit of $1,200, earning 9.5% interest compounded semiannually for 10 years.
$3,035.72

Careers
Exercise 19 Loan officers determine whether a customer should receive a loan, and the amount of the loan. Many factors go into this decision, including the customer's credit rating, income, investments, and other loans.

Test Prep

📁 **Resources**
For additional practice with a variety of test item formats:
- Test Prep, p. 393
- Test-Taking Strategies, p. 388
- Test-Taking Strategies With Transparencies

Reteaching 7-8 Simple and Compound Interest

Find the balance in an account when $500 is deposited at 4% interest compounded semi-annually for 2 years.
The table shows the interest and balance for each half year.

Principal at Beginning of Period	Interest	Balance
½ year: $500	$10	$510
1 year: $510	$10.20	$520.20
1½ year: $520.20	$10.40	$530.60
2 year: $530.60	$10.61	$541.21

The balance after 2 years is $541.21.
You can also find the balance with the formula $B = p(1 + r)^n$, where B is the ending balance. The principal p is 500. The rate is for a half year; 4% annual interest equals 2% per half year. Thus r is 0.02. The number of compounding periods n is 4, because there are 4 half years in 2 years.
$B = p(1 + r)^n$
$B = 500(1 + 0.02)^4$ Substitute.
$B = 541.22 Use a calculator. Round to the nearest cent.
With the formula, the ending balance is $541.22. The difference is due to rounding error.

Find the ending balance when $1,500 is deposited at 6% interest compounded semi-annually for 2 years.

1. Use a table.

Principal at Beginning of Period	Interest	Balance
½ year: $1,500	$45	$1,545
1 year: $1,545	$46.35	$1,591.35
1½ year: $1,591.35	$47.74	$1,639.09
2 year: $1,639.09	$49.17	$1,688.26

2. Use the formula:
$B = p(1 + r)^n = 1,500(1 + 0.03)^4 =$ _____ $1,688.26

 Challenge 🌐 **19. Borrowing** Leroy borrows $800 at 10% annual interest compounded semiannually. He makes no payments.
  a. How much will he owe after four years? **$1,181.96**
  b. How much interest will he owe in four years? **$381.96**

🌐 **20. Investing** Ling invests $1,000 in an account paying 8% interest.
  a. Compare the account balances after 5 years of simple interest and after 5 years of interest compounded annually. **See below.**
  b. After how many years of compounded interest will the account balance be about twice Ling's initial investment? **9**
  c. **Reasoning** What would the simple interest rate have to be for the investment to double in the same amount of time?
  20a. $1,400 and $1,469.33   **about 11.1%**

Writing in Math
Many banks compound interest on a daily basis. Explain what it means to compound interest daily. See back of book.

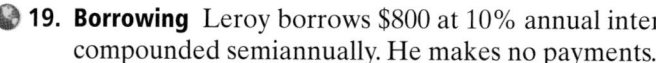

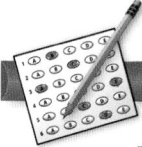 **Test Prep**

Multiple Choice

21. Matthew invests $5,000 at 14% simple interest. About how much interest will he earn in eight months? **A**
A. $467   B. $700   C. $5,467   D. $5,700

22. Which formula could be used to find the balance on a deposit of $520, earning 7% interest compounded semiannually for 3 years? **H**
F. $B = 520(1 + 0.035)^3$ G. $B = 520(0.07)^3$
H. $B = 520(1 + 0.035)^6$ I. $B = 520(0.07)^6$

23. What is the balance after 8 years on a deposit of $500, earning 7% interest compounded semiannually? **B**
A. $657.97   B. $658.40   C. $856.91   D. $859.09

Short Response

24. [2] $128.00; $32.00
[1] one correct answer

24. A savings account pays 4% simple interest.
  a. How much interest does an $800 deposit earn in 4 years?
  b. How much more would the $800 earn in 4 years at 5%?
  See left.

Take It to the NET
Online lesson quiz at
www.PHSchool.com
Web Code: ada-0708

25. Greg deposits $800 into a savings account that earns 10% interest compounded annually. **See margin.**
  a. What is Greg's balance after four years?
  b. Make a table to explain your answer.

🔵 **Mixed Review**

Lesson 7-6   **Solve for the variable indicated in red.**

26. $f = \dfrac{15m}{a}$ **27.** $y = 4x - 9$ **28.** $d = \dfrac{5}{8}k + 1$
$m = \dfrac{fa}{15}$ $x = \dfrac{1}{4}y + \dfrac{9}{4}$ $k = \dfrac{8}{5}d - \dfrac{8}{5}$

Lesson 6-3 🌐 **29. Architecture** A floor plan has a scale of $\frac{1}{4}$ in. : 5 ft. Find the length on the drawing for an actual length of 60 ft. **3 in.**

Lesson 1-10   **Graph each point on a coordinate plane. 30–32. See back of book.**

30. $A(-2, 0)$ **31.** $C(-4, -5)$ **32.** $D(1, -3)$

---

386   **Chapter 7**   Solving Equations and Inequalities

Alternative Assessment

Have students find the interest rates paid locally by banks for savings accounts and certificates of deposit. Using these rates and the formulas in this lesson, have students describe an investment plan that would earn the most for an investment of $10,000 for 5 years.

25. [2] $1,171.28

Yr. Start	Interest	Yr. End
800	80	880
880	88	968
968	96.8	1,064.80
1,064.80	106.48	1,171.28

[1] minor error OR answer only

Credit-Card Interest

When you use a credit card, you are charged interest each month on the balance in your account. You can use a spreadsheet to investigate the interest charged on a credit-card account.

You use a credit card to buy a $450 airline ticket. You are charged 1.8% monthly interest on your account balance, and you make a $40 payment each month. Using a spreadsheet program, create a spreadsheet with the formulas shown in red.

	A	B	C	D	E	F
1	Month	Balance	Planned Monthly Payment	Interest	New Balance	Total Interest
2	1	450	40	=B2*0.018	=B2+D2−C2	=D2
3	=A2+1	=E2				=F2+D3
4						
	.	.	.	.	.	.

The arrows indicate you should use the Fill Down feature of your spreadsheet program. This will calculate successive months for you.

EXERCISES

Use your spreadsheet. Round any totals to the nearest cent.

1. a. In which month is the balance less than the monthly payment? 13
    b. Your last payment is the balance plus the interest in the month you found in part (a). What is the amount of the last payment? $27.41
    c. What is the total interest paid on this account? $57.42

2. a. Change the monthly payment to $60 a month. In which month is the balance less than the monthly payment? 9
    b. What is the total interest paid on this account? $37.82

3. a. Create a new spreadsheet using a beginning balance of $1,200, 2.1% monthly interest, and a monthly payment of $100. What is the total interest paid on this account in 5 months? $109.96
    b. Change the monthly payment to $200. What is the total interest paid on this account in 5 months? $88.51
    c. **Reasoning** What can you conclude about the relationship between the size of monthly payments and the amount of interest charges? If you increase the monthly payments, the interest charges will be less.

Technology

Credit-Card Interest

This Technology extension shows students how to use a spreadsheet to calculate credit card interest. You can also use this spreadsheet to calculate how long it will take to pay off the balance, and to calculate the amount of interest you will pay on a balance.

Resources

Students may use any spreadsheet software program to calculate credit card interest.

Teaching Notes

Error Prevention!

If the spreadsheet shows the same values in each row, students may have copied and pasted the formulas in each column instead of using the spreadsheet's Fill Down feature.

Inclusion

Pair students who do not have good eye-hand coordination with students who do. The first student can direct the second one as to what to type and when to use the Fill Down feature.

Diversity

Some students may have never used a credit card. Explain to them how a credit card is used. A credit card company pays the store for your purchase. Then it charges you interest for what it paid until you have paid the company back for the amount of the purchase plus the interest. Ask student volunteers to discuss the advantages and disadvantages of charging purchases using credit cards. You may also wish to point out the high rates of interest that many credit card companies charge. Include in your discussion the pitfalls of credit cards that offer extremely low interest rates for the first months after you sign up, and then raise their rates.

Eliminating Answers

This feature helps students understand the advantage of eliminating answer choices on multiple-choice test items.

Resources

Test-Taking Strategies With Transparencies
• Transparency 7
• Practice sheet, p. 7

Teaching Notes

Teaching Tip
Eliminating answer choices increases the probability of choosing the correct answer if you have to make a random guess.

Test-Taking Strategies With Transparencies

Chapter 7: Eliminating Answers

Exercises

Identify the answer choices you can immediately eliminate. Cross the choices out and explain why you eliminated them. Then solve the problem.

1. Sandra is making 4 batches of cookies, so she will need to use 4 times the amount of flour the recipe calls for. The recipe calls for $3\frac{1}{4}$ cups of flour. How much flour does Sandra need?

   A. $1\frac{1}{4}$ cups   B. 12 cups   C. 13 cups   D. 17 cups

2. Alice's grandmother made a quilt that is $9\frac{1}{2}$ feet wide and $12\frac{5}{8}$ feet long. Alice plans to make a quilt that is half as wide and half as long. What will be the dimensions of Alice's quilt?

   F. $4\frac{3}{4}$ ft wide by $6\frac{7}{16}$ ft long   G. $4\frac{5}{8}$ ft wide by $6\frac{5}{8}$ ft long
   H. 4 ft wide by 6 ft long   I. $18\frac{1}{2}$ ft wide by $24\frac{1}{2}$ ft long

3. There are 95 different kinds of butterflies in a zoo. There are $\frac{4}{5}$ as many different kinds of beetles as butterflies at the zoo. How many different kinds of beetles are at the zoo?

   A. 50 beetles   B. 75 beetles   C. 76 beetles   D. 120 beetles

Test-Taking Strategies   Pre-Algebra   **7**

Before you do all the work involved in solving a multiple-choice problem, you usually can eliminate some answer choices. This can save you time in finding the correct answer. Also, it improves your chances of making a correct guess.

1 EXAMPLE

What is the solution to $\frac{3}{4}(x - 2) = \frac{3}{2}$?

   A. −2   B. 2   C. 3   D. 4

The product on the left must equal the positive number on the right. Thus, since $\frac{3}{4}$ is positive, the value of $(x - 2)$ must also be positive.

The choices −2 and 2 do not give positive values for $(x - 2)$. You can eliminate choices A and B. Then substitute 4 for x and use mental math to find that D is the correct choice.

2 EXAMPLE

What is the solution to $x + 0.05x = 420$?

   F. 400   G. 410   H. 420   I. 450

On the left, a fraction of x is added to x and the result is 420. Thus the value of x must be less than 420. You can eliminate choices H and I. Then check 400 in the equation to find that F is the correct choice.

EXERCISES

Show how you can eliminate one or two of the answer choices for each multiple-choice question. 1–4. See margin.

1. What is the solution to $\frac{x - 2}{-3} = -4$?

   A. −13   B. −10   C. 11   D. 14

2. What is the solution to $x - 0.15x = 680$?

   F. 620   G. 675   H. 760   I. 800

3. On a field trip to the zoo, 21 students voted to have sandwiches for lunch. This represents $\frac{7}{8}$ of the class. How many students are in the class?

   A. 24   B. 25   C. 38   D. 40

4. The area of a rectangle is 64 in.^{2}. If the area is increased by 25%, which of the following could be the dimensions of the new rectangle?

   F. 6 in. by 8 in.   G. 10 in. by 8 in.   H. 10 in. by 10 in.   I. 8 in. by 8 in.

---

1. The left side of the equation must equal the negative number on the right. Thus, since the denominator is negative, the value of the numerator must be positive. The choices −13 and −10 do not give positive values for the numerator. You can eliminate choices A and B.

2. On the left, a fraction of x is subtracted from x and the result is 680. Thus the value of x must be greater than 680. You can eliminate choices A and B.

3. The value of $\frac{7}{8}$ is very close to the value of 1. Thus 21 is very close to the total number of students in the class. The choices 38 and 40 are not close to 21. You can eliminate choices C and D.

4. See back of book.

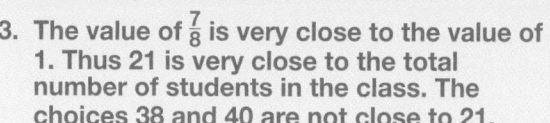

Chapter Review

Vocabulary

balance (p. 383)
compound inequality (p. 377)
compound interest (p. 383)

consecutive integers (p. 353)
interest (p. 382)
interest rate (p. 382)

principal (p. 382)
simple interest (p. 382)

Reading Math
Understanding
Vocabulary

Choose the vocabulary term that correctly completes the sentence.

1. A bank pays __?__ when it pays interest on the principal and on the interest an account has earned. **compound interest**

2. The amount of money first deposited into a savings account is called the __?__. **principal**

3. The principal plus the interest is the __?__ of the account. **balance**

4. When you count by 1s from any integer, you are counting __?__.
   consecutive integers

5. A bank pays interest based on its advertised __?__. **interest rate**

6. __?__ is paid only on the principal of an account. **simple interest**

Take It to the NET
Online vocabulary quiz
at www.PHSchool.com
Web Code: adj-0751

7. A bank pays you __?__ for the use of your money. **interest**

Skills and Concepts

7-1 Objectives

▼ To solve two-step equations (p. 348)

▼ To use two-step equations to solve problems (p. 349)

To solve two-step equations, undo addition and subtraction, then undo multiplication and division.

Solve each equation.

8. $2a - 7 = -15$ **-4**   9. $3 = -6x + 15$ **2**   10. $\frac{c}{4} + 10 = 22$ **48**

11. $1.5y + 3.4 = 7.9$ **3** 12. $\frac{2}{3}y - 9 = 5$ **21**   13. $8 = 9x - 7$ **$1\frac{2}{3}$**

7-2 and 7-3 Objectives

▼ To combine like terms to simplify an equation (p. 352)

▼ To use the Distributive Property to simplify an equation (p. 354)

▼ To solve multi-step equations with fractions (p. 357)

▼ To solve multi-step equations with decimals (p. 358)

To solve multi-step equations, remove grouping symbols and combine like terms first. Then follow the steps for solving two-step equations.

Solve each equation.

14. $8m - 3m = 4$ **$\frac{4}{5}$**

15. $6 - 2y - y = 12$ **-2**

16. $\frac{2}{3}q + 5 = \frac{3}{4}$ **$-6\frac{3}{8}$**

17. $\frac{1}{4}(b - 7) = 8$ **39**

18. $1.06x - 3 = 0.71$ **3.5**

19. $-2(5 + 6c) + 16 = -90$ **8**

20. **Number Sense** Find four consecutive integers with a sum of -66.
    $-18, -17, -16, -15$

Resources

Student Edition
Extra Practice, Ch. 7, p. 750
English/Spanish Glossary, p. 782
Table of Symbols, p. 777

 Reaching All Students
Reading and Math Literacy 7D
Spanish Reading and Math
Literacy 7D

 **ASSESSMENT SYSTEM**

Test Preparation
• Chapter 7 practice in test
  formats

 www.PHSchool.com
Student Site
• Self-grading vocabulary test
PH SuccessNet Teacher Center
• Resources

Plus

Spanish Reading and Math Literacy

Reading and Math Literacy

7D: Vocabulary   For use with Chapter Review

Study Skill Often when you learn about a new topic in mathematics, you also learn several new words. To understand the new vocabulary, take the time to review some of the vocabulary terms from previous topics, and see how they relate to the new words. In general, you will keep adding to your active math vocabulary and reusing the terms you learned before.

Many mathematical ideas are opposites, inverses, or contrasts. For each pair, write a brief explanation of how to tell the difference between the two mathematical ideas in the pair. For help, use the Glossary in your textbook.

1. simple interest
   compound interest
   Simple interest is interest paid only on the principal, while compound interest is interest paid on the principal and on the interest the account has earned.

2. principal
   interest
   Principal is the amount originally deposited or invested. Interest is the amount that the principal earns because the institution is paying for the use of that money.

3. consecutive even integers
   consecutive odd integers
   Consecutive even integers are integers that you get by starting with an integer that is divisible by two (or even) and counting by twos. To get consecutive odd integers, you start with an odd integer (not divisible by two) and count by twos.

4. equation
   expression
   An equation is a mathematical sentence with an equal sign, and an expression is a mathematical statement without an equal sign.

5. interest
   interest rate
   The interest rate is the percent of interest paid per year, while the interest is the amount of money paid.

6. ratio
   proportion
   A ratio is the quotient of two numbers, while a proportion is the statement that two ratios are equal.

7-4 Objectives

▼ To write an equation to solve a problem (p. 362)

One strategy for solving problems is to write an equation and then solve the equation.

Write an equation. Then solve.

21. A pair of jeans is on sale for 15% off the original price. The sale price of the jeans is $29.74. What was the original price?
$p - 0.15p = 29.74$; $34.99

22. A bank teller is counting his money and notices that he has an equal number of tens and twenties. He also has $147 in other bills. If the total value of the bills he has is $1,167, how many tens and twenties does he have?
$10n + 20n + 147 = 1,167$; 34 tens, 34 twenties

🌐 23. **Finance** Jalisha invested some money and made an 8% profit. The current value of her investment is $1,296. How much did she invest initially? $a + 0.08a = 1,296$; $1,200

7-5 Objectives

▼ To solve equations with variables on both sides (p. 367)

▼ To use equations with variables on both sides (p. 368)

To solve equations with variables on both sides, first simplify both sides of the equation. Then use properties of equality to get the variable alone on one side of the equation.

Solve each equation.

24. $7x = 33 - 4x$ 3
25. $2a - 24 - 3a = 5a$ -4
26. $5x + 7 = -5x + 19$ $1\frac{1}{5}$
27. $4x - 26 = 5(2 - x)$ 4
28. $8(b + 3) = 4b - 4$ -7
29. $2x - (9 - 3x) = 8x - 11$ $\frac{2}{3}$

🌐 30. **Travel Time** A refrigerated truck leaves a rest stop traveling at a steady rate of 56 mi/h. A car leaves the same rest stop $\frac{1}{4}$ h later following the truck at a steady rate of 64 mi/h. How long after the truck leaves the rest stop will the car overtake the truck?   2 h

7-6 Objectives

▼ To solve two-step inequalities (p. 373)

▼ To use two-step inequalities to solve problems (p. 374)

Solving two-step inequalities involves the same steps as solving two-step equations. Reverse the direction of the inequality symbol when you multiply or divide by a negative number.

Solve and graph each inequality. 31–38. For graphs, see margin.

31. $2a - 3 > 11$ $a > 7$
32. $9y + 13 \leq -14$ $y \leq -3$
33. $-6c + 12 \geq 8$ $c \leq \frac{2}{3}$
34. $23 < 7 - 4x$ $x < -4$
35. $\frac{8}{9}x + 5 < -3$ $x < -9$
36. $-\frac{b}{2} + 14 > 13$ $b < 2$
37. $-17 > \frac{x}{3} - 19$ $x < 6$
38. $x + 4x + 9 \geq 6$ $x \geq -\frac{3}{5}$

31.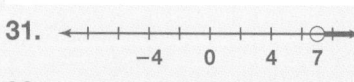
   −4   0   4   7

32.
   −3   −1 0   1

33.
   −2   0 $\frac{2}{3}$ 2

34.
   −4   −2   0   2

35.
   −9 −4 0   4

36.
   −2   0   2

37.
   −2 0   2   6

38.
   −2 −$\frac{3}{5}$ 0   2

39. Computers Last year's computer model is on sale for $799. You can add more memory to the computer. Each chip of 8 megabytes of memory costs $25. How many megabytes of memory can you add if you have at most $1,000 to spend? Write and solve an inequality. $799 + 25\left(\frac{c}{8}\right) \le 1,000$; **about 64 megabytes**

7-7 Objectives

▼ To solve a formula for a given variable (p. 378)

▼ To use formulas to solve problems (p. 379)

Use the properties of equality to transform a formula.

Solve for the variable indicated in red.

40. $r = 6km$ $m = \frac{r}{6k}$

41. $8x = 6y$ $y = \frac{4}{3}x$

42. $Q = gp$ $g = \frac{Q}{p}$

43. $a = b - 2c$ $b = a + 2c$

44. $w = 3a + 5n$ $a = \frac{1}{3}w - \frac{5}{3}n$

45. $e = \frac{h}{6} + 11$ $h = 6e - 66$

7-8 Objectives

▼ To solve simple-interest problems (p. 382)

▼ To solve compound-interest problems (p. 383)

You can calculate **simple interest** using the formula $I = prt$, where I is the interest, p is the **principal** (original amount deposited), r is the **interest rate** per year, and t is the time in years.

Compound interest is interest paid on both the principal and interest. It is found using the formula $B = p(1 + r)^n$, where B is the final **balance**, p is the principal, r is the interest rate for each interest period, and n is the number of interest periods.

Find the simple interest.

46. $150 deposited at an interest rate of 9% for 2 years $27

47. $2,525 deposited at an interest rate of 2.5% for 4 years $252.50

48. $6,000 deposited at an interest rate of 3% for 6 months $90.00

Find each balance.

49. $8,000 at 12% compounded annually for 3 years $11,239.42

50. $17,500 at 17% compounded annually for 6 years $44,890.37

51. $22,000 at 6% compounded semiannually for 8 years $35,303.54

52. $33,800 at 18% compounded semiannually for 5 years $80,016.89

53. The more interest periods there are, the more interest you make on an investment. Do you agree with this statement? Explain. **Answers may vary. Sample: Yes; with more interest periods, the interest would start earning interest earlier.**

Chapter Test

Resources

📁 **Teaching Resources**
Ch. 7 Test, Forms A & B
Ch. 7 Alternative Assessment,
   Form C

 Reaching All Students
Spanish Ch. 7 Test, Forms A & B
Spanish Ch. 7 Alternative
   Assessment, Form C

ASSESSMENT SYSTEM

Assessment Resources
• Ch. 7 Test, Forms A & B
• Ch. 7 Alternative Assessment,
   Form C
Computer Test Generator CD-ROM
• Instant Chapter Test™ for Ch. 7

 **www.PHSchool.com**
Student Site
• Self-grading Ch. 7 Test
PH SuccessNet Teacher Center
• Resources

Plus 🅸 TEXT

Chapter Test – Form B

Chapter Test – Form A

Chapter 7 Test • Form A

Circle the letter of the best answer.
1. Solve $\frac{1}{3}(b-4) = 1$.
   A. $b = 5$ B. $b = -1$ C. $b = 7$ D. $b = 1\frac{3}{4}$
2. Solve $3w - 4 = w + 8$.
   F. $w = 30$ G. $w = -20$ H. $w = -6$ J. $w = 6$
3. Solve $2.4(n-1) = 12$.
   A. $n = 6$ B. $n = 1.5$ C. $n = 5$ D. $n = -5$
4. Solve $5t + 1 > 3t - 13$.
   F. $t > -6$ G. $t > -7$ H. $t > 6$ J. $t < 7$
5. Solve $3n - 16 \le 8n + 29$.
   A. $-n \le -9$ B. $n \ge 9$ C. $n \ge -9$ D. $n \le -9$
6. Find the simple interest on $750 deposited at an interest rate of 3.5% for 3 years.
   F. $828.75   G. $262.50   H. $67.50   J. $78.75
7. Find the balance on $1,800 deposited at 5% compounded annually for 4 years.
   A. $1,986.86   B. $2,187.91   C. $186.86   D. $387.91
8. Find the balance on $6,000 deposited at 6% compounded semi-annually for 3 years.
   F. $7,164.31   G. $7,146.10   H. $8,511.11   J. $6,556.36
9. Which equation does *not* represent the problem? Sebastian's school bus averages 28 mi/h, including stops. One day Sebastian forgot his backpack. His mom left home 15 minutes (0.25 h) after Sebastian and traveled at an average speed of 42 mi/h. How long did it take Sebastian's mom to catch the bus?
   A. $42t = 28(t + 0.25)$ B. $42t = 28t + 0.25$
   C. $14t = 7$ D. $42t = 28t + 7$
Solve each equation.
10. $5 - 2y = 7$ $y = -1$
11. $\frac{3}{4}x + 8 = 5$ $x = -4$
12. $5(x - 3) = 2x + 6$ $x = 7$
13. $-12 + 4n = 6(n - 2)$ $n = 0$

Solve each equation.

1. $3x + 4 = 19$ 5
2. $5 + \frac{c}{9} = -31$ −324
3. $2y - 15 = 11$ 13
4. $8a + 3 = -12.2$ −1.9
5. $\frac{3}{5}b - 8 = 4$ 20
6. $\frac{m}{2} - 5 = 7$ 24
7. $-83 = 9x - 2$ −9
8. $18 - \frac{a}{4} = -5$ 92
9. $\frac{3}{5}y + \frac{2}{5} = \frac{4}{5}$ $\frac{2}{3}$
10. $-23 - c = -19$ −4
11. $3x + 4x = 21$ 3
12. $\frac{1}{2}(10y + 4) = 17$ 3
13. $2(7b - 6) - 4 = 12$ 2
14. $2m - 6 = m$ 6
15. $\frac{2}{3}a - 5 + \frac{8}{9}a = -19$ −9
16. $0.015x + 3.45 = 4.65$ 80
17. $12y + 3 = 9y - 15$ −6
18. $3(2b + 6) = 4b - 8$ −13

Write an equation. Then solve.

19. **Number Sense** Find three consecutive integers with a sum of 267.
   $n + (n + 1) + (n + 2) = 267$; 88, 89, 90
20. A rental car company charges $35 a day plus $.15/mi for a mid-size car. A customer owes $117.15 for a three-day rental. How many miles did the customer drive?
   $35(3) + 0.15m = 117.15$; 81 mi
21. **Travel Time** A moving truck leaves a house and travels at a steady rate of 40 mi/h. The family leaves the house 1 h later following the same route in a car. They travel at a steady rate of 60 mi/h. How long after the moving truck leaves the house will the car catch up with the truck? $40t = 60(t - 1)$;3 h
22. **Coin Collections** The Jaspers collect nickels, dimes, and quarters in a jar. When they count the change in the jar, there are twice as many nickels as there are quarters. If there is $15.30 in dimes and $74.80 in all, how many quarters are there?
   $0.05(2q) + 0.25q + 15.30 = 74.80$; 170 quarters

Solve and graph each inequality.
23–30. For graphs, see margin.

23. $7m - 8 > 6$
   $m > 2$
24. $2x - 6 \ge -9$
   $x \ge -\frac{3}{2}$
25. $-9a - 1 \le 26$
   $a \ge -3$
26. $22 < 6c + 4$
   $c > 3$
27. $\frac{b}{3} + 12 > -3$
   $b > -45$
28. $-\frac{2}{3}x + 8 \le 2$
   $x \ge 9$
29. $11 > -3y + 2$
   $y > -3$
30. $16 - 4a > 8$
   $a < 2$

31. **Commissions** An insurance salesperson earns a salary of $1,200 per month plus a commission of 3% of sales. How much must the salesperson sell to have a monthly income of at least $1,500? ≥ $10,000

32. **Writing in Math** How is solving a two-step inequality different from solving a two-step equation? See below.

Solve for the variable indicated in red.

33. $H = 3w + 2$
   $w = \frac{1}{3}H - \frac{2}{3}$
34. $g = cst$ $s = \frac{g}{ct}$
35. $R = 6n + 4p$
   $p = \frac{1}{4}R - \frac{3}{2}n$
36. $y = \frac{x}{5} - 4$
   $x = 5y + 20$

Find the simple interest.

37. $800 deposited at an interest rate of 1.5% for 3 years $36
38. $1,050 deposited at an interest rate of 2% for 9 months $15.75
39. $2,500 deposited at an interest rate of 8% for 5 years $1,000

Find each balance.

40. $12,000 at 8% compounded annually for 4 years $16,325.87
41. $1,950 at 5% compounded annually for 2 years $2,149.88
42. $18,500 at 9% compounded semiannually for 5 years $28,729.93
43. $75,000 at 15% compounded semiannually for 8 years $238,559.49

32. Answers may vary. Sample: You must reverse the direction of the inequality when multiplying or dividing by a negative number.

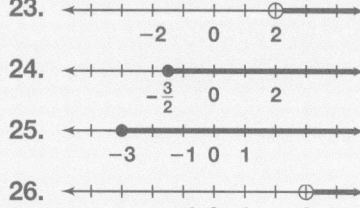

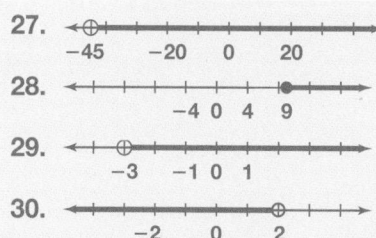

23.
24.
25.
26.
27.
28.
29.
30.

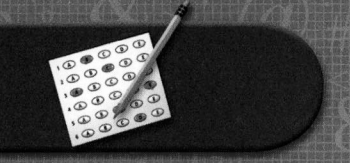

Reading Comprehension Read the passage below. Then answer the questions on the basis of what is *stated* or *implied* in the passage.

Income Tax The United States Tax Relief Act of 2001 lowered the percentage of tax that individuals must pay on their taxable income. The table below compares the tax rate for 2001 with the new, lower tax rate for 2002 for unmarried individuals.

Taxable Income	2001 Tax	2002 Tax
Up to $27,050	15% of taxable income	15% of taxable income
$27,051 to $65,550	$4,057.50 + 28% of excess over $27,050	$4,057.50 + 27.5% of excess over $27,050
$65,551 to $136,750	$14,837.50 + 31% of excess over $65,550	$14,465 + 30.5% of excess over $65,550
$136,751 to $297,350	$36,909.50 + 36% of excess over $136,750	$36,361 + 35.5% of excess over $136,750
Over $297,350	$94,725.50 + 39.6% of excess over $297,350	$93,374 + 39.1% of excess over $297,350

1. Why was the United States Tax Relief Act called a "Tax Relief" act? **See below.**

2. Which expression shows the amount of tax owed by an unmarried person with taxable income of $40,000 for 2002? **B**
   A. 0.275(40,000)
   B. 4,057.50 + 0.275(12,950)
   C. 4,057.50 + 0.275
   D. 4,057.50 + 0.275(40,000)

3. Which expression shows the amount of tax owed by an unmarried person with taxable income of $72,000 for 2002? **H**
   F. 14,465 + 0.305(72,000)
   G. 0.305(65,500)
   H. 14,465 + 0.305(72,000 − 65,550)
   I. 0.305(72,000)

1. It "relieved" individuals by lowering the percentage of tax they must pay on taxable income.

7. $0; The tax relief act only lowers taxes for individuals who earn more than $27,500.

4. About how much tax will an unmarried person with taxable income of $27,500 owe for 2002? **B**
   A. $0   B. $4,000 C. $7,500 D. $27,000

5. About how much tax will an unmarried person with taxable income of $300,000 owe for 2002? **G**
   F. $90,000   G. $95,000
   H. $117,000   I. $210,000

6. About how much less tax would an unmarried person whose taxable income is $50,000 owe for 2002 than for 2001? **C**
   A. $0   B. $10   C. $100   D. $1,000

7. In 2002, his first year out of high school, Joacquim expected to have a taxable income of $25,000. How much tax relief did Joacquim gain for 2002 compared to what he would have had to pay for 2001? **See left.**

Test Prep

Resources

Students must be able to extract information from reading passages, answer multiple-choice questions, and construct responses in order to be successful in current state and national assessments.

📁 **Teaching Resources**
Cumulative Review

👥 **Reaching All Students**
Spanish Cumulative Review

ASSESSMENT SYSTEM

Test Prep
• Ch. 7 Test Prep
Assessment Resources
• Cumulative Review
Computer Test Generator CD-ROM
• Test Prep

💻 **www.PHSchool.com**
• Test Prep
• Resources

Plus **iTEXT**

Cumulative Review

▪ **Chapter 7 Cumulative Review**

Circle the letter of the best answer.

1. Simplify $5z + 3y - (z + y)$.
   A. $4z + 2y$ B. $4z + 4y$ C. $8z - 2y$ D. $6z + 4y$

2. Use the formula $t = \frac{d}{r}$ for $t = 3.5$ h and $r = 60$ mi/h. Find the distance driven, d.
   F. 17 mi G. 180 mi H. 200 mi J. 210 mi

3. Find the GCF of $5a^3b^2$ and $15ab^4$.
   A. $5ab$ B. $5ab^2$ C. $15ab^2$ D. $15a^3b^4$

4. Teresa is training for a 10,000-meter race. Her goal is to be able to run $6\frac{1}{2}$ miles, which is very close to 10,000 meters. Yesterday she ran $5\frac{1}{10}$ miles. How far is she from her goal?
   F. $\frac{2}{5}$ mi G. $\frac{3}{5}$ mi H. $\frac{1}{4}$ mi J. $1\frac{1}{2}$ mi

5. Twenty-one of the 25 members of the Science club had an entry in the science fair. What percent of the club had an entry.
   A. 84% B. 80% C. 21% D. 16%

6. Which is the graph of the solution of $-9 > 4x - 1$?
   F. G. H. J.

7. Ali's little sister takes 5 steps to cover the same distance that Ali covers in 3 steps. If Ali takes 82 steps walking home from school, how many steps does his sister take?.
   A. about 123 steps B. about 75 steps
   C. about 49 steps D. about 137 steps

8. A car costs $29 a day plus $.25 a mile to rent. The rental company uses the formula $c = 29 + 0.25m$ to find the daily cost c for m miles. Solve the formula for m.
   F. $m = c - 29$ G. $m = \frac{c - 29}{0.25}$ H. $m = 4c + 29$ J. $m = \frac{c}{0.25} - 29$

9. Use the formula you found in the previous exercise to find the number of miles driven in a day for a total cost of $60.25.
   A. about 31 mi B. 212 mi C. 125 mi D. 270 mi

10. Which expression is equal to $2\frac{4}{5}$?
    F. $4\frac{1}{2} - 1\frac{7}{10}, b = 6$ G. $\frac{2}{a} - \frac{2}{5}a, a = 5.5$ H. $3\frac{1}{3} - 1\frac{2}{3}$ J. $\frac{-7}{3} - \frac{1}{3}$

11. Which statement is *not* true?
    A. $\frac{4}{9} > 44\%$ B. $0.25\% < \frac{1}{4}$ C. $150\% = 1.5$ D. $0.375 > 40\%$

Assessment

393

Wireless Style

Students will use the information on these two pages to answer questions.

Activating Prior Knowledge

Ask students whether they or any members of their families have a cell phone. Let volunteers explain the cell-phone calling plans they have. Ask whether any student knows the difference in the way service providers count long-distance minutes for cell phones versus land-line phones. **Answers may vary. Sample: For cell phones, providers start counting minutes the moment you press the send button. For land lines, providers start counting when you actually have a connection, with any partial minute rounded up.**

Teaching Notes

Diversity

Some students may not have had the opportunity to see or hold a cell phone. Bring one to class for these students to see. You may wish to have a student show other functions of the phone, such as the calculator and the storage of phone numbers.

English Learners

Explain that *circuit* sometimes refers to a path you can follow. In an electrical object, a circuit is a path that electricity follows.

Teaching Tip

Ask students why cell phone companies often camouflage their towers. **Answers may vary. Sample: They camouflage towers so the towers fit in with the scenery.**

Real-World Snapshots

Wireless Style

Applying Equations Cell-phone use has increased dramatically since the mid-1990s. Millions of people worldwide own cell phones. If you are one of them, you probably purchased a calling plan from a service provider. These providers charge different fees for a variety of services.

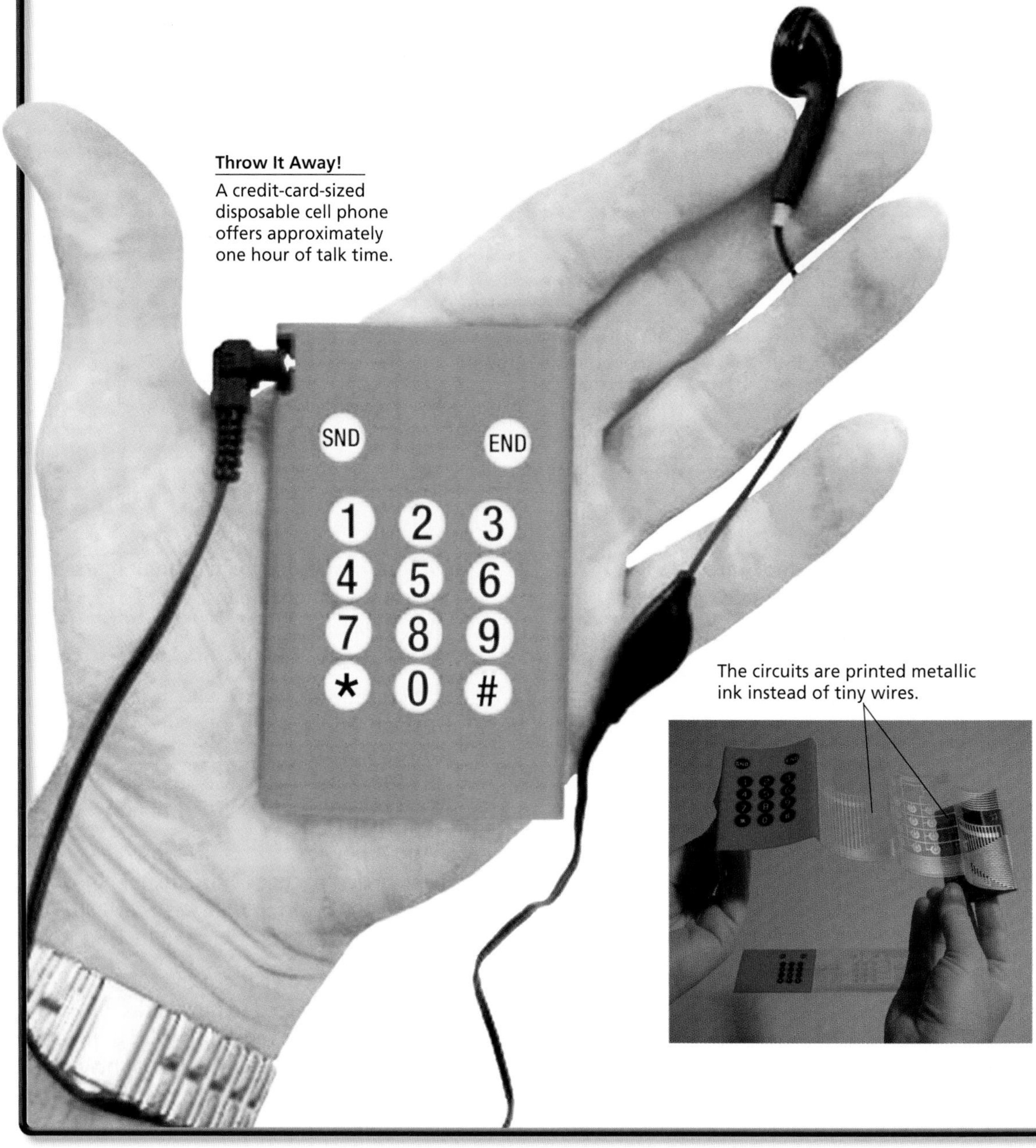

Throw It Away!
A credit-card-sized disposable cell phone offers approximately one hour of talk time.

The circuits are printed metallic ink instead of tiny wires.

Activity 1–3. See margin.

1. Suppose you are shopping for a calling plan. You expect to use 10 long-distance minutes per month.
   a. Use the table below and the total-cost equation to find out how much you will pay for the first month of each calling plan.
   b. **Writing in Math** Which plan would you choose? Explain.

2. Suppose a friend is also shopping for a calling plan. Your friend expects to use 60 long-distance minutes each month.
   a. Use the table below and the total-cost equation to find out how much your friend will pay for the first month of each calling plan.
   b. Which plan do you think your friend would choose? Explain.

3. **Number Sense** Without calculating, which plan would be the least expensive to use in the second month? Explain.

Calling Plan	A	B	C	D
Monthly Fee	$19.99	$34.99	$19.99	$29.99
Long-Distance Rate	$.15	$.15	$.00	$.20
Activation Fee	$36.00	$24.00	$30.00	$35.00

Total-Cost Equation
$$c = m + d\ell + a$$
c = total cost
m = monthly fee
ℓ = long-distance rate
d = long-distance minutes
a = activation fee

Monthly Fee The amount a customer pays each month for basic service

Long-Distance Rate The amount a customer pays for each minute of a call made outside the local calling area

Activation Fee A one-time fee paid to start phone service

Where's the Cell-Phone Tower?
Cell phone companies often camouflage their towers to make them blend in with the surrounding landscape.

Antenna

Antenna

Take It to the NET For more information about cell phones, go to **www.PHSchool.com**.
Web Code ade-0753

Students must be able to extract information from tables in order to make good choices about real-world opportunities for which a variety of information is available.

Ask students whether they know of other situations in which you may have an activation fee, a monthly fee, and a rate for an item or a service. **Answers may vary. Sample: cable television service with movie rental choices, Internet provider**

Exercise 1 Have students note that the plans charge only for a long-distance rate. Many plans do not charge for what are considered local calls. Different plans may have different local-calling areas.

Exercise 3 Point out that the activation fee is charged only the first month. You need to compare only the monthly fees and long-distance rates.

1a. Plan A: $57.49
    Plan B: $60.49
    Plan C: $49.99
    Plan D: $66.99
  b. Plan C; it is the least expensive of the four plans for 10 long-distance minutes

2a. Plan A: $64.99
    Plan B: $67.99
    Plan C: $49.99
    Plan D: $76.99
  b. Plan C; it is the least expensive of the four plans for 60 long-distance minutes

3. Plan C; it has the lowest monthly fee and there are no long-distance costs

Chapter 8

Linear Functions and Graphing

Chapter at a Glance

8-1 Relations and Functions
pp. 400–404

Objectives
1. Identifying Relations and Functions
2. Graphing Relations and Functions

New Vocabulary
relation, domain, range, function, vertical-line test

NCTM Standards
2, 6, 7, 8, 9, 10

Local Standards

8-2 Equations With Two Variables
pp. 405–409

Objectives
1. Finding Solutions
2. Graphing Equations With Two Variables

New Vocabulary
solution, linear equation

NCTM Standards
2, 6, 7, 8, 9, 10

Local Standards

8-3 Slope and y-intercept
pp. 411–416

Objectives
1. Finding the Slope of a Line
2. Using Slope to Graph Linear Equations

New Vocabulary
slope, y-intercept, slope-intercept form

Material
graph paper

NCTM Standards
2, 8, 9, 10

Local Standards

8-4 Writing Rules for Linear Functions
pp. 418–422

Objectives
1. Writing Rules From Words
2. Writing Rules From Tables or Graphs

New Vocabulary
function notation, function rule

NCTM Standards
2, 7, 8, 9, 10

Local Standards

✓ **Checkpoint Quiz 1**

8-5 Scatter Plots
pp. 423–428

Objectives
1. Interpreting and Drawing Scatter Plots
2. Using Scatter Plots to Find Trends

New Vocabulary
scatter plot, positive correlation, negative correlation, no correlation

Material
graph paper

NCTM Standards
2, 5, 6, 8, 9, 10

Local Standards

8-6  Solve by Graphing
pp. 430–433

Objective
1. Solve by Graphing

New Vocabulary
trend line

NCTM Standards
2, 5, 6, 8, 9, 10

Local Standards

8-7 Solving Systems of Linear Equations
pp. 435–440

Objectives
1. Graphing Systems of Linear Equations
2. Writing Systems of Linear Equations

New Vocabulary
system of linear equations

NCTM Standards
2, 6, 8, 9, 10

Local Standards

✓ **Checkpoint Quiz 2**

8-8 Graphing Linear Inequalities
pp. 441–446

Objectives
1. Graphing Linear Inequalities
2. Graphing Systems of Linear Inequalities

New Vocabulary
linear inequality, system of linear inequalities

NCTM Standards
2, 8, 9, 10

Local Standards

Correlation to Standardized Tests

Lesson	NAEP	Terra Nova		ITBS	SAT10	Local Test
		CAT/6	CTBS			
8-1	A2a, A2c				■	
8-2	A2a, A2b, A2c				■	
8-3	A4d					
8-4	A1a, A1b, A1c				■	
8-5	D1b, D1d				■	
8-6	D1a					
8-7	A2a, A2b,					
8-8	A3a		■		■	

NAEP National Assessment of Educational Progress
     N = Number Sense, Properties, and Operations
     M = Measurement
     G = Geometry and Spatial Sense
     D = Data Analysis, Statistics and Probability
     A = Algebra and Functions
CAT/6 California Achievement Test, 6th Ed.
CTBS Comprehensive Test of Basic Skills
ITBS Iowa Test of Basic Skills, Form M
SAT10 Stanford Achievement Test, 10th Ed.

NCTM STANDARDS 2000

1	Number and Operations	6	Problem Solving
2	Algebra	7	Reasoning and Proof
3	Geometry	8	Communication
4	Measurement	9	Connections
5	Data Analysis and Probability	10	Representation

Pacing Options

This chart suggests pacing for only the core lessons and their parts. It is provided as a possible guide. It will help you determine how much time you have in your schedule to cover other components, such as the features, chapter projects, Chapter Review, and Chapter Test.

Day	Traditional 45-minute class periods	Two-Year 45-minute class periods	Block 90-minute class periods
1	8-1 ⅴ ⅴ	8-1 ⅴ	8-1 ⅴ ⅴ 8-2 ⅴ ⅴ
2	8-2 ⅴ	8-1 ⅴ	8-3 ⅴ ⅴ
3	8-2 ⅴ	8-1 ⅴ	8-4 ⅴ ⅴ 8-5 ⅴ
4	8-3 ⅴ	8-2 ⅴ	8-5 ⅴ 8-6 ⅴ
5	8-3 ⅴ	8-2 ⅴ	8-7 ⅴ ⅴ 8-8 ⅴ ⅴ
6	8-4 ⅴ ⅴ	8-2 ⅴ	
7	8-5 ⅴ ⅴ	8-2 ⅴ	
8	8-6 ⅴ	8-3 ⅴ	
9	8-7 ⅴ	8-3 ⅴ	
10	8-7 ⅴ	8-3 ⅴ	
11	8-8 ⅴ ⅴ	8-3 ⅴ	
12		8-4 ⅴ	
13		8-4 ⅴ	
14		8-4 ⅴ	
15		8-5 ⅴ	
16		8-5 ⅴ	
17		8-5 ⅴ	
18		8-6 ⅴ	
19		8-6 ⅴ	
20		8-7 ⅴ	
21		8-7 ⅴ	
22		8-7 ⅴ	
23		8-7 ⅴ	
24		8-8 ⅴ ⅴ	

Math Background

Skills Trace

BEFORE Chapter 8

Students have been working with patterns that represent functional relationships between quantities in most of the previous chapters, but they were not identified as functions.

DURING Chapter 8

Students formalize their informal experiences with functions from previous chapters. This chapter makes connections between tabular, symbolic, verbal, and graphical representations for functions.

AFTER Chapter 8

Functions are used and reviewed throughout the remainder of this course. Chapter 13 introduces nonlinear functions. Functions are reviewed and extended in Algebra 1.

8-1 Relations and Functions

Consider this set of ordered pairs:

$$(2, 4), (3, 6), (5, 10)$$

These pairs of numbers are called *ordered* pairs because the order of the numbers makes a difference; the pair (2, 4) is not the same as the pair (4, 2). A *relation* is a set of ordered pairs such as this. The first numbers, or *coordinates,* in a relation form the *domain* of the relation, and the second coordinates form the *range* of the relation.

You can also express this relation in the form of an equation: $y = 2x$. The relation defined by the equation $y = 2x$ includes an infinite number of ordered pairs, unless you restrict the domain to, for example, the numbers 2, 3, and 5.

Another way to represent the relation (2, 4), (3, 6), (5, 10) is to graph the points on a coordinate plane.

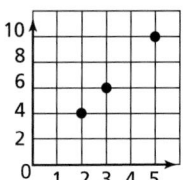

One special kind of relation is called a *function*. A function is a relation in which one element in the domain is paired with exactly one element in the range. (In mathematics, the words *exactly one* mean that there is always one, neither more nor less.) The relation (2, 4), (3, 6), (5, 10) is a function because each number in the domain (2, 3, and 5) has exactly one partner, or match, in the range.

However, the relation (2, 4), (3, 6), (5, 10), (3, 9) is *not* a function because 3 is matched with two numbers, 6 and 9.

8-2 Equations With Two Variables

A *linear* equation (*linear* because its graph is a straight line) is generally written with two variables, such as $y = 3x - 2$. An equation with two variables can have many solutions. One way to show these solutions is to draw their graph.

A linear equation is a function unless it is of the form $x = b$. Notice that $x = b$ has no y-term and its graph will always be a vertical line $|b|$ units from the y-axis.

The one-variable equations of Chapter 7 are linear equations that simplify to the form $x = b$ when you solve them. For example, $2x + 1 = 5$ simplifies to $x = 2$.

8-3 Slope and *y*-intercept

When the equation of a line written in *slope-intercept form*, $y = mx + b$, has $m > 0$, then the right end of its graph is higher than the left end and the line has a *positive slope*. If you think of the graph as a ramp, you are climbing from left to right.

On the other hand, if you write the equation of a line in slope-intercept form and $m < 0$, then the left end of its graph is higher than the right end and the line has a *negative slope*. If you think of the graph as a ramp, you are descending from left to right.

8-4 Writing Rules for Linear Functions

When the value of *y* depends on the value of *x*, as in $y = 5x - 2$, then you can say "*y* is a function of *x*." To say that *y* is a function of *x* means, informally, "Give me a value for *x* and I'll give you the corresponding *y*-value."

For many students, the idea of function may be new. The notation may also be confusing. You write the statement "*y* is a function of *x*" as $y = f(x)$. This does not mean that *f* is a variable, nor that it is multiplied by *x*. The letter *f* and the parentheses have a special meaning in this notation, so you say $f(x) = 5x - 2$ as "*f* of *x* is five *x* minus two" or "the function of *x* is five *x* minus two." In this case, the equation $y = 5x - 2$ is a function rule that can be written as the function $f(x) = 5x - 2$.

8-5 8-6 Scatter Plots and Solve by Graphing

When a relation is a set of ordered pairs, or of data, that consist of separate points (called *discrete values*), rather than every point on a line (called *continuous values*), then the graph of the relation is a collection of points called a *scatter plot*.

The points on a scatter plot show a *positive correlation* when an increase in *x* shows a corresponding increase in *y*. When an increase in *x* shows a corresponding decrease in *y*, the scatter plot shows a *negative correlation*. Some sets of data will show neither; they have *no correlation*.

To find whether a correlation exists and what kind it is, you can plot data pairs to get a scatter plot. If there is a correlation, you can draw a *trend line* that approximates the data points in the scatter plot. A trend line with a positive slope (right end higher) indicates a positive correlation for the data.

8-7 8-8 Solving Systems of Linear Equations; Graphing Linear Inequalities

You can graph the relation $y = 5x - 2$ as a line. Every solution of $y = 5x - 2$ is an ordered pair that makes the equation true and corresponds to a point on the graph. Every point on the graph represents an ordered pair that makes the equation true.

You can find the common solution of two or more linear equations by graphing. The point where the graphs intersect, if there is one, is a solution for both equations. This is called the *solution of the system* of the two equations.

When the graphs are parallel lines, the system has no solution. When the graphs of two equations are the same line, the system has infinitely many solutions.

If you replace the equal sign (=) in a linear equation with an inequality sign ($<$, $\leq$, $>$, $\geq$) the result is called a *linear inequality*. When the inequality sign shows that the border is included (as with $\leq$ or $\geq$), then the graph is a region (or half-plane) with a solid line on the border. When the border is excluded ($<$ or $>$), you use a dotted line for the edge of the half-plane that contains the solutions to the inequality.

You can find the solutions of a system of linear inequalities by graphing the inequalities on the same coordinate plane. The solutions that the inequalities have in common (indicated by the overlapping graphs) are the solutions of the system.

Additional Professional Development Opportunities

Chapter 8 Math Background notes:
pp. 401, 406, 412, 419, 424, 431, 436, 442

Professional Development, Content Facilitator Guide: Pre-Algebra, Chapter 8

Additional resources available from SkyLight Professional Development: On-site courses, workshops, summer institutes. Online courses and chat rooms. Videocassettes and books. Visit www.skylightedu.com.

Ongoing Assessment and Intervention

The *Prentice Hall Pre-Algebra* program provides many options for assessment in the Student Edition, Teacher's Edition, and teaching resources. From these options you may choose instructional materials that are appropriate for your students and support your district's curriculum requirements.

Daily Assessment

Instant Check System™ in Chapter 8

Allows students to check their own learning before, during, and after each lesson.

Diagnosing Readiness before the chapter (p. 396)

Check Skills You'll Need exercises in each lesson (pp. 400, 405, 411, 418, 423, 430, 435, 441)

Check Understanding questions with each Example (pp. 401, 402, 405, 406, 407, 411, 412, 413, 418, 419, 423, 424, 425, 431, 435, 436, 442, 443)

Checkpoint Quiz (pp. 422, 440)

Formal Assessment

In Chapter 8 and Additional Resources

Assesses student progress throughout the *Pre-Algebra* text and with blackline masters and CD-ROM.

Student Edition
- Chapter 8 Review, with Vocabulary Skills and Concepts Review, pp. 449–451
- Chapter 8 Test, p. 452

Assessment Resources   *Spanish versions available.*
- Checkpoint Quizzes 1 & 2
- Chapter Test, Forms A & B
- Chapter Alternative Assessment

Computer Test Generator CD-ROM
- Instant Chapter Tests™ — pre-made tests with items that vary every time you print.
- Online Testing allows you to give tests online and receive progress reports.
- Diagnose readiness with questions on prerequisite skills.
- Prepare students by making tests based on standardized test objectives.

Algebra Readiness Tests
- Includes Basic Skills Tests and Concept-Readiness Tests.
- Assess understanding of skills and concepts needed for success in algebra.

Standardized Test Preparation

Test Prep in Chapter 8

Teaches students strategies and gives them practice with all the test item formats they will encounter on high-stakes tests.

Test Prep exercises in each lesson (pp. 404, 409, 416, 422, 428, 433, 439, 446)

Test-Taking Strategies (p. 448: Finding Multiple Correct Answers)

Test Prep (p. 453: Cumulative Review)

PRENTICE HALL ASSESSMENT *SYSTEM*

Provides a three-step approach to preparing students for high-stakes, national, and state exams.

1 Diagnose & Prescribe   **2 Review & Reteach**

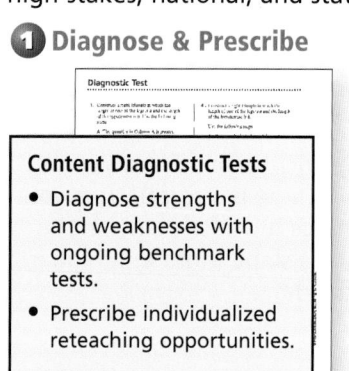

Content Diagnostic Tests
- Diagnose strengths and weaknesses with ongoing benchmark tests.
- Prescribe individualized reteaching opportunities.

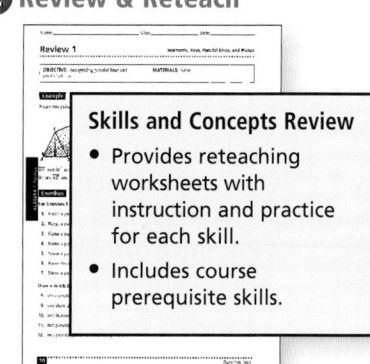

Skills and Concepts Review
- Provides reteaching worksheets with instruction and practice for each skill.
- Includes course prerequisite skills.

3 Practice & Assess

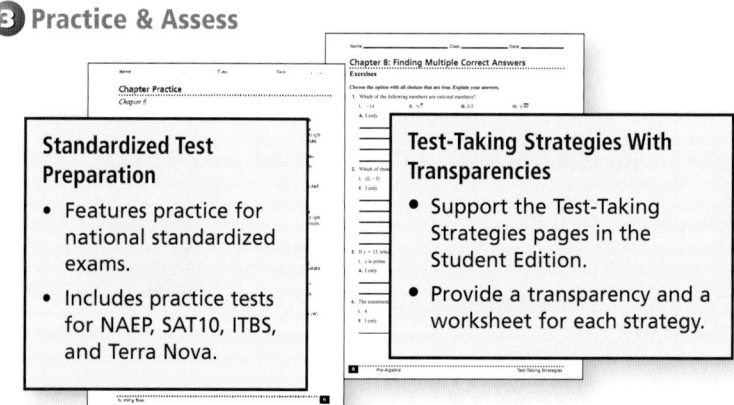

Standardized Test Preparation
- Features practice for national standardized exams.
- Includes practice tests for NAEP, SAT10, ITBS, and Terra Nova.

Test-Taking Strategies With Transparencies
- Support the Test-Taking Strategies pages in the Student Edition.
- Provide a transparency and a worksheet for each strategy.

Reaching All Students

The textbook, the iText, and other technology components provide numerous opportunities to reach students of various ability levels and learning styles. Each Teacher's Edition lesson suggests how you can help all your students be successful and understand the mathematics in Chapter 8.

Below Level

Student Edition
- Diagnosing Readiness*: p. 396
- Check Skills You'll Need*: pp. 400, 405, 411, 418, 423, 430, 435, 441

Reteaching
Chapter 8 Grab & Go™ File: pp. 9–16

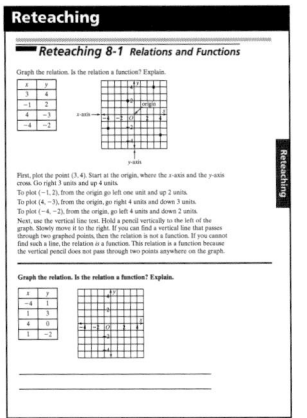

* Can be used with all ability levels to ensure mastery of prerequisite skills.

Advanced Learners

Student Edition
- Challenge exercises: pp. 404, 408, 409, 415, 421, 427, 433, 439, 445
- Extension: p. 410

Enrichment
Chapter 8 Grab & Go™ File: pp. 17–24

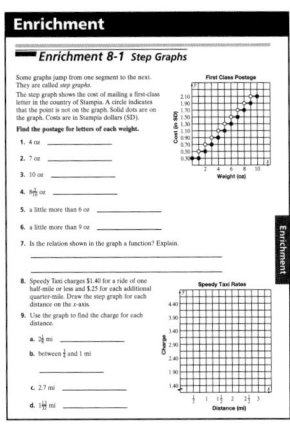

Problem Solving

Student Edition
- Strategies: pp. 430–433
- Real-World Problem Solving: pp. 401, 405, 413, 418, 423, 424, 425, 430, 442

Guided Problem Solving Masters
Chapter 8: pp. 65–72

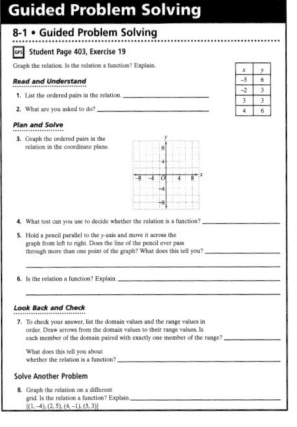

Reading and Math Literacy

Student Edition
- Vocabulary: pp. 397, 449, plus in every lesson
- Reading Math: pp. 413, 419, 425, 426, 429, 449
- Writing in Math: pp. 404, 408, 415, 420, 421, 422, 427, 432, 439, 444, 445, 452
- Illustrated Glossary: pp. 782–826

Reading and Math Literacy Masters
Chapter 8: pp. 29–32

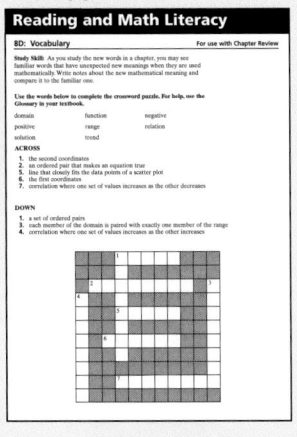

English Learners

Student Edition
- English/Spanish Illustrated Glossary: pp. 782–826

Workbook and Masters
Spanish Practice Workbook: pp. 65–72
Spanish Reading and Math Literacy Masters: pp. 29–32

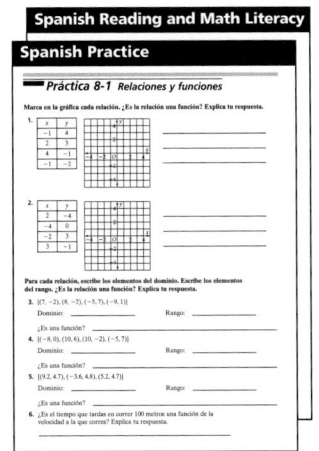

Learning Styles

Student Edition
- Investigation: pp. 398, 411, 423
- Technology: pp. 417, 447
- DK Activities: pp. 454–455
- Chapter Project: pp. 741

Activity Masters
Hands-On Activities: 1
Technology Activities: 14, 15

Program Resources

	Resources in Grab & Go™ Files				Resources for Reaching All Students				Spanish Resources			Transparencies				Presentation Assistant Plus!
	Practice	Reteach	Enrich	Checkpt Quiz	Reading & Math Literacy	Technology Activities	Hands-On Activities	Guided Problem Solving	Practice	Reading & Math Literacy	Checkpt Quiz	Skills Check	Additional Examples	Answers to Exercises	Lesson Quiz	Prentice Hall Presentation Pro CD-ROM
8-1	■	■	■		■				■	■		■	■	■	■	■
8-2	■	■	■				■		■			■	■	■	■	■
8-3	■	■	■				■		■			■	■	■	■	■
8-4	■	■	■	■	■				■		■	■	■	■	■	■
8-5	■	■	■				■		■			■	■	■	■	■
8-6	■	■	■				■		■			■	■	■	■	■
8-7	■	■	■				■		■			■	■	■	■	■
8-8	■	■	■		■			■	■			■	■	■	■	■
For the Chapter	Chapter Projects, Chapter Tests, Alternative Assessment, Cumulative Review, Cumulative Assessment				**On Web site only:** Home Activities, Algebra Readiness Puzzles, Interdisciplinary Activities				Spanish Chapter Tests, Alternative Assessment, Cumulative Review, Cumulative Assessment			Classroom Aid Transparencies				

Also available for use with the chapter:
- Practice Workbook
- Solution Key
- MathNotes folder
- For additional online and technology resources, see below.
- For teacher support and access to student Web site materials, use Web Code adk-5500.

 **PRENTICE HALL ASSESSMENT SYSTEM**

Program assessment and test preparation, all in one place.

See page 396E.

 Skills Intervention Kit

A *complete* system for the student who is struggling with course-level work

How to Use With Chapter 8

8-1, 8-8   Pre-Algebra Basics

 **Online Intervention**

Integrated within the iText, this online intervention system includes diagnostic tests and prescribed remediation, plus reports to track student mastery.

Technology

 Online and on CD-ROM

Complete Interactive Student Text online and on CD-ROM—with instant-feedback assessment, tutorial help, dynamic activities, instructional and real-world videos, audio, and additional practice.

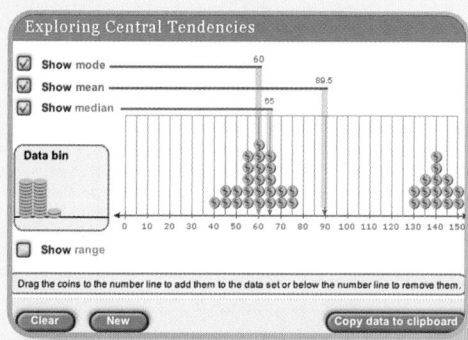

www.PHSchool.com For Students

Use Web Codes for easy access to online activities, chapter projects, self-grading lesson quizzes, chapter tests, vocabulary quizzes, updated data sources, graphing calculator procedures, and more.

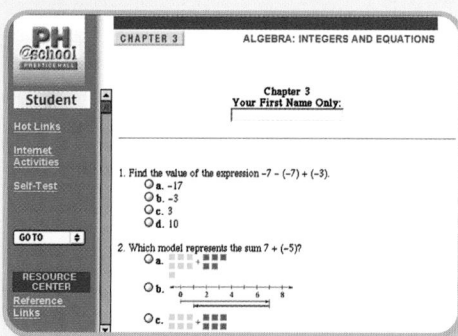

PHSuccessNet For Teachers

Online lesson planning with built-in state correlations, all the teaching resources, complete reference library, your own calendar and Teacher Web page, professional development, and more.

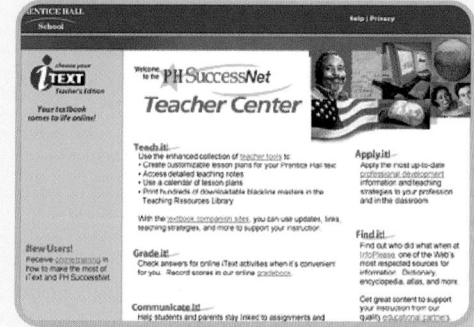

Presentation Assistant Plus!

The Prentice Hall *Presentation Assistant Plus!* provides you with the material you need to teach a lesson from beginning to end. Two easy-to-use formats—Transparencies and CD-ROM—allow you to present a lesson the way you are most comfortable.

 ## Transparencies

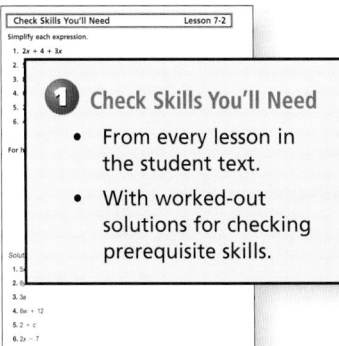

1 Check Skills You'll Need
- From every lesson in the student text.
- With worked-out solutions for checking prerequisite skills.

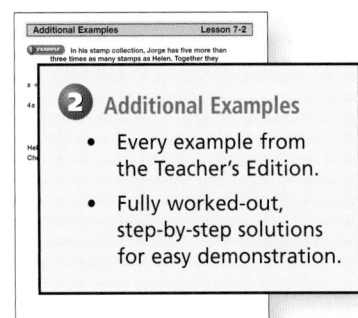

2 Additional Examples
- Every example from the Teacher's Edition.
- Fully worked-out, step-by-step solutions for easy demonstration.

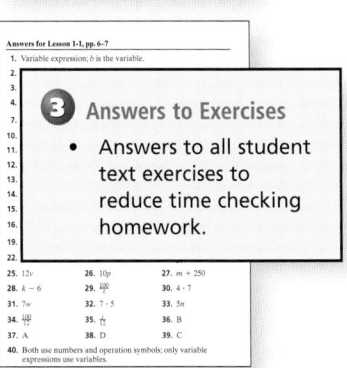

3 Answers to Exercises
- Answers to all student text exercises to reduce time checking homework.

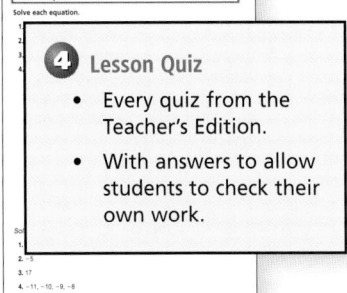

4 Lesson Quiz
- Every quiz from the Teacher's Edition.
- With answers to allow students to check their own work.

PowerPoint Throughout the Teacher's Edition, this symbol indicates material that is available in the Presentation Assistant Plus!

PowerPoint ## Prentice Hall Presentation Pro CD-ROM

- Includes all Transparencies as PowerPoint® presentations.
- Conveniently organized by lesson so you can easily **1** Introduce, **2** Teach, **3** Check Homework, and **4** Assess each lesson.
- Animated examples allow step-by-step instruction at your own pace.
- Easy to edit so you can create custom presentations.

Teaching Chapter 8 Using Presentation Assistant Plus!

	1 Introduce	**2 Teach**	**3 Check Homework**	**4 Assess**
	Check Skills You'll Need	Additional Examples	Student Edition Answers	Lesson Quiz
8-1	p. 66	pp. 101–102	✔	p. 66
8-2	p. 67	pp. 103–105	✔	p. 67
8-3	p. 68	pp. 105–107	✔	p. 68
8-4	p. 69	pp. 108–109	✔	p. 69
8-5	p. 70	pp. 109–111	✔	p. 70
8-6	p. 71	pp. 111–112	✔	p. 71
8-7	p. 72	pp. 113–114	✔	p. 72
8-8	p. 73	pp. 115–119	✔	p. 73

 ### Prentice Hall Presentation Pro

CD-ROM with dynamic Powerpoint® presentations for every lesson. Helps you introduce and develop concepts, check homework, and assess progress. Part of Presentation Assistant Plus! *(See above.)*

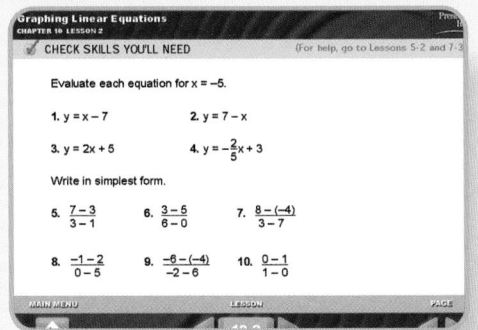

 ### Computer Test Generator

CD-ROM to create practice sheets and tests for course objectives and standardized tests. Includes Instant Chapter Tests™, online testing, and student reports. Part of the PH Assessment System. *(See page 396E.)*

 ### Resource Pro® with Planning Express®

CD-ROM with a lesson planning tool that allows you to import state and local objectives. Includes electronic versions of all the teaching resources.

Chapter 8

Linear Functions and Graphing

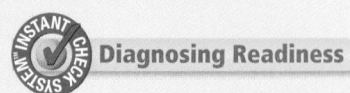
11–16.

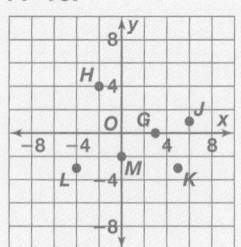

Where You've Been

- In Chapter 1, you used inductive reasoning to write rules for patterns. You also graphed points in a coordinate plane.

- In Chapter 4, you simplified fractions by finding the GCF of the numerator and denominator.

- In Chapter 7, you solved two-step and multi-step equations and inequalities using inverse operations.

iTEXT Instant self-check online and on CD-ROM

 **Diagnosing Readiness**   (For help, go to the lesson in green.)

Describing Number Patterns (Lesson 1-7)

Write the next two numbers in each pattern.

1. 8, 5, 2, −1, ...
$-4, -7$

2. 43, 37, 31, 25, ...
19, 13

3. 4.5, 6, 7.5, 9, ...
10.5, 12

4. −3, −5, −7, −9, ...
$-11, -13$

Graphing Points (Lesson 1-10)

Write the coordinates of each point.

5. *A* (5, 2)

6. *B* (−3, 4)

7. *C* (4, 0)

8. *D* (6, −3)

9. *E* (−4, −3)

10. *F* (0, 3)

Draw a coordinate plane. Graph each point.
11–16. See margin.

11. $M(0, -2)$

12. $H(-2, 4)$

13. $J(6, 1)$

14. $K(5, -3)$

15. $L(-4, -3)$

16. $G(3, 0)$

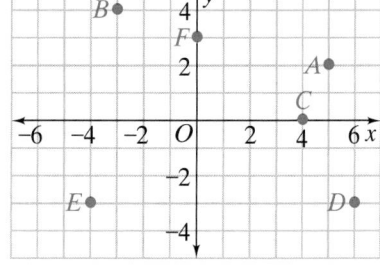

Simplifying Fractions (Lesson 4-4)

Write each fraction in simplest form.

17. $\dfrac{-5 - (-4)}{12 - (-6)}$
$-\frac{1}{18}$

18. $\dfrac{15 - (-12)}{17 - 8}$ 3

19. $\dfrac{-4 - 1}{-7 - (-2)}$ 1

20. $\dfrac{4.3 - 3.5}{7.1 - 4.7}$ $\frac{1}{3}$

Transforming Equations (Lesson 7-7)

Solve each equation for *y*.

21. $4x + y = 3$
$y = -4x + 3$

22. $y - 4 = -2x$
$y = -2x + 4$

23. $2x - y = 6$
$y = 2x - 6$

24. $8 + y + 6x = 0$
$y = -6x - 8$

25. $12 - y = x$
$y = -x + 12$

26. $2y + x = 5$
$y = -\frac{1}{2}x + \frac{5}{2}$

27. $5y - 20 = x$
$y = \frac{1}{5}x + 4$

28. $3x + 4y = 12$
$y = -\frac{3}{4}x + 3$

Linear Functions and Graphing

Where You're Going

In this chapter, you will learn how to

- Determine whether a relation is a function.
- Solve linear equations.
- Solve systems of linear equations and inequalities.
- Solve a problem by graphing.

 **Real-World Snapshots** Applying what you learn, on pages 454–455 you will solve problems about electronic devices.

LESSONS

Key Vocabulary

- domain (p. 400)
- function (p. 400)
- function notation (p. 418)
- function rule (p. 418)
- linear equation (p. 406)
- linear inequality (p. 441)
- negative correlation (p. 425)
- no correlation (p. 425)
- positive correlation (p. 425)
- range (p. 400)
- relation (p. 400)
- scatter plot (p. 423)
- slope (p. 411)
- slope-intercept form (p. 413)
- solution (p. 405)
- system of linear equations (p. 435)
- system of linear inequalities (p. 443)
- trend line (p. 430)
- vertical-line test (p. 401)
- *y*-intercept (p. 413)

397

Chapter 8 Overview

In Chapter 8 students identify relations and functions, and then graph linear equations, learning that nonvertical lines represent linear functions. Students graph lines by first plotting points and then using the slope and *y*-intercept. Students learn to write rules for linear functions from words and from tables. They use their graphing knowledge to find trends and make predictions from scatter plots. Students also solve systems of linear equations and inequalities by graphing.

Activating Prior Knowledge

In Chapter 1 students learned to graph points in a coordinate plane. Ask: *In which direction do you move first to graph a point?* **right or left**

 Reading Math

- Reading a Graph, p. 429
- **Vocabulary** A complete list of terms, plus vocabulary exercises, appears in the Chapter Review on p. 449.
- **Illustrated Glossary** Examples for each vocabulary term, plus definitions in both English and Spanish, appear starting on p. 782.

Test-Taking Strategies

Finding Multiple Correct Answers, p. 448

Real-World Problem Solving

- **Strategy:** Solve by Graphing, pp. 430–433
- **DK Real-World Snapshots:** Applying Graphs, pp. 454–455
- **Chapter Project:** Rental Math, p. 741

 www.PHSchool.com

Internet support includes:
- Self-grading Vocabulary and Chapter 8 Tests
- Activity Masters
- Chapter Project support
- Chapter Planner
- Chapter 8 Resources

Plus **iTEXT**

397

Relating Graphs to Events

This Investigation shows students how a graph expresses the relationship between two variables. Students sketch a graph to describe a situation.

Teaching Notes

A graph can show the relationship between two variables. When time is one of the variables of a graph, you often represent it on the *x*-axis, increasing from left to right on the graph. The other variable is represented on the *y*-axis.

Error Prevention!

Students may forget to label their graphs. Suggest that students begin a graph by labeling both axes. Remind them that time is often represented along the *x*-axis.

Additional Examples

1 Ask: *Suppose the graph in Example 1 related the distance from school (instead of from home) to time. How would the graph differ from the one shown?* **The distance from the school would be greatest at the start and end of the trip and would be zero while you were at school. The graph would be like the one shown turned upside down.**

2 Ask: *Suppose you took an airplane to get to your summer-vacation destination. Sketch a graph to show your height above the ground while you are on the plane. Identify your axes and include labels for each part.* **Sample:**

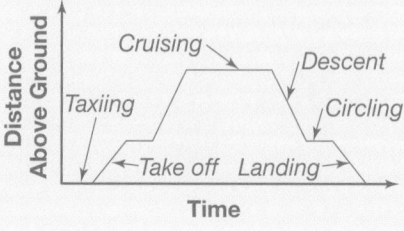

Modeling: Relating Graphs to Events

For Use With Lesson 8-1

You can use graphs to show real-world relationships visually. Labels can help explain the parts of a graph.

1 EXAMPLE

Transportation The graph at the right shows one trip from home to school and back. The trip combines walking and getting a ride from a neighbor. Tell what the graph shows by labeling each part.

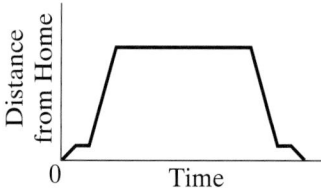

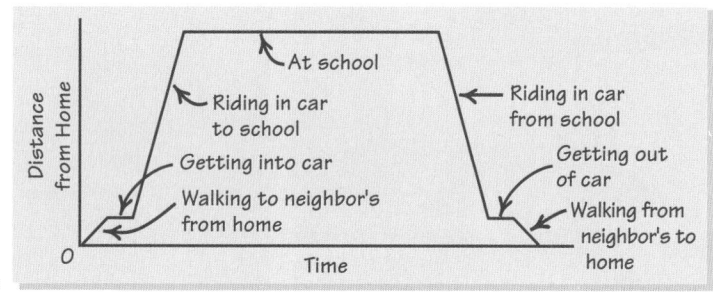

Label the parts of each graph. See right.

1.

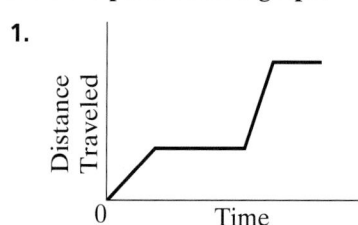

2.

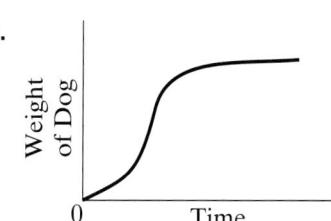

3. The graph at the right is a *step graph*. It shows the prices at a parking garage.
   a. How much does parking cost for an hour or less? **$2**
   b. How much does parking cost for 4 hours and 20 minutes? **$6**
   c. A receipt from the parking garage is for $7. What is the greatest length of time the car could have been in the garage? **6 h**

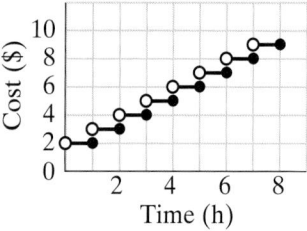

1–2. Answers may vary. Samples are given.
1.

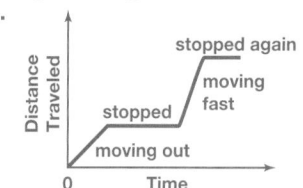

2.

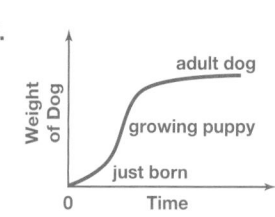

4. Reasoning Use the graph at the right. Jolene and Tamika were sprinting. Which girl ran faster? Explain.

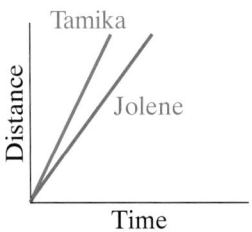

Tamika; Tamika took less time to run the same distance as Jolene ran.

When you draw a graph without actual data, you are making a sketch. A sketch can help you visualize relationships.

2 EXAMPLE

You go to an amusement park and ride a moving horse on a carousel. Sketch a graph to show your height above the ground. Identify your axes and include labels for each part.

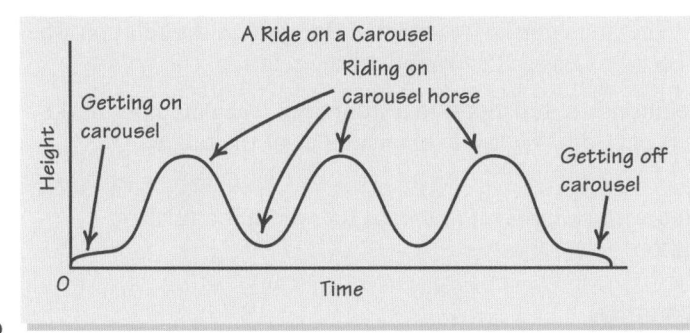

Sketch a graph for each situation. Identify your axes and include labels for each part. 5–9. See above right. Answers may vary. Samples are given.

5. the temperature outside during one 24-hour period

6. your speed as you take a trip on a train

7. the total distance you travel as you go to a concert and return home

8. the distance above ground of a pole vaulter's feet at a track meet

9. You pour water at a constant rate into the container shown at the right. Sketch a graph of the water level as you fill the container.

5.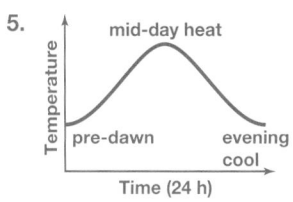

6.

7.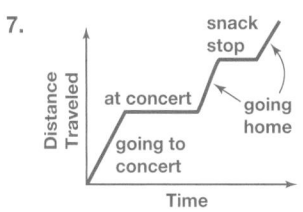

8.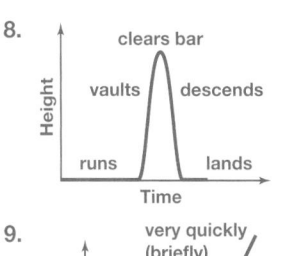

9.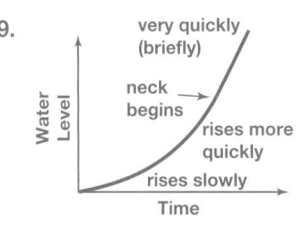

Investigation Modeling: Relating Graphs to Events **399**

8-1

8-1

Relations and Functions

What You'll Learn

 OBJECTIVE 1
To determine whether a relation is a function

 OBJECTIVE 2
To graph relations and functions

. . . And Why

To solve real-world problems involving cooking

 Check Skills You'll Need

Graph each point.
1–6. See below.
1. $A(3, 4)$ **2.** $B(-3, 1)$

3. $F(2, 0)$ **4.** $D(2, -2)$

5. $C(-4, -3)$

6. $E(0, -4)$

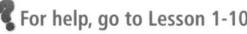 For help, go to Lesson 1-10.

New Vocabulary

• relation
• domain
• range
• function
• vertical-line test

1–6.
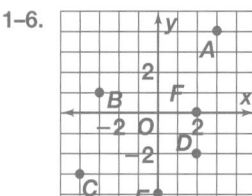

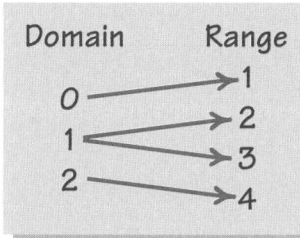 Interactive lesson includes instant self-check, tutorials, and activities.

OBJECTIVE

1 Identifying Relations and Functions

The table shows the results of a canned-food drive.

You can write the data in the table as a **relation,** a set of ordered pairs. The first coordinate of each ordered pair is the number of students in a homeroom. The second coordinate is the number of cans the students in that homeroom collected.

Food for Life Canned-Food Drive

Homeroom	Number of Students	Number of Cans
101	25	133
102	22	216
103	24	148
104	22	195
105	20	74
106	21	150

Here is the relation represented by the table:
  {(25, 133), (22, 216), (24, 148), (22, 195), (20, 74), (21, 150)}.
The braces, { }, indicate that these are all the ordered pairs in this relation. The first coordinates are the **domain** of the relation. The second coordinates are the **range** of the relation.

Some relations are functions. In a **function,** each member of the domain is paired with exactly one member of the range.

You can draw a *mapping diagram* to see whether a relation is a function.

1 EXAMPLE   Identifying a Function

Is each relation a function? Explain.

a. {(0, 1), (1, 2), (1, 3), (2, 4)}

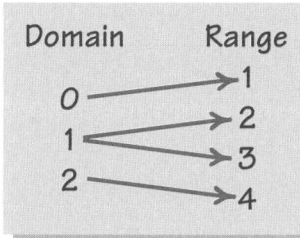

List the domain values and the range values in order.

Draw arrows from the domain values to their range values.

There are two range values for the domain value 1. This relation is *not* a function.

Ongoing Assessment and Intervention

Before the Lesson
Diagnose prerequisite skills using:
• Check Skills You'll Need

During the Lesson
Monitor progress using:
• Check Understanding
• Additional Examples
• Test Prep

After the Lesson
Assess knowledge using:
• Lesson Quiz
• Computer Test Generator CD-ROM

b. {(0, 1), (1, 2), (2, 2), (3, 4)}   **c.** {(0, 1), (1, 3), (2, 2), (3, 4)}

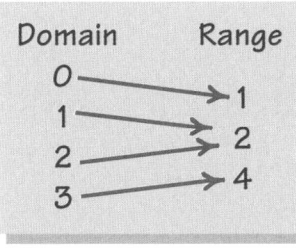

There is one range value
for each domain value.
This relation is a function.

There is one range value
for each domain value.
This relation is a function.

✓ **Check Understanding** Example 1

1. Is each relation a function? Explain. 1a–b. See right.

   a. {(−2, 3), (2, 2), (2, −2)}   **b.** {(−5, −4), (0, −4), (5, −4)}

Functions can model many everyday situations when one quantity
depends on another. One quantity *is a function of* the other.

2 **EXAMPLE** Real-World Problem Solving

**Cooking Is the time needed to cook a turkey a function of the
weight of the turkey? Explain.**

The time the turkey cooks (range value) is determined by the
weight of the turkey (domain value). This relation is a function.

✓ **Check Understanding** Example 2

2. **a.** For the United States Postal Service, is package weight
   a function of the postage paid to mail the package?
   Explain.
   b. Is the cost of postage a function of package weight?
   Explain.
   2a–b. See below right.

OBJECTIVE

2 Graphing Relations and Functions

Graphing a relation on a coordinate plane gives you a visual way to
tell whether the relation is a function. If the relation is a function, then
any vertical line passes through at most one point on the graph. If you
can find a vertical line that passes through two points on the graph,
then the relation is *not* a function. This is the **vertical-line test.**

1a. No; there are two range
values for the domain
value 2.
1b. Yes; there is one range
value for each domain
value.

Real-World Connection

You can estimate the
cooking time of a turkey:
20 minutes per pound
unstuffed, or 30 minutes
per pound stuffed.

2a. No; a specific postage
cost (domain value) can
mail packages of
different weights (range
values).
2b. Yes; for each package
weight (domain value)
there is one postage
cost to the same zip
code (range value).

2. Teach

Professional
Development

Math Background

You can think of a function as a
number generator. If you *input*
one number into the function,
the function *outputs* a second
number. The first coordinate in
each ordered pair is the input
number, a member of the
domain. The second coordinate in
each ordered pair is an output
number, a member of the range.

Teaching Notes

1 EXAMPLE Visual Learners

Have students compare the
domain and range lists for all
three parts of Example 1. Help
them see (in the finite case) that
when a relation is a function, the
amount of numbers in the
domain list is either greater than
or equal to the amount of
numbers in the range list.

2 EXAMPLE Error Prevention

Students may not realize that the
order in which the quantities are
named is important. Use a few
situations that are common to the
students' everyday lives to stress
the importance of the order. For
example: Is the time it takes to fix
a bike a function of the type of
repair, or is a type of repair a
function of the time it takes to fix
it? Help students realize that the
type of repair affects the time
needed to fix it, not vice versa.
Therefore, the time it takes to fix
the bike is a function of the type
of repair.

PowerPoint

Additional Examples

❶ Is each relation a function?
Explain. a–c. See back of book.
   a. {(0, 5), (1, 6), (2, 4), (3, 7)}
   b. {(0, 5), (1, 5), (2, 6), (3, 7)}
   c. {(0, 5), (0, 6), (1, 6), (2, 7)}

❷ Is the time needed to mow a
lawn a function of the size of
the lawn? Explain.
See back of book.

👥 **Reaching All Students**

| **Below Level** Have students come up with ways to associate "domain" with *x*-values and "range" with *y*-values. One way is to note that alphabetically *x* comes before *y*, and "domain" comes before "range." | **Advanced Learners** Ask: *Is the relation {(0, −2)} a function? Explain.* Yes; there is no repeated domain value, and it passes the vertical-line test. | **Visual Learners** See note on page 401. **Tactile Learners** See note on page 402. |

a.

Domain Value	Range Value
−3	5
−5	3
3	5
5	3

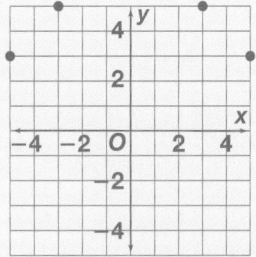

b. Use the vertical-line test. Is the relation a function? Explain. **Yes; no vertical line passes through two points on the graph.**

3 EXAMPLE **English Learners**

Help students understand the difference between *vertical* and *horizontal*. Suggest that they think of *horizon* to remember *horizon*tal.

3 EXAMPLE **Tactile Learners**

Students may have difficulty understanding why this test for a function is called a *vertical*-line test when their pencils are likely *horizontal* on their desks. Have students hold their papers up vertically and perform the test. Have them tack their papers to a corkboard or use a grid on the chalkboard. Remind them that the use of "horizontal" and "vertical" provide different ways to refer to the two axes.

Closure

Ask students to describe the difference between a relation and a function. **Any set of ordered pairs is a relation. A function is a relation with the restriction that no two of its ordered pairs have the same first coordinate.**

402

Need Help?

The first value in an ordered pair, the *x*-coordinate, shows horizontal position.

The second value in an ordered pair, the *y*-coordinate, shows vertical position.

---

3 EXAMPLE **Using the Vertical-Line Test**

a. Graph the relation shown in the table.

x-coordinates   *y*-coordinates

Domain Value	Range Value
−4	−3
2	0
2	3
4	3
5	−4

Graph the ordered pairs (−4, −3), (2, 0), (2, 3), (4, 3), and (5, −4).

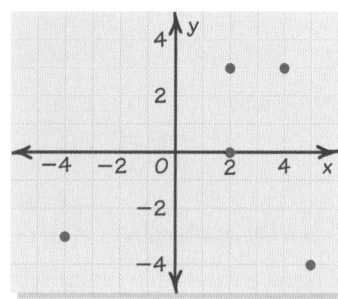

b. Use the vertical-line test. Is the relation a function? Explain.

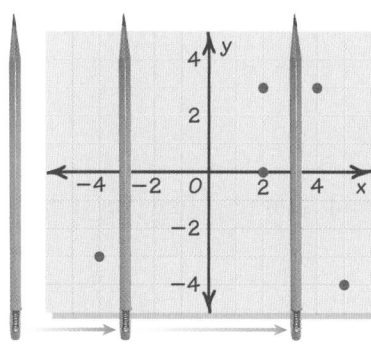

Pass a pencil across the graph as shown. Keep the pencil vertical (parallel to the *y*-axis) to represent a vertical line.

The pencil held vertically would pass through both $(2, 0)$ and $(2, 3)$, so the relation is *not* a function.

✓ Check Understanding Example 3

3. **Algebra** Graph the relation shown in each table. Use the vertical-line test. Is the relation a function? Explain.
a–c. See back of book.

a.
x	y
−6	−5
−3	−2
0	−2
1	0
4	3
5	7

b.
x	y
−7	4
−2	6
−1	−1
−1	3
0	5
1	5

c.
x	y
−5	4
−4	4
−3	4
0	0
1	4
2	4

EXERCISES

Practice and Problem Solving

 A Practice by Example

Example 1
(page 400)

Is each relation a function? Explain. 1–5. See below left.

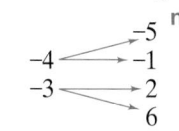

1. Domain Range   **2.** Domain Range   **3.** Domain Range

4. $\{(3, -1), (3, 0), (-3, 4), (3, 8)\}$ **5.** $\{(-3, -2), (-1, 0), (1, 0), (5, -2)\}$
no   yes

Example 2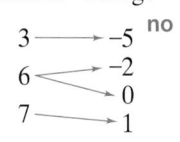
(page 401)

1. Yes; there is one range value for each domain value.
2. No; there are two range values for the domain values −4 and −3.
3. No; there are two range values for the domain value 6.
4. No; there are three range values for the domain value 3.
5. Yes; there is one range value for each domain value.

Example 3
(page 402)

6. Walking Is the time you take to go to the library a function of the distance to the library? Explain. 6–10. See back of book.

7. Is the price of a one-year subscription to your favorite magazine a function of the age of the subscriber? Explain.

8. Sewing Is the price of a piece of cloth a function of the length of the cloth? Explain.

9. Is the number of students on a field trip a function of the number of buses used? Explain.

10. Is the number of buses used for a field trip a function of the number of students on the field trip? Explain.

Graph the relation shown in each table. Use the vertical-line test. Is the relation a function? Explain. 11–14. See back of book.

11.

x	y
−5	2
−1	4
2	−5
4	−1

12.

x	y
−5	−5
−3	−3
1	1
2	2

13.

x	y
−1	3
−1	2
0	−4
4	2

14.

x	y
3	−1
2	−1
−4	0
2	4

B Apply Your Skills

Graph each relation. Is the relation a function? Explain.
15–22. See back of book.

15. $\{(0, 1), (3, 5), (2, 2), \left(-\frac{1}{2}, \frac{4}{5}\right)\}$ **16.** $\{(-1, 9), (0, -1), (-1, 4), (4, 9)\}$

17. $\{(-1, 1), (-2, 1), (-2, 2), (0, 2)\}$

18. $\{(4, -8), (4, -6), (1, 2), (1, 5), (1, -6)\}$

19.

GPS

x	y
−5	6
−2	3
3	2
6	4

20.

x	y
3	−7
1	−5
−1	−5
−3	−7

21.

x	y
−7	3
−5	1
−5	−1
−7	−3

22.

x	y
6	−2
1	−1
0	−2
−1	−3

GPS Use the Guided Problem Solving worksheet with Exercise 19.

Assignment Guide

1 Objective 1
  A **B** Core 1–10, 23–25
  C Extension 26–29

2 Objective 2
  A **B** Core 11–22
  C Extension 30

Test Prep 31–33
Mixed Review 34–37

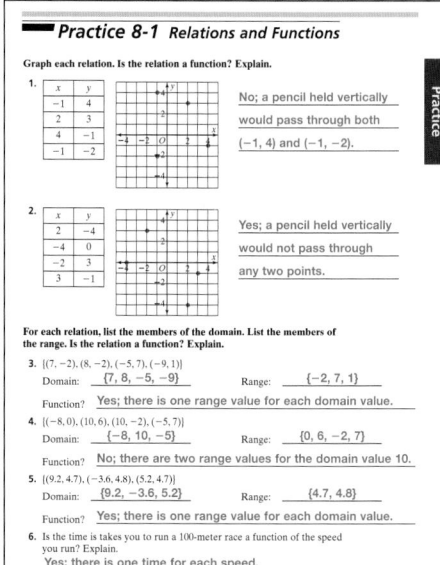

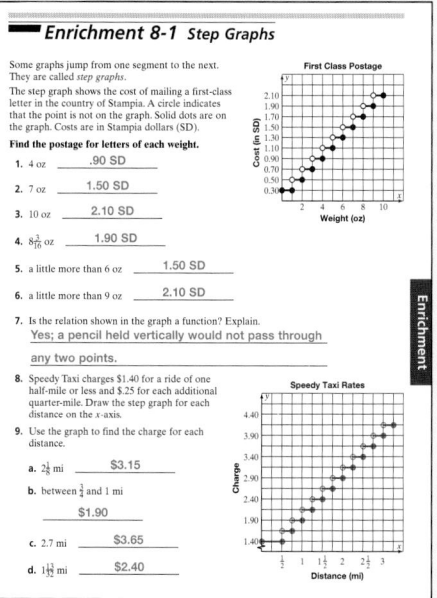

PowerPoint **Lesson Quiz 8-1**

Is each relation a function? Explain.

1. {(−2, −1), (4, 2), (−8, −4), (6, 3)} Yes; there is only one range value for each domain value.

2. {(5, 0), (7, 2), (9, 4), (5, 1)} No; the domain value 5 has two range values, 0 and 1.

3. Graph the relation in the table. Is the relation a function? Explain. Yes; there is one range value for each domain value. Check students' graphs.

x	y
−1	7
0	7
1	7
2	7

Teaching Tip
Exercises 26–29 Students can use words or write an equation in terms of *x* and *y* to describe each pattern.

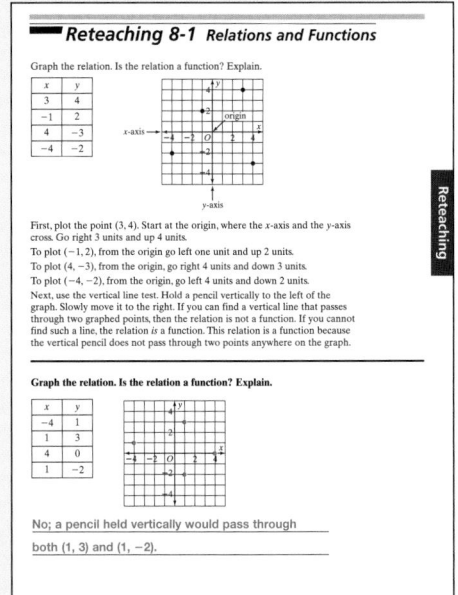

---

25. A function can have the same *y*-coordinate with different *x*-coordinates, but it cannot have the same *x*-coordinate with different *y*-coordinates.

C Challenge

---

23. **Writing in Math**  Is every relation a function? Is every function a relation? Explain. **See back of book.**

24. **Geometry** Explain why the area of a square is a function of the length of a side of the square. **For each side length, there is one and only one area of the square.**

25. **Error Analysis** Your friend says that a relation is not a function when two ordered pairs have the same *y*-coordinate. Explain your friend's error. **See left.**

Patterns In each function below, there is a pattern to how the range values relate to the domain values. Describe the pattern. 26–29. **See back of book.**

26. {(−2, 0), (0, 2), (3, 5), (8, 10)}   27. {(−5, 5), (−1, 1), (0, 0), (3, −3)}

28. {(−1, −0.5), (2, 1), (7, 3.5)}   29. {(1, 1), (2, 4), (3, 9), (4, 16)}

30. a. **Open-Ended** Write two different relations for which the domain is {−1, 0, 1} and the range is {1, 2}.
    b. Graph your relations. Use the vertical-line test to tell whether each relation is a function. **a–b. See back of book.**

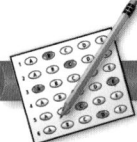

Test Prep

Multiple Choice

For Exercises 31 and 32, which choice best explains why the relation IS or IS NOT a function?

31. {(−5, 7), (−2, −1), (0, 3), (4, 7)} A
    A. A function; only one range value exists for each domain value.
    B. A function; two domain values exist for range value 7.
    C. Not a function; the relation passes the vertical line test.
    D. Not a function; two domain values exist for range value 7.

Take It to the NET
Online lesson quiz at
www.PHSchool.com
Web Code: ada-0801

32. {(−8, −4), (−2, 0), (1, 3), (−2, 6)} I
    F. A function; only one range value exists for each domain value.
    G. A function; two range values exist for domain value −2.
    H. Not a function; the relation passes the vertical line test.
    I. Not a function; two range values exist for domain value −2.

Short Response

33. Answer and explain. **(a)** Is the number of people expected to attend a picnic a function of the number of sandwiches made for the picnic? **(b)** Is the number of sandwiches made for a picnic a function of the number of people expected to attend? **See back of book.**

Mixed Review

Lesson 7-8 34. **Banking** You invest $1,200 in an account that earns 3.5% interest compounded annually. Find the account balance after four years. $1,377.03

Lessons 7-1 and 7-3 **Solve each equation.**

35. $-42 + 3c = -6$ 12   36. $\frac{3}{2}t - 4 = \frac{1}{2}$ 3   37. $2m - 4.9 = -3.6$ 0.65

Alternative Assessment

Have students write some "If . . . then . . ." statements to summarize how they can determine whether a relation is a function. Be sure students write statements that describe the definition, the vertical-line test, the mapping diagrams, and the repetition of a domain value.

Test Prep

Resources
For additional practice with a variety of test item formats:
• Test Prep, p. 453
• Test-Taking Strategies, p. 448
• Test-Taking Strategies With Transparencies

Equations With Two Variables

8-2

OBJECTIVE

1 Finding Solutions of Two-Variable Equations

In previous chapters, you solved equations with one variable, such as $2x + 5 = 7x$. In this chapter, you will find solutions of equations with two variables, such as $y = 3x + 4$. An ordered pair that makes such an equation a true statement is a **solution** of the equation.

1 EXAMPLE   Finding a Solution

Find the solution of $y = 3x + 4$ for $x = -1$.

$y = 3x + 4$

$y = 3(-1) + 4$ **Replace x with -1.**

$y = -3 + 4$ **Multiply.**

$y = 1$ **Add.**

• A solution of the equation is $(-1, 1)$.

✓ Check Understanding   Example 1

1. Find the solution of each equation for $x = -3$.

  a. $y = 2x + 1$ **b.** $y = -4x + 3$ **c.** $y = 0x - 4$
    $(-3, -5)$ $(-3, 15)$ $(-3, -4)$

You can use two-variable equations to model real-world situations.

2 EXAMPLE   Real-World 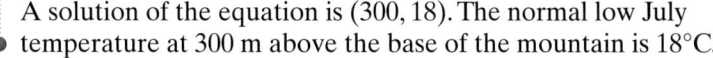 Problem Solving

Meteorology The equation $t = 21 - 0.01n$ models the normal low July temperature in degrees Celsius at Mount Rushmore, South Dakota. In the equation, t is the temperature at n meters above the base of the mountain. Find the normal low July temperature at 300 m above the base.

$t = 21 - 0.01n$

$t = 21 - 0.01(300)$ **Replace n with 300.**

$t = 21 - 3$ **Multiply.**

$t = 18$ **Subtract.**

• A solution of the equation is $(300, 18)$. The normal low July temperature at 300 m above the base of the mountain is 18°C.

What You'll Learn

OBJECTIVE 1 To find solutions of equations with two variables

OBJECTIVE 2 To graph linear equations with two variables

. . . And Why

To solve real-world problems involving meteorology and oceanography

✓ Check Skills You'll Need

Evaluate each expression for $x = 2$.

1. $2 + x$ **2.** $x - 12$
    4   -10

3. $8x - 13$ **4.** $24 \div 2x$
    3   6

? For help, go to Lesson 1-3.

New Vocabulary

• solution
• linear equation

 TEXT Interactive lesson includes instant self-check, tutorials, and activities.

---

1. Plan

Lesson Preview

✓ **Check Skills You'll Need**

Evaluating Expressions
Lesson 1-3: Example 1;
Exercises 1–6.
Extra Practice, p. 744.

Lesson Resources

📁 **Teaching Resources**
Practice, Reteaching, Enrichment

👥 **Reaching All Students**
Practice Workbook 8-2
Spanish Practice Workbook 8-2
Guided Problem Solving 8-2
Technology Activities 14

⏰ **Presentation Assistant Plus!**
Transparencies and PowerPoint™
• Check Skills You'll Need 8-2
• Additional Examples 8-2
• Student Edition Answers 8-2
• Lesson Quiz 8-2
• Classroom Aid 2
PH Presentation Pro CD-ROM 8-2

ASSESSMENT SYSTEM

Computer Test Generator CD-ROM

💻 **Technology**
Resource Pro® CD-ROM
Computer Test Generator CD-ROM
PH Presentation Pro CD-ROM

💻 **www.PHSchool.com**
Student Site
• Teacher Web Code: adk-5500
• Algebra Readiness Puzzles 63, 87
• Graphing Calculator, Procedure 4, 5
• Self-grading Lesson Quiz
PH SuccessNet Teacher Center
• Lesson Planner
• Resources

Plus **TEXT**

Ongoing Assessment and Intervention

Before the Lesson	**During the Lesson**	**After the Lesson**
Diagnose prerequisite skills using:	Monitor progress using:	Assess knowledge using:
• Check Skills You'll Need	• Check Understanding • Additional Examples • Test Prep	• Lesson Quiz • Computer Test Generator CD-ROM

Math Background

The coordinates of every point on a line in a coordinate plane make the equation of the line a true statement. Since a line has infinite length, a linear equation has an infinite number of solutions. Any equation that can be written in the form $y = mx + b$ is a linear function whose graph is a line. So $y = 3$, where $m = 0$ and $b = 3$, is a linear function. However, the equation $x = 3$ is *not* a function. It is a vertical line and therefore does not pass the vertical-line test.

Teaching Notes

1 EXAMPLE Teaching Tip

Ask: *Why does the last line of the example say, "A solution of the equation . . . " instead of "The solution . . . ?"* The ordered pair $(-1, 1)$ is not the only solution. For example, $(0, 4)$ is another solution.

2 EXAMPLE Science Connection

Temperature is a function of altitude. The higher you go, the cooler it becomes. On average, temperature drops about 6.5°C for every kilometer of altitude. Altitude also has an effect on the day-night temperature range. The higher you go, the thinner the atmosphere, which allows for a greater amount of incoming radiation during the day and outgoing radiation at night.

3 EXAMPLE English Learners

Anything described by the adjective *linear* is related to a *line* that generally is regarded as a *straight line*.

4 EXAMPLE Error Prevention

Students may incorrectly assume that all linear equations are functions. Remind them that linear equations with vertical-line graphs are not functions.

✓ **Check Understanding**   Example 2

2. Find the normal low July temperature at 700 m above the base of Mount Rushmore.   **14°C**

OBJECTIVE

2   **Graphing Equations With Two Variables**

An equation with two variables can have many solutions. One way to show these solutions is to graph them, which also gives a graph of the equation. A **linear equation** is any equation whose graph is a line. All the equations in this lesson are linear equations.

3 EXAMPLE   **Graphing a Linear Equation**

Graph $y = -\frac{1}{2}x + 3$.

Make a table of values to show ordered-pair solutions.

x	$-\frac{1}{2}x + 3$	(x, y)
-2	$-\frac{1}{2}(-2) + 3 = 1 + 3 = 4$	$(-2, 4)$
0	$-\frac{1}{2}(0) + 3 = 0 + 3 = 3$	$(0, 3)$
4	$-\frac{1}{2}(4) + 3 = -2 + 3 = 1$	$(4, 1)$

Graph the ordered pairs. Draw a line through the points.

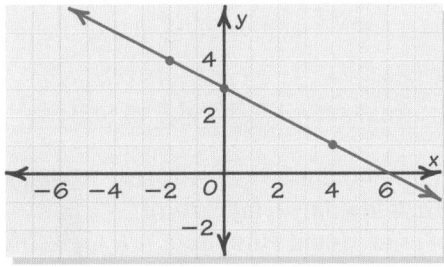

✓ **Check Understanding**   Example 3

3. Graph each linear equation.

   a. $y = 2x + 1$ **b.** $y = 3x - 2$ **c.** $y = -\frac{1}{2}x + 4$
     See above left.   b–c. See left.

If you use the vertical-line test on the graph in Example 3, you see that every x-value has exactly one y-value. This means that the relation $y = -\frac{1}{2}x + 3$ is a function. A linear equation is a function *unless* its graph is a vertical line.

? Need Help?

The expression $-\frac{1}{2}x$ means "the opposite of $\frac{1}{2}x$." So when the value of x is -2, the expression $-\frac{1}{2}x$ represents the opposite of one half of -2, which is 1.

3a.

3b.

3c.

👥 **Reaching All Students**

Below Level Have students think of different combinations of nickels and quarters they can use to make a dollar. Have them draw five of their combinations and then list them in words (e.g., 5 nickels, 3 quarters).	**Advanced Learners** Challenge students to graph $y = |x|$. Ask: *Is the relation a function? Is it linear? Explain.* It is a function since it passes the vertical-line test, but it is not linear.	**English Learners** See note on page 406. **Error Prevention** See note on page 409.

4 EXAMPLE Graphing y = a and x = b

Graph each equation. Is the equation a function?

a. $y = 2$

For every value of x, $y = 2$.

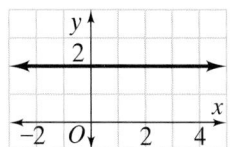

This is a horizontal line. The equation $y = 2$ is a function.

b. $x = 2$

For every value of y, $x = 2$.

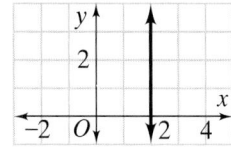

This is a vertical line. The equation $x = 2$ is *not* a function.

✓ Check Understanding   Example 4

4. Graph each equation. Is the equation a function?
   a–c. See right for graphs.
   a. $x = 1$ no   **b.** $y = -4$ yes   **c.** $x = 0$ no

You may find it helpful to solve an equation for y before you find solutions and graph the equation.

5 EXAMPLE   Graphing by Solving for y

Solve $3x + y = -5$ for y. Then graph the equation.

Solve the equation for y.

$$3x + y = -5$$
$$3x + y - 3x = -5 - 3x \quad \text{Subtract 3x from each side.}$$
$$y = -3x - 5 \quad \text{Simplify.}$$

Make a table of values.

x	−3x − 5	(x, y)
−2	−3(−2) − 5 = 1	(−2, 1)
−1	−3(−1) − 5 = −2	(−1, −2)
0	−3(0) − 5 = −5	(0, −5)

Graph.

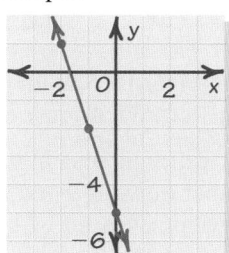

✓ Check Understanding   Example 5

5. Solve each equation for y. Then graph the equation.

a. $2x + y = 3$
$y = -2x + 3$
See right.

b. $y - x = 5$
$y = x + 5$
See right.

c. $-3x + 2y = 6$
$y = \frac{3}{2}x + 3$
See margin.

8-2 Equations With Two Variables   **407**

4a.
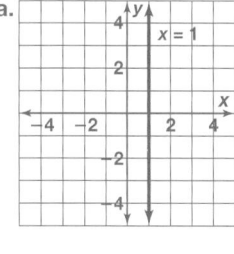

4b.
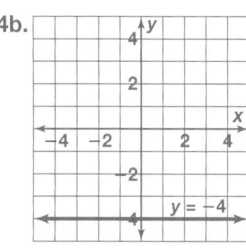

4c.
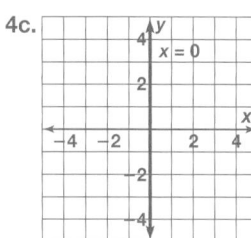

5a.
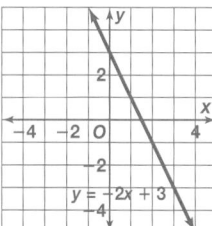

5b.
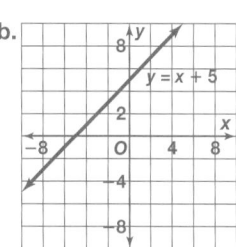

5c.
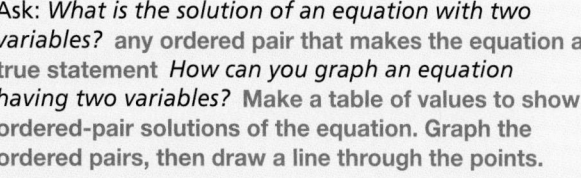

5 EXAMPLE Teaching Tip

Suggest students substitute 0 and numbers close to 0 for x. Using numbers like −2, −1, 0, 1, and 2 as x-values may simplify calculations.

PowerPoint
Additional Examples

1 Find the solution of $y = 4x - 3$ for x = 2. **(2, 5)**

2 The equation $a = 5 + 3p$ gives the price for admission to a park. In the equation, a is the admission price for one car with p people in it. Find the price of admission for a car with 4 people in it. **$17**

3 Graph $y = 4x - 2$.
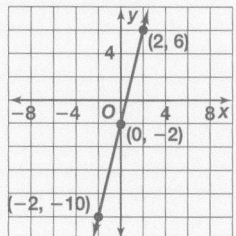

4 Graph each equation. Is the equation a function?
a. $y = -3$ yes
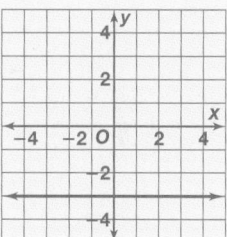

b. $x = 4$ no
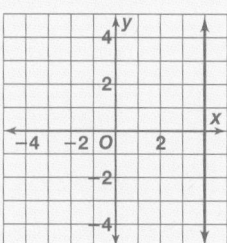

5 Solve $y - \frac{1}{2}x = 3$ for y. Then graph the equation.
$y = \frac{1}{2}x + 3$
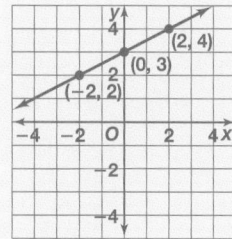

Closure

Ask: *What is the solution of an equation with two variables?* any ordered pair that makes the equation a true statement *How can you graph an equation having two variables?* Make a table of values to show ordered-pair solutions of the equation. Graph the ordered pairs, then draw a line through the points.

Assignment Guide

1 Objective 1
Ⓐ Ⓑ Core 1–11, 27–36

2 Objective 2
Ⓐ Ⓑ Core 12–26
Ⓒ Extension 37

Test Prep 38–41
Mixed Review 42–46

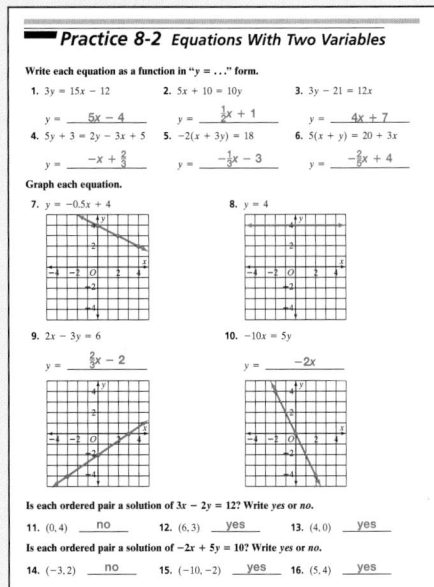

EXERCISES

❓ For more exercises, see *Extra Practice.*

Practice and Problem Solving

Ⓐ **Practice by Example**

Example 1
(page 405)

Find the solution of each equation for $x = -5$.

1. $y = 4x + 2$
$(-5, -18)$

2. $y = -3x - 1$
$(-5, 14)$

3. $y = 8x$
$(-5, -40)$

Find the solution of $y = -x - 3$ for the given value of x.

4. -2 -1 **5.** -1 -2 **6.** 0 -3 **7.** 1 -4 **8.** 2 -5 **9.** 3 -6

Example 2
(page 405)

The equation $k = 1.6d$ gives an approximate relationship between d miles and k kilometers. Express each distance in kilometers.

10. the 430 miles between Boise, Idaho, and Reno, Nevada
about 688 km
11. the 665 miles between Columbus, Ohio, and Des Moines, Iowa
about 1,064 km

Examples 3 and 4
(pages 406 and 407)

Graph each linear equation. Is the equation a function?
12–20. See margin for graphs.

12. $y = x - 3$ yes   **13.** $y = -x - 2$ yes   **14.** $y = \frac{2}{3}x - 2$ yes

15. $y = x + 3$ yes   **16.** $y = x - 10$ yes   **17.** $y = 2x - 1$ yes

18. $x = 7$ no   **19.** $y = 0$ yes   **20.** $x = -2$ no

Example 5
(page 407)

21–26.
Solve each equation for y. Then graph the equation. See back of book.

21. $-4x + y = 16$ **22.** $-3y = 3x - 9$ **23.** $2x - 4y = 12$

24. $y - 6 = 0.5x$ **25.** $-3x = 2y$ **26.** $2y - 3x = 10$

Ⓑ **Apply Your Skills**

28. yes; $12 - 6 = 6$
29. no; $-12 + 6 \neq 6$
30. no; $0 - 6 \neq 6$
31. no; $8 - 0 \neq 6$
32. $(-2, 13), (1, 4), (4, -5)$
33. $(-2, 5\frac{1}{2}), (1, 6\frac{1}{4}), (4, 7)$
34. $(-2, -7\frac{1}{5}), (1, -5\frac{2}{5}), (4, -3\frac{3}{5})$

27. Writing in Math Explain how you can determine from a linear equation whether the solutions of the equation form a function.
Answers may vary. Sample: If you can solve the equation for y, you have a function.

Is each ordered pair a solution of $4x - 3y = 6$? Explain. 28–31.
See left.

28. $(3, 2)$ **29.** $(-3, -2)$ **30.** $(0, 2)$ **31.** $(2, 0)$

Find the solutions of each equation for $x = -2, 1$, and 4.

32. $y = 7 - 3x$ **33.** $y = \frac{1}{4}x + 6$ **34.** $y = \frac{3}{5}x - 6$
32–34. See left.

$3x + 4y = 12$

$4y = 12 - 3x$

$y = 3 - 3x$

35. Error Analysis A student solved $3x + 4y = 12$ for y. Her work is at the left. What error did the student make? **The student forgot to divide $-3x$ by 4.**

GPS **36.** José is driving on a highway. The equation $d = 55t$ relates the number of miles d and the amount of time in hours t. About how many hours does José spend driving 100 mi? **1.8 h**

Ⓒ **Challenge**

37a. (0, 30) and (40, 0);
You burn 360 cal by
swimming only the
butterfly stroke for
30 min or only the
backstroke for 40 min.

37. If you swim the backstroke, you burn 9 cal/min (calories per minute). If you swim the butterfly stroke, you burn 12 cal/min. The equation $9x + 12y = 360$ models how you can burn 360 cal by swimming the backstroke for x min and the butterfly for y min.
a. Find the solutions of the equation for $x = 0$ and $y = 0$. Explain what your solutions mean. See left.

408 Chapter 8 Linear Functions and Graphing

GPS Use the Guided Problem Solving worksheet with Exercise 36.

12.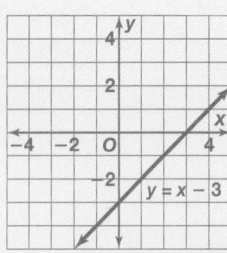

13.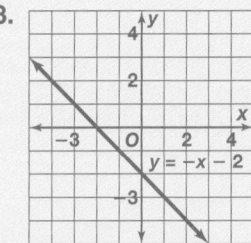

14–20. See back of book.

37c. (0, 30) is the point at which the graph and the *y*-axis intercept each other; (40, 0) is the point at which the graph and the *x*-axis intercept each other.

b. Graph the solutions you found in part (a). Draw a line through the two points. **See back of book.**

🌐 **c. Language Arts** The solutions you found in part (a) are the *y*-intercept and the *x*-intercept of the line. Explain why these names are appropriate. **See left.**

d. Use your graph from part (b). If you swim the butterfly stroke for 10 min, how long should you swim the backstroke to burn a total of 360 calories? **about 27 min**

Test Prep

Multiple Choice   For Exercises 38 and 39, which ordered pair is a solution for the given equation?

38. $y = 2x + 7$ **B**
  A. (13, 3)   **B.** (3, 13)   **C.** (2, 8)   **D.** (8, 2)

39. $y = -3x - 4$ **I**
  F. (1, −1)   **G.** (1, 1)   **H.** (−7, 1)   **I.** (1, −7)

Reading Comprehension   Read the passage below before doing Exercises 40 and 41.

Mountains Under the Sea

There is a mountain range in the Pacific Ocean far beneath the surface. Jacques Piccard and Donald Walsh descended to 35,814 ft to make a record dive in these mountains in a submersible.

There is tremendous pressure at these depths. The pressure of the air at sea level is 14.7 lb/in.^{2}, and the pressure increases about 0.44 lb/in.^{2} for every foot an object descends below sea level.

40. What is the pressure at 10 ft below sea level? **19.1 lb/in.^{2}**

Take It to the NET
Online lesson quiz at
www.PHSchool.com
  Web Code: ada-0802

41. The equation $y = 14.7 + 0.44x$ gives the pressure *y* in pounds per square inch at a depth of *x* feet below sea level.
  a. Find the pressure at the depth of the record dive.
  b. Find the pressure at half the depth of the record dive.
  41a. about 15,773 lb/in.^{2}
  41b. about 7,894 lb/in.^{2}

Mixed Review

Lesson 8-1   **Is each relation a function? Explain.** **42–45. See back of book.**

42. {(2, 4), (3, 6), (−3, 6), (1, 2)}   **43.** {(0, 3), (2, 1), (−7, 2), (1, 1)}

44. {(3, 4), (2.3, 6), (3, −7)}   **45.** {(0, −1), (0, 0), (−1, 0), (−2, −1)}

Lessons 4-9 and 5-5 🌐 **46. Astronomy** The sun orbits the Milky Way galaxy at about 135 mi/s. How far does the sun travel in an hour? In a week? Write your answers in scientific notation.
  about 4.86×10^5 mi; about 8.16×10^7 mi

8-2 Equations With Two Variables   **409**

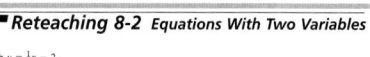
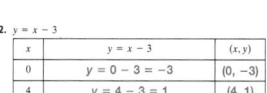
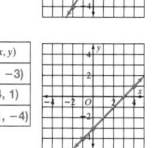
409

Direct Variation

This Extension shows students how to write the equation for a direct variation from a single pair of coordinates.

Teaching Notes

The equations for direct variations have the form $y = mx$, $m \neq 0$, and thus are a special subset of linear equations of the form $y = mx + b$. In direct variations, the slope is never 0 and the y-intercept is always 0.

2 EXAMPLE Teaching Tip

Help students carry through both steps of the two-step process: first, substituting the coordinates to solve for k, and, second, substituting the found value of k in the equation along with an x-value to find the corresponding y-value.

Additional Example

The speed limit on major highways in Austria is 130 km/h, which is the same as 80.6 mi/h. Speed in miles/hour varies directly with speed in kilometers/hour. Write a direct variation to convert kilometers/hour to miles/hour. The speed limit on smaller highways in Austria is 80 km/h. Use your equation to convert this to miles/hour.

$y = 0.62x$; 49.6 mi/h

Extension   **Direct Variation**

For Use With Lesson 8-2

A *direct variation* is a linear function modeled by the equation $y = kx$, where $k \neq 0$. The coefficient k is the *constant of variation*. In a direct variation, you can find k from one ordered pair (x, y). The graph of a direct variation always includes the origin.

1 EXAMPLE

Write an equation for the direct variation that includes $A(3, 5)$.

Step 1 First find the value of k.

$y = kx$	direct-variation equation
$5 = k(3)$	Replace y with 5 and x with 3.
$k = \frac{5}{3}$	Solve for k.

Step 2 Write the equation using the value of k.

$y = kx$	direct-variation equation
$y = \frac{5}{3}x$	Replace k with $\frac{5}{3}$.

You can write a direct variation to find the conversion factor between two measurement systems.

2 EXAMPLE

Measurement A segment measures 5 in., or 12.7 cm. Let x represent inches and let y represent centimeters. Write a direct variation to convert inches to centimeters. Then convert 24 in. to centimeters.

$y = kx$	Use the equation for a direct variation.
$12.7 = k(5)$	Replace x with 5 and y with 12.7.
$2.54 = k$	Solve for k.
$y = 2.54x$	Replace k with 2.54 to write a direct variation.
$y = 2.54(24)$	Solve for $x = 24$.
$y = 60.96$	Multiply.

24 in. is also 60.96 cm.

EXERCISES

Write an equation for a direct variation that includes each point.

1. $(4, 3)$ $y = \frac{3}{4}x$ **2.** $(2, 3)$ $y = \frac{3}{2}x$ **3.** $(8, 3)$ $y = \frac{3}{8}x$ **4.** $(5.9, 22.42)$ $y = 3.8x$

5. Measurement A carton contains 2 qt, or 1.89 L, of juice. Write a direct variation for the relationship between quarts and liters. Find the number of liters in 8 quarts. **See above right.**

5. $y = 0.945x$ (y is the number of liters and x is the number of quarts) or $y = 1.058x$ (y is the number of quarts and x is the number of liters); 7.56 L

Slope and *y*-intercept

Finding the Slope of a Line

**vestigation**

Understanding Slope

1a. See back of book.
1. **a.** Graph $y = x$, $y = 2x$, and $y = 3x$ on one coordinate plane.
   b. How does the graph of $y = kx$ change as k, the coefficient of x, increases? **It becomes steeper.**
   2a. See back of book.
2. **a.** Graph $y = x$ and $y = -x$ on the same coordinate plane.
   b. How are the graphs of $y = x$ and $y = -x$ alike? Different?
   Answers may vary. Sample: They both are lines through the origin. From left to right, one rises while the other falls.

The ratio that describes the tilt of a line is its slope. If a line slants upward from left to right, it has positive slope. If it slants downward, it has negative slope. To calculate slope, you use this ratio.

$$\textbf{slope} = \frac{\text{vertical change}}{\text{horizontal change}} = \frac{\text{rise}}{\text{run}}$$

1 **EXAMPLE** **Using Rise and Run to Find Slope**

Find the slope of each line.

a.
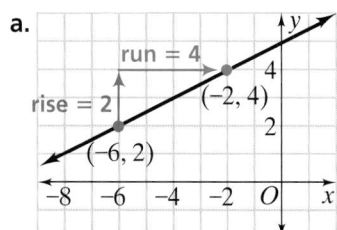

b.
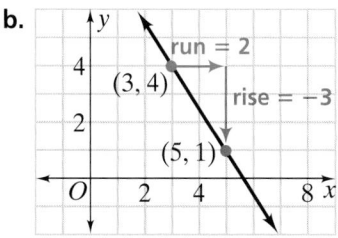

$$\text{slope} = \frac{\text{rise}}{\text{run}} = \frac{2}{4} = \frac{1}{2}$$

$$\text{slope} = \frac{\text{rise}}{\text{run}} = \frac{-3}{2} = -\frac{3}{2}$$

✔ **Check Understanding** **Example 1**

1. What is the slope of the ski trail at the right? $-\frac{3}{4}$

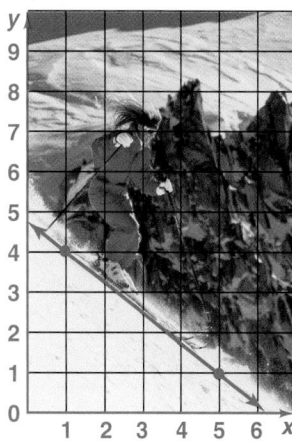

TEXT Interactive lesson includes instant self-check, tutorials, and activities.

8-3 Slope and *y*-intercept **411**

What You'll Learn

OBJECTIVE **1** To find the slope of a line

OBJECTIVE **2** To use slope-intercept form in graphing a linear equation

. . . And Why

To solve real-world problems involving the incline of a ramp or the slant of a roof

✔ **Check Skills You'll Need**

Find each difference.

1. $-4 - 5$ **2.** $3 - (-2)$
    -9 5
3. $6 - 9$ **4.** $-1 - (-1)$
    -3 0

❓ For help, go to Lesson 1-6.

New Vocabulary

• slope
• *y*-intercept
• slope-intercept form

Lesson Preview

✔ **Check Skills You'll Need**

Subtracting Integers
Lesson 1-6: Example 3;
Exercises 18–29.
Extra Practice, p. 744.

Lesson Resources

📁 **Teaching Resources**
Practice, Reteaching, Enrichment

👥 **Reaching All Students**
Practice Workbook 8-3
Spanish Practice Workbook 8-3
Guided Problem Solving 8-3
Technology Activities 14

⏱ **Presentation Assistant Plus!**
Transparencies and PowerPoint™
• Check Skills You'll Need 8-3
• Additional Examples 8-3
• Student Edition Answers 8-3
• Lesson Quiz 8-3
• Classroom Aid 2, 18
PH Presentation Pro CD-ROM 8-3

ASSESSMENT SYSTEM

Computer Test Generator CD-ROM

💻 **Technology**
Resource Pro® CD-ROM
Computer Test Generator CD-ROM
PH Presentation Pro CD-ROM

💻 **www.PHSchool.com**
Student Site
• Teacher Web Code: adk-5500
• Algebra Readiness Puzzles 64, 65
• Graphing Calculator, Procedure 6
• Self-grading Lesson Quiz
PH SuccessNet Teacher Center
• Lesson Planner
• Resources

Plus **TEXT**

Ongoing Assessment and Intervention

Before the Lesson
Diagnose prerequisite skills using:
• Check Skills You'll Need

During the Lesson
Monitor progress using:
• Check Understanding
• Additional Examples
• Test Prep

After the Lesson
Assess knowledge using:
• Lesson Quiz
• Computer Test Generator CD-ROM

411

Math Background

A formula for the slope of a nonvertical line is $m = \dfrac{y_2 - y_1}{x_2 - x_1}$, where m is the slope and (x_1, x_2) and (y_1, y_2) are two points on the line. You may choose any two points on the line to calculate the slope.

Teaching Notes

Investigation (Optional)
Help students see that the coefficient k of x in the linear equation $y = kx$ describes the steepness, or slope, of the graph of the equation. Remind students that x by itself has an unwritten coefficient of 1.

Teaching Tip
Students may observe that all lines that are not vertical or horizontal slant both upward and downward. To avoid confusion, suggest students always "read" the slant of lines from left to right, in the same way they read text from left to right.

2 EXAMPLE Visual Learners
Invite students to develop visual or mnemonic devices to help distinguish between a slope of zero and an undefined slope. One suggestion might be that a bicyclist might have "zero" difficulty riding on a flat road, but riding up a vertical wall would be impossible (undefined).

3 EXAMPLE Error Prevention
It is natural to write the difference of the x-coordinates in the numerator since the x-coordinates are written first in ordered pairs. Students might remember to write the difference of the y-coordinates in the numerator by noting the rhyming of *rise* and *y's,* or if they circle the y-coordinates.

4 EXAMPLE Auditory Learners
Help students remember how to start graphing a function of the form $y = mx + b$ by having them repeat "Begin at *b*." Stress the two b's.

412

If you know two points of a line, you can find the slope of the line using the following formula.

$$\text{slope} = \frac{\text{difference in } y\text{-coordinates}}{\text{difference in } x\text{-coordinates}}$$

The y-coordinate you use first in the numerator must correspond to the x-coordinate you use first in the denominator.

2 EXAMPLE Using Coordinates to Find Slope

Find the slope of the line through $C(-2, 6)$ and $D(4, 3)$.

$$\text{slope} = \frac{\text{difference in } y\text{-coordinates}}{\text{difference in } x\text{-coordinates}} = \frac{3 - 6}{4 - (-2)} = \frac{-3}{6} = \frac{-1}{2} = -\frac{1}{2}$$

✓ **Check Understanding   Example 2**

   2. Find the slope of the line through each pair of points.

   a. $V(8, -1), Q(0, -7)$ $\frac{3}{4}$ **b.** $S(-4, 3), R(-10, 9)$ -1

Horizontal and vertical lines are special cases for slope.

3 EXAMPLE   Finding Slope for Special Cases

Find the slope of each line.

a.
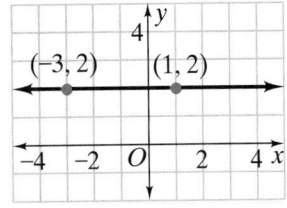

b.
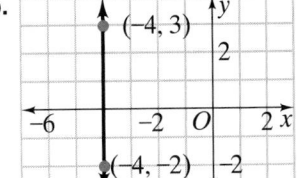

$$\text{slope} = \frac{2 - 2}{1 - (-3)} = \frac{0}{4} = 0$$

Slope is 0 for a horizontal line.

$$\text{slope} \frac{-2 - 3}{-4 - (-4)} = \frac{-5}{0}$$

Division by zero is undefined. Slope is *undefined* for a vertical line.

✓ **Check Understanding   Example 3**

   3. Find the slope of each line.

   a.
   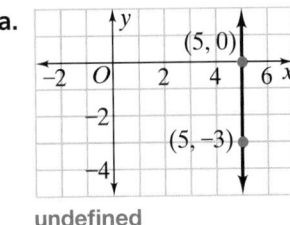
   undefined

   b.
   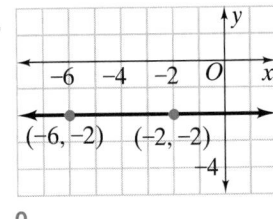
   0

412 Chapter 8 Linear Functions and Graphing

Test-Taking Tip
You may say that a vertical line has *no slope*. But be sure that you do not confuse *no slope* with *slope 0.*

👥 Reaching All Students

Below Level Have students measure the steepness, or slope, of various stairs and ramps around the school. For stairs, you may want to advise them on how to measure rise and run.	**Advanced Learners** Challenge students to find the slope and y-intercept of the equation $14x + 21y = 63$. $-\frac{2}{3}$; 3	**Visual Learners** See note on page 412. **Diversity** See note on page 413.

2 Using Slope to Graph Linear Equations

Here is the graph of $y = -\frac{1}{2}x + 3$.

The slope of the line is $\frac{-2}{4}$, or $-\frac{1}{2}$.

The **y-intercept** of the line is the point where the line crosses the y-axis. The constant in the equation is the y-intercept.

$$y = -\frac{1}{2}x + 3$$
$$\uparrow \qquad \uparrow$$
$$\text{slope} \quad y\text{-intercept}$$

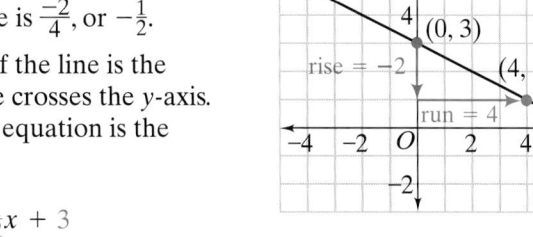

rise = −2   (4, 1)

run = 4

(0, 3)

> **Reading Math**
>
> The word *intercept* sounds like *intersect,* which means "to cross." Think of the *y*-intercept as where the line crosses the *y*-axis.

Key Concepts   Slope-Intercept Form

The equation $y = mx + b$ is the **slope-intercept form.** In this form, m is the slope of the line, and b is the y-intercept.

You can use slope-intercept form to help you graph an equation.

4 EXAMPLE   Real-World   Problem Solving

Engineering A ramp slopes from a warehouse door down to a street. The function $y = -\frac{1}{3}x + 2$ models the ramp, where x is the horizontal distance in feet from the bottom of the door and y is the height in feet above the street. Graph the equation.

Step 1 Since the y-intercept is 2, graph $(0, 2)$.

Step 2 Since the slope is $-\frac{1}{3}$ or $\frac{-1}{3}$, move 1 unit down from $(0, 2)$. Then move 3 units right to graph a second point.

Step 3 Draw a line through the points.

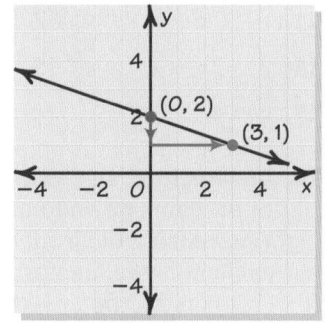

(0, 2)

(3, 1)

4a.

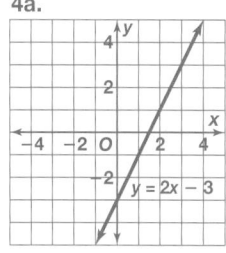

$y = 2x - 3$

4b.

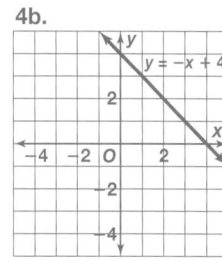

$y = -x + 4$

✓ Check Understanding   Example 4

4. Graph each equation. a–b. See right.

   a. $y = 2x - 3$ **b.** $y = -x + 4$

4.

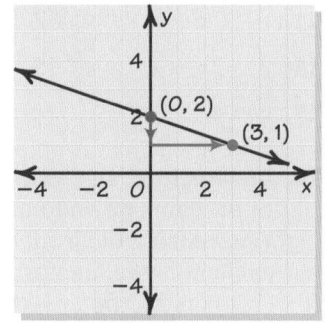

(0, 4)   (5, 3)

Closure

Have students draw the graph of a line with positive slope. **Check students' graphs.** Have students select two points on their line and find the slope. Repeat for negative, zero, and undefined slopes.

---

4 EXAMPLE   Diversity

Lead a discussion on how the slope of a staircase or ramp affects either the ease of use or the likelihood of falls. Discuss how the physical needs of people influence the slope. You may want to use measurements obtained in the Below Level activity on page 412. Have students research building regulations on the steepness of stairs or ramps.

PowerPoint

Additional Examples

1 Find the slope of each line.

   a.   4

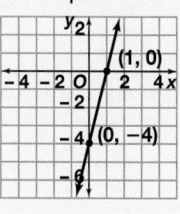

(1, 0)

(0, −4)

   b.   −2

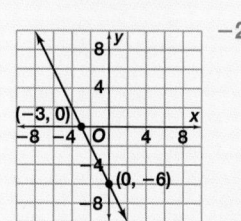

(−3, 0)

(0, −6)

2 Find the slope of the line through $E(7, 5)$ and $F(-2, 0)$. $\frac{5}{9}$

3 Find the slope of each line.

   a.   0

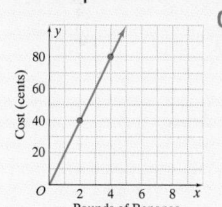

Cost (cents)

Pounds of Bananas

   b.

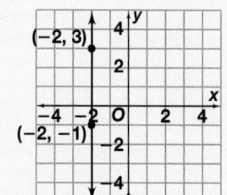

(−2, 3)

(−2, −1)

undefined

4 A ramp slopes from a warehouse door down to a street. The function $y = -\frac{1}{5}x + 4$ models the ramp, where x is the horizontal distance in feet from the bottom of the door and y is the height in feet above the street. Graph the equation. **See left.**

413

3. Practice

Assignment Guide

1 Objective 1
  Ⓐ Ⓑ Core 1–10, 21–29, 39, 40
  Ⓒ Extension 44, 45

2 Objective 2
  Ⓐ Ⓑ Core 11–20, 30–38
  Ⓒ Extension 41–43

Test Prep 46–51
Mixed Review 52–58

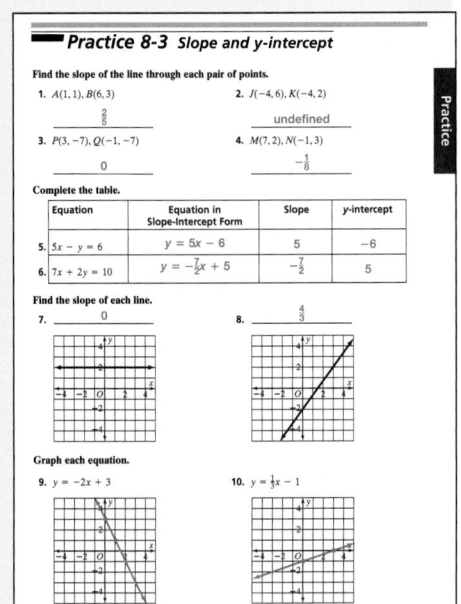

Practice 8-3 *Slope and y-intercept*

Find the slope of the line through each pair of points.
1. $A(1, 1), B(6, 3)$ 2. $J(-4, 6), K(-4, 2)$
   $\frac{2}{5}$ undefined
3. $P(3, -7), Q(-1, -7)$ 4. $M(7, 2), N(-1, 3)$
   0 $-\frac{1}{8}$

Complete the table.

Equation	Equation in Slope-Intercept Form	Slope	y-intercept
5. $5x - y = 6$	$y = 5x - 6$	5	-6
6. $7x + 2y = 10$	$y = -\frac{7}{2}x + 5$	$-\frac{7}{2}$	5

Find the slope of each line.
7. ____ 0 8. ____ $\frac{4}{3}$

Graph each equation.
9. $y = -2x + 3$ 10. $y = \frac{1}{3}x - 1$

Enrichment 8-3 *Linear Relationships*

Use slope and y-intercept to see relationships among lines.
Graph the given equations on the coordinate axes.
1. a. $y = \frac{1}{2}x - 3$ 2. a. $y = -x + 2$
   b. $y = \frac{1}{2}x - 1$ b. $y = -x + 1$
   c. $y = \frac{1}{2}x + 1$ c. $y = -x - 3$
   d. $y = \frac{1}{2}x + 3$ d. $y = -x - 1$

3. What kind of lines did you draw in Exercises 1 and 2?
   parallel lines
4. Complete: If two lines have the same ___slope___ but
   different ___y-intercepts___, then the lines are
   ___parallel___.

Graph the given equations on the coordinate axes.
5. a. $y = \frac{3}{2}x + 2$ 6. a. $y = 4x - 3$
   b. $y = -\frac{2}{3}x - 1$ b. $y = -\frac{1}{4}x + 1$

7. What kind of lines did you draw in each set?
   perpendicular
8. Find the product of the slopes in Exercise 5 ___−1___;
   In Exercise 6. ___−1___
9. Complete: If the product of the slopes of two lines is ___−1___, then
   the lines are
   ___perpendicular___.

EXERCISES

For more exercises, see *Extra Practice*.

Practice and Problem Solving

Ⓐ **Practice by Example**

Example 1
(page 411)

Find the slope of each line.

1. 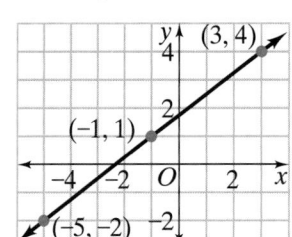 $\frac{3}{4}$

2. 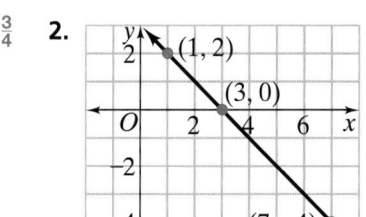 -1

Example 2
(page 412)

Find the slope of the line through each pair of points.

3. $A(2, 6), B(8, 1)$ $-\frac{5}{6}$ 4. $E(1, -2), F(4, -8)$ -2

5. $N(-5, 2), Q(1, -4)$ -1 6. $G(3, 4), H(6, 10)$ 2

7. $P(-3, 0), Q(4, -5)$ $-\frac{5}{7}$ 8. $A(2, 4), B(-1, -2)$ 2

Example 3
(page 412)

Find the slope of each line.

9.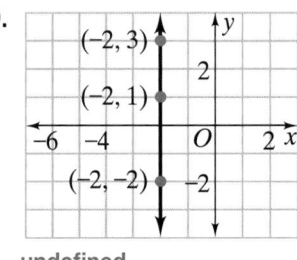
   undefined

10.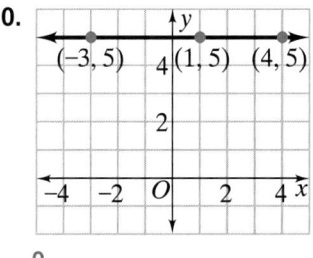
    0

Example 4
(page 413)

Identify the slope and y-intercept of the graph of each equation. Then graph the equation. 11–19. See back of book.

11. $y = 7x + 3$ 12. $y = -x$ 13. $y = \frac{1}{2}x - 8$

14. $y = 2x + 1$ 15. $y = -3x - 1$ 16. $y = x - 4$

17. $y = 4$ 18. $y = -3x + 3$ 19. $y = -\frac{3}{2}x + 6$

20. Architecture The roof of an A-frame cabin slopes from the peak of the cabin down to the ground. It suggests the letter A when viewed from the front or the back. The equation $y = -3x + 15$ can model the line formed by one side of the roof. For a point (x, y) on the roof, x is the horizontal distance in feet from the center of the base of the house, and y is the height of the roof in feet. Graph the equation. **See back of book.**

Ⓑ **Apply Your Skills**

21. The student could have calculated
    difference in *x*-coordinates / difference in *y*-coordinates.

21. Error Analysis A student said that the slope of the line through $(8, 4)$ and $(2, 2)$ is 3. What error could this student have made? See left.

22. Open-Ended Write equations for five different lines that intersect at $(0, 3)$.
Answers may vary. Sample: $y = 3, y = \frac{1}{2}x + 3, y = x + 3, y = 2x + 3, y = 4x + 3$.

414 Chapter 8 Linear Functions and Graphing

Find the slope of each line.

23.

$(-5, 2)$ y
$(-2, 1)$ $(1, 0)$
-4 -2 O 4 x
$(4, -1)$ $-\frac{1}{3}$

24.   0

y
-2 O 2 4 x
-2
$(-2, -3)$ $(4, -3)$

25. The upper roof has the steeper pitch because it has the greater slope.

9 ft

🌎 **25. Construction** The slope of a roof is its *pitch*. You indicate the pitch of a roof by a ratio $a : b$, where a is the number of feet of rise for every b feet of run. In the photos at the left, which house has a roof with steeper pitch? Explain. **See above left.**

3 ft
10 ft

Find the slope of the line through each pair of points.

26. $C\left(\frac{1}{2}, \frac{3}{4}\right), D\left(\frac{1}{4}, \frac{3}{4}\right)$ 0 **27.** $L(7, -6.3), M(5, -1.3)$ $-\frac{5}{2}$

28. $J(2.1, 3), K(2.1, 4.2)$ undefined **29.** $A\left(\frac{2}{3}, 2\frac{2}{3}\right), B\left(2\frac{2}{3}, \frac{2}{3}\right)$ -1

Solve each equation for y. Then graph the equation.
30–38. See margin.
30. $y - 2x = 4$ **31.** $y + 3 = 5x$ **32.** $2y + 2x = 2$

33. $3y + 2x = 3$ **34.** $y - \frac{1}{2}x = 0$ **35.** $y + 3 = 0$

36. $2y = x - 8$ **37.** $-4y = x + 48$ **38.** $3y - 2x = 15$

39. Does the point $(-3, 4)$ lie on the graph of $y = -2x + 1$? Explain.
no; $4 \neq -2(-3) + 1$
40. Does the point $(-2, -4)$ lie on the graph of $2y - 6x = 4$? Explain.
yes; $2(-4) - 6(-2) = 4$

C Challenge **Graph each line.** 41–42. See back of book.

41. no slope, through $(4, -2)$ **42.** slope $\frac{2}{3}$, through $(0, -4)$

43. a. Graph the groups of equations on three coordinate planes.
See back of book.

Group 1	Group 2	Group 3
$y = 2x - 5$	$y = -3x - 1$	$y = -6$
$y = 2x$	$y = -3x$	$y = 1$
$y = 2x + 3$	$y = -3x + 4$	$y = 4.5$

43b. The lines are parallel. Explanations may vary. Sample: Their $\frac{rise}{run}$ ratios are the same, so they never meet.

b. Writing in Math How are the lines in each group related to each other? Explain. **See above left.**

c. Reasoning What is the coefficient of x in the equation of a graph that has slope 0? 0

🌎 **44. Construction** The slope of a road is its *grade*. What do you think it means for the grade of a road to be 4%? $\frac{rise}{run} = \frac{4}{100}$. As you "run" 100 ft horizontally, you rise 4 ft vertically.

45. Find the slope of the line at the left using two points. Then find the slope using two other points. Are the slopes the same? Explain. **Answers may vary. Sample:** $\frac{4 - 2}{6 - 3} = \frac{2}{3}$ and $\frac{0 - (-2)}{0 - (-3)} = \frac{2}{3}$. Yes, the slope of the line is the same all along it.

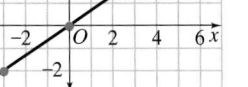

y
4
2
-2 O 2 4 6 x
-2

30. $y = 2x + 4$

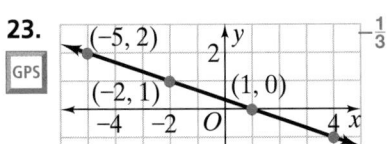

$y = 2x + 4$

31. $y = 5x - 3$

$y = 5x - 3$

32. $y = -x + 1$

$y = -x + 1$

33. $y = -\frac{2}{3}x + 1$

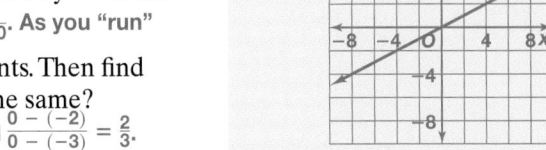

$y = -\frac{2}{3}x + 1$

34. $y = \frac{1}{2}x$

$y = \frac{1}{2}x$

35–38. See back of book.

GPS Use the Guided Problem Solving worksheet with Exercise 23.

Lesson Quiz 8-3

Find the slope of the line through each pair of points.

1. $A(2, 4)$, $B(-2, -4)$ **2**

2. $F(-5, 1)$, $G(0, -9)$ **−2**

3. Identify the slope and y-intercept of $y = -\frac{4}{3}x + 3$. Then graph the line. $-\frac{4}{3}$; 3

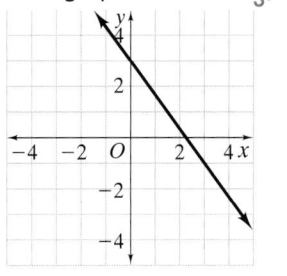

Test Prep

📁 Resources

For additional practice with a variety of test item formats:
- Test Prep, p. 453
- Test-Taking Strategies, p. 448
- Test-Taking Strategies With Transparencies

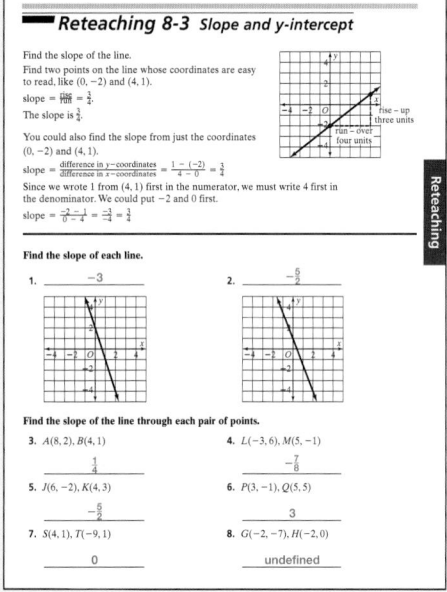

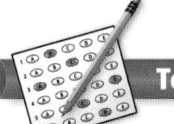

Test Prep

Gridded Response For Exercises 46–48, what is the slope of the line through the points of each pair?

 **Take It to the NET**
Online lesson quiz at
www.PHSchool.com
Web Code: ada-0803

46. $T(0, 5)$, $U(-3, -2)$ **47.** $Q(9, 5)$, $R(4, -5)$ **48.** $C(1, 7)$, $D(-8, 7)$
   7/3   2   0

For Exercises 49–51, what is the y-intercept of the graph of each equation?

49. $y = -4x + 7$ 7 **50.** $y = -2x$ 0 **51.** $y = 1.9$ 1.9

⬤ Mixed Review

Lesson 7-6 **Solve and graph each inequality.** 52–54. See back of book.

52. $4x + 5 < 17$ **53.** $18 \le 5 - 2x$ **54.** $-x + 6 > 31$

Lesson 6-8 **Find each percent of change. Tell whether the change is an increase or a decrease.**

55. from 10 to 9   **56.** from 20 to 30   **57.** from 52 to 39
   10% decrease   50% increase   25% decrease

Lesson 6-7 🌐 **58. Ticket Sales** During the 1998–1999 season, New York theater goers bought 11.7 million tickets for a total of $588.5 million. Theater goers spent a total of 5.5% more than the season before. What was the total amount spent during the 1997–1998 season? about $557.8 million

Math at Work

Movie-Camera Operator

Lights . . . camera . . . action! These are familiar words for movie-camera operators. When the action begins, movie-camera operators are responsible for capturing the action on film. One scene in a movie can cost hundreds of thousands of dollars, so a scene has to be filmed correctly in as few tries as possible. Camera operators are trained in the effective use of lighting, lens filters, and camera angles. The operators determine the precise movements of the camera and its platform and the camera angles in advance of the actual shooting. It takes a good understanding of algebra and coordinate geometry to do that!

💻 **Take It to the NET** For more information about movie-camera operators, go to **www.PHSchool.com**.
Web Code: adb-2031

416 Chapter 8 Linear Functions and Graphing

Alternative Assessment

Give each student a laminated coordinate plane and a piece of uncooked spaghetti. On the chalkboard, write equations for lines (in slope-intercept form) whose y-intercepts are integers. Have students use the spaghetti to graph each equation.

Technology

Graphing Lines

You can use a graphing calculator to graph equations in slope-intercept form and find solutions.

EXAMPLE

Graph $y = 3x - 2$.

Step 1 Press the **Y=** key.
Enter $3x - 2$.

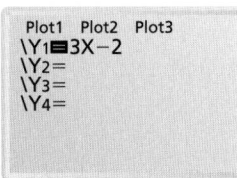

Step 2 Press **ZOOM** **6** to graph your equation with the standard viewing window.

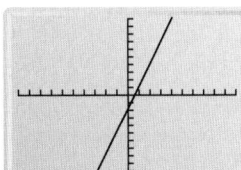

Step 3 Press **TABLE** to see solutions.

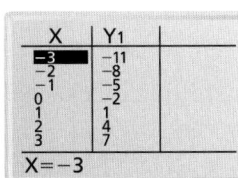

Step 4 Sketch the graph using values from the table of solutions.

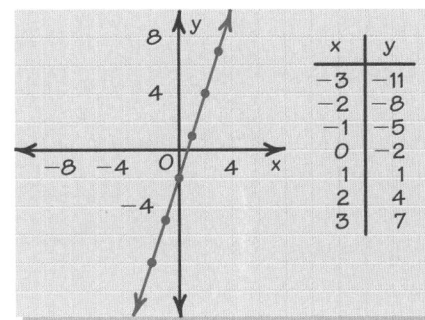

EXERCISES

Graph each equation. 1–9. See margin.

1. $y = 2x + 1$

2. $y = x - 4$

3. $y = 3x + 2$

4. $y = -x$

5. $y = -x + 4$

6. $y = 4x - 3$

7. $y = -3x - 2$

8. $y = \frac{1}{2}x - 5$

9. $y = -\frac{1}{2}x + 2$

10. Graph $y = \frac{2}{3}x - 2$, $y = \frac{2}{3}x + 2$, and $y = \frac{2}{3}x + 6$, in the standard viewing window. Tell what you observe, and explain. **The lines are parallel; the lines have the same slope, but different y-intercepts.**

1.

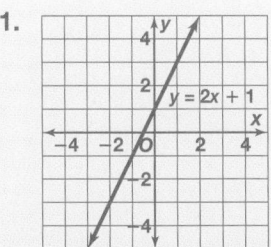

2.

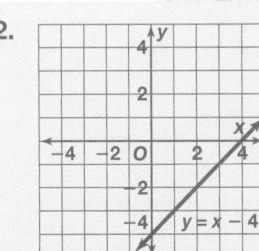

3.

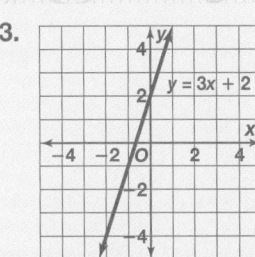

Graphing Lines

This Technology extension shows students how to graph linear equations and find ordered-pair solutions with a graphing calculator.

Teaching Notes

Graphing linear equations is an important skill in pre-algebra and algebra, as well as in advanced mathematics courses.

Visual Learners
Some students may not make the connection between the graphed line and the table. Pair students. Have one student's calculator display the table. Instruct the other student to display the graph in the ZInteger viewing window and then **TRACE** on the graph. Have the students compare the integer coordinates shown by the trace with the coordinates shown in the table.

Error Prevention!

Stress the importance of entering keystrokes carefully and following the procedures in the Example.

4.

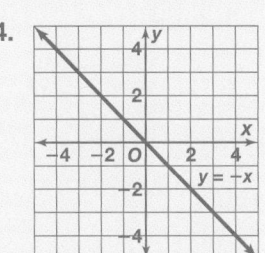

5.

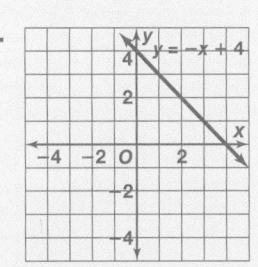

6–9. See back of book.

417

8-4

1. Plan

Lesson Preview

 Check Skills You'll Need

Slope
Lesson 8-3: Example 2;
Exercises 3–8.
Extra Practice, p. 751.

Lesson Resources

 Teaching Resources
Practice, Reteaching, Enrichment
Checkpoint Quiz 1

 Reaching All Students
Practice Workbook 8-4
Spanish Practice Workbook 8-4
Reading and Math Literacy 8B
Spanish Reading and Math
  Literacy 8B
Spanish Checkpoint Quiz 1
Guided Problem Solving 8-4

 Presentation Assistant Plus!
Transparencies and PowerPoint™
• Check Skills You'll Need 8-4
• Additional Examples 8-4
• Student Edition Answers 8-4
• Lesson Quiz 8-4
• Classroom Aid 2, 18
PH Presentation Pro CD-ROM 8-4

 ASSESSMENT *SYSTEM*

Checkpoint Quiz 1
Computer Test Generator CD-ROM

 Technology
Resource Pro® CD-ROM
Computer Test Generator CD-ROM
PH Presentation Pro CD-ROM

 www.PHSchool.com
Student Site
• Teacher Web Code: adk-5500
• Algebra Readiness Puzzles 66, 67
• Self-grading Lesson Quiz
PH SuccessNet Teacher Center
• Lesson Planner
• Resources

Plus

418

 **8-4**

What You'll Learn

 OBJECTIVE 1 To write a function rule for a word relationship

OBJECTIVE 2 To write a function rule by analyzing a table or graph

. . . And Why

To solve real-world problems involving measurements

 Check Skills You'll Need

Find the slope of the line through each pair of points.

1. $A(3, 1)$, $B(2, 1)$ 0

2. $S(3, 4)$, $T(1, 2)$ 1

3. $P(0, -2)$, $Q(0, 2)$
  undefined

4. $C(-5, 2)$, $D(4, -1)$ $-\frac{1}{3}$

For help, go to Lesson 8-3.

New Vocabulary

• function notation
• function rule

iTEXT Interactive lesson includes instant self-check, tutorials, and activities.

Writing Rules for Linear Functions

OBJECTIVE
1 Writing Rules From Words

You can write a function using **function notation,** in which you use $f(x)$ instead of y. You read $f(x)$ as "f of x." You can think of a domain value as an *input* and the resulting range value as the *output*. A **function rule** is an equation that describes a function.

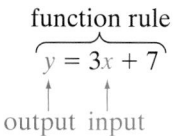 function rule
$$y = 3x + 7$$
output input

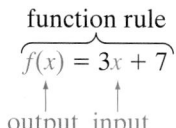 function rule
$$f(x) = 3x + 7$$
output input

1 EXAMPLE **Real-World** 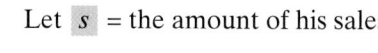 **Problem Solving**

Sales Commissions Paulo works at a local store. Each week he earns a $300 salary plus a 3% commission on his sales.

a. Write a function rule that relates total earnings to sales.

Words total earnings   are $300   plus   3% of sales

Let s = the amount of his sales.

Let $t(s)$ = total earnings, a function of his sales.

Rule $t(s)$ =   300   +   0.03 · s

A rule for the function is $t(s) = 300 + 0.03s$.

b. Find Paulo's earnings for one week if his sales are $2,500.

$t(s) = 300 + 0.03s$

$t(2,500) = 300 + 0.03(2,500)$ **Replace s with 2,500.**

$t(2,500) = 300 + 75$ **Multiply.**

$t(2,500) = 375$ **Add.**

Paulo earns $375 if his sales are $2,500.

 Check Understanding Example 1

1. Scrumptious Snack Mix is sold by mail order. It costs $3/lb, plus $4 for shipping and handling. Write a function rule for the total cost $c(p)$ based on the number of pounds p bought. Use your function to find the total cost of 5 lb of snack mix.
$c(p) = 3p + 4;$ $19

INSTANT CHECK SYSTEM **Ongoing Assessment and Intervention**

Before the Lesson Diagnose prerequisite skills using:	**During the Lesson** Monitor progress using:	**After the Lesson** Assess knowledge using:
• Check Skills You'll Need	• Check Understanding • Additional Examples • Test Prep	• Lesson Quiz • Computer Test Generator CD-Rom • Chapter Checkpoint 1 (p. 422)

To write a function rule from a table, look for a pattern. The slope m is $\dfrac{\text{difference in } f(x) \text{ values}}{\text{difference in } x \text{ values}}$, and b is the value of $f(x)$ when $x = 0$.

2 EXAMPLE   **Writing a Function Rule From a Table**

Write a rule for the linear function in the table below.

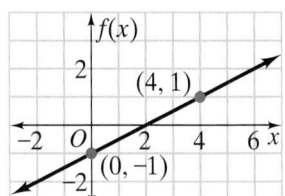

x	f(x)
−2	−5
0	1
2	7
4	13

As the x values increase by 2, the $f(x)$ values increase by 6.

So $m = \dfrac{6}{2} = 3$.

When $x = 0$, $f(x) = 1$. So $b = 1$.

● A rule for the function is $f(x) = 3x + 1$.

✓ Check Understanding   Example 2

2. Write a rule for each linear function.

a.

x	f(x)
−1	−2
0	0
1	2
2	4

$f(x) = 2x$

b.

x	f(x)
−3	6
0	0
3	−6
6	−12

$f(x) = -2x$

c.

x	y
−6	−11
−4	−7
−2	−3
0	1

$y = 2x + 1$

You can use slope-intercept form, $f(x) = mx + b$ or $y = mx + b$, when you write a rule for a linear function.

3 EXAMPLE   **Writing a Function Rule From a Graph**

Write a rule for the linear function graphed below.

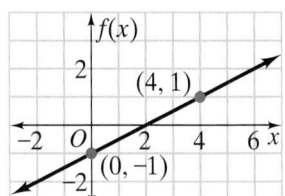

slope $= \dfrac{1 - (-1)}{4 - 0} = \dfrac{2}{4} = \dfrac{1}{2}$

y-intercept $= -1$

A rule for the function is $f(x) = \dfrac{1}{2}x - 1$.

Reading Math

y and $f(x)$ may be used interchangeably in a function rule.

✓ Check Understanding   Example 3

3. Write a rule for the function graphed at the right.
$y = -x + 2$

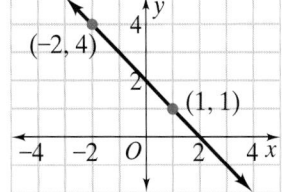

Reaching All Students

Below Level Have students form an "assembly line." On a piece of paper, student A writes a number (input). Student B writes the product of the number and 3 (output). Student C reads the input/output result.

Advanced Learners Challenge students to write one rule for finding the positive difference between any two temperatures.

Error Prevention See note on page 421.
English Learners See note on page 421.

---

2. Teach

Professional Development

Math Background

When the value of y depends on the value of x, you can say "y is a function of x." For the function $f(x) = 3x + 7$, you evaluate the function for $x = -2$, or find $f(-2)$, by substituting -2 for x:
$f(-2) = 3(-2) + 7$
$f(-2) = 1$
You may state the result as "f of negative two is one."

PowerPoint

📖 Additional Examples

1 A long-distance phone company charges its customers a monthly fee of \$4.95 plus 9¢ for each minute of a long-distance call.
a. Write a function rule that relates the total monthly bill to the number of minutes a customer spent on long-distance calls.
$t(m) = 4.95 + 0.09m$
b. Find the total monthly bill if the customer made 90 minutes of long-distance calls. **\$13.05**

2 Write a rule for the linear function in the table below.

x	2	0	−2	−4
f(x)	3	−5	−13	−21

$f(x) = 4x - 5$

3 Write a rule for the linear function graphed below.

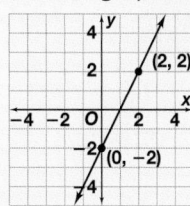

$f(x) = 2x - 2$

Closure

Ask students how to write a function rule from a table that shows x and $f(x)$ values of a linear function. **See back of book.**

Assignment Guide

 **Objective 1**
- Ⓐ Ⓑ **Core** 1–3, 10–12
- Ⓒ **Extension** 26, 27

 **Objective 2**
- Ⓐ Ⓑ **Core** 4–9, 13–24
- Ⓒ **Extension** 25

Test Prep 28–31
Mixed Review 32–38

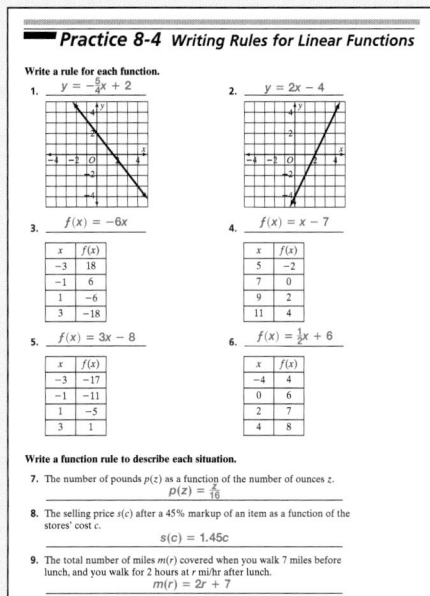

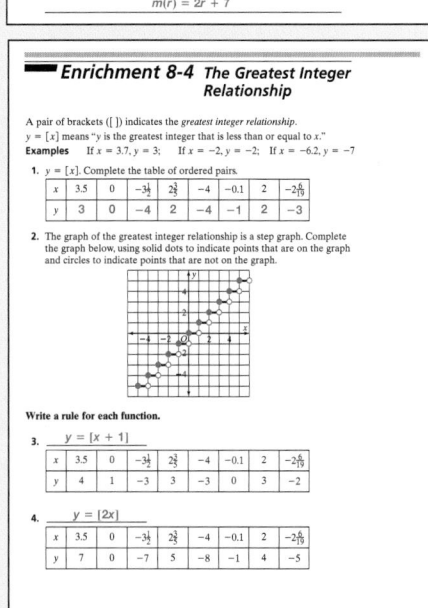

EXERCISES

? For more exercises, see *Extra Practice*.

Practice and Problem Solving

Ⓐ **Practice by Example**

Example 1
(page 418)

Write a function rule for each situation. Then use your function as indicated.

🌐 **1. Money** You give a salesperson $20 for a purchase and receive change. Use your function to find the amount of change from a $4.50 purchase. $a(c) = 20 - c$; $15.50

🌐 **2. Science** The temperature t in *Kelvin* is 273.15 more than the temperature c in degrees *Celsius*. Use your function to find the equivalent temperature in Kelvin for 100°C.
$t(c) = c + 273.15$; 373.15 K

🌐 **3. Physics** The force of gravity is less on Mars than it is on Earth. As a result, the weight of an object on Mars m is 40% of its weight on Earth w. Use your function to find the weight on Mars of a space probe that weighs 15 lb on Earth. $m(w) = 0.4w$; 6 lb

Example 2
(page 419)

In Exercises 4–8, write a rule for each linear function. 4–6. See left.

4.

x	f(x)
−9	−18
0	−9
9	0
18	9

5.

x	f(x)
−4	4
−2	2
0	0
2	−2

6.

x	y
0	−2.4
2	−4.8
4	−7.2
6	−9.6

4. $f(x) = x - 9$
5. $f(x) = -x$
6. $y = -1.2x - 2.4$

Example 3
(page 419)

7.

$(0, 2)$
$(5, -2)$
$y = -\frac{4}{5}x + 2$

8.

$f(x)$
$(5, 3)$
$(0, 1)$
$f(x) = \frac{2}{5}x + 1$

9a. A rule is a concise way of showing a function.

9b. A rule does not give specific x and y values.

10a. $q(p) = \frac{1}{2}p$

10b. $q(f) = \frac{f}{32}$

9. a. Writing in Math Describe the advantages you see in using a rule for a function rather than listing function values in a table.
b. Describe the disadvantages. 9a–b. See above left.

Ⓑ **Apply Your Skills**

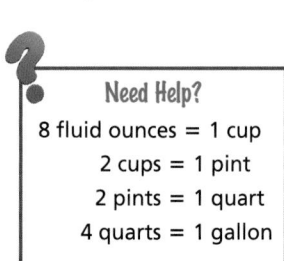

Need Help?

8 fluid ounces = 1 cup
2 cups = 1 pint
2 pints = 1 quart
4 quarts = 1 gallon

10. Measurement Write a rule that expresses the number of quarts q of a liquid as a function of each of the following.
a. the number of pints p **b.** the number of fluid ounces f
a–b. See above left.

11. a. Measurement Express the number of inches $n(d)$ as a function of the number of yards d. $n(d) = 36d$
b. Use your function to find the number of inches in 4 yards.
$n(4) = 36(4) = 144$; 144 inches.

12. a. Geometry Write a rule that expresses the perimeter $p(s)$ of a square as a function of the length s of one side. $p(s) = 4s$
b. Use your function to find the perimeter of a square with side length 7 cm. $p(7) = 4(7) = 28$; 28 cm

 GPS

420 Chapter 8 Linear Functions and Graphing

GPS Use the Guided Problem Solving worksheet with Exercise 12.

Examples 2 and 3 suggest that you can write a rule for a linear function if you know any of the following about its graph.
(a) the slope *m* and *y*-intercept *b*;
(b) the slope *m* and any point *(p, q)* of the graph;
(c) any two points *(r, s)* and *(u, v)* of the graph.

Sample A line through points $(-2, 6)$ and $(4, 3)$ has slope

$$\frac{3 - 6}{4 - (-2)} = -\frac{1}{2}.$$

Using $-\frac{1}{2}$ for the slope, an equation of the line is $\quad y = -\frac{1}{2}x + b.$

Using $(4, 3)$, substitute 4 for *x* and 3 for *y*: $\quad 3 = -\frac{1}{2}(4) + b$

So, $3 = -2 + b$, and the *y*-intercept *b* is 5. The rule is $\quad y = -\frac{1}{2}x + 5.$

Write a rule for the linear function whose graph has slope *m* and *y*-intercept *b*.

13. $m = 2, b = -4$
$y = 2x - 4$

14. $m = -\frac{1}{3}, b = -2$
$y = -\frac{1}{3}x - 2$

15. $m = 0, b = 2$
$y = 2$

Write a rule for the linear function whose graph has slope *m* and contains the given point.

16. $m = -\frac{1}{4}; (4, 0)$
$y = -\frac{1}{4}x + 1$

17. $m = 3; (-2, -2)$
$y = 3x + 4$

18. $m = \frac{3}{4}; (6, 4)$
$y = \frac{3}{4}x - \frac{1}{2}$

Write a rule for the linear function whose graph contains the two given points. 19–24. See left.

19. $(1, 1), (2, 5)$

20. $(3, 0), (8, 2)$

21. $(11, 19), (-6, -15)$

22. $(-3, 2), (4, -1.5)$ **23.** $(1, -1), (4, -1)$ **24.** $(1, 2.4), (-1, 3.8)$

19. $y = 4x - 3$
20. $y = \frac{2}{5}x - 1\frac{1}{5}$
21. $y = 2x - 3$
22. $y = -0.5x + 0.5$
23. $y = -1$
24. $y = -0.7x + 3.1$

 Challenge

25. a. Choose two points from the table and write a rule for the linear function.
b. Choose two other points from the table and write a rule for the linear function.
c. **Writing in Math** Compare the rules from parts (a) and (b) Justify your observations. See left.

25a–b. $y = 2x - 3$
c. The rules are the same because all points are on the same line.

x	y
−6	−15
1	−1
7	11
11	19

Data Analysis For Exercises 26 and 27, use the data below.

26. Write a function rule for the total monthly cost for electric space heating.
$c(k) = 0.05691k + 7.77$

27. a. Write a function rule for the total monthly bill of a home customer. See left.
b. Suppose a home customer receives a bill for $22.52 one month. How many kilowatt-hours did the customer use that month? 315 kWh

27a. $c(k) = 0.04968k + 6.87$

Electricity Rates

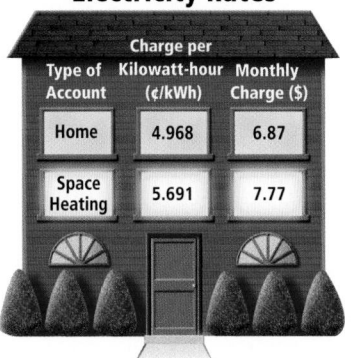

Type of Account	Charge per Kilowatt-hour (¢/kWh)	Monthly Charge ($)
Home	4.968	6.87
Space Heating	5.691	7.77

Science Connection
Exercise 2 The Kelvin temperature scale is also known as the "absolute-temperature scale." William Thompson, Lord Kelvin, developed it in the mid-1800s. The zero point on the Kelvin scale is equivalent to −273.15°C. This "absolute zero" point is considered the lowest possible temperature of anything in the universe.

Error Prevention!

Exercises 4–6, 25 Each ordered pair in a table represents an ordered pair of the function. As a check of their work, suggest that students substitute ordered pairs from the table into the rules they find.

English Learners
Exercise 27 Explain to students that electric *space* heating refers to the heating of living space, such as rooms in a home.

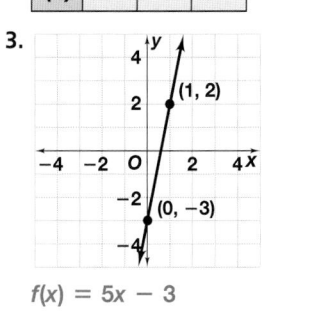
Lesson Quiz 8-4

Write a rule for each function.

1. Sarena earns a salary of $150 a week plus a 10% commission on each sale. $f(x) = 0.10x + 150$

2.

x	0	1	2
f(x)	0	1	2

$f(x) = x$

3.

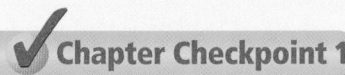

$f(x) = 5x - 3$

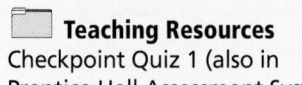**Chapter Checkpoint 1**

To check understanding of Lessons 8-1 to 8-4:

Checkpoint Quiz 1 (p. 422)

📁 **Teaching Resources**
Checkpoint Quiz 1 (also in Prentice Hall Assessment System)

👥 **Reaching All Students**
Reading and Math Literacy 8B

Spanish versions available.

Reteaching 8-4 *Writing Rules for Linear Functions*

Write a rule for the function.

x	f(x)
-2	-12
0	-2
2	8
4	18

As the x values increase by 2, the f(x) values increase by 10. So $m = \frac{10}{2} = 5$. When $x = 0$, $f(x) = -2$. So $b = -2$. Substitute $m = 5$ and $b = -2$ into $f(x) = mx + b$.
$f(x) = 5x + (-2)$
$f(x) = 5x - 2$

Write a rule for each function.

1. $f(x) = 7x$

x	f(x)
-1	-7
0	0
1	7
2	14

2. $f(x) = x - 8$

x	f(x)
-9	-17
0	-8
9	1
18	10

3. $f(x) = -2x + 9$

x	f(x)
0	9
2	5
4	1
6	-3

4. $f(x) = \frac{1}{3}x + 9$

x	f(x)
-6	7
-3	8
0	9
3	10

5. $f(x) = -\frac{1}{4}x - 7$

x	f(x)
-4	-6
0	-7
4	-8
8	-9

6. $f(x) = 6x - 11$

x	f(x)
-12	-83
-6	-47
0	-11
6	25

422

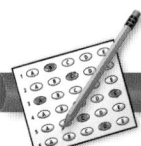 **Test Prep**

Multiple Choice

28. Which rule gives the same relationship between x and y as $x + y = 6$?
A. $y = x + 6$ **B.** $y = x - 6$ **C.** $y = 6 - x$ **D.** $y = -6 - x$
C

Take It to the NET
Online lesson quiz at
www.PHSchool.com
Web Code: ada-0804

29. Which function rule describes the number of centimeters y as a function of a number of millimeters x? **H**
F. $y = 100x$ **G.** $y = 10x$ **H.** $y = 0.1x$ **I.** $y = 0.01x$

30. Which rule shows the relationship of pounds, p, to ounces, z? **A**
A. $z = 16p$ **B.** $z = 32p$ **C.** $p = 16z$ **D.** $p = 32z$

Short Response

31. a. One gallon equals 4 quarts. Write a rule that expresses the number of quarts q as a function of the number of gallons g.
b. Use your function from part (a) to find the number of quarts in 17 gallons. **See back of book.**

Mixed Review

Lesson 8-3 **Find the slope of the line through each pair of points.**

32. $C(0, -2), D(2, 1)$ $\frac{3}{2}$ **33.** $J(3, -1), K(6, 1)$ $\frac{2}{3}$ **34.** $G(12, 8), H(6, 2)$ 1

Lesson 6-4 **Probability** **Find each probability for choosing a letter at random from the letters in the word FUNCTION.**

35. $P(\text{N or C})$ $\frac{3}{8}$ **36.** $P(\text{consonant})$ $\frac{5}{8}$ **37.** $P(\text{not T})$ $\frac{7}{8}$

Lesson 3-5 🌐 **38. Sports** In 1999, Hicham El Guerrouj of Morocco ran the mile in world-record time. Had he taken 1.26 seconds longer, his time would have matched the previous record of 3 min, 44.39 s. Write and solve an equation to find the 1999 record time. $r + 1.26 = 44.39$; $r = 43.13$ for a 1999 record time of 3 min 43.13 s

---

 **Checkpoint Quiz 1**   **Lessons 8-1 through 8-4**

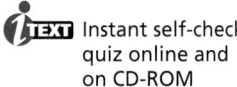 **Instant self-check quiz online and on CD-ROM**

3. Yes; there is one range value for each domain value.

4. Answers may vary. Sample: If every vertical line passes through just one graphed point, then the relation is a function.

1. Find three solutions of $9x - 2y = 18$.
Answers may vary. Sample: (0, -9), (2, 0), (1, $-4\frac{1}{2}$)

2. Graph $3x - y = 5$ on a coordinate plane. **See back of book.**

3. Is $\{(-2, 0), (-1, 3), (0, -2), (3, -1)\}$ a function? Explain. **See left.**

4. **Writing in Math** Explain how to use the vertical-line test to determine whether a relation is a function. **See left.**

Find the slope of the line through the given points.

5. $A(1, 5), B(3, 15)$ **6.** $D(-2, -4), F(0, -6)$ **7.** $G(-3, 4), H(-3, -6)$
5   -1   undefined

8. What are the slope and the y-intercept of $y = -2x + 5$? **-2, 5**

9. **Measurement** Write a rule to describe the number of pounds $p(n)$ as a function of a number of tons n. $p(n) = 2{,}000n$

422 Chapter 8 Linear Functions and Graphing

Alternative Assessment

Have students pick a standard unit of measurement, such as a quart, and write a function rule that converts quart measurements into measurements using a metric unit, such as liters. Have them refer to the table on page 292. $y = 1.06q$

Test Prep

📁 **Resources**
For additional practice with a variety of test item formats:
• Test Prep, p. 453
• Test-Taking Strategies, p. 448
• Test-Taking Strategies With Transparencies

Scatter Plots

Interpreting and Drawing Scatter Plots

 **In**vestigation

Making Scatter Plots

1. **Data Collection** For each person in your group, measure the height and *hand span*, the greatest distance possible between the tips of the thumb and little finger on one hand.
   Check students' work.
2. Graph the lengths as ordered pairs (height, hand span).
   Check students' work.
3. **a.** Share your data with the class. Make a graph of the class data. Check students' work.
   b. **Reasoning** Compare the two graphs you made. Does one graph show a relationship between heights and hand spans more clearly than the other? Explain. The class data should show a clearer relationship because more points are plotted, making unusual points less important.

A **scatter plot** is a graph that shows the relationship between two sets of data. To make a scatter plot, graph the data as ordered pairs.

1 EXAMPLE <u>Real-World</u> 🌐 <u>Problem Solving</u>

Income The scatter plot shows education and income data.

a. Describe the person represented by point _A_.

This person has 12 years of education and earns $20,000 in a year.

b. How many years of education does the person who earns $100,000 have?

The point (16, 100) has income coordinate 100. The person earning $100,000 in a year has 16 years of education.

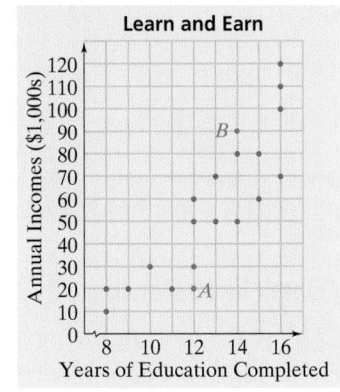

Learn and Earn

✓ **Check Understanding** Example 1

1. **a.** Describe the person represented by point _B_. See right.
   b. How many people have exactly 12 years of education?
   4 people

What You'll Learn

To interpret and draw scatter plots

To use scatter plots to find trends

. . . And Why

To solve real-world problems involving trends

✓ **Check Skills You'll Need**

Write the coordinates of each point.
1–4. See below.
1. _A_
2. _B_
3. _C_
4. _D_

❓ For help, go to Lesson 1-10.

New Vocabulary

- scatter plot
- positive correlation
- negative correlation
- no correlation

1. (−2, 2)
2. (0, 3)
3. (−3, 0)
4. (2, 3)

1a. The person has 14 years of education and earns $90,000 in a year.

📱**TEXT** Interactive lesson includes instant self-check, tutorials, and activities.

Lesson Preview

✓ **Check Skills You'll Need**

Graphing Points
Lesson 1-10: Example 1;
Exercises 1–12.
Extra Practice, p. 744.

Lesson Resources

📁 **Teaching Resources**
Practice, Reteaching, Enrichment

👥 **Reaching All Students**
Practice Workbook 8-5
Spanish Practice Workbook 8-5
Guided Problem Solving 8-5
Technology Activities 15

⏱ **Presentation Assistant Plus!**
Transparencies and PowerPoint™
- Check Skills You'll Need 8-5
- Additional Examples 8-5
- Student Edition Answers 8-5
- Lesson Quiz 8-5
- Classroom Aid 22, 23
PH Presentation Pro CD-ROM 8-5

🔄 **ASSESSMENT SYSTEM**

Computer Test Generator CD-ROM

💻 **Technology**
Resource Pro® CD-ROM
Computer Test Generator CD-ROM
PH Presentation Pro CD-ROM

💻 **www.PHSchool.com**
Student Site
- Teacher Web Code: adk-5500
- Updated Data
- Self-grading Lesson Quiz
PH SuccessNet Teacher Center
- Lesson Planner
- Resources

Plus 📱**TEXT**

Ongoing Assessment and Intervention

Before the Lesson	**During the Lesson**	**After the Lesson**
Diagnose prerequisite skills using:	Monitor progress using:	Assess knowledge using:
• Check Skills You'll Need	• Check Understanding	• Lesson Quiz
	• Additional Examples	• Computer Test Generator CD-ROM
	• Test Prep	

2. Teach

Math Background

In a scatter plot, discrete points show the relationship (if any) between two sets of data. A scatter plot can help reveal trends in such relationships.

Teaching Notes

Investigation (Optional)
Help students see that a rule can be written to represent the relationship even though not all the data points—possibly none of them—satisfy the rule.

1 EXAMPLE Teaching Tip

Point out that most data sets used for scatter plots involve positive measurements, so your scatter plots need show only Quadrant I of the coordinate plane. Also point out the "break" on each axis in this example. Explain that you can use a break when you need to skip a large interval before starting to graph. Using only one quadrant and a break on either, or each, axis saves space when graphing.

2 EXAMPLE Geography Connection

Every point on Earth has a specific location on a grid of "lines" denoting *latitude* and *longitude*. Latitude gives location north or south of the equator and is expressed as an angle measurement ranging from 0° at the equator to 90° at the poles. Longitude gives location east or west of a north-south line called the *prime meridian*, and is expressed as an angle measurement ranging from 0° at the prime meridian to 180° at the International Date Line.

2 EXAMPLE Alternative Method

Let students use a graphing calculator to create the scatter plot in this example. They can enter all the data at one time into lists L_1, L_2, and L_3, and then select the two lists they need for each scatter plot in the Example and Check Understanding.

2 EXAMPLE Real-World 🌐 Problem Solving

Climate Use the table to make a scatter plot of the latitude and temperature data.

Climate Data

City	Location (degrees north latitude)	Daily Mean Temperature (°F)	Mean Annual Precipitation (inches)
Atlanta, GA	34	61	51
Boston, MA	42	51	42
Chicago, IL	42	49	36
Duluth, MN	47	39	30
Honolulu, HI	21	77	22
Houston, TX	30	68	46
Juneau, AK	58	41	54
Miami, FL	26	76	56
Phoenix, AZ	33	73	8
Portland, ME	44	45	44
San Diego, CA	33	64	10
Wichita, KS	38	56	29

SOURCES: *The World Almanac* and *The Statistical Abstract of the United States*. Go to **www.PHSchool.com** for a data update. Web Code: adg-2041

2a.
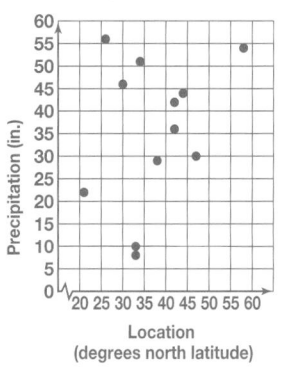

2b.
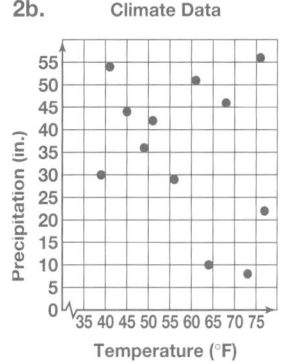

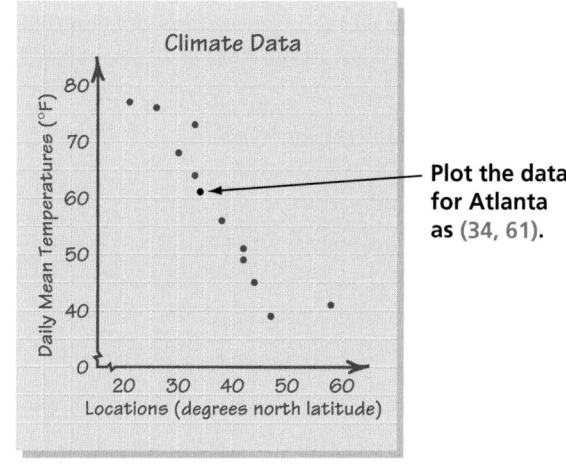

Plot the data for Atlanta as (34, 61).

✓ **Check Understanding** Example 2

2. Use the table in Example 2. a–b. See left.
   a. Make a scatter plot of the latitude and precipitation data.
   b. Make a scatter plot of the temperature and precipitation data. Plot temperatures along the horizontal axis of the graph.

424 Chapter 8 Linear Functions and Graphing

👥 Reaching All Students

Below Level Bring in publications with articles that contain sets of related data and possibly some scatter plots. Point out that scatter plots can sometimes convey information more readily than written articles.	**Advanced Learners** Ask: *If there is a positive correlation between data, does it matter which set of data is represented on the x-axis?* Explain. No; both sets of data increase.	**Alternative Method** See note on page 424. **Error Prevention** See note on page 427.

424

2 Using Scatter Plots to Find Trends

You can use scatter plots to look for trends. The next three scatter plots show the types of relationships two sets of data may have.

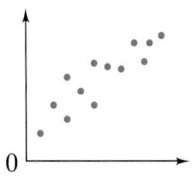

Positive correlation
As one set of values increases, the other set tends to increase.

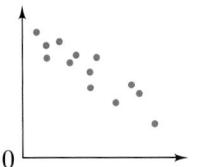

Negative correlation
As one set of values increases, the other set tends to decrease.

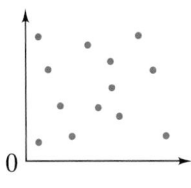

No correlation
The values show no relationship.

> **Reading Math**
> "Positive slope" in a scatter plot suggests a positive correlation. "Negative slope" suggests a negative correlation.

3 EXAMPLE Real-World Problem Solving

Sports Use the scatter plot below. Is there a *positive correlation,* a *negative correlation,* or *no correlation* between the years and the winning times? Explain.

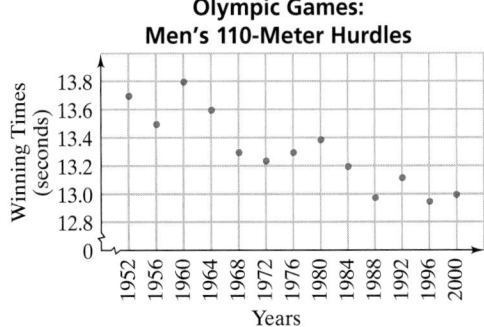

Olympic Games: Men's 110-Meter Hurdles

Since 1952, the winning times have generally decreased. There is a negative correlation.

✔ Check Understanding Example 3

3. Sports Use the scatter plot at the right. Is there a *positive correlation,* a *negative correlation,* or *no correlation* between the years and the winning distances? Explain.
Positive correlation; as time goes by, the winning distances have tended to increase.

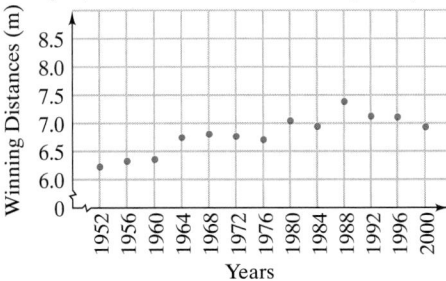

Olympic Games: Women's Long Jump

8-5 Scatter Plots **425**

Additional Examples
1a. This person has 10 years of education and earns $30,000 in a year.
1b. 3 people; $50,000, $80,000, and $90,000
3. No correlation; the values show no relationship.

Closure

Ask students how they can use scatter plots to find positive and negative correlations.

Two sets of data have a positive correlation if the values in one set tend to increase as the values in the other set tend to increase. Two sets of data have a negative correlation if values in one set increase as the values in the other set tend to decrease.

Additional Examples

1 Use the scatter plot in Example 1.
   a. Describe the person represented by the point with coordinates (10, 30).
   b. How many people have exactly 14 years of education? What are their incomes?
   a–b. See bottom margin.

2 Use the table to make a scatter plot of the elevation and precipitation data.

City	Elevation Above Sea Level (ft)	Mean Annual Precipitation (in.)
Atlanta	1,050	51
Boston	20	42
Chicago	596	36
Honolulu	18	22
Miami	11	56
Phoenix	1,072	8
Portland	75	44
San Diego	40	10
Wichita	1,305	29

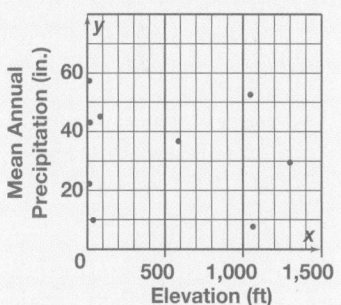

3 Use the scatter plot below. Is there a *positive correlation,* a *negative correlation,* or *no correlation* between temperatures and amounts of precipitation? Explain.

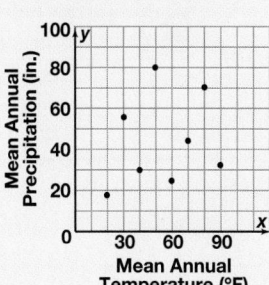

See left.   **425**

EXERCISES

For more exercises, see Extra Practice.

Practice and Problem Solving

Assignment Guide

1 Objective 1
- Ⓐ Ⓑ Core 1–6, 13–15
- Ⓒ Extension 22, 23

2 Objective 2
- Ⓐ Ⓑ Core 7–12, 16–21
- Ⓒ Extension 24, 25

Test Prep 26–30
Mixed Review 31–37

Ⓐ Practice by Example
Example 1
(page 423)

Statistics The scatter plot shows the average times that 15 students spent watching television and on physical activities in a day.

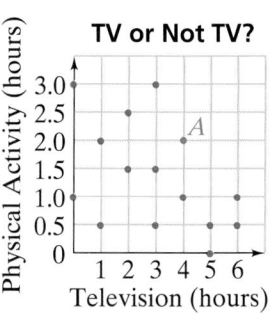

TV or Not TV?

1. Describe the student represented by point *A*. **See below left.**

2. How many students averaged 1 hour of physical activity? **3 students**

3. How many students averaged 5 hours of watching television? **2 students**

Reading Math

For help with reading and solving Exercises 1–3, see page 429.

Example 2
(page 424)

🌐 **Nutrition** For Exercises 4–6, use the table below. Make a scatter plot for the data indicated. Graph calories on the horizontal axis.

Nutritional Values for 100 Grams of Food

Food	Fat (grams)	Protein (grams)	Carbohydrate (grams)	Energy (calories)
Bread	4	8	50	267
Cheese	33	25	1	403
Chicken	4	31	0	165
Eggs	11	13	1	155
Ground beef	19	27	0	292
Milk	3	3	5	61
Peanuts	49	26	16	567
Pizza	5	12	33	223
Tuna	1	26	0	116

SOURCE: U. S. Department of Agriculture Nutrient Database for Standard Reference

7. No correlation; there is no apparent relationship.
8. Positive correlation; as one set of values increases, the other set tends to increase.
9. Negative correlation; as one set of values increases, the other set tends to decrease.

GPS **4.** calories and grams of protein **4–6. See back of book.**

5. calories and grams of fat

6. calories and grams of carbohydrates

Example 3
(page 425)

Is there a *positive correlation*, a *negative correlation*, or *no correlation* between the sets of data in each scatter plot? Explain.
7–12. See left.

10. Positive; as one set of values increases, the other set tends to increase.
11. Negative; as one set of values increases, the other set tends to decrease.
12. No correlation; there is no apparent relationship.

7. 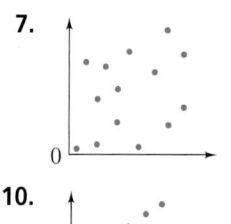   **8.** 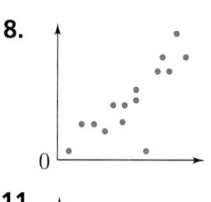   **9.**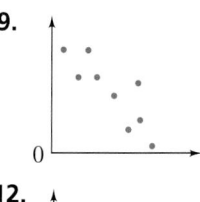

10. 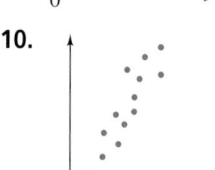   **11.** 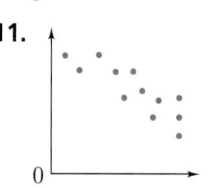   **12.**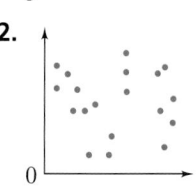

---

426 Chapter 8 Linear Functions and Graphing

GPS Use the Guided Problem Solving worksheet with Exercise 4.

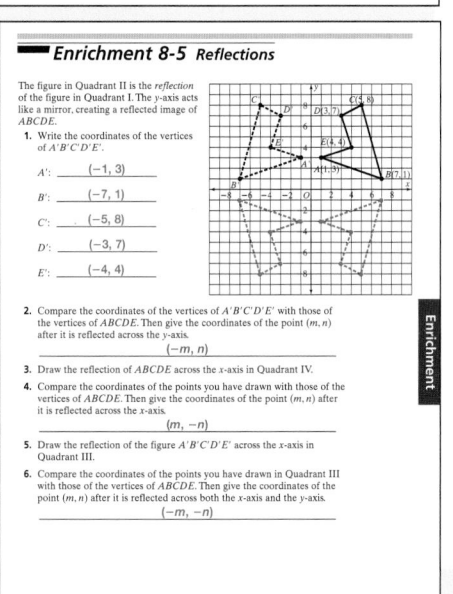

B Apply Your Skills

Data Analysis The scatter plot below shows the relationship between the distances from school and the times it takes to get to school for the students in one class.

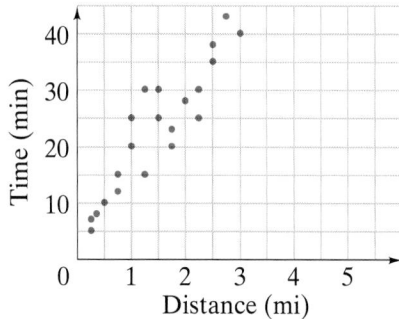

13. How long does it take the student who lives 0.5 mi from school to get to school? **10 min**

14. How many students live closer than 1 mi from school? **6 students**

15. How many students take longer than 35 min to get to school? **3 students**

Would you expect a *positive correlation,* a *negative correlation,* or *no correlation* between each pair of data sets? Explain.

16. the age of pets in a home and the number of pets in that home
No correlation; the sets of data are not related.

17. the temperature outside and the number of layers of clothing
Negative; the lower the temperature, the more layers of clothing you wear.

18. your grade on a test and the amount of time you studied
Positive; the more you study, the better your grade will be.

19. the shoe sizes and the shirt sizes for men
Positive; larger men usually have larger feet.

20. the times candles take to burn and their original heights
Positive; the taller a candle is, the longer it can burn.

21. the number of students in a school and the number of stores near a school   No correlation; the sets of data are not related.

22. latitude and precipitation (see p. 424 Check Understanding 2a)
No correlation; the sets of data are not related.

23. temperature and precipitation (see p. 424 Check Understanding 2b)
No correlation; the sets of data are not related.

C Challenge

24. Sample: number of miles a car has been driven and the value of the car; cars that have been driven more miles are usually bought or sold for less money.

25a.

25b. positive correlation
25c. Yes; interchanging the axes doesn't affect the relationship between the variables.

24. **Writing in Math** Describe a pair of data sets, different from any in this lesson, for which you would expect to see a scatter plot with a negative correlation. Explain. **Answers may vary. Sample at left.**

25. **Ticket Prices** The table at the right shows the average prices of movie tickets and the numbers of movie admissions. **a–c. See left.**

  a. Make a scatter plot of the data in the table. Graph the prices of tickets on the horizontal axis.

  b. **Data Analysis** Is there a *positive correlation,* a *negative correlation,* or *no correlation* between the numbers of admissions and the prices of tickets?

  c. **Reasoning** Would your answer to part (b) be the same if you graphed ticket prices on the vertical axis instead? Explain.

Year	Number of Admissions (millions)	Average Ticket Price
1990	1,189	$4.23
1992	1,173	$4.15
1994	1,292	$4.18
1996	1,339	$4.42
1998	1,481	$4.69

SOURCE: Motion Picture Association of America

8-5 Scatter Plots   **427**

427

Lesson Quiz 8-5

Answer the following questions based on the graph.

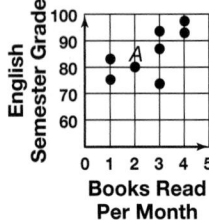

1. What do you know about the student at point *A*?
read 2 books per month, grade: 80

2. How many students read 3 books per month?
3 students

3. Is there a *positive correlation*, a *negative correlation*, or *no correlation* between books read and semester grades?
positive correlation

Test Prep

📁 Resources

For additional practice with a variety of test item formats:
• Test Prep, p. 453
• Test-Taking Strategies, p. 448
• Test-Taking Strategies With Transparencies

Reteaching 8-5 *Scatter Plots*

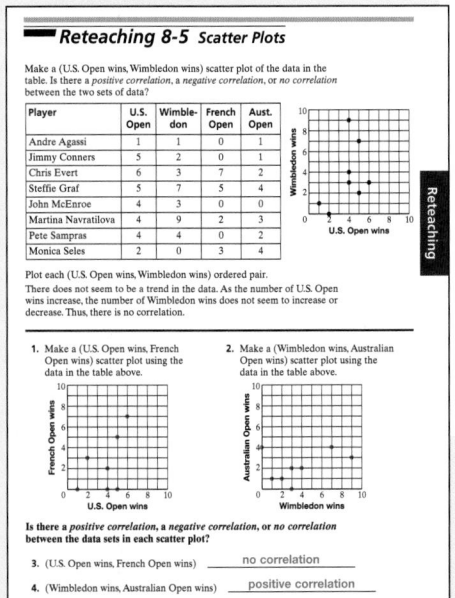

Test Prep

Multiple Choice

26. Which scatter plot shows that as the numbers of pages in magazines increase, the weights of the magazines increase? **A**

A.
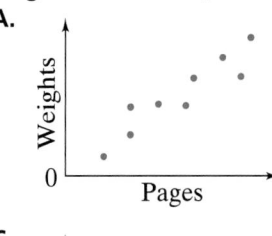

B.

Take It to the NET
Online lesson quiz at **www.PHSchool.com**
Web Code: ada-0805

C.
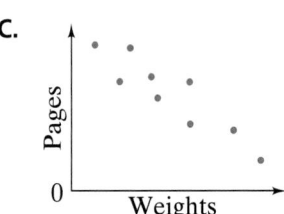

D.
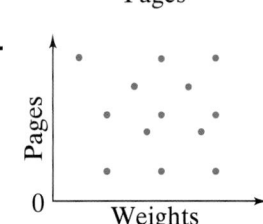

27. Which pair of data sets would most likely have no correlation? **H**
F. the distances cars can travel on full tanks of gasoline and the amounts of gasoline their tanks can hold
G. the ages of children under 12 years old and their heights
H. people's ring sizes and the numbers of rings they own
I. the numbers of students and the numbers of teachers in each school in your state

Short Response

In Exercises 28–30, **(a)** describe a graph with each given type of correlation. **(b)** Sketch a graph showing each type of correlation.
28–30. See margin.
28. positive   **29.** negative   **30.** no correlation

Mixed Review

Lesson 8-4

Write a rule for each function. 31–33. See left.

31. $y = \frac{5}{2}x$

32. $y = -\frac{2}{3}x + 1$

33. $f(x) = -x + 7$

31.

x	y
−4	−10
−2	−5
0	0
2	5

32.

x	y
−6	5
−3	3
0	1
3	−1

33.

x	f(x)
−2	9
1	6
4	3
7	0

Lesson 7-7

Solve each formula for the variable indicated in red.

34. $V = \frac{1}{3}Bh$
$B = \frac{3V}{h}$

35. $A = \frac{1}{2}(b + c)h$
$h = \frac{2A}{b + c}$

36. $S = \frac{a}{1 - r}$
$a = S(1 - r)$

Lesson 6-7 🌐 **37. Personal Finance** Ms. Jimenez earns $27,000 per year. She is paid weekly. She puts 8% of her salary in a retirement fund. How much money goes into this fund each week? **$41.54**

Alternative Assessment

Ask students to check newspapers and magazines for articles that compare two sets of data. Have them use the data to make scatter plots. Then have them describe whether there is a *positive correlation*, a *negative correlation*, or *no correlation*, and explain.

28. [2] The *y*-values increase as the *x*-values increase; correct graph
[1] correct description; incorrect or no sketch
29–30. See back of book.

Reading Math

Reading a Graph

To read a graph, you must understand its parts. You must also be able to analyze what it shows. Graphs called *scatter plots* show correlations. They tell you how, if at all, pairs of data sets are related.

EXAMPLE

Statistics The scatter plot shows the average times that 15 students spent watching television and the average times they spent on physical activity in a day.

1. Describe the student represented by point *A*.

2. How many students averaged 1 hour of physical activity?

3. How many students averaged 5 hours of watching television?

• **Understand the parts.**

The labeling of the axes provides the key to understanding the graph. You find hours of TV viewing on the horizontal axis. You find hours of physical activity on the vertical axis. A plotted point corresponds to an ordered pair (TV hours, activity hours).

1. **Describe the student represented by point *A*.**
   This student averaged 4 hours of TV viewing and 2 hours of physical activity daily.

2. **How many students averaged 1 hour of physical activity?**
   Find 1 hour of physical activity on the vertical axis. Look across and find three points. Three students averaged 1 hour of physical activity.

3. **How many students averaged 5 hours of watching TV?**
   Find 5 hours of television viewing on the horizontal axis. Look above and find two points. Two students averaged 5 hours watching TV.

• **Analyze what the graph shows.**

This graph is a scatter plot. You should decide what kind of correlation, if any, the graph shows.

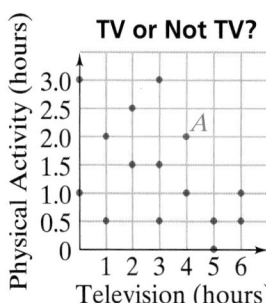

TV or Not TV?

EXERCISES

1. Would you expect there to be a positive correlation, a negative correlation, or no correlation between hours of physical activity and hours of watching television? Justify your choice.
   See right.

2. Does the scatter plot suggest a positive correlation, a negative correlation, or no correlation? Explain.
   No correlation; the number of television hours does not appear to be related to physical activity hours.

Reading Math

Reading a Graph

In this feature, students will read and analyze scatter plots.

Teaching Notes

Students must be able to make a meaningful connection between the graph and the situation described. They will use the graph to answer questions and determine the correlation.

Teaching Tip
Suggest that students work in pairs after they have solved the exercises. Have them explain their thinking to each other and see whether they understand and agree with each other's justifications and answers.

Inclusion
Reproduce a larger version of the scatter plot *TV or Not TV* onto poster board for students who may have vision impairment. You may also want to reproduce large versions of scatter plots that show positive or negative correlations between two sets of data.

1. Answers may vary. Sample: Negative correlation; the more physical activity you do, the less time you have for watching television.

Lesson Preview

 Check Skills You'll Need

Writing Rules
Lesson 8-4: Example 3;
Exercises 7, 8.
Extra Practice, p. 751.

Lesson Resources

📁 **Teaching Resources**
Practice, Reteaching, Enrichment

👥 **Reaching All Students**
Practice Workbook 8-6
Spanish Practice Workbook 8-6
Guided Problem Solving 8-6
Technology Activities 14

⏱ **Presentation Assistant Plus!**
Transparencies and PowerPoint™
• Check Skills You'll Need 8-6
• Additional Examples 8-6
• Student Edition Answers 8-6
• Lesson Quiz 8-6
• Classroom Aid 2
PH Presentation Pro CD-ROM 8-6

ASSESSMENT SYSTEM

Computer Test Generator CD-ROM

💻 **Technology**
Resource Pro® CD-ROM
Computer Test Generator CD-ROM
PH Presentation Pro CD-ROM

💻 **www.PHSchool.com**
Student Site
• Teacher Web Code: adk-5500
• Updated Data
• Graphing Calculator,
  Procedure 22
• Self-grading Lesson Quiz
PH SuccessNet Teacher Center
• Lesson Planner
• Resources

Plus 📲 **TEXT**

What You'll Learn

 OBJECTIVE
1 To solve problems by
graphing

. . . And Why
To solve real-world
problems involving
wildlife populations

✓ **Check Skills You'll Need**

**Write a rule for each
linear function.**

1.

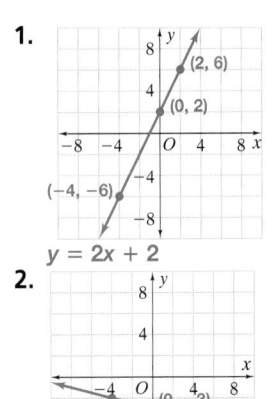

$y = 2x + 2$

2.

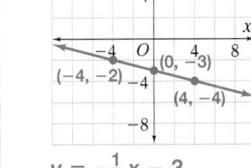

$y = -\frac{1}{4}x - 3$
❓ For help, go to Lesson 8–4.

New Vocabulary
• trend line

OBJECTIVE
1 Solve by Graphing

Math Strategies in Action
Businesses and government
agencies use scatter plots to
look for trends and make
predictions.

For example, the park service
at Isle Royale, Michigan,
surveys the moose and wolf
populations each spring. They
use a scatter plot to show the
relationship between them.

On the scatter plot they draw a
trend line that closely fits the
data points in the scatter plot.
Using the trend line, they can
predict the size of one population
from the size of the other.

Real-World 🌐 Connection

Moose, like the one shown
above, have wolves as a
principal predator.

1 EXAMPLE **Real-World 🌐 Problem Solving**

Wildlife Use the data in the table below. Suppose there were
18 wolves one year. About how many moose would you expect to
be on the island that year?

Isle Royale Populations

Year	Wolf	Moose	Year	Wolf	Moose	Year	Wolf	Moose
1982	14	700	1988	12	1,653	1994	15	1,800
1983	23	900	1989	11	1,397	1995	16	2,400
1984	24	811	1990	15	1,216	1996	22	1,200
1985	22	1,062	1991	12	1,313	1997	24	500
1986	20	1,025	1992	12	1,600	1998	14	700
1987	16	1,380	1993	13	1,880	1999	25	750

SOURCE: Isle Royale National Park Service

✓ **Ongoing Assessment and Intervention**

Before the Lesson
Diagnose prerequisite skills
using:
• Check Skills You'll Need

During the Lesson
Monitor progress using:
• Check Understanding
• Additional Examples
• Test Prep

After the Lesson
Assess knowledge using:
• Lesson Quiz
• Computer Test Generator
  CD-ROM

2. Teach

Read and Understand

1. What are the two variables?
   the number of wolves and the number of moose
2. What are you trying to predict?
   the number of moose when there are 18 wolves

Plan and Solve

You can graph the data in a scatter plot. If the points show a correlation, you can draw a trend line. You can then use the line to predict other data values.

Step 1 Make a scatter plot by graphing the (wolf, moose) ordered pairs. Use the x-axis for wolves and the y-axis for moose.

Step 2 Sketch a trend line. The line should be as close as possible to each data point. There should be about as many points above the trend line as below it.

Step 3 To predict the number of moose when there are 18 wolves, find 18 along the horizontal axis. Look up to find the point on the trend line that corresponds to 18 wolves. Then look across to the value on the vertical axis, which is about 1,200.

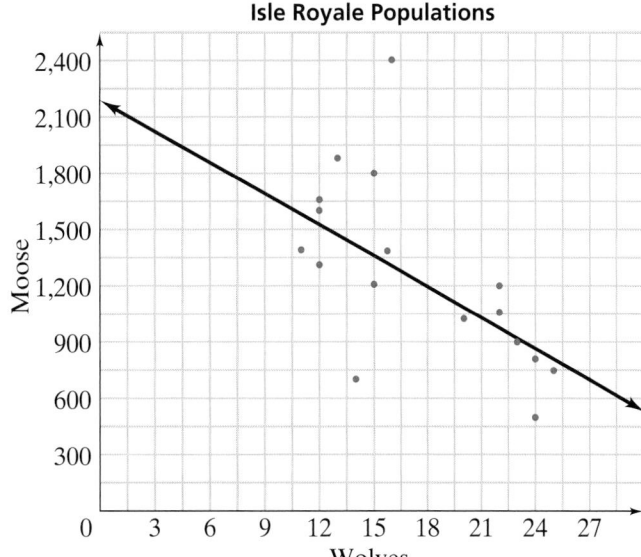

Isle Royale Populations

There will be about 1,200 moose when there are 18 wolves.

Look Back and Check

You can write an equation for a trend line. You can use the equation to make predictions.

✓ **Check Understanding**   a–d. Answers may vary. Samples are given.

3. **a.** What is the y-intercept of the trend line above? about 2,175
   b. Locate one other point on the trend line. Then find the slope of the trend line. about –55
   c. Write an equation for the trend line in slope-intercept form. $y = -55x + 2,175$
   d. Use the equation you wrote in part (c). Find the solution of the equation when $x = 18$. 1,185

Math Background

When a scatter plot shows a trend, you can draw a *trend line* on the graph to model the trend. The trend line passes through the middle of the data points. About half of the points that are not on the line should be above it, the other half below it. You can also write an equation for the trend line to help predict new data points on the graph.

Teaching Notes

Visual Learners
Where you draw a trend line on a scatter plot affects the predictions you make about the situation. However, one scatter plot can have more than one appropriate trend line. Place a blank transparency over a scatter plot on the overhead. Ask a volunteer to draw a trend line and discuss whether it is reasonable. Have other volunteers do the same on other blank transparencies. After four or five students have drawn lines, place all of the lines on the scatter plot. Make it clear that all trend lines are appropriate even though they may be positioned differently. Help students see that different predictions can be reasonable.

PowerPoint
Additional Examples

1 Use the data in the table in Example 1. Suppose this year there are 16 wolves on the island. Predict how many moose are on the island.
about 1,300 moose

Closure

Ask: *How are trend lines helpful?*
A trend line suggests a relationship that helps you make a prediction.

👥 Reaching All Students

| **Below Level** Ask a student to draw a scatter plot using 4 points from the Example. Add 10 more points. Have the student draw another trend line to show that more points yield a better trend line. | **Advanced Learners** Have students select a vacation place and research its weather for the past 2 weeks. Make a scatter plot and predict the weather for the next day. Have them check their predictions. | **Visual Learners** See note on page 431. **Error Prevention** See note on page 433. |

431

3. Practice

Assignment Guide

▼ 1 Objective 1

Ⓐ Ⓑ Core 1–7

Ⓒ Extension 8, 9

Test Prep 10–14
Mixed Review 15–22

▬ Practice 8-6 *Solve by Graphing*

A giraffe was 1 ft tall at birth, 7 ft tall at the age of 4, and 11½ ft tall at the age of 7.

1. Use the data to make a (age, height) scatter plot.

2. Draw a trend line.

3. Write an equation for your trend line in slope-intercept form.

  $y = \frac{3}{2}x + 1$

4. Use your equation to find the following information.

a. the giraffe's height at the age of 5

  8½ ft

b. the age at which the giraffe was 16 ft tall

  10 yrs

A hippopotamus weighed 700 lb at the age of 1 and 1,900 lb at the age of 3, and 2,500 lb at the age of 4.

5. Use the data to make a (age, weight) scatter plot.

6. Draw a trend line.

7. Write an equation for your trend line.

  $y = 600x + 100$

8. Use the equation to predict the following information.

a. the hippo's weight at the age of 8

  4,900 lb

b. the age at which the hippo weighed 7,900 lb

  13 yrs

9. Can this equation be used to predict the hippo's weight at any age? Explain.

  Sample answer is shown: No; the hippo will not

  continue to gain weight indefinitely.

Giraffe Height

Hippopotamus Weight

▬ Enrichment 8-6 *Technology at Home*

The table shows the percentage of U.S. households owning a computer and having cable TV in several years.

1. Use the data to make a (computer, cable) scatter plot.

Percentage of U.S. Households

Year	Owning a Computer	Having Cable TV
1990	22%	59%
1991	25%	61%
1992	27%	62%
1993	30%	63%
1994	33%	63%
1995	37%	66%
1996	40%	67%

U.S. Households

2. Draw a trend line through the data for 1990 and 1993.

3. Predict the percentage of households that will have cable TV when 45% of U.S. households own a computer.

  70%

4. Find the slope of your trend line. $m = \frac{1}{2}$

5. Find the y-intercept by substituting the slope you found and the point (22, 59) into the equation $y = mx + b$. Solve for b.

  $b = 48$

6. Write an equation for your trend line.

  $y = \frac{1}{2}x + 48$

7. Use the equation to predict the percentage of households with cable TV when 50% of households own a computer.

  73%

8. Use the equation to predict the percentage of households owning a computer when 80% of households have cable TV.

  64%

EXERCISES

❓ For more exercises, see *Extra Practice*.

Practice and Problem Solving

Ⓐ Practice by Example

Example 1
(page 430)

Solve each problem by graphing.

Statistics For Exercises 1 and 2, use the data below. The table shows the populations of some states and the numbers of cars registered in those states.

State Populations and Cars

State	Population (millions)	Registered Cars (millions)	State	Population (millions)	Registered Cars (millions)
FL	14.4	7.2	NY	18.1	7.9
GA	7.3	3.8	OH	11.2	6.6
IL	11.8	6.2	PA	12.0	5.9
KS	2.6	1.2	SC	3.7	1.8
ME	1.2	0.6	TN	5.3	3.0
MS	2.7	1.3	TX	19.1	7.4
NV	1.6	0.6	WA	5.5	2.6

SOURCE: *Statistical Abstract of the United States.* Go to **www.PHSchool.com** for a data update. Web Code: adg-2041

1. a. Use the data to make a scatter plot of the data. Use the population data for the horizontal axis.

b. Draw a trend line. **a–b. See back of book.**

c. Predict how many cars are registered by the 32.2 million people in California. **about 16 million cars**

d. Write an equation for your trend line. Predict the number of cars registered by the 7.3 million people in North Carolina.

  $y = 0.5x$; about 3.6 million cars

2. Writing in Math Is there a correlation between the two data sets? Explain. **As the populations increase, the numbers of cars also increase. So, there is a positive correlation between the data sets.**

3. Data Analysis Use the data in the table below. Predict the number
 [GPS] of gallons bought for $15. **Answers may vary. Sample: 8.4 gal**

Gasoline Purchases

Dollars Spent	12	14	11	12	10	6	10	8
Gallons Bought	7.3	8.0	5.9	6.5	5.7	3.5	5.1	4.4

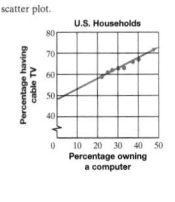

Strategies

- Account for All Possibilities
- Draw a Diagram
- Look for a Pattern
- Make a Model
- Make a Table
- Simplify the Problem
- Simulate the Problem
- Solve by Graphing
- Try, Test, Revise
- Use Multiple Strategies
- Work Backward
- Write an Equation
- Write a Proportion

Ⓑ Apply Your Skills

Solve using any strategy.

4. Elections Four candidates are running for president of the student council. Three other candidates are running for vice-president. How many different ways can the two offices be filled?
 12 different ways

5. Business A supermarket charges $1.17 for a 12-oz jar of salsa and $1.89 for a 20-oz jar. Now the producer is introducing a 16-oz jar of the same salsa. What do you think would be a fair price for this new size? Justify your answer to the manager of the store.
 Answers may vary. Sample: $1.55; (16, 1.55) is on the line through the two points (12, 1.17) and (20, 1.89).

Writing in Math

For help with justifying your answer to Exercise 5, see page 434.

432 Chapter 8 Linear Functions and Graphing

[GPS] Use the Guided Problem Solving worksheet with Exercise 3.

6. (Algebra) A plumber charges $45 for a service call, plus $70/h for her time.
  a. Find the cost of a two-hour service call. **$185**
  b. How long was a service call that cost $150? **1.5 h**

🌐 **7. Engineering** To provide wheelchair access, a ramp with a slope of $\frac{1}{15}$ is being built to a door of a building. Suppose that the bottom of the door is 3 ft above street level. How far will the ramp extend from the building? **45 ft**

C Challenge 🌐 **8. Physics** As the weight held by a spring increases, the length of the spring increases proportionally. Suppose a 2-lb weight stretches a spring to 15 in., and a 12-lb weight stretches the same spring to 20 in. What is the length of the spring with no weight attached? **14 in.**

9. The data table on page 430 shows 18 data pairs. Its scatter plot (page 431) shows 17 plotted points. Make a conjecture as to why this is so. Study the table to verify or disprove your conjecture. **The 1982 and 1998 values are the same.**

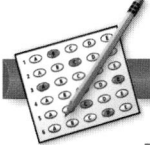

Test Prep

Multiple Choice

10. Which ordered pair is a solution for $4x - 3y = 6$? **B**
   A. $(-3, 2)$ **B.** $(3, 2)$ **C.** $(3, -2)$ **D.** $(-3, -2)$

11. What is the slope of the line through $A(2, 6)$ and $B(8, -1)$? **I**
   F. $-\frac{6}{7}$ **G.** $-\frac{4}{9}$ **H.** $\frac{5}{6}$ **I.** $-\frac{7}{6}$

Take It to the NET
Online lesson quiz at
www.PHSchool.com
Web Code: ada-0806

12. What is the slope of the graph of $3x - 2y = 6$? **D**
   A. $-\frac{3}{2}$ **B.** $-\frac{2}{3}$ **C.** $\frac{2}{3}$ **D.** $\frac{3}{2}$

13. What is the y-intercept of the graph of $3x - 2y = 6$? **F**
   F. -3 **G.** 2   **H.** 3   **I.** 6

Short Response

14. One gallon equals 4 quarts. **(a)** Write a rule that expresses the number of gallons g of a liquid as a function of the number of quarts q. **(b)** Use the rule to find the number of gallons in 30 quarts.
   [2] $g(q) = \frac{q}{4}$; 7.5 gallons
   [1] correct rule OR answer only

Mixed Review

Lesson 8-2

17. $(-3, -3.5)$, $(0, -2)$, $(2, -1)$

Find the solutions of each equation for $x = -3, 0,$ and 2.

15. $y = -3x$ **16.** $y = \frac{1}{3}x + 4$ **17.** $y = 0.5x - 2$
   $(-3, 9)$, $(0, 0)$, $(2, -6)$ $(-3, 3)$, $(0, 4)$, $(2, 4\frac{2}{3})$ See left.

Lessons 7-2 and 7-5 **Solve each equation.**

18. $3x + 7 = 4x - 12$ **19**   **19.** $7t + 3 - 4t = -6$ **-3**

20. $8(2 - c) - 12 = -3c$ **$\frac{4}{5}$**   **21.** $-2x + 3(5 - x) = 5$ **2**

Lesson 6-6 🌐 **22. Food** About 150 million of the 20 billion hot dogs consumed in the United States each year are eaten during the Fourth of July weekend. What percent of the hot dogs are eaten at this time? **about 0.75%**

8-6 Solve by Graphing **433**

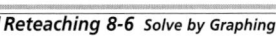
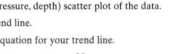
Alternative Assessment

Have students research census data for the United States for the past century. Have them use data from each census year to draw a scatter plot, and then a trend line on the plot. Finally, have them use their trend line to predict the population of the United States in 2010 and 2050.

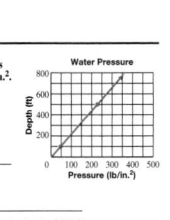

433

Writing to Persuade

Students learn to present mathematical information to an audience. They summarize the information and present a visual display.

Teaching Notes

Visual Learners
Exercise 2 Have students work independently to complete the exercise on a transparency. Then let volunteers explain their work to the class.

Teaching Tip
Provide students with advertisements from grocery stores. Have students work in groups to select products and then come up with reasonable prices for other sizes of the products. Make a visual display and have volunteers present their information to the class.

Writing in Math

Writing to Persuade

For Use With Page 432, Exercise 5

When you present mathematical information to persuade someone to your point of view, you should do the following:
- Identify your audience and your goal.
- Summarize the mathematics behind your view.
- Create a graph or other visual display to support your view.

EXAMPLE

Business A supermarket charges $1.17 for a 12-oz jar of salsa and $1.89 for a 20-oz jar. Now the manufacturer is introducing a 16-oz jar of the same salsa. What do you think would be a fair price for this new size? Justify your answer.

- Identify your audience and your goal.

  Your audience is the manager. Your goal is to decide on a price for the 16-oz jar and then convince the manager that this price is fair.

- Summarize the mathematics behind your thinking.

  Writing solutions to word problems is excellent practice for this. Here, you find the unit price for each jar size.

  $$\frac{\$1.17}{12 \text{ oz}} = \$.0975/\text{oz} \quad \textbf{Find the 12-oz-jar unit price.}$$

  $$\frac{\$1.89}{20 \text{ oz}} = \$.0945/\text{oz} \quad \textbf{Find the 20-oz-jar unit price.}$$

  16 oz is halfway between 12 oz and 20 oz. A unit price halfway between $.0975 and $.0945 seems fair.

  $$\frac{\$.0975 + \$.0945}{2} = \$.096 \quad \textbf{Find the average.}$$

  $$16 \cdot \$.096 \approx \$1.54 \quad \textbf{Find the 16-oz-jar price.}$$

  A fair price for a 16-oz jar is $1.54.

- Make a visual display (at right) to support your view.

A Fair Price for 16 oz

EXERCISES

1. What do you think would be a reasonable price for an 18-oz jar of the salsa in the example? **about $1.72**

2. Your family eats two boxes of cereal each week. Your family buys 15-oz boxes costing $2.89 each. A 28-oz box of the same cereal is $4.79. You think that buying the larger size is better. Persuade your family to your point of view using mathematics, explanation, and a visual display. (*Hint:* Show what happens over an extended length of time, such as a year.) **See above.**

2. Answers may vary. Sample:

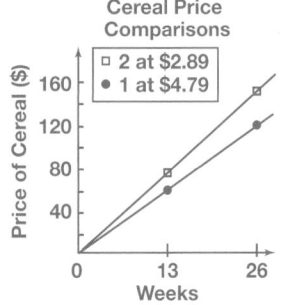

Cereal Price Comparisons
- □ 2 at $2.89
- ● 1 at $4.79

The family can probably manage with one 28-oz box each week. For 26 weeks, the large boxes would cost about $125 and pairs of small boxes would cost about $145.

Solving Systems of Linear Equations

OBJECTIVE

1 Graphing Systems of Linear Equations

Two or more linear equations form a **system of linear equations.** A *solution of the system* is any ordered pair that is a solution of each equation in the system.

You can solve some systems of equations by graphing the equations on a coordinate plane and identifying the point(s) of intersection.

1 EXAMPLE   Solving a System by Graphing

Solve the system $y = -x + 1$ **and** $y = 2x + 4$ **by graphing.**

Step 1 Graph each line.

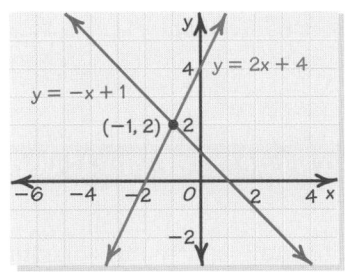

Step 2 Find the point of intersection.

The lines intersect at one point, $(-1, 2)$. The solution is $(-1, 2)$.

Check See whether $(-1, 2)$ makes both equations true.

$y = -x + 1$		$y = 2x + 4$
$2 \stackrel{?}{=} -(-1) + 1$	← **Replace x with -1 and y with 2.** →	$2 \stackrel{?}{=} 2(-1) + 4$
$2 = 2$ ✔	**The solution checks.**	$2 = 2$ ✔

✓ Check Understanding Example 1

1. Solve each system of equations by graphing. Check each solution.
   a–b. See back of book.
   a. $y = x - 6$ **b.** $y = 3x - 3$
   $\quad y = -2x$ $\quad x + y = 1$

When the graphs of two equations are parallel, there is no point of intersection. The system has *no solution*.

When the graphs of two equations are the same line, all the points on the line are solutions. The system has *infinitely many solutions*.

What You'll Learn

OBJECTIVE 1 To solve systems of linear equations by graphing

OBJECTIVE 2 To use systems of linear equations to solve problems

. . . And Why

To solve real-world problems involving carpentry

✓ Check Skills You'll Need

Graph each equation.
1–4. See back of book.
1. $y = -x - 4$

2. $y = 2x - 1$

3. $-4x = 6y$

4. $3x - 2y = 5$

 For help, go to Lesson 8-2.

New Vocabulary

• system of linear equations

 **Interactive lesson** includes instant self-check, tutorials, and activities.

8-7 Solving Systems of Linear Equations   **435**

---

1. Plan

Lesson Preview

✓ **Check Skills You'll Need**

Equations With Two Variables
Lesson 8-2: Example 5;
Exercises 21–26.
Extra Practice, p. 751.

Lesson Resources

 Teaching Resources
Practice, Reteaching, Enrichment
Checkpoint Quiz 2

Reaching All Students
Practice Workbook 8-7
Spanish Practice Workbook 8-7
Reading and Math Literacy 8C
Spanish Reading and Math
  Literacy 8C
Spanish Checkpoint Quiz 2
Guided Problem Solving 8-7

 Presentation Assistant Plus!
Transparencies and PowerPoint™
• Check Skills You'll Need 8-7
• Additional Examples 8-7
• Student Edition Answers 8-7
• Lesson Quiz 8-7
• Classroom Aid 2
PH Presentation Pro CD-ROM 8-7

ASSESSMENT SYSTEM

Checkpoint Quiz 2
Computer Test Generator CD-ROM

Technology
Resource Pro® CD-ROM
Computer Test Generator CD-ROM
PH Presentation Pro CD-ROM

www.PHSchool.com
Student Site
• Teacher Web Code: adk-5500
• Updated Data
• Algebra Readiness
  Puzzles 68, 69
• Graphing Calculator, Procedure 9
• Self-grading Lesson Quiz
PH SuccessNet Teacher Center
• Lesson Planner
• Resources

Plus

✓ Ongoing Assessment and Intervention

Before the Lesson	**During the Lesson**	**After the Lesson**
Diagnose prerequisite skills using:	Monitor progress using:	Assess knowledge using:
• Check Skills You'll Need	• Check Understanding	• Lesson Quiz
	• Additional Examples	• Computer Test Generator CD-ROM
	• Test Prep	• Chapter Checkpoint 2 (p. 440)

2. Teach

Math Background

Any two nonparallel lines on a coordinate plane intersect. The coordinates of the point of intersection form a solution of the equations for both lines.

Teaching Notes

1 EXAMPLE Visual Learners

Explain that graphing can be a difficult way to find the solution for a system of equations. It is very difficult to graph a line precisely, so the point of intersection may be "off" a little. The solutions to all systems in this lesson have integer coordinates. If a point of intersection is not at such a point, students should first check their graphs. If the graphs seem correct, then they should use the point with integer coordinates that appears to be closest to the intersection. They can use substitution to check whether this is the solution.

2 EXAMPLE Visual Learners

Ask: *Why do you not have to graph the system of equations in part (b) to know the solution?* When you put the equations into $y = mx + b$ form, you see they are the same equation. Each solution of the equation is a solution of the system, so there are infinitely many solutions.

Tactile Learners

Have students place two pencils on a coordinate grid to represent a system of two linear equations with no solution. Then have them represent a system with one solution, and then a system with infinitely many solutions.

3 EXAMPLE Error Prevention

The two numbers asked for in Example 3 are 5 and 1. Remind students that the example defines x to be the greater number, so the solution of the system is (5, 1) and not (1, 5). Show these two points with the lines to stress the importance of determining the correct x- and y-coordinates.

436

2a. infinitely many solutions

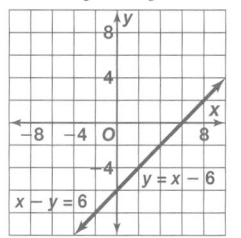

2b. no solutions

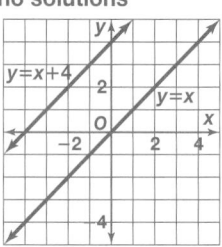

Graphing Calculator Hint

You can use a graphing calculator to check your solution of a system. Write the equations in slope-intercept form, press $\boxed{Y=}$, and enter them as Y_1 and Y_2. Then use the **CALC** menu to find the coordinates of the intersection point.

2 EXAMPLE Solving Special Systems

Solve each system of equations by graphing.

a. $x + y = 1$; $y = -x + 3$ b. $x - 2y = 4$; $2x - 4y = 8$

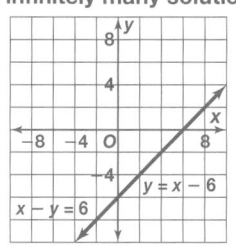   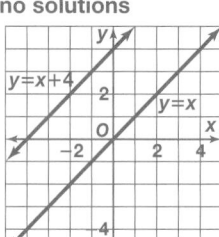

The lines are parallel. They do not intersect. There is no solution.

The graphs are the same line. There are infinitely many solutions.

✓ **Check Understanding** Example 2

2. Solve each system by graphing.

a. $y = x - 6$; See left.   b. $y = x + 4$; See left.
   $x - y = 6$ $y = x$

OBJECTIVE

2 Using Systems of Linear Equations

You can write and graph systems of equations to solve problems.

3 EXAMPLE Using a System of Equations

Find two numbers with a sum of 6 and a difference of 4.

Step 1 Write equations.

Let x = the greater number.
Let y = the lesser number.

Equation 1 Sum   is   6.
           $x + y$ =   6

Equation 2 Difference is 4.
           $x - y$ =   4

Step 2 Graph the equations.

The lines intersect at (5, 1). The numbers are 5 and 1.

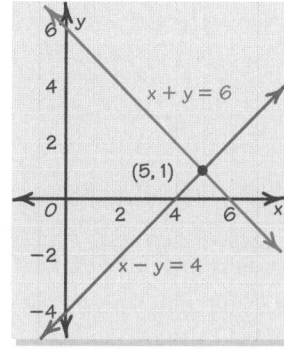

Check Since the sum of 5 and 1 is 6 and the difference of 5 and 1 is 4, the answer is correct.

✓ **Check Understanding** Example 3

3. Find two numbers with a difference of 2 and a sum of -8. -3, -5

436 Chapter 8 Linear Functions and Graphing

👥 Reaching All Students

Below Level Ask students to describe the intersection of two streets. Discuss how the intersection is a part of both streets. It is the region that the two streets have in common.

Advanced Learners Ask : *How can you tell that a system of equations has no solution by looking at the equations?* The equations, written in slope-intercept form, have the same slope, but different y-intercepts.

Visual Learners See note on page 436.
Tactile Learners See note on page 436.

You can solve some problems involving two variables by writing and graphing a system of equations, or you may be able to use one variable to write and solve an equation.

More Than One Way

Carpentry A carpenter cuts an 8-ft board into two pieces. One piece is three times as long as the other. What is the length of each piece?

Roberto's Method

Write and graph a system of equations.

Let x = length of longer piece; y = length of shorter piece.

Equation 1 Longer piece is three times shorter piece.

$$x = 3 \cdot y$$

Equation 2 Sum of lengths is eight.

$$x + y = 8$$

Graph the equations.

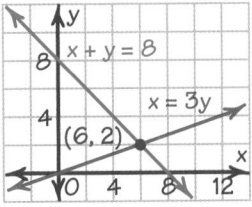

The lines intersect at (6, 2). The lengths are 6 ft and 2 ft.

Michelle's Method

Write a one-variable equation.

Let x = length of shorter piece; 3x = length of longer piece.

Equation Shorter piece plus longer piece is 8 feet.

$$x + 3x = 8$$
$$4x = 8$$
$$x = 2$$

The shorter piece is 2 ft, and the longer piece is 3(2) = 6 ft.

Choose a Method See above right.

1. Which method would you use to find the lengths? Explain.

2. In Roberto's Method, suppose x = length of shorter piece. What difference would this make in the equations and the graph?

1. Answers may vary. Sample: Michelle's Method; it is easier than graphing.

2. The first equation would be y = 3x. Its graph is steeper than the graph of x = 3y and the graphs would intersect at (2, 6).

Additional Examples

① Solve the system y = x − 7 and y = 4x + 2 by graphing. (−3, −10)

② Solve each system of equations by graphing.
   a. 27x + 9y = 36; y = 4 − 3x infinitely many solutions
   b. 8 = 4x + 2y; 2x + y = 5 no solution

③ Find two numbers with a sum of 10 and a difference of 2. 6, 4

Closure

Have students describe systems with no solution, one solution, and infinitely many solutions. Two equations that have the same slope and different y–intercepts have no solution. Two equations that have different slopes have one solution. Two equations that have the same slope and the same y–intercept have infinitely many solutions.

3. Practice

Assignment Guide

1 Objective 1

Ⓐ Ⓑ **Core** 1–15, 20–22, 30

Ⓒ **Extension** 34, 35

2 Objective 2

Ⓐ Ⓑ **Core** 16–19, 23–29

Ⓒ **Extension** 31–33

Test Prep 36–39

Mixed Review 40–48

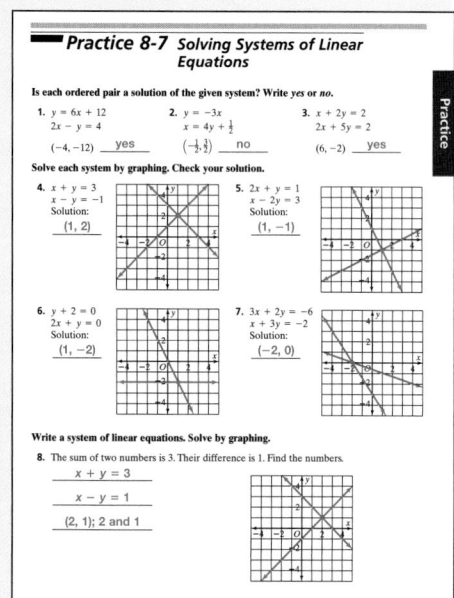

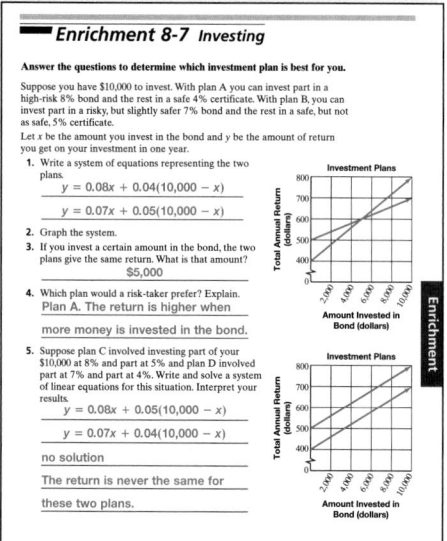

EXERCISES

🔎 For more exercises, see *Extra Practice*.

Practice and Problem Solving

Ⓐ **Practice by Example**

Example 1
(page 434)

Check whether $(-1, 5)$ is a solution of each system of equations. Show your work.

1. $x + y = 4$ no
$x - y = 6$

2. $y = -2x + 3$ no
$y = x - 4$

3. $2x = y - 7$ yes
$2y = -x + 9$

Solve each system of equations by graphing. Check each solution.

4. $y = x + 1$ (4, 5)
$y = 3x - 7$

5. $y = 2x + 5$ (1, 7)
$x + y = 8$

6. $y = x + 1$ (−2, −1)
$y = -x - 3$

7. $y = x + 5$ (1, 6)
$y = -2x + 8$

8. $y = x - 4$ (−2, −6)
$y = 3x$

9. $y = 2x - 2$ (4, 6)
$y = 6$

10–15. See left.

Example 2
(page 435)

10. no solution
11. no solution
12. infinitely many solutions
13. no solution
14. infinitely many solutions
15. infinitely many solutions

10. $-3x + y = 5$
$y = 3x - 7$

11. $y = -x - 3$
$y = -x + 2$

12. $y = -6 - 2x$
$2x + y = -6$

13. $y = -2x + 1$
$2x + y = -1$

14. $y = 3x$
$-y = -3x$

15. $y = x + 2$
$x - y = -2$

Example 3
(page 435)

16. Find two numbers with a sum of -8 and a difference of 4. Let x be the greater number and y be the lesser number. $-2, -6$

Ⓑ **Apply Your Skills**

Is each ordered pair a solution of the given system of equations? Show your work.

17. $2x + 5y = 3$
$y = 7.5x; (1.5, 0.2)$ no

18. $6x - 6y = 2$
$3x + 9y = -7; \left(-\frac{1}{3}, -\frac{2}{3}\right)$ yes

🌐 **19. Kites** A four-foot-long wooden rod is cut into two pieces to make a kite. One piece is three times as long as the other.
  a. Let $x =$ the length of the longer piece. $x + y = 4$
  Let $y =$ the length of the shorter piece. $x = 3y$
  Write a system of equations to find the length of each piece.
  b. Solve the system by graphing. State the length of each piece.
  (3, 1); 3 ft, 1 ft

Solve each system of equations by graphing. Check each solution.

20. no solution
21. infinitely many solutions
23. infinitely many solutions
25. infinitely many solutions

20. $x + y = 3$
$2x = 10 - 2y$
See left.

21. $y = 2x - 4$
$2x - y = 4$
See left.

22. $x - y = -4$
$x + y = 6$
(1, 5)

23. $2x - 4y = 4$
$y = 0.5x - 1$
See left.

24. $y = x - 2$
$x + 3y = 6$
(3, 1)

25. $3y - 2x = 3$
$6y = 4x + 6$
See left.

26. Geometry The perimeter of a rectangle is 24 ft. Its length is five times its width. Let x be the length and y be the width. What is the area of the rectangle? 20 ft²

27. The difference of two numbers is 5. The result when the greater number is decreased by twice the lesser is 9. Let x be the greater number and y be the lesser number. Find the numbers. 1, −4

Practice 8-7 *Solving Systems of Linear Equations*

Is each ordered pair a solution of the given system? Write *yes* or *no*.

1. $y = 6x + 12$
$2x - y = 4$
$(-4, -12)$ __yes__

2. $y = -3x$
$x = 4y + \frac{1}{2}$
$\left(-\frac{1}{2}, \frac{3}{2}\right)$ __no__

3. $x + 2y = 2$
$2x + 5y = 2$
$(6, -2)$ __yes__

Solve each system by graphing. Check your solution.

4. $x + y = 3$
$x - y = -1$
Solution: __(1, 2)__

5. $2x + y = 1$
$x - 2y = 3$
Solution: __(1, −1)__

6. $y + 2 = 0$
$2x + y = 0$
Solution: __(1, −2)__

7. $3x + 2y = -6$
$x + 3y = -2$
Solution: __(−2, 0)__

Write a system of linear equations. Solve by graphing.

8. The sum of two numbers is 3. Their difference is 1. Find the numbers.
$x + y = 3$
$x - y = 1$
(2, 1); 2 and 1

Enrichment 8-7 *Investing*

Answer the questions to determine which investment plan is best for you.

Suppose you have $10,000 to invest. With plan A you can invest part in a high-risk 8% bond and the rest in a safe 4% certificate. With plan B, you can invest part in a risky, but slightly safer 7% bond and the rest in a safe, but not as safe, 5% certificate.

Let x be the amount you invest in the bond and y be the amount of return you get on your investment in one year.

1. Write a system of equations representing the two plans.
$y = 0.08x + 0.04(10,000 - x)$
$y = 0.07x + 0.05(10,000 - x)$

2. Graph the system.

3. If you invest a certain amount in the bond, the two plans give the same return. What is that amount? $5,000

4. Which plan would a risk-taker prefer? Explain.
Plan A. The return is higher when more money is invested in the bond.

5. Suppose plan C involved investing part of your $10,000 at 8% and part at 5% and plan D involved part at 7% and part at 4%. Write and solve a system of linear equations for this situation. Interpret your results.
$y = 0.08x + 0.05(10,000 - x)$
$y = 0.07x + 0.04(10,000 - x)$
no solution
The return is never the same for these two plans.

438 Chapter 8 Linear Functions and Graphing

28. There are 11 animals in a barnyard. Some are chickens and some
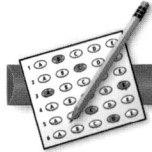 are cows. There are 38 legs in all. Let x be the number of chickens
and y be the number of cows. How many of each animal are in
the barnyard? **3 chickens, 8 cows**

29. One sales position pays \$200/wk plus 10% commission. Another
sales position pays \$150/wk plus 20% commission. **a–c. See margin.**
 a. For each job, write an equation that relates the amount of
 sales x for one week to the money earned y.
 b. Solve the system from part (a) to find the amount of sales in
 a week that will earn the same amount from each job. Show
 your work.
 c. If weekly sales at each job are about \$600, at which job can you
 earn more money? Explain.

31. $y = 3x$
 $y = 3x + 2$
32. $y = x + 1$
 $y = 2x$
33. $y - x = 2$
 $y = x + 2$

30. a. Graph each system of equations on a separate coordinate
 plane. **See margin.**
 $y = 3x + 1; y = 3x - 2$ $y = -2x - 1; y = -2x + 4$
 b. Writing in Math Based on part (a), write a conjecture about
 solutions to systems of equations that have the same slope.
 Conjectures may vary. Sample: A system of equations with the
 same slope but different y-intercepts has no solutions.

C Challenge **Open-Ended Write a system of equations with the given solutions.**
31–33. Answers may vary. See above left for samples.
31. no solution **32.** one solution **33.** infinitely many

34. Geometry The graphs of $y = 3$, $y = 7$, $x = 2$, and $x = 5$ contain
the sides of a rectangle. Find the area of the rectangle. **12 units²**

35. Solve the system $y = x + 2$, $y = 4x + 11$, and $y = -2x - 7$. **(−3, −1)**

Test Prep

Multiple Choice

36. What is the solution of the system **D**
 $y = x + 4; y = 4x + 1$?
 A. (0, 1) **B.** (0, 4) **C.** (1, 4) **D.** (1, 5)

37. How many solutions does the system have **F**
 $2x + 4y = 10; x + 2y = 10$?
 F. 0 **G.** 1 **H.** 2 **I.** infinitely many

38. Use the system $x + y = -6; x - y = 2$. How are the x-coordinate
and the y-coordinate of the solution related? **B**
 A. $y = -2x$ **B.** $y = 2x$ **C.** $x = -2y$ **D.** $x = 2y$

Extended Response

39. There are 16 questions on a test. Each question is worth either
5 points or 10 points. The total is 100 points. **a–c. See back of book.**
 a. Let x = the number of 5-point questions.
 Let y = the number of 10-point questions.
 Write a system of equations to find the number of each
 type of question.
 b. Solve the system by graphing.
 c. How many questions of each type are on the test?

Take It to the NET
Online lesson quiz at
www.PHSchool.com
Web Code: ada-0807

8-7 Solving Systems of Linear Equations **439**

Teaching Tip
Exercises 10–15 Remind students
that they do not have to
necessarily graph a system to find
the solutions. Equations with the
same slope and different
y-intercepts have no solution,
and equations that are
equivalent have infinitely
many solutions.

29a. $y = 200 + 0.10x$ and
 $y = 150 + 0.20x$

29b.
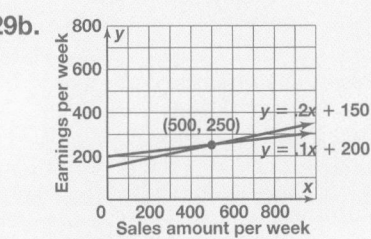

\$500

29c. If weekly sales are
about \$600, you would
earn more money at the
position that pays
\$150/wk plus 20%
commission. If $x = 600$,
$y = 270$. If $x = 600$ in the
other equation, $y = 260$,
which is less than 270.

30a.
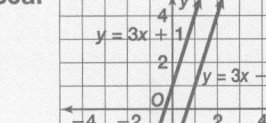
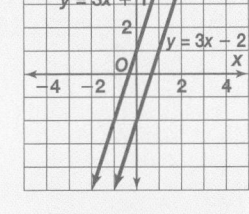

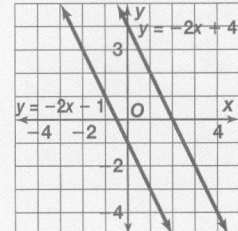

Solve each system by graphing.

1. $y = -x - 4$ and $y = 4x + 1$
($-1, -3$)

2. $y = -3x + 12$ and
$18x + 6y = 42$ **no solution**

3. Find two numbers with a
sum of 15 and a difference
of 1. Show your work. **(8, 7)**

✓ Chapter Checkpoint 2

To check understanding of
Lessons 8-5 to 8-7:

Checkpoint Quiz 2 (p. 440)

📁 **Teaching Resources**
Checkpoint Quiz 2 (also in
Prentice Hall Assessment System)

👥 **Reaching All Students**
Reading and Math Literacy 8C

Spanish versions available.

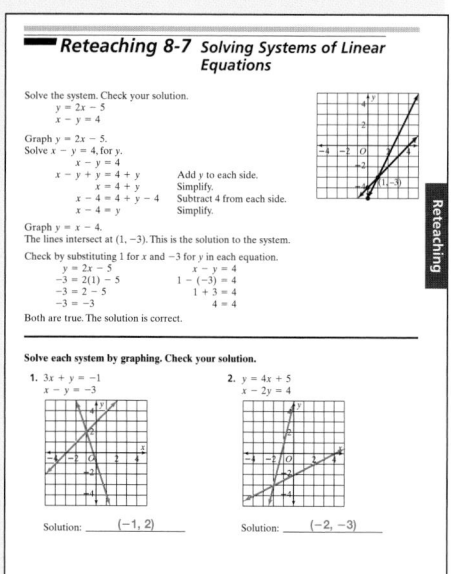

Mixed Review

Lesson 8-5

40. Use the scatter plot at the right.
  a. How much time did the
  person who saw four
  movies spend? **5 h**
  b. How many people saw more
  than three movies? **3 people**
  c. How many people spent
  less than three hours
  watching movies? **2 people**

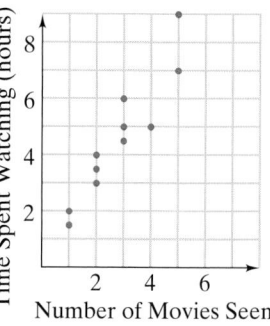

Lesson 7-6 **Solve each inequality.**

41. $1 - x < 5$ **$x > -4$**   **42.** $3t - 1 \le 17$ **$t \le 6$**

43. $-2c + 5 \ge 3$ **$c \le 1$**   **44.** $m + 4 > -10$ **$m > -14$**

Lesson 6-4 **Probability** **Find each probability for one roll of a number cube.**

45. $P(2)$ $\frac{1}{6}$ **46.** $P(6 \text{ or } 5)$ **47.** $P(-1)$ **0**   **48.** $P(4, 2, \text{ or } 5)$
$\frac{2}{6}$, or $\frac{1}{3}$ $\frac{3}{6}$, or $\frac{1}{2}$

✓ Checkpoint Quiz 2   Lessons 8-5 through 8-7

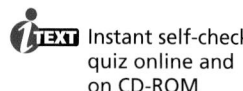 **Instant self-check quiz online and on CD-ROM**

1. a. Statistics Use the table at the
right. Make a scatter plot
relating daily newspaper
circulation and television sets.
  b. Is there is a *positive correlation*,
  a *negative correlation*, or *no
  correlation* between daily
  newspaper circulation and the
  number of television sets in
  homes? Explain.
  c. Data Analysis Draw a trend
  line on your scatter plot. Use
  it to predict the number of
  television sets when newspaper
  circulation is 55 million. **a–c. See back of book.**

Media in the United States

Year	Daily Newspaper Circulation (millions)	Television Sets in Homes (millions)
1980	62	128
1985	63	155
1990	62	193
1991	61	193
1992	60	192
1993	60	201
1994	59	211
1995	57	217
1996	57	223

SOURCE: *Statistical Abstract of the United States*.
Go to **www.PHSchool.com** for a data update.
Web Code: adg-2041

Solve each system by graphing.

2. $y = -4x$ **($-2, 8$)**   **3.** $x - y = 1$ **($-3, -4$)**   **4.** $6x + 2y = 12$ **(1, 3)**
$y = -x + 6$ $x + y = -7$ $y = 3x$

5. Measurement One gallon of liquid occupies 231 cubic inches.
Write a rule that expresses the number of gallons $g(c)$ as a
function of the number of cubic inches c. **$g(c) = \frac{c}{231}$**

6. Find two numbers with a sum of -4 and a difference of 10. **3, -7**

Alternative Assessment

Give students the graphs of $y = 2x$ and $y = 2$
(without showing the equations) and have them
write the system of linear equations for the lines.
Also have them give the solution of the system.

Test Prep

 **Resources**
For additional practice with a variety of
test item formats:
• Test Prep, p. 453
• Test-Taking Strategies, p. 448
• Test-Taking Strategies With Transparencies

Graphing Linear Inequalities

OBJECTIVE

1 Graphing Linear Inequalities

If you replace the equal sign in a linear equation with $>$, $<$, $\geq$, or $\leq$, the result is a **linear inequality.** The graph of a linear inequality is a region of the coordinate plane bounded by a line. Every point in the region is a solution of the inequality.

1 EXAMPLE Graphing a Linear Inequality

Graph each inequality on a coordinate plane.

a. $y \leq x + 2$ **b.** $y < -2x$

Step 1 Graph the boundary line.

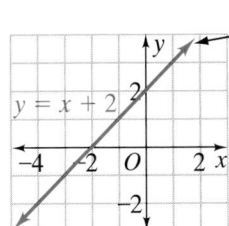

Points on the boundary line make $y \leq x + 2$ true. Use a solid line.

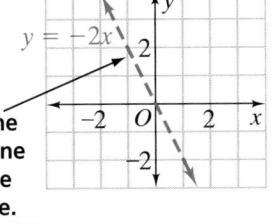

Points on the boundary line do *not* make $y < -2x$ true. Use a dashed line.

Step 2 Test a point not on the boundary line.

Test $(0, 0)$
in the inequality.

$y \leq x + 2$

$0 \overset{?}{\leq} 0 + 2$ **Substitute.**

$0 \leq 2$ ✔ **true**

Test $(1, 1)$
in the inequality.

$y < -2x$

$1 \overset{?}{<} -2(1)$ **Substitute.**

$1 < -2$ ✘ **false**

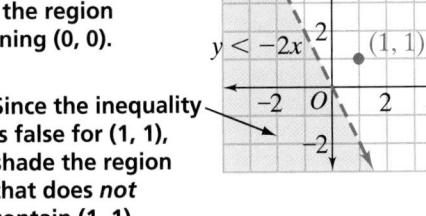

Since the inequality is true for (0, 0), shade the region containing (0, 0).

Since the inequality is false for (1, 1), shade the region that does *not* contain (1, 1).

i TEXT Interactive lesson includes instant self-check, tutorials, and activities.

What You'll Learn

OBJECTIVE 1 To graph linear inequalities

OBJECTIVE 2 To graph systems of linear inequalities

. . . And Why

To solve real-world situations involving grocery shopping and earnings from jobs

✓ Check Skills You'll Need

Is the given value of x a solution of the inequality? Explain.

1. $x + 3 \geq -2$; $x = -5$

2. $5 - x < 4$; $x = 1$

3. $-2 - 2x \leq 6$; $x = -4$

4. $4x + 1 > -7$; $x = -2$
1–4. See margin.

? For help, go to Lesson 7-6.

New Vocabulary

• linear inequality

• system of linear inequalities

8-8

1. Plan

Lesson Preview

✓ Check Skills You'll Need

Solving One-Step Inequalities
Lesson 7-6: Examples 1 and 2;
Exercises 3–14.
Extra Practice, p. 750.

Lesson Resources

📁 **Teaching Resources**
Practice, Reteaching, Enrichment

👥 **Reaching All Students**
Practice Workbook 8-8
Spanish Practice Workbook 8-8
Guided Problem Solving 8-8

⏱ **Presentation Assistant Plus!**
Transparencies and PowerPoint™
• Check Skills You'll Need 8-8
• Additional Examples 8-8
• Student Edition Answers 8-8
• Lesson Quiz 8-8
• Classroom Aid 2
PH Presentation Pro CD-ROM 8-8

ASSESSMENT SYSTEM

Computer Test Generator CD-ROM

💻 **Technology**
Resource Pro® CD-ROM
Computer Test Generator CD-ROM
PH Presentation Pro CD-ROM

💻 **www.PHSchool.com**
Student Site
• Teacher Web Code: adk-5500
• Graphing Calculator, Procedure 8
• Self-grading Lesson Quiz
PH SuccessNet Teacher Center
• Lesson Planner
• Resources

Plus **i TEXT**

🔄 Ongoing Assessment and Intervention

Before the Lesson
Diagnose prerequisite skills using:
• Check Skills You'll Need

During the Lesson
Monitor progress using:
• Check Understanding
• Additional Examples
• Test Prep

After the Lesson
Assess knowledge using:
• Lesson Quiz
• Computer Test Generator CD-ROM

1. yes; $-5 + 3 \geq -2$
2. no; $5 - 1 \not< 4$
3. yes; $-2 - 2(-4) \leq 6$
4. no; $4(-2) + 1 \not> -7$

Math Background

A system of linear equations whose graphs intersect in one point has only one solution. A system of linear inequalities whose graphs intersect has infinitely many solutions.

Teaching Notes

1 EXAMPLE Visual Learners

Help students connect graphing a solid boundary line for a two-variable inequality containing $\geq$ and $\leq$ with graphing a solid dot for a one-variable inequality. Write $y \leq 2$ on the board and have two volunteers graph it, one on a number line and the other in the coordinate plane. Also show the connection of a dashed line with the open dot by repeating the activity for $y < -2$.

1 EXAMPLE Error Prevention

For lines that are nearly vertical, it may be difficult to tell what is "above" and what is "below" the boundary line. In these cases, it is always best to test a point that is clearly on one side of the line to decide which side to shade.

PowerPoint

Additional Examples

1 Graph each inequality on a coordinate plane.

a. $y > 2x + 1$

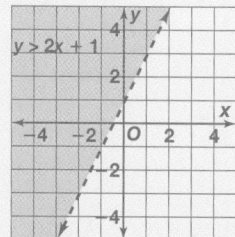

b. $y \leq 3x - 2$

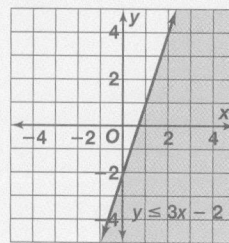

Need Help?

< means "is less than."
> means "is greater than."
$\leq$ means "is less than or equal to."
$\geq$ means "is greater than or equal to."

Real-World Connection

There are over 3,100 farmers markets in the United States.

1a.
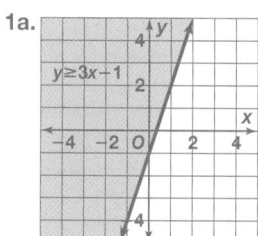

1b.
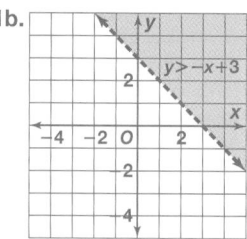

✓ Check Understanding Example 1

1. Graph each inequality on its own coordinate plane.

a. $y \geq 3x - 1$ b. $y > -x + 3$ c. $y < 2x - 4$
   a–b. See below left.   See back of book.

2 EXAMPLE Real-World Problem Solving

Grocery Shopping Apricots cost \$3/lb. Tomatoes cost \$1/lb. You plan to spend no more than \$10. How many pounds of each can you buy?

Step 1 Write an inequality.

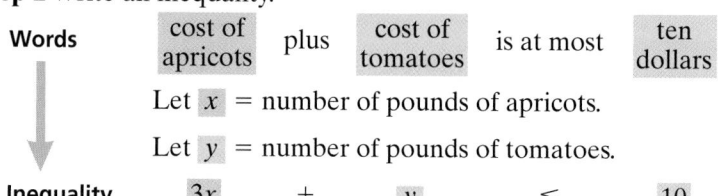

Let x = number of pounds of apricots.

Let y = number of pounds of tomatoes.

Inequality $3x$ + y $\leq$ 10

Step 2 Write the equation of the boundary line in slope-intercept form.

$3x + y \leq 10$
$\quad y \leq -3x + 10$
$\quad y = -3x + 10$

Step 3 Graph $y = -3x + 10$ in Quadrant I since weight is not negative.

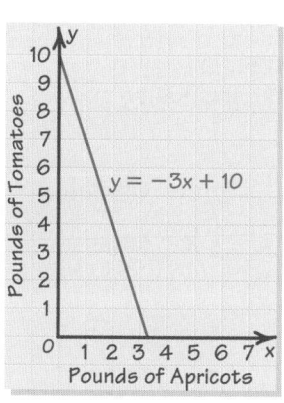

Step 4 Test $(1, 1)$.

$y \leq -3x + 10$
$1 \overset{?}{\leq} -3(1) + 10$
$1 \leq 7$ ✔

The inequality is true. $(1, 1)$ is a solution.

Step 5 Shade the region containing $(1, 1)$.

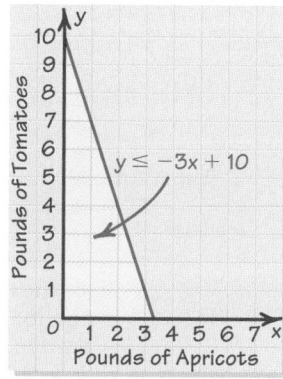

The graph shows the possible solutions. For example, you could buy 1 pound of apricots and 5 pounds of tomatoes.

👥 Reaching All Students

Below Level Help students see that they are first graphing a linear equation. Then they use the inequality symbol to determine a solid or dashed boundary line and which side of the boundary line to shade.

Advanced Learners Challenge students to describe the solutions of the system $y < x + 1$, $y > x + 1$ without graphing. No solutions; shaded regions will be on opposite sides of the dashed boundary line.

Visual Learners
See note on page 442.
Inclusion
See note on page 443.

✓ **Check Understanding** Example 2

2. Adult tickets to the school play cost $4. Children's tickets cost $2. Your goal is to sell tickets worth at least $30. Let x be the number of children's tickets and y be the number of adult tickets. Graph a linear inequality to show how many of each type of ticket you must sell to reach your goal.
See right.

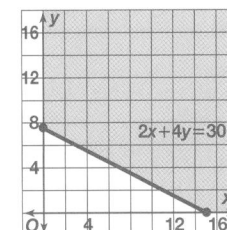

OBJECTIVE

2 **Graphing Systems of Linear Inequalities**

Two or more linear inequalities form a **system of linear inequalities.** A *solution of a system of linear inequalities* is any ordered pair that makes each inequality in the system true. To solve a system, graph the inequalities on one coordinate plane.

3 **EXAMPLE** **Solving a System of Linear Inequalities**

Solve the system $y > x$ and $y \leq -x + 2$ by graphing.

Step 1 Graph $y > x$ on a coordinate plane.

Step 2 Graph $y \leq -x + 2$ on the same coordinate plane.

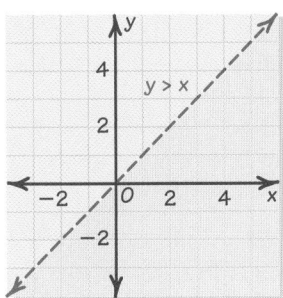

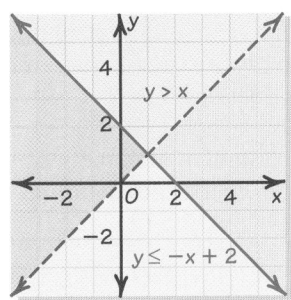

The solutions are the coordinates of all the points in the region that is shaded in both colors.

Check The point $(-1, 0)$ is in the solution region. Check whether $(-1, 0)$ makes both of the inequalities true.

$y > x$
$0 \overset{?}{>} -1$ **Replace x with −1 and y with 0.** $0 \overset{?}{\leq} -(-1) + 2$
$0 > -1$ ✔   **The solution checks.** $0 \leq 3$ ✔

$y \leq -x + 2$

✓ **Check Understanding** Example 3

3. Solve each system by graphing. **a–b. See right.**

a. $y \leq -2x - 5$
$y < \frac{1}{2}x$

b. $y > x - 1$
$y < 3x + 4$

3a.

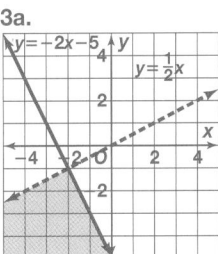

3b.

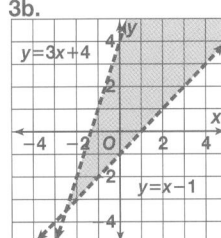

2 Cashews cost $2/lb. Pecans cost $4/lb. You plan to spend no more than $20. How many pounds of each can you buy?

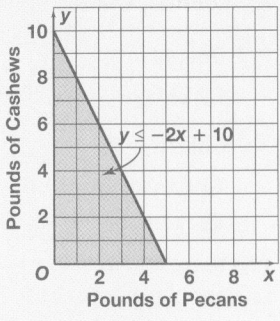

3 Solve the system $y \geq x + 1$ and $y < 2x + 3$ by graphing.

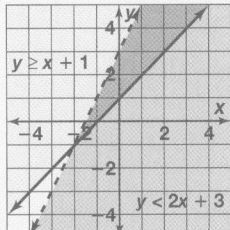

3 **EXAMPLE** **Visual Learners**

Have students use two different colored pencils to shade the solution regions. Stress the importance of shading lightly to be able to see the graphs beneath the two colors. On the overhead you can use different colored transparencies to represent different regions. Colored, clear-plastic report binders also work well as colored transparencies.

3 **EXAMPLE** **Inclusion**

Pair students who do not have good eye-hand coordination with those who do to graph the systems of equations. The student lacking the coordination can direct the partner as to how to graph the boundary line, whether to make the line dashed or solid, and which side of the line to shade.

Closure

Ask students how to determine whether the point where the boundary lines of a system of linear inequalities intersect is a solution of the system. **See left.**

Closure

If either of the inequalities is > or <, then the boundary line for that inequality does not contain solutions for that inequality. Therefore, the point at which the boundary lines intersect is not a solution of the system.

Assignment Guide

 **Objective 1**
Ⓐ Ⓑ **Core** 1–15, 20–36, 43

Objective 2
Ⓐ Ⓑ **Core** 16–19, 37–42
Ⓒ **Extension** 44–48

Test Prep 49–54
Mixed Review 55–65

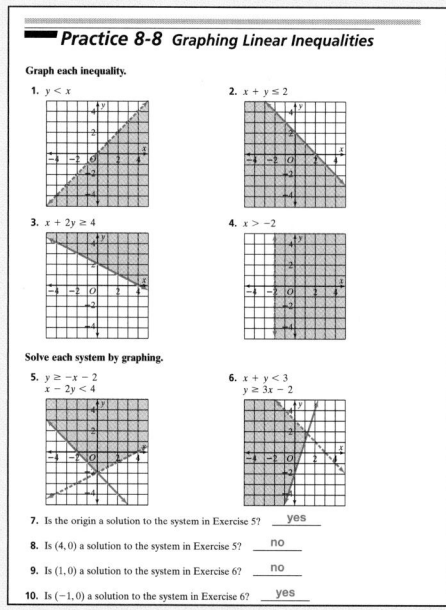

Practice 8-8 **Graphing Linear Inequalities**

Graph each inequality.
1. $y < x$
2. $x + y \le 2$
3. $x + 2y \ge 4$
4. $x > -2$

Solve each system by graphing.
5. $y \ge -x - 2$
   $x - 2y < 4$
6. $x + y < 3$
   $y \ge 3x - 2$

7. Is the origin a solution to the system in Exercise 5? yes
8. Is $(4, 0)$ a solution to the system in Exercise 5? no
9. Is $(1, 0)$ a solution to the system in Exercise 6? no
10. Is $(-1, 0)$ a solution to the system in Exercise 6? yes

Enrichment 8-8 **Mathematician Turned Architect**

London's Great Fire of 1666 changed a professor of mathematics and physics into a world-renowned architect. This learned man oversaw the rebuilding of much of London, including St. Paul's Cathedral.

To find the name of this mathematician/architect, decide which of the two inequalities has the given ordered pair as a solution. Circle the inequality. Then write the letter of the inequality above the number of the exercise in the answer grid at the bottom of the page.

1. $(1, 6)$ Ⓡ $y < 2x + 5$ A: $y > 2x + 5$
2. $(-3, -11)$ Ⓔ $y \ge 3x - 2$ N: $y > 3x - 2$
3. $(-10, 0)$ Ⓒ $y \le \frac{1}{2}x + 5$ I: $y < \frac{1}{2}x + 5$
4. $(3, -20)$ Ⓦ $y > 8 - 12x$ O: $y < 8 - 12x$
5. $(-1, 0)$ M: $5 + 4x < y$ Ⓢ $5 + 4x > y$
6. $(-8, -7)$ Ⓛ $x \le y$ G: $x \ge y$
7. $(6, -5)$ Ⓞ $x > -3$ C: $x < -3$
8. $(-2, 2)$ S: $y - 4 > x$ Ⓣ $y - 4 \ge x$
9. $(-3, 3)$ R: $x + y > y$ Ⓗ $x + y > x$
10. $(-\frac{4}{5}, \frac{1}{5})$ Ⓗ $-x > 0$ P: $-x < 0$
11. $(2, 1.2)$ E: $x < 3y - 2$ Ⓡ $x > 3y - 2$
12. $(4.5, 3.4)$ Ⓡ $3x < 4y$ T: $3x > 4y$
13. $(-5, 3)$ M: $2x + 3y > 0$ Ⓛ $2x + 3y < 0$
14. $(2.7, 4.8)$ Ⓢ $-3x + 5y < 16$ R: $-3x + 5y > 16$
15. $(0.8, 0.2)$ W: $8 - 8x > 9y$ Ⓔ $8 - 8x < 9y$
16. $(-3.9, -6.5)$ S: $7x - 4y < -2$ Ⓡ $7x - 4y > -2$
17. $(5, 8)$ Ⓟ $x \le 5$ A: $x > 5$
18. $(-3, -10)$ Ⓝ $y \le x + 7$ P: $y \ge x - 5$

S I R   C H R I S T O P H E R   W R E N
14 6 12   3 9 1 13 5 8 7 17 10 2 16   4 11 15 18

EXERCISES

❓ For more exercises, see *Extra Practice*.

Practice and Problem Solving

Ⓐ **Practice by Example**

Example 1
(page 441)

The graph of each inequality is bounded by a line. State whether the boundary line is solid or dashed.

1. $y > x$ dashed   2. $y \le -x + 1$ solid   3. $y \ge x - 1$ solid

Graph each inequality on its own coordinate plane. 4–9. See margin.

4. $y > x - 6$ 5. $y \le -x + 8$ 6. $y > x + 2$
7. $y \ge 2x - 1$ 8. $y < -\frac{1}{3}x + 1$ 9. $y \le 2x + 1$

Example 2
(page 442)

Solve each inequality for y.

10. $4x + y < -3$
    $y < -4x - 3$
11. $-y \le 2x$
    $y \ge -2x$
12. $2x + 3y \le 7$
    $y \le -\frac{2}{3}x + \frac{7}{3}$

For Exercises 13–15, show all the solutions by writing and graphing a linear inequality. 13–15. See back of book.

13. Find two nonnegative numbers with a sum greater than three.

14. A number is greater than or equal to three times another number. What are the numbers?
    (GPS)

🌐 15. **Collections** Melissa has a collection of dimes and nickels with a total face value of less than one dollar. Let x be the number of dimes and y be the number of nickels. How many of each type of coin does she have?

Example 3
(page 443)

Solve each system of inequalities by graphing. Use a point on the x- or y-axis to check each solution. 16–19. See back of book.

16. $y > -x$
    $y < x + 6$
17. $y \le x$
    $y \ge -x - 4$
18. $y > -x$
    $y > 2x + 3$
19. $y \le -x + 1$
    $y > x - 5$

Ⓑ **Apply Your Skills**

Choose a linear inequality to match each graph.

20. 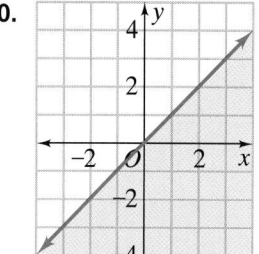   21.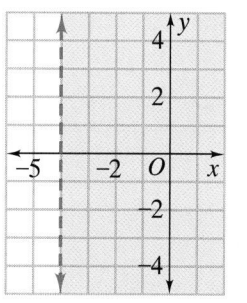

A. $-y \ge x$ B. $-y \le x$
C. $-y \ge -x$ D. $-y \le -x$

F. $x < -4$ G. $x > -4$
H. $-x < -4$ I. $-x > -4$

22. Multiply both sides of $-y < x$ by -1 to get $y > -x$. The graph of $y < -x$ is the set of points below the graph of $y = -x$. The graph of $y > -x$ is the set of points above the graph of $y = -x$.

22. **Writing in Math** Describe the difference between the graph of $y < -x$ and the graph of $-y < x$. See left.

444 Chapter 8 Linear Functions and Graphing

(GPS) Use the Guided Problem Solving worksheet with Exercise 14.

4.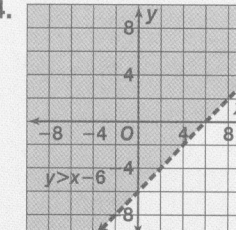
   $y > x - 6$

5.
   $y \le -x + 8$

6–9. See back of book.

Graph each inequality on its own coordinate plane. 23–28. See margin.

23. $x - y > 10$ **24.** $y \leq 5$ **25.** $y \geq -\frac{2}{3}x$

26. $9x + 3y < 3$ **27.** $x - 2y \geq -12$ **28.** $-6x - 4y > 8$

29. a. Income You can earn $6/h mowing lawns and $3/h baby-sitting. You want to earn at least $45. Let x = number of hours mowing lawns and y = number of hours baby-sitting. Write a linear inequality to model this situation. $6x + 3y \geq 45$

  b. Graph the linear inequality. See margin.

  c. If you baby-sit for 6 hours, what is the number of hours you will need to mow lawns to earn $45? $4\frac{1}{2}$ h

30. $y = -x - 3$; dashed
31. $y = x - 7$; solid
32. $y = -4x$; dashed
33. $y = \frac{1}{2}x$; solid
34. $y = -\frac{5}{3}x + 3$; solid
35. $y = 2x - 5$; dashed

Write the equation of each boundary line in slope-intercept form. State whether the boundary line is solid or dashed. 30–35. See left.

30. $x + y < -3$ **31.** $x - y \geq 7$ **32.** $-y > 4x$

33. $-y \leq -\frac{1}{2}x$ **34.** $5x + 3y \leq 9$ **35.** $4x - 2y > 10$

36. Medium drinks cost $2 and large drinks cost $3. Let x be the number of medium drinks sold and y be the number of large drinks sold. How many drinks must the vendor sell to have at least $60 in sales? Show all possible solutions by graphing a linear inequality. See margin.

Solve each system of inequalities by graphing. 37–42. See back of book.

37. $2x + y \leq 4$
   $y + 1 \geq -2x$

38. $x + y > -3$
   $x - y < 5$

39. $x < 6$
   $y \leq 2x$

40. $y < 4$
   $x > -5$

41. $-2x + y > 1$
   $x + 2y < 2$

42. $3x + y > 5$
   $y \geq -2$

43. Answers may vary. Sample: When you graph inequalities, you show a set of solutions. When you graph on a number line, you show single-number solutions for one variable. When you graph on a coordinate plane, you show ordered-pair solutions for two variables.

43. Writing in Math How is graphing an inequality on a coordinate plane similar to graphing an inequality on a number line? How is it different? See left.

C Challenge

Open-Ended Write a system of inequalities with the solutions indicated. If such a system is not possible, tell why. 44–46. See left.

44. no solutions **45.** all real numbers **46.** the points of a line

44. Answers may vary. Sample: $y > x + 5$, $y < x + 3$

45. Answers may vary. Sample: Not possible; some real numbers will be on the "other" side of the boundary lines.

46. Answers may vary. Sample: $y \geq 0$, $y \leq 0$

Reasoning Write a system of inequalities to describe each graph.

47.

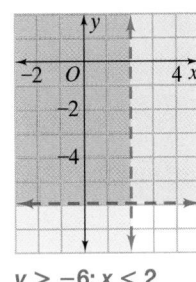

$y > -6$; $x < 2$

48.

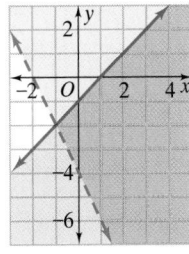

$y \leq x - 1$; $y > -2x - 4$

8-8 Graphing Linear Inequalities **445**

29b.

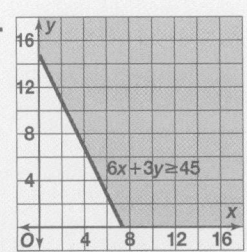

36.

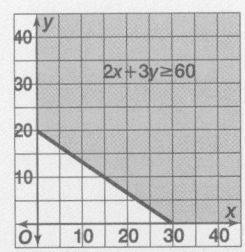

23.

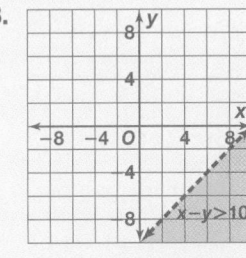

24.

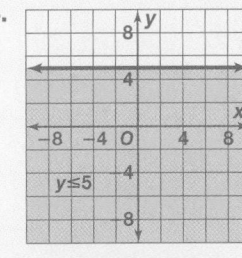

25.

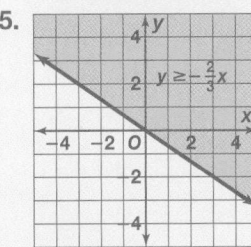

26.

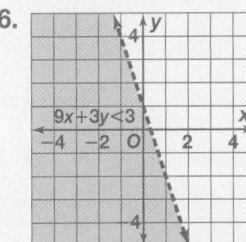

27.

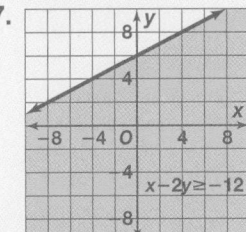

28.

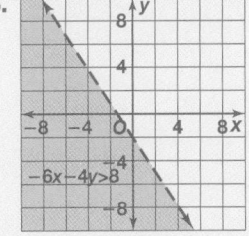

4. Assess

Lesson Quiz 8-8

Tell whether the ordered pair is a solution of the inequality. Justify your response.

1. $y < 4x$; (3, 0) yes; $0 < 12$

2. $y > -x - 1$; (2, -3) no; $3 \not> -3$

3. $y \le 4x - 2$; (-1, 1) no; $1 \not\le -6$

4. Solve the system $y \le 3x + 1$ and $y > -2x + 2$ by graphing.

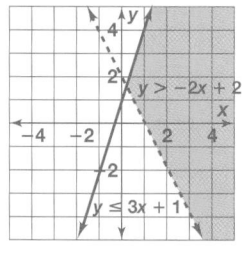

Test Prep

📁 **Resources**

For additional practice with a variety of test item formats:
• Test Prep, p. 453
• Test-Taking Strategies, p. 448
• Test-Taking Strategies With Transparencies

Reteaching 8-8 *Graphing Linear Inequalities*

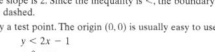 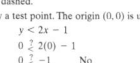 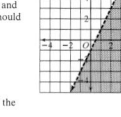

Graph $y < 2x - 1$.

Graph the boundary line $y = 2x - 1$. The y-intercept is -1 and the slope is 2. Since the inequality is $<$, the boundary line should be dashed.

Try a test point. The origin (0, 0) is usually easy to use.

$y < 2x - 1$
$0 \stackrel{?}{<} 2(0) - 1$
$0 \stackrel{?}{<} -1$ No

(0, 0) is not in the solution of $y < 2x - 1$. Shade the side of the boundary line *not* containing the origin.

Tell whether the boundary line of the graph of each inequality is *solid* or *dashed*.

1. $4x - 5y \ge 3$ solid
2. $y < \frac{2}{3}x + 2$ dashed
3. $2x > 3 - 2y$ dashed
4. $y \le -5$ solid
5. $-x + 2y > -3$ dashed
6. $8 \le 5y - 3x$ solid

Tell whether the region containing the origin would be shaded in the graph of each inequality. Write *yes* or *no*.

7. $4x - 5y \ge 3$ no
8. $y < \frac{2}{3}x + 2$ yes
9. $2x > 3 - 2y$ no
10. $y \le -5$ no
11. $-x + 2y > -3$ yes
12. $8 \le 5y - 3x$ no
13. $4x < y$ no
14. $\frac{1}{2}x > 2y$ no

446

Multiple Choice

49. Which inequality has the same solutions as $y \ge -2x + 1$? **B**
    A. $2x + y \le 1$
    B. $2x + y \ge 1$
    C. $2x - y \le 1$
    D. $2x - y \ge 1$

💻 **Take It to the NET**
Online lesson quiz at **www.PHSchool.com**
Web Code: ada-0808

50. Which describes the graph of $y \le -x + 2$? **G**
    F. shading above a solid boundary line
    G. shading below a solid boundary line
    H. shading above a dashed boundary line
    I. shading below a dashed boundary line

51. You want to spend less than \$20 on asparagus and green beans. Asparagus costs \$3.00 per pound and green beans cost \$.50 per pound. Let a represent the asparagus and g represent the green beans. Which inequality models what you can spend? **C**
    A. $3a + 0.5g > 20$
    B. $3a + 0.5g \ge 20$
    C. $3a + 0.5g < 20$
    D. $3a + 0.5g \le 20$

52. Which inequality has a graph with shading below a dashed boundary line? **I**
    F. $2x + y > -3$
    G. $2x + y \ge -3$
    H. $2x + y \le -3$
    I. $2x + y < -3$

53. Which point is a solution of the system $y \ge 0$; $x \le 0$? **B**
    A. (1, 1)   B. (-1, 1)   C. (1, -1)   D. (-1, -1)

Short Response

54. Explain how to graph $y \ge 2x + 3$. Then graph the inequality. See back of book.

Mixed Review

Lesson 8-7 **Solve each system of equations by graphing. Check each solution.**

55. $x + y = 8$
    $x - y = -2$
    (3, 5)

56. $y = 2x - 1$
    $2x - y = 3$
    no solution

57. $3y = -2x - 3$
    $3y = x - 12$
    (3, -3)

Lesson 6-6 🌐 58. **Endangered Animals** In 1999, there were 162 California condors. Of these birds, 113 were in captivity, 29 were living free in California, and 20 were living free in Arizona.
    a. What percent of the condors were living free in Arizona? Round your answer to the nearest tenth of a percent. **12.3%**
    b. What percent of the condors were living free in all? Round your answer to the nearest tenth of a percent. **30.2%**

Lessons 5-7 and 5-8 **Solve each equation.**

59. $m - \frac{2}{3} = \frac{1}{6}$ $\frac{5}{6}$

60. $\frac{5}{4}c = \frac{3}{2}$ $1\frac{1}{5}$

61. $\frac{3}{4} + w = \frac{9}{10}$ $\frac{3}{20}$

Lesson 4-6 **Evaluate each expression for $c = 4$ and $m = -3$.**

62. $\frac{c + m}{5}$ $\frac{1}{5}$
63. $\frac{m - c}{2}$ $-3\frac{1}{2}$
64. $\frac{2c - m}{-4}$ $-2\frac{3}{4}$
65. $\frac{4m}{2 - c}$ 6

446 Chapter 8 Linear Functions and Graphing

Alternative Assessment

Create a coordinate plane on a classroom bulletin board. Have students use string, thumbtacks, and construction paper to show graphs of systems of linear equations. If an inequality contains $>$ or $<$, have the students use a marker to "dash" the string.

Technology

Graphing Inequalities

For Use With Lesson 8-8

Graphing an inequality on a calculator is similar to graphing an equation. If your calculator does not graph dashed lines, you have to remember the type of boundary line you need for the inequality.

EXAMPLE

Graph $y > -x + 4$.

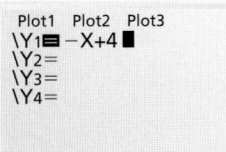

Step 1 Press the Y= key.
Enter $-x + 4$.

Step 2 Press ◄ to move to the left of Y1.
Press ENTER twice when
y is greater than the right side of the equation.
Press ENTER three times when
y is less than the right side of the equation.

Step 3 Press ZOOM 6 to graph the inequality with the standard viewing window. Then sketch the inequality.

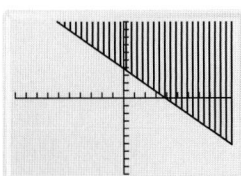
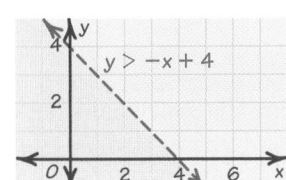

EXERCISES

1–4. See above right. 5–8. See margin.

Graph each inequality. Be sure your boundary line is correct.

1. $y > 3x + 1$ **2.** $y \le 2x$ **3.** $y < -x - 5$ **4.** $y \ge 4x + 6$

5. $y \le -2x - 4$ **6.** $y < x + 7$ **7.** $y > -3x + 4$ **8.** $y \ge -\frac{2}{5}x + 1$

Graph each system of inequalities. Sketch the solutions. See answers for Ex. 16–19, p. 444.

9. $y > -x$
$y < x + 6$

10. $y \le x$
$y \ge -x - 4$

11. $y > -x$
$y > 2x + 3$

12. $y \le -x + 1$
$y > x - 5$

13. Find and graph a system of inequalities that has no solution. Answers may vary.
Sample: $y > x + 1$
$y < x - 2$

14. Find and graph a system of inequalities whose solutions are the points of a line. Answers may vary. Sample: $y \ge x$
$y \le x$

1.
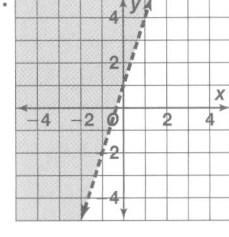

2.
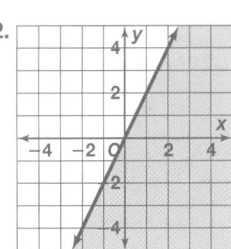

3.
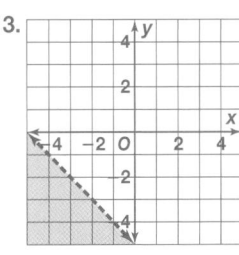

4.
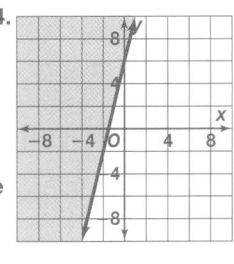

Technology Graphing Inequalities **447**

Technology

Graphing Inequalities

In this Technology extension students graph linear inequalities using a graphing calculator.

Teaching Notes

Error Prevention!

Remind students to clear the Y= list first. If students get an error message when they graph the line, have them make sure they pressed the negative key and not the minus key when they entered $-x$.

Error Prevention!

Remind students that in a sketch of an inequality, the boundary line is dashed or solid according to the type of inequality symbol used.

Inclusion

Pair a student who lacks good eye-hand coordination with someone who can easily enter information into the calculator. Have the student who lacks good eye-hand coordination give instructions to the partner.

5.
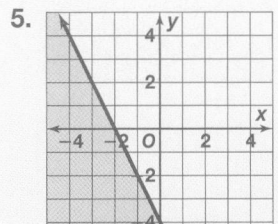

6.
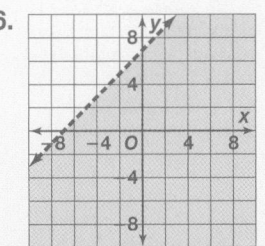

7.
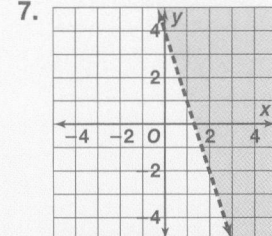

8.
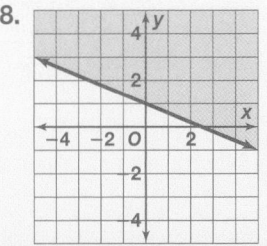

447

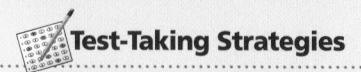

Finding Multiple Correct Answers

This feature helps students develop strategies for answering questions that have more than one correct response. Students need to look at each statement and test to see whether it is true or false. This type of problem requires logical reasoning in addition to problem-solving skills.

Resources

Test-Taking Strategies With Transparencies
• Transparency 8
• Practice Sheet, p. 8

Teaching Notes

Visual Learners
Suggest that students use colored pencils. Have students mark the *true* statements one color and the *not true*, or *false*, statements a different color.

Test-Taking Strategies With Transparencies

Chapter 8: Finding Multiple Correct Answers
Exercises

Choose the option with all choices that are true. Explain your answers.

1. Which of the following numbers are rational numbers?
   I. −14   II. √7   III. 0.3   IV. √49
   A. I only   B. I and III   C. II and IV   D. I, III, and IV

2. Which of these ordered pairs is a solution to the equation $y = 2x - 5$?
   I. (0, −5)   II. (4, 3)   III. (2, 1)
   F. I only   G. I and II   H. II and III   I. I, II, and III

3. If $y = 13$, which of the statements are true?
   I. y is prime   II. y is divisible by 3   III. y is odd
   A. I only   B. I and II   C. I and III   D. I, II, and III

4. The statement $x > 3$ and $x < 5$ is true for which values of x?
   I. 4   II. 6   III. 4.5   IV. $\frac{25}{6}$
   F. I only   G. I and II   H. II and III   I. I, III, and IV

8   Pre-Algebra   Test-Taking Strategies

Finding Multiple Correct Answers

A multiple-correct-answer test item presents you with a question and several possible answers labeled with Roman numerals. You have to decide which of the answers are correct. Then you pick your list of correct answers from the lettered choices given.

A good strategy to follow is to test each answer and mark it if correct.

EXAMPLE

For which equation(s) is (4, 6) a solution?
   I. $x - y = -2$ II. $-x - y = -10$ III. $x - y = 2$ IV. $y - x = 2$

   A. I and II only   B. I, II, and III only   C. I, II, and IV only   D. III only

Test each answer.

Substitute 4 for x and 6 for y.

I. $x - y = -2$	II. $-x - y = -10$	III. $x - y = 2$	IV. $y - x = 2$
$4 - 6 = -2$	$-4 - 6 = -10$	$4 - 6 = 2$	$6 - 4 = 2$
true	true	not true	true

Statements I, II, and IV (only) are correct; choice C.

EXERCISES

1. The slope of a line is –2. Through which pairs of points could the line pass? C
   I. (0, 3) and (–2, 7)   II. (0, –1) and (2, –5)   III. (0, 0) and (3, 6)   IV. (2, –3) and (–1, 3)

   A. I and II only   B. I, II, and III only   C. I, II, and IV only   D. III only

2. For which system(s) of equations is (2, 3) the solution? G
   I. $y = x + 1$ and $y = -x + 5$ II. $y = 2x - 1$ and $y = \frac{1}{2}x + 2$
   III. $y = 3x - 3$ and $y = -2x + 7$ IV. $y = \frac{1}{4}x + \frac{5}{2}$ and $y = -3x + 3$

   F. I and III only   G. I, II, and III only   H. I, II, and IV only   I. III and IV only

3. Which system(s) of equations has no solution? B
   I. $y = 3x - 1$ and $y = -3x + 1$ II. $y = 1.5x - 2$ and $y = \frac{3}{2}x + 2$
   III. $x + y = 1$ and $y = -x + 3$ IV. $2x + y = 4$ and $2y = 4x + 2$

   A. III only   B. II and III only   C. I, II, and III only   D. I, II, III, and IV

Chapter Review

Vocabulary

domain (p. 400)
function (p. 400)
function notation (p. 418)
function rule (p. 418)
linear equation (p. 406)
linear inequality (p. 441)
negative correlation (p. 425)
no correlation (p. 425)

positive correlation (p. 425)
range (p. 400)
relation (p. 400)
scatter plot (p. 423)
slope (p. 411)
slope-intercept form (p. 413)
solution (p. 405)

system of linear
   equations (p. 435)
system of linear
   inequalities (p. 443)
trend line (p. 430)
vertical-line test (p. 401)
y-intercept (p. 413)

Reading Math
Understanding
Vocabulary

Choose the vocabulary term that correctly completes the sentence.

1. The tilt or slant of a line is its __?__. slope

2. To determine whether the graph shows a function, use the __?__.
   vertical-line test

3. On a scatter plot, when one set of values increases while the other
   decreases, the data is said to have a __?__. negative correlation

4. When each member of a relation's domain is paired with exactly
   one member of the range, the relation is a __?__. function

5. Any equation whose graph is a line is a __?__. linear equation

6. The first coordinates in a set of ordered pairs is the __?__ of the relation.
   domain

7. The second coordinates in a set of ordered pairs is the __?__ of
   the relation. range

Take It to the NET
Online vocabulary quiz
at **www.PHSchool.com**
Web Code: adj-0851

8. An ordered pair that makes an equation a true statement is a __?__
   of the equation. solution

Skills and Concepts

8-1 Objectives

▼ To determine whether
   a relation is a function
   (p. 400)

▼ To graph relations and
   functions (p. 401)

Any set of ordered pairs is a **relation.** The **domain** of a relation is the
set of first coordinates of the ordered pairs. The **range** is the set of
second coordinates. A **function** is a relation in which no two ordered
pairs have the same first coordinate.

Is each relation a function? Explain.

9. Yes; there is one range value
   for each domain value.

9. $\{(2, 3), (4, 3), (0, 1), (-2, 3)\}$ See left.

10.

x	−3	4	−1	−4
y	0	2	0	1

Yes; there is one range value
for each domain value.

11. Domain   Range
    2 ——→ −1
    3 ——→ 0
    4 ——→ 3
    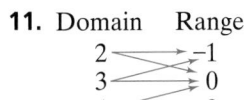
    See left.

11. No; there are domain values
    for which there is more than
    one range value.

12. No; one length of time (for
    different distances) could
    result in different costs.

12. Is the amount of a long-distance telephone bill a function of time
    spent talking on the telephone? Explain. See left.

Resources

Student Edition
Extra Practice, Ch. 8 p. 751
English/Spanish Glossary, p. 782
Table of Symbols, p. 777

 Reaching All Students
Reading and Math Literacy 8D
Spanish Reading and Math
   Literacy 8D

ASSESSMENT SYSTEM

Test Preparation
• Chapter 8 practice in test
  formats

www.PHSchool.com
Student Site
• Self-grading vocabulary test
PH SuccessNet Teacher Center
• Resources

Plus **iTEXT**

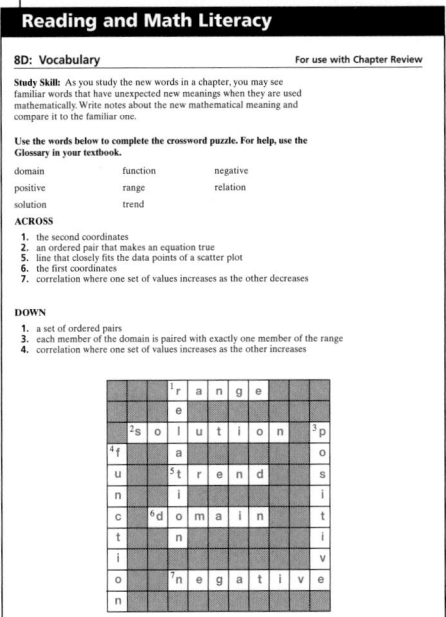

17.

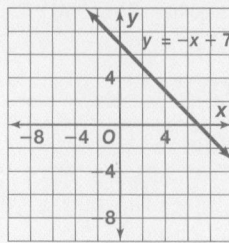

18.

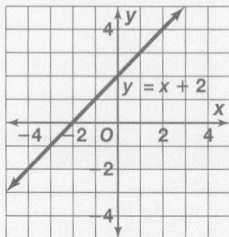

19.

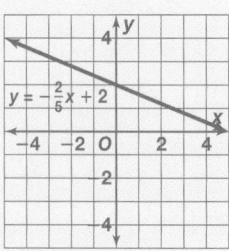

20.

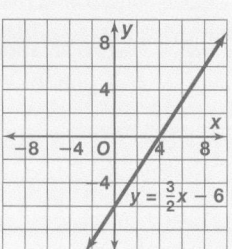

8-2 Objectives

▼ To find solutions of equations with two variables (p. 405)

▼ To graph linear equations with two variables (p. 406)

A solution of an equation with two variables is any ordered pair that makes the equation true. The graph of a **linear equation** is a line.

Find the solutions of each equation for $x = -3, 0$, and 2.

13. $y = x + 5$
(−3, 2), (0, 5), (2, 7)

14. $y = -4x$
(−3, 12), (0, 0), (2, −8)

15. $y = \frac{1}{2}x + 3$
(−3, 1½), (0, 3), (2, 4)

16. $y = 6 - 2x$
(−3, 12), (0, 6), (2, 2)

8-3 Objectives

▼ To find the slope of a line (p. 411)

▼ To use slope-intercept form in graphing a linear equation (p. 413)

Slope is a measure describing the tilt of a line, which you can calculate using the ratio $\frac{\text{vertical change}}{\text{horizontal change}}$, or $\frac{\text{difference in } y\text{-coordinates}}{\text{difference in } x\text{-coordinates}}$.

One form of a linear equation is the slope-intercept form, $y = mx + b$, where m is the slope and b is the y-intercept.

Identify the slope and y-intercept of each equation. Then graph each equation. See margin for graphs.

17. $x + y = 7$ −1, 7

18. $x - y = -2$ 1, 2

19. $2x + 5y = 10$ $-\frac{2}{5}$, 2

20. $3x - 2y = 12$ $\frac{3}{2}$, −6

Find the slope of each line.

21.

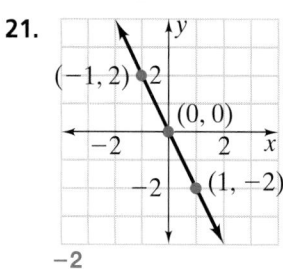

−2

22.

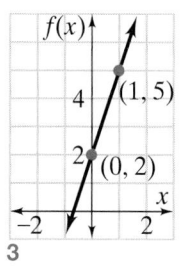

3

23.

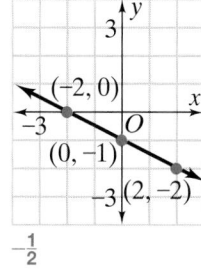

$-\frac{1}{2}$

8-4 Objectives

▼ To write a function rule for a word relationship (p. 418)

▼ To write a function rule by analyzing a table or graph (p. 419)

You can write a **function rule** from a verbal description, from a table of values, or from a graph.

Write a rule for each function.

24.

x	f(x)
−2	2
−1	1
0	0
1	−1

$f(x) = -x$

25.

x	y
−3	−5
−2	−3
−1	−1
0	1

$y = 2x + 1$

26.

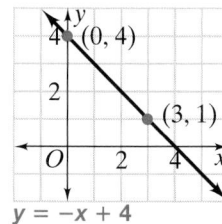

$y = -x + 4$

27. Tickets to a play cost $14 each by mail, plus a $2 processing fee for each order of one or more tickets. Write a rule to describe total cost $c(t)$ as a function of the number of tickets t.
$c(t) = 14t + 2$

8-5 and 8-6 Objectives

▼ To interpret and draw scatter plots (p. 423)

▼ To use scatter plots to find trends (p. 425)

▼ To solve problems by graphing (p. 430)

A **scatter plot** is a graph that shows the relationship between two sets of data. A scatter plot can help you find trends between sets of data.

Use the scatter plot at the right.

28. How long did the person who used 240 calories ride a bicycle? **30 min**

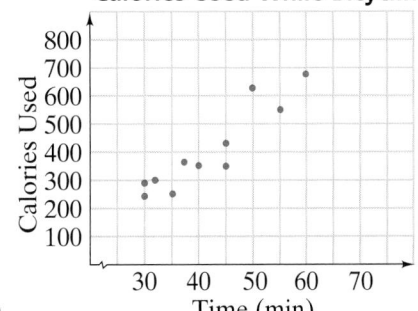

Calories Used While Bicycling

29. How many calories did the person who bicycled 50 minutes use?
about 620 calories

30. Data Analysis Is there a positive correlation, a negative correlation, or no correlation between the time spent bicycling and the calories used? Explain. **Positive correlation; as the time bicycling increases, the calories used increases.**

31. Data Analysis Carefully place a straightedge (preferably transparent) on the scatter plot to serve as a trend line. Use the trend line to predict the number of calories a person uses on a 70-min bicycle ride. **about 800 calories**

8-7 and 8-8 Objectives

▼ To solve systems of linear equations by graphing (p. 435)

▼ To use systems of linear equations to solve problems (p. 436)

▼ To graph linear inequalities (p. 441)

▼ To graph systems of linear inequalities (p. 443)

Two or more linear equations with the same variables form a **system of linear equations.** A solution of a system of equations is any ordered pair that makes each equation true.

Two or more linear inequalities with the same variables form a **system of linear inequalities.** A solution of a system of inequalities is any ordered pair that makes both inequalities true. You can solve a system by graphing.

Graph each inequality. **32–35. See margin.**

32. $y > 2x + 5$

33. $y \le -x + 1$

34. $y \ge \frac{1}{2}x - 3$

35. $y < 3x - 2$

Solve each system by graphing.

36. $y = \frac{1}{2}x - 3$ **(4, −1)**
    $y = -\frac{1}{2}x + 1$

37. $3x + 2y = 6$ **(4, −3)**
    $x + 4y = -8$

38. $y = x - 5$ **(2, −3)**
    $y = -2x + 1$

39. $y < 3x + 2$ **infinitely many solutions**
    $y > 3x - 1$

40. Explain why it is possible for a system of linear equations to have no solutions. **The graphs could be parallel lines, so there is no common solution.**

Chapter 8 Chapter Review **451**

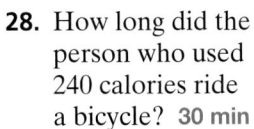
32.

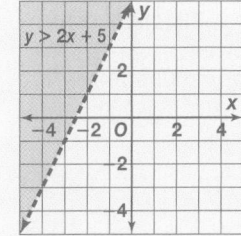

33.

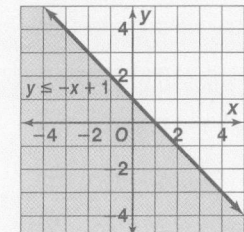

34.

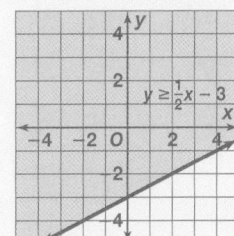

35.

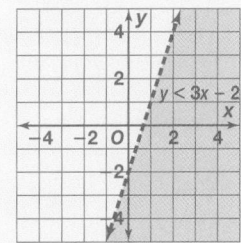

Chapter 8

Chapter Test

Take It to the NET
Online chapter test at
www.PHSchool.com
Web Code: ada-0852

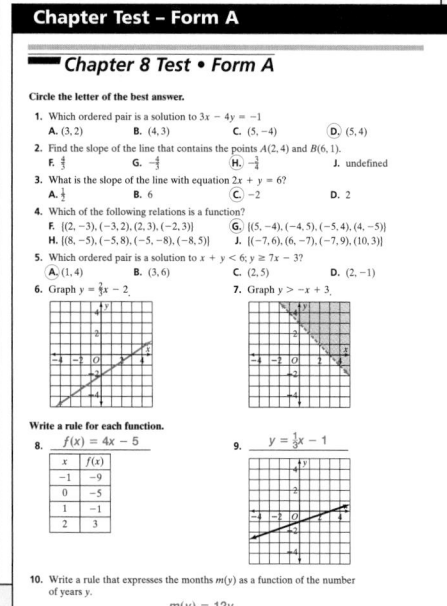

Is each relation a function? Explain.

1. $\{(-2, -12), (-2, 0), (-2, 4), (-2, 11)\}$ no

2. $\{(8, 1), (4, 1), (0, 1), (-15, 1)\}$ yes

3. $\{(-4, -6), (-3, -2), (1, -2), (1, 0), (1, 3)\}$
no

4. $\{(0, 1), (0, 2), (1, 2), (1, 3), (3, 1), (4, 2)\}$
no

Graph each equation. 5–8. See margin.

5. $y = 2x$

6. $y = -x - 2$

7. $2x - y = 4$

8. $3y = x - 6$

Find the slope of the line through each pair of points.

9. $C(0, 1)$ and $D(-5, 1)$ 0

10. $M(-4, 1)$ and $N(6, 3)$ $\frac{1}{5}$

11. $J(-1, -2)$ and $K(2, 7)$ 3

12. $P(4, 9)$ and $Q(-6, 12)$ $-\frac{3}{10}$

Write a rule for each function.

13.

x	f(x)
−2	−3
−1	−5
0	−7
1	−9

$f(x) = -2x - 7$

14.

x	f(x)
−3	4
0	1
3	−2
6	−5

$f(x) = -x + 1$

Is there a *positive correlation*, a *negative correlation*, or *no correlation* between the sets of data in each scatter plot? Explain.

15.

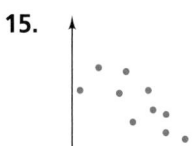

16.

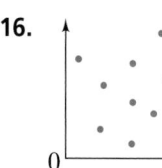

15. Negative correlation; as one value increases the other decreases.

16. No correlation; there is no apparent relationship.

Graph each inequality. 17–18. See back of book.

17. $y \geq 3x - 1$

18. $y < -x + 5$

Solve each system by graphing.

19. $y = x - 1$
$x = 2y$ (2, 1)

20. $x + y = 4$
$2x + 2y = 8$
infinitely many solutions

21. $x + y = 3$
$y = x - 5$ (4, −1)

22. $y \leq 3x - 2$
$y > x + 4$
See back of book.

23. **Writing in Math** Is the amount of sales tax paid a function of the labeled price of a taxable item? Explain. See back of book.

24. **Writing in Math** Is a person's age a function of his or her height? Explain.
See back of book.

25. Use the data in the table below.

New York Thruway Tolls

Distance (miles)	Toll (dollars)	Distance (miles)	Toll (dollars)
112	3.50	125	3.90
137	3.75	100	3.10
112	3.40	22	0.70
69	1.65	58	1.80
69	2.15	137	4.25
169	5.70	43	1.80
90	2.80	84	3.05
188	5.85	164	5.10

See back of book.

a. Make a (distance, toll) scatter plot.
b. Draw a trend line. Predict the toll if a car travels 200 mi on the toll road. See back of book.
c. Use your trend line to predict how far a car traveled on the toll road if there was a $4.50 toll. See back of book.
d. Write an equation of your trend line. See back of book.

26. **Open-Ended** The slope of a line through the origin is $-\frac{2}{3}$. Find the coordinates of two points on the line.

Answers may vary. Sample: (3, –2), (–3, 2)

5.
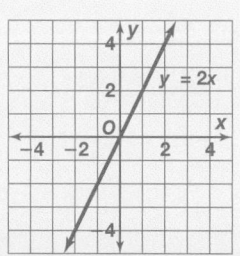

6.
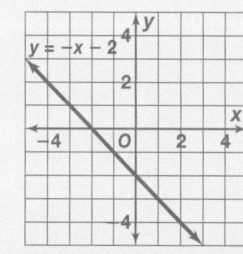

7.
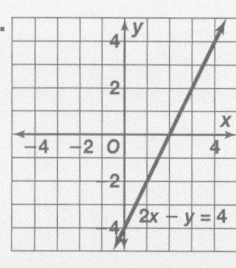

8.
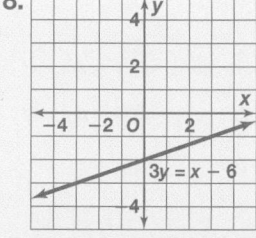

Test Prep

Multiple Choice

1. An empty pot weighs 1 lb 11 oz. With oatmeal in it, the pot weighs 3 lb 7 oz. How much does the oatmeal weigh? **C**
A. 5 lb 2 oz
B. 2 lb 3 oz
C. 1 lb 12 oz
D. 1 lb 4 oz

2. Which equation has a solution of 8? **I**
F. $8x + 8 = 64$
G. $\frac{b}{2} + 7 = 10$
H. $2z + 5 = 11$
I. $5n - 13 = 27$

3. Four friends split the cost of renting a car for a snorkeling trip. Each person also rents a snorkel for $2. Each person pays a total of $15. Which equation will help find the cost c of renting the car? **A**
A. $\frac{c}{4} + 2 = 15$
B. $15 - 2^4 = c$
C. $15 - 4c = 2$
D. $\frac{c}{2} + 4 = 15$

4. Sara and Juan collect soccer cards. Sara has 6 fewer than three times the number of cards Juan has. Together they have 42 cards. Solve $c + (3c - 6) = 42$ to answer: How many cards does each have? **I**
F. Sara has 9 cards; Juan has 33 cards.
G. Sara has 33 cards; Juan has 9 cards.
H. Sara has 12 cards; Juan has 30 cards.
I. Sara has 30 cards; Juan has 12 cards.

5. Which ordered pair is *not* a solution of $4x + 2y = 16$? **C**
A. $(-2, 12)$
B. $(5, -2)$
C. $(2, 5)$
D. $(1, 6)$

6. Which function represents the number of kilograms $k(n)$ as a function of the number of grams n? **I**
F. $k(n) = 100n$
G. $k(n) = 0.01n$
H. $k(n) = 1,000n$
I. $k(n) = 0.001n$

7. Which point is a solution of the system?
$y = x + 2; y = 2x - 2$ **C**
A. $(6, 4)$
B. $(1, 3)$
C. $(4, 6)$
D. no solution

8. What is the solution of $-2(x - 1) \le -6$? **H**
F. $x \le 4$
G. $x \le -4$
H. $x \ge 4$
I. $x \ge -4$

Gridded Response

9. The probability that a couple will give birth to a pair of twins is 1 in 90. About how many pairs of twins would you expect to find in 250,000 births? **2778**

10. Find the slope of the line through $(3, 2)$ and $(1, -2)$. **2**

11. In the scatter plot below, each point represents an athlete who ran in the 100-m race. Greg won the race in the least amount of time. What is Greg's age in years? **15**

Athletes' Ages and Times

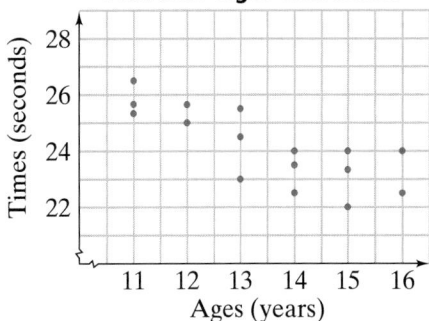

Short Response

Find the solutions of each equation for the given values of x. Show your work.
12–13. See back of book.
12. $y = x + 12; x = -3, 0,$ and 2

13. $4x - 4y = 8; x = 0, 2,$ and 4

Extended Response

14. a. Write the equation $x + \frac{1}{2}y = 4$ in slope-intercept form.
b. Find the slope and the y-intercept of the line in part (a).
c. Graph the equation in part (a).
a–c. See back of book.

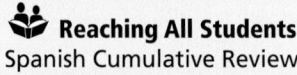
Item	1	2	3	4	5	6	7	8	9	10	11	12	13	14
Lesson	5-5	7-1	7-1	7-2	8-2	8-4	8-7	7-6	6-4	8-3	8-5	8-2	8-2	8-3

Real-World Snapshots

Virtual Progress

In this activity, students solve problems by analyzing information provided in a bar graph, a paragraph, and captioned illustrations, and by applying their knowledge of graphs and percents to compare numbers in millions.

Activating Prior Knowledge

Ask students what technological changes they have experienced in their own lifetime. What new technology being advertised today would they like to use? **Answers may vary. Sample: Students may have used smaller and faster computers, CD burners, DVD and MP3 players, satellite TV, or digital cameras. Technology to try might include plasma TVs, satellite navigation systems in cars, newer DVD game consoles, and 3-D games.**

Teaching Notes

Teaching Tip

Have a volunteer read the introductory paragraph. Ask: *What do you think is the best technology that has been invented since your grandparents were young? What do you think is the worst?* **Answers may vary. Sample: the computer or the cell phone might be the best invention; high-tech weapons might be the worst.**

Inclusion

Examine the graph with students. Note that the data on the graph are for the year 2001. Point out that the numbers on the vertical axis stand for the numbers of millions. Have volunteers read the names of the electronic devices. Ask students to name the two devices found in the greatest number of households. Ask which device is found in the fewest households. **Answers: Televisions and videocassette recorders are in the most homes; DVD game consoles are in the fewest homes.**

Real-World Snapshots

Virtual Progress

Applying Graphs Technology changes every day. When your grandparents were kids, they watched black-and-white TVs, listened to records, and used typewriters. Today, people watch color TVs, listen to compact discs, and use computers. Tired of walking your dog? Robotic pets hit the market in 2000. Interested in becoming an astronaut? Pilots and astronauts train with virtual reality gear.

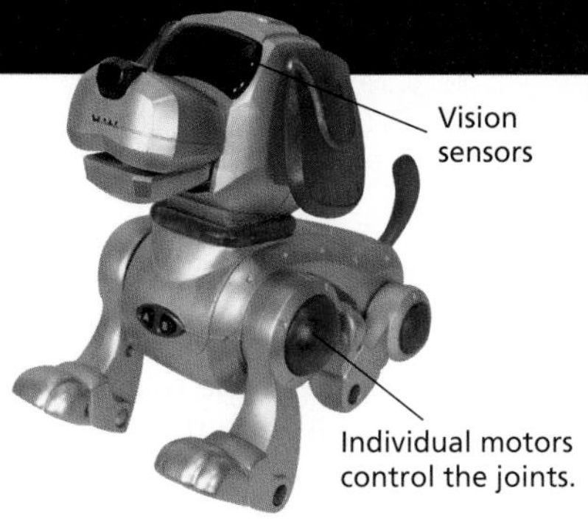
Vision sensors
Individual motors control the joints.

New and Different Pets

Robotic pets use computers and artificial intelligence to interact with their environments.

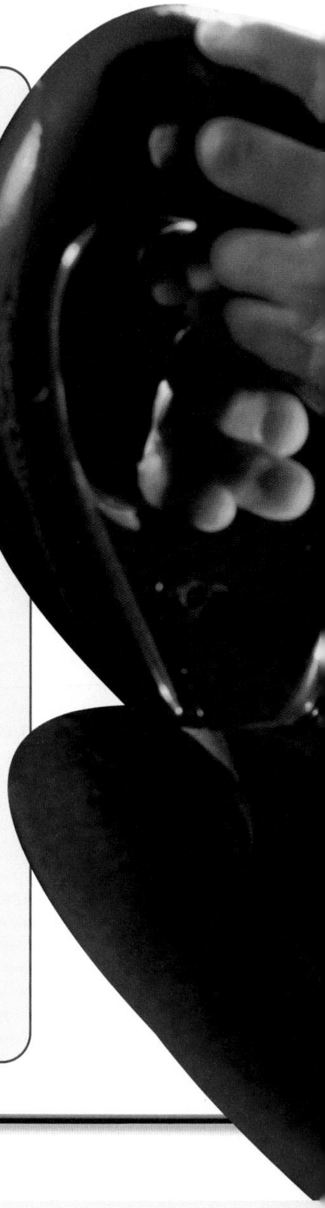

Activity

Use the information on these two pages to answer the questions.

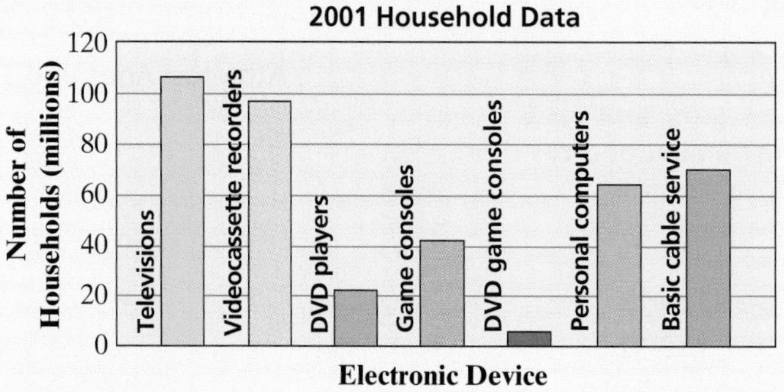
2001 Household Data
Number of Households (millions)
120
100
80
60
40
20
0
Televisions
Videocassette recorders
DVD players
Game consoles
DVD game consoles
Personal computers
Basic cable service
Electronic Device

1–7. See margin.

1. How many households have a television and not a VCR?
2. How many households with televisions do not have basic cable?
3. The number of households with personal computers is how many times the number with DVD game consoles?
4. How many times as many households have a television as have a DVD player?
5. How many households will get their first DVD player between 2001 and 2006?
6. a. About 70% of DVD households rent at least one DVD movie per month. How many households is this?
   b. Suppose this percent stays constant. About how many households will rent at least one DVD movie in December 2006?
7. **Reasoning** What do you think is likely to happen to the number of households with VCRs by 2006? Explain.

1. about 12 million
2. about 37 million
3. about 12 times
4. about 5 times
5. about 48 million

6a. about 15 million
b. about 48 million

7. The number of households is likely to decrease as the number with DVD players increases.

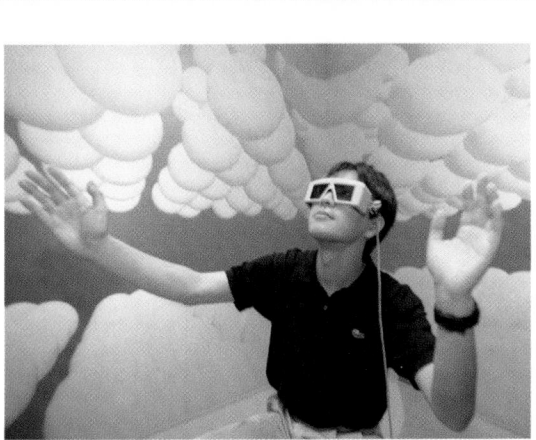

Intelligent Modeling

3-D glasses help this researcher "touch" carbon atoms from a microscopic world in a virtual reality room.

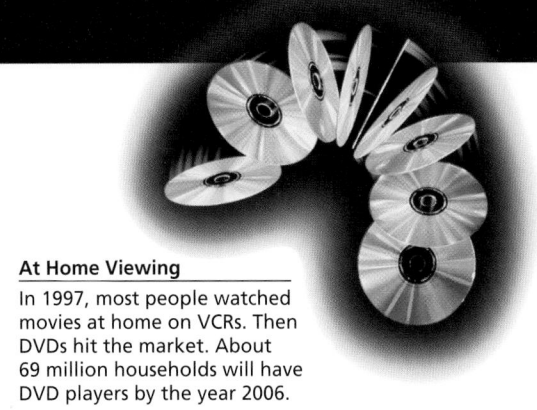

At Home Viewing

In 1997, most people watched movies at home on VCRs. Then DVDs hit the market. About 69 million households will have DVD players by the year 2006.

Take It to the NET For more information about DVDs, go to **www.PHSchool.com**.
Web Code: ade-0853

Put It All Together

Students must be able to interpret graph data in order to compare the numbers of electronic devices in millions of households now and in the future.

Teaching Tip

Before students begin the activity, discuss the illustrations and their captions. Students should read through the activity before beginning to work.

Diversity

Have students interview an adult member of their family about the kinds of electronic devices the family member used when he or she was the student's age. **Answers may vary. Sample: calculators, computers, AM radios, wired telephones, microwave ovens, VCRs**

English Learners

Have students read aloud the names of the electronic devices on the graph. Provide magazine, newspaper, or catalog advertisements that show these devices. Pairs of students should cut out pictures of several of the devices from the ads, mount them on paper, and label them correctly.

Careers

Have students research and report to the class about someone who has made a great contribution to technology in the last decade. **Answers may vary. Sample: George Lucas's company, Industrial Light and Magic, has revolutionized special effects in movies. Bill Gates of Microsoft Corporation has had a major effect on software for personal computers.**

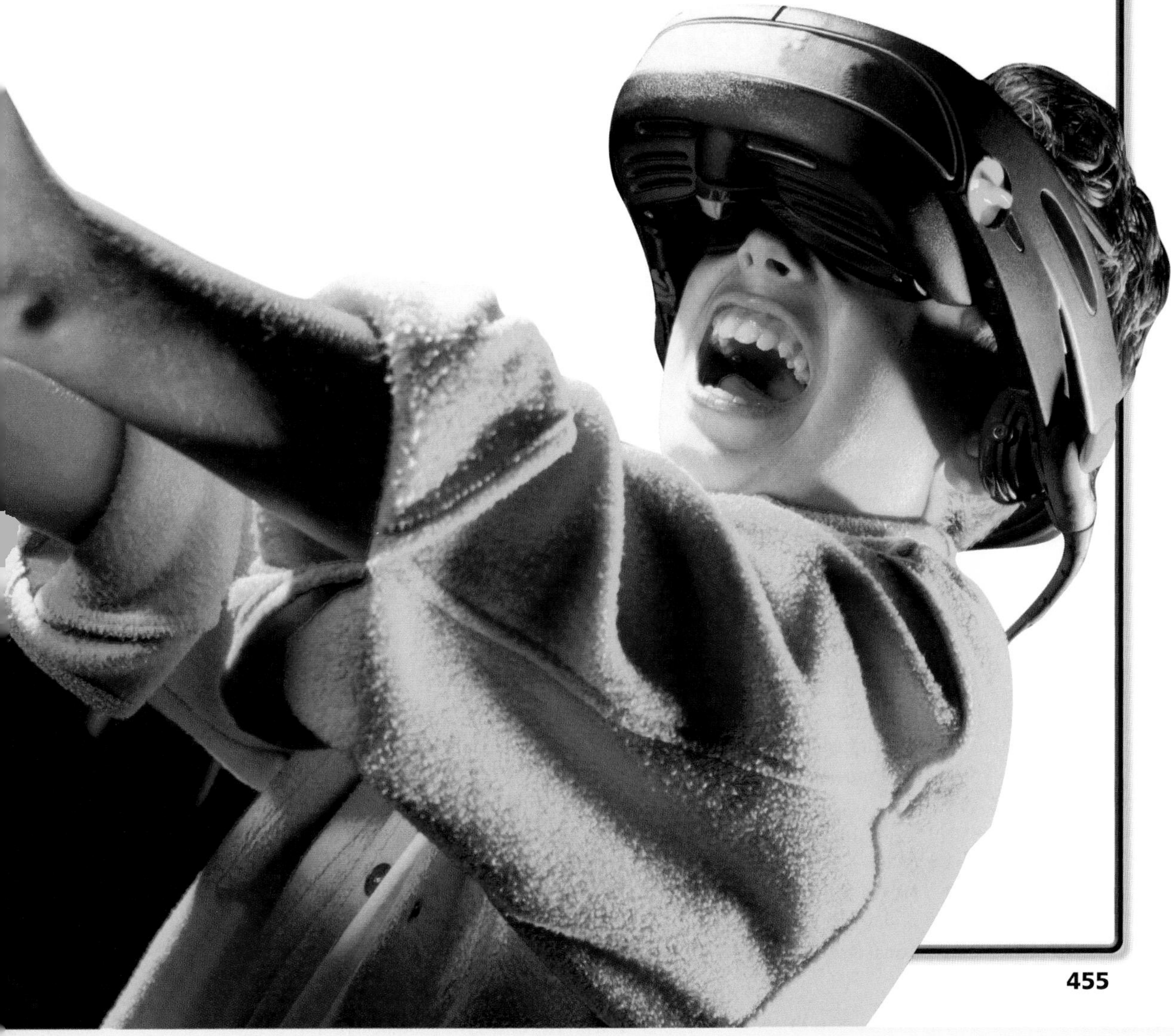

Chapter at a Glance

9-1

Introduction to Geometry: Points, Lines, and Planes

pp. 458–463

Objectives

▼ Points, Lines, and Planes

▼ Intersecting, Parallel, and Skew Lines

New Vocabulary

point, plane, ray, skew, line, segment, parallel

NCTM Standards

3, 6, 7, 8, 9, 10

Local Standards

9-2

Angle Relationships and Parallel Lines

pp. 465–469

Objectives

▼ Adjacent and Vertical Angles

▼ Relating Angles and Parallel Lines

New Vocabulary

angles: adjacent, vertical, congruent, supplementary, complementary, corresponding, alternate interior; transversal

NCTM Standards

3, 4, 7, 8, 10

Local Standards

9-3

Classifying Polygons

pp. 470–474

Objectives

▼ Classifying Triangles

▼ Classifying Quadrilaterals

New Vocabulary

polygon, regular polygon

NCTM Standards

3, 4, 7, 8, 9, 10

Local Standards

9-4 Problem Solving

Draw a Diagram

pp. 476–479

Objective

▼ Drawing a Diagram

NCTM Standards

3, 4, 6, 7, 8, 9, 10

Local Standards

9-5

Congruence

pp. 480–484

Objectives

▼ Identifying Corresponding Parts

▼ Identifying Congruent Triangles

Materials

plastic straws, string

NCTM Standards

3, 4, 6, 7, 8, 9, 10

Local Standards

✔ **Checkpoint Quiz 1**

9-6

Circles

pp. 486–490

Objectives

▼ Finding Circumference

▼ Making Circle Graphs

New Vocabulary

circle, central angle

Materials

ruler, string, several circular objects

NCTM Standards

3, 4, 6, 8, 9, 10

Local Standards

9-7

Constructions

pp. 491–495

Objectives

▼ Congruent Segments and Angles

▼ Constructing Bisectors

New Vocabulary

perpendicular lines, segment bisector, perpendicular bisector, angle bisector

Materials

compass, straightedge

NCTM Standards

3, 4, 8, 10

Local Standards

9-8

Translations

pp. 497–501

Objectives

▼ Graphing Translations

▼ Describing Translations

New Vocabulary

transformation, translation, image

NCTM Standards

3, 8, 9, 10

Local Standards

✔ **Checkpoint Quiz 2**

9-9

Symmetry and Reflections

pp. 503–506

Objectives

▼ Identifying Lines of Symmetry

▼ Graphing Reflections

New Vocabulary

reflectional symmetry, line of symmetry, reflection, line of reflection

NCTM Standards

3, 8, 10

Local Standards

9-10

Rotations

pp. 507–510

Objectives

▼ Graphing Rotations

▼ Identifying Rotational Symmetry

New Vocabulary

rotation, center of rotation, angle of rotation, rotational symmetry

NCTM Standards

3, 7, 8, 9, 10

Local Standards

Correlation to Standardized Tests

Lesson	NAEP	Terra Nova CAT/6	CTBS	ITBS	SAT10	Local Test
9-1	G3g				■	
9-2	G3g				■	
9-3	G1b, G3F					
9-4		■				
9-5	G2e	■	■			
9-6	M1h		■		■	
9-7	G3b					
9-8	G2c	■	■			
9-9	G2c					
9-10	G2c	■	■			

NAEP National Assessment of Educational Progress
   N = Number Sense, Properties, and Operations
   M = Measurement
   G = Geometry and Spatial Sense
   D = Data Analysis, Statistics and Probability
   A = Algebra and Functions

CAT/6 California Achievement Test, 6th Ed.
CTBS Comprehensive Test of Basic Skills
ITBS Iowa Test of Basic Skills, Form M
SAT10 Stanford Achievement Test, 10th Ed.

NCTM STANDARDS 2000

1	Number and Operations	6	Problem Solving
2	Algebra	7	Reasoning and Proof
3	Geometry	8	Communication
4	Measurement	9	Connections
5	Data Analysis and Probability	10	Representation

Pacing Options

This chart suggests pacing for only the core lessons and their parts. It is provided as a possible guide. It will help you determine how much time you have in your schedule to cover other components, such as the features, chapter projects, Chapter Review, and Chapter Test.

Day	Traditional 45-minute class periods	Two-Year 45-minute class periods	Block 90-minute class periods
1	9-1 ⅴ	9-1 ⅴ	9-1 ⅴ ⅴ 9-2 ⅴ ⅴ ⅴ
2	9-1 ⅴ	9-1 ⅴ	9-3 ⅴ ⅴ 9-4 ⅴ
3	9-3 ⅴ	9-2 ⅴ	9-5 ⅴ ⅴ
4	9-3 ⅴ	9-2 ⅴ	9-6 ⅴ ⅴ
3	9-2 ⅴ ⅴ	9-1 ⅴ	9-7 ⅴ ⅴ 9-8 ⅴ ⅴ
5	9-3 ⅴ	9-2 ⅴ	9-9 ⅴ ⅴ 9-10 ⅴ ⅴ
7	9-5 ⅴ ⅴ	9-3 ⅴ	
8	9-6 ⅴ ⅴ	9-3 ⅴ	
9	9-7 ⅴ	9-3 ⅴ	
10	9-7 ⅴ	9-4 ⅴ	
11	9-8 ⅴ ⅴ	9-4 ⅴ	
12	9-9 ⅴ ⅴ	9-5 ⅴ	
13	9-10 ⅴ ⅴ	9-5 ⅴ	
14		9-6 ⅴ	
15		9-6 ⅴ	
16		9-6 ⅴ	
17		9-7 ⅴ	
18		9-7 ⅴ	
19		9-7 ⅴ	
20		9-8 ⅴ	
21		9-8 ⅴ	
22		9-9 ⅴ ⅴ	
23		9-10 ⅴ ⅴ	
24			

Math Background

Skills Trace

BEFORE Chapter 9
Students should have encountered most of the basic ideas and concepts in this chapter in previous courses.

DURING Chapter 9
This chapter reviews basic geometric ideas and concepts. Congruence postulates (e.g., Side-Angle-Side) are introduced, and basic constructions are developed.

AFTER Chapter 9
Geometric ideas and concepts are used in Chapter 10 (Area and Volume) and Chapter 11 (Right Triangles in Algebra). The work in this chapter is foundational for some work in Algebra 1 and most of Geometry.

9-1 Introduction to Geometry: Points, Lines, and Planes

Geometry comes from two Greek words that mean "measure the earth." Geometry deals with figures and space and such properties of figures as size and shape. The picture that follows shows the basic figures in geometry, described below.

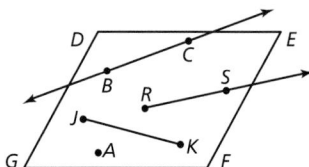

a *point*, *A*, which has location and no size

a *line*, $\overleftrightarrow{BC}$, a series of points that extends in opposite directions without end

a *plane*, *DEFG*, a flat surface with no thickness that extends without end in the directions of all the lines it contains

a *line segment*, $\overline{JK}$, part of a line with two endpoints and length *JK*

a *ray*, $\overrightarrow{RS}$, part of a line that has exactly one endpoint, *R*

9-2 Angle Relationships and Parallel Lines

If two lines in the same plane are not parallel, then they must intersect. An angle is formed where the two lines intersect. An angle consists of two rays with a common endpoint.

Angles have special relationships that, once identified, can help to solve problems regarding the measurement of angles. Some of these special relationships have to do with adjacent angles, vertical angles, congruent angles, supplementary angles, complementary angles, corresponding angles, and alternate interior angles. Some of these angles pairs are shown in the figure below.

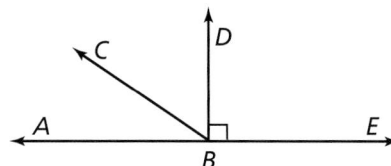

$\angle ABC$ and $\angle CBD$ are *adjacent angles.* They share a vertex and a side but no points in their interiors. These two adjacent angles are also *complementary* since the sum of their measures is 90°. The two adjacent angles $\angle ABC$ and $\angle CBE$ are *supplementary* since the sum of their measures is 180°.

9-3 Classifying Polygons

Polygons are closed plane figures, the simplest of which is the three-sided figure called a *triangle.* Four-sided polygons are called *quadrilaterals.*

Within the quadrilaterals are subcategories of polygons that are classified according to whether their sides are parallel, congruent, or both, and whether their angles measure 90°. For example, a *trapezoid* has exactly one pair of parallel sides. If both sides are parallel, the quadrilateral is a *parallelogram.* If both sides are parallel and congruent, then the quadrilateral is a *rhombus.* If both sides are parallel and the angles measure 90°, it is a *rectangle.* Finally, if both sides are parallel and congruent, and the angles measure 90°, then the quadrilateral is a *square.*

9-4 Draw a Diagram

Drawing a diagram can help you model a relationship, keep track of facts, and understand a situation more clearly. It should be a key strategy for visual learners. It also can help reinforce connections between algebraic and geometric concepts.

9-5 Congruence

Congruent polygons have the same size and shape. You can superimpose one on the other so that they coincide. The corresponding parts of congruent polygons have the same measure.

You can be sure that two triangles are congruent if these corresponding parts are congruent.

Side-Side-Side (SSS ≅ SSS)
Side-Angle-Side (SAS ≅ SAS)
Angle-Side-Angle (ASA ≅ ASA)

Notice that the angle in SAS must be the angle *included* between the two congruent sides, and the side in ASA must be the side included between the two congruent angles.

9-6 Circles

The ratio of the distance around any circle (circumference, or C) to the distance across the same circle (diameter, or d) is always the same number. This constant ratio $\frac{C}{d}$ is a number called *pi*, written with the Greek letter π. The number π is irrational and is equal to a decimal that never ends and never shows a repeating pattern.

Students usually have their first encounter with π when learning about circles. It is very important to stress the fact that 3.14, $\frac{22}{7}$, and whatever a calculator displays when you press the π key are all approximations for π, because π is irrational. (Students will learn more about irrational numbers in Chapter 11.)

Whenever you use an approximation for π to solve a problem, it is important to record the answer as *about*, or *approximately*. Today, π has been calculated to over a million places, but it is usually approximated as 3.14.

9-7 Constructions

A geometric construction is a figure that is made using only two tools, an unmarked straightedge and a compass. When you make a construction, the arcs that you draw are left in place rather than erased because they show the steps you used in the construction. You should make constructions with a fine pencil to approach the theoretical idea of lines and points without thickness.

9-8, 9-9, 9-10 Translations; Symmetry and Reflections; Rotations

A *transformation* is a change in the position or size of a figure. The figure that results after a transformation is called the *image* of the original figure. One kind of transformation is a *translation,* or slide. Another kind is a *reflection,* or flip. A third transformation is a *rotation,* or turn.

A translation must specify how far and in what direction you move the figure. A reflection must specify a *line of reflection* over which you flip the figure. A rotation specifies a fixed point, called the *center of rotation,* about which you rotate the figure, and an *angle of rotation* (understood in this text to be counterclockwise).

Additional Professional Development Opportunities

Chapter 9 Math Background notes:
pp. 459, 466, 471, 477, 481, 487, 492, 498, 504, 508

Additional resources available from SkyLight Professional Development: On-site courses, workshops, summer institutes. Online courses and chat rooms. Videocassettes and books. Visit www.skylightedu.com.

Professional Development, Content Facilitator Guide: Pre-Algebra, Chapter 9

Ongoing Assessment and Intervention

The *Prentice Hall Pre-Algebra* program provides many options for assessment in the Student Edition, Teacher's Edition, and teaching resources. From these options you may choose instructional materials that are appropriate for your students and support your district's curriculum requirements.

Daily Assessment

 Instant Check System™ in Chapter 9

Allows students to check their own learning before, during, and after each lesson.

Diagnosing Readiness before the chapter (p. 456)

Check Skills You'll Need exercises in each lesson (pp. 458, 465, 470, 476, 480, 486, 491, 497, 503, 507)

Check Understanding questions with each Example (pp. 459, 460, 466, 467, 470, 471, 472, 477, 481, 487, 488, 491, 492, 493, 497, 498, 503, 504, 508)

Checkpoint Quiz (pp. 484, 501)

Formal Assessment

In Chapter 9 and Additional Resources

Assesses student progress throughout the *Pre-Algebra* text and with blackline masters and CD-ROM.

Student Edition
- Chapter 9 Review, with Vocabulary Skills and Concepts Review, pp. 513–515
- Chapter 9 Test, p. 516

Assessment Resources   *Spanish versions available.*
- Checkpoint Quizzes 1 & 2
- Chapter Test, Forms A & B
- Chapter Alternative Assessment

 Computer Test Generator CD-ROM
- Instant Chapter Tests™ — pre-made tests with items that vary every time you print.
- Online Testing allows you to give tests online and receive progress reports.
- Diagnose readiness with questions on prerequisite skills.
- Prepare students by making tests based on standardized test objectives.

Algebra Readiness Tests
- Includes Basic Skills Tests and Concept-Readiness Tests.
- Assess understanding of skills and concepts needed for success in algebra.

Standardized Test Preparation

 Test Prep in Chapter 9

Teaches students strategies and gives them practice with all the test item formats they will encounter on high-stakes tests.

Test Prep exercises in each lesson (pp. 463, 469, 474, 479, 484, 490, 495, 501, 506, 510)

Test-Taking Strategies (p. 512: Drawing a Diagram)

Test Prep (p. 517: Reading Comprehension)

PRENTICE HALL ASSESSMENT SYSTEM

Provides a three-step approach to preparing students for high-stakes, national, and state exams.

1 Diagnose & Prescribe   **2 Review & Reteach**

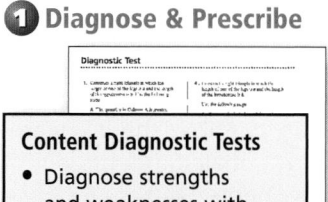

Content Diagnostic Tests
- Diagnose strengths and weaknesses with ongoing benchmark tests.
- Prescribe individualized reteaching opportunities.

Skills and Concepts Review
- Provides reteaching worksheets with instruction and practice for each skill.
- Includes course prerequisite skills.

3 Practice & Assess

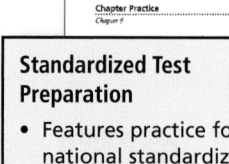

Standardized Test Preparation
- Features practice for national standardized exams.
- Includes practice tests for NAEP, SAT10, ITBS, and Terra Nova.

Test-Taking Strategies With Transparencies
- Support the Test-Taking Strategies pages in the Student Edition.
- Provide a transparency and a worksheet for each strategy.

Reaching All Students

The textbook, the iText, and other technology components provide numerous opportunities to reach students of various ability levels and learning styles. Each Teacher's Edition lesson suggests how you can help all your students be successful and understand the mathematics in Chapter 9.

Below Level

Student Edition
- Diagnosing Readiness*: p. 456
- Check Skills You'll Need*: pp. 458, 465, 470, 476, 480, 486, 491, 497, 503, 507

Reteaching
Chapter 9 Grab & Go™ File: pp. 11–20

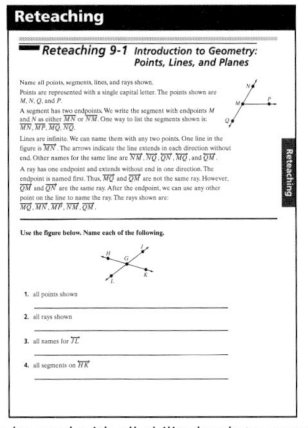

* Can be used with all ability levels to ensure mastery of prerequisite skills.

Advanced Learners

Student Edition
- Challenge exercises: pp. 462, 469, 474, 479, 483, 490, 495, 500, 506, 510
- Extension: pp. 475, 502, 511

Enrichment
Chapter 9 Grab & Go™ File: pp. 21–30

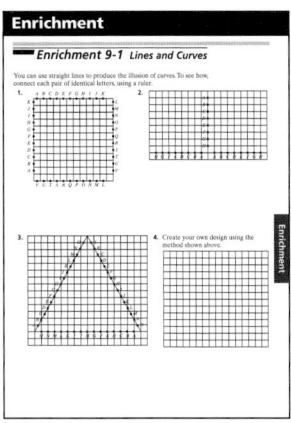

Problem Solving

Student Edition
- Strategies: pp. 476–479
- Real-World Problem Solving: pp. 460, 472, 476, 480, 487, 488, 508

Guided Problem Solving Masters
Chapter 9: pp. 73–82

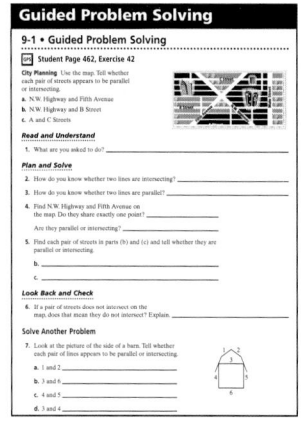

Reading and Math Literacy

Student Edition
- Vocabulary: pp. 457, 513, plus in most lessons
- Reading Math: pp. 459, 471, 483, 485, 487, 492, 513
- Writing in Math: pp. 462, 468, 475, 478, 483, 489, 494, 500, 505, 509, 516
- Illustrated Glossary: pp. 782–826

Reading and Math Literacy Masters
Chapter 9: pp. 33–36

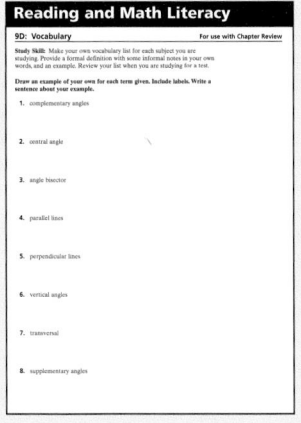

English Learners

Student Edition
- English/Spanish Illustrated Glossary: pp. 782–826

Workbook and Masters
Spanish Practice Workbook: pp. 73–82
Spanish Reading and Math Literacy Masters: pp. 33–36

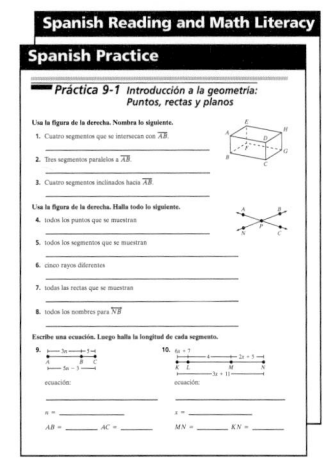

Learning Styles

Student Edition
- Investigation: pp. 480, 486
- Technology: p. 496
- DK Activities: pp. 518–519
- Chapter Project: p. 742

Activity Masters
Hands-On Activities: 17, 19, 20, 21, 27, 30
Technology Activities: 16, 17, 18, 19, 20, 21

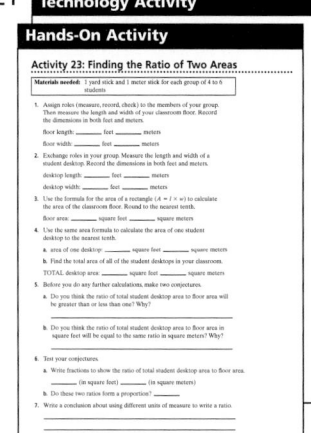

Program Resources

Presentation Assistant Plus!

	Resources in Grab & Go™ Files				Resources for Reaching All Students				Spanish Resources			Transparencies				Prentice Hall Presentation Pro CD-ROM
	Practice	Reteach	Enrich	Checkpt Quiz	Reading & Math Literacy	Technology Activities	Hands-On Activities	Guided Problem Solving	Practice	Reading & Math Literacy	Checkpt Quiz	Skills Check	Additional Examples	Answers to Exercises	Lesson Quiz	
9-1	■	■	■		■		■	■	■			■	■	■	■	■
9-2	■	■	■			■	■	■	■			■	■	■	■	■
9-3	■	■	■				■	■	■			■	■	■	■	■
9-4	■	■	■					■	■			■	■	■	■	■
9-5	■	■	■	■	■	■		■	■		■	■	■	■	■	■
9-6	■	■	■				■	■	■			■	■	■	■	■
9-7	■	■	■					■	■			■	■	■	■	■
9-8	■	■	■	■	■	■		■	■			■	■	■	■	■
9-9	■	■	■			■	■	■	■			■	■	■	■	■
9-10	■	■	■			■	■	■	■			■	■	■	■	■
For the Chapter	Chapter Projects, Chapter Tests, Alternative Assessment, Cumulative Review, Cumulative Assessment				On Web site only: Home Activities, Algebra Readiness Puzzles, Interdisciplinary Activities				Spanish Chapter Tests, Alternative Assessment, Cumulative Review, Cumulative Assessment			Classroom Aid Transparencies				

Also available for use with the chapter:

- Practice Workbook
- Solution Key
- MathNotes folder
- For additional online and technology resources, see below.
- For teacher support and access to student Web site materials, use Web Code adk-5500.

 **PRENTICE HALL ASSESSMENT SYSTEM**

Program assessment and test preparation, all in one place.

See page 456E.

 Skills Intervention Kit

A *complete* system for the student who is struggling with course-level work

How to Use With Chapter 9

9-1, 9-10   Geometry

 **Online Intervention**

Integrated within the iText, this online intervention system includes diagnostic tests and prescribed remediation, plus reports to track student mastery.

Technology

 iTEXT   Online and on CD-ROM

Complete Interactive Student Text online and on CD-ROM—with instant-feedback assessment, tutorial help, dynamic activities, instructional and real-world videos, audio, and additional practice.

 www.PHSchool.com For Students

Use Web Codes for easy access to online activities, chapter projects, self-grading lesson quizzes, chapter tests, vocabulary quizzes, updated data sources, graphing calculator procedures, and more.

PH SuccessNet   For Teachers

Online lesson planning with built-in state correlations, all the teaching resources, complete reference library, your own calendar and Teacher Web page, professional development, and more.

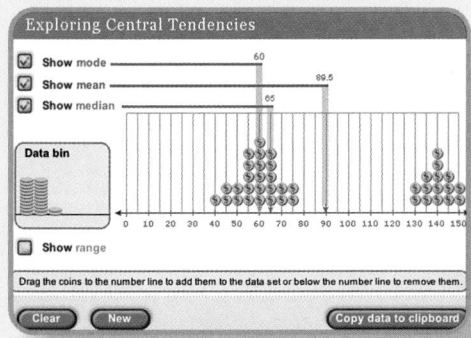

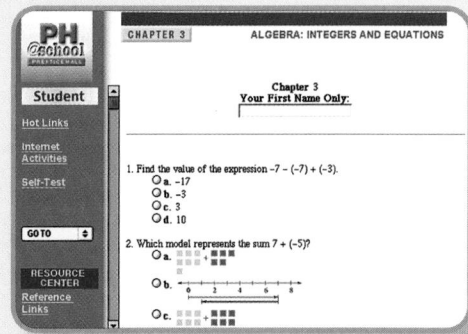

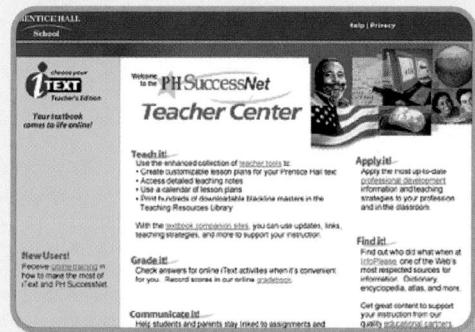

Presentation Assistant Plus!

The Prentice Hall *Presentation Assistant Plus!* provides you with the material you need to teach a lesson from beginning to end. Two easy-to-use formats—Transparencies and CD-ROM—allow you to present a lesson the way you are most comfortable.

Transparencies

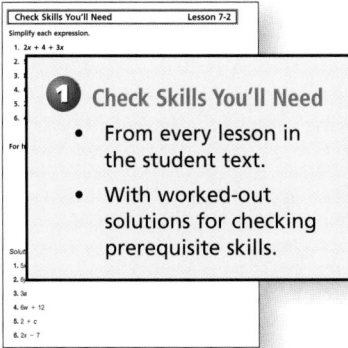

① Check Skills You'll Need
- From every lesson in the student text.
- With worked-out solutions for checking prerequisite skills.

② Additional Examples
- Every example from the Teacher's Edition.
- Fully worked-out, step-by-step solutions for easy demonstration.

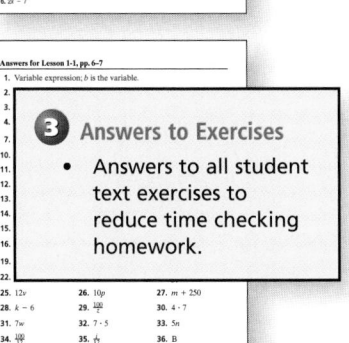

③ Answers to Exercises
- Answers to all student text exercises to reduce time checking homework.

④ Lesson Quiz
- Every quiz from the Teacher's Edition.
- With answers to allow students to check their own work.

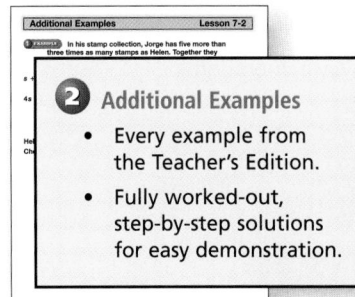
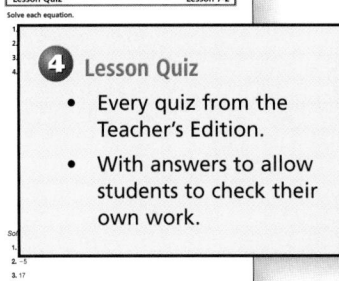

 **PowerPoint** Throughout the Teacher's Edition, this symbol indicates material that is available in the Presentation Assistant Plus!

PowerPoint Prentice Hall Presentation Pro CD-ROM

- Includes all Transparencies as PowerPoint® presentations.
- Conveniently organized by lesson so you can easily ❶ Introduce, ❷ Teach, ❸ Check Homework, and ❹ Assess each lesson.
- Animated examples allow step-by-step instruction at your own pace.
- Easy to edit so you can create custom presentations.

Teaching Chapter 9 Using Presentation Assistant Plus!

	❶ Introduce	❷ Teach	❸ Check Homework	❹ Assess
	Check Skills You'll Need	Additional Examples	Student Edition Answers	Lesson Quiz
9-1	p. 74	pp. 120–121	✔	p. 74
9-2	p. 75	p. 122	✔	p. 75
9-3	p. 76	p. 123	✔	p. 76
9-4	p. 77	p. 124	✔	p. 77
9-5	p. 78	p. 125	✔	p. 78
9-6	p. 79	pp. 126–127	✔	p. 79
9-7	p. 80	pp. 128–131	✔	p. 80
9-8	p. 81	pp. 132–133	✔	p. 81
9-9	p. 82	pp. 134–135	✔	p. 82
9-10	p. 83	p. 136	✔	p. 83

Prentice Hall Presentation Pro

CD-ROM with dynamic Powerpoint® presentations for every lesson. Helps you introduce and develop concepts, check homework, and assess progress. Part of Presentation Assistant Plus! *(See above.)*

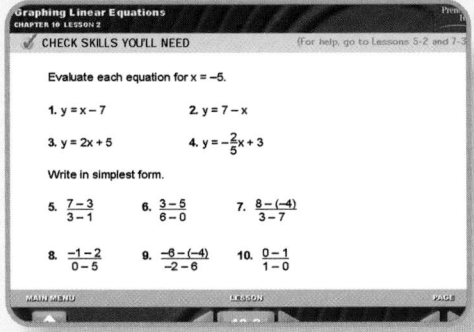

Computer Test Generator

CD-ROM to create practice sheets and tests for course objectives and standardized tests. Includes Instant Chapter Tests™, online testing, and student reports. Part of the PH Assessment System. *(See page 456E.)*

Resource Pro® with Planning Express®

CD-ROM with a lesson planning tool that allows you to import state and local objectives. Includes electronic versions of all the teaching resources.

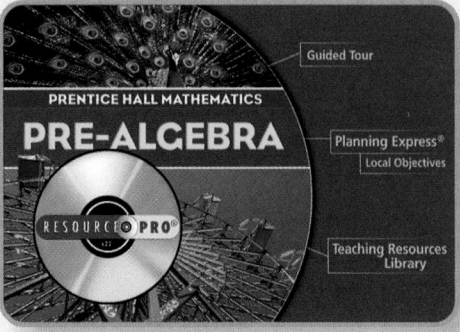

Spatial Thinking

Diagnosing Readiness

Students will find the answers to these exercises in the back of their textbooks.

Prescribing Intervention
For intervention, direct students to:

Naming Polygons
Previous Course

Identifying Radius
Previous Course

Graphing on the Coordinate Plane
Lesson 1-10: Example 2;
Exercises 13–28.
Extra Practice, p. 744.

Where You've Been

- In Chapter 3, you learned how to solve equations by multiplying or dividing decimals, and how to use formulas.
- In Chapter 5, you learned how to solve equations by multiplying fractions.
- In Chapter 7, you learned how to solve multi-step equations by using inverse operations.

Instant self-check online and on CD-ROM

Diagnosing Readiness   (For help, go to the lesson in green.)

Naming Polygons (Previous Course)

Match each polygon to its name.

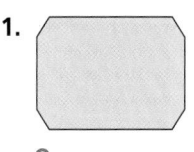

1.
C

2. B

3. D

4. A

A. quadrilateral   **B.** pentagon   **C.** octagon   **D.** hexagon

Identifying Radius (Previous Course)

Give the radius of each circle.

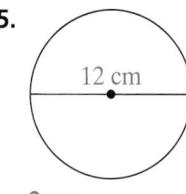

5. 12 cm

6. 1 in.

7. 5.6 cm

8. 15 ft

6 cm $\frac{1}{2}$ in.   2.8 cm   7.5 ft

Graphing on the Coordinate Plane (Lesson 1-10)

Graph each point on the same coordinate plane. See margin.

9. $A(0, 7)$ **10.** $B(-2, 5)$ **11.** $E(4, 0)$ **12.** $D(2, -4)$ **13.** $C(-3, -1)$

14. $F\left(1\frac{1}{2}, -3\right)$ **15.** $G(0, 0)$ **16.** $J(0, -1)$ **17.** $I(-4, -5)$ **18.** $H(-5, -5)$

9–18.

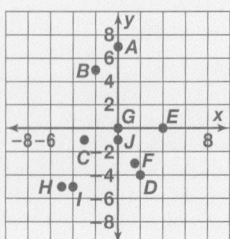

Spatial Thinking

Chapter 9

Where You're Going

In this chapter, you will learn how to

- Use properties of figures to solve problems.
- Classify geometric figures.
- Construct figures.
- Solve a problem by drawing a diagram.

Real-World Snapshots Applying what you learn, on pages 518–519 you will solve problems about Ferris wheels.

Key Vocabulary

- adjacent angles (p. 465)
- alternate interior angles (p. 466)
- angle bisector (p. 493)
- complementary (p. 465)
- congruent angles (p. 465)
- congruent figures (p. 480)
- corresponding angles (p. 466)
- parallel (p. 459)
- perpendicular bisector (p. 492)
- perpendicular lines (p. 492)
- polygon (p. 470)
- reflection (p. 504)
- regular polygon (p. 472)
- rotation (p. 507)
- segment (p. 458)
- segment bisector (p. 492)
- supplementary (p. 465)
- symmetry (pp. 503, 508)
- translation (p. 497)
- vertical angles (p. 465)

457

Chapter 9 Overview

Students begin this chapter learning the basic figures of geometry. They identify special pairs of angles and lines and apply what they learn about angle measures and line relationships to classify triangles and quadrilaterals. Students identify corresponding parts of polygons and determine whether two triangles are congruent. They apply their knowledge of proportions to make circle graphs. Then they use a compass and straightedge to construct congruent segments and angles, and bisect segments and angles. The chapter concludes with the study of translations, reflections, and rotations of geometric figures.

Activating Prior Knowledge

Students apply skills learned in Chapter 1 for graphing points on a coordinate plane. Ask students to describe how to graph (2, −3). Start at origin. Move right 2 units and then down 3 units.

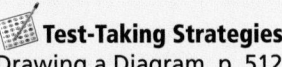 Reading Math

- Reading a Diagram, p. 485
- **Vocabulary** A complete list of terms, plus vocabulary exercises, appears in the Chapter Review on p. 513.
- **Illustrated Glossary** Examples for each vocabulary term, plus definitions in both English and Spanish, appear starting on p. 782.

Test-Taking Strategies

Drawing a Diagram, p. 512

Real-World Problem Solving

- **Strategy:** Draw a Diagram, pp. 476–479
- **DK Real-World Snapshots:** Applying Circles, pp. 518–519
- **Chapter Project:** Treasure Hunt, p. 742

www.PHSchool.com

Internet support includes:
- Self-grading Vocabulary and Chapter 9 Tests
- Activity Masters
- Chapter Project support
- Chapter Planner
- Chapter 9 Resources

Plus

Introduction to Geometry: Points, Lines, and Planes

 Check Skills You'll Need

Inequalities and Their Graphs
Lesson 2-8: Example 2;
Exercises 13–16.
Extra Practice, p. 745.

Lesson Resources

 Teaching Resources
Practice, Reteaching, Enrichment

Reaching All Students
Practice Workbook 9-1
Spanish Practice Workbook 9-1
Reading and Math Literacy 9A
Spanish Reading and Math
  Literacy 9A
Spanish Checkpoint Quiz 1
Guided Problem Solving 9-1
Hands-On Activities 19

 Presentation Assistant Plus!
Transparencies and PowerPoint™
• Check Skills You'll Need 9-1
• Additional Examples 9-1
• Student Edition Answers 9-1
• Lesson Quiz 9-1
PH Presentation Pro CD-ROM 9-1

 **ASSESSMENT SYSTEM**

Checkpoint Quiz 1
Computer Test Generator CD-ROM

 Technology
Resource Pro® CD-ROM
Computer Test Generator CD-ROM
PH Presentation Pro CD-ROM

 **www.PHSchool.com**
Student Site
• Teacher Web Code: adk-5500
• Self-grading Lesson Quiz
PH SuccessNet Teacher Center
• Lesson Planner
• Resources

Plus *iTEXT*

458

What You'll Learn

OBJECTIVE 1 To name basic geometric figures

OBJECTIVE 2 To recognize intersecting lines, parallel lines, and skew lines

. . . And Why

To build a basic vocabulary in geometry and to solve problems in architecture

 Check Skills You'll Need

Describe the number-line graph of each inequality.
1–4. See back of book.
1. $a \geq 3$ **2.** $a \leq 0$

3. $a \leq 5$ **4.** $a \geq -2$

 For help, go to Lesson 2-8.

New Vocabulary

• point   • line
• plane   • segment
• ray   • parallel
• skew

iTEXT Interactive lesson includes instant self-check, tutorials, and activities.

OBJECTIVE

1 Points, Lines, and Planes

Geometric shapes are evident in many human-made and natural structures. Notice the hexagonal shape of each cell of the honeycomb in the photo below. Two other examples of geometry in nature are the spiral structure of a snail's shell and the shape of a snowflake.

Basic Geometric Figures

Name	Sample	Symbolic Name	Description
Point	• *A*	Point *A*	A **point** is a location in space. It has no size.
Line	*A*, *B*, *n*	$\overleftrightarrow{AB}$, $\overleftrightarrow{BA}$, or *n*	A **line** is a series of points that extends in opposite directions without end. A lowercase letter can name a line.
Plane	*A*, *B*, *M*, *D*, *C*	*ABCD* or *M*	A **plane** is a flat surface with no thickness. It contains many lines and extends without end in the directions of all its lines.
Line segment or segment	*Q*, *P*	$\overline{PQ}$, or $\overline{QP}$	A **segment** is a part of a line. It has two endpoints. *PQ* represents the length of $\overline{PQ}$.
Ray	*C*, *R*	$\overrightarrow{CR}$	A **ray** is a part of a line. It has exactly one endpoint. Name its endpoint first.

Ongoing Assessment and Intervention

Before the Lesson
Diagnose prerequisite skills using:
• Check Skills You'll Need

During the Lesson
Monitor progress using:
• Check Understanding
• Additional Examples
• Test Prep

After the Lesson
Assess knowledge using:
• Lesson Quiz
• Computer Test Generator CD-ROM

You can combine the basic geometric figures to create many other geometric figures.

1 EXAMPLE Naming Geometric Figures

Name each figure in the diagram.

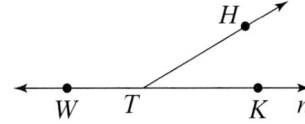

a. **Name four points.**
   $H, K, T,$ and W .... Name a point with a capital letter.

b. **Name four different segments.**
   $\overline{HT}, \overline{WT}, \overline{TK},$ and $\overline{WK}$ .... Name a segment by its endpoints.

c. **Write five other names for** $\overleftrightarrow{WT}$.
   $\overleftrightarrow{WK}, \overleftrightarrow{TK}, \overleftrightarrow{KT}, \overleftrightarrow{KW},$ or $\overleftrightarrow{TW}$ ..... There is one line pictured. It has several names.

d. **Name five different rays.**
   $\overrightarrow{TH}, \overrightarrow{TW}, \overrightarrow{TK}, \overrightarrow{WK},$ or $\overrightarrow{KW}$ ..... The first letter names the endpoint of the ray.

✓ Check Understanding Example 1

1. Name each figure in the diagram.

   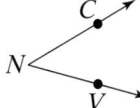

   a. three points C, N, V
   b. two segments $\overline{NC}, \overline{NV}$
   c. two rays $\overrightarrow{NC}, \overrightarrow{NV}$

OBJECTIVE

2 Intersecting, Parallel, and Skew Lines

Two lines *intersect* if they have exactly one point in common. Two lines that lie in the same plane and do not intersect are **parallel.** You use the symbol ∥ to indicate "is parallel to." Segments and rays are parallel if they lie in parallel lines.

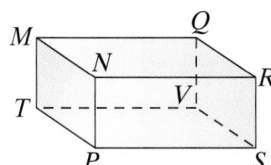

$\overline{MN}$ intersects $\overline{NP}$.
$\overline{MN} \parallel \overline{QR}$

> **Reading Math**
> The symbol ∥ used for "parallel" looks like two parallel lines.

Skew lines are lines that do not lie in the same plane. They are not parallel and they do not intersect. Skew segments must be parts of skew lines. In the diagram above, $\overline{MN}$ and $\overline{RS}$ are skew.

👥 Reaching All Students

| **Below Level** Ask students to point out basic geometric figures they see in the classroom. | **Advanced Learners** Ask students to explain why two different lines can intersect only once. Lines are straight. For two lines to intersect more than once, at least one of the lines would have to curve. | **English Learners** See note on page 459. **Inclusion** See note on page 460. |

---

2. Teach

Math Background

Point, line, and plane are basic geometric concepts that usually are left undefined. A point has no dimensions. A line is one-dimensional having no width or height. You cannot measure length of a line because it has no end. A plane has two dimensions, length and width, but no height. You cannot measure length or width of a plane because it extends forever. The simplest figure you can measure is a line segment. You can associate its two endpoints with points on a number line, often in the form of a ruler.

Teaching Notes

English Learners

Discuss the differences in the meaning and spelling of *plane* (as a geometric figure) and *plain* (as in ordinary, or a region of level land).

Auditory Learners

Group students in pairs. Have one student read the names of and describe the basic figures while the other draws them according to what she or he hears.

1 EXAMPLE Error Prevention

Students may think that $\overrightarrow{WK}$ and $\overrightarrow{KW}$ are the same ray, or may want to write $\overleftrightarrow{WK}$. Stress that the arrow always points to the right in the symbol, and begins with the endpoint.

📊 Additional Examples

1. Use the figure to name each of the following.

   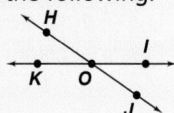

   a. four points $H, I, J,$ and K
   b. four different segments
      $\overline{HO}, \overline{HJ}, \overline{KI}, \overline{OI}$
   c. five other names for $\overleftrightarrow{KI}$
      $\overleftrightarrow{IK}, \overleftrightarrow{KO}, \overleftrightarrow{OK}, \overleftrightarrow{IO}, \overleftrightarrow{OI}$
   d. five different rays
      $\overrightarrow{HO}, \overrightarrow{OJ}, \overrightarrow{KI}, \overrightarrow{OK}, \overrightarrow{JH}$

459

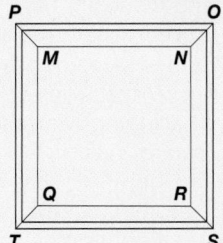

Need Help?

One way to find skew segments in this figure is to look for a vertical segment and a horizontal segment that do not intersect.

2 EXAMPLE Real-World 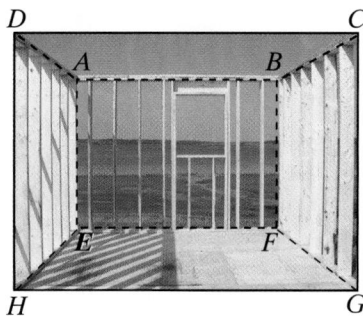 Problem Solving

Architecture **This structure is the frame of a room. Name the figures described below.**

a. four segments that intersect $\overline{DH}$ $\overline{AD}, \overline{CD}, \overline{EH}, \overline{GH}$

b. three segments parallel to $\overline{DH}$ $\overline{AE}, \overline{BF}, \overline{CG}$

c. four segments skew to $\overline{DH}$ $\overline{AB}, \overline{BC}, \overline{EF}, \overline{FG}$

✓ Check Understanding Example 2

2. Use the diagram above. Name each of the following.

a. four segments that intersect $\overline{EF}$ **EH, FG, AE, BF**

b. three segments parallel to $\overline{EF}$ **HG, DC, AB**

c. four segments skew to $\overline{EF}$ **DH, CG, AD, BC**

3 EXAMPLE **Drawing Lines**

Draw two parallel lines. Then draw a segment that intersects the parallel lines.

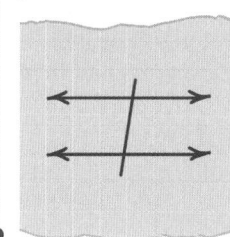

Use the lines on a piece of notebook paper or graph paper to help you draw parallel lines. Then draw a segment that intersects the two lines.

✓ Check Understanding Example 3

3. Use notebook paper or graph paper. Draw the figures indicated.
a–e. See margin.
a. three parallel segments
b. a ray that intersects the parallel segments of part (a)
c. a segment, $\overline{AB}$ **d.** a ray, $\overrightarrow{QR}$ **e.** a line, $\overleftrightarrow{LM}$

3a.

3b.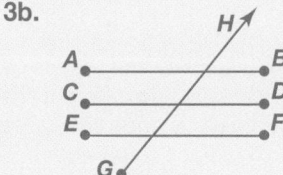

3c.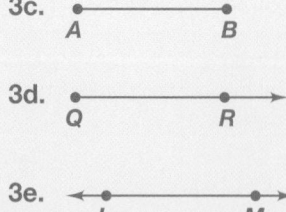

EXERCISES

For more exercises, see Extra Practice.

Practice and Problem Solving

A Practice by Example

Name the indicated figures in each diagram.

Example 1
(page 459)

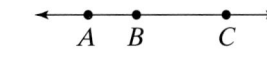

1. three points *A, B, C*

2. three different segments
$\overline{AB}, \overline{BC}, \overline{AC}$

6. Answers may vary.
Sample: $\overrightarrow{ZR}, \overrightarrow{RF}, \overrightarrow{ZF}$

3. four different rays
$\overrightarrow{AC}, \overrightarrow{BC}, \overrightarrow{BA}, \overrightarrow{CA}$

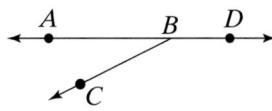

4. all points *Z, R, F*

5. all segments $\overline{ZR}, \overline{RF}, \overline{ZF}$

6. all lines See left.

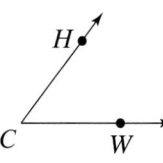

7. all segments $\overline{AB}, \overline{AD}, \overline{BD}, \overline{BC}$

8. Answers may vary.
Sample: $\overrightarrow{DA}$

8. all lines See left.

9. all rays $\overrightarrow{BA}, \overrightarrow{BC}, \overrightarrow{BD}, \overrightarrow{AD}, \overrightarrow{DA}$

10. all rays $\overrightarrow{CH}, \overrightarrow{CW}$

11. all points *H, C, W*

Example 2
(page 460)

Name all indicated segments.

12. $\overline{KD}, \overline{DG}, \overline{EH}, \overline{EF}$
13. $\overline{GF}, \overline{JI}, \overline{KH}$
14. $\overline{GJ}, \overline{FI}, \overline{KJ}, \overline{HI}$
15. $\overline{ML}, \overline{NK}, \overline{MR}, \overline{NS}$
16. $\overline{RS}, \overline{QP}, \overline{LK}$
17. $\overline{PS}, \overline{RQ}, \overline{PK}, \overline{QL}$

12–17. See left.

12. that intersect $\overline{DE}$

13. that are parallel to $\overline{DE}$

14. that are skew to $\overline{DE}$

15. that intersect $\overline{MN}$

16. that are parallel to $\overline{MN}$

17. that are skew to $\overline{MN}$

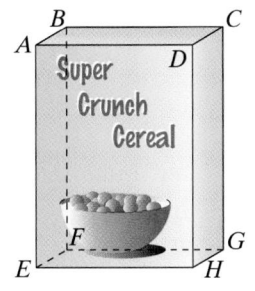

Packaging For the cereal box (left), name each of the following.

18. four segments that intersect $\overline{AE}$ $\overline{AB}, \overline{AD}, \overline{EF}, \overline{EH}$

19. three segments parallel to $\overline{AE}$ $\overline{BF}, \overline{CG}, \overline{DH}$

20. four segments skew to $\overline{AE}$ $\overline{FG}, \overline{BC}, \overline{DC}, \overline{HG}$

Example 3
(page 460)

21. Use notebook paper or graph paper. Draw three segments that are parallel to each other. Draw a line that intersects the parallel segments. See margin.

22. Draw two parallel rays.

23. Draw $\overleftrightarrow{VB}$. 22–24. See margin.

24. Draw $\overleftrightarrow{CD}$ so that it intersects two segments, $\overline{FG}$ and $\overline{HJ}$.

B Apply Your Skills

Modeling Draw each of the following. If not possible, explain.

25. $\overleftrightarrow{PQ} \parallel \overleftrightarrow{RS}$ **26.** $\overrightarrow{AB} \parallel \overline{BC}$ **27.** $\overrightarrow{JK}$ skew to $\overleftrightarrow{LM}$
25–27. See p. 462 margin.

9-1 Introduction to Geometry: Points, Lines, and Planes **461**

21. Answers may vary. Sample:

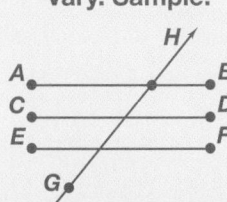

22. Answers may vary. Sample:

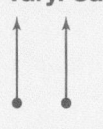

23.

V   B

24. Answers may vary. Sample:

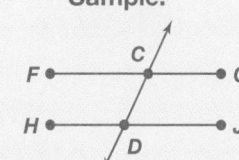

Practice 9-1 Introduction to Geometry: Points, Lines, and Planes

Use the figures at the right. Name each of the following.

1. Four segments that intersect $\overline{AB}$.
   $\overline{BC}, \overline{BF}, \overline{AE}, \overline{AD}$

2. Three segments parallel to $\overline{AB}$.
   $\overline{DC}, \overline{EF}, \overline{GH}$

3. Four segments skew to $\overline{AB}$.
   $\overline{DH}, \overline{FG}, \overline{EH}, \overline{CG}$

Use the figure at the right. Find each of the following.

4. all points shown
   A, B, C, P, N

5. all segments
   $\overline{AP}, \overline{PC}, \overline{AC}, \overline{NP}, \overline{PB}, \overline{NB}$

6. five different rays Sample answer is shown.
   $\overrightarrow{PA}, \overrightarrow{PC}, \overrightarrow{PB}, \overrightarrow{PN}, \overrightarrow{NB}$

7. all lines shown
   $\overleftrightarrow{AC}, \overleftrightarrow{NB}$

8. all names for $\overleftrightarrow{NB}$
   $\overleftrightarrow{NB}, \overleftrightarrow{BN}, \overleftrightarrow{PN}, \overleftrightarrow{NP}, \overleftrightarrow{BP}, \overleftrightarrow{PB}$

Write an equation. Then find the length of each segment.

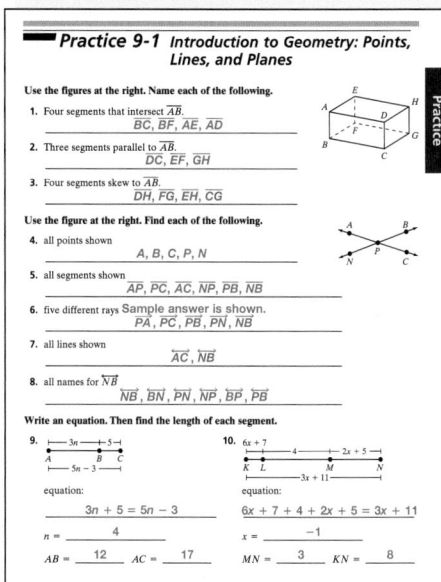

9.
equation:
$3n + 5 = 5n - 3$

$n = \underline{\quad 4 \quad}$

$AB = \underline{\quad 12 \quad}$ $AC = \underline{\quad 17 \quad}$

10.
equation:
$6x + 7 + 4 + 2x + 5 = 3x + 11$

$x = \underline{\quad -1 \quad}$

$MN = \underline{\quad 3 \quad}$ $KN = \underline{\quad 8 \quad}$

Enrichment 9-1 Lines and Curves

You can use straight lines to produce the illusion of curves. To see how, connect each pair of identical letters, using a ruler.

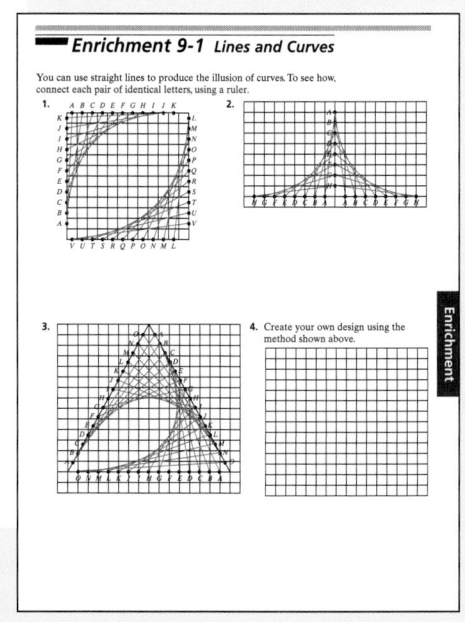

4. Create your own design using the method shown above.

25. Answers may vary.
Sample:

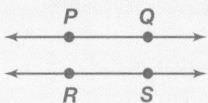

26. Answers may vary.
Sample: Not possible;
$\overrightarrow{AB}$ and $\overrightarrow{BC}$ both contain point *B*.

27. Answers may vary.
Sample:

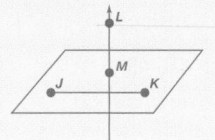

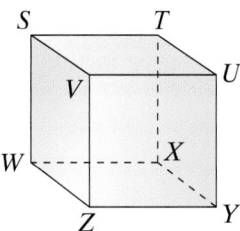

Use the figure at the left. Name a segment to make each statement true. 28–31. Answers may vary. Samples are given.

28. ▦ ‖ $\overline{XY}$ $\overline{WZ}$ **29.** ▦ ‖ $\overline{YZ}$ $\overline{WX}$ **30.** ▦ ‖ $\overline{WX}$ $\overline{ST}$ **31.** ▦ ‖ $\overline{SV}$ $\overline{TU}$

Complete with *always*, *sometimes*, or *never* to make a true statement.

32. $\overrightarrow{AB}$ and $\overrightarrow{BC}$ are __?__ on the same line. sometimes

33. $\overrightarrow{AB}$ and $\overrightarrow{AC}$ are __?__ the same ray. sometimes

34. $\overline{AX}$ and $\overline{XA}$ are __?__ the same segment. always

35. $\overleftrightarrow{TQ}$ and $\overleftrightarrow{QT}$ are __?__ the same line. always

36. Skew lines are __?__ in the same plane. never

37. Two lines in the same plane are __?__ parallel. sometimes

⟨Algebra⟩ **Write an equation. Then find the length of each segment.**

38.

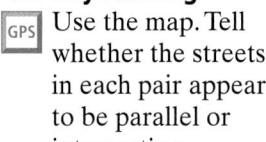

2*x* + 3 = 8*x*; 1, 3, 4

39.

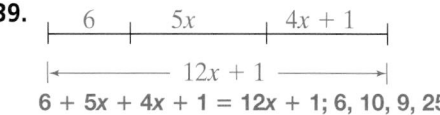

6 + 5*x* + 4*x* + 1 = 12*x* + 1; 6, 10, 9, 25

40. $\overline{AB}$ is the segment from *A* to *B*. *AB* is a number, the length of $\overline{AB}$.

41. Answers may vary.
Sample: $\overrightarrow{AB}$ and $\overrightarrow{BA}$ have different endpoints.

40. Writing in Math Explain what the symbols $\overline{AB}$ and *AB* represent. Use examples. See left.

41. Error Analysis A student says that $\overrightarrow{AB}$ is the same ray as $\overrightarrow{BA}$. Explain the student's error. See left.

42a. intersecting
b. intersecting
c. parallel
d. parallel
e. intersecting

42. City Planning

▢GPS Use the map. Tell whether the streets in each pair appear to be parallel or intersecting.

a. N.W. Highway and Fifth Avenue

b. N.W. Highway and B Street

c. A and C Streets   d. B and C Streets   e. C and Main Streets
a–e. See left.

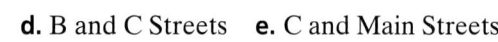

Ⓒ Challenge

43. a. Suppose a town installs a mailbox at a point *P*. How many straight roads can the town plan that lead to *P*? infinitely many

b. Suppose a town installs mailboxes at points *P* and *R*. How many straight roads might the town plan to build that pass by both mailboxes? one straight road

44a.

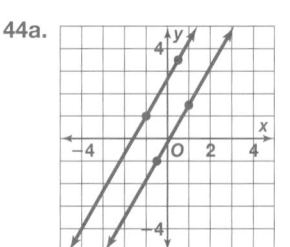

44. a. On a coordinate plane, draw a line through $\left(-\frac{1}{2}, -1\right)$ and $\left(1, 1\frac{1}{2}\right)$. Then draw a line through $(-1, 1)$ and $\left(\frac{1}{2}, 3\frac{1}{2}\right)$. See left.

b. What appears to be true of the two lines that you drew in part (a)? parallel

c. Find the slope of each line. $\frac{5}{3}$, $\frac{5}{3}$

d. Inductive Reasoning Make a conjecture based on your answer to parts (b) and (c). If the slopes are equal, the lines are parallel.

462 Chapter 9 Spatial Thinking

 Use the Guided Problem Solving worksheet with Exercise 42.

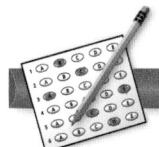
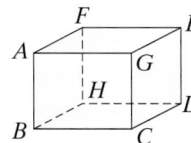
Multiple Choice

Use the figure at the left for Exercises 45–48.

45. Which segment is skew to $\overline{AB}$? **B**
  A. $\overline{BC}$ **B.** $\overline{CD}$ **C.** $\overline{DE}$ **D.** $\overline{GC}$

46. Which segment is parallel to $\overline{ED}$? **H**
  F. $\overline{BH}$ **G.** $\overline{AF}$ **H.** $\overline{AB}$ **I.** $\overline{GE}$

Take It to the NET
Online lesson quiz at
www.PHSchool.com
Web Code: ada-0901

47. Which segment does NOT intersect $\overline{AG}$? **D**
  A. $\overline{AB}$ **B.** $\overline{GC}$ **C.** $\overline{AF}$ **D.** $\overline{BC}$

48. Which describes *BHDC*? **H**
  F. point **G.** line **H.** plane **I.** ray

Short Response

49. Draw a line and label three of its points as *A*, *B* and *C*.
  a. Explain why both $\overleftrightarrow{AB}$ and $\overleftrightarrow{BA}$ are names for your line.
  b. State another name for your line.
  a–b. See back of book.

Mixed Review

Lesson 8-8

Graph each inequality in its own coordinate plane.
50–52. See back of book.
50. $y \geq -2x + 6$ **51.** $y > x + 1$ **52.** $x \leq -4$

Lessons 5-3 and 5-4

Simplify each expression.

53. $\frac{3}{8} + \frac{7}{12}$ $\frac{23}{24}$ **54.** $2\frac{3}{4} - 1\frac{5}{6}$ $\frac{11}{12}$ **55.** $1\frac{1}{3} + 2\frac{1}{6}$ $3\frac{1}{2}$ **56.** $2\frac{1}{2} - 3\frac{2}{3}$ $-1\frac{1}{6}$

57. $\frac{5}{8} \cdot \frac{3}{4}$ $\frac{15}{32}$ **58.** $2\frac{2}{3} \div \frac{3}{8}$ $7\frac{1}{9}$ **59.** $1\frac{1}{4} \cdot 3$ $3\frac{3}{4}$ **60.** $4\frac{3}{8} \div 4$ $1\frac{3}{32}$

Math at Work

Choreographer

Choreographers are usually experienced dancers whose hard work and dedication have earned them the opportunity to create original dances. Choreographers have an excellent sense of timing and spatial positioning.

Many choreographed dance numbers reflect geometric shapes such as triangles and quadrilaterals. Next time you see a dance group perform, be on the lookout for geometry—it will help you think like a choreographer!

Take It to the NET For more information about choreographers, go to **www.PHSchool.com**.
Web Code: adb-2031

9-1 Introduction to Geometry: Points, Lines, and Planes **463**

Alternative Assessment

From old magazines or newspapers have students cut pictures that suggest each of the basic geometric figures and the three types of line relationships: parallel, intersecting, and skew. Ask students to outline each figure with a wide black marker, and

display them on a poster or in a booklet. Have them label each geometric shape.

---

4. Assess

PowerPoint Lesson Quiz 9-1

Use the figure. Name each of the following.

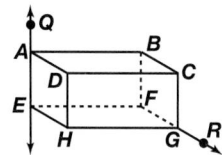

1. four points *A, B, C, D*

2. another name for $\overleftrightarrow{AE}$ $\overleftrightarrow{EQ}$

3. three different rays
  $\overrightarrow{AQ}, \overrightarrow{AE}, \overrightarrow{GR}$

4. three segments that are parallel to $\overline{HG}$ $\overline{EF}, \overline{DC}, \overline{AB}$

5. four segments that are skew to $\overline{CG}$ $\overline{AB}, \overline{AD}, \overline{EF}, \overline{EH}$

6. four segments that intersect $\overline{AE}$ $\overline{AB}, \overline{AD}, \overline{EF}, \overline{EH}$

Test Prep

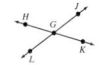 **Resources**

For additional practice with a variety of test item formats:
• Test Prep, p. 517
• Test-Taking Strategies, p. 512
• Test-Taking Strategies With Transparencies

Reteaching 9-1 Introduction to Geometry: Points, Lines, and Planes

Name all points, segments, lines, and rays shown.

Points are represented with a single capital letter. The points shown are *M, N, Q,* and *P.*

A segment has two endpoints. We write the segment with endpoints *M* and *N* as either $\overline{MN}$ or $\overline{NM}$. One way to list the segments shown is: $\overline{MN}, \overline{MP}, \overline{MQ}, \overline{NQ}$.

Lines are infinite. We can name them with any two points. One line in the figure is $\overleftrightarrow{MN}$. The arrows indicate the line extends in each direction without end. Other names for the same line are $\overleftrightarrow{NM}, \overleftrightarrow{NQ}, \overleftrightarrow{QN}, \overleftrightarrow{MQ}$, and $\overleftrightarrow{QM}$.

A ray has one endpoint and extends without end in one direction. The endpoint is named first. Thus, $\overrightarrow{MQ}$ and $\overrightarrow{QM}$ are not the same ray. However, $\overrightarrow{QM}$ and $\overrightarrow{QN}$ are the same ray. After the endpoint, we can use any other point on the line to name the ray. The rays shown are: $\overrightarrow{MQ}, \overrightarrow{MN}, \overrightarrow{MP}, \overrightarrow{NM}, \overrightarrow{QM}$.

Use the figure below. Name each of the following.

1. all points shown
  G, H, J, K, L

2. all rays shown
  $\overrightarrow{GJ}, \overrightarrow{GK}, \overrightarrow{GL}, \overrightarrow{GH}, \overrightarrow{LG}, \overrightarrow{KG}, \overrightarrow{JG}, \overrightarrow{HG}$

3. all names for $\overleftrightarrow{JL}$
  $\overleftrightarrow{JL}, \overleftrightarrow{LJ}, \overleftrightarrow{JG}, \overleftrightarrow{GJ}, \overleftrightarrow{LG}, \overleftrightarrow{GL}$

4. all segments on $\overleftrightarrow{HK}$
  $\overline{HG}, \overline{HK}, \overline{GK}$

Reteaching

Drawing and Measuring Angles

This Review defines an angle and its parts, and classifies angles by their measures. Students should use protractors to draw and measure angles.

Teaching Notes

You can name an angle by a single letter or number at its vertex, or by three letters that name points on the angle. The middle letter must be the vertex and the other letters must name a point on each of the two rays.

Teaching Tip

Point out to students that if they think of an angle with a hinge at its vertex, the measure of an angle indicates how much one ray has turned from the other.

Error Prevention!

The two scales on the protractor can be confusing. Encourage students to have a mental picture of the angle they are going to draw (acute or obtuse), or an estimate of the measure they are going to find. Either idea will help them choose the correct scale on the protractor.

An *angle* is formed by two rays with a common endpoint. The rays are the *sides* of the angle. The common endpoint is the *vertex*. You can name the angle at the right $\angle ABC$, $\angle CBA$, $\angle B$, or $\angle 1$.

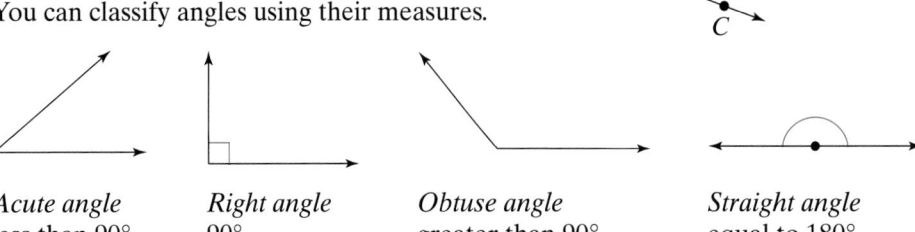

You can classify angles using their measures.

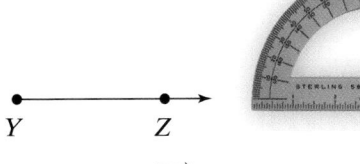

Acute angle
less than 90°

Right angle
90°

Obtuse angle
greater than 90°
and less than 180°

Straight angle
equal to 180°

You can use a protractor to draw and to measure angles.

EXAMPLE

Draw a 120° angle.

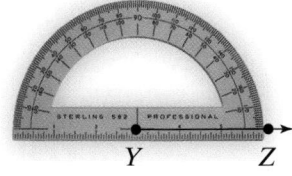 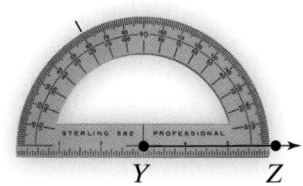 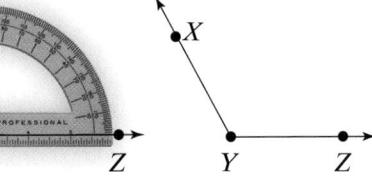

Step 1 Draw $\overrightarrow{YZ}$.

Step 2 Place the center of the protractor over Y. Make sure $\overrightarrow{YZ}$ passes through zero on the protractor scale.

Step 3 Place a mark on your paper at 120° such that $\angle XYZ$ will be obtuse.

Step 4 Draw $\overrightarrow{YX}$. The measure of $\angle XYZ$ is 120°.

EXERCISES

Draw an angle with the given measure. 1–6. See margin.

1. 45°	**2.** 110°	**3.** 80°	**4.** 60°	**5.** 30°	**6.** 150°

Measure each angle. Then classify it as *acute*, *right*, or *obtuse*.

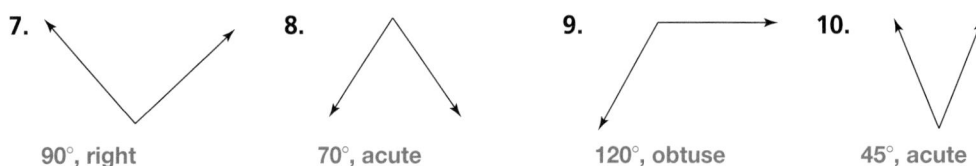

7. 90°, right   **8.** 70°, acute   **9.** 120°, obtuse   **10.** 45°, acute

464   Review   Drawing and Measuring Angles

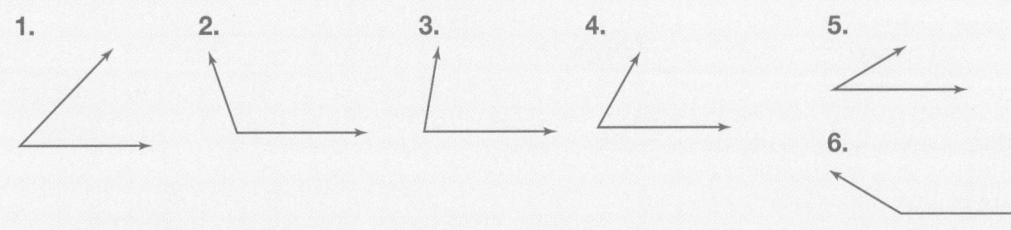

1.   2.   3.   4.   5.

6.

Angle Relationships and Parallel Lines

1. Plan

OBJECTIVE
1 Adjacent and Vertical Angles

In this lesson you will learn to identify special pairs of angles.

Adjacent angles share a vertex and a side but no points in their interiors.

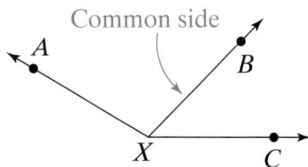

Common side

$\angle AXB$ and $\angle BXC$ are adjacent angles.

$\angle AXC$ and $\angle BXC$ are not adjacent angles.

Vertical angles are formed by two intersecting lines and are opposite each other. Vertical angles have the same measure.

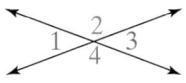

$\angle 1$ and $\angle 3$ are vertical angles.
$\angle 2$ and $\angle 4$ are vertical angles.

Angles that have the same measure are **congruent angles.** In the diagram above, $\angle 1$ is congruent to $\angle 3$. You can write this as $\angle 1 \cong \angle 3$. You can write *the measure of $\angle 1$ as $m\angle 1$.* Since $\angle 1 \cong \angle 3, m\angle 1 = m\angle 3$.

If the sum of the measures of two angles is 180°, the angles are **supplementary.**

If the sum of the measures of two angles is 90°, the angles are **complementary.**

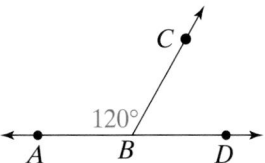

$\angle ABC$ and $\angle CBD$ are supplementary.

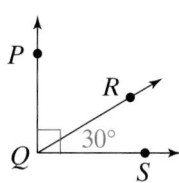

$\angle ABC$ and $\angle X$ are supplementary.
$\angle X$ and $\angle RQS$ are complementary.

$\angle PQR$ and $\angle RQS$ are complementary.

What You'll Learn

OBJECTIVE 1
To identify adjacent and vertical angles

OBJECTIVE 2
To relate angles formed by parallel lines and a transversal

... And Why

To use the relationships of angles formed by parallel lines in real-world situations, such as setting leaded window panes

✓ Check Skills You'll Need

Solve.

1. $n + 45 = 180$ 135

2. $75 + x = 90$ 15

3. $3y = 2y + 90$ 90

4. $2a + 15 = a + 45$ 30

❓ For help, go to Lesson 7-5.

New Vocabulary

• adjacent angles
• vertical angles
• congruent angles
• supplementary
• complementary
• transversal
• corresponding angles
• alternate interior angles

📱 **iTEXT** Interactive lesson includes instant self-check, tutorials, and activities.

Lesson Preview

✓ **Check Skills You'll Need**

Solving Equations
Lesson 7-5: Example 1.
Exercises 1–8.
Extra Practice, p. 750.

Lesson Resources

📁 **Teaching Resources**
Practice, Reteaching, Enrichment

👥 **Reaching All Students**
Practice Workbook 9-2
Spanish Practice Workbook 9-2
Guided Problem Solving 9-2
Technology Activities 16
Hands-On Activities 19

⏱ **Presentation Assistant Plus!**
Transparencies and PowerPoint™
• Check Skills You'll Need 9-2
• Additional Examples 9-2
• Student Edition Answers 9-2
• Lesson Quiz 9-2
• Classroom Aid 3, 24
PH Presentation Pro CD-ROM 9-2

ASSESSMENT SYSTEM

Computer Test Generator CD-ROM

💻 **Technology**
Resource Pro® CD-ROM
Computer Test Generator CD-ROM
PH Presentation Pro CD-ROM

💻 **www.PHSchool.com**
Student Site
• Teacher Web Code: adk-5500
• Self-grading Lesson Quiz
PH SuccessNet Teacher Center
• Lesson Planner
• Resources

Plus 📱**iTEXT**

Ongoing Assessment and Intervention

Before the Lesson
Diagnose prerequisite skills using:
• Check Skills You'll Need

During the Lesson
Monitor progress using:
• Check Understanding
• Additional Examples
• Test Prep

After the Lesson
Assess knowledge using:
• Lesson Quiz
• Computer Test Generator CD-ROM

Professional Development

Math Background

Special relationships exist between some angles. These special relationships are useful in solving everyday problems in many areas, including art, nature, and architecture.

Teaching Notes

Tactile Learners

Have students carefully draw two intersecting lines and then measure the four angles formed to verify that vertical angles are congruent.

Error Prevention!

Some students may think that two angles with the same degree measure are not congruent because their sides are drawn with different lengths. Remind students that the measure of an angle indicates only the amount of turn from one side of the angle to the other. Point out that the hands of a large clock and the much smaller hands of a small wristwatch form congruent right angles at 3:00.

Auditory Learners

Some students confuse *complementary* and *supplementary* angles. As a memory aid, have them say, "C (complementary) comes before S (supplementary) and 90 comes before 180."

1 EXAMPLE Visual Learners

Have students draw the figure on paper. Then have them shade one pair of vertical angles with one color and the other pair with a second color.

English Learners

Help students relate the term *transversal* to other words, like *transfer, transact,* and *transmission,* that begin with the same prefix *trans,* the Latin word for "across." Have students think of other words with the prefix *trans.*

1 EXAMPLE Finding the Measure of an Angle

In the diagram at the left, find the measure of $\angle 1$ if $m\angle 4 = 135°$.

$$m\angle 1 + m\angle 4 = 180° \qquad \text{$\angle 1$ and $\angle 4$ are supplementary.}$$
$$m\angle 1 + 135° = 180° \qquad \text{Replace $m\angle 4$ with 135°.}$$
$$m\angle 1 + 135° - 135° = 180° - 135° \qquad \text{Solve for $m\angle 1$.}$$
$$m\angle 1 = 45°$$

✓ **Check Understanding**   Example 1

1. If $m\angle 8 = 20°$, find the measures of $\angle 5$, $\angle 6$, and $\angle 7$. 160°, 20°, 160°

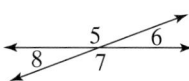

OBJECTIVE

2 **Relating Angles and Parallel Lines**

A line that intersects two other lines in different points is a **transversal.** Some pairs of angles formed by transversals and two lines have special names.

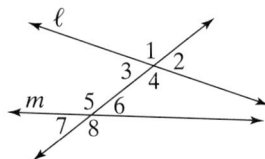

Corresponding angles lie on the same side of the transversal and in corresponding positions. $\angle 1$ and $\angle 5$, $\angle 3$ and $\angle 7$, $\angle 2$ and $\angle 6$, and $\angle 4$ and $\angle 8$ are corresponding angles.

Alternate interior angles are in the interior of a pair of lines and on opposite sides of the transversal. $\angle 3$ and $\angle 6$, and $\angle 4$ and $\angle 5$ are alternate interior angles.

When a transversal intersects two parallel lines, corresponding angles are congruent. Alternate interior angles are also congruent.

2 EXAMPLE Identifying Congruent Angles

In the diagram, $\ell \parallel m$. Identify each of the following.

a. congruent corresponding angles

$\angle 1 \cong \angle 3, \angle 2 \cong \angle 4, \angle 8 \cong \angle 6,$
$\angle 7 \cong \angle 5$

b. congruent alternate interior angles

$\angle 3 \cong \angle 7, \angle 2 \cong \angle 6$

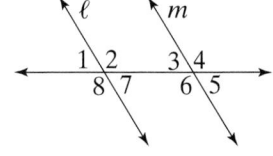

466   Chapter 9   Spatial Thinking

 Reaching All Students

| **Below Level** Ask students to give examples of lines in their surroundings that appear to be parallel. **Answers may vary. Samples: lines in the flooring, lines on highways** | **Advanced Learners** Have students draw two lines intersecting to form vertical angles. Ask: *If all four angles in your drawing are congruent, what is the measure of each one? Explain.* **90°; 360 ÷ 4 = 90** | **Visual Learners** See note on page 466. **English Learners** See note on page 466. |

✓ Check Understanding   Example 2

2. In the diagram, $a \parallel b$. Name four pairs of congruent corresponding angles and two pairs of congruent alternate interior angles. $\angle 1 \cong \angle 5$, $\angle 2 \cong \angle 6$, $\angle 3 \cong \angle 7$, $\angle 4 \cong \angle 8$; $\angle 3 \cong \angle 5$, $\angle 4 \cong \angle 6$

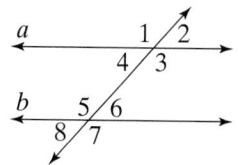

When solving a problem that involves parallel lines, you can often choose whether to use corresponding angles or alternate interior angles.

More Than One Way

The windowpanes at the right are held in place by parallel strips of lead. Lines r and s are parallel and line q is a transversal. If $m\angle 1 = 65°$, what is $m\angle 4$?

Nicole's Method

Use corresponding angles.

$\angle 1 \cong \angle 3$ because they are corresponding angles, so $m\angle 3 = 65°$. $\angle 3$ and $\angle 4$ are supplementary, so $m\angle 3 + m\angle 4 = 180°$.

$$m\angle 3 + m\angle 4 = 180°$$
$$65° + m\angle 4 = 180°$$
$$65° + m\angle 4 - 65° = 180° - 65°$$
$$m\angle 4 = 115°$$

Eric's Method

Use alternate interior angles.

$\angle 1$ and $\angle 2$ are supplementary.

$$m\angle 1 + m\angle 2 = 180°$$
$$65° + m\angle 2 = 180°$$
$$65° + m\angle 2 - 65° = 180° - 65°.$$
$$m\angle 2 = 115°$$

$\angle 2$ and $\angle 4$ are alternate interior angles, so they are congruent. If $m\angle 2 = 115°$, then $m\angle 4 = 115°$.

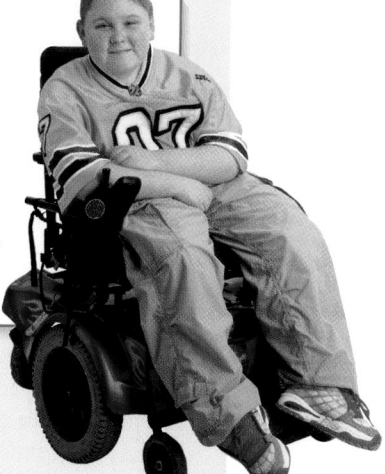

Choose a Method   1–2. See margin.

1. Which method do you prefer? Explain why.
2. What is another way to solve the problem?

1. Answers may vary. Sample: Nicole's Method; it is easier using corresponding angles.

2. Answers may vary. Sample: $\angle 1$ is congruent to its vertical angle. That angle is congruent to $\angle 3$. $\angle 3$ and $\angle 4$ are supplementary.

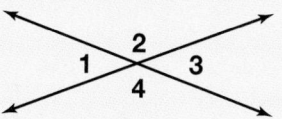
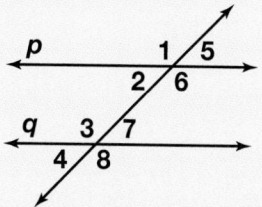
467

3. Practice

Assignment Guide

▼1 Objective 1
- Ⓐ Ⓑ **Core** 1–5, 10–13
- Ⓒ **Extension** 17

▼2 Objective 2
- Ⓐ Ⓑ **Core** 6–9, 14–16

Test Prep 18–21
Mixed Review 22–29

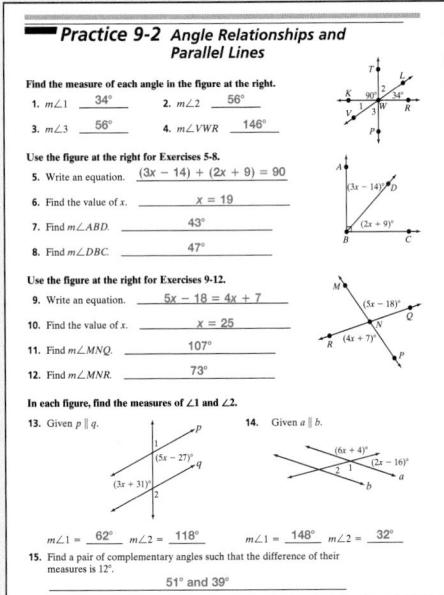

Practice 9-2 Angle Relationships and Parallel Lines

Find the measure of each angle in the figure at the right.
1. $m\angle1$ ___34°___   2. $m\angle2$ ___56°___
3. $m\angle3$ ___56°___   4. $m\angle VWR$ ___146°___

Use the figure at the right for Exercises 5-8.
5. Write an equation. ___$(3x - 14) + (2x + 9) = 90$___
6. Find the value of x. ___$x = 19$___
7. Find $m\angle ABD$. ___43°___
8. Find $m\angle DBC$. ___47°___

Use the figure at the right for Exercises 9-12.
9. Write an equation. ___$5x - 18 = 4x + 7$___
10. Find the value of x. ___$x = 25$___
11. Find $m\angle MNQ$. ___107°___
12. Find $m\angle MNR$. ___73°___

In each figure, find the measures of $\angle1$ and $\angle2$.
13. Given $p \parallel q$.   14. Given $a \parallel b$.

$m\angle1 = $ ___62°___ $m\angle2 = $ ___118°___ $m\angle1 = $ ___148°___ $m\angle2 = $ ___32°___
15. Find a pair of complementary angles such that the difference of their measures is 12°.
___51° and 39°___

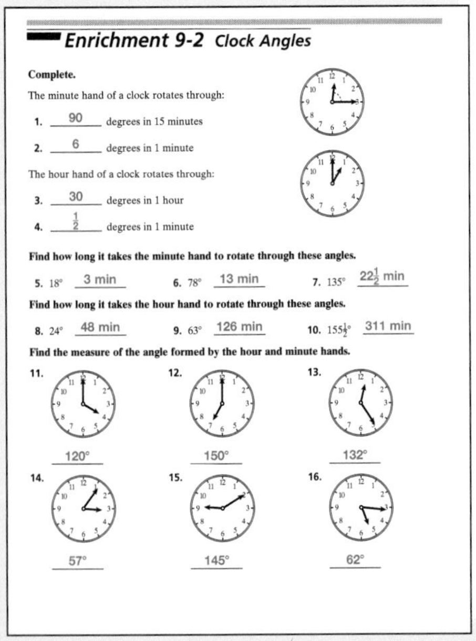

Enrichment 9-2 Clock Angles

Complete.
The minute hand of a clock rotates through:
1. ___90___ degrees in 15 minutes
2. ___6___ degrees in 1 minute
The hour hand of a clock rotates through:
3. ___30___ degrees in 1 hour
4. ___½___ degrees in 1 minute
Find how long it takes the minute hand to rotate through these angles.
5. 18° ___3 min___   6. 78° ___13 min___   7. 135° ___22½ min___
Find how long it takes the hour hand to rotate through these angles.
8. 24° ___48 min___   9. 63° ___126 min___   10. 155½° ___311 min___
Find the measure of the angle formed by the hour and minute hands.
11. 120°   12. 150°   13. 132°
14. 57°   15. 145°   16. 62°

EXERCISES

❓ For more exercises, see *Extra Practice*.

Practice and Problem Solving

Ⓐ **Practice by Example**

Example 1
(page 466)

For Exercises 1 and 2, copy and complete the sentence.

1. $\angle1$ and $\angle2$ are ___?___ angles. **supplementary**

2. $\angle1$ and $\angle3$ are ___?___ angles. **vertical**

3. Find the measures of $\angle1$, $\angle2$, and $\angle3$ if $m\angle4 = 100°$.
$m\angle1 = 80°$, $m\angle2 = 100°$, $m\angle3 = 80°$

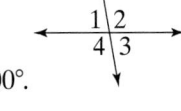

For Exercises 4 and 5, name the angle vertical to $\angle1$. Name an angle adjacent to $\angle1$. Then find $m\angle1$. **4–5. See left.**

4. $\angle3$ is vertical to $\angle1$. $\angle2$ is adjacent to $\angle1$. $m\angle1 = 40°$
5. $\angle3$ is vertical to $\angle1$. $\angle2$ is adjacent to $\angle1$. $m\angle1 = 110°$

4.    5.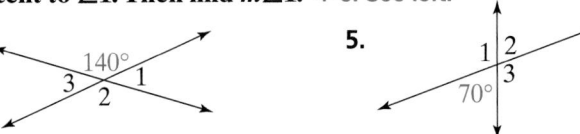

Example 2
(page 466)

6. $\angle1$ and $\angle5$, $\angle2$ and $\angle6$, $\angle3$ and $\angle7$, $\angle4$ and $\angle8$

7. $\angle2$ and $\angle8$, $\angle3$ and $\angle5$

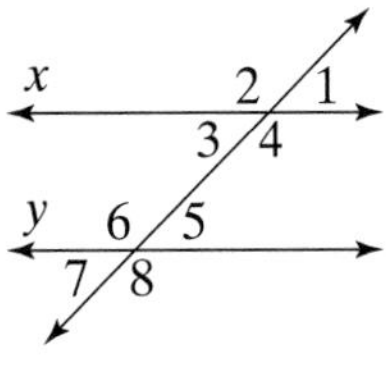

For Exercises 6–8, use the figure at the right.

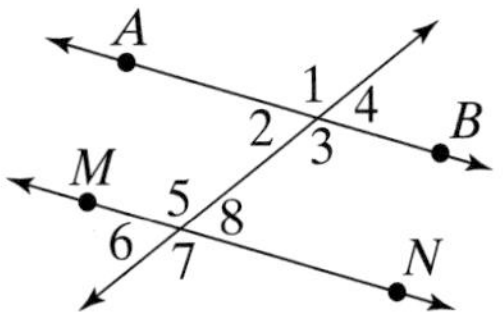

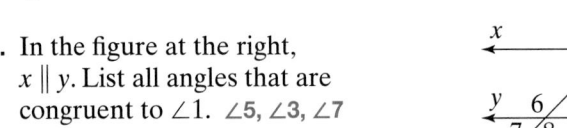

6. Name four pairs of corresponding angles. **See left.**
7. Name the alternate interior angles. **See left.**
8. Suppose $\overleftrightarrow{AB} \parallel \overleftrightarrow{MN}$. Name all angles congruent to $\angle8$. **$\angle6$, $\angle2$, $\angle4$**

9. **a.** In the figure at the right, $x \parallel y$. List all angles that are congruent to $\angle1$. **$\angle5$, $\angle3$, $\angle7$**
   b. If $m\angle5 = 45°$, what are the measures of the other angles? **See margin.**

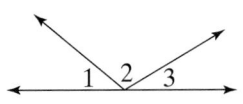

Ⓑ **Apply Your Skills**

10. In the figure at the right, find the sum of the measures of $\angle1$, $\angle2$, and $\angle3$. **180°**

11. Fill in the blank. The sum of the measures of two angles is 90°. The angles are ___?___ angles. **complementary**

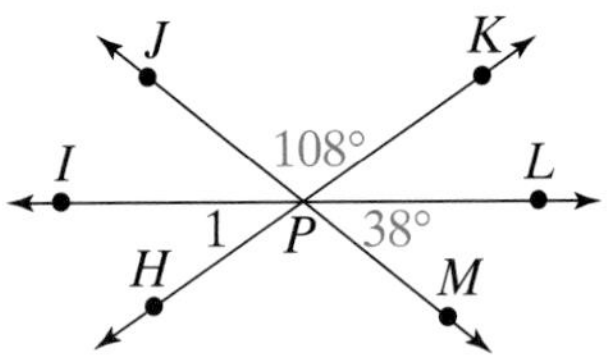

12. In the figure at the left, name the angle vertical to $\angle1$. Name an angle adjacent to $\angle1$. Then find $m\angle1$. **See margin.**

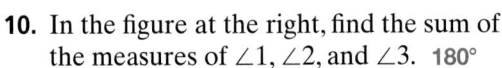

13. **Writing in Math** Describe how you will keep from confusing the definitions of supplementary angles and complementary angles.
See below left.

14. **Reasoning** Angles on the "outside" of two lines and on opposite sides of a transversal are called *alternate exterior angles*. The transversal q intersects two parallel lines m and n. If $m\angle1 = 84°$, what is the measure of $\angle5$? Explain your reasoning. **See margin.**

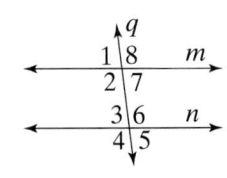

15. **Algebra** Use the figure for Exercise 14. If $m\angle8 = 2x + 5$ and $m\angle4 = x + 10$, what is the value of x? **5**

13. Answers may vary. Sample: Supplementary angles can form a straight angle and both supplementary and straight begin with "s".

468 **Chapter 9** Spatial Thinking

9b. $m\angle6 = 135°$, $m\angle7 = 45°$, $m\angle8 = 135°$, $m\angle3 = 45°$, $m\angle2 = 135°$, $m\angle1 = 45°$, $m\angle4 = 135°$

12. $\angle KPL$ is vertical to $\angle1$. $\angle JPI$ and $\angle HPM$ are adjacent to $\angle1$. $m\angle1 = 34°$.

14. Answers may vary. Sample: $\angle1 \cong \angle3$ because they are corresponding angles. So $m\angle3 = 84°$. $\angle5 \cong \angle3$, so $m\angle5 = 84°$.

16. (Algebra) Given $a \parallel b$ at the right, find the
measures of $\angle 1$ and $\angle 2$. $m\angle 1 = 60°$, $m\angle 2 = 60°$

C Challenge

17. a. (Algebra) Write an equation and find
the value of x. $3x = x + 30$, $x = 15$

b. Find $m\angle KQB$. 45°

c. Find $m\angle KQR$.
135°

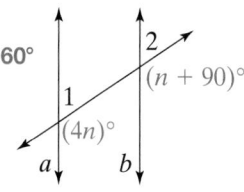

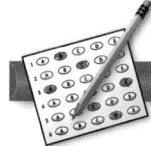

Multiple Choice

18. What is $m\angle 3$? A

A. 22° B. 68°

C. 158° D. 202°

19. If $\ell \parallel m$, what is $m\angle 6$? H

F. 22° G. 68°

H. 158° I. 202°

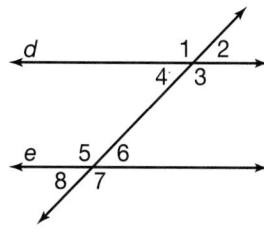

Reading Comprehension

Read the passage below before doing Exercises 20 and 21.

New Road Approved

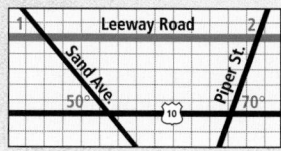

The Middleton City Board approved the proposal for a new road parallel to Highway 10. This new road, to be called Leeway Road, will help ease traffic flow in downtown Middleton during rush hour. Leeway Road will intersect both Sand Avenue and Piper Street.

Take It to the NET
Online lesson quiz at
www.PHSchool.com
Web Code: ada-0902

20. When Leeway Road is built, what will $m\angle 1$ be? Justify
your answer. 50°; corresponding angles are congruent.

21. If $m\angle 2$ is 130° when Leeway Road is built, what criterion is
Leeway Road NOT meeting? Leeway Road is not parallel to
Highway 10.

Lesson 9-1

Draw each figure. 22–26. See back of book.

22. $\overline{AB}$ **23.** $\overrightarrow{CD}$ **24.** $\overrightarrow{DC}$ **25.** $\overleftrightarrow{EF}$ **26.** $\angle GHI$

Lesson 6-9

Find the sale price.

27. $25 at 10% discount $22.50 **28.** $324 at 20% discount $259.20

Lesson 4-5

29. In a single-elimination tournament, a team plays until it loses.
Eight teams play in a tournament. How many games must be
played to decide a tournament winner? seven games

9-2 Angle Relationships and Parallel Lines **469**

Alternative Assessment

Let students work in pairs. Have one student
draw two parallel lines cut by a transversal
and number the angles. The other student
lists all pairs of adjacent angles, vertical
angles, supplementary angles, corresponding
angles, and alternate interior angles.

Use the Guided Problem
Solving worksheet with
Exercise 16.

---

4. Assess

PowerPoint **Lesson Quiz 9-2**

In the diagram, $d \parallel e$.

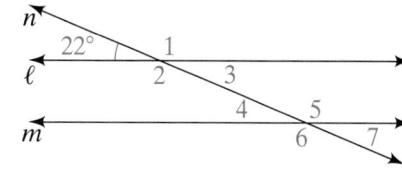

1. Find $m\angle 5$, if $m\angle 8$ is 35°.
145°

2. Name the congruent
corresponding angles.
$\angle 1 \cong \angle 5$, $\angle 2 \cong \angle 6$,
$\angle 4 \cong \angle 8$, $\angle 3 \cong \angle 7$

3. Name the congruent
alternate interior angles.
$\angle 4 \cong \angle 7$, $\angle 2 \cong \angle 5$

Test Prep

Resources

For additional practice with a
variety of test item formats:
• Test Prep, p. 517
• Test-Taking Strategies, p. 512
• Test-Taking Strategies With
Transparencies

Reteaching 9-2 *Angle Relationships and Parallel Lines*

Find the measures of $\angle 1$ and $\angle 2$. Given: $r \parallel s$.
Write an equation and solve for x.

$(5x + 7) + (15x - 7) = 180$	These angles are supplementary.
$5x + 15x + 7 - 7 = 180$	Simplify.
$20x = 180$	Simplify.
$\frac{20x}{20} = \frac{180}{20}$	Divide each side by 20.
$x = 9$	Simplify.

Find the measure of the angle marked $(5x + 7)°$ by
substituting $x = 9$.
$5x + 7 = 5(9) + 7 = 45 + 7 = 52$
Since this angle and $\angle 1$ are vertical, they have the same measure.
Thus, $m\angle 1 = 52°$.
We can find the measure of $\angle 2$ several ways. The angle marked $(15x - 7)°$
and $\angle 2$ are corresponding angles, so they have the same measure. We can
find this measure by substituting $x = 9$ into $15x - 7$ or by realizing that this
angle and $\angle 1$ are supplementary.
$180 - 52 = 128$
$15x - 7 = 15(9) - 7 = 135 - 7 = 128$
Either way, $m\angle 2 = 128°$.

Use the figure at the right.

Given: $p \parallel q$.

1. Write an equation.
$(6x + 60) + 9x = 180$

2. Find the value of x.
$x =$ 8

3. Find $m\angle 1$.
$m\angle 1 =$ 72°

4. Find $m\angle 2$.
$m\angle 2 =$ 108°

469

Lesson Preview

 Check Skills You'll Need

Angle Relationships
Lesson 9-2: Example 1;
Exercises 1–5.
Extra Practice, p. 752.

Lesson Resources

 Teaching Resources
Practice, Reteaching, Enrichment

Reaching All Students
Practice Workbook 9-3
Spanish Practice Workbook 9-3
Guided Problem Solving 9-3
Technology Activities 17
Hands-On Activities 20, 21

Presentation Assistant Plus!
Transparencies and PowerPoint™
• Check Skills You'll Need 9-3
• Additional Examples 9-3
• Student Edition Answers 9-3
• Lesson Quiz 9-3
• Classroom Aid 9, 10, 25
PH Presentation Pro CD-ROM 9-3

ASSESSMENT SYSTEM

Computer Test Generator CD-ROM

Technology
Resource Pro® CD-ROM
Computer Test Generator CD-ROM
PH Presentation Pro CD-ROM

www.PHSchool.com
Student Site
• Teacher Web Code: adk-5500
• Self-grading Lesson Quiz
PH SuccessNet Teacher Center
• Lesson Planner
• Resources

Plus

 **9-3**

Classifying Polygons

What You'll Learn

OBJECTIVE 1 To classify triangles

OBJECTIVE 2 To classify quadrilaterals

. . . And Why

To use polygons in real-world situations involving design and construction

 Check Skills You'll Need

For the angle measures given, classify the angle as *acute*, *right*, or *obtuse*.
1–6. See below.
1. 85° **2.** 95° **3.** 160°

4. 90° **5.** 36° **6.** 127°

For help, go to Lesson 9-2.

New Vocabulary

• polygon
• regular polygon

---

1. acute
2. obtuse
3. obtuse
4. right
5. acute
6. obtuse

iTEXT Interactive lesson includes instant self-check, tutorials, and activities.

A **polygon** is a *closed* plane figure with at least three *sides*. The sides meet only at their endpoints.

A triangle is a polygon with three sides. You can classify triangles by angle measures. In the Review on page 464 you reviewed how to classify angles. You can also classify triangles by side lengths. Tick marks are used to indicate congruent sides of a figure.

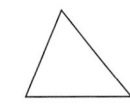
Acute triangle
three acute angles

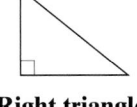
Right triangle
one right angle

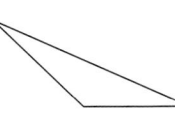
Obtuse triangle
one obtuse angle

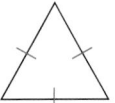
Equilateral triangle
three congruent sides

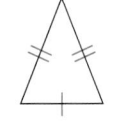
Isosceles triangle
at least two congruent sides

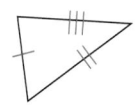
Scalene triangle
no congruent sides

1 EXAMPLE **Classifying a Triangle**

Classify the triangle by its sides and angles.

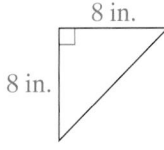
8 in.

8 in.

The triangle has two congruent sides and one right angle.

● The triangle is an isosceles right triangle.

 Check Understanding Example 1

1. Judging by appearance, classify each triangle by its sides and angles.

a.

b.

c.

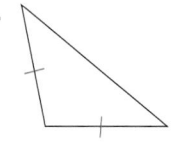
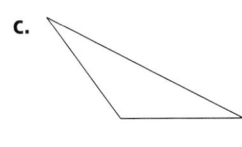

scalene right triangle

isosceles obtuse triangle

scalene obtuse triangle

470 Chapter 9 Spatial Thinking

Ongoing Assessment and Intervention

Before the Lesson
Diagnose prerequisite skills using:
• Check Skills You'll Need

During the Lesson
Monitor progress using:
• Check Understanding
• Additional Examples
• Test Prep

After the Lesson
Assess knowledge using:
• Lesson Quiz
• Computer Test Generator CD-ROM

OBJECTIVE
2 Classifying Quadrilaterals

You can also classify quadrilaterals by their sides and angles.

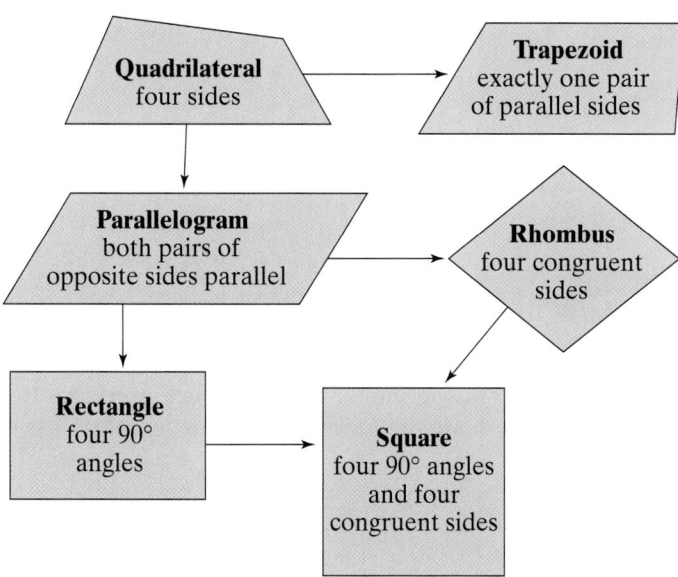

Professional Development

Math Background

The prefixes *penta-*, meaning five, *hexa-*, meaning six, and *octo-*, meaning eight, come from the Greek language. The term *polygon* has Greek roots as well. *Polygon* is based on the Greek words *polus,* meaning "many," and *gonia,* meaning "angle."

Teaching Notes

Teaching Tip

Ask students to draw a triangle with more than one right angle or more than one obtuse angle. They will soon see that this is impossible. Remind students that in previous courses they learned the sum of the measures of the angles of a triangle is 180°. Ask how they can use this rule to explain why you cannot draw the triangles as requested above. *Answers may vary. Sample: The two right angles have a sum of 180°, and the two obtuse angles have a sum that is greater than 180°. Therefore, there are no degrees "left" for the third angle.*

2 EXAMPLE   Classifying Quadrilaterals

Name the types of quadrilaterals that have both pairs of opposite sides parallel.

All parallelograms have opposite sides parallel. Parallelograms include rectangles, rhombuses, and squares.

✓ Check Understanding   Example 2

2. Name the types of quadrilaterals that have four right angles.
rectangles and squares

In later math courses, you will prove that a parallelogram has opposite sides congruent and opposite angles congruent.

Polygons are named using their vertices. Start at one vertex and list them in consecutive order.

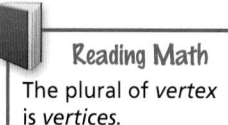

1 EXAMPLE Error Prevention

Stress to students that you may classify a triangle *by appearance* only when a problem asks you to do so. In geometry, you are not supposed to *assume* any information about a diagram.

PowerPoint
Additional Examples

1 Classify the triangle by its sides and angles.

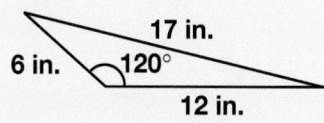

scalene obtuse triangle

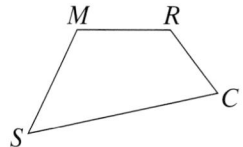

Starting from *M*, the name of this figure is quadrilateral *MRCS* or quadrilateral *MSCR*.

Reading Math
The plural of *vertex* is *vertices*.

2 Name the types of quadrilaterals that have at least one pair of parallel sides.
parallelograms (rectangles, rhombuses, squares) and trapezoids

👥 Reaching All Students

| **Below Level** Have students name all the geometric shapes they can think of, besides triangles. Have a volunteer sketch the shapes on the board. | **Advanced Learners** Ask: *You use P = 10(7) to find the perimeter of a decagon that has a side with length 7 in. However, the actual perimeter is 62 in. What must be the problem?* The decagon is not regular. | **English Learners** See note on page 472. **Diversity** See note on page 474. |

471

3 A contractor is framing the wooden deck shown below in the shape of a regular dodecagon (12 sides). Write a formula to find the perimeter of the deck. Evaluate the formula for a side length of 3 ft. $P = 12x$; 36 ft

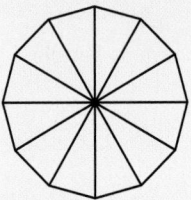

Tactile Learners

Let students use toothpicks to model various regular polygons. Include heptagons (7 sides), octagons (8 sides), decagons (10 sides), and dodecagons (12 sides).

English Learners

Have students brainstorm a list of words having prefixes *tri-, penta-,* or *oct-.* The words must have meanings associated with the numbers that the prefixes represent. Students can find these words in a dictionary. Discuss the meanings of the prefixes and words, and what each student's three words/definitions have in common.

3 EXAMPLE Teaching Tip

Ask students why the formula $P = 8x$ can be used to find the perimeter of an octagon, only if the octagon is regular. **To multiply a side length *x* by 8 to get the perimeter, all sides must have the same length *x*, meaning that the octagon must be regular.**

Closure

Ask students to tell what a polygon is. Also have students list five types of quadrilaterals. **A polygon is a closed plane figure with at least three sides that meet only at their endpoints; trapezoid, parallelogram, rectangle, rhombus, square.**

472

A **regular polygon** has all sides congruent and all angles congruent. Some regular polygons are shown below.

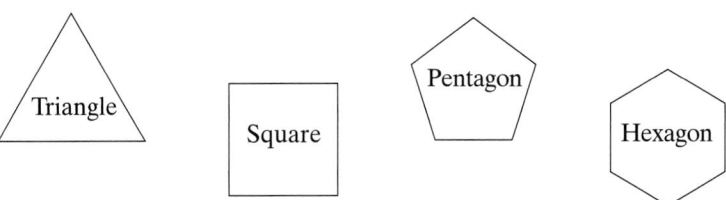

You can use algebra to write a formula for the perimeter of a regular polygon.

3 **EXAMPLE** Real-World 🌐 Problem Solving

Algebra **A contractor is framing a regular octagonal gazebo. Write a formula for the perimeter of the gazebo in terms of the length of a side. Evaluate the formula for a side length of 7 ft.**

To write a formula, let $x =$ the length of each side. The perimeter of the regular octagon is
  $x + x + x + x + x + x + x + x$.
Therefore the formula for the perimeter is $P = 8x$.

  $P = 8x$ **Write the formula.**

  $= 8(7)$ **Substitute 7 for *x*.**

  $= 56$ **Simplify.**

● For a side length of 7 ft, the perimeter is 56 ft.

✓ **Check Understanding** Example 3

  3. a. **Algebra** Write a formula to find the perimeter of a regular hexagon. $P = 6x$
  b. Use the formula to find the perimeter if one side is 16 cm. 96 cm

Real-World 🌐 Connection

Most gazebos are regular hexagons or regular octagons.

14–19. Answers may vary. Samples are given.

14.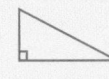

15.

16.

17.

18.

19.

EXERCISES

Practice and Problem Solving

 For more exercises, see Extra Practice.

 Practice by Example

Example 1
(page 470)

1. equilateral acute triangle
2. isosceles right triangle
3. scalene acute triangle

Judging by appearance, classify each triangle by its sides and angles.
1–3. See left.

1. 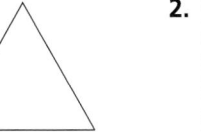   **2.**    **3.**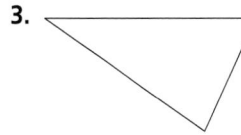

Example 2
(page 471)

Name the types of quadrilaterals that have the given property.

4. four congruent sides
    square, rhombus
5. exactly one pair of parallel sides
    trapezoid
6. two pairs of parallel sides
    6–9. See below left.
7. opposite sides congruent
8. four congruent angles
9. opposite angles congruent

Example 3
(page 472)

6. parallelogram, rhombus, square, rectangle
7. rectangle, square, rhombus, parallelogram
8. rectangle, square
9. rectangle, parallelogram, square, rhombus

(Algebra) **Write and use a formula for the perimeter of each figure. Use the formula to find the perimeter.**

10. an equilateral triangle with one side 3.5 cm $P = 3x$; 10.5 cm

11. a square with one side 12.5 in. $P = 4x$; 50 in.

12. a regular hexagon with one side $\frac{5}{8}$ in. $P = 6x$; $3\frac{3}{4}$ in.

 13. Architecture The Pentagon is a pentagonal-shaped building near Washington, D.C., that is home to the United States Department of Defense. Write a formula for the perimeter of a regular pentagon in terms of the length of a side. Evaluate the formula to find the perimeter of the Pentagon, which has a side length of 921 ft.
$P = 5x$; 4,605 ft

 Apply Your Skills

Open-Ended Sketch each figure. 14–19. See p. 472 margin.

14. an isosceles right triangle   **15.** a scalene obtuse triangle

16. an isosceles obtuse triangle   **17.** an isosceles acute triangle

18. a scalene right triangle   **19.** an equilateral triangle

20. Judging by appearance at the left, classify the triangle suggested by the edges of the piano, the piano lid, and the prop.
scalene acute triangle

21. Draw a parallelogram without a right angle but with four congruent sides. What is another name for this figure? See margin.

Find the perimeter of each figure.

22. an isosceles triangle with congruent sides of 16.2 cm and a third side half that length   40.5 cm

23. a scalene triangle with two side lengths of 8 in. and 5 in., and a third side length that is the average of the other two side lengths
19.5 in.

Name the types of quadrilaterals that do *not* have the given property.

24. trapezoid, parallelogram, rectangle

24. four congruent sides
See left.
25. four 90° angles
trapezoid, parallelogram, rhombus

9-3 Classifying Polygons   **473**

21.

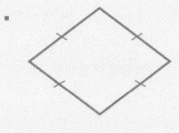

rhombus

GPS Use the Guided Problem Solving worksheet with Exercise 13.

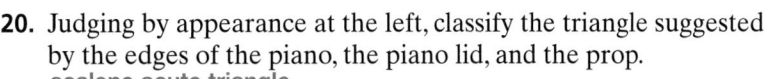

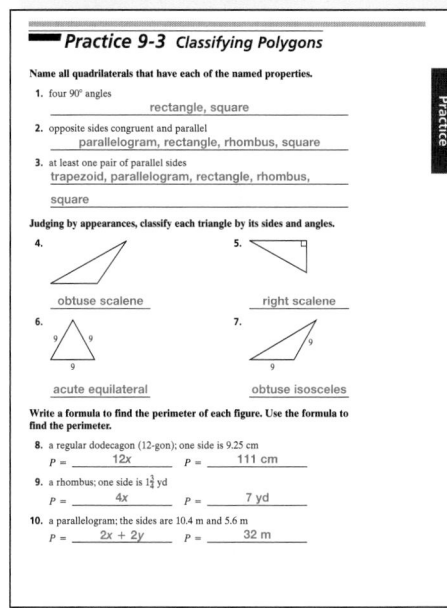

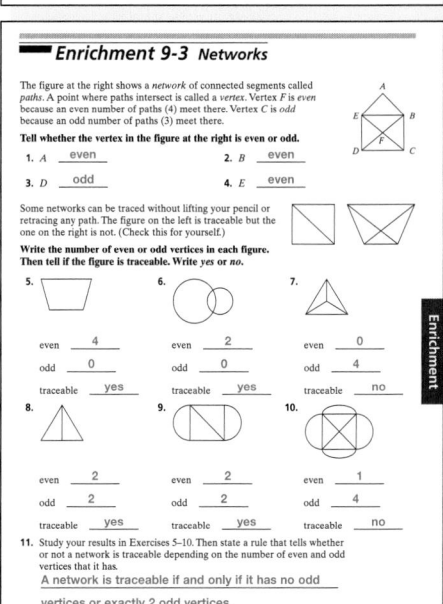

 **Lesson Quiz 9-3**

Name the following.

1. a type of triangle that has at least two congruent sides and one right angle
isosceles right triangle

2. a type of quadrilateral that can have opposite sides parallel and no right angles
parallelogram, rhombus

3. Write a formula for the perimeter of a regular heptagon (7 sides). Evaluate for a side of 12 in. **P = 7x; 84 in.**

Diversity
Exercises 26, 27 Ask students who are from countries other than the United States to bring to class their country's flag or a picture of it. Have the class name all the geometric shapes in the flags.

Test Prep

Resources
For additional practice with a variety of test item formats:
• Test Prep, p. 517
• Test-Taking Strategies, p. 512
• Test-Taking Strategies With Transparencies

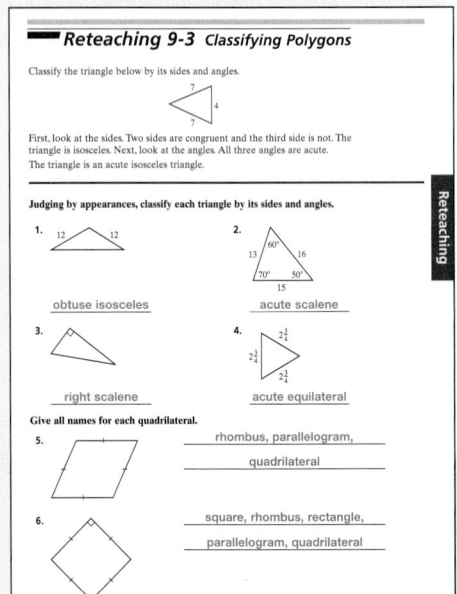

C Challenge

Name three different figures in each flag. For each triangle, state the type of triangle.

26. Answers may vary. Sample: trapezoid, equilateral triangle, rectangle
27. Answers may vary. Sample: trapezoid, isosceles triangle, right triangle

 **Writing in Math**

Are all equilateral triangles isosceles? Are all isosceles triangles equilateral? Explain.

See back of book.

26.
Flag of Philippines
See left.

27.
Flag of Antigua
See left.

The lengths of two sides of an isosceles triangle are given. What is the perimeter? Explain. 28–30. See margin.

28. 10 cm, 12 cm   **29.** 5 cm, 12 cm   **30.** 12 cm, 12 cm

31. a. ⎡Algebra⎤ A decagon is a polygon with 10 sides. Write a formula for the perimeter of a regular decagon. **P = 10x**
   b. Find the perimeter of a regular decagon with sides of 14.5 m.
   c. Find the length of a side of a regular decagon that has a **b. 145 m** perimeter of 22 ft. **2.2 ft**

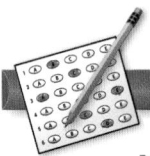  **Test Prep**

Multiple Choice

Take It to the NET
Online lesson quiz at
www.PHSchool.com
Web Code: ada-0903

32. What is the perimeter of a regular pentagon with a side length of 4.9 cm? **C**
   A. 4.9 cm   **B.** 14.7 cm   **C.** 24.5 cm   **D.** 29.4 cm

33. What is the perimeter of a square that has a side length of $\frac{3}{4}$ ft? **H**
   F. $\frac{3}{16}$ ft   **G.** $\frac{3}{4}$ ft   **H.** 3 ft   **I.** 4 ft

Short Response

34. Is a square a rhombus? Explain your answer. **See back of book.**

35. Is a square a rectangle? Explain your answer. **See back of book.**

Mixed Review

Lesson 9-2
36. A transversal intersects two parallel lines, forming eight angles. One angle measures 60°. Sketch a diagram showing the measures of all eight angles. **See back of book.**

Lesson 8-7 ● **37. Parades** A town parade included modern and antique cycles. The modern cycles had two wheels and the antique cycles had three wheels. Altogether there were 64 wheels on the 28 cycles. How many of the cycles had three wheels? **8 antique cycles**

Lessons 7-2 and 7-5 **Solve each equation.**

38. $x + 20 + 2x = 41$ **7**   **39.** $53 - 6x = 13 - 2x$ **10**

Reteaching 9-3 Classifying Polygons

Classify the triangle below by its sides and angles.

First, look at the sides. Two sides are congruent and the third side is not. The triangle is isosceles. Next, look at the angles. All three angles are acute. The triangle is an acute isosceles triangle.

Judging by appearances, classify each triangle by its sides and angles.

1. **obtuse isosceles**
2. **acute scalene**
3. **right scalene**
4. **acute equilateral**

Give all names for each quadrilateral.

5. rhombus, parallelogram, quadrilateral
6. square, rhombus, rectangle, parallelogram, quadrilateral

Alternative Assessment

Have students write a note to an absent classmate explaining various ways to classify the types of triangles and polygons studied in this lesson. Have them include sketches.

28. If the congruent sides are 10 cm, then the perimeter is 32 cm. If the congruent sides are 12 cm, then the perimeter is 34 cm.
29–30. See back of book.

Angles of a Polygon

For Use With Lesson 9-3

In previous courses, you learned that the sum of the measures of the angles of a triangle is 180°. Now you have the tools to prove that this is true with deductive reasoning.

In the figure, $\overleftrightarrow{AC} \parallel \overleftrightarrow{DE}$. If two parallel lines are cut by a transversal, then alternate interior angles are congruent. Therefore, $\angle 1 \cong \angle 4$, or $m\angle 1 = m\angle 4$. Similarly, $m\angle 3 = m\angle 5$. $\angle ABC$ is a straight angle, so $m\angle 1 + m\angle 2 + m\angle 3 = 180°$. Substitute $m\angle 4$ for $m\angle 1$ and $m\angle 5$ for $m\angle 3$ and you get $m\angle 4 + m\angle 2 + m\angle 5 = 180°$. These are the angles of $\triangle DBE$.

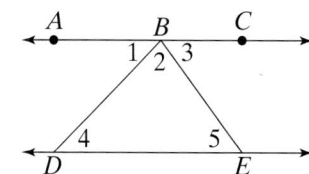

You can use triangles to find the sum of the measures of the angles of any polygon.

EXAMPLE

Find the sum of the measures of the angles of a hexagon.

The hexagon has **6** vertices.
From vertex A, there are **5** segments to the other vertices.
The segments determine **4** triangles.

number of triangles	·	number of degrees in angles of triangle	=	sum of measures of angles of hexagon
4	·	180°	=	720°

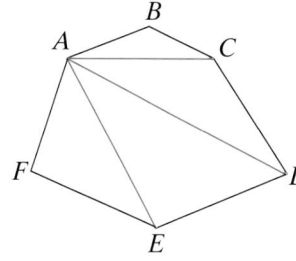

EXERCISES

Find the sum of the measures of the angles of each polygon.

1. a quadrilateral **360°**

2. a decagon (10 sides) **1,440°**

3. an octagon **1,080°**

4. a dodecagon (12 sides) **1,800°**

5. Reasoning Write a formula for the sum of the measures of the angles of an n-gon (n sides). **$s = 180(n - 2)$**

6. Find the value of x in the figure at the right. **105°**

7. Writing in Math The sum of the measures of the angles of a polygon is 1,260°. Explain how you can find the number of sides. See below.

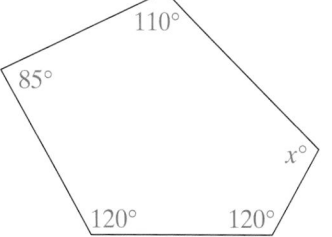

Find the number of sides in the polygon whose angle measures have the given sum.

8. 540° **5**

9. 900° **7**

10. 1,620° **11**

11. 18,000° **102**

7. Answers may vary. Sample:
Use the formula $s = 180(n - 2)$.
Substitute 1,260 for s and solve.
There are 9 sides.

Teaching Notes

Teaching Tip
Point out to students that by drawing all the diagonals from one vertex of a polygon, you can see that any polygon can be divided into a certain number of triangles. The number of triangles for a polygon of n sides is always $n - 2$.

Teaching Tip

EXAMPLE
Some students may not understand why you multiply by 180°. Help students see that angles from 4 different triangles form $\angle A$, and the other angles from those same triangles form the other angles of the hexagon. Therefore, you can add the measures of the angles of the triangles to get the sum of the measures of the angles of the hexagon. Since there are four triangles, you are essentially adding 180 four times.

Additional Example

Find the sum of the measures of the angles of a polygon with 15 sides. **2,340°**

1. Plan

Lesson Preview

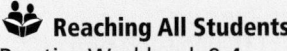
Check Skills You'll Need

Classifying Polygons
Lesson 9-3: Examples 1 and 2;
Exercises 1–9.
Extra Practice, p. 752.

Lesson Resources

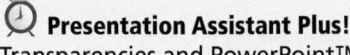
Teaching Resources
Practice, Reteaching, Enrichment

Reaching All Students
Practice Workbook 9-4
Spanish Practice Workbook 9-4
Guided Problem Solving 9-4

Presentation Assistant Plus!
Transparencies and PowerPoint™
• Check Skills You'll Need 9-4
• Additional Examples 9-4
• Student Edition Answers 9-4
• Lesson Quiz 9-4
PH Presentation Pro CD-ROM 9-4

ASSESSMENT SYSTEM

Computer Test Generator CD-ROM

Technology
Resource Pro® CD-ROM
Computer Test Generator CD-ROM
PH Presentation Pro CD-ROM

www.PHSchool.com

Student Site
• Teacher Web Code: adk-5500
• Algebra Readiness
  Puzzles 105, 106
• Self-grading Lesson Quiz
PH SuccessNet Teacher Center
• Lesson Planner
• Resources

Plus *i*TEXT

What You'll Learn

OBJECTIVE 1 To draw a diagram to solve a problem

...And Why

To find the number of diagonals in an octagon

Check Skills You'll Need

Sketch each figure.
1–5. See below.
1. equilateral triangle

2. rectangle

3. pentagon

4. hexagon

5. octagon

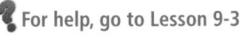
For help, go to Lesson 9-3.

1.
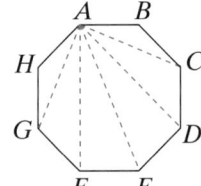

2.

3.

4.

5.

TEXT Interactive lesson includes instant self-check, tutorials, and activities.

OBJECTIVE
1 Draw a Diagram

Math Strategies in Action
Car designers rely on computer-design programs to create, test, and modify their plans. The process of drawing a diagram helps them discover any problems they may have and see possible solutions.

Drawing a diagram is an important problem-solving tool.

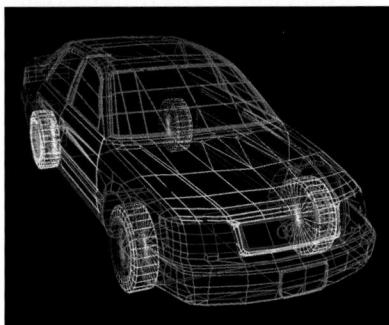

1 EXAMPLE Real-World Problem Solving

How many diagonals does an octagon have?

Read and Understand

In reading the problem, make sure you understand the meanings of all of the terms.

1. What is an octagon? a polygon with 8 sides

2. What is a diagonal?
   a line segment that connects two nonconsecutive vertices

Plan and Solve

One strategy for solving this problem is to draw a diagram and count the diagonals. An octagon has eight sides. You can draw five diagonals from one vertex of an octagon.

$\overline{AG}, \overline{AF}, \overline{AE}, \overline{AD}$, and $\overline{AC}$ are some of the diagonals.

3. There are 5 diagonals drawn from vertex A. Copy the diagram. Now find the number of diagonals you can draw from vertex B. 5

4. How many new diagonals can you draw from vertex C? 4

476 Chapter 9 Spatial Thinking

Ongoing Assessment and Intervention

Before the Lesson
Diagnose prerequisite skills using:
• Check Skills You'll Need

During the Lesson
Monitor progress using:
• Check Understanding
• Additional Examples
• Test Prep

After the Lesson
Assess knowledge using:
• Lesson Quiz
• Computer Test Generator CD-ROM

It may be helpful to organize your results as you count the diagonals.

Make a table similar to the one below and fill in the number of diagonals from each vertex. Do not count a diagonal twice. (The segment from A to C is the same segment as the one from C to A.)

Then add to find the total number of diagonals.

Vertex	Number of Diagonals
A	5
B	5
C	4
D	■ 3
E	■ 2
F	■ 1
G	■ 0
H	■ 0
Total	■ 20

Look Back and Check

Counting the diagonals after they have all been drawn is not an easy task. To check your results, you may want to try a different approach.

Start with figures with fewer sides and see whether there is a pattern to the total numbers of diagonals as you increase the number of sides.

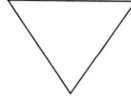  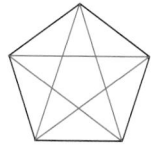 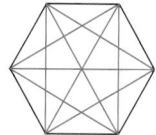

Figure	Number of Sides	Number of Diagonals
Triangle	3	0
Quadrilateral	4	2
Pentagon	5	5
Hexagon	6	9

Notice that the total number of diagonals increases as you increase the number of sides of the polygon. First the number increases by 2, then by 3, and then by 4. Continue this pattern to check your results.

✓ **Check Understanding**

5. How many diagonals does a decagon have? 35

Reaching All Students

Below Level Ask students to tell how they have used a diagram to explain something to someone.
Answers may vary. Sample: drawing a map to give directions

Advanced Learners Challenge students to write an equation that relates the number of diagonals d to the number of vertices n of a regular n-gon. $d = \frac{n(n-3)}{2}$ or $d = \frac{n^2-3n}{2}$.

Error Prevention See note on page 477.
Tactile Learners See note on page 477.

Math Background

Drawing a diagram often helps you model relationships or understand a situation more clearly. A diagram can also serve as a written record of your thought processes and lets you see the steps you have taken to solve a problem. By analyzing the data and organizing it into your diagram, you may see patterns, or even an algebraic equation, to use in solving the problem.

Teaching Notes

1 EXAMPLE Error Prevention
To help students avoid counting diagonals twice in their diagrams, suggest that they put a tick mark on each diagonal as they count it.

Tactile Learners
Have students use geoboards to model the diagonals of a quadrilateral, a pentagon, and a hexagon.

Additional Examples

 How many diagonals does a nonagon (9 sides) have?
27 diagonals

Closure

Ask students: *How can drawing a diagram help you solve a problem?*
Answers may vary. Sample: Drawing a diagram gives a visual representation of the problem.

3. Practice

Assignment Guide

1 Objective 1
Ⓐ Ⓑ **Core** 1–13
Ⓒ **Extension** 14, 15

Test Prep 16–19
Mixed Review 20–30

Practice 9-4 Draw a Diagram

Solve by drawing a diagram.

1. How many diagonals does a quadrilateral have?

   2

2. Which quadrilaterals always have congruent diagonals?

   square, rectangle, isosceles trapezoid

3. Find a formula for the number of diagonals d in a polygon with n sides. Complete the table to help you. Look for a pattern.

Figure	Number of sides	Number of vertices	Number of diagonals from each vertex	Total number of diagonals
triangle	3	3	0	0
quadrilateral	4	4	1	2
pentagon	5	5	2	5
hexagon	6	6	3	9
octagon	8	8	5	20
n-gon	n	n	$n-3$	$\frac{n(n-3)}{2}$

$d = \frac{n(n-3)}{2}$

4. One day in the lunch line, Maurice was ahead of Aquia and behind Rochelle. Rochelle was ahead of Shequille and behind Whitney. Shequille was ahead of Maurice. Who was last?

   Aquia

5. A mail carrier leaves the post office at 10:00 A.M. and travels 4 miles south, then 7 miles east, then 5 miles south, then 10 miles west, and 9 miles north. At the end of her route, how far and in which direction is the mail carrier from the post office?

   She is 3 miles west of the post office.

Enrichment 9-4 Angles of Regular Polygons

In a regular polygon, all sides are congruent and all angles are congruent. Each interior angle of any regular n-gon has a certain measure. You can write a formula to find this measure based on the number of sides n.

1. An equilateral triangle is regular. What is the measure of each interior angle of an equilateral triangle? Explain how you know.

   60°; The sum of the measures of the angles of a

   triangle is 180°. An equilateral triangle has 3 angles

   that are all the same size, so each is 180 ÷ 3 = 60°.

A quadrilateral can be divided into two triangles by a diagonal from a single vertex. The sum of the angles of any quadrilateral is 2(180) = 360°.

Complete the table. Look for a pattern. Use diagrams if necessary.

	Polygon	n	Number of triangles	Sum of interior angles	Measure of one angle in regular n-gon
2.	Triangle	3	1	180°	60°
3.	Quadrilateral	4	2	2(180) = 360°	90°
4.	Pentagon	5	3	3(180) = 540°	108°
5.	Hexagon	6	4	4(180) = 720°	120°
6.	Octagon	8	6	6(180) = 1,080°	135°
7.	Decagon	10	8	8(180) = 1,440°	144°
8.	Dodecagon	12	10	10(180) = 1,800°	150°
9.	n-gon	n	$n-2$	$(n-2)(180)$	$\frac{180(n-2)}{n}$

10. Complete the conjecture:
    The measure of an interior angle of a regular n-gon is $\frac{180(n-2)}{n}$.

EXERCISES

For more exercises, see Extra Practice.

Practice and Problem Solving

Ⓐ **Practice by Example**

Example 1
(page 476)

Solve by drawing a diagram.

1. **Retail Delivery** A furniture delivery truck leaves the store at 8 A.M. It travels 6 miles east, then 4 miles south, then 2 miles west, and then 4 miles north. At the end of this route, how far is the truck from the store? **4 mi**

2. Bill is older than Jim and younger than Jose. Jose is older than Chris and younger than Tandala. Chris is older than Jim. Bill is younger than Tandala. Chris is older than Bill. Who is youngest? **Jim**

3. **Geometry** How many triangles can you form in a hexagon if you draw all of the diagonals from only one vertex? **4 triangles**

4. **Game Schedules** Eight soccer teams are to play each other two times in a season. How many games will be played? **56 games**

5. There are 25 students in a math class. Ten students are in the math club. Twelve students are in the band. Five students are in both. **GPS** How many students in the math class are members of neither club? **8 students**

10. Answers may vary. Sample: Count out a substantial number of sheets, perhaps 200. Then measure the thickness of that stack and divide the measurement by 200.

Ⓑ **Apply Your Skills**

Strategies

- Account for All Possibilities
- Draw a Diagram
- Look for a Pattern
- Make a Model
- Make a Table
- Simplify the Problem
- Simulate the Problem
- Solve by Graphing
- Try, Test, Revise
- Use Multiple Strategies
- Work Backward
- Write an Equation
- Write a Proportion

Solve using any strategy.

6. **Geometry** Snoozles are always born as twins, and each snoozle always moves in the opposite direction from its twin. Twin snoozles are at the origin of a coordinate plane. One follows the path $(0, 0)$ to $(1, 3)$ to $(2, 2)$ to $(4, 7)$. What path will its twin travel?
   $(0, 0)$ to $(-1, -3)$ to $(-2, -2)$ to $(-4, -7)$

7. **Measurement** Maureen cut a 20-cm ribbon into exactly three pieces. The first piece is 3 cm shorter than the second piece. The third piece is 4 cm shorter than the second piece. Find the length of the shortest piece. **5 cm**

8. **Car Rental** A rental car costs $34.95 for the first 150 miles and $.35 for each additional mile. How much will the rental car cost for driving 275 miles? **$78.70**

9. A student was standing in the middle of a line. Twenty-three students were ahead of her. How many students were in the line? **47 students**

10. **Writing in Math** Suppose you want to find the thickness of one sheet of paper. Describe the problem solving method you would use. **See above left.**

11. Shana has three pets, a dog, a cat, and a bird. One of them is named Sammy. Noodles is younger than both the bird and the dog. Fluffy is green. Which pet has the name Sammy? **the dog**

12. **Geometry** You can draw one segment to connect two points and three distinct segments to connect three named points. How many segments can you draw to connect five points if no three of the points lie on the same line? **10 segments**

GPS Use the Guided Problem Solving worksheet with Exercise 5.

13. Two friends rented a canoe for 10 days. One friend used the canoe for 6 days. The other friend used the canoe for 4 days. How much of the $150 rental fee should each friend pay? **$90, $60**

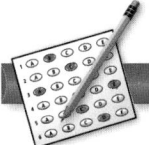 **Challenge**

14. Container A has twice the capacity of container B. Container A is full of sand and container B is empty. Suppose $\frac{1}{8}$ of the sand in container A is poured into container B. What fractional part of container B will contain sand? $\frac{1}{4}$

15. Points P, Q, R, and S appear in that order on a line. The ratio $PQ : QR$ is 3 : 4, and the ratio $QR : RS$ is 2 : 5. The length PQ is 6 in. Find the length PS. **34 in.**

Test Prep

Multiple Choice

16. How many diagonals does a hexagon have? **B**
A. 6   **B.** 9   **C.** 12   **D.** 18

17. Some taxicabs begin each trip by setting the meter to $1.50. The meter then adds $.40 for each $\frac{1}{4}$ mi traveled. If a trip costs $7.90, how far did the cab travel? **I**
F. 160 mi   **G.** 16 mi   **H.** 8 mi   **I.** 4 mi

 Take It to the NET
Online lesson quiz at
www.PHSchool.com
Web Code: ada-0904

18. What is the perimeter of a regular hexagon with side length of 6.3 cm? **C**
A. 25.2 cm   **B.** 31.5 cm   **C.** 37.8 cm   **D.** 50.4 cm

Short Response

19. A coin collector has 53 rare coins. This is 12 fewer than 5 times the number there were a year ago. **(a)** Write an equation you could use to find out how many coins the collector had a year ago. **(b)** Solve the equation and show your work. See margin.

Mixed Review

Lesson 9-3

Classify each triangle by its sides and angles.

20. no congruent sides and one right angle scalene right triangle

21. three congruent sides equilateral triangle

22. one obtuse angle and no congruent sides scalene obtuse triangle

23. a 90° angle and two congruent sides isosceles right triangle

Lesson 8-8 **24. Ticket Sales** Adult tickets for the school musical sell for $8 and student tickets sell for $5 each. Let x be the number of adult tickets sold and y be the number of student tickets sold. The school hopes to make at least $1,000. Write an inequality to model the situation. Show all solutions by graphing the inequality. See back of book.

25. $\frac{7}{50}$, 14%
26. $4\frac{1}{2}$, 450%
27. $\frac{11}{100}$, 11%
28. $\frac{1}{50}$, 2%
29. $\frac{1}{8}$, 12.5%
30. 1 and 100%

Lesson 6-5

Write each decimal as a fraction in simplest form and as a percent.
25–30. See left.
25. 0.14   **26.** 4.5   **27.** 0.11   **28.** 0.02   **29.** 0.125   **30.** 1

9-4   Draw a Diagram   **479**

19. [2] 53 = 5x − 12;
53 = 5x − 12
65 = 5x
13 = x
13 coins

[1] minor error
OR answer
only

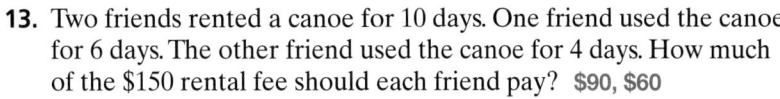

4. Assess

PowerPoint Lesson Quiz 9-4
Solve.
1. How many diagonals does a quadrilateral have?
2 diagonals
2. How many triangles can you form if you draw all the diagonals from one vertex of a pentagon? 3 triangles
3. How many triangles can you form if you draw all the diagonals of a rectangle?
8 triangles

Tactile Learners
Exercise 14 Have students work in pairs. Provide them with 2-cup and 1-cup measuring cups and sand to aid in solving this problem. Make sure both measuring cups are marked in fourths.

Test Prep

Resources
For additional practice with a variety of test item formats:
• Test Prep, p. 517
• Test-Taking Strategies, p. 512
• Test-Taking Strategies With Transparencies

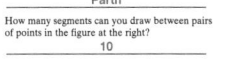

Reteaching 9-4 *Draw a Diagram*

Solve by drawing a diagram.
Kara and Karl are twins with the same tastes. They like pizza more than tacos, but less than steak. They like mashed potatoes more than tacos, but less than hamburgers. They like hamburgers more than pizza, but less than steak. Which of these foods do they like the most?
Let p = pizza, t = tacos, s = steak, m = mashed potatoes, and h = hamburgers.
Draw a diagram with 5 blanks. Since Kara and Karl like pizza more than tacos, but less than steak, start by putting s, p, and t in the first 3 blanks.

  s p t

They like mashed potatoes more than tacos, but less than hamburgers. This moves tacos down. Tentatively, we have:

  s p h m t

They like hamburgers more than pizza but less than steak.

  s h p m t

We still cannot be sure if they like pizza more or less than mashed potatoes, but that is not important for answering the question. Kara and Karl like steak the most.

Solve by drawing a diagram.

1. Mindy is taller than Olga, but shorter than Thomas. Thomas is taller than Sven, but shorter than Parth. Sven is taller than Olga, but shorter than Mindy. Who's the tallest?

_____ _____ _____ _____ _____
Parth

2. How many segments can you draw between pairs of points in the figure at the right?
10

Alternative Assessment

Group students in pairs. Have each pair collaborate to write a word problem that can be solved using a diagram. Have pairs exchange problems and use a diagram to solve each other's problem.

479

1. Plan

Lesson Preview

✔ Check Skills You'll Need

Similar Figures
Lesson 6-3: Example 1;
Exercises 1–3.
Extra Practice, p. 749.

Lesson Resources

📁 **Teaching Resources**
Practice, Reteaching, Enrichment
Checkpoint Quiz 1

👥 **Reaching All Students**
Practice Workbook 9-5
Spanish Practice Workbook 9-5
Reading and Math Literacy 9B
Spanish Reading and Math
  Literacy 9B
Spanish Checkpoint Quiz 1
Guided Problem Solving 9-5
Technology Activities 18

⏱ **Presentation Assistant Plus!**
Transparencies and PowerPoint™
• Check Skills You'll Need 9-5
• Additional Examples 9-5
• Student Edition Answers 9-5
• Lesson Quiz 9-5
PH Presentation Pro CD-ROM 9-5

♻ **ASSESSMENT SYSTEM**

Checkpoint Quiz 1
Computer Test Generator CD-ROM

💻 **Technology**
Resource Pro® CD-ROM
Computer Test Generator CD-ROM
PH Presentation Pro CD-ROM

💻 **www.PHSchool.com**
Student Site
• Teacher Web Code: adk-5500
• Algebra Readiness Puzzles 70
• Self-grading Lesson Quiz
PH SuccessNet Teacher Center
• Lesson Planner
• Resources

Plus 📱 **iTEXT**

480

What You'll Learn

OBJECTIVE 1 To identify corresponding parts of congruent triangles

OBJECTIVE 2 To determine whether triangles are congruent

. . . And Why

To use congruent figures for finding distance

✔ Check Skills You'll Need

$\triangle ABC \sim \triangle XYZ$. **For the given part of $\triangle ABC$, find the corresponding part of $\triangle XYZ$.**

1. $\angle A$ $\angle X$ **2.** $\angle C$ $\angle Z$
3. $\overline{AB}$ $\overline{XY}$ **4.** $\overline{CA}$ $\overline{ZX}$

❓ For help, go to Lesson 6-3.

New Vocabulary
• congruent figures

OBJECTIVE

1 Identifying Corresponding Parts

Investigation

Exploring Congruence

1. Have each member of your group cut plastic straws 3 cm, 6 cm, and 7 cm long. String an 18-cm string through the three straws. Tie the string just tight enough to form a strong triangle without bending any straws. **Check students' work.**

2. Hold the triangles up to one another to compare. Are they the same size and shape? Describe how the angle measures compare. **Yes; all the triangles have sides of the same three lengths and angles with the same three measures.**

Congruent figures have the same size and shape, and their corresponding parts have equal measures.

The triangles at the right are congruent. You use tick marks to indicate congruent segments, and arcs to mark congruent angles. You write a congruence statement by listing the corresponding angles in the same order.

You can use corresponding parts of congruent triangles to find distance.

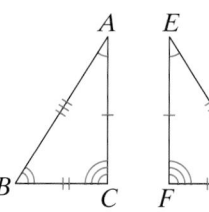

$\triangle ABC \cong \triangle EDF$

$\angle A \cong \angle E$ $\overline{AB} \cong \overline{ED}$
$\angle B \cong \angle D$ $\overline{BC} \cong \overline{DF}$
$\angle C \cong \angle F$ $\overline{AC} \cong \overline{EF}$

Test-Taking Tip
When two triangles are congruent, you can sketch the shapes side by side to help identify congruent parts.

📱 **iTEXT** Interactive lesson includes instant self-check, tutorials, and activities.

1 EXAMPLE **Real-World** 🌐 **Problem Solving**

Measurement $\triangle AMN \cong \triangle ABC$. **Name the corresponding parts.**

a. congruent angles
$\angle M \cong \angle B, \angle N \cong \angle C,$
$\angle MAN \cong \angle BAC$

b. congruent sides
$\overline{MN} \cong \overline{BC}, \overline{NA} \cong \overline{CA}, \overline{MA} \cong \overline{BA}$

c. Find the distance from M to N.
Since $\overline{MN} \cong \overline{BC}$ and $BC = 100$ yd, $MN = 100$ yd.

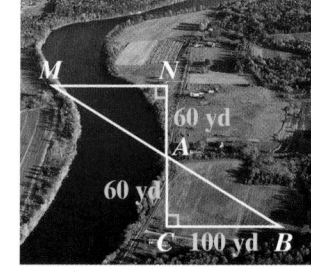

480 Chapter 9 Spatial Thinking

 Ongoing Assessment and Intervention

Before the Lesson	**During the Lesson**	**After the Lesson**
Diagnose prerequisite skills using: • Check Skills You'll Need	Monitor progress using: • Check Understanding • Additional Examples • Test Prep	Assess knowledge using: • Lesson Quiz • Computer Test Generator CD-ROM • Chapter Checkpoint 1 (p. 484)

1. $\triangle ABC \cong \triangle DEC$. List all pairs of congruent corresponding sides and angles. Then find AC. $\overline{AB} \cong \overline{DE}$, $\overline{BC} \cong \overline{EC}$, $\overline{AC} \cong \overline{DC}$, $\angle A \cong \angle D$, $\angle B \cong \angle E$, $\angle BCA \cong \angle ECD$, $AC = 50$ m

OBJECTIVE

2 **Identifying Congruent Triangles**

You use corresponding parts of triangles to identify congruent triangles. Below are three of the ways to show that two triangles are congruent.

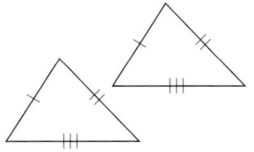
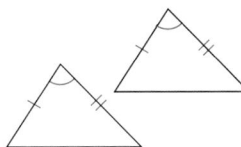
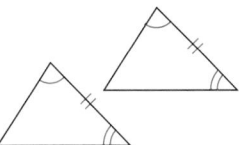

Side–Side–Side
(SSS)

Side–Angle–Side
(SAS)

Angle–Side–Angle
(ASA)

2 EXAMPLE **Identifying Congruent Triangles**

List the congruent corresponding parts of each pair of triangles. Write a congruence statement for the triangles.

a.
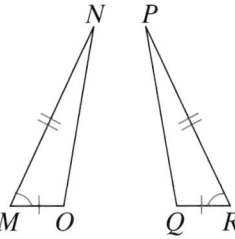

b.
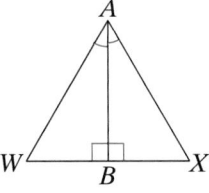

$\overline{MO} \cong \overline{RQ}$ **Side**

$\angle M \cong \angle R$ **Angle**

$\overline{MN} \cong \overline{RP}$ **Side**

$\triangle MNO \cong \triangle RPQ$ by SAS.

$\angle WAB \cong \angle XAB$ **Angle**

$\overline{AB} \cong \overline{AB}$ **Side**

$\angle ABW \cong \angle ABX$ **Angle**

$\triangle WAB \cong \triangle XAB$ by ASA.

✓ **Check Understanding** Example 2

2. For the two highlighted triangles, list the congruent corresponding parts. Write a congruence statement (and reason) for the triangles. $\overline{FJ} \cong \overline{FG}$, $\overline{JI} \cong \overline{GH}$, $\overline{FI} \cong \overline{FH}$, $\triangle JFI \cong \triangle GFH$ by SSS

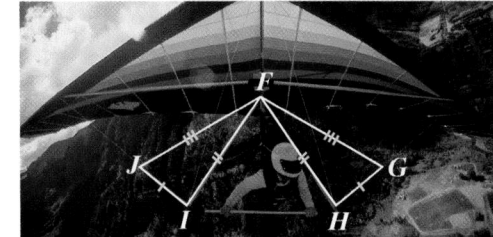

9-5 Congruence   **481**

👥 **Reaching All Students**

| **Below Level** Ask: *In Example 2b, how do you know that* $\angle ABW \cong$ $\angle ABX$? They are both right angles. | **Advanced Learners** Ask: *If two triangles are marked congruent by SAS, are the other two pairs of corresponding angles congruent?* Yes; all pairs of corresponding angles are congruent. | **Error Prevention** See note on page 483. |

---

2. Teach

Professional Development

Math Background

Congruent polygons have the same size and shape. However, congruent polygons are not considered "equal." The *measures* of corresponding parts of congruent polygons are equal.

Teaching Notes

Investigation (Optional)

Point out that these are approximate models of the triangles, so students can overlook small variations caused by differences in how tightly the strings are tied or other mechanical considerations.

PowerPoint

🖥 Additional Examples

1 In the figure, $\triangle TUV \cong \triangle WUX$.
See back of book.

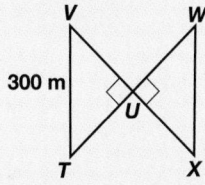

a. Name the corresponding congruent angles.
b. Name the corresponding congruent sides.
c. Find the length of $\overline{WX}$.

2 List the congruent corresponding parts of each pair of triangles. Write a congruence statement for the triangles.
See back of book.

a.
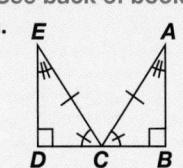

b.
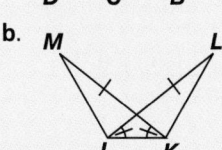

Closure

Ask students to name the three ways to show that two triangles are congruent. See back of book.

481

Assignment Guide

1 Objective 1
- Ⓐ Ⓑ Core 1–16, 20–22
- Ⓒ Extension 33, 34

2 Objective 2
- Ⓐ Ⓑ Core 17–19, 23–32
- Ⓒ Extension 35–37

Test Prep 38–40
Mixed Review 41–47

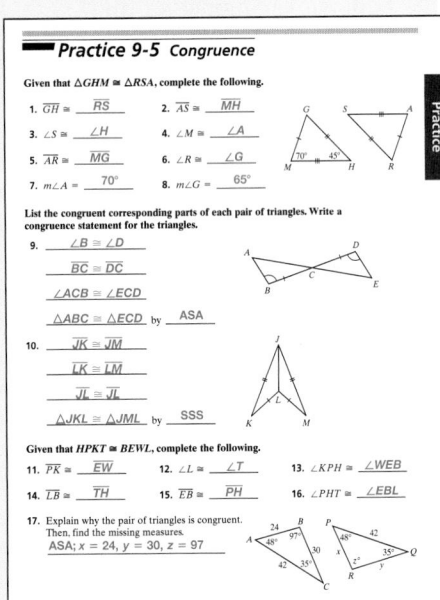

Practice 9-5 *Congruence*

Given that △GHM ≅ △RSA, complete the following.

1. $\overline{GH} \cong$ ___ $\overline{RS}$ 2. $\overline{AS} \cong$ ___ $\overline{MH}$

3. ∠S ≅ ___ ∠H   4. ∠M ≅ ___ ∠A

5. $\overline{AR} \cong$ ___ $\overline{MG}$ 6. ∠R ≅ ___ ∠G

7. m∠A = ___ 70°   8. m∠G = ___ 65°

List the congruent corresponding parts of each pair of triangles. Write a congruence statement for the triangles.

9. ∠B ≅ ∠D
   $\overline{BC} \cong \overline{DC}$
   ∠ACB ≅ ∠ECD
   △ABC ≅ △ECD by ___ ASA

10. $\overline{JK} \cong \overline{JM}$
   $\overline{LK} \cong \overline{LM}$
   $\overline{JL} \cong \overline{JL}$
   △JKL ≅ △JML by ___ SSS

Given that HPKT ≅ BEWL, complete the following.

11. $\overline{PK} \cong$ ___ $\overline{EW}$ 12. ∠L ≅ ___ ∠T   13. ∠KPH ≅ ___ ∠WEB

14. $\overline{LB} \cong$ ___ $\overline{TH}$ 15. $\overline{EB} \cong$ ___ $\overline{PH}$ 16. ∠PHT ≅ ___ ∠EBL

17. Explain why the pair of triangles is congruent.
   Then, find the missing measures.
   ASA; x = 24, y = 30, z = 97

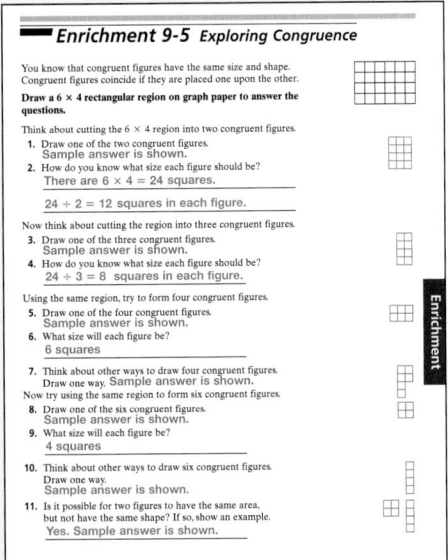

Enrichment 9-5 *Exploring Congruence*

You know that congruent figures have the same size and shape. Congruent figures coincide if they are placed one upon the other.

Draw a 6 × 4 rectangular region on graph paper to answer the questions.

Think about cutting the 6 × 4 region into two congruent figures.
1. Draw one of the two congruent figures. Sample answer is shown.
2. How do you know what size each figure should be? There are 6 × 4 = 24 squares.
   24 ÷ 2 = 12 squares in each figure.

Now think about cutting the region into three congruent figures.
3. Draw one of the three congruent figures. Sample answer is shown.
4. How do you know what size each figure should be? 24 ÷ 3 = 8 squares in each figure.

Using the same region, try to form four congruent figures.
5. Draw one of the four congruent figures. Sample answer is shown.
6. What size will each figure be? 6 squares

7. Think about other ways to draw four congruent figures. Draw one way. Sample answer is shown.
Now try using the same region to form six congruent figures.
8. Draw one of the six congruent figures. Sample answer is shown.
9. What size will each figure be? 4 squares

10. Think about other ways to draw six congruent figures. Draw one way. Sample answer is shown.

11. Is it possible for two figures to have the same area, but not have the same shape? If so, show an example. Yes. Sample answer is shown.

EXERCISES

🔖 *For more exercises, see Extra Practice.*

Practice and Problem Solving

Ⓐ **Practice by Example**

Example 1
(page 480)

△ABC ≅ △DEF.
Complete each statement.

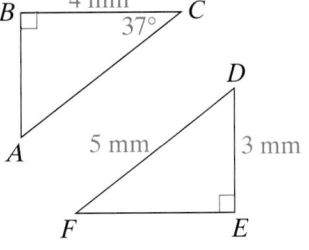

1. ∠A ≅ ___ ∠D   2. ∠B ≅ ___ ∠E

3. m∠C = ___ m∠F
   m∠F, or 37°
4. m∠B = ___
   m∠E, or 90°

5. m∠A = ___
   m∠D, or 53°
6. $\overline{AC} \cong$ ___ $\overline{DF}$

7. $\overline{EF} \cong$ ___ $\overline{BC}$ 8. $\overline{BA} \cong$ ___ $\overline{ED}$

9. AC = ___
   DF, or 5 mm
10. FE = ___
   CB, or 4 mm

11. △CBA ≅ ___
   △FED
12. △BAC ≅ ___
   △EDF
13. △ACB ≅ ___
   △DFE

🌐 **Quilt Patterns** Use the quilt design for Exercises 14–16.

14. ∠A ≅ ∠C ≅ ∠M ≅ ∠K,
   ∠E ≅ ∠D ≅ ∠I ≅ ∠J,
   ∠B ≅ ∠H ≅ ∠L ≅ ∠F

14. The yellow triangles are congruent. Name the corresponding congruent angles.
   See left.

15. $\overline{EB} \cong \overline{JF} \cong \overline{IL} \cong \overline{DH}$,
   $\overline{BD} \cong \overline{FE} \cong \overline{LJ} \cong \overline{HI}$,
   $\overline{DE} \cong \overline{EJ} \cong \overline{JI} \cong \overline{ID}$

15. The red-and-blue triangles are congruent. Name the corresponding congruent sides.
   See left.

16. The dark blue triangles are isosceles and congruent, and GD = 10 in. Find the distance from G to I.
   10 in.

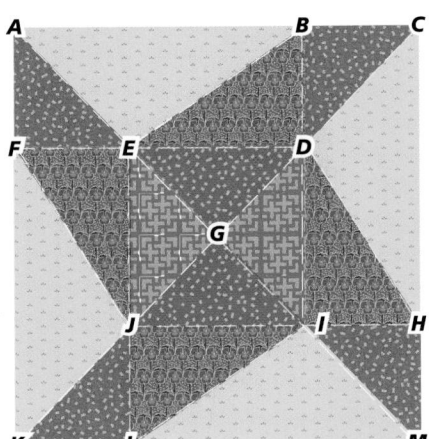

Example 2
(page 481)

For each pair of triangles, list the congruent corresponding parts. Write a congruence statement (and reason) for the triangles.

18. $\overline{DF} \cong \overline{SF}$, $\overline{EF} \cong \overline{TF}$,
   ∠DFE ≅ ∠SFT,
   △DFE ≅ △SFT by SAS

17. $\overline{BC} \cong \overline{HG}$, $\overline{AB} \cong \overline{KH}$,
   ∠B ≅ ∠H, △ABC ≅ △KHG
   by SAS

18. See left.

19. $\overline{ON} \cong \overline{RQ}$, $\overline{OM} \cong \overline{RP}$,
   $\overline{NM} \cong \overline{QP}$, △ONM ≅ △RQP
   by SSS

Ⓑ **Apply Your Skills**

21. $\overline{AB} \cong \overline{XY}$, $\overline{BC} \cong \overline{YZ}$,
   $\overline{AC} \cong \overline{XZ}$

Assume that △ABC ≅ △XYZ. Answer the following.

20. Name the corresponding congruent angles.
   ∠A ≅ ∠X, ∠B ≅ ∠Y, ∠C ≅ ∠Z

21. Name the corresponding congruent sides. See left.

22. If AB = 12 cm and BC = 15 cm, what is the length of $\overline{YZ}$? 15 cm

For each pair of triangles, list the congruent corresponding parts. Write a congruence statement (and reason) for the triangles.

23.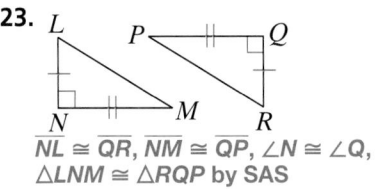

$\overline{NL} \cong \overline{QR}$, $\overline{NM} \cong \overline{QP}$, $\angle N \cong \angle Q$, $\triangle LNM \cong \triangle RQP$ by SAS

24.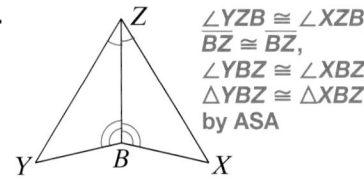

$\angle YZB \cong \angle XZB$, $\overline{BZ} \cong \overline{BZ}$, $\angle YBZ \cong \angle XBZ$, $\triangle YBZ \cong \triangle XBZ$ by ASA

25.

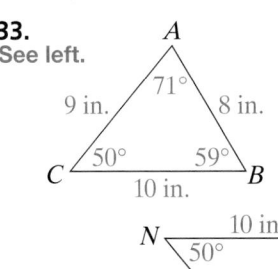
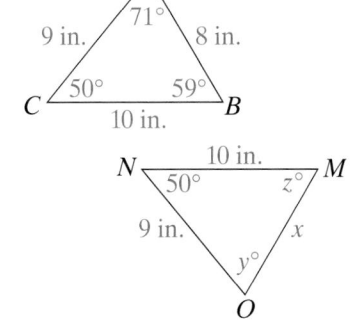

$\overline{KM} \cong \overline{JM}$, $\overline{ML} \cong \overline{ML}$, $\angle KML \cong \angle JML$, $\triangle KML \cong \triangle JML$ by SAS

26.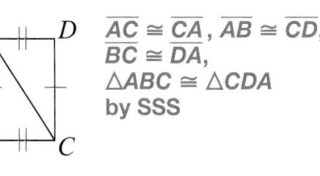

$\overline{AC} \cong \overline{CA}$, $\overline{AB} \cong \overline{CD}$, $\overline{BC} \cong \overline{DA}$, $\triangle ABC \cong \triangle CDA$ by SSS

Error Analysis The two figures in the diagram (left) are congruent. State whether each congruence statement is correct and explain.

27. $RAVK \cong NLUC$ Incorrect; $\angle R$ does not correspond with $\angle N$.

28. $RKVA \cong ULNC$ Incorrect; $\angle R$ does not correspond with $\angle U$.

29. $ARKV \cong CULN$ Incorrect; $\angle A$ does not correspond with $\angle C$.

30. $\overline{NL} \cong \overline{KV}$ Correct; these are corresponding sides.

31. $\angle V \cong \angle C$ Incorrect; $\angle V$ and $\angle C$ are not corresponding angles.

32. $\angle VAR \cong \angle LUC$ Correct; these are corresponding angles.

C Challenge

Explain why the triangles in each pair are congruent. Then find the missing measures in each diagram.

33. congruent by SAS; $y = 71$, $z = 59$, $x = 8$ in.

33. See left.

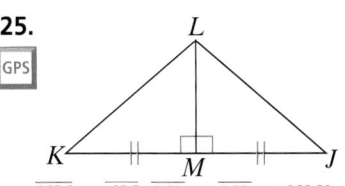

34.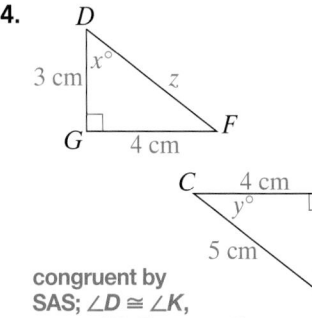

congruent by SAS; $\angle D \cong \angle K$, so $x = 53$. Because the sum of the angle measures in a triangle is 180°, $y = 37$ and $z = 5$ cm.

35a. $\triangle CDH$; congruent by SSS or by SAS

35b. $\triangle CBA$; congruent by SSS or by SAS

35. **Containers** The end of the shipping container at the left is a rectangle. The diagonals are congruent and intersect at point H. $\overline{HB} \cong \overline{HD}$ and $\overline{AH} \cong \overline{CH}$. Which triangle is congruent to the given triangle? Explain.
a. $\triangle ABH$
b. $\triangle ADC$ a–b. See above left.

36. **Reasoning** $\triangle KWR$ is *equiangular* (all angles are congruent). $\triangle ABJ$ is also equiangular. Can you use **Angle-Angle-Angle** (**AAA**) to show that two triangles are congruent? Use diagrams to justify your conclusion. See margin.

37. **Writing in Math** $\triangle ABC \cong \triangle XYZ$. What can you conclude about the perimeters of the triangles? Explain. The perimeters are equal. Since the sides of the triangles are congruent, the sums of their side lengths will be equal.

9-5 Congruence **483**

36. No; $\triangle ABJ$ and $\triangle KWR$ are both equiangular but the sides are not congruent.

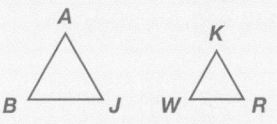

 Use the Guided Problem Solving worksheet with Exercise 25.

PowerPoint Lesson Quiz 9-5

Given that △ JKL ≅ △MNO, complete the following.

1. ∠L ≅ ∠O

2. $\overline{JK}$ ≅ $\overline{MN}$

3. $\overline{JL}$ ≅ $\overline{MO}$

4. If two sides and the angle between those sides of one triangle are congruent to two sides and the angle between those sides of another triangle, why can you conclude that the two triangles are congruent? **SAS**

✓ **Chapter Checkpoint 1**

To check understanding of Lessons 9-1 to 9-5:

Checkpoint Quiz 1 (p. 484)

📁 **Teaching Resources**
Checkpoint Quiz 1 (also in Prentice Hall Assessment System)

👥 **Reaching All Students**
Reading and Math Literacy 9B

Spanish versions available.

Reteaching 9-5 Congruence

List the congruent corresponding parts of the pair of triangles. Write a congruence statement for the triangles.

∠ACB = ∠ACD because both are right angles.
$\overline{BC}$ ≅ $\overline{DC}$ because they are marked.
$\overline{AC}$ ≅ $\overline{AC}$ because these are the same segment in each triangle.
Thus, △ABC ≅ △ADC by SAS (side-angle-side).
The vertices must be listed in the same order that they correspond.

A ↔ A
B ↔ D
C ↔ C

List the congruent corresponding parts of each pair of triangles. Write a congruence statement for the triangles.

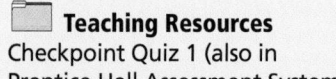

1. ∠JLK ≅ ∠JLM
   ∠LJK ≅ ∠LJM
   $\overline{JL}$ ≅ $\overline{JL}$
   △JLK ≅ △JLM by **ASA**

2. $\overline{PQ}$ ≅ $\overline{RQ}$
   $\overline{SQ}$ ≅ $\overline{TQ}$
   ∠PQS ≅ ∠RQT
   △PQS ≅ △RQT by **SAS**

3. ∠ZWY ≅ ∠XWY
   ∠ZYW ≅ ∠XYW
   $\overline{WY}$ ≅ $\overline{WY}$
   △ZWY ≅ △XWY by **ASA**

Reteaching

Test Prep

Multiple Choice

38. If △AND ≅ △PCK, which statement must be true? **B**
   A. $\overline{AN}$ ≅ $\overline{PK}$ B. ∠N ≅ ∠C   C. $\overline{ND}$ ≅ $\overline{PC}$ D. ∠AND ≅ ∠PKC

39. Which is the correct congruence statement? **F**
   F. △BCD ≅ △FED by ASA
   G. △BCD ≅ △FED by SSS
   H. △CDB ≅ △DEF by ASA
   I. △BDC ≅ △FED by SAS

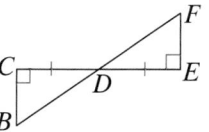

💻 **Take It to the NET**
Online lesson quiz at
www.PHSchool.com
Web Code: ada-0905

40. Quadrilateral JKLM ≅ quadrilateral PQRS. Which is a correct congruence statement? **C**
   A. $\overline{JK}$ ≅ $\overline{RS}$ B. $\overline{LM}$ ≅ $\overline{QR}$ C. ∠K ≅ ∠Q   D. ∠M ≅ ∠P

⬤ **Mixed Review**

Lesson 9-4

41. Students are evenly spaced as they sit around a round table. The fourth student is directly across from the eleventh student. How many students are seated at the table? **14 students**

Lesson 6-7   **Algebra** Write and solve an equation.

42. What percent of 50 is 20?
   x · 50 = 20, 40%

43. 15% of what number is 12?
   0.15 · x = 12, 80

44. Find 125% of 200.
   1.25 · 200 = x, 250

Lesson 5-1   **Order from least to greatest.**

45. $\frac{1}{2}, \frac{5}{6}, \frac{3}{8}, \frac{2}{3}$ $\frac{3}{8}, \frac{1}{2}, \frac{2}{3}, \frac{5}{6}$

46. $\frac{3}{8}, \frac{2}{3}, \frac{3}{4}, \frac{4}{5}$ $\frac{3}{8}, \frac{2}{3}, \frac{3}{4}, \frac{4}{5}$

47. $\frac{1}{6}, \frac{1}{5}, \frac{1}{7}, \frac{1}{4}$ $\frac{1}{7}, \frac{1}{6}, \frac{1}{5}, \frac{1}{4}$

✓ **Checkpoint Quiz 1**   **Lessons 9-1 through 9-5**

📱 **TEXT** Instant self-check quiz online and on CD-ROM

Name the figure that has the properties described.

1. a part of a line with one endpoint   **ray**

2. a series of points that extends in two directions without end   **line**

3. a segment congruent to $\overline{PR}$ when △LMN ≅ △PQR $\overline{LN}$

4. two rays with a common endpoint   **angle**

5a. 6x + 16 + 2x + 12 = 180, x = 19

5. **Algebra** In the diagram at the right, a ∥ b.
   a. Write an equation to find x.   **See left.**
   b. Find m∠TAV.   **50°**
   c. Find m∠TAN.   **130°**
   d. Find m∠DNK.   **130°**

6.

6. **Open-Ended** Draw a triangle that is scalene and has a right angle.
   Answers may vary. See left for sample.

Alternative Assessment

Have pairs of students cut congruent triangles out of tagboard and label the vertices differently. Collect and mix up the triangles. Then give one triangle to each student. Have students find matching triangles. Then have them write a congruence statement.

Test Prep

📁 **Resources**
For additional practice with a variety of test item formats:
• Test Prep, p. 517
• Test-Taking Strategies, p. 512
• Test-Taking Strategies With Transparencies

Read the exercise below and then follow along with how Shelley reads the diagram. Check your understanding by solving the problem at the bottom of the page.

List the congruent corresponding parts of the triangles.
Write a congruence statement (and reason) for the triangles.

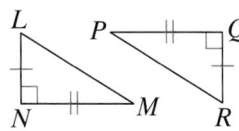

What Shelley Asks

What does the diagram show?

What are the corresponding points?

What congruent parts do I know?

Can I write a congruence statement?

Do I have SSS, SAS, or ASA?

Do I have SAS?

I must write the congruence statement (and reason).

What Shelley Thinks and Writes

Two triangles
The little squares show right angles.
The tick marks show congruent sides.

Points L, N, M correspond to R, Q, and P.

The single ticks show $\overline{LN} \cong \overline{RQ}$.
The double ticks show $\overline{NM} \cong \overline{QP}$.
I also know right angles are congruent.
I'll write:

$$\overline{LN} \cong \overline{RQ}$$
$$\overline{NM} \cong \overline{QP}$$
$$\angle N \cong \angle Q$$

I can write a congruence statement if I have SSS, SAS, or ASA.

I have congruence for two sides and an angle. SAS is the only possibility.

The angles have to be between the sides. They are! I have SAS.

I'll write:

$$\triangle LNM \cong \triangle RQP \text{ by SAS}$$

EXERCISES

Write a congruence statement (and reason) for the triangles.

1.

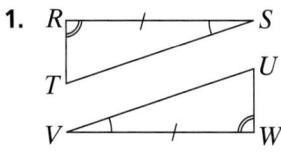

$\triangle RST \cong \triangle WVU$; ASA

2.

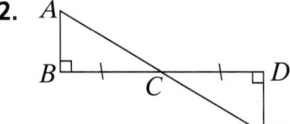

$\triangle ABC \cong \triangle EDC$; ASA

3.

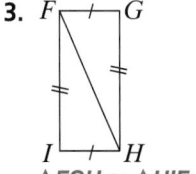

$\triangle FGH \cong \triangle HIF$; SSS

Reading Math

Reading a Diagram

In this feature, students read the diagram and extract the needed information in order to solve the problem.

Teaching Notes

Some students might not view reading a diagram as actual reading. Remind them that the broad definition of reading is to be able to interpret and understand the symbols on the page. In this case, the symbols on the page are triangles.

Auditory Learners
Have students work in pairs. Ask students to take turns stating their congruence statements and reasons quietly aloud.

Tactile Learners
Encourage students to trace the triangles on different pieces of paper and label the vertices. Have them compare triangles by placing one tracing over the other.

Inclusion
Have students slowly and carefully describe the triangles for other students who may be visually impaired.

Teaching Tip
Ask students to work independently to complete the exercises. Then have volunteers show their work on the overhead projector or chalkboard and explain.

1. Plan

Lesson Preview

 **Check Skills You'll Need**

Proportions
Lesson 6-2: Example 1;
Exercises 1–12.
Extra Practice, p. 749.

Lesson Resources

 Teaching Resources
Practice, Reteaching, Enrichment

Reaching All Students
Practice Workbook 9-6
Spanish Practice Workbook 9-6
Guided Problem Solving 9-6
Hands-On Activities 17, 27

Presentation Assistant Plus!
Transparencies and PowerPoint™
• Check Skills You'll Need 9-6
• Additional Examples 9-6
• Student Edition Answers 9-6
• Lesson Quiz 9-6
• Classroom Aid 8
PH Presentation Pro CD-ROM 9-6

ASSESSMENT SYSTEM

Computer Test Generator CD-ROM

Technology
Resource Pro® CD-ROM
Computer Test Generator CD-ROM
PH Presentation Pro CD-ROM

www.PHSchool.com

Student Site
• Teacher Web Code: adk-5500
• Self-grading Lesson Quiz
PH SuccessNet Teacher Center
• Lesson Planner
• Resources

Plus **iTEXT**

9-6 Circles

What You'll Learn

OBJECTIVE 1 To find circumferences

OBJECTIVE 2 To find central angles and to make circle graphs

. . . And Why

To display statistics using circle graphs

 Check Skills You'll Need

Solve each proportion. Round to the nearest whole number where necessary.

1. $\frac{10}{100} = \frac{x}{360}$ 36

2. $\frac{75}{100} = \frac{x}{360}$ 270

3. $\frac{0.8}{5.3} = \frac{x}{360}$ 54

4. $\frac{1.6}{5.3} = \frac{x}{360}$ 109

For help, go to Lesson 6-2.

New Vocabulary
• circle
• central angle

4. Answers may vary.
Sample: 3.1

iTEXT Interactive lesson includes instant self-check, tutorials, and activities.

Investigation

Exploring Pi

1. Work in groups. Each member of your group should have a ruler, string, and several circular objects, such as jar lids. Make a chart similar to the chart below. Record your results.
1–3. Check students' work.

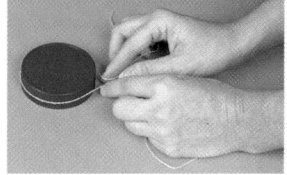

Object	Diameter	Circumference	Ratio $\frac{Circumference}{Diameter}$
▦	▦	▦	▦
▦	▦	▦	▦

2. Measure the diameter of each circle to the nearest millimeter.

3. Find the circumference of each circle by wrapping a string around the outside of the circle. Then straighten the string and measure its length to the nearest millimeter.

4. Calculate the ratio $\frac{circumference}{diameter}$ to the nearest tenth.
See below left.

5. Make a conjecture about the relationship between the circumference of a circle and its diameter.
The ratio is approximately 3.1.

A **circle** is the set of all points in a plane that are the same distance from a given point, called the *center* of the circle.

Radius is a segment that has one endpoint at the center and the other point on the circle.

Circumference is the distance around the circle.

Diameter is a chord that passes through the center of a circle.

Chord is a segment whose endpoints are on the circle.

The ratio of every circle's circumference C to its diameter d is the same. It has a special symbol, π, which is pronounced "pie." Both 3.14 and $\frac{22}{7}$ are good approximations for this ratio. Use $\frac{22}{7}$ for π when calculations involve fractions, and use 3.14 when they do not.

 Ongoing Assessment and Intervention

Before the Lesson
Diagnose prerequisite skills using:
• Check Skills You'll Need

During the Lesson
Monitor progress using:
• Check Understanding
• Additional Examples
• Test Prep

After the Lesson
Assess knowledge using:
• Lesson Quiz
• Computer Test Generator CD-ROM

If you multiply both sides of the equation $\frac{C}{d} = \pi$ by d, you get $C = \pi d$, which is a formula for the circumference of a circle.

The symbol π is a letter from the Greek alphabet. Leonhard Euler, an 18th-century Swiss mathematician, popularized the use of the symbol to represent the ratio of a circle's circumference to its diameter.

Key Concepts **Circumference of a Circle**

The circumference of a circle is π times the diameter.

$$C = \pi d \qquad C = 2\pi r$$

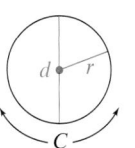

1 EXAMPLE **Finding Circumference**

Find the circumference of the circle at the right.

$C = \pi d$ **Write the formula.**

$C \approx (3.14)6$ **Replace π with 3.14 and d with 6.**

$= 18.84$ **Simplify.**

● The circumference of the circle is about 18.84 ft.

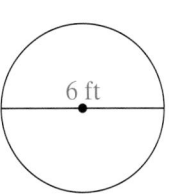

6 ft

✓ **Check Understanding** **Example 1**

1. Find the circumference of each circle.

  a. diameter $= 2\frac{4}{5}$ in.   **b.** radius $= 30$ mm   **c.** diameter $= 200$ mi
     about $8\frac{4}{5}$ in.   about 188.4 mm   about 628 mi

OBJECTIVE

2 Making Circle Graphs

To make a circle graph, you find the measure of each *central angle*. A **central angle** is an angle whose vertex is the center of a circle. There are 360° in a circle.

2 EXAMPLE **Real-World Problem Solving**

Budget Make a circle graph for Juan's weekly budget shown at the right.

Use proportions to find the measures of the central angles.

$$\frac{20}{100} = \frac{r}{360} \qquad \frac{25}{100} = \frac{\ell}{360} \qquad \frac{15}{100} = \frac{c}{360} \qquad \frac{40}{100} = \frac{s}{360}$$

$r = 72° \qquad\quad \ell = 90° \qquad\quad c = 54° \qquad\quad s = 144°$

● • Use a compass to draw a circle.
  • Draw the central angles with a protractor.
  • Label each section.
  • Add a title and necessary information.

Juan's Weekly Budget

Recreation (r)	20%
Lunch (ℓ)	25%
Clothes (c)	15%
Savings (s)	40%

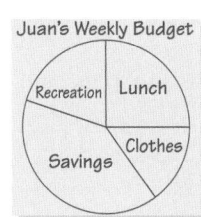

Juan's Weekly Budget

🌿 Reaching All Students

Below Level Have students list phrases like 10-in. pizza and 14-in. tire, and discuss their meanings. **10 in. and 14 in. are the distances across.**	**Advanced Learners** Ask students how many times the 26-in. tires on a bicycle turn while it is ridden 1.2 mi. **931 times**	**Auditory Learners** See note on page 487. **English Learners** See note on page 488.

2. Teach

Professional Development

Math Background

The number π is irrational. It cannot be written as the ratio of two integers. You may use $\frac{22}{7}$ or 3.14 as an approximation of π. Results of calculations using any approximation of π, including π on a calculator, should be expressed using $\approx$.

Teaching Notes

Investigation (Optional)
You can also use a measuring tape to measure the circumference.

Auditory Learners
Students often confuse the terms *radius* and *diameter*. Encourage them to think of mnemonics or other devices to help distinguish the two. For example, the word *diameter* is longer than the word *radius*, and a diameter of a circle is longer than a radius.

2 EXAMPLE Error Prevention

Students may confuse percents with degrees. Remind them that percent represents part of a whole. The whole is 360°. To check, tell students that the sum of all the percents should be 100%, while the sum of all their degree measurements should be 360° (100% of the circle).

PowerPoint
📖 Additional Examples

1 Find the circumference of the circle.

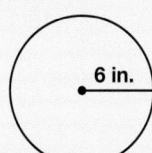

6 in.

about 37.68 in.

2 Make a circle graph for Jackie's weekly budget.

Jackie's Weekly Budget	
Entertainment	20%
Food	20%
Transportation	10%
Savings	50%

See back of book.

487

488

3 Draw a circle graph of the data.

Spring Dance Attendance	
Freshmen	120
Sophomores	82
Juniors	137
Seniors	101

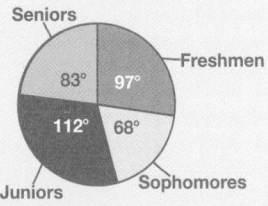

Seniors 83° — Freshmen 97° — Juniors 112° — Sophomores 68°

3 EXAMPLE English Learners

Students may hear others refer to circle graphs as "pie graphs." Show or remind students what a cut pie looks like and make the connection with pie graph. Make sure they understand that the *pie* in *pie graph* is not the same as *pi*, the letter π from the Greek alphabet. When scientists and mathematicians use π, it represents the irrational number that is the ratio of a circle's circumference to its diameter.

History Connection

Historians have found that π was known in very ancient times, although mathematicians approximated it as 3. The ancient Greek mathematician Archimedes seems to have been the first person to write about calculating π, which he approximated in the third century B.C. as $\frac{22}{7}$. Currently, scientists have used computers to calculate π to more than 100,000,000 decimal places.

Closure

Have students explain what the symbol π represents; also, how to find the measure of a central angle in a circle graph given the percent of the circle graph that the angle is to represent.

The symbol π represents the ratio of a circle's circumference to its diameter. Use a proportion or a percent equation to find the measure of the central angle.

488

---

2. Blood Types of Population

Type O 155°
Type A 144°
Type AB 18°
Type B 43°

3. Student Jobs at Western High School

Restaurant 158°
Retail 84°
Auto 68°
Library 17°
Other 34°

488 Chapter 9 Spatial Thinking

✓ Check Understanding   Example 2

2. Make a circle graph for the data. Round the measure of each central angle to the nearest degree. See left.

Blood Types of Population

Type A	Type B	Type AB	Type O
40%	12%	5%	43%

3 EXAMPLE   Real-World 🌐 Problem Solving

National Parks **Draw a circle graph of the data below.**

First add to find the total number of visits (in millions).

$$0.3 + 0.4 + 1.3 + 1.8 = 3.8$$

Use proportions to find the measures of the central angles.

$\frac{0.3}{3.8} = \frac{a}{360}$ $\frac{0.4}{3.8} = \frac{b}{360}$

$a \approx 28°$ $b \approx 38°$

$\frac{1.3}{3.8} = \frac{c}{360}$ $\frac{1.8}{3.8} = \frac{d}{360}$

$c \approx 123°$ $d \approx 171°$

Visits to Kentucky's National Recreation Areas

Site	Visits (millions)
Abraham Lincoln's Birthplace	0.3
Big South Fork	0.4
Cumberland Gap	1.3
Mammoth Caves	1.8

Use a compass to draw a circle. Draw the central angles with a protractor. Label each section. Add a title and necessary information.

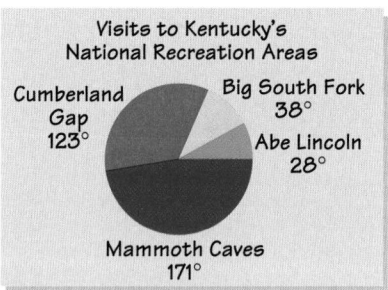

Visits to Kentucky's National Recreation Areas

Cumberland Gap 123°
Big South Fork 38°
Abe Lincoln 28°
Mammoth Caves 171°

✓ Check Understanding   Example 3

3. Students at Western High School work in the following places: restaurants, 140; library, 15; auto shop, 60; retail stores, 75; and other places, 30. Draw a circle graph to show where students at Western High School work. Round the measures of the central angles to the nearest degree. See left.

EXERCISES

❓ For more exercises, see *Extra Practice*.

Practice and Problem Solving

 Practice by Example

Find the circumference of each circle.

Example 1
(page 487)

1.

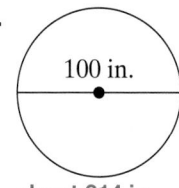

100 in.

about 314 in.

2.

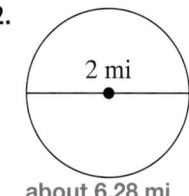

2 mi

about 6.28 mi

3.

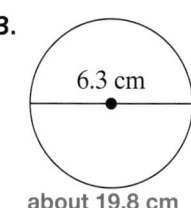

6.3 cm

about 19.8 cm

Find the circumference of each circle with the given radius or diameter.

4. radius = 3.5 cm
about 21.98 cm

5. radius = $4\frac{2}{3}$ ft
about $29\frac{1}{3}$ ft

6. diameter = 0.1 m
about 0.314 m

7. radius = 18 in.
about 113 in.

8. radius = 90 ft
about 565.2 ft

9. diameter = $\frac{1}{2}$ yd
about $1\frac{4}{7}$ yd

Examples 2 and 3
(pages 487 and 488)

Find the measures of the central angles that you would draw to represent each percent in a circle graph. Round to the nearest degree.

10. 35%
126°

11. 50%
180°

12. 30%
108°

13. 1%
4°

14. 25%
90°

15. 75%
270°

16.

What College Students Earn

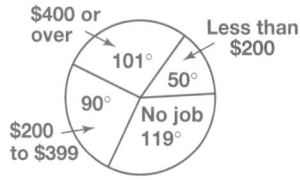

$400 or over 101°
Less than $200 50°
No job 119°
$200 to $399 90°

🌐 **16. Income** Make a circle graph for the data. **See left.**

What College Students Earn

Monthly Income from Jobs	No job	Less than $200	$200 to $399	$400 or over
Percent of Total Number of Students	33%	14%	25%	28%

 Apply Your Skills

Find the circumference of each circle with the given radius or diameter.

17. radius = 0.6 in
about 3.8 in.

18. radius = 10.25 mi
about 64.37 mi

19. diameter = 4.6 yd
about 14.4 yd

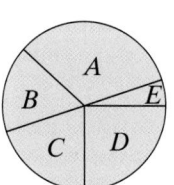

A
B
E
C
D

🌐 **20. Personal Finance** Nancy spends a third of her salary on rent, a fifth on utilities, a fourth on food, 5% on transportation, and she saves a sixth. Which section of the graph (at left) represents rent? Utilities? Food? Transportation? Savings? *A, C, D, E, B*

21. How Students Travel to School

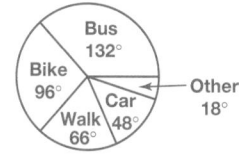

Bus 132°
Bike 96°
Other 18°
Walk 66°
Car 48°

21. The data below show how a group of students travel to school each day. Make a circle graph for the data. **See left.**

How Students Travel to School

Transportation	Walk	Bicycle	Bus	Car	Other
Number of Students	55	80	110	40	15

22. Extra Income Spending

Movies 37°
Eat out 57°
Vacation 140°
Savings 126°

🌐 **22. Finance** In a recent survey, families were asked how they spend extra income. Twenty-two families said they went to the movies, 34 said they eat out, 83 went on vacations, and the remaining 75 put it into savings. Make a circle graph for the data. **See left.**

23. Writing in Math Write a paragraph to a student who was not in class describing how to make a circle graph. **See margin.**

23. Answers may vary. Sample: Draw a circle using a compass. Then, use proportions to find the central-angle measures of all the sections of your circle graph. Use a protractor to draw the angles accurately. Finally, label each section and add a title and other necessary information.

GPS Use the Guided Problem Solving worksheet with Exercise 21.

Assignment Guide

1 **Objective 1**
Ⓐ Ⓑ **Core** 1–9, 17–19
Ⓒ **Extension** 24

2 **Objective 2**
Ⓐ Ⓑ **Core** 10–16, 20–23
Ⓒ **Extension** 25

Test Prep 26–28
Mixed Review 29–33

Practice 9-6 Circles

Find the measures of the central angles that you would draw to represent each percent in a circle graph. Round to the nearest degree.

	Voter Preference for Senator		Central Angle
1.	Peterson	40%	144°
2.	Washington	30%	108°
3.	Gomez	15%	54°
4.	Thomson	10%	36°
5.	Miller	5%	18°

6. Draw a circle graph for the data on voter preference.

Voter Preference for Senator

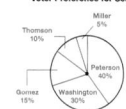

Thomson 10%
Miller 5%
Peterson 40%
Gomez 15%
Washington 30%

7. The total number of voters surveyed was 5,000. How many voters preferred Gomez?
750

Find the circumference of each circle with the given radius or diameter. Use 3.14 for π.

8. d = 25.8 m
C = 81.012 m

9. r = 9.1 cm
C = 57.148 cm

10. r = 0.28 km
C = 1.7584 km

11. d = 14 ft
C = 43.96 ft

12. d = 5 in.
C = 15.7 in.

13. r = $\frac{7}{8}$ in.
C = 5.495 in.

Enrichment 9-6 How Old Are You?

Mercury, the planet nearest the sun, orbits the sun at an average distance of 3.6×10^7 mi. Its average speed in orbit is 1.07×10^5 mi/h.

Solve. Use 3.14 for π. Give answers in scientific notation rounded to three decimal places unless otherwise instructed.

1. Find the circumference of Mercury's orbit.
2.261×10^8 mi

2. Find the number of hours it takes Mercury to complete one orbit of the sun.
2.113×10^3 h

3. Convert the above answer to days. Round to the nearest day and express your answer in standard form.
88 days

A "year" on a planet is the length of time it takes the planet to travel once around the sun. One Earth year is about 365 days.

4. About how many Mercury years are there in one Earth year? Round to the nearest year.
4 yr

5. Find your age in Mercury years.
Student's age × 4

Pluto, the planet farthest from the sun, orbits the sun at an average distance of 3.67×10^9 mi. Its average speed in orbit is 1.06×10^4 mi/h.

6. What is the circumference of Pluto's orbit?
2.305×10^{10} mi

7. What is the length of a year on Pluto in days, rounded to the nearest day?
90,596 days

8. What is the number of Earth years in one Pluto year, rounded to the nearest year?
248 yr

9. What is your age in Pluto years?
Student's age ÷ 248

Lesson Quiz 9-6

Solve.

1. Find the circumference of a circle with a diameter of 2.5 in. **about 7.85 in.**

2. Ten out of 22 students surveyed prefer milk with their breakfast. Find the measure of the central angle to represent this data in a circle graph. **about 164°**

3. Draw a circle graph of the data.

After-School Activities (for one class)	Number of Students
Band	5
Basketball	8
Baby-sitting	10
Library	7

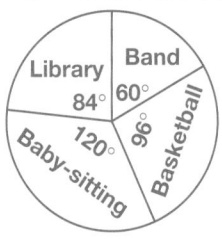

Reteaching 9-6 Circles

Find the measures of the central angles that you would draw to represent each percent in a circle graph. Round to the nearest degree.

Employment Distribution in California

Service	Trade	Manufacturing	Government	Other
31%	23%	15%	17%	14%

You can use proportions to find the measures of the central angles. You also can use equations.

What is 31% of 360?	What is 23% of 360?	What is 15% of 360?
$n = (0.31)(360)$	$n = (0.23)(360)$	$n = (0.15)(360)$
$n \approx 112°$	$n \approx 83°$	$n \approx 54°$

What is 17% of 360?	What is 14% of 360?
$n = (0.17)(360)$	$n = (0.14)(360)$
$n \approx 61°$	$n \approx 50°$

Find the measures of the central angle that you would draw to represent each percent in a circle graph. Round to the nearest degree.

	Employment Distribution in Texas		Measure of central angle
1.	Service	27%	97°
2.	Trade	24%	86°
3.	Manufacturing	13%	47°
4.	Government	18%	65°
5.	Other	18%	65°

Challenge

24. Answers may vary.
Sample:
a. $\overline{DC}$
b. $\overline{OC}, \overline{OD}, \overline{OB}, \overline{OA}$
c. $\overleftrightarrow{DB}, \overleftrightarrow{AB}$
d. $\overline{DB}, \overline{AB}, \overline{CD}$
e. $\overrightarrow{EF}, \overrightarrow{EB}$

Diameter	Circumference
1 in.	3.14 in.
5 in.	15.7 in.
8 in.	25.1 in.
10 in.	31.4 in.

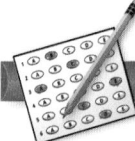

24. A *tangent* to a circle is a line, segment, or ray in the same plane as the circle and which intersects the circle in exactly one point. A *secant* is a line, segment, or ray that intersects a circle in two points. Use the diagram to identify the following. **a–e. See left.**
a. one diameter   **b.** four radii
c. two secants   **d.** three chords
e. two tangents

25. The data at the left represent the circumference and the diameter of four circles of different sizes. **a–b. See back of book.**
a. Graph the points on a coordinate plane. Use the diameter as the *x*-coordinate and the circumference as the *y*-coordinate.
b. Connect the points with a line.
c. Find the slope of the line. **3.14**
d. **Reasoning** Explain the meaning of slope in this situation. **The slope is the value of π. For every increase of 1 in. diameter, the circumference increases by about 3.14 in.**

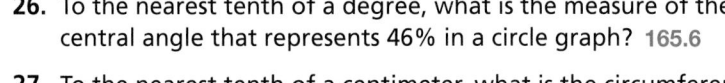
Test Prep

Gridded Response

26. To the nearest tenth of a degree, what is the measure of the central angle that represents 46% in a circle graph? **165.6**

Take It to the NET
Online lesson quiz at
www.PHSchool.com
Web Code: ada-0906

27. To the nearest tenth of a centimeter, what is the circumference of a circle with a radius of 2.5 cm? Use 3.14 for π. **15.7**

28. To the nearest hundredth of an inch, what is the circumference of a circle with a diameter of 8 in.? Use 3.14 for π. **25.12**

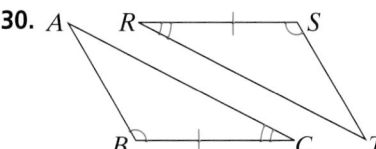
Mixed Review

Lesson 9-5

List the congruent corresponding parts of each pair of triangles. Write a congruence statement for the triangles. **29–30. See left.**

29. $\overline{AD} \cong \overline{CD}, \overline{BD} \cong \overline{BD},$
$\angle ADB \cong \angle CDB,$
$\triangle ADB \cong \triangle CDB$ by SAS

30. $\angle B \cong \angle S, \angle C \cong \angle R,$
$\overline{BC} \cong \overline{SR},$
$\triangle ABC \cong \triangle TSR$ by ASA

29.

30.

Lesson 8-1

31. Yes; there is one range value for each domain value.
32. No; there are three range values for the domain value 1.

Is each relation a function? Explain. **31–32. See left.**

31. $\left\{ \left(4, \frac{1}{2}\right), \left(6, \frac{1}{2}\right), \left(-2, \frac{1}{2}\right) \right\}$ **32.** $\left\{ (1, 0), (1, 5), \left(1, 3\frac{1}{4}\right) \right\}$

Lesson 6-2 **33. Physical Fitness** While exercising, your heart beats 32 times in 15 s. At this rate, how many times will it beat in 2 min? **256 times**

490   Chapter 9   Spatial Thinking

Alternative Assessment

Have students compute the central angles needed for a circle graph of a set of data. Then have students calculate the length of the part of the circumference for each section of the circle graph with a radius of 10 cm.

Test Prep

📁 **Resources**
For additional practice with a variety of test item formats:
• Test Prep, p. 517
• Test-Taking Strategies, p. 512
• Test-Taking Strategies With Transparencies

Constructions

OBJECTIVE

1 Congruent Segments and Angles

In constructions, you use only a *compass* and *straightedge* (an unmarked ruler) to accurately copy a segment or an angle, or draw an accurate bisector. A compass is a tool used to draw circles or parts of circles. An *arc* is part of a circle.

1 EXAMPLE   Constructing a Congruent Segment

Construct a segment congruent to $\overline{AB}$.

Step 1 Draw a ray with endpoint *C*.

Step 2 Open the compass to the length of $\overline{AB}$.

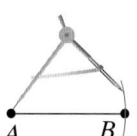

Step 3 With the *same* compass setting, put the compass tip on *C*. Draw an arc that intersects the ray. Label the intersection *D*.

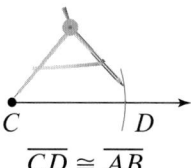

$\overline{CD} \cong \overline{AB}$

✓ Check Understanding   Example 1

1. Draw a segment. Construct a segment twice the length of the segment you drew. Sample:

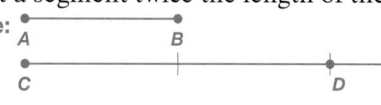

What You'll Learn

OBJECTIVE 1 To construct a segment or an angle congruent to a given segment or angle

OBJECTIVE 2 To construct segment bisectors and angle bisectors

. . . And Why

To construct precise drawings such as those that architects use

✓ Check Skills You'll Need

State the meaning of each symbol.
1–4. See below.

1. *B*   2. $\overline{AB}$

3. $\overrightarrow{AB}$ 4. $\overleftrightarrow{AB}$

❓ For help, go to Lesson 9-1.

New Vocabulary

- **perpendicular lines**
- **segment bisector**
- **perpendicular bisector**
- **angle bisector**

1. point *B*
2. a line segment with endpoints *A* and *B*
3. a ray with endpoint *A* and containing point *B*
4. a line containing points *A* and *B*

TEXT Interactive lesson includes instant self-check, tutorials, and activities.

9-7 Constructions   **491**

9-7

1. Plan

Lesson Preview

✓ **Check Skills You'll Need**

Points, Lines, and Planes
Lesson 9-1: Example 1;
Exercises 1–11.
Extra Practice, p. 752.

Lesson Resources

📁 **Teaching Resources**
Practice, Reteaching, Enrichment

👥 **Reaching All Students**
Practice Workbook 9-7
Spanish Practice Workbook 9-7
Guided Problem Solving 9-7
Technology Activities 19

⏱ **Presentation Assistant Plus!**
Transparencies and PowerPoint™
- Check Skills You'll Need 9-7
- Additional Examples 9-7
- Student Edition Answers 9-7
- Lesson Quiz 9-7
PH Presentation Pro CD-ROM 9-7

ASSESSMENT SYSTEM

Computer Test Generator CD-ROM

💻 **Technology**
Resource Pro® CD-ROM
Computer Test Generator CD-ROM
PH Presentation Pro CD-ROM

💻 **www.PHSchool.com**
Student Site
- Teacher Web Code: adk-5500
- Self-grading Lesson Quiz
PH SuccessNet Teacher Center
- Lesson Planner
- Resources

Plus TEXT

🔄 **Ongoing Assessment and Intervention**

Before the Lesson
Diagnose prerequisite skills using:
- Check Skills You'll Need

During the Lesson
Monitor progress using:
- Check Understanding
- Additional Examples
- Test Prep

After the Lesson
Assess knowledge using:
- Lesson Quiz
- Computer Test Generator CD-ROM

2. Teach

Professional Development

Math Background

When you do geometric constructions, you draft a figure using only two tools, a compass and a straightedge (which cannot be used for measuring). Euclid stated these limitations in his book, *Elements,* about 300 B.C. With the compass you can compare two lengths, though you cannot measure them in units. Do constructions carefully. Use a finely-sharpened pencil to find points of intersection accurately.

Teaching Notes

English Learners

The word *compass* names two very different tools. You use one to draw circles and the other to indicate direction. If possible, bring in a magnetic compass so that students can see both instruments.

Inclusion

Some students may not physically be able to use a compass and straightedge. Have these students work in pairs with others who can do the physical work. Have the physically challenged student give directions to his or her partner.

1 EXAMPLE Teaching Tip

Help students understand why you use arcs to mark equal distances. An *arc* is a curve that is part of a circle. Remind students that all points on a circle are the same distance from the center. When students are drawing with a compass, the compass tip locates the center of the circle and all marks made by the pencil represent points on the circle.

1 EXAMPLE Error Prevention

Some students may unwittingly squeeze the compass too hard and change the setting. Some compasses may "slip" by themselves. Have students draw a few arcs without changing the setting to check for slippage. Stress that students can avoid squeezing the compass by holding it as shown in the photo, or by its pointed "leg."

492

Real-World Connection

To work with a compass easily, here is one way to hold it.

2 EXAMPLE Constructing a Congruent Angle

Construct an angle congruent to ∠E.

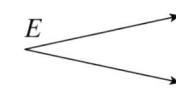

Step 1 Draw a ray with endpoint Q.

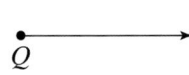

Step 2 With the compass point at E, draw an arc that intersects the sides of ∠E. Label the intersection points F and G.

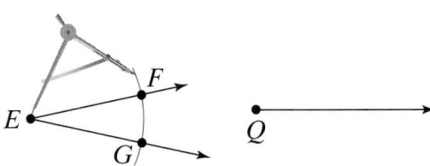

Step 3 With the *same* compass setting, put the compass tip on Q. Draw an arc intersecting the ray at point P.

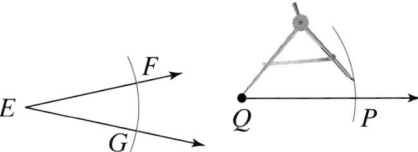

Step 4 Open the compass to the length of $\overline{FG}$. Using this setting, put the compass tip at P. Draw an arc to determine the point R. Draw $\overrightarrow{QR}$.

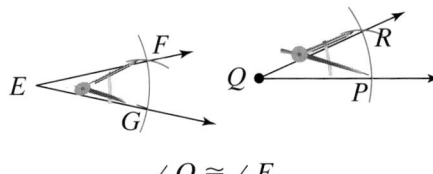

$$\angle Q \cong \angle E$$

✔ Check Understanding Example 2

2. Draw an obtuse angle. Construct an angle congruent to the angle you drew. **See back of book.**

OBJECTIVE
2 Constructing Bisectors

The figures below show some special relationships intersecting lines may have.

Reading Math

To *bisect* means to divide into two equal parts. Therefore a bisector divides a segment or angle into two congruent parts.

  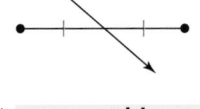 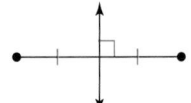

Perpendicular lines, segments, or rays intersect to form right angles.

A **segment bisector** is a line, segment, or ray that divides a segment into two congruent segments.

A **perpendicular bisector** is a line, segment, or ray that is perpendicular to the segment it bisects.

492   Chapter 9 Spatial Thinking

👥 Reaching All Students

Below Level Ask students to describe a situation in which they had to make a measurement without a ruler or tape measure. Ask how they solved the problem.

Advanced Learners Ask students how to construct an angle with twice the measure of a given angle. Construct one congruent angle, and then construct another adjacent congruent angle.

English Learners See note on page 492.
Inclusion See note on page 492.

3 EXAMPLE   Constructing a Perpendicular Bisector

Construct the perpendicular bisector of $\overline{PQ}$.

Step 1 Open the compass to more than half the length of $\overline{PQ}$. Put the compass tip at P. Draw an arc intersecting $\overline{PQ}$. With the same compass setting, repeat from point Q.

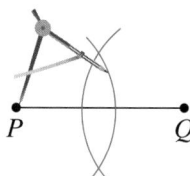

Step 2 Label the points of intersection of the two arcs as S and T. Draw $\overleftrightarrow{ST}$. Label the intersection of $\overleftrightarrow{ST}$ and $\overline{PQ}$ as point M.

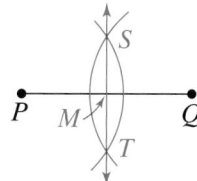

• $\overleftrightarrow{ST}$ is perpendicular to $\overline{PQ}$ and $\overleftrightarrow{ST}$ bisects $\overline{PQ}$.

✓ Check Understanding   Example 3

3. Draw a segment. Construct its perpendicular bisector.
See margin.

An **angle bisector** is a ray that divides an angle into two congruent angles.

4 EXAMPLE   Constructing an Angle Bisector

Construct the bisector of $\angle A$.

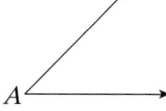

Step 1 Put the compass tip at A. Draw an arc that intersects the sides of $\angle A$. Label the points of intersection B and C.

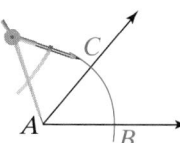

Step 2 Put the compass tip at B. Draw an arc. With the same compass setting, repeat with the compass tip at C. Make sure the arcs intersect. Label the intersection of the arcs D. Draw $\overrightarrow{AD}$.

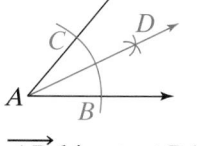

$\overrightarrow{AD}$ bisects $\angle BAC$.

✓ Check Understanding   Example 4

4. Draw an obtuse angle. Construct its angle bisector.
See margin.

9-7 Constructions **493**

3.

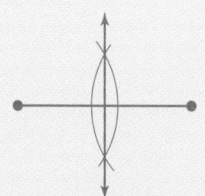

4.

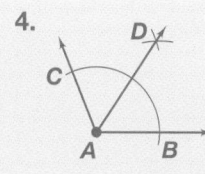

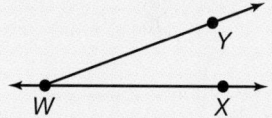
493

3. Practice

Assignment Guide

1 **Objective 1**
  A B Core 1–5, 12, 14, 15
  C Extension 21

2 **Objective 2**
  A B Core 6–11, 13, 16–19
  C Extension 20

Test Prep 22–24
Mixed Review 25–31

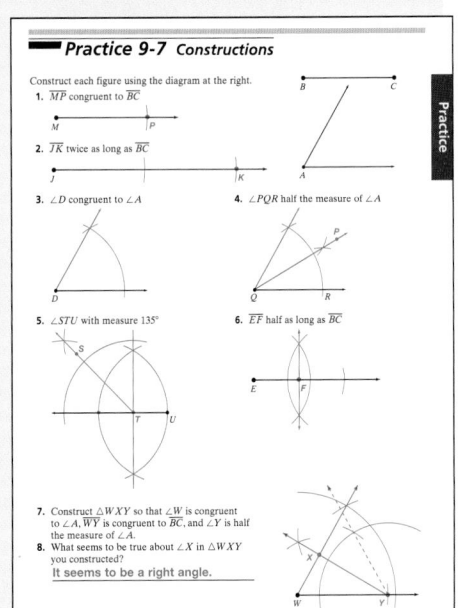

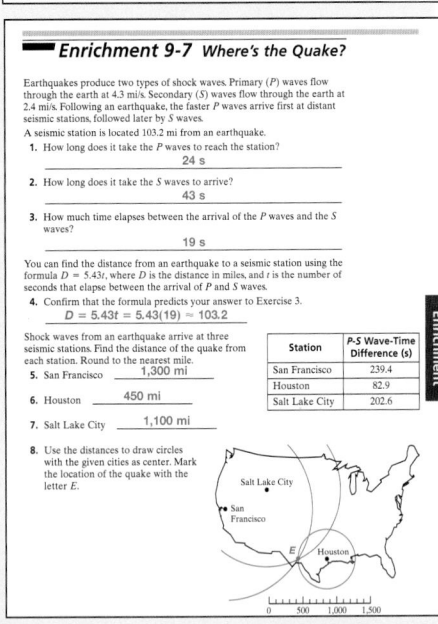

EXERCISES

For more exercises, see *Extra Practice*.

Practice and Problem Solving

A **Practice by Example**

Example 1
(page 491)

Example 2
(page 492)

For Exercises 1–4, draw a diagram similar to one that is given. Then construct each figure. 1–4. See margin.

1. $\overline{EF}$ congruent to $\overline{XY}$

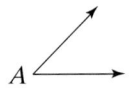

2. $\overline{GH}$ twice the length of $\overline{XY}$

3. $\angle D$ congruent to $\angle A$ **4.** $\angle Y$ congruent to $\angle X$

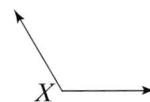

5. Draw an acute angle. Construct an angle congruent to the angle you drew. **See back of book.**

Example 3
(page 493)

For Exercises 6 and 7, first draw diagrams similar to ones shown. 6–8. Check students' work.

6. Construct the perpendicular bisector of $\overline{MN}$.

7. Construct the perpendicular bisector of $\overline{CD}$.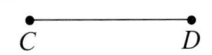

8. Draw $\overline{DE}$ at least 4 in. long. Then construct its perpendicular bisector.

Example 4
(page 493)

For Exercises 9 and 10, first draw diagrams similar to ones shown. 9–10. See back of book.

9. Construct the bisector of $\angle J$.

10. Construct the bisector of $\angle K$.

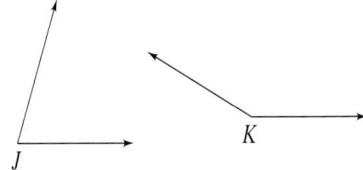

11. Use a protractor to draw a right angle. Construct its angle bisector. **See back of book.**

B **Apply Your Skills**

For Exercises 12–14, draw a figure similar to the one that is given. Then construct each figure. 12–14. See back of book.

12. $\overline{MN}$ three times the length of $\overline{CD}$

13. $\overline{PQ}$ 1.5 times the length of $\overline{CD}$

14. $\triangle ABF$ with two angles congruent to $\angle X$

15. Draw an angle and label it $\angle A$. Then construct $\angle I$ so that $m\angle I = 2m\angle A$. **See back of book.**

16. Construct a 90° angle. **See back of book.**

17. **Writing in Math** How are constructing a segment bisector and constructing an angle bisector alike? **Answers may vary. Sample: In both constructions, you use the compass to draw intersecting arcs, and then use the points of intersection to draw the bisectors.**

494 Chapter 9 Spatial Thinking

1.

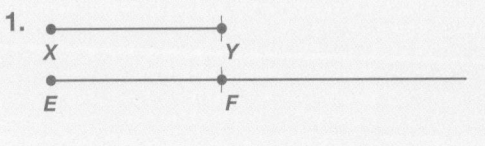

2.

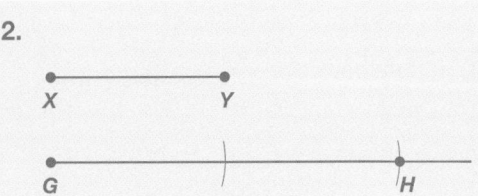

3–4. See back of book.

18. Open-Ended Use your compass to make a design. Decorate your design. **Check students' work.**

19. The bisector of $\angle XYZ$ is $\overrightarrow{YN}$. If the measure of $\angle XYN$ is 55°, what is the measure of $\angle XYZ$? **110°**

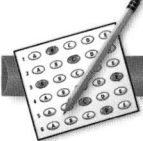 **C Challenge**

20. a. Draw a point and a line. Construct the perpendicular segment from the point to the line. (*Hint:* Place your compass tip at the point. Open your compass far enough to draw an arc that intersects the line in two points. Construct the perpendicular bisector of the segment between the two points.) **See back of book.**

b. An *altitude* of a triangle is a perpendicular segment from a vertex to a line containing the side opposite the vertex. Draw a large acute triangle. Construct its three altitudes. **Check students' work.**

21. Draw $\triangle PQR$. To construct $\triangle ABC$ congruent to $\triangle PQR$, first construct $\overline{AB}$ congruent to $\overline{PQ}$. Use a compass setting the length of $\overline{PR}$. Draw an arc with the compass tip at A. Then use a compass setting the length of $\overline{QR}$. With the compass tip at B draw an arc that intersects the first arc. Label the intersection C. Draw $\overline{AC}$ and $\overline{BC}$. **See back of book.**

 **Test Prep**

Multiple Choice

22. The bisector of $\angle ABC$ is $\overrightarrow{BD}$. If the measure of $\angle ABD$ is 50°, what is the measure of $\angle ABC$? **C**

 A. 25° **B.** 50° **C.** 100° **D.** 130°

23. $\overrightarrow{DB}$ is the bisector of $\angle CDE$. Which statement must be true? **H**

 F. $\angle CDE \cong \angle BDE$ **G.** $\angle CDB \cong \angle EDC$
 H. $\angle CDB \cong \angle BDE$ **I.** $\angle EDC \cong \angle EBC$

Extended Response

24. Explain how to construct each figure. **See back of book.**

 a. a 45° angle **b.** a $22\frac{1}{2}°$ angle **c.** a $67\frac{1}{2}°$ angle
 d. Do one of the constructions (a)–(c).

Take It to the NET
Online lesson quiz at
www.PHSchool.com
Web Code: ada-0907

Mixed Review

Lesson 9-6 **Find the measure of the central angle that would represent each percent in a circle graph. Round your answer to the nearest degree.**

25. 12% **43°** **26.** 45% **162°** **27.** 5% **18°** **28.** 25% **90°**

Lesson 8-7 **29. Number Sense** Find two numbers with a sum of 25 and a difference of 15. **5 and 20**

Lesson 7-8 **Find the simple interest.**

30. $1,000 deposited at an interest rate of 2% for 3 years **$60**

31. $150 deposited at an interest rate of 4% for 6 months **$3**

9-7 Constructions **495**

Use the Guided Problem Solving worksheet with Exercise 19.

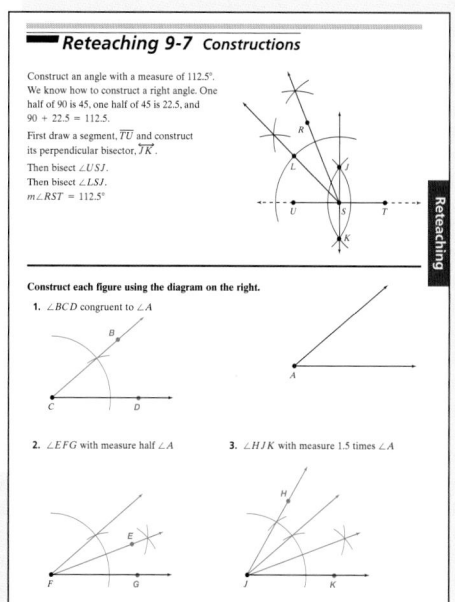
495

Exploring Constructions

This Technology extension explains the special meaning of "construct" as it is used in geometry software.

Resources

Students may use any type of geometry software.

Teaching Notes

Auditory Learners
Encourage students to say the steps quietly aloud as they work through the Example.

Inclusion
Pair a student who does not have good motor control with another student who can complete the steps using the software. Have the first student state the steps aloud while viewing the computer.

Technology

Exploring Constructions

You can use geometry software to construct a geometric figure quickly and accurately. In such software, "construct" has a special meaning.

● EXAMPLE

Construct $\overleftrightarrow{CD}$, the perpendicular bisector of $\overline{AB}$. Tell what happens when you do the following.

a. Drag A toward B.   **b.** Drag A in a path parallel to $\overleftrightarrow{CD}$.

Step 1   Use the Segment tool to draw a segment. Label its endpoints A and B.

Step 2   Highlight $\overline{AB}$. Use the Construct menu and construct the midpoint of $\overline{AB}$. Label the midpoint C.

Step 3   Highlight C and $\overline{AB}$. Use the Construct menu and construct a perpendicular through $\overline{AB}$ at C. Construct a second point on this perpendicular line and label it D.

$\overleftrightarrow{CD}$ is the perpendicular bisector of $\overline{AB}$.

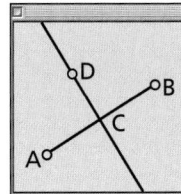

a.   As you drag A toward B, point C moves half as fast as A to remain the midpoint of $\overline{AB}$. $\overleftrightarrow{CD}$ moves to stay perpendicular to $\overline{AB}$.

b.   As you drag A in a path parallel to $\overleftrightarrow{CD}$, $\overline{AB}$ changes size and position, but $\overleftrightarrow{CD}$ moves also to remain the perpendicular bisector of $\overline{AB}$.

EXERCISES

1. Use the Segment tool to draw $\angle JKL$ as shown at the right. Then use the Construct menu and construct $\overrightarrow{KM}$, the bisector of $\angle JKL$.
   a. Predict what will happen if you change the size of $\angle JKL$ by dragging point J. Use the software to test your prediction. **See margin.**
   b. Is there a way to move J so that $\overrightarrow{KM}$ does not change? Use the software to check your answer. **See margin.**

   c. Predict what will happen if you drag point K so that $\angle JKL$
        i. has measure 180°. $\overrightarrow{KM}$ **would be perpendicular to** $\overleftrightarrow{JL}$.
        ii. has measure 0°. $\overrightarrow{KM}$ **would be part of** $\overleftrightarrow{JL}$.
        Use the software to test each prediction.

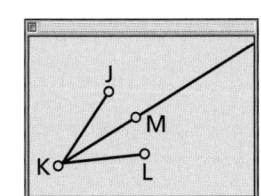

2. **Writing in Math**   Describe what is special about a figure you *construct* with geometry software. **Answers may vary.**
   Sample: The constructed properties do not change when you move the figure.

1a. Answers may vary. Sample: Point M will move half as fast as J so that $\overrightarrow{KM}$ will remain the bisector of $\angle JKL$.

1b. Answers may vary. Sample: You can move J along $\overrightarrow{KJ}$ without changing the size of the angle, so $\overrightarrow{KM}$ will not need to change.

Translations

OBJECTIVE

1 Graphing Translations

You can move pattern blocks by sliding them, flipping them, or turning them. Each of these moves is a type of transformation. A **transformation** is a change of position or size of a figure.

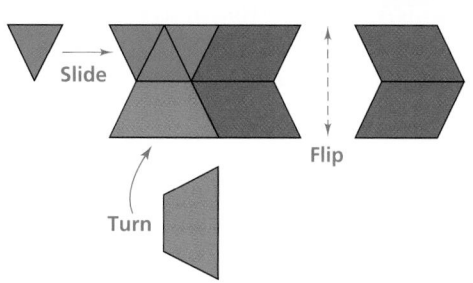

Slide

Flip

Turn

A **translation** is a transformation that moves points the same distance and in the same direction. A figure and its translated image are congruent. You can see examples of translations or slides in wallpaper, fabric, and wrapping paper.

The figure you get after a transformation is called the **image.** To name the image of a point, you use *prime* notation. The figure at the right shows the translation of A to its image A'.

Image of A

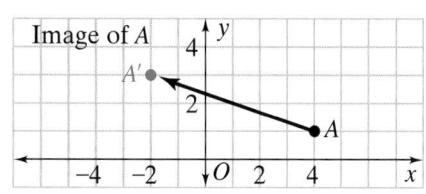

1 EXAMPLE   Translating a Figure

Graph the image of $\triangle KRT$ after a translation 5 units to the right and 3 units down.

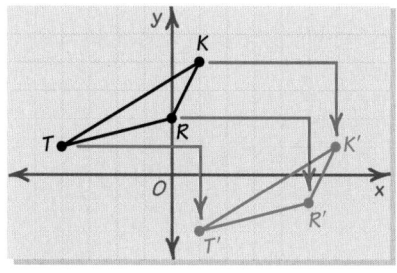

✓ Check Understanding   Example 1

1. On a coordinate plane, draw $\triangle KRT$. Graph the image of $\triangle KRT$ after each translation. **See back of book.**
   a. 4 units to the left   **b.** 5 units down
   c. 4 units to the left and 5 units down

What You'll Learn

OBJECTIVE 1 To graph translations

OBJECTIVE 2 To describe translations

. . . And Why

To use translations in describing real-world situations, such as moves in a chess game

✓ Check Skills You'll Need

Graph each point.
1–5. See back of book.
1. $A(-4, 3)$ **2.** $B(0, 2)$

3. $C(1, 4)$ **4.** $D(4, -2)$

5. $E(-2, -3)$

❓ For help, go to Lesson 1-10.

New Vocabulary

- **transformation**
- **translation**
- **image**

Need Help?

Always use the prime symbol (') with letters naming the image. This will help you keep track of which figure is the image.

❓TEXT Interactive lesson includes instant self-check, tutorials, and activities.

---

1. Plan

Lesson Preview

✓ **Check Skills You'll Need**

The Coordinate Plane
Lesson 1-10: Example 2;
Exercises 13–28.
Extra Practice, p. 744.

Lesson Resources

📁 **Teaching Resources**
Practice, Reteaching, Enrichment
Checkpoint Quiz 2

👥 **Reaching All Students**
Practice Workbook 9-8
Spanish Practice Workbook 9-8
Reading and Math Literacy 9C
Spanish Reading and
  Math Literacy 9C
Spanish Checkpoint Quiz 2
Guided Problem Solving 9-8
Technology Activities 20
Hands-On Activities 30

⏱ **Presentation Assistant Plus!**
Transparencies and PowerPoint™
- Check Skills You'll Need 9-8
- Additional Examples 9-8
- Student Edition Answers 9-8
- Lesson Quiz 9-8
- Classroom Aid 2, 26
PH Presentation Pro CD-ROM 9-8

ASSESSMENT SYSTEM

Checkpoint Quiz 2
Computer Test Generator CD-ROM

💻 **Technology**
Resource Pro® CD-ROM
Computer Test Generator CD-ROM
PH Presentation Pro CD-ROM

💻 **www.PHSchool.com**
Student Site
- Teacher Web Code: adk-5500
- Graphing Calculator, Procedure 13
- Self-grading Lesson Quiz
PH SuccessNet Teacher Center
- Lesson Planner
- Resources
Plus ❓TEXT

Ongoing Assessment and Intervention

Before the Lesson
Diagnose prerequisite skills using:
- Check Skills You'll Need

During the Lesson
Monitor progress using:
- Check Understanding
- Additional Examples
- Test Prep

After the Lesson
Assess knowledge using:
- Lesson Quiz
- Computer Test Generator
  CD-ROM
- Chapter Checkpoint 2 (p. 501)

2. Teach

Math Background

Transformation geometry is the study of *rigid motions* of a figure in a plane. Rigid motions (translations, rotations, and reflections) preserve the shape and size of a figure while changing its location.

Additional Examples

1 Graph the image of △*BCD* after a translation 3 units to the left and 4 units down.

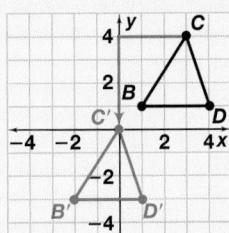

2 Use arrow notation to describe the translation of *X* to *X'*.

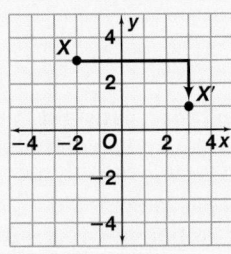

$X(-2, 3) \rightarrow X'(3, 1)$.

3 Write a rule to describe the translation of △*RST* to △*R'S'T'*.

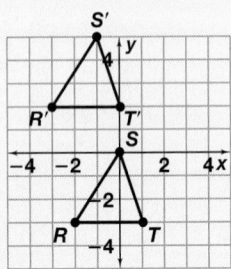

$(x, y) \rightarrow (x - 1, y + 5)$

Closure

Ask students to write a rule to describe the translation of $P(-3, 4)$ to $P'(-1, -1)$.
$(x, y) \rightarrow (x + 2, y - 5)$

498

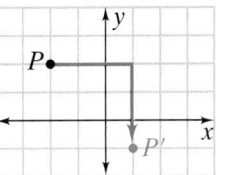

Real-World Connection

In chess, the move of a knight is a translation. The translation of piece *A* is $(x, y) \rightarrow (x + 1, y - 2)$.

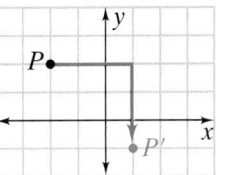

OBJECTIVE

2 Describing Translations

You can describe a transformation using arrow (→) notation, which describes the *mapping* of a figure onto its image.

2 EXAMPLE Using Arrow Notation

The movement of point *P* is both horizontal and vertical. Use arrow notation to describe this translation.

The point moves from $P(-2, 2)$ to $P'(1, -1)$, so the translation is $P(-2, 2) \rightarrow P'(1, -1)$.

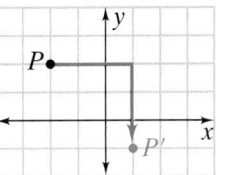

✓ **Check Understanding** Example 2

2. Use arrow notation to describe a translation of $B(-1, 5)$ to $B'(3, 1)$. $B(-1, 5) \rightarrow B'(3, 1)$

You can also use arrow notation to write a general rule that describes a transformation. To write a rule for a translation, choose corresponding points on a figure and its image. Subtract the coordinates of the figure from the coordinates of its image.

3 EXAMPLE Writing a Rule

Write a rule to describe the translation of △*PQR* to △*P'Q'R'*.

Use $P(3, 2)$ and its image $P'(-2, 5)$ to find the horizontal and vertical translations.

Horizontal translation: $-2 - 3 = -5$
Vertical translation: $5 - 2 = 3$

The rule is $(x, y) \rightarrow (x - 5, y + 3)$

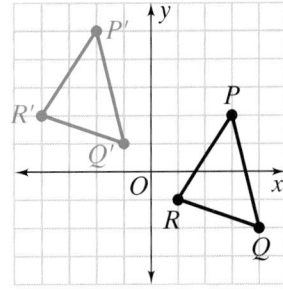

✓ **Check Understanding** Example 3

3. Write a rule to describe the translation of quadrilateral *ABCD* to quadrilateral *A'B'C'D'*. $(x, y) \rightarrow (x + 5, y - 1)$

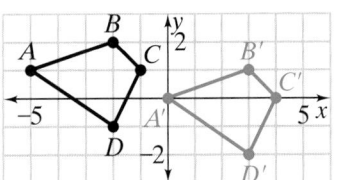

498 Chapter 9 Spatial Thinking

👥 Reaching All Students

| **Below Level** Ask a volunteer who has played chess to describe the moves made by the different pieces. Point out to students that these moves are similar to translations of figures on a plane. | **Advanced Learners** Ask: *A circle has radius 3 units and center C(−2, −2). You translate the circle 4 units right and 2 units down. What is the greatest possible y-coordinate for a point on the image of the circle?* −1 | **Error Prevention** See note on page 500. **Inclusion** See note on page 500. |

EXERCISES

 For more exercises, see *Extra Practice.*

Practice and Problem Solving

 Practice by Example

Example 1
(page 497)

Graph the image of △QRS for the given translation. 1–6. See margin.

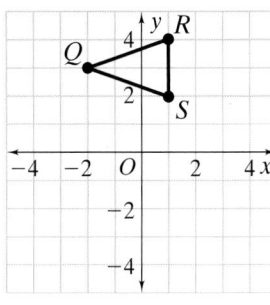

1. 2 units to the right

2. 5 units down

3. 3 units to the right and 5 units down

4. 1 unit to the left and 3 units down

5. 2 units to the right and 1 unit up

6. 3 units to the left and 2 units up

△HIJ has the coordinates given. Graph the triangle and its translation 3 units to the right and 2 units down.
7–10. See p. 500 margin.

7. $H(-1, 1), I(1, 4), J(1, 3)$

8. $H(0, 0), I(-3, -1), J(-1, -2)$

9. $H(-1, -2), I(0, 1), J(1, -2)$

10. $H(-4, 3), I(-2, 0), J(-4, 1)$

Use arrow notation to describe the translation.

Example 2
(page 498)

11. $A(1, 5)$ to $A'(2, 7)$
$A(1, 5) \rightarrow A'(2, 7)$

12. $W(-2, -6)$ to $W'(4, 9)$
$W(-2, -6) \rightarrow W'(4, 9)$

13. $S(3, 3)$ to $S'(11, 1)$
$S(3, 3) \rightarrow S'(11, 1)$

14. $D(-9, -4)$ to $D'(0, 1)$
$D(-9, -4) \rightarrow D'(0, 1)$

Example 3
(page 498)

Write a rule to describe each translation. 15–18. See below left.

15. (x, y) → (x + 4, y + 3)
16. (x, y) → (x + 5, y − 2)
17. (x, y) → (x − 4, y + 1)
18. (x, y) → (x − 6, y − 2)

15.

16.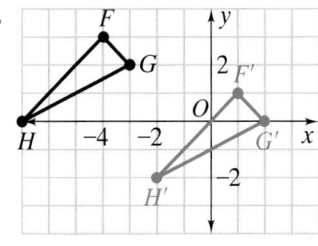

17.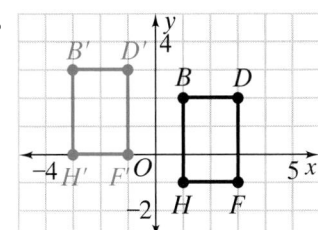

18.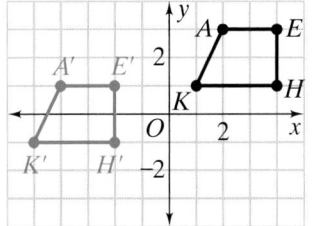

19. translation 11 units to the left and 4 units up
20. translation 5 units to the right and 2 units down
21. translation 6 units to the left and 3 units down
22. translation 3 units to the right and 9 units up

Write a description of each rule. 19–22. See left.

19. $(x, y) \longrightarrow (x - 11, y + 4)$

20. $(x, y) \longrightarrow (x + 5, y - 2)$

21. $(x, y) \longrightarrow (x - 6, y - 3)$

22. $(x, y) \longrightarrow (x + 3, y + 9)$

Assignment Guide

▼1 **Objective 1**
Ⓐ Ⓑ **Core** 1–10, 23–30, 37
Ⓒ **Extension** 38

▼2 **Objective 2**
Ⓐ Ⓑ **Core** 11–22, 31–36
Ⓒ **Extension** 39, 40

Test Prep 41–44
Mixed Review 45–49

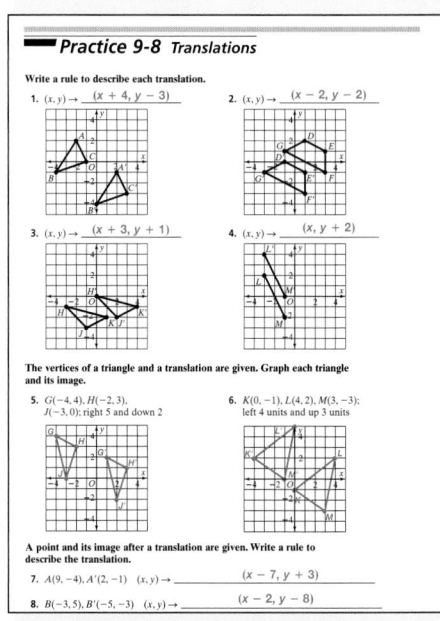

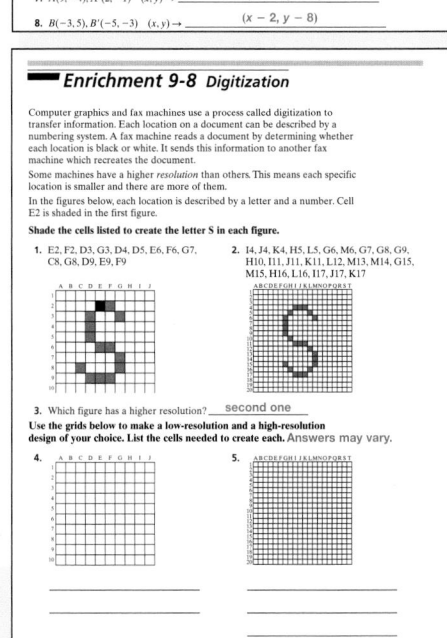

1.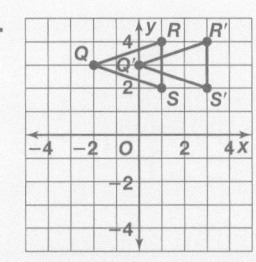

2.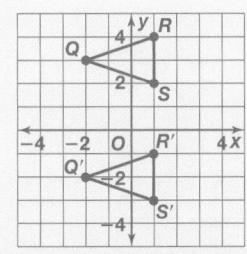

3.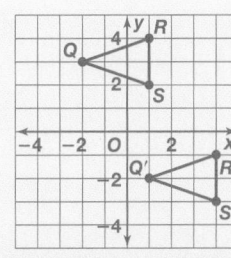

4–6. See page 500 margin. **499**

page 499

4.

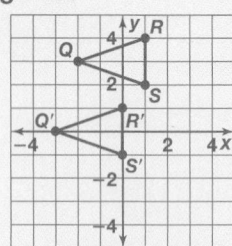

5.

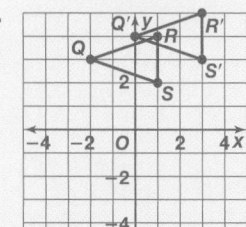

6.

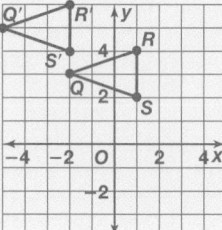

7.

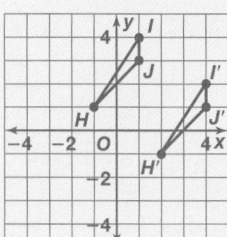

8.

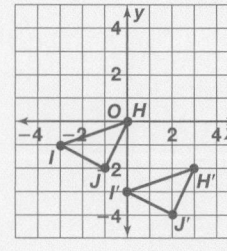

B Apply Your Skills

Complete with *horizontal* or *vertical* to make a true statement.

23. In a __?__ translation, the y-coordinate changes and the x-coordinate stays the same. **vertical**

24. In a __?__ translation, the x-coordinate changes and the y-coordinate stays the same. **horizontal**

The endpoints of a segment are given. Graph each segment and its image for the given translation. 25–30. See back of book.

25. $A(0,0), B(0,5)$; 2 units left   **26.** $C(0,0), D(0,2)$; 2 units up

27. $E(0,0), F(2,0)$; 4 units down   **28.** $G(0,0), H(-4,0)$; 4 units up

29. $J(0,0), K(5,5)$; 1 unit right   **30.** $L(-1,3), M(2,1)$; 5 units left

Write a rule to describe each translation.

31.

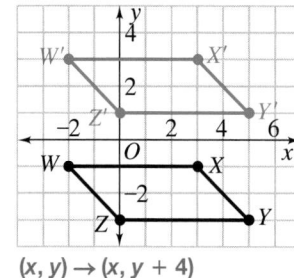

$(x, y) \rightarrow (x, y + 4)$

32.

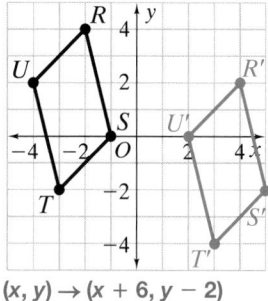

$(x, y) \rightarrow (x + 6, y - 2)$

The endpoints of a segment are given. Graph each segment and its image for the given translation. 33–36. See back of book.

33. $N(3,3), P(-3,4)$;
3 units left, 2 units down

34. $Q(2, -1), R(-2, 1)$;
2 units right, 3 units up

35. $S(4,3), T(1, -5)$;
4 units left, 1 unit up

36. $U(-4, -5), V(2,1)$;
3 units right, 2 units down

37. Translate point $T(2, 5)$ 2 units to the right and 6 units up.
Translate its image, point T', 4 units to the left and 1 unit down.
What are the coordinates of the image of point T'? **(0, 10)**

C Challenge

38. **Writing in Math** Describe and explain the result of moving a figure a units horizontally and then $-a$ units horizontally.
See above left.

39.

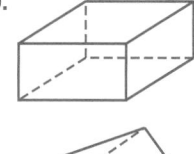
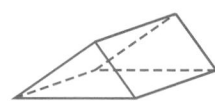

38. You move the figure a number of units one way horizontally and then the same number of units in the opposite direction. The result is an image in the same position as the original figure.

39. Art You can use translations to draw three-dimensional figures. First draw a figure on graph paper. Translate the figure. Connect each vertex with its image. Use dashes for sides that are not visible. Try this, first with a rectangle; then begin with a triangle. See left.

40. A rule like $(x, y) \rightarrow (2x, 2y)$ describes a dilation (see p. 304) of the coordinate plane. This dilation has center $(0, 0)$ and scale factor 2.
  a. $\overline{AB}$ has endpoints $A(4, 0)$ and $B(0, 3)$. Describe its image, $\overline{A'B'}$, for the dilation above. How do lengths AB and $A'B'$ compare?
  b. Describe a coordinate-plane dilation that has center $(0, 0)$ and scale factor $\frac{1}{2}$. Describe its effect on $\overline{AB}$ from part (a).
  a. $\overline{A'B'}$ has endpoints $A'(8, 0)$ and $B'(0, 6)$. $A'B' = 2AB$
  b. $\overline{A'B'}$ has endpoints $A'(2, 0)$ and $B'(0, 1\frac{1}{2})$. $A'B' = \frac{1}{2}AB$

500 Chapter 9 Spatial Thinking

GPS Use the Guided Problem Solving worksheet with Exercise 37.

9.

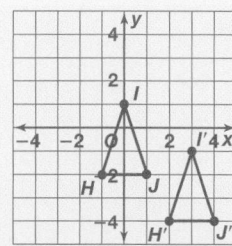

10.

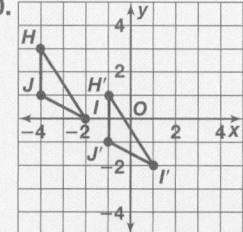

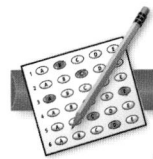

Multiple Choice

41. Which coordinates represent a translation of $B(-4, 1)$ 3 units to the right and 2 units down? **C**

   A. $B'(-7, 3)$ **B.** $B'(-6, 4)$ **C.** $B'(-1, -1)$ **D.** $B'(-2, -4)$

42. Which points show the translation $(x, y) \rightarrow (x - 1, y + 4)$? **G**

   F. $A(4, 2), A'(5, -2)$ **G.** $A(4, 2), A'(3, 6)$

   H. $A(4, 2), A'(8, 1)$ **I.** $A(4, 2), A'(0, 3)$

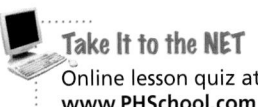
Take It to the NET
Online lesson quiz at
www.PHSchool.com
Web Code: ada-0908

43. Quadrilateral $WXYZ$ has vertices $W(0, 0)$, $X(-4, 2)$, $Y(-4, 6)$, and $Z(0, 4)$. Quadrilateral $W'X'Y'Z'$ has vertices $W'(2, -3)$, $X'(-2, -1)$, $Y'(-2, 3)$, and $Z'(2, 1)$. Which rule describes the translation? **B**

   A. $(x, y) \rightarrow (x - 3, y + 2)$ **B.** $(x, y) \rightarrow (x + 2, y - 3)$

   C. $(x, y) \rightarrow (x - 2, y + 3)$ **D.** $(x, y) \rightarrow (x + 3, y - 2)$

Short Response

44. [2] $(x, y) \rightarrow (x + 4, y - 3)$; 2
[1] Rule is correct, but slope is incorrect or not given OR slope is correct, but rule is incorrect or not given.

44. You translate the graph of $y = 2x + 4$ by 3 units down and 4 units right. **See left.**

   a. Write a rule to describe the translation.

   b. What is the slope of the graph of the image?

Mixed Review

Lesson 9-7   **45.** Draw an acute angle and construct its bisector. **See back of book.**

Lesson 5-4   **Simplify each product.**

   46. $\frac{3}{7} \cdot \frac{7}{9}$ $\frac{1}{3}$ **47.** $\frac{1}{2} \cdot \frac{8}{11}$ $\frac{4}{11}$ **48.** $\frac{1}{2} \cdot \frac{1}{8}$ $\frac{1}{16}$

Lesson 4-5   **49.** Amanda, Adam, and Ann ate salad, chicken, or tofu for lunch. Amanda did not eat chicken or tofu. Ann did not eat chicken. Each one had a different meal. What did each person eat?
Amanda had salad, Adam had chicken, and Ann had tofu.

✓ **Checkpoint Quiz 2**   **Lessons 9-6 through 9-8**

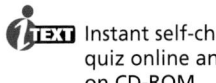 Instant self-check quiz online and on CD-ROM

Use the circle graph.

1. Eighty people attended a catered meal. Twenty-eight people ordered fish, half ordered chicken, and twelve ordered the vegetarian meal. Which section represents each of the meals?
A is chicken, B is fish, and C is vegetarian.

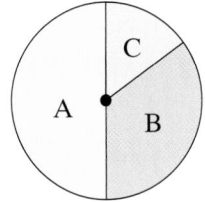

2. Determine the measure of the central angle of each section in the circle graph. **Section A: 180°; section B: 126°; section C: 54°**

3.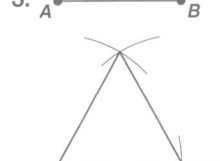

3. **Open-Ended** Draw a segment about $\frac{3}{4}$ in. long. Construct an equilateral triangle with sides of this length. **See left.**

4. Graph $\overline{NR}$ with endpoints $N(2, 7)$ and $R(-4, 0)$. Then graph its image after a translation 4 units right and 3 units down.
See back of book.

Alternative Assessment

Have students make a map of the classroom on a coordinate plane. Then ask them to describe a translation from their desk to another desk.

Test Prep

 **Resources**
For additional practice with a variety of test item formats:
- Test Prep, p. 517
- Test-Taking Strategies, p. 512
- Test-Taking Strategies With Transparencies

---

4. Assess

✓ **Chapter Checkpoint 2**

To check understanding of Lessons 9-6 to 9-8:
Checkpoint Quiz 2 (p. 501)

 **Teaching Resources**
Checkpoint Quiz 2 (also in Prentice Hall Assessment System)

Reaching All Students
Reading and Math Literacy 9C

Spanish versions available.

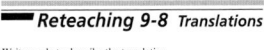
Reteaching 9-8 *Translations*

Write a rule to describe the translation.
Point A has coordinates $(-2, 3)$. It's image A' has coordinates $(-1, -2)$. To move from A to A' on the graph, we go right one unit $(+1)$ and down 5 units (-5). So the rule is $(x, y) \rightarrow (x + 1, y - 5)$. We could also subtract coordinates:
$x: -1 - (-2) = -1 + 2 = 1$
$y: -2 - 3 = -2 + (-3) = -5$

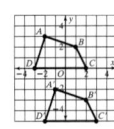

Write a rule to describe each translation.

1. $(x, y) \rightarrow$ ___ $(x + 3, y - 1)$ **2.** $(x, y) \rightarrow$ ___ $(x - 4, y + 6)$

3. $(x, y) \rightarrow$ ___ $(x - 2, y)$ **4.** $(x, y) \rightarrow$ ___ $(x, y + 4)$

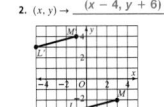 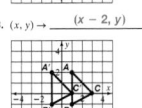 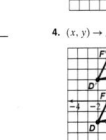

5. The translation that takes $A(8, -6)$ to $A'(9, -3)$.
$(x, y) \rightarrow$ ___ $(x + 1, y + 3)$

6. The translation that takes $B(2, -10)$ to $B'(-7, -12)$.
$(x, y) \rightarrow$ ___ $(x - 9, y - 2)$

501

Matrices and Translations

For Use With Lesson 9-8

A matrix is a rectangular arrangement of numbers. Each number is a matrix entry. You can write the coordinates of the vertices of a figure as a matrix.

$$\begin{array}{c} \\ x\text{-coordinate} \\ y\text{-coordinate} \end{array} \begin{array}{ccc} A & B & C \\ \begin{bmatrix} 0 & -1 & -4 \\ 0 & 4 & 0 \end{bmatrix} \end{array}$$

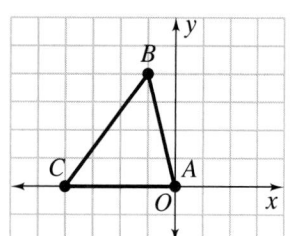

You can use matrices to translate figures.

● **EXAMPLE**

Geometry Use a matrix to find the vertices of the image of quadrilateral $ABCD$ using the rule $(x, y) \longrightarrow (x + 3, y - 2)$.

vertices of quadrilateral + translation matrix = vertices of image

Add 3 to each x-coordinate.

Add -2 to each y-coordinate.

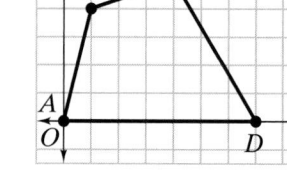

$$\begin{array}{cccc} A & B & C & D \\ \begin{bmatrix} 0 & 1 & 4 & 7 \\ 0 & 4 & 5 & 0 \end{bmatrix} \end{array} + \begin{bmatrix} 3 & 3 & 3 & 3 \\ -2 & -2 & -2 & -2 \end{bmatrix} = \begin{array}{cccc} A' & B' & C' & D' \\ \begin{bmatrix} 3 & 4 & 7 & 10 \\ -2 & 2 & 3 & -2 \end{bmatrix} \end{array}$$

● The vertices of the image are $A'(3, -2)$, $B'(4, 2)$, $C'(7, 3)$, and $D'(10, -2)$.

EXERCISES

Use matrix addition to find the vertices of the image of the given figure under each translation. 1–4. See margin.

1. $\triangle TRI$ with vertices
   $T(-5, -5), R(-3, -1), I(-1, -3)$;
   translation: $(x, y) \longrightarrow (x + 6, y + 6)$

2. square $SQRE$ with vertices
   $S(1, 2), Q(4, 2), R(4, 5), E(1, 5)$;
   translation: $(x, y) \longrightarrow (x + 1, y - 3)$

3. $\triangle NGL$ with vertices
   $N(4, 4), G(7, 4), L(5, 0)$;
   translation matrix: $\begin{bmatrix} -9 & -9 & -9 \\ -4 & -4 & -4 \end{bmatrix}$

4. square $RECT$ with vertices
   $R(0, 0), E(0, -4), C(-4, -4), T(-4, 0)$;
   translation matrix: $\begin{bmatrix} -1 & -1 & -1 & -1 \\ 2 & 2 & 2 & 2 \end{bmatrix}$

5. **a.** What matrix would you use to translate a triangle 1 unit to the left and 4 units down? $\begin{bmatrix} -1 & -1 & -1 \\ -4 & -4 & -4 \end{bmatrix}$

   b. Use your answer from part (a) to translate $\triangle ABC$ with vertices $A(2, 2), B(3, 5), C(3, 0)$ The vertices of the image are $A'(1, -2)$, $B'(2, 1)$, and $C'(2, -4)$.

Symmetry and Reflections

OBJECTIVE

1 Identifying Lines of Symmetry

A figure has **reflectional symmetry** when one half is a mirror image of the other half. A **line of symmetry** divides a figure with reflectional symmetry into two congruent halves.

A pattern for the back of a shirt is shown below. To make a shirt, you place the pattern on a folded piece of material, with the dashed lines of the pattern on the fold. After cutting the material, the back of the shirt will look like this.

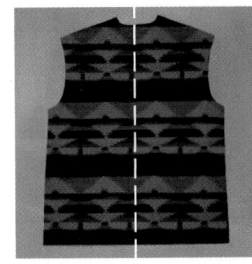

The fold is the line of symmetry.

The shirt has one line of symmetry.

It is possible for a figure to have more than one line of symmetry.

1 EXAMPLE Finding Lines of Symmetry

Draw the lines of symmetry. Tell how many there are.

a.

one line of symmetry

b.

six lines of symmetry

✓ Check Understanding Example 1

1. Copy each figure. Draw all lines of symmetry. a–b. See right.

a.
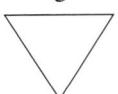

b.
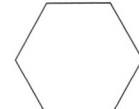

What You'll Learn

OBJECTIVE 1 To identify a line of symmetry

OBJECTIVE 2 To graph a reflection of a geometric figure

. . . And Why

To use symmetry and reflections in real-world situations, such as sewing

✓ Check Skills You'll Need

Graph each line.
1–6. See back of book.
1. $x = 0$ **2.** $y = 0$

3. $x = 3$ **4.** $y = 2$

5. $x = -1$ **6.** $x = y$

For help, go to Lesson 8-3.

New Vocabulary

• reflectional symmetry
• line of symmetry
• reflection
• line of reflection

a.
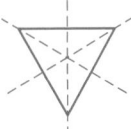

b.
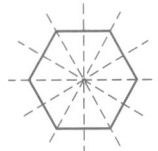

iTEXT Interactive lesson includes instant self-check, tutorials, and activities.

---

1. Plan

Lesson Preview

✓ Check Skills You'll Need

Slope and *y*-intercept
Lesson 8-3: Example 4;
Exercises 11–19.
Extra Practice, p. 751.

Lesson Resources

Teaching Resources
Practice, Reteaching, Enrichment

Reaching All Students
Practice Workbook 9-9
Spanish Practice Workbook 9-9
Guided Problem Solving 9-9
Technology Activities 20, 21
Hands-On Activities 30

Presentation Assistant Plus!
Transparencies and PowerPoint™
• Check Skills You'll Need 9-9
• Additional Examples 9-9
• Student Edition Answers 9-9
• Lesson Quiz 9-9
• Classroom Aid 2, 26
PH Presentation Pro CD-ROM 9-9

ASSESSMENT SYSTEM
Computer Test Generator CD-ROM

Technology
Resource Pro® CD-ROM
Computer Test Generator CD-ROM
PH Presentation Pro CD-ROM

www.PHSchool.com
Student Site
• Teacher Web Code: adk-5500
• Self-grading Lesson Quiz
PH SuccessNet Teacher Center
• Lesson Planner
• Resources

Plus **iTEXT**

Ongoing Assessment and Intervention

Before the Lesson
Diagnose prerequisite skills using:
• Check Skills You'll Need

During the Lesson
Monitor progress using:
• Check Understanding
• Additional Examples
• Test Prep

After the Lesson
Assess knowledge using:
• Lesson Quiz
• Computer Test Generator CD-ROM

Math Background

You can think of a line of symmetry as a line along which you can fold a figure in half so that both halves match at every point. You can fold along a line of reflection and the figure and its image will coincide.

Teaching Notes

1 EXAMPLE Visual Learners

Ask students to cut out photos of objects from newspapers or magazines and draw the lines of symmetry. Have them display their pictures on posters.

2 EXAMPLE Inclusion

Students with vision problems may have difficulty with reflections. Have a volunteer draw △ABC on graph paper and mark the axes using a thick marker. Then have students draw the image and fold along the line of reflection (the y–axis in this case) to check the image.

PowerPoint

Additional Examples

1 Identify the lines of symmetry.

a.   b.

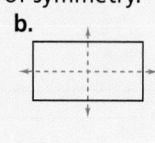

8 lines   2 lines

2 $\overline{FG}$ has endpoints $F(-4, -2)$ and $G(-2, -4)$. Graph $\overline{FG}$ and the image of $\overline{FG}$ after a reflection over the x-axis.
See back of book.

3 $\overline{FG}$ has endpoints $F(-4, -2)$ and $G(-2, -4)$. Graph $\overline{FG}$ and the image of $\overline{FG}$ after a reflection over $y = -1$.
See back of book.

Closure

Ask students: *What is a reflection? What is a line of symmetry?* See back of book.

504

---

2 Graphing Reflections

A **reflection** is a transformation that flips a figure over a **line of reflection.** The reflected figure, or image, is congruent to the original figure. Together, an image and its reflection have line symmetry, the line of reflection being the line of symmetry.

2 EXAMPLE   Reflecting Over an Axis

Graph the image of △ABC after a reflection over the y-axis.

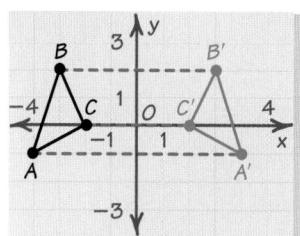

Since A is 4 units to the left of the y-axis, A′ is 4 units to the right of the y-axis. Reflect the other vertices. Draw △A′B′C′.

✓ **Check Understanding**   Example 2

2. Graph the image of △ABC after a reflection over the x-axis.
See left.

You can reflect images over lines other than the axes.

3 EXAMPLE   Reflecting Over a Line

Graph the image of △PQR after a reflection over $y = 2$.

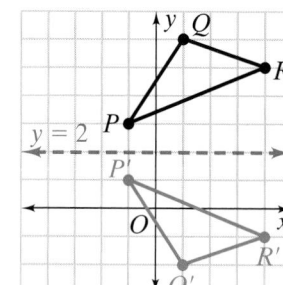

Graph $y = 2$. Since P is 1 unit above the red line, P′ is 1 unit below the red line.

Reflect the other vertices. Draw △P′Q′R′.

✓ **Check Understanding**   Example 3

3. Graph the image △ABC with vertices $A(3, 0)$, $B(2, 3)$, and $C(5, -1)$ after a reflection over each line. a–b. See left.

   a. $x = 2$ **b.** $y = -1$

👥 Reaching All Students

| **Below Level** Have students hold a mirror next to several block capital letters and compare each letter with its reflection. Some, but not all, letters appear flipped, or backward. | **Advanced Learners** Ask students how many lines of symmetry a circle has and to explain. Infinitely many; each diameter is a line of symmetry and a circle has infinitely many diameters. | **Visual Learners** See note on page 504. **Inclusion** See note on page 504. |

EXERCISES

Practice and Problem Solving

 For more exercises, see *Extra Practice*.

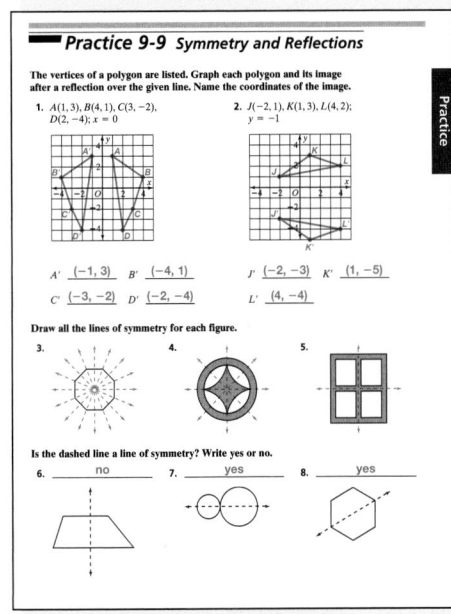

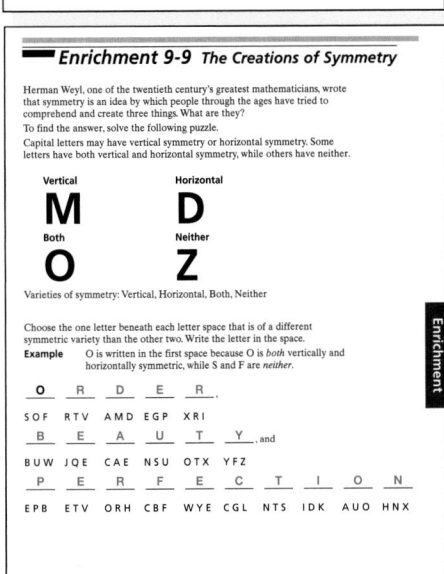

A Practice by Example

Example 1
(page 503)

Copy each figure. Draw all lines of symmetry. See below left.

1.  **2.**  **3.**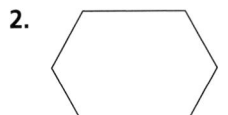

1. no line of symmetry because no half is a mirror reflection of the other half

2.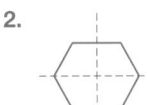

3.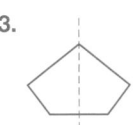

Example 2
(page 504)

In Exercises 4–8, graph each figure and its image after a reflection over the given line. 4–8. See margin.

4.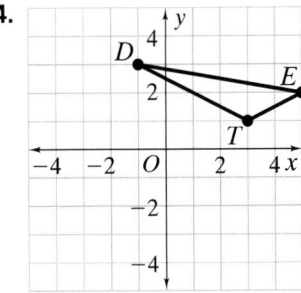

the *x*-axis

5.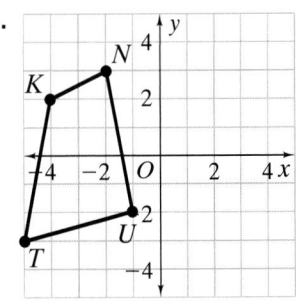

the *y*-axis

Example 3
(page 504)

6. △ABC with A(2, 0), B(6, 0), C(2, −6); line x = 1

7. △KLM with K(−1, 1), L(3, 2), M(0, 3); line y = −1

GPS **8.** △WXY with W(−1, −1), X(0, 0), Y(−5, 0); line y = 2

B Apply Your Skills

Draw each figure. Draw all the lines of symmetry. 9–11. See left.

9. rhombus **10.** square **11.** isosceles triangle

9–11. Drawings may vary. Samples are given.

9.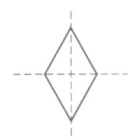

10.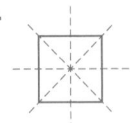

11.

12. Writing in Math Can a reflection image of an angle have a measure that is different from the measure of the original angle? Explain. No, a figure and its reflection image are congruent.

Graph each point and its image after a reflection over the given line. Name the coordinates of the image. 13–18. See back of book.

13. H(−8, 3); y = 4 **14.** J(−8, 3); y = 2 **15.** V(5, 0); x = −2

16. A(2, 5); y = x **17.** B(0, 3); y = 0 **18.** C(4, 0); x = 0

Reasoning Decide whether each statement is *always* true, *sometimes* true, or *never* true.

19. The image of a polygon reflected over a line is congruent to the original polygon. always

20. When corresponding points of an original figure and its reflection are connected, the resulting segments are all perpendicular to the line of reflection. always

21. When a point is reflected over a horizontal line, the *y*-coordinate of the point stays the same. sometimes

9-9 Symmetry and Reflections **505**

4.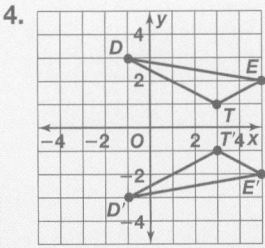

5.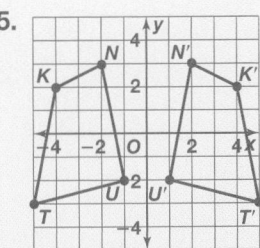

 Use the Guided Problem Solving worksheet with Exercise 8.

6–8. See back of book.

505

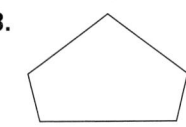

Lesson Quiz 9-9

Use a graph of $\triangle WXY$ with vertices $W(-3, 3)$, $X(-2, 0)$, and $Y(0, 2)$.

1. Graph $\triangle WXY$. How many lines of symmetry does $\triangle WXY$ have? **1**

2. Give the vertices of $\triangle W'X'Y'$, the image of $\triangle WXY$ after a reflection over the x-axis. **$W'(-3,-3)$, $X'(-2, 0)$, $Y'(0, -2)$**

3. Give the vertices of $\triangle W''X''Y''$, the image of $\triangle WXY$ after a reflection over the y-axis. **$W''(3, 3)$, $X''(2, 0)$, $Y''(0, 2)$**

Error Prevention!

Exercises 13–15, 17, 18 Remind students that lines for which y equals a constant are horizontal lines. Lines for which x equals a constant are vertical lines.

Test Prep

📁 **Resources**

For additional practice with a variety of test item formats:
- Test Prep, p. 517
- Test-Taking Strategies, p. 512
- Test-Taking Strategies With Transparencies

Reteaching 9-9 *Symmetry and Reflections*

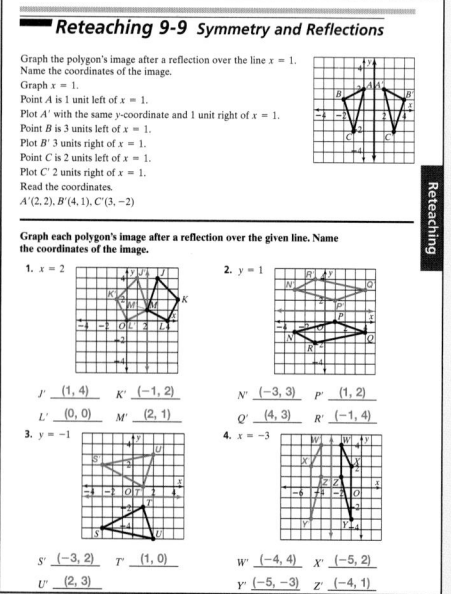

506

© **Challenge**

The given point is reflected over line 1. Then the image is reflected over line 2. Name the coordinates of the second image.

22. $A(3, -2)$ $(-3, 2)$
   line 1: y-axis
   line 2: x-axis

23. $B(-1, 5)$ $(-1, 11)$
   line 1: x-axis
   line 2: $y = 3$

24. $C(-5, -1)$ $(-9, -1)$
   line 1: $x = 2$
   line 2: y-axis

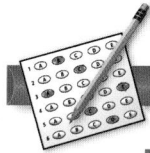

Writing in Math

How many lines of symmetry does a circle have? Explain.

There are infinitely many symmetry lines that pass through the center of a circle.

25. **a.** On a coordinate plane, graph the line $y = x$ and $\triangle ABC$ with vertices $A(5, 3)$, $B(6, -1)$, and $C(2, -1)$. **a–c. See back of book.**

   b. To graph the image of $\triangle ABC$ over the line $y = x$, trace the axes and $\triangle ABC$ on tracing paper. Fold the paper along $y = x$. Trace over the triangle so that it makes an impression on your original graph. Label A', B', and C' appropriately and draw $\triangle A'B'C'$.

   c. Connect A to A', B to B', and C to C'. What do you notice about the line $y = x$ and these segments?

   d. Complete: The line of reflection is the _?_ of the segment that connects a point to its image. **perpendicular bisector**

Test Prep

Multiple Choice

26. Which type of figure has at least two lines of symmetry? **D**
   A. parallelogram
   B. trapezoid
   C. isosceles triangle
   D. rhombus

27. How many lines of symmetry does a rectangle have? **H**
   F. 0
   G. 1
   H. 2
   I. 4

Short Response

In Exercises 28 and 29, **(a)** state whether each statement is *always* true, *sometimes* true, or *never* true. **(b)** Explain your reasoning.

28. When a point is reflected over a horizontal line, the x–coordinate stays the same. **See back of book.**

🖥️ **Take It to the NET**
Online lesson quiz at
www.PHSchool.com
Web Code: ada-0909

29. When a point is reflected over a horizontal line and is NOT on the line, the y–coordinate stays the same. **See back of book.**

Mixed Review

Lesson 9-8

The endpoints of a segment are given. Graph the segment and its image for the given translation. **30–31. See back of book.**

30. $A(4, 3)$, $B(5, 7)$;
   3 units left, 2 units down

31. $X(0, -1)$, $Y(2, 7)$;
   2 units right, 3 units up

Lesson 8-2

Graph each equation. **32–34. See back of book.**

32. $x + 3 = y$

33. $y - 8 = x$

34. $2y = x + 10$

Lesson 1-8

35. If six people meet, and each person shakes every other person's hand, how many handshakes are there in all? **15 handshakes**

Alternative Assessment

Have each student draw four separate figures—the first with no line of symmetry, the second with one, the third with two, and the fourth with more than two. Have them trade papers and draw the lines of symmetry. Then have students draw a fifth figure on graph paper along with a line of reflection. Trade papers again and draw each reflection image.

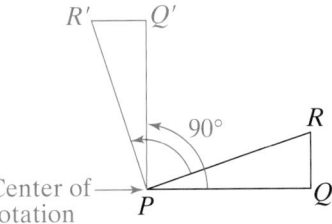

OBJECTIVE

1 **Graphing Rotations**

A **rotation** is a transformation that turns a figure about a fixed point called the **center of rotation.** The angle measure of the rotation is the **angle of rotation.**

R' Q'

$90°$ R

Center of → rotation P Q

In the diagram, $\triangle QPR$ is rotated 90° about the center of rotation, point P. Notice that $m\angle QPQ' = 90°$ and $m\angle RPR' = 90°$. A figure and its rotation image are congruent.

In the diagram, the direction of the rotation is *counterclockwise.* All rotations in this book will be counterclockwise.

You can graph a rotation on a coordinate plane.

1 **EXAMPLE** **Finding a Rotation Image**

Find the vertices of the image of $\triangle ABC$ after a rotation of 180° about the origin.

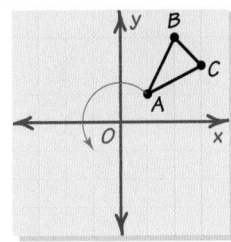

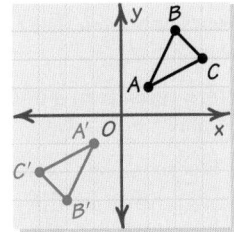

Step 1 Draw $\triangle ABC$. Place a piece of tracing paper over the graph. Trace the vertices of the triangle, the *x*-axis, and the *y*-axis. Then place your pencil at the origin to rotate the paper.

Step 2 Rotate the paper 180°. Make sure the axes line up. Mark the position of each vertex by pressing through the paper. Connect the vertices of the rotated triangle.

The vertices of the image are $A'(-1, -1), B'(-2, -3),$ and $C'(-3, -2).$

What You'll Learn

OBJECTIVE
1 To graph rotations

OBJECTIVE
2 To identify rotational symmetry

. . . And Why

To use rotations in describing real objects

✔ Check Skills You'll Need

Graph each triangle.
1–3. See back of book.
1. $A(1, 3), B(4, 1),$
$C(3, -2)$

2. $J(-2, 1), K(1, -3),$
$L(1, 4)$

3. $X(4, 0), Y(0, 2)$
$Z(-2, -3)$

 For help, go to Lesson 1-10.

New Vocabulary

• rotation
• center of rotation
• angle of rotation
• rotational symmetry

 TEXT Interactive lesson includes instant self-check, tutorials, and activities.

Lesson Preview

✔ Check Skills You'll Need

The Coordinate Plane
Lesson 1-10: Example 2;
Exercises 13–28.
Extra Practice, p. 744.

Lesson Resources

📁 **Teaching Resources**
Practice, Reteaching, Enrichment

👥 **Reaching All Students**
Practice Workbook 9-10
Spanish Practice Workbook 9-10
Guided Problem Solving 9-10
Technology Activities 20
Hands-On Activities 30

⏰ **Presentation Assistant Plus!**
Transparencies and PowerPoint™
• Check Skills You'll Need 9-10
• Additional Examples 9-10
• Student Edition Answers 9-10
• Lesson Quiz 9-10
• Classroom Aid 2, 26
PH Presentation Pro CD-ROM 9-10

 ASSESSMENT *SYSTEM*

Computer Test Generator CD-ROM

💻 **Technology**
Resource Pro® CD-ROM
Computer Test Generator CD-ROM
PH Presentation Pro CD-ROM

💻 **www.PHSchool.com**
Student Site
• Teacher Web Code: adk-5500
• Self-grading Lesson Quiz
PH SuccessNet Teacher Center
• Lesson Planner
• Resources

Plus  **TEXT**

✔ Ongoing Assessment and Intervention

Before the Lesson
Diagnose prerequisite skills using:
• Check Skills You'll Need

During the Lesson
Monitor progress using:
• Check Understanding
• Additional Examples
• Test Prep

After the Lesson
Assess knowledge using:
• Lesson Quiz
• Computer Test Generator CD-ROM

Math Background

A figure has rotational symmetry if you can turn it about a point and, at some place prior to a complete turn, the turning figure matches the original figure.

Teaching Notes

English Learners
Make sure students understand that *clockwise* means a direction of rotation identical to the direction followed by the hands of a clock, and that *counterclockwise* means the opposite direction of rotation.

Additional Examples

1 Find the vertices of the image of △RST after a rotation of 90° about the origin.

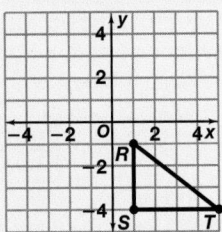

R′(1, 1), S′(4, 1), and T′(4, 5)

2 Judging from appearance, tell whether the star has rotational symmetry. If so, what is the angle of rotation?

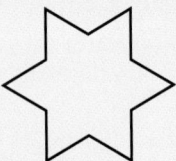

The figure has rotational symmetry; 60°.

Closure

Ask students to explain how to recognize rotational symmetry
A figure has rotational symmetry when an image matches the original figure exactly after a rotation of 180° or less.

508

✔ **Check Understanding**   Example 1

1. Copy the graph of △ABC in Example 1. Draw its image after a rotation of 90° about the origin. Name the coordinates of the vertices of the image. **See back of book.**

OBJECTIVE

2   **Identifying Rotational Symmetry**

A figure has **rotational symmetry** if you can rotate it 180°, or less, so that its image matches the original figure. The angle (or its measure) through which the figure rotates is the angle of rotation.

The wheel at the right has rotational symmetry. You can turn the wheel from its original position to four other positions (five positions in all) and its picture will be as you see here. The smallest such turn moves A to A′. The angle of rotation is 360° ÷ 5, or 72°.

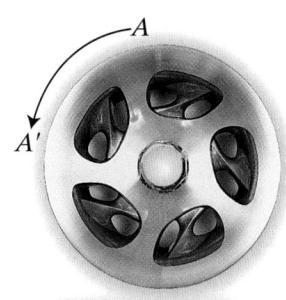

2 EXAMPLE   **Real-World** 🌐 **Problem Solving**

Botany Judging from appearance, state whether the flower has rotational symmetry. If so, what is the angle of rotation?

The flower can match itself in 3 positions.

The pattern repeats in 3 equal intervals. 360° ÷ 3 = 120°

The figure has rotational symmetry.
● The angle of rotation is 120°.

✔ **Check Understanding**   Example 2

2. Judging from appearance, tell whether each figure has rotational symmetry. If so, what is the angle of rotation?

a.
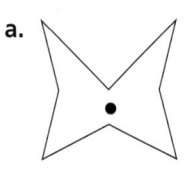

b.
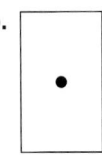

c.
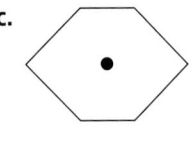

no   yes, 180°   yes, 180°

508   **Chapter 9**   Spatial Thinking

👥 Reaching All Students

| **Below Level** Ask students to give examples of things that rotate. **Answers may vary. Sample: tire, fan blade, music box, jewelry case in a store, Ferris wheel, merry-go-round** | **Advanced Learners** Ask: *Suppose you have a gear with 50 teeth. How many degrees must you rotate the gear to move one tooth to the position of the next tooth?* **7.2°** | **English Learners** See note on page 508. **Inclusion** See note on page 510. |

EXERCISES

Practice and Problem Solving

For more exercises, see *Extra Practice*.

A Practice by Example

Example 1
(page 507)

In Exercises 1–8, graph each figure and its image after a rotation of
(a) 180° and **(b)** 90° about the origin. **1–8. See margin.**

1.

2.

3. point $D(-1, -3)$

4. point $E(3, 2)$

5. $\triangle KLM$ with $K(3, 0)$, $L(2, 4)$, $M(2, 2)$

6. $\triangle STU$ with $S(0, -4)$, $T(-4, -4)$, $U(-4, -3)$

7. $\triangle CDE$ with $C(-2, 0)$, $D(-3, 5)$, $E(-1, 2)$

8. $\triangle GHI$ with $G(-4, -1)$, $H(-2, -5)$, $I(-2, -1)$

Example 2
(page 508)

Natural Science Judging from appearance, tell whether each figure
has rotational symmetry. If so, what is the angle of rotation?
9–12. See left.

9. yes, 90°
10. yes, 60°
11. yes, 60°
12. no

9.

10.

11.

12.

B Apply Your Skills

13. The vertices of a triangle are $V(0, 0)$, $W(2, 5)$, and $X(1, 5)$. On
separate coordinate planes, graph the triangle and its images after
rotations of **(a)** 90° and **(b)** 180° about $(1, 1)$. **See back of book.**

14. Writing in Math Describe something in your classroom that has
rotational symmetry. What is the angle of rotation?
Check students' work.

9-10 Rotations **509**

1a.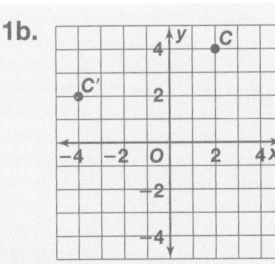

1b.

GPS Use the Guided Problem
Solving worksheet with
Exercise 13.

2–8. See back of book.

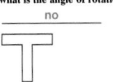 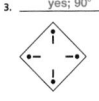
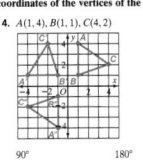 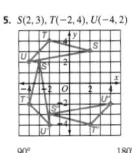
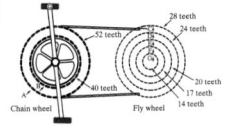

4. Assess

 **PowerPoint** **Lesson Quiz 9-10**

1. $\triangle DFG$ has vertices $D(-2, 4)$, $F(-3,1)$, and $G(-1,2)$. Find the vertices of the image $\triangle D'F'G'$ after a rotation of 180° about the origin.
$D'(2, -4)$, $F'(3, -1)$, $G'(1, -2)$

Judging from appearance, tell whether each figure has rotational symmetry. If so, what is the angle of rotation? If not, explain.

2. 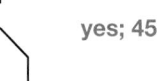 yes; 45°

3.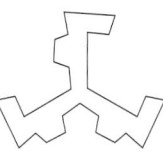

No; you cannot rotate the figure 180° or less so that its image matches the original figure.

Inclusion

Exercises 15–17 Some students may have difficulty differentiating the colors in the figures. Draw each figure on the overhead and label each section appropriately with Y (yellow), O (orange), B (blue), or G (green).

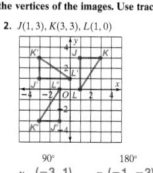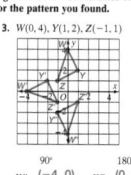
Reteaching 9-10 *Rotations*

$\triangle PQR$ has vertices $P(1, 4)$, $Q(2, 1)$ and $R(4, 2)$. Graph the triangle and its image after a rotation of (a) 90° and (b) 180° about the origin.

Graph $\triangle PQR$. Trace it onto tracing paper and label the vertices. Also trace the axes. Place your pencil at the origin. Turn the paper counterclockwise until the y-axis on the tracing paper is on top of the x-axis of the graph. Mark the position of each vertex by pressing through the paper. Connect the vertices of the rotated triangle and label them P', Q', and R'. The coordinates are $P'(-4, 1)$, $Q'(-1, 2)$, and $R'(-2, 4)$. Put your tracing paper back in its original position. Now turn it until $+5$ on the tracing paper x-axis is by -5 on the graph's x-axis. Mark the vertices, connect them, and label them P'', Q'', and R''. The coordinates are $P''(-1, -4)$, $Q''(-2, -1)$, and $R''(-4, -2)$.

1. The coordinates of $\triangle PQR$, its image after a 90° rotation $\triangle P'Q'R'$, and its image after a 180° rotation $\triangle P''Q''R''$ are listed in the table. Look for a pattern. What is the result on any point (x, y) of (a) a 90° rotation, (b) an 180° rotation? Complete the table.

Point	Image	
	90° Rotation	180° Rotation
$P(1,4)$	$P'(-4,1)$	$P''(-1,-4)$
$Q(2,1)$	$Q'(-1,2)$	$Q''(-2,-1)$
$R(4,2)$	$R'(-2,4)$	$R''(-4,-2)$
(x, y)	$(-y, x)$	$(-x, -y)$

The vertices of a triangle are given. Graph each triangle and its image after a rotation of (a) 90° and (b) 180° about the origin. Name the coordinates of the images. Use tracing paper or the pattern you found.

2. $J(1, 3), K(3, 3), L(1, 0)$ **3.** $W(0, 4), Y(1, 2), Z(-1, 1)$

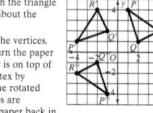

	90°	180°
J'	$(-3, 1)$	$(-1, -3)$
K'	$(-3, 3)$	$(-3, -3)$
L'	$(0, 1)$	$(-1, 0)$

	90°	180°
W'	$(-4, 0)$	$(0, -4)$
Y'	$(-2, 1)$	$(-1, -2)$
Z'	$(-1, -1)$	$(1, -1)$

510

Each figure below is an image formed by rotating the figure at the left. What is each angle of rotation?

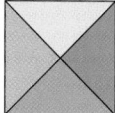 **15.** 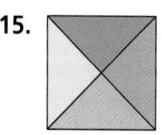 90° **16.** 270° **17.** 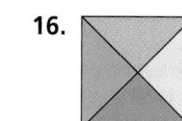 180°

In Exercises 18–21, does the figure have rotational symmetry? If so, what is the angle of rotation?

18. equilateral triangle yes, 120°   **19.** rectangle yes, 180°

20. regular pentagon yes, 72°   **21.** trapezoid no

22. For Exercises 18–21, tell (a) whether each figure has line symmetry and (b) the number of lines of symmetry. yes, 3; yes, 2; yes, 5; yes, 1 if its nonparallel sides are congruent

C Challenge

23. $\triangle JKL$ has vertices $J(4, 4)$, $K(3, 2)$ and $L(5, 1)$.
  a. Graph its image, $\triangle J'K'L'$, after a rotation of 90° about the origin. Name the coordinates of the vertices of the image.
  b. Graph the image of $\triangle J'K'L'$ after a reflection over the y-axis.
  a–b. See back of book.
24. Reasoning Is a rotation of 180° the same as a reflection over the y-axis? Justify your answer.
  No; the reflection of (2, 5) across the y-axis is $(-2, 5)$. A 180° rotation image of (2, 5) is $(-2, -5)$.

Test Prep

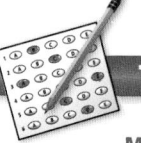

Multiple Choice

25. Which letter has rotational symmetry? A
  A. H   **B.** J   **C.** K   **D.** L

Take It to the NET
Online lesson quiz at
www.PHSchool.com
Web Code: ada-0910

26. Which number has rotational symmetry? I
  F. 2   **G.** 4   **H.** 6   **I.** 8

27. Which object does NOT have rotational symmetry? C
  A. daisy   **B.** ceiling fan   **C.** glove   **D.** picture frame

Short Response

28. Which types of triangles have rotational symmetry? Explain.
  See back of book.

Mixed Review

Lesson 9-9

The vertices of $\triangle ABC$ are $A(5, 6)$, $B(0, 3)$, and $C(3, 2)$. Graph $\triangle ABC$ and its image after a reflection over the given line.
29–31. See back of book.
29. $x = -2$ **30.** $y = -2$ **31.** x-axis

Lesson 8-3

Find the slope of the line through each pair of points.

32. $A(5, 9)$, $B(5, 14)$ undefined   **33.** $E(2, 1)$, $F(8, 4)$ $\frac{1}{2}$ **34.** $C(-2, 4)$, $D(-7, 14)$ -2

Lesson 4-5

35. Number Sense How many three-digit numbers greater than 500 can you form using the digits 2, 6, and 8 exactly once each? four

510   **Chapter 9**   Spatial Thinking

Alternative Assessment

Provide students with a small equilateral triangle and a square. Have them trace each shape anywhere on a coordinate plane. Then find the images after rotations of 90° and 180° about the origin. Also, have them find the angle of rotation for an equilateral triangle and a square. Check students' work.

Test Prep

 Resources
For additional practice with a variety of test item formats:
• Test Prep, p. 517
• Test-Taking Strategies, p. 512
• Test-Taking Strategies With Transparencies

Extension

Tessellations

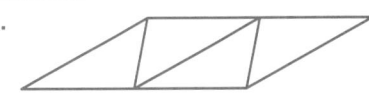

For Use With Lesson 9-10

A tessellation is a repeating pattern of figures that completely covers a plane without gaps or overlaps. You can see tessellations in art, architecture, and nature.

You can use translations, rotations, and reflections to make a tessellation.

1.

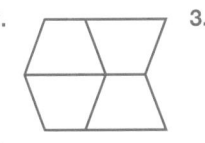

EXAMPLE

Show how the figure at the right forms a tessellation.

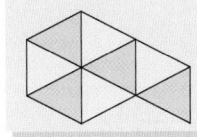

Rotate and translate the figure to cover the plane.

2.

3. will not tessellate

4.

Tessellations

In this Extension, students use transformations to create their own tessellations.

Teaching Notes

Teaching Tip

A tessellation can be a mosaic pattern formed by fitting together repeating polygons to completely cover a plane (without overlapping or leaving spaces). The ancient Greeks proved that the only regular polygons you can use to tessellate are equilateral triangles, squares, and regular hexagons.

Exercise 5 Error Prevention

Remind students that success with tessellations depends on drawing figures accurately and cutting out each one carefully.

EXERCISES

Make multiple copies of each figure on graph paper. Determine whether each figure can form a tessellation. If it can, show the tessellation. 1–4. See above.

1.
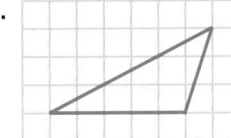

2.
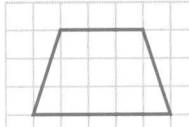

3.
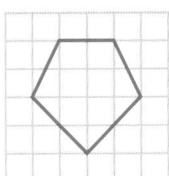

4.
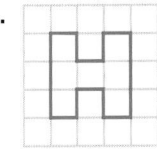

5. **Open-Ended** The diagram below shows how to make a shape to use as a repeating figure for a tessellation. Follow the diagram and make your own tessellation. **Check students' work.**

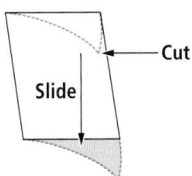
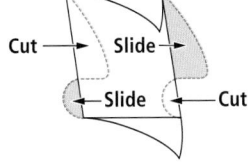

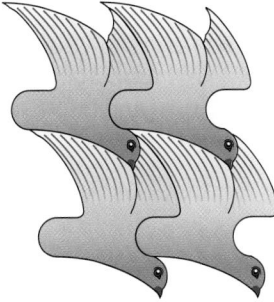

6. **Reasoning** Draw regular polygons with 3, 4, 5, 6, 7, and 8 sides. Which ones can you use to make a tessellation? **3, 4, and 6**

Drawing a Diagram

This strategy helps students understand the advantages of drawing a diagram to help solve a problem. A diagram enables students to organize and visualize multiple pieces of information. Once students can visualize a problem, a solution strategy will begin to emerge.

Resources

Test-Taking Strategies With Transparencies
• Transparency 9
• Practice sheet, p. 9

Teaching Notes

Remind students to always label the parts of the diagram. This will help prevent errors.

Auditory Learners
Suggest that students read the example problems softly aloud as they follow along.

Sometimes for a problem, you may find it helpful to draw a diagram to keep track of the facts and actually see how the given information is related. Then you can use the diagram to help you solve the problem.

1 EXAMPLE

Shayna has nearly completed the annual Walk for Hunger. She began at the Start/Finish line and walked south for $\frac{1}{2}$ mile. Then she walked $1\frac{1}{2}$ miles east. She walked 1 mile north and then walked $\frac{1}{4}$ mile west. She turned right and walked $\frac{1}{4}$ mile. Then she turned left and walked $1\frac{1}{4}$ miles. Then she walked $\frac{1}{2}$ mile south. How far is it directly back to the Start/Finish line?

A. $\frac{1}{4}$ mile   B. $\frac{1}{2}$ mile   C. $1\frac{1}{4}$ miles   D. $1\frac{1}{2}$ miles

Draw a diagram on grid paper if possible. ⟶
Label each segment with its distance. If you draw the diagram carefully, it will show that Shayna is $\frac{1}{4}$ mile from the Start/Finish line. The correct choice is A.

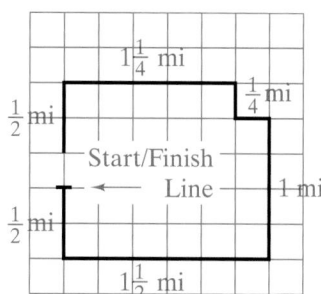

2 EXAMPLE

The endpoints of the diameter of a circle are at $(-4, 5)$ and $(4, 5)$ in a coordinate plane. At what points does the circle intersect the y-axis?

F. $(0, 0), (0, 8)$ G. $(0, 1), (0, 8)$ H. $(0, 0), (0, 9)$ I. $(0, 1), (0, 9)$

On grid paper locate the given points $(-4, 5)$ and $(4, 5)$. Sketch the diameter. Locate its midpoint, $(0, 5)$, the center of the circle. The radius is 4. Sketch the circle. The circle must intersect the y-axis 4 units above and below $(0, 5)$. The points of intersection are $(0, 1)$ and $(0, 9)$, choice I.

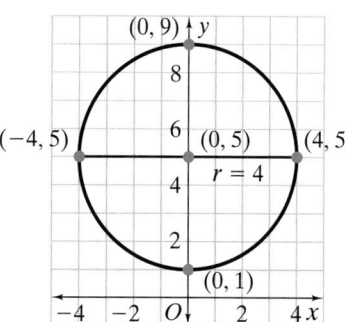

EXERCISES

1. In Example 1, how far has Shayna walked? **C**
   A. $4\frac{1}{4}$ miles   B. $4\frac{1}{2}$ miles   C. $5\frac{1}{4}$ miles   D. $5\frac{1}{2}$ miles

2. A triangle has vertices $(-2, 1), (5, 1),$ and $(0, 6)$. What is its area? **F**
   F. $17\frac{1}{2}$ units^2 G. 21 units^2 H. 35 units^2 I. 42 units^2

Chapter Review

Vocabulary

adjacent angles (p. 465)	line (p. 458)	regular polygon (p. 472)
alternate interior angles (p. 466)	line of reflection (p. 504)	rotation (p. 507)
angle bisector (p. 493)	line of symmetry (p. 503)	rotational symmetry (p. 508)
angle of rotation (p. 507)	parallel (p. 459)	segment (p. 458)
center of rotation (p. 507)	perpendicular bisector (p. 492)	segment bisector (p. 492)
central angle (p. 487)	perpendicular lines (p. 492)	skew (p. 459)
circle (p. 486)	plane (p. 458)	supplementary (p. 465)
complementary (p. 465)	point (p. 458)	transformation (p. 497)
congruent angles (p. 465)	polygon (p. 470)	translation (p. 497)
congruent figures (p. 480)	ray (p. 458)	transversal (p. 466)
corresponding angles (p. 466)	reflection (p. 504)	vertical angles (p. 465)
image (p. 497)	reflectional symmetry (p. 503)	

Resources

Student Edition
Extra Practice, Ch. 9 p. 752
English/Spanish Glossary, p. 782
Table of Symbols, p. 777

 **Reaching All Students**
Reading and Math Literacy 9D
Spanish Reading and Math Literacy 9D

 ASSESSMENT *SYSTEM*

Test Preparation
• Chapter 9 practice in test formats

www.PHSchool.com
Student Site
• Self-grading vocabulary test
PH SuccessNet Teacher Center
• Resources

 **Reading Math**
Understanding Vocabulary

Match the vocabulary terms on the right with their descriptions on the left.

1. Angles that have the same measure, are opposite each other, and are formed by two intersecting lines e

2. A flip of a figure over a line of reflection c

3. A ? divides a figure with reflectional symmetry in half. b

4. An angle whose vertex is the center of a circle a

5. A change of position or size of a figure d

6. A location in space g

7. In a plane, all points the same distance from a given point h

8. A line that intersects two other lines at different points f

    a. central angle
    b. line of symmetry
    c. reflection
    d. transformation
    e. vertical angles
    f. transversal
    g. point
    h. circle

 **Take It to the NET**
Online vocabulary quiz at www.PHSchool.com
Web Code: adj-0951

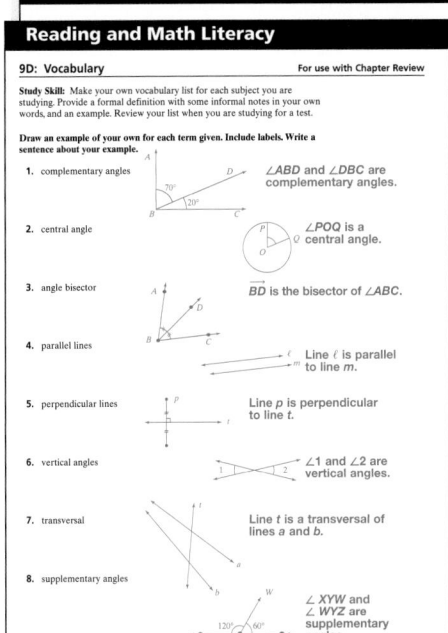

Skills and Concepts

9-1 Objectives

▼ To name basic geometric figures (p. 458)

▼ To recognize intersecting lines, parallel lines, and skew lines (p. 459)

9. ∠RPD, ∠DPL, ∠RPL
10. $\overrightarrow{PR}$, $\overrightarrow{PD}$, $\overrightarrow{PL}$
11. Answers may vary. Sample: $\overleftrightarrow{RL}$
12. R, P, D, L
13. $\overline{RP}$, $\overline{PD}$, $\overline{PL}$, $\overline{RL}$

A **point** is a position in space. All geometric figures are made up of points. A **line** is a series of points that extend in two directions without end. A **segment** is a part of a line and has two endpoints. A **ray** is a part of a line with exactly one endpoint. An angle is two rays that intersect at their endpoints.

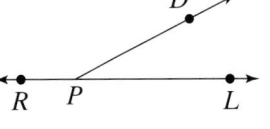

Name the following in the figure above. 9–13. See left.

  9. 3 angles **10.** 3 rays **11.** a line **12.** 4 points **13.** 4 segments

Chapter 9 Chapter Review **513**

▼ To identify adjacent and vertical angles (p. 465)

▼ To relate angles formed by parallel lines and a transversal (p. 466)

Adjacent angles share a vertex and a side but no points in their interiors. **Vertical angles** are formed by intersecting lines and are **congruent.** If parallel lines are crossed by a **transversal** their **corresponding angles** are congruent. **Alternate interior angles** formed by a transversal and parallel lines are also congruent.

In the diagram at the right, m ∥ n.

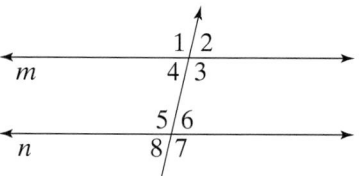

14. Name all angles congruent to ∠1. **∠3, ∠5, ∠7**

15. Answers may vary. Samples: ∠2 and ∠3, ∠5 and ∠6

15. Name two pairs of supplementary angles. **See left.**

16. Name all pairs of corresponding angles.
    ∠1 and ∠5, ∠2 and ∠6, ∠3 and ∠7, ∠4 and ∠8
17. Name all pairs of alternate interior angles.
    ∠4 and ∠6, ∠3 and ∠5
18. If $m \angle 2 = 75°$, find the measures of all the other angles.
    **$m\angle 1 = 105°, m\angle 3 = 105°, m\angle 4 = 75°, m\angle 5 = 105°,$
    $m\angle 6 = 75°, m\angle 7 = 105°, m\angle 8 = 75°$**

9-3 and 9-5 Objectives

▼ To classify triangles (p. 470)

▼ To classify quadrilaterals (p. 471)

▼ To identify corresponding parts of congruent triangles (p. 480)

▼ To determine whether triangles are congruent (p. 481)

A **polygon** is a closed figure with at least three sides. Polygons with the same size and shape are **congruent.** A triangle can be classified by its angles and its sides. You can show two triangles are congruent using **Side-Side-Side, Side-Angle-Side,** and **Angle-Side-Angle.** You can classify some quadrilaterals as parallelograms, rectangles, squares, rhombuses, or trapezoids.

Use the most precise name for each figure described.

19. a triangle with all sides congruent **equilateral triangle**

20. a parallelogram with all sides congruent and four 90° angles
    square
21. a triangle with all acute angles and exactly two congruent sides
    isosceles acute triangle
22. a quadrilateral with exactly one pair of parallel sides **trapezoid**

List the congruent corresponding parts of each of the triangles below. Write a congruence statement (and reason) for the triangles.

23.
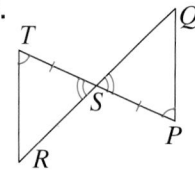

∠T ≅ ∠P, $\overline{ST} ≅ \overline{SP}$,
∠RST ≅ ∠QSP
△RST ≅ △QSP by ASA

24.

$\overline{DE} ≅ \overline{FE}, \overline{CE} ≅ \overline{GE}$,
∠DEC ≅ ∠FEG
△CDE ≅ △GFE by SAS

9-4 Objectives

▼ To draw a diagram to solve a problem (p. 476)

Drawing a diagram can help you visualize a problem.

25. A house is to be built on a lot 70 ft wide by 100 ft deep. The shorter side of the lot faces the street. The house must be set back from the street at least 25 ft. It must be 20 ft from the back lot line and 10 ft from each side lot line. What are the maximum length and width of the house? **55 ft long by 50 ft wide**

9-6 Objectives

▼ To find circumferences (p. 486)

▼ To find central angles and to make circle graphs (p. 487)

You can use these formulas to find the circumference of a circle:
$$C = \pi d \text{ and } C = 2\pi r.$$
There are 360° in a circle. An angle whose vertex is the center of a circle is a **central angle.**

26. Find the circumference of a circle with a diameter of 14 cm.
about 44 cm

🌐 **27. Television Programming** Suppose a survey indicates that at 8 P.M. 40% of viewers watched channel X, 25% watched channel Y, and 35% watched channel Z. Make a circle graph of the data.
See margin.

9-7 Objectives

▼ To construct a segment or angle congruent to a given segment or angle (p. 491)

▼ To construct segment bisectors and angle bisectors (p. 492)

You can use a compass and straightedge to construct congruent segments, congruent angles, **segment bisectors,** and **angle bisectors.**

Draw △CDE with an obtuse ∠D. 28–29. **Drawings may vary.**
See margin for samples.
28. Construct the bisector of ∠D.

29. Construct the perpendicular bisector of $\overline{DE}$.

9-8, 9-9, and 9-10 Objectives

▼ To graph translations (p. 497)

▼ To describe translations (p. 498)

▼ To identify a line of symmetry (p. 503)

▼ To graph a reflection of a geometric figure (p. 504)

▼ To graph rotations (p. 507)

▼ To identify rotational symmetry (p. 508)

A **transformation** is a change of position or size of a figure. The figure after the transformation is called the **image.** You can transform figures in a plane by a **translation,** a **reflection,** or a **rotation.**

What is the image of point $A(7, -2)$ after each transformation?

30. 4 units right, 3 units up
$A'(11, 1)$

31. reflection over the y-axis
$A'(-7, -2)$

32. rotation of 90° about $(0, 0)$
$A' (2, 7)$

33. reflection over the line $y = -1$
$A'(7, 0)$

34. How do translations, reflections, and rotations affect the size and shape of an image? Explain. **They have no effect on size or shape. In each case the image is congruent to the original figure.**

27. Television Programming

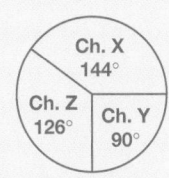

28.

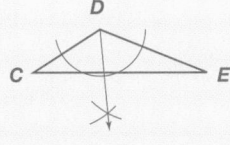

29.

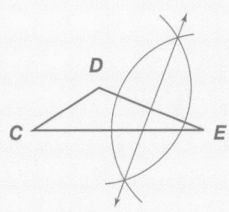

 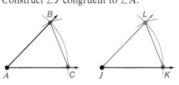

Resources

Teaching Resources
Ch. 9 Test, Forms A & B
Ch. 9 Alternative Assessment,
Form C

Reaching All Students
Spanish Ch. 9 Test, Forms A & B
Spanish Ch. 9 Alternative
Assessment, Form C

ASSESSMENT SYSTEM

Assessment Resources
• Ch. 9 Test, Forms A & B
• Ch. 9 Alternative Assessment,
Form C
Computer Test Generator CD-ROM
• Instant Chapter Test™ for Ch. 9

www.PHSchool.com
Student Site
• Self-grading Chapter 9 Test
PH SuccessNet Teacher Center
• Resources

Plus **iTEXT**

Chapter Test – Form B

Chapter Test – Form A

Chapter 9 Test • Form A

Chapter Test

Take It to the NET
Online chapter test at
www.PHSchool.com
Web Code: ada-0952

Use the diagram to name the following.

1. all segments
containing point G
$\overline{GQ}, \overline{GD}$

2. all pairs of
vertical angles
See right.

3. all rays containing point M 2. $\angle GQT$ and $\angle MQD$,
$\overrightarrow{MQ}, \overrightarrow{QM}, \overrightarrow{TM}, \overrightarrow{MT}, \overrightarrow{TQ}$ $\angle GQM$ and $\angle TQD$

4. a line containing point T
$\overleftrightarrow{MT}$

Use the diagram to name the following.

5. four segments that
intersect $\overline{AB}$
$\overline{AC}, \overline{AE}, \overline{BD}, \overline{BF}$

6. three segments
parallel to $\overline{AB}$
$\overline{CD}, \overline{EF}, \overline{GH}$

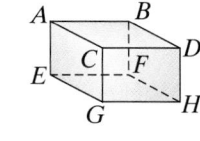

For Exercises 7 and 8, name all possible polygons for each description.

7. quadrilateral with at least one pair of
parallel sides and at least two right angles
trapezoid, rectangle, square

8. quadrilateral with one diagonal
that divides it into two congruent
equilateral triangles
a rhombus that is not a square

9. Find the perimeter of an equilateral
triangle that has a side measure of 60 cm.
180 cm

10. Find the perimeter of a square that has a
side measure of 60 cm. **240 cm**

11. The perimeter of a rectangle is 58 cm. One
side is 18 cm. Find the lengths of the other
three sides. **18 cm, 11 cm, 11 cm**

**A segment has endpoints $A(-3, -6)$ and
$M(-3, -4)$. Find the coordinates of the
endpoints after each transformation.**

12. a translation of 4 units right and 3 units up
$A'(1, -3), M'(1, -1)$

13. a reflection over the y-axis
$A'(3, -6), M'(3, -4)$

14. a rotation of 90° about the origin
about the origin $A'(6, -3), M'(4, -3)$

15. Draw a segment. Construct its
perpendicular bisector. **See margin.**

16. Draw an obtuse angle. Construct its angle
bisector. **See margin.**

Use the diagram for Exercises 17 and 18.

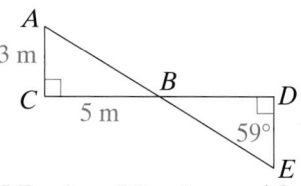

17. If $m\angle 2 = 130°$,
find $m\angle 4$. **130°**

18. **Writing in Math**
Describe how you
can find $m\angle 1$ if you know $m\angle 2$.
Subtract the measure of $\angle 2$ from 180°.

19. **Statistics** Forty two-year-old children were
asked to name their favorite color. Five
chose yellow, seven chose blue, and fourteen
chose red. The rest chose other colors.
a. To make a circle graph, what should be
the measure of the central angle
representing blue, red, and yellow?
Round to the nearest degree. **blue: 63°;**
b. Create a circle graph for   **red: 126°;**
the information.   **yellow: 45°**
See margin.

20. If $\overline{AB} \cong \overline{CD}$, $\angle A \cong \angle D$, and $\angle B \cong \angle C$,
what method can you use to show that
$\triangle ABE \cong \triangle DCF$? **ASA**

21. **Open-Ended** Draw and describe a figure
that has rotational symmetry.
Check students' work.

22. a. The measures of two angles of a triangle
are 50° and 35°. What is the measure of
the third angle? **95°**
b. Classify the triangle by its angles.
obtuse

23. $\triangle CAB \cong \triangle DEB$. Find as many angle
measures and side lengths as you can.

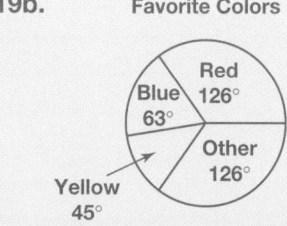

$DE = 3$ m, $BD = 5$ m, $m\angle C = 90°$, $m\angle D = 90°$,
$m\angle ABC = 31°$, $m\angle EBD = 31°$, $m\angle A = 59°$

15.

16.

19b.

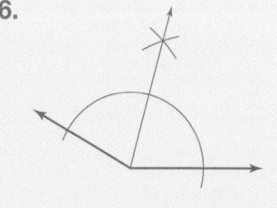

Favorite Colors
Red 126°
Blue 63°
Other 126°
Yellow 45°

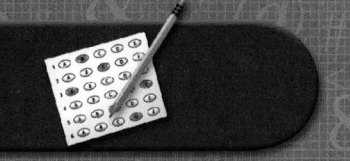
Reading Comprehension Read each passage below. Then answer the questions on the basis of what is *stated* or *implied* in the passage.

> **A Day in a Life** A market research firm studied the activities of a large group of people during a 24-hour day. The firm then found their average numbers of hours for certain activities. It found people spent 8 hours sleeping, 6 hours working, 3 hours on leisure activities, 1 hour eating, and the rest of the day on other activities.

1. On the average, how many hours did people spend daily doing other activities? **D**
   A. 3 h   **B.** 4 h   **C.** 5 h   **D.** 6 h

2. On the average, how many hours did people spend sleeping each week? **I**
   F. 7 h   **G.** 8 h   **H.** 48 h   **I.** 56 h

3. A circle graph for the daily activities would show how many regions? **B**
   A. 4   **B.** 5   **C.** 6   **D.** 8

4. In a circle graph for the daily activities, what would be the measure of the central angle for time spent working? **H**
   F. 6°   **G.** 45°   **H.** 90°   **I.** 120°

5. In a circle graph for the daily activities, what region would be half the size of another region? **B**
   A. Working
   B. Leisure activities
   C. Eating
   D. Other activities

> **In Line With New Friends** Anna had doubts about her first day at the new school, but they faded quickly when she found herself next to Biff and Carly at lunch. They quickly discovered that Anna was the new girl who had moved into the house that sits between theirs on Poplar Road. Anna watched Biff scratch a line on a napkin. "Look Anna. My house is here, at *B*. Carly's is here at *C*. Carly's is five times as far from my house as your house is. She's 100 yards away from you. Guess that means you're going to have to be my next best friend!"

Let *A, B,* and *C* represent the homes of Anna, Biff, and Carly, respectively.

6. Which statements are true? **G**
   I. *A, B,* and *C* are all on Poplar Road.
   II. *B* is between *A* and *C*.
   III. *A* is closer to *B* than to *C*.

   F. I only
   G. I and III only
   H. II and III only
   I. I, II, and III

7. How far apart are *A* and *C*? **C**
   A. 25 yd   **B.** 50 yd
   C. 100 yd   **D.** 125 yd

8. How far apart are *B* and *C*? Show your work. **See margin.**

9. About how long did it take for Anna's doubts about her first day at the new school to fade? **G**
   F. 1 h   **G.** 4 h   **H.** 8 h   **I.** 1 day

8.
$$5x = x + 100$$
$$5x - x = x - x + 100$$
$$4x = 100$$
$$\frac{4x}{4} = \frac{100}{4}$$
$$x = 25$$
$$5(25) = 125$$
B and *C* are 125 yd apart.

Test Prep

Students must be able to extract information from reading passages, answer multiple-choice questions, and construct responses in order to be successful in current state and national assessments.

Resources

 Teaching Resources
Cumulative Review
Quarter 3 Tests, Forms A & B

Reaching All Students
Spanish Cumulative Review
Spanish Quarter 3 Tests

 ASSESSMENT *SYSTEM*

Test Preparation
• Ch. 9 Test Prep

Assessment Resources
• Cumulative Review
• Quarter 3 Tests, Forms A & B
Computer Test Generator CD-ROM
• Test Prep

 www.PHSchool.com
• Test Prep
• Resources

Plus

Cumulative Assessment

— Chapter 9 Cumulative Review

Circle the letter of the best answer.

1. Which expression simplifies to *x* + 2?
   A. $\frac{1}{3}(3x + 6)$ **B.** 5 − *x* − 3   **C.** $\frac{1}{3}(x + 12) − 2$ **D.** 7*x* − 5*x* + 2

2. Find the mean of 12, 15, 18, and 23.
   F. 15   **G.** 17   **H.** 18   **J.** 16

3. Which expression is equivalent to *x* · *x* · *y* · 2 · (−*y*) · *x* · 5?
   A. −10*x*²*y*³   **B.** 10*x*³*y*²   **C.** 10*x*²*y*³   **D.** −10*x*³*y*²

4. Simplify −5 + $\frac{5}{6}$.
   F. −5$\frac{5}{6}$ **G.** 4$\frac{5}{6}$ **H.** −4$\frac{1}{6}$ **J.** 5$\frac{5}{6}$

5. Which measure is equivalent to $\frac{2}{3}$ yd?
   A. 1 ft   **B.** 2 ft   **C.** 12 in.   **D.** 18 in.

6. 70% of *z* is 140. Find *z*.
   F. 98   **G.** 200   **H.** 500   **J.** 0.005

7. Solve 5*x* − 3 = 7*x* + 11.
   A. *x* = −7   **B.** *x* = 4   **C.** *x* = $\frac{3}{4}$ **D.** *x* = 7

8. Find the slope of the line through (4, 2) and (−2, 6).
   F. −1$\frac{1}{2}$ **G.** 1$\frac{1}{2}$ **H.** −$\frac{2}{3}$ **J.** $\frac{2}{3}$

9. The measure of the complement of an angle with measure 18° is what?
   A. 81°   **B.** 72°   **C.** 162°   **D.** 82°

10. Which number is less than 10?
   F. the LCM of 4 and 3   **G.** the GCF of 32 and 48
   H. the GCF of 24 and 36   **J.** the LCM of 3 and 9

11. In △*PQR*, *m*∠*P* = 38° and *m*∠*Q* = 52°. Classify △*PQR*.
   A. acute   **B.** right   **C.** obtuse   **D.** equilateral

12. Simplify $\frac{8 − 4(2 \cdot 4)}{-6}$.

13. Given: △*JKL* ≅ △*PQR*. Complete the following:
   ∠*K* = ____   ∠*Q* ____ $\overline{TJ}$ ≅ ____ $\overline{RP}$

14. Name all the different rays shown in the figure.
   $\overrightarrow{DE}, \overrightarrow{ED}, \overrightarrow{EF}, \overrightarrow{FE}, \overrightarrow{DF}, \overrightarrow{FD}$

Assessment

517

Circle Riding

In this activity, students apply their knowledge of circles to solve problems related to real-world Ferris wheels.

Activating Prior Knowledge

Have students share their memories of riding a Ferris wheel. Discuss where they were and what they remember about the experience, such as the number of passengers in each car and how old they were. **Answers may vary. Sample: Students may have ridden on a Ferris wheel at a state fair or an amusement park. The cars may have held 2 to 4 people.**

Teaching Notes

Teaching Tip

Have a volunteer read the introductory paragraph. Ask: *Why do you think so many people bought tickets to ride the first Ferris wheel at the 1893 World's Fair?* **Answers may vary. Sample: No one had ever seen a ride like this before, so it was an engineering marvel and a novelty.**

Connection to Science

Invite students to find out more about George W. Ferris and the construction of the first Ferris wheel. **Answers may vary. Sample: George Ferris was a 32-year-old bridge builder from Pittsburgh, Pennsylvania, with an engineering degree from Rensselaer Polytechnic Institute. The wheel cost $380,000. It had an axle of 45 feet, was powered by a 1,000 horsepower engine, and used an air brake. Wooden cars were suspended from the wheel and axle by iron clamps.**

Inclusion

Examine the table with students. Look at each measure for both Ferris wheels. Ask a volunteer to tell which is the only measure that is greater for the first Ferris wheel than for the Cosmo Clock 21.

Circle Riding

Applying Circles Have you ever ridden on a Ferris wheel? Since its introduction in 1893, millions of people worldwide have enjoyed riding Ferris wheels. The basic structure of Ferris wheels remains quite similar to the one George W. Ferris created.

The First Ferris Wheel

George W. Ferris built his ride for the 1893 World's Fair in Chicago. It was an instant success.

Each car held 60 people.

Ticket Sales

The ride sold more than $725,000 worth of tickets during the exposition.

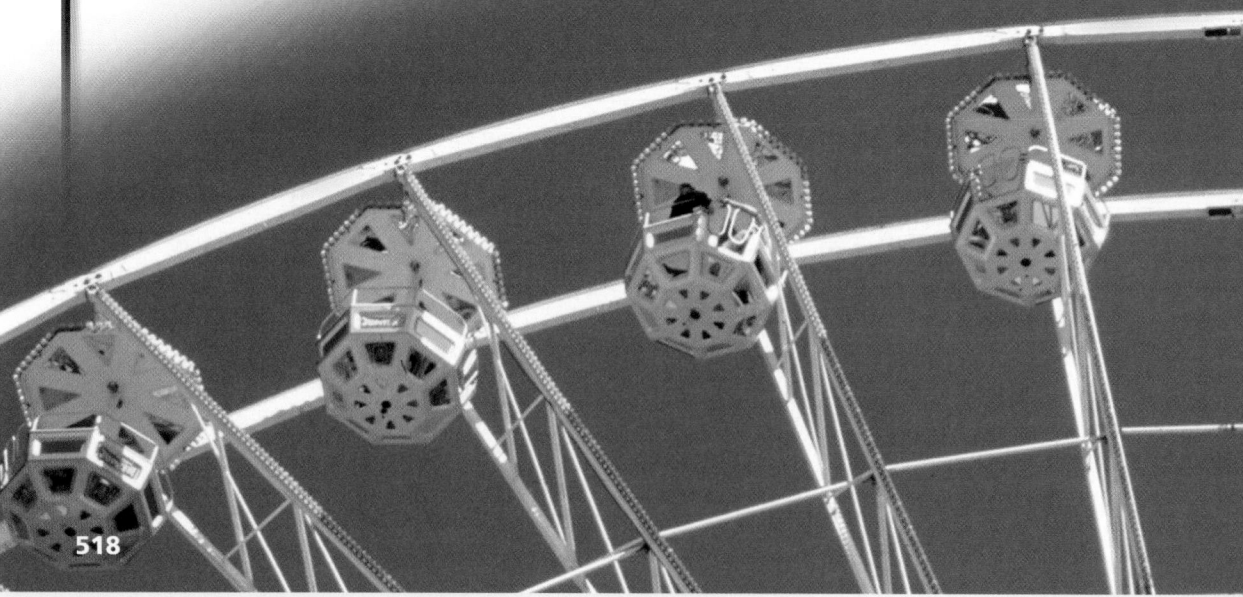

518

Answer: Number of People per Car is 60 for the first Ferris wheel and 8 for the Cosmo Clock 21.

Activity

Use the information on these two pages to answer these questions. 1–5. See margin.

1. How far does a rider travel in one turn of each Ferris wheel?

2. For each wheel, estimate the number of turns needed for a rider to travel one mile.

3. Tickets for a ride on George W. Ferris's wheel cost $.50.
   a. At least how many tickets were sold?
   b. Suppose every ticket-holder rode for two turns of the wheel. At least how many turns did the wheel have to make?

4. Cosmo Clock 21 makes one rotation in 15 min. Find your car's location and the angle of rotation after the given time.
   a. 3 min   **b.** 5 min   **c.** 9 min   **d.** 12 min

5. **Writing in Math** Explain why 28 · 60 more people could ride at one time on the first Ferris wheel than on Cosmo Clock 21.

Ferris Wheel Statistics

Measure	First Ferris Wheel	Cosmo Clock 21
Diameter (ft)	250	328
Height, including base (ft)	264	369
Number of Passenger Cars	36	60
Number of People per Car	60	8

The Biggest Ride

With a maximum capacity of 480 riders, Cosmo Clock 21, in Yokohama, Japan, holds more riders than any other operating Ferris wheel. Even so, waiting time for this attraction is often more than one hour.

 Take It to the NET For more information about Ferris wheels, go to **www.PHSchool.com**.
Web Code: ade-0953

1. First Ferris wheel: about 785 ft; Cosmo Clock 21: about 1,030 ft

2. First Ferris wheel: about 7 rotations; Cosmo Clock 21: about 5 rotations

3a. about 1,450,000 tickets
   b. about 1,343 turns

4a. $\frac{1}{5}$ of the way around, 72° from the start
   b. $\frac{1}{3}$ of the way around, 120° from the start
   c. $\frac{3}{5}$ of the way around, 216° from the start
   d. $\frac{4}{5}$ of the way around, 288° from the start

5. The total number of people in the first Ferris wheel is 36 · 60. The total number of people in Cosmo Clock 21 is 60 · 8. The difference is 36 · 60 − 60 · 8 = (36 − 8) · 60 = 28 · 60.

Area and Volume

Chapter at a Glance

10-1

Area: Parallelograms
pp. 522–526

Objectives
1. Finding Areas of Rectangles
2. Finding Areas of Parallelograms

New Vocabulary
area, altitude

Materials
index cards, scissors

NCTM Standards
3, 4, 6, 7, 8, 9, 10

Local Standards

10-2

Area: Triangles and Trapezoids
pp. 527–531

Objectives
1. Finding Areas of Triangles
2. Finding Areas of Trapezoids

New Vocabulary
altitude of a triangle

NCTM Standards
3, 4, 7, 8, 9, 10

Local Standards

10-3

Area: Circles
pp. 532–537

Objectives
1. Finding Areas of Circles
2. Finding Areas of Irregular Figures

Materials
protractor, scissors

NCTM Standards
3, 4, 6, 8, 9, 10

Local Standards

✓ **Checkpoint Quiz 1**

10-4

Space Figures
pp. 539–543

Objectives
1. Naming Space Figures
2. Identifying Space Figures From Nets

New Vocabulary
space figures, prism, pyramid, cylinder, cone, sphere, net

NCTM Standards
3, 8, 10

Local Standards

10-5

Surface Area: Prisms and Cylinders
pp. 545–550

Objectives
1. Finding Surface Areas of Prisms
2. Finding Surface Areas of Cylinders

New Vocabulary
surface area, lateral area

NCTM Standards
3, 4, 6, 7, 8, 9, 10

Local Standards

10-6

Surface Area: Pyramids, Cones, and Spheres *pp. 552–556*

Objectives
1. Finding Surface Areas of Pyramids
2. Finding Surface Areas of Cones and Spheres

New Vocabulary
slant height

NCTM Standards
3, 4, 6, 7, 8, 9, 10

Local Standards

10-7

Volume: Prisms and Cylinders
pp. 557–560

Objectives
1. Finding the Volumes of Prisms
2. Finding the Volumes of Cylinders

New Vocabulary
volume, cubic unit

NCTM Standards
3, 4, 6, 8, 9, 10

Local Standards

10-8 — Problem Solving

Make a Model
pp. 562–565

Objective
1. Making a Model

NCTM Standards
3, 4, 6, 9, 10

Local Standards

✓ **Checkpoint Quiz 2**

10-9

Volume: Pyramids, Cones, and Spheres
pp. 566–569

Objectives
1. Finding the Volumes of Cones and Pyramids
2. Finding the Volumes of Spheres

NCTM Standards
3, 4, 6, 9, 10

Local Standards

Correlation to Standardized Tests

Lesson	NAEP	Terra Nova		ITBS	SAT10	Local Test
		CAT/6	CTBS			
10-1	M1h, M1a, N2d	■			■	
10-2	M1h, M2a, M2d	■			■	
10-3	M1h		■		■	
10-4	G1c, G1e, G1f	■	■		■	
10-5	M1j					
10-6	M1j					
10-7	M1j		■		■	
10-8						
10-9	M1j					

NAEP National Assessment of Educational Progress
  N = Number Sense, Properties, and Operations
  M = Measurement
  G = Geometry and Spatial Sense
  D = Data Analysis, Statistics and Probability
  A = Algebra and Functions

CAT/6 California Achievement Test, 6th Ed.
CTBS Comprehensive Test of Basic Skills
ITBS Iowa Test of Basic Skills, Form M
SAT10 Stanford Achievement Test, 10th Ed.

NCTM STANDARDS 2000

1	Number and Operations	6	Problem Solving
2	Algebra	7	Reasoning and Proof
3	Geometry	8	Communication
4	Measurement	9	Connections
5	Data Analysis and Probability	10	Representation

Pacing Options

This chart suggests pacing for only the core lessons and their parts. It is provided as a possible guide. It will help you determine how much time you have in your schedule to cover other components, such as the features, chapter projects, Chapter Review, and Chapter Test.

Day	Traditional 45-minute class periods	Two-Year 45-minute class periods	Block 90-minute class periods
1	10-1 ▼ ▼	10-1 ▼	10-1 ▼ ▼ / 10-2 ▼ ▼
2	10-2 ▼ ▼	10-1 ▼	10-3 ▼ ▼ / 10-4 ▼ ▼
3	10-3 ▼	10-2 ▼	10-5 ▼ ▼
4	10-3 ▼	10-2 ▼	10-6 ▼ ▼
5	10-4 ▼ ▼	10-2 ▼	10-7 ▼ ▼
6	10-5 ▼	10-3 ▼	10-8 ▼ / 10-9 ▼ ▼
7	10-5 ▼	10-3 ▼	
8	10-6 ▼ ▼	10-3 ▼	
9	10-7 ▼ ▼	10-4 ▼	
10	10-8 ▼	10-4 ▼	
11	10-9 ▼ ▼	10-5 ▼	
12		10-5 ▼	
13		10-5 ▼	
14		10-6 ▼	
15		10-6 ▼	
16		10-6 ▼	
17		10-7 ▼	
18		10-7 ▼	
19		10-8 ▼	
20		10-8 ▼	
21		10-9 ▼	
22		10-9 ▼	
23		10-9 ▼	

Math Background

Skills Trace

BEFORE Chapter 10

Chapter 9 reviewed plane figures that appear in Chapter 10. Students were introduced to area, surface area, and volume in previous courses.

DURING Chapter 10

This chapter reviews concepts and formulas for area. Solids, or space figures, are reviewed. Surface area and volume formulas are developed for various space figures.

AFTER Chapter 10

The remainder of this course reviews the ideas in this chapter. The formulas developed here are used in both Algebra 1 and Geometry.

10-1 10-2   Area: Parallelograms, Triangles, and Trapezoids

The area of a plane figure is the number of square unit regions the figure contains. You calculate the area by counting or approximating the number of square-unit regions covered by the surface. In many cases, you can use a formula to shortcut the counting process. You can easily divide some rectangular figures, such as this one, into square units.

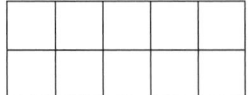

Notice in the following figures that the area does not change as the rectangle is skewed into a parallelogram.

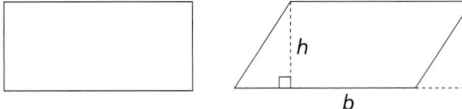

The formula for the area of a parallelogram is the same as that for a rectangle, but the length and width are usually called the *base* and the *height*. The formula for the area of a parallelogram is $A = bh$.

The following figure shows that the area of a triangle is one-half the area of a corresponding parallelogram.

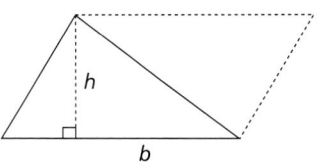

The formula for the area of a triangle is $A = \frac{1}{2}bh$. Notice that the height is the length of the perpendicular segment from one vertex to the line containing the opposite side.

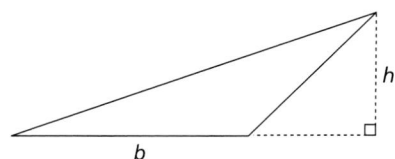

10-3   Area: Circles

You can approximate the area of a circle by dividing it into wedges, or *sectors*. These sectors can be arranged to approximate a parallelogram with a height that is about the same as the radius of the circle and a base that is about the same as half the circumference of the circle.

The following steps show how to substitute these measures of the circle to derive the formula for the area of a circle.

$A = bh$	area of a parallelogram
$A = \frac{1}{2}Cr$	Base is half the circumference and height is the radius.
$A = \frac{1}{2}(2\pi r)r$	Substitute for C. ($C = 2\pi r$)
$A = \pi r^2$	Simplify.

Notice that the formula for the area of a circle, $A = \pi r^2$, contains r^2. Since area is measured in square units, this will help students distinguish it from the formula for the circumference, $C = 2\pi r$.

10-4 Space Figures

Solid geometry is the geometry of figures in three-dimensional space. These figures are often called *space figures.* The lesson discusses the various aspects and properties of space figures, along with the nets of space figures.

A pattern that you can cut out and fold into a model for a space figure is called a *net.* If you take a shoe box with the top glued on, for example, and cut along the edges to flatten it out, the result is a net for a rectangular prism. You can draw several different nets for such a shoe box. Here is one:

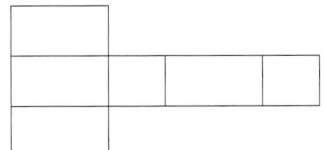

- For a prism, you can use these two formulas, L.A = hp, or ph, and S.A = L.A. + 2B, where B is the area of one base.

- For a cylinder, since the perimeter, or circumference, of a circle is $2\pi r$, these two formulas become L.A = $2\pi rh$ and S.A. = L.A. + 2B.

All the pyramids in this text are *regular* pyramids with bases that are regular polygons and lateral faces that are congruent isosceles triangles. The height of one of the triangular faces is called the slant height (ℓ) of the pyramid.

For a pyramid,
L.A. = $n\left(\frac{1}{2}b\ell\right) = \frac{1}{2}p\ell$, where n is the number of lateral faces, and
S.A. = L.A. + B.

- For a right circular cone with a slant height of ℓ, L.A. = $\frac{1}{2}(2\pi r)\ell$, or L.A. = $\pi r\ell$, and S.A. = L.A. + B.

- For a sphere, S.A. = $4\pi r^2$.

10-5 10-6 Surface Area: Prisms, Cylinders, Pyramids, Cones, and Spheres

If the axis of a cylinder or the lateral faces of a prism make right angles with the bases, then the figure is a *right* cylinder or prism; otherwise it is *oblique*. In this text, if it is not otherwise stated, figures are assumed to be right. The cones and pyramids are also right space figures because the perpendicular segment from the vertex to the base hits the center of the base.

In a rectangular prism, if the sides of the base are called s_1, s_2, s_3, and s_4, for example, then the lateral area (L.A.) of the faces is
   $hs_1 + hs_2 + hs_3 + hs_4$,
where h is the height of the prism. But this is
   $h(s_1 + s_2 + s_3 + s_4)$
which is the same as h(perimeter of the base), or hp.

10-7, 10-8, 10-9 Volume: Prisms, Cylinders, Pyramids, Cones, and Spheres

The *volume* of a space figure is the number of cubic units needed to fill the figure. A *cubic unit* is the space occupied by a cube with edges of one unit. Sometimes it is helpful to make a model of a space figure to help solve a problem.

An interesting experiment to convince students that the formula for the volume of a cone makes sense is to have them cut two figures out of paper: a cone and a cylinder that have exactly the same height and circumference. Then ask students to fill the cone with rice and pour the rice into the cylinder. Most students are surprised to discover that it takes three cones of rice to fill the cylinder.

Additional Professional Development Opportunities

Chapter 10 Math Background notes:
pp. 523, 528, 533, 540, 546, 553, 558, 563, 567

SkyLight
Professional
Development

Additional resources available from SkyLight Professional Development: On-site courses, workshops, summer institutes. Online courses and chat rooms. Videocassettes and books. Visit www.skylightedu.com.

Professional Development, Content Facilitator Guide: Pre-Algebra, Chapter 10

Ongoing Assessment and Intervention

The *Prentice Hall Pre-Algebra* program provides many options for assessment in the Student Edition, Teacher's Edition, and teaching resources. From these options you may choose instructional materials that are appropriate for your students and support your district's curriculum requirements.

Daily Assessment

 Instant Check System™ in Chapter 10

Allows students to check their own learning before, during, and after each lesson.

Diagnosing Readiness before the chapter (p. 520)

Check Skills You'll Need exercises in each lesson (pp. 522, 527, 532, 539, 545, 552, 557, 562, 566)

Check Understanding questions with each Example (pp. 523, 527, 528, 529, 533, 534, 540, 545, 546, 547, 553, 554, 558, 563, 566, 567)

Checkpoint Quiz (pp. 537, 565)

Formal Assessment

In Chapter 10 and Additional Resources

Assesses student progress throughout the *Pre-Algebra* text and with blackline masters and CD-ROM.

Student Edition

- Chapter 10 Review, with Vocabulary Skills and Concepts Review, pp. 571–573
- Chapter 10 Test, p. 574

Assessment Resources   *Spanish versions available.*

- Checkpoint Quizzes 1 & 2
- Chapter Test, Forms A & B
- Chapter Alternative Assessment

 Computer Test Generator CD-ROM

- Instant Chapter Tests™ — pre-made tests with items that vary every time you print.
- Online Testing allows you to give tests online and receive progress reports.
- Diagnose readiness with questions on prerequisite skills.
- Prepare students by making tests based on standardized test objectives.

Algebra Readiness Tests

- Includes Basic Skills Tests and Concept-Readiness Tests.
- Assess understanding of skills and concepts needed for success in algebra.

Standardized Test Preparation

 Test Prep in Chapter 10

Teaches students strategies and gives them practice with all the test item formats they will encounter on high-stakes tests.

Test Prep exercises in each lesson (pp. 525, 531, 536, 543, 550, 556, 560, 565, 569)

Test-Taking Strategies (p. 570: Choosing "Cannot Be Determined")

Test Prep (p. 575: Cumulative Review)

Provides a three-step approach to preparing students for high-stakes, national, and state exams.

❶ Diagnose & Prescribe

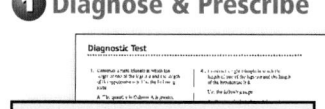

Content Diagnostic Tests

- Diagnose strengths and weaknesses with ongoing benchmark tests.
- Prescribe individualized reteaching opportunities.

❷ Review & Reteach

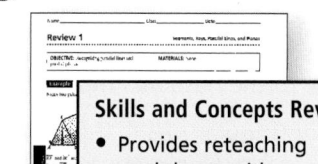

Skills and Concepts Review

- Provides reteaching worksheets with instruction and practice for each skill.
- Includes course prerequisite skills.

❸ Practice & Assess

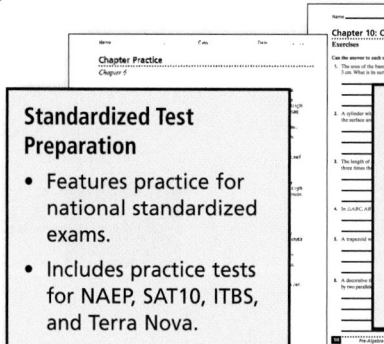

Standardized Test Preparation

- Features practice for national standardized exams.
- Includes practice tests for NAEP, SAT10, ITBS, and Terra Nova.

Test-Taking Strategies With Transparencies

- Support the Test-Taking Strategies pages in the Student Edition.
- Provide a transparency and a worksheet for each strategy.

Reaching All Students

The textbook, the iText, and other technology components provide numerous opportunities to reach students of various ability levels and learning styles. Each Teacher's Edition lesson suggests how you can help all your students be successful and understand the mathematics in Chapter 10.

Below Level

Student Edition
- Diagnosing Readiness*: p. 520
- Check Skills You'll Need*: pp. 522, 527, 532, 539, 545, 552, 557, 562, 566

Reteaching
Chapter 10 Grab & Go™ File: pp. 10–18

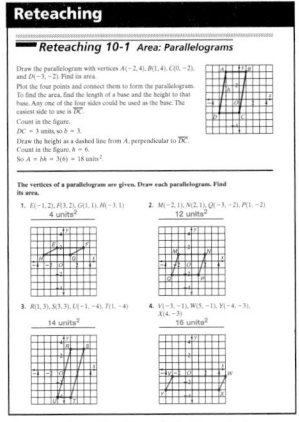

* Can be used with all ability levels to ensure mastery of prerequisite skills.

Advanced Learners

Student Edition
- Challenge exercises: pp. 525, 531, 536, 542, 549, 550, 555, 556, 560, 564, 569
- Extension: pp. 538, 544

Enrichment
Chapter 10 Grab & Go™ File: pp. 19–27

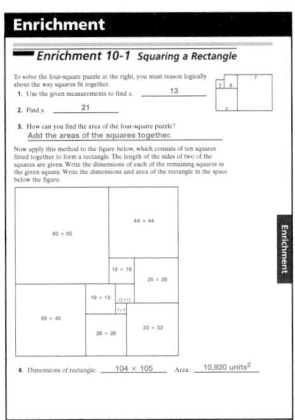

Problem Solving

Student Edition
- Strategies: pp. 562–565
- Real-World Problem Solving: pp. 522, 528, 529, 533, 534, 554, 558, 562, 567

Guided Problem Solving Masters
Chapter 10: pp. 83–91

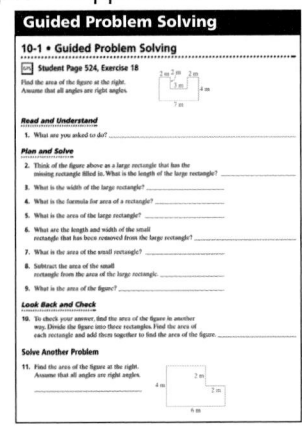

Reading and Math Literacy

Student Edition
- Vocabulary: pp. 521, 571, plus in most lessons
- Reading Math: pp. 523, 541, 546, 551, 571
- Writing in Math: pp. 525, 530, 536, 542, 549, 555, 559, 561, 564, 568, 574
- Illustrated Glossary: pp. 782–826

Reading and Math Literacy Masters
Chapter 10: pp. 37–40

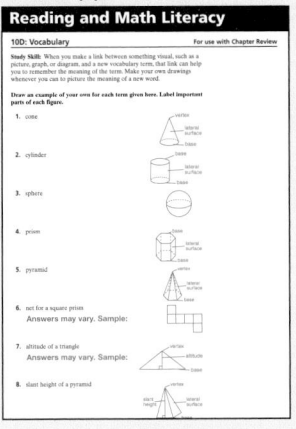

English Learners

Student Edition
- English/Spanish Illustrated Glossary: pp. 782–826

Workbook and Masters
Spanish Practice Workbook: pp. 83–91
Spanish Reading and Math Literacy Masters: pp. 37–40

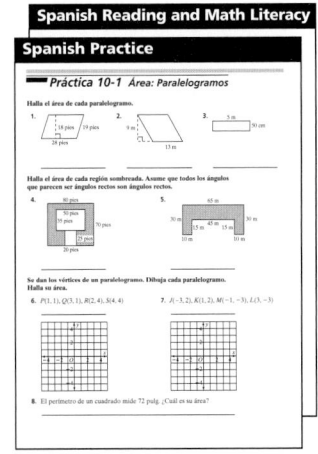

Learning Styles

Student Edition
- Investigation: pp. 522, 532
- Technology: p. 561
- DK Activities: pp. 576–577
- Chapter Project: p. 742

Activity Masters
Hands-On Activities: 24, 25, 26, 27, 28
Technology Activities: 22, 23, 24, 25, 26, 27

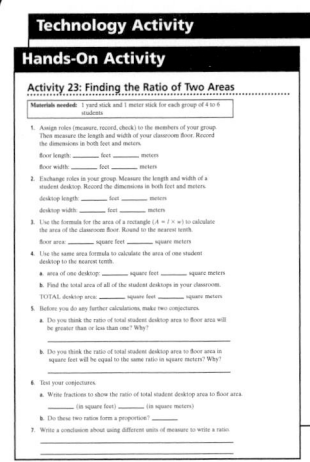

Program Resources

	Resources in Grab & Go™ Files				Resources for Reaching All Students				Spanish Resources			Presentation Assistant Plus! Transparencies				Prentice Hall Presentation Pro CD-ROM
	Practice	Reteach	Enrich	Checkpt Quiz	Reading & Math Literacy	Technology Activities	Hands-On Activities	Guided Problem Solving	Practice	Reading & Math Literacy	Checkpt Quiz	Skills Check	Additional Examples	Answers to Exercises	Lesson Quiz	
10-1	■	■	■		■		■	■	■	■		■	■	■	■	■
10-2	■	■	■			■		■	■			■	■	■	■	■
10-3	■	■	■	■	■			■	■	■	■	■	■	■	■	■
10-4	■	■	■						■			■	■	■	■	■
10-5	■	■	■			■	■	■	■			■	■	■	■	■
10-6	■	■	■				■	■	■			■	■	■	■	■
10-7	■	■	■				■	■	■			■	■	■	■	■
10-8	■	■	■	■				■	■		■	■	■	■	■	■
10-9	■	■	■				■	■	■			■	■	■	■	■
For the Chapter	Chapter Projects, Chapter Tests, Alternative Assessment, Cumulative Review, Cumulative Assessment				On Web site only: Home Activities, Algebra Readiness Puzzles, Interdisciplinary Activities				Spanish Chapter Tests, Alternative Assessment, Cumulative Review, Cumulative Assessment			Classroom Aid Transparencies				

Also available for use with the chapter:
- Practice Workbook
- Solution Key
- MathNotes folder
- For additional online and technology resources, see below.
- For teacher support and access to student Web site materials, use Web Code adk-5500.

PRENTICE HALL
ASSESSMENT *SYSTEM*

Program assessment and test preparation, all in one place.

See page 520E.

Skills Intervention Kit

A *complete* system for the student who is struggling with course-level work

How to Use With Chapter 10

10-1, 10-4	Geometry
10-6	Operations With Fractions
10-7–10-9	Geometry

Online Intervention

Integrated within the iText, this online intervention system includes diagnostic tests and prescribed remediation, plus reports to track student mastery.

Technology

 Online and on CD-ROM

Complete Interactive Student Text online and on CD-ROM—with instant-feedback assessment, tutorial help, dynamic activities, instructional and real-world videos, audio, and additional practice.

 www.PHSchool.com For Students

Use Web Codes for easy access to online activities, chapter projects, self-grading lesson quizzes, chapter tests, vocabulary quizzes, updated data sources, graphing calculator procedures, and more.

PH SuccessNet **For Teachers**

Online lesson planning with built-in state correlations, all the teaching resources, complete reference library, your own calendar and Teacher Web page, professional development, and more.

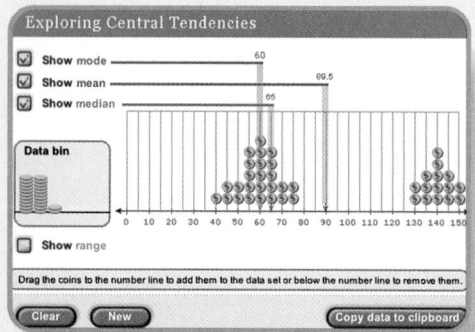

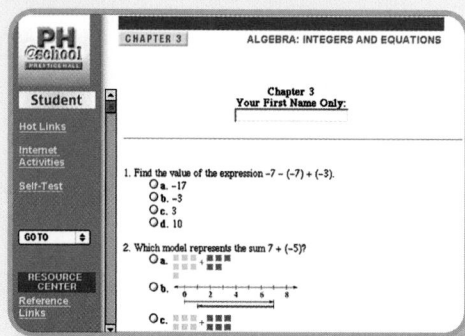

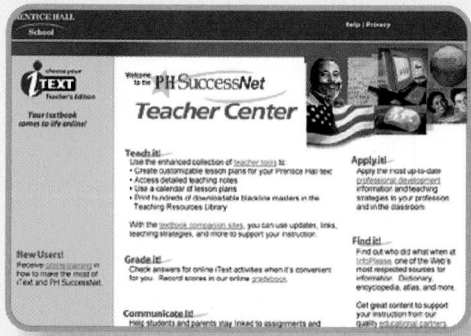

Presentation Assistant Plus!

The Prentice Hall *Presentation Assistant Plus!* provides you with the material you need to teach a lesson from beginning to end. Two easy-to-use formats—Transparencies and CD-ROM—allow you to present a lesson the way you are most comfortable.

 ## Transparencies

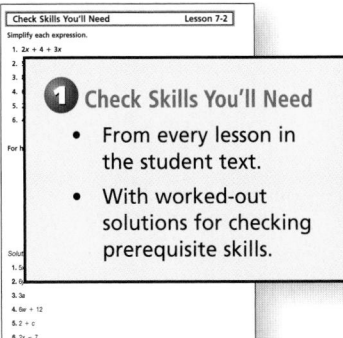

1 Check Skills You'll Need
- From every lesson in the student text.
- With worked-out solutions for checking prerequisite skills.

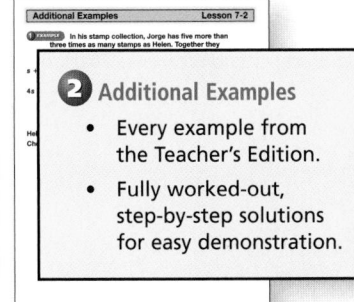

2 Additional Examples
- Every example from the Teacher's Edition.
- Fully worked-out, step-by-step solutions for easy demonstration.

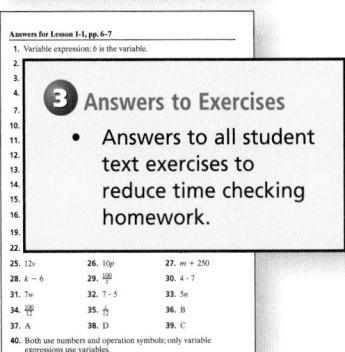

3 Answers to Exercises
- Answers to all student text exercises to reduce time checking homework.

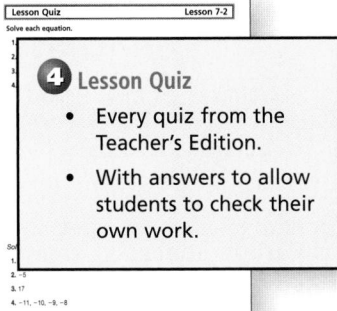

4 Lesson Quiz
- Every quiz from the Teacher's Edition.
- With answers to allow students to check their own work.

 Throughout the Teacher's Edition, this symbol indicates material that is available in the Presentation Assistant Plus!

 Prentice Hall Presentation Pro CD-ROM

- Includes all Transparencies as PowerPoint® presentations.
- Conveniently organized by lesson so you can easily **1** Introduce, **2** Teach, **3** Check Homework, and **4** Assess each lesson.
- Animated examples allow step-by-step instruction at your own pace.
- Easy to edit so you can create custom presentations.

Teaching Chapter 10 Using Presentation Assistant Plus!

	1 Introduce	**2 Teach**	**3 Check Homework**	**4 Assess**
	Check Skills You'll Need	Additional Examples	Student Edition Answers	Lesson Quiz
10-1	p. 84	p. 137	✔	p. 84
10-2	p. 85	pp. 138–139	✔	p. 85
10-3	p. 86	pp. 140–141	✔	p. 86
10-4	p. 87	p. 142	✔	p. 87
10-5	p. 88	pp. 143–144	✔	p. 88
10-6	p. 89	pp. 144–145	✔	p. 89
10-7	p. 90	p. 146	✔	p. 90
10-8	p. 91	p. 147	✔	p. 91
10-9	p. 92	pp. 148–149	✔	p. 92

 Prentice Hall Presentation Pro

CD-ROM with dynamic Powerpoint® presentations for every lesson. Helps you introduce and develop concepts, check homework, and assess progress. Part of Presentation Assistant Plus! *(See above.)*

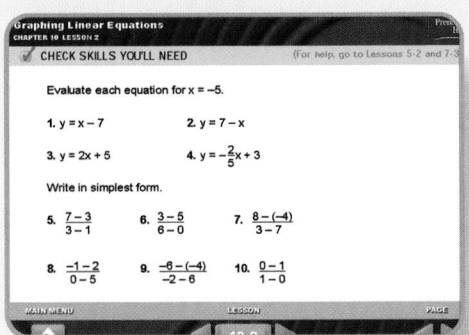

 Computer Test Generator

CD-ROM to create practice sheets and tests for course objectives and standardized tests. Includes Instant Chapter Tests™, online testing, and student reports. Part of the PH Assessment System. *(See page 520E.)*

 Resource Pro® with Planning Express®

CD-ROM with a lesson planning tool that allows you to import state and local objectives. Includes electronic versions of all the teaching resources.

Area and Volume

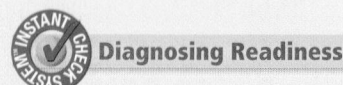
Diagnosing Readiness

Students will find the answers to these exercises in the back of their textbooks.

Prescribing Intervention
For intervention, direct students to:

Finding the Areas of Rectangles and Squares
Geometric Formulas, p. 780

Simplifying Expressions With Exponents
Lesson 4-7: Example 1;
Exercises 1–9.
Extra Practice, p. 747.

Multiplying by a Fraction
Lesson 5-4: Example 2;
Exercises 1–8.
Extra Practice, p. 748.

Finding the Circumferences of Circles
Lesson 9-6: Example 1;
Exercises 1–9.
Extra Practice, p. 752.

Where You've Been

● In Chapter 7, you learned to solve multi-step equations and inequalities using inverse operations.

● In Chapter 8, you graphed and solved linear equations and inequalities.

● In Chapter 9, you learned how to classify polygons and identify corresponding parts of congruent triangles.

iTEXT Instant self-check online and on CD-ROM

Diagnosing Readiness   (For help, go to the lesson in green.)

Finding the Areas of Rectangles and Squares (Geometric Formulas, p. 780)

Find the area of each figure.

1.
6 m
6 m
36 m^2

2.
2.5 in.
8 in.
20 in.^2

3.
5 cm
9 cm
45 cm^2

Simplifying Expressions With Exponents (Lesson 4-7)

Simplify each product.

4. $5 \cdot 3^2$ 45   **5.** $3.14 \cdot 5^2$ 78.5   **6.** $6 \cdot 12^2$ 864   **7.** $4^2 \cdot 3$ 48   **8.** $10^2 \cdot 3$ 300   **9.** $3.14 \cdot 12^2$ 452.16

Multiplying by a Fraction (Lesson 5-4)

Find each product.

10. $\frac{1}{2} \cdot 12$ 6   **11.** $\frac{1}{2} \cdot 13 \cdot 3$ $19\frac{1}{2}$ **12.** $\frac{1}{2}(10 + 8)$ 9

13. $\frac{1}{2} \cdot 20x$ 10x   **14.** $\frac{1}{2} \cdot 5x \cdot 2x$ $5x^2$ **15.** $\frac{1}{2}(10)(6 + 5)$ 55

16. $\frac{1}{2}(62)(30 + 14)$ 1,364   **17.** $\frac{1}{3}(20)(35 + 40)$ 500   **18.** $\frac{1}{3}(3)(5 + 3)$ 8

Finding the Circumferences of Circles (Lesson 9-6)

Find the circumference of each circle. Use 3.14 for π.

19. $d = 50$ yd
157 yd

20. $r = 100$ m
628 m

21. $d = 5.5$ in.
17.27 in.

Area and Volume

Chapter 10

Where You're Going

In this chapter, you will learn how to

- Find the areas of figures.
- Find the surface areas of space figures.
- Find the volumes of space figures.
- Solve a problem by making a model.

Real-World Snapshots Applying what you learn, on pages 576–577 you will solve problems about playing fields.

Key Vocabulary

- altitude (p. 523)
- altitude of a triangle (p. 527)
- area (p. 522)
- cone (p. 539)
- cubic unit (p. 557)
- cylinder (p. 539)
- lateral area (p. 546)
- net (p. 540)
- prism (p. 539)
- pyramid (p. 539)
- slant height (p. 552)
- space figure (p. 539)
- sphere (p. 539)
- surface area (p. 545)
- volume (p. 557)

521

Chapter 10 Overview

Chapter 10 shows how to find the areas, surface areas, and volumes of some basic geometric figures. Students find the areas of parallelograms. Then they use the formula for the area of a parallelogram to develop and use area formulas for triangles and trapezoids. Students use all these formulas and the formula for the area of a circle to find the areas of irregular shapes. Students learn about space figures and identify them from nets. They find surface areas first by finding the areas of nets. Then they find surface areas and volumes by using formulas.

Activating Prior Knowledge
Ask students to recall as many area formulas as they can and list them on the board.

📘 Reading Math
- Reading a Formula, p. 551
- **Vocabulary** A complete list of terms, plus vocabulary exercises, appears in the Chapter Review on p. 571.
- **Illustrated Glossary** Examples for each vocabulary term, plus definitions in both English and Spanish, appear starting on p. 782.

📝 Test-Taking Strategies
Choosing "Cannot Be Determined," p. 570

🌐 Real-World Problem Solving
- **Strategy:** Make a Model, pp. 562–565
- **DK Real-World Snapshots:** Applying Area, pp. 576–577
- **Chapter Project:** Making a Splash, p. 742

💻 www.PHSchool.com
Internet support includes:
- Self-grading Vocabulary and Chapter 10 Tests
- Activity Masters
- Chapter Project support
- Chapter Planner
- Chapter 10 Resources

Plus

Lesson Preview

✓ Check Skills You'll Need

Using Formulas
Lesson 3-4: Example 1;
Exercises 1–4.
Extra Practice, p. 746.

Lesson Resources

📁 **Teaching Resources**
Practice, Reteaching, Enrichment

👥 **Reaching All Students**
Practice Workbook 10-1
Spanish Practice Workbook 10-1
Reading and Math Literacy 10A
Spanish Reading and Math
  Literacy 10A
Guided Problem Solving 10-1
Hands-On Activities 26

⏰ **Presentation Assistant Plus!**
Transparencies and PowerPoint™
• Check Skills You'll Need 10-1
• Additional Examples 10-1
• Student Edition Answers 10-1
• Lesson Quiz 10-1
• Classroom Aid 9, 10
PH Presentation Pro CD-ROM 10-1

ASSESSMENT SYSTEM

Computer Test Generator CD-ROM

💻 **Technology**
Resource Pro® CD-ROM
Computer Test Generator CD-ROM
PH Presentation Pro CD-ROM

💻 **www.PHSchool.com**
Student Site
• Teacher Web Code: adk-5500
• Graphing Calculator, Procedure 2
• Self-grading Lesson Quiz
PH SuccessNet Teacher Center
• Lesson Planner
• Resources

Plus 📘 **iTEXT**

What You'll Learn

OBJECTIVE 1 To find areas of rectangles

OBJECTIVE 2 To find areas of parallelograms

. . . And Why

To use formulas in finding areas of objects, such as the area of a banner

✓ Check Skills You'll Need

Use $A = \ell w$ and find the third value.
1–4. See below.

1. $A = 54$ in.^{2}, $w = 6$ in.

2. $\ell = 35$ m, $w = 7$ m

3. $A = 25$ cm^2, $\ell = 2.5$ cm

4. $\ell = 7.2$ ft, $w = 7.2$ ft

📗 For help, go to Lesson 3-4.

New Vocabulary

• area
• altitude

1. $\ell = 9$ in.
2. $A = 245$ m^2
3. $w = 10$ cm
4. $A = 51.84$ ft^2

📘 **iTEXT** Interactive lesson includes instant self-check, tutorials, and activities.

OBJECTIVE

1 Finding Areas of Rectangles

Investigation

Discovering an Area Formula

1. Use a 3 in.-by-5 in. index card. Find the area of the card. **15 in.^{2}**

2. Draw a line from one vertex to a point on another side to create a triangle. Cut along that line. **Check students' work.**

3. Use the pieces to form a parallelogram that is not a rectangle. **Check students' work.**

4. What is the area of your parallelogram? Explain.
   15 in.^{2}; the shapes have the same amount of paper in them.

The **area** of a figure is the number of square units it encloses. The rectangle outlined in red encloses 8 square units, each with area 1 cm^2 (1 square centimeter). So, the area of the rectangle is 8 cm^2.

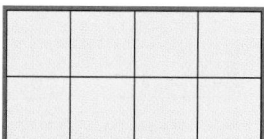

You can use the formula $A = bh$ to find the area of a rectangle, where b is the length of one side and h is the length of the other. For the rectangle above, $A = 4 \cdot 2 = 8$. So, the area is 8 cm^2.

When you find area, the dimensions must be in the same unit.

1 EXAMPLE **Real-World 🌐 Problem Solving**

Parades Find the area of the marching band's rectangular banner.

Step 1 Change the units so that they are the same.

  1 yd = 3 ft   **Change 1 yard to feet.**

Step 2 Find the area.

  $A = bh$ **Use the formula for the area of a rectangle.**

  $= (7)(3)$ **Replace b and h with the dimensions 7 and 3.**

  $= 21$ **Simplify.**

• The area of the banner is 21 ft^2.

Ongoing Assessment and Intervention

Before the Lesson
Diagnose prerequisite skills using:
• Check Skills You'll Need

During the Lesson
Monitor progress using:
• Check Understanding
• Additional Examples
• Test Prep

After the Lesson
Assess knowledge using:
• Lesson Quiz
• Computer Test Generator CD-ROM

✓ Check Understanding   Example 1

1. Find the area of each rectangle.

a.
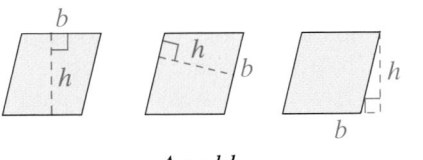
1 m
10 cm

1,000 cm², or 0.1 m²

b.
2 yd
2 ft

12 ft², or 1⅓ yd²

OBJECTIVE

2 Finding Areas of Parallelograms

A rectangle is a special kind of parallelogram. The formula for the area of a parallelogram follows from the formula for the area of a rectangle. The height *h* of a parallelogram is the length of an *altitude*.

An **altitude** is a line segment perpendicular to the line containing a base of the figure and drawn from the side opposite that base.

Key Concepts   **Area of a Parallelogram**

The area of a parallelogram is the product of any base length *b* and the corresponding height *h*.

b

[parallelogram diagrams with *h* and *b*]

$$A = bh$$

Reading Math

For any base in a figure, the *corresponding height* is the length of an altitude to that base.

---

2 EXAMPLE   Finding Area of a Parallelogram

Find the area of each parallelogram.

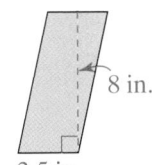
8 in.
3.5 in.

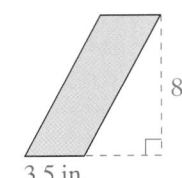
8 in.
3.5 in.

$$
\begin{aligned}
A &= bh && \text{area formula} \\
&= (3.5)(8) && \text{Substitute.} \\
&= 28 && \text{Simplify.}
\end{aligned}
$$

The area of each is 28 in.²

✓ Check Understanding   Example 2

2. Find the area of each parallelogram.

a.

3 m   6 m²
2 m

b.
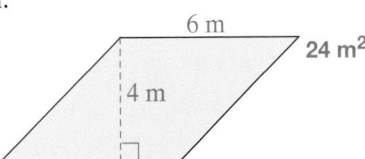
6 m
24 m²
4 m

c. How do the areas of two parallelograms compare when the dimensions of one are twice the dimensions of the other?
The area of the larger parallelogram is 4 times the area of the smaller parallelogram.

10-1   Area: Parallelograms   **523**

🧑‍🤝‍🧑 Reaching All Students

Below Level Ask students for examples of items that are sold by the square unit. **Answers may vary.** Sample: carpeting, flooring	**Advanced Learners** Ask: *A parallelogram has an area of 198 in.² and a base of 18 in. What is the height of the parallelogram?* 11 in.	**Tactile Learners** See note on page 523. **Error Prevention** See note on page 525.

---

2. Teach

Math Background

Professional Development

To find the area of a parallelogram, you can cut off a right triangle from one end and move it to the opposite end to form a rectangle. Because of this, the area formulas for rectangles and parallelograms are the same.

Teaching Notes

Investigation (Optional)
Show how to find the area of the index card by drawing a one-inch grid on the card and then counting the squares.

2 EXAMPLE Tactile Learners

Some students may not understand why height for a parallelogram is not the length of one of its sides. Have a volunteer stand and lean to one side. Ask another volunteer to measure the height of the student's chin above the floor. Lead students to see that you measure height perpendicular to the base, or floor in this case, and not along a "slant."

PowerPoint

Additional Examples

1 Find the area of the rectangle.
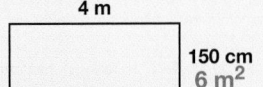
4 m
150 cm
6 m²

2 Find the area of each parallelogram.

a.
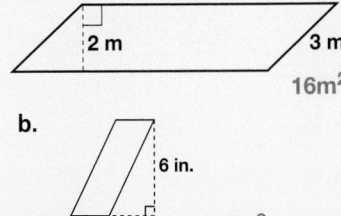
8 m
2 m
3 m
16m²

b.
6 in.
2.5 in.
15 in.²

Closure

Ask students: *How are the methods for finding the area of a rectangle and the area of a parallelogram similar?* For both, you multiply the length of a base and its corresponding height.

523

Assignment Guide

1 Objective 1
- Ⓐ Ⓑ **Core** 1–3, 11, 12, 14, 18
- Ⓒ **Extension** 20–22, 25

2 Objective 2
- Ⓐ Ⓑ **Core** 4–10, 13, 15–17, 19
- Ⓒ **Extension** 23, 24

Test Prep 26–31
Mixed Review 32–39

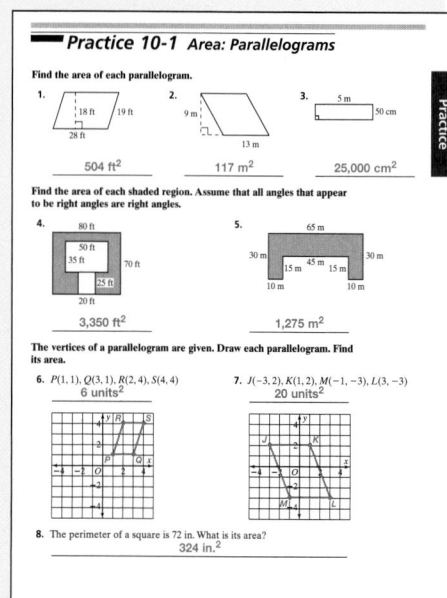

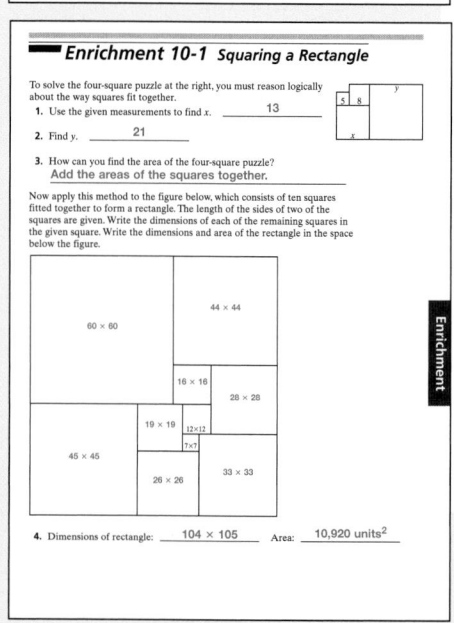

EXERCISES

For more exercises, see Extra Practice.

Practice and Problem Solving

Ⓐ **Practice by Example**

Find the area of each parallelogram.

Example 1
(page 522)

1. 3 yd, 15 ft
135 ft², or 15 yd²

2. 100 cm, 1 m
1 m², or 10,000 cm²

3. 4 ft, 1 yd
12 ft², or 1⅓ yd²

Example 2
(page 523)

4. 23 ft, 17 ft, 16 ft
368 ft²

5. 2 m, 1.5 m
3 m²

6. ⟵0.5 m⟶ 20 cm
1,000 cm², or 0.1 m²

7. ⟵10 in.⟶ 10 in.
100 in.²

8. 5.5 ft, 8 ft, 5 ft
40 ft²

9. 2 in., 4.5 in., 4 in.
8 in.²

10c. The area of the larger parallelogram is 9 times the area of the smaller parallelogram.

10. Find the area of a parallelogram with the given dimensions.
  a. base 3 cm, height 5 cm **15 cm²**   **b.** base 9 cm, height 15 cm **135 cm²**
  c. How do the areas of two parallelograms compare when the dimensions of one are three times the dimensions of the other? **See left.**

Ⓑ **Apply Your Skills** 🌐 **11. Sports** A football field is 300 ft long, from goal line to goal line, and 160 ft wide, from sideline to sideline. What is the area of a football field? **48,000 ft²**

16. 9 square units

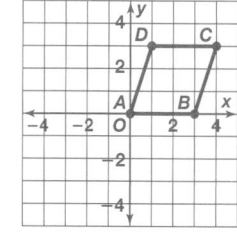

17. 12 square units

Find the area of each parallelogram.

12. 10,560 ft, 2 mi
4 mi², or 111,513,600 ft²

13. ⟵7 cm⟶ 20 mm
1,400 mm², or 14 cm²

14. 5 m, 200 cm
10 m², or 100,000 cm²

15. 22 in., 30 in., ⟵77 in.⟶
1,694 in.²

Coordinate Geometry **The vertices of a parallelogram are given. Draw each parallelogram. Find its area.** **16–17. See left.**

16. $A(0,0), B(3,0), C(4,3), D(1,3)$

17. $W(-2,0), X(-3,3), Y(2,0), Z(1,3)$

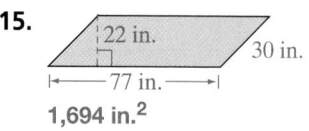

18. Find the area of the figure at the right.
GPS Assume that all angles are right angles.
22 m²

524 Chapter 10 Area and Volume

 GPS Use the Guided Problem Solving worksheet with Exercise 18.

19. No; the left parallelogram has an area of 6 m² while the right parallelogram has 4.5 m².

19. Writing in Math The two parallelograms below have the same perimeter. Are the areas the same? Explain. **See left.**

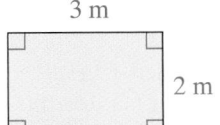
3 m
2 m

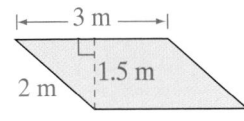
3 m
2 m
1.5 m

C Challenge

20a–b. Answers may vary. Samples are given.
a. 80 ft × 5 ft,
40 ft × 10 ft,
20 ft × 20 ft;
check students'
work for
drawings.
b. 20 ft × 20 ft

20. Open-Ended You want to make a 400-ft² vegetable garden. You plan to build a fence to keep the rabbits out. To spend the least amount of money, you want to use as little fencing as possible.
  a. Draw and list three possible dimensions for your garden.
  b. Which of the three will need the least amount of fencing?
  a–b. See left.

Find the area of each shaded region. Assume that all angles that appear to be right angles are right angles.

23. ½; the area of a parallelogram is *bh*, so doubling one dimension doubles the area.

21.

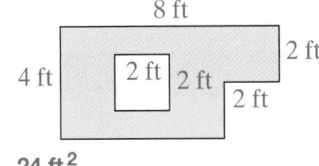
8 ft
2 ft
4 ft
2 ft 2 ft
2 ft

24 ft²

22.

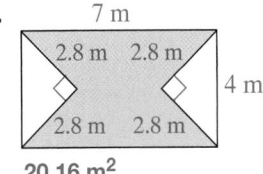
7 m
2.8 m   2.8 m
4 m
2.8 m   2.8 m

20.16 m²

24. ¼; the area of a parallelogram is *bh*, so doubling both dimensions quadruples the area.

Reasoning In Exercises 23 and 24, find the ratio of the areas of the parallelograms (smaller to larger). Justify each answer.

23. The bases are the same length. The height of one parallelogram is twice the height of the other. **See above left.**

24. The height and the length of a base of one parallelogram are both twice those of the other parallelogram. **See left.**

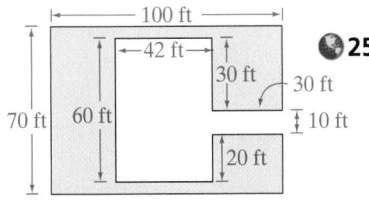
100 ft
42 ft
30 ft   30 ft
70 ft 60 ft   10 ft
20 ft

25. a. Landscaping Find the area of the yard at the left. Assume that all angles that appear to be right angles are right angles.
  b. How many square yards of sod do you need to cover the yard?
  c. One bag of fertilizer covers approximately 2,000 ft². How many bags should you buy to cover the yard? **3 bags**
  25a. 4,180 ft²   25b. 464.$\overline{4}$ yd²

Test Prep

Multiple Choice

26. Square *ABCD* has perimeter *x* units. What is its area in terms of *x*? **A**
  A. $\frac{x^2}{16}$ units²   **B.** $4x^2$ units²   **C.** $\frac{x^2}{4}$ units²   **D.** $\frac{x}{16}$ units²

27. A parallelogram has base 18 cm and height 9 cm. What is its area? **H**
  F. 27 cm²   **G.** 81 cm²   **H.** 162 cm²   **I.** 324 cm²

28. What is the side length of a square with area 16 cm²? **D**
  A. 256 cm²   **B.** 32 cm²   **C.** 8 cm   **D.** 4 cm

29. A rectangle has base *r* and height *s*. Which formula gives its area? **H**
  F. $A = r^2$ **G.** $A = s^2$ **H.** $A = rs$ **I.** $A = 2r + 2s$

Error Prevention!

Exercises 4–9 Tell students to look for two segments that form a right angle when determining a corresponding base and height.

Lesson Quiz 10-1

Find each area.

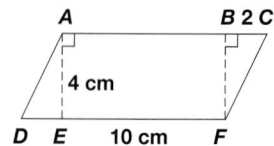

1. rectangle *ABFE* 40 cm²

2. parallelogram *ACFD* 48 cm²

3. a rectangle with a base of 50 cm and a height of 5 cm 250 cm²

Alternative Assessment

Have students use graph paper to draw a rectangle and a parallelogram, each with an area of 30 square units. **Answers may vary. Sample: Rectangle may have unit dimensions of 1 by 30, 2 by 15, 3 by 10, or 5 by 6; parallelogram should have a base and height matching one pair of the dimensions given.**

Test Prep

Resources

For additional practice with a variety of test item formats:
• Test Prep, p. 575
• Test-Taking Strategies, p. 570
• Test-Taking Strategies With Transparencies

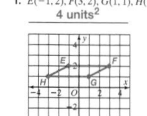

Reteaching 10-1 Area: Parallelograms

Draw the parallelogram with vertices $A(-2, 4)$, $B(1, 4)$, $C(0, -2)$, and $D(-3, -2)$. Find its area.

Plot the four points and connect them to form the parallelogram. To find the area, find the length of a base and the height to that base. Any one of the four sides could be used as the base. The easiest side to use is $\overline{DC}$.

Count in the figure.
$\overline{DC} = 3$ units, so $b = 3$.
Draw the height as a dashed line from A, perpendicular to $\overline{DC}$.
Count in the figure, $h = 6$.
So $A = bh = 3(6) = 18$ units².

The vertices of a parallelogram are given. Draw each parallelogram. Find its area.

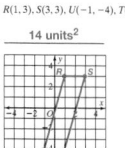

1. $E(-1, 2)$, $F(3, 2)$, $G(1, 1)$, $H(-3, 1)$ 4 units²

2. $M(-2, 1)$, $N(2, 1)$, $Q(-3, -2)$, $P(1, -2)$ 12 units²

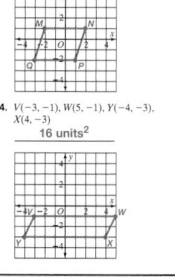

3. $R(1, 3)$, $S(3, 3)$, $U(-1, -4)$, $T(1, -4)$ 14 units²

4. $V(-3, -1)$, $W(5, -1)$, $Y(-4, -3)$, $X(4, -3)$ 16 units²

526

Reading Comprehension   Read the passage below before doing Exercises 30 and 31.

Political Sign Regulations Set

The City Council issued the following regulations for political signs in the upcoming election:
1. Only one sign may be posted on a single lot of land.
2. Sign areas may not exceed 32 ft².
3. Signs cannot be more than 6 ft in height.
4. All signs must be removed no later than 7 days after the election.

Take It to the NET
Online lesson quiz at
www.PHSchool.com
Web Code: ada-1001

30. You wish to display a sign that is 6 ft high. What is the greatest width it can have? $5\frac{1}{3}$ ft

31. A sign with area 24 ft² is at least 1 ft high. Write an inequality that shows all possible values for its base length *b*. $b \le 24$

Mixed Review

Lesson 9-10 **The endpoints of a segment are given. Graph each segment and its image after a rotation of 90° about the origin. 32–34. See margin.**

32. $A(5, 8)$, $B(2, 4)$ **33.** $C(0, 3)$, $D(3, -5)$ **34.** $E(-2, -3)$, $F(-2, 4)$

Lesson 9-2 **35.** Find the measures of two supplementary angles if the difference of their measures is 56°. 118°, 62°

Lesson 5-4 **Simplify each expression.**

36. $\frac{2}{5} \cdot 2\frac{1}{2}$ 1   **37.** $\frac{2}{5} \div 2\frac{1}{2}$ $\frac{4}{25}$ **38.** $3\frac{2}{3} \cdot \frac{3}{4}$ $2\frac{3}{4}$ **39.** $3\frac{2}{3} \div \frac{3}{4}$ $4\frac{8}{9}$

Math at Work

Pharmacist

Pharmacists dispense medications. They also talk to their customers about the possible side effects of medications. To do this, they must thoroughly understand how prescription drugs are made.

Sometimes a doctor prescribes a special medication that a pharmacist must mix. The pharmacist must measure the ingredients in the exact proportions that the patient needs. In a situation such as this, mathematics is essential.

Take It to the NET For more information about pharmacists, go to **www.PHSchool.com**.
Web Code: adb-2031

32.
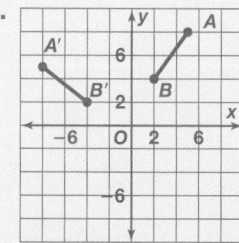

33.
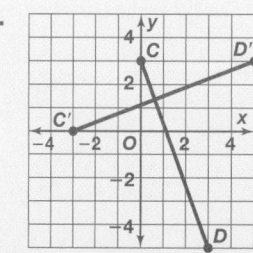

34.
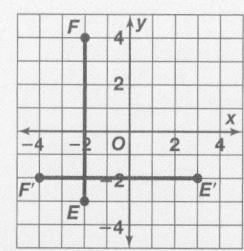

Area: Triangles and Trapezoids

OBJECTIVE

1 Finding Areas of Triangles

A diagonal divides a parallelogram into two congruent triangles.

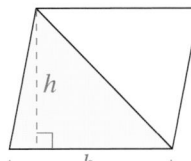 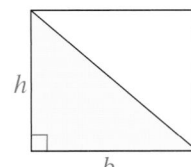 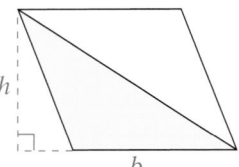

You can see that the area of a triangle is half the area of a parallelogram. An **altitude of a triangle** is the perpendicular segment from a vertex of a triangle to the line containing the opposite side. The height is the length of the altitude.

Key Concepts | Area of a Triangle

The area of a triangle equals half the product of any base length b and the corresponding height h.

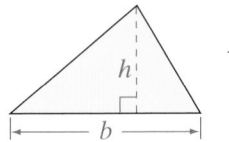

$A = \frac{1}{2}bh$

1 EXAMPLE | Finding Area of a Triangle

Find the area of the triangle.

$A = \frac{1}{2}bh$ **Use the formula for the area of a triangle.**

$= \frac{1}{2} \cdot 8 \cdot 3$ **Replace b with 8 and h with 3.**

$= 12$ **Simplify.**

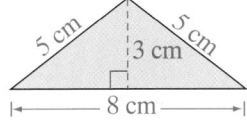

● The area is 12 cm².

✓ Check Understanding   Example 1

1. Find the area of each triangle.

a.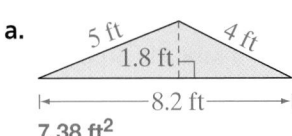

7.38 ft²

b.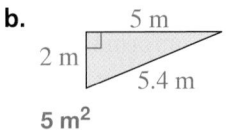

5 m²

What You'll Learn

OBJECTIVE 1 To find areas of triangles

OBJECTIVE 2 To find areas of trapezoids

. . . And Why

To find areas in real-world situations, such as construction

✓ Check Skills You'll Need

Find each product.

1. $\frac{1}{2} \cdot 16$ 8   2. $\frac{1}{2} \cdot 14 \cdot 6$ 42

3. $\frac{1}{2} \cdot 5 \cdot 15$ $37\frac{1}{2}$

4. $\frac{1}{2} \cdot 2\frac{1}{2} \cdot 8$ 10

❓ For help, go to Lesson 5-4.

New Vocabulary

• altitude of a triangle

 TEXT Interactive lesson includes instant self-check, tutorials, and activities.

---

1. Plan

Lesson Preview

✓ **Check Skills You'll Need**

Multiplying Fractions
Lesson 5-4: Example 2;
Exercises 1–8.
Extra Practice, p. 748.

Lesson Resources

📁 **Teaching Resources**
Practice, Reteaching, Enrichment

👥 **Reaching All Students**
Practice Workbook 10-2
Spanish Practice Workbook 10-2
Guided Problem Solving 10-2
Technology Activities 22

⏱ **Presentation Assistant Plus!**
Transparencies and PowerPoint™
• Check Skills You'll Need 10-2
• Additional Examples 10-2
• Student Edition Answers 10-2
• Lesson Quiz 10-2
• Classroom Aid 9, 10
PH Presentation Pro CD-ROM 10-2

ASSESSMENT SYSTEM
Computer Test Generator CD-ROM

💻 **Technology**
Resource Pro® CD-ROM
Computer Test Generator CD-ROM
PH Presentation Pro CD-ROM

💻 **www.PHSchool.com**
Student Site
• Teacher Web Code: adk-5500
• Algebra Readiness Puzzles 107
• Self-grading Lesson Quiz
PH SuccessNet Teacher Center
• Lesson Planner
• Resources

Plus **TEXT**

Ongoing Assessment and Intervention

Before the Lesson
Diagnose prerequisite skills using:
• Check Skills You'll Need

During the Lesson
Monitor progress using:
• Check Understanding
• Additional Examples
• Test Prep

After the Lesson
Assess knowledge using:
• Lesson Quiz
• Computer Test Generator CD-ROM

2. Teach

Math Background

Students know how to find the area of a parallelogram. In this lesson, students adapt the formula for the area of a parallelogram to find the areas of triangles and trapezoids. A triangle can be viewed as half of a parallelogram that has the same base and height as the triangle. A trapezoid can be viewed as two triangles with the same height.

Teaching Notes

1 EXAMPLE **Visual Learners**

Have students draw a parallelogram and one of its diagonals on graph paper, making sure the base and height are whole units. Have them count to find the area of the parallelogram and the area of one triangle to verify the formula for a triangle.

Teaching Tip

Show that using either diagonal of a trapezoid will result in the same area formula, $\frac{1}{2}h(b_1 + b_2)$.

3 EXAMPLE **English Learners**

Explain to students that a *cross section* is the plane figure that results by slicing through a space figure. Ask students to picture an orange. Slicing it in half exposes a cross section with a shape very near that of a circle.

3 EXAMPLE **Error Prevention**

Remind students that the bases of a trapezoid are the two sides parallel to each other, even if the figure is turned so that the bases are vertical. Use the lengths of these two sides when calculating the area of a trapezoid. Draw trapezoids in different orientations on the board or overhead, and have students identify the bases.

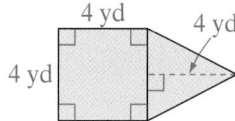

2 EXAMPLE  Real-World  Problem Solving

Construction How much siding does a builder need to cover the side of the house shown at the left?

Area of triangle	Area of rectangle
$A = \frac{1}{2}bh$	$A = bh$
$= \frac{1}{2} \cdot 16 \cdot 9$	$= 16 \cdot 10$
$= 72$	$= 160$

Add to find the total: $72 + 160 = 232$.

● The builder needs 232 ft^2 of siding.

✓ **Check Understanding** Example 2

2. Find the area of the shaded figure. **24 yd^2**

4 yd   4 yd

4 yd

OBJECTIVE

2 Finding Areas of Trapezoids

A diagonal divides a trapezoid into two triangles. Notice that the triangles have the same height but different bases.

You can add the areas of the triangles to find the area of the trapezoid.

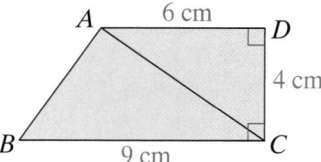

Area of $\triangle ABC$	Area of $\triangle ADC$
$A = \frac{1}{2}bh$	$A = \frac{1}{2}bh$
$= \frac{1}{2} \cdot 9 \cdot 4$	$= \frac{1}{2} \cdot 6 \cdot 4$
$= 18$	$= 12$

The areas of the two triangles are 18 cm^2 and 12 cm^2. The area of the trapezoid is the sum of the areas of the two triangles, 30 cm^2.

You can use this information to find a formula for the area of a trapezoid.

528 Chapter 10 Area and Volume

👥 Reaching All Students

Below Level Let students look through periodicals to find examples of triangles and trapezoids used in architecture.	**Advanced Learners** Display a map of Nevada. Ask: *How can you approximate the area of Nevada?* Sample: Find the area of a rectangle and a triangle.	**Visual Learners** See note on page 528. **English Learners** See note on page 528.

In a trapezoid, the parallel sides are its bases. For the figure at the right the bases are b_1 and b_2. The height is h.

The area of the trapezoid is $\frac{1}{2}b_1h + \frac{1}{2}b_2h$.

By using the Distributive Property, you can see that

$\frac{1}{2}b_1h + \frac{1}{2}b_2h$ is $\frac{1}{2}h(b_1 + b_2)$.

So, the area of the trapezoid is $\frac{1}{2}h(b_1 + b_2)$.

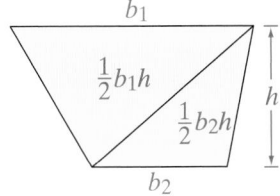

Key Concepts — Area of a Trapezoid

The area of a trapezoid is half the product of the height and the sum of the lengths of the bases.

$$A = \frac{1}{2}h(b_1 + b_2)$$

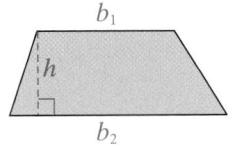

3 EXAMPLE   Real-World Problem Solving

Erie Canal The Erie Canal opened in 1825 and was hailed as an engineering marvel. Below is a cross section of the Erie Canal. Find the area of the trapezoidal cross section.

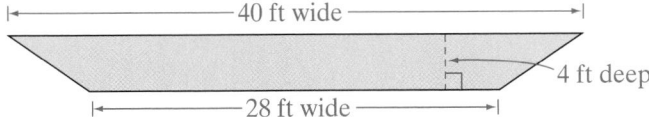

$A = \frac{1}{2}h(b_1 + b_2)$ **Use the formula for the area of a trapezoid.**

$A = \frac{1}{2} \cdot 4(28 + 40)$ **Replace h with 4, b_1 with 28, and b_2 with 40.**

$= \frac{1}{2} \cdot 4(68)$ **Simplify.**

$= 2 \cdot 68$

$= 136$

● The area of the cross section is 136 ft².

✓ Check Understanding   Example 3

3. Find the area of each trapezoid.

a.
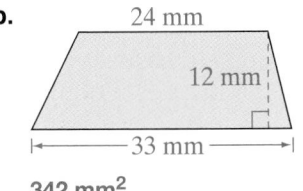

13 ft²

b.

24 mm

12 mm

33 mm

342 mm²

Real-World Connection

The Erie Canal is 363 miles in length.

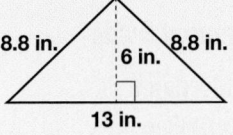
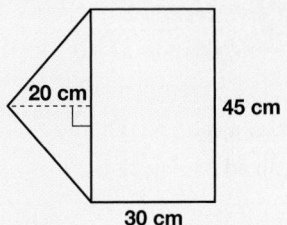
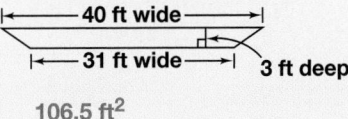

3. Practice

Assignment Guide

▼1 Objective 1
- Ⓐ Ⓑ **Core** 1–6, 11, 12, 14–16
- Ⓒ **Extension** 17, 18

▼2 Objective 2
- Ⓐ Ⓑ **Core** 7–10, 13
- Ⓒ **Extension** 19

Test Prep 20–23
Mixed Review 24–29

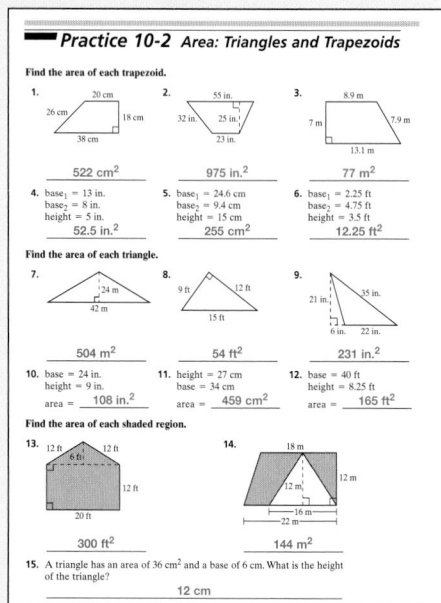

■ **Practice 10-2** *Area: Triangles and Trapezoids*

Find the area of each trapezoid.
1. 522 cm²   2. 975 in.²   3. 77 m²
4. base₁ = 13 in., base₂ = 8 in., height = 5 in. 52.5 in.²
5. base₁ = 24.6 cm, base₂ = 9.4 cm, height = 15 cm 255 cm²
6. base₁ = 2.25 ft, base₂ = 4.75 ft, height = 3.5 ft 12.25 ft²

Find the area of each triangle.
7. 504 m²   8. 54 ft²   9. 231 in.²
10. base = 24 in., height = 9 in., area = 108 in.²
11. height = 27 cm, base = 34 cm, area = 459 cm²
12. base = 40 ft, height = 8.25 ft, area = 165 ft²

Find the area of each shaded region.
13. 300 ft²   14. 144 m²

15. A triangle has an area of 36 cm² and a base of 6 cm. What is the height of the triangle? 12 cm

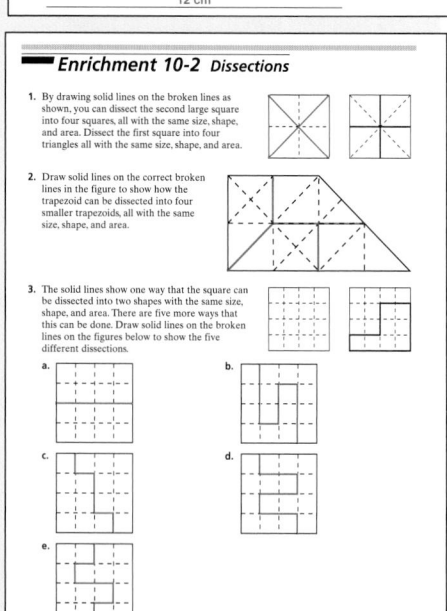

■ **Enrichment 10-2** *Dissections*

1. By drawing solid lines on the broken lines as shown, you can dissect the second large square into four squares, all with the same size, shape, and area. Dissect the first square into four triangles all with the same size, shape, and area.

2. Draw solid lines on the correct broken lines in the figure to show how the trapezoid can be dissected into four smaller trapezoids, all with the same size, shape, and area.

3. The solid lines show one way that the square can be dissected into two shapes with the same size, shape, and area. There are five more ways that this can be done. Draw solid lines on the broken lines on the figures below to show the five different dissections.
a.   b.   c.   d.   e.

EXERCISES

? For more exercises, see *Extra Practice*.

Practice and Problem Solving

Ⓐ **Practice by Example**

Find the area of each triangle.

Example 1
(page 527)

1.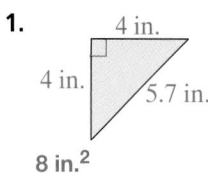
8 in.²

2.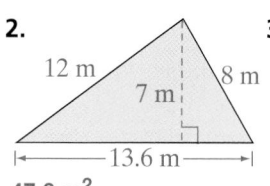
47.6 m²

3.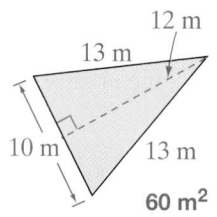
60 m²

Example 2
(page 528)

Find the area of each shaded figure.

4. 20 cm²

5. 130 m²

🌐 6. **Interior Design** A designer wants to cover the wall shown at the left below with wallpaper. How much wallpaper does she need?
234 ft²

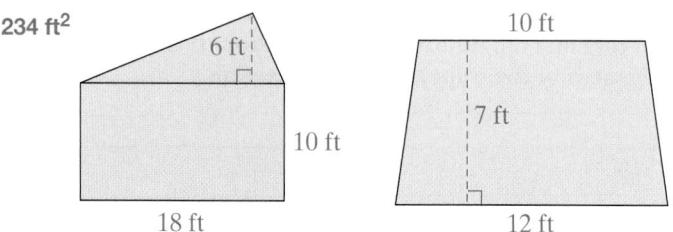

Example 3 🌐 7. **Shipping** One end of an air cargo container has the shape shown at the right above. Find the area of the trapezoid. **77 ft²**
(page 529)

Find the area of each trapezoid.

8. 22 cm²   9. 63 ft²   10. 15 in.²

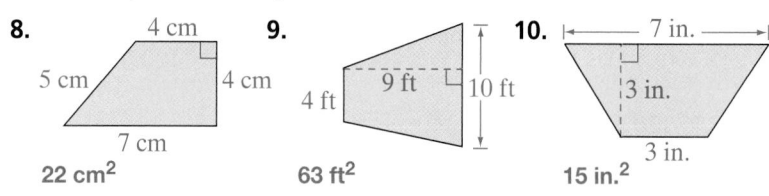

Ⓑ **Apply Your Skills**

11. The triangle is two times as high as the parallelogram.

12. Yes, by the Commutative and Associative Properties. Regrouping factors can make it easier to find the area by mental math.

11. **Reasoning** A triangle and a parallelogram both have areas of 20 cm² and bases of 5 cm. How do their heights compare? **See left.**

12. **Writing in Math** Are $\left(\frac{1}{2} \cdot 3\right) \cdot 8$ and $3 \cdot \left(\frac{1}{2} \cdot 8\right)$ equal? Explain how this can help in finding the area of a triangle. **See left.**

13. A trapezoid has area 50 in.². The two bases are 5 in. and 15 in. **GPS** What is the height of the trapezoid? **5 in.**

14. **Open-Ended** Sketch and label two different triangles so that both have areas of 180 in.². **See margin.**

GPS Use the Guided Problem Solving worksheet with Exercise 13.

14. Answers may vary.
Samples:

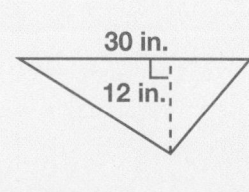

Find the area of each shaded region.

15.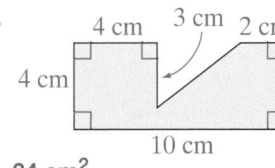

4 cm 3 cm 2 cm

4 cm

10 cm

34 cm²

16.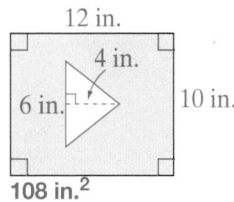

12 in.

4 in.

6 in.

10 in.

108 in.²

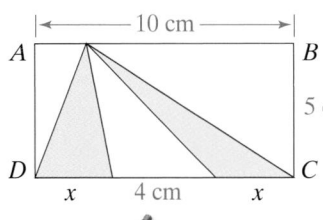

10 cm

A   B

5 cm

D   C

x   4 cm   x

C Challenge

Reasoning In Exercises 17 and 18, find the ratios of the areas of the triangles (smaller to larger). Justify each answer.

17. The height and the lengths of the bases of one trapezoid are all twice those of the other trapezoid. $\frac{1}{2}(2h)(2b_1 + 2b_2) : \frac{1}{2}h(b_1 + b_2) = 4 : 1$

18. The trapezoids have the same height. One trapezoid has base lengths b and $2b$. The other has base lengths b and $4b$. **See below.**

19. *ABCD* (left) is a rectangle. What is the area of the shaded region? **15 cm²**

18. $\frac{1}{2}h(b + 4b) : \frac{1}{2}h(b + 2b) = 5b : 3b = 5 : 3$

 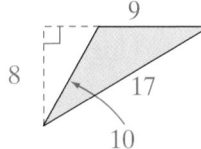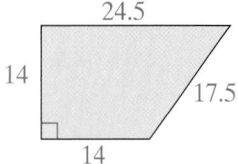
Mixed Review

Lesson 10-1 **Find the area of each parallelogram.**

24.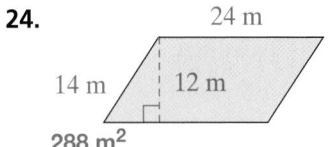

24 m

14 m   12 m

288 m²

25.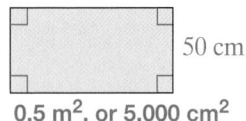

1 m

50 cm

0.5 m², or 5,000 cm²

Lessons 7-1 and 7-3 **Solve each equation.**

26. $16 + 2y = 9$ $-3\frac{1}{2}$ **27.** $5.5a + 2 = 10.5$ **28.** $\frac{1}{2}b - 10 = 24$ **68**
                                    1.54

Lesson 6-9 **29.** Suppose you bought two books for $15. The original prices of the two books were the same, but you were able to buy one for half price. What was the full price of each book? **$10**

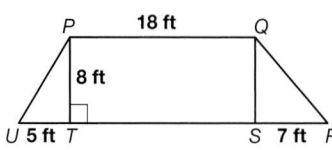
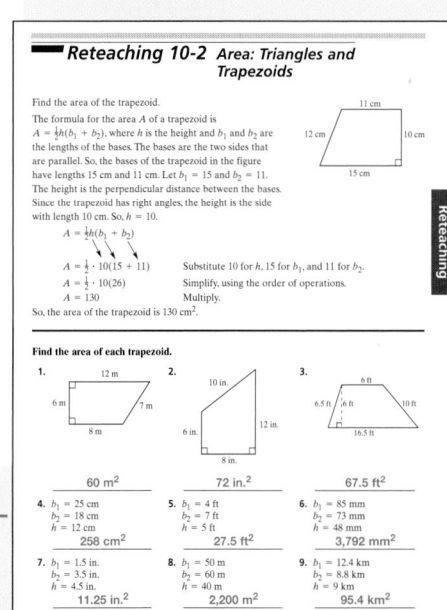
531

10-3

1. Plan

Lesson Preview

 Check Skills You'll Need

Exponents and Multiplication
Lesson 4–2: Examples 2 and 3;
Exercises 7–19.
Extra Practice, p. 747.

Lesson Resources

 **Teaching Resources**
Practice, Reteaching, Enrichment
Checkpoint Quiz 1

 Reaching All Students
Practice Workbook 10-3
Spanish Practice Workbook 10-3
Reading and Math Literacy 10B
Spanish Reading and Math
 Literacy 10B
Spanish Checkpoint Quiz 1
Guided Problem Solving 10-3

 Presentation Assistant Plus!
Transparencies and PowerPoint™
• Check Skills You'll Need 10-3
• Additional Examples 10-3
• Student Edition Answers 10-3
• Lesson Quiz 10-3
• Classroom Aid 8
PH Presentation Pro CD-ROM 10-3

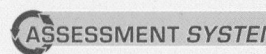 **ASSESSMENT SYSTEM**

Checkpoint Quiz 1
Computer Test Generator CD-ROM

 Technology
Resource Pro® CD-ROM
Computer Test Generator CD-ROM
PH Presentation Pro CD-ROM

 www.PHSchool.com
Student Site
• Teacher Web Code: adk-5500
• Self-grading Lesson Quiz
PH SuccessNet Teacher Center
• Lesson Planner
• Resources

 Plus **iTEXT**

532

 **10-3**

Area: Circles

What You'll Learn

 OBJECTIVE 1
To find areas of circles

 OBJECTIVE 2
To find areas of irregular figures that include parts of circles

. . . And Why

To use area formulas in real-world situations, such as finding the amount of grass needed to cover a circular region

 **Check Skills You'll Need**

Simplify each expression.

1. $3.14 \cdot 4^2$ 50.24

2. $3.14 \cdot 5^2$ 78.5

3. $3.14 \cdot 9^2$ 254.34

4. $3.14 \cdot 0.5^2$ 0.785

? For help, go to Lesson 4-2.

5. The base is $\frac{1}{2}$ the circumference. The height is the radius of the circle.

iTEXT Interactive lesson includes instant self-check, tutorials, and activities.

OBJECTIVE
 **1** Finding Areas of Circles

Investigation .....

Finding the Formula for Area of a Circle

1. Use a compass to draw a circle. Cut out the circle.
 Check students' work.
2. Fold the circle in half, and then in half again. Fold it in half a third and fourth time. Check students' work.

3. Cut out the 16 wedges that you have formed with the folds.
 Check students' work.
4. Arrange the wedges in a row as shown below.

5. Notice that the new shape resembles a parallelogram. How does the base of the parallelogram (the side shown in red) relate to the circumference of the circle? How does the height of the parallelogram relate to the radius of the circle?
 See left.
6. Use the formula for the area of a parallelogram to estimate the area of your circle. Check students' work.

The diagram above shows the relationship between the area of a circle and a figure that is like a parallelogram. The height h of the parallelogram is about the same as the radius r of the circle. The base b is about half the circumference C of the circle.

You can use the formula for the area of a parallelogram to suggest the formula for the area of a circle.

$A = bh$ **Use the formula for the area of a parallelogram.**

$A = \left(\frac{1}{2}C\right)(r)$ **Substitute $\frac{1}{2}C$ for b and r for h.**

$A = \frac{1}{2}(2\pi r) \cdot r$ **Substitute $2\pi r$ for C.**

$A = \pi r^2$ **Simplify.**

532 Chapter 10 Area and Volume

Ongoing Assessment and Intervention

Before the Lesson
Diagnose prerequisite skills using:
• Check Skills You'll Need

During the Lesson
Monitor progress using:
• Check Understanding
• Additional Examples
• Test Prep

After the Lesson
Assess knowledge using:
• Lesson Quiz
• Computer Test Generator CD-ROM
• Chapter Checkpoint 1 (p. 537)

Area of a Circle

The area of a circle equals the product of π and the square of the radius r.

$$A = \pi r^2$$

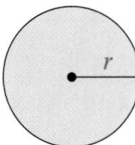

You can express the *exact area* of a circle by using π.

---

1 EXAMPLE **Finding Area of a Circle**

Find the exact area of a circle with diameter 12 cm.

$A = \pi r^2$

$= \pi(6)^2$ **$r = \frac{1}{2}d; r = 6$**

$= 36\pi$ **Simplify.**

The area is 36π cm^2.

✓ **Check Understanding**   **Example 1**

1. Find the exact area of a circle with radius 50 in.   **2,500π in.^{2}**

For real-world situations, you usually want an approximate value for the area of a circle. If you are finding an approximate area, use 3.14 or the value provided by a calculator for π.

---

2 EXAMPLE   **Real-World** 🌐 **Problem Solving**

Biology **The size of a jaguar's territory depends on how much food is available. In a situation where there is plenty of food, the circular territory of the jaguar may be as small as 3 mi in diameter. Find the area of such a region to the nearest square mile.**

$A = \pi r^2$

$= \pi(1.5)^2$ **$r = \frac{1}{2}d; r = 1.5$**

$= 2.25\pi$ **exact area**

$\approx (2.25)(3.14)$ **Use 3.14 for π.**

$= 7.065$ **approximate area**

The area of the region is about 7 mi^2.

✓ **Check Understanding**   **Example 2**

2. Find the approximate area of a circle with radius 6 mi.   **about 113 mi^2**

Real-World 🌐 **Connection**

During a drought a jaguar may need to search for food in a territory as large as 6 mi in diameter.

👥 **Reaching All Students**

| **Below Level** Stress to students that they must use the radius, not the diameter, in the formula for finding the area of a circle. | **Advanced Learners** Tell students to visualize a castle with circular towers built at its corners. Have them sketch a "footprint" for their castle, including dimensions. Ask what areas they can find. | **Auditory Learners** See note on page 533. **Tactile Learners** See note on page 534. |

Professional Development

Math Background

The formula for area of a circle is $A = \pi r^2$. Since π is irrational and a decimal that never terminates, the *exact* area of a circle must be written with π shown as a factor. An approximate area of a circle can be found by using a decimal approximation, such as 3.14, for π.

Teaching Notes

Investigation (Optional)
Provide students with circular coffee filters to cut. Explain to them that the resulting figure only *approximates* a parallelogram because the outside edge of each wedge is slightly curved. If you increase the number of wedges, the figure will more closely resemble a rectangle with base closer to half the circumference and height closer to the radius.

1 EXAMPLE **Auditory Learners**
Tell students to read carefully to determine whether a problem gives radius or diameter. Draw several circles on the board. Label the lengths of radii in some of the circles, and lengths of diameters in others. Have volunteers say aloud the formula they can use to find the area of each circle.

2 EXAMPLE **Careers**
A wildlife biologist rides a helicopter in a grid pattern over a region and takes "game counts" to find the number of a certain species living there.

PowerPoint
📋 Additional Examples

1 Find the exact area of a circle with diameter 20 in. **100π in.^{2}**

2 A TV station's weather radar can detect precipitation in a circular region having a diameter of 100 mi. Find the area of the region. **about 7,850 mi^2**

Additional Examples

3 A pound of grass seed covers approximately 675 ft². Find the area of the lawn below. Then find the number of bags of grass seed you need to buy to cover the lawn. Grass seed comes in 3-lb bags.
one 3-lb bag

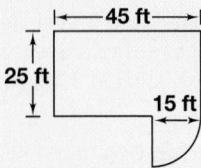

3 EXAMPLE Tactile Learners

When trying to find the areas of irregular figures, some students may confuse when to add and when to subtract. Have them sketch the shape in Example 3 on graph paper, including the line that is between the half-circle and the rectangle. (Let each grid unit equal 5 ft.) Have students cut along each line to have two shapes, a rectangle and a half-circle. Help students see that the area of the half-circle in the figure is in addition to the area of the rectangle. Then have students sketch the figure in Check Understanding 3. Have them cut out the shaded region. Help them see that they have to "take away" the half-circle from the rectangle.

Closure

Have students explain how to find the area of a circle. Use the formula $A = \pi r^2$, with A equal to the area of the circle and r equal to the radius of the circle.

To find the area of an irregular figure, you can sometimes separate it into figures with areas you know how to find.

3 EXAMPLE <u>Real-World</u> 🌐 <u>Problem Solving</u>

Landscaping A pound of grass seed covers approximately 675 ft². Find the area of the lawn below. Then find the amount of grass seed you need to buy to cover the lawn. Grass seed comes in 3-lb bags.

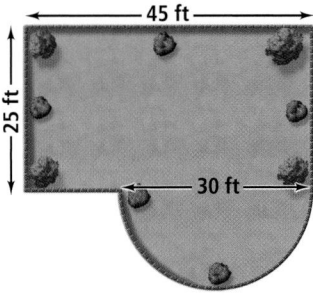

Area of region that is one half of a circle

area of circle $= \pi r^2$

area of half circle $= \frac{1}{2}\pi r^2$

$A \approx \frac{1}{2}(3.14)(15)^2$ **Replace π with 3.14 and r with 15.**

$A = 353.25$

Area of region that is a rectangle

area of rectangle $= bh$

$A = 45 \cdot 25$ **Replace b with 45 and h with 25.**

$A = 1,125$

The area of the lawn is about 353 ft² + 1,125 ft² = 1,478 ft².

$1,478 \div 675 \approx 2.19$ **Divide to find the amount of seed.**

● You need to buy one 3-lb bag of grass seed.

Need Help?

To find how much grass seed, use dimensional analysis:

$ft^2 \div \frac{ft^2}{lb} =$

$ft^2 \cdot \frac{lb}{ft^2} = lb$

✓ **Check Understanding** Example 3

3. Find the area of the shaded region to the nearest tenth. 40.2 cm²

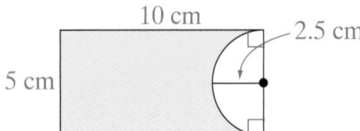

EXERCISES

 For more exercises, see *Extra Practice.*

Practice and Problem Solving

A Practice by Example
Examples 1 and 2
(page 533)

Find the area of each circle. Give the exact area, and an approximate area to the nearest square unit.

1.
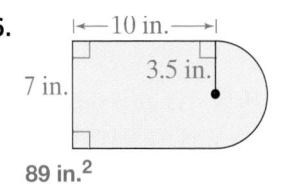
12 ft

144π ft^2; 452 ft^2

2.
16 m

64π m^2; 201 m^2

3.
60 cm

900π cm^2; 2,826 cm^2

 4. Recreation A standard dartboard has a diameter of 18 in. What is its area to the nearest square inch? **254 in.^{2}**

 5. Culinary Arts A culinary student decorates an 8-in.-diameter round cake. What is the approximate area of the top of the cake? **50 in.^{2}**

Example 3
(page 534)

Find the area of each figure to the nearest square unit.

6.
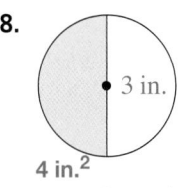
|← 10 in. →|
7 in.
3.5 in.

89 in.^{2}

7.
|← 40 yd →|
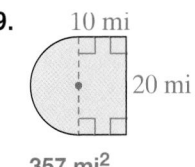
40 yd

2,856 yd^2

Find the area of each shaded region to the nearest square unit.

8.
3 in.

4 in.^{2}

9.
10 mi
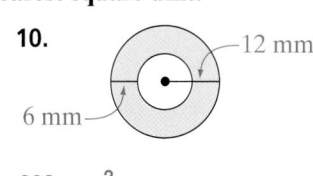
20 mi

357 mi^2

10.
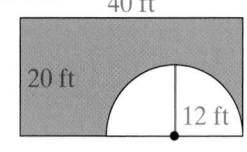
12 mm
6 mm

339 mm^2

 11. Lawn Care A groundskeeper wants to use sod to cover the lawn shown in green in the diagram. Each piece of sod covers 3 ft^2. About how many pieces of sod are needed?
about 191 pieces

40 ft
20 ft
12 ft

B Apply Your Skills
Number Sense **Match each object with its most likely area.**

12. dinner plate E

13. quarter A

14. 12-in. circular pizza B

15. jar lid C

16. the center circle on a basketball court D

A. 0.8 in.^{2}

B. 110 in.^{2}

C. 7 in.^{2}

D. 16,000 in.^{2}

E. 80 in.^{2}

 17. Pool Design Covering for the pool border is sold by the square yard (whole-number amounts only). It costs $20/yd^2.
a. What is the area of the border in square feet? **about 392.5 ft^2**
b. About how much will the covering cost? **about $880**

Pool
10 ft
15 ft
Border

Assignment Guide

▼1 Objective 1
A B Core 1–5, 12–16, 18–24, 28
C Extension 30

▼2 Objective 2
A B Core 6–11, 17, 25–27
C Extension 29

Test Prep 31–34
Mixed Review 35–41

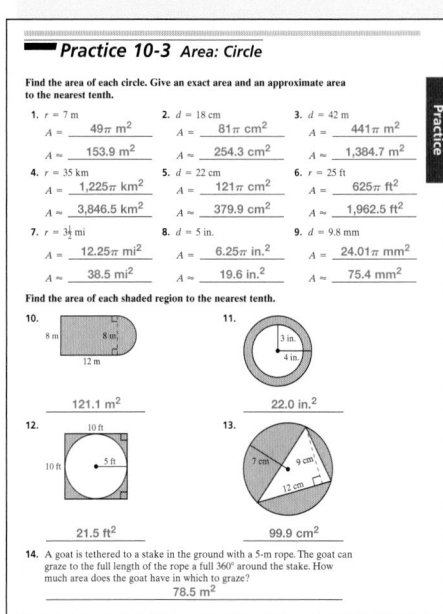

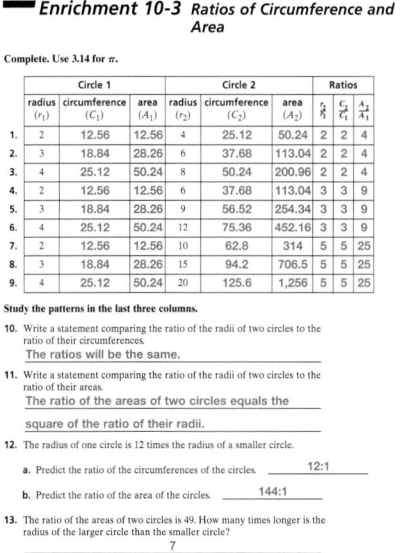

18. 144π mi^2; 452.2 mi^2
19. 0.09π m^2; 0.3 m^2
20. 0.5625π in.^{2}; 1.8 in.^{2}
21. 17.64π mm^2; 55.4 mm^2

22. Answers may vary. Sample: Find the area of a circular stage for a play.

23. The circle with radius 4 m has greater area because the four circles have a total area of 4π m^2, but the circle with radius 4 m has an area of 16π m^2.

28. 16π cm^2; the square will have a side length of 8 cm. The radius of the circle inside is $\frac{1}{2} \cdot 8 =$ 4 cm. The area is $\pi(4)^2$, or 16π.

Find the area of each circle. Give the exact area, and an approximate area to the nearest tenth. 18–21. See left.

18. $r = 12$ mi   19. $r = 0.3$ m   20. $d = 1.5$ in.   21. $d = 8.4$ mm

22. **Open-Ended** Describe a real-life situation, not used in this lesson, where you might use the formula for the area of a circle. See left.

23. Which has a greater area, four circles, each with radius 1 m, or one circle with radius 4 m? Explain. See left.

24. How many circles with radius 2 cm will have the same total area as a circle with radius 4 cm? 4 circles

Find the area of each shaded region to the nearest square unit.

25.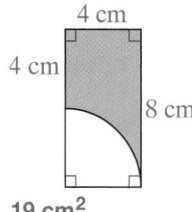
19 cm^2

26.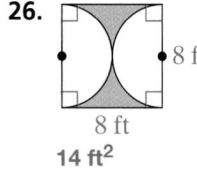
14 ft^2

27.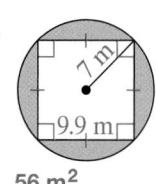
56 m^2

28. **Writing in Math** What is the area of the largest circle that will fit in a square with area 64 cm^2? Explain. See left.

C Challenge

29. **Can Lids** A manufacturer cuts lids for eight cans from one rectangular sheet of aluminum as shown at the left.
  a. What is the radius of each lid? 3 in.
  b. How many square inches of aluminum do the lids require?
  c. How many square inches of aluminum are wasted?
  b. about 226 in.^{2} c. about 62 in.^{2}

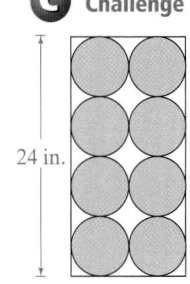
24 in.
|← 12 in. →|

30. **Consumer Issues** You can buy a 10-in. diameter pizza for \$6.50, a 12-in. pizza for \$8.50, or a 14-in. pizza for \$10.50.
  a. What is the area of each pizza to the nearest square inch?
  b. What is the price per square inch of each pizza?
  c. **Reasoning** Is the largest pizza the best buy? Explain.
  a–c. See margin.

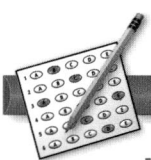

Test Prep

Multiple Choice

For Exercises 31–33, what is the exact area of each circle having radius r or diameter d?

31. $r = 11$ mi **D**
  A. 5.5π mi^2 B. 11π mi^2 C. 22π mi^2 D. 121π mi^2

32. $r = \frac{1}{2}$ m **F**
  F. $\frac{1}{4}\pi$ m^2 G. $\frac{1}{2}\pi$ m^2 H. π m^2 I. 2π m^2

33. $d = 1.2$ in. **C**
  A. 2.4π in.^{2} B. 1.44π in.^{2} C. 0.36π in.^{2} D. 0.18π in.^{2}

Short Response

34. Which has a greater area, **(a)** a circle with radius 2 m or a square with side length 2 m? **(b)** Explain your answer. See margin.

536   Chapter 10   Area and Volume

 Use the Guided Problem Solving worksheet with Exercise 23.

34. [2] The circle has greater area; a circle with a radius of 2 m has an area of 4π m^2 whereas a square of side length 2 m has an area of 4 m^2.
  [1] minor error OR answer only

Lesson 10-2   **Find the area of each figure.**

35.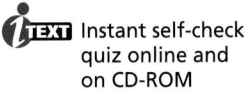
5 mi
3 mi
$6\frac{1}{2}$ mi
17.25 mi²

36.
1.5 yd
7 yd
5.25 yd²

Lesson 9-4   **37.** Square $ABCD$ has side length 8 in. $\triangle BXY$ is isosceles. Its congruent sides have length 2 in. How many triangles congruent to $\triangle BXY$ can you cut from square $ABCD$?
32 triangles

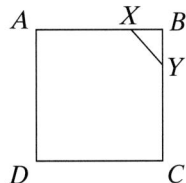

Lesson 5-3   **Find each sum or difference.**

38. $4\frac{3}{5} + 5\frac{2}{3}$
$10\frac{4}{15}$

39. $5\frac{2}{3} - 4\frac{3}{5}$
$1\frac{1}{15}$

40. $\frac{7}{8} + \frac{5}{6}$
$1\frac{17}{24}$

41. $\frac{7}{8} - \frac{5}{6}$
$\frac{1}{24}$

✓ Checkpoint Quiz 1   Lessons 10-1 through 10-3

iTEXT Instant self-check quiz online and on CD-ROM

Find the area of each figure.

1.
10 in.
10 in.
100 in.²

2.
10 in.
10 in.
50 in.²

3.
20 in.
15 in.
300 in.²

4.
20 yd
12 yd   13 yd
30 yd
300 yd²

5.
35 cm
30 cm
70 cm
2,100 cm²

6.
25 m
15 m
20 m
150 m²

Find the area of each figure. Give the exact area, and an approximate area to the nearest square unit.

7.
10 yd
100π yd²; 314 yd²

8.
16 ft
64π ft²; 201 ft²

9.
40 cm
20 cm
(800 + 50π) cm²; 957 cm²

10. A trapezoid has an area of 45 cm². The two bases are 6 cm and 12 cm. What is the height of the trapezoid? **5 cm**

10-3   Area: Circles   **537**

---

4. Assess

Find the area.

1. Find the exact area of a circle with diameter 32 in.
256π in.²

2. A 5-ft-diameter round table is in a 12 ft-by-15 ft room.
   a. What is the area covered by the table? Round to the nearest unit. **20 ft²**
   b. What is the area of the rest of the room? Round to the nearest unit.
   160 ft²

✓ Chapter Checkpoint 1

To check understanding of Lessons 10-1 to 10-3:
Checkpoint Quiz 1 (p. 537)

📁 **Teaching Resources**
Checkpoint Quiz 1 (also in Prentice Hall Assessment System)

👥 **Reaching All Students**
Reading and Math Literacy 10B

Spanish versions available.

Reteaching 10-3 *Area: Circles*

Find the area of the circle. Give an exact area and an approximate area.
The formula for the area A of a circle is $A = \pi r^2$, where r is the radius of the circle and π is a number that is close to 3.14, but not exactly 3.14.
In the circle shown, the diameter is 48 cm. The radius of any circle is half its diameter.
48 cm
$\frac{1}{2} \cdot 48 = 24$
So, $r = 24$ cm.
$A = \pi r^2$
$A = \pi(24)^2$ Substitute 24 for r in the formula.
$A = 576\pi$ Simplify.
The exact area of the circle is 576π cm².
To find the approximate area, substitute 3.14 for π.
$A = 576\pi \approx 576(3.14) = 1,808.64$
Note: The symbol ≈ is read "is approximately equal to."
The approximate area is 1,808.64 cm².

Find the area of each circle. Give an exact area and an approximate area to the nearest tenth.

1. 3 m
$A =$ __9π m²__
$A \approx$ __28.3 m²__

2. 140 in.
$A =$ __4,900π in.²__
$A \approx$ __15,386 in.²__

3. 4.5 ft
$A =$ __20.25π ft²__
$A \approx$ __63.6 ft²__

4. $r = 15$ cm
$A =$ __225π cm²__
$A \approx$ __706.5 cm²__

5. $d = 16$ in.
$A =$ __64π in.²__
$A \approx$ __201.0 in.²__

6. $d = 7$ m
$A =$ __12.25π m²__
$A \approx$ __38.5 m²__

7. $r = 3.4$ ft
$A =$ __11.56π ft²__
$A \approx$ __36.3 ft²__

8. $d = 29$ cm
$A =$ __210.25π cm²__
$A \approx$ __660.2 cm²__

9. $d = 284$ mi
$A =$ __20,164π mi²__
$A \approx$ __63,315.0 mi²__

Alternative Assessment

Using compasses, rulers, tape, scissors, and index cards, have students make irregular shapes that are combinations of parallelograms and circles or half-circles. Have them exchange shapes and find the areas of the figures.

Test Prep

📁 **Resources**
For additional practice with a variety of test item formats:
• Test Prep, p. 575
• Test-Taking Strategies, p. 570
• Test-Taking Strategies With Transparencies

Three Views of an Object

This Extension shows students how to draw different views of three-dimensional figures.

Teaching Notes

A polyhedron is one type of solid, or space figure. Its faces are formed from polygons. All the polyhedrons in this extension have rectangular faces. Architects and builders use top views, front views, right-side views, and corner views to help them represent and analyze three-dimensional figures.

Error Prevention!

Exercises 1–4 Encourage students to build models with cubes. Make sure they examine them carefully from several viewpoints. This will aid in completing correct drawings.

Inclusion

Exercises 1–5 The ability to visualize three-dimensional figures varies widely. Help students who have difficulty use models. It may take extra time for some students to "see" how the drawings relate to the models.

Additional Example

Draw the top, front, and right-side views of this solid.

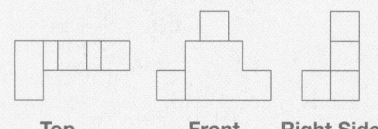

Top   Front   Right Side

538

A solid is a three-dimensional figure.

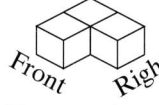

You can draw a solid *in perspective* (p. 542) to show that it is three-dimensional.

Isometric Dot Paper

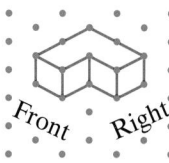

You can use isometric dot paper to draw a three-dimensional view.

Rectangular Graph Paper

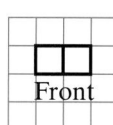
Front

You can use rectangular graph paper to draw top, front, and side views.

EXAMPLE

Draw the top, front, and right-side views of the solid.

Isometric   Top   Front   Right Side

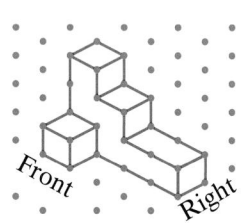   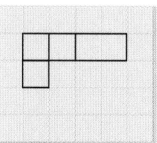   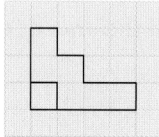   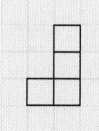

EXERCISES

Draw the top, front, and right-side views of each solid. 1–4. See margin.

1.   2.   3.   4.

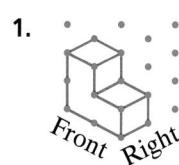   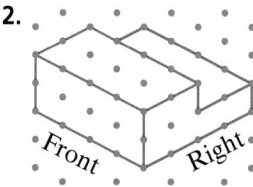   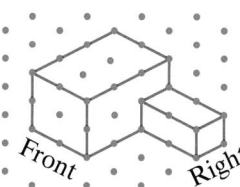   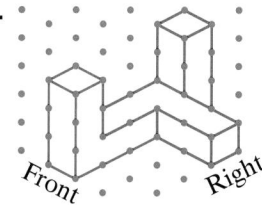

5. The top, front, and right-side views are given. Draw an isometric view on isometric dot paper.

Top   Front   Right Side   5.

            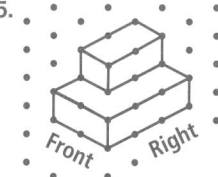

1.

   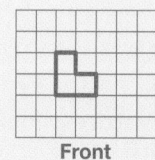   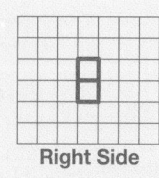

Top   Front   Right Side

2–4. See back of book.

OBJECTIVE
1 Naming Space Figures

The figures below are common three-dimensional figures, also called **space figures** or solids. The space figures you will study in this book are prisms, pyramids, cylinders, cones, and spheres.

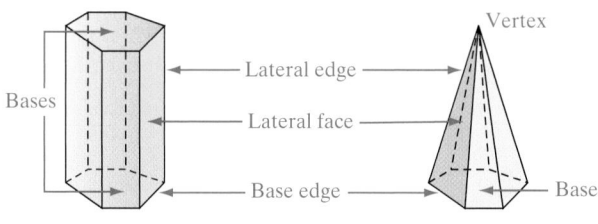

Prism

Pyramid

A **prism** has two parallel bases that are congruent polygons, and lateral faces that are parallelograms.

A **pyramid** has a base that is a polygon. The lateral faces are triangles.

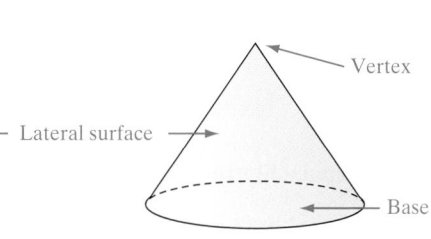

Cylinder

Cone

A **cylinder** has two parallel bases that are congruent circles.

A **cone** has one circular base and one vertex.

Sphere

A **sphere** is the set of all points in space that are a given distance from a given point called the center.

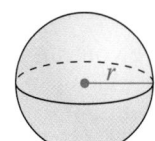

What You'll Learn

OBJECTIVE 1 To identify common space figures

OBJECTIVE 2 To identify space figures from nets

. . . And Why

To identify the space figures often used in constructing buildings

✔ Check Skills You'll Need

Judging by appearance, classify each polygon.

1.

triangle

2.

square

3.

rectangle

4.

hexagon

❓ For help, go to Lesson 9-3.

New Vocabulary

• space figures
• prism
• pyramid
• cylinder
• cone
• sphere
• net

 Interactive lesson includes instant self-check, tutorials, and activities.

10-4 Space Figures **539**

Lesson Preview

 **Check Skills You'll Need**

Classifying Polygons
Lesson 9-3: Examples 1 and 2;
Exercises 1–9.
Extra Practice, p. 752.

Lesson Resources

📁 **Teaching Resources**
Practice, Reteaching, Enrichment

👥 **Reaching All Students**
Practice Workbook 10-4
Spanish Practice Workbook 10-4
Guided Problem Solving 10-4
Technology Activities 23
Hands-On Activities 24

⏱ **Presentation Assistant Plus!**
Transparencies and PowerPoint™
• Check Skills You'll Need 10-4
• Additional Examples 10-4
• Student Edition Answers 10-4
• Lesson Quiz 10-4
• Classroom Aid 4, 11, 12
PH Presentation Pro CD-ROM 10-4

Computer Test Generator CD-ROM

💻 **Technology**
Resource Pro® CD-ROM
Computer Test Generator CD-ROM
PH Presentation Pro CD-ROM

💻 **www.PHSchool.com**
Student Site
• Teacher Web Code: adk-5500
• Self-grading Lesson Quiz
PH SuccessNet Teacher Center
• Lesson Planner
• Resources

Plus

⬦ Ongoing Assessment and Intervention

Before the Lesson	**During the Lesson**	**After the Lesson**
Diagnose prerequisite skills using:	Monitor progress using:	Assess knowledge using:
• Check Skills You'll Need	• Check Understanding	• Lesson Quiz
	• Additional Examples	• Computer Test Generator CD-ROM
	• Test Prep	

539

2. Teach

Math Background

A *space figure* is a three-dimensional figure. A *net* is a two-dimensional pattern for a three-dimensional figure. To help identify the type of figure that is modeled by a net, look at the shapes in the net.

Teaching Notes

2 EXAMPLE Tactile Learners

Provide students with large versions of the nets in the textbook. Have students use scissors and tape to cut out and form the space figures.

PowerPoint

Additional Examples

1 Describe the bases and name the figure.

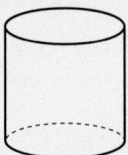

circles; cylinder

2 Name the space figure you can form from the net.

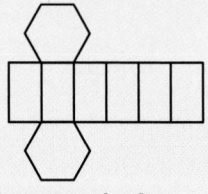

hexagonal prism

Closure

Have students explain the differences between prisms and pyramids. **Sample: Prisms have two parallel bases that are congruent polygons. Pyramids have only one polygonal base. The lateral faces of prisms are parallelograms. The lateral faces of pyramids are triangles.**

540

Real-World Connection

This space figure displays the 73,000-ft² "Rainbow" by Corita Kent.

You can use the shape of a base to help you name a space figure.

1 EXAMPLE Naming Space Figures

For each figure, describe the bases and name the figure.

a.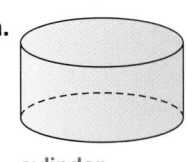

The bases are triangles. The figure is a triangular prism.

b.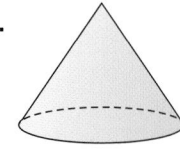

The bases of the prism are trapezoids. The figure is a trapezoidal prism.

✓ Check Understanding Example 1

1. Name each figure.

a. [cylinder figure]   b. [cone figure]

cylinder   cone

OBJECTIVE

2 Identifying Space Figures From Nets

A **net** is a pattern you can form into a space figure.

2 EXAMPLE Naming Space Figures From Nets

Name the space figure you can form from each net.

a. [six-pointed star net]

With a hexagonal base and triangular sides, you can form a hexagonal pyramid.

b. [triangular prism net]

With two triangular bases and rectangular sides, you can form a triangular prism.

✓ Check Understanding Example 2

Need Help?
Recall that a *cube* is a rectangular prism with six congruent square faces.

2. Name the space figure you can form from each net.

a. 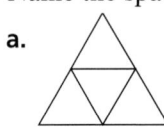 With a triangular base and three faces that are triangles, you can form a triangular pyramid.

b. 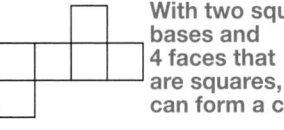 With two square bases and 4 faces that are squares, you can form a cube.

540 Chapter 10 Area and Volume

👥 Reaching All Students

Below Level Ask students to find examples of various types of space figures in the classroom. **Answers may vary. Samples: globe (sphere), book, file box (rectangular prism)**	**Advanced Learners** Challenge students to draw as many different nets for a cube as they can. Students may want to cut out and fold their nets to check their drawings.	**Tactile Learners** See note on page 540. **Error Prevention** See note on page 542.

EXERCISES

For more exercises, see Extra Practice.

Practice and Problem Solving

A Practice by Example

Example 1
(page 540)

For each figure, describe the base(s), if any, and name the figure.
1–6. See below left.

1.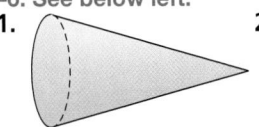

2.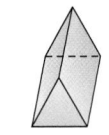

3.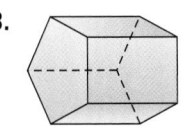

4.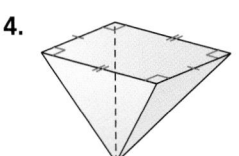

5.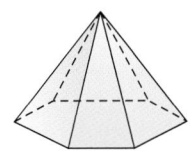

6.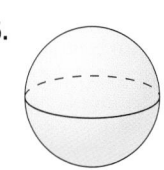

Example 2
(page 540)

Name the space figure you can form from each net.

7.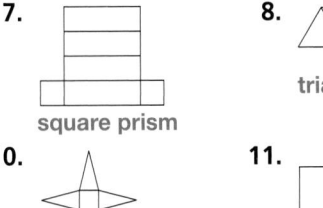
square prism

8.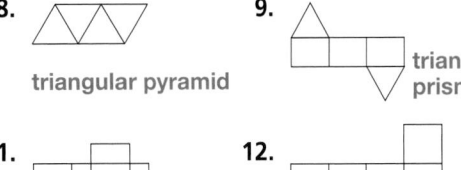
triangular pyramid

9.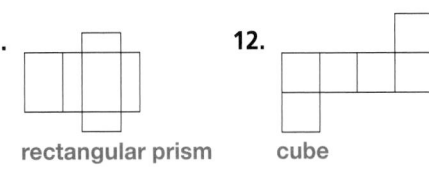
triangular prism

10.
square pyramid

11.
rectangular prism

12.
cube

B Apply Your Skills

Reading Math

Lateral means "on the side." The lateral faces of a prism or pyramid are the surfaces that connect with a base. See page 539.

1. The base is a circle. The figure is a cone.
2. The bases are triangles. The figure is a triangular prism.
3. The bases are pentagons. The figure is a pentagonal prism.
4. The base is a rectangle. The figure is a rectangular pyramid.
5. The base is a hexagon. The figure is a hexagonal pyramid.
6. There are no bases. The figure is a sphere.

For Exercises 13–15, write the most precise name for each space figure that has the given properties.

13. four lateral faces that are triangles pyramid

14. three lateral faces that are rectangles triangular prism

15. a lateral surface and one circular base cone

16. What type of space figure does each object suggest?
   a. a shoe box   b. a teepee   c. a basketball
      rectangular prism   cone   sphere

Open Ended Draw a net for each space figure.

17. pentagonal pyramid   18. an object in your classroom
                              Check students' work.

19. **Error Analysis** A student explains that since each figure below has six square faces, each can be folded to make a cube. Explain the error the student might have made.

Figure A   Figure B   Figure C   Figure D

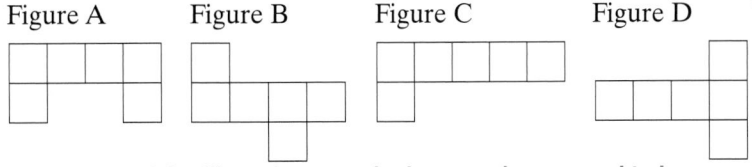

Figures A and C will not form a cube because bases need to be on both ends of the vertical faces.

10-4 Space Figures **541**

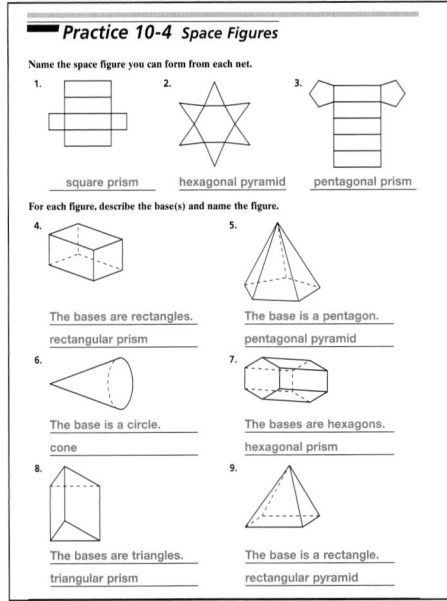
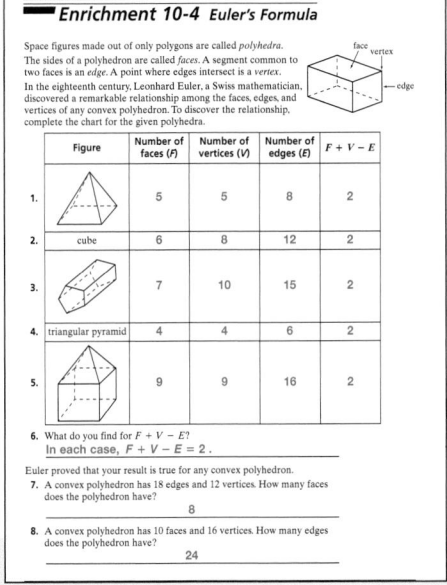

20. A net is made of 4 congruent rectangles and 2 congruent squares whose sides are the same length as the shorter sides of the rectangles. Name a space figure you can form from this net.
square prism

Match each container with the correct net.

24. Answers may vary. Sample: A net for a rectangular prism has two rectangular bases with four rectangular faces attached. A net for a rectangular pyramid has one rectangular base with four triangular faces attached.

21. C 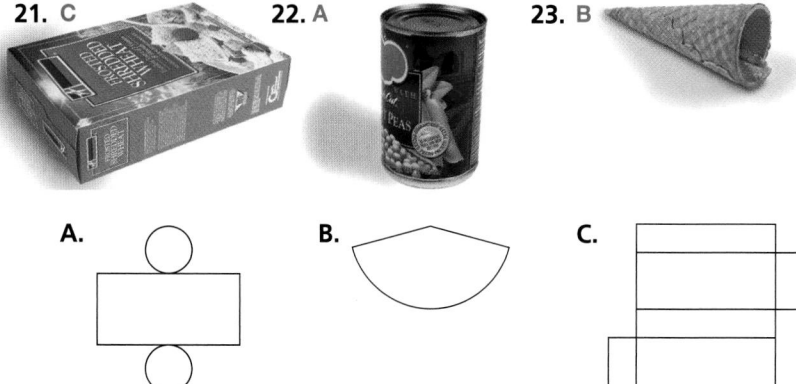 **22.** A **23.** B

A.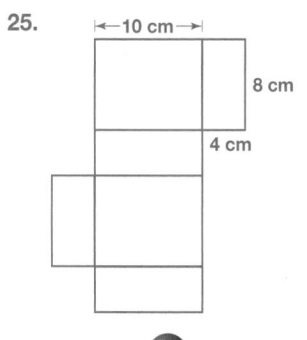

B.

C.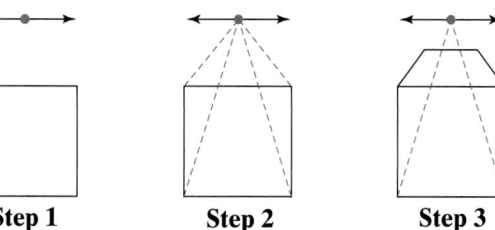

24. Writing in Math Suppose you see a net for a rectangular prism and [GPS] a net for a rectangular pyramid. Explain how you can match each net with its name. **See above left.**

25.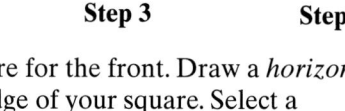
Draw a net to represent a rectangular box that is 10 cm long, 8 cm wide, and 4 cm high. Label dimensions on the net. **See left.**

C Challenge

26. A cube is easy to draw in *one-point perspective*. Draw a cube in one-point perspective by following the steps below.

Step 1   **Step 2**   **Step 3**   **Step 4**

Step 1 Begin by drawing a square for the front. Draw a *horizon line* parallel to one horizontal edge of your square. Select a *vanishing point* on the horizon line.

Step 2 Draw lines, called *vanishing lines,* from the vertices of the square to the vanishing point.

Step 3 Draw a line segment parallel to the horizon line. Use this segment to determine the top and back edges.

Step 4 Draw dashed lines for the hidden back vertical and horizontal edges. Erase the horizon line and unnecessary parts of the vanishing lines. **Check students' work.**

27. Using steps like those suggested in Exercise 26, make a one-point perspective drawing of each figure. **a–b. See margin.**
  a. triangular prism   **b.** cylinder

[GPS] Use the Guided Problem Solving worksheet with Exercise 24.

27a.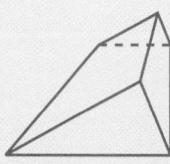

27b.

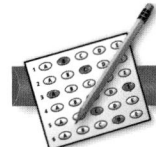

Test Prep

Multiple Choice

28. Which of the following is a net for a cylinder? **B**

A.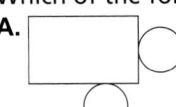

B.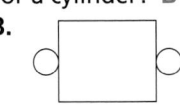

C.

D.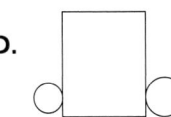

33. [2]

6 in.

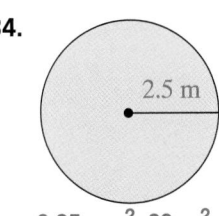

4 in.   4 in.

[1] correct drawing, but incorrect or no labels

29. Which space figure can you form from the net? **I**
  F. hexagonal pyramid
  G. triangular pyramid
  H. triangular prism
  I. hexagonal prism

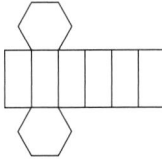

30. Which space figure has three lateral faces that are triangles? **A**
  A. triangular pyramid   **B.** pentagonal prism
  C. square prism   **D.** triangular prism

31. Which space figure has 6 faces that are all regular quadrilaterals? **H**
  F. triangular pyramid   **G.** pentagonal prism
  H. square prism   **I.** triangular prism

Take It to the NET
Online lesson quiz at
www.PHSchool.com
Web Code: ada-1004

32. A rectangular prism has how many faces? **C**
  A. 2   **B.** 4   **C.** 6   **D.** 8

Short Response

33. **a.** Draw a net for a cylinder that has diameter 4 in. and height 6 in.
  b. Label your drawing. See above left.

Mixed Review

Lesson 10-3 For each circle, find the exact area and an approximate area.

34.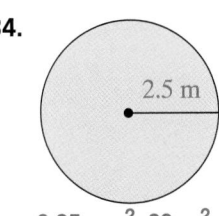
2.5 m

6.25π m²; 20 m²

35.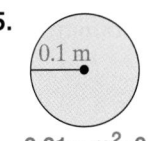
0.1 m

0.01π m²; 0.0314 m²

36.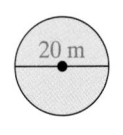
20 m

100π m²; 314 m²

Lessons 9-4 **37. Mowing Lawns** A rectangular yard is 20 ft by 40 ft. Your lawn mower will mow a 2-ft-wide path. What is the least number of turns you must make to mow the lawn? **9 turns**

Lesson 8-3 Write each equation in slope-intercept form.

38. $3x - y = 6$
$y = 3x - 6$

39. $2x - 2y = 10$
$y = x - 5$

40. $-8y - 16 = 24x$
$y = -3x - 2$

10-4 Space Figures **543**

Alternative Assessment

Have students work in groups of four to play this memory game. On index cards, have them draw space figures from the lesson, one figure per card. On different index cards, write the names of the figures. Place the cards face down and mix them. Each player picks two cards. If the cards "match," the player keeps the cards and then picks two more. If not, the player places the cards facedown again and another player picks two cards. Repeat until all "matches" have been found.

543

4. Assess

PowerPoint Lesson Quiz 10-4

Describe the base(s) and name each solid.

1.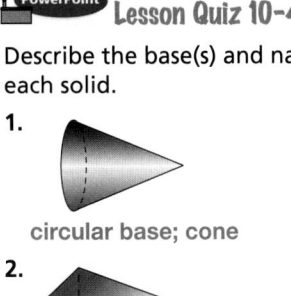

circular base; cone

2.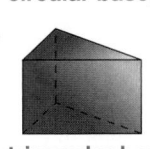

triangular bases; triangular prism

3. Name the solid you can form from this net.

octagonal pyramid

Test Prep

 Resources
For additional practice with a variety of test item formats:
• Test Prep, p. 575
• Test-Taking Strategies, p. 570
• Test-Taking Strategies With Transparencies

Reteaching 10-4 *Space Figures*

Name the space figure you can form from the net.

The net has a square and four triangles. So, the square must be the base. A pyramid has triangular sides and only one base. So, the net is for a triangular pyramid. You might try to picture what the figure looks like when it is cut out and folded. See the space figure at the right.

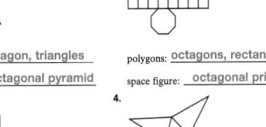

Name the space figure you can form from each net. Start by naming the polygons in the net.

1.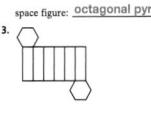
polygons: octagon, triangles
space figure: octagonal pyramid

2.
polygons: octagons, rectangles
space figure: octagonal prism

3.
polygons: hexagons, rectangles
space figure: hexagonal prism

4.
polygons: triangles
space figure: triangular pyramid

Extension

Cross Sections of Space Figures

For Use With Lesson 10-5

In this Extension, students analyze the intersections of planes and solids to describe the cross sections formed.

Teaching Notes

Cross sections are easiest to see and sketch when the plane that intersects the solid is horizontal, or vertical, and parallel to a base or face. In most instances, the cross section will resemble the base (horizontal) or the face (vertical). However, the plane can intersect the solid at any angle. Locating points of intersection along the edges of the solid and then joining them along the surfaces of the solid will help reveal the cross section.

Error Prevention!

Exercises 1–4 Help students visualize each situation by using a model or a cube, perhaps built out of toothpicks held together at the corners with miniature marshmallows. Use a piece of paper or plastic to model the intersecting plane.

Tactile Learners

Exercise 9 To help understand this exercise, have students shape a piece of clay in the form of a sphere. Then use dental floss pulled tightly to cut cross sections.

The intersection of a plane and a space figure is a *cross section* of the space figure. This cross section of a block of cheese is a rectangle.

● **EXAMPLE**

Sketch a plane intersecting a cube in three different ways to show a rectangular cross section.

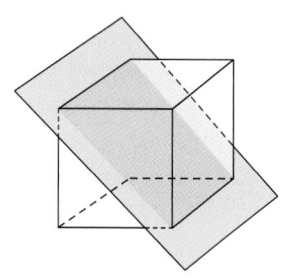 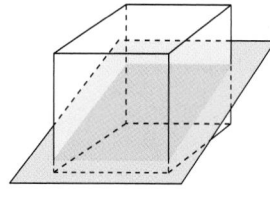 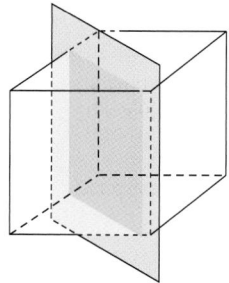

EXERCISES

Use the name of a polygon to describe each cross section of the cube. Points *M, N, P, Q,* and *R* are midpoints of edges.

1. through *M, P, Q,* and *R* square
2. through *E, A, C,* and *G* rectangle
3. through *B, E,* and *G* equilateral triangle
4. through *M, N, D,* and *B* trapezoid

Sketch a cube to show each cross section. 5–8. See margin.

5. a scalene triangle
6. a trapezoid
7. a square
8. an isosceles triangle

9. Describe the possible cross sections of a sphere. They are all circles.

10. Sketch and describe two possible cross sections of a cylinder. See margin.

5.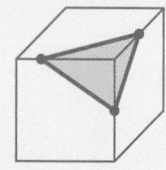

6.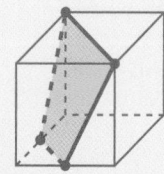

7.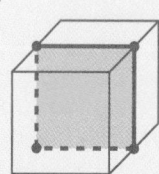

8.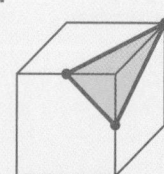

10.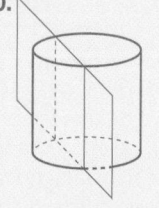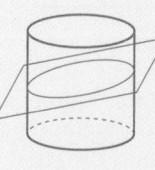

Surface Area: Prisms and Cylinders

OBJECTIVE 1 Finding Surface Areas of Prisms

Prisms and cylinders can be *right* or *oblique*.

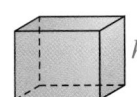 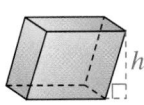 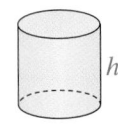 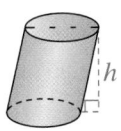

Right prism   Oblique prism   Right cylinder   Oblique cylinder

In this text, you may assume that prisms and cylinders are right unless otherwise stated.

Surface area (S.A.) is the sum of the areas of the base(s) and the lateral faces of a space figure. One way to find the surface area of a space figure is to find the area of its net. You measure surface area in square units.

1 EXAMPLE Finding Surface Area Using a Net

Find the surface area of the rectangular prism using a net.

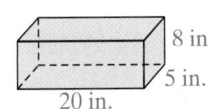

8 in.
5 in.
20 in.

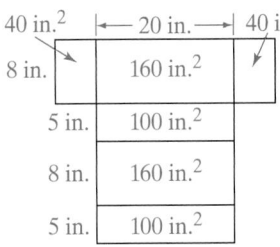

40 in.^{2} |← 20 in. →| 40 in.^{2}
8 in. 160 in.^{2}
5 in. 100 in.^{2}
8 in. 160 in.^{2}
5 in. 100 in.^{2}

Draw and label a net.

Find the area of each rectangle in the net.

$40 + 40 + 160 + 100 + 160 + 100 = 600$ **Add the areas.**

• The surface area is 600 in.^{2}.

✓ Check Understanding Example 1

1. a. Find the surface area of the triangular prism. **84 yd^2**

  b. A similar triangular prism has dimensions twice those shown here. Find its surface area. **336 yd^2**

  c. How do surface areas of similar prisms compare when dimensions are doubled? **See above right.**

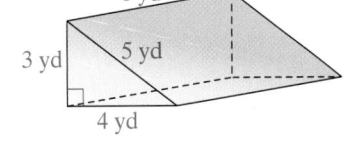

6 yd
3 yd 5 yd
4 yd

1c. The surface area of the larger prism is 4 times the surface area of the smaller prism.

What You'll Learn

OBJECTIVE 1 To find surface areas of prisms

OBJECTIVE 2 To find surace areas of cylinders

. . . And Why

To find the amount of material needed in packaging

✓ Check Skills You'll Need

Find the circumference of each circle with the given radius or diameter.

1. $r = 5$ in. **31.4 in.**

2. $r = 4.2$ cm **26.4 cm**

3. $d = 8$ ft **25.1 ft**

4. $d = 6.8$ in. **21.4 in.**

❓ For help, go to Lesson 9-6.

New Vocabulary

• surface area
• lateral area

📄 Interactive lesson includes instant self-check, tutorials, and activities.

Lesson Preview

✓ **Check Skills You'll Need**

Circles
Lesson 9-6: Example 1;
Exercises 1–9.
Extra Practice, p. 752.

Lesson Resources

📁 **Teaching Resources**
Practice, Reteaching, Enrichment

👥 **Reaching All Students**
Practice Workbook 10-5
Spanish Practice Workbook 10-5
Guided Problem Solving 10-5
Technology Activities 23, 24, 25
Hands-On Activities 25

⏰ **Presentation Assistant Plus!**
Transparencies and PowerPoint™
• Check Skills You'll Need 10-5
• Additional Examples 10-5
• Student Edition Answers 10-5
• Lesson Quiz 10-5
• Classroom Aid 11, 12, 27
PH Presentation Pro CD-ROM 10-5

ASSESSMENT SYSTEM

Computer Test Generator CD-ROM

💻 **Technology**
Resource Pro® CD-ROM
Computer Test Generator CD-ROM
PH Presentation Pro CD-ROM

💻 **www.PHSchool.com**
Student Site
• Teacher Web Code: adk-5500
• Self-grading Lesson Quiz
PH SuccessNet Teacher Center
• Lesson Planner
• Resources

Plus 📄

⟲ Ongoing Assessment and Intervention

Before the Lesson	During the Lesson	After the Lesson
Diagnose prerequisite skills using:	**Monitor progress using:**	**Assess knowledge using:**
• Check Skills You'll Need	• Check Understanding • Additional Examples • Test Prep	• Lesson Quiz • Computer Test Generator CD-ROM

2. Teach

Professional Development

Math Background

The bases of prisms are various polygons. You cannot use a single formula for the areas of the bases of all prisms. Therefore, B is used to represent "area of the base." The bases of cylinders are always circles. Therefore you can use the formula S.A. $= 2\pi rh + 2\pi r^2$ for the surface area of a cylinder. However, it is easier to remember just one formula for surface area of either a prism or cylinder: S.A. $=$ L.A. $+ 2B$.

Teaching Notes

1 EXAMPLE Tactile Learners

Let students cut different-shaped boxes into nets. Then have them find the surface area of each box by finding the area of each rectangle in its net. Tissue boxes work well.

2 EXAMPLE Visual Learners

Have students sketch the figure for Example 2. Have them use a colored pencil to shade the lateral faces and then use a different color to shade the bases. Repeat for different prisms.

3 EXAMPLE Tactile Learners

Give solid figures and clay to students grouped in pairs. Be sure to include a cylinder for each pair. Have students press the sides of the geometric solids into the clay. Have them roll a cylinder in the clay for one turn to form a rectangle. This will reinforce how the curved part of a cylinder can be matched with a rectangle as shown at the top of the student page.

? Need Help?

B represents the area of a base. For a list of area formulas, see the table on page 780.

Reading Math

For help with reading a formula, see page 551.

Another way to find the surface area of a prism is to use the *lateral area* and the base areas. **Lateral area (L.A.)** of a prism is the sum of the areas of the lateral faces.

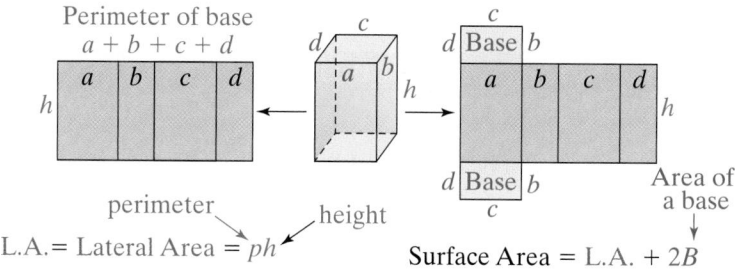

Perimeter of base
$a + b + c + d$

perimeter   height

L.A.$=$ Lateral Area $= ph$

Surface Area $=$ L.A. $+ 2B$

Area of a base

To find surface area, it is a good idea to find lateral area first.

Key Concepts   **Surface Area of a Prism**

The lateral area of a prism is the product of the perimeter of the base and the height.

$$\text{L.A.} = ph$$

The surface area of a prism is the sum of the lateral area and the areas of the two bases.

$$\text{S.A.} = \text{L.A.} + 2B$$

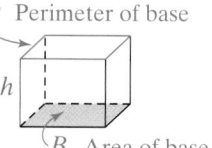

P Perimeter of base

h

B Area of base

---

2 EXAMPLE   Finding Surface Area Using Formulas

Find the surface area of the triangular prism at the right.

Step 1 Find the lateral area.

$$\text{L.A.} = ph \qquad \text{Use the formula for lateral area.}$$
$$= (5 + 5 + 6)12 \qquad p = 5 + 5 + 6 \text{ and } h = 12.$$
$$= 192$$

Step 2 Find the surface area.

$$\text{S.A.} = \text{L.A.} + 2B \qquad \text{Use the formula for surface area.}$$
$$= 192 + 2\left(\tfrac{1}{2} \cdot 6 \cdot 4\right) \qquad \text{L.A.} = 192 \text{ and } B = \tfrac{1}{2} \cdot 6 \cdot 4.$$
$$= 192 + 24$$
$$= 216$$

• The surface area of the triangular prism is 216 cm^2.

✓ Check Understanding   Example 2

2. Find the surface area of the prism at the right.
108 m^2

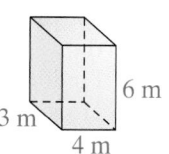

👪 Reaching All Students

| Below Level Ask students how they would determine the least amount of paper needed to cover a box. Answers may vary. Sample: Cut pieces of paper the same sizes as the faces and tape the pieces to the box. | Advanced Learners Ask students to write a formula for the surface area of a food can that has one end removed. The surface area equals the sum of the lateral area and the area of one base: S.A. = L.A. + B | Tactile Learners See note on page 546. Visual Learners See note on page 546. |

2 Finding Surface Areas of Cylinders

If you cut a label from a soup can, you will see that the label is a rectangle. The height of the rectangle is the height of the can. The base length of the rectangle is the circumference of the can.

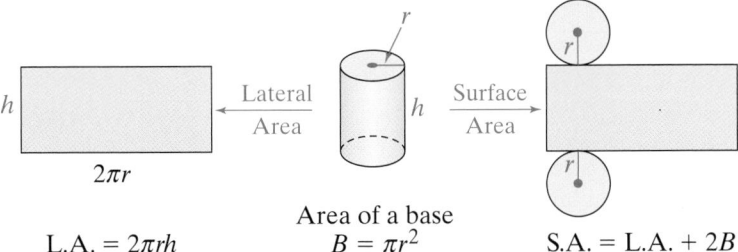

h Lateral Area h Surface Area

$2\pi r$

Area of a base

L.A. $= 2\pi rh$ $B = \pi r^2$ S.A. $=$ L.A. $+ 2B$

Key Concepts   **Surface Area of a Cylinder**

The lateral area of a cylinder is the product of the circumference of the base and the height of the cylinder.

B is the area of a base.

$$\text{L.A.} = 2\pi rh$$

The surface area of a cylinder is the sum of the lateral area and the areas of the two bases.

$$\text{S.A.} = \text{L.A.} + 2B$$

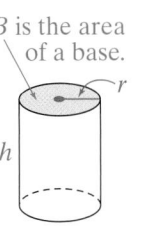

---

3 EXAMPLE   **Finding Surface Area of a Cylinder**

Packaging **Find the surface area of the can at the right.**

Step 1 Find the lateral area.

L.A. $= 2\pi rh$ **Use the formula for lateral area.**

     $\approx 2(3.14)(3.5)(11.5)$ $r = 3.5$ and $h = 11.5$.

     ≈ 253

Step 2 Find the surface area.

S.A. $=$ L.A. $+ 2B$ **Use the formula for surface area.**

     $\approx 253 + 2(3.14)(3.5)^2$ **L.A. $\approx$ 253 and $B = \pi(3.5)^2$.**

     $\approx 253 + 77$

     $= 330$

3.5 cm

11.5 cm

The surface area of the can is about 330 cm^2.

✓ Check Understanding   **Example 3**

3. Find the surface area of a can with radius 5 cm and height 20 cm.   about 785 cm^2

Additional Examples

1 Find the surface area of the rectangular prism using a net.

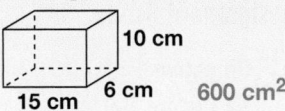

10 cm

15 cm   6 cm   600 cm^2

2 Find the surface area of the rectangular prism.   500 in.^{2}

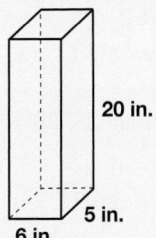

20 in.

5 in.

6 in.

3 Find the surface area of the cylindrical water tank.

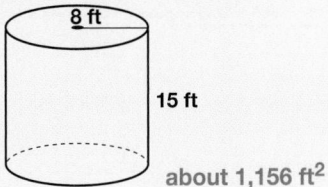

8 ft

15 ft

about 1,156 ft^2

Closure

Have students explain how to find the surface areas of both a prism and a cylinder. **The surface area in each case is the sum of the lateral area and the areas of the two bases.**

547

3. Practice

Assignment Guide

1 **Objective 1**
  Ⓐ Ⓑ Core 1–9, 15, 17, 19, 22, 23
  Ⓒ Extension 24

2 **Objective 2**
  Ⓐ Ⓑ Core 10–14, 16, 18, 20, 21
  Ⓒ Extension 25, 26

Test Prep 27–30
Mixed Review 31–37

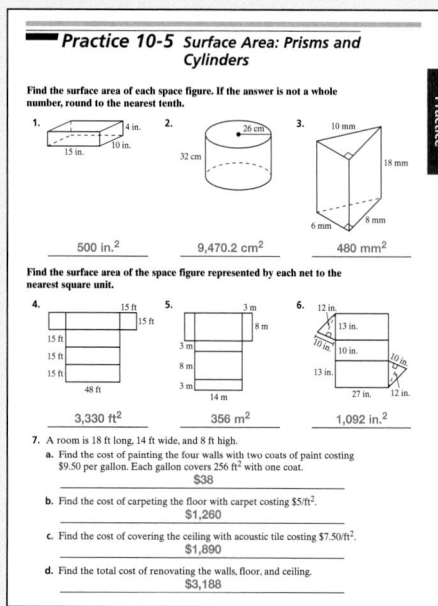

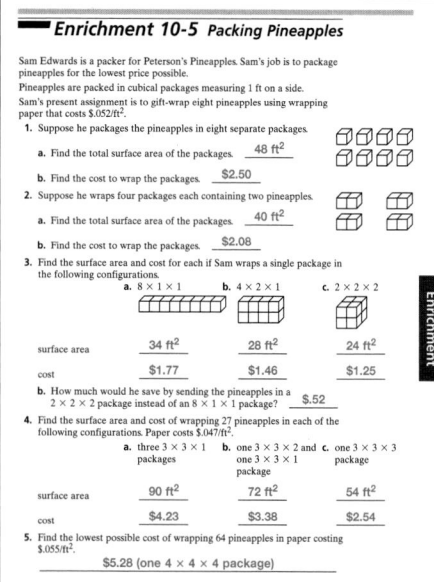

EXERCISES

For more exercises, see *Extra Practice*.

Practice and Problem Solving

Ⓐ **Practice by Example**

Example 1
(page 545)

3a. |←—11 in.—→|

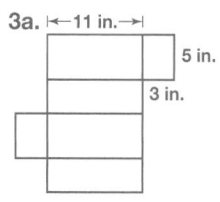

3d. The surface area of the larger prism is 9 times the surface area of the smaller prism.

Find, to the nearest square unit, the surface area of the space figure represented by each net.

1.

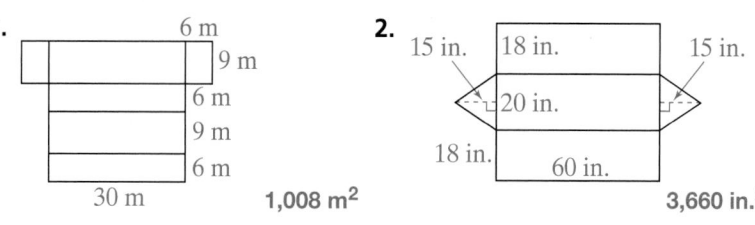

1,008 m²

2.

3,660 in.²

3. The base of a rectangular prism is 3 in. by 5 in. The height is 11 in.
   a. Draw and label a net for the prism. **See left.**
   b. Find the surface area of the prism. **206 in.²**
   c. A similar rectangular prism has dimensions three times the dimensions of the given prism. Find its surface area. **1,854 in.²**
   d. How do surface areas of similar prisms compare when dimensions are tripled? **See left.**

Example 2
(page 546)

Find the surface area of each prism.

4. **1,056 mm²**

5. **11,988 in.²**

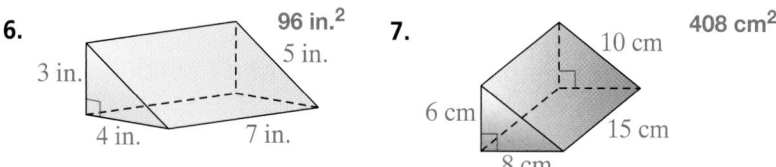

6. **96 in.²**

7. **408 cm²**

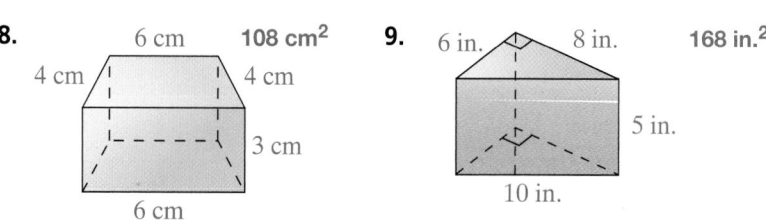

8. **108 cm²**

9. **168 in.²**

Example 3
(page 547)

Find the surface area of the cylinder shown or represented. Round to the nearest tenth.

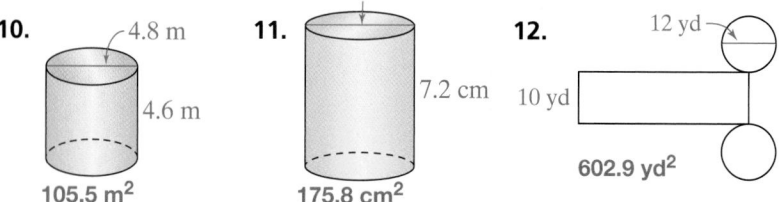

10. **105.5 m²**

11. **175.8 cm²**

12. **602.9 yd²**

13. Gift Wrapping Juliet is trying to wrap a can of mixed nuts that is a birthday gift for her brother. The can has a radius of 8 cm and a height of 10 cm. Approximately how many square centimeters of wrapping paper will cover the gift? **904 cm²**

B **Apply Your Skills**

14.

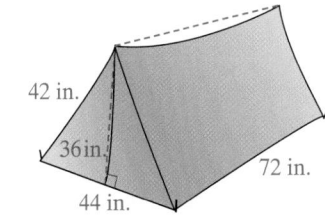

8 ft
12 ft

14. A cylinder has radius 8 ft and height 12 ft. Draw and label a net for the cylinder. Find its surface area. **See left; about 1,004.8 ft²**

15. Find the surface area of a square prism with base edge 7 m and height 15 m. **518 m²**

16. Find the area of the top and lateral surface of a cylindrical water tank with radius 20 ft and height 30 ft. **5,024 ft²**

17. Camping A tent is approximately the shape of a triangular prism. Approximate the area of the tent, including the bottom, by finding the surface area of the prism. **10,800 in.²**

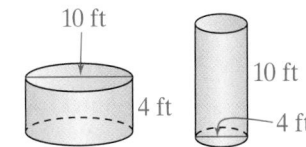

42 in.
36 in.
44 in.
72 in.

18. Find the surface area of a cylinder with radius 10 cm and height 8 cm. **about 1,130.4 cm²**

19. Painting The neighborhood swimming pool needs to be painted. The pool is 40 ft by 60 ft. The depth of the pool is 6 ft throughout.
  a. How many sides need to be painted? **5 sides**
  b. What is the total number of square feet to be painted? **3,600 ft²**
  c. The materials for painting the pool cost $1.50 per square yard. What is the cost of the materials for painting the pool? **$600**

20. Answers may vary. Sample: The student thought that you can interchange diameter and height and have the same surface areas.

20. Error Analysis A student explains that the two cylinders at the right have the same surface area. Explain the student's error. **See left.**

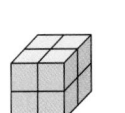
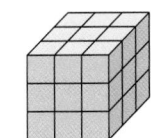

10 ft
10 ft
4 ft
4 ft

21. Open-Ended Describe a real-world situation in which you need to know the surface area of a space figure. **See margin.**

22. The height of the base is the height of the triangular base, but the height of the prism is the length of a segment perpendicular to the two bases.

22. Writing in Math In a triangular prism, what is the difference between the height of a base and the height of the prism? **See left.**

23. Packaging You have made two boxes with lids. Which box required more cardboard, a box 8 in. by 6.25 in. by 10.5 in., or a box 9 in. by 5.5 in. by 11.75 in.? Explain. **See margin.**

C **Challenge**

24a. 6 square units; 24 square units; 54 square units

24. Reasoning Use the cubes with side lengths of 1, 2, and 3 units.
  a. Find the surface area of each cube. **See left.**
  b. If the length of each side of a cube is doubled, how does that affect the surface area? **It is quadrupled.**
  c. If the length of each side of a cube is tripled, how does that affect the surface area? **It increases by a factor of nine.**

10-5 Surface Area: Prisms and Cylinders **549**

21. Answers may vary. Sample: When you paint a room, you need to find the surface area of the walls to buy the correct amount of paint.

23. The first box requires 399.25 in.² of cardboard. The second requires 439.75 in.² of cardboard. So the second box requires more cardboard.

Use the Guided Problem Solving worksheet with Exercise 16.

Lesson Quiz 10-5

Find the surface area of each figure rounded to the nearest whole unit.

1. triangular prism with base perimeter 24 cm, base area 24 cm², and height 15 cm
408 cm²

2. rectangular prism with base perimeter 30 cm, base area 50 cm², and height 150 cm
4,600 cm²

3. cylindrical candle with radius 2 cm and height 16 cm **about 226 cm²**

Test Prep

Resources

For additional practice with a variety of test item formats:
• Test Prep, p. 575
• Test-Taking Strategies, p. 570
• Test-Taking Strategies With Transparencies

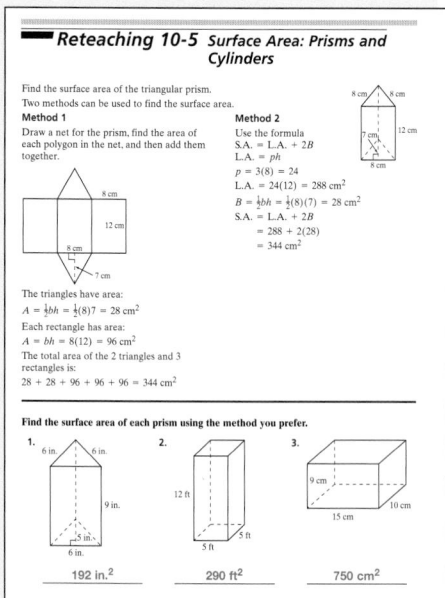

Reteaching 10-5 **Surface Area: Prisms and Cylinders**

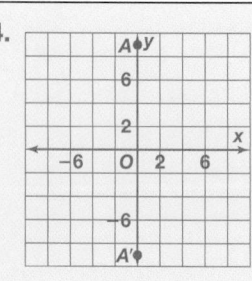

34.

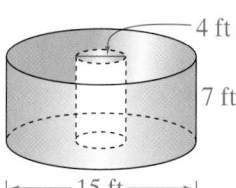
4 ft
7 ft
|←——— 15 ft ———→|

25. Construction The concrete figure at the left has a hole in it. The surface will be painted except for the inside of the hole. Find the total surface area to be painted to the nearest square foot. **658 ft²**

26. Reasoning Which has the greater effect on the surface area of a cylinder: doubling the base radius or doubling the height? Justify your answer. **Doubling the radius has a greater effect on the surface area. Doubling the radius or the height results in the same change in lateral area, but doubling the radius also increases the base area.**

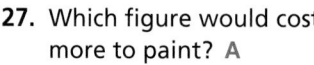
Test Prep

Multiple Choice

27. Which figure would cost more to paint? **A**
   A. the square prism
   B. the cylinder
   C. They would cost the same.
   D. cannot be determined

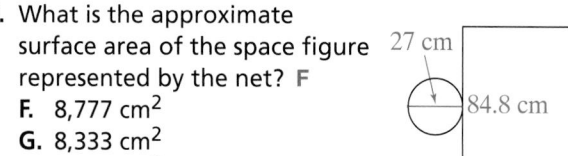
8 cm   5 cm   5 cm   10 cm   5 cm

Test-Taking Tip
When a test question asks for the surface area of a prism, you can sketch the net of the prism to help visualize the entire surface.

28. What is the approximate surface area of the space figure represented by the net? **F**
   F. 8,777 cm²
   G. 8,333 cm²
   H. 8,202 cm²
   I. 4,387 cm²

27 cm   84.8 cm   90 cm   27 cm

29. Each edge of cube is 40 cm long. What is the surface area of the cube? Use 2.5 cm ≈ 1 in. **B**
   A. 256 in.²   **B.** 1,536 in.²   **C.** 3,840 in.²   **D.** 9,600 in.²

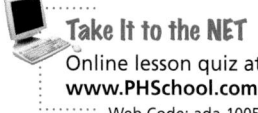
Take It to the NET
Online lesson quiz at
www.PHSchool.com
Web Code: ada-1005

30. A cylinder has height 10 in. and base radius 2.5 in. What is its lateral area, to the nearest whole unit? **I**
   F. 235 in.²   **G.** 215 in.²   **H.** 196 in.²   **I.** 157 in.²

Mixed Review

Lesson 10-4   **Name each space figure.**

31.   **32.**   **33.**

hexagonal prism   pentagonal pyramid   cone

Lesson 9-9   **Graph each point and its image after a reflection over the given line.**

34. $A(0, 9)$; x-axis   **35.** $B(-3, 5)$; y-axis   **36.** $C(3, -1)$; $x = 2$
34–36. See margin.

Lesson 6-2 **37. Recipes** A recipe that serves 6 people calls for $\frac{1}{2}$ teaspoon of salt. In preparing this recipe for 25 people, about how many teaspoons of salt should you use? **2 teaspoons**

Alternative Assessment

Name a space figure and have students write a description of how to find its surface area using a net. For example: *triangular prism*—sum of the areas of three rectangles and two triangles.

35.

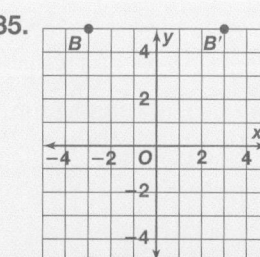

36. See back of book.

Reading a Formula

For the example below, follow along with how Diana reads and uses the formulas. Check your understanding by solving the exercises at the bottom of the page.

Find the surface area of the triangular prism at the right.

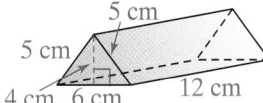

What Diana Reads

Step 1 Find the lateral area.

$$L.A. = ph$$
$$= (5 + 5 + 6)12$$
$$= 192$$

Step 2 Find the surface area.

$$S.A. = L.A. + 2B$$
$$= 192 + 2\left(\tfrac{1}{2} \cdot 6 \cdot 4\right)$$
$$= 192 + 24$$
$$= 216$$

The surface area of the triangular prism is 216 cm^2.

What Diana Thinks

Surface area means lateral area plus base areas.

In the Step 1 formula,

L.A. is the lateral area.

p is the perimeter of the base, so $p = 5 + 5 + 6$.

h is the height of the prism, so $h = 12$.

Using these values, the Step 1 formula gives L.A. = 192 cm^2.

In the Step 2 formula,

S.A. is the surface area.

L.A. is the lateral area, 192, from Step 1.

$2B$ is the area of the 2 bases.

Each base is a triangle with area B. Use the formula for area of a triangle and find $B = \tfrac{1}{2}(\text{base})(\text{height}) = \tfrac{1}{2}(6)(4)$.

Using these values, the Step 2 formula gives S.A. = 216 cm^2.

EXERCISES

Write the formulas you use to find the surface area of each figure. Give the meaning and value of each letter or letters in the formula.   1–3. See margin.

1.

3 in. / 5 in. / 20 in.

2.

3 cm / 4 cm / 5 cm / 10.5 cm

3.

1 m / 2 m

1. $ph + 2(\ell w)$; p = perimeter of base, so $p = 50$. h = height of prism, so $h = 3$. ℓ = length of base, so $\ell = 20$. w = width of base, so $w = 5$.

2. $PH + 2\left(\tfrac{1}{2}bh\right)$; P = perimeter of base, so $P = 12$; H = height of prism, so $H = 10.5$. b = length of triangular base, so $b = 4$. h = height of triangular base, so $h = 3$.

3. $2\pi rh + 2\pi r^2$, r = radius of the circular base, so $r = 1$. h = height of the cylinder, so $h = 2$.

In this feature, students interpret and use formulas to solve problems.

Teaching Notes

Students need to understand that each variable or symbol in a formula represents a quantity. Students must know what the symbols in the formula mean, what the formula itself means, and how to substitute the information they have into the formula.

Teaching Tip

To help students remember what it means to find the surface area of an object, tell them to think of the object suspended in air. The surface area is the sum of the areas of all the surfaces they can touch.

Error Prevention!

Have students sketch nets of the geometric solids in the exercises and label all known parts before solving the problems.

Visual Learners

Provide geometric solids for the students to view as they complete the problems.

Surface Area: Pyramids, Cones, and Spheres

552

What You'll Learn

OBJECTIVE 1 To find surface areas of pyramids

OBJECTIVE 2 To find surface areas of cones and spheres

. . . And Why

To find surface areas of real-world objects, such as a basketball

 Check Skills You'll Need

Use the Order of Operations to simplify each expression.

1. $\frac{2}{3}(9\pi) + \frac{1}{2}(8\pi)$ 10π

2. $\frac{3}{4}(12\pi) + \frac{2}{5}(15\pi)$ 15π

3. $\frac{1}{6}(24\pi) + \frac{1}{3}(3\pi)$ 5π

4. $\frac{5}{8}(32\pi) + \frac{1}{7}(14\pi)$ 22π

For help, go to Lesson 5-4.

New Vocabulary

• slant height

 Interactive lesson includes instant self-check, tutorials, and activities.

In this text, all pyramids are *regular* pyramids. They have regular polygons for bases and congruent isosceles triangles for lateral faces.

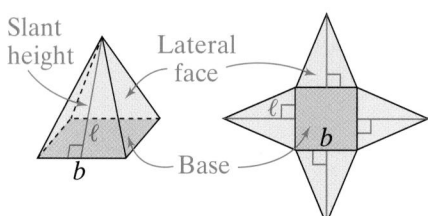

You can use the **slant height** ℓ, the height of a face, to find the area of the lateral faces. If n is the number of lateral triangular faces,

$$\text{L.A. is } n\left(\tfrac{1}{2}b\ell\right) \text{ or } \tfrac{1}{2}p\ell.$$

Key Concepts   **Surface Area of a Pyramid**

The lateral area of a pyramid is one half the product of the perimeter of the base and the slant height.

The surface area of a pyramid is the sum of the lateral area and the area of the base.

$$\text{L.A.} = \tfrac{1}{2}p\ell \qquad \text{S.A.} = \text{L.A.} + B$$

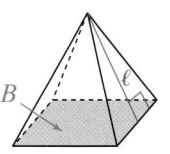

1 EXAMPLE   **Finding Surface Area of a Pyramid**

Find the surface area of the square pyramid.

Step 1 Find the lateral area.

$\text{L.A.} = \tfrac{1}{2}p\ell$ **Use the formula for lateral area.**

$= \tfrac{1}{2} \cdot 48 \cdot 16$ $p = 4(12)$ **and** $\ell = 16$.

$= 384$

Step 1 Find the surface area.

$\text{S.A.} = \text{L.A.} + B$ **Use the formula for surface area.**

$= 384 + 12^2$ **L.A. = 384 and** $B = 12^2$.

$= 384 + 144$

$= 528$

The surface area of the pyramid is 528 cm².

 Ongoing Assessment and Intervention

Before the Lesson
Diagnose prerequisite skills using:
• Check Skills You'll Need

During the Lesson
Monitor progress using:
• Check Understanding
• Additional Examples
• Test Prep

After the Lesson
Assess knowledge using:
• Lesson Quiz
• Computer Test Generator CD-ROM

✓ Check Understanding Example 1

1. A pyramid has a square base with edge 20 ft. The slant height is 8 ft. Find the surface area. **720 ft²**

OBJECTIVE

2 Finding Surface Areas of Cones and Spheres

In this text, every cone is a right circular cone with the vertex of the cone directly over the center of the circular base.

L.A. is $\frac{1}{2}(2\pi r)\ell$ or L.A. $= \pi r\ell$.

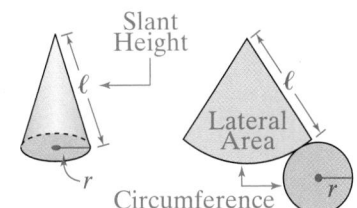

Slant Height

Lateral Area

Circumference

Key Concepts Surface Area of a Cone

The surface area (S.A.) of a cone is the sum of the lateral area and base area.

$$\text{L.A.} = \pi r\ell \qquad \text{S.A.} = \text{L.A.} + B$$

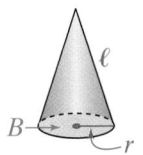

2 EXAMPLE Finding Surface Area of a Cone

Find the surface area of the cone at the right.

L.A. $= \pi r\ell$ Use the formula for lateral area.
  $\approx 3.14(4)(10)$ $r = 4$ and $\ell = 10$.
  $= 125.6$

10 cm

4 cm

S.A. $= $ L.A. $+ B$ Use the formula for surface area.
  $\approx 125.6 + 3.14(4)^2$ L.A. ≈ 125.6 and $B = \pi(4)^2$.
  $= 125.6 + 50.24$
  $= 175.84$

● The surface area of the cone is about 176 cm².

✓ Check Understanding Example 2

2. A cone has slant height 39 ft and radius 7 ft. Find it surface area. **about 1,011 ft²**

A sphere has the same area as four circles with the same radius.

Key Concepts Surface Area of a Sphere

The surface area of a sphere of radius r is
$$\text{S.A.} = 4\pi r^2.$$

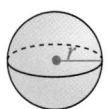

👪 Reaching All Students

| **Below Level** Have students give examples of pyramids, cones, and spheres they have seen. They may also find pictures in magazines. | **Advanced Learners** Ask students how they would find the surface area of a structure that is a combination of more than one geometric solid. | **English Learners** See note on page 553. **Tactile Learners** See note on page 553. |

---

2. Teach

Professional Development

Math Background

Note the similarity between the formulas for area of a rectangle and lateral areas of prisms and cylinders:
  $A = bh$, L.A. $= ph$
(p is perimeter or circumference). Note also the similarity between the formulas for area of a triangle and lateral areas of pyramids and cones:
  $A = \frac{1}{2}bh$, L.A. $= \frac{1}{2}p\ell$.
These are handy analogies that can help you remember not only the lateral-area formulas, but also the surface-area formulas, each of which involves adding lateral area and base area(s).

Teaching Notes

English Learners
The *slant height* of a pyramid or cone is the height of the slanted surfaces. It is different from the perpendicular distance from the vertex to the base (height of the pyramid or cone). See the Teaching Tip on page 554.

Tactile Learners
To clarify the difference between the slant height and height, have students make a net for a pyramid. Draw a segment for the (slant) height from the vertex to the opposite side on one of the triangular faces. As students fold the net to make the pyramid, help them see that the line segment they drew is not perpendicular to the base of the pyramid, but remains perpendicular to the base of the triangle.

1 EXAMPLE Teaching Tip

The formula for lateral area of a pyramid is derived from L.A. $= n(\frac{1}{2}b\ell)$, where n is the number of sides and b is the length of one side of the base.
  L.A. $= n(\frac{1}{2}b\ell)$
  L.A. $= nb(\frac{1}{2}\ell)$
  L.A. $= p(\frac{1}{2}\ell)$
  L.A. $= \frac{1}{2}p\ell$
Therefore, the lateral area of a prism is half the perimeter times the slant height.

553

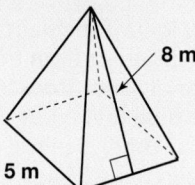
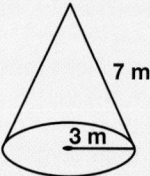

— 10 in. —

❸ **EXAMPLE** Real-World 🌐 Problem Solving

Basketball Calculate the surface area of a basketball.

$$\text{S.A.} = 4\pi r^2 \qquad \text{Use the formula for surface area.}$$
$$\approx 4(3.14)(5)^2 \qquad r = 5$$
$$= 314$$

● The surface area of the basketball is about 314 in.²

✓ **Check Understanding** Example 3

3. A sphere has a radius of 6 cm. Find its surface area. **about 452 cm²**

You can find the surface area of a space figure that combines two or more figures you have studied.

More Than One Way

Find the surface area of the silo formed by a half sphere and a cylinder. The diameter of the silo is 20 ft.

10 ft

72 ft

Roberto's Method

Find the area of each space figure. Then find their sum.

One half sphere	Cylinder
S.A. $= \frac{1}{2}(4\pi r^2)$	L.A. $= 2\pi rh$
$\approx \frac{1}{2}(4)(3.14)(10^2)$	$\approx 2(3.14)(10)(72)$
$= 628$	$= 4{,}521.6$

Surface area of silo is about 628 + 4,521.6, or 5,149.6 ft².

Jasmine's Method

Combine formulas before substituting values.

$$\begin{aligned} \text{Surface area} &= \tfrac{1}{2}\text{S.A.} \qquad + \text{ L.A.}\\ \text{of silo} &\quad \text{of sphere} \quad \text{of cylinder}\\ &= \tfrac{1}{2}(4\pi r^2) + 2\pi rh\\ &= 2\pi r^2 + 2\pi rh\\ &= 2\pi r(r + h)\\ &\approx 2(3.14)(10)(10 + 72)\\ &= 5{,}149.6 \end{aligned}$$

Surface area of silo is about 5,149.6 ft².

Choose a Method

1. Which method do you prefer? Explain. **Answers may vary. Sample: Jasmine's Method; it is easier to manipulate symbols than numbers.**

Practice and Problem Solving

A Practice by Example

Examples 1–3
(pages 552 and 553)

Find the surface area of each space figure, to the nearest square unit.

1.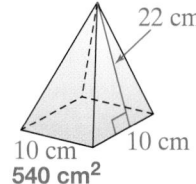
22 cm
10 cm 10 cm
540 cm²

2.
15 in.
6 in.
396 in.²

3.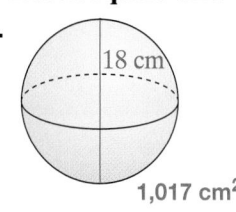
18 cm
1,017 cm²

4.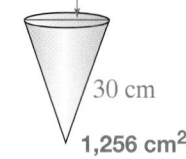
4 yd
3 yd
3 yd
33 yd²

5.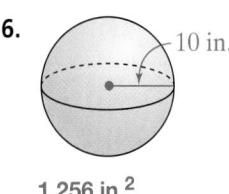
20 cm
30 cm
1,256 cm²

6.
10 in.
1,256 in.²

7. The length of the base of a square pyramid is 5 cm. Its slant height is 8 cm. Find the surface area of the square pyramid.
105 cm²

8. The base of a cone has radius 3 ft. Its slant height is 8 ft. Find the surface area of the cone. **about 104 ft²**
GPS

9. Engineering A spherical ball bearing has a radius of 8 mm. Find the surface area of the ball bearing. **about 804 mm²**

B Apply Your Skills

14. Answers may vary. Sample: My friend forgot that the lateral area of the pyramid is half of the lateral area of the prism. Also, it is necessary to add the area of the second base of the prism.

15. Use the slant height to find the lateral area using the formula L.A. = $\pi r \ell$: 3.14 · 8 · 10, then add the area of the base, 3.14 · 8², to the lateral area to find the surface area.

C Challenge

16. 216 m²
17. 122 m²
18. 2,185 ft²

Find the surface area of each space figure, to the nearest square unit.

10.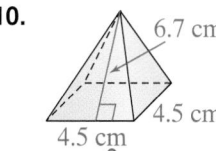
6.7 cm
4.5 cm
4.5 cm
81 cm²

11.
1.5 m
4.5 m
28 m²

12.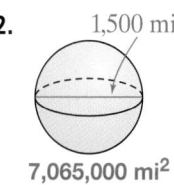
1,500 mi
7,065,000 mi²

13. Geography A globe has a diameter of 18 inches. What is the surface area of the globe to the nearest square inch? **1,018 in.²**

14. Error Analysis A friend tells you that the surface area of a square prism with base length 4 m and height 5 m is the same as the surface area of a square pyramid with base length 4 m and height 5 m. Explain your friend's error. **See above left.**

15. Writing in Math Write a paragraph explaining how to find the surface area of a cone with slant height 10 in. and base radius 8 in. **See left.**

Find the surface area of each figure to the nearest square unit. 16–18. **See left.**

16.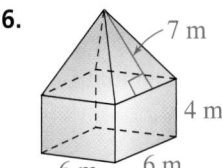
7 m
4 m
6 m 6 m

17.
3 m
6 m
2 m

18.
12 ft
11 ft

10-6 Surface Area: Pyramids, Cones, and Spheres **555**

GPS Use the Guided Problem Solving worksheet with Exercise 8.

Assignment Guide

1 Objective 1
A B Core 1, 4, 7, 10, 14
C Extension 16

2 Objective 2
A B Core 2, 3, 5, 6, 8, 9, 11–13, 15
C Extension 17–21

Test Prep 22–24
Mixed Review 25–31

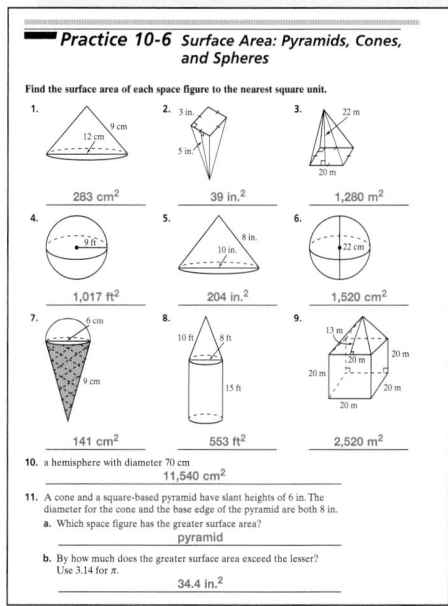

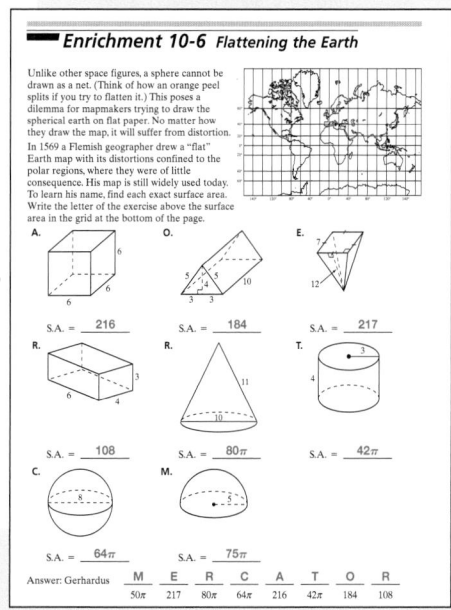

4. Assess

Error Prevention!

Students may forget formulas and leave out variables if they try to use them from memory. Have students write formulas on an index card for quick reference.

Test Prep

Resources

For additional practice with a variety of test item formats:
- Test Prep, p. 575
- Test-Taking Strategies, p. 570
- Test-Taking Strategies With Transparencies

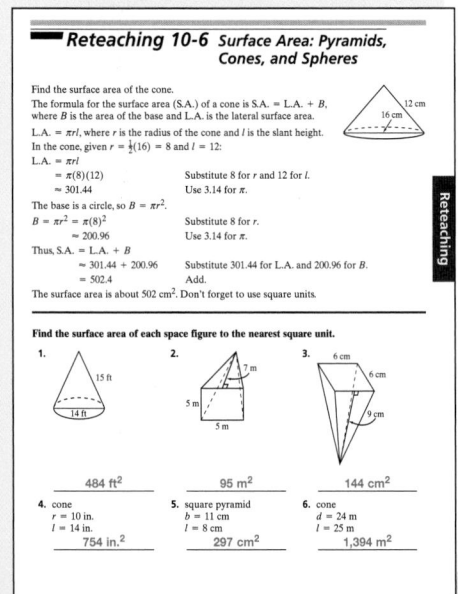

19. Architecture The spherical planetarium (left) at the American Museum of Natural History in New York City is 87 ft in diameter.
   a. What is the surface area of the sphere? about 23,800 ft²
   b. The sphere is covered by 2,474 panels to absorb sound. What is the average area of each panel, to the nearest tenth of a square foot? 9.6 ft²

20. Reasoning Which has the greater surface area, a cylinder with height 2 in. and radius of base 2 in., or a sphere with radius 2 in.? Justify your answer. Both have the same surface area of 16π in.².

21. Geography Approximately 70% of Earth's surface is covered by water. If the diameter of Earth is approximately 13,000 km, find the approximate surface area *not* covered by water. 159,198,000 km²

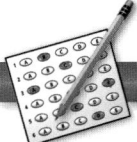 **Test Prep**

Multiple Choice

22. What is the surface area of the figure at the right? B
   A. 2,150 in.²
   B. 2,600 in.²
   C. 3,000 in.²
   D. 3,200 in.²

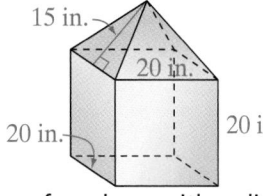
15 in.
20 in.
20 in.
20 in.

Take It to the NET
Online lesson quiz at
www.PHSchool.com
Web Code: ada-1006

23. What is the ratio of the surface area of a sphere with radius 2 ft to the surface area of a sphere with radius 5 ft? G
   F. 2 to 5   **G.** 4 to 25   **H.** 16 to 125   **I.** 18 to 20

Extended Response

24. A water storage tank with a roof that is in the shape of a cone has a diameter of 10 ft. The height of the cylindrical part of the tank is 15 ft. The slant height of the roof is 8 ft. **(a)** What is the radius of the tank? **(b)** What is the lateral area of the cylindrical part of the tank? **(c)** What is the surface area of the entire tank?
See back of book.

Mixed Review

Lesson 10-5 **Find the surface area to the nearest square unit.**

25.
24 in.
12 in.
1,130 in.²

26.
22 cm
10 cm
14 cm
848 cm²

Lesson 8-7 **27.** Under rate plan A a new computer costs $200 down and $20 a month. Under rate plan B the computer costs $175 down and $25 a month. After how many months will the amount paid be the same for both plans? 5 months

Lesson 4-1 **List all the factors of each number.**

28. 21
1, 3, 7, 21

29. 100
1, 2, 4, 5, 10, 20, 25, 50, 100

30. 25
1, 5, 25

31. 32
1, 2, 4, 8, 16, 32

556 Chapter 10 Area and Volume

Alternative Assessment

Give pairs of students different-sized cones and spheres. Use conical paper cups, snow-cone holders, ice cream cones, and various balls. Have them find the surface area of each figure using rulers to find diameters. Include or omit the base of a cone according to what seems appropriate. Measuring

the diameter or radius of a sphere is a little difficult. Tell the students to do the best they can.

Volume: Prisms and Cylinders

 10-7

OBJECTIVE
1 Finding the Volumes of Prisms

The **volume** of a three-dimensional figure is the number of cubic units needed to fill it. A **cubic unit** is the space occupied by a cube with edges one unit long.

Consider filling the rectangular prism at the right with centimeter cubes.

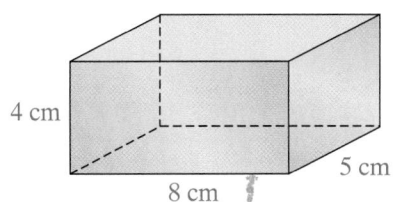

4 cm

8 cm   5 cm

The bottom layer of the prism contains $8 \cdot 5 = 40$ centimeter cubes, or a volume of 40 cm³ (cubic centimeters).

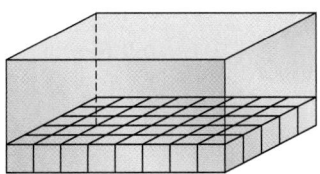

The prism has four layers of cubes, so it contains $4 \cdot 40$, or 160, centimeter cubes in all.

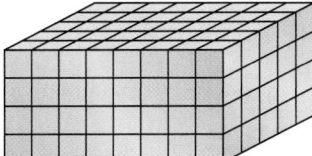

The volume of the prism is 160 cm³.

The volume found for the rectangular prism above suggests the following formula.

Key Concepts   **Volume of a Prism**

The volume V of a prism is the product of the base area B and the height h.
$$V = Bh$$

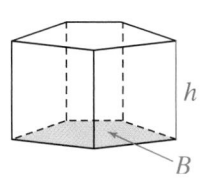

h

B

What You'll Learn

OBJECTIVE 1 To find volumes of prisms

OBJECTIVE 2 To find volumes of cylinders

. . . And Why

To solve real-world problems, such as finding volumes of containers

✔ Check Skills You'll Need

Find the area of each circle.

1. radius = 8 cm
   about 201 cm²
2. radius = 12 cm
   about 452 cm²
3. diameter = 20 cm
   about 314 cm²

For help, go to Lesson 10-3.

New Vocabulary
- volume
- cubic unit

TEXT Interactive lesson includes instant self-check, tutorials, and activities.

1. Plan

Lesson Preview

 Check Skills You'll Need

Area of Circles
Lesson 10-3: Example 1; Exercises 1–3.
Extra Practice, p. 753.

Lesson Resources

 Teaching Resources
Practice, Reteaching, Enrichment

 Reaching All Students
Practice Workbook 10-7
Spanish Practice Workbook 10-7
Guided Problem Solving 10-7
Technology Activities 26, 27
Hands-On Activities 25, 28

 Presentation Assistant Plus!
Transparencies and PowerPoint™
- Check Skills You'll Need 10-7
- Additional Examples 10-7
- Student Edition Answers 10-7
- Lesson Quiz 10-7
- Classroom Aid 11, 12, 29
PH Presentation Pro CD-ROM 10-7

 ASSESSMENT SYSTEM

Computer Test Generator CD-ROM

 Technology
Resource Pro® CD-ROM
Computer Test Generator CD-ROM
PH Presentation Pro CD-ROM

 www.PHSchool.com
Student Site
- Teacher Web Code: adk-5500
- Self-grading Lesson Quiz
PH SuccessNet Teacher Center
- Lesson Planner
- Resources

Plus

 Ongoing Assessment and Intervention

Before the Lesson
Diagnose prerequisite skills using:
- Check Skills You'll Need

During the Lesson
Monitor progress using:
- Check Understanding
- Additional Examples
- Test Prep

After the Lesson
Assess knowledge using:
- Lesson Quiz
- Computer Test Generator CD-ROM

Professional Development

Math Background

As in the formulas for surface areas, you can use B to represent the area of a base in formulas for volumes. The formula $V = Bh$ covers all of the possibilities of base shapes for prisms and cylinders.

Teaching Notes

1 EXAMPLE Visual Learners

Some students may not understand why the unit of measure for volume has the appearance of a third power. Remind students that exponents represent repeated multiplication and write the following on the board:

$V = \frac{1}{2} \cdot 10$ cm $\cdot 6$ cm $\cdot 21$ cm

$\quad = \frac{1}{2} \cdot 10 \cdot 6 \cdot 21 \cdot$ cm $\cdot$ cm $\cdot$ cm

$\quad = 630$ cm^3

Relate "cm^3" to *cubic* centimeters.

PowerPoint

Additional Examples

1 Find the volume of the triangular prism. **1,260 cm^3**

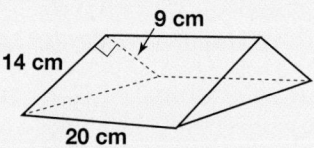

2 Find the volume of the juice can to the nearest cubic centimeter. **581 cm^3**

Closure

Ask students how to find the volumes of prisms and cylinders. Use the formula $V = Bh$ where V is volume, B is the area of a base, and h is the height of the prism or cylinder.

558

---

1 EXAMPLE Finding Volume of a Prism

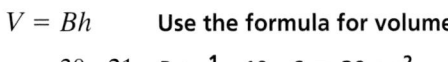

Find the volume of the triangular prism at the left.

$\quad V = Bh \qquad$ Use the formula for volume.

$\quad\quad = 30 \cdot 21 \quad B = \frac{1}{2} \cdot 10 \cdot 6 = 30$ cm^2

$\quad\quad = 630 \qquad$ Simplify.

● The volume is 630 cm^3.

✓ Check Understanding   Example 1

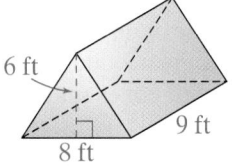

1. Find the volume of the triangular prism.
   216 ft^3

OBJECTIVE

2 Finding the Volumes of Cylinders

You can calculate the volume of a cylinder in much the same way that you calculate the volume of a prism.

Key Concepts   Volume of a Cylinder

The volume V of a cylinder is the base area B times the height h.

$\quad\quad V = Bh$

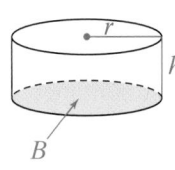

2 EXAMPLE   Real-World   Problem Solving

Packaging Find the volume of the juice can to the nearest cubic centimeter.

$\quad V = Bh \qquad\qquad$ Use the formula for volume.

$\quad V = \pi r^2 h \qquad\qquad B = \pi r^2$

$\quad\quad \approx 3.14 \cdot 3.4^2 \cdot 12 \quad$ Replace r with 3.4, and h with 12.

$\quad\quad = 435.5808 \qquad$ Simplify.

● The volume is about 436 cm^3.

✓ Check Understanding   Example 2

2. a. Find the volume of the cylinder to the nearest cubic foot. **1,900 ft^3**
   b. How does the volume of this cylinder compare with one having twice its dimensions? **See left.**

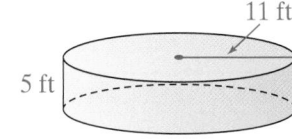

b. The volume of the larger cylinder is 8 times the volume of the smaller cylinder.

558 Chapter 10 Area and Volume

👥 Reaching All Students

| **Below Level** Review the formulas used so far in this chapter by having volunteers list them on the board. Leave the list on the board for a quick, as-needed reference. Add to the list as appropriate. | **Advanced Learners** Have groups fill a cylinder with water, calculate the volume in cubic units (their choice), and then pour the water into a cylinder graduated in milliliters. Challenge students to write a conversion factor. | **Visual Learners** See note on page 558. **Error Prevention** See note on page 560. |

EXERCISES

🔎 For more exercises, see *Extra Practice*.

Practice and Problem Solving

Assignment Guide

▼ **1 Objective 1**
  🅐 🅑 Core 1–3, 8–10, 12, 14, 16
  🅒 Extension 17, 18

▼ **2 Objective 2**
  🅐 🅑 Core 4–7, 11, 13, 15
  🅒 Extension 19

Test Prep 20–22
Mixed Review 23–27

🅐 Practice by Example

Example 1
(page 558)

Find the volume of each prism.

1.

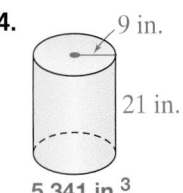

3 cm   4 cm   9 cm

54 cm³

2.

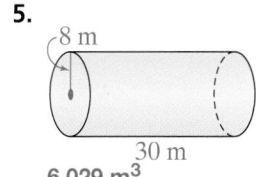

10 cm   8 cm   18 cm

720 cm³

3.

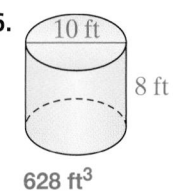

2 m   3 m   4 m

24 m³

Example 2
(page 558)

For Exercises 4–7, find the volume of each cylinder to the nearest cubic unit.

4.

9 in.   21 in.

5,341 in.³

5.

8 m   30 m

6,029 m³

6.

10 ft   8 ft

628 ft³

7. a. a mailing tube 25 in. long with a diameter of 4 in. **314 in.³**
   b. a mailing tube with double the dimensions in part (a) **2,512 in.³**
   c. How do the volumes of the two mailing tubes compare? The volume of the larger tube is 8 times the volume of the smaller tube.

🅑 Apply Your Skills 🌐 **8. Firewood** Wood for a fireplace is often sold by the cord. A cord is 8 ft by 4 ft by 4 ft. How many cubic feet are in a cord of wood? **128 ft³**

🌐 **9. Storage** An under-the-bed storage box measures 24 in. by 12 in. by 3 in. Find its volume to the nearest cubic centimeter (1 in. = 2.54 cm). **14,158 cm³**
[GPS]

Find each missing dimension. Use $\pi \approx 3.14$.

10.

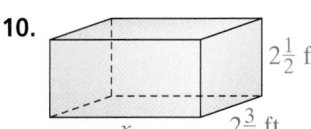

$2\frac{1}{2}$ ft x $2\frac{3}{4}$ ft

$V = 38.5$ ft³
Length = ▦ $5\frac{3}{5}$ ft

11.

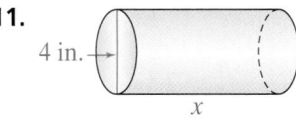

4 in. x

$V = 125.6$ in.³
Height ≈ ▦ **10 in.**

12.

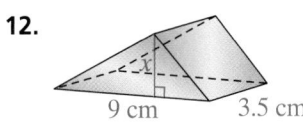

x 9 cm   3.5 cm

$V = 50.4$ cm³
Height of triangle = ▦
3.2 cm

13.

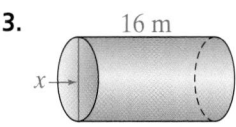

16 m x

$V = 1,256$ m³
Diameter ≈ ▦
10 m

Writing in Math Describe one real object with the given shape. Explain why you might want to find the volume of the object.

14. triangular prism   **15.** cylinder   **16.** rectangular prism
14–16. Answers may vary. See margin for samples.

10-7 Volume: Prisms and Cylinders   **559**

14. A tent; you may need to see how many of your friends can fit in a tent on a camping trip.
15. A food container; you may have to estimate the amount of food you can store.

[GPS] Use the Guided Problem Solving worksheet with Exercise 9.

16. A large box; you may need to find how much the box can hold when you store items.

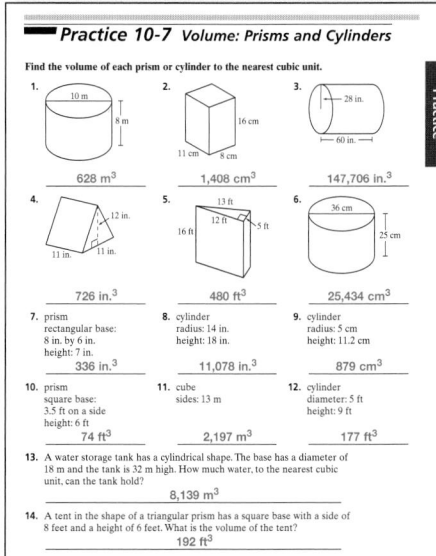

Practice 10-7 *Volume: Prisms and Cylinders*

Find the volume of each prism or cylinder to the nearest cubic unit.

1. 10 m, 8 m, 11 cm, 8 cm   **628 m³**
2. 16 cm   **1,408 cm³**
3. 28 in., 60 in.   **147,706 in.³**
4. 12 in., 11 in., 11 in.   **726 in.³**
5. 13 ft, 12 ft, 5 ft, 16 ft   **480 ft³**
6. 36 cm, 25 cm   **25,434 cm³**

7. prism
   rectangular base:
   8 in. by 6 in.
   height: 7 in.   **336 in.³**
8. cylinder
   radius: 14 in.
   height: 18 in.   **11,078 in.³**
9. cylinder
   radius: 5 cm
   height: 11.2 cm   **879 cm³**

10. prism
    square base:
    3.5 ft on a side
    height: 6 ft   **74 ft³**
11. cube
    sides: 13 m   **2,197 m³**
12. cylinder
    diameter: 5 ft
    height: 9 ft   **177 ft³**

13. A water storage tank has a cylindrical shape. The base has a diameter of 18 m and the tank is 32 m high. How much water, to the nearest cubic unit, can the tank hold?   **8,139 m³**

14. A tent in the shape of a triangular prism has a square base with a side of 8 feet and a height of 6 feet. What is the volume of the tent?   **192 ft³**

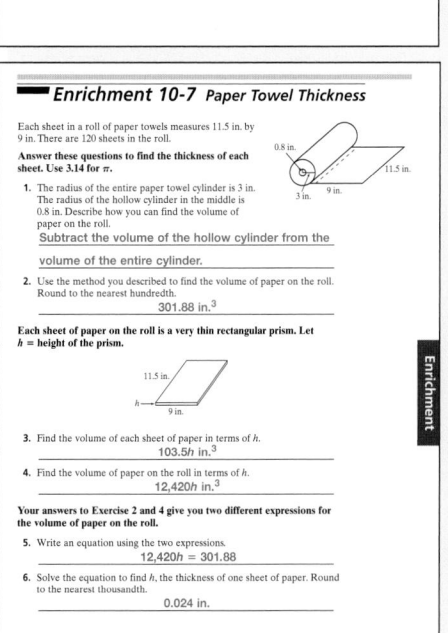

Enrichment 10-7 *Paper Towel Thickness*

Each sheet in a roll of paper towels measures 11.5 in. by 9 in. There are 120 sheets in the roll.

Answer these questions to find the thickness of each sheet. Use 3.14 for π.

1. The radius of the entire paper towel cylinder is 3 in. The radius of the hollow cylinder in the middle is 0.8 in. Describe how you can find the volume of paper on the roll.
   Subtract the volume of the hollow cylinder from the volume of the entire cylinder.

2. Use the method you described to find the volume of paper on the roll. Round to the nearest hundredth.   **301.88 in.³**

Each sheet of paper on the roll is a very thin rectangular prism. Let h = height of the prism.

3. Find the volume of each sheet of paper in terms of h.   **103.5h in.³**

4. Find the volume of paper on the roll in terms of h.   **12,420h in.³**

Your answers to Exercise 2 and 4 give you two different expressions for the volume of paper on the roll.

5. Write an equation using the two expressions.   **12,420h = 301.88**

6. Solve the equation to find h, the thickness of one sheet of paper. Round to the nearest thousandth.   **0.024 in.**

4. Assess

Find the volume of each space figure.

1. rectangular prism with base 12 m by 14 m and height 50 m 8,400 m³

2. cylindrical pool with diameter 24 ft and height 4 ft about 1,809 ft³

3. right triangular prism with base legs 8 cm and 10 cm and height 20 cm 800 cm³

Error Prevention!

Exercises 1, 2, 12 Remind students that in a prism, a face that is not a rectangle must be a base.

Test Prep

For additional practice with a variety of test item formats:
• Test Prep, p. 575
• Test-Taking Strategies, p. 570
• Test-Taking Strategies With Transparencies

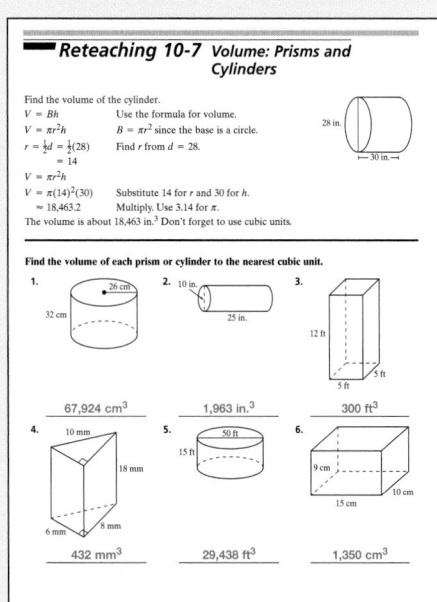

Reteaching 10-7 Volume: Prisms and Cylinders

Ⓒ Challenge 🌐 **17. Construction** Concrete is sold by the yard, which means by the cubic yard. It costs $70 per yard. How many cubic feet are in a cubic yard? How much would it cost to pour a slab that is 14 ft by 16 ft by 6 in. for a patio?
27; $290.37

18. Reasoning The two stacks of paper in the photo at the left contain the same number of sheets. The first stack forms an oblique prism; the second forms a right prism. The stacks have the same height, base, and volume. Use this information to find the volume of the oblique prism shown below the stacks. 27 in.³

19. Error Analysis A student explains that a cylinder with radius 1 in. and height 3 in. has half the volume of one with radius 2 in. and height 3 in. Explain the student's error.
Answers may vary. Sample: The student used the ratio of the radii, 1 : 2, to form the conclusion.

Test Prep

Multiple Choice **20.** One side of a triangle is 5 cm and its corresponding height is 15 cm. The triangle is the base of a triangular prism with height 5 cm. What is the volume of the prism? **C**
A. 12.5 cm³ **B.** 37.5 cm³ **C.** 187.5 cm³ **D.** 375.0 cm³

21. What is the height of a rectangular prism with length 5 ft, width 2 ft, and volume 120 ft³? **F**
F. 12 ft **G.** 10 ft **H.** 6 ft **I.** 2 ft

Extended Response **22.** A manufacturer is deciding whether to package table salt in a cylinder or in a rectangular prism made of cardboard. The cylinder has radius 4 cm and height 13.5 cm. The prism is 7 cm by 7 cm by 13.5 cm.
a. What volume of salt will each package hold?
b. Each package will use how many square centimeters of cardboard?
c. Which seems to be the better type of package? Explain.
a–c. See back of book.

Mixed Review

Lesson 10-6 **Find the surface area of each figure, to the nearest square unit.**

23. 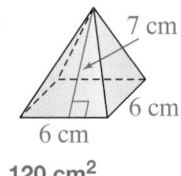 5 cm, 13 cm
283 cm²

24. 7 cm, 6 cm, 6 cm
120 cm²

25. 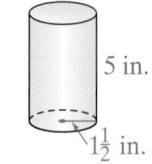 5 in., 1½ in.
61 in.²

26. m∠4, m∠5, m∠8 = x°;
m∠2, m∠3, m∠6, m∠7 = (180 − x)°

Lesson 9-2 **26.** If a ∥ b in the figure at the right, find the measures of angles 2–8 in terms of x.
See left.

Lesson 5-6 🌐 **27. Money** Juan has $3.80 in coins. He has 6 quarters and 12 dimes. The rest are nickels. How many nickels does he have? 22 nickels

Alternative Assessment

Divide students into small groups and have them write lessons to teach the concept of volume to a younger class. Remind them to avoid language or descriptions the younger students might not understand.

Technology

Rounding Error

For Use With Lesson 10-7

A calculator can help you avoid a *rounding error*. However, you have to know how to work with exact values in unsimplified form.

EXAMPLE

Find the volume of a cylinder with height 6 and circumference 15. Round to the nearest tenth.

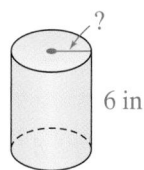

6 in.

Method 1		**Method 2**
$C = 2\pi r$	formula for circumference	$C = 2\pi r$
$15 = 2\pi r$	$C = 15$	$15 = 2\pi r$
$\frac{15}{2\pi} = r$	Divide by 2π.	$\frac{15}{2\pi} = r$
$2.4 \approx r$	Simplify (at left).	
$V = Bh$	formula for volume	$V = Bh$
$= \pi r^2 h$	$B = \pi r^2$	$= \pi r^2 h$
$\approx \pi(2.4)^2(6)$	Replace r and h.	$= \pi\left(\frac{15}{2\pi}\right)^2(6)$
≈ 108.6	Use a calculator.	≈ 107.4

In Method 1, the intermediate value $r \approx 2.4$ gives a final result that has a greater *rounding error*. In Method 2, note that the formula for volume uses the exact value of the radius, $\frac{15}{2\pi}$.

EXERCISES

What intermediate value must you find to solve the problem?
Give its exact value and its approximate value to the nearest tenth.

1. Find the area of a circle with circumference 12. $r = \frac{6}{\pi}, r \approx 1.9$

2. Find the volume of a cylinder with radius 3 and lateral area 10. $h = \frac{5}{3\pi}, h \approx 0.5$

Solve each problem to the nearest tenth by two methods. In one method, use an approximate intermediate value. In the other method, use the exact intermediate value.

3. Find the surface area of a cone with slant height 5 and lateral area 9. **10.1, 10.0**

4. Find the surface area of a sphere with circumference 13. **55.4, 53.8**

5. Find the surface area and volume of a cylinder with lateral area 10 and height 8. **10.3, 10.2; 1.0, 1.0**

6. **Writing in Math** In the Example, which method do you think makes better use of the calculator? Explain. **Answers may vary. Sample: Method 2 makes better use of the calculator. There is no need to round in the middle of the solution.**

Technology Rounding Error **561**

Technology

Rounding Error

This Technology extension explores how a calculator can help you avoid rounding errors.

Teaching Notes

Teaching Tip
Have students note that neither the radius nor the diameter of the cylinder is shown on the figure or given in the problem. The volume formula requires that the radius be known, so it must be found first. Since the formula for circumference includes the radius, and the circumference is a given value, you use the circumference formula to find the radius.

Teaching Tip
Ask: *Why is the value found for the volume in Method 1 more than the value found for the volume in Method 2?* In Method 1, the value for $\frac{15}{2\pi}$ is rounded up to 2.4 from 2.3873. . .

Lesson Preview

 Check Skills You'll Need

Classifying Polygons
Lesson 9-3: Example 2;
Exercises 4–9.
Extra Practice, p. 752.

Lesson Resources

Teaching Resources
Practice, Reteaching, Enrichment
Checkpoint Quiz 2

 Reaching All Students
Practice Workbook 10-8
Spanish Practice Workbook 10-8
Reading and Math Literacy 10C
Spanish Reading and Math
   Literacy 10C
Spanish Checkpoint Quiz 2
Guided Problem Solving 10-8

 Presentation Assistant Plus!
Transparencies and PowerPoint™
• Check Skills You'll Need 10-8
• Additional Examples 10-8
• Student Edition Answers 10-8
• Lesson Quiz 10-8
PH Presentation Pro CD-ROM 10-8

ASSESSMENT SYSTEM

Checkpoint Quiz 2
Computer Test Generator CD-ROM

Technology
Resource Pro® CD-ROM
Computer Test Generator CD-ROM
PH Presentation Pro CD-ROM

 **www.PHSchool.com**
Student Site
• Teacher Web Code: adk-5500
• Self-grading Lesson Quiz
PH SuccessNet Teacher Center
• Lesson Planner
• Resources

Plus **iTEXT**

OBJECTIVE

1 Make a Model

What You'll Learn

OBJECTIVE 1 To make a model

. . . And Why

To build the largest box possible from a given rectangle

 Check Skills You'll Need

Draw each figure described below.
1–3. See back of book.
1. a rectangle with small squares drawn in each corner

2. a rectangle divided into eight congruent rectangles

3. two parallelograms that have different shapes but the same perimeter

For help, go to Lesson 9-3.

Math Strategies in Action Architects build and use models when they plan. When they design buildings, they experiment with models. When they design packaging, they first create prototype models.

1 EXAMPLE   Real-World Problem Solving

Packaging A box company makes boxes to hold popcorn. Each box is made by cutting the square corners out of a rectangular sheet of cardboard. The rectangle is $8\frac{1}{2}$ in. by 11 in. What are the dimensions of the box that will hold the most popcorn if the square corners have side lengths 1 in., 2 in., 3 in., and 4 in.?

Read and Understand

1. What is the goal of the problem? The goal is to find the dimensions of the box that will hold the most popcorn.
2. What information do you have to help you build a model? The size of the piece of cardboard is known, as well as the size of the square corners.

Plan and Solve

To find the size that will hold the greatest amount of popcorn, you must find the dimensions that will give you the greatest volume.

Ongoing Assessment and Intervention

Before the Lesson
Diagnose prerequisite skills using:
• Check Skills You'll Need

During the Lesson
Monitor progress using:
• Check Understanding
• Additional Examples
• Test Prep

After the Lesson
Assess knowledge using:
• Lesson Quiz
• Computer Test Generator CD-ROM
• Chapter Checkpoint 2 (p. 565)

Build four boxes using sheets of $8\frac{1}{2}$ in.-by-11 in. paper. Test four whole-number lengths of cuts.

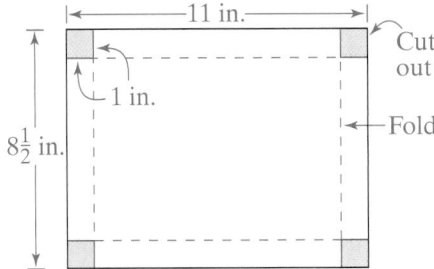

3. **a.** What are the dimensions of the box with corners 1 in. by 1 in.? $6\frac{1}{2}$ **in. by 9 in. by 1 in.**
   b. What is the volume of this box? $58\frac{1}{2}$ **in.³**

4. When you cut a 2 in.-by-2 in. square from each corner, what effect does that have on the length, width, and height of the box? **The length and width are decreased by 4 in., and the height is increased by 2 in.**

Measure to find the dimensions of each of your boxes. Then find the volume of each box.

5. Which box has the greatest volume?
   The box with 2 in.-by-2 in. corners.
6. Is it possible to create a box that has 5 in.-by-5 in. corners? Explain. **No; such a box would require more cardboard than is actually available in an $8\frac{1}{2}$ in.-by-11 in. piece of cardboard.**

Look Back and Check

A table is another way to organize your information and solve the problem.

7. List the size of the cut, and then find the length, width, and height of the box. Find each volume.

Size of Cut	Length	Width	Height	Volume
1 in.	9 in.	6.5 in.	1 in.	58.5 in.³
2 in.	7 ▦ in.	4.5 ▦ in.	2 ▦ in.	63 ▦ in.³
3 in.	5 ▦ in.	2.5 ▦ in.	3 ▦ in.	37.5 ▦ in.³
4 in.	3 ▦ in.	0.5 ▦ in.	4 ▦ in.	6 ▦ in.³

✓ **Check Understanding**

8. **a.** Use a table to find the volume of a box folded from an $8\frac{1}{2}$ in.-by-11 in. sheet of paper if the square corners are $1\frac{1}{2}$ in.; $2\frac{1}{2}$ in.; $3\frac{1}{2}$ in. **66 in.³; 52.5 in.³; 21 in.³**
   b. Did you find dimensions of a box that holds a greater volume than you did in Question 7? Which dimensions are they?
   Yes; $5\frac{1}{2}$ in. by 8 in. by $1\frac{1}{2}$ in.

10-8 Make a Model **563**

🌱 **Reaching All Students**

| **Below Level** As you discuss Example 1, have students look at the diagram to help them understand the situation. | **Advanced Learners** Ask: *In Example 1, would a 2-in. cut or a 3-in. cut result in the greater volume if the original piece of paper were 16 in. by 22 in. and the other conditions stayed the same?* **a 3-in. cut** | **Inclusion** See note on page 563. **Tactile Learners** See note on page 563. |

2. Teach

Math Background

Making a model to represent a problem is useful when you need to see, examine, or measure to solve the problem. When you make a model, you represent a situation or an actual object, although the size and exact materials may differ and be easier to work with. If the model you make is a fairly accurate scale model, you can take measurements in order to answer questions.

Teaching Notes

Inclusion
Some students may find it difficult to use scissors and tape on small edges. Pair them with students who are experienced with building models.

1 EXAMPLE Tactile Learners
Help students develop a connection between the two-dimensional abstract drawing and the real three-dimensional object. Organize the class into 8 groups. Assign each group a box to make from Example 1 so that there are two of each box. Groups who make same-sized boxes can compare their boxes for accuracy. Then display the boxes to show the different shapes.

PowerPoint
Additional Examples

1 A can company rolls rectangular pieces of metal that measure 8 in. by 10 in. to make the sides of cans. Which height, 8 in. or 10 in., will make the can with the greater volume? **8-in. height**

Closure

Ask students how making a model may help solve a problem.
Answers may vary. Sample: Making a model is useful when you need to examine, manipulate, or measure to solve a problem.

563

3. Practice

Assignment Guide

Objective 1

Ⓐ Ⓑ Core 1–7
Ⓒ Extension 8, 9

Test Prep 10–12
Mixed Review 13–18

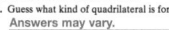

Practice 10-8 *Make a Model*

Solve by making a model.

1. A narrow strip of paper is twisted once, then joined at the ends with glue or tape. The strip is then cut lengthwise along the dotted line shown.
   a. Guess the results.
   Answers may vary.
   b. Make and cut a model as directed. What are the results?
   A single loop results.

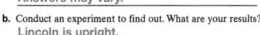

2. The midpoint of a segment is the point that divides the segment into two segments of equal length. A quadrilateral with unequal sides is drawn. The midpoints of the four sides are found and connected in order.
   a. Guess what kind of quadrilateral is formed.
   Answers may vary.
   b. Draw four quadrilaterals with unequal sides and connect the midpoints of adjacent sides. What kind of quadrilaterals appear to have been formed?
   parallelograms

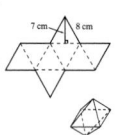

3. A penny with Lincoln's head upright is rolled along the edge of another penny as shown in the figure.
   a. At the end, do you think Lincoln will be right-side-up or upside-down?
   Answers may vary.
   b. Conduct an experiment to find out. What are your results?
   Lincoln is upright.

4. A net for an octahedron is shown. All the sides are congruent, equilateral triangles. Cut and fold on the dotted lines. Find the surface area of the octahedron.
   224 cm²

Enrichment 10-8 *Regular Polyhedra*

Polyhedra are space figures with polygons as sides. Regular polyhedra have regular polygons as sides and a special arrangement at each vertex. There are only five regular polyhedra.
You can use the patterns on this page to construct models of three of the five regular polyhedra.
Cut out the patterns. Fold on the dotted lines and fasten the edges with tape to construct the models.

Regular Tetrahedron   Regular Octahedron

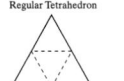   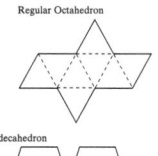

Regular Dodecahedron

Analyze Euler's Formula for these regular polyhedra.

	Regular Figure	Number of faces (F)	Number of vertices (V)	Number of edges (E)	F + V − E
1.	Tetrahedron	4	4	6	2
2.	Octahedron	8	6	12	2
3.	Dodecahedron	12	15	25	2

4. Does F + V − E = 2 for each regular polyhedron? yes

EXERCISES

❓ For more exercises, see *Extra Practice*.

Practice and Problem Solving

Ⓐ **Practice by Example**

Example 1
(page 562)

8-Page Signature

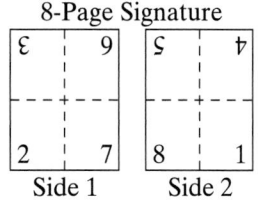

Side 1   Side 2

Solve by making a model.

1. You cut square corners off a piece of cardboard with dimensions 16 in. by 20 in. You then fold the cardboard to create a box with no lid. To the nearest inch, what dimensions will give you the greatest volume? 10 in. by 14 in. by 3 in.

2. **Publishing** Newspapers, books, and magazines often are printed in groups of 8, 16, or 32 pages, called *signatures*. The diagram at the left shows how pages should be positioned for an 8-page signature. The pages are positioned to print on both sides of the paper that is fed through the printing press. When the paper is folded, the pages are in order. Make a model to show one way to position the pages in a 16-page book. See back of book.

Ⓑ **Apply Your Skills**

Solve using any strategy.

3. The length of a rectangle is twice its width. The perimeter of the rectangle is 90 cm. What are the length and width? 30 cm, 15 cm

Strategies

- Account for All Possibilities
- Draw a Diagram
- Look for a Pattern
- Make a Model
- Make a Table
- Simplify the Problem
- Simulate the Problem
- Solve by Graphing
- Try, Test, Revise
- Use Multiple Strategies
- Work Backward
- Write an Equation
- Write a Proportion

4. **Packaging** A company packages snack mix in cylindrical tubes. Each tube is made from a rectangle of cardboard. The bases of the cylinder are plastic. The cardboard comes in $8\frac{1}{2}$ in.-by-11 in. sheets. To hold the greatest amount of mix, should the longer side or shorter side be the height? Justify your answer. See below left.

5. **Pets** A dog owner wants to use 200 ft of fencing to enclose the greatest possible area for his dog. He wants the fenced area to be rectangular. What dimensions should he use? 50 ft by 50 ft

6. **Writing in Math** You want to find how the length of a pendulum affects the time the pendulum takes to swing back and forth. Explain how you would model the situation. See margin.

7. An alphabet book will have one letter on each page. Eight pages will be printed on a single piece of paper. You fold the paper in half. Then you fold it in half again and trim the edges. The eight pages appear in order. Draw the layout for two sides of the large sheet for the letters A–H. Explain why two layouts are possible. See back of book.

Ⓒ **Challenge**

4. The shorter side should be the height because it will yield a volume of 81.8 in.³, and using the longer side as the height yields a volume of only 63.3 in.³.

8. **Reasoning** In the parts (a)–(c), how many of the indicated cubes are there in this 3-by-3-by-3 cube?
   a. 1-by-1-by-1 cubes 27 cubes
   b. 2-by-2-by-2-cubes 8 cubes
   c. 3-by-3-by-3 cubes 1 cube
   d. How many 3-by-3-by-3 cubes would be in a 5-by-5-by-5 cube? 15 cubes

9. One base of a trapezoid is twice as long as the other base. The height is the same as the shorter base. If the area is 24 cm², what is the height of the trapezoid? 4 cm

GPS Use the Guided Problem Solving worksheet with Exercise 5.

6. Answers may vary. Sample: Use several different lengths of string and a single weight. Record the time it takes the weight to swing back and forth when tied to each of the strings.

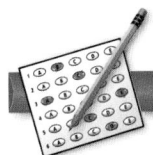

Multiple Choice

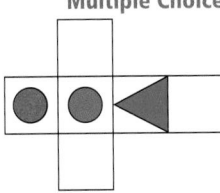

10. Which space figure below can you fold from the net at the left? **C**

A. 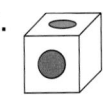 **B.** **C.** **D.**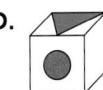

11. A rectangle has a perimeter of 24. The length and width are integers. For the least possible area, what are its dimensions? **F**

F. 1 by 11 **G.** 1 by 24 **H.** 2 by 4 **I.** 6 by 6

Take It to the NET
Online lesson quiz at
www.PHSchool.com
Web Code: ada-1008

12. A pyramid and a rectangular prism have the same base and height. The volume of the rectangular prism is how many times the volume of the pyramid? **D**

A. $\frac{1}{3}$ **B.** $\frac{1}{2}$ **C.** 2 **D.** 3

Mixed Review

Lesson 10-7

Find the volume of each figure, to the nearest tenth.

13.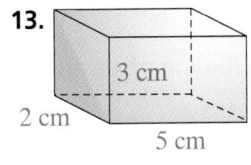
3 cm
2 cm
5 cm
30.0 cm³

14. 5.5 cm
5.5 cm
130.6 cm³

15.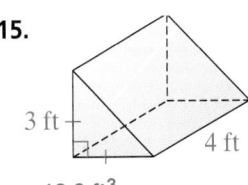
3 ft
4 ft
18.0 ft³

Lesson 8-2

Find the solutions of each equation when x is 0, 1, and −1.

16. $2x - y = 10$
−10, −8, −12

17. $5x + y = 15$
15, 10, 20

18. $2x + 3y = 6$
2, $1\frac{1}{3}$, $2\frac{2}{3}$

✓ Checkpoint Quiz 2

Lessons 10-4 through 10-8

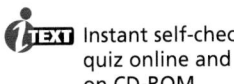 Instant self-check quiz online and on CD-ROM

Name each space figure. Find its surface area, to the nearest square unit.

1.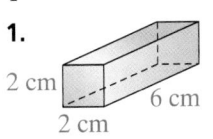
2 cm
2 cm
6 cm
square prism, 56 cm²

2. 3 in.
8 in.
cylinder, 207 in.²

3.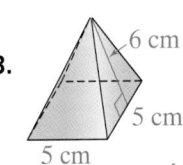
6 cm
5 cm
5 cm
square pyramid, 85 cm²

Find the volume of each figure to the nearest tenth.

4.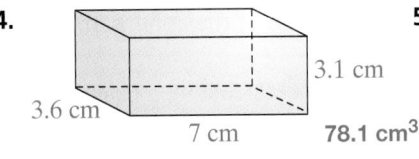
3.1 cm
3.6 cm
7 cm
78.1 cm³

5. 3 in.
6 in.
169.6 in.³

6. Open-Ended Choose a space figure. Draw its net. **Check students' work.**

10-8 Make a Model **565**

PowerPoint Lesson Quiz 10-8

1. You cut square corners from a piece of cardboard that has dimensions 32 cm by 40 cm. You then fold the cardboard to create a box with no lid. To the nearest centimeter, what are the dimensions of the box that will have the greatest volume? **20 cm by 28 cm by 6 cm**

✓ Chapter Checkpoint 2

To check understanding of Lessons 10-4 to 10-8:

Checkpoint Quiz 2 (p. 565)

📁 **Teaching Resources**
Checkpoint Quiz 2 (also in Prentice Hall Assessment System)

👥 **Reaching All Students**
Reading and Math Literacy 10C

Spanish versions available.

Reteaching 10-8 *Make a Model*

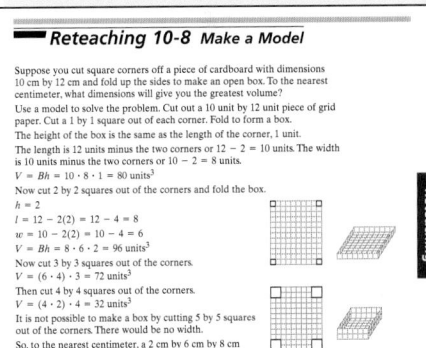

Suppose you cut square corners off a piece of cardboard with dimensions 10 cm by 12 cm and fold up the sides to make an open box. To the nearest centimeter, what dimensions will give you the greatest volume?
Use a model to solve the problem. Cut out a 10 unit by 12 unit piece of grid paper. Cut a 1 by 1 square out of each corner. Fold to form a box.
The height of the box is the same as the length of the corner, 1 unit.
The length is 12 units minus the two corners or $12 - 2 = 10$ units. The width is 10 units minus the two corners or $10 - 2 = 8$ units.
$V = Bh = 10 \cdot 8 \cdot 1 = 80$ units³
Now cut 2 by 2 squares out of the corners and fold the box.
$h = 2$
$l = 12 - 2(2) = 12 - 4 = 8$
$w = 10 - 2(2) = 10 - 4 = 6$
$V = Bh = 8 \cdot 6 \cdot 2 = 96$ units³
Now cut 3 by 3 squares out of the corners.
$V = (6 \cdot 4) \cdot 3 = 72$ units³
Then cut 4 by 4 squares out of the corners.
$V = (4 \cdot 2) \cdot 4 = 32$ units³
It is not possible to make a box by cutting 5 by 5 squares out of the corners. There would be no width.
So, to the nearest centimeter, a 2 cm by 6 cm by 8 cm box gives the greatest volume.

Suppose you cut square corners off a piece of cardboard with dimensions 12 cm by 15 cm to make an open box. Use a model to find the dimensions, to the nearest centimeter of each box. Record your work in the table.

	Length of side of corner	Length	Width	Height	Volume
1.	1 cm	13 cm	10 cm	1 cm	130 cm³
2.	2 cm	11 cm	8 cm	2 cm	176 cm³
3.	3 cm	9 cm	6 cm	3 cm	162 cm³
4.	4 cm	7 cm	4 cm	4 cm	112 cm³
5.	5 cm	5 cm	2 cm	5 cm	50 cm³

6. Which dimensions give the greatest volume? **2 cm by 8 cm by 11 cm**

Reteaching

Alternative Assessment

Give students stiff paper and have them make boxes (without tops). Have students find and compare the dimensions and volumes of their boxes. Then have students display the boxes in order from least to greatest volume.

Test Prep

📁 **Resources**
For additional practice with a variety of test item formats:
• Test Prep, p. 575
• Test-Taking Strategies, p. 570
• Test-Taking Strategies With Transparencies

565

10-9

Lesson Preview

 Check Skills You'll Need

Multiplying Fractions
Lesson 5-4: Example 1;
Exercises 1–8.
Extra Practice, p. 748.

Lesson Resources

 Teaching Resources
Practice, Reteaching, Enrichment

 Reaching All Students
Practice Workbook 10-9
Spanish Practice Workbook 10-9
Guided Problem Solving 10-9
Hands-On Activities 27

 Presentation Assistant Plus!
Transparencies and PowerPoint™
• Check Skills You'll Need 10-9
• Additional Examples 10-9
• Student Edition Answers 10-9
• Lesson Quiz 10-9
• Classroom Aid 12
PH Presentation Pro CD-ROM 10-9

ASSESSMENT *SYSTEM*

Computer Test Generator CD-ROM

 Technology
Resource Pro® CD-ROM
Computer Test Generator CD-ROM
PH Presentation Pro CD-ROM

 www.PHSchool.com
Student Site
• Teacher Web Code: adk-5500
• Self-grading Lesson Quiz
PH SuccessNet Teacher Center
• Lesson Planner
• Resources

Plus

Volume: Pyramids, Cones, and Spheres

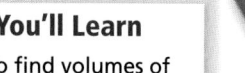

What You'll Learn

 OBJECTIVE 1 To find volumes of pyramids and cones

OBJECTIVE 2 To find volumes of spheres

. . . And Why

To find out how much water is displaced by a space figure

 Check Skills You'll Need

Multiply.

1. $\frac{1}{3}(3.14)(2)^2(5)$ **20.9$\overline{3}$**

2. $\frac{1}{3}(4)^2(6)$ **32**

3. $\frac{4}{3}(3.14)(2)^3$ **33.49$\overline{3}$**

4. $\frac{4}{3}(3.14)(0.5)^3$ **0.52$\overline{3}$**

 For help, go to Lesson 5-4.

OBJECTIVE

1 **Finding Volumes of Cones and Pyramids**

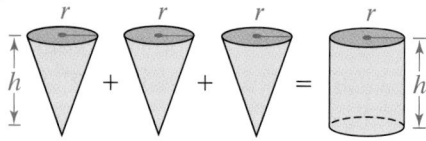

You can fill three cones with sand and pour the contents into a cylinder with the same height and radius. You will fill the cylinder evenly to the top.

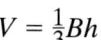

The volume of the cone is one third the volume of the cylinder.

The same relationship is true of a pyramid and a prism with the same base and height.

Key Concepts | **Volume of a Cone and of a Pyramid**

The volume V of a cone or a pyramid is $\frac{1}{3}$ the product of the base area B and the height h.

$$V = \frac{1}{3}Bh$$

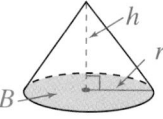 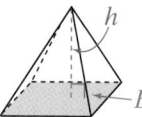

1 **EXAMPLE** **Finding Volume of a Cone**

Find the volume of the cone.

$V = \frac{1}{3}Bh$ **Use the formula for volume.**

$V = \frac{1}{3}\pi r^2 h$ $B = \pi r^2$

$\approx \frac{1}{3}(3.14)(3)^2(10)$ **Replace *r* with 3 and *h* with 10. Simplify.**

$= 94.2$

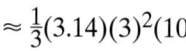

The volume of the cone is about 94 ft³.

 Check Understanding   **Example 1**

1. Find the volume, to the nearest cubic unit, of a cone with height 5 cm and radius of base 2 cm. **21 cm³**

 TEXT Interactive lesson includes instant self-check, tutorials, and activities.

Ongoing Assessment and Intervention

Before the Lesson	**During the Lesson**	**After the Lesson**
Diagnose prerequisite skills using:	Monitor progress using:	Assess knowledge using:
• Check Skills You'll Need	• Check Understanding	• Lesson Quiz
	• Additional Examples	• Computer Test Generator CD-ROM
	• Test Prep	

2 EXAMPLE Finding Volume of a Pyramid

Find the volume of the square pyramid.

$V = \frac{1}{3}Bh$ **Use the formula for volume.**

$V = \frac{1}{3}s^2h$ **$B = s^2$**

$= \frac{1}{3}(6)^2(10)$ **Replace s with 6 and h with 10.**

$= 120$ **Simplify.**

• The volume of the pyramid is 120 ft^3.

✓ **Check Understanding** Example 2

2. Find the volume of a square pyramid that has a side of 5 ft and a height of 20 ft. **167 ft^3**

OBJECTIVE

2 Finding Volumes of Spheres

Below is the formula for the volume of a sphere.

> **Key Concepts** **Volume of a Sphere**
>
> The volume V of a sphere with radius r is $\frac{4}{3}\pi$ times the cube of the radius.
>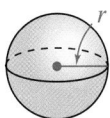
> $$V = \frac{4}{3}\pi r^3$$

3 EXAMPLE Real-World Problem Solving

Snow Spheres You build a snow statue with snow spheres. **What is the volume of the snow in the bottom sphere?**

$V = \frac{4}{3}\pi r^3$ **Use the volume formula.**

$\approx \frac{4}{3}(3.14)(1.5)^3$ **Replace r with 1.5.**

$= 14.13$ **Simplify.**

• The volume of the bottom snow sphere is about 14 ft^3.

✓ **Check Understanding** Example 3

3. Find the volume of each sphere to the nearest whole number.

a. radius = 15 m
14,130 m^3

b. diameter = 7 mi
180 mi^3

.3 ft

10-9 Volume: Pyramids, Cones, and Spheres **567**

2. Teach

Professional Development

Math Background

It is important to note that the formula for the volumes of cones and pyramids uses each figure's height, not slant height. The height of a cone or pyramid is the length of the segment from the vertex perpendicular to the base.

Teaching Notes

3 EXAMPLE **Error Prevention**
Make sure students realize that the formula for the volume of a sphere is the only one they have studied that involves a third power of a variable.

PowerPoint

Additional Examples

1 Find the volume of the cone.
about 50 in.^{3}
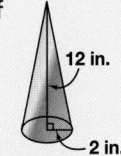
12 in.
2 in.

2 Find the volume of the square pyramid.
256 in.^{3}
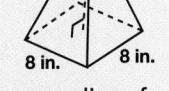
12 in.
8 in. 8 in.

3 Earth has an average radius of 3,963 mi. What is Earth's approximate volume to the nearest 1,000,000 mi^3? Assume that Earth is a sphere.
260,578,000,000 mi^3

Closure

Ask: *How are volumes of pyramids and cones related to volumes of prisms and cylinders?*
The volumes of pyramids and cones are one-third the volumes of prisms and cylinders that have the same base areas and heights, respectively.

3. Practice

Assignment Guide

▼ **Objective 1**
  Ⓐ Ⓑ **Core** 1–8, 15, 17, 20, 21, 23
  Ⓒ **Extension** 24

▼ **Objective 2**
  Ⓐ Ⓑ **Core** 9–14, 16, 18, 19, 22
  Ⓒ **Extension** 25

Test Prep 26–30
Mixed Review 31–38

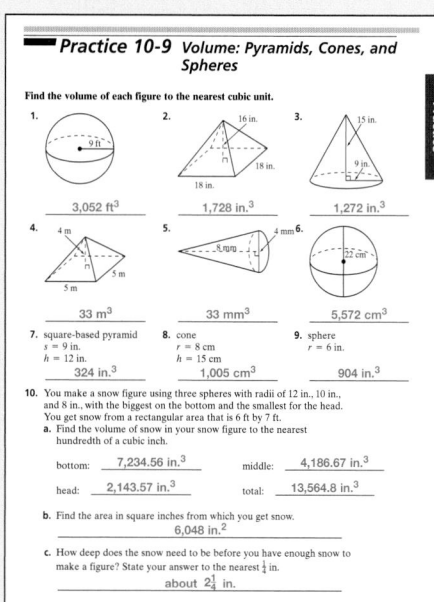

Practice 10-9 *Volume: Pyramids, Cones, and Spheres*

Find the volume of each figure to the nearest cubic unit.

1. 3,052 ft³   2. 1,728 in.³   3. 1,272 in.³

4. 33 m³   5. 33 mm³   6. 5,572 cm³

7. square-based pyramid
$s = 9$ in.
$h = 12$ in.
324 in.³

8. cone
$r = 8$ cm
$h = 15$ cm
1,005 cm³

9. sphere
$r = 6$ in.
904 in.³

10. You make a snow figure using three spheres with radii of 12 in., 10 in., and 8 in., with the biggest on the bottom and the smallest for the head. You get snow from a rectangular area that is 6 ft by 7 ft.
a. Find the volume of snow in your snow figure to the nearest hundredth of a cubic inch.

bottom: 7,234.56 in.³   middle: 4,186.67 in.³
head: 2,143.57 in.³   total: 13,564.8 in.³

b. Find the area in square inches from which you get snow.
6,048 in.²

c. How deep does the snow need to be before you have enough snow to make a figure? State your answer to the nearest ¼ in.
about 2¼ in.

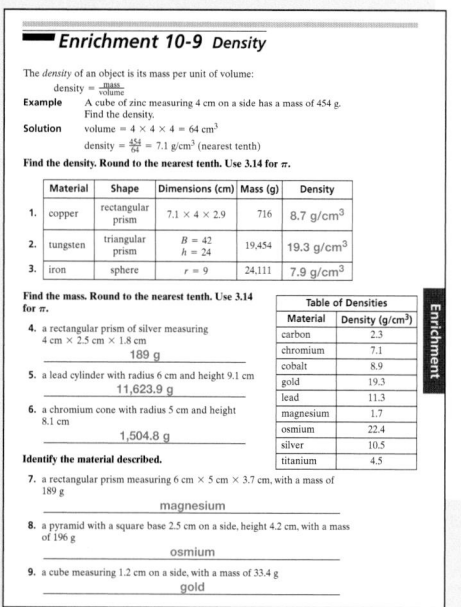

Enrichment 10-9 *Density*

The *density* of an object is its mass per unit of volume:
density = mass/volume

Example A cube of zinc measuring 4 cm on a side has a mass of 454 g. Find the density.

Solution volume = 4 × 4 × 4 = 64 cm³
density = 454/64 = 7.1 g/cm³ (nearest tenth)

Find the density. Round to the nearest tenth. Use 3.14 for π.

	Material	Shape	Dimensions (cm)	Mass (g)	Density
1.	copper	rectangular prism	7.1 × 4 × 2.9	716	8.7 g/cm³
2.	tungsten	triangular prism	B = 42 h = 24	19,454	19.3 g/cm³
3.	iron	sphere	r = 9	24,111	7.9 g/cm³

Find the mass. Round to the nearest tenth. Use 3.14 for π.

4. a rectangular prism of silver measuring 4 cm × 2.5 cm × 1.8 cm
189 g

5. a lead cylinder with radius 6 cm and height 9.1 cm
11,623.9 g

6. a chromium cone with radius 5 cm and height 8.1 cm
1,504.8 g

Table of Densities	
Material	Density (g/cm³)
carbon	2.3
chromium	7.1
cobalt	8.9
gold	19.3
lead	11.3
magnesium	1.7
osmium	22.4
silver	10.5
titanium	4.5

Identify the material described.

7. a rectangular prism measuring 6 cm × 5 cm × 3.7 cm, with a mass of 189 g
magnesium

8. a pyramid with a square base 2.5 cm on a side, height 4.2 cm, with a mass of 196 g
osmium

9. a cube measuring 1.2 cm on a side, with a mass of 33.4 g
gold

EXERCISES

? For more exercises, see *Extra Practice*.

Practice and Problem Solving

Ⓐ Practice by Example

In Exercises 1–4, find the volume of each cone to the nearest cubic unit.

Example 1 (page 566)

1. 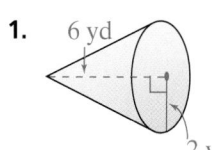 6 yd, 2 yd   25 yd³

2. 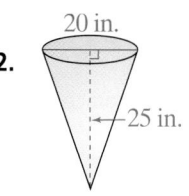 20 in., 25 in.   2,617 in.³

3. height 12 cm, radius 21 cm
5,539 cm³

4. height 7 in., radius 7 in.
359 in.³

Example 2 (page 567)

In Exercises 5–8, find the volume of each square pyramid.

5. 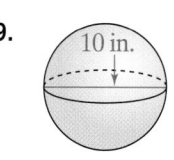 8 in., 9 in., 9 in.   216 in.³

6. 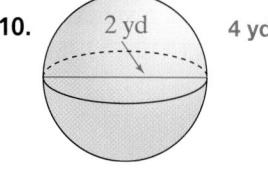 9 ft, 10 ft, 10 ft   300 ft³

7. edge 3.2 cm, height 6 cm
20.48 cm³

8. edge 90 mm, height 300 mm
810,000 mm³

Example 3 (page 567)

Find the volume of each sphere to the nearest whole number.

9. 10 in.   523 in.³

10. 2 yd   4 yd³

18. The volume of a pyramid is a variation on the volume of a rectangular solid. The volume of a cone or a sphere is a variation on the volume of a cylinder.

11. $r = 12$ cm
7,235 cm³

12. $r = 3.5$ in.
180 in.³

13. $d = 60$ yd
113,040 yd³

14. $d = 30$ m
14,130 m³

Ⓑ Apply Your Skills

🌐 15. **Plants** A cone-shaped paper cup is 7 cm high with a diameter of 6 cm. If the ivy plant on Julia's desk needs 240 mL of water, about how many paper cups of water will she use to water it? (1 mL = 1 cm³)
4 cups

🌐 16. **Snacks** How much frozen yogurt can you pack inside a cone that is 5 in. high with a radius of 1.25 in.? about 8.2 in.³

 TENNIS BALLS

🌐 17. **Packaging** Tennis balls with a diameter of 2.5 in. are sold in cans of three (left). The can is a cylinder. What is the volume of the space in the can not occupied by tennis balls? Assume the balls touch the can on the sides, top, and bottom. about 12.3 in.³

18. **Writing in Math** Explain how you remember formulas for finding volumes of prisms and pyramids, cylinders and cones, and spheres. See above left.

🌐 19. **Physics** You place a steel ball with diameter 4 cm in a water-filled cylinder that is 5 cm in diameter and 10 cm high. What volume of water will spill out of the cylinder? about 33.5 cm³

 GPS Use the Guided Problem Solving worksheet with Exercise 16.

Find the missing dimension. Round to the nearest unit.

20.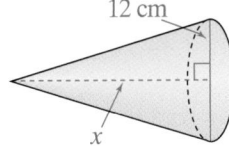

12 cm

x

$V = 819 \text{ cm}^3$
Height ≈ ▮ 22 cm

21.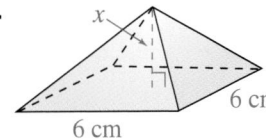

x

6 cm

6 cm

$V = 38 \text{ cm}^3$
Height = ▮ 3 cm

22. Sphere: volume = 36π yd³, diameter = ▮ 6 yd

23. Cone: volume = 424 m³, diameter = 18 m, height ≈ ▮ 5 m

C Challenge

24. You want to fill the top part of an hourglass $\frac{2}{3}$ full of salt. The height of the hourglass is 20 cm, and the radius of the base is 8 cm. Find the volume of salt needed. **about 447 cm³**

25. Error Analysis A student tells a class that if you double the radius of a sphere, the volume will be multiplied by 6. Explain the student's error. **The student multiplied 2 by 3 instead of finding 2^3.**

Test Prep

Gridded Response

26. The eight segments from the center of a cube to the eight corners of the cube form the edges of six pyramids. If one edge of the cube is 4 in., what is the volume of each pyramid, to the nearest cubic inch? **11**

27. What is the volume of a square pyramid with height 3.25 yd and base edge 5.5 yd, to the nearest tenth of a cubic yard? **32.8**

28. What is the volume of a sphere with diameter 5.5 m, to the nearest cubic meter? **87**

Take It to the NET
Online lesson quiz at
www.PHSchool.com
Web Code: ada-1009

29. What is the volume of a cone with radius 4.8 cm and height 12 cm, to the nearest tenth of a cubic centimeter? Use 3.14 for π. **289.4**

30. How many cones of radius 1 m and height 1 m have total volume equal to the volume of a sphere with radius 1 m? **4**

Mixed Review

Lesson 7-5 **Solve each equation.**

31. $\frac{5}{6}x = \frac{1}{6}x + 12$ **32.** $5y + 2 = 3y - 10$ **33.** $3a + 10 = 12 - 2a$

18   −6 $\frac{2}{5}$

Lesson 5-9 **Simplify each expression.**

34. $(3ab^2)^3$ **35.** $-(4x)^2$ **36.** $(-2p^2)^4$ **37.** $\left(-\frac{3}{8}\right)^2$ **38.** $\left(\frac{2x}{y^3}\right)^2$

$27a^3b^6$ $-16x^2$ $16p^8$ $\frac{9}{64}$ $\frac{4x^2}{y^6}$

10-9 Volume: Pyramids, Cones, and Spheres **569**

Alternative Assessment

Have each student draw a pyramid, cone, and sphere, and label the dimensions. Then have them find the volume of each figure and write the volumes on a separate piece of paper. Have students exchange drawings and find the volumes. Have them compare results to check their work.

Choosing "Cannot Be Determined"

This strategy helps students understand that "cannot be determined" is the answer choice if there is not enough information given to find the answer.

Resources

Test-Taking Strategies With Transparencies
• Transparency 10
• Practice sheet, p. 10

Teaching Notes

Error Prevention!

Point out to students that "cannot be determined" can be given as an answer choice to distract from the correct answer.

Test-Taking Strategies With Transparencies

Chapter 10: Choosing "Cannot Be Determined"
Exercises

Can the answer to each exercise be determined? Explain your choice.

1. The area of the base of a rectangular prism is 6 cm². Its height is 3 cm. What is its surface area?

2. A cylinder with height 3 ft fits inside a cube as shown. What is the surface area of the cylinder?

3. The length of a rectangle is twice the width. The perimeter is three times the length. What are the dimensions of the rectangle?

4. In △ABC, AB = 5 cm. The height to $\overline{AB}$ is twice the height to $\overline{BC}$. What is the length of $\overline{BC}$?

5. A trapezoid with height 3 cm has area 15 cm². What is the perimeter of the trapezoid?

6. A decorative tile is shown at the right. The shaded section is formed by two parallelograms. What is the total area of the two parallelograms?

10   Pre-Algebra   Test-Taking Strategies

Some multiple-choice questions cannot be answered because there is insufficient information or there is more than one possible answer. If so, then one of the answer choices will be "cannot be determined."

1 EXAMPLE

What is the surface area of the figure at the right?   D

A. 2,600 in.²   **B.** 3,200 in.²   **C.** 8,600 in.²   **D.** cannot be determined

The bottom part is a cube. You know its length, width, and height, so you can find its base area and its lateral area. The top part is a pyramid. You know the perimeter of the base, but you need to know the slant height of its faces to find its lateral area.

● There is insufficient information. The correct choice is D.

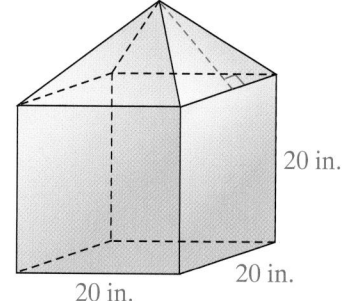

20 in.

20 in.

20 in.

2 EXAMPLE

A rectangular prism with height 5 cm has volume 60 cm³. What is the perimeter of the base?   I

F. 14 cm   **G.** 16 cm   **H.** 26 cm   **I.** cannot be determined

You know $V = Bh$.

$60 = B(5)$ **Replace V with 60 and h with 5.**

$12 = B$ **Solve for B.**

For $B = 12$ cm², the rectangular base can be 1 cm by 12 cm, 2 cm by 6 cm, or 3 cm by 4 cm. The perimeter can be 26 cm (choice H), 16 cm (choice G), or 14 cm (choice A).

● There is more than one possible answer. The correct choice is I.

EXERCISES

If the answer to an exercise cannot be determined, choose "cannot be determined" and explain your reasoning.

1. The base of a square prism has sides of 14 in. What is the surface area of the prism?   D; you need to know the height of the prism.

   A. 56 in.²   **B.** 196 in.²   **C.** 784 in.²   **D.** cannot be determined

2. A trapezoid has height 8 and area 28. What are the lengths of its bases?

   F. 6 and 1   **G.** 5 and 2   **H.** 4 and 3   **I.** cannot be determined

   I; you have to know at least one base because there are three possible combinations of base sizes that have the needed sum of 7.

Chapter Review

Vocabulary

altitude (p. 523)
altitude of a triangle (p. 527)
area (p. 522)
cone (p. 539)
cubic unit (p. 557)

cylinder (p. 539)
lateral area (p. 546)
net (p. 540)
prism (p. 539)
pyramid (p. 539)

slant height (p. 552)
space figure (p. 539)
sphere (p. 539)
surface area (p. 545)
volume (p. 557)

Reading Math
Understanding
Vocabulary

Choose the vocabulary term that correctly completes the sentence.

1. The sum of the areas of the lateral faces of a prism is the __?__ of a prism. **lateral area**

2. A __?__ is a space figure with one circular base and one vertex. **cone**

3. The __?__ of a parallelogram is a line segment drawn from the side opposite the base to the base, that is perpendicular to the base. **altitude**

4. The __?__ of a three-dimensional figure is the number of cubic units needed to fill it. **volume**

Take It to the NET
Online vocabulary quiz
at www.PHSchool.com
Web Code: adj-1051

5. The set of all points in space that are a given distance from a given point called the center is a __?__. **sphere**

6. A __?__ has two parallel bases that are congruent circles. **cylinder**

7. The __?__ of a figure is the number of square units it encloses. **area**

Skills and Concepts

10-1 and 10-2 Objectives

▼ To find areas of rectangles (p. 522)

▼ To find areas of parallelograms (p. 523)

▼ To find areas of triangles (p. 527)

▼ To find areas of trapezoids (p. 528)

The **area** of a polygon is the number of square units enclosed by the polygon. To find the areas of parallelograms, triangles, or trapezoids, use the appropriate formulas.

parallelogram
$A = bh$

triangle
$A = \frac{1}{2}bh$

trapezoid
$A = \frac{1}{2}h(b_1 + b_2)$

Find the area of the shaded region in each figure.

8. Parallelogram

21 m
9 m
189 m²

9. Trapezoid

2 cm
4 cm
5 cm
14 cm²

10.

5 yd
2.5 yd
6.25 yd²

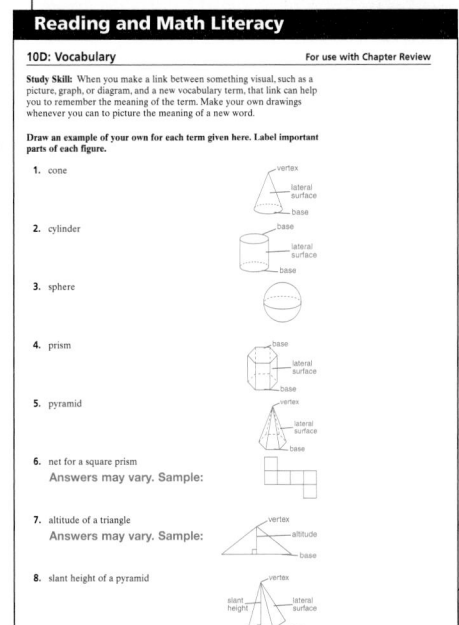

10-3 Objectives

▼ To find areas of circles (p. 532)

▼ To find areas of irregular figures that include parts of circles (p. 534)

To find the area of a circle, use the formula $A = \pi r^2$. Use 3.14 for π.

Find the area of each figure to the nearest square unit.

11.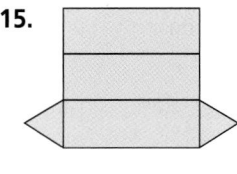
12.
13.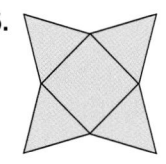
14.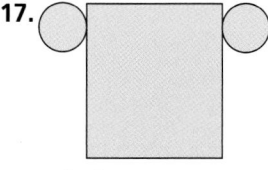

79 m²   201 mm²   57 m²   31 in.²

10-4 Objectives

▼ To identify common space figures (p. 539)

▼ To identify space figures from nets (p. 540)

Name **pyramids** and **prisms** by the shapes of their bases. A **cylinder** is a space figure with two circular bases. **Cones** have one circular base and one vertex. **Nets** are flat patterns for space figures.

Name the space figure represented by each net.

15.
16.
17.

triangular prism   square pyramid   cylinder

10-5 Objectives

▼ To find surface areas of prisms (p. 545)

▼ To find surface areas of cylinders (p. 547)

The **lateral area** of a prism is the sum of the areas of the lateral faces. The lateral area of a cylinder is the area of the curved surface. The **surface area** of a prism or a cylinder is the sum of the lateral area and the areas of the two bases.

To find surface area, use the appropriate formula.

prism   cylinder
L.A. = ph L.A. = $2\pi rh$
S.A. = L.A. + $2B$ S.A. = L.A. + $2B$

Find the surface area to the nearest square unit. Use 3.14 for π.

18. 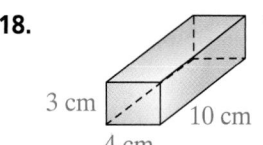 164 cm²
19. 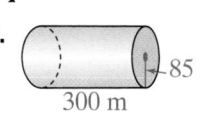 205,513 m²

20. 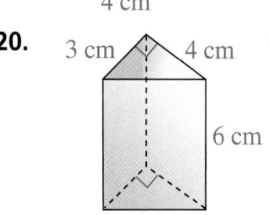 84 cm²
21. 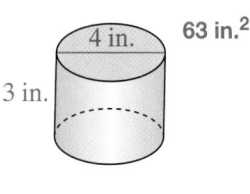 63 in.²

10-6 Objectives

▼ To find surface areas of pyramids (p. 552)

▼ To find surface areas of cones and spheres (p. 553)

For pyramids and cones, use **slant height** ℓ to find the lateral area. For a regular pyramid, if n is the number of lateral faces, you can find the area of one face and then multiply by n. The lateral area of a cone is the area of the curved surface. The surface area of a pyramid or a cone is the sum of the lateral area and the base area.

To find surface area, use the appropriate formula.

pyramid	cone	sphere
$L.A. = n\left(\frac{1}{2}b\ell\right)$	$L.A. = \pi r\ell$	
$S.A. = L.A. + B$	$S.A. = L.A. + B$	$S.A. = 4\pi r^2$

Find the surface area of each figure, to the nearest square unit.

22.	23.	24.	25.

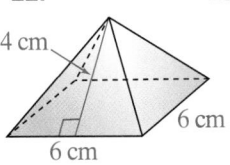
4 cm
6 cm

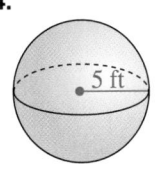
6 cm
3 cm

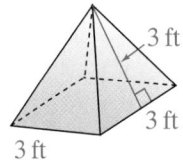
5 ft

3 ft
3 ft
3 ft

84 cm²   85 cm²   314 ft²   27 ft²

10-8 Objective

▼ To make a model (p. 562)

To solve some problems, make a model.

26. A gift box measures 6 in. along each edge. You cut a rectangular sheet of wrapping paper to get a single piece with which you can cover the box without overlapping. What are the smallest possible dimensions of the original sheet of wrapping paper? **24 in. by 18 in.**

27. A 12 m-by-15 m rectangular garden has a walk 1 m wide around it. Describe how you would find the area of the walk. **Find the area of the walk and garden, and then subtract the area of the garden.**

10-7 and 10-9 Objectives

▼ To find volumes of prisms (p. 557)

▼ To find volumes of cylinders (p. 558)

▼ To find volumes of cones and pyramids (p. 566)

▼ To find volumes of spheres (p. 567)

Volume is the measure of how much a space figure can hold.

To find volume, use the appropriate formula.

prisms and cylinders	pyramids and cones	spheres
$V = Bh$	$V = \frac{1}{3}Bh$	$V = \frac{4}{3}\pi r^3$

Find each volume to the nearest cubic unit.

28.	29.	30.	31.

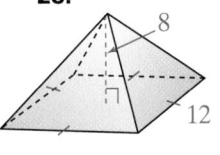
8
12

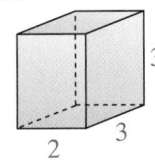
3
2
3

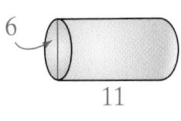
6
11

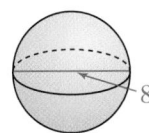
8

384 units³   18 units³   311 units³   268 units³

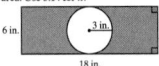
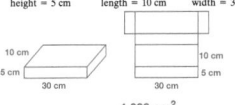

Resources

Teaching Resources
Ch. 10 Test, Forms A & B
Ch. 10 Alternative Assessment, Form C

Reaching All Students
Spanish Ch. 10 Test, Forms A & B
Spanish Ch. 10 Alternative Assessment, Form C

ASSESSMENT SYSTEM

Assessment Resources
• Ch. 10 Test, Forms A & B
• Ch. 10 Alternative Assessment, Form C
Computer Test Generator CD-ROM
• Instant Chapter Test™ for Ch. 10

www.PHSchool.com
Student Site
• Self-grading Chapter 10 Test
PH SuccessNet Teacher Center
• Resources

Plus  **TEXT**

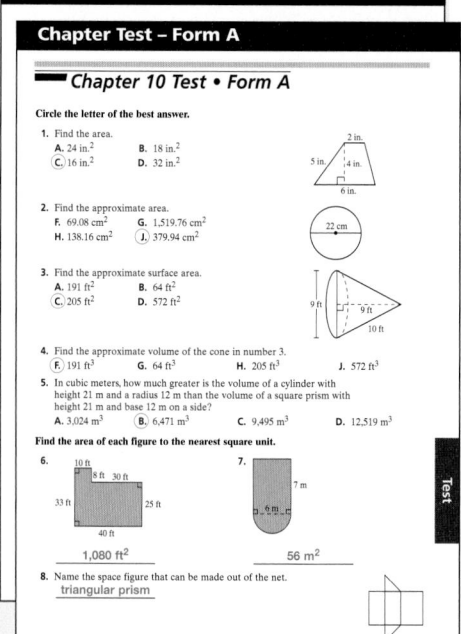

Chapter Test

Take It to the NET
Online chapter test at
www.PHSchool.com
Web Code: ada-1052

Use 3.14 for π as needed on this page.

Find the area of each figure.

1.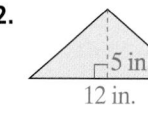
12 m²

2.
30 in.²

3. 6 yd
4. 78.5 ft²
21 yd²
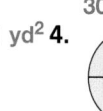 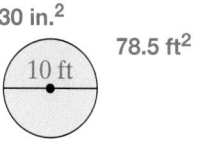

5.
12 m²

6.
4 m²

Find the missing measures.

7. circle 12.56
$d = 4$ cm
$A = \blacksquare$ cm²

8. triangle 14
$b = 7$ m
$h = 4$ m
$A = \blacksquare$ m²

Name the space figure for each net.

9.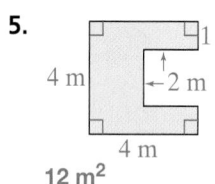
triangular pyramid

10.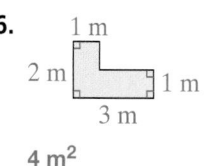
triangular prism

Find the surface area of each figure.

11.
12 m
10 m
340 m²

12.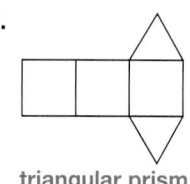
2 cm
4 cm
31.4 cm²

13.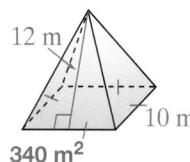
15 m
706.5 m²

14.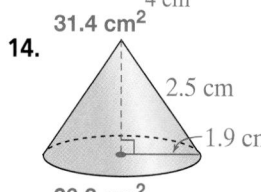
2.5 cm
1.9 cm
26.3 cm²

Find the volume of each figure to the nearest cubic unit.

15.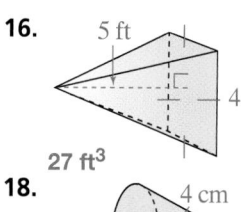
5 m
65 m³

16.
5 ft
4 ft
27 ft³

17.
2 in.
2 in.
4 in.
16 in.³

18.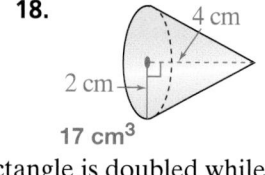
4 cm
2 cm
17 cm³

19. The height of a rectangle is doubled while the base is unchanged. How does this affect the area? Explain. **See margin.**

20. In cubic feet, how much greater is the volume of a cone with height 10 ft and radius 6 ft than the volume of a square pyramid with height 10 ft and base edge length 6 ft? **256.8 ft³**

21. The diameter of Mars is about 4,000 mi.
   a. Find the approximate surface area.
   b. Find the approximate volume.
   a–b. See below.

22. A box is 25.5 cm by 17 cm by 5 cm.
   a. How much dry dishwashing detergent can it hold? **2,167.5 cm³**
   b. Without overlap, how much cardboard is needed to make the box? **1,292 cm²**

23. **Writing in Math** How is the formula for volume of a prism like the formula for volume of a pyramid? How are the formulas different? **See margin.**

24. A rectangular piece of sheet metal measures 26 in. by 20 in. A square measuring 2 in. by 2 in. is cut out of each corner, and the sides are folded to form a box. What is the volume of the box? **704 in.³**

25. **Open-Ended** Draw a net for a rectangular prism. **Answers may vary. See margin.**

21a. 50,240,000 mi²   21b. 33,493,000,000 mi³

---

19. Since the formula for the area of a rectangle is $A = bh$, doubling the height doubles the area.

23. Both formulas use the general form $V = Bh$ where B is the area of the base, and h the height. The formula for the volume of a pyramid has a factor of $\frac{1}{3}$.

25. Sample:
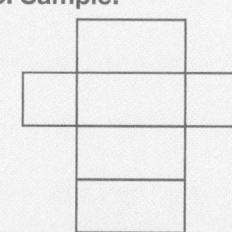

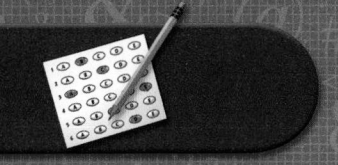

Multiple Choice

Choose the best answer.

1. The average nose has about 6,000,000 cells that detect odors. What is this number in scientific notation? **B**
   A. $6 \cdot 10^5$　　B. $6 \cdot 10^6$
   C. $6 \cdot 10^7$　　D. $6 \cdot 10^8$

2. Which equation represents the statement *The sum of twice a number and five times another number is 40?* **F**
   F. $40 = 2x + 5y$　　G. $5y = \frac{40}{2x}$
   H. $2x \cdot 5y = 40$　　I. $5y = \frac{1}{2}x + 40$

3. In which situation are two angles supplementary? **A**
   A. The sum of their measures is 180°.
   B. They share a vertex.
   C. The sum of their measures is 90°.
   D. They have the same measure.

4. What space figure can you form from the net? **H**
   F. square pyramid
   G. triangular pyramid
   H. triangular prism
   I. hexagonal prism

5. Figure A is a rectangle 10 in. long and 7.5 in. wide. Figure B is a parallelogram with height 12 in. and base length 7.5 in. Which statement is true? **B**
   A. area of A > area of B
   B. area of A < area of B
   C. area of A = area of B
   D. cannot be determined

Gridded Response

Find each area.

6.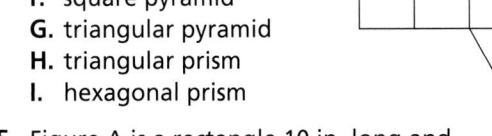

7.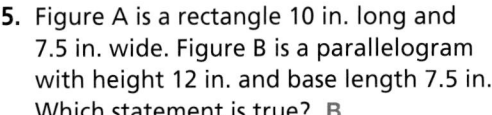

Find each area to the nearest square unit.

8. 452
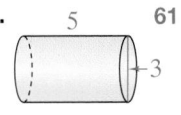

9. 113

Find the surface area of each figure to the nearest square unit.

10. 288
11. 5　61
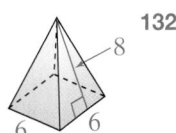 3

12. 21.2　**1,095**
13. 132
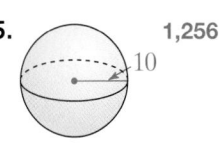 8

14. 955
15. 1,256

Short Response

Find the volume of each figure, to the nearest cubic unit. Show your work. 16–21. See back of book.

16. 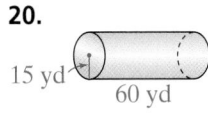 6 mm　8.5 mm　10 mm

17. 8 m　5 m　12 m

18. 75 ft　40 ft

19. 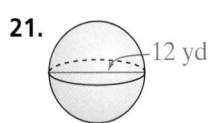 5.5 m　8 m　8 m

20. 15 yd　60 yd

21. 12 yd

Extended Response

22. A cylinder has diameter 3 cm and height 6 cm. **(a)** Draw and label a net. **(b)** Find the surface area of the cylinder to the nearest square centimeter. **(c)** Find the volume.
See back of book.

Chapter 10 Test Prep **575**

Cumulative Review

Chapter 10 Cumulative Review

Circle the letter of the best answer.

1. $3(x + y) - x + y =$
   A. $2x + 2y$　B. $2x + 4y$　C. $4x + 4y$　D. $4x + 2y$
2. Estimate 79.783×31.6691.
   F. 240　G. 2,400　H. 24,000　J. 240,000
3. In standard notation, 9.03×10^7 is
   A. 9,030,000,000　B. 9,030,000　C. 90,300,000　D. 903,000,000
4. Which equation describes *four less than twice a number is negative eight?*
   F. $2x - 4 = -8$　G. $4 - 2x = -8$　H. $2(x - 4) = -8$　J. $4x - 2 = -8$
5. Which fraction is equal to 0.125?
   A. $\frac{1}{6}$　B. $\frac{1}{4}$　C. $\frac{1}{12}$　D. $\frac{1}{8}$
6. Which equation has y-intercept -3?
   F. $3x - y = 3$　G. $x - 3y = 3$　H. $x + 3y = 3$　J. $3x + 3 = y$
7. The measure of the supplement of a 71° angle is
   A. 19°　B. 17°　C. 109°　D. 107°
8. Find the circumference of a circle with radius 18 cm.
   F. 18π cm　G. 324π cm　H. 36π cm　J. $1,296\pi$ cm
9. What space figure can you form from the net at the right?
   A. square pyramid　B. triangular prism
   C. triangular pyramid　D. square prism
10. Figure A is a rectangle 8 in. long and 6.5 in. high. Figure B is a triangle 8 in. long and 6.5 in. high. Which statement is true about the areas of Figures A and B?
   F. $A = B$　G. $A < B$　H. $A = \frac{1}{4}B$　J. $A = 2B$
11. A rectangle has a perimeter of 110 ft and a length of 23 ft. What is its area?
   A. $2,530$ ft²　B. 32 ft²　C. $2,001$ ft²　D. 736 ft²

Find the area of each figure to the nearest tenth.

12. 14 in.　7 in.　15 in.　26 in.
91 in.²
13. 30 ft
706.5 ft²
14. 8 cm　7 cm　11 cm
66.5 cm²

Item	1	2	3	4	5	6	7	8	9	10	11	12	13	14	15	16	17	18	19	20	21	22
Lesson	4-9	8-2	9-2	10-4	10-1	10-2	10-2	10-3	10-3	10-5	10-5	10-5	10-6	10-6	10-6	10-7	10-7	10-9	10-9	10-7	10-9	10-5

Playing Fields

In this activity, students use information in a table and apply their knowledge of area to calculate and compare areas of different sports playing fields.

Activating Prior Knowledge

Ask students which sports they play or have watched in person or on TV. Discuss similarities and differences among the sports shown on these pages. **Answers may vary. Sample: Similarities: two teams compete, uniforms, field with special markings, timed playing periods, score by getting object into specific place, penalties for breaking rules; Differences: unique kind of ball or puck, number of players, playing periods, playing fields, scoring methods and points**

Teaching Notes

Teaching Tip

Have a volunteer read the introductory paragraph. Ask: *Why does every sport have rules and officials to enforce them?*
Answers may vary. Sample: to make sure players do not cheat or injure each other

Visual Learners

Take students to look at the school soccer field or basketball court. Have them measure the diameter of a circle on the field or court and calculate its radius and area.

Inclusion

Examine the table with students. Note the pictures of the different kinds of balls and the puck. Discuss why the correct solutions to Exercises 2, 3, 5, 6, 7, and 8 depend in part on the answers to Exercise 1. **Answers may vary. Sample: In Exercise 1, you calculate the area of each field. In the following exercises, you must use the field areas to figure out comparisons and to find partial areas.**

576

Playing Fields

Applying Area Have you ever played a team sport such as soccer, basketball, or ice hockey? If so, you had to follow the rules of the game. You probably found that these include rules about your appearance and the equipment you use, as well as other game equipment such as goals, backboards, or hockey pucks. There are even rules for the space in which you play. One purpose of these rules is to provide all players with an equal chance of success.

Football Gridiron

Parallel lines run 5 yd apart from goal line to goal line along the playing area of a football field. The playing area, or gridiron, is 300 ft long.

Take It to the NET For more information about sports, go to **www.PHSchool.com**.
Web Code: ade-1053

576

Hockey Rink

A hockey rink uses quarter circles with 28-ft radii to keep the puck from getting caught in the corners.

Basketball Court

A basketball court can be up to 2 yd shorter than regulation size and up to 4 yd narrower. Its dimensions must remain in proportion.

Soccer Field

Each soccer team plays both ends of the field during a game, switching goals after the first 45-min half.

Activity

1. Copy the table. Find the area of each field.
   1–8. See margin.

For Exercises 2 and 3, how many times the area of the smaller field is the area of the larger field?

2. a soccer field and a football field

3. a professional basketball court and a junior high basketball court

4. <u>Writing in Math</u> Why do you think the basketball courts are different sizes?

For Exercises 5–7, on each field, how much playing area is outside the indicated part? Round to the nearest whole number where necessary.

5. a professional basketball court, outside the two rectangular free-throw lanes, each 19 ft by 14 ft

6. **a.** a soccer field, outside two penalty areas, each 44 yd wide and 18 yd deep, in front of each goal
   b. the same field, outside the two penalty areas and the 10-yd-radius center circle

7. a hockey rink, outside its five face-off circles, each with a radius of 15 ft

8. In the New York Giants' football stadium, the grass surface is 433 ft long and 269 ft wide. What is the area of the grass surface outside the playing field?

Playing Fields

Sport		Length	Width	Area
Basketball				
Professional and college		94 ft	50 ft	■
High school		82 ft	46 ft	■
Junior high school		74 ft	42 ft	■
Football (with end zones)		120 yd	$53\frac{1}{3}$ yd	■
Ice hockey		200 ft	85 ft	■
Soccer (maximum)		130 yd	100 yd	■

577

Chapter 11 Right Triangles in Algebra

Chapter at a Glance

11-1
Square Roots and Irrational Numbers
pp. 580–583

Objectives
- Finding Square Roots
- Classifying Real Numbers

NCTM Standards
1, 2, 3, 6, 8, 9

New Vocabulary
perfect square, square root, irrational number

Local Standards

11-2
The Pythagorean Theorem
pp. 584–589

Objectives
- Using the Pythagorean Theorem
- Identifying Right Triangles

New Vocabulary
legs, hypotenuse

Material
graph paper

NCTM Standards
1, 2, 3, 4, 6, 8, 9, 10

Local Standards

11-3
Distance and Midpoint Formulas
pp. 592–596

Objectives
- Finding Distance
- Finding the Midpoint

New Vocabulary
distance, midpoint

NCTM Standards
2, 3, 4, 10

Local Standards

 **Checkpoint Quiz 1**

11-4 Problem Solving
Write a Proportion
pp. 598–601

Objective
- Writing a Proportion

NCTM Standards
2, 3, 4, 6, 9, 10

Local Standards

11-5
Special Right Triangles
pp. 602–606

Objectives
- Using 45°-45°-90° Triangles
- Using 30°-60°-90° Triangles

NCTM Standards
1, 2, 3, 6, 8, 9, 10

Local Standards

11-6
Sine, Cosine, and Tangent Ratios
pp. 608–612

Objectives
- Finding Ratios in Right Triangles
- Using Ratios to Solve Problems

New Vocabulary
trigonometry, trigonometric ratio, sine, cosine, tangent

NCTM Standards
2, 3, 4, 6, 8, 9, 10

Local Standards

 Checkpoint Quiz 2

11-7
Angles of Elevation and Depression
pp. 614–618

Objectives
- Angles of Elevation
- Angles of Depression

New Vocabulary
angle of elevation, angle of depression

NCTM Standards
2, 3, 4, 6, 8, 9, 10

Local Standards

Correlation to Standardized Tests

Lesson	NAEP	Terra Nova		ITBS	SAT10	Local Test
		CAT/6	CTBS			
11-1	N2d					
11-2	G3d		■			
11-3	M1k					
11-4	N4c					
11-5	G3d					
11-6						
11-7						

NAEP National Assessment of Educational Progress
    N = Number Sense, Properties, and Operations
    M = Measurement
    G = Geometry and Spatial Sense
    D = Data Analysis, Statistics and Probability
    A = Algebra and Functions

CAT/6 California Achievement Test, 6th Ed.
CTBS Comprehensive Test of Basic Skills
ITBS Iowa Test of Basic Skills, Form M
SAT10 Stanford Achievement Test, 10th Ed.

NCTM STANDARDS 2000

1	Number and Operations	6	Problem Solving
2	Algebra	7	Reasoning and Proof
3	Geometry	8	Communication
4	Measurement	9	Connections
5	Data Analysis and Probability	10	Representation

Pacing Options

This chart suggests pacing for only the core lessons and their parts. It is provided as a possible guide. It will help you determine how much time you have in your schedule to cover other components, such as the features, chapter projects, Chapter Review, and Chapter Test.

Day	Traditional 45-minute class periods	Two-Year 45-minute class periods	Block 90-minute class periods
1	11-1 ▼ ▼	11-1 ▼	11-1 ▼ ▼ / 11-2 ▼ ▼
2	11-2 ▼	11-1 ▼	11-3 ▼ ▼ / 11-4 ▼
3	11-2 ▼	11-1 ▼	11-5 ▼ ▼
4	11-3 ▼ ▼	11-2 ▼	11-6 ▼ ▼
5	11-4 ▼	11-2 ▼	11-7 ▼ ▼
6	11-5 ▼ ▼	11-2 ▼	
7	11-6 ▼ ▼	11-2 ▼	
8	11-7 ▼ ▼	11-3 ▼	
9		11-3 ▼	
10		11-3 ▼	
11		11-4 ▼	
12		11-4 ▼	
13		11-5 ▼	
14		11-5 ▼	
15		11-5 ▼	
16		11-6 ▼	
17		11-6 ▼	
18		11-6 ▼	
19		11-7 ▼	
20		11-7 ▼	
21		11-7 ▼	
22			
23			
24			

Math Background

Skills Trace

BEFORE Chapter 11

Students may have been introduced to some of the basic ideas in this chapter in previous courses, but they were not developed in as much depth as they are here.

DURING Chapter 11

This chapter introduces square roots and irrational numbers, which are used in applications of the Pythagorean Theorem and other relationships for right triangles.

AFTER Chapter 11

The ideas in this chapter are reviewed throughout the remainder of this course. The ideas and formulas developed here are used both in Algebra 1 and Geometry.

11-1 Square Roots and Irrational Numbers

You read the expression 3^2 as "three squared" because a number used twice as a factor gives the area of a square whose sides have lengths equal to that number, that is, $3 \cdot 3 = 3^2$.

Area $= 3^2$ square units $= 3^2$ units^2

3

3

The inverse of squaring a number is *finding the square root*. If, for example, you know that the area of a square is 25 square units, to find the side of that square, you find the positive square root of 25 (written $\sqrt{25}$).

You use the *radical sign* (from the Latin word *radix*, meaning "root") when you want the nonnegative root. Since $(-5)(-5)$ also equals 25, -5 is a square root of 25, but $\sqrt{25} = 5$. The square of an integer (such as $3^2 = 9$ or $(-5)^2 = 25$) is called a *perfect square*.

A rational number can be written as the ratio of two integers, $\frac{a}{b}$, where $b \neq 0$. A number that cannot be expressed as the ratio of integers, such as π or $\sqrt{2}$, is *irrational*. The square root of an integer that is not a perfect square, such as $\sqrt{7}$, $\sqrt{101}$, or $\sqrt{33}$, is irrational.

An irrational number can be expressed as a decimal that does not end or repeat a set of digits. Although 5.26226222622226 . . . shows a predictable pattern, it is an irrational number because it never ends and never shows a repeating pattern.

11-2 The Pythagorean Theorem

The longest side of a right triangle, which is always opposite the right angle, is called the *hypotenuse*. The other two sides, which form the sides of the right angle, are called the *legs*.

If the hypotenuse of a right triangle is c and the legs are a and b, then $a^2 + b^2 = c^2$. This relationship is called the *Pythagorean Theorem*, and it is true for any right triangle. The *Converse of the Pythagorean Theorem* is also true: If $a^2 + b^2 = c^2$, where a, b, and c are the sides of a triangle, then you can be sure that the triangle is a right triangle.

11-3 Distance and Midpoint Formulas

One application of the Pythagorean Theorem is finding the distance between two points whose coordinates you know; for example, the points (x_1, y_1) and (x_2, y_2) are graphed here.

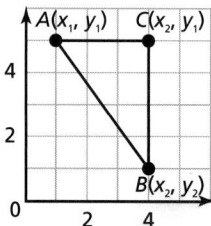

By drawing the right triangle shown, with point C at (x_2, y_1), you can solve for d, the distance between points A and B, with the following steps.

$(AB)^2 = (AC)^2 + (CB)^2$ by the Pythagorean Theorem.

$(d)^2 = (x_2 - x_1)^2 + (y_2 - y_1)^2$

$d = \sqrt{(x_2 - x_1)^2 + (y_2 - y_1)^2}$

This is the *Distance Formula* for finding d, the distance between two points, (x_1, y_1) and (x_2, y_2).

11-4 Write a Proportion

Proportions provide the mathematical models for proportional thinking. If a post appears to be "half again" as tall as another post, then the proportion $\frac{H}{h} = \frac{1.5}{1}$ allows you to find the height of either post if you know the height of the other. If one triangle appears to be similar to another, proportions allow you to find the lengths of some sides if you know the lengths of others.

11-5 Special Right Triangles

You get special results when you use the Pythagorean Theorem with certain special right triangles. For example, in an isosceles right triangle, the two acute angles each measure 45°. In any 45° right triangle, if each leg is x units long, the length of the hypotenuse is equal to $x\sqrt{2}$.

$h^2 = x^2 + x^2$ the Pythagorean Theorem

$h^2 = 2x^2$ Add.

$h = \sqrt{2x^2}$ Find the square root of each side.

To simplify $\sqrt{2x^2}$, use the Rule for Multiplying Square Roots, which says that if $a \geq 0$ and $b \geq 0$, then $\sqrt{ab} = \sqrt{a} \cdot \sqrt{b}$. So, $\sqrt{2x^2}$ simplifies to $\sqrt{2} \cdot \sqrt{x^2}$, or $\sqrt{2}x$, and $h = x\sqrt{2}$ by the Commutative Property of Multiplication.

Another special right triangle is the 30°-60°-90° triangle. In every 30°-60°-90° triangle, the side *opposite* the 30° angle is one-half the length of the hypotenuse.

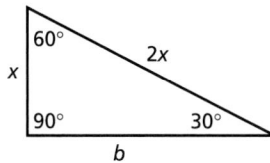

Solving for b, the third side, which is opposite the 60° angle, gives the result $b = x\sqrt{3}$. (The steps are given in the text.)

In any 30°-60°-90° triangle, if the leg opposite the 30° angle is x, then the hypotenuse is $2x$ and the longer leg is $x\sqrt{3}$.

11-6 / 11-7 Sine, Cosine, and Tangent Ratios; Angles of Elevation and Depression

There are other relationships that are always true in right triangles, and these are part of the branch of mathematics called *trigonometry*.

Any two right triangles with a common acute angle are similar. This means that for all right triangles containing a given angle A, the ratio of side a to side c will be constant, as will the other ratios of the sides.

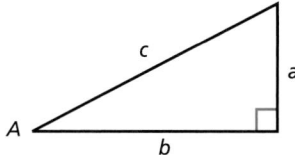

There are six *trigonometric* ratios defined in terms of angle A, the hypotenuse (c), the side of the triangle that is opposite angle A (a), and the side that is adjacent to angle A (b). This text introduces three of these six ratios.

$$sine \angle A = \frac{\text{side opposite}}{\text{hypotenuse}} = \frac{a}{c}$$

$$cosine \angle A = \frac{\text{side adjacent}}{\text{hypotenuse}} = \frac{b}{c}$$

$$tangent \angle A = \frac{\text{side opposite}}{\text{side adjacent}} = \frac{a}{b}$$

These ratios are usually abbreviated as *sin A*, *cos A*, and *tan A*.

You can use a scientific calculator or a table of trigonometric ratios to find the values of these ratios for any given angle. You can use these ratios to indirectly find the lengths of sides or the measures of angles in right triangles. You can use these trigonometric ratios to solve real-world problems involving *angles of elevation* or *angles of depression*.

Additional Professional Development Opportunities

Chapter 11 Math Background notes:
pp. 581, 585, 593, 599, 603, 609, 615

Professional Development, Content Facilitator Guide: Pre-Algebra, Chapter 11

Additional resources available from SkyLight Professional Development: On-site courses, workshops, summer institutes. Online courses and chat rooms. Videocassettes and books. Visit www.skylightedu.com.

Ongoing Assessment and Intervention

The *Prentice Hall Pre-Algebra* program provides many options for assessment in the Student Edition, Teacher's Edition, and teaching resources. From these options you may choose instructional materials that are appropriate for your students and support your district's curriculum requirements.

Daily Assessment

 Instant Check System™ in Chapter 11

Allows students to check their own learning before, during, and after each lesson.

Diagnosing Readiness before the chapter (p. 578)

Check Skills You'll Need exercises in each lesson (pp. 580, 584, 592, 598, 602, 608, 614)

Check Understanding questions with each Example (pp. 580, 581, 585, 586, 593, 594, 599, 603, 604, 609, 610, 615, 616)

Checkpoint Quiz (pp. 596, 612)

Formal Assessment

In Chapter 11 and Additional Resources

Assesses student progress throughout the *Pre-Algebra* text and with blackline masters and CD-ROM.

Student Edition
- Chapter 11 Review, with Vocabulary Skills and Concepts Review, pp. 621–623
- Chapter 11 Test, p. 624

Assessment Resources   *Spanish versions available.*
- Checkpoint Quizzes 1 & 2
- Chapter Test, Forms A & B
- Chapter Alternative Assessment

 Computer Test Generator CD-ROM
- Instant Chapter Tests™ — pre-made tests with items that vary every time you print.
- Online Testing allows you to give tests online and receive progress reports.
- Diagnose readiness with questions on prerequisite skills.
- Prepare students by making tests based on standardized test objectives.

Algebra Readiness Tests
- Includes Basic Skills Tests and Concept-Readiness Tests.
- Assess understanding of skills and concepts needed for success in algebra.

Standardized Test Preparation

 Test Prep in Chapter 11

Teaches students strategies and gives them practice with all the test item formats they will encounter on high-stakes tests.

Test Prep exercises in each lesson (pp. 583, 589, 596, 601, 606, 612, 618)

Test-Taking Strategies (p. 620: Using a Variable)

Test Prep (p. 625: Reading Comprehension)

PRENTICE HALL
ASSESSMENT SYSTEM

Provides a three-step approach to preparing students for high-stakes, national, and state exams.

1 Diagnose & Prescribe   **2 Review & Reteach**

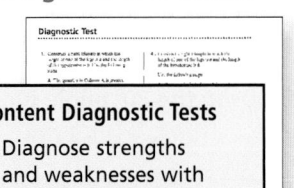

Content Diagnostic Tests
- Diagnose strengths and weaknesses with ongoing benchmark tests.
- Prescribe individualized reteaching opportunities.

Skills and Concepts Review
- Provides reteaching worksheets with instruction and practice for each skill.
- Includes course prerequisite skills.

3 Practice & Assess

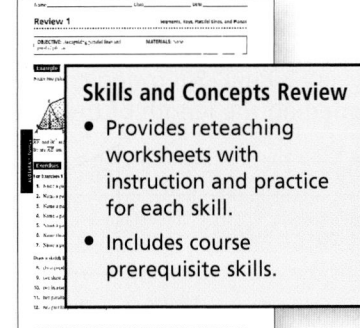
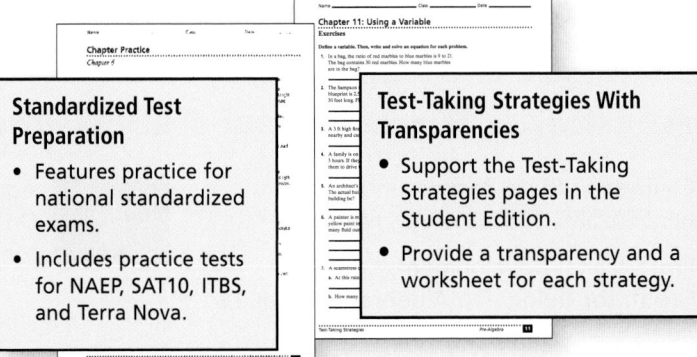

Standardized Test Preparation
- Features practice for national standardized exams.
- Includes practice tests for NAEP, SAT10, ITBS, and Terra Nova.

Test-Taking Strategies With Transparencies
- Support the Test-Taking Strategies pages in the Student Edition.
- Provide a transparency and a worksheet for each strategy.

Reaching All Students

The textbook, the iText, and other technology components provide numerous opportunities to reach students of various ability levels and learning styles. Each Teacher's Edition lesson suggests how you can help all your students be successful and understand the mathematics in Chapter 11.

Below Level

Student Edition
- Diagnosing Readiness*: p. 578
- Check Skills You'll Need*: pp. 580, 584, 592, 598, 602, 608, 614

Reteaching
Chapter 11 Grab & Go™ File: pp. 8–14

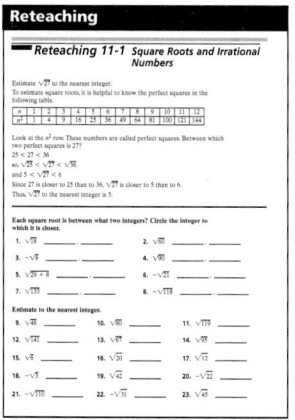

* Can be used with all ability levels to ensure mastery of prerequisite skills.

Advanced Learners

Student Edition
- Challenge exercises: pp. 583, 588, 596, 601, 605, 606, 611, 618
- Extension: pp. 590, 607, 613

Enrichment
Chapter 11 Grab & Go™ File: pp. 15–21

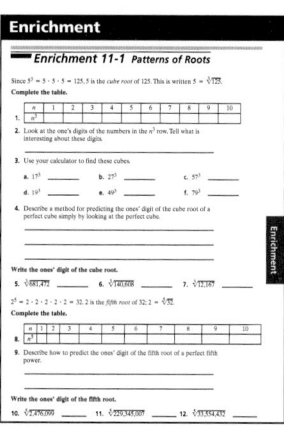

Problem Solving

Student Edition
- Strategies: pp. 598–601
- Real-World Problem Solving: pp. 581, 586, 598, 603, 610, 614, 615, 616

Guided Problem Solving Masters
Chapter 11: pp. 92–98

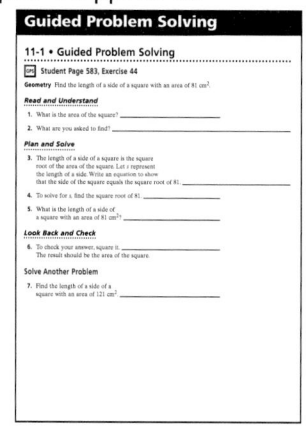

Reading and Math Literacy

Student Edition
- Vocabulary: pp. 579, 621, plus in most lessons
- Reading Math: pp. 580, 593, 609, 616, 617, 619, 621
- Writing in Math: pp. 582, 588, 596, 597, 605, 611, 617, 624
- Illustrated Glossary: pp. 782–826

Reading and Math Literacy Masters
Chapter 11: pp. 41–44

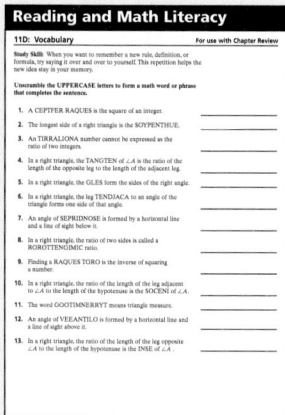

English Learners

Student Edition
- English/Spanish Illustrated Glossary: pp. 782–826

Workbook and Masters
Spanish Practice Workbook: pp. 92–98
Spanish Reading and Math Literacy Masters: pp. 41–44

Learning Styles

Student Edition
- Investigation: pp. 584, 608
- DK Activities: pp. 626–627
- Chapter Project: p. 743

Activity Masters
Hands-On Activities: 16, 36
Technology Activities: 28, 29, 30, 31

Program Resources

	Resources in Grab & Go™ Files				Resources for Reaching All Students				Spanish Resources			Transparencies				Prentice Hall Presentation Pro CD-ROM
	Practice	Reteach	Enrich	Checkpt Quiz	Reading & Math Literacy	Technology Activities	Hands-On Activities	Guided Problem Solving	Practice	Reading & Math Literacy	Checkpt Quiz	Skills Check	Additional Examples	Answers to Exercises	Lesson Quiz	
11-1	■	■	■		■	■		■	■			■	■	■	■	■
11-2	■	■	■		■		■	■	■			■	■	■	■	■
11-3	■	■	■	■	■			■	■		■	■	■	■	■	■
11-4	■	■	■			■	■	■	■			■	■	■	■	■
11-5	■	■	■					■	■			■	■	■	■	■
11-6	■	■	■	■			■	■	■			■	■	■	■	■
11-7	■	■	■						■			■	■	■	■	■
For the Chapter	Chapter Projects, Chapter Tests, Alternative Assessment, Cumulative Review, Cumulative Assessment				**On Web site only:** Home Activities, Algebra Readiness Puzzles, Interdisciplinary Activities				Spanish Chapter Tests, Alternative Assessment, Cumulative Review, Cumulative Assessment			Classroom Aid Transparencies				

Presentation Assistant Plus!

Also available for use with the chapter:
- Practice Workbook
- Solution Key
- MathNotes folder
- For additional online and technology resources, see below.
- For teacher support and access to student Web site materials, use Web Code adk-5500.

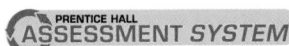
PRENTICE HALL ASSESSMENT SYSTEM

Program assessment and test preparation, all in one place.
See page 578E.

Skills Intervention Kit

A *complete* system for the student who is struggling with course-level work

How to Use With Chapter 11

11-2	Whole Numbers
11-3	Geometry
11-4	Ratio, Proportion, and Percent
11-6, 11-7	Operations/Fractions

Online Intervention

Integrated within the iText, this online intervention system includes diagnostic tests and prescribed remediation, plus reports to track student mastery.

Technology

iTEXT Online and on CD-ROM

Complete Interactive Student Text online and on CD-ROM—with instant-feedback assessment, tutorial help, dynamic activities, instructional and real-world videos, audio, and additional practice.

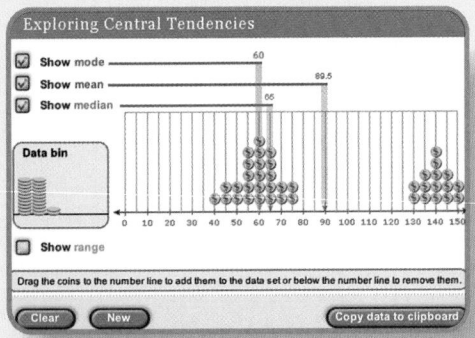

www.PHSchool.com For Students

Use Web Codes for easy access to online activities, chapter projects, self-grading lesson quizzes, chapter tests, vocabulary quizzes, updated data sources, graphing calculator procedures, and more.

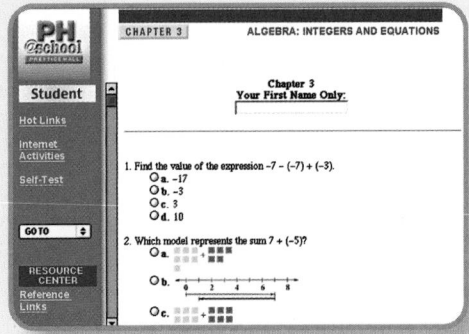

PH SuccessNet For Teachers

Online lesson planning with built-in state correlations, all the teaching resources, complete reference library, your own calendar and Teacher Web page, professional development, and more.

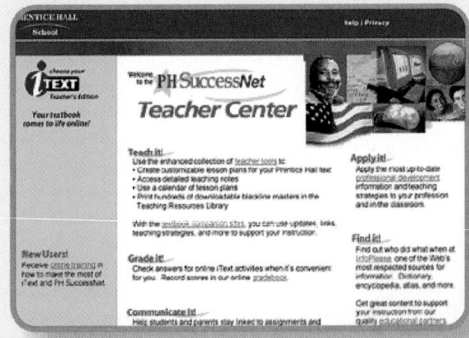

Presentation Assistant Plus!

The Prentice Hall *Presentation Assistant Plus!* provides you with the material you need to teach a lesson from beginning to end. Two easy-to-use formats—Transparencies and CD-ROM—allow you to present a lesson the way you are most comfortable.

Transparencies

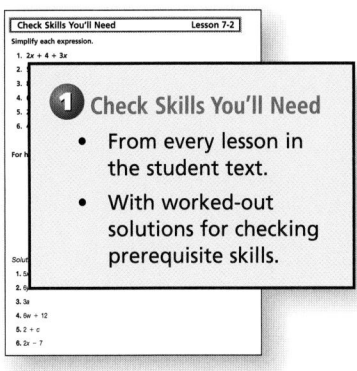

1 Check Skills You'll Need
- From every lesson in the student text.
- With worked-out solutions for checking prerequisite skills.

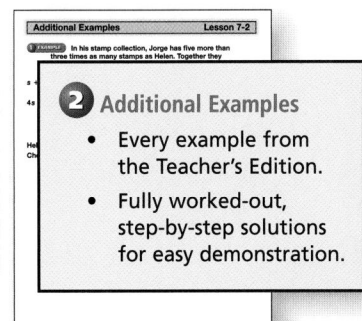

2 Additional Examples
- Every example from the Teacher's Edition.
- Fully worked-out, step-by-step solutions for easy demonstration.

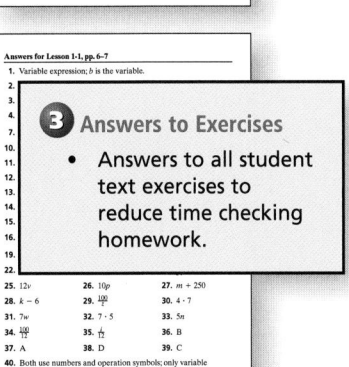

3 Answers to Exercises
- Answers to all student text exercises to reduce time checking homework.

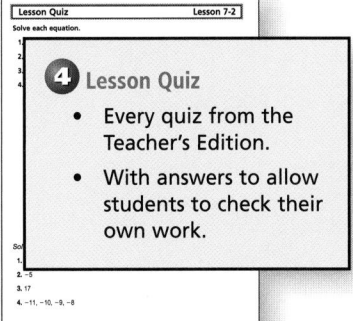

4 Lesson Quiz
- Every quiz from the Teacher's Edition.
- With answers to allow students to check their own work.

 Throughout the Teacher's Edition, this symbol indicates material that is available in the Presentation Assistant Plus!

PowerPoint Prentice Hall Presentation Pro CD-ROM

- Includes all Transparencies as PowerPoint® presentations.
- Conveniently organized by lesson so you can easily **1** Introduce, **2** Teach, **3** Check Homework, and **4** Assess each lesson.
- Animated examples allow step-by-step instruction at your own pace.
- Easy to edit so you can create custom presentations.

Teaching Chapter 11 Using Presentation Assistant Plus!

	1 Introduce	**2 Teach**	**3 Check Homework**	**4 Assess**
	Check Skills You'll Need	Additional Examples	Student Edition Answers	Lesson Quiz
11-1	p. 93	pp. 150–151	✔	p. 93
11-2	p. 94	pp. 152–153	✔	p. 94
11-3	p. 95	pp. 154–156	✔	p. 95
11-4	p. 96	p. 157	✔	p. 96
11-5	p. 97	pp. 158–159	✔	p. 97
11-6	p. 98	pp. 160–161	✔	p. 98
11-7	p. 99	pp. 162–164	✔	p. 99

 Prentice Hall Presentation Pro

CD-ROM with dynamic Powerpoint® presentations for every lesson. Helps you introduce and develop concepts, check homework, and assess progress. Part of Presentation Assistant Plus! *(See above.)*

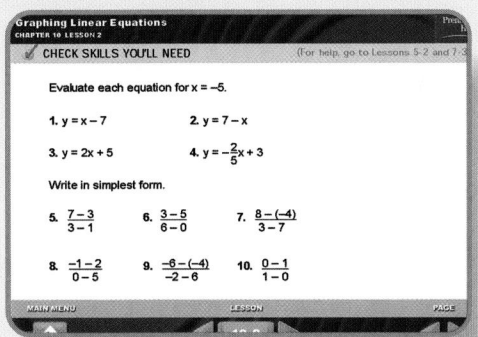

 Computer Test Generator

CD-ROM to create practice sheets and tests for course objectives and standardized tests. Includes Instant Chapter Tests™, online testing, and student reports. Part of the PH Assessment System. *(See page 578E.)*

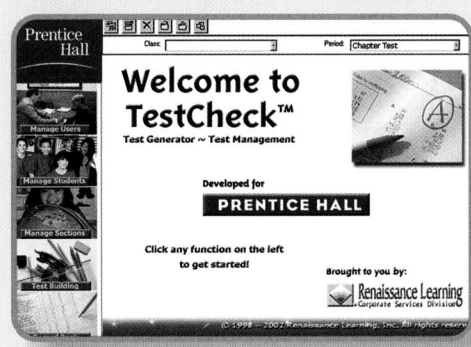

 Resource Pro® with Planning Express®

CD-ROM with a lesson planning tool that allows you to import state and local objectives. Includes electronic versions of all the teaching resources.

Right Triangles in Algebra

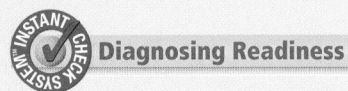

Diagnosing Readiness

Students will find the answers to these exercises in the back of their textbooks.

Prescribing Intervention
For intervention, direct students to:

Understanding Coordinates
Lesson 1-10: Example 1;
Exercises 7–12.
Extra Practice, p. 744.

**Simplifying Numbers
With Exponents**
Lesson 4-2: Example 2;
Exercises 7–12.
Extra Practice, p. 747.

Solving Proportions
Lesson 6-2: Example 1;
Exercises 1–12.
Extra Practice, p. 749.

Where You've Been

- In Chapter 7, you learned to solve two-step equations and inequalities, multi-step equations, equations with variables on both sides, and to transform formulas.

- In Chapter 9, you learned about points, lines, and planes; congruence, constructions, translations, symmetry, and reflections.

- In Chapter 10, you learned to calculate areas, surface areas, and volumes.

iTEXT Instant self-check
online and on CD-ROM

Diagnosing Readiness

(For help, go to the lesson in green.)

Understanding Coordinates (Lesson 1-10)

Name the point with the given coordinates.

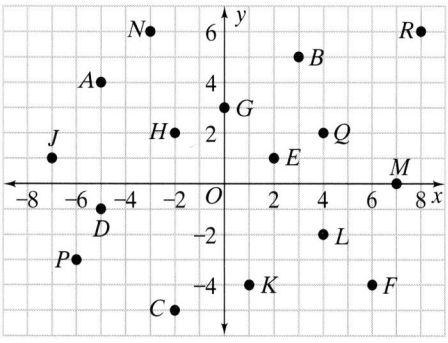

1. $(0, 3)$ **G**   **2.** $(1, -4)$ **K**   **3.** $(-2, 2)$**H**

4. $(-5, -1)$ **D** **5.** $(3, 5)$ **B**   **6.** $(6, -4)$**F**

Write the coordinates of each point.

7. A **(−5, 4)**   **8.** E **(2, 1)**   **9.** M **(7, 0)**

10. J **(−7, 1)** **11.** L **(4, −2)** **12.** P **(−6, −3)**

Simplifying Numbers With Exponents (Lesson 4-2)

Simplify each expression.

13. 10^2 100   **14.** 6^2 36   **15.** 2^2 4   **16.** 9^2 81   **17.** 11^2 121

18. 0.2^2 0.04   **19.** 7^2 49   **20.** 2.3^2 5.29   **21.** 4^2 16   **22.** 5^2 25

Solving Proportions (Lesson 6-2)

Solve each proportion.

23. $\frac{1}{3} = \frac{a}{12}$ 4   **24.** $\frac{h}{5} = \frac{20}{25}$ 4   **25.** $\frac{24}{6} = \frac{4}{x}$ 1   **26.** $\frac{2}{7} = \frac{c}{35}$ 10

27. $\frac{e}{5} = \frac{32}{80}$ 2   **28.** $\frac{18}{g} = \frac{3}{10}$ 60   **29.** $\frac{4}{11} = \frac{28}{m}$ 77   **30.** $\frac{21}{13} = \frac{42}{a}$ 26

31. $\frac{2}{15} = \frac{c}{75}$ 10   **32.** $\frac{1}{4} = \frac{8}{x}$ 32   **33.** $\frac{13}{p} = \frac{39}{51}$ 17   **34.** $\frac{x}{20} = \frac{40}{100}$ 8

Right Triangles in Algebra

LESSONS

Key Vocabulary

- angle of depression (p. 616)
- angle of elevation (p. 614)
- cosine (p. 608)
- distance (p. 592)
- hypotenuse (p. 584)
- irrational number (p. 581)
- legs (p. 584)
- midpoint (p. 594)
- perfect square (p. 580)
- sine (p. 608)
- square root (p. 580)
- tangent (p. 608)
- trigonometric ratio (p. 608)
- trigonometry (p. 608)

Where You're Going

In this chapter, you will learn how to

- Find the square roots of numbers.
- Find the missing measures of right triangles.
- Use the Distance and Midpoint Formulas.
- Solve a problem by writing a proportion.

Real-World Snapshots Applying what you learn, on pages 626–627 you will apply ratios to solve problems about proportions in rectangles.

Chapter 11 Overview

Students begin this chapter by finding square roots and classifying real numbers. They use the Pythagorean Theorem and its converse to find missing sides of right triangles and to determine whether triangles are right triangles. Students find the distance between two points and the midpoint of a segment using the Distance and Midpoint Formulas. They use proportions to solve real-world problems that can be modeled with similar triangles. Students learn the special relationships between the sides of 45°-45°-90° triangles and 30°-60°-90° triangles and use the relationships to find missing sides of these triangles. They use the trigonometric ratios sine, cosine, and tangent, and angles of elevation and depression to find missing sides of right triangles.

Activating Prior Knowledge

Students apply the order of operations learned in Lesson 4-2. Ask students to simplify $(6 - 1)^2 + (9 - 3)^2$. **61**

Reading Math

- Reading for Problem Solving, p. 619
- **Vocabulary** A complete list of terms, plus vocabulary exercises, appears in the Chapter Review on p. 621.
- **Illustrated Glossary** Examples for each vocabulary term, plus definitions in both English and Spanish, appear starting on p. 782.

Test-Taking Strategies

Using a Variable, p. 620

Real-World Problem Solving

Strategy: Write a Proportion, pp. 598–601
DK Real-World Snapshots: Applying Ratios, pp. 626–627
Chapter Project: Tree Angles, p. 743

www.PHSchool.com

Internet support includes:
- Self-grading Vocabulary and Chapter 11 Tests
- Activity Masters
- Chapter Project support
- Chapter Planner
- Chapter 11 Resources

Plus  **579**

Lesson Preview

✓ **Check Skills You'll Need**

Exponents
Lesson 4-2: Example 2;
Exercises 7–12.
Extra Practice, p. 747.

Lesson Resources

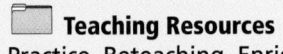 **Teaching Resources**
Practice, Reteaching, Enrichment

 **Reaching All Students**
Practice Workbook 11-1
Spanish Practice Workbook 11-1
Reading and Math Literacy 11A
Spanish Reading and Math
  Literacy 11A
Guided Problem Solving 11-1
Technology Activities 28

⏱ **Presentation Assistant Plus!**
Transparencies and PowerPoint™
• Check Skills You'll Need 11-1
• Additional Examples 11-1
• Student Edition Answers 11-1
• Lesson Quiz 11-1
PH Presentation Pro CD-ROM 11-1

ASSESSMENT SYSTEM

Computer Test Generator CD-ROM

💻 **Technology**
Resource Pro® CD-ROM
Computer Test Generator CD-ROM
PH Presentation Pro CD-ROM

💻 **www.PHSchool.com**
Student Site
• Teacher Web Code: adk-5500
• Algebra Readiness Puzzles 90, 91
• Graphing Calculator, Procedure 1
• Self-grading Lesson Quiz
PH SuccessNet Teacher Center
• Lesson Planner
• Resources

Plus

580

Square Roots and Irrational Numbers

What You'll Learn

OBJECTIVE 1 To find square roots of numbers

OBJECTIVE 2 To classify real numbers

. . . And Why

To use square roots in real-world situations, such as finding the distance to the horizon

✓ **Check Skills You'll Need**

Write the numbers in each list without using exponents.

1. $1^2, 2^2, 3^2, \ldots, 12^2$

2. $10^2, 20^2, 30^2, \ldots, 120^2$
1–2. See back of book.

🔊 For help, go to Lesson 4-2.

New Vocabulary
• perfect square
• square root
• irrational number

Reading Math
The symbol $\sqrt{100}$ is the positive square root of 100, so you may read $-\sqrt{100}$ as the negative square root of 100.

TEXT Interactive lesson includes instant self-check, tutorials, and activities.

OBJECTIVE

1 Finding Square Roots

Consider the three squares shown below.

Each square has sides with integer length. The area of a square is the *square* of the length of a side. The square of an integer is a **perfect square**.

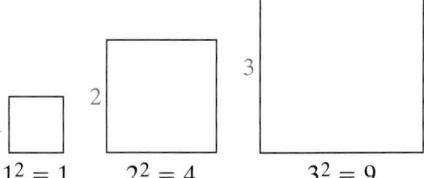

$1^2 = 1$ $2^2 = 4$ $3^2 = 9$

The inverse of squaring a number is finding a **square root**. The square-root radical, $\sqrt{}$, indicates the nonnegative square root of a number. In this book, you may assume that an expression under a square-root radical is greater than or equal to zero.

1 EXAMPLE **Simplifying Square Roots**

Simplify each square root.

a. $\sqrt{64}$ **b.** $-\sqrt{121}$

   $\sqrt{64} = 8$ $-\sqrt{121} = -11$

✓ **Check Understanding** Example 1

1. Simplify each square root.

   a. $\sqrt{100}$ 10   **b.** $-\sqrt{100}$ −10 **c.** $\sqrt{16}$ 4   **d.** $-\sqrt{16}$ −4

The first thirteen perfect squares are
   0, 1, 4, 9, 16, 25, 36, 49, 64, 81, 100, 121, and 144.
Memorizing these will help you solve problems efficiently.

For an integer that is not a perfect square, you can estimate a square root. For example, 8 is between the perfect squares 4 and 9.

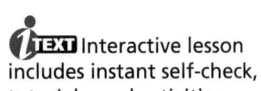 $\sqrt{8}$ is between $\sqrt{4}$ and $\sqrt{9}$.

Since 8 is closer to 9 than to 4, $\sqrt{8}$ is closer to 3 than to 2. So, $\sqrt{8} \approx 3$.

580 Chapter 11 Right Triangles in Algebra

 Ongoing Assessment and Intervention

Before the Lesson	**During the Lesson**	**After the Lesson**
Diagnose prerequisite skills using:	Monitor progress using:	Assess knowledge using:
• Check Skills You'll Need	• Check Understanding	• Lesson Quiz
	• Additional Examples	• Computer Test Generator
	• Test Prep	CD-ROM

2 EXAMPLE Real-World Problem Solving

Lifeguarding You can use the formula $d = \sqrt{1.5h}$ to estimate the distance d, in miles, to a horizon line when your eyes are h feet above the ground. Estimate the distance to the horizon seen by a lifeguard whose eyes are 10 feet above the ground.

$$d = \sqrt{1.5h}$$ Use the formula.

$$d = \sqrt{15}$$ Replace h with 10 and multiply.

$$\sqrt{9} < \sqrt{15} < \sqrt{16}$$ Find perfect squares close to 15.

$$\sqrt{16} = 4$$ Find the square root of the closest perfect square.

● The lifeguard can see about 4 miles to the horizon.

✓ Check Understanding Example 2

2. Estimate to the nearest integer.

   a. $\sqrt{27}$ 5   **b.** $-\sqrt{72}$ –8   **c.** $\sqrt{50}$ 7   **d.** $-\sqrt{22}$ –5

Real-World Connection

This lifeguard can see nearly 1 mile farther than he can standing on the beach.

OBJECTIVE

2 Classifying Real Numbers

You can express a rational number as the ratio of two integers $\frac{a}{b}$, with $b \neq 0$. In decimal form, a rational number either terminates or repeats. An **irrational number** has decimal form that neither terminates nor repeats, and it cannot be written as the ratio of two integers. Together, rationals and irrationals form the real numbers.

If an integer is not a perfect square, its square root is irrational.

Need Help?

To review rational numbers, see Lesson 4-6.

3 EXAMPLE Identifying Irrational Numbers

Identify each number as rational or irrational. Explain.

a. $\sqrt{18}$ irrational, because 18 is not a perfect square

b. $\sqrt{121}$ rational, because 121 is a perfect square

c. 432.8   rational, because it is a terminating decimal

d. 0.1212 . . .   rational, because it is a repeating decimal

e. 0.120120012 . . .   irrational; it neither terminates nor repeats

f. π irrational; it cannot be represented as $\frac{a}{b}$, where a and b are integers

✓ Check Understanding Example 3

3. Identify each number as rational or irrational. Explain.

   a. $\sqrt{2}$ **b.** $-\sqrt{81}$ **c.** 0.53   **d.** $\sqrt{42}$

   a–d. See right.

3a. irrational; because 2 is not a perfect square
3b. rational; because 81 is a perfect square
3c. rational; because it is a terminating decimal
3d. irrational; because 42 is not a perfect square

11-1 Square Roots and Irrational Numbers **581**

Professional Development

Math Background

A positive number n has two square roots. The radical sign is used to indicate its positive square root. We often use $\sqrt{n}$ and speak of *the* square root, with "positive" being understood. In working with real numbers, there is no square root of a negative number because the product of any two nonzero numbers must be positive.

Teaching Notes

Visual Learners
Write "$4^2 = 16$ and $(-4)^2 = 16$" on the board. Then write "What is the square root of 16?" 4 and –4 Write "What is $\sqrt{16}$?" on the board, aligning "What" and "is" with their matching words in the first question. Explain that the answer is only 4 because $\sqrt{}$ indicates the positive square root.

PowerPoint

Additional Examples

1 Simplify each square root.
   a. $\sqrt{144}$ 12   **b.** $-\sqrt{81}$ –9

2 You can use the formula $d = \sqrt{1.5h}$ to estimate the distance d, in miles, to a horizon line when your eyes are h feet above the ground. Estimate the distance to the horizon seen by a lifeguard whose eyes are 20 feet above the ground. **about 5 miles**

3 Identify each number as rational or irrational.
   a. $\sqrt{49}$ rational
   b. 0.16 rational
   c. $\sqrt{3}$ irrational
   d. 0.3333. . . rational
   e. $-\sqrt{15}$ irrational
   f. 12.69 rational
   g. 0.1234567. . . irrational

👥 Reaching All Students

Below Level List and review the list of the first thirteen perfect squares. Students may benefit from listing them and their square roots in a notebook for reference.	**Advanced Learners** Ask: *If the length of each side of a square with an area of 144 cm² is increased by 25%, what is the area of the new square?* 225 cm² *What is the percent of increase in the area?* about 56%	**Visual Learners** See note on page 581.

Closure

Ask: *How are the operations squaring and finding a square root related?* inverse operations

Assignment Guide

1 Objective 1
- **Ⓐ Ⓑ Core** 1–13, 22–25, 37, 38, 40–44
- **Ⓒ Extension** 45–49

2 Objective 2
- **Ⓐ Ⓑ Core** 14–21, 26–36, 39
- **Ⓒ Extension** 50–53

Test Prep 54–56
Mixed Review 57–65

Practice 11-1 *Square Roots and Irrational Numbers*

Estimate to the nearest integer.

1. $\sqrt{18}$ ___4___ 2. $\sqrt{24}$ ___5___ 3. $\sqrt{50}$ ___7___
4. $\sqrt{8}$ ___3___ 5. $\sqrt{62}$ ___8___ 6. $\sqrt{78}$ ___9___
7. $\sqrt{98}$ ___10___ 8. $\sqrt{46}$ ___7___ 9. $\sqrt{38}$ ___6___

Simplify each square root.

10. $\sqrt{144}$ ___12___ 11. $\sqrt{9+16}$ ___5___ 12. $\sqrt{900}$ ___30___
13. $\sqrt{169}$ ___13___ 14. $-\sqrt{100}$ ___-10___ 15. $\sqrt{0.16}$ ___0.4___
16. $\sqrt{\frac{16}{81}}$ ___$\frac{4}{9}$___ 17. $\sqrt{\frac{4}{25}}$ ___$\frac{2}{5}$___ 18. $\sqrt{\frac{121}{144}}$ ___$\frac{11}{12}$___

Identify each number as rational or irrational.

19. $\sqrt{289}$ ___Rational___ 20. 5.7777... ___Rational___
21. $\sqrt{41}$ ___Irrational___ 22. 0.62662... ___Irrational___
23. $\sqrt{49}$ ___Rational___ 24. $\sqrt{52}$ ___Irrational___

Find two integers that make each equation true.

25. $x^2 = 16$ ___4, -4___ 26. $3m^2 = 147$ ___7, -7___

Use the formula $d = \sqrt{1.5h}$ to estimate the distance to the horizon d in miles for each viewer's eye height h, in feet.

27. $h = 12$ ft — about 4 mi
28. $h = 216$ ft — 18 mi
29. $h = 412$ ft — about 25 mi

30. The Moon has a surface area of approximately 14,650,000 mi². Estimate its radius to the nearest mile. ___1,080 mi___

Enrichment 11-1 *Patterns of Roots*

Since $5^3 = 5 \cdot 5 \cdot 5 = 125$, 5 is the *cube root* of 125. This is written $5 = \sqrt[3]{125}$.

Complete the table.

n	1	2	3	4	5	6	7	8	9	10
1. n^3	1	8	27	64	125	216	343	512	729	1,000

2. Look at the one's digits of the numbers in the n^3 row. Tell what is interesting about these digits.
   each of the digits 0-9 occurs once

3. Use your calculator to find these cubes.

   a. 17^3 ___4,913___ b. 27^3 ___19,683___ c. 57^3 ___185,193___
   d. 19^3 ___6,859___ e. 49^3 ___117,649___ f. 79^3 ___493,039___

4. Describe a method for predicting the ones' digit of the cube root of a perfect cube simply by looking at the perfect cube.
   Find the cube in the table with the same ones' digit as the given cube. The two roots will have the same ones' digit.

Write the ones' digit of the cube root.

5. $\sqrt[3]{681,472}$ ___8___ 6. $\sqrt[3]{140,608}$ ___2___ 7. $\sqrt[3]{12,167}$ ___3___

$2^5 = 2 \cdot 2 \cdot 2 \cdot 2 \cdot 2 = 32$. 2 is the *fifth root* of 32; $2 = \sqrt[5]{32}$.

Complete the table.

n	1	2	3	4	5	6	7	8	9	10
8. n^5	1	32	243	1,024	3,125	7,776	16,807	32,768	59,049	100,000

9. Describe how to predict the ones' digit of the fifth root of a perfect fifth power.
   The fifth power and its root have the same ones' digit.

Write the ones' digit of the fifth root.

10. $\sqrt[5]{2,476,099}$ ___9___ 11. $\sqrt[5]{229,345,007}$ ___7___ 12. $\sqrt[5]{33,554,432}$ ___2___

EXERCISES

For more exercises, see *Extra Practice*.

Practice and Problem Solving

Ⓐ Practice by Example

Example 1
(page 580)

Simplify each square root.

1. $\sqrt{4}$ 2 2. $-\sqrt{36}$ -6 3. $\sqrt{1}$ 1 4. $\sqrt{25}$ 5
5. $-\sqrt{49}$ -7 6. $\sqrt{81}$ 9 7. $-\sqrt{9}$ -3 8. $-\sqrt{169}$ -13

Example 2
(page 581)

Estimate to the nearest integer.

9. $\sqrt{10}$ 3 10. $\sqrt{17}$ 4 11. $-\sqrt{39}$ -6 12. $-\sqrt{55}$ -7

🌐 13. **Viewing Distance** The observation windows at the top of the Washington Monument in Washington, D.C., are 500 ft high. Using the formula $d = \sqrt{1.5h}$ of Example 2, estimate the distance you can see to the horizon from the observation windows. 27 mi

Example 3
(page 581)

Identify each number as rational or irrational. Explain.
14–21. See margin.

14. 4.1010010001... 15. $\sqrt{87}$
16. $-\sqrt{16}$ 17. $-0.\overline{3}$
18. $\sqrt{5}$ 19. 2,222,222
20. $\sqrt{144}$ 21. 0.31311...

Ⓑ Apply Your Skills

Simplify each square root.

22. $\sqrt{196}$ 14 23. $\sqrt{\frac{4}{9}}$ $\frac{2}{3}$ 24. $\sqrt{\frac{25}{49}}$ $\frac{5}{7}$ 25. $\sqrt{\frac{36}{64}}$ $\frac{3}{4}$

Estimate to the nearest integer.

26. $\sqrt{7}$ 3 27. $\sqrt{2}$ 1 28. $\sqrt{40}$ 6 29. $-\sqrt{80}$ -9
30. $\sqrt{58}$ 8 31. $-\sqrt{98}$ -10 32. $\sqrt{14}$ 4 33. $\sqrt{105}$ 10

Identify each number as rational or irrational. Explain.

34. $\sqrt{0}$ rational; can be expressed as $\frac{a}{b}$
35. 1.001001001... rational; repeating decimal
36. 2.3010010001... See above left.

37. **Reasoning** What do you get when you square $\sqrt{x}$? x

38. **Writing in Math** A classmate was absent for today's lesson. Explain to him or her how to estimate $\sqrt{30}$. See left.

39. a. **Patterns** You can create irrational numbers. For example, the number 1.010010001... shows a pattern, yet it is irrational. What pattern do you see? a–b. See left.
   b. **Open-Ended** Name three irrational numbers between 9 and 10.

36. irrational; it neither terminates nor repeats

38. Answers may vary. Sample: Think of the perfect squares closest to 30, one less than 30 and one greater than 30. Take the square root of the one closest to 30.

39a. In each repetition of the pattern there is one more zero than in the previous one.
   b. Answers may vary. Sample: 9.010010001..., 9.121121112..., 9.565665666...

582 Chapter 11 Right Triangles in Algebra

14. irrational; it neither terminates nor repeats
15. irrational; because 87 is not a perfect square
16. rational; because 16 is a perfect square
17. rational; because it is a repeating decimal
18. irrational; because 5 is not a perfect square
19. rational; it can be expressed as a ratio of two numbers
20. rational; because 144 is a perfect square
21. irrational; it neither terminates nor repeats

 **Algebra** Find two integers that make each equation true.

40. $a^2 = 9$
3, −3

41. $b^2 = 25$
5, −5

42. $y^2 = 100$
10, −10

43. $m^2 = \frac{100}{25}$
2, −2

[GPS] **44. Geometry** Find the length of a side of a square with area 81 cm².
9 cm

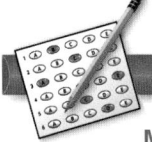 **C** Challenge **45. Geometry** The area of a circle is 12 in.². Estimate its radius to the nearest inch. **2 in.**

If a number is the product of three identical factors, each factor is the *cube root* of the number. Since $2^3 = 8$, 2 is the cube root of 8. In Exercises 46–49, find the number *n* that makes each equation true.

46. $n^3 = -8$
−2

47. $n^3 = 27$
3

48. $n^3 = -27$
−3

49. $n^3 = 343$
7

On your graphing calculator, press [MATH] 4 to show the cube-root radical $\sqrt[3]{}$. Use it to find each cube root.

50. $\sqrt[3]{-8}$
−2

51. $\sqrt[3]{125}$
5

52. $\sqrt[3]{-1{,}331}$
−11

53. $\sqrt[3]{15{,}625}$
25

 **Test Prep**

Multiple Choice

Joe is hiking in national park wilderness. His radio transmits signals as far as the horizon. Use the formula $d = \sqrt{1.5h}$, where *d* is the line-of-sight distance to the horizon in miles and *h* is height in feet, to answer the following questions.

Take It to the NET
Online lesson quiz at
www.PHSchool.com
Web Code: ada-1101

54. Joe has the transmitter at a height of 6 ft. About how far is it from the transmitter to the horizon? **A**
 A. 3 mi **B.** 5 mi **C.** 7 mi **D.** 9 mi

55. Joe sets his receiver on the ground. What is the farthest away that a transmitter 4 ft above the ground can be in order to reach Joe? **H**
 F. 0 mi **G.** 1.2 mi **H.** 2.4 mi **I.** 6 mi

Short Response

56. Joe wants to talk with his base camp that he knows is 6 mi away.
 (a) Explain how Joe could find the height at which he should have the transmitter. **(b)** Find that height.
 [2] He can use the equation $d = \sqrt{1.5h}$ where *d* is 6. Since $\sqrt{36}$ is 6, he can conclude that $1.5h = 36$; 24 ft.
 [1] minor error OR answer only

 Mixed Review

Lesson 10-9 Find the volume of each figure in cubic centimeters.

57. sphere with $r = 0.03$ m
about 113 cm³

58. cone with $r = 4$ cm, $h = 10$ cm
about 167 cm³

Lesson 6-5 **59.** Shannon scored 17 correct on a 25-item test. The passing grade was 65%. Did Shannon pass? Explain. Yes; $\frac{17}{25}$ is 0.68, or 68%. Since 68% ≥ 65%, Shannon passed the test.

Lesson 4-1 List the positive factors of each number. 60–65. See margin.

60. 18 **61.** 22 **62.** 33 **63.** 45 **64.** 50 **65.** 90

11-1 Square Roots and Irrational Numbers **583**

Alternative Assessment

With students in pairs, have one estimate the square root of a number that is not a perfect square (such as 11, 37, 84), while the other student uses a calculator and finds the square root to the nearest integer. Ask the students to compare their findings. Then have them switch roles and repeat with a different number.

[GPS] Use the Guided Problem Solving worksheet with Exercise 44.

60. 1, 2, 3, 6, 9, 18
61. 1, 2, 11, 22
62. 1, 3, 11, 33
63. 1, 3, 5, 9, 15, 45
64. 1, 2, 5, 10, 25, 50
65. 1, 2, 3, 5, 6, 9, 10, 15, 18, 30, 45, 90

583

The Pythagorean Theorem

1. Plan

Lesson Preview

 Check Skills You'll Need

Exponents
Lesson 4-2: Example 2;
Exercises 7–12.
Extra Practice, p. 747.

Lesson Resources

 Teaching Resources
Practice, Reteaching, Enrichment

Reaching All Students
Practice Workbook 11-2
Spanish Practice Workbook 11-2
Guided Problem Solving 11-2
Technology Activities 29
Hands-On Activities 16

Presentation Assistant Plus!
Transparencies and PowerPoint™
• Check Skills You'll Need 11-2
• Additional Examples 11-2
• Student Edition Answers 11-2
• Lesson Quiz 11-2
• Classroom Aid 30
PH Presentation Pro CD-ROM 11-2

ASSESSMENT SYSTEM

Computer Test Generator CD-ROM

 Technology
Resource Pro® CD-ROM
Computer Test Generator CD-ROM
PH Presentation Pro CD-ROM

www.PHSchool.com
Student Site
• Teacher Web Code: adk-5500
• Algebra Readiness Puzzles 50, 51
• Graphing Calculator, Procedure 2
• Self-grading Lesson Quiz
PH SuccessNet Teacher Center
• Lesson Planner
• Resources

Plus

584

What You'll Learn

OBJECTIVE 1 To use the Pythagorean Theorem

OBJECTIVE 2 To identify right triangles

. . . And Why

To use the Pythagorean Theorem in real-world situations, such as carpentry

 Check Skills You'll Need

Simplify.

1. $4^2 + 6^2$ **2.** $5^2 + 8^2$
    52   89
3. $7^2 + 9^2$ **4.** $9^2 + 3^2$
    130   90
For help, go to Lesson 4-2.

New Vocabulary

• legs
• hypotenuse

Need Help?
A right triangle is a triangle with a 90° angle.

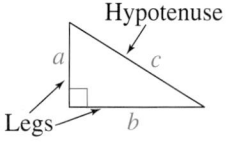 **TEXT** Interactive lesson includes instant self-check, tutorials, and activities.

OBJECTIVE 1 Using the Pythagorean Theorem

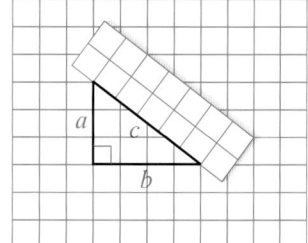

Investigation

Exploring Right Triangles

1. On graph paper, create right triangles with legs a and b. Measure the length of the third side c with another piece of graph paper.

Copy and complete the table below.

a	b	c	a^2	b^2	c^2
3	4	▓	9	16	▓ 5, 25
5	12	▓	25	144	▓ 13, 169
9	12	▓	81	144	▓ 15, 225

2. Based on your table, use $>$, $<$, or $=$ to complete the following statement.

$$a^2 + b^2 \ \blacksquare \ c^2 \ =$$

In a right triangle, the two shortest sides are **legs.** The longest side, which is opposite the right angle, is the **hypotenuse.** The Pythagorean Theorem shows how the legs and hypotenuse of a right triangle are related.

Key Concepts **Pythagorean Theorem**

In any right triangle, the sum of the squares of the lengths of the legs is equal to the square of the length of the hypotenuse.

$$a^2 + b^2 = c^2$$

You will prove the Pythagorean Theorem in a future math class. For now, you will use the theorem to find the length of a leg or the length of a hypotenuse.

Ongoing Assessment and Intervention

Before the Lesson	During the Lesson	After the Lesson
Diagnose prerequisite skills using:	**Monitor progress using:**	**Assess knowledge using:**
• Check Skills You'll Need	• Check Understanding	• Lesson Quiz
	• Additional Examples	• Computer Test Generator
	• Test Prep	CD-ROM

1 EXAMPLE   Using the Pythagorean Theorem

Find c, the length of the hypotenuse, in the triangle at the right.

$$c^2 = a^2 + b^2$$ **Use the Pythagorean Theorem.**

$$c^2 = 6^2 + 8^2$$ **Replace a with 6 and b with 8.**

$$c^2 = 100$$ **Simplify.**

$$c = \sqrt{100} = 10$$ **Find the positive square root of each side.**

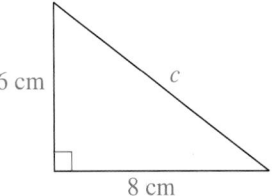

6 cm · c · 8 cm

● The length of the hypotenuse is 10 cm.

✔ Check Understanding   Example 1

1. The lengths of two sides of a right triangle are given. Find the length of the third side.

    a. legs: 3 ft and 4 ft **5 ft**   **b.** leg: 12 m; hypotenuse: 15 m
                                                       9 m

You can use a calculator or a table of square roots to find approximate values for square roots.

2 EXAMPLE   Finding an Approximate Length

Find the value of x in the triangle at the right. Round to the nearest tenth.

$$a^2 + b^2 = c^2$$ **Use the Pythagorean Theorem.**

$$6^2 + x^2 = 9^2$$ **Replace a with 6, b with x, and c with 9.**

$$36 + x^2 = 81$$ **Simplify.**

$$x^2 = 45$$ **Subtract 36 from each side.**

$$x = \sqrt{45}$$ **Find the positive square root of each side.**

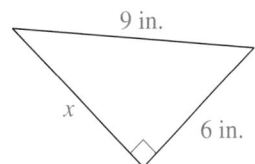

9 in. · x · 6 in.

Then use one of the two methods below to approximate $\sqrt{45}$.

Method 1 Use a calculator.
A calculator value for $\sqrt{45}$ is *6.7082039*.

    $x \approx 6.7$ **Round to the nearest tenth.**

Method 2 Use a table of square roots.
Use the table on page 778. Find 45 in the N column. Then find the corresponding value in the $\sqrt{N}$ column. It is 6.708.

    $x \approx 6.7$ **Round to the nearest tenth.**

● The value of x is about 6.7 in.

✔ Check Understanding   Example 2

2. In a right triangle, the length of the hypotenuse is 15 m and the length of a leg is 8 m. What is the length of the other leg, to the nearest tenth of a meter? **12.7 m**

Math Background

The general theorem for any right triangle is named after the Greek mathematician Pythagoras, who lived about 580–500 B.C. Evidence shows that as much as fifteen hundred years earlier, the Babylonians knew the properties of this theorem. An ancient Hindu handbook for temple builders, written around 600 B.C., states the theorem. However, scholars credit Pythagoras for first demonstrating the truth of this theorem.

Teaching Notes

Investigation (Optional)
Have students note that the longest side of each triangle is always the side that is not part of the right angle.

Visual Learners
To help students remember which two sides of a right triangle are the legs, have them hold their thumb and forefinger so they are perpendicular to form an L. Point out the mnemonic that the *Legs* form an **L**, or right angle.

2 EXAMPLE Teaching Tip

Explain that $a^2 + b^2 = c^2$ for every right triangle, even when the lengths of sides are irrational numbers.

PowerPoint
Additional Examples

1 Find c, the length of the hypotenuse. **35 cm**

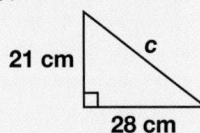

21 cm · c · 28 cm

2 Find the value of x in the triangle. Round to the nearest tenth. **12.1 in.**

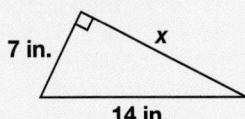

7 in. · x · 14 in.

👥 Reaching All Students

| **Below Level** Remind students that they cannot accurately identify a right triangle just because it *looks* like one. | **Advanced Learners** Have students research the appearance and use of the Pythagorean Theorem and its converse in ancient civilizations. | **Visual Learners** See note on page 586. **Tactile Learners** See note on page 588. |

Additional Examples

❸ The carpentry terms *span*, *rise*, and *rafter length* are illustrated in Example 3. A carpenter wants to make a roof that has a span of 20 ft and a rise of 10 ft. What should the rafter length be?
about 14.1 ft

❹ Is a triangle with sides 10 cm, 24 cm, and 26 cm a right triangle? **yes**

❸ EXAMPLE Inclusion

Some students may have difficulty determining which right triangle to use in the diagram. Sketch the diagram on a transparency. Show that the rise and half of the span are the lengths of the legs by tracing over their segments with a red marker. Then trace the appropriate rafter with a different color to show the hypotenuse.

❹ EXAMPLE Visual Learners

Introduce Pythagorean triples such as 3, 4, 5 and 5, 12, 13. Have students use the Converse of the Pythagorean Theorem to show that these "triples" are the lengths of sides of right triangles. Then have volunteers substitute multiples of the triples, such as 6, 8, 10 and 10, 24, 26, to show that multiples of a triple will also be lengths of sides of right triangles. Learning to recognize a few of these triples can save time in future work.

Closure

Have students explain how to use the Pythagorean Theorem to find a missing side length and how to use the Converse of the Pythagorean Theorem to prove a triangle is a right triangle.

When you know two side lengths, substitute those lengths into the Pythagorean Theorem equation and solve for the third side length. When you know three side lengths, test whether those lengths make the equation $a^2 + b^2 = c^2$ true.

---

❸ EXAMPLE Real-World Problem Solving

Carpentry The carpentry terms *span*, *rise*, and *rafter length* are illustrated in the diagram at the left. A carpenter wants to make a roof that has a span of 24 ft and a rise of 8.5 ft. What should the rafter length be?

$c^2 = a^2 + b^2$	Use the Pythagorean Theorem.
$c^2 = 12^2 + 8.5^2$	Use half the span, 12 ft. Replace *a* with 12 and *b* with 8.5.
$c^2 = 144 + 72.25$	Square 12 and 8.5.
$c^2 = 216.25$	Add.
$c = \sqrt{216.25}$	Find the positive square root.
$c \approx 14.7$	Round to the nearest tenth.

● The rafter length should be about 14.7 ft.

✔ **Check Understanding** Example 3

3. **Carpentry** What is the rise of a roof if the span is 22 feet and the rafter length is 14 feet? Round to the nearest tenth of a foot. **8.7 ft**

OBJECTIVE

2 Identifying Right Triangles

The *Converse of the Pythagorean Theorem* allows you to substitute the lengths of the sides of a triangle into the equation $a^2 + b^2 = c^2$ to check whether a triangle is a right triangle. If the equation is true, the triangle is a right triangle.

❹ EXAMPLE Finding a Right Triangle

Is a triangle with sides 12 m, 15 m, and 20 m a right triangle?

$a^2 + b^2 = c^2$	Write the equation for the Pythagorean Theorem.
$12^2 + 15^2 \stackrel{?}{=} 20^2$	Replace *a* and *b* with the shorter lengths and *c* with the longest length.
$144 + 225 \stackrel{?}{=} 400$	Simplify.
$369 \neq 400$	

● The triangle is not a right triangle.

✔ **Check Understanding** Example 4

4. Can you form a right triangle with the three lengths given? Explain.
   a. 7 in., 8 in., $\sqrt{113}$ in. **b.** 5 mm, 6 mm, 10 mm
   Yes, $7^2 + 8^2 = 113$. No, $5^2 + 6^2 \neq 10^2$.

🔎 For more exercises, see *Extra Practice*.

Practice and Problem Solving

 Practice by Example

Examples 1 and 2
(page 585)

In each right triangle, find each missing length to the nearest tenth.

1. 13 cm, 5 cm, c, 12 cm

2. 11.3 m, 8 m, 8 m, k

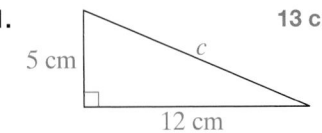

3. 8 in., 6 in., 10 in., b

4. 5.2 mm, 6 mm, h, 3 mm

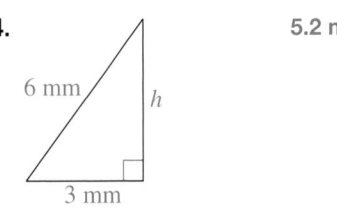

The lengths of two sides of a right triangle are given. Find the length of the third side. Round to the nearest tenth where necessary.

5. legs: 12 in. and 16 in. **20 in.**

6. legs: 21 ft and 28 ft **35 ft**

7. leg: 48 ft; hypotenuse: 50 ft **14 ft**

8. leg: 33 ft; hypotenuse: 55 ft **44 ft**

Example 3
(page 586)

Use the Pythagorean Theorem to solve each problem.

🌐 **9. Carpentry** Use the diagram in Example 3 on page 586. A carpenter wants to make a roof that has a rise of 5 ft and a rafter length of 16 ft. What is the half span? The span?
about 15.2 ft; about 30.4 ft

🌐 **10. House Painting** A painter places an 11-ft ladder against a house.
GPS The base of the ladder is 3 ft from the house. How high on the house does the ladder reach? **about 10.6 ft**

🌐 **11. Hiking** Darla hikes due north for 6 km. She then turns due east and hikes 3 km. What is the direct distance between her starting point and stopping point, rounded to the nearest tenth of a kilometer?
6.7 km

Example 4
(page 586)

12. no; $4^2 + 6^2 \neq 7^2$

13. no; $4^2 + 5^2 \neq 6^2$

Can you form a right triangle with the three lengths given? Explain.
12–13. See left.

12. 4 m, 6 m, 7 m

13. 4 mi, 5 mi, 6 mi

14. 7 in., 24 in., 25 in.
yes; $7^2 + 24^2 = 25^2$

15. 6, 7, $\sqrt{85}$
yes; $6^2 + 7^2 = 85$

16. 8 in., 10 in., 12 in.
no; $8^2 + 10^2 \neq 12^2$

17. 5 cm, 12 cm, 13 cm
yes; $5^2 + 12^2 = 13^2$

 **Apply Your Skills**

Use the triangle at the right. Find the missing length to the nearest tenth of a unit.

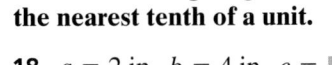

18. $a = 2$ in., $b = 4$ in., $c = \blacksquare$
4.5 in.

19. $a = 1.4$ m, $b = 2.8$ m, $c = \blacksquare$
3.1 m

20. $a = 3$ ft, $c = 5$ ft, $b = \blacksquare$
4 ft

21. $b = 2.7$ km, $c = 3.4$ km, $a = \blacksquare$
2.1 km

22. Reasoning Is a triangle with side lengths of $\sqrt{12}$ cm, $\sqrt{7}$ cm, and $\sqrt{5}$ cm a right triangle? Explain. **yes; $\left(\sqrt{5}\right)^2 + \left(\sqrt{7}\right)^2 = \left(\sqrt{12}\right)^2$**

 Use the Guided Problem Solving worksheet with Exercise 10.

Assignment Guide

 Objective 1
Ⓐ Ⓑ **Core** 1–11, 18–21, 23–28, 31
Ⓒ **Extension** 34–37

 Objective 2
Ⓐ Ⓑ **Core** 12–17, 22, 29, 30, 32
Ⓒ **Extension** 33

Test Prep 38–40
Mixed Review 41–51

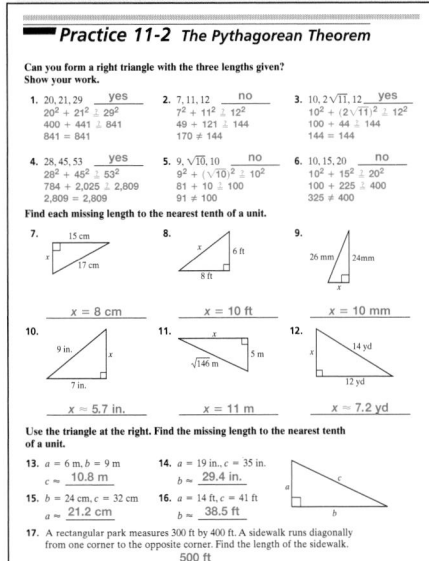

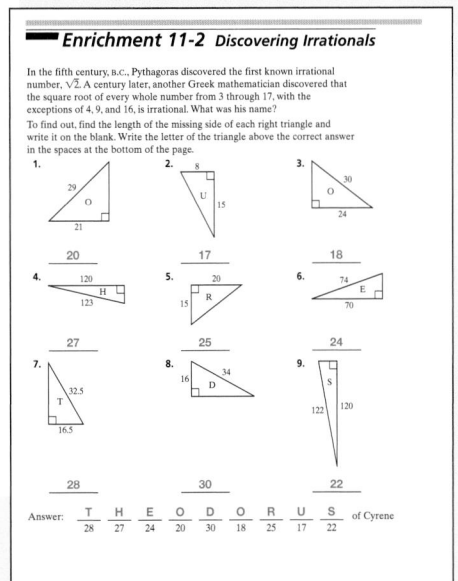

23. yes; $3^2 + 4^2 = 5^2$
24. yes; $7^2 + 24^2 = 25^2$
25. no; $10^2 + 24^2 \neq 25^2$
26. yes; $5^2 + 12^2 = 13^2$
27. yes, $6^2 + 8^2 = 10^2$;
    yes, $14^2 + 48^2 = 50^2$;
    yes, $10^2 + 24^2 = 26^2$

Any three positive integers that make $a^2 + b^2 = c^2$ true form a *Pythagorean triple*. Does each group of three integers below form a Pythagorean triple? Show your work. 23–26. See left.

23. 3, 4, 5   **24.** 7, 24, 25   **25.** 10, 24, 25   **26.** 5, 12, 13

27. For each group in Exercises 23–26 that forms a Pythagorean triple, multiply the integers by 2. Do the three new numbers form a Pythagorean triple? Show your work. See left.

🌐 **28. Landscaping** Jim works for a landscaping company. He must plant and stake a tree. The stakes are 2 ft from the base of the tree. They are connected to wires that attach to the trunk at a height of 5 ft. If there is 6 in. of extra length at both ends of each wire, how long must each wire be, to the nearest tenth of a foot? **6.4 ft**

Can you form a right triangle having the three given lengths? Explain.

29. $\sqrt{5}$ yd, $\sqrt{3}$ yd, $\sqrt{2}$ yd   **30.** 1 m, 0.54 m, 0.56 m
yes; $\left(\sqrt{2}\right)^2 + \left(\sqrt{3}\right)^2 = \left(\sqrt{5}\right)^2$ no; $0.56^2 + 0.54^2 \neq 1^2$

🌐 **31. Quilting** The diagonals for a quilting frame must be the same length to ensure the frame is rectangular. What should the lengths of the diagonals be for a quilting frame 86 in. by 100 in.? Draw a sketch and then solve. **For sketch, see below left; about 131.9 in.**

32. Writing in Math Can you form a right triangle having side lengths of $3p$ ft, $4p$ ft, and $5p$ ft? Explain. **Yes; $(3p)^2 + (4p)^2 = (5p)^2$ for any value of p.**

C Challenge

33. Geometry In the rectangular prism at the left, d_1 is the diagonal of the base of the prism, and d_2 is the *diagonal of the prism*.
  a. Find d_1. **10 in.**
  b. The triangle formed by d_1, d_2, and the side that is 4 in. is a right triangle. Use your answer to part (a) to find d_2. **about 10.8 in.**
  c. Find the diagonal of a rectangular prism with dimensions 9 in., 12 in., and 5 in. **about 15.8 in.**

31.

Find the value of n in each diagram. Give your answer as a square root.

34. 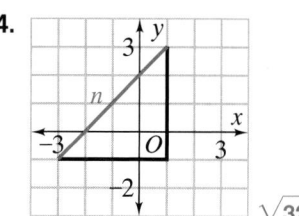 $\sqrt{32}$

35. 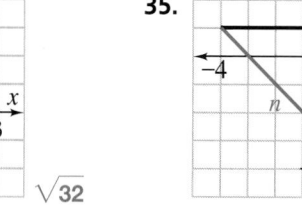 $\sqrt{50}$

36. 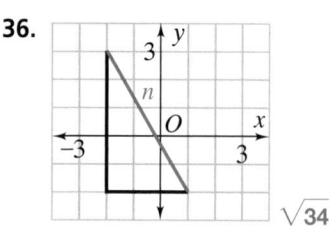 $\sqrt{34}$

37. 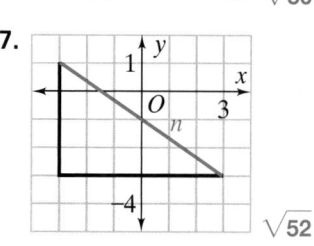 $\sqrt{52}$

Multiple Choice For Exercises 38 and 39, the lengths of two sides of a right triangle are given. What is the length of the third side?

38. legs: 36 m and 48 m **D**
  A. 5 m **B.** 12 m **C.** 50 m **D.** 60 m

39. leg: 6 m; hypotenuse: $\sqrt{85}$ m **F**
  F. 7 m **G.** 8 m **H.** 9 m **I.** 10 m

Extended Response **40. a.** Can segments with lengths 3 ft, 4 ft, and 5 ft form a right triangle? Explain.
  b. Ancient builders are said to have used ropes with 12 equally-spaced knots to make sure that square corners were indeed right angles. How could you use such a rope to determine whether a corner in your room forms a right angle?
  c. Explain your answer in part (b). See back of book.

Take It to the NET
Online lesson quiz at
www.PHSchool.com
Web Code: ada-1102

Mixed Review

Lesson 11-1 **Identify each number as rational or irrational.**

41. $\sqrt{36}$ **42.** $0.\overline{6}$ **43.** $-\sqrt{12}$ **44.** -33.3 **45.** $0.\overline{654}$
41–45. See margin.

Lesson 5-9 **Simplify each expression.**

46. $(bc)^5$ **47.** $(2x^2)^4$ **48.** $(-3b)^3$ **49.** $(a^5b^2)^4$ **50.** $\left(\frac{3m}{5}\right)^2$ $\frac{9m^2}{25}$
  b^5c^5 $16x^8$ $-27b^3$ $a^{20}b^8$

Lesson 4-9 🌐 **51. Geography** Greenland is the world's largest island and has an area of 2,175,600 km². Express this area in scientific notation.
  2.1756×10^6 km²

Math at Work

Air-Traffic Controller

When we think of airline safety, many of us think of pilots. But there is also a network of people, the air-traffic controllers, who work hard to ensure the safe operation of aircraft. Using radar and visual observation, they closely monitor the location of each plane. They coordinate the movement of air traffic to make certain that aircraft stay a safe distance apart. They also coordinate landings and takeoffs to keep delays at a minimum.

In their jobs, air-traffic controllers use angle measurements in some of the same ways you do when you solve problems in algebra and geometry.

Take It to the NET For more information about air-traffic controllers, go to **www.PHSchool.com**.
Web Code: adb-2031

11-2 The Pythagorean Theorem **589**

41. rational; because 36 is a perfect square
42. rational; because it is a repeating decimal
43. irrational; because 12 is not a perfect square
44. rational; because it is a terminating decimal
45. rational; because it is a terminating decimal

Alternative Assessment

Have students look for examples of right triangles in photos and illustrations in books, magazines, or other periodicals. Have them verify that these are right triangles by using a ruler and the Converse of the Pythagorean Theorem.

4. Assess

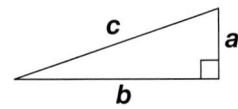
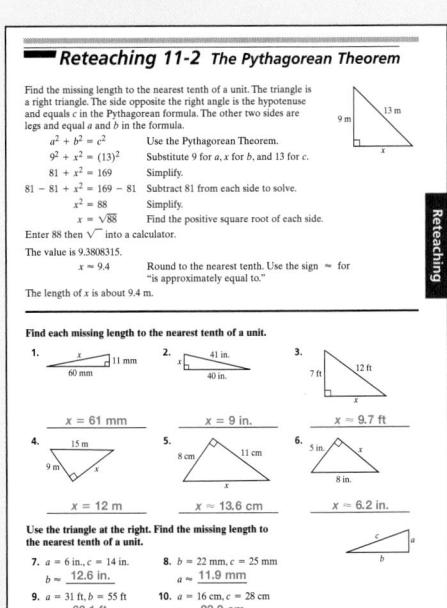

The Pythagorean Theorem and Circles

This Extension leads students to discover that the perpendicular bisector of a chord passes through the center of the circle. Students then use the Pythagorean Theorem to find the distance from the center to a chord of the circle, the length of a chord, or the radius.

Teaching Notes

Geometry Connection
A *chord* of a circle is any line segment that connects two points on the circle. A diameter is a chord that passes through the center of the circle. The diameters of a circle are the longest chords.

The distance from a point to a line is defined to be the length of the perpendicular segment from the point to the line. This means that the distance from the center to a chord of a circle is the length of the perpendicular segment from the center to the chord.

Inclusion
Pair students who may have trouble handling a compass with students who have full dexterity.

Teaching Tip
Emphasize that one leg of the right triangle in each diagram is half the chord, not the entire chord.

Follow the steps below to discover a characteristic of circle chords and their perpendicular bisectors.

Step 1 With a compass, construct a large circle. Label the center O.

Step 2 Draw a chord $\overline{AB}$ that is not a diameter.

Step 3 Construct the perpendicular bisector of the chord with a compass and straightedge or by folding the circle so that A lies on B.

Step 4 Label the point where the perpendicular bisector intersects the chord as point D.

1. Write a conjecture about the perpendicular bisector of a chord and the center of the circle. **See right.** The perpendicular bisector of a chord of a circle passes through the center of the circle.

2. Classify $\triangle AOD$ by its angles. **right triangle**

The distance from the center of a circle to a chord is the length of the perpendicular segment with endpoints at the center and on the chord. You can use the radius of a circle and the length of a chord to find the distance from the center of a circle to the chord.

1 EXAMPLE

Circle O has a radius of 10 cm. Chord FG is 12 cm long. $\overline{OM}$ is the perpendicular bisector of $\overline{FG}$. How far is $\overline{FG}$ from O?

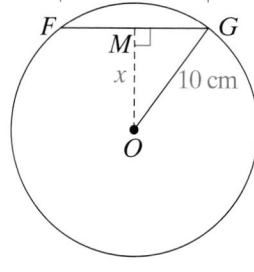

$\triangle OMG$ is a right triangle with legs $\overline{OM}$ and $\overline{MG}$, and hypotenuse $\overline{OG}$.

OM = distance to chord = x

OG = radius = 10 cm

$MG = \frac{1}{2}FG = \frac{1}{2}(12) = 6$

Use the Pythagorean Theorem to find x.

$OG^2 = OM^2 + MG^2$

$10^2 = x^2 + 6^2$

$100 = x^2 + 36$

$100 - 36 = x^2 + 36 - 36$

$64 = x^2$

$8 = x$

● The distance from the center to the chord is 8 cm.

590   Extension   The Pythagorean Theorem and Circles

Find x, the distance from the center O of each circle to chord $\overline{JK}$. Round to the nearest tenth.

3. 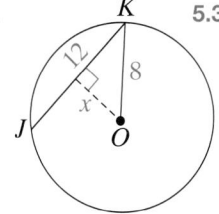 5.3

4. 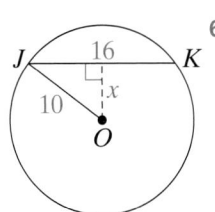 6

5. 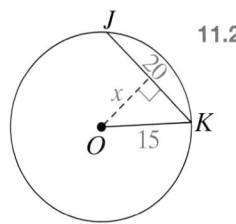 11.2

For a given circle, you can also find the length of a chord or the length of the radius if you know two other lengths.

2 EXAMPLE

Chord PT is 24 in. long and 5 in. from the center O of the circle. Find the length of the radius.

Use the Pythagorean Theorem to find the radius r.

$PM = \frac{1}{2}(PT) = 12$

$r^2 = 12^2 + 5^2$

$r^2 = 144 + 25$

$r^2 = 169$

$r = 13$

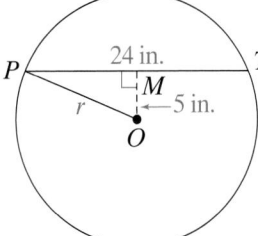

● The radius is 13 in.

Find x. If your answer is not an integer, round to the nearest tenth.

6. 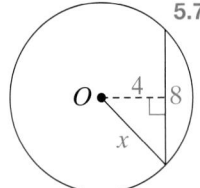 5.7

7. 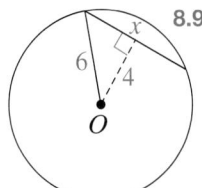 8.9

8. 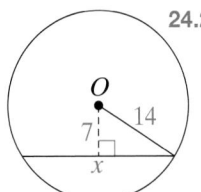 24.2

9. 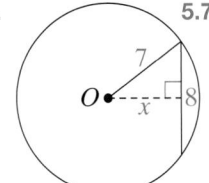 5.7

10. 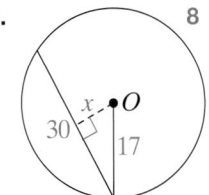 8

11. 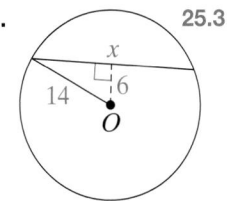 25.3

1. Plan

Lesson Preview

 Check Skills You'll Need

The Coordinate Plane
Lesson 1-10: Example 1;
Exercises 7–12.
Extra Practice, p. 744.

Lesson Resources

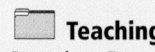 **Teaching Resources**
Practice, Reteaching, Enrichment
Checkpoint Quiz 1

 **Reaching All Students**
Practice Workbook 11-3
Spanish Practice Workbook 11-3
Reading and Math Literacy 11A
Spanish Reading and Math
  Literacy 11A
Spanish Checkpoint Quiz 1
Guided Problem Solving 11-3

Presentation Assistant Plus!
Transparencies and PowerPoint™
• Check Skills You'll Need 11-3
• Additional Examples 11-3
• Student Edition Answers 11-3
• Lesson Quiz 11-3
• Classroom Aid 31
PH Presentation Pro CD-ROM 11-3

ASSESSMENT SYSTEM

Checkpoint Quiz 1
Computer Test Generator CD-ROM

 Technology
Resource Pro® CD-ROM
Computer Test Generator CD-ROM
PH Presentation Pro CD-ROM

 www.PHSchool.com
Student Site
• Teacher Web Code: adk-5500
• Graphing Calculator, Procedure 19
• Self-grading Lesson Quiz
PH SuccessNet Teacher Center
• Lesson Planner
• Resources

Plus

What You'll Learn

OBJECTIVE 1 To find the distance between two points using the Distance Formula

OBJECTIVE 2 To find the midpoint of a segment using the Midpoint Formula

. . . And Why

To find the perimeters of figures on the coordinate plane

 Check Skills You'll Need

Write the coordinates of each point.
1-4. See below.
1. A **2.** D **3.** G **4.** J

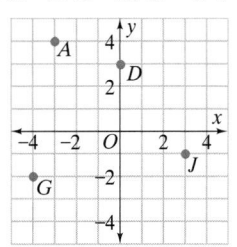

 For help, go to Lesson 1-10.

New Vocabulary

• distance
• midpoint

1. $(-3, 4)$
2. $(0, 3)$
3. $(-4, -2)$
4. $(3, -1)$

iTEXT Interactive lesson includes instant self-check, tutorials, and activities.

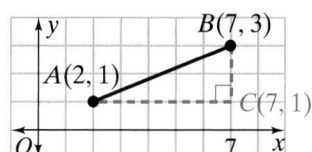

In the graph at the right, you can locate point $C(7, 1)$ to form a right triangle with points $A(2, 1)$ and $B(7, 3)$. Using the Pythagorean Theorem, you can find AB.

$$(AB)^2 = (AC)^2 + (BC)^2$$

$$(AB)^2 = (7 - 2)^2 + (3 - 1)^2$$

$$(AB)^2 = 5^2 + 2^2$$

$$AB = \sqrt{25 + 4} = \sqrt{29} \approx 5.4$$

AC equals the difference in *x* values.
BC equals the difference in *y* values.

Simplify.

Find the square root.

You can use the Pythagorean Theorem to find the length of a segment on a coordinate plane, or you can use the *Distance Formula*. The Distance Formula is based on the Pythagorean Theorem.

Key Concepts   **Distance Formula**

You can find the **distance** d between any two points (x_1, y_1) and (x_2, y_2):

$$d = \sqrt{(x_2 - x_1)^2 + (y_2 - y_1)^2}$$

1 EXAMPLE   **Using the Distance Formula**

Find the distance between $A(6, 3)$ and $B(1, 9)$.

$$d = \sqrt{(x_2 - x_1)^2 + (y_2 - y_1)^2}$$ Use the Distance Formula.

$$d = \sqrt{(1 - 6)^2 + (9 - 3)^2}$$ Replace (x_2, y_2) with (1, 9) and (x_1, y_1) with (6, 3).

$$d = \sqrt{(-5)^2 + 6^2}$$ Simplify.

$$d = \sqrt{61}$$ Find the exact distance.

$$d \approx 7.8$$ Round to the nearest tenth.

● The distance between A and B is about 7.8 units.

INSTANT CHECK **Ongoing Assessment and Intervention**

Before the Lesson
Diagnose prerequisite skills using:
• Check Skills You'll Need

During the Lesson
Monitor progress using:
• Check Understanding
• Additional Examples
• Test Prep

After the Lesson
Assess knowledge using:
• Lesson Quiz
• Computer Test Generator
  CD-ROM
• Chapter Checkpoint 1 (p. 596)

✓ **Check Understanding** Example 1

1. Find the distance between the two points in each pair. Round to the nearest tenth.

   a. $(3, 8), (2, 4)$ 4.1   **b.** $(10, -3), (1, 0)$ 9.5

You can also use the Distance Formula to solve geometry problems. Wait until the last step to round your answer.

> **Reading Math**
>
> The Distance Formula indicates that you subtract (twice), square (twice), and add before you find the square root.

② EXAMPLE **Finding Perimeter**

Find the perimeter of *ABCD*.

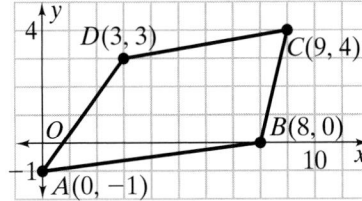

Use the Distance Formula to find the side lengths.

$AB = \sqrt{(8-0)^2 + (0-(-1))^2}$ **Replace (x_2, y_2) with (8, 0) and (x_1, y_1) with (0, −1).**

$= \sqrt{64 + 1} = \sqrt{65}$ **Simplify.**

$BC = \sqrt{(9-8)^2 + (4-0)^2}$ **Replace (x_2, y_2) with (9, 4) and (x_1, y_1) with (8, 0).**

$= \sqrt{1 + 16} = \sqrt{17}$ **Simplify.**

$CD = \sqrt{(3-9)^2 + (3-4)^2}$ **Replace (x_2, y_2) with (3, 3) and (x_1, y_1) with (9, 4).**

$= \sqrt{36 + 1} = \sqrt{37}$ **Simplify.**

$DA = \sqrt{(0-3)^2 + ((-1)-3)^2}$ **Replace (x_2, y_2) with (0, −1) and (x_1, y_1) with (3, 3).**

$= \sqrt{9 + 16} = \sqrt{25} = 5$ **Simplify.**

perimeter $= \sqrt{65} + \sqrt{17} + \sqrt{37} + 5 \approx 23.268126$

● The perimeter is about 23.3 units.

✓ **Check Understanding** Example 2

2. Find the perimeter of $\triangle DEF$ at the right. Round to the nearest tenth. **17.5**

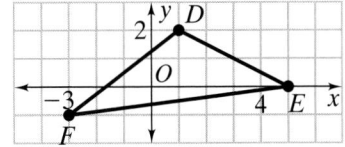

Math Background

The Distance Formula uses the fact that the line segment between two points on a coordinate plane is the hypotenuse of a particular right triangle. The difference in the *x*-coordinates is the length of one leg, and the difference in the *y*-coordinates is the length of the other leg. By the Pythagorean Theorem, the square root of the sum of the squares of these lengths is the length of the hypotenuse, or the distance between the two original points.

Teaching Notes

① EXAMPLE **Error Prevention**

Show students that it does not matter which coordinates are used as (x_1, y_1). Have students calculate the distance using A as (x_1, y_1) and then B as (x_1, y_1). Students will see that the differences of the *x*-coordinates are opposites. The same is true for the differences of the *y*-coordinates. When opposites are squared, the results are the same positive number.

① EXAMPLE **Visual Learners**

Students may calculate $(x_1 - y_1)$ and $(x_2 - y_2)$ instead of $(x_2 - x_1)$ and $(y_2 - y_1)$. Have them first circle the *x*-coordinate in each pair to remind them to subtract *x*-coordinates in the first parentheses, and noncircled *y*-coordinates in the second parentheses.

PowerPoint

📖 Additional Examples

① Find the distance between $T(3, -2)$ and $V(8, 3)$. about 7.1 units

② Find the perimeter of *WXYZ*.

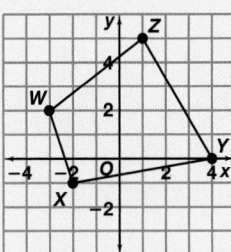

about 20.1 units

👥 Reaching All Students

| **Below Level** Help students understand how to view an oblique segment between two points on a coordinate plane as the hypotenuse of a right triangle. | **Advanced Learners** Ask: *How can you use the Distance Formula to verify the Midpoint Formula?* The distances between the midpoint and each endpoint must be the same. | **Visual Learners** See note on page 593. **English Learners** See note on page 594. |

Additional Examples

3 Find the midpoint of $\overline{TV}$.

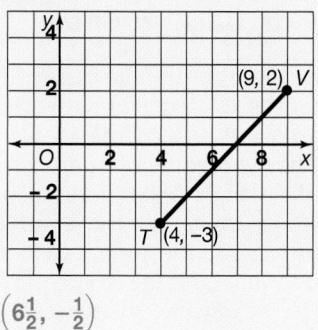

$\left(6\frac{1}{2}, -\frac{1}{2}\right)$

Teaching Tip

Point out that the Midpoint Formula does not use the Pythagorean Theorem. To find the coordinates of the midpoint of a segment, you find the average of the x–coordinates and the average of the y–coordinates of the endpoints of the segment. You may wish to demonstrate on a number line that the average value of two coordinates is the coordinate halfway between them.

3 EXAMPLE **English Learners**

Have students think of another way to express the term *midpoint*. Halfway point is one example.

Closure

Ask students: *What is the Distance Formula and what do you find with it? What is the Midpoint Formula and what do you find with it?* **The Distance Formula is** $d = \sqrt{(x_2 - x_1)^2 + (y_2 - y_1)^2}$. **You use it to find the distance between any two points (x_1, y_1) and (x_2, y_2). The Midpoint Formula is** $M\left(\frac{x_1 + x_2}{2}, \frac{y_1 + y_2}{2}\right)$. **You use it to find the point that is halfway between any two points (x_1, y_1) and (x_2, y_2).**

The **midpoint** of a segment $\overline{AB}$ is the point M on $\overline{AB}$ halfway between the endpoints A and B where $AM = MB$.

Reading Math

Each coordinate of a midpoint is the mean of the corresponding coordinates of the endpoints.

Key Concepts   Midpoint Formula

You can find the midpoint of a line segment with endpoints $A(x_1, y_1)$ and $B(x_2, y_2)$:

$$M\left(\frac{x_1 + x_2}{2}, \frac{y_1 + y_2}{2}\right)$$

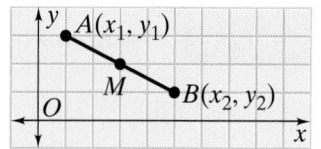

3 EXAMPLE   **Finding the Midpoint of a Segment**

Find the midpoint of $\overline{GH}$.

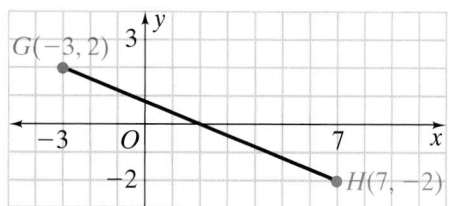

$\left(\frac{x_1 + x_2}{2}, \frac{y_1 + y_2}{2}\right)$ **Use the Midpoint Formula.**

$= \left(\frac{-3 + 7}{2}, \frac{2 + (-2)}{2}\right)$ **Replace (x_1, y_1) with $(-3, 2)$ and (x_2, y_2) with $(7, -2)$.**

$= \left(\frac{4}{2}, \frac{0}{2}\right)$ **Simplify the numerators.**

$= (2, 0)$ **Write the fractions in simplest form.**

The coordinates of the midpoint of $\overline{GH}$ are $(2, 0)$.

✓ **Check Understanding**   Example 3

3. Find the midpoint of each segment.

a.

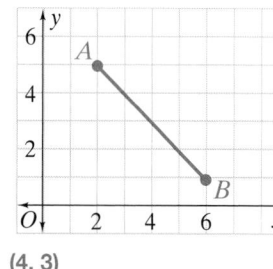

(4, 3)

b.

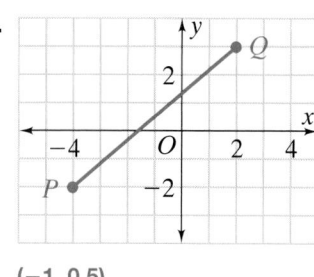

(−1, 0.5)

EXERCISES

 For more exercises, see *Extra Practice*.

Practice and Problem Solving

3. Practice

Assignment Guide

1 Objective 1
Ⓐ Ⓑ Core 1–8, 16
Ⓒ Extension 18

2 Objective 2
Ⓐ Ⓑ Core 9–15, 17
Ⓒ Extension 19

Test Prep 20–22
Mixed Review 23–30

Ⓐ **Practice by Example**

Find the distance between the two points of each pair. Round to the nearest tenth.

Example 1
(page 592)

1. $(1, 5), (5, 2)$ 5
2. $(6, 0), (-6, 5)$ 13
3. $(-5, 10), (11, -7)$
   23.3
4. $(-6, 12), (-3, -7)$
   19.2
5. $(8, -1), (-5, 11)$
   17.7
6. $(12, 3), (-12, 4)$
   24.0

Example 2
(page 593)

Geometry Find the perimeter of each figure.

7.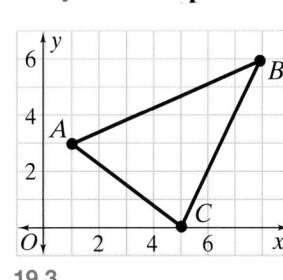
19.3

8.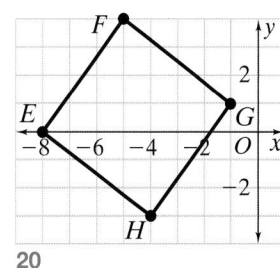
20

Example 3
(page 594)

Find the midpoint of each segment.

9. 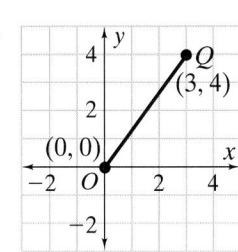 (1.5, 2)

10. 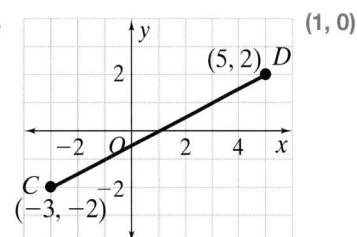 (1, 0)

Ⓑ **Apply Your Skills**

For Exercises 11 and 12, find both the length and the midpoint of the segment joining the two given points. Round to the nearest tenth.

11. $S(9, 12)$ and $U(-9, -12)$
    30; (0, 0)
12. $K(23, 4)$ and $W(-2, 16)$
    27.7; (10.5, 10)

13. The student used subtraction in the numerators instead of addition.
15. No; addition is commutative.
16. No; the square of a number $(x_1 - x_2)$ and the square of its opposite $(x_2 - x_1)$ are equal.

13. **Error Analysis** A student's calculation of the midpoint of the segment with endpoints $A(-4, 2)$ and $B(6, 6)$ is shown at the right. What mistake did the student make?
See left.

$$\left(\frac{(6 - (-4)}{2}, \frac{(6 - 2)}{2}\right)$$
$$= \left(\frac{10}{2}, \frac{4}{2}\right)$$
$$= (5, 2)$$

14. **Reasoning** The midpoint of $\overline{AB}$ is (3, 5). The coordinates of A are $(-6, 1)$. What are the coordinates of B? (12, 9) [GPS]

When you use the indicated formula, does it matter which point you choose as (x_1, y_1)? Explain. 15–16. See left.

15. the Midpoint Formula
16. the Distance Formula

Writing in Math

For help with writing a solution for Exercise 17, see page 597.

17. A segment has endpoints $A(-3, 5)$ and $B(2, 1)$.
   a. Find the midpoint M of the segment. $(-0.5, 3)$
   b. Use the Distance Formula to verify that $AM = MB$.
   See margin.

11-3 Distance and Midpoint Formulas **595**

17b. $AM = \sqrt{(-3 - (-0.5))^2 + (5 - 3)^2} = \sqrt{10.25}$
     $MB = \sqrt{(2 - (-0.5))^2 + (1 - 3)^2} = \sqrt{10.25}$

[GPS] Use the Guided Problem Solving worksheet with Exercise 14.

 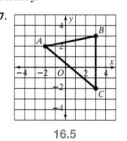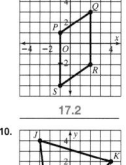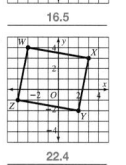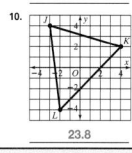

4. Assess

Lesson Quiz 11-3

Find the length (to the nearest tenth) and midpoint of each segment with the given endpoints.

1. $A(-2, -5)$ and $B(-3, 4)$
9.1; $(-2\frac{1}{2}, -\frac{1}{2})$

2. $D(-4, 6)$ and $E(7, -2)$
13.6; $(1\frac{1}{2}, 2)$

3. Find the perimeter of $\triangle ABC$, with coordinates $A(-3, 0)$, $B(0, 4)$, and $C(3, 0)$. **16**

✓ Chapter Checkpoint 1

To check understanding of Lessons 11-1 to 11-3:

Checkpoint Quiz 1 (p. 596)

📁 **Teaching Resources**
Checkpoint Quiz 1 (also in Prentice Hall Assessment System)

👥 **Reaching All Students**
Reading and Math Literacy 11B

Spanish versions available.

Reteaching 11-3 *Distance and Midpoint Formulas*

Find the perimeter of the figure. Round to the nearest tenth where necessary.
Use the distance formula to find the lengths of the sides.
$d = \sqrt{(x_2 - x_1)^2 + (y_2 - y_1)^2}$
First, find the coordinates of the vertices.
$A(-3, 2), B(3, -1)$ and $C(-4, -4)$.
$AB = \sqrt{[3 - (-3)]^2 + [-1 - 2]^2}$ Replace (x_2, y_2) with $(3, -1)$ and (x_1, y_1) with $(-3, 2)$.
$= \sqrt{6^2 + (-3)^2}$ Simplify.
$= \sqrt{36 + 9}$ Find the squares.
$= \sqrt{45}$ Add.
Similarly,
$BC = \sqrt{[3 - (-4)]^2 + [-1 - (-4)]^2}$ $AC = \sqrt{[(-3) - (-4)]^2 + [2 - (-4)]^2}$
$= \sqrt{7^2 + 3^2}$ $= \sqrt{1^2 + 6^2}$
$= \sqrt{49 + 9}$ $= \sqrt{1 + 36}$
$= \sqrt{58}$ $= \sqrt{37}$
The perimeter is the sum of the lengths of the sides.
perimeter $= \sqrt{45} + \sqrt{58} + \sqrt{37} \approx 20.4$
The perimeter is about 20.4 units.

Find the perimeter of each figure. Round to the nearest tenth when necessary.

1.   **2.**

$MN = \underline{5\sqrt{2}}$ $NQ = \underline{\sqrt{13}}$ $UV = \underline{4\sqrt{2}}$ $VW = \underline{\sqrt{53}}$
$MQ = \underline{5}$ $P \approx \underline{15.7}$ $UW = \underline{3\sqrt{5}}$ $P \approx \underline{19.6}$

 **Challenge**

18. Geometry The three vertices of a triangle have coordinates $P(-3, 1)$, $Q(2, -5)$, and $R(4, 6)$. Determine whether the triangle is scalene, isosceles, or equilateral. Show your work.
Scalene; check students' work.

19. Writing in Math Explain how using the Midpoint Formula involves finding averages. Each coordinate of the midpoint is the average of the corresponding coordinates of the endpoints.

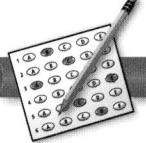

Test Prep

Gridded Response

Use the diagram for Exercises 20 and 21.

20. What is the number of square units in the square? **18**

21. What is the perimeter of the square, to the nearest tenth? **17.0**

💻 **Take It to the NET**
Online lesson quiz at
www.PHSchool.com
Web Code: ada-1103

22. What is the length, to the nearest tenth, of the segment whose endpoints are $A(3, 7)$ and $B(8, 21)$? **14.9**

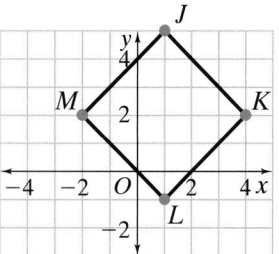

Mixed Review

Lesson 11-2   **Can you form a right triangle with the lengths given?**

23. 8 m, 15 m, 17 m   **24.** 5 in., 8 in., 5 in.   **25.** 20 yd, 12 yd, 16 yd
yes; $8^2 + 15^2 = 17^2$ no; $5^2 + 5^2 \neq 8^2$ yes; $12^2 + 16^2 = 20^2$

Lesson 10-4   **26. Geometry** Draw a net to represent a rectangular prism that is 4 in. long, 3 in. wide, and 2 in. high. Label dimensions on the net.
See below left.

Lesson 6-2   **Solve each proportion.**

27. $\frac{3}{8} = \frac{a}{24}$ **9**   **28.** $\frac{11}{c} = \frac{66}{72}$ **12**   **29.** $\frac{5}{6} = \frac{n}{15}$ **12.5**   **30.** $\frac{b}{1.9} = \frac{7}{9.5}$ **1.4**

26.

4 in.
2 in. | 2 in. | 2 in.
3 in.
2 in.
3 in.

✓ Checkpoint Quiz 1   Lessons 11-1 through 11-3

📱 **TEXT** Instant self-check quiz online and on CD-ROM

Estimate to the nearest integer.

1. $-\sqrt{3}$ **2.** $\sqrt{14}$ **3.** $\sqrt{27}$ **4.** $\sqrt{90}$ **5.** $-\sqrt{45}$ **6.** $\sqrt{105}$
-2   4   5   9   -7   10

The lengths of two legs of a right triangle are given. Find the length of the hypotenuse. Round to the nearest tenth.

7. 6 ft, 8 ft   **8.** 8 m, 14 m   **9.** 7 yd, 24 yd   **10.** 5 cm, 5 cm
10 ft   16.1 m   25 yd   7.1 cm

Find the length of $\overline{AB}$ and the midpoint of $\overline{AB}$. Round the length of $\overline{AB}$ to the nearest tenth.

11. $A(0, -2)$ and $B(-6, -9)$ **12.** $A(8, 11)$ and $B(-5, 2)$
9.2; $(-3, -5.5)$ 15.8; $(1.5, 6.5)$

13. Open-Ended Name three irrational numbers between 10 and 20.
Answers may vary. Sample: $\sqrt{120}$, $\sqrt{299}$, 15.010010001 . . .

596   Chapter 11   Right Triangles in Algebra

Alternative Assessment

Give students a number cube and a counter with "−" marked or taped on one side. Have them form the coordinates of two points by tossing both the number cube and the counter four times. Have the students find the length and midpoint of the segment joining the two points.

Test Prep

📁 **Resources**
For additional practice with a variety of test item formats:
• Test Prep, p. 625
• Test-Taking Strategies, p. 620
• Test-Taking Strategies With Transparencies

Writing in Math

Writing to Justify

For Use With Page 595, Exercise 17

One way to justify your solution of a problem is to give a reason for each step you take, keeping in mind the persons who will read your work. Acceptable reasons include properties and procedures that you and your audience have agreed upon.

EXAMPLE

A segment has endpoints $A(-3, 5)$ and $B(2, 1)$.
a. Find the midpoint M of the segment.
b. Use the Distance Formula to verify that $AM = MB$.

a. First find the midpoint of $\overline{AB}$.

Steps	Reasons
$\left(\dfrac{-3 + 2}{2}, \dfrac{5 + 1}{2}\right)$	Use the Midpoint Formula. Replace (x_1, y_1) with $(-3, 5)$ and (x_2, y_2) with $(2, 1)$.
$\left(-\dfrac{1}{2}, 3\right)$ or $(-0.5, 3)$	Simplify.

b. Next verify that this is the midpoint M by showing that $AM = MB$.

Steps	Reasons
$AM = \sqrt{(-0.5 - (-3))^2 + (3 - 5)^2}$	Find *AM*. Use the Distance Formula.
$AM = \sqrt{10.25}$	Simplify.
$MB = \sqrt{(2 - (-0.5))^2 + (1 - 3)^2}$	Find *MB*. Use the Distance Formula.
$MB = \sqrt{10.25}$	Simplify.

Since AM and MB are both $\sqrt{10.25}$, $AM = MB$ and $(-0.5, 3)$ is the midpoint of $\overline{AB}$.

EXERCISES

Solve each problem. Justify your steps to verify your answer.

1. Find the perimeter of the triangle with vertices located at $(5, 9)$, $(7, 4)$, and $(-3, 7)$. **See right.**

2. The vertices of a triangle are located at $(-1, 5), (2, 5)$, and $(2, 1)$. Show that this is a right triangle. (*Hint:* Use the Distance Formula and the Converse of the Pythagorean Theorem.) **See right.**

1. Answers may vary. Sample: Using the Distance Formula, the three sides are $\sqrt{29}$, $\sqrt{109}$, and $\sqrt{68}$. Rounded to the nearest tenth, the perimeter is 24.1.

2. Answers may vary. Sample: The sides are 3, 4, and 5. It is a right triangle because $3^2 + 4^2 = 5^2$.

Teaching Notes

Auditory Learners
Have students quietly read aloud to themselves the steps and reasons in the Example.

Visual Learners
Have students draw diagrams to aid in solving the exercises.

Error Prevention!

Remind students, when using the Distance Formula, to carefully substitute the *x*- and *y*- coordinates.

Teaching Tip
Have students solve the exercises independently. Then have them share their steps and justifications with each other.

Tactile Learners
If the floor of the classroom has square floor tiles, ask for three volunteers to represent the three vertices of the triangle in each exercise. Have the students display pieces of paper listing their coordinates. Then ask a volunteer to describe the steps needed to solve the problem.

11-4

Lesson Preview

 Check Skills You'll Need

Proportions
Lesson 6-2: Example 1;
Exercises 1–12.
Extra Practice, p. 749.

Lesson Resources

 Teaching Resources
Practice, Reteaching, Enrichment

 **Reaching All Students**
Practice Workbook 11-4
Spanish Practice Workbook 11-4
Guided Problem Solving 11-4
Technology Activities 30
Hands-On Activities 16

 Presentation Assistant Plus!
Transparencies and PowerPoint™
• Check Skills You'll Need 11-4
• Additional Examples 11-4
• Student Edition Answers 11-4
• Lesson Quiz 11-4
PH Presentation Pro CD-ROM 11-4

ASSESSMENT SYSTEM

Computer Test Generator CD-ROM

 Technology
Resource Pro® CD-ROM
Computer Test Generator CD-ROM
PH Presentation Pro CD-ROM

 www.PHSchool.com
Student Site
• Teacher Web Code: adk-5500
• Self-grading Lesson Quiz
PH SuccessNet Teacher Center
• Lesson Planner
• Resources

Plus

 11-4 Problem Solving

Write a Proportion

OBJECTIVE

1 Write a Proportion

Math Strategies in Action You can't measure distance across the Grand Canyon with a tape measure. Yet, distances across it have been measured. How were they measured?

Surveyors sometimes find such distances indirectly using similar triangles and proportions. You learned about these in Lessons 6-2 and 6-3. Now let's see how you can use similar right triangles and proportions to find measurements indirectly.

1 EXAMPLE Real-World 🌐 Problem Solving

Surveying To find the distance from P to P across a canyon, a surveyor picks points R and S such that $\overline{RS}$ is perpendicular to $\overline{RP}$. He locates point T on $\overline{SP}$ such that $\overline{QT}$ is perpendicular to $\overline{RP}$. The two triangles, $\triangle PRS$ and $\triangle PQT$, are similar. He then measures $\overline{RS}$, $\overline{RQ}$, and $\overline{QT}$. What is the distance QP across the canyon?

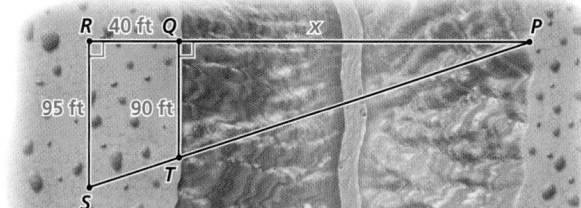

Not drawn to scale

Test-Taking Tip

If problems involving distance do not include diagrams, draw your own to help you solve the problem.

Interactive lesson includes instant self-check, tutorials, and activities.

Read and Understand

1. What information is given?

2. What are you asked to find? *QP*

1. $\overline{RS}$ is perpendicular to $\overline{RP}$; $\overline{QT}$ is perpendicular to $\overline{RP}$; $\triangle PRS \sim \triangle PQT$; lengths *RS*, *RQ*, and *QT*

Ongoing Assessment and Intervention

Before the Lesson	**During the Lesson**	**After the Lesson**
Diagnose prerequisite skills using:	Monitor progress using:	Assess knowledge using:
• Check Skills You'll Need	• Check Understanding	• Lesson Quiz
	• Additional Examples	• Computer Test Generator
	• Test Prep	CD-ROM

Plan and Solve

Since $\triangle PQT \sim \triangle PRS$ and you know three lengths, writing and solving a proportion is a good strategy to use. It is helpful to draw the triangles as separate figures.

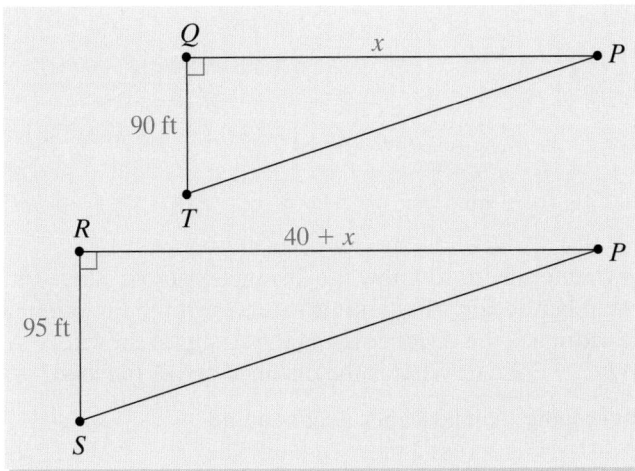

Write a proportion using the legs of the similar right triangles.

$\dfrac{x}{40 + x} = \dfrac{90}{95}$ **Write a proportion.**

$95x = 90(40 + x)$ **Write cross products.**

$95x = 3{,}600 + 90x$ **Use the Distributive Property.**

$5x = 3{,}600$ **Subtract 90x from each side.**

$x = 720$ **Divide each side by 5.**

The distance QP across the canyon is 720 ft.

Look Back and Check

Solving problems that involve indirect measurement often makes use of figures that *overlap*. Use the diagram on page 598 to answer the following questions.

✓ **Check Understanding**

3. Which segments overlap? $\overline{RQ}$ and $\overline{RP}$, $\overline{ST}$ and $\overline{SP}$

4. A common error students make is to use part of a side in a proportion. For example, some students might think $\frac{40}{95}$ is equal to $\frac{x}{90}$. How does drawing the triangles as separate figures help you avoid this error? It allows you to draw the entire $40 + x$ side to complete the larger triangle.

Professional Development

Math Background

If $\triangle ABC$ is similar to $\triangle DEF$, then $\frac{AB}{DE} = \frac{BC}{EF} = \frac{AC}{DF}$. You can use proportions like these to find lengths of the sides in similar triangles. Substitute three known lengths into a proportion and solve for the unknown length.

Teaching Notes

1 EXAMPLE   **Visual Learners**

Draw the diagram on the board. Draw a bracket from R to P and write $40 + x$ over the bracket to help students see that they need to add 40 and x to represent the length of the side of the larger triangle.

Geography Connection

Scientists have tried to use math to measure the height of Mt. Everest, whose peak is the highest point above sea level on Earth. Methods have included reflecting light off mirrors, using radar, and bouncing signals off satellites.

PowerPoint

Additional Examples

1 At a given time of day, a building of unknown height casts a shadow that is 24 feet long. At the same time of day, a post that is 8 feet tall casts a shadow that is 4 feet long. What is the height x of the building? 48 ft

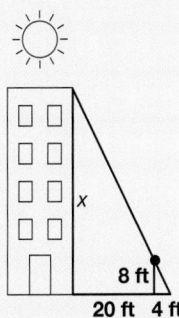

Reaching All Students

Below Level Review similar figures in Lesson 6-3. Remind students that corresponding angles are congruent and corresponding sides are in proportion.

Advanced Learners After working Example 1, ask: *What is another method you could use to find TP once you know QP and QT?* the Pythagorean Theorem

Visual Learners See note on page 599. **Error Prevention** See note on page 601.

Closure

Ask: *How can you measure a distance indirectly using similar triangles?* Find three lengths, write a proportion, and solve for the fourth length.

3. Practice

Assignment Guide

1 Objective 1

Ⓐ Ⓑ **Core** 1–9
Ⓒ **Extension** 10–12

Test Prep 13–15
Mixed Review 16–20

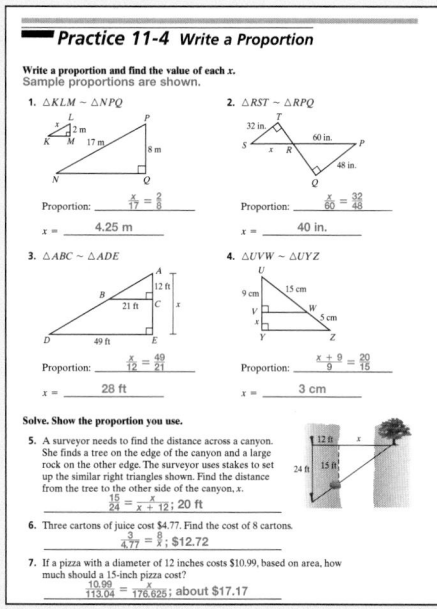

Practice 11-4 *Write a Proportion*

Write a proportion and find the value of each *x*.
Sample proportions are shown.

1. △KLM ~ △NPQ

2. △RST ~ △RPQ

Proportion: $\frac{x}{17} = \frac{2}{8}$ Proportion: $\frac{x}{60} = \frac{32}{48}$

x = ____ 4.25 m   *x* = ____ 40 in.

3. △ABC ~ △ADE

4. △UVW ~ △UYZ

Proportion: $\frac{x}{12} = \frac{49}{21}$ Proportion: $\frac{x+9}{9} = \frac{20}{15}$

x = ____ 28 ft   *x* = ____ 3 cm

Solve. Show the proportion you use.

5. A surveyor needs to find the distance across a canyon. She finds a tree on the edge of the canyon and a large rock on the other edge. The surveyor uses stakes to set up the similar right triangles shown. Find the distance from the tree to the other side of the canyon, *x*.
$\frac{15}{24} = \frac{x}{x+12}$; 20 ft

6. Three cartons of juice cost $4.77. Find the cost of 8 cartons.
$\frac{3}{4.77} = \frac{8}{x}$; $12.72

7. If a pizza with a diameter of 12 inches costs $10.99, based on area, how much should a 15-inch pizza cost?
$\frac{10.99}{113.04} = \frac{x}{176.625}$; about $17.17

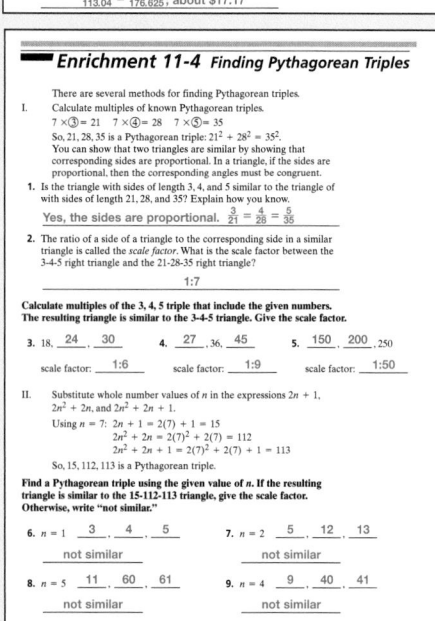

Enrichment 11-4 *Finding Pythagorean Triples*

There are several methods for finding Pythagorean triples.

I. Calculate multiples of known Pythagorean triples.
7 ×③ = 21   7 ×④ = 28   7 ×⑤ = 35
So, 21, 28, 35 is a Pythagorean triple: $21^2 + 28^2 = 35^2$.
You can show that two triangles are similar by showing that corresponding sides are proportional. In a triangle, if the sides are proportional, then the corresponding angles must be congruent.

1. Is the triangle with sides of length 3, 4, and 5 similar to the triangle of with sides of length 21, 28, and 35? Explain how you know.
Yes, the sides are proportional. $\frac{3}{21} = \frac{4}{28} = \frac{5}{35}$

2. The ratio of a side of a triangle to the corresponding side in a similar triangle is called the *scale factor*. What is the scale factor between the 3-4-5 right triangle and the 21-28-35 right triangle?
1:7

Calculate multiples of the 3, 4, 5 triple that include the given numbers. The resulting triangle is similar to the 3-4-5 triangle. Give the scale factor.

3. 18, __24__, __30__   **4.** __27__, 36, __45__   **5.** __150__, __200__, 250
scale factor: __1:6__   scale factor: __1:9__   scale factor: __1:50__

II. Substitute whole number values of *n* in the expressions $2n + 1$, $2n^2 + 2n$, and $2n^2 + 2n + 1$.
Using $n = 7$: $2n + 1 = 2(7) + 1 = 15$
$2n^2 + 2n = 2(7)^2 + 2(7) = 112$
$2n^2 + 2n + 1 = 2(7)^2 + 2(7) + 1 = 113$
So, 15, 112, 113 is a Pythagorean triple.

Find a Pythagorean triple using the given value of *n*. If the resulting triangle is similar to the 15-112-113 triangle, give the scale factor. Otherwise, write "not similar."

6. *n* = 1   __3__, __4__, __5__   **7.** *n* = 2   __5__, __12__, __13__
__not similar__   __not similar__

8. *n* = 5   __11__, __60__, __61__   **9.** *n* = 4   __9__, __40__, __41__
__not similar__   __not similar__

EXERCISES

🔍 For more exercises, see *Extra Practice*.

Practice and Problem Solving

Ⓐ **Practice by Example**

Example 1
(page 598)

1. $\frac{20}{x+20} = \frac{13}{21}$; 12.3 m

2. $\frac{x}{15} = \frac{60}{25}$; 36 yd

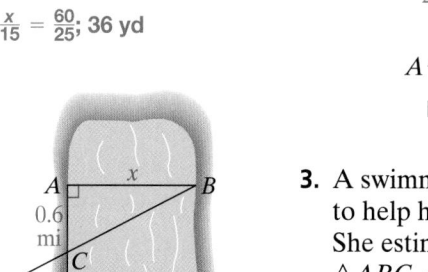

Ⓑ **Apply Your Skills** 🌐

Strategies

- Account for All Possibilities
- Draw a Diagram
- Look for a Pattern
- Make a Model
- Make a Table
- Simplify the Problem
- Simulate the Problem
- Solve by Graphing
- Try, Test, Revise
- Use Multiple Strategies
- Work Backward
- Write an Equation
- Write a Proportion

In Exercises 1–5, write a proportion and find the value of each *x*.

1. △ABE ~ △ACD
See left.

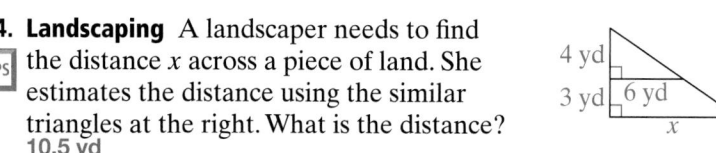

2. △GHI ~ △KJI
See left.

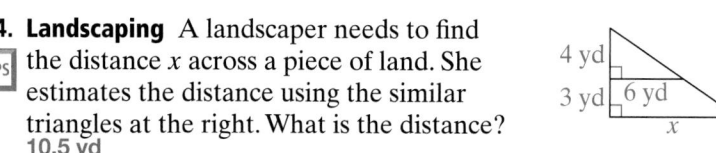

3. A swimmer needs to know the distance *x* across a lake (at left) to help her decide whether it is safe to swim to the other side. She estimates the distance using the triangles shown. △ABC ~ △EDC. What is the distance across the lake? **1.2 mi**

4. Landscaping A landscaper needs to find the distance *x* across a piece of land. She estimates the distance using the similar triangles at the right. What is the distance? **10.5 yd**

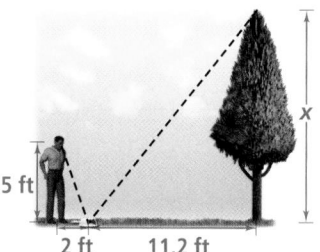

5. Indirect Measurement To estimate the height of a tree, Milton positions a mirror on the ground so he can see the top of the tree reflected in it. His height, his distance from the mirror, and his line of sight to the mirror determine a triangle. The tree's height, its distance from the mirror, and the distance from the top of the tree to the mirror form a similar triangle. Use the measurements shown to determine the height of the tree. **28 ft**

Solve using any strategy.

6. There are 30 students in a math class. Twelve belong to the computer club, and eight belong to the photography club. Three belong to both clubs. How many belong to neither club?
13 students

7. Jake spent $\frac{3}{8}$ of his money on a book and $\frac{1}{2}$ of what was left on a magazine. He now has $6.25. How much money did he start with?
$20

8. Hai takes 12 minutes to walk to school. He wants to get there 15 minutes early to meet with his lab partner. What time should he leave his house if school starts at 8:10 A.M.? **7:43 A.M.**

9. Number Sense Christa thought of a number. She added 4, multiplied the sum by −5, and subtracted 12. She then doubled the result and got −34. What number did Christa start with? **−3**

600 Chapter 11 Right Triangles in Algebra

GPS Use the Guided Problem Solving worksheet with Exercise 4.

Real-World Connection

The Eiffel Tower was named for its designer, Gustave Eiffel, who also designed the Statue of Liberty framework.

C Challenge

10. The height of the Eiffel Tower is 984 ft. A souvenir model of the tower is 6 in. tall. At 5 P.M. in Paris, the shadow of the souvenir model is 8 in. long. The Eiffel Tower and its shadow determine two legs of a right triangle that are similar to the two legs of a right triangle determined by the souvenir model and its shadow. About how long is the shadow of the Eiffel Tower? **1,312 ft**

11. **Architecture** Madison Square Garden in New York City is built in the shape of a circle. Its diameter is 404 ft and it accommodates 20,234 spectators. To the nearest tenth of a square foot, how much area is there for each spectator? **6.3 ft²**

12. **Algebra** You serve a tennis ball from one end of a tennis court, 39 ft from the net. You hit the ball at 9 feet above the ground. It travels in a straight path down the middle of the court, and just clears the top of the 3-ft net. This is illustrated in the diagram. $\triangle PQR \sim \triangle MQS$. How far from the net does the ball land? **19.5 ft**

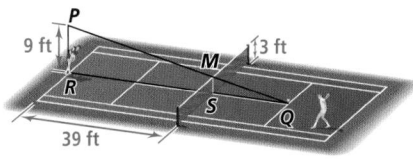

Test Prep

Multiple Choice

13. In the diagram at the right, what is x? **B**
   A. 43.75 B. 28
   C. 26.25 D. 17

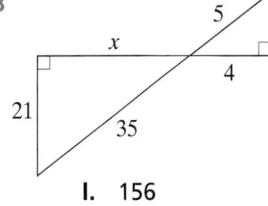

Take It to the NET
Online lesson quiz at
www.PHSchool.com
Web Code: ada-1104

14. What is the value of x in this proportion, $\frac{65}{50} = \frac{x + 36}{x}$? **H**
   F. 15   G. 60   H. 120   I. 156

Short Response

15. Suppose a friend says to you "x is to $x + 1.5$ as 64 is to 72."
   a. Write a proportion to solve for x.
   b. Solve your proportion. **See back of book.**

Mixed Review

Lesson 11-3   **Find the midpoint of each segment with given endpoints.**

16. $A(2, 3)$ and $B(4, 7)$ **(3, 5)**   17. $L(-1, 2)$ and $M(2, 6)$ **(0.5, 4)**

Lessons 9-3   **Sketch each figure.** **18–19. See margin.**

18. isosceles right triangle   19. scalene obtuse triangle

Lesson 7-4   20. **Fundraising** Keith collected twice as much money as Lucy for a walkathon. Together they collected $120. How much money did each person collect? **Keith $80, Lucy $40**

11-4 Write a Proportion   **601**

---

4. Assess

PowerPoint Lesson Quiz 11-4

Write a proportion and solve.

1. On the blueprints for a rectangular floor, the width of the floor is 6 in. The diagonal distance across the floor is 10 in. If the width of the actual floor is 32 ft, what is the actual diagonal distance across the floor?
   about 53 ft

2. A right triangle with side lengths 3 cm, 4 cm, and 5 cm is similar to a right triangle with a 20-cm hypotenuse. Find the perimeter of the larger triangle. **48 cm**

3. A 6-ft-tall man standing near a geyser has a shadow 4.5 ft long. The geyser has a shadow 15 ft long. What is the height of the geyser?
   20 ft

Error Prevention!

Exercise 10 Encourage students to draw a sketch for the problem to help them set up the necessary proportions correctly.

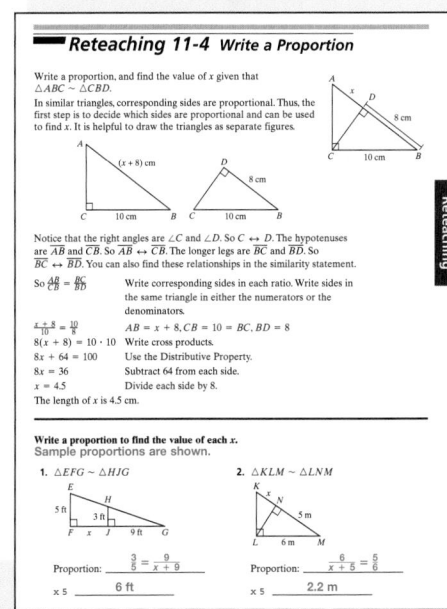

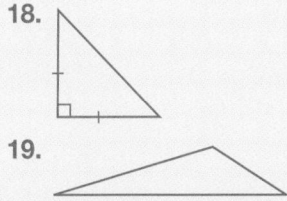

Alternative Assessment

Place students in small groups. Ask each group to find a height around the school that they can measure only by using similar triangles and proportions. Have students present their measurements and explain their methods.

Test Prep

Resources
For additional practice with a variety of test item formats:
• Test Prep, p. 625
• Test-Taking Strategies, p. 620
• Test-Taking Strategies With Transparencies

601

Lesson Preview

 Check Skills You'll Need

The Pythagorean Theorem
Lesson 11-2: Examples 1 and 2;
Exercises 1–8.
Extra Practice, p. 754.

Lesson Resources

 **Teaching Resources**
Practice, Reteaching, Enrichment

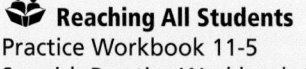 **Reaching All Students**
Practice Workbook 11-5
Spanish Practice Workbook 11-5
Guided Problem Solving 11-5

Presentation Assistant Plus!
Transparencies and PowerPoint™
• Check Skills You'll Need 11-5
• Additional Examples 11-5
• Student Edition Answers 11-5
• Lesson Quiz 11-5
PH Presentation Pro CD-ROM 11-5

ASSESSMENT SYSTEM

Computer Test Generator CD-ROM

 Technology
Resource Pro® CD-ROM
Computer Test Generator CD-ROM
PH Presentation Pro CD-ROM

 www.PHSchool.com
Student Site
• Teacher Web Code: adk-5500
• Self-grading Lesson Quiz
PH SuccessNet Teacher Center
• Lesson Planner
• Resources

Plus **iTEXT**

 **11-5**

Special Right Triangles

 1 **Using 45°-45°-90° Triangles**

The Pythagorean Theorem requires that you understand square roots. The rule for Multiplying Square Roots will help you work with square roots more efficiently.

Key Concepts **Multiplying Square Roots**

For nonnegative numbers, the square root of a product equals the product of the square roots.

Arithmetic	**Algebra**
$\sqrt{9 \cdot 2} = \sqrt{9} \cdot \sqrt{2}$	If $a \geq 0$ and $b \geq 0$, then $\sqrt{ab} = \sqrt{a} \cdot \sqrt{b}$.

The rule for Multiplying Square Roots is especially useful with an isosceles right triangle, which is also known by its angle measures as a 45°-45°-90° triangle. You can use the rule to relate the lengths of the sides and the hypotenuse in such a triangle.

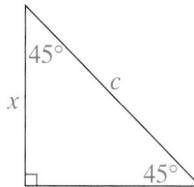

$c^2 = a^2 + b^2$	**Use the Pythagorean Theorem.**
$c^2 = x^2 + x^2$	**Replace a and b with x.**
$c^2 = 2x^2$	**Simplify.**
$c = \sqrt{2x^2}$	**Find the square root.**
$c = \sqrt{2} \cdot \sqrt{x^2}$	**Use the rule for Multiplying Square Roots.**
$c = \sqrt{2} \cdot x$, or $x\sqrt{2}$	**Simplify.**

This shows the following special relationship.

Key Concepts **45°-45°-90° Triangles**

In a 45°-45°-90° triangle, the legs are congruent and the length of the hypotenuse is the length of a leg times $\sqrt{2}$.

$$\text{hypotenuse} = \text{leg} \cdot \sqrt{2}$$

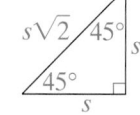

What You'll Learn

OBJECTIVE
1 To use the relationships in 45°-45°-90° triangles

OBJECTIVE
2 To use the relationships in 30°-60°-90° triangles

. . . And Why

To find distances in real-world situations, such as in sports

 Check Skills You'll Need

Find the missing side of each right triangle.

1. legs: 6 m and 8 m
10 m
2. leg: 9 m; hypotenuse: 15 m
12 m
3. legs: 27 m and 36 m
45 m
4. leg: 48 m; hypotenuse: 60 m
36 m

 For help, go to Lesson 11-2.

iTEXT Interactive lesson includes instant self-check, tutorials, and activities.

INSTANT CHECK SYSTEM

Ongoing Assessment and Intervention

Before the Lesson	**During the Lesson**	**After the Lesson**
Diagnose prerequisite skills using:	**Monitor progress using:**	**Assess knowledge using:**
• Check Skills You'll Need	• Check Understanding	• Lesson Quiz
	• Additional Examples	• Computer Test Generator CD-ROM
	• Test Prep	

1 EXAMPLE Finding Length of the Hypotenuse

Find the length of the hypotenuse in the triangle at the right.

hypotenuse = leg · $\sqrt{2}$ **Use the 45°-45°-90° relationship.**

$x = 6 · \sqrt{2}$ **The length of the leg is 6.**

≈ 8.5 **Use a calculator.**

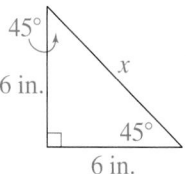

● The length of the hypotenuse is about 8.5 in.

✓ **Check Understanding** Example 1

1. The length of each leg of an isosceles right triangle is 4.2 cm. Find the length of the hypotenuse. Round to the nearest tenth. **5.9 cm**

You can use 45°-45°-90° triangles in real-world situations.

2 EXAMPLE Real-World 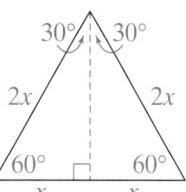 Problem Solving

Baseball **A baseball diamond is a square. The distance from any base to the next is 90 ft. How far is it from home plate to second base?**

hypotenuse = leg · $\sqrt{2}$ **Use the 45°-45°-90° relationship.**

$= 90 · \sqrt{2}$ **The length of the leg is 90.**

≈ 127.28 **Use a calculator.**

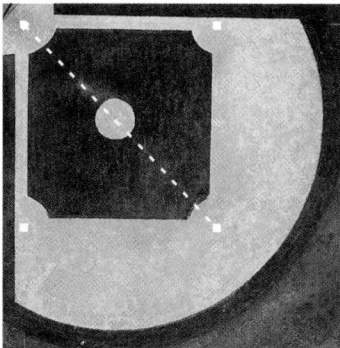

● The distance from home plate to second base is about 127 ft.

✓ **Check Understanding** Example 2

2. Gymnasts use mats that are 12 m by 12 m for floor exercises. A gymnast does cartwheels across the diagonal of a mat. What is the length of the diagonal to the nearest meter? **17 m**

OBJECTIVE

2 Using 30°-60°-90° Triangles

Another special right triangle is the 30°-60°-90° triangle. You can form two congruent 30°-60°-90° triangles by bisecting an angle of an equilateral triangle. This is shown in the diagram.

In the diagram, the length of the hypotenuse of each 30°-60°-90° triangle is twice the length of the shorter leg. You can use the Pythagorean Theorem to find the length of the longer leg.

11-5 Special Right Triangles **603**

Reaching All Students

Below Level Have students use rulers and protractors to draw right triangles, each with congruent legs. Have them measure the acute angles to verify the acute angles are always 45°.

Advanced Learners Challenge students to find the longer leg of a 30°-60°-90° triangle with a hypotenuse of b ft. $\frac{b\sqrt{3}}{2}$ **ft**

Tactile Learners See note on page 604.
Error Prevention See note on page 604.

Math Background

You can check the rule for Multiplying Square Roots by finding $\sqrt{36}$ and comparing it to $\sqrt{9} · \sqrt{4}$. **6 = 3 · 2** You can use the rule for Multiplying Square Roots to simplify many square roots. For example, $\sqrt{27} = \sqrt{9} · \sqrt{3}$. Since 9 is a perfect square, $\sqrt{27} = 3\sqrt{3}$.

Teaching Notes

Geometry Connection
The sum of the measures of the angles of a triangle is 180°. If, for a right triangle, you subtract 90° for the right angle, then 90° remain to be shared by the two other angles. In particular, the acute angles of any isosceles right triangle are congruent and hence 45° each.

1 EXAMPLE Teaching Tip

With some calculators, you press the square root key after entering the number, and with others you press the square root key first. Have students test their calculators so they know which order to use.

PowerPoint
Additional Examples

1 Find the length of the hypotenuse in the triangle.

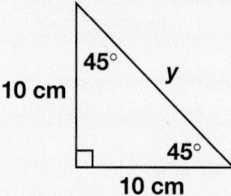

about 14.1 cm

2 Patrice folds square napkins diagonally to put on a table. The side length of each napkin is 20 in. How long is the diagonal? **about 28.3 in.**

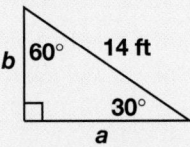
❸ Find the missing lengths in the triangle.

b | 60° | 14 ft

30°

a

b = 7 ft; *a* ≈ 12.1 ft

Tactile Learners

Point out that the shortest side of a triangle is across from the smallest angle and the longest side is across from the largest angle. Have students draw a large scalene right triangle and measure the angles and sides to verify this. So, for a 30°-60°-90° triangle, students can place a finger on the 30° angle, and then move the finger across the triangle to find the shortest side.

Teaching Tip

On the board, label the shorter leg of a 30°-60°-90° triangle as *s*. Then label the longer leg $s\sqrt{3}$ and the hypotenuse 2*s*. Help students see that if they are given the longer leg or the hypotenuse and have to find the other two sides, then they should first find the shorter leg. Both of the other sides have the value of the shorter leg (*s* in your diagram) in their formulas. Therefore, calculations are easier if they find the shorter leg first.

❸ **EXAMPLE** **Error Prevention**

Students sometimes confuse which square root, $\sqrt{2}$ or $\sqrt{3}$, to use when working with a special right triangle. To help, point out that there are two congruent angles in a 45°-45°-90° triangle. The two congruent angles can serve as a reminder to use $\sqrt{2}$. There are three different angles in a 30°-60°-90° triangle. The three different angles can serve as a reminder to use $\sqrt{3}$.

Closure

Ask: *What special relationships exist in a 45°-45°-90° triangle? In a 30°-60°-90° triangle?*
45°-45°-90°: The length of the hypotenuse is the length of a leg

For the figure at the right, find the length of the longer leg.

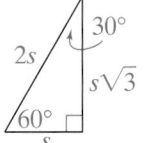

$$(2x)^2 = x^2 + b^2 \quad \textbf{Use the Pythagorean Theorem.}$$
$$4x^2 = x^2 + b^2 \quad \textbf{Simplify.}$$
$$3x^2 = b^2 \quad \textbf{Subtract } x^2 \textbf{ from each side.}$$
$$\sqrt{3x^2} = b \quad \textbf{Find the square root.}$$
$$\sqrt{3} \cdot \sqrt{x^2} = b \quad \textbf{Rule for Multiplying Square Roots}$$
$$b = \sqrt{3} \cdot x, \text{ or } x\sqrt{3} \quad \textbf{Simplify.}$$

This shows the special relationship of the hypotenuse and the legs in a 30°-60°-90° triangle.

> **Key Concepts** **30°-60°-90° Triangle**
>
> In a 30°-60°-90° triangle, the length of the hypotenuse is 2 times the length of the shorter leg. The length of the longer leg is the length of the shorter leg times $\sqrt{3}$.
>
> $$\text{hypotenuse} = 2 \cdot \text{shorter leg}$$
> $$\text{longer leg} = \text{shorter leg} \cdot \sqrt{3}$$

❸ **EXAMPLE** **Finding Lengths in a 30°-60°-90° Triangle**

Find the missing lengths in the triangle.

$$\text{hypotenuse} = 2 \cdot \text{shorter leg}$$
$$x = 2 \cdot 5 \quad \textbf{The length of the shorter leg is 5.}$$
$$x = 10 \quad \textbf{Simplify.}$$
$$\text{longer leg} = \text{shorter leg} \cdot \sqrt{3}$$
$$y = 5 \cdot \sqrt{3} \quad \textbf{The length of the shorter leg is 5.}$$
$$y \approx 8.7 \quad \textbf{Use a calculator.}$$

The length of the hypotenuse is 10 ft, and the length of the longer leg is about 8.7 ft.

✔ **Check Understanding** Example 3

3a. *a* ≈ 6.9 cm
    b = 8 cm
3b. *e* = 6 in.
    f ≈ 10.4 in.

3. Find the missing lengths in each 30°-60°-90° triangle. **a–b. See left.**

a.

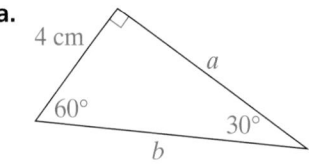

b.

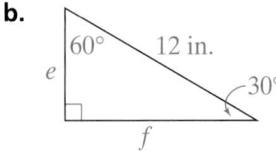

times $\sqrt{2}$. 30°-60°-90°: The length of the hypotenuse is 2 times the length of the shorter leg, and the length of the longer leg is the length of the shorter leg times $\sqrt{3}$.

EXERCISES

For more exercises, see *Extra Practice*.

Practice and Problem Solving

A Practice by Example

Example 1
(page 603)

The lengths of the legs of an isosceles right triangle are given. Find the length of each hypotenuse to the nearest tenth.

1.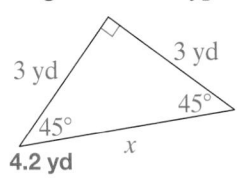

3 yd
3 yd
45°
45°
4.2 yd   x

2.

x
45°
9 cm
12.7 cm

3. legs: 5.4 in.   **7.6 in.**   **4.** legs: 17 ft   **24.0 ft**   **5.** legs: 21 m   **29.7 m**

Example 2
(page 603)

6. Ballet A ballet teacher wants to divide his square classroom in half diagonally with masking tape. How much tape will he need if the side length of the classroom is 40 ft?   **about 56.6 ft**

7. Flooring A square piece of tile with sides 12 in. is cut along a diagonal. What is the length of the diagonal rounded to the nearest inch?   **17 in.**

Example 3
(page 604)

Find the missing lengths. Round to the nearest tenth.

8.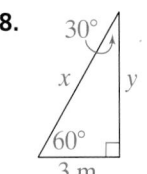

30°   x = 6 m, y ≈ 5.2 m
x   y
60°
3 m

9.

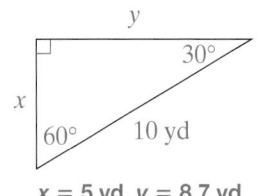

y
30°
x
60°   10 yd

x = 5 yd, y = 8.7 yd

B Apply Your Skills

10.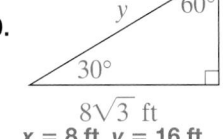

y   60°
30°   x
8√3 ft
x = 8 ft, y = 16 ft

11.

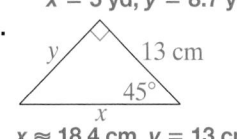

y   13 cm
45°
x

x ≈ 18.4 cm, y = 13 cm

13. Answers may vary. Sample: The hypotenuse is twice the shorter leg. Since the shorter leg is 10 ft, the hypotenuse is 20 ft. The longer leg is √3 times the shorter leg, which is 10√3, or about 17.3 ft.

12. Error Analysis A student says that a right triangle with a hypotenuse of length 2√2 in. has to be an isosceles right triangle. What mistake might the student have made?   **See margin.**

13. Writing in Math Explain how to find the lengths of the longer leg and hypotenuse of a 30°-60°-90° triangle if the shorter leg is 10 ft. See left.

14. Mrs. Fernandez wants to string a rope diagonally across her square classroom for her students to hang their completed art projects. If one side of the room measures 20 ft, what is the minimum length of rope she can use?   **about 28.3 ft**

Simplify. Use the rule for Multiplying Square Roots.

15. $\sqrt{3} \cdot \sqrt{27}$ **9**   **16.** $\sqrt{50} \cdot \sqrt{2}$ **10**   **17.** $\sqrt{36} \cdot \sqrt{4}$ **12**

C Challenge

18. Reasoning The smaller angles of a 30°-60°-90° triangle are in the ratio 1:2. Are the shorter sides also in the ratio 1:2? Explain.
No, the ratio of the shorter leg to the longer leg is 1 : √3. The ratio of the shorter leg to the hypotenuse is 1 : 2.

11-5 Special Right Triangles   **605**

12. Answers may vary. Sample: The student knows that the length of the hypotenuse of an isosceles right triangle with leg length 2 is 2√2. Because of this, the student might assume that a right triangle with hypotenuse length 2√2 must be isosceles. However, a triangle with legs √2 and √6, for example, has hypotenuse length 2√2.

 Use the Guided Problem Solving worksheet with Exercise 14.

---

3. Practice

Assignment Guide

1 Objective 1
A **B** Core 1–7, 11, 12, 14
C Extension 20

2 Objective 2
A **B** 8–10, 13, 15–17
C Extension 18, 19

Test Prep 21–25
Mixed Review 26–31

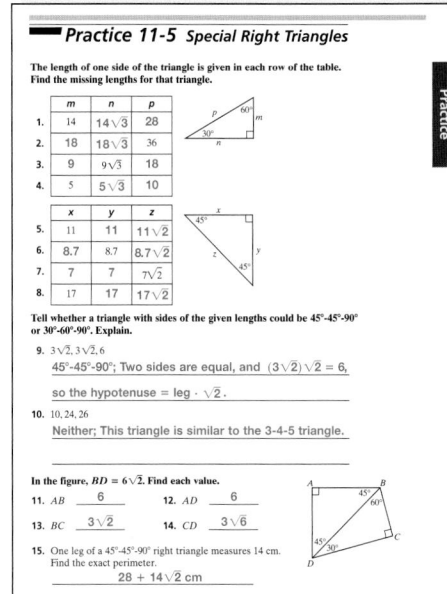

Practice 11-5 *Special Right Triangles*

The length of one side of the triangle is given in each row of the table. Find the missing lengths for that triangle.

	m	n	p
1.	14	14√3	28
2.	18	18√3	36
3.	9	9√3	18
4.	5	5√3	10

	x	y	z
5.	11	11	11√2
6.	8.7	8.7	8.7√2
7.	7	7	7√2
8.	17	17	17√2

Tell whether a triangle with sides of the given lengths could be 45°-45°-90° or 30°-60°-90°. Explain.

9. 3√2, 3√2, 6
45°-45°-90°; Two sides are equal, and (3√2)√2 = 6, so the hypotenuse = leg · √2.

10. 10, 24, 26
Neither; This triangle is similar to the 3-4-5 triangle.

In the figure, BD = 6√2. Find each value.

11. AB __6__   12. AD __6__
13. BC __3√2__   14. CD __3√6__

15. One leg of a 45°-45°-90° right triangle measures 14 cm. Find the exact perimeter.
28 + 14√2 cm

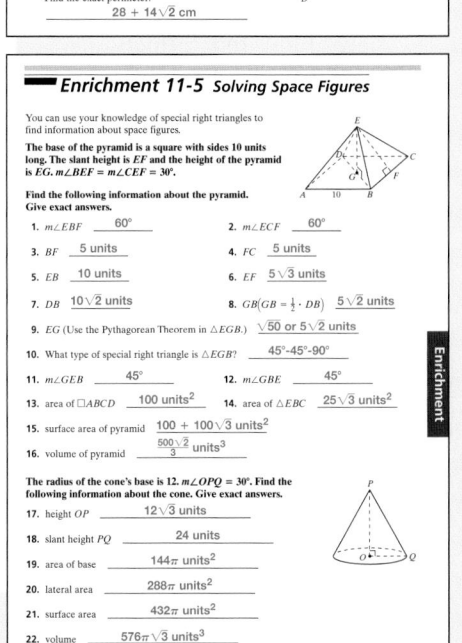

Enrichment 11-5 *Solving Space Figures*

You can use your knowledge of special right triangles to find information about space figures.

The base of the pyramid is a square with sides 10 units long. The slant height is EF and the height of the pyramid is EG. m∠BEF = m∠CEF = 30°.

Find the following information about the pyramid. Give exact answers.

1. m∠EBF __60°__   2. m∠ECF __60°__
3. BF __5 units__   4. FC __5 units__
5. EB __10 units__   6. EF __5√3 units__
7. DB __10√2 units__   8. GB (GB = ½ · DB) __5√2 units__
9. EG (Use the Pythagorean Theorem in △EGB.) √50 or 5√2 units
10. What type of special right triangle is △EGB? __45°-45°-90°__
11. m∠GEB __45°__   12. m∠GBE __45°__
13. area of □ABCD __100 units²__   14. area of △EBC __25√3 units²__
15. surface area of pyramid 100 + 100√3 units²
16. volume of pyramid 500√2/3 units³

The radius of the cone's base is 12. m∠OPQ = 30°. Find the following information about the cone. Give exact answers.

17. height OP __12√3 units__
18. slant height PQ __24 units__
19. area of base __144π units²__
20. lateral area __288π units²__
21. surface area __432π units²__
22. volume __576π√3 units³__

Find each missing length.

1. Find the length of the legs of a 45°-45°-90° triangle with a hypotenuse of $4\sqrt{2}$ cm. **4 cm**

2. Find the length of the longer leg of a 30°-60°-90° triangle with a hypotenuse of 6 in. **$3\sqrt{3}$ in.**

3. Kit folds a bandana diagonally before tying it around her head. The side length of the bandana is 16 in. About how long is the diagonal? **about 22.6 in.**

Teaching Tip

Encourage students to memorize the approximate values 1.4 for the square root of 2 and 1.7 for the square root of 3. These are helpful when a calculator is not available and for checking the reasonableness of an answer.

Test Prep

 **Resources**

For additional practice with a variety of test item formats:
• Test Prep, p. 625
• Test-Taking Strategies, p. 620
• Test-Taking Strategies With Transparencies

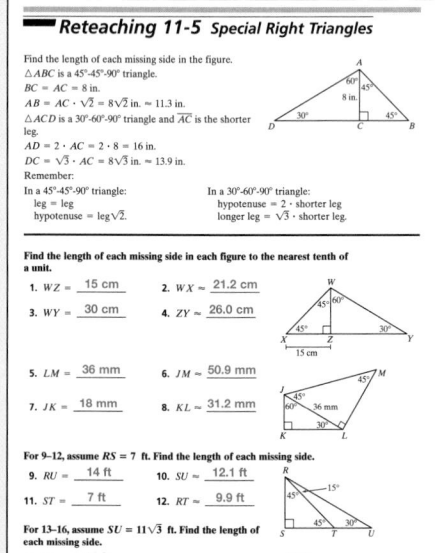

Reteaching 11-5 *Special Right Triangles*

Find the length of each missing side in the figure.
$\triangle ABC$ is a 45°-45°-90° triangle.
$BC = AC = 8$ in.
$AB = AC \cdot \sqrt{2} = 8\sqrt{2}$ in. ≈ 11.3 in.
$\triangle ACD$ is a 30°-60°-90° triangle and $\overline{AC}$ is the shorter leg.
$AD = 2 \cdot AC = 2 \cdot 8 = 16$ in.
$DC = \sqrt{3} \cdot AC = 8\sqrt{3}$ in. ≈ 13.9 in.
Remember:
In a 45°-45°-90° triangle:
leg = leg
hypotenuse = leg $\sqrt{2}$.
In a 30°-60°-90° triangle:
hypotenuse = 2 · shorter leg
longer leg = $\sqrt{3}$ · shorter leg.

Find the length of each missing side in each figure to the nearest tenth of a unit.
1. $WZ =$ __15 cm__   2. $WX \approx$ __21.2 cm__
3. $WY =$ __30 cm__   4. $ZY \approx$ __26.0 cm__
5. $LM =$ __36 mm__   6. $JM \approx$ __50.9 mm__
7. $JK =$ __18 mm__   8. $KL \approx$ __31.2 mm__

For 9–12, assume $RS = 7$ ft. Find the length of each missing side.
9. $RU =$ __14 ft__   10. $SU \approx$ __12.1 ft__
11. $ST =$ __7 ft__   12. $RT \approx$ __9.9 ft__

For 13–16, assume $SU = 11\sqrt{3}$ ft. Find the length of each missing side.
13. $RS =$ __11 ft__   14. $RU =$ __22 ft__
15. $ST =$ __11 ft__   16. $RT \approx$ __15.6 ft__

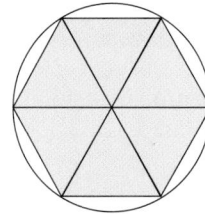

Sketch a 45°-45°-90° triangle. Use x for the length of one leg. Explain how to find the lengths of the other sides of the triangle.

See back of book.

19. **Geometry** A polygon is inscribed in a circle if all of its vertices lie on the circle. To find the area of the hexagon inscribed in a circle with a diameter of 8 in., answer each of the following.
   a. The segments shown form 6 congruent equilateral triangles. What is the length of each side of each triangle? **4 in.**
   b. What is the height of one triangle? **$2\sqrt{3}$ in., or about 3.5 in.**
   c. What is the area of one triangle? **$4\sqrt{3}$ in.^{2}, or about 6.9 in.^{2}**
   d. What is the area of the hexagon? **$24\sqrt{3}$ in.^{2}, or about 41.6 in.^{2}**

20. **Geometry** You can inscribe a regular hexagon in a circle using a compass and straightedge.
   a. Use your compass to construct a circle. Keep the compass at the same setting. Place the tip of the compass on the circle. Mark an arc on the circle. Place the tip of the compass where the arc intersects the circle and mark another arc. Continue around the circle until you have six arcs on the circle. Join consecutive arcs with segments.
   b. Measure the diameter of the circle. Use this measure and Exercise 19 to find the area of your hexagon.
   a–b. See back of book.

Test Prep

Multiple Choice

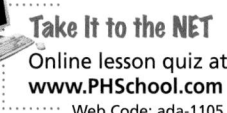
Take It to the NET
Online lesson quiz at
www.PHSchool.com
Web Code: ada-1105

21. In the triangle at the right, what is x, to the nearest tenth?
   A. 8.7   **B.** 8   **C.** 5.7   **D.** 2   **C**

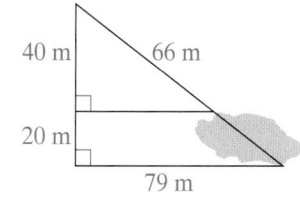

22. In a 30°-60°-90° triangle, the length of the longer leg is 10. What is the length of the hypotenuse, to the nearest tenth? **H**
   F. 5.0   **G.** 5.8   **H.** 11.5   **I.** 17.3

Short Response

In Exercises 23–25, **(a)** tell whether a triangle with sides of the given lengths could be 45°-45°-90° or 30°-60°-90°. **(b)** Explain your answers.
23–25. See back of book.
23. 6, 8, 10   24. 5, 5, $5\sqrt{2}$ 25. 15, 7.5$\sqrt{3}$, 7.5

Mixed Review

Lesson 11-4

26. **Surveying** A surveyor needs to find the distance across a lake. He estimates the distance using the similar triangles at the right. What is the distance? **33 m**

40 m   66 m
20 m
79 m

Lesson 9-6

Find the circumference of each circle with the given radius or diameter.

27. radius = 4 in. **about 25.1 in.**
28. diameter = 6 m **about 18.8 m**
29. radius = 2.5 ft **about 15.7 ft**

Lesson 8-1

Is each relation a function? Explain.

30. $\{(-1, 3), (0, 4), (1, 5)\}$
31. $\{(2, 3), (3, 4), (4, 5), (5, 6)\}$
30–31. See back of book.

Alternative Assessment

Have students use a protractor and ruler to draw a 45°-45°-90° triangle and a 30°-60°-90° triangle. Have them measure the length of one side of each triangle and then calculate the lengths of the other sides. Have them use their rulers to verify their answers.

Square Roots of Expressions With Variables

For Use With Lesson 11-5

You can simplify square roots of expressions that contain variables. Assume that the value of each variable is not negative.

1 EXAMPLE

Write each square root without a radical sign.

a. $\sqrt{25x^2}$

$\sqrt{25x^2} = \sqrt{(5x)^2}$ **Write $25x^2$ as the square of $5x$.**

$\qquad\qquad = 5x$ **Simplify.**

b. $\sqrt{p^6}$

$\sqrt{p^6} = \sqrt{(p^3)^2}$ **Use the rule for the Power of a Power.**

$\qquad = p^3$ **Simplify.**

You can also simplify expressions that have nonsquare factors by using the rule for Multiplying Square Roots.

2 EXAMPLE

Simplify each square root.

a. $\sqrt{x^9}$

$\sqrt{x^9} = \sqrt{x^8 \cdot x}$ **Use the rule for Multiplying Powers with the Same Base.**

$\qquad = \sqrt{x^8} \cdot \sqrt{x}$ **Use the rule for Multiplying Square Roots.**

$\qquad = x^4\sqrt{x}$ **Simplify.**

b. $\sqrt{48x}$

$\sqrt{48x} = \sqrt{16 \cdot 3x}$ **Find a perfect square factor.**

$\qquad = \sqrt{16} \cdot \sqrt{3x}$ **Use the rule for Multiplying Square Roots.**

$\qquad = 4\sqrt{3x}$ **Simplify.**

EXERCISES

Write each square root without the radical sign.

1. $\sqrt{49y^2}$ $7y$ **2.** $\sqrt{100m^{12}}$ $10m^6$ **3.** $-\sqrt{25x^6}$ $-5x^3$ **4.** $\sqrt{a^2b^{10}}$ ab^5 **5.** $-\sqrt{169w^{26}}$ $-13w^{13}$

Simplify each square root.

6. $\sqrt{a^{12}}$ a^6 **7.** $\sqrt{36x^4}$ $6x^2$ **8.** $\sqrt{81b^8}$ $9b^4$ **9.** $-\sqrt{64a^{16}}$ $-8a^8$ **10.** $-\sqrt{x^4y^{12}}$ $-x^2y^6$

11. $\sqrt{c^7}$ $c^3\sqrt{c}$ **12.** $\sqrt{x^{23}}$ $x^{11}\sqrt{x}$ **13.** $-\sqrt{20m}$ $-2\sqrt{5m}$ **14.** $\sqrt{27b^{11}}$ $3b^5\sqrt{3b}$ **15.** $-\sqrt{72a^{19}}$ $-6a^9\sqrt{2a}$

Square Roots of Expressions With Variables

This Extension shows students how to find or simplify square roots of expressions with variables.

Teaching Notes

Teaching Tip

You can simplify a square root when the <u>constant</u> is a perfect square ($\sqrt{36} = 6$), when the variable expression is a perfect square and the variable is nonnegative ($\sqrt{x^2} = x$), or both ($\sqrt{36x^2} = 6x$). You can also simplify square roots by factoring perfect squares from variable expressions and using the rule for Multiplying Square Roots. For example:

$\sqrt{32v^3} = \sqrt{16v^2 \cdot 2v} = 4v\sqrt{2v}$

Error Prevention!

Remind students that exponents are multiplied, not added, in a power of a power. For example, $\sqrt{x^{10}}$ can be rewritten as $\sqrt{(x^5)^2}$, *not* $\sqrt{(x^8)^2}$, and then simplified to x^5.

Lesson Preview

 Check Skills You'll Need

Similar Figures
Lesson 6-3: Example 2;
Exercises 8 and 9.
Extra Practice, p. 749.

Lesson Resources

 Teaching Resources
Practice, Reteaching, Enrichment
Checkpoint Quiz 2

 Reaching All Students
Practice Workbook 11-6
Spanish Practice Workbook 11-6
Reading and Math Literacy 11C
Spanish Reading and Math
  Literacy 11C
Spanish Checkpoint Quiz 2
Guided Problem Solving 11-6
Technology Activities 31
Hands-On Activities 16

 Presentation Assistant Plus!
Transparencies and PowerPoint™
• Check Skills You'll Need 11-6
• Additional Examples 11-6
• Student Edition Answers 11-6
• Lesson Quiz 11-6
• Classroom Aid 32
PH Presentation Pro CD-ROM 11-6

ASSESSMENT *SYSTEM*

Checkpoint Quiz 2
Computer Test Generator CD-ROM

 Technology
Resource Pro® CD-ROM
Computer Test Generator CD-ROM
PH Presentation Pro CD-ROM

 www.PHSchool.com

Student Site
• Teacher Web Code: adk-5500
• Self-grading Lesson Quiz
PH SuccessNet Teacher Center
• Lesson Planner
• Resources

Plus

608

OBJECTIVE 1 To find trigonometric ratios in right triangles

OBJECTIVE 2 To use trigonometric ratios to solve problems

. . . And Why

To find lengths that cannot be measured directly

 Check Skills You'll Need

Solve each problem.

1. A 6-ft man casts an 8-ft shadow while a nearby flagpole casts a 20-ft shadow. How tall is the flagpole? **15 ft**

2. When a 12-ft tall building casts a 22-ft shadow, how long is the shadow of a nearby 14-ft tree? **$25\frac{2}{3}$ ft**

For help, go to Lesson 6-3.

New Vocabulary
• trigonometry
• trigonometric ratio
• sine
• cosine
• tangent

 TEXT Interactive lesson includes instant self-check, tutorials, and activities.

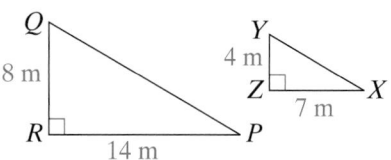
Investigation

Exploring Ratios in Similar Right Triangles

1. In the diagram at the right, $\triangle PQR \sim \triangle XYZ$. Find the length of the hypotenuse of each triangle. **16 m, 8 m**

2. In the triangles above, $\angle P$ is the smallest angle of $\triangle PQR$ and $\angle X$ is the smallest angle of $\triangle XYZ$. For each figure, write the following ratios in simplest form.

a. $\dfrac{\text{length of leg opposite smallest angle}}{\text{length of hypotenuse}}$ $\quad \frac{8}{16} = \frac{1}{2}, \frac{4}{8} = \frac{1}{2}$

b. $\dfrac{\text{length of leg adjacent to smallest angle}}{\text{length of hypotenuse}}$ $\quad \frac{14}{16} = \frac{7}{8}, \frac{7}{8}$

c. $\dfrac{\text{length of leg opposite smallest angle}}{\text{length of leg adjacent to smallest angle}}$ $\quad \frac{8}{14} = \frac{4}{7}, \frac{4}{7}$

3. What do you notice about the two ratios you wrote for each part of Question 2? **They are equal.**

The word **trigonometry** means triangle measure. The ratio of the lengths of two sides of a right triangle is a **trigonometric ratio.** To write trigonometric ratios, you must identify sides that are opposite and adjacent to the acute angles of a triangle.

Trigonometric Ratios

sine $\angle A = \dfrac{\text{length of leg opposite } \angle A}{\text{length of hypotenuse}} = \dfrac{CB}{AB}$

cosine $\angle A = \dfrac{\text{length of leg adjacent to } \angle A}{\text{length of hypotenuse}} = \dfrac{AC}{AB}$

tangent $\angle A = \dfrac{\text{length of leg opposite } \angle A}{\text{length of leg adjacent to } \angle A} = \dfrac{CB}{AC}$

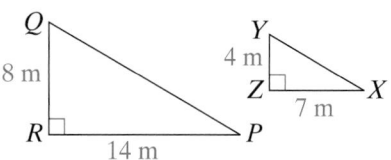 **Ongoing Assessment and Intervention**

Before the Lesson	**During the Lesson**	**After the Lesson**
Diagnose prerequisite skills using:	Monitor progress using:	Assess knowledge using:
• Check Skills You'll Need	• Check Understanding	• Lesson Quiz
	• Additional Examples	• Computer Test Generator
	• Test Prep	CD-ROM
		• Chapter Checkpoint 2 (p. 612)

You can use these abbreviations when you find trigonometric ratios for a given acute $\angle N$.

$$\sin N = \frac{\text{opposite}}{\text{hypotenuse}} \qquad \cos N = \frac{\text{adjacent}}{\text{hypotenuse}} \qquad \tan N = \frac{\text{opposite}}{\text{adjacent}}$$

Reading Math

The abbreviations for sine, cosine, and tangent are sin, cos, and tan, respectively.

1 EXAMPLE Writing Trigonometric Ratios

For $\triangle XYZ$, find the sine, cosine, and tangent of $\angle X$.

$$\sin X = \frac{\text{opposite}}{\text{hypotenuse}} = \frac{5}{13}$$

$$\cos X = \frac{\text{adjacent}}{\text{hypotenuse}} = \frac{12}{13}$$

$$\tan X = \frac{\text{opposite}}{\text{adjacent}} = \frac{5}{12}$$

✓ Check Understanding Example 1

1. For $\triangle XYZ$ above, find the sine, cosine, and tangent of $\angle Y$.
   $\sin Y = \frac{12}{13}$, $\cos Y = \frac{5}{13}$, $\tan Y = \frac{12}{5}$

Trigonometric ratios are usually expressed in decimal form as approximations. If you know the measure of an acute angle of a right triangle, you can use a calculator or a table of trigonometric ratios to find approximate values for the sine, cosine, and tangent of the angle.

2 EXAMPLE Using a Calculator

Find the trigonometric ratios of 42° using a calculator or the table on page 779. Round to four decimal places.

$\sin 42° \approx 0.6691$ **Scientific calculator:** Enter 42 and press the key labeled SIN, COS, or TAN.

$\cos 42° \approx 0.7431$ **Table:** Find 42° in the first column.

$\tan 42° \approx 0.9004$ Look across to find the appropriate ratio.

Graphing Calculator Hint

If you use a graphing calculator, enter the trigonometric ratio name before you enter the angle measure. Be sure the calculator is in degree mode.

✓ Check Understanding Example 2

2. Find each value. Round to four decimal places.

   a. $\sin 10°$ **b.** $\cos 75°$ **c.** $\tan 53°$ **d.** $\cos 22°$
   0.1736   0.2588   1.3270   0.9272

OBJECTIVE

2 Using Trigonometric Ratios to Solve Problems

You can use trigonometric ratios to find measures in right triangles indirectly. The advantage to using trigonometric ratios is that you need only an acute angle measure and the length of one side to find the lengths of the other two sides.

👥 Reaching All Students

| **Below Level** Draw right triangles in various orientations on the board. Point to an acute angle and have students locate the adjacent and opposite legs. | **Advanced Learners** Ask: *What is the relationship between the sines and cosines of the acute angles of a right triangle?* The sine of one angle equals the cosine of the other. | **English Learners** See note on page 609. **Visual Learners** See note on page 610. |

---

2. Teach

Math Background

Remind students that for similar right triangles, ratios of lengths of corresponding sides are the same. For example, the ratio of the opposite leg to the hypotenuse for a 50° angle in any right triangle is about 0.7660.

Teaching Notes

Investigation (Optional)

Students may be confused as to which leg is *adjacent* to a given angle. Point out that in a right triangle, a leg adjacent to an acute angle is a side of both the acute angle and the right angle.

English Learners

Students are probably unfamiliar with the terms *sine, cosine,* and *tangent.* Point out that you read the abbreviations "sin" as "sine," "cos" as "cosine," and "tan" as "tangent."

1 EXAMPLE Auditory Learners

Students may have trouble remembering the trigonometric ratios. Have them write the following: $S = \frac{O}{H}$, $C = \frac{A}{H}$, $T = \frac{O}{A}$ (O (opposite side), A (adjacent side), H (hypotenuse), S (sine), C (cosine), and T (tangent)). Encourage them to create mnemonic devices to help remember the ratios. One example is: Some Old Horses Can't Always Hide Their Old Age.

📊 Additional Examples

1 Find the sine, cosine, and tangent of $\angle A$.

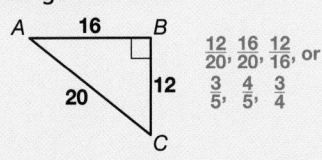

$\frac{12}{20}$, $\frac{16}{20}$, $\frac{12}{16}$, or $\frac{3}{5}$, $\frac{4}{5}$, $\frac{3}{4}$

2 Find the trigonometric ratios of 18°. Round to four decimal places.

$\sin 18° \approx 0.3090$
$\cos 18° \approx 0.9511$
$\tan 18° \approx 0.3249$

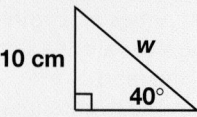
③ The diagram shows a doorstop with the shape of a wedge. What is the length of the hypotenuse of the doorstop?

10 cm *w* 40°

about 15.6 cm

③ **EXAMPLE** Visual Learners

To help students determine which trigonometric ratio to use, have them place a finger on the given acute angle, $\angle A$, and another finger on the given leg measure. This will help them see whether the leg is adjacent to or opposite the given angle. Then they can determine the relationship between that angle, the known side, and the missing side.

Closure

Ask students to give the definitions of the trigonometric ratios without using terms such as adjacent, opposite, leg, or hypotenuse. **Answers may vary. Sample:** Sine of an angle is the side directly across from the angle divided by the longest side. Cosine is the shorter side next to the angle divided by the longer side. Tangent is the side directly across from the angle, divided by the shorter side next to the angle.

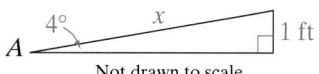

A 4° x 1 ft

Not drawn to scale

3 **EXAMPLE**   **Real-World**  **Problem Solving**

Ramps **What is the length of the wheelchair ramp at the left?**

You know the angle and the side opposite the angle. You want to find x, the length of the hypotenuse.

$$\sin A = \frac{\text{opposite}}{\text{hypotenuse}}$$ Use the sine ratio.

$$\sin 4° = \frac{1}{x}$$ Substitute 4° for the angle and 1 for the side opposite.

$$x(\sin 4°) = 1$$ Multiply each side by x.

$$x = \frac{1}{\sin 4°}$$ Divide each side by sin 4°.

$$x \approx 14.3$$ Use a calculator.

● The ramp is about 14.3 ft long.

✓ **Check Understanding**   Example 3

3. How long is the longer leg under the ramp in Example 3?
   about 14.3 ft

More Than One Way

Ladders **Find the height, x, that the ladder reaches.**

8 ft   x

68°

3 ft

Kevin's Method

Use the Pythagorean theorem.
$$3^2 + x^2 = 8^2$$
$$9 + x^2 = 64$$
$$x^2 = 55$$
$$x = \sqrt{55} \approx 7.4$$
The ladder reaches about 7.4 ft.

Tina's Method

Use a trigonometric ratio.
$$\sin 68° = \frac{x}{8}$$
$$8(\sin 68°) = x$$
$$7.4 \approx x$$
The ladder reaches about 7.4 ft.

Choose a Method   1–2. See margin.

1. Which method do you prefer to use? Explain.

2. What information is needed for each method?

610   **Chapter 11**   Right Triangles in Algebra

1. Answers may vary. Sample: Tina's Method; it usually requires fewer steps.
2. For Tina's Method you need the acute angle measure and the ladder length; For Kevin's Method you need the distance between the foot of the ladder and the building as well as the ladder length.

EXERCISES

Practice and Problem Solving

 Practice by Example

Example 1
(page 609)

For Exercises 1–3, find the length of the indicated side.

1. the leg opposite ∠A **4**

2. the leg adjacent to ∠A **3**

3. the hypotenuse of △ABC **5**

4. Find the sine, cosine, and tangent of ∠A.
$\frac{4}{5}, \frac{3}{5}, \frac{4}{3}$

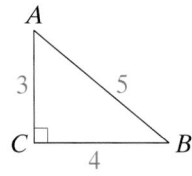

Use △QRS for Exercises 5 and 6.

5. $\frac{9}{15}$ or $\frac{3}{5}$, $\frac{12}{15}$ or $\frac{4}{5}$, $\frac{9}{12}$ or $\frac{3}{4}$

5. Find the sine, cosine, and tangent of ∠R.
See left.

6. Find the sine, cosine, and tangent of ∠S.
$\frac{12}{15}$ or $\frac{4}{5}$, $\frac{3}{5}$ or $\frac{9}{15}$, $\frac{12}{9}$ or $\frac{4}{3}$

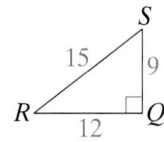

Example 2
(page 609)

Find each value. Round to four decimal places.

7. tan 89°   **8.** sin 30°   **9.** cos 14°   **10.** sin 67°
57.2900   **0.5000**   **0.9703**   **0.9205**

11. tan 28°   **12.** cos 89°   **13.** tan 11°   **14.** sin 83°
0.5317   **0.0175**   **0.1944**   **0.9925**

Example 3 **15. Waterskiing** The angle that a waterskiing ramp forms with the
(page 610)   surface of the water is 15°, and the ramp rises 5 ft. Approximately
how long is the ramp? **19.3 ft**

🌐 **16. Loading Ramps** The ramp on the back of a mover's truck is 12 ft
long. If the angle of the ramp with the ground is 22°, about how
high is the floor of the truck above the ground? **4.5 ft**

B **Apply Your Skills**

Use right triangles to find the ratios. Show your diagrams.
17–20. See margin.

17. tan 45°   **18.** cos 60°   **19.** sin 30°   **20.** cos 30°

21. Both are correct. The
ratios include *h*, a
known side length, and
a known angle measure.

21. Writing in Math Tom says the missing length in
the triangle at the right can be found using the
tangent ratio. Jed says it can be found using the
sine ratio. Who is correct? Explain. **See left.**

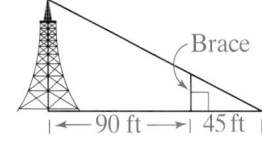

🌐 **22. Hot-Air Balloons** A hot-air balloon climbs continuously along a
GPS 30° angle to a height of 5,000 feet. To the nearest tenth of a foot,
how far has the balloon traveled to reach 5,000 feet? Draw a
sketch, and then solve. **See margin.**

C **Challenge**

23. Reasoning Find the sine of an angle and the cosine of its
complement. Do this for several angles. Make a conjecture.
The sine of an angle equals the cosine of its complement.

24. A wire from a radio tower is supported
by a 23-ft brace.
a. How tall is the radio tower? **69 ft**
b. What is the measure of the angle
formed by the wire and the ground?
about 27°

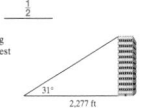

17. 1

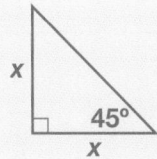

18. $\frac{1}{2}$

19. $\frac{1}{2}$

GPS Use the Guided Problem
Solving worksheet with
Exercise 22.

20. See back of book.

---

22. 10,000 ft

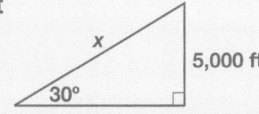

611

4. Assess

 Lesson Quiz 11-6

Solve.

1. In $\triangle ABC$, $AB = 5$, $AC = 12$, and $BC = 13$. If $\angle A$ is a right angle, find the sine, cosine, and tangent of $\angle B$.
$\frac{12}{13}, \frac{5}{13}, \frac{12}{5}$

2. One angle of a right triangle is 35°, and the adjacent leg is 15.
   a. What is the length of the opposite leg? **about 10.5**
   b. What is the length of the hypotenuse? **about 18.3**

3. Find the sine, cosine, and tangent of 72° using a calculator or a table.
   0.9511, 0.3090, 3.0777

✓ Chapter Checkpoint 2

To check understanding of Lessons 11-4 to 11-6:

Checkpoint Quiz 2 (p. 612)

📁 Teaching Resources
Checkpoint Quiz 2 (also in Prentice Hall Assessment System)

👥 Reaching All Students
Reading and Math Literacy 11C

Spanish versions available.

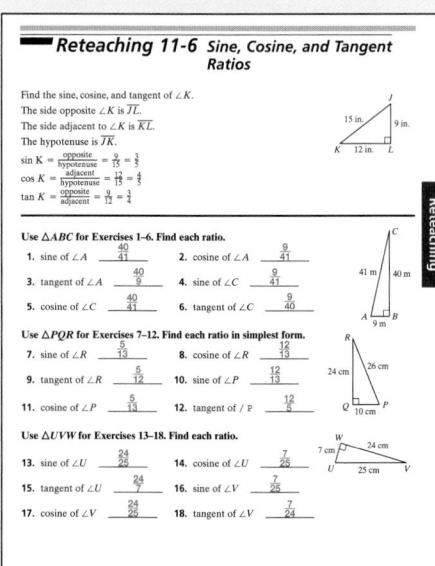

Test Prep

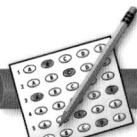

Multiple Choice In Exercises 25 and 26, how high on a wall does a 12-ft ladder reach?

25. The base of the ladder is 3 ft from the wall. **C**
    A. 4.0 ft   **B.** 10.0 ft   **C.** 11.6 ft   **D.** 12 ft

26. The ladder forms a 60° angle with the ground. **F**
    F 10.4 ft   **G.** 8.0 ft   **H.** 6.9 ft   **I.** 6.0 ft

Reading Comprehension Read the passage below before doing Exercises 27 and 28.

The Tilting Tower

Building began on the bell tower at Pisa, Italy, in 1173. Shortly after that, the 55.9-m tower began to lean and has continued to lean even more over the centuries. In 1993, the tower had a tilt that was 5.5° from the vertical. In the spring of 1999, engineering experts began work at the base to correct some of the lean. They completed the work in 2001 after decreasing the lean by 0.5°. The engineers hope their work will stabilize the tower for the next 300 years.

Take It to the NET
Online lesson quiz at
www.PHSchool.com
Web Code: ada-1106

27. In 2001, what was the tilt of the tower in degrees? **5.0°**

28. In 2001, about how many meters from the vertical was the top of the tower? **4.9 m**

⬤ Mixed Review

Lesson 11-5 **Find the missing lengths.**

29. $4\sqrt{2}$ m, or about 5.7 m

31. $13\sqrt{3}$ in., or about 22.5 in.

29. 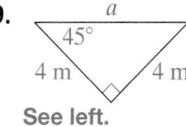 See left.

30.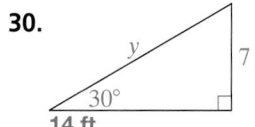

31. See left.

Lesson 9-7 **32. Geometry** $\overleftrightarrow{GT}$ is the perpendicular bisector of $\overline{RA}$ at point E. Name two congruent segments. $\overline{RE} \cong \overline{EA}$

Lesson 8-2 **Find the solutions of each equation for $x = -1, 0,$ and 3.**

33. $y = -3x + 2$
    5, 2, −7

34. $x + y = 20$
    21, 20, 17

35. $6x - 2y = 12$
    −9, −6, 3

✓ Checkpoint Quiz 2   Lessons 11-4 through 11-6

 **Instant self-check quiz online and on CD-ROM**

Tell whether a triangle with sides of the given lengths is 45°-45°-90°, 30°-60°-90°, or neither.

1. $8, 8, 8\sqrt{2}$
   45°-45°-90°

2. $1, 2, \sqrt{3}$
   30°-60°-90°

3. $12\sqrt{3}, 12, 24$
   30°-60°-90°

Find each value. Round to four decimal places.

4. $\cos 61°$
   0.4848

5. $\tan 30°$
   0.5774

6. $\sin 32°$
   0.5299

7. $\sin 87°$
   0.9986

Alternative Assessment

Organize students into pairs. Give each pair a protractor and a yardstick or meter stick. In the classroom, have them find right triangles. For each triangle, have them measure one acute angle and one side. Then have them use trigonometric ratios to find the lengths of the other sides.

Test Prep

📁 Resources
For additional practice with a variety of test item formats:
• Test Prep, p. 625
• Test-Taking Strategies, p. 620
• Test-Taking Strategies With Transparencies

Technology

Finding Angle Measures

For Use With Lesson 11-6

You can use a calculator or a trigonometric-ratio table to find the degree measure of an acute angle of a right triangle if two sides of the triangle are known. If you are using a graphing calculator, be sure you are in degree mode.

EXAMPLE

You have a map charting a ship's course. The ship is traveling from the port along the course shown. What is the angle from due north of the ship's course?

The angle formed by due north, the port, and the ship is the angle at which the ship is traveling. This is angle X.

$$\cos X = \frac{191}{325}$$

To find $m\angle X$ with a calculator:

Press **TRIG cos⁻¹** 191 ÷ 325 **ENTER**.

$m\angle X \approx 54°$

To find $m\angle X$ using the table of trigonometric ratios on page 779:

$\cos X = \frac{191}{325} \approx 0.5877$ **Divide.**

$m\angle X \approx 54°$ **In the cosine column, find the decimal closest to 0.5877, which is 0.5878. Read the angle measure across from 0.5878.**

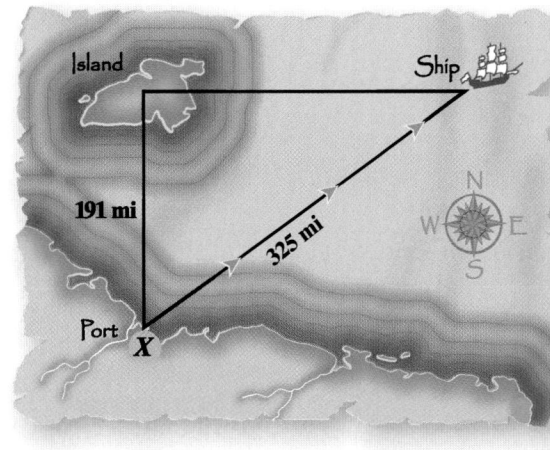

• The ship is traveling at a 54° angle from due north.

EXERCISES   1. $m\angle X \approx 44°, m\angle Y \approx 46°$ 2. $m\angle H \approx 28°, m\angle K \approx 62°$ 3. $m\angle C \approx 36°, m\angle D \approx 54°$

Find the measure of each acute angle. Round to the nearest degree.   1–3. See above.

1.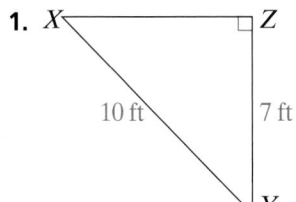

2.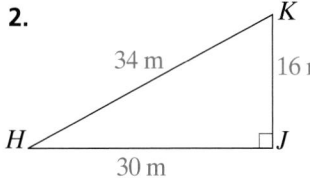

3.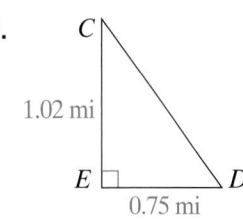

In $\triangle PQR$, $\angle Q$ is a right angle. Find the measures of $\angle P$ and $\angle R$ to the nearest tenth.   4–6. See below.

4. $PQ = 3, PR = 5$
4. $m\angle P \approx 53.1°, m\angle R \approx 36.9°$
5. $m\angle P \approx 67.4°, m\angle R \approx 22.6°$
6. $m\angle P \approx 46.4°, m\angle R \approx 43.6°$

5. $RQ = 12, PR = 13$

6. $PQ = 20, RQ = 21$

Extension   Finding Angle Measures   **613**

613

1. Plan

Lesson Preview

 Check Skills You'll Need

Trigonometric Ratios
Lesson 11-6: Example 2;
Exercises 7–14.
Extra Practice, p. 754.

Lesson Resources

 **Teaching Resources**
Practice, Reteaching, Enrichment

 **Reaching All Students**
Practice Workbook 11-7
Spanish Practice Workbook 11-7
Guided Problem Solving 11-7

Presentation Assistant Plus!
Transparencies and PowerPoint™
• Check Skills You'll Need 11-7
• Additional Examples 11-7
• Student Edition Answers 11-7
• Lesson Quiz 11-7
• Classroom Aid 32
PH Presentation Pro CD-ROM 11-7

 ASSESSMENT SYSTEM

Computer Test Generator CD-ROM

 **Technology**
Resource Pro® CD-ROM
Computer Test Generator CD-ROM
PH Presentation Pro CD-ROM

 www.PHSchool.com
Student Site
• Teacher Web Code: adk-5500
• Self-grading Lesson Quiz
PH SuccessNet Teacher Center
• Lesson Planner
• Resources
Plus 𝒊TEXT

 **11-7**

What You'll Learn

OBJECTIVE 1 To use trigonometry to find angles of elevation

OBJECTIVE 2 To use trigonometry to find angles of depression

. . . And Why

To solve real-world problems in subjects such as surveying and navigation

 Check Skills You'll Need

Find each trigonometric ratio.
1–6. See below.
1. $\sin 45°$ **2.** $\cos 32°$

3. $\tan 18°$ **4.** $\sin 68°$

5. $\cos 88°$ **6.** $\tan 84°$

 For help, go to Lesson 11-6.

New Vocabulary

• angle of elevation
• angle of depression

1. 0.7071
2. 0.8480
3. 0.3249
4. 0.9272
5. 0.0349
6. 9.5144

𝒊TEXT Interactive lesson includes instant self-check, tutorials, and activities.

Angles of Elevation and Depression

OBJECTIVE
1 Angles of Elevation

Civil engineers and navigators use the terms *angle of elevation* and *angle of depression* to describe the angles at which they observe things. An **angle of elevation** is formed by a horizontal line and a line of sight above it. It is used when you must look up at an object.

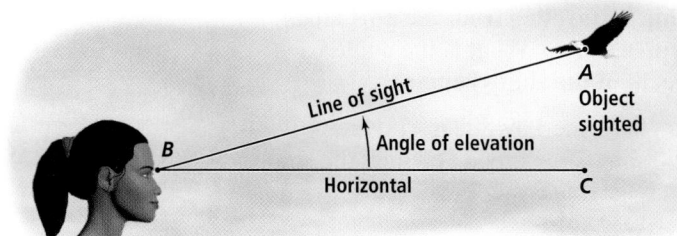

$\angle ABC$ is an angle of elevation.

1 EXAMPLE <u>Real-World</u> 🌐 <u>Problem Solving</u>

Kite Flying **Marcus is flying a kite. He lets out 40 yd of string and anchors it to the ground. He determines that the angle of elevation of the kite is 52°. What is the height x of the kite from the ground?**

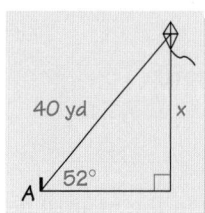

Draw a picture.

$\sin A = \dfrac{\text{opposite}}{\text{hypotenuse}}$ **Choose an appropriate trigonometric ratio.**

$\sin 52° = \dfrac{x}{40}$ **Substitute 52° for the angle measure and 40 for the hypotenuse.**

$40(\sin 52°) = x$ **Multiply each side by 40.**

$32 \approx x$ **Simplify.**

• The kite is about 32 yd from the ground.

Ongoing Assessment and Intervention

Before the Lesson
Diagnose prerequisite skills using:
• Check Skills You'll Need

During the Lesson
Monitor progress using:
• Check Understanding
• Additional Examples
• Test Prep

After the Lesson
Assess knowledge using:
• Lesson Quiz
• Computer Test Generator CD-ROM

✓ Check Understanding Example 1

1. The angle of elevation from a ship to the top of a lighthouse is 12°. The lighthouse is known to be 30 m tall. How far is the ship from the base of the lighthouse? **about 141 m**

In real life, a person's line of sight is parallel to the ground at eye height. In some problems you must account for this.

2 EXAMPLE Real-World 🌐 Problem Solving

Indirect Measurement **Felicia wants to determine the height of a tree. From her position 20 ft from the base of the tree, she sees the top of the tree at an angle of elevation of 73°. Felicia's eyes are 5 ft from the ground. How tall is the tree, to the nearest foot?**

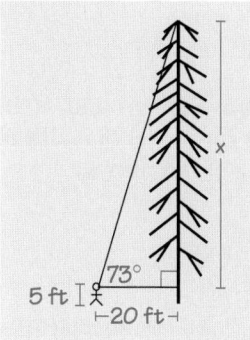

Draw a picture.

$$\tan = \frac{\text{opposite}}{\text{adjacent}}$$ **Choose an appropriate trigonometric ratio.**

$$\tan 73° = \frac{x}{20}$$ **Substitute 73 for the angle measure and 20 for the adjacent side.**

$$20(\tan 73°) = x$$ **Multiply each side by 20.**

$$65 \approx x$$ **Use a calculator or a table.**

$$65 + 5 = 70$$ **Add 5 to account for the height of Felicia's eyes from the ground.**

● The tree is about 70 ft tall.

✓ Check Understanding Example 2

2. A rock climber looks at the top of a vertical rock wall at an angle of elevation of 74°. He is standing 4.2 m from the base of the wall and his eyes are 1.5 m from the ground. How high is the wall, to the nearest tenth of a meter? **16.1 m**

11-7 Angles of Elevation and Depression **615**

👥 Reaching All Students

| **Below Level** Have students look at triangles used in this lesson. Guide them to see that the angle of elevation or depression is always formed by one leg and the hypotenuse. | **Advanced Learners** For Example 3, have students find the line-of-sight distance and tell why it is close to the ground distance. The angle of depression is very small. | **Tactile Learners** See note on page 615. **English Learners** See note on page 616. |

---

2. Teach

Professional Development

Math Background

Angles of elevation and depression occur in right triangle models that represent "vertical situations." The situations usually involve an unknown distance or height that would be difficult to measure directly. You are given the angle and height, and have to find the distance. Or you are given the angle and the distance, and have to find the height.

Teaching Notes

1 EXAMPLE Tactile Learners

To demonstrate an angle of elevation, have students hold their arms out in front of them and parallel to the floor. Identify an object that is up high and have them raise their right arms to point at the object. Point out that the angle formed by the two arms of each student suggests an angle of elevation. Have them demonstrate angles of depression in a similar manner.

2 EXAMPLE Teaching Tip

Ask students why the tangent ratio was used for this problem. Tangent is a ratio of the two legs of a right triangle. The given value is one leg and the value to be found is the other leg.

PowerPoint
Additional Examples

❶ Janine is flying a kite. She lets out 30 yd of string and anchors it to the ground. She determines that the angle of elevation of the kite is 52°. What is the height h of the kite from the ground? **about 24 yd**

❷ Greg wants to find the height of a tree. From his position 30 ft from the base of the tree, he sees the top of the tree at an angle of elevation of 61°. Greg's eyes are 6 ft from the ground. How tall is the tree, to the nearest foot? **60 ft**

615

2 Angles of Depression

Reading Math

With an angle of elevation, the object sighted is elevated, or above the horizontal line. With an angle of depression, the object is depressed, or below the horizontal line.

An **angle of depression** is formed by a horizontal line and a line of sight below it. It is used when you must look down at an object.

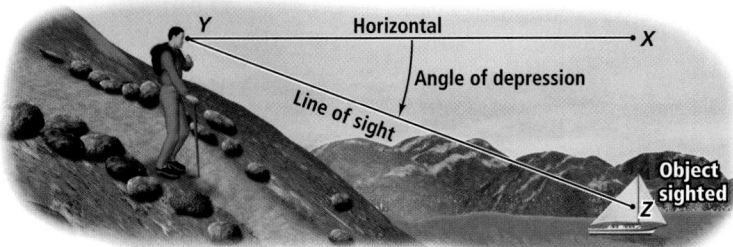

$\angle XYZ$ is an angle of depression.

3 **EXAMPLE** Real-World 🌐 Problem Solving

Navigation **An airplane is flying 0.5 mi above the ground. If the pilot must begin a 3° descent to an airport runway at that altitude, how far is the airplane from the beginning of the runway (in ground distance)?**

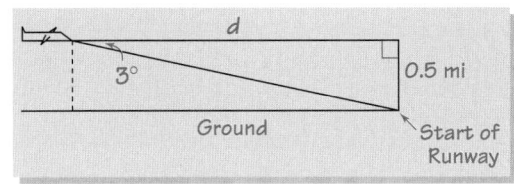

Draw a picture.

Not drawn to scale

$\tan 3° = \dfrac{0.5}{d}$ **Choose an appropriate trigonometric ratio.**

$d \tan 3° = 0.5$ **Multiply each side by *d*.**

$\dfrac{d \tan 3°}{\tan 3°} = \dfrac{0.5}{\tan 3°}$ **Divide each side by tan 3°.**

$d = \dfrac{0.5}{\tan 3°}$ **Simplify.**

$d \approx 9.5$ **Use a calculator.**

The airplane is about 9.5 mi from the airport.

✓ **Check Understanding** Example 3

3. A group of people in a hang-gliding class are standing on top of a cliff 70 m high. They spot a hang glider landing on the beach below them. The angle of depression from the top of the cliff to the hang glider is 72°. How far is the hang glider from the base of the cliff? **about 22.7 m**

EXERCISES

For more exercises, see *Extra Practice.*

Practice and Problem Solving

 Practice by Example

Examples 1 and 2
(pages 614 and 615)

1. In Example 1, Marcus's kite drops so that the angle of elevation is 48°. Find the height of the kite above the ground. **about 30 yd**

2. In Example 2, Felicia spots a nest in the tree at an angle of elevation of 65°. How high above the ground is the nest?
about 48 ft

Find x to the nearest tenth.

3.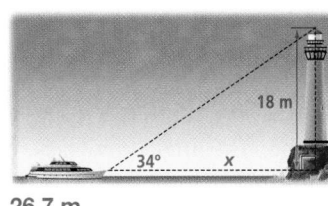
18 m
34° x
26.7 m

4.
E
x
A   20°   B
D   25 ft   C   5.4 ft
14.5 ft

Example 3
(page 616)

For Exercises 5 and 6, draw a sketch and solve.

5. An airplane descends at an angle of 2°. Its altitude decreases by 2.5 miles. What is the ground distance covered by the airplane?
about 71.6 mi

6. An airplane descends at an angle of 22.5° over a ground distance of 0.5 mi. By how many miles, to the nearest tenth, does its altitude decrease? **0.2 mi**

 Apply Your Skills

Name the angles of elevation and depression in each figure.

7.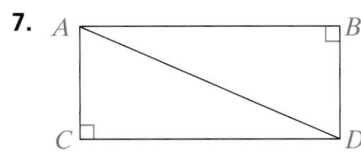
A   B
C   D

8.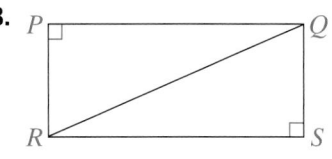
P   Q
R   S

7–8. See margin.

Reading Math

For help with reading and solving Exercise 9, see page 619.

---

11. Answers may vary.
Sample: You need to use a ratio that involves the side length you are looking for and a known side length.

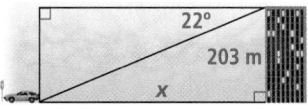
22°
203 m
x

9. Bird Watching A rare bird is spotted in a tree by a bird-watching group. The group is 9.5 yd from the base of the tree. The angle of elevation to the bird is 57°. How far is the bird from the group along the line of sight? Draw a sketch, and then solve.
See margin.

10. Navigation The angle of elevation from a ship to the top of a lighthouse is 4°. If the top of the lighthouse is known to be 50 m above sea level, how far is the ship from the lighthouse?
about 715 m

11. Writing in Math How do you decide which trigonometric ratio to use to solve a problem? **See left.**

12. Find the distance x of the car from the office building at the left. **about 502.4 m**

13. Meteorology A meteorologist measures the angle of elevation of a weather balloon as 53°. A radio signal from the balloon indicates that it is 1,620 m (line-of-sight) from the meteorologist's location. How high above ground is the weather balloon? **about 1,293.8 m**

Assignment Guide

1 Objective 1
Ⓐ Ⓑ Core 1–4, 9–11, 13

2 Objective 2
Ⓐ Ⓑ Core 5–8, 12, 14, 15
Ⓒ Extension 16, 17

Test Prep 18, 19
Mixed Review 20–29

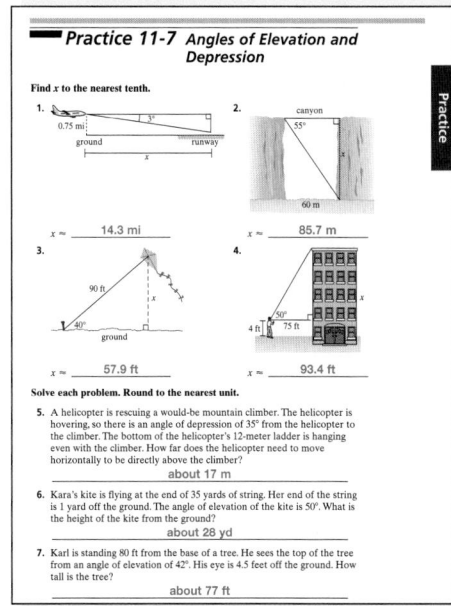

Practice 11-7 *Angles of Elevation and Depression*

Find x to the nearest tenth.

1.
0.75 mi   3°
ground   runway
x
$x \approx$ **14.3 mi**

2.
canyon
55°
x
60 m
$x \approx$ **85.7 m**

3.
90 ft x
40°
ground
$x \approx$ **57.9 ft**

4.
50°
4 ft   75 ft x
ground
$x \approx$ **93.4 ft**

Solve each problem. Round to the nearest unit.

5. A helicopter is rescuing a would-be mountain climber. The helicopter is hovering, so there is an angle of depression of 35° from the helicopter to the climber. The bottom of the helicopter's 12-meter ladder is hanging even with the climber. How far does the helicopter need to move horizontally to be directly above the climber?
about 17 m

6. Kara's kite is flying at the end of 35 yards of string. Her end of the string is 1 yard off the ground. The angle of elevation of the kite is 50°. What is the height of the kite from the ground?
about 28 yd

7. Karl is standing 80 ft from the base of a tree. He sees the top of the tree from an angle of elevation of 42°. His eye is 4.5 feet off the ground. How tall is the tree?
about 77 ft

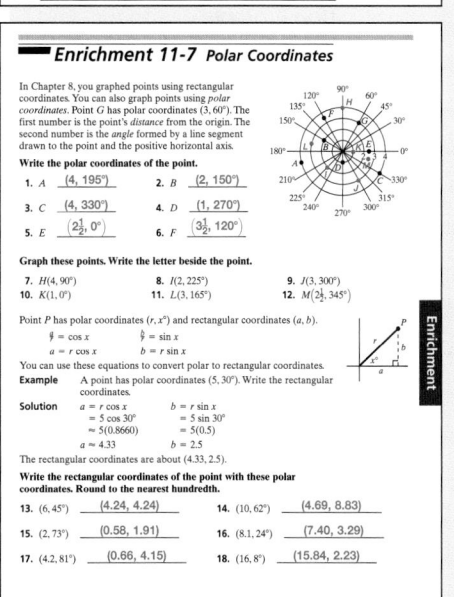

Enrichment 11-7 *Polar Coordinates*

In Chapter 8, you graphed points using rectangular coordinates. You can also graph points using *polar coordinates.* Point *G* has polar coordinates (3, 60°). The first number is the point's *distance* from the origin. The second number is the *angle* formed by a line segment drawn to the point and the positive horizontal axis.

Write the polar coordinates of the point.

1. A   **(4, 195°)**   2. B   **(2, 150°)**

3. C   **(4, 330°)**   4. D   **(1, 270°)**

5. E   **(2½, 0°)**   6. F   **(3½, 120°)**

Graph these points. Write the letter beside the point.

7. H(4, 90°)   8. I(2, 225°)   9. J(3, 300°)
10. K(1, 0°)   11. L(3, 165°)   12. M(2½, 345°)

Point *P* has polar coordinates (*r*, *x*°) and rectangular coordinates (*a*, *b*).

$\frac{a}{r} = \cos x$ $\frac{b}{r} = \sin x$
$a = r \cos x$ $b = r \sin x$

You can use these equations to convert polar to rectangular coordinates.
Example A point has polar coordinates (5, 30°). Write the rectangular coordinates.

Solution $a = r \cos x$ $b = r \sin x$
$= 5 \cos 30°$ $= 5 \sin 30°$
$\approx 5(0.8660)$ $= 5(0.5)$
$a \approx 4.33$ $b = 2.5$
The rectangular coordinates are about (4.33, 2.5).

Write the rectangular coordinates of the point with these polar coordinates. Round to the nearest hundredth.

13. (6, 45°)   **(4.24, 4.24)**   14. (10, 62°)   **(4.69, 8.83)**

15. (2, 73°)   **(0.58, 1.91)**   16. (8.1, 24°)   **(7.40, 3.29)**

17. (4.2, 81°)   **(0.66, 4.15)**   18. (16, 8°)   **(15.84, 2.23)**

---

7. angle of elevation = ∠ADC,
   angle of depression = ∠BAD
8. angle of elevation = ∠QRS,
   angle of depression = ∠PQR

9. about 17.4 yd
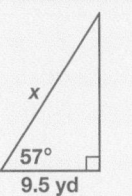
x
57°
9.5 yd

617

Lesson Quiz 11-7

Solve. Round answers to the nearest unit.

1. The angle of elevation from a boat to the top of a lighthouse is 35°. The lighthouse is 96 ft tall. How far from the base of the lighthouse is the boat? **137 ft**

2. Ming launched a model rocket from 20 m away. The rocket traveled straight up. Ming saw it peak at an angle of 70°. If she is 1.5 m tall, how high did the rocket fly? **57 m**

3. An airplane is flying 2.5 mi above the ground. If the pilot must begin a 3° descent to an airport runway at that altitude, how far is the airplane from the beginning of the runway (in ground distance)? **48 mi**

Test Prep

Resources

For additional practice with a variety of test item formats:
• Test Prep, p. 625
• Test-Taking Strategies, p. 620
• Test-Taking Strategies With Transparencies

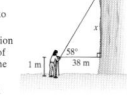

Reteaching 11-7 Angles of Elevation and Depression

A surveyor stands 38 meters from the base of a sheer cliff. Using equipment that sites from 1 meter off the ground, the surveyor measures the angle of elevation from her position to the top of the cliff as 58°. What is the height of the cliff?

Start by drawing a diagram and labeling it with the information given. Label x in the right triangle. Remember the height h of the cliff is actually $x + 1$, since the surveyor is siting from one meter off the ground.

Determine what information is given. The angle of elevation is 58°. The side adjacent to the 58° angle is 38 meters.

The surveyor needs to determine x, the side opposite the 58° angle. The tangent ratio uses the opposite side and the adjacent side, so use that.

$\tan = \frac{\text{opposite}}{\text{adjacent}}$

$\tan 58° = \frac{x}{38}$ Substitute 58° for the angle measure, 38 for the adjacent side, and x for the opposite side.

$38(\tan 58°) = x$ Multiply each side by 38.

$61 \approx x$ Use a calculator or a table.

$h = x + 1 = 61 + 1 = 62$ Add one meter for the tripod's height.

The cliff is about 62 meters high.

Find x to the nearest whole unit.

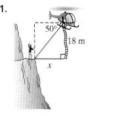
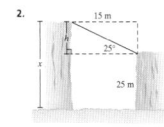

1.   2.

$x \approx$ ___ **15 m** $x \approx$ ___ **32 m**

3. Thomas' kite is flying at the end of 82 feet of string. His end of the string is 3 feet off the ground. The angle of elevation of the kite is 55°. What is the height of the kite from the ground? **about 70 ft**

618

---

14. **Error Analysis** A student made the drawing at the right to solve an angle-of-depression problem. What mistake has the student made? The angle of depression is between the line of sight and the horizontal.

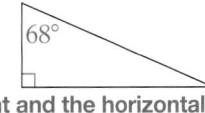

15. **Aeronautics** The pilot of a helicopter at an altitude of 6,000 ft sees a second helicopter at an angle of depression of 43°. The altitude of the second helicopter is 4,000 ft. What is the distance from the first helicopter to the second along the line of sight? **about 2,932.6 ft**

C **Challenge**

16. **Astronomy** The diagram suggests a method for finding depths of moon craters from Earth. Astronomers calculate that the distance from R to H is 3 km when the angle of depression of the sun's rays is 12°.

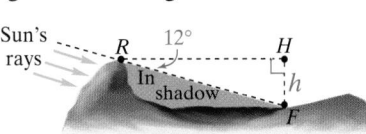

a. about 0.64 km
a. How high is the rim of the crater from the floor of the crater?
b. When the angle increases to 14°, how much shorter is the crater's shadow on the crater floor? **about 0.43 km**

17. **Surveying** Surveyors find that a canyon is 4 km wide. From one canyon rim, the angle of depression to the base of the canyon wall below the other rim is 7°. The angle of depression to a river is 8°. How far is the river from the far canyon wall? **about 0.51 km**

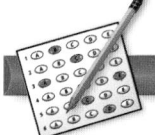

Test Prep

Multiple Choice

18. A ramp has an angle of elevation of 19° and a length of 35 ft. What is the height in inches of the ramp at its high end? **C**
   A. 11 in.   **B.** 12 in.   **C.** 137 in.   **D.** 145 in.

19. A radio transmitting tower casts a shadow that extends 344 feet from the base of the tower. A line connecting the sun, the top of the tower, and the end of the shadow forms an angle of depression of 16°. Approximately how high is the tower? **G**
   F. 344 ft   **G.** 99 ft   **H.** 1,200 ft   **I.** 1,248 ft

Mixed Review

Lesson 11-6   **Find each value. Round to four decimal places.**

20. $\tan 29°$ 21. $\sin 80°$ 22. $\cos 34°$ 23. $\sin 76°$ 24. $\cos 45°$
0.5543   0.9848   0.8290   0.9703   0.7071

Lesson 10-3   **Find the area of each circle. Give an exact area using π and an approximate area to the nearest tenth.**

26. 3.61π cm²; 11.3 cm²
27. 100π mm²; 314.0 mm²
28. 20.25π in.²; 63.6 in.²

25. $r = 8$ in.   26. $r = 1.9$ cm   27. $r = 10$ mm   28. $r = 4.5$ in.
64π in.²; 201.0 in.²   26–28. See left.

Lesson 6-2   29. **Baking** A recipe that serves four people calls for $1\frac{1}{2}$ c of flour. How many cups of flour are needed to serve ten people? $3\frac{3}{4}$ c

17.

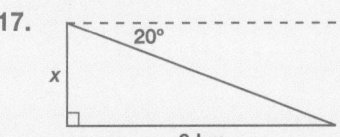

20°

x

9 km

Alternative Assessment

Have pairs of students find the height of the school's flagpole, the height of the school building, or some other height in the schoolyard using a method from this lesson.

Reading for Problem Solving

For Use With Page 617, Exercise 9

Reading for Problem Solving

Students read someone else's method of solving a right-triangle problem before solving a similar type of problem.

Teaching Notes

Suggest that students use a diagram to model the Exercise, before solving the problem.

Visual Learners
Have students copy the Exercise on their own paper or an overhead transparency. Then have them underline the information given with a colored pencil or marker. Have them underline what they are to find with a pencil or marker of a different color.

Read the problem. Then follow along with what Cheryl thinks as she solves it. Check your understanding by solving the exercise at the bottom of the page.

Bird Watching A rare bird is spotted in a tree by a bird-watching group. The group is 9.5 yd from the base of the tree. The angle of elevation to the bird is 57°. How far is the bird from the group along the line of sight? Draw a sketch, and then solve.

What Cheryl Thinks

I'll draw a sketch. In it, I'll show:
angle of elevation = 57°,
distance from tree = 9.5 yd,
right angle near base of tree.

I must find the line-of-sight distance to the bird. That's along the hypotenuse of the right triangle. I'll name it x.

I know an angle and the adjacent leg.
I want to find the hypotenuse.
I'll use the cosine ratio.

I can solve this equation.

I'll use a calculator and round.

Now I can write the answer.

What Cheryl Writes

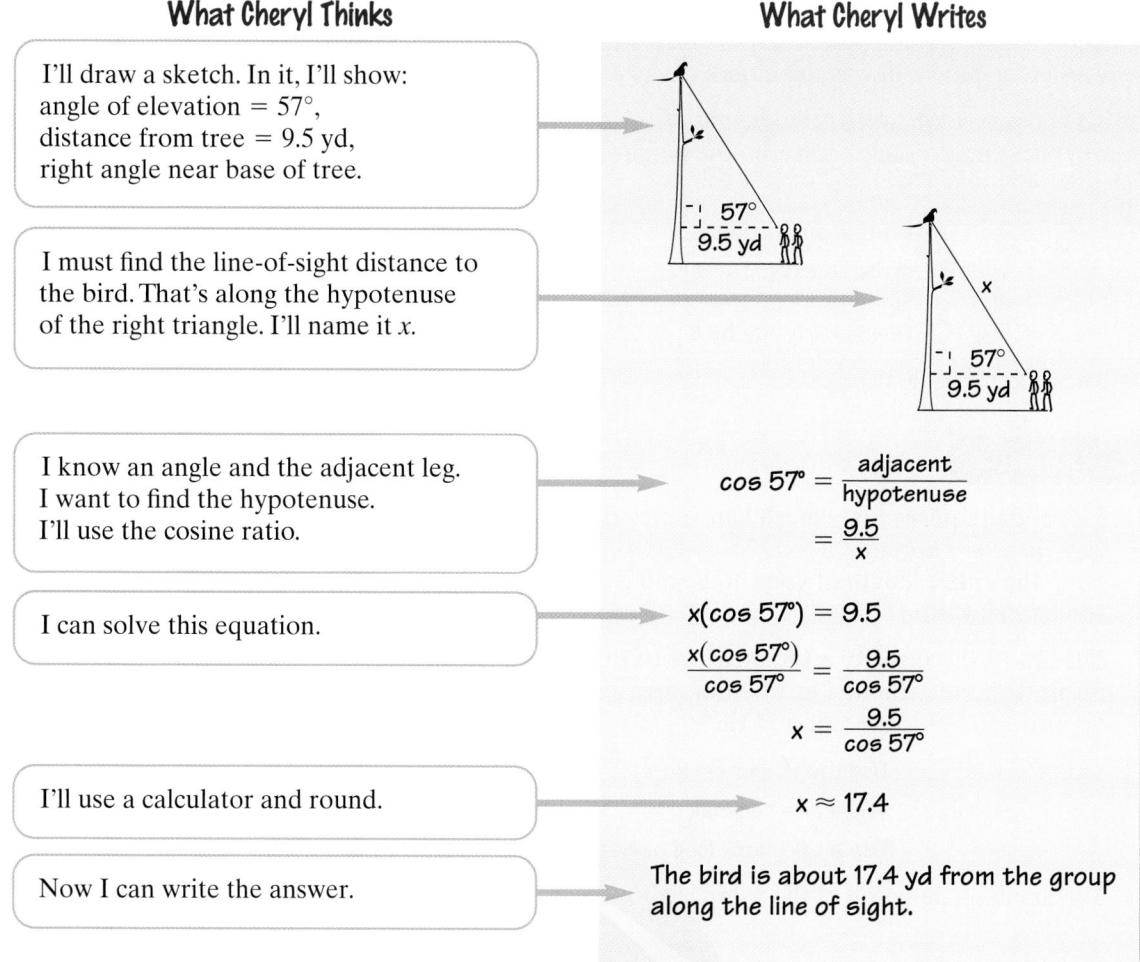

$$\cos 57° = \frac{\text{adjacent}}{\text{hypotenuse}}$$

$$= \frac{9.5}{x}$$

$$x(\cos 57°) = 9.5$$

$$\frac{x(\cos 57°)}{\cos 57°} = \frac{9.5}{\cos 57°}$$

$$x = \frac{9.5}{\cos 57°}$$

$$x \approx 17.4$$

The bird is about 17.4 yd from the group along the line of sight.

EXERCISE

1. A hot-air balloon is 150 feet high. The angle of depression from the pilot to her assistant on the ground is 25°. What is the line-of-sight distance from the pilot to her assistant, to the nearest foot? **355 ft**

Using a Variable

This strategy helps students understand the advantages of representing the unknown with a variable and writing an equation that accurately reflects the given information.

Resources

Test-Taking Strategies With Transparencies
- Transparency 11
- Practice sheet, p. 11

Teaching Notes

Teaching Tip

Suggest that students, after solving the problem, read the question again to see whether the answer makes sense.

Test-Taking Strategies With Transparencies

Chapter 11: Using a Variable

Exercises

Define a variable. Then, write and solve an equation for each problem.

1. In a bag, the ratio of red marbles to blue marbles is 9 to 21. The bag contains 30 red marbles. How many blue marbles are in the bag?

2. The Sampson family is building a playhouse. The scale of their blueprint is 2.5 cm : 12 ft. The playhouse will be 24 feet wide and 30 feet long. Find the dimensions on the blueprint.

3. A 3 ft high fire hydrant casts a 5 ft long shadow. Gena is standing nearby and casts an 8.5 ft long shadow. How tall is Gena?

4. A family is on a 520-mi road trip. They have driven 195 miles in 3 hours. If they continue driving at this rate, how long will it take them to drive the entire 520 mi?

5. An architect's drawing of a museum is 18 cm wide by 28 cm long. The actual building is going to be 45 m wide. How long will the building be?

6. A painter is mixing paint. The directions say to mix red, blue, and yellow paint in a ratio of 3 : 7 : 6. He needs a gallon of paint. How many fluid ounces of each color does the painter need?

7. A seamstress can make two dresses in nine hours.
  a. At this rate, how long will it take her to make seven dresses?
  b. How many dresses can she make in 15 hours?

Test-Taking Strategies — Pre-Algebra — 11

You can solve many problems by letting a variable be an unknown quantity you want to find. Use the variable in an equation. Then solve the equation to help solve the problem.

1 EXAMPLE

When José visited France he saw a large model of the Statue of Liberty. He wondered how tall the model was, so he measured its shadow. The shadow was 100 feet. He measured the height and shadow of a vertical pole. The pole measured 4 feet and its shadow was 5 feet. How tall was the model of the Statue of Liberty?

The unknown quantity is the height of the model. Sketch similar triangles (not to scale). Let x be the height. Then write a proportion using x.

$\dfrac{5}{100} = \dfrac{4}{x}$ **Write a proportion.**

$5x = 100(4)$ **Write cross products.**

$5x = 400$ **Simplify.**

$x = 80$ **Divide each side by 5.**

4 ft   5 ft   x   100 ft

● The model was 80 ft tall.

2 EXAMPLE

City code requires that wheelchair ramps rise no more than 1 in. for every horizontal foot. To meet the code, you build a ramp the entire length of your house, 36 ft. What is the ramp's angle of elevation?

The unknown quantity is the measure of the angle that the ramp forms with the ground. Let x be that measure. You know the side opposite and the side adjacent the angle.

$\tan x = \dfrac{3}{36}$ **Use the tangent ratio.**

≈ 0.0833 **Write as a decimal.**

$x \approx 5$ **Use a calculator (see page 613).**

3 ft   36 ft   ?

● The angle of elevation of the ramp is about 5°.

EXERCISE

1. You are flying a kite at the end of 200 ft of string. The angle of elevation is 30°. You are holding the end of the string at eye level, 5 ft above the ground. How high is the kite from the ground? Draw a diagram. Show how to use a variable. Then find how high the kite is.
  $\sin 30° = \frac{x}{200}$; 105 feet

Chapter Review

Vocabulary

angle of depression (p. 616)
angle of elevation (p. 614)
cosine (p. 608)
distance (p. 592)
hypotenuse (p. 584)

irrational number (p. 581)
legs (p. 584)
midpoint (p. 594)
perfect square (p. 580)
sine (p. 608)

square root (p. 580)
tangent (p. 608)
trigonometric ratio (p. 608)
trigonometry (p. 608)

Reading Math
Understanding Vocabulary

Match the vocabulary terms on the right with their descriptions on the left.

1. the two shortest sides of a right triangle **c**

2. an angle formed by a horizontal line and a line of sight above it **f**

3. the ratio of the lengths of two sides of a right triangle **d**

4. the longest side of a right triangle, opposite the right angle **e**

5. a number that cannot be expressed as a ratio of two integers **a**

6. The inverse of squaring a number is finding this. **b**

a. irrational number
b. square root
c. legs
d. trigonometric ratio
e. hypotenuse
f. angle of elevation

Take It to the NET
Online vocabulary quiz at www.PHSchool.com
Web Code: adj-1151

Skills and Concepts

11-1 Objectives

▼ To find square roots of numbers (p. 580)

▼ To classify real numbers (p. 581)

17. rational; because it is a terminating decimal
18. rational; because 64 is a perfect square
19. rational; because it is a repeating decimal
20. irrational; because 15 is not a perfect square
21. rational; because it is a repeating decimal

The square of an integer is a **perfect square.** The inverse of squaring a number is finding a **square root.** The symbol $\sqrt{}$ indicates the positive square root of a number. A number that cannot be expressed as the ratio of two integers $\frac{a}{b}$, where b is not zero, is **irrational.** If a positive integer is not a perfect square, its square root is irrational.

Simplify each square root.

7. $\sqrt{1}$ 1   8. $-\sqrt{16}$ −4   9. $\sqrt{49}$ 7   10. $\sqrt{64}$ 8   11. $-\sqrt{36}$ −6

Estimate to the nearest integer.

12. $\sqrt{5}$ 2   13. $\sqrt{11}$ 3   14. $\sqrt{33}$ 6   15. $\sqrt{62}$ 8   16. $\sqrt{91}$ 10

Identify each number as rational or irrational. Explain.

17. 0.55 18. $\sqrt{64}$ 19. $0.\overline{45}$ 20. $\sqrt{15}$ 21. $0.123123\ldots$
17–21. See left.

22. Explain why $0.12122122212222\ldots$ is an irrational number. It is irrational because the decimal neither terminates nor repeats.

Chapter 11 Chapter Review   **621**

Chapter Review

Resources

Student Edition
Extra Practice, Ch. 11 p. 754
English/Spanish Glossary, p. 782
Table of Symbols, p. 777

Reaching All Students
Reading and Math Literacy 11D
Spanish Reading and Math Literacy 11D

ASSESSMENT *SYSTEM*

Test Preparation
• Chapter 11 practice in test formats

www.PHSchool.com

Student Site
• Self-Grading vocabulary test
PH SuccessNet Teacher Center
• Resources

Plus **iTEXT**

Spanish Reading and Math Literacy

Reading and Math Literacy

11D: Vocabulary   For use with Chapter Review

Study Skill: When you want to remember a new rule, definition, or formula, try saying it over and over to yourself. This repetition helps the new idea stay in your memory.

Unscramble the UPPERCASE letters to form a math word or phrase that completes the sentence.

1. A CEPTFER RAQUES is the square of an integer. — PERFECT SQUARE

2. The longest side of a right triangle is the SOYPENTHUE. — HYPOTENUSE

3. A TIRRALIONA number cannot be expressed as the ratio of two integers. — IRRATIONAL

4. In a right triangle, the TANGTEN of ∠A is the ratio of the length of the opposite leg to the length of the adjacent leg. — TANGENT

5. In a right triangle, the GLES form the sides of the right angle. — LEGS

6. In a right triangle, the leg TENDJACA to an angle of the triangle forms one side of that angle. — ADJACENT

7. An angle of SEPRIDNOSE is formed by a horizontal line and a line of sight below it. — DEPRESSION

8. In a right triangle, the ratio of two sides is called a ROROTTENGIMIC ratio. — TRIGONOMETRIC

9. Finding a RAQUES TORO is the inverse of squaring a number. — SQUARE ROOT

10. In a right triangle, the ratio of the length of the leg adjacent to ∠A to the length of the hypotenuse is the SOCENI of ∠A. — COSINE

11. The word GOOTIMNERRYT means triangle measure. — TRIGONOMETRY

12. An angle of VEEANTILO is formed by a horizontal line and a line of sight above it. — ELEVATION

13. In a right triangle, the ratio of the length of the leg opposite ∠A to the length of the hypotenuse is the INSE of ∠A. — SINE

621

11-2 Objectives

▼ To use the Pythagorean Theorem (p. 584)

▼ To identify right triangles (p. 586)

In a right triangle, the two shortest sides are the **legs.** The longest side, which is opposite the right angle, is the **hypotenuse.** The Pythagorean Theorem states that in any right triangle the sum of the squares of the lengths of the legs is equal to the square of the length of the hypotenuse ($a^2 + b^2 = c^2$).

Can you form a right triangle with the three lengths given? Show your work.

24. yes; $8^2 + 15^2 = 17^2$

23. 1 mi, 3 mi, 3 mi   no; $1^2 + 3^2 \ne 3^2$ **24.** 8 yd, 15 yd, 17 yd
See left.

25. $\sqrt{6}$ ft, $\sqrt{10}$ ft, 4 ft   **26.** 30 m, 40 m, 50 m
yes; $(\sqrt{6})^2 + (\sqrt{10})^2 = 4^2$ yes; $30^2 + 40^2 = 50^2$

11-3 Objectives

▼ To find the distance between two points using the Distance Formula (p. 592)

▼ To find the midpoint of a segment using the Midpoint Formula (p. 594)

The Distance Formula states that the **distance** d between any two points (x_1, y_1) and (x_2, y_2) is $d = \sqrt{(x_2 - x_1)^2 + (y_2 - y_1)^2}$.

The Midpoint Formula states that the **midpoint** of a line segment with endpoints $A(x_1, y_1)$ and $B(x_2, y_2)$ is $\left(\frac{x_1 + x_2}{2}, \frac{y_1 + y_2}{2}\right)$.

Find the distance between each pair of points. Round to the nearest tenth.

27. $(3, 0), (0, 2)$ 3.6   **28.** $(-1, 7), (3, 10)$ 5

29. $(4, -5), (-8, -1)$ 12.6   **30.** $(-10, -12), (-8, -11)$ 2.2

31. $(2, -14), (9, -20)$ 9.2   **32.** $(10, 4), (-2, -2)$ 13.4

Find the midpoint of each segment with the given endpoints.

33. $H(0, 1)$ and $J(4, 7)$ (2, 4)   **34.** $K(2, 6)$ and $L(4, 2)$ (3, 4)

35. $M(-7, 8)$ and $P(3, -4)$ (−2, 2)   **36.** $A(4, 9)$ and $B(5, 11)$ (4.5, 10)

37. $X(-15, -12)$ and $Y(-9, -4)$ (−12, −8)   **38.** $D(20, 18)$ and $E(-15, -19)$ (2.5, −0.5)

11-4 Objectives

▼ To write a proportion from similar triangles (p. 598)

You can write a proportion to solve indirect measurement problems using similar triangles.

⬤ **39. Engineering** An engineer needs to know what length to plan for a bridge across a river. She estimates the distance using the similar triangles $\triangle ABC$ and $\triangle DEC$ in the figure at the right. What is the distance a across the river? about 337.5 ft

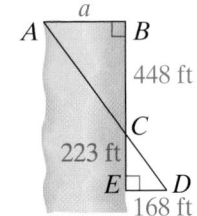

11-5 Objectives

▼ To use the relationships in 45°-45°-90° triangles (p. 602)

▼ To use the relationships in 30°-60°-90° triangles (p. 603)

In a 45°-45°-90° triangle, the length of the hypotenuse is the length of a leg times $\sqrt{2}$.

In a 30°-60°-90° triangle, the length of the hypotenuse is 2 times the length of the shorter leg, and the length of the longer leg is the length of the shorter leg times $\sqrt{3}$.

Find the values of the variables, rounded to the nearest tenth, if necessary.

40.

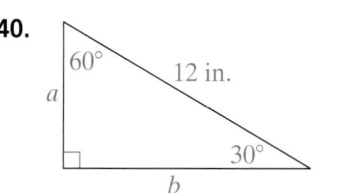

$a = 6$ in., $b \approx 10.4$ in.

41.

$y \approx 9.9$ m

42.

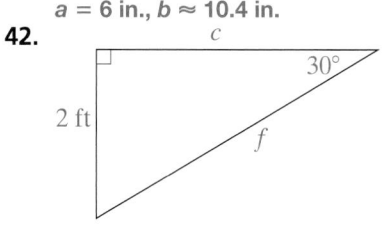

$f = 4$ ft, $c \approx 3.5$ ft

43.

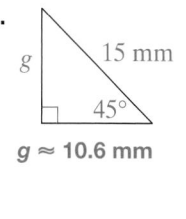

$g \approx 10.6$ mm

11-6 and 11-7 Objectives

▼ To find trigonometric ratios in right triangles (p. 608)

▼ To use trigonometric ratios to solve problems (p. 609)

▼ To use trigonometry to find angles of elevation (p. 614)

▼ To use trigonometry to find angles of depression (p. 616)

The ratios of the lengths of two sides of a right triangle are **trigonometric ratios.** Three trigonometric ratios are **sine, cosine,** and **tangent.** You can use these abbreviations when you find trigonometric ratios for a given acute $\angle N$.

$$\sin N = \frac{\text{opposite}}{\text{hypotenuse}} \qquad \cos N = \frac{\text{adjacent}}{\text{hypotenuse}} \qquad \tan N = \frac{\text{opposite}}{\text{adjacent}}$$

An **angle of elevation** is formed by a horizontal line and a line of sight above it. An **angle of depression** is formed by a horizontal line and a line of sight below it.

Find each value. Round to four decimal places.

44. sin 16° 0.2756	**45.** tan 82° 7.1154	**46.** cos 25° 0.9063	**47.** tan 3° 0.0524	**48.** sin 87° 0.9986
49. cos 73° 0.2924	**50.** cos 46° 0.6947	**51.** tan 45° 1.0000	**52.** sin 79° 0.9816	**53.** tan 13° 0.2309

Solve each problem. Round to the nearest unit.

54. A loading ramp forms a 28° angle with the ground. If the base of the ramp is 15 ft long, how high does the ramp reach? **8 ft**

55. Melanie is flying a kite and lets out 100 ft of string. Rosa determines that from Melanie's hands the angle of elevation of the kite is 71°. Melanie's hands are 4.3 ft from the ground. What is the height of the kite? **99 ft**

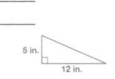

Chapter Test

Take It to the NET
Online chapter test at
www.PHSchool.com
Web Code: ada-1152

Simplify each square root.

1. $\sqrt{25}$ 5   2. $-\sqrt{81}$ −9   3. $\sqrt{100}$ 10

4. $-\sqrt{4}$ −2   5. $\sqrt{16}$ 4   6. $\sqrt{49}$ 7

Estimate to the nearest integer.

7. $\sqrt{6}$ 2   8. $\sqrt{12}$ 3   9. $\sqrt{45}$ 7

10. $\sqrt{78}$ 9   11. $\sqrt{85}$ 9   12. $\sqrt{118}$ 11

Identify each number as rational or irrational.

13. $0.999\ldots$ rational   14. $\sqrt{24}$ irrational

15. $\sqrt{100}$ rational   16. $420,420$ rational

Find each missing length to the nearest tenth of a unit.

17.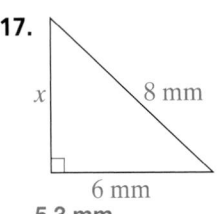
x, 8 mm
6 mm
5.3 mm

18.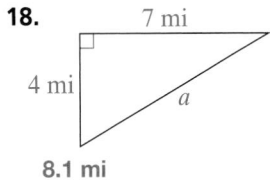
7 mi
4 mi, a
8.1 mi

19.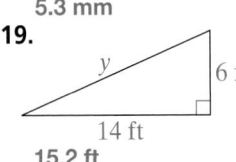
y, 6 ft
14 ft
15.2 ft

20.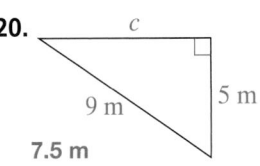
c
9 m, 5 m
7.5 m

Find the distance between the points of each pair. Round to the nearest tenth.

21. $(0,0), (4,6)$ 7.2   22. $(5,-3), (-6,2)$
                                          12.1
23. $(-8,-9), (1,2)$ 24. $(-1,-3), (-4,-7)$
    14.2   5

Find the midpoint of each segment with the given endpoints.

25. $C(5,0)$ and $D(3,6)$ (4, 3)

26. $M(9,-4)$ and $P(2,8)$ (5.5, 2)

27. To estimate the height of a tree, Joan positions a mirror on the ground so she can see the top of the tree reflected in it. Joan's height, her distance from the mirror, and her line of sight to the mirror determine a triangle. The tree's height, its distance from the mirror, and the distance from the top of the tree to the mirror determine a similar triangle. Use the measurements below to find the height of the tree. **16 ft**

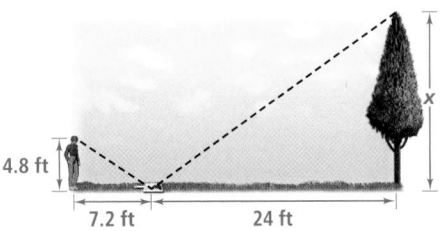
4.8 ft
7.2 ft   24 ft   x

Find the missing lengths.

28.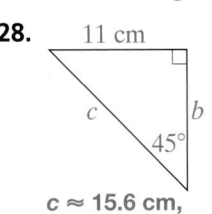
11 cm
c, b
45°
$c \approx 15.6$ cm,
$b = 11$ cm

29.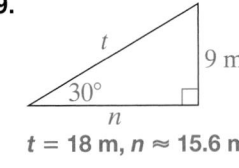
t, 9 m
30°
n
$t = 18$ m, $n \approx 15.6$ m

Find each value. Round to four decimal places.

30. $\sin 47°$ 31. $\tan 75°$ 32. $\cos 86°$
    0.7314   3.7321   0.0698
33. $\tan 29°$ 34. $\cos 60°$ 35. $\sin 67°$
    0.5543   0.5000   0.9205

36. **Writing in Math** Explain how a trigonometric ratio can be used to find a measurement indirectly. See below.

37. **Navigation** The captain of a ship sights the top of a lighthouse at an angle of elevation of 12°. The captain knows that the top of the lighthouse is 24 m above sea level. What is the distance from the ship to the lighthouse? about 113 m

   36. Answers may vary. Sample: If an unknown measurement can be placed into a trigonometric ratio with two known measurements, you can solve for the unknown measurement.

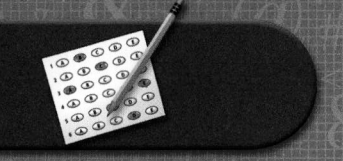
Reading Comprehension Read the passage below. Then answer the questions on the basis of what is *stated* or *implied* in the passage.

Early Geometry The early Babylonians and Egyptians used practical geometry in their buildings, but it was a Greek named Thales who first wrote down the formal abstract geometry that we know today.

Thales, an olive-oil merchant, lived from about 600 to 550 B.C. One of the unchanging properties of triangles that he discovered was that a triangle drawn in a semicircle (half a circle), with the diameter as a hypotenuse, will always be a right triangle.

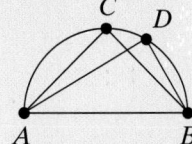

Around 540 B.C. a student of Thales, Pythagoras, founded a group that studied, among other things, mathematics. One of the rules of the *Pythagoreans* was never to eat beans! At first, they believed that the entire universe was made of only rational numbers, but working with right triangles convinced them that they could draw lines that have lengths equal to the square root of 2, the square root of 5, and so on.

1. What is the name of a teacher of Pythagoras? **Thales**

2. What was the name of a group founded by Pythagoras? **Pythagoreans**

3. What is the measure of $\angle C$? **C**
   A. 360°   B. 180°   C. 90°   D. 45°

4. Which term best describes $\overline{AC}$? **F**
   F. leg   G. sine
   H. hypotenuse   I. tangent

5. If $AC = CB = 1$ in., what is AB? **C**
   A. 2 in.   B. $\sqrt{3}$ in.   C. $\sqrt{2}$ in.   D. 1 in.

6. If $AB = 6$ in. and $DB = 3$ in., what is AD? **G**
   F. $3\sqrt{2}$ in.   G. $3\sqrt{3}$ in.
   H. $6\sqrt{2}$ in.   I. $6\sqrt{3}$ in.

7. If AB is $\sqrt{8}$ cm *and* $AC = CB$, what are AC and CB? **2 cm**

8. Which term does NOT apply to $\overline{AB}$? **C**
   A. diameter   B. hypotenuse
   C. leg   D. line segment

9. How does the measure of $\angle D$ compare with the measure of $\angle C$? $m\angle D = m\angle C$

10. What country was Thales from? **Greece**

11. How long did Thales live? **about 50 years**

12. What must be true of $\sqrt{2}$? **G**
    I. It is not a rational number.
    II. A segment can have length $\sqrt{2}$.
    III. It is equal to $\sqrt{5}$.
    F. I only   G. I and II
    H. I and III   I. II and III only

 **Test Prep**

Students must be able to extract information from reading passages, answer multiple-choice questions, and construct responses in order to be successful in current state and national assessments.

Resources

Teaching Resources
Cumulative Review

Reaching All Students
Spanish Cumulative Review

 ASSESSMENT *SYSTEM*

Test Preparation
• Ch. 11 Test Prep
Assessment Resources
• Cumulative Review
Computer Test Generator CD-ROM
• Test Prep

 **www.PHSchool.com**
• Test Prep
• Resources

Plus **iTEXT**

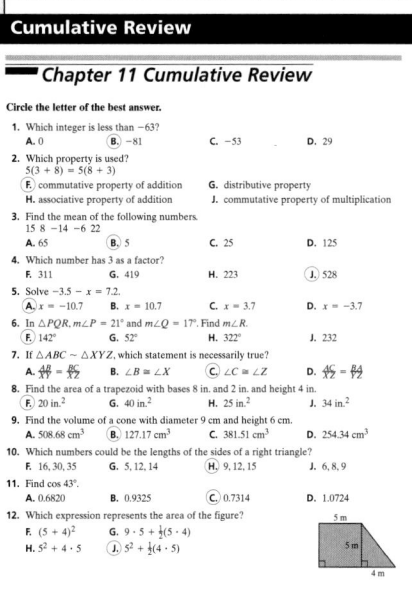

Picture Perfect

In this activity, students use information from a paragraph and captioned illustrations and diagrams, and apply their knowledge of ratios to complete a table and interpret its data.

Activating Prior Knowledge

Ask students if they have heard of the golden rectangle. Review the proportion that indicates a golden rectangle: **a is to b as (a + b) is to a.** Have volunteers suggest some objects to measure in the classroom. Write the measurements on the board and determine whether any have the dimensions of a golden rectangle. **Answers may vary. Sample: classroom objects to measure might include books, desktops, windows, doors, papers, posters, chalkboards**

Teaching Notes

Teaching Tip

Have a volunteer read the introductory paragraph. Ask: *Do you think artists and architects deliberately incorporate the golden rectangle in their work?* **Answers may vary. Sample: yes, because many artists and architects have studied mathematics; no, because they probably are not aware of the golden rectangle proportion and happen to use it because it is pleasing to the eye**

Visual Learners

Show students reproductions of the *Mona Lisa* by Leonardo da Vinci and *Composition in Red, Yellow, and Blue* by modern Dutch painter Piet Mondrian. Ask students to look for golden rectangles in these paintings. **Answers may vary. Sample: There is a golden rectangle around Mona Lisa's face. There are several golden rectangles in Mondrian's work.**

626

Picture Perfect

Applying Ratios Ancient Greeks realized that rectangles with certain dimensions were especially pleasing to the eye. A golden rectangle has sides that form the proportion $\frac{a}{b} = \frac{a + b}{a}$. The ratio of two sides of a golden rectangle is called the *golden ratio*. Artists make paintings with dimensions close to the golden ratio. Photographers often *crop*, or cut, their photographs to be golden rectangles.

Golden Rectangle Proportion
a is to *b* as (*a* + *b*) is to *a*.

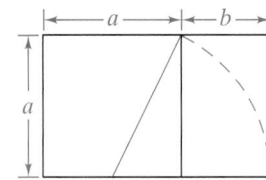

How to Make a Golden Rectangle
Start with a square with side length *a*. Open a compass the length from the midpoint of one side of the square to a corner on the opposite side. Make an arc. Extend the side containing the midpoint to intersect the arc. Make a rectangle using lengths *b* and *a*.

The Parthenon
The front of the Parthenon, in Athens, Greece, approximates a golden rectangle.

x

1.62*x*

626

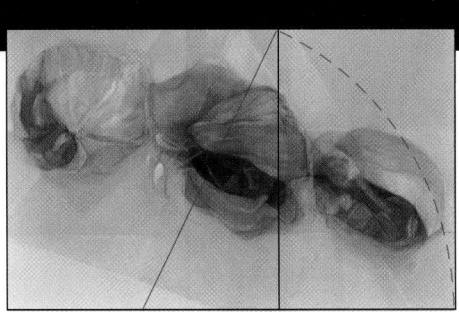

The Golden Rectangle in Art

Artist Sydney McGinley makes pastel paintings of flowers, such as *Pyramidal Fuschia*, using a golden rectangle to position the flowers within the painting.

The Villa Savoye

The Swiss architect Charles Le Corbusier designed the Villa Savoye, outside Paris, France, based on the golden rectangle, among other things. The house, built in 1930, looks different from each side.

Activity 1–4. See margin.

1. a. Copy the table. For each rectangle, find the ratios $\frac{a}{b}$ and $\frac{a+b}{a}$. Write the ratios in decimal form, rounding to the nearest tenth. Write *yes* if the decimals are approximately equal.

Rectangle Dimensions (inches)

Side *a*	Side *a + b*	$\frac{a}{b}$	$\frac{(a+b)}{a}$	Golden Ratio?
5	8	$\frac{5}{3}=1.\overline{6}\approx 1.7$	$\frac{8}{5}=1.6$	Yes
3	4	▧	▧	▧
6	10	▧	▧	▧
14	22	▧	▧	▧
12	16	▧	▧	▧
15	24	▧	▧	▧
18	26	▧	▧	▧
21	33	▧	▧	▧

b. Which rectangles are close to a golden rectangle? Explain.

2. Photo labs make prints in several sizes, including 3×5, 4×6, and 8×10. Which of these sizes is closest to a golden rectangle?

3. Open-Ended From the table, choose one pair of dimensions that do not form a golden rectangle. Change the value of *a* to a whole number that makes the rectangle closer to a golden rectangle. Justify your choice by showing your work.

4. Research Find at least three images from magazines or catalogs that you think approximate golden rectangles. Measure the images and calculate the ratio of length to width.

Take It to the NET For more information about the golden ratio, go to **www.PHSchool.com**.
Web Code: ade-1153

627

1a. See back of book.

 b. 5 × 8 and 15 × 24 are similar rectangles and are equally close to golden rectangles.

2. 3 × 5

3. Answers may vary. Sample: Suppose $a = 3$ and $a + b = 4$. $\frac{a}{b} = 3$ and $\frac{(a+b)}{a} = 1.\overline{3}$. If the value of *a* is 2 and $a + b = 3$, $\frac{a}{b} = 2$ and $\frac{(a+b)}{a} = 1.5$, which are closer to the golden-rectangle ratios.

4. Check students' work.

Chapter 12

Data Analysis and Probability

Chapter at a Glance

12-1

Frequency Tables and Line Plots

pp. 630–633

Objectives

1. Using Frequency Tables to Display Data
2. Using Line Plots to Display Data

New Vocabulary
frequency table, line plot, range

NCTM Standards
1, 5, 6, 7, 9, 10

Local Standards

12-2

Box-and-Whisker Plots

pp. 635–639

Objectives

1. Making Box-and-Whisker Plots
2. Analyzing Box-and-Whisker Plots

New Vocabulary
box-and-whisker plot, quartiles

NCTM Standards
5, 6, 7, 8, 9, 10

Local Standards

12-3

Using Graphs to Persuade

pp. 642–647

Objectives

1. Using Breaks in Scales
2. Using Different Scales

NCTM Standards
5, 6, 8, 9, 10

Local Standards

12-4

Counting Outcomes and Theoretical Probability *pp. 649–653*

Objectives

1. Counting Possible Choices
2. Counting Outcomes to Find Probability

New Vocabulary
counting principle, theoretical probability, sample space

NCTM Standards
5, 6, 7, 8, 9, 10

Local Standards

✔ **Checkpoint Quiz 1**

12-5

Independent and Dependent Events

pp. 654–658

Objectives

1. Independent Events
2. Dependent Events

New Vocabulary
independent events, dependent events

Materials
blank cards

NCTM Standards
5, 6, 8, 9

Local Standards

12-6

Permutations and Combinations

pp. 659–663

Objectives

1. Permutations
2. Combinations

New Vocabulary
permutation, combination

NCTM Standards
5, 6, 8, 9

Local Standards

12-7

Experimental Probability

pp. 665–668

Objectives

1. Finding Experimental Probability
2. Using Simulations

New Vocabulary
experimental probability, simulation

NCTM Standards
5, 6, 7, 8, 9

Local Standards

12-8

Random Samples and Surveys

pp. 669–672

Objectives

1. Choosing Samples for Surveys
2. Making Estimates About Populations

New Vocabulary
population, sample, random sample

NCTM Standards
5, 6, 8, 9

Local Standards

✔ **Checkpoint Quiz 2**

12-9 **Problem Solving**

Simulate the Problem

pp. 674–677

Objective

1. Simulating the Problem

NCTM Standards
5, 6, 9

Local Standards

Correlation to Standardized Tests

Lesson	NAEP	Terra Nova CAT/6	Terra Nova CTBS	ITBS	SAT10	Local Test
12-1	D1b, D1d				■	
12-2	D2b, D2d					
12-3	D1d, D1e		■		■	
12-4	D4b, D4e				■	
12-5	D4a, D4h		■			
12-6		■			■	
12-7	D4d				■	
12-8	D3a, D3b, D3d		■			
12-9	D4c					

NAEP National Assessment of Educational Progress
  N = Number Sense, Properties, and Operations
  M = Measurement
  G = Geometry and Spatial Sense
  D = Data Analysis, Statistics and Probability
  A = Algebra and Functions
CAT/6 California Achievement Test, 6th Ed.
CTBS Comprehensive Test of Basic Skills
ITBS Iowa Test of Basic Skills, Form M
SAT10 Stanford Achievement Test, 10th Ed.

NCTM STANDARDS 2000

1	Number and Operations	6	Problem Solving
2	Algebra	7	Reasoning and Proof
3	Geometry	8	Communication
4	Measurement	9	Connections
5	Data Analysis and Probability	10	Representation

Pacing Options

This chart suggests pacing for only the core lessons and their parts. It is provided as a possible guide. It will help you determine how much time you have in your schedule to cover other components, such as the features, chapter projects, Chapter Review, and Chapter Test.

Day	Traditional 45-minute class periods	Two-Year 45-minute class periods	Block 90-minute class periods
1	12-1 ▼ ▼	12-1 ▼	12-1 ▼ ▼ / 12-2 ▼ ▼
2	12-2 ▼	12-1 ▼	12-3 ▼ ▼ / 12-4 ▼
3	12-2 ▼	12-2 ▼	12-4 ▼ / 12-5 ▼
4	12-3 ▼ ▼	12-2 ▼	12-5 ▼ / 12-6 ▼ ▼
5	12-4 ▼	12-2 ▼	12-7 ▼ ▼
6	12-4 ▼	12-3 ▼	12-8 ▼ ▼ / 12-9 ▼
7	12-5 ▼ ▼	12-3 ▼	
8	12-6 ▼	12-3 ▼	
9	12-6 ▼	12-4 ▼	
10	12-7 ▼ ▼	12-4 ▼	
11	12-8 ▼ ▼	12-4 ▼	
12	12-9 ▼	12-5 ▼	
13		12-5 ▼	
14		12-5 ▼	
15		12-6 ▼	
16		12-6 ▼	
17		12-6 ▼	
18		12-7 ▼	
19		12-7 ▼	
20		12-8 ▼	
21		12-8 ▼	
22		12-9 ▼	
23		12-9 ▼	

Math Background

Skills Trace

BEFORE Chapter 12

Students should have encountered in previous courses some of the concepts developed in this chapter. Box-and-whisker plots and some of the formulas introduced here may not have been learned in previous courses.

▼

DURING Chapter 12

This chapter develops data distributions (line plots, box-and-whisker plots) and introduces the ways graphs can convey a particular message. Concepts and formulas for probability, permutations, and combinations are developed.

▼

AFTER Chapter 12

Graphical representations are used in Chapter 13 and throughout most subsequent math courses. Algebra 1 revisits probability concepts. Geometry develops geometric probability.

12-2
12-3
Box-and-Whisker Plots; Using Graphs to Persuade

In addition to organizing and displaying data, you may want to summarize the data. One way to do this along a number line is to use a *box-and-whisker plot.* A box-and-whisker plot groups the data into four equal parts using three numbers called *quartiles.*

To make such a plot, you first arrange the data in order from least to greatest. The median of all the scores is the point called the *middle quartile.* The median of the lower half is the *lower quartile.* The median of the upper half is the *upper quartile.* The least value gives the first point of the plot and the greatest value gives the last point of the plot. You draw the box to include the values from the lower quartile to the upper quartile (the middle half of the values). You draw the whiskers as lines from the box to the least value and the greatest value. The text shows several plots of this type.

You can use a box-and-whisker plot to show where the data are concentrated and how they are spread out.

You can organize and summarize collected facts and display them in ways that communicate clearly and also try to persuade the reader. However, some ways of picturing data may be misleading. These include using different units on the *x*-axis and *y*-axis, using a break in the scale on either axis, and using different widths for the bars on a bar graph.

12-1 ## Frequency Tables and Line Plots

One way to organize data is with a table showing the number of items in each category. This is called a *frequency table.* The table lists each data item along with a tally or number that shows how many times (or how frequently) that value occurs.

A frequency table orders the data. Other ways to order data include tally marks, a bar graph, or a line plot. A *line plot* uses a number line. Above each value, you mark an x for each appearance of that value in the data set. The following line plot shows how many times each digit appears in the counting numbers from 5 to 15, inclusive.

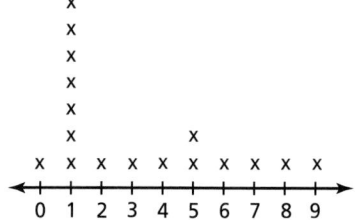

12-4
12-5
Counting Outcomes and Theoretical Probability; Independent and Dependent Events

The *theoretical probability* of an event in which all outcomes are equally likely is this:

$$P(\text{event}) = \frac{\text{number of favorable outcomes}}{\text{number of possible outcomes}}$$

If you want to find the theoretical probability of tossing two cubes and getting a 2 and a 6 in either order, use the sample space of 36 possible outcomes. The favorable outcomes would be either (2 and 6) or (6 and 2). The theoretical probability is this:

$$P(\text{2 and 6 in either order}) = \frac{2}{36}, \text{ or } \frac{1}{18}$$

Does this mean that if you toss two cubes 18 times you are sure to get one toss of 2 and 6? No, the theoretical probability of $\frac{1}{18}$ means that if you toss the cubes a great many times, then you can expect to get this result on about $\frac{1}{18}$ of the tosses.

When you toss one number cube and then toss a second, the result you get on the first toss has no influence on the second toss. Two events for which the occurrence of one *does not* affect the probability of the occurrence of the other are called *independent events.*

For two independent events, A and B, the probability that both events occur is the product of the probabilities that each event will occur. For independent events, $P(A \text{ and } B) = P(A) \cdot P(B)$.

What happens when the occurrence of one event *does* affect the probability of the occurrence of the other? Suppose you want to draw at least one even number in two draws from nine cards numbered 1 to 9. On your first draw, you have 9 possible outcomes. You draw and do not replace that card. For the second draw, you now have only 8 possible outcomes. This means that the first outcome affects probabilities for the second; if you draw a 7 first, then 7 is no longer a possibility for the second draw. Events in which the first event occurring *does affect* the probability of the second event are called *dependent events.*

For two dependent events A and B, the probability that both events occur is the product of the probability of the first event and the probability that, after the first event, the second event occurs. For dependent events, $P(A, \text{ then } B) = P(A) \cdot P(B \text{ after } A)$.

12-6   **Permutations and Combinations**

When the *order* of an arrangement matters, then the arrangement is a *permutation.* When the order of an arrangement is not important, then the arrangement is a *combination.*

For example, if you choose 3 people from a club of 10 members to represent the club at a meeting, then the order *does not* matter. The choice of (Bill, Irene, and Lynn) is the same as the choice of (Lynn, Bill, and Irene). You can write the number of such combinations as $_{10}C_3$. In general, $_nC_r$ represents the number of combinations of n objects chosen r at a time.

However, if you choose 3 people from the 10-member club to be the president, vice-president, and secretary of the club, the order *does* matter. The choice of (Lynn as president, Irene as vice-president, and Bill as secretary) is not the same as the choice of (Irene as president, Bill as vice-president, and Lynn as secretary). You can write the number of such permutations as $_{10}P_3$. In general, $_nP_r$ represents the number of permutations of n objects chosen r at a time.

You can find $_{10}P_3$ by using the Counting Principle.

$$_{10}P_3 = 10 \cdot 9 \cdot 8$$

The number $_nP_n$ of permutations of n things taken n at a time is given by

$$_nP_n = n(n - 1)(n - 2)\ldots(3)(2)(1), \text{ so}$$

$$_{10}P_{10} = 10 \cdot 9 \cdot 8 \cdot 7 \cdot 6 \cdot 5 \cdot 4 \cdot 3 \cdot 2 \cdot 1.$$

In later courses, students will learn that this product of all the integers from 10 to 1 is called *10 factorial* (symbolized as 10!), or, in general, $_nP_n = n!$

To find the number of combinations, use the following formula:

$$_nC_r = \frac{_nP_r}{_rP_r}.$$

12-7

    Experimental Probability

When you find a probability for an event based on performing an actual experiment, you are finding *experimental probability.* One way to find an experimental probability is with a model or a *simulation.*

Additional Professional Development Opportunities

Chapter 12 Math Background notes:
pp. 631, 636, 643, 650, 655, 660, 666, 670, 675

Additional resources available from SkyLight Professional Development: On-site courses, workshops, summer institutes. Online courses and chat rooms. Videocassettes and books. Visit www.skylightedu.com.

Professional Development, Content Facilitator Guide: Pre-Algebra, Chapter 12

Ongoing Assessment and Intervention

The *Prentice Hall Pre-Algebra* program provides many options for assessment in the Student Edition, Teacher's Edition, and teaching resources. From these options you may choose instructional materials that are appropriate for your students and support your district's curriculum requirements.

Daily Assessment

 Instant Check System™ in Chapter 12

Allows students to check their own learning before, during, and after each lesson.

Diagnosing Readiness before the chapter (p. 628)

Check Skills You'll Need exercises in each lesson (pp. 630, 635, 642, 649, 654, 659, 665, 669, 674)

Check Understanding questions with each Example (pp. 631, 636, 637, 642, 643, 644, 649, 650, 651, 655, 656, 659, 660, 661, 665, 666, 669, 670, 675)

Checkpoint Quiz (pp. 653, 672)

Formal Assessment

In Chapter 12 and Additional Resources

Assesses student progress throughout the *Pre-Algebra* text and with blackline masters and CD-ROM.

Student Edition

- Chapter 12 Review, with Vocabulary Skills and Concepts Review, pp. 679–681
- Chapter 12 Test, p. 682

Assessment Resources *Spanish versions available.*

- Checkpoint Quizzes 1 & 2
- Chapter Test, Forms A & B
- Chapter Alternative Assessment

 Computer Test Generator CD-ROM

- Instant Chapter Tests™ — pre-made tests with items that vary every time you print.
- Online Testing allows you to give tests online and receive progress reports.
- Diagnose readiness with questions on prerequisite skills.
- Prepare students by making tests based on standardized test objectives.

Algebra Readiness Tests

- Includes Basic Skills Tests and Concept-Readiness Tests.
- Assess understanding of skills and concepts needed for success in algebra.

Standardized Test Preparation

 Test Prep in Chapter 12

Teaches students strategies and gives them practice with all the test item formats they will encounter on high-stakes tests.

Test Prep exercises in each lesson (pp. 633, 639, 647, 653, 658, 663, 668, 671, 677)

Test-Taking Strategies (p. 678: Answering True/False Questions)

Test Prep (p. 683: Cumulative Review)

Provides a three-step approach to preparing students for high-stakes, national, and state exams.

① Diagnose & Prescribe

Content Diagnostic Tests

- Diagnose strengths and weaknesses with ongoing benchmark tests.
- Prescribe individualized reteaching opportunities.

② Review & Reteach

Skills and Concepts Review

- Provides reteaching worksheets with instruction and practice for each skill.
- Includes course prerequisite skills.

③ Practice & Assess

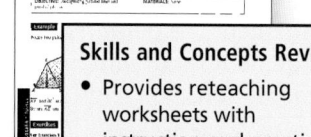

Standardized Test Preparation

- Features practice for national standardized exams.
- Includes practice tests for NAEP, SAT10, ITBS, and Terra Nova.

Test-Taking Strategies With Transparencies

- Support the Test-Taking Strategies pages in the Student Edition.
- Provide a transparency and a worksheet for each strategy.

Reaching All Students

The textbook, the iText, and other technology components provide numerous opportunities to reach students of various ability levels and learning styles. Each Teacher's Edition lesson suggests how you can help all your students be successful and understand the mathematics in Chapter 12.

Below Level

Student Edition
- Diagnosing Readiness*: p. 628
- Check Skills You'll Need*: pp. 630, 635, 642, 649, 654, 659, 665, 669, 674

Reteaching
Chapter 12 Grab & Go™: pp. 10–18

Reteaching master image

* Can be used with all ability levels to ensure mastery of prerequisite skills.

Advanced Learners

Student Edition
- Challenge exercises: pp. 633, 639, 646, 652, 658, 662, 663, 668, 671, 677
- Extension: pp. 640, 664

Enrichment
Chapter 12 Grab & Go™ File: pp. 19–27

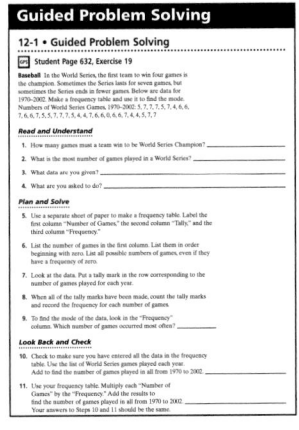

Problem Solving

Student Edition
- Strategies: pp. 674–677
- Real-World Problem Solving: pp. 631, 635, 636, 637, 642, 643, 644, 651, 655, 660, 665, 669, 670, 674

Guided Problem Solving Masters
Chapter 12: pp. 99–107

Guided Problem Solving master image

Reading and Math Literacy

Student Edition
- Vocabulary: pp. 629, 679, plus in most lessons
- Reading Math: pp. 631, 646, 648, 679
- Writing in Math: pp. 633, 638, 646, 652, 657, 663, 668, 671, 673, 677, 682
- Illustrated Glossary: pp. 782–826

Reading and Math Literacy Masters
Chapter 12: pp. 45–48

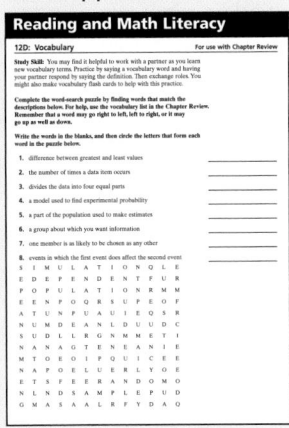

English Learners

Student Edition
- English/Spanish Illustrated Glossary: pp. 782–826

Workbook and Masters
Spanish Practice Workbook: pp. 99–107
Spanish Reading and Math Literacy Masters: pp. 45–48

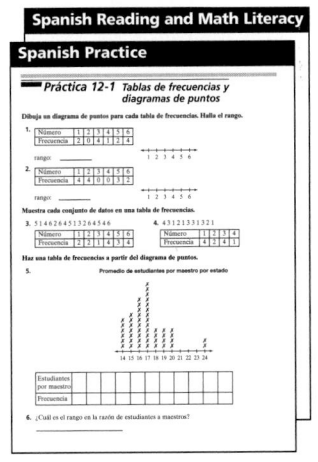

Learning Styles

Student Edition
- Investigation: pp. 630, 649, 654
- Technology: pp. 634, 673
- DK Activities: pp. 684–685
- Chapter Project: p. 743

Activity Masters
Hands-On Activities: 18, 31, 33, 34
Technology Activities: 32, 33, 34, 35

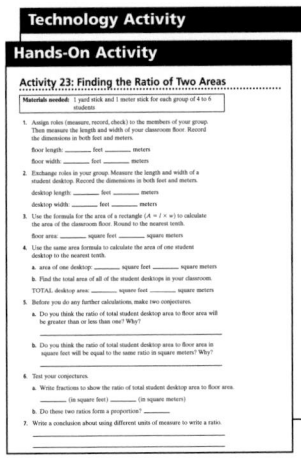

Program Resources

	Resources in Grab & Go™ Files				Resources for Reaching All Students				Spanish Resources			Presentation Assistant Plus! Transparencies				Prentice Hall Presentation Pro CD-ROM
	Practice	Reteach	Enrich	Checkpt Quiz	Reading & Math Literacy	Technology Activities	Hands-On Activities	Guided Problem Solving	Practice	Reading & Math Literacy	Checkpt Quiz	Skills Check	Additional Examples	Answers to Exercises	Lesson Quiz	
12-1	■	■	■		■		■	■	■	■		■	■	■	■	■
12-2	■	■		■			■	■	■			■	■	■	■	■
12-3	■	■		■			■	■	■			■	■	■	■	■
12-4	■	■	■	■			■	■	■	■		■	■	■	■	■
12-5	■	■	■				■	■	■			■	■	■	■	■
12-6	■	■	■			■	■	■	■			■	■	■	■	■
12-7	■	■	■				■	■	■			■	■	■	■	■
12-8	■	■	■	■			■	■	■		■	■	■	■	■	■
12-9	■	■	■			■		■	■			■	■	■	■	■
For the Chapter	Chapter Projects, Chapter Tests, Alternative Assessment, Cumulative Review, Cumulative Assessment				**On Web site only:** Home Activities, Algebra Readiness Puzzles, Interdisciplinary Activities				Spanish Chapter Tests, Alternative Assessment, Cumulative Review, Cumulative Assessment			Classroom Aid Transparencies				

Also available for use with the chapter:
- Practice Workbook
- Solution Key
- MathNotes folder
- For additional online and technology resources, see below.
- For teacher support and access to student Web site materials, use Web Code adk-5500.

 PRENTICE HALL **ASSESSMENT** *SYSTEM*

Program assessment and test preparation, all in one place.

See page 628E.

 Skills Intervention Kit

A *complete* system for the student who is struggling with course-level work

How to Use With Chapter 12

12-1, 12-2, 12-4, 12-6, 12-8, 12-9	Whole Numbers
12-3	Decimals
12-7	Operations/Fractions

 **Online Intervention**

Integrated within the iText, this online intervention system includes diagnostic tests and prescribed remediation, plus reports to track student mastery.

Technology

 iTEXT Online and on CD-ROM

Complete Interactive Student Text online and on CD-ROM—with instant-feedback assessment, tutorial help, dynamic activities, instructional and real-world videos, audio, and additional practice.

 www.PHSchool.com For Students

Use Web Codes for easy access to online activities, chapter projects, self-grading lesson quizzes, chapter tests, vocabulary quizzes, updated data sources, graphing calculator procedures, and more.

PH SuccessNet For Teachers

Online lesson planning with built-in state correlations, all the teaching resources, complete reference library, your own calendar and Teacher Web page, professional development, and more.

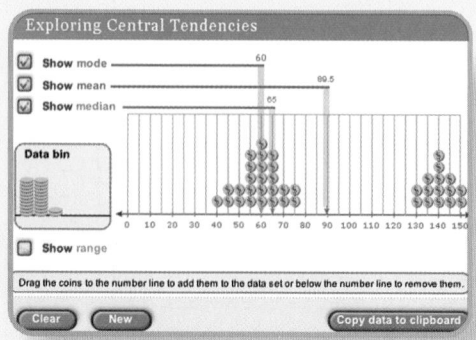

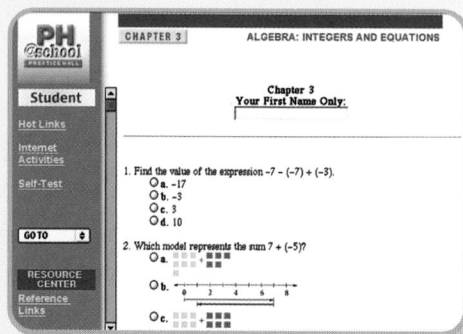

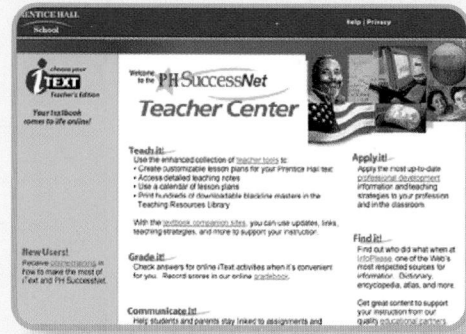

Presentation Assistant Plus!

The Prentice Hall *Presentation Assistant Plus!* provides you with the material you need to teach a lesson from beginning to end. Two easy-to-use formats—Transparencies and CD-ROM—allow you to present a lesson the way you are most comfortable.

 ## Transparencies

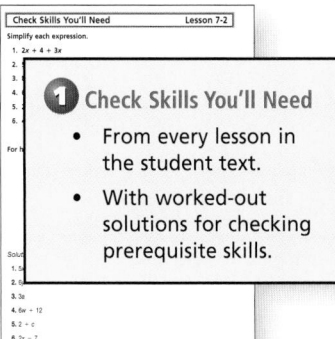

1 Check Skills You'll Need
- From every lesson in the student text.
- With worked-out solutions for checking prerequisite skills.

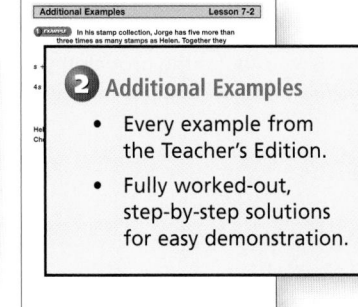

2 Additional Examples
- Every example from the Teacher's Edition.
- Fully worked-out, step-by-step solutions for easy demonstration.

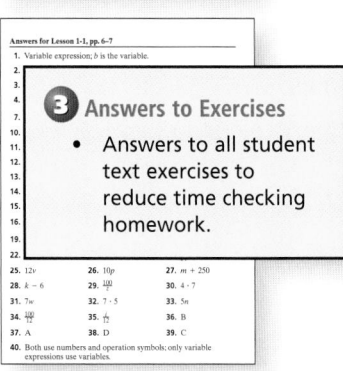

3 Answers to Exercises
- Answers to all student text exercises to reduce time checking homework.

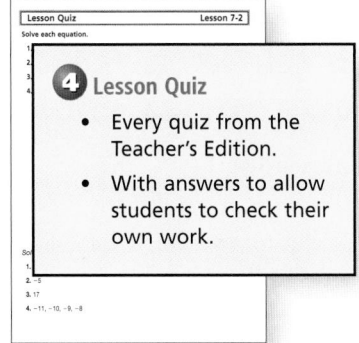

4 Lesson Quiz
- Every quiz from the Teacher's Edition.
- With answers to allow students to check their own work.

 **PowerPoint** Throughout the Teacher's Edition, this symbol indicates material that is available in the Presentation Assistant Plus!

PowerPoint ## Prentice Hall Presentation Pro CD-ROM

- Includes all Transparencies as PowerPoint® presentations.
- Conveniently organized by lesson so you can easily **1** Introduce, **2** Teach, **3** Check Homework, and **4** Assess each lesson.
- Animated examples allow step-by-step instruction at your own pace.
- Easy to edit so you can create custom presentations.

Teaching Chapter 12 Using Presentation Assistant Plus!

	1 Introduce	**2 Teach**	**3 Check Homework**	**4 Assess**
	Check Skills You'll Need	Additional Examples	Student Edition Answers	Lesson Quiz
12-1	p. 100	pp. 165–166	✔	p. 100
12-2	p. 101	pp. 167–169	✔	p. 102
12-3	p.103	pp. 170–172	✔	p. 103
12-4	p. 104	pp. 172–174	✔	p. 104
12-5	p. 105	pp. 174–175	✔	p. 105
12-6	p. 106	pp. 176–177	✔	p. 107
12-7	p. 108	p. 178	✔	p. 108
12-8	p. 109	p. 179	✔	p. 109
12-9	p. 110	p. 180	✔	p. 110

 ### Prentice Hall Presentation Pro

CD-ROM with dynamic Powerpoint® presentations for every lesson. Helps you introduce and develop concepts, check homework, and assess progress. Part of Presentation Assistant Plus! *(See above.)*

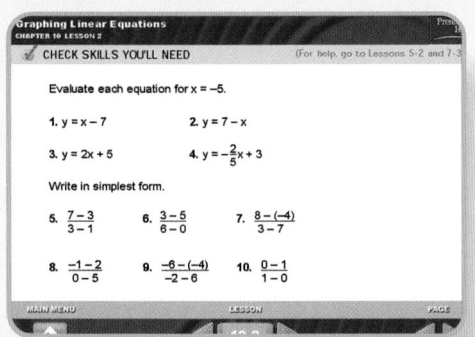

 ### Computer Test Generator

CD-ROM to create practice sheets and tests for course objectives and standardized tests. Includes Instant Chapter Tests™, online testing, and student reports. Part of the PH Assessment System. *(See page 628E.)*

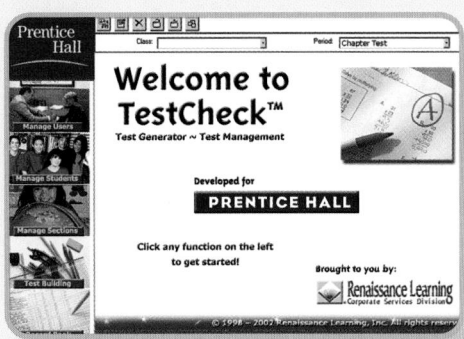

 ### Resource Pro® with Planning Express®

CD-ROM with a lesson planning tool that allows you to import state and local objectives. Includes electronic versions of all the teaching resources.

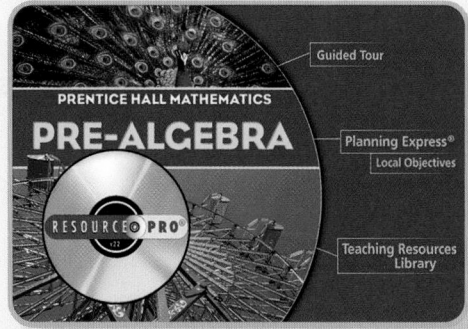

Chapter 12

Data Analysis and Probability

Diagnosing Readiness

Students will find the answers to these exercises in the back of their textbooks.

Prescribing Intervention
For intervention, direct students to:

Finding the Median
Lesson 3-3: Example 1;
Exercises 1–4.
Extra Practice, p. 746.

Multiplying Fractions
Lesson 5-4: Example 2;
Exercises 1–8.
Extra Practice, p. 748.

Finding Probability
Lesson 6-4: Examples 1 and 2;
Exercises 1–13.
Extra Practice, p. 749.

Fractions, Decimals, and Percents
Lesson 6-5: Examples 2–4;
Exercises 11–41.
Extra Practice, p. 749.

Where You've Been

- In Chapter 3, you investigated measures of central tendency for sets of data.

- In Chapter 4, you simplified fractions by dividing the numerator and denominator by the GCF.

- In Chapter 5, you performed operations with fractions.

- In Chapter 6, you found the probability of events. You also wrote fractions and decimals as percents.

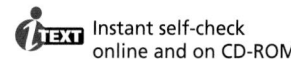 Instant self-check online and on CD-ROM

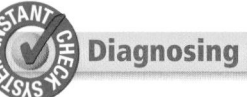
Diagnosing Readiness   (For help, go to the lesson in green.)

Finding the Median (Lesson 3-3)

Find the median.

1. $12, 14, 10, 9, 13, 12, 15, 12, 11$ **12**   **2.** $55, 53, 67, 52, 50, 49, 51, 52, 52$ **52**

3. $101, 100, 100, 105, 102, 101$ **101**   **4.** $0.2, 0.5, 0.11, 0.25, 0.34, 0.19$ **0.225**

Multiplying Fractions (Lesson 5-4)

Find each product.

5. $\frac{2}{3} \cdot \frac{1}{2}$ $\frac{1}{3}$ **6.** $\frac{7}{8} \cdot \frac{6}{7}$ $\frac{3}{4}$ **7.** $\frac{9}{10} \cdot \frac{8}{9}$ $\frac{4}{5}$ **8.** $\frac{5}{6} \cdot \frac{4}{5}$ $\frac{2}{3}$ **9.** $\frac{3}{4} \cdot \frac{2}{3}$ $\frac{1}{2}$ **10.** $\frac{7}{8} \cdot \frac{6}{7} \cdot \frac{5}{6}$ $\frac{5}{8}$

Finding Probability (Lesson 6-4)

Find the probability for one roll of a number cube.

11. $P(2)$ $\frac{1}{6}$ **12.** $P(5)$ $\frac{1}{6}$ **13.** $P(2 \text{ or } 5)$ $\frac{2}{6}$, or $\frac{1}{3}$ **14.** $P(8)$ 0

15. $P(1, 2, \text{or } 3)$ $\frac{3}{6}$, or $\frac{1}{2}$ **16.** $P(\text{less than } 1)$ 0 **17.** $P(\text{not } 3)$ $\frac{5}{6}$ **18.** $P(\text{greater than } 4)$ $\frac{2}{6}$, or $\frac{1}{3}$

A student is chosen at random from a class of 15 boys and 18 girls.
Find each probability.

19. $P(\text{girl})$ $\frac{18}{33}$, or $\frac{6}{11}$ **20.** $P(\text{boy})$ $\frac{15}{33}$, or $\frac{5}{11}$ **21.** $P(\text{not a girl})$ $\frac{15}{33}$, or $\frac{5}{11}$ **22.** $P(\text{not a boy})$ $\frac{18}{33}$, or $\frac{6}{11}$

Fractions, Decimals, and Percents (Lesson 6-5)

Write each percent as a decimal, and each decimal or fraction as a percent.

23. 50% **0.50**   **24.** 36% **0.36**   **25.** 20% **0.20**   **26.** 5% **0.05**

27. $\frac{1}{5}$ **20%**   **28.** $\frac{7}{8}$ **87.5%**   **29.** 0.28 **28%**   **30.** 0.3 **30%**

Data Analysis and Probability

Where You're Going

In this chapter, you will learn how to

- Use graphs to represent data.
- Find theoretical probability and experimental probability.
- Find permutations and combinations.
- Solve problems by doing simulations.

Real-World Snapshots Applying what you learn, on pages 684–685 you will solve problems about goal scoring in World Cup soccer.

LESSONS

12-1 Frequency Tables and Line Plots

12-2 Box-and-Whisker Plots

12-3 Using Graphs to Persuade

12-4 Counting Outcomes and Theoretical Probability

12-5 Independent and Dependent Events

12-6 Permutations and Combinations

12-7 Experimental Probability

12-8 Random Samples and Surveys

12-9 Problem Solving: Simulate the Problem

Key Vocabulary

- box-and-whisker plot (p. 635)
- combination (p. 660)
- counting principle (p. 650)
- dependent events (p. 656)
- experimental probability (p. 665)
- frequency table (p. 630)
- independent events (p. 654)
- line plot (p. 631)
- permutation (p. 659)
- quartiles (p. 635)
- random sample (p. 669)
- range (p. 631)
- sample (p. 669)
- sample space (p. 650)
- simulation (p. 665)
- theoretical probability (p. 650)

629

Chapter 12 Overview

Chapter 12 shows how to display data in different forms, such as frequency tables, line plots, and box-and-whisker plots. The students learn how graphs can be persuasive, or even deceiving, due to breaks in scales, spacing, and sizes of images used. Students find probabilities for independent and dependent events, and learn the differences between theoretical and experimental probabilities. They distinguish between permutations and combinations and calculate both. They also evaluate sampling plans for surveys and make estimates about populations. Students finish the chapter by learning to use simulations.

Activating Prior Knowledge
Ask students how to simplify a fraction. Divide both the numerator and denominator by their GCF.

Reading Math
- Reading for Problem Solving, p. 648
- **Vocabulary** A complete list of terms, plus vocabulary exercises, appears in the Chapter Review on p. 679.
- **Illustrated Glossary** Examples for each vocabulary term, plus definitions in both English and Spanish, appear starting on p. 782.

Test-Taking Strategies
Answering True/False Questions, p. 678

Real-World Problem Solving
Strategy: Simulate the Problem, pp. 674–677
DK Real-World Snapshots: Applying Data Analysis, pp. 684–685
Chapter Project: The Good Times Poll, p. 743

 www.PHSchool.com
Internet support includes:
- Self-grading Vocabulary and Chapter 12 Tests
- Activity Masters
- Chapter Project support
- Chapter Planner
- Chapter 12 Resources

Plus

Frequency Tables and Line Plots

 Check Skills You'll Need

Mean, Median, and Mode
Lesson 3-3: Example 1;
Exercises 1–4.
Extra Practice, p. 746.

Lesson Resources

 Teaching Resources
Practice, Reteaching, Enrichment

 Reaching All Students
Practice Workbook 12-1
Spanish Practice Workbook 12-1
Reading and Math Literacy 12A
Spanish Reading and Math
  Literacy 12A
Guided Problem Solving 12-1
Hands-On Activities 18

 Presentation Assistant Plus!
Transparencies and PowerPoint™
• Check Skills You'll Need 12-1
• Additional Examples 12-1
• Student Edition Answers 12-1
• Lesson Quiz 12-1
• Classroom Aid 1
PH Presentation Pro CD-ROM 12-1

 ASSESSMENT SYSTEM

Computer Test Generator CD-ROM

 Technology
Resource Pro® CD-ROM
Computer Test Generator CD-ROM
PH Presentation Pro CD-ROM

 www.PHSchool.com
Student Site
• Teacher Web Code: adk-5500
• Graphing Calculator,
  Procedure 20
• Self-grading Lesson Quiz
PH SuccessNet Teacher Center
• Lesson Planner
• Resources

Plus

What You'll Learn

 To display data in frequency tables

 To display data in line plots

. . . And Why

To solve real-world problems involving surveys

 **Check Skills You'll Need**

Find the median and mode of each data set.

1. 6, 9, 9, 5, 9
   9; 9
2. 73, 78, 77, 73, 79
   77; 73
3. 300, 100, 200, 150, 300
   200; 300
4. 3, 5, 7, 9, 3, 4, 6, 3, 7
   5; 3

For help, go to Lesson 3-3.

New Vocabulary

• frequency table
• line plot
• range

OBJECTIVE

1 Using Frequency Tables to Display Data

 **In**vestigation

Exploring Frequency Tables

Surveys Many people have favorite colors. Do people also have favorite numbers? Take a survey of your classmates.

1. Ask each person to choose an integer from 0 to 9. Use a table to record the responses. **1–3. Check students' work.**

2. Which number was chosen most frequently? How many times was each of the other numbers chosen?

3. Suppose you want to continue your survey by asking more people. Looking back, would you use the same type of table you used for Question 1? Can you make improvements? Explain.

You can display data in a **frequency table,** which lists each data item with the number of times it occurs.

1 EXAMPLE Building a Frequency Table

A number cube was rolled 20 times. The results are shown at the right. Display the data in a frequency table.

```
5 2 5 4 1 6 5 2 5 1
3 6 1 3 4 5 3 5 3 4
```

List the numbers on the cube in order. | **Use a tally mark for each result.** | **Count the tally marks and record the frequency.**

Number	Tally	Frequency
1					3
2				2
3						4
4					3
5							6
6				2

 iTEXT Interactive lesson includes instant self-check, tutorials, and activities.

Ongoing Assessment and Intervention

Before the Lesson
Diagnose prerequisite skills using:
• Check Skills You'll Need

During the Lesson
Monitor progress using:
• Check Understanding
• Additional Examples
• Test Prep

After the Lesson
Assess knowledge using:
• Lesson Quiz
• Computer Test Generator CD-ROM

✓ Check Understanding Example 1

1. Display the data below in a frequency table. See right.

10 12 13 15 10 11 14 13 10 11 11 12 10 10 15

1.

Number	Frequency
10	5
11	3
12	2
13	2
14	1
15	2

You can organize numerical data into frequency tables and line plots to help others understand it quickly and efficiently. A frequency table shows each data item and a count of how many times that item occurs. A line plot pictures frequencies in the form of marks above a number line.

OBJECTIVE 2 Using Line Plots to Display Data

A **line plot** displays data with **X** marks above a number line.

The **range** of the data is the difference between the greatest and the least values in the data set.

Reading Math

This is the second use of the word *range*. The first appears in Lesson 8-1. You must read and use "range" *in context*, that is, according to the meanings of the words that appear with it.

Teaching Notes

Investigation (Optional)

Help students see how much more quickly they can get certain information (such as which result occurs most often) from the data when the data are organized in a frequency table.

2 EXAMPLE Tactile Learners

Have students model a line plot of their birthdays by having each stand in one of 12 rows, based on the month in which he or she was born.

2 EXAMPLE Real-World 🌐 Problem Solving

Surveys Twenty-five students in a school hallway were asked how many books they were carrying. The frequency table at the right shows their responses. Display the data in a line plot. Then find the range.

"How many books are you carrying?"

Number	Frequency
0	3
1	7
2	6
3	2
4	4
5	3

For a line plot, follow steps ①, ②, and ③.

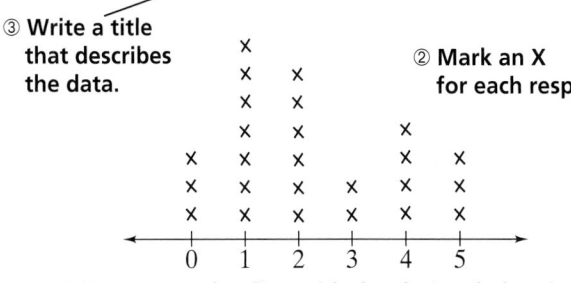

Students Carrying Books

③ Write a title that describes the data.

② Mark an X for each response.

① Draw a number line with the choices below it.

The greatest value in the data set is 5 and the least value is 0.
So the range is 5 − 0, or 5.

PowerPoint

Additional Examples

1 A survey asked 22 students how many hours of TV they watched daily. The results are shown below. Display the data in a frequency table.
1 3 4 3 1 1 2 3 4 1 3
2 2 1 3 2 1 2 3 2 4 3
See back of book.

2 Twenty-one judges were asked how many cases they were trying on Monday. The frequency table below shows their responses. Display the data in a line plot. Then find the range.

"How many cases are you trying?"

Number	Frequency
0	3
1	5
2	4
3	5
4	4

See back of book for line plot; range: 4

✓ Check Understanding Example 2

2. a. Display the data below in a line plot. Then find the range.
miles from home to the mall: 2, 4, 3, 7, 3, 1, 4, 2, 2, 6, 3, 5, 1, 8, 3
  b. What is the range of the data below? See right.
prices of a gallon of regular gas at different gas stations:
$1.48, $1.32, $1.30, $1.35, $1.41, $1.29, $1.32, $1.43, $1.36 $.19

2a. Miles to the Mall

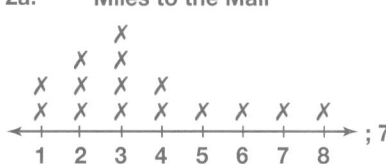

; 7

Closure

Ask: *What are frequency tables and line plots?* See back of book.

👥 Reaching All Students

Below Level Explain that data need not be numerical. Data can also be such things as colors of cars or sets of names.	**Advanced Learners** Suggest students conduct a survey similar to the one in Example 2. Ask students to report on how the numbers of students they survey affect their data.	**Tactile Learners** See note on page 631. **Auditory Learners** See note on page 633.

3. Practice

Assignment Guide

1 Objective 1
Ⓐ Ⓑ Core 1–6, 19

2 Objective 2
Ⓐ Ⓑ Core 7–18, 20–25
Ⓒ Extension 26, 27

Test Prep 28–31
Mixed Review 32–37

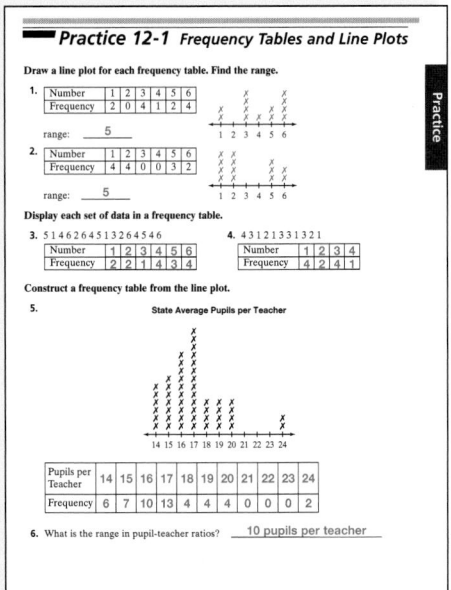

EXERCISES

Q For more exercises, see *Extra Practice*.

Practice and Problem Solving

Ⓐ **Practice by Example**

Display each set of data in a frequency table. 1–6. See margin.

Example 1
(page 630)

1. 1 4 0 3 0 1 3 2 2 4   **2.** 6 2 8 7 9 3 5 4 8 2 4 6 4 1

3. 10 30 20 30 50 10 40 30 50 40 30 50

4. 25 29 28 28 30 25 26 28 27 29 26 30

5. rolls of a number cube: 4 1 3 4 2 1 2 5 2 3 5 1 6 1 3 5 6

6. test scores: 100 90 70 60 95 65 85 70 70 75 80 85 75 70 100 90

Example 2
(page 631)

Draw a line plot for each frequency table. 7–8. See back of book.

7.

Number	1	2	3	4	5	6
Frequency	2	5	7	8	4	3

8.

Number	1	2	3	4	5	6
Frequency	1	3	5	8	8	5

In Exercises 9–14, display each set of data in a line plot. Find the range. 9–13. See back of book.

9. 0 2 1 1 4 0 4 3 2   **10.** 5 2 1 3 3 6 4 5 4 2

11. 5 0 2 1 4 3 4 0 2 5   **12.** 4 2 4 12 8 12 10 6 4
   4 3 2 0 4   8 6 8 12

🌐 **13. Literature** the number of letters in each of the first twenty-five words of *Alice's Adventures in Wonderland* by Lewis Carroll:
4 3 10 5 3 9 2 3 4 5 2 7 2 3 6 2 3 4 3 2 6 7 2 2 4

Ⓑ **Apply Your Skills**

14. the weekly earnings in dollars of the employees at Industrial Enterprises: 320, 320, 320, 400, 400, 400, 400, 400, 400, 480, 480, 480, 720, 720, 720, 1000 See left.

14. $680

Weekly Earnings

```
X
X
X
X      X
X  X   X
X  X   X          X
─────────────────────────
300 400 500 600 700 800 900 1000
        Earnings ($)
```

Display each set of data in a frequency table and in a line plot. Find the range. 15–18. See back of book.

15. ages of club members:
14 16 14 16 14 13 12 15 16 12 12 15 14 15 15

16. heights of plants (inches):
25 25 20 25 16 20 25 30 25 31 26 28 30

17. 7 11 10 10 8 11 9 7 9 8 11 11

18. 17 20 16 17 19 18 17 20 17 18 18 19 18 17

🌐 **19. Baseball** In the World Series, the first team to win four games is the champion. Sometimes the Series lasts for seven games, but sometimes the Series ends in fewer games. Below are data for 1970–2002. Make a frequency table and use it to find the mode. Numbers of World Series Games, 1970–2002: 5, 7, 7, 7, 5, 7, 4, 6, 6, 7, 6, 6, 7, 5, 5, 7, 7, 7, 5, 4, 4, 7, 6, 6, 0, 6, 6, 7, 4, 4, 5, 7, 7
See back of book.

Use the Guided Problem Solving worksheet with Exercise 19.

1.

Number	Frequency
0	2
1	2
2	2
3	2
4	2

3.

Number	Frequency
10	2
20	1
30	4
40	2
50	3

2, 4–6. See back of book.

A frequency table or line plot may allow you to readily "see" the mode and find the median. Find the mode and the median for the data set in each exercise.

20. Exercise 11 4; 3
21. Exercise 12
4, 8, 12; 8
22. Exercise 13 2; 3
23. Exercise 14
400; 400
24. Exercise 15
14, 15; 14
25. Exercise 16
25; 25

C Challenge

26. Reasoning A magazine line plot shows results of a survey. Explain how to use the line plot to find each of the following:
a. the number of people who answered the survey. Count the x's.
b. the mode, median, and mean See back of book.

27. Writing in Math Describe a set of data that would be easier to display with a frequency table than with a line plot.
Answers may vary. Sample: data in which one or more numbers occur with a high frequency.

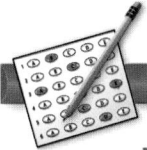

Test Prep

Multiple Choice

28. Below is a list of the ages of first-year teachers in one school system. What is the mode of the ages? A
23, 42, 21, 25, 23, 24, 23, 24, 37, 23, 39, 51, 63, 24, 55
A. 23   **B.** 24   **C.** 37   **D.** 51

31. [2] Chicken; more students chose chicken as their favorite lunch.
[1] minor error OR answer only

29. What is the range of the data below? I
99.2, 101.5, 97.9, 102.1, 98.6, 100.4, 102.2, 99.9
F. 3.7   **G.** 3.9
H. 4.0   **I.** 4.3

Short Response

The line plot (right) represents the results of a class survey in which students were asked to name their favorite lunch.

30. a. How many students were surveyed?
b. How do you know?
See back of book.
31. a. What is the mode of the survey?
b. Explain your answer for part (a).
See above left.

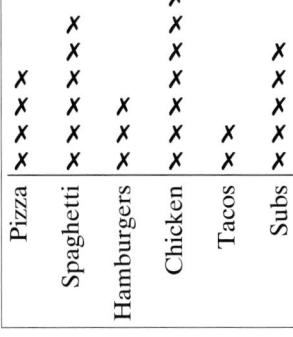

Take It to the NET
Online lesson quiz at
www.PHSchool.com
Web Code: ada-1201

Mixed Review

Lesson 11-7
32. Measurement The angle of elevation to a treetop from a point 10 ft out from the tree's base is 70°. Find the height of the tree.
about 27 ft

Lesson 9-5
Given that $\triangle LMN \cong \triangle PQR$, **complete each statement.**

33. $\angle N \cong$ ■ $\angle R$ **34.** $\overline{MN} \cong$ ■ $\overline{QR}$ **35.** $PQ =$ ■ LM

Lesson 3-3
Find the mean, median, and mode for each data set.

36. 12 13 14 16 16 17 18 18
15.5, 16, 16 and 18
37. 8 15 22 9 11 16 20 10
13.875, 13, no mode

12-1 Frequency Tables and Line Plots   **633**

 **Lesson Quiz 12-1**

Solve.
1. Maria surveyed friends to find out how many pets each one has. The responses are below. Display the data in a frequency table.
0, 1, 1, 2, 3, 0, 1, 1, 3, 2, 1, 2, 1, 0, 1, 0, 0
See back of book.

2. Here are the numbers of books students read in the last month: 5, 4, 0, 12, 4, 5, 4, 3, 10, 5, 12, 3, 5, 7, 3, 10, 5, 0, 6.
Display the data in a line plot. Then find the range.
See back of book.
range: 12

Auditory Learners
Exercises 7–12 Have students work in pairs to draw each line plot. Have one student read the data items aloud as the other marks them on the line plot. Then have students switch roles and do another exercise.

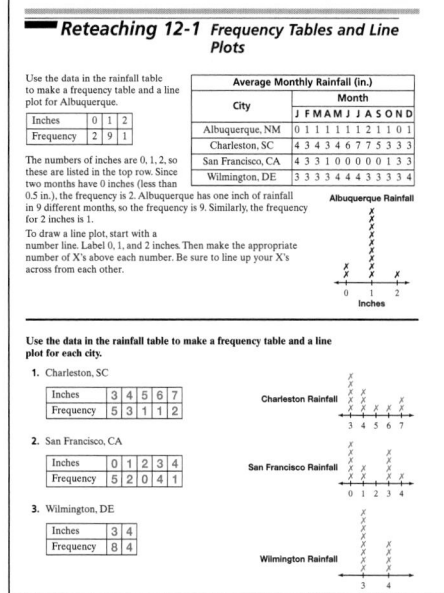

Reteaching 12-1 *Frequency Tables and Line Plots*

Alternative Assessment

Have groups of students use number cubes or spinners from various board games. Have them record the results they get from rolling the number cubes or spinning the spinners. Then have them organize the data in frequency tables and as line plots. Have them find the ranges for their data.

Test Prep

Resources
For additional practice with a variety of test item formats:
• Test Prep, p. 683
• Test-Taking Strategies, p. 678
• Test-Taking Strategies With Transparencies

633

Making Histograms

This Technology extension shows students how to use a graphing calculator to make a histogram. A histogram is a special type of bar graph that has no spaces between the bars.

Resources

Students may use any graphing calculator.

Teaching Notes

Error Prevention!

Remind students that, as they work with the graphing calculator, they must be alert for screen information that is left over from previous use. They should "clear" such information before proceeding.

 **Technology**

Making Histograms

For Use With Lesson 12-1

A histogram shows the frequencies of data items as a graph. You can use a graphing calculator to make a histogram.

EXAMPLE

Make a histogram of the data below.
21, 23, 20, 22, 23, 21, 24, 26, 23, 21, 20, 23, 21, 23, 20, 24

Step 1 Press **LIST** to find list L_1. Enter the data in L_1. (To first remove any data already in L_1, select L_1, then `CLEAR` `ENTER`.)

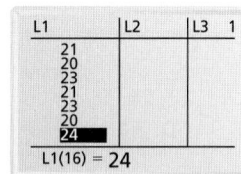

Step 2 In **PLOT**, enter 1 and select **On**. Select the Type of graph that looks like a histogram and `ENTER`.

Step 3 In the **ZOOM** menu, select item 7 "ZoomStat" and `ENTER`. In `WINDOW`, set Xscl = 1. Then `GRAPH`.

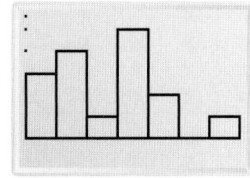

Step 4 To see the frequency of each number, press `TRACE`, and move the cursor across the histogram. Sketch the histogram.

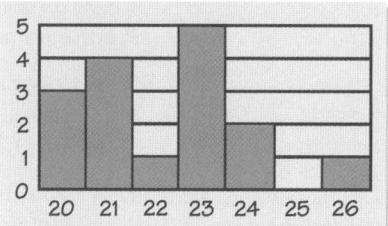

EXERCISES

Use a graphing calculator to make a histogram of each set of data.
Then sketch the histogram. 1–4. See margin.

1. 11, 12, 12, 11, 10, 12, 13, 15, 9, 10, 12, 13

2. 9, 7, 6, 9, 8, 5, 9, 2, 2, 5, 8, 4, 6, 3, 8, 7, 8, 5

3. 23, 26, 25, 26, 23, 25, 25, 24, 21, 21, 22, 23

4. 95, 90, 92, 91, 95, 94, 93, 92, 94, 93, 95, 91

5. In Step 3 above, `ENTER` showed one histogram and then `GRAPH` showed another. They are histograms of the same data. Explain the difference in how they look. **Answers will vary. Sample: The scales of the histogram are different.**

1.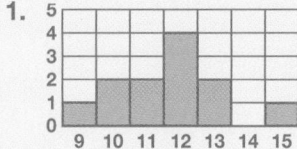

2.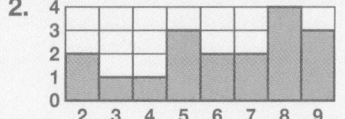

3.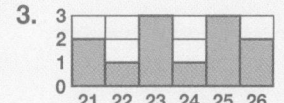

4.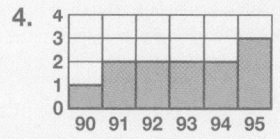

Box-and-Whisker Plots

OBJECTIVE 1 Making Box-and-Whisker Plots

A **box-and-whisker plot** displays the distribution of data items along a number line. **Quartiles** divide the data into four equal parts. The median is the middle quartile.

Box-and-Whisker Plot

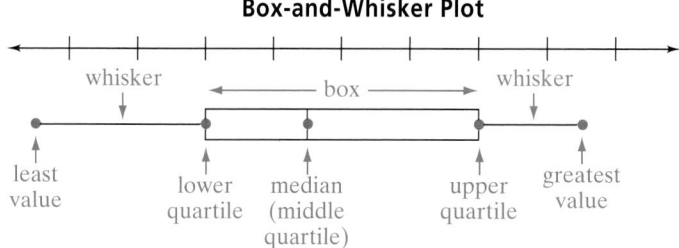

1 EXAMPLE Real-World Problem Solving

Statistics The table, below right, shows United States crops harvested from 1988 to 2000. Make a box-and-whisker plot.

Step 1 Arrange the data in order from least to greatest. Find the median.

298 308 314 317 318 318 321 322 323 326 326 327 333

Step 2 Find the lower quartile and upper quartile, which are the medians of the lower and upper "halves."

298 308 314 317 318 318 321 322 323 326 326 327 333

$$\text{lower quartile} = \frac{314 + 317}{2} = \frac{631}{2} = 315.5$$

$$\text{upper quartile} = \frac{326 + 326}{2} = \frac{652}{2} = 326$$

Step 3 Draw a number line. Mark the least and greatest values, the median, and the quartiles. Draw a box from the first to the third quartiles. Mark the median with a vertical segment. Draw whiskers from the box to the least and greatest values.

Crops Harvested (millions of acres)

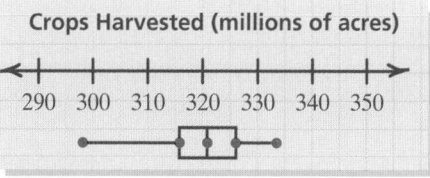

What You'll Learn

 OBJECTIVE 1 To make box-and-whisker plots

OBJECTIVE 2 To analyze data in box-and-whisker plots

... And Why

To solve real-world problems involving large data sets

✓ Check Skills You'll Need

Find each median.

1. 12, 10, 11, 7, 9, 8, 10, 5
   9.5

2. 4.5, 3.2, 6.3, 5.2, 5, 4.8, 6, 3.9
   4.9

3. 55, 53, 67, 52, 50, 49, 51, 52, 52, 52
   52

4. 101, 100, 100, 105, 102, 101
   101

 For help, go to Lesson 3-3.

New Vocabulary

• box-and-whisker plot
• quartiles

Crops Harvested

Year	Acres (millions)	Year	Acres (millions)
1988	298	1995	314
1989	318	1996	326
1990	322	1997	333
1991	318	1998	326
1992	317	1999	327
1993	308	2000	323
1994	321		

SOURCE: *Statistical Abstract of the United States.* Go to to **www.PHSchool.com** for a data update. Web Code: adg-2041

 TEXT Interactive lesson includes instant self-check, tutorials, and activities.

12-2 Box-and-Whisker Plots **635**

---

1. Plan

Lesson Preview

✓ **Check Skills You'll Need**

Mean, Median, and Mode
Lesson 3-3: Example 1;
Exercises 1–4.
Extra Practice, p. 746.

Lesson Resources

📁 **Teaching Resources**
Practice, Reteaching, Enrichment

👥 **Reaching All Students**
Practice Workbook 12-2
Spanish Practice Workbook 12-2
Guided Problem Solving 12-2
Technology Activities 33
Hands-On Activities 18

⏱ **Presentation Assistant Plus!**
Transparencies and PowerPoint™
• Check Skills You'll Need 12-2
• Additional Examples 12-2
• Student Edition Answers 12-2
• Lesson Quiz 12-2
• Classroom Aid 33, 34, 35
PH Presentation Pro CD-ROM 12-2

(ASSESSMENT *SYSTEM*)

Computer Test Generator CD-ROM

💻 **Technology**
Resource Pro® CD-ROM
Computer Test Generator CD-ROM
PH Presentation Pro CD-ROM

💻 **www.PHSchool.com**
Student Site
• Teacher Web Code: adk-5500
• Updated Data
• Graphing Calculator, Procedure 21
• Self-grading Lesson Quiz
PH SuccessNet Teacher Center
• Lesson Planner
• Resources

Plus **TEXT**

⟳ Ongoing Assessment and Intervention

Before the Lesson	**During the Lesson**	**After the Lesson**
Diagnose prerequisite skills using:	Monitor progress using:	Assess knowledge using:
• Check Skills You'll Need	• Check Understanding	• Lesson Quiz
	• Additional Examples	• Computer Test Generator CD-ROM
	• Test Prep	

Math Background

You can summarize data by grouping them into fourths with a *box-and-whisker plot*. You group the middle two fourths inside a *box*. You show the first fourth and last fourth as *whiskers* (horizontal segments) extending from the sides of the box.

Teaching Notes

English Learners

Ask students what the term *quartile* sounds like. They will likely say *quarter*. Therefore, some students may think that there are four quartiles. Point out that there are only 3 quartiles, but they separate the data into 4 sets.

1 EXAMPLE Error Prevention

Students may want to make the spaces between the quartiles the same size. Explain that quartiles divide the number of data items into four equal parts. However, the ranges of the *values* of the data points in the four parts may be different, which leads to the different sizes.

1 EXAMPLE Tactile Learners

Have students use masking tape to make a number line on the floor for Example 1. Then have them write each data value on a small card and place each card in the proper place on the line. Students can use more masking tape to make the box-and-whisker plot around the cards.

3 EXAMPLE Teaching Tip

Have students list what they know about a set of data from looking at a box-and-whisker plot. For example, they can see the least and greatest values, the median and quartiles, and the distances between these points.

Real-World Connection

DNA evidence suggests that whales and hippopotamuses are closely related genetically.

✓ Check Understanding Example 1

1. Draw a box-and-whisker plot for the distances of migration of birds (thousands of miles): 5, 2.5, 6, 8, 9, 2, 1, 4, 6.2, 18, 7.
See back of book.

You can compare two sets of data by making two box-and-whisker plots below one number line.

2 EXAMPLE Real-World 🌐 Problem Solving

Biology Use box-and-whisker plots to compare orca whale masses and hippopotamus masses.

Orca whale masses (kg)

| 3,900 | 2,750 | 2,600 | 3,100 | 4,200 | 2,600 | 3,700 | 3,000 | 2,200 |

Hippopotamus masses (kg)

| 1,800 | 2,000 | 3,000 | 2,500 | 3,600 | 2,700 | 1,900 | 3,100 | 2,300 |

Draw a number line for both sets of data. Use the range of data points to choose a scale.

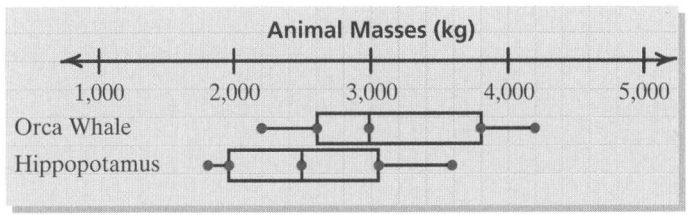

Draw the second box-and-whisker plot below the first one.

✓ Check Understanding Example 2

2. Compare annual video sales and CD sales by making two box-and-whisker plots below one number line.

videos (millions of units): 28, 24, 15, 21, 22, 16, 22, 30, 24, 17

CDs (millions of units): 16, 17, 22, 16, 18, 24, 15, 16, 25, 18
See back of book.

OBJECTIVE

2 Analyzing Box-and-Whisker Plots

Although you cannot see every data point in a box-and-whisker plot, you can use the quartiles and the greatest and least values to analyze and describe a data set.

👥 Reaching All Students

Below Level Display the data: 1, 1, 3, 3, 4, 5, 7, 7, 8, 9, 9. Ask students: *What is the median?* 5 *The median of the data that are less than the median?* 3 *The median of the data that are greater than the median?* 8

Advanced Learners Ask: *Why can't you be sure from looking at a box-and-whisker plot that the median and quartiles are actual values from the data set?* A median or quartile could be an average of 2 data values.

English Learners
See note on page 636.
Tactile Learners
See note on page 636.

3 EXAMPLE Describing Data

Describe the data in the box-and-whisker plot.

Exam Scores

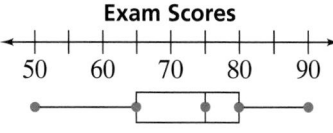

The highest score is 90 and the lowest is 50. At least half of the scores are within 10 points of the median, 75.

✔ **Check Understanding** Example 3

3. Describe the data in each box-and-whisker plot. a–b. See right.

a.
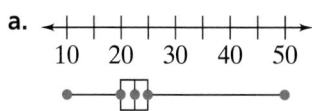

b.
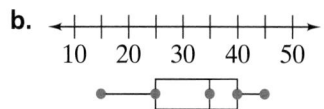

You can compare box-and-whisker plots to analyze two sets of data.

3a. The highest value is 50 and the lowest is 10. The median is 22.5. At least half of the values are within 2.5 units of the median.

3b. The highest value is 45 and the lowest is 15. The median is 35. At least half of the values are within 10 units of the median.

4 EXAMPLE Real-World 🌐 Problem Solving

Social Studies The plots below compare the percents of the voting-age population who said they registered to vote in U.S. elections to the percents who said they voted. What conclusions can you draw?

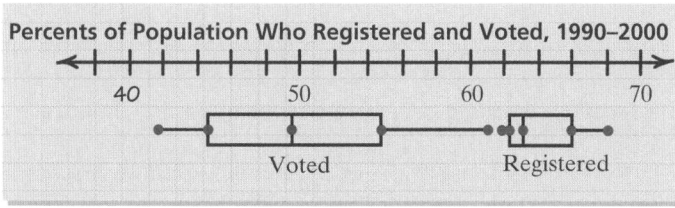

The percent registered was fairly constant, since the box-and-whisker plot is narrow. The percent who voted varied more. You can conclude that in an election, on average, the percent of people who voted was about 15 less than the percent of people who were registered.

✔ **Check Understanding** Example 4

4. Use box-and-whisker plots below. What conclusions can you draw about heights of Olympic basketball players? See right.

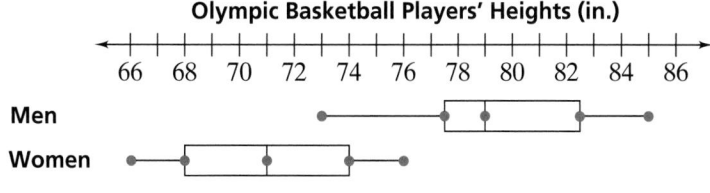

4. The women's heights have a median of 71 in. and a range of 10 in. The men's heights have a median of 79 in. and a range of 12 in. Most of the men are taller than the tallest woman.

12-2 Box-and-Whisker Plots **637**

Additional Example 4
Answers may vary. Sample: About 95% of the students were eligible to participate in extracurricular activities. Around 60% of the students did participate. A little less than two thirds of the eligible students participated in extracurricular activities.

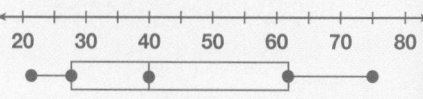
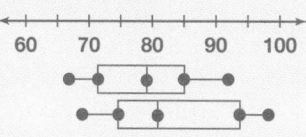
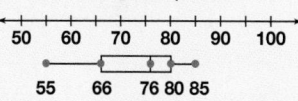

3. Practice

Assignment Guide

1 Objective 1
- **A** **B** Core 1–3, 10, 11
- **C** Extension 12

2 Objective 2
- **A** **B** Core 4–9
- **C** Extension 13

Test Prep 14–16
Mixed Review 17–23

Practice 12-2 Box-and-Whisker Plots

Use the box-and-whisker plot to answer each question.

Weekly Mileage Totals, 24 Runners

10 15 20 25 30 35 40 45 50 55 60

1. What is the highest weekly total? __55 miles__ the lowest? __15 miles__

2. What is the median weekly total? __35 miles__

3. What percent of runners run less than 40 miles a week? __75%__

4. How many runners run less than 20 miles a week? __6 runners__

Make a box-and-whisker plot for each set of data.

5. 16 20 30 15 23 11 15 21 30 29 13 16
   10   15   20   25   30

6. 9 12 10 3 2 3 9 11 5 1 10 4 7 12 3 10
   0   5   10   15

7. 70 77 67 65 79 82 70 68 75 73 69 66
   70 73 89 72
   60 65 70 75 80 85 90

Use box-and-whisker plots to compare data sets. Use a single number line for each comparison.

8. 1st set: 7 12 25 3 1 29 30 7 15 2 5
   10 29 1 10 30 18 8 7 29
   2nd set: 37 17 14 43 27 19 32 1 8 48
   26 16 28 6 25 18
   0 5 10 15 20 25 30 35 40 45 50
   1st Set
   2nd Set

9. Area in 1,000 mi²
   Midwestern states:
   45 36 58 97 56 65 87 82 77
   Southern states:
   52 59 48 52 42 32 54 43 70 53 66
   30 40 50 60 70 80 90 100
   Midwestern States
   Southern States

Enrichment 12-2 Plot the Answer

To answer each of the following questions, make a box and whisker plot for the given set of data. Then write the first quartile, the median, and the third quartile in the answer boxes.

Example
6 7 8 9 10 11 12 13
[6] [7] [1] [3]

1. What was the year of the birth of the famous mathematician Pythagoras?
   Data: 6, 10, 2, 7, 6, 12, 8, 6, 4, 13, 2, 6
   2   4   6   8   10   12   14
   [5] [6] [9] B.C.

2. The Caspian Sea is the largest lake in the world. What is its area?
   Data: 38, 7, 50, 17, 11, 39, 25, 55, 8, 27, 42, 5, 37, 57, 46, 23
   0 10 20 30 40 50 60
   [1] [4] [3].[2] [4] [4] mi²

3. The Pacific Ocean, the world's largest, is also the deepest. What is the average depth of the Pacific Ocean?
   Data: 26, 53, 32, 0, 33, 1, 13, 1, 36, 34, 41, 0
   0 10 20 30 40 50 60
   [1] [2].[9] [3] [5] ft

4. The greatest recorded snowfall in the United States in a single year fell at Mount Rainier, Washington, in 1971–1972. What was the total amount of snow that fell?
   Data: 58, 9, 14, 33, 60, 12, 15, 37, 59, 13, 60, 42, 40, 7, 12, 4
   0 10 20 30 40 50 60
   [1].[2] [2] [4].[5] [0] in.

EXERCISES

❓ For more exercises, see *Extra Practice*.

Practice and Problem Solving

A Practice by Example 🌐

Example 1
(page 635)

1. **Biology** Use the data at the right to make a box-and-whisker plot for the maximum speeds of animals.
   See margin.

2. Make a box-and-whisker plot for this set of data:
   16, 18, 59, 75, 30, 34, 25, 49, 27, 16, 21, 58, 71, 19, 50
   See back of book.

Example 2
(page 636)

3. Compare the data sets by making two box-and-whisker plots below one number line.
   set A: 3, 7, 9, 12, 2, 1, 6, 5, 4, 3, 7, 10, 13, 8, 1, 9
   set B: 9, 8, 1, 7, 6, 3, 7, 9, 8, 6, 4, 7, 8, 9, 10, 10
   See back of book.

Maximum Speeds of Animals for a Quarter Mile

Animal	Maximum Speed (mi/h)
Cheetah	70
Lion	50
Quarter horse	47.5
Coyote	43
Hyena	40
Rabbit	35
Giraffe	32
Grizzly bear	30
Cat (domestic)	30
Elephant	25
Squirrel	12

SOURCE: *The World Almanac*

Example 3
(page 637)

Answer each question for the data in the box-and-whisker plot below.

4. What are the highest and lowest prices for the CD players?
   $115, $50

5. What is the lower quartile price? The median price? The upper quartile price? $60; $70; $85

Prices of Portable CD Players ($)

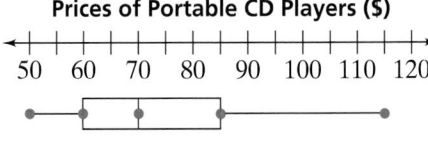

50   60   70   80   90   100 110 120

6. About half of the prices are within what amount of the median?
   $15

Example 4
(page 637)

7. In Example 2 on page 636, what conclusions can you draw?
   See below left.

B Apply Your Skills 🌐

GPS

7. Answers may vary. Sample: The orca weights have a median of 3,000 lb and a range of 2,000 lb. The hippopotamus weights have a median of 2,500 lb and a range of 1,800 lb. A significant number of the orcas and hippos in this comparison fall within the same weight range.

9. The acreages vary considerably, from about 25 acres to about 650 acres. However, about half of the parks are between 50 and 250 acres, with a median of 125 acres.

8. **a. Olympics** Compare the ages of male and female soccer players by making two box-and-whisker plots below one number line.

Ages of U.S. Olympic Soccer Team Players

men: 22, 21, 22, 26, 20, 26, 23, 21, 22, 22, 22, 22, 21, 22, 23, 21, 20, 22

women: 30, 27, 28, 25, 31, 24, 31, 24, 21, 23, 27, 18, 19, 24, 23, 20

b. Compare the box-and-whisker plots. What can you conclude?
a–b. See back of book.

9. Use the box-and-whisker plot below. What can you conclude about acreages of state parks? See below left.

Areas of State Parks (acres)

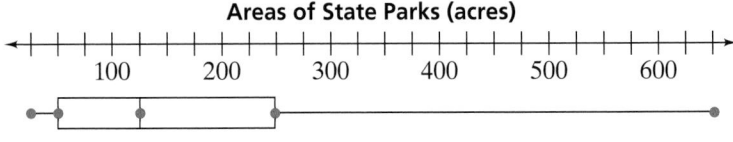

100   200   300   400   500   600

10. **Writing in Math** Explain how you can find the quartiles of a set of data. The lower quartile is the median of the lower half of the data; the upper quartile is the median of the upper half of the data. The middle quartile is the median of the data.

638 Chapter 12 Data Analysis and Probability

GPS Use the Guided Problem Solving worksheet with Exercise 8.

1. **Maximum Speeds of Animals (mi/h)**

   0 10 20 30 40 50 60 70 80 90 100

11. Error Analysis A student made a box-and-whisker plot. The student marked the greatest and least data values and then divided the distance between those points into four equal parts. What error did the student make? **See back of book.**

Challenge

12. Open-Ended Write a set of data whose box-and-whisker plot has a long box and short whiskers. **Answers may vary. Sample: 10, 12, 12, 30, 31, 45, 47**

13. Reasoning Can you find the mean, median, and mode of a set of data by looking at a box-and-whisker plot? Explain. **See back of book.**

Test Prep

Multiple Choice For Exercises 14–16, use the table.

14. What is the median of the maximum life spans of the animals in the table? **B**
  A. 18 yr   **B.** 31 yr
  C. 34 yr   **D.** 50 yr

Take It to the NET
Online lesson quiz at **www.PHSchool.com**
Web Code: ada-1202

15. What is the median of the maximum life spans of the animals if you exclude the mouse and chipmunk? **G**
  F. 50 yr   **G.** 43 yr
  H. 26 yr   **I.** 18 yr

Short Response
16. a. Make a box-and-whisker plot to represent the maximum life spans.
  b. Identify and label the median, the lower and upper quartiles, and the least and greatest maximum life spans. **See back of book.**

Animals' Maximum Life Spans

Animal	Years
Beaver	50
Black bear	36
Chimpanzee	53
Chipmunk	8
Elephant	77
Goat	18
Horse	50
Mouse	6
Squirrel	23
Tiger	26

Mixed Review

Lesson 12-1   **Display each set of data in a frequency table.**

17.

Number	Frequency
4	2
5	3
6	5
7	4
8	4

17. 6 8 7 6 5 8 5 6 4 8 7 5
    4 7 6 8 6 7
  See left.

18. 32 31 29 33 31 32 35 33
    32 31 32 30
  See back of book.

Lesson 11-3   **Find the distance between the points in each pair to the nearest tenth.**

19. $D(3, -2), S(-3, 2)$ **7.2**
20. $A(0, 4), W(-7, -5)$ **11.4**
21. $Y(6, 4), K(-1, 3)$ **7.1**
22. $Z(9, 0), M(-8, 11)$ **20.2**

Lessons 4-9 and 5-5   **23.** Lawns can have 850 blades of grass per square foot. **a–b. See left.**
  a. About how many blades of grass are in one square yard?
  b. The area of all lawns in the United States equals an area twice as large as that of Pennsylvania. Pennsylvania's area is 46,058 mi². Estimate the number of blades of grass in lawns in the United States. Write your answer in scientific notation. (*Hint:* A mile equals 5,280 feet.)

23a. 7,650 blades of grass
23b. about 2.18×10^{15} blades of grass

---

4. Assess

 **Lesson Quiz 12-2**

Solve.

1. Use the data to make a box-and-whisker plot. Student heights (in.) are: 60, 66, 59, 67, 68, 63, 62, 61, 69, 64, 61.
See back of book.
  a. What is the median height? **63 in.**
  b. Between what heights do 50% of the students fall? **61 in. and 67 in.**

2. The box-and-whisker plots below compare prices for the same items at Mary's Discount Store and Ed's Clothing. What conclusions can you draw?

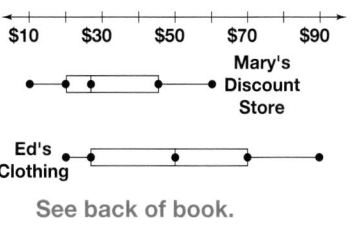

See back of book.

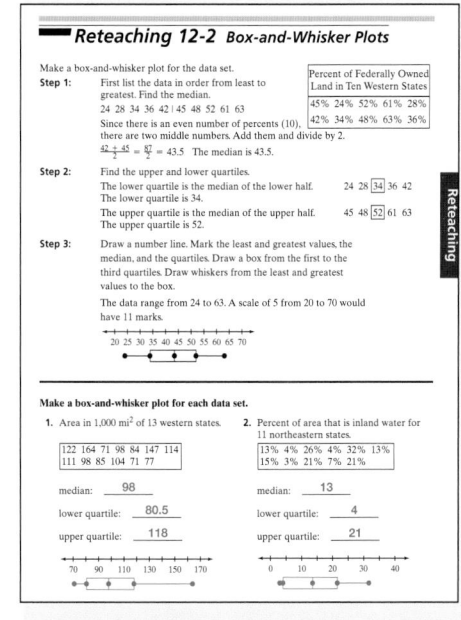

Reteaching 12-2 *Box-and-Whisker Plots*

Alternative Assessment

Have students find data in newspaper or magazine articles that they can represent with box-and-whisker plots. Have them make box-and-whisker plots of the data in the articles, and share the articles and plots with the class.

Test Prep

Resources
For additional practice with a variety of test item formats:
- Test Prep, p. 683
- Test-Taking Strategies, p. 678
- Test-Taking Strategies With Transparencies

Stem-and-Leaf Plots

In this Extension, students learn to make and interpret stem-and-leaf plots. A stem-and-leaf plot can make working with data easier because it shows numbers arranged in order in a compact space.

Teaching Notes

Teaching Tip

A stem-and-leaf plot differs from a box-and-whisker plot in that it shows all data values. You arrange the data by separating the last digit (leaf) of each data value from the other digit(s) (stem) and then making two separate, ordered lists of the data. The stems are ordered vertically and the leaves are ordered horizontally outward on one side of the stem. A back-to-back stem-and-leaf plot shows leaves to both the left and the right of the stems, with the leaves on each side representing a single data set.

Error Prevention!

To help prevent confusion in separating the stems from the leaves, have students ring the stems before stacking them in order. Remind students to include a key for each stem-and-leaf plot.

1 EXAMPLE Auditory Learners

Have students practice reading data from the stem-and-leaf plot. Have one student name a stem and another student name a corresponding leaf. Then a third student names the number that the stem and leaf represents.

1b. Animal Life Spans

```
0 | 1 7
1 | 0 0 2 2 5 5 5
2 | 0 5
3 |
4 | 1

1 | 0  means 10
```

640

Stem-and-Leaf Plots

For Use With Lesson 12-2

A *stem-and-leaf plot* organizes data by showing the items in order. The leaf is the last digit to the right. The stem is the remaining digit or digits.

stem→ 15.7 ←leaf

stem→ 32 ←leaf

1 EXAMPLE

Use the table at the right to construct a stem-and-leaf plot. Then find the median, mode, and range.

Choose the stems. For this data set, use the values in the tens place. Draw a line to the right of the stems.

stems ——→
```
2
3
```

Leaves are single digits, so for this data set the leaves will be the values in the ones place.

```
2 | 9 8
3 | 7 8 7 3 9 7
```
←—— leaves

Broadway Productions

Arrange the leaves on each stem from least to greatest. Include a title and a key that shows how to read your stem-and-leaf plot.

```
2 | 9 8
3 | 7 8 7 3 9 7

2 | 8 means 28
```
←—— key

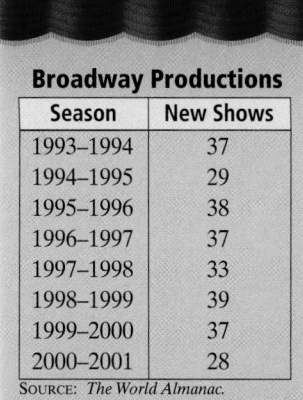

Broadway Productions

Season	New Shows
1993–1994	37
1994–1995	29
1995–1996	38
1996–1997	37
1997–1998	33
1998–1999	39
1999–2000	37
2000–2001	28

SOURCE: *The World Almanac.*

Since the data items are in order, the median is the midpoint. The median is the mean of the fourth and fifth values, or 37.

The mode corresponds to the most repeated leaf. The mode is 37.

The range is the difference of the greatest and least values, or 11.

1. Biology Use the table at the right.
   a. Reasoning What number should you use as the stem for the kangaroo and the opossum? **0**
   b. Construct a stem-and-leaf plot. **See margin.**
   c. Find the median. **13.5**
   d. Find the mode. **15**
   e. Find the range. **40**

Average Longevity

Animal	Years	Animal	Years
Grizzly bear	25	Hippopotamus	41
Kangaroo	7	Pig	10
Cow	15	Lion	15
Dog	12	Opossum	1
Giraffe	10	Cat	12
Gorilla	20	Zebra	15

SOURCE: *The World Almanac*

Make a stem-and-leaf plot for each set of data. Then find the median, the mode, and the range. **2–5. See margin.**

2. 15, 22, 25, 10, 36, 15, 28, 35, 18

3. 47, 41, 60, 75, 85, 53, 57, 76, 79, 81, 84, 86

4. 785, 785, 776, 772, 792, 788, 761, 768, 768

5. 4.5, 4.3, 0.8, 3.5, 2.6, 1.4, 0.2, 0.8, 4.3, 6.0

2.
```
1 | 0 5 5 8
2 | 2 5 8
3 | 5 6

2 | 2  means 22
```
22, 15, 26

3, 5. See back of book.

4.
```
76 | 1 8 8
77 | 2 6
78 | 5 5 8
79 | 2

76 | 1  means 761
```
776; 768 and 785; 31

A back-to-back stem-and-leaf plot uses two sets of data. The side-by-side display makes the data easier to compare.

② **EXAMPLE**

Draw a back-to-back stem-and-leaf plot for the winning times in the Olympic 100-m dash. Find each median and mode.

Use seconds for the stem and tenths of seconds for the leaves. Put the leaves in ascending order starting at the stem.

Winning Times, 100-m Dash

Men's Times (tenths of second)	Stem (seconds)	Women's Times (tenths of second)
9 9 9 8	9	
3 2 1 1 0 0 0	10	5 8 8 9
	11	0 0 0 1 1 1 4

means 10.0 ⟵ 0 | 10 | 5 ⟶ means 10.5

The median of the times for men is 10.0 s. The median of the times for women is 11.0 s. The modes of the times for men are 9.9 s and 10.0 s. The modes of the times for women are 11.0 s and 11.1 s.

Winning Times, 100-m Dash (seconds)

Year	Men	Women
1960	10.2	11.0
1964	10.0	11.4
1968	9.9	11.0
1972	10.1	11.1
1976	10.1	11.1
1980	10.3	11.1
1984	10.0	11.0
1988	9.9	10.5
1992	10.0	10.8
1996	9.8	10.9
2000	9.9	10.8

SOURCE: *Sports Illustrated Sports Almanac*

Make a back-to-back stem-and-leaf plot for each pair of data sets. Then find each median and mode.

6. set A: 9.1, 8.2, 7.3, 6.4, 7.3, 8.5   set B: 7.6, 9.2, 8.2, 8.3, 9.7, 7.6
   See margin.
7. set C: 236, 237, 241, 250, 242   set D: 262, 251, 248, 243, 257
   7–8. See back of book.
8. Annual video sales (millions):   Annual CD sales (millions):
   28, 24, 15, 21, 22, 16, 22, 30, 24, 17   16, 17, 22, 16, 18, 24, 15, 16, 25, 18

Use the stem-and-leaf plot at the right. The plot shows the time spent on homework by students in two classes.

9. Which numbers are the stems?
   6, 7, 8, and 9
10. What is the least time spent for each set of data?
    Class A: 63 min; Class B: 61 min
11. What is the median for each set of data?
    Class A: 79.5; Class B: 84
12. What is the mode for each set of data?
    Class A: 74, 79, and 96; Class B: 99
13. What is the range for each set of data?
    Class A: 34; Class B: 38

Time Spent on Homework (min)

Class A		Class B
7 4 3	6	1 1 3 5 5
9 9 8 5 4 4	7	0 2 2 4
5 2 1 0	8	4 5 8 9
7 6 6 4 2	9	3 6 7 9 9 9

means 63 ⟵ 3 | 6 | 1 ⟶ means 61

6.

Set B		Set A
	6	4
6 6	7	3 3
3 2	8	2 5
7 2	9	1

means 7.6 ⟵ 6 | 7 | 3 ⟶ means 7.3

Set A: 7.75; 7.3
Set B: 8.25; 7.6

641

12-3

1. Plan

Lesson Preview

 Check Skills You'll Need

Slope
Lesson 8-3: Example 1;
Exercises 1 and 2.
Extra Practice, p. 751.

Lesson Resources

 **Teaching Resources**
Practice, Reteaching, Enrichment

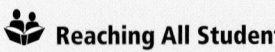 **Reaching All Students**
Practice Workbook 12-3
Spanish Practice Workbook 12-3
Guided Problem Solving 12-3
Technology Activities 32

Presentation Assistant Plus!
Transparencies and PowerPoint™
• Check Skills You'll Need 12-3
• Additional Examples 12-3
• Student Edition Answers 12-3
• Lesson Quiz 12-3
• Classroom Aid 1, 36
PH Presentation Pro CD-ROM 12-3

ASSESSMENT SYSTEM

Computer Test Generator CD-ROM

 Technology
Resource Pro® CD-ROM
Computer Test Generator CD-ROM
PH Presentation Pro CD-ROM

 www.PHSchool.com
Student Site
• Teacher Web Code: adk-5500
• Updated Data
• Self-grading Lesson Quiz
PH SuccessNet Teacher Center
• Lesson Planner
• Resources

Plus

Using Graphs to Persuade

What You'll Learn

OBJECTIVE 1 To recognize the use of breaks in the scales of graphs

OBJECTIVE 2 To recognize the use of different scales

. . . And Why

To solve real-world problems involving population and cost of living

 Check Skills You'll Need

Find the slope of $\overline{AB}$ in each graph.
1–2. See below
1.

2.

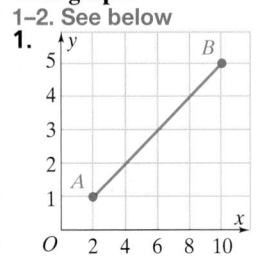

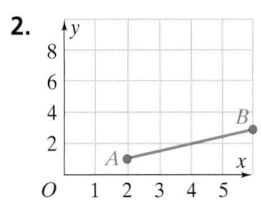

For help, go to Lesson 8-3.

1. $\frac{1}{2}$
2. $\frac{1}{2}$

iTEXT Interactive lesson includes instant self-check, tutorials, and activities.

OBJECTIVE 1 Using Breaks in Scales

You can draw graphs of a data set in different ways in order to give different impressions.

You can use a break in the scale on one or both axes of a line graph or a bar graph. This lets you show more detail and emphasize differences. However, it can also give a distorted picture of the data.

1 EXAMPLE Real-World Problem Solving

Population Which title would be more appropriate for the graph below: "Los Angeles Overwhelms Chicago" or "Populations of Chicago and Los Angeles"? Explain.

Because of the break in the vertical axis, the bar for Los Angeles appears to be more than three times as tall as the bar for Chicago. Actually, the population of Los Angeles is a little less than 3.6 million, and the population of Chicago is about 2.7 million. So the population of Los Angeles is about 1.3 times that of Chicago.

The title "Los Angeles Overwhelms Chicago" could be misleading. "Populations of Chicago and Los Angeles" better describes the information in the graph.

✓ **Check Understanding** Example 1

1. Use the data in the graph in Example 1. Redraw the graph without a break. **See back of book.**

Ongoing Assessment and Intervention

Before the Lesson
Diagnose prerequisite skills using:
• Check Skills You'll Need

During the Lesson
Monitor progress using:
• Check Understanding
• Additional Examples
• Test Prep

After the Lesson
Assess knowledge using:
• Lesson Quiz
• Computer Test Generator CD-ROM

2 Using Different Scales

You can use different scales or spacing along axes. This lets you emphasize (or de-emphasize) how changes in data are related.

2 EXAMPLE Real-World Problem Solving

Cost of Living Study the graphs below. Which graph gives the impression of a sharper increase in price? Explain.

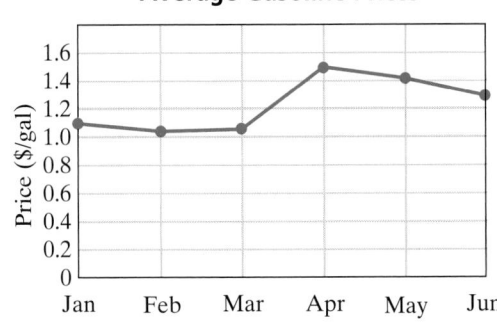

In the graph at the right, the months are much closer together, so the line appears to climb more rapidly. This graph suggests that prices are going up faster than suggested by the graph at the left.

✓ Check Understanding Example 2

2. Use the data in the table at the right.

   a. Make a graph that suggests a rapid decrease in the total weight of fish caught. **a–b. See back of book.**

   b. Make a graph that suggests a slow decrease in the total weight of fish caught.

   c. **Reasoning** A group is planning a campaign to protect the supply of fish. They are proposing a regulation that would limit the number of pounds of fish caught annually. Would they more likely use the graph from part (a) or part (b) in their proposal? Explain. **See right.**

There is a fine line between using graphs to persuade and using graphs to mislead.

Fish Caught for Food in the U.S.

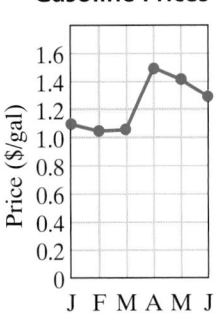

Year	Fish Caught (billions of pounds)
1993	8.2
1994	7.9
1995	7.7
1996	7.5

SOURCE: *Statistical Abstract of the United States.* Go to **www.PHSchool.com** for a data update. Web Code: adg-2041

2c. Answers may vary. Sample: They would use the graph from part (a) to show that the supply of fish is decreasing rapidly. Using this graph emphasizes the need for the limit.

👥 Reaching All Students

| **Below Level** As you work through this lesson, have students make a list of all the things they should look for in a graph to help understand the graph. **labels, scales, broken scales, differing shapes** | **Advanced Learners** Ask students how to make a graph that highlights differences in percentages that vary by only a few tenths of a percent. **Show a scale marked in tenths, or even hundredths, of a percent.** | **Visual Learners** See note on page 643. **Auditory Learners** See note on page 646. |

---

2. Teach

Math Background

To interpret a graph accurately, you should pay attention to the title, the labels on the axes, and the scales on the axes. You can construct graphs in different ways for different emphases. The graph is "honest" if you clearly provide the information the user needs to correctly interpret the graph. The graph may be misleading if you require the user to make inferences to correctly interpret the graph.

Teaching Notes

1 EXAMPLE Visual Learners

Point out the visual cue on the graph that shows a break in the scale. A break in the scale indicates part of the scale is missing. When there is a break, then part of each bar is missing, or a line graph is positioned much closer to the horizontal axis than it otherwise would be. Point out that a break can save space and can also allow for a scale that helps distinguish the data being graphed.

PowerPoint ▶ Additional Examples

1 Which title would be more appropriate for the graph below: "Texas Overwhelms California" or "Areas of California and Texas"? Explain.

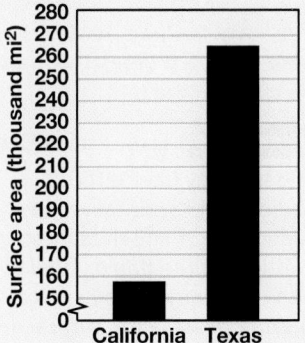

See back of book.

643

2 Study the graphs below. Which graph gives the impression of a sharper increase in rainfall from March to April? Explain.

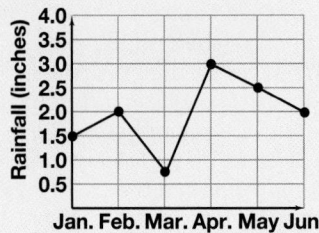

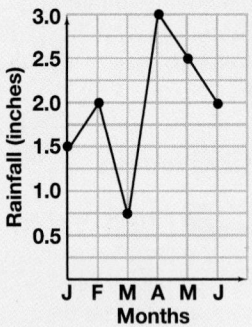

The second graph; its horizontal scale values are closer together and its vertical scale values are farther apart than in the first graph, so its line from March to April appears to climb more rapidly.

3 What makes the graph misleading? Explain.

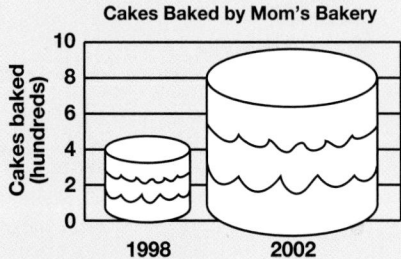

The "cake" on the right has much more than two times the area of the cake on the left.

3 EXAMPLE Error Prevention

Students may have difficulty reading graphs critically. Have students ask themselves these questions: *Is the title or label used in the graph trying to lead me to a conclusion? Have the vertical or horizontal scales been numbered so that the visual display is distorted?*

Closure

Ask students how they can study claims based on a graphical display.
See back of book.

644

Bar graphs can be misleading if their "bars" change in more than one dimension. This can happen when graphs use realistic images for the bars. These images make the graphs more interesting but also can give false impressions.

3 EXAMPLE Real-World 🌐 Problem Solving

Reasoning What makes the graph misleading? Explain.

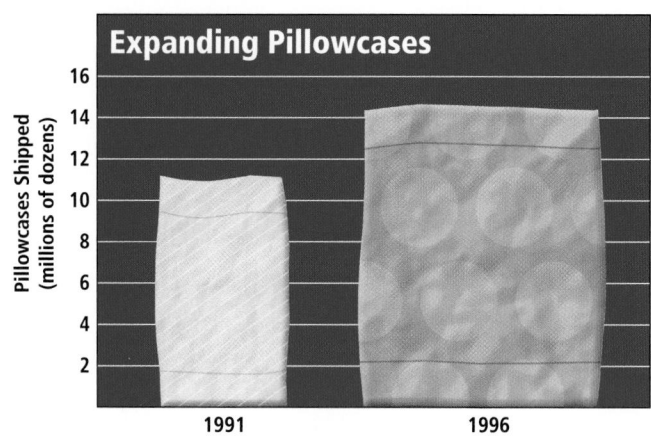

By reading the vertical axis, you can see that the number of pillowcases shipped increased by about one fourth.

However, the bar on the right has not only increased in height, but has also nearly doubled in width. The area of the second bar is more than two times the area of the first bar.

Because of this, you might get the impression that the increase
● was much greater than it really was.

✔ **Check Understanding** Example 3

3. Use the data in the table below.

Prices of Field-Grown Tomatoes in the United States

Year	Price of Tomatoes (cents per pound)
1990	86
1997	162

Source: *Statistical Abstract of the United States.* Go to **www.PHSchool.com** for a data update. Web Code: adg-2041

a. Draw a graph that suggests that the price of tomatoes nearly doubled. a–b. See back of book.
b. Draw a graph that suggests that the price of tomatoes more than doubled.

EXERCISES

Practice and Problem Solving

For more exercises, see *Extra Practice*.

(A) Practice by Example

Example 1
(page 642)

For Exercises 1–4, use the graph at the right.

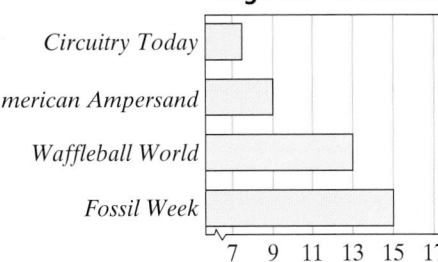
Magazine Circulation

Circuitry Today
American Ampersand
Waffleball World
Fossil Week

7 9 11 13 15 17
Circulation (millions)

1. Which magazine *appears* to have about twice the circulation of *Circuitry Today?* **American Ampersand**

2. Which magazine *actually* has twice the circulation of *Circuitry Today?* **Fossil Week**

3. **You might compare the lengths of the bars without noticing the break in the scale.**

3. Explain why the graph might mislead you. **See left.**

4. Redraw the graph without a break in the horizontal axis. **See back of book.**

Example 2
(page 643)

Statistics For Exercises 5–7, use the graph at the right.

5. **It suggests that the percent is rising rapidly, by putting 1989 and 1993 very close together.**

🌐 5. **School Computers** Does the graph suggest a rapid increase or a slow increase in the percent of students using a computer at school? **See left.**

6. Redraw the graph. Change the horizontal scale to suggest a slower increase from 1989 to 1993. **See margin.**

7. Redraw the graph. Suggest a slower increase from 1989 to 1993 by changing the vertical scale. **See back of book.**

Percent of Students Using Computers at School

Percent
80
70
60
50
40
30
20
10
0
1989   1993
Year

Example 3 🌐 **Food Service For Exercises 8–10, use the graph below.**
(page 644)

8. **It suggests that sales more than quadrupled. Yes; rather than looking at just the heights of the boxes, one tends to compare areas. The big box looks like it could contain perhaps five times as much milk.**

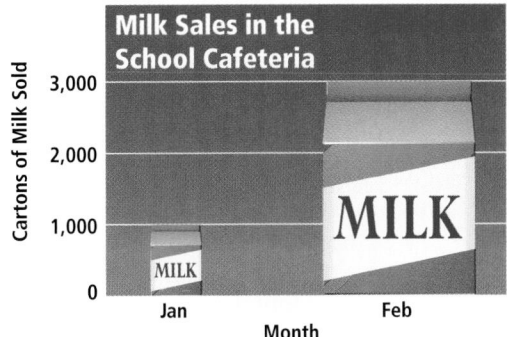
Milk Sales in the School Cafeteria

Cartons of Milk Sold
3,000
2,000
1,000
0
MILK   MILK
Jan   Feb
Month

8. What impression does the graph give you about milk sales in the school cafeteria? Is the graph misleading? Explain. **See left.**

9. Redraw the graph to represent the data accurately. **See back of book.**

10. Redraw the graph to suggest that milk sales changed very little. **See back of book.**

12-3 Using Graphs to Persuade **645**

6.
Percent of Students Using Computers at School

Percent
100
80
60
40
20
0
1989 1990 1991 1992 1993
Year

---

3. Practice

Assignment Guide

1 Objective 1
  (A)(B) Core 1–4, 11–14

2 Objective 2
  (A)(B) Core 5–10, 15, 16
  (C) Extension 17–19

Test Prep 20–22
Mixed Review 23–30

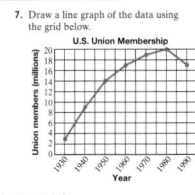

Practice 12-3 Using Graphs to Persuade

Use the graph at the right for Exercises 1–5.

1. Which group of animals appears to have more than twice as many endangered species as mammals? **birds**

2. Does one group actually have twice as many endangered species as mammals? **no**

3. What gives the impression that one group has twice as many endangered species as mammals? **The break in the vertical axis.**

4. Redraw the graph without a break.

5. Describe the effect the change in scale has on what the graph suggests. **The differences seem much less.**

U.S. Endangered Species
Number of Species
80 75 70 65 60 55 50
Mammals Birds Fish
Group

U.S. Endangered Species
Number of Species
80 70 60 50 40 30 20 10 0
Mammals Birds Fish
Group

Use the data in the table for Exercises 6–8.

U.S. Union Membership
Year	1930	1940	1950	1960	1970	1980	1990
Union members (millions)	3	9	14	17	19	20	17

6. Draw a line graph of the data using the grid below.

7. Draw a line graph of the data using the grid below.

U.S. Union Membership

U.S. Union Membership

8. What gives the different impressions in the two graphs? **The horizontal scales are different.**

Enrichment 12-3 Computer Graphing

The 20 members of the Student Council sold T-shirts as a school fund raiser. Four teams of 5 students sold 1,000 T-shirts at $6.50 each.
Use a computer to graph and analyze the data.

Teams	Number Sold
blue	250
red	375
gold	125
white	250

Construct a bar graph that shows the number of shirts sold by each team. Use unbroken axes.

1. Which team sold the greatest number of shirts? **red**

2. About how many times as great as the gold team was the number of shirts sold by the white team? **two times**

3. Change the graph so there is a break in one axis. Also change the scale. Make your new graph give the impression that the white team sold about three times as many shirts as the gold team. What scale did you use for the number sold? **Sample answer is shown. 62.5 to 412.5 by 50**

4. About how many times as great as the gold team was the number of shirts sold by the red team? **3 times**

5. About how many times as great as the gold team does the number of shirts sold by the red team seem based on your second graph? **Sample answer is shown: 5 times**

6. Which bar graph would members of the red team prefer? **the second graph**

Construct a line graph that compares the number of shirts sold and the amount of money raised. Show data for 100, 200, 300, . . . 1,000 shirts sold.

7. What scale did you use for "Money Raised"? **Sample answer is shown. 0 to 6,500 by 500's**

8. What unbroken scale could you use for "Shirts Sold" to give the impression that the money raised increases more rapidly with each shirt sold than your first graph implies? **Sample answer is shown. 0 to 1,000 by 200's**

9. Which line graph would members of the gold team prefer? **the first graph**

11a.

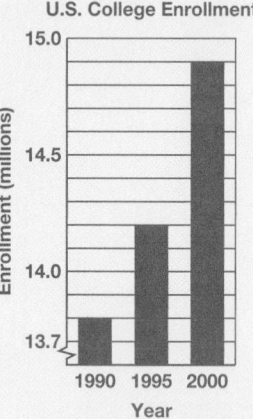

U.S. College Enrollment

11b.

U.S. College Enrollment

14. Answers may vary. Sample:

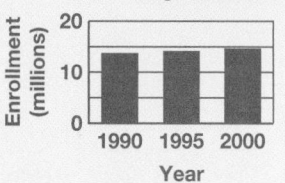

Average Number of Students per Computer

There is only a small decrease in the number of students per computer between elementary and middle school and between middle school and high school.

18. The intervals are not comparable. Each of the three tallest bars spans 10 years, while the shorter one spans more than 10 years.

646

 **B** **Apply Your Skills**

> **Reading Math**
>
> For help with reading the table and drawing the graph in Exercise 11, see page 648.

12. No; 11.2 is only about 1.3 times 8.5. The break in the axis causes the misinterpretation.

Average Annual Tuition and Fees for Four-Year Public Colleges

Year	Tuition and Fees
1980–1981	$1,647
1990–1991	$2,529
2000–2001	$3,535

Source: The College Board

 C **Challenge**

Percent of Milk Sold That Was Low-Fat

Year	Percent
1980	38%
1990	59%

19a. You can make the scale of the *x*-axis half of the scale on the *y*-axis.
19b. You can use the same scale on each axis.
19c. You can make the scale of the *x*-axis twice the scale on the *y*-axis.

---

11. a. Statistics Use the data at the right. Draw a graph with an axis break to suggest that enrollment in 2000 was many times the enrollment in 1990.
b. Draw a second graph of the data, without using a break. Choose a scale that suggests that enrollment did not increase much from 1990 to 2000.
a–b. See margin.

U.S. College Enrollment

Year	Enrollment
1990	13.8 million
1995	14.2 million
2000	14.9 million

Source: U.S. Education Department

For Exercises 12–14, use the graph at the right.

12. Writing in Math The graph suggests that the number of students per computer in elementary schools is three times the number of students per computer in high schools. Is this true? Explain. **See left.**

Average Number of Students per Computer

High School
Middle School
Elementary

8 9 10 11 12
Students per Computer

13. What does the graph suggest is the ratio of middle school students per computer to high school students per computer? What is the actual ratio? **nearly 2 to 1; about 1.14 to 1**

14. Redraw the graph without a break. Describe the effect this has on what the graph suggests. **See margin.**

15. Use the data at the left. Draw a line graph that gives the impression of a gradual increase in college tuition and fees from 1980 to 2001. **See back of book.**

16. Open-Ended Find a graph in a newspaper or magazine that could be misleading. Explain how it could be misleading. **Check students' work.**

17. Use the data at the left to make two different graphs. Draw one of the graphs to suggest that the percent of low-fat milk sold in 1990 was double the percent in 1980. **See back of book.**

18. Statistics Use the graph at the right. Explain why the intervals on the horizontal axis could make the graph misleading. **See margin.**

19. Tell how to scale the *x*- and *y*-axes so that $\overline{AB}$ joining points $A(4, 2)$ and $B(8, 6)$ appears to have the slope given. **a–c. See left.**
a. $\frac{1}{2}$ **b.** 1   **c.** 2

Home Ownership Rates, by Age

Age	Percent
Under 35	38.7
35–44	66.1
45–54	75.8
55–64	80.1

 GPS Use the Guided Problem Solving worksheet with Exercise 15.

Multiple Choice   For Exercises 20 and 21, use the graph below.

20. The graph makes it appear that there are how many times as many students per teacher at North HS as there are at West HS? **B**

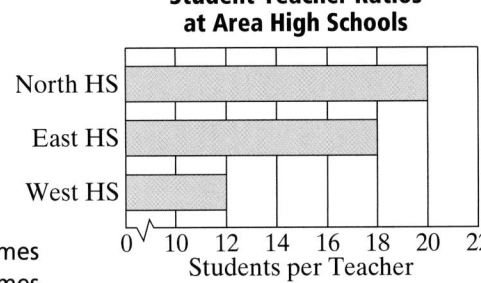

Student-Teacher Ratios at Area High Schools

Students per Teacher

A. 2 times   **B.** 3 times
C. 4 times   **D.** 5 times

21. Why might this graph give a distorted picture of the data? **H**
F. The longest horizontal bar is on top.
G. The vertical lines are evenly spaced.
H. There is a break in the horizontal axis.
I. The horizontal bars are different lengths.

Short Response   **22.** Use the table at the right to make two different line graphs.
a. Draw one graph to suggest that sales more than doubled from 1996 to 1999.
b. Draw the other graph to suggest that sales increased only slightly during the same period.
a–b. See back of book.

Annual Sales

Year	Sales
1996	$87 million
1997	$87 million
1998	$88 million
1999	$90 million

Take It to the NET
Online lesson quiz at
www.PHSchool.com
Web Code: ada-1203

Mixed Review

Lesson 12-2   **Make a box-and-whisker plot for each set of data.**   **23–25. See back of book.**

23. 27, 25, 23, 29, 25, 28, 26, 27, 23, 21, 20, 24, 25, 28, 30, 19, 25

24. 2, 6, 3, 9, 15, 4, 9, 20, 6, 7, 2, 3, 8, 4, 1, 5, 6, 8, 5, 4, 9, 3, 2, 8, 7

25. 100, 95, 102, 101, 96, 100, 104, 115, 102, 108, 92, 97, 103, 106

Lessons 10-5   **26. Geometry** The Museum of Health and Medical Science in Houston, Texas, has one of the largest kaleidoscopes in the world. It is a cylinder 10 feet long and 22 inches in diameter. What is the surface area of the kaleidoscope? about 9,050 in.^{2} or 63 ft^2

Lesson 6-4   **Find each probability for choosing a letter at random from the word STATISTICS.**

27. P(vowel)   **28.** P(S)   **29.** P(not T)   **30.** P(A or C)
$\frac{3}{10}$ $\frac{3}{10}$ $\frac{7}{10}$ $\frac{2}{10}$, or $\frac{1}{5}$

12-3 Using Graphs to Persuade   **647**

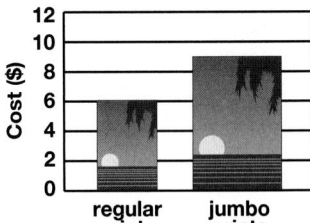
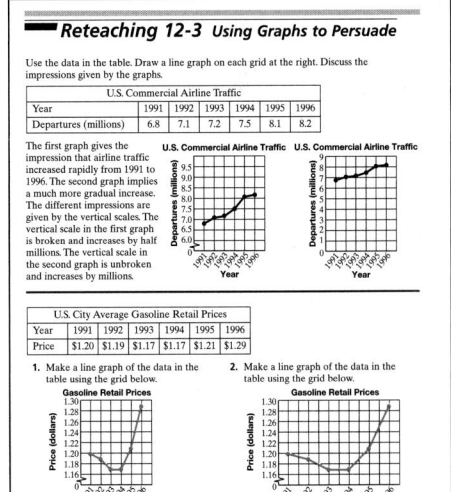

Reading for Problem Solving

Students follow and understand someone else's method of solving a problem before solving a similar type of problem.

Teaching Notes

Teaching Tip

Have students bring graphs to class from magazines and newspapers. Ask students to describe what kind of impression each graph gives. Then ask students to use the same data and draw a graph that will give a different impression.

Reading Math

Reading for Problem Solving

For Use With Page 646, Exercise 11

Read the problems below. Then follow along with what Kayla thinks as she solves them. Check your understanding by solving the exercise at the bottom of the page.

a. Statistics Use the data at the right. Draw a graph with a break to suggest that enrollment in 2000 was many times the enrollment in 1990.

b. Draw a second graph of the data without using a break. Choose a scale that suggests that enrollment did not increase much from 1990 to 2000.

U.S. College Enrollment

Year	Enrollment
1990	13.8 million
1995	14.2 million
2000	14.9 million

SOURCE: U.S. Education Department

What Kayla Thinks

Part (a) asks me to draw a graph with a break that makes enrollment in 2000 look *many times* the enrollment in 1990.

I'll use a bar graph. The table shows the 1990 enrollment was 13.8 million. I'll break the vertical scale right before 13.8 to make the 1990 bar look small.

The table shows a 2000 enrollment of 14.9 million. I'll use vertical intervals of 0.3. That makes the top mark 15.0.

The bar for 14.9 is as tall as possible. It looks nearly 4 times as tall as 1990!

Part (b) asks for no break. I'll scale by 2 on the vertical axis. This will make 1990 and 2000 almost the same height.

What Kayla Draws

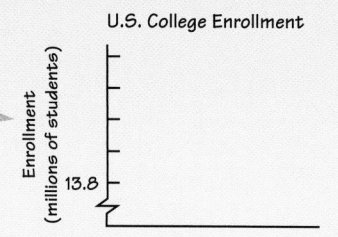

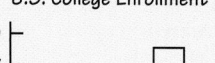
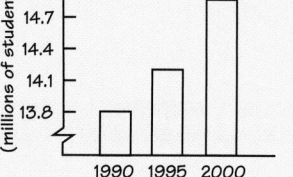

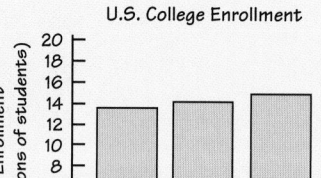

EXERCISE

1. Two months ago, the price for Technostar stock was $32. Last month it was $32.40. Now it is $32.80. Draw graphs suggesting each of the following about the stock price. **a–b. See margin.**

   a. a large increase   **b.** a small increase

1a.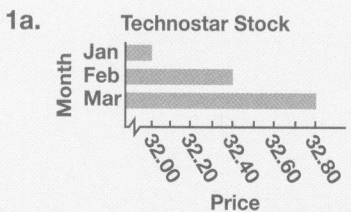

1b.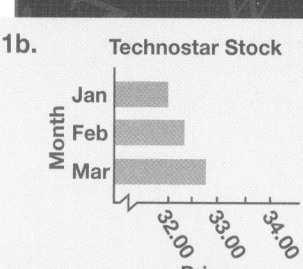

Counting Outcomes and Theoretical Probability

OBJECTIVE

1 Counting Possible Choices

Investigation

Exploring Possible Outcomes

Congratulations! Your application to run the pizza stand at school home games has been accepted. Now you have to decide which pizzas to sell. You plan to offer two or three choices in each of three categories—size, crust, and topping. The more types of pizza the better, but you're limited by kitchen space to a total of 18 types.

1. Decide which types of pizza you will offer. Make a menu that shows your customers their options. **Check students' work.**

2. Reasoning Suppose you decide to offer three choices of size and three choices of crust. How many choices of toppings can you offer? **2 choices of toppings**

You can use a tree diagram to display and count possible choices.

1 EXAMPLE Drawing a Tree Diagram

A school team sells caps in two colors (blue or white), two sizes (child or adult), and two fabrics (cotton or polyester). Draw a tree diagram to find the number of cap choices.

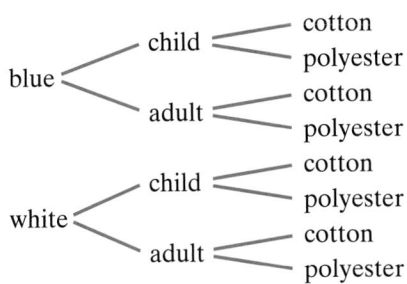

Each branch of the "tree" represents one choice—for example, blue-child-cotton.

● There are 8 possible cap choices.

✓ **Check Understanding Example 1**

1. Suppose the caps in Example 1 also come in black. Draw a tree diagram. How many cap choices are there? **See back of book.**

What You'll Learn

OBJECTIVE 1 To use a tree diagram and the Counting Principle to count possible choices

OBJECTIVE 2 To find theoretical probability by counting outcomes

. . . And Why

To solve real-world problems involving probabilities and outcomes

✓ **Check Skills You'll Need**

A bag has 5 blue (B) chips, 4 red (R) chips, and 3 tan (T) chips. Find each probability for choosing a chip at random from the bag.
1–6. See below.

1. $P(\text{R})$ **2.** $P(\text{not R})$

3. $P(\text{B})$ **4.** $P(\text{R or B})$

5. $P(\text{T})$ **6.** $P(\text{B or T})$

 For help, go to Lesson 6-4

New Vocabulary

• counting principle
• theoretical probability
• sample space

1. $\frac{4}{12}$, or $\frac{1}{3}$ 4. $\frac{9}{12}$, or $\frac{3}{4}$

2. $\frac{8}{12}$, or $\frac{2}{3}$ 5. $\frac{3}{12}$, or $\frac{1}{4}$

3. $\frac{5}{12}$ 6. $\frac{8}{12}$, or $\frac{2}{3}$

 iTEXT Interactive lesson includes instant self-check, tutorials, and activities.

Lesson Preview

✓ **Check Skills You'll Need**

Probability
Lesson 6-4: Example 1; Exercises 1–3.
Extra Practice, p. 749.

Lesson Resources

 Teaching Resources
Practice, Reteaching, Enrichment
Checkpoint Quiz 1

Reaching All Students
Practice Workbook 12-4
Spanish Practice Workbook 12-4
Reading and Math Literacy 12B
Spanish Reading and Math Literacy 12B
Spanish Checkpoint Quiz 1
Guided Problem Solving 12-4
Hands-On Activities 34

Presentation Assistant Plus!
Transparencies and PowerPoint™
• Check Skills You'll Need 12-4
• Additional Examples 12-4
• Student Edition Answers 12-4
• Lesson Quiz 12-4
PH Presentation Pro CD-ROM 12-4

ASSESSMENT SYSTEM

Checkpoint Quiz 1
Computer Test Generator CD-ROM

 Technology
Resource Pro® CD-ROM
Computer Test Generator CD-ROM
PH Presentation Pro CD-ROM

 www.PHSchool.com
Student Site
• Teacher Web Code: adk-5500
• Graphing Calculator, Procedure 16
• Self-grading Lesson Quiz
PH SuccessNet Teacher Center
• Lesson Planner
• Resources

Plus  **iTEXT**

Ongoing Assessment and Intervention

Before the Lesson
Diagnose prerequisite skills using:
• Check Skills You'll Need

During the Lesson
Monitor progress using:
• Check Understanding
• Additional Examples
• Test Prep

After the Lesson
Assess knowledge using:
• Lesson Quiz
• Computer Test Generator CD-ROM
• Chapter Checkpoint 1 (p. 653)

2. Teach

Math Background

The theoretical probability of an event is the ratio of the number of favorable outcomes to the number of possible outcomes. Tree diagrams are useful for finding the number of possible outcomes when the number is small. When the number is large, the Counting Principle is easier to use.

Teaching Notes

Investigation (Optional)

Have students work in small groups to list the 18 different pizzas they could offer in Part 2 of the Investigation.

1 EXAMPLE Visual Learners

Some students may think there are 14 different choices since there are 14 words in the tree diagram. Have students write a list of each choice (blue-child-cotton) so they can see that there are only 8 possible choices.

2 EXAMPLE Auditory Learners

One way students can remember how to use the Counting Principle is to say "choices times choices times choices . . . ," saying the word "choices" the same number of times that different choices are to be made.

4 EXAMPLE Diversity

Students from other countries may not be familiar with American lotteries. Describe lotteries to these students and ask them to share with the class any lotteries that they may have in their country of origin.

Science Connection

You use theoretical probability when you study heredity. Heredity is the study of the biological process by which traits are passed from parents to their offspring. In the mid-1800s, the Austrian monk Gregor Mendel discovered that you could predict the probability of whether certain traits would be passed from parent to offspring.

Test-Taking Tip
The Counting Principle is sometimes called the "Multiplication Counting Principle."

Real-World 🌐 Connection

A monogram is made up of two or more letters, such as your initials.

 iTEXT Interactive lesson includes instant self-check, tutorials, and activities.

Another way to count choices is to use the **Counting Principle.**

Key Concepts | Counting Principle

If there are m ways of making one choice, and n ways of making a second choice, then there are $m \cdot n$ ways of making the first choice followed by the second.

The Counting Principle is particularly useful when a tree diagram would be too large to draw.

2 EXAMPLE Using the Counting Principle

How many two-letter monograms are possible?

first letter		second letter		monograms
possible choices		possible choices		possible choices
26	$\cdot$	26	$=$	676

● There are 676 possible two-letter monograms.

✓ **Check Understanding** Example 2

2. **a.** How many three-letter monograms are possible? **17,576 three-letter monograms**

   b. How many five-letter license plates can be made if the letters O and I cannot be used? **7,962,624 license plates**

OBJECTIVE

2 Finding Probability by Counting Outcomes

You can count outcomes to help you find the **theoretical probability** of an event in which outcomes are equally likely.

Key Concepts | Theoretical Probability

$$P(\text{event}) = \frac{\text{number of favorable outcomes}}{\text{number of possible outcomes}}$$

A **sample space** is a list of all possible outcomes. You can use a tree diagram to find a sample space. Then you can calculate probability.

👥 Reaching All Students

Below Level Help students determine how many three-number combinations are possible for a combination lock that has digits from 0 to 99. $100 \cdot 100 \cdot 100 =$ 1,000,000 combinations	**Advanced Learners** Have students explain why the sum seven is considered to be "easiest" to roll with two number cubes. A sample shows that a sum of 7 has the greatest theoretical probability.	**Auditory Learners** See note on page 650. **Diversity** See note on page 650.

3 EXAMPLE Using a Tree Diagram

Use a tree diagram to find the sample space for tossing two coins. Then find the probability of tossing two tails.

heads — heads
heads — tails
tails — heads
tails — tails

The tree diagram shows there are four possible outcomes, one of which is tossing two tails.

$P(\text{event}) = \dfrac{\text{number of favorable outcomes}}{\text{number of possible outcomes}}$ Use the probability formula.

$P(\text{two tails}) = \dfrac{\text{number of two-tail outcomes}}{\text{number of possible outcomes}}$

$= \dfrac{1}{4}$

● The probability of tossing two tails is $\frac{1}{4}$.

✓ Check Understanding Example 3

3. You toss two coins. Find $P(\text{one head and one tail})$. $\frac{1}{2}$

You can also use the Counting Principle to find probability.

4 EXAMPLE Real-World Problem Solving

Many people play lottery games without knowing the probability of winning. In some state lotteries, the winning number is made up of four digits chosen at random. Suppose a player buys two tickets with different numbers. What is the probability that the player has a winning ticket?

First find the number of possible outcomes. For each digit, there are 10 possible outcomes, 0 through 9.

1st digit outcomes		2nd digit outcomes		3rd digit outcomes		4th digit outcomes		total outcomes
10	·	10	·	10	·	10	=	10,000

Then find the probability when there are two favorable outcomes.

$P(\text{winning ticket}) = \dfrac{\text{number of favorable outcomes}}{\text{number of possible outcomes}} = \dfrac{2}{10,000}$

● The probability is $\frac{2}{10,000}$, or $\frac{1}{5,000}$.

✓ Check Understanding Example 4

4. A lottery uses five digits chosen at random. Find the probability of buying a winning ticket. $\frac{1}{100,000}$

Additional Examples

1 The school cafeteria sells sandwiches for which you can choose one item from each of the following categories: two breads (wheat or white), two meats (ham or turkey), and two condiments (mayonnaise or mustard). Draw a tree diagram to find the number of sandwich choices.

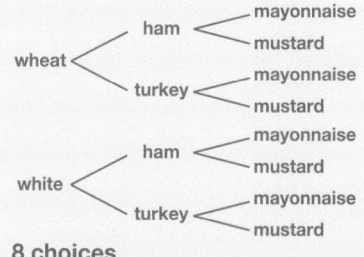

8 choices

2 How many two-digit numbers can be formed for which the first digit is odd and the second digit is even? **25 numbers**

3 Use a tree diagram to show the sample space for *guessing* right or wrong on two true-false questions. Then find the probability of guessing correctly on both questions. $\frac{1}{4}$

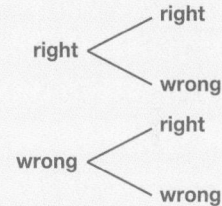

4 In some state lotteries, the winning number is made up of five digits chosen at random. Suppose a player buys 5 tickets with different numbers. What is the probability that the player has a winning number? $\frac{1}{20,000}$

Closure

Ask students to name two ways to find the number of possible outcomes. **You can use a tree diagram to display the possible outcomes, or use the Counting Principle.**

3. Practice

Assignment Guide

1 Objective 1
- Ⓐ Ⓑ Core 1–4, 10, 11
- Ⓒ Extension 17

2 Objective 2
- Ⓐ Ⓑ Core 5–9, 12–15
- Ⓒ Extension 16

Test Prep 18–20
Mixed Review 21–24

Practice 12-4 *Counting Outcomes and Theoretical Probability*

A computer store sells 4 models of a computer (m1, m2, m3, and m4). Each model can be fitted with 3 sizes of hard drive (A, B, and C).

1. Find the sample space.
   m1A, m1B, m1C, m2A, m2B, m2C, m3A, m3B, m3C,
   m4A, m4B, m4C

2. What is the probability of choosing a computer with a size C hard drive at random? $\frac{1}{3}$

3. What is the probability of choosing a model 2 computer with a size A hard drive at random? $\frac{1}{12}$

Solve each problem by drawing a tree diagram.

4. A ballot offered 3 choices for president (A, B, C) and 2 choices for vice president (M, N). How many choices for a combination of the two offices did it offer? List them.
   6 choices; AM, AN, BM, BN, CM, CN

5. The Cougar baseball team has 4 pitchers (P1, P2, P3, P4) and 2 catchers (C1, C2). How many pitcher-catcher combinations are possible? List them.
   8 combinations; P1C1, P1C2, P2C1, P2C2, P3C1,
   P3C2, P4C1, P4C2

Solve each problem by using the counting principle.

6. There are 5 roads from Allen to Baker, 7 roads from Baker to Carlson, and 4 roads from Carlson to Dodge. How many different routes from Allen to Dodge by way of Baker and Carlson are possible?
   140 routes

7. Drapery is sold in 4 different fabrics. Each fabric comes in 13 different patterns. Each pattern is offered in 9 different colors. How many fabric-pattern-color combinations are there?
   468 combinations

Enrichment 12-4 *Counting Trails*

The diagram shows trails leading from Camp Alpha (A), where you are camped, to the river. You may walk only in a southerly direction.

How many routes can you choose to get from A to:

1. B? __1__   2. C? __1__

3. D? __1__   4. F? __1__

5. G? __1__   6. J? __1__

7. Find the number of routes you can choose to get from A to E.
   2

8. Find the number of choices you have for walking from A to H and from A to I.
   A to H __3__   A to I __3__

9. Use the above method to find the number of trails from Camp Alpha to the Rainbow Desert. Write the number of choices to each point in the open circles.

Camp Alpha

① ① ① ① ① ②① ① ③③① ① ④⑥④① ①⑤⑩⑩⑤① ①⑥⑮⑳⑮⑥①

Rainbow Desert

You may recognize the triangle of numbers you have written as Pascal's triangle, an array with wide applications in mathematics.

EXERCISES

For more exercises, see *Extra Practice*.

Practice and Problem Solving

Ⓐ **Practice by Example**

Example 1
(page 649)

You can choose a burrito having one filling wrapped in one tortilla. Draw a tree diagram to count the number of burrito choices.
1–2. See back of book.

1. tortillas: flour or corn; fillings: beef, chicken, bean, cheese, or vegetable

2. tortillas: whole wheat flour, blue corn, or white corn; fillings: chicken, tofu, grilled fish, or vegetable

Example 2
(page 650)

There are four roads from Marsh to Taft and seven roads from Taft to Polk. Use the Counting Principle to find the number of routes below.

3. from Marsh to Polk through Taft 28 routes

4. from Marsh to Polk after a new road opens from Marsh to Taft
   35 routes

Example 3
(page 651)

Use a tree diagram to find the sample space for tossing three coins. Then find each probability.

5. P(three heads) $\frac{1}{8}$ 6. P(two tails) $\frac{3}{8}$ 7. P(at least one head) $\frac{7}{8}$

Example 4
(page 651)

Use the Counting Principle to help you find each probability.

8. Rolling a 3 on each of two number cubes $\frac{1}{36}$

9. **Lottery** Choosing the three winning lottery numbers when the numbers are chosen at random from 1 to 50. Numbers can repeat. $\frac{1}{125,000}$

Ⓑ **Apply Your Skills**

10. **Snacks** You can choose chocolate, strawberry, or vanilla frozen yogurt, and red, blue, or green sprinkles. A sundae has one yogurt flavor and two different colors of sprinkles. How many different kinds of sundaes can you order? List them. **See back of book.**

Sweaters

Colors	Styles
Blue	Cardigan
Pink	Crewneck
Red	V-neck
Brown	
Black	

You have one sweater of each possible color and style in the table (left).

11. How many sweaters do you have? 15 sweaters

12. What is the probability of choosing a brown sweater at random? $\frac{3}{15}$, or $\frac{1}{5}$

13. What is the probability of choosing a cardigan at random? $\frac{5}{15}$, or $\frac{1}{3}$

Find the probability of each event.

14. You toss tails and roll an even number (when you toss a coin and roll a number cube). $\frac{1}{4}$ GPS

15. You roll two odd numbers and pick a vowel (when you roll two number cubes and pick a letter of the alphabet at random). $\frac{5}{104}$

17. Answers may vary. Sample: Suppose you have 4 kinds of meat and 5 kinds of bread. Find the number of sandwiches you can make with one meat and one bread; 20 different sandwiches.

Ⓒ **Challenge**

16. **Reasoning** You have a bag containing an equal number of nickels, dimes, and quarters. You reach into the bag and choose a coin. Are all outcomes equally likely? Explain. See margin.

17. **Writing in Math** Write a problem (unlike any in this lesson) that you can solve using the Counting Principle. Then solve.
    See above left.

652 Chapter 12 Data Analysis and Probability

GPS Use the Guided Problem Solving worksheet with Exercise 14.

16. No. You might tend to pick up a larger coin. Also, larger coins might tend to go to the bottom, so you might be more likely to pick a lighter coin.

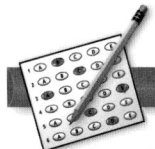
Multiple Choice

18. You are writing a three-digit number. The first digit must be 2 or 8. The second digit must be 1, 3, or 9. The third digit must be 4, 5, 6, 7, or 8. Which expression can you use to find how many different three-digit numbers you can write? **A**

A. $2 \cdot 3 \cdot 5$ **B.** $5 \cdot 4 \cdot 3 \cdot 2 \cdot 1$

C. $(1 \cdot 2) + (2 \cdot 3) + (3 \cdot 5)$ **D.** $2 + 3 + 5$

19. An ice-cream vendor sells small or large cones and has chocolate, vanilla, rocky road, pecan, and strawberry flavors. To help a customer select a flavor and size, the vendor has a spinner. What is the probability that the spinner will choose a large strawberry for a customer? **G**

F. $\frac{1}{14}$ **G.** $\frac{1}{10}$ **H.** $\frac{1}{7}$ **I.** $\frac{1}{3}$

Extended Response

Take It to the NET
Online lesson quiz at
www.PHSchool.com
Web Code: ada-1204

20. You roll two number cubes. List all possible outcomes. Find the probability of each event. Show your work.
a. rolling a 1 and a 2
b. rolling the same numbers
c. rolling different numbers
a–c. See back of book.

 Mixed Review

Lesson 12-1 **Display each data set in a line plot. Find the range.**

21. 3 4 5 4 7 7 3 6 5   **22.** 19 18 19 17 17 16 19 18 17 19
21–22. See back of book.

Lesson 11-3 **Find the midpoint of a segment with the given endpoints.**

23. $X(3, -2)$ and $Y(-3, 6)$ **(0, 2)**   **24.** $A(-1, 0)$ and $B(2, 1)$ **(0.5, 0.5)**

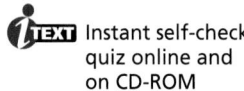 **Checkpoint Quiz 1**   **Lessons 12-1 through 12-4**

TEXT Instant self-check quiz online and on CD-ROM

1. Display the data below in a frequency table. **See back of book.**
47 51 50 52 50 47 48 50 49 51 48 52

2. Make a box-and-whisker plot for the data below. **See back of book.**
31, 33, 74, 90, 44, 49, 40, 64, 42, 31, 36, 73, 86, 34, 46, 65

3. Open-Ended Use the data in the table.
a. Draw a graph that could be misleading. Explain.
b. Draw a second graph that is not misleading.
a–b. See back of book.

Year	Hourly Minimum Wage
1996	$4.75
1997	$5.15

SOURCE: *Wall Street Journal Almanac*

4. Olivia and Oliver each choose a number from 1 to 10 at random. What is the probability that both numbers are odd numbers? $\frac{1}{4}$

Alternative Assessment

Organize the class into small groups. Have each group create a simple board game based on chance outcomes (such as in rolling a number cube). Ask students to write instructions for their games. The groups can take turns playing each other's games.

Test Prep

Resources
For additional practice with a variety of test item formats:
• Test Prep, p. 683
• Test-Taking Strategies, p. 678
• Test-Taking Strategies With Transparencies

---

4. Assess

 PowerPoint **Lesson Quiz 12-4**

Use the following information for Questions 1 and 2. In a game, a number cube is tossed to determine the number of spaces to move, and a coin is tossed to determine forward or backward movement.

1. How many possible outcomes are there? **12**

2. What is the theoretical probability you will move four spaces? $\frac{1}{6}$

3. How many different three-digit whole numbers are possible using the digits 1, 2, 3, 4, and 5? **125**

✔ **Chapter Checkpoint 1**

To check understanding of Lessons 12-1 to 12-4:
Checkpoint Quiz 1 (p. 653)

 **Teaching Resources**
Checkpoint Quiz 1 (also in Prentice Hall Assessment System)

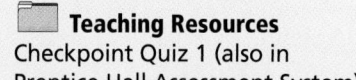 **Reaching All Students**
Reading and Math Literacy 12B

Spanish versions available.

Reteaching 12-4 *Counting Outcomes and Theoretical Probability*

A basketball team has 2 centers (C1 and C2), 2 point guards (P1 and P2), and 3 shooting guards (S1, S2, S3). Find the sample space and the probability that the first point guard (P1), starts a game if players for the 3 positions are chosen randomly.

You can use a tree diagram to find the sample space.
The tree diagram shows there are 12 possible outcomes. Of the 12 outcomes, 6 include P1:

C1-P1-S1, C1-P1-S2, C1-P1-S3
C2-P1-S1, C2-P1-S2, C2-P1-S3

$P(\text{P1 starts}) = \frac{\text{number of favorable outcomes}}{\text{number of possible outcomes}} = \frac{6}{12} = \frac{1}{2}$

You could also find the number of outcomes in the same space and the favorable outcomes with the Counting Principle.

2 center choices × 2 point guard choices × 3 shooting guard choices = 12
There are 12 possible outcomes. The favorable outcomes include 2 choices for center and three choices for shooting guard. However, only one choice for point guard is favorable.

2 center choices × 1 point guard choice × 3 shooting guard choices = 6
There are 6 favorable outcomes.

$P(\text{P1 starts}) = \frac{\text{number of favorable outcomes}}{\text{number of possible outcomes}} = \frac{6}{12} = \frac{1}{2}$

A basketball team has 2 centers (C1 and C2), 3 shooting guards (S1, S2, S3), and 3 power forwards (F1, F2, and F3). Players for the 3 positions are chosen randomly to start the game.

1. How many possible outcomes are there in the sample space?
18 possible outcomes

2. List the sample space.
C1-S1-F1, C1-S1-F2, C1-S1-F3, C1-S2-F1, C1-S2-F2, C1-S2-F3, C1-S3-F1, C1-S3-F2, C1-S3-F3, C2-S1-F1, C2-S1-F2, C2-S1-F3, C2-S2-F1, C2-S2-F2, C2-S2-F3, C2-S3-F1, C2-S3-F2, C2-S3-F3

3. Find $P(\text{F2 starts})$. $\frac{1}{3}$ **4.** Find $P(\text{S1 and F1})$ start. $\frac{1}{9}$

Lesson Preview

 Check Skills You'll Need

Multiplying Fractions
Lesson 5-4: Examples 1 and 2;
Exercises 1–8.
Extra Practice, p. 748.

Lesson Resources

 Teaching Resources
Practice, Reteaching, Enrichment

 Reaching All Students
Practice Workbook 12-5
Spanish Practice Workbook 12-5
Guided Problem Solving 12-5

 Presentation Assistant Plus!
Transparencies and PowerPoint™
• Check Skills You'll Need 12-5
• Additional Examples 12-5
• Student Edition Answers 12-5
• Lesson Quiz 12-5
PH Presentation Pro CD-ROM 12-5

 ASSESSMENT SYSTEM

Computer Test Generator CD-ROM

 Technology
Resource Pro® CD-ROM
Computer Test Generator CD-ROM
PH Presentation Pro CD-ROM

 www.PHSchool.com
Student Site
• Teacher Web Code: adk-5500
• Self-grading Lesson Quiz
PH SuccessNet Teacher Center
• Lesson Planner
• Resources

Plus

Independent and Dependent Events

What You'll Learn

OBJECTIVE 1 To calculate probabilities of independent events

OBJECTIVE 2 To calculate probabilities of dependent events

. . . And Why

To solve real-world problems involving games and science

 Check Skills You'll Need

Multiply.

1. $\frac{3}{5} \cdot \frac{1}{5}$ $\frac{3}{25}$ 2. $\frac{1}{4} \cdot \frac{2}{4}$ $\frac{1}{8}$

3. $\frac{4}{10} \cdot \frac{2}{10}$ $\frac{2}{25}$ 4. $\frac{5}{9} \cdot \frac{4}{8}$ $\frac{5}{18}$

5. $\frac{4}{7} \cdot \frac{3}{6}$ $\frac{2}{7}$ 6. $\frac{9}{10} \cdot \frac{8}{9}$ $\frac{4}{5}$

 For help, go to Lesson 5-4.

New Vocabulary

• independent events
• dependent events

3.
$\frac{1}{5}$	$\frac{1}{5}$	$\frac{1}{5}$	$\frac{3}{19}$
$\frac{1}{10}$	$\frac{1}{10}$	$\frac{1}{10}$	$\frac{1}{19}$
$\frac{3}{10}$	$\frac{3}{10}$	$\frac{3}{10}$	$\frac{5}{19}$
$\frac{2}{5}$	$\frac{2}{5}$	$\frac{2}{5}$	$\frac{7}{19}$

 Interactive lesson includes instant self-check, tutorials, and activities.

OBJECTIVE 1 Independent Events

Investigation

Exploring Probability in Games

You have four cards with an M written on them, two with an A, six with a T, and eight with an H.

1. You draw an M card at random and replace it. What is the probability that the next card you draw at random will also be an M card? $\frac{4}{20}$, or $\frac{1}{5}$

2. You draw an M card at random and do not replace the card. What is the probability that the next card you draw at random will also be an M card? $\frac{3}{19}$

3. Make a table to find the probability of matching cards.
See below left.

Probability With Replacement		**Probability Without Replacement**	
First Card	**Second Card Matches**	**First Card**	**Second Card Matches**
$P(M) = $ ▨	$P(M) = $ ▨	$P(M) = $ ▨	$P(M) = $ ▨
$P(A) = $ ▨	$P(A) = $ ▨	$P(A) = $ ▨	$P(A) = $ ▨
$P(T) = $ ▨	$P(T) = $ ▨	$P(T) = $ ▨	$P(T) = $ ▨
$P(H) = $ ▨	$P(H) = $ ▨	$P(H) = $ ▨	$P(H) = $ ▨

4. **Reasoning** For any letter, why is the probability for selecting the second card with replacement of the first card different from the probability of selecting the second card without replacement of the first card?
Without replacement, both the number of the first card selected and the total number of cards have been reduced by one.

Suppose the numbers from 1 to 10 are written on 10 cards, one number to a card. You are interested in drawing one card at random and getting an even number, and then drawing a second card and getting an even number again.

If you *replace* your first card, the probability of getting an even number on the second card is unaffected.

Independent events are events for which the occurrence of one event *does not affect* the probability of the occurrence of the other.

Ongoing Assessment and Intervention

Before the Lesson
Diagnose prerequisite skills using:
• Check Skills You'll Need

During the Lesson
Monitor progress using:
• Check Understanding
• Additional Examples
• Test Prep

After the Lesson
Assess knowledge using:
• Lesson Quiz
• Computer Test Generator CD-ROM

Key Concepts — Probability of Independent Events

For two independent events A and B, the probability of both events occurring is the product of the probabilities of each event occurring.

$$P(A, \text{then } B) = P(A) \cdot P(B)$$

1 EXAMPLE — Finding Probability for Independent Events

You roll a number cube once. Then you roll it again. What is the probability that you get 2 on the first roll and a number greater than 4 on the second roll?

$P(2) = \frac{1}{6}$ **There is one 2 among 6 numbers on a number cube.**

$P(\text{greater than } 4) = \frac{2}{6}$ **There are two numbers greater than 4 on a number cube.**

$P(2, \text{then greater than } 4) = P(2) \cdot P(\text{greater than } 4)$

$\qquad = \frac{1}{6} \cdot \frac{2}{6}$

$\qquad = \frac{2}{36}, \text{ or } \frac{1}{18}$

The probability is $\frac{1}{18}$.

✓ Check Understanding   Example 1

1. You toss a coin twice. Find the probability of getting two heads. $\frac{1}{4}$

You can use fractions, decimals, or percents to represent probabilities and to find the probability of two events occurring.

2 EXAMPLE — Real-World  Problem Solving

Botany Under the best conditions, a wild bluebonnet seed has a 20% probability of growing. If you select two seeds at random, what is the probability that both will grow, under the best conditions?

$P(\text{a seed grows}) = 20\%, \text{ or } 0.20$ **Write the percent as a decimal.**

$P(\text{two seeds grow}) = P(\text{a seed grows}) \cdot P(\text{a seed grows})$

$\qquad = 0.20 \cdot 0.20$ **Substitute.**

$\qquad = 0.04$ **Multiply.**

$\qquad = 4\%$ **Write 0.04 as a percent.**

The probability that two seeds grow is 4%.

Real-World 🌐 Connection
Bluebonnets grow wild in the southwestern United States.

12-5   Independent and Dependent Events   **655**

🌱 Reaching All Students

Below Level Place a group of objects in front of the class. Have students remove one object at a time. Ask: *How does the group change after each item is taken?* There is one fewer item in the group.

Advanced Learners Ask: *A bag holding red (R) and white (W) buttons. If P(R) is $\frac{3}{5}$, and, without replacement, P(R, then R) is $\frac{3}{10}$, what is the probability of choosing red on your second draw?* $\frac{1}{2}$

Visual Learners
See note on page 656.
Error Prevention
See note on page 656.

---

2. Teach

Professional Development

Math Background

Suppose you put five white marbles and one red marble in a bag. You reach in without looking to draw a marble, look at it, and put it back in the bag. A second person draws a marble. The probability that the second person will draw the red marble is the same as it was for you because the bag contains the same five white marbles and one red marble. The two draws are *independent* events. However, if you keep your marble when you draw it, the probability that the second person will draw the red marble is different because there is one fewer marble in the bag. The two draws now are *dependent* events.

Teaching Notes

Investigation (Optional)
Help students understand that when a card is not replaced, there are fewer outcomes possible for the next drawing.

2 EXAMPLE — Science Connection

Bluebonnet seeds have a very tough outer covering, and it may take several years for one to germinate. Delayed germination assures that a plant species will survive periods of drought or other adverse growing conditions.

PowerPoint
💻 Additional Examples

1 You roll a number cube once. Then you roll it again. What is the probability that you get 5 on the first roll and a number less than 4 on the second roll? $\frac{1}{12}$

2 Suppose you plant bluebonnet seeds in your garden and use a fertilizer that increases to 50% the probability that a seed will grow. If you select two seeds at random, what is the probability that both will grow in your garden? 25%

3 Three girls and two boys volunteer to represent their class at a school assembly. The teacher selects one name and then another from a bag containing the five students' names. What is the probability that both representatives will be boys? $\frac{1}{10}$

2. Botany Chemically treated bluebonnet seeds have a 30% probability of growing. You select two such seeds at random. What is the probability that both will grow? **9%**

OBJECTIVE

2 Dependent Events

Teaching Tip

To help students understand why *dependent* events are so named, point out that the probability of the second event *depends* on the first outcome.

Suppose you want to draw two even-numbered cards from cards showing numbers from 1 to 10. You draw one card. Then, *without replacing* the first card, you draw a second card. The probability of drawing an even number on the second card is affected.

Dependent events are events for which the occurrence of one event *affects* the probability of the occurrence of the other.

3 **EXAMPLE** Visual Learners

Have three girls and two boys stand at the front of the class to help model the problem. Ask: *What is the probability that a girl will be chosen?* $\frac{3}{5}$ Have one girl go back to her desk. Ask: *Now, what is the probability that a boy will be chosen from the remaining students?* $\frac{2}{4}$

Key Concepts Probability of Dependent Events

For two dependent events *A* and *B,* the probability of both events occurring is the product of the probability of the first event and the probability that, after the first event, the second event occurs.

$$P(A, \text{then } B) = P(A) \cdot P(B \text{ after } A)$$

3 **EXAMPLE** Error Prevention

Some students may think that the probability of both choices should be the same. Help students see that when they find the probability for the second choice, both the number of girls and the total number of students have been reduced by 1.

3 **EXAMPLE** Finding Probability for Dependent Events

Three girls and two boys volunteer to represent their class at a school assembly. The teacher selects one name and then another from a bag containing the five students' names. What is the probability that both representatives will be girls?

$P(\text{girl}) = \frac{3}{5}$ **Three of five students are girls.**

$P(\text{girl after girl}) = \frac{2}{4}$ **If a girl's name is drawn, two of the four remaining students are girls.**

$P(\text{girl, then girl}) = P(\text{girl}) \cdot P(\text{girl after girl})$

$\qquad = \frac{3}{5} \cdot \frac{2}{4}$ **Substitute.**

$\qquad = \frac{6}{20}, \text{ or } \frac{3}{10}$ **Simplify.**

• The probability that both representatives will be girls is $\frac{3}{10}$.

Closure

Ask students to explain the difference between *independent events* and *dependent events.* Independent events are those in which the first event *does not* affect the second. Dependent events are those in which the first event *does* affect the second.

✔ **Check Understanding** Example 3

3. a. For Example 3, find $P(\text{boy, then girl})$. $\frac{3}{10}$
b. Find $P(\text{girl, then boy})$. $\frac{3}{10}$

EXERCISES

❓ For more exercises, see *Extra Practice*.

Practice and Problem Solving

Ⓐ Practice by Example
Example 1
(page 655)

You roll a number cube twice. What is the probability that you roll each pair of numbers?

1. 6, then 5 $\frac{1}{36}$

2. 6, then a number less than 4 $\frac{3}{36}$, or $\frac{1}{12}$

3. 6, then 2 or 5 $\frac{2}{36}$, or $\frac{1}{18}$

4. an even number, then 2 or 5 $\frac{6}{36}$, or $\frac{1}{6}$

5. 1, then 1 $\frac{1}{36}$

6. an even number, then an odd number $\frac{9}{36}$, or $\frac{1}{4}$

Example 2 🌐
(page 655)

7. Weather Forecasting Weather forecasters are accurate 91% of the time when predicting precipitation for the day. What is the probability that a forecaster will make correct precipitation predictions two days in a row? **about 83%**

Example 3
(page 656)

You select a card at random from those below. Without replacing the card, you select a second card. Find the probability of selecting each set of letters.

P R E A L G E B R A

8. P, then G $\frac{1}{90}$

9. E, then A $\frac{4}{90}$, or $\frac{2}{45}$

10. E, then a second vowel
See left.

11. G, then R or A $\frac{4}{90}$, or $\frac{2}{45}$

10. $\frac{6}{90}$, or $\frac{1}{15}$

12. P or E, then A $\frac{6}{90}$, or $\frac{1}{15}$

13. a consonant, then a vowel $\frac{24}{90}$, or $\frac{4}{15}$

Ⓑ Apply Your Skills

Are the events independent or dependent? Explain.

14. You select a card. Without putting the card back, you select a second card.
Dependent; the total number of cards has been reduced by 1.

15. You roll a number cube. You roll it again. **Independent; the possibilities on the second roll are the same as on the first.**

You pick a marble from a bag containing 1 green marble, 4 red marbles, 2 yellow marbles, and 3 black marbles. You replace the first marble and then select a second one. Find each probability.

16. P(red, then yellow) $\frac{8}{100}$, or $\frac{2}{25}$

17. P(black, then black) $\frac{9}{100}$

18. P(red, then black) $\frac{12}{100}$, or $\frac{3}{25}$

19. P(yellow, then black) $\frac{6}{100}$, or $\frac{3}{50}$

Gino has 5 blue socks and 4 black socks. He selects one sock at random. Without replacing the sock, he selects a second sock at random. Find each probability.

24. For independent events, the occurrence of the first does not affect the probability of the occurrence of the second. In dependent events, it does.

20. P(blue, then black) $\frac{20}{72}$, or $\frac{5}{18}$

21. P(black, then blue) $\frac{20}{72}$, or $\frac{5}{18}$

22. P(black, then black) $\frac{12}{72}$, or $\frac{1}{6}$

23. P(blue, then blue) $\frac{20}{72}$, or $\frac{5}{18}$

24. Writing in Math Explain the difference between independent and dependent events. **See left.**

---

3. Practice

Assignment Guide

1 Objective 1
- Ⓐ Ⓑ Core 1–7, 15–19
- Ⓒ Extension 26

2 Objective 2
- Ⓐ Ⓑ Core 8–14, 20–25
- Ⓒ Extension 27

Test Prep 28–31
Mixed Review 32–34

Practice 12-5 Independent and Dependent Events

Practice

A shelf holds 3 novels, 2 biographies, and 1 history book. Two students in turn choose a book at random. What is the probability that the students choose each of the following?

1. both novels $\frac{1}{5}$

2. both biographies $\frac{1}{15}$

3. a history, then a novel $\frac{1}{10}$

4. both history books 0

Meg flipped a penny the given number of times. What is the probability the results were as follows?

5. 2; two heads $\frac{1}{4}$

6. 3; three tails $\frac{1}{8}$

7. 2; a tail, then a head $\frac{1}{4}$

8. 5; five tails $\frac{1}{32}$

Two puppies are chosen at random from a box at the mall. What is the probability of these outcomes?

Free Puppies for Adoption!
5 black retrievers
3 brown hounds
4 black setters

9. both black $\frac{6}{11}$

10. both brown $\frac{1}{22}$

11. a setter, then a hound $\frac{1}{11}$

12. a retriever, then a setter $\frac{5}{33}$

13. both setters $\frac{1}{11}$

Are the events independent or dependent? Explain.

14. A guest at a party takes a sandwich from a tray. A second guest then takes a sandwich.
Dependent; the second guest's choice is limited by the first guest's choice.

15. Sam flips a coin and gets heads. He flips again and gets tails.
Independent; the second flip is not affected by the first.

You can select only two cards from the right. Find the probability of selecting a T and an N for each condition.

M A T H
I S
F U N

16. You replace the first card before drawing the second. $\frac{1}{81}$

17. You do not replace the first card before drawing the second. $\frac{1}{72}$

Enrichment 12-5 Odds and Dependent Events

Enrichment

Odds are a way of comparing favorable and unfavorable outcomes.

odds in favor = $\frac{\text{number of favorable outcomes}}{\text{number of unfavorable outcomes}}$

odds against = $\frac{\text{number of unfavorable outcomes}}{\text{number of favorable outcomes}}$

A record is chosen at random from a sale bin. Find the odds.

Record Sale!
8 jazz
6 classical
2 rock

1. in favor of classical $\frac{3}{5}$

2. in favor of rock $\frac{1}{7}$

3. against jazz $\frac{1}{4}$

Example: Two records are chosen at random from the sale bin. Find the odds in favor of both being jazz.

Solution: You can use probability to find odds.
$P(\text{both jazz}) = \frac{8}{16} \cdot \frac{7}{15} = \frac{7}{30}$
There are $30 - 7 = 23$ unfavorable outcomes out of 30.
Odds in favor of both being jazz = $\frac{7}{23}$

Two records are chosen at random from the sale bin described above. Find the odds in favor of each.

4. both are rock $\frac{1}{119}$

5. the first is jazz and the second is rock $\frac{1}{14}$

6. the first is classical and the second is jazz $\frac{1}{4}$

7. both are classical $\frac{1}{7}$

Two records are chosen at random from the sale bin described above. Find the odds against each.

8. both are rock $\frac{119}{1}$

9. the first is jazz and the second is rock $\frac{14}{1}$

10. the first is classical and the second is jazz $\frac{4}{1}$

11. both are classical $\frac{7}{1}$

---

4. Assess

Solve.

1. You roll a number cube once. Then you roll it again. What is the probability that you will get 6 on the first roll and a number greater than 3 on the second roll? $\frac{1}{12}$

2. Suppose there are three white marbles and three black marbles in a bag and you want to remove two marbles. What is the probability that you will select a white marble and then a black marble? Express your answer as a percent. **30%**

3. Each of five girls and seven boys wants to be one of the two announcers for a variety show. To be fair, a teacher puts the names of the twelve students in a hat and draws two. What is the probability that the teacher will draw the names of two boys? Of two girls? $\frac{7}{22}$; $\frac{5}{33}$

 **C Challenge**

30. [2] Carolyn selects 49 and Jamie selects 49. Independent; Carolyn's choice of a number does not affect the probability of Jamie's choice.
[1] minor error OR answer only

25. A refrigerator contains 12 orange drinks, 4 grape drinks, and 25 apple drinks. Ann is first in the line for drinks. Mark is second. What is the probability that Ann gets an apple drink and Mark gets a grape drink, if they are given drinks at random? $\frac{5}{82}$

26. On a multiple-choice test you randomly guess the answers to two questions. Each question has five choices.
   a. What is the probability that you get both answers correct? $\frac{1}{25}$
   b. What is the probability that you get both answers incorrect? $\frac{16}{25}$

27. Mrs. Kendall's wallet contains 3 one-dollar bills, 2 five-dollar bills, and 3 ten-dollar bills. She randomly selects one bill and then another. Find the probability that she selects the given bills.
   a. a one-dollar bill and then a ten-dollar bill $\frac{9}{56}$
   b. a ten-dollar bill and then a five-dollar bill $\frac{6}{56}$, or $\frac{3}{28}$

Test Prep

Multiple Choice

28. There are 6 girls and 5 boys in a debate class. The teacher chooses two students at random to lead a class discussion. What is the probability of selecting a girl and then a boy? **B**

   A. $\frac{30}{121}$ B. $\frac{3}{11}$ C. $\frac{36}{121}$ D. $\frac{6}{11}$

29. Mike asks Carolyn to pick a number at random from 1 to 100, and then asks Jamie to do the same. What is the probability that both girls will select 49? **I**

   F. $\frac{1}{50}$ G. $\frac{1}{100}$ H. $\frac{1}{9,900}$ I. $\frac{1}{10,000}$

Short Response

30. a. Exercise 29 involves two events. What are they?
   b. Are they independent or dependent? Explain.
   See above left.

31. In a game, Teri and Hector take turns choosing cards at random from a basket. Each card shows a "T" or "H". A player chooses a card, records the letter, and puts the card in a discard pile.
   a. Are the letters drawn independent or dependent events?
   b. Explain your answer.
   See back of book.

Take It to the NET
Online lesson quiz at
www.PHSchool.com
Web Code: ada-1205

Mixed Review

Lesson 12-4 32. **Travel** From Compt there are four ways to get to Murch. From Murch there are five ways to get to Toll. How many ways are there from Compt to Toll through Murch? **20 ways**

Lesson 11-6 **For each triangle, find the sine, cosine, and tangent of angle A.**

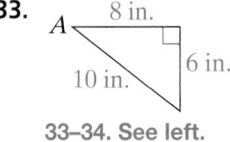
33.

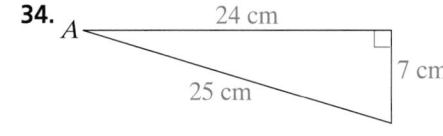
34.

33. $\frac{6}{10}$ or $\frac{3}{5}$, $\frac{8}{10}$ or $\frac{4}{5}$, $\frac{6}{8}$ or $\frac{3}{4}$

34. $\frac{7}{25}$, $\frac{24}{25}$, $\frac{7}{24}$

33–34. See left.

658 Chapter 12 Data Analysis and Probability

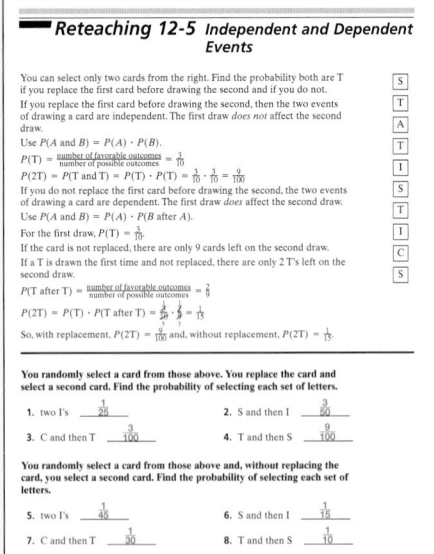

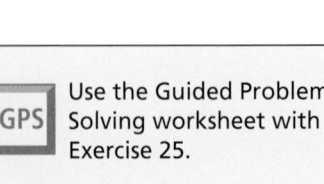
GPS Use the Guided Problem Solving worksheet with Exercise 25.

Alternative Assessment

Organize students into groups of four. Give each group a coin, a bag of marbles, a number cube, a stack of cards, and a blank spinner. Have the students use any of these items to create two problems: one that involves two independent events and one that involves two dependent events.

Test Prep

Resources
For additional practice with a variety of test item formats:
• Test Prep, p. 683
• Test-Taking Strategies, p. 678
• Test-Taking Strategies With Transparencies

Permutations and Combinations

OBJECTIVE

1 Permutations

An arrangement in which order is important is a **permutation.** For the letters O, P, S, and T, the permutations *STOP* and *POTS* are different because the order of the letters is different.

You can use the Counting Principle to find the number of possible permutations.

1 EXAMPLE Counting Permutations

Find the number of permutations possible for the letters O, P, S, and T.

1st letter	2nd letter	3rd letter	4th letter
4 choices	3 choices	2 choices	1 choice
4 ·	3 ·	2 ·	1 = 24

● There are 24 permutations of the letters O, P, S, and T.

✔ Check Understanding Example 1

1. Use the Counting Principle to find the number of permutations possible for the letters W, A, T, E, and R. **120**

A track team has seven members. In how many ways could four team members line up for a relay race?

You can use *permutation notation* to represent this problem.

7 members ─┐ ┌─ Choose 4.

$$_7P_4 = 7 \cdot 6 \cdot 5 \cdot 4 = 840$$

1st   2nd   3rd   4th
member member member member

Four of seven team members could line up in 840 ways.

Key Concepts Permutation Notation

The expression $_nP_r$ stands for the number of permutations of n objects chosen r at a time.

What You'll Learn

OBJECTIVE 1   To use permutations

OBJECTIVE 2   To use combinations

. . . And Why

To solve real-world problems involving sports and geography

✔ Check Skills You'll Need

Use the Counting Principle to find the number of outcomes.

1. Roll 2 number cubes.
   36 outcomes
2. Choose three different letters.
   15,600 outcomes
3. Select a month and a day of the week.
   84 outcomes
4. Toss a coin 4 times.
   16 outcomes

🔍 For help, go to Lesson 12-4.

New Vocabulary

• permutation

• combination

 iTEXT Interactive lesson includes instant self-check, tutorials, and activities.

Lesson Preview

✔ **Check Skills You'll Need**

Counting Outcomes
Lesson 12-4: Example 2; Exercises 3 and 4.
Extra Practice, p. 755.

Lesson Resources

📁 **Teaching Resources**
Practice, Reteaching, Enrichment

👥 **Reaching All Students**
Practice Workbook 12-6
Spanish Practice Workbook 12-6
Guided Problem Solving 12-6
Technology Activities 34
Hands-On Activities 31

🕐 **Presentation Assistant Plus!**
Transparencies and PowerPoint™
• Check Skills You'll Need 12-6
• Additional Examples 12-6
• Student Edition Answers 12-6
• Lesson Quiz 12-6
PH Presentation Pro CD-ROM 12-6

ASSESSMENT SYSTEM

Computer Test Generator CD-ROM

💻 **Technology**
Resource Pro® CD-ROM
Computer Test Generator CD-ROM
PH Presentation Pro CD-ROM

💻 **www.PHSchool.com**
Student Site
• Teacher Web Code: adk-5500
• Self-grading Lesson Quiz
PH SuccessNet Teacher Center
• Lesson Planner
• Resources

Plus **iTEXT**

✔ Ongoing Assessment and Intervention

Before the Lesson
Diagnose prerequisite skills using:
• Check Skills You'll Need

During the Lesson
Monitor progress using:
• Check Understanding
• Additional Examples
• Test Prep

After the Lesson
Assess knowledge using:
• Lesson Quiz
• Computer Test Generator CD-ROM

2. Teach

Math Background

Order distinguishes permutations from combinations. If you arrange the letters *T, H,* and *E* as *THE* and *HTE*, their orders are different. The arrangements are different *permutations*. *THE* and *HTE* are the same *combination*.

Teaching Notes

1 EXAMPLE Error Prevention

Students may think the only plausible combinations of letters are the ones that spell a word. Explain that each unique arrangement of letters, regardless of whether it spells a word, is a permutation of those letters.

2 EXAMPLE Teaching Tip

Show students how to set up the multiplication to find the number of permutations $_nP_r$. The number *n* shows the greatest whole number in the expression, and the number *r* shows how many consecutive whole numbers to multiply. For example, for $_9P_5$, you find the product of 5 consecutive whole numbers, with the greatest being 9.

3 EXAMPLE Teaching Tip

Ask students why the combination CA was left off the list. **CA is the same combination as AC.** Stress that you would include both CA and AC in a list of permutations because CA and AC are in different orders and are, therefore, different permutations.

4 EXAMPLE Auditory Learners

Have students read aloud $_5C_3$ as "the number of combinations of five sandwich fillings chosen three at a time." Urge them to read combination (and permutation) notation aloud, softly, to themselves, each time they see it.

5 EXAMPLE Tactile Learners

Have students work in groups and actually use five books and three CDs (all different).

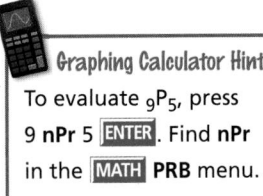
Graphing Calculator Hint
To evaluate $_9P_5$, press 9 **nPr** 5 **ENTER**. Find **nPr** in the **MATH PRB** menu.

2 EXAMPLE Simplifying Permutation Notation

You have 9 books and want to display 5 on a shelf. How many different 5-book arrangements are possible?

9 books ⌐ Choose 5.
$$_9P_5 = 9 \cdot 8 \cdot 7 \cdot 6 \cdot 5 = 15{,}120 \qquad \textbf{Simplify.}$$

● There are 15,120 arrangements possible.

✔ Check Understanding Example 2

2. Simplify each expression.

   a. $_5P_2$ 20   **b.** $_5P_3$ 60   **c.** $_5P_4$ 120   **d.** $_5P_5$ 120

OBJECTIVE

2 Combinations

Sometimes the order of items is not important. For instance, a ham and cheese sandwich is the same as a cheese and ham sandwich. An arrangement in which order does not matter is a **combination.**

3 EXAMPLE Real-World 🌐 Problem Solving

Inland Water	
Country	**Water Area (mi²)**
Australia	26,610
Canada	291,573
Ethiopia	46,680
India	121,391
Tanzania	22,799
United States	79,541

Source: *The Top 10 of Everything*

Geography **In how many ways could you choose two countries from the table when you write reports about inland water?**

Make an organized list of all the combinations.

AC	AE	AI	AT	AU
	CE	CI	CT	CU
		EI	ET	EU
			IT	IU
				TU

Abbreviate by using the first letter of each country's name. First, list all pairs containing Australia. Continue until every pair of countries is listed.

● There are fifteen ways to choose two countries from the list of six.

✔ Check Understanding Example 3

3. In how many ways could you choose three different items from a menu containing six items? **20 ways**

Key Concepts   Combination Notation

The expression $_nC_r$ stands for the number of combinations of *n* objects chosen *r* at a time.

660 Chapter 12 Data Analysis and Probability

👥 Reaching All Students

Below Level Have the students write the letters C, A, and T. Then have them make an organized list of all the different ways the letters can be arranged. **CAT, CTA, ATC, ACT, TAC, TCA**	**Advanced Learners** Have students research what factorial notation (*n*!) is. **Factorial notation names a number, *n*! (read *n* factorial), that is the product of the first *n* whole numbers.**	**Auditory Learners** See note on page 660. **Tactile Learners** See note on page 660.

In general, there are fewer combinations than permutations. To find the number of combinations, $_nC_r$, of r items chosen from n items, find the total number of permutations $_nP_r$, and then divide by the number of possible permutations, $_rP_r$, for any group of r items.

$$_nC_r = \frac{_nP_r}{_rP_r}.$$

4 EXAMPLE   Simplifying Combination Notation

You have five choices of sandwich fillings. How many different sandwiches could you make by choosing three of the five fillings?

5 fillings ⌐ ⌐Choose 3.

$_5C_3 = \dfrac{_5P_3}{_3P_3}$

$= \dfrac{5 \cdot 4 \cdot 3}{3 \cdot 2 \cdot 1} = 10$ **Simplify.**

● You could make 10 different sandwiches.

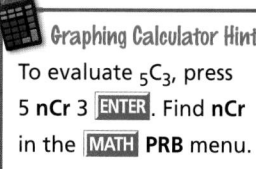

Graphing Calculator Hint

To evaluate $_5C_3$, press
5 nCr 3 [ENTER]. Find **nCr**
in the **[MATH] PRB** menu.

✔ Check Understanding   Example 4

4. Simplify each expression.

a. $_8C_2$ 28   **b.** $_8C_3$ 56   **c.** $_8C_4$ 70   **d.** $_8C_5$ 56

You can tell whether a problem requires permutations or combinations by asking yourself, *Does order matter?* If the answer is *yes,* use permutations. If it is *no,* use combinations.

5 EXAMPLE   Identifying Whether Order Is Important

Tell which type of arrangement each problem involves. Explain.

a. How many different groups of three books could you choose from five books?

Combinations; the order of the books selected does not matter.

b. In how many different orders could you play three CDs?

Permutations; the order in which you play the CDs matters.

✔ Check Understanding   Example 5

5. Tell which type of arrangment is involved. Explain. a–b. See right.

a. A teacher selects a committee of 4 students from 25 students. How many different committees could the teacher select?

b. Class officers are president, vice-president, secretary, and treasurer. From a class of 25 students, how many different groups of officers could students elect?

5a. Combinations; the order in which the teacher selects the students does not matter.

5b. Permutations; the order in which students are chosen matters.

PowerPoint

Additional Examples

1 Find the number of permutations possible for the letters H, O, M, E, and S.
120 permutations

2 In how many ways can you line up 3 students chosen from 7 students for a photograph?
210 ways

3 In how many ways can you choose two states from the table when you write reports about the areas of states?
10 ways

State	Area (mi²)
Alabama	50,750
Colorado	103,729
Maine	30,865
Oregon	96,003
Texas	261,914

4 How many different pizzas can you make if you can choose exactly 5 toppings from 9 that are available?
126 pizzas

5 Tell which type of arrangement—permutations or combinations—each problem involves. Explain.
a. How many different groups of three vegetables could you choose from six different vegetables?
Combinations: the order of the vegetables selected does not matter.
b. In how many different orders can you play 4 DVDs?
Permutations: the order in which you play the DVDs matters.

Closure

Ask students to explain the difference between a permutation and a combination.
A permutation is an arrangement in which order is important. A combination is an arrangement in which order is not important.

3. Practice

Assignment Guide

▼1 Objective 1
- Ⓐ Ⓑ Core 1–8, 20–22, 24, 27–29
- Ⓒ Extension 32

▼2 Objective 2
- Ⓐ Ⓑ Core 9–19, 23, 25, 26, 30, 31
- Ⓒ Extension 33

Test Prep 34–36
Mixed Review 37–40

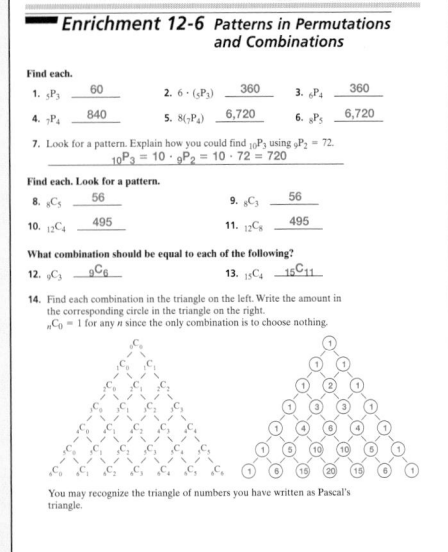

Practice 12-6 *Permutations and Combinations*

Simplify each expression.
1. $_7P_2$ ___42___   2. $_7C_2$ ___21___   3. $_8P_3$ ___336___
4. $_9P_4$ ___3,024___   5. $_3C_2$ ___3___   6. $_{10}C_4$ ___210___

7. Art, Becky, Carl, and Denise are lined up to buy tickets.
   a. How many different permutations of the four are possible?
      ___24___
   b. Suppose Ed was also in line. How many permutations would there be?
      ___120___
   c. In how many of the permutations of the five is Becky first?
      ___24___
   d. What is the probability that a permutation of this five chosen at random will have Becky first?
      $\frac{1}{5}$

8. Art, Becky, Carl, Denise, and Ed all want to go to the concert. However, there are only 3 tickets. How many ways can they choose the 3 who get to go to the concert?
   ___10___

9. A combination lock has 36 numbers on it. How many different 3-number combinations are possible if no number may be repeated?
   ___42,840___

Numbers are to be formed using the digits 1, 2, 3, 4, 5, and 6. No digit may be repeated.
10. How many two-digit numbers can be formed? ___30___
11. How many three-digit numbers can be formed? ___120___
12. How many four-digit numbers can be formed? ___360___
13. How many five-digit numbers can be formed? ___720___
14. How many six-digit numbers can be formed? ___720___

Enrichment 12-6 *Patterns in Permutations and Combinations*

Find each.
1. $_5P_3$ ___60___   2. $6 \cdot (_5P_3)$ ___360___   3. $_6P_4$ ___360___
4. $_7P_4$ ___840___   5. $8(_7P_4)$ ___6,720___   6. $_8P_5$ ___6,720___

7. Look for a pattern. Explain how you could find $_{10}P_3$ using $_9P_2 = 72$.
   $_{10}P_3 = 10 \cdot _9P_2 = 10 \cdot 72 = 720$

Find each. Look for a pattern.
8. $_8C_5$ ___56___   9. $_8C_3$ ___56___
10. $_{12}C_4$ ___495___   11. $_{12}C_8$ ___495___

What combination should be equal to each of the following?
12. $_9C_3$ __$_9C_6$__   13. $_{15}C_4$ __$_{15}C_{11}$__

14. Find each combination in the triangle on the left. Write the amount in the corresponding circle on the right. $_nC_0 = 1$ for any n since the only combination is to choose nothing.

You may recognize the triangle of numbers you have written as Pascal's triangle.

EXERCISES

For more exercises, see *Extra Practice*.

Practice and Problem Solving

Ⓐ **Practice by Example**

Example 1
(page 659)

Use the Counting Principle to find the number of permutations possible for all the letters in each group.

1. S, I, T 6   2. P, L, U, S 24   3. W, O, R, L, D 120

Example 2
(page 660)

Simplify each expression.

4. $_4P_2$ 12   5. $_6P_4$ 360   6. $_9P_4$ 3,024   7. $_{10}P_8$ 1,814,400

8. How many different arrangements of four books on a shelf could you make from eight books? **1,680 arrangements**

Example 3
(page 660)

9. 3; CA, CT, AT
10. 6; MA, MT, MH, AT, AH, TH
11. 10; VA, VL, VU, VE, AL, AU, AE, LU, LE, UE

In how many ways could you choose two different items from each group? Make an organized list of all the combinations. 9–11. See left.

9. C, A, T   10. M, A, T, H   11. V, A, L, U, E

Example 4
(page 661)

Simplify each expression.

12. $_4C_2$ 6   13. $_6C_4$ 15   14. $_9C_4$ 126   15. $_{10}C_8$ 45

16. **Literature** Louisa May Alcott published 13 novels during her lifetime. In how many ways could you select three of these books?
    286 ways
17. You have six choices of sandwich fillings. How many different sandwiches could you make by choosing three of the six fillings?
    20 sandwiches

Example 5
(page 661)

Does each problem involve *permutations* or *combinations*? Explain.

18. In how many different ways could three students form a line?
    Permutations; order is important in a line.
19. In how many ways could you choose three shirts from seven shirts?
    Combinations; the order of the shirts selected does not matter.

Ⓑ **Apply Your Skills**

Find the number of possible 5-letter permutations of the given letters.

20. D, E, C, I, M, A, L   21. F, A, C, T, O, R   22. T, R, I, A, N, G, L, E
    2,520   720   6,720

23. Use the different letters from your last name.
    a. Find the number of two-letter permutations.
    b. Find the number of two-letter combinations.
       a–b. Check students' work.

Simplify each expression.

24. $_6P_3$ 120   25. $_6C_3$ 20   26. $_2C_1$ 2   27. $_2P_1$ 2

28. $_{12}P_9$ 79,833,600   29. $_{10}P_5$ 30,240   30. $_{10}C_5$ 252   31. $_{20}C_{19}$ 20

Ⓒ **Challenge**

32a. 24 arrangements

32. Use the letters E, P, S, and T.
    a. How many possible arrangements of the letters are there? See left.
    b. Add a second letter T to the list. How many distinct arrangements of the five letters are possible? **60 arrangements**

GPS Use the Guided Problem Solving worksheet with Exercise 16.

33. Writing in Math To open a combination lock, you turn a dial to match three whole numbers from 0 to 39. You alternate directions of the turns. Explain why 128,000 combinations are possible.
(2 choices of first-turn directions) · 40 · 40 · 40 = 128,000 combinations

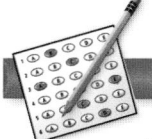

Test Prep

Multiple Choice

34. What is the value of $_{10}C_2$? **A**
  A. 45   **B.** 90   **C.** 180   **D.** 360

35. A teacher is organizing a class of 24 students into eight groups of three. In how many different ways could she form groups of three? **G**
  F. 56   **G.** 2,024   **H.** 12,144   **I.** 735,471

Short Response

36. a. How many three-letter permutations are possible for the letters H, E, X, A, G, O, N?
  b. How many four-letter permutations are possible?
  See margin.

Mixed Review

Lesson 12-5   On each of five cards there is one of the letters A, B, C, D, and E. You select two cards. Find $P(A, \text{then } B)$ in each situation.

37. with first card replaced $\frac{1}{25}$ **38.** with first card not replaced $\frac{1}{20}$

Lessons 10-2 and 11-2   **39.** Find the area of the triangle at the right. **120 in.²**

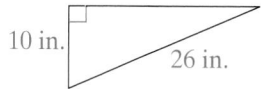
10 in.   26 in.

Lesson 6-9 **40. Consumer Issues** A coat is on sale for $80. Its original price was $120. What is the percent of discount? **33.3̄%**

Math at Work

Wildlife Statistician

Wildlife statisticians study the growth or decline of plant and animal life in a geographical region. They make observations and collect data for a small portion, or sample, of an animal or plant population. Then they draw conclusions about the entire population. If you enjoy studying wildlife, this may be the job for you.

Take It to the NET For more information about statisticians, go to **www.PHSchool.com.**
Web Code: adb-2031

12-6 Permutations and Combinations   **663**

36. [2] 210, 840
  [1] one correct answer

Alternative Assessment

Have students work in pairs. Instruct each student to write two problems, one that can be solved using permutations and one that can be solved using combinations. Have partners exchange papers and solve the two problems. Then have them check each other's answers.

663

Pascal's Triangle

This Extension leads students to discover that Pascal's triangle can be used to find combinations.

Teaching Notes

Teaching Tip
Point out to students that while Pascal's triangle shows numbers of combinations, it does not show numbers of permutations.

Visual Learners
When copying or constructing Pascal's triangle, have students use a different color of pencil for each row of numbers.

The structure of Pascal's triangle is described below.

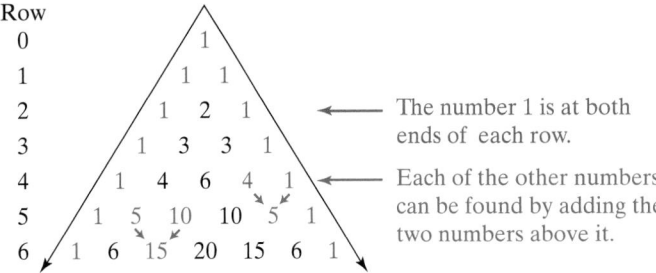

← The number 1 is at both ends of each row.

← Each of the other numbers can be found by adding the two numbers above it.

You can use Pascal's triangle to find combinations.

EXAMPLE

Find $_5C_3$ using Pascal's triangle.

Row 5 of Pascal's triangle gives all the values of $_5C_r$, for $r = 0$ to 5.

1   5   10   10   5   1   ← **row 5**

$_5C_0 \quad _5C_1 \quad _5C_2 \quad _5C_3 \quad _5C_4 \quad _5C_5$ ← **combinations in the form $_5C_r$, for $r = 0$ to 5**

$$_5C_3 = 10$$

Note that $_nC_0$ equals 1.

EXERCISES

1. Copy and extend Pascal's triangle to Row 10. **See right.**

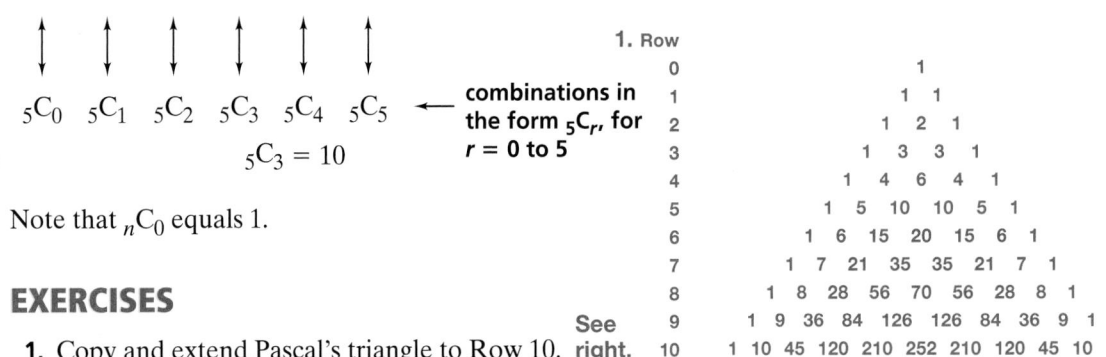

2. **a.** Find the sum of the numbers in each row of the triangle. 1, 2, 4, 8, 16, 32, 64, 128, 256, 512, 1,024
   b. Write each sum as a power of 2. $2^0, 2^1, 2^2, 2^3, 2^4, 2^5, 2^6, 2^7, 2^8, 2^9, 2^{10}$
   c. Complete: The sum of the numbers in row n is ▇. 2^n

Use Pascal's triangle to find each value.

3. $_5C_2$ 10
4. $_3C_2$ 3
5. $_4C_3$ 4
6. $_6C_4$ 15
7. $_7C_2$ 21

8. $_8C_6$ 28
9. $_9C_3$ 84
10. $_9C_5$ 126
11. $_{10}C_0$ 1
12. $_{10}C_{10}$ 1

13. **Reasoning** Explain how to display the values in Row 27 of Pascal's triangle using a calculator. **Answers may vary. Sample: Press** Y= **27** $_nC_r$ **X, then** TABLE **with TblStart = 0 and △Tbl = 1.**

664   Extension   Pascal's Triangle

Experimental Probability 12-7

OBJECTIVE

1 Finding Experimental Probability

Experimental probability is probability based on experimental data.

> **Key Concepts** **Experimental Probability**
>
> $$P(\text{event}) = \frac{\text{number of times an event occurs}}{\text{number of times experiment is done}}$$

1 EXAMPLE Real-World Problem Solving

Medical Science **A medical study tests a new medicine on 3,500 people. It is effective for 3,010 people. Find the experimental probability that the medicine is effective.**

$$P(\text{event}) = \frac{\text{number of times an event occurs}}{\text{number of times experiment is done}}$$
$$= \frac{3,010}{3,500} = 0.86, \text{ or } 86\%$$

✔ **Check Understanding** **Example 1**

1. Another medicine is effective for 1,183 of 2,275 people. Find the experimental probability that the medicine is effective. **52%**

OBJECTIVE

2 Using Simulations

A **simulation** is a model used to find experimental probability.

2 EXAMPLE **Using a Simulation**

Simulate the correct guessing of true-false answers.

Toss a coin to simulate each guess. Heads represents a correct guess. Here are the results of 50 trials:

HHTTT   THHTT   THTHH   HTTTH   TTHTT   THTHT
HHTTT   HTHHH   THTHT   THTHT

$$P(\text{heads}) = \frac{\text{number of heads}}{\text{number of tosses}} = \frac{22}{50} = \frac{11}{25}$$

The experimental probability of guessing correctly is $\frac{11}{25}$.

What You'll Learn

 To find experimental probability

 To use simulations

. . . And Why

To solve real-world problems involving medical science and test-taking

✔ **Check Skills You'll Need**

Write each decimal or fraction as a percent.
1–6. See below.
1. 0.8   **2.** 0.53   **3.** 0.625
4. $\frac{3}{5}$ **5.** $\frac{7}{12}$ **6.** $\frac{5}{8}$

 For help, go to Lesson 6-5.

New Vocabulary

- experimental probability
- simulation

1. 80%
2. 53%
3. 62.5%
4. 60%
5. 58.$\overline{3}$%
6. 62.5%

 iTEXT Interactive lesson includes instant self-check, tutorials, and activities.

12-7

1. Plan

Lesson Preview

✔ **Check Skills You'll Need**

Fractions, Decimals, and Percent
Lesson 6-5: Examples 3 and 4;
Exercises 22–41.
Extra Practice, p. 749.

Lesson Resources

 Teaching Resources
Practice, Reteaching, Enrichment

 Reaching All Students
Practice Workbook 12-7
Spanish Practice Workbook 12-7
Guided Problem Solving 12-7
Hands-On Activities 34

 Presentation Assistant Plus!
Transparencies and PowerPoint™
- Check Skills You'll Need 12-7
- Additional Examples 12-7
- Student Edition Answers 12-7
- Lesson Quiz 12-7
PH Presentation Pro CD-ROM 12-7

 **ASSESSMENT** *SYSTEM*

Computer Test Generator CD-ROM

Technology
Resource Pro® CD-ROM
Computer Test Generator CD-ROM
PH Presentation Pro CD-ROM

www.PHSchool.com
Student Site
- Teacher Web Code: adk-5500
- Self-grading Lesson Quiz
PH SuccessNet Teacher Center
- Lesson Planner
- Resources

Plus

Ongoing Assessment and Intervention

Before the Lesson
Diagnose prerequisite skills using:
- Check Skills You'll Need

During the Lesson
Monitor progress using:
- Check Understanding
- Additional Examples
- Test Prep

After the Lesson
Assess knowledge using:
- Lesson Quiz
- Computer Test Generator CD-ROM

Math Background

Professional Development

You can base experimental probabilities on experiences. You can also base experimental probabilities on simulations. A simulation can model chance occurrences when an experiment may be too difficult or costly to carry out. The more trials done in a simulation, the closer the match between experimental and theoretical probabilities.

Teaching Notes

1 EXAMPLE **Error Prevention**
Remind students that the denominator in an experimental probability ratio is the number of trials, not the number of possible outcomes.

Diversity
Have students brainstorm to name events that have different probabilities of occurring in your community than in others. A certain type of weather condition might be one example.

PowerPoint
Additional Examples

1 A medical study tests a new medicine on 3,500 people. It produces side effects for 1,715 people. Find the experimental probability that the medicine will cause side effects. **49%.**

2 Simulate the correct guessing of answers on a multiple-choice test where each problem has four answer choices (A, B, C, and D). **Check students' work.**

Closure

Ask students to explain the difference between theoretical and experimental probability. **Theoretical probability is the ratio of the number of favorable outcomes to the number of possible outcomes. Experimental probability is the ratio of the number of times an event occurs to the number of times an experiment is done.**

666

2a. The experimental probability is less than the theoretical probability of $\frac{1}{2}$.

2b. The experimental probability is likely to get closer to the theoretical probability.

✓ **Check Understanding** **Example 2**

2. a. In Example 2, compare the experimental probability with the theoretical probability. **See left.**

b. If you try the experiment 100 times, what is likely to happen to the experimental probability? **See left.**

More Than One Way

Use theoretical and experimental probabilities to find a probability for correctly guessing all four answers on a four-question true-false quiz.

Nicole's Method

Each guess is independent. Find the probability of one correct guess. Then find the probability of four independent correct guesses.

$$P(1 \text{ correct guess}) = \frac{1}{2}$$
$$P(4 \text{ correct guesses}) = \frac{1}{2} \cdot \frac{1}{2} \cdot \frac{1}{2} \cdot \frac{1}{2} = \frac{1}{16}$$

The theoretical probability is $\frac{1}{16}$.

Daryl's Method

Simulate the problem by tossing a coin. Let heads stand for a correct guess and tails for an incorrect guess. Use the results of 120 tosses given at the left. Separate the results into 30 groups of 4. Count the groups with 4 heads. There are two.

HTTT HTTT HHHT TTTT TTHT THTT
THHH THHH HTTT TTHH HTTT HTHH
HTHH THTT TTHT THTH HHTT THTH
HHHH TTHT HHHH THTT TTTH HHHT
HHTT HTTT THTT HHTT HHTH HTHH

Find the experimental probability.

$$P(\text{event}) = \frac{\text{number of times an event occurs}}{\text{number of times experiment is done}}$$
$$= \frac{2}{30} = \frac{1}{15}$$

The experimental probability is $\frac{1}{15}$.

120 Coin Tosses

```
HTTTHTTTHHHT
TTTTTHTTHTT
THHHTHHHHTTT
TTHHHTTTHTHH
HTHHTHTTTTHT
THTHHHTTTHTH
HHHHTTHTHHHH
THTTTTHHHHT
HHTTHTTTTHTT
HHTTHHTHHTHH
```

For Daryl's simulation, the experimental probability is a little greater than the theoretical probability.

Choose a Method

1. Which method would you use to solve the problem? Explain. **Answers may vary. Sample: Nicole's Method; it is a simple multiplication of fractions.**

 Reaching All Students

| **Below Level** Have students roll a number cube 10 times. Ask: *Which did you roll more, 3 or 6?* **Answers may vary.** *Do you have a better chance of rolling one number than the other? Explain.* **Answers may vary.** | **Advanced Learners** Ask: *If you get heads on five straight tosses of a coin, what is the probability that you will get heads on a sixth toss?* **50%** | **Error Prevention** See note on page 666. **Diversity** See note on page 666. |

EXERCISES

For more exercises, see *Extra Practice.*

Practice and Problem Solving

A **Practice by Example**

Example 1
(page 665)

7a. Answers may vary.
Sample: Use a spinner
divided into four equal
areas.
b. Check students' work.
c. The theoretical
probability is $\frac{1}{4}$ for
each choice.

A student randomly selected 68 vehicles
in a large parking lot and noted the color
of each. Use the results to find the
experimental probability that a vehicle
chosen at random in the lot is the given
color. Write the probability as a percent,
to the nearest tenth of a percent.

Color	Number of Vehicles
Black	9
Blue	10
Brown	13
Green	7
Red	12
White	11
Gray	6

1. red 17.6%

2. white 16.2%

3. black 13.2%

4. blue or green 25%

5. not black or gray 77.9%

6. purple 0%

Example 2
(page 665)

8. Answers may vary.
Sample: Simulate
getting a sticker by
rolling a number cube.
Each number on the
cube represents a
sticker number. Sample
results of 12 rolls: 3 4 1
6 2 2 1 4 5 2 6 5.
$P(3 \text{ or } 4) = \frac{3}{12}$, or $\frac{1}{4}$

7. In a multiple-choice test, each item
has four choices. a–c. See left.
a. Tell how to simulate the correct
guessing of the correct choice.
b. Carry out your simulation. What
do you find for the experimental probability?
c. Compare your result to the theoretical probability.

8. A cereal company randomly puts one of six different stickers in
each box of its cereal. Use a simulation to find the experimental
probability of getting sticker 3 or sticker 4. See left.

B **Apply Your Skills**

13a. Toss 3 coins
repeatedly and record
the results. The
percent of the time
that you get 3 heads
is the experimental
probability.
13b. Find the experimental
probability as in part
(a). Calculate the
theoretical probability:
$\frac{1}{2} \cdot \frac{1}{2} \cdot \frac{1}{2} = \frac{1}{8}$. Compare
the probabilities. They
will not necessarily be
the same. As one
performs many
experiments,
experimental
probability is likely to
approach theoretical.

Students were surveyed about the
numbers of pencils in their book bags.
The table shows the results. Write each
experimental probability as a fraction
in simplest form.

Pencils in Students' Book Bags

Number of pencils	Number of students
0	4
1	16
2 or more	12

9. $P(\text{one pencil})$ $\frac{1}{2}$

10. $P(\text{no pencils})$ $\frac{1}{8}$

11. $P(\text{two or more pencils})$ $\frac{3}{8}$ **12.** $P(\text{at least one pencil})$ $\frac{7}{8}$

13. a. How would you find an experimental probability for tossing
three coins and getting three heads? See left.
b. Reasoning How would you compare an experimental
probability for getting three heads to the theoretical
probability? Would you expect the probabilities to be equal?
Explain. See left.

14. Error Analysis A student wants to do a simulation to find a
probability for correctly guessing a number from 1 to 5 two times
in a row. He decides to roll a number cube 100 times, separating the
results into 50 groups of two and letting a roll of 1 stand for a
correct guess. Explain why the student's simulation will not give
good results. See margin.

12-7 Experimental Probability **667**

14. In the actual situation,
the student's theoretical
probability of making a
correct guess is $\frac{1}{5}$.
In the simulation with a
six-sided number cube,
the theoretical probability
of rolling a 1 is $\frac{1}{6}$.

3. Practice

Assignment Guide

1 **Objective 1**
A **B** Core 1–6, 9–12

2 **Objective 2**
A **B** Core 7, 8, 13, 14, 15
C Extension 16

Test Prep 17–19
Mixed Review 20–26

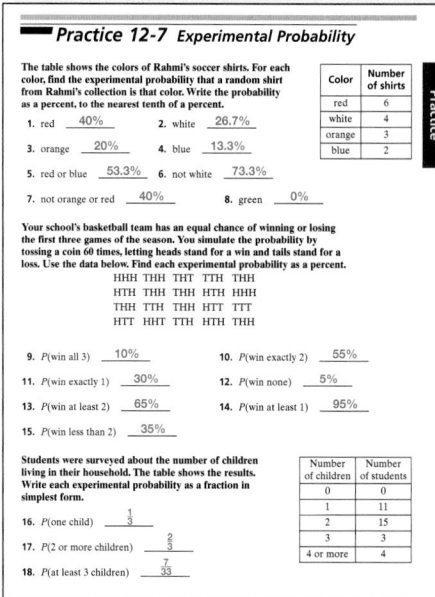

Practice 12-7 *Experimental Probability*

The table shows the colors of Rahmi's soccer shirts. For each
color, find the experimental probability that a random shirt
from Rahmi's collection is that color. Write the probability
as a percent, to the nearest tenth of a percent.

Color	Number of shirts
red	6
white	4
orange	3
blue	2

1. red 40%   **2.** white 26.7%

3. orange 20%   **4.** blue 13.3%

5. red or blue 53.3% **6.** not white 73.3%

7. not orange or red 40%   **8.** green 0%

Your school's basketball team has an equal chance of winning or losing
the first three games of the season. You simulate the probability by
tossing a coin 60 times, letting heads stand for a win and tails for a
loss. Use the data below. Find each experimental probability as a percent.

HHH THH THT TTH TTH
HTH THH THH HTH HHH
THH TTH THH HTT TTT
HTT HHT TTH HTH THH

9. $P(\text{win all 3})$ 10%   **10.** $P(\text{win exactly 2})$ 55%

11. $P(\text{win exactly 1})$ 30%   **12.** $P(\text{win none})$ 5%

13. $P(\text{win at least 2})$ 65% **14.** $P(\text{win at least 1})$ 95%

15. $P(\text{win less than 2})$ 35%

Students were surveyed about the number of children
living in their household. The table shows the results.
Write each experimental probability as a fraction in
simplest form.

Number of children	Number of students
0	0
1	11
2	15
3	3
4 or more	4

16. $P(\text{one child})$ $\frac{1}{3}$

17. $P(\text{2 or more children})$ $\frac{2}{3}$

18. $P(\text{at least 3 children})$ $\frac{7}{33}$

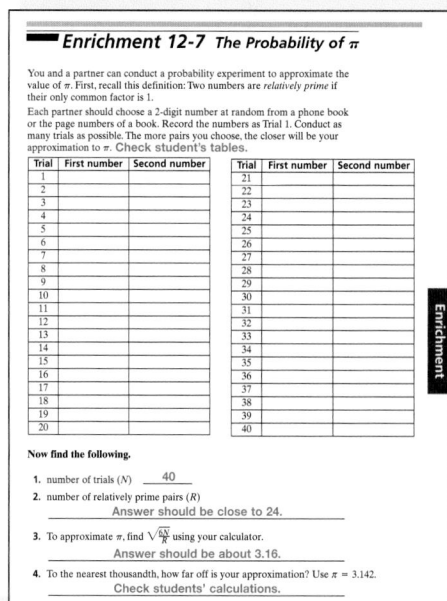

Enrichment 12-7 *The Probability of π*

You and a partner can conduct a probability experiment to approximate the
value of π. First, recall this definition: Two numbers are *relatively prime* if
their only common factor is 1.

Each partner should choose a 2-digit number at random from a phone book
or the page numbers of a book. Record the numbers as Trial 1. Conduct as
many trials as possible. The more pairs you choose, the closer will be your
approximation to π. Check student's tables.

Trial	First number	Second number		Trial	First number	Second number
1				21		
2				22		
3				23		
4				24		
5				25		
6				26		
7				27		
8				28		
9				29		
10				30		
11				31		
12				32		
13				33		
14				34		
15				35		
16				36		
17				37		
18				38		
19				39		
20				40		

Now find the following.

1. number of trials (N) 40

2. number of relatively prime pairs (R)
Answer should be close to 24.

3. To approximate π, find $\sqrt{\frac{6N}{R}}$ using your calculator.
Answer should be about 3.16.

4. To the nearest thousandth, how far off is your approximation? Use π = 3.142.
Check students' calculations.

667

4. Assess

PowerPoint Lesson Quiz 12-7

Solve.

1. Jenny made 42 out of 70 free throws. What is the experimental probability that she will make her next free throw? 60%

2. If 152 of 722 students would choose fish for lunch, what is the experimental probability that a student chosen at random will choose fish? about 21%

Test Prep

Resources

For additional practice with a variety of test item formats:
- Test Prep, p. 683
- Test-Taking Strategies, p. 678
- Test-Taking Strategies With Transparencies

Reteaching 12-7 *Experimental Probability*

The table shows the colors of Lisa's baseball caps. Find the probability that a random cap from Lisa's collection is green or orange. Round to the nearest tenth of a percent.

Color	Number of Caps
blue	7
green	5
orange	3
white	9
red	6

$P(\text{event}) = \frac{\text{number of times the event occurs}}{\text{number of trials}}$

Since there are 30 caps in Lisa's collection, the number of trials is 30. Five caps are green and 3 are orange, so $5 + 3 = 8$ are either green or orange.

$P(\text{green or orange}) = \frac{8}{30} \approx 26.7\%$

Use the data in the table above. For each color, find the experimental probability that a random cap from Lisa's collection is that color. Write the probability as a percent, to the nearest tenth of a percent.

1. blue	23.3%	2. green	16.7%
3. red	20%	4. red or white	50%
5. blue or orange	33.3%	6. not white	70%
7. not green or red	63.3%	8. pink	0%
9. not pink	100%	10. red, white, or blue	73.3%
11. green, orange, or white	56.7%	12. not green, orange, or white	43.3%

GPS Use the Guided Problem Solving worksheet with Exercise 15.

---

15. Two players played a number-cube game. **GPS** The table shows the results.
  a. Find P(A wins) and P(B wins).
  b. **Writing in Math** A *fair game* is one in which each player has the same chance of winning. Do you think the game that A and B played is fair? Explain.
  a–b. See left.

Game Results

A Wins	B Wins
⊞⊞⊞⊞ ⊞IIII	⊞⊞⊞⊞ ⊞⊞⊞ ⊞⊞II

15a. $\frac{29}{81}, \frac{52}{81}$
15b. It is probably not a fair game because B is winning far more often than A.

C Challenge

16. a. Open-Ended Write an experimental probability problem that you can solve with a simulation. Your problem should be different from any in this lesson.
  b. Solve the problem. a–b. Check students' work.

Test Prep

Gridded Response

17. A baseball manufacturer checked 250 of its baseballs and found that 8 were defective. What is the experimental probability, to the nearest tenth of a percent, that a baseball is NOT defective? 96.8

18. Suki tosses two number cubes 100 times. In 19 of the tosses, the sum of the two cubes equals 7. What is Suki's experimental probability of getting a sum of 7 when tossing two number cubes? 0.19

19. A medical experiment finds that 232 out of 1,000 patients did NOT respond to the same medication. What is the experimental probability, to the nearest tenth of a percent, that a patient will respond to the medication? 76.8

Take It to the NET
Online lesson quiz at
www.PHSchool.com
Web Code: ada-1207

Mixed Review

Lesson 12-6 **Evaluate each expression.**

20. $_4P_2$ 12   **21.** $_{10}P_3$ 720   **22.** $_4C_3$ 4   **23.** $_6C_3$ 20

Lesson 10-9 **24. Geometry** Find the volume of a spherical globe with a diameter of 0.9 m. Round to the nearest tenth. 0.4 m³

Lesson 9-8 **Geometry Write a rule to describe each translation.**

25.
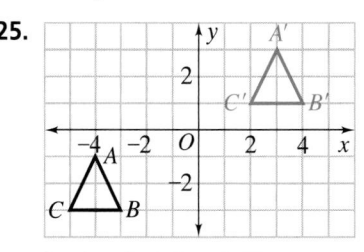
$(x, y) \rightarrow (x + 7, y + 4)$

26.
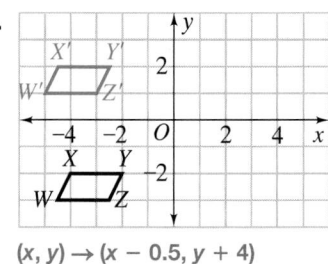
$(x, y) \rightarrow (x - 0.5, y + 4)$

---

668 Chapter 12 Data Analysis and Probability

Alternative Assessment

Assign partners. Have students find an experimental probability that students have an even house or apartment number. They should toss a coin to simulate the last digit of the house and apartment numbers, with *heads* representing an even number and *tails* representing an odd number. After 20 coin tosses, have each group share their probability with the class. Then poll the class to see how many students actually have an even house or apartment number.

Random Samples and Surveys

 **12-8**

 OBJECTIVE

1 Choosing Samples for Surveys

How many books do you read each week? What are your hobbies? Statisticians use questions like these in surveys to get information about specific groups.

A **population** is a group about which you want information. A **sample** is a part of the population you use to make estimates about the population. The larger your sample, the more reliable your estimates will be.

For a **random sample** each member of the population has an equal chance to be selected. A random sample is likely to be representative of the whole population.

1 EXAMPLE **Real-World** **Problem Solving**

Recycling You want to find out whether students will participate if you start a recycling program at your school. Tell whether each survey plan describes a good sample.

a. **Interview every tenth teenager you see at a mall.**
This sample will probably include students who do not go to your school. It is not a good sample because it is not taken from the population you want to study.

b. **Interview the students in your ecology class.**
The views of students in an ecology class may not represent the views about recycling of students in other classes. This is not a good sample because it is not random.

c. **Interview every tenth student leaving a school assembly.**
This is a good sample. It is selected at random from the population you want to study.

✓ **Check Understanding** Example 1

1. Explain whether each plan describes a good sample.

   a. You want to know which bicycle is most popular. You plan to survey entrants in a bicycle race.
   b. You want to know how often teens rent videos. You plan to survey teens going into the local video rental store.
   c. You want to know the most popular breakfast cereal. You plan to survey people entering a grocery store. **a–c. See right.**

What You'll Learn

 OBJECTIVE 1 To choose a sample for a survey of a population

 OBJECTIVE 2 To make estimates about populations

. . . And Why

To solve real-world problems involving recycling and quality control

✓ **Check Skills You'll Need**

Solve each proportion.

1. $\frac{8}{32} = \frac{n}{450}$ 112.5

2. $\frac{7}{25} = \frac{n}{24,000}$ 6,720

3. $\frac{2}{250} = \frac{n}{50,000}$ 400

4. $\frac{4}{100} = \frac{n}{144,000}$ 5,760

 For help, go to Lesson 6-2.

New Vocabulary

• **population**
• **sample**
• **random sample**

1a. Not a good sample; these students would be most interested in racing bikes.
1b. Not a good sample; this sample would not include teens who do not rent videos.
1c. This is a good sample, because there is little built-in bias for or against any cereal.

 Interactive lesson includes instant self-check, tutorials, and activities.

Lesson Preview

✓ **Check Skills You'll Need**

Proportions
Lesson 6-2: Example 1;
Exercises 1–12.
Extra Practice, p. 749.

Lesson Resources

📁 **Teaching Resources**
Practice, Reteaching, Enrichment
Checkpoint Quiz 2

👥 **Reaching All Students**
Practice Workbook 12-8
Spanish Practice Workbook 12-8
Reading and Math Literacy 12C
Spanish Reading and Math
  Literacy 12C
Spanish Checkpoint Quiz 2
Guided Problem Solving 12-8
Hands-On Activities 33

⏱ **Presentation Assistant Plus!**
Transparencies and PowerPoint™
• Check Skills You'll Need 12-8
• Additional Examples 12-8
• Student Edition Answers 12-8
• Lesson Quiz 12-8
PH Presentation Pro CD-ROM 12-8

ASSESSMENT SYSTEM

Checkpoint Quiz 2
Computer Test Generator CD-ROM

💻 **Technology**
Resource Pro® CD-ROM
Computer Test Generator CD-ROM
PH Presentation Pro CD-ROM

 www.PHSchool.com
Student Site
• Teacher Web Code: adk-5500
• Self-grading Lesson Quiz
PH SuccessNet Teacher Center
• Lesson Planner
• Resources

Plus

 ## Ongoing Assessment and Intervention

Before the Lesson
Diagnose prerequisite skills using:
• Check Skills You'll Need

During the Lesson
Monitor progress using:
• Check Understanding
• Additional Examples
• Test Prep

After the Lesson
Assess knowledge using:
• Lesson Quiz
• Computer Test Generator CD-ROM
• Chapter Checkpoint 2 (p. 672)

Professional Development

Math Background

The results from a random sample tend to reflect the results you would get for the whole population. The larger the sample, the more reliable its results will be.

Teaching Notes

1 EXAMPLE Auditory Learners

Begin a class discussion about how random samples produce more reliable survey results because there are no intentional or unintentional biases in selecting the samples. Have students work in groups to plan surveys and good random samples, and discuss possible biases.

2 EXAMPLE Error Prevention

Emphasize for students that a sample can be used to make only an *estimate* about the population. Confidence in the estimate depends on many factors.

PowerPoint

Additional Examples

1 You want to find out how many people in the community use computers on a daily basis. Tell whether each survey plan describes a good sample. Explain.
a. Interview every tenth person leaving a computer store.
b. Interview people at random at the shopping center.
c. Interview every tenth student who arrives at school on a school bus.
See back of book.

2 From 20,000 calculators produced, a manufacturer takes a random sample of 300 calculators. The sample has 2 defective calculators. Estimate the total number of defective calculators. about 133 calculators

Closure

Ask students to explain how they could best find a random sample of their peers to survey about their favorite music groups.
See back of book.

OBJECTIVE

2 Making Estimates About Populations

You can use a sample to make an estimate about a population by writing and solving a proportion.

2 EXAMPLE Real-World Problem Solving

Quality Control From 20,000 calculators produced, a manufacturer takes a random sample of 500 calculators. The sample has 3 defective calculators. Estimate the total number of defective calculators.

$$\frac{\text{defective sample calculators}}{\text{sample calculators}} = \frac{\text{defective calculators}}{\text{calculators}}$$ Write a proportion.

$$\frac{3}{500} = \frac{n}{20,000}$$ Substitute.

$$3(20,000) = 500n$$ Write cross products.

$$\frac{3(20,000)}{500} = \frac{500n}{500}$$ Divide each side by 500.

$$120 = n$$ Simplify.

● Estimate: About 120 calculators are defective.

✓ **Check Understanding** Example 2

2. Use the data in the table below.

Calculator Samples

Sample	Number Sampled	Number Defective
A	500	3
B	200	2
C	50	0

a. Using Sample B, how many of 20,000 calculators would you estimate to be defective? **200 calculators**
b. **Reasoning** Would you expect an estimate based on Sample C to be more accurate or less accurate than one based on Sample B? Explain. **See left.**
c. Explain why you would take a sample rather than counting or surveying an entire population. **See left.**

2b. Less accurate; a larger sample is likely to be more representative of the population.

2c. The entire population might be too large to be surveyed. Also, the testing might be destructive, as would occur in testing light-bulb life.

In Example 2, you can think of the sample as giving an experimental probability $(\frac{3}{500} = 0.006)$. Then you can multiply this probability by the total number of calculators $(0.006 \cdot 20,000)$ to estimate the total number of defective calculators.

670 Chapter 12 Data Analysis and Probability

Reaching All Students

| Below Level Find out whether any students have been part of a survey. Discuss what kinds of questions the survey asked. | Advanced Learners Ask: *You use a survey to buy sport drinks for Track and Field Day. You run out of the flavor that your survey showed was the least popular. What happened?* See back of book. | Auditory Learners See note on page 670. Error Prevention See note on page 670. |

EXERCISES

For more exercises, see *Extra Practice*.

Practice and Problem Solving

A Practice by Example **Sports** You want to find how popular basketball is at your school.
State whether each survey plan describes a good sample. Explain.

Example 1
(page 669)

1–3. See margin.

1. Interview the 10 tallest students in the school.

2. Interview 20 students after picking their ID numbers at random.

3. Interview 30 students watching a basketball game.

Example 2
(page 670)

4. Quality Control A worker takes 100 eggs at random from a
shipment of 120,000 eggs. The worker finds that four eggs are bad.
Estimate the total number of bad eggs. **4,800 eggs**

5. Estimation Of 75 pairs of jeans, 7 have flaws. Estimate how many
of 24,000 pairs of jeans are flawed. **2,240 pairs**

B Apply Your Skills

You want to find which restaurants in your city are most popular.
State whether each survey plan describes a good sample. Explain.

8. Not a good sample;
restaurant critics may
be looking for things
the general public pays
little attention to.

10. No; the sample is
biased toward students
who use the gym.

6. Choose people to interview at random from the city phone book.
A good sample, since there is little bias built into it.

7. Interview every fifth person leaving a restaurant in the city.
See margin.

8. Interview all the restaurant critics in the state. See left.

9. Error Analysis Eight of the 32 students in your math class have
a cold. The school population is 450. A student estimates that
112 students in the school have a cold. **a–b. See back of book.**
a. Why is your math class not representative of the population?
b. Describe a survey plan you could use to better estimate the
number of students who have a cold.

10. Reasoning You survey every fifth student leaving volleyball
practice. Of those surveyed, 92% support a proposal to buy
new bleachers for the gym. Should you report that there is
overwhelming support for the proposal? Explain. See above left.

C Challenge

11. Open-Ended Describe a survey question, a population, and a sample
you could use to make an estimate. **Check students' work.**

12. Writing in Math From 50,000 computer chips produced, you
sample 250 chips and find that 0.8% are defective. Explain how
you could estimate the total number of defective chips.
Find 0.8% of 50,000.
0.008 · 50,000 = 400 defective chips (estimate)

Test Prep

Multiple Choice

13. Out of 6,000 radios tested, 12 are defective. What is the estimated
total number of defective radios in a group of 250,000? **D**
   A. 60   **B.** 120   **C.** 200   **D.** 500

12-8 Random Samples and Surveys **671**

---

1. Not a good sample; tall
students are more likely
to be basketball players
than other students.

2. This is a good sample,
since there is no bias
built into the sample.

3. Not a good sample; it

excludes students not
interested in basketball.

7. Not a good sample; it
excludes people who
dislike that particular
restaurant.

GPS Use the Guided Problem
Solving worksheet with
Exercise 5.

Assignment Guide

1 Objective 1
   A B Core 1–3, 6–8
   C Extension 11

2 Objective 2
   A B Core 4, 5, 9, 10
   C Extension 12

Test Prep 13–16
Mixed Review 17–24

Practice 12-8 *Random Samples and Surveys*

A school has 800 students. Two
random surveys are conducted to
determine students' favorite sport.
Use the data in the table to estimate
the total number of students who
prefer each sport.

Sample	Number Sampled	Favorite sport Basketball	Football	Baseball
A	40	16	14	10
B	50	22	16	12

1. basketball based on Sample A 320 students

2. basketball based on Sample B 352 students

3. baseball based on Sample A 200 students

4. baseball based on Sample B 192 students

You want to find out if a school bond issue for a new computer center is
likely to pass in the next election. State whether each survey plan
describes a good sample. Explain your reasoning.

5. You interview people coming out of a computer store in your town.
The views of people coming out of a computer
store may not represent the views of other voters.
This is not a good sample because it is not random.

6. You choose people to interview at random from the city telephone
book.
The city telephone book may cover more than one
school district. It would also include people who do
not vote. This is not a good sample because it does
not represent the population.

7. You interview every tenth person leaving each voting place in your
school district.
This is a good sample. It is selected at random from
the population you want to study.

Enrichment 12-8 *Coin Toss Simulation*

You can use a graphing calculator to simulate the toss of a coin. Highlight
randInt(in the **MATH PRB** menu. Press **ENTER**. After the parenthesis,
type "0, 99" and press **ENTER** repeatedly to create a list of random integers
between 0 and 99.

To simulate a coin toss, use your calculator to generate a list of random
numbers. You can treat each random number as the result of a coin toss using
the following rule: A number less than 50 will represent "heads," and a
number greater than or equal to 50 will represent "tails."

Here is a sample of 40 randomly generated numbers:

25	71	47	46	66	13	63	36	1	59
22	7	83	25	72	24	73	22	59	81
14	9	40	64	81	72	2	38	21	9
92	10	93	34	36	45	53	18	23	75

1. The probability of getting heads when tossing a coin is $\frac{1}{2}$. If a coin is
tossed 10 times, how many times can you expect heads to result?
5 times
Check students' work for exercises 2–4 and 6.

2. Toss a coin 10 times by hand. What results did you get?
heads _____   tails _____

3. Use your calculator to simulate 10 coin tosses, or use the first row of the
sample given above. Write the results.
heads _____   tails _____

4. How do the results compare to what you expected?

5. Do you think the results of the tosses will be closer to the expected
probability if you increase the number of tosses?
yes

6. Test your answer. Use your calculator to simulate 40 coin tosses, or use
the sample given above. Write the results.
heads _____   tails _____

7. You toss one coin 40 times and 40 coins one time each. Are the
expectations the same? Explain.
Answers may vary. Sample: Yes; tossing 40 coins at
once results in 40 independent events, the same
as if you tossed one coin 40 times.

Lesson Quiz 12-8

Solve.

1. To find out the type of music the general population prefers, you survey people at random at a local art museum. Does the survey plan describe a good sample? **Not a good sample; it includes only people who visit the art museum.**

2. Of 80 sweaters, 6 have flaws. Estimate how many of 38,000 sweaters have flaws. **2,850 sweaters**

✓ Chapter Checkpoint 2

To check understanding of Lessons 12-5 to 12-8:

Checkpoint Quiz 2 (p. 672)

📁 Teaching Resources

Checkpoint Quiz 2 (also in Prentice Hall Assessment System)

👥 Reaching All Students

Reading and Math Literacy 12C

Spanish versions available.

Reteaching 12-8 *Random Samples and Surveys*

From 8,000 sports shirts produced, a manufacturer takes several random samples. Use the data in the table to estimate the total number of defective shirts based on Sample A.

Sample	Number Sampled	Number Defective
A	250	6
B	400	8
C	500	9

Set up a proportion.

$\frac{\text{defective sample shirts}}{\text{sample shirts}} = \frac{\text{defective shirts}}{\text{shirts produced}}$

$\frac{6}{250} = \frac{x}{8,000}$ Substitute.

$250x = 6(8,000)$ Find cross products.

$250x = 48,000$ Simplify.

$\frac{250x}{250} = \frac{48,000}{250}$ Divide each side by 250.

$x = 192$ Simplify.

The total number of defective shirts based on Sample A is about 192.

Use the data in the table above to estimate the number of defective shirts out of 8,000 based on each sample.

1. Sample B **160 shirts** proportion used: $\frac{8}{400} = \frac{x}{8,000}$

2. Sample C **144 shirts** proportion used: $\frac{9}{500} = \frac{x}{8,000}$

From 12,000 computer games produced, a manufacturer takes several random samples. Use the data in the table to estimate the total number of defective games based on each sample.

Sample	Number Sampled	Number Defective
A	400	16
B	800	30
C	500	19

3. Sample A **480 games**
proportion: $\frac{16}{400} = \frac{x}{12,000}$

4. Sample B **450 games**
proportion: $\frac{30}{800} = \frac{x}{12,000}$

5. Sample C **456 games**
proportion: $\frac{19}{500} = \frac{x}{12,000}$

6. All 3 samples combined **459 games**
proportion: $\frac{65}{1,700} = \frac{x}{12,000}$

---

14. All students at a local elementary school eat lunch at school. You want to find how many students bring their lunches. Which group would be a good sample? **I**

F. students on one school bus **G.** one first-grade classroom
H. the cafeteria workers **I.** all third-grade classrooms

Short Response For Exercises 15 and 16, **(a)** state whether each survey plan describes a good sample. **(b)** Explain your answer. **15–16. See back of book.**

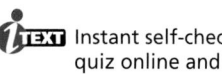

Take It to the NET
Online lesson quiz at
www.PHSchool.com
Web Code: ada-1208

15. You want to find how often teens get haircuts. You plan to survey customers in a barbershop.

16. You want to find students' favorite foods. You plan to survey every fourth student leaving the library.

Mixed Review

Lesson 12-7 Use the survey data at the right. Write each experimental probability as a fraction.

18. $\frac{5}{26}$

17. P(no pets) $\frac{9}{26}$ **18.** P(two or more pets) See left.

19. P(one pet) $\frac{12}{26}$, or $\frac{6}{13}$ **20.** P(at least one pet) $\frac{17}{26}$

Students' Pets

Number of Pets	Number of Students
0	9
1	12
2 or more	5

Lesson 12-6 **21.** How many combinations of four flowers can you choose from a bouquet of one dozen different flowers? **495 combinations**

Lesson 10-3 **Geometry** Find the area of each circle. Give the exact area and area rounded to the nearest whole number of units. Use 3.14 for π.

22. $r = 24$ cm
576π cm^2; 1,809 cm^2

23. $d = 45$ in.
506.25π in.^{2}; 1,590 in.^{2}

24. $r = 50$ mi
$2,500\pi$ mi^2; 7,850 mi^2

✓ Checkpoint Quiz 2 Lessons 12-5 through 12-8

Instant self-check quiz online and on CD-ROM

1. A bag contains 10 cards labeled 1–10. You draw one card and then another, without replacing the first card before drawing the second. Find the probability of drawing two even numbers. $\frac{2}{9}$

2. a. A club of 20 students chooses a president and a vice-president. How many different outcomes are possible? **380 outcomes**

b. A club of 20 students chooses two committee members. How many different committees may be chosen? **190 committees**

3. A hockey player attempts 15 goals and makes 2. Find the experimental probability of making a goal. Predict the number of goals the player will make in the next game if the player attempts 23 goals. $\frac{2}{15}$; **3 goals**

4. Of 450 oranges from a crop of 50,000 oranges, 85 are "premium." Estimate the number of premium oranges in the whole crop.
9,444 premium oranges

Alternative Assessment

Ask students to find results of surveys in newspapers or magazines. Have them identify the sample size and the population that is represented by the sample. Have volunteers share their findings with the class.

Test Prep

📁 Resources

For additional practice with a variety of test item formats:

• Test Prep, p. 683
• Test-Taking Strategies, p. 678
• Test-Taking Strategies With Transparencies

Using Random Numbers

For Use With Lesson 12-9

Some calculators and computer programs can generate *random numbers*. You can use random numbers for simulations.

To make a list of random integers on a graphing calculator, highlight **randInt** in the MATH **PRB** menu. Press ENTER, and enter "0,9999." Press ENTER repeatedly for a list of four-digit random numbers. Note that the calculator suppresses any zeros at the front of a number. For example, 45 represents the four-digit number 0045.

EXAMPLE

There is a 30% probability of being stopped by a red light at each of four traffic lights. Use a simulation to find an experimental probability of being stopped by at least two red lights.

Use your calculator to generate 20 random 4-digit numbers.

There is a 30% chance of a red light, so let three of the ten digits represent a red light. For this simulation let 1, 2, and 3 represent a red light. Let 4, 5, 6, 7, 8, 9, and 0 represent a yellow or green light.

5186	8918	4275	4285
8124	9619	2517	9964
0912	2759	2329	1666
8938	0357	6755	2227
0201	6325	1905	6885

Any group with two or more of the digits 1, 2, or 3 represents being stopped by at least two red lights. There are seven such groups in this list.

P(at least two red lights) $= \frac{7}{20}$, or 35%

EXERCISES

1. Use the information in the example. What is the experimental probability of being stopped by exactly three red lights? By four red lights? **10%; 0**

2. What would be the result in the example if you had chosen 8, 9, and 0 instead of 1, 2, and 3 to represent red lights? **40%**

3. **a.** Make a new random number list by using randInt(0,999) in place of randInt(0,9999). How many digits are in each random number? **3 digits**
   b. How can you make a 6-digit random number? **randInt (0,999999) enter**

4. **Writing in Math** Suppose the probability of being stopped by a red light at each of four lights is 50%. Describe how you would use random numbers to find the probability of getting a red light at two or more lights. **Let an even digit represent being stopped by a red light. Generate 4-digit random numbers. Look for groups with 2 or more even digits.**

5. About 20% of high school students in the United States say they would like to be president. Use random numbers to find the probability that at least three of the next five high school students you see would like to be president. **Check students' work.**

Technology

Using Random Numbers

This Technology investigation shows students how to use random numbers generated by a calculator for simulations that yield experimental probabilities.

Resources

Students may use any graphing calculator.

Teaching Notes

EXAMPLE Teaching Tip

A random-number generator provides a tool for constructing simulations. In Example 1, you use random numbers to represent experimental results. You use 4-digit numbers because there are 4 traffic lights. The more 4-digit random numbers you test, the more confidence you can place in your experimental probability.

EXAMPLE Teaching Tip

Help students understand that on a computer they can easily run a simulation like this a great many times and compile the results. They can put much confidence in results from a large number of trials. However, they also have to understand all the assumptions behind the simulation.

Inclusion

Pair a student who may not be able to operate a calculator with a partner who has no such difficulties. Have them work together to complete the Exercises.

Additional Example

Describe what you would do differently in the example if 30% were replaced by 40%. **Select four digits to each represent a red light.**

1. Plan

Lesson Preview

 Check Skills You'll Need

Frequency Tables and Line Plots
Lesson 12-1: Example 1;
Exercises 1–6.
Extra Practice, p. 755.

Lesson Resources

📁 **Teaching Resources**
Practice, Reteaching, Enrichment

👥 **Reaching All Students**
Practice Workbook 12-9
Spanish Practice Workbook 12-9
Guided Problem Solving 12-9
Technology Activities 35

⏰ **Presentation Assistant Plus!**
Transparencies and PowerPoint™
• Check Skills You'll Need 12-9
• Additional Examples 12-9
• Student Edition Answers 12-9
• Lesson Quiz 12-9
PH Presentation Pro CD-ROM 12-9

ASSESSMENT SYSTEM

Computer Test Generator CD-ROM

💻 **Technology**
Resource Pro® CD-ROM
Computer Test Generator CD-ROM
PH Presentation Pro CD-ROM

💻 **www.PHSchool.com**
Student Site
• Teacher Web Code: adk-5500
• Graphing Calculator, Procedure 15
• Self-grading Lesson Quiz
PH SuccessNet Teacher Center
• Lesson Planner
• Resources

Plus 📘iTEXT

What You'll Learn

OBJECTIVE 1 To solve problems by simulation

. . . And Why

To solve real-world problems involving sports

✔ **Check Skills You'll Need**

Create a frequency table showing the number of times each letter of the alphabet appears in the sentence below.

A simulation is a model of a real experience.
See back of book.
❓ For help, go to Lesson 12-1.

---

2. Answers may vary. Sample: Use two sets of 5 cards numbered 1 to 5. Selecting 1–4 indicates "makes the shot" and selecting 5 indicates "misses the shot." Perform a number of trials.

📘**iTEXT** Interactive lesson includes instant self-check, tutorials, and activities.

Math Strategies in Action
Do you dream of flying your own airplane? Can you picture yourself in a space shuttle? Flight simulators help pilots train for real flying. Simulators are models of the real experience.

You can use simulations to investigate real-world problems. First develop a model, and then conduct an experiment.

1 EXAMPLE Real-World 🌐 Problem Solving

Basketball As time is running out in the basketball game, your team is behind by one point. You are fouled and go to the free-throw line. If you miss the shot, your team loses. If you make it, the score is tied and you get another shot. If you miss the second shot, the game ends in a tie. If you make both shots, your team wins. Your average at free throws is four out of five. Simulate the situation and find an experimental probability for each event.
  a. You tie the game.   b. You win the game.   c. You tie or win the game.

Read and Understand

Think about the problem.

1. Based on your average, what is the probability of making one free throw? $\frac{4}{5}$

2. What methods could you use to simulate the problem?
   See left.

Plan and Solve

You can use a spinner to simulate the problem. Construct a spinner with five congruent sections. Make four of the sections blue and one of them red. The blue section represents *makes the shot* and the red section represents *misses the shot.* Each spin represents one shot.

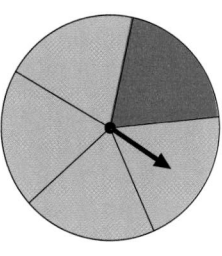

674 Chapter 12 Data Analysis and Probability

✔ **Ongoing Assessment and Intervention**

Before the Lesson	**During the Lesson**	**After the Lesson**
Diagnose prerequisite skills using:	Monitor progress using:	Assess knowledge using:
• Check Skills You'll Need	• Check Understanding	• Lesson Quiz
	• Additional Examples	• Computer Test Generator
	• Test Prep	CD-ROM

3. How many spins will you make for each experiment?
One or two spins, depending on the result of the first spin.
4. How many experiments will you do?
many—perhaps 100

Use the results given in the table below. "B" stands for blue and "R" stands for red. Note that there is no second shot when the first shot is a miss (R).

Results of 100 Experiments

BR	BB	BB	BB	BB	BR	BB	BB	BB	BB
BR	BB	BR	BB	R	BB	R	BB	BR	BB
BB	BB	BB	R	BB	BB	BB	BB	BB	BB
BB	R	BB	BB	BB	BB	BB	BB	BB	BB
BB	R	BR	BR	BB	BB	BB	R	BB	BR
BB	BR	BB	BB	BB	R	BB	R	BB	BB
BB	R	BR	BB	BB	R	BB	BR	BB	R
BB	BB	BB	BB	BB	BB	BB	BR	BB	BB
BB	R	BR	BB	R	BB	BB	BB	R	BB
BR	BR	BB	R	BB	R	BB	BB	BB	BB

Make a frequency table.

Misses the first shot (R)	Makes the first shot and misses the second shot (BR)	Makes the first shot and makes the second shot (BB)
⁄⁄⁄⁄ ⁄⁄⁄⁄ ⁄⁄⁄⁄ I	⁄⁄⁄⁄ ⁄⁄⁄⁄ ⁄⁄⁄⁄	⁄⁄⁄⁄ ⁄⁄⁄⁄ ⁄⁄⁄⁄ ⁄⁄⁄⁄ ⁄⁄⁄⁄ ⁄⁄⁄⁄ ⁄⁄⁄⁄ ⁄⁄⁄⁄ ⁄⁄⁄⁄ ⁄⁄⁄⁄ ⁄⁄⁄⁄ ⁄⁄⁄⁄ ⁄⁄⁄⁄ IIII

5. Find each experimental probability.
   a. Your team ties the game. 15%
   b. Your team wins the game. 69%
   c. Your team ties or wins the game. 84%

[**Look Back and Check**]

Simulations can give different results. You may find a different probability if you do another simulation. The more experiments you do, the closer the results of different simulations are likely to be.

✓ **Check Understanding**

6. Continue the simulation with another 100 experiments. Combine the results with the results of the first 100 experiments.
Check students' work.
7. Based on the second simulation, what is the probability that your team wins? Check students' work.

2. Teach

Professional Development

Math Background

There is often a difference between the theoretical and an experimental probability of an event. As you increase the number of trials, the experimental probability gets closer to the theoretical probability.

Teaching Notes

1 EXAMPLE **Error Prevention**
Make sure students see the difference between the number of trials and the number of shots. While there were 100 trials, many of the trials involved two shots, so the total number of shots is greater then 100.

Diversity
Have a volunteer student from another country explain or teach a game that is popular in his or her country of origin. Then have students work together in groups to identify and simulate a situation in the game.

Inclusion
Some students may have trouble answering the Questions because of reading or comprehension difficulties. Organize the class into groups. Have students read and discuss the problems before they solve them.

PowerPoint
Additional Examples

1 A softball player has an average of getting a base hit 2 times in every 7 times at bat. What is an experimental probability that she will get a base hit the next time she is at bat? Check students' work.

Closure

Have students explain why using a *simulation* is a helpful problem-solving technique.
See back of book.

👥 **Reaching All Students**

Below Level Ask students who play team sports whether they have ever participated in a scrimmage or practice game. Have volunteers explain the purpose of such games.

Advanced Learners Ask: *What are some aspects of shooting a free throw in a big game that practice (simulation) cannot duplicate?*
Answers may vary. Sample: crowd noise, stress, fatigue

Diversity
See note on page 675.
Inclusion
See note on page 675.

Assignment Guide

1 Objective 1
Ⓐ Ⓑ Core 1–9
Ⓒ Extension 10, 11

Test Prep 12–14
Mixed Review 15–20

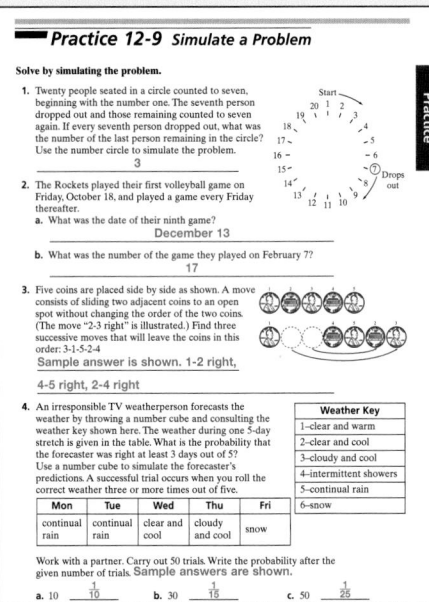

EXERCISES

🔖 *For more exercises, see Extra Practice.*

Practice and Problem Solving

Ⓐ **Practice by Example**

Example 1
(page 674)

Solve by simulating the problem.

1. What is the experimental probability that exactly three children in a family of five children will be boys? Assume that $P(\text{boy}) = P(\text{girl})$. **See margin.**

2. You take a three-question multiple-choice test. Each question has four choices. You don't know any of the answers. What is the experimental probability that you will guess exactly two out of three correctly? **See back of book.**

Ⓑ **Apply Your Skills**

Solve using any strategy.

3. Thirteen of 25 students are going on a field trip. Six students are traveling in a van. What is the theoretical probability that a student chosen at random from those going on the trip is *not* traveling in the van? $\frac{7}{13}$

4. A student draws a card at random from the cards below. What is the theoretical probability that the student will draw a card showing A or B? $\frac{3}{11}$

5. **Prices** The original cost of a jacket is $72. During a sale, the store reduces the jacket price by 25%. After the sale, the store raises the reduced jacket price by 25%. What is the price of the jacket after it is increased? **$67.50**

6. **Geometry** A farmer uses 24 yd of fencing to make a rectangular pen. The pen is 6 yd longer than it is wide. What are the dimensions of the pen? **3 yd by 9 yd**

7. **Reasoning** The circumference of the peg is 3 in. Will the peg go through the hole? Explain. **Yes. Since circumference equals πd, $d = \frac{3 \text{ in.}}{\pi} \approx \frac{3 \text{ in.}}{3.14}$, which is less than 1 in.**

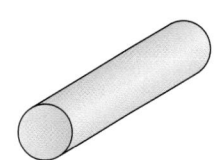 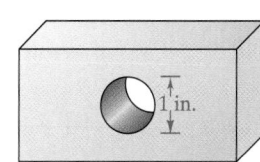

8. You toss five coins. What is the theoretical probability that you will get five heads? $\frac{1}{32}$

9. Many sweepstakes contests have an elimination round. In the elimination round, half of the entrants are chosen at random to go on to the final round. Then one person is chosen as the winner. What is the theoretical probability that a person who enters a contest with 10,000 entrants will be the winner? $\frac{1}{10,000}$

Strategies

- Account for All Possibilities
- Draw a Diagram
- Look for a Pattern
- Make a Model
- Make a Table
- Simplify the Problem
- Simulate the Problem
- Solve by Graphing
- Try, Test, Revise
- Use Multiple Strategies
- Work Backward
- Write an Equation
- Write a Proportion

676 **Chapter 12** Data Analysis and Probability

GPS Use the Guided Problem Solving worksheet with Exercise 3.

1. Answers may vary. Sample: Simulate the problem by tossing a coin. Let heads be a girl and tails be a boy. Toss the coin 100 times and organize the results into 20 groups of five. Count the number of groups with exactly three tails. Divide this number by 20 to get the experimental probability.

 **Challenge**

11. Answers may vary.
Sample: Simulate the problem by constructing a spinner with four congruent sections. Label the sections "1," "2," "3," and "4" to represent the four prizes. Spin 100 times and organize the results into 10 groups of 10. Count the number of groups with all four numbers. Divide this number by 10 to get the experimental probability.

10. On a TV game show, you try to win a prize that is hidden behind one of three doors. After you choose a door, but before it is opened, the host opens one of the other doors, behind which there is no prize. You can then switch to the remaining closed door or stay with your original choice. **a–c. See back of book.**

   a. Find the experimental probability of winning if your strategy is to stay with your original choice. (*Hint:* Simulate by using one marked index card and two unmarked index cards.)

   b. Find the experimental probability of winning if your strategy is to switch to the other door.

   c. Writing in Math Should you stay or switch in this game? Explain.

11. Each box of Tastycrunch cereal contains a prize. There are four possible prizes. The prizes are equally likely. You purchase 10 boxes of Tastycrunch. Simulate the problem to find the experimental probability that you will get all four prizes.
See above left.

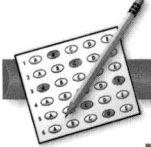

Test Prep

Multiple Choice

12. Raul has 4 pairs of shoes to choose from each day. He wants to find the experimental probability of choosing his favorite pair of shoes at random. Which simulation should Raul use? **C**
   A. Tossing a coin
   B. Rolling a number cube
   C. Spinning a spinner with 4 congruent sections
   D. Drawing chips from a bag with 8 different-colored chips

13. Angela conducts a simulation in which she gets a favorable outcome 230 times out of 500 trials. What is the experimental probability of a favorable outcome? **H**
   F. 2.3%   **G.** 23%   **H.** 46%   **I.** 230%

14. Jerome constructs a spinner that has 5 congruent sections. He writes "yes" in one section and "no" in the other four sections. Jerome uses this spinner to simulate making free-throw shots. What experimental probability is he most likely to find? **C**
   A. 1%   **B.** 5%   **C.** 20%   **D.** 80%

Take It to the NET
Online lesson quiz at **www.PHSchool.com**
Web Code: ada-1209

Mixed Review

Lesson 12-8   **15. Quality Control** Six out of every 80 wrenches are found to be defective. For a batch of 3,200 wrenches, estimate the number of wrenches that will *not* have any flaw. **2,960 wrenches**

Lesson 11-5   **16. Geometry** Each side of a square kite is to be 20 in. long. To the nearest inch, what length of wood do you need to make the diagonals? **57 in.**

Lesson 11-1   **Estimate to the nearest integer.**
   17. $\sqrt{15}$ **4**   **18.** $\sqrt{10}$ **3**   **19.** $\sqrt{50}$ **7**   **20.** $-\sqrt{82}$ **−9**

4. Assess

 **Lesson Quiz 12-9**

1. You and a friend play a game in which you each toss a coin. You score a point for each head and your friend scores a point for each tail. The first person to score ten points wins. The score is 8 to 6 in your favor. Describe a simulation that completes the game and use it to find an experimental probability that your friend will win. **Check students' work.**

Test Prep

Resources
For additional practice with a variety of test item formats:
• Test Prep, p. 683
• Test-Taking Strategies, p. 678
• Test-Taking Strategies With Transparencies

Reteaching 12-9 *Simulate a Problem*

Each carton of monster yogurt contains a card with a monster cartoon character on it. Each of the 6 characters is equally likely. You purchase 8 cartons of yogurt. Find the probability that you get at least 5 different cards. Simulate the problem.

Since there are 6 characters, you can use a number cube to simulate the problem. A trial consists of rolling the cube 8 times. The results of 5 trials are shown in the table.

Trial 1	6 6 1 5 1 6 6 4
Trial 2	1 6 2 4 4 2 6 5
Trial 3	5 6 3 1 1 6 2 1
Trial 4	6 2 1 2 3 3 2 6
Trial 5	3 5 4 4 3 2 4 6

In trials 1, 4, and 5, four different numbers were rolled, representing 4 different cards. In trials 2 and 3, five different numbers were rolled, representing 5 different cards.

So, at least 5 different cards were found in 2 of the 5 trials and the probability is $\frac{2}{5}$ or 40%. Note that "at least 5" means 5 or 6.

Use the table above combined with the one on the right to find each probability based on 10 trials. Write each probability as a percent.

Trial 6	5 6 1 1 5 1 1 3
Trial 7	2 4 4 6 5 6 2 6
Trial 8	2 4 4 2 2 6 6 4
Trial 9	1 4 6 4 4 2 3 4
Trial 10	4 4 4 2 4 5 3 6

1. Complete the frequency table for the ten trials.
2. Find the probability that you get exactly 4 different cards.
   50%
3. Find the probability that you get exactly 5 different cards.
   40%
4. Find the probability that you get at least 4 different cards.
   90%
5. Find the probability that you get at least 5 different cards.
   40%
6. Find the probability that you get no more than 4 different cards.
   60%

Number of Different Cards	Tally	Frequency (number of trials)
3	I	1
4	ℍℍ	5
5	IIII	4
6		0

Alternative Assessment

Have small groups of students write problems like the Example that can be solved with a simulation. Have groups exchange problems and solve using a simulation.

Answering True/False Questions

In this strategy, students find counterexamples to help answer true/false questions.

Resources

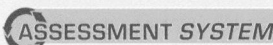
ASSESSMENT *SYSTEM*

Test-Taking Strategies With Transparencies
• Transparency 12
• Practice sheet, p. 12

Teaching Notes

Help students understand that if part of a statement is false, the whole statement is false.

Test-Taking Strategies With Transparencies

Name _____ Class _____ Date _____

Chapter 12: Answering True/False Questions
Exercises

Determine whether each statement is true or false. Explain your answer.

1. True or False? When x is a positive integer, then x^3 is also positive.
   _____

2. True or False? The expression x^0 equals y^0 for all nonzero values of x and y.
   _____

3. True or False? The expression 5^9 equals $5^4 \times 5^2$.
   _____

4. True or False? The value of x^3 is never less than the value of x^2.
   _____

5. True or False? The expression $(x^5y^4)^3$ is equal to $x^{15}y^{12}$ for all nonzero values of x and t.
   _____

6. True or False? The expression $(x - y)^2$ equals $x^2 - y^2$ for all values of x and y.
   _____

7. True or False? The expression $\frac{9^x}{9^y}$ equals 81.
   _____

8. True or False? The expression 9.8×10^{-4} is greater than 6.4×10^{-3}.
   _____

9. True or False? If you toss a penny four times and get four tails, then on the fifth toss $P(\text{tails}) \approx 1$.
   _____

10. True or False? The expression 4×6^3 equals $2^5 \times 3^3$.
    _____

11. True or False? If $270,000 \times 21,000 = 5.67 \times 10^P$, then $P = 7$.
    _____

12 Pre-Algebra   Test-Taking Strategies

In true/false questions, the entire statement must be true. Otherwise, the statement is false. A statement may be true for many cases and false for just one. This one case is called a *counterexample.* If you think a statement is false, try to find a counterexample.

1 EXAMPLE

True or False? The mean of a set of values is always different from the median of the same set of values.

Choose a simple example that has an odd number of values, and that is "evenly balanced" above and below the middle value.

   8, 10, 12, 14, and 16

Find the median: 8, 10, **12**, 14, 16
Find the mean: $(8 + 10 + 12 + 14 + 16) \div 5 = 12$

● This is a counterexample to the statement, so the statement is false.

2 EXAMPLE

Suppose two events are independent and the probability of each is less than 1. Is the following statement true or false? The probability that the two events occur is less than the probability of either event.

Since the events are independent, $P(A \text{ and } B) = P(A) \cdot P(B)$. $P(A)$ and $P(B)$ are both less than 1. The product of two (proper) fractions is less than either fraction. Test some cases:

$$\frac{1}{2} \times \frac{1}{4} = \frac{1}{8} \qquad \frac{1}{8} \text{ is less than both } \frac{1}{2} \text{ and } \frac{1}{4}.$$

$$\frac{3}{4} \times \frac{1}{2} = \frac{3}{8} \qquad \frac{3}{8} \text{ is less than both } \frac{3}{4} \text{ and } \frac{1}{2}.$$

It seems likely that $P(A \text{ and } B) < P(A)$ and $P(A \text{ and } B) < P(B)$ are
● always true.

EXERCISES

Determine whether each statement is *true* or *false*. Explain.

1. The median of a data set is always one of the data values.
   False; in the data set 10, 20, 22, 28, 31, 44, the median is 25, which is not in the set.

2. The number of permutations of two items from a data set is always two times the number of combinations when taking two objects at a time from the same data set. See right.

3. In large data sets (1,000 or more values), the mean is always one of the data values. False; it may or may not be one of the data values.

2. True; the number of combinations when you take objects two at a time is the number of permutations divided by $_2P_2$, or 2.

Chapter Review

Vocabulary

box-and-whisker plot (p. 635)
combination (p. 660)
counting principle (p. 650)
dependent events (p. 656)
experimental probability (p. 665)
frequency table (p. 630)

independent events (p. 654)
line plot (p. 631)
permutation (p. 659)
population (p. 669)
quartiles (p. 635)
random sample (p. 669)

range (p. 631)
sample (p. 669)
sample space (p. 650)
simulation (p. 665)
theoretical probability (p. 650)

 **Reading Math**
Understanding
Vocabulary

Choose the vocabulary term that correctly completes the sentence.

1. An arrangement in which order does not matter is a ___?___.
   combination

2. The part of a population used to make estimates about the entire population is a ___?___. sample

3. The ratio of the number of favorable outcomes to the number of possible outcomes is the ___?___ of an event. theoretical probability

4. An arrangement in which order is important is a ___?___. permutation

5. The difference between the greatest and the least values in a data set is the ___?___ of the data set. range

6. A listing of a data set that shows the number of times each data item occurs is a ___?___. frequency table

7. Events in which the first event *does* affect the second event are ___?___. dependent events

8. In a ___?___ each member of the population has an equal chance of being selected. random sample

Take It to the NET
Online vocabulary quiz
at www.PHSchool.com
Web Code: adj-1251

Skills and Concepts

12-1 Objectives

▼ To display data in frequency tables (p. 630)

▼ To display data in line plots (p. 631)

You can show data in a **frequency table,** which lists each data item with the number of times it occurs, or a **line plot,** which displays data with **X** marks on a number line. The **range** is the difference between the greatest and the least values in a set of data.

Display each set of data in a frequency table. 9–10. See margin.

9. 11 10 12 10 12 11 13 12 11 9 12 10

10. 47 48 46 47 45 49 46 48 50 48 46 49

Draw a line plot for each frequency table. Find the range.

11.
Number	1	2	3	4	5	6
Frequency	6	4	5	2	3	1

12.
Number	1	2	3	4	5	6
Frequency	2	8	6	7	3	1

11–12. See margin.

9.
Number	Frequency
9	1
10	3
11	3
12	4
13	1

10.
Number	Frequency
45	1
46	3
47	2
48	3
49	2
50	1

11.
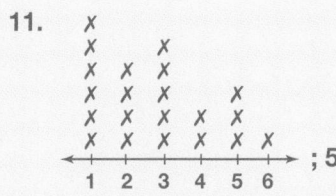
; 5

Resources

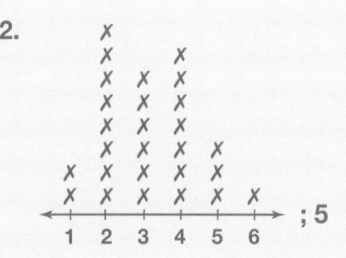

12.
; 5

13.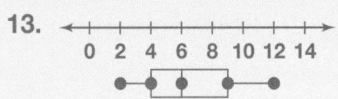

14.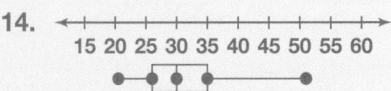

15. It increased gradually.

16. Answers may vary. Sample: Break the vertical axis and mark a scale from 50 to 60 above the break.

12-2 Objectives

▼ To make box-and-whisker plots (p. 635)

▼ To analyze data in box-and-whisker plots (p. 636)

A **box-and-whisker plot** displays data items below a number line. **Quartiles** divide the data into four parts. The median is the middle quartile. You can compare two sets of related data by making two box-and-whisker plots on one number line.

Make a box-and-whisker plot for each set of data. 13–14. See margin.

13. 6 9 6 5 8 2 3 9 4 8 5 7 12 9 4

14. 21 35 26 32 24 30 29 38 27 32 51

12-3 Objectives

▼ To recognize the use of breaks in the scales of graphs (p. 642)

▼ To recognize the use of different scales (p. 643)

A graph can give a different impression if a break is used in the scale. A graph can be misleading when a scale is distorted.

For Exercises 15 and 16, use the graph showing wheat production.
15–16. See margin.

15. What does the graph suggest about U.S. wheat production?

16. Explain how you could redraw the graph so that production seems to be increasing dramatically.

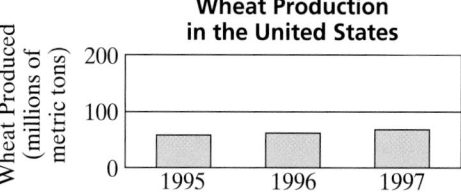

12-4 Objectives

▼ To use a tree diagram and the Counting Principle to count possible choices (p. 649)

▼ To find theoretical probability by counting outcomes (p. 650)

A **sample space** is all the possible outcomes of an event. Use a tree diagram or the **Counting Principle** to count the number of outcomes. You can count outcomes to help find **theoretical probability.**

17. Volunteers have made a large number of sandwiches for a school party. The sandwiches come on white bread, on whole wheat bread, or on a roll. Each contains one of five fillings: turkey, chicken, egg salad, cheese, or peanut butter.
  a. How many different types of sandwich are possible? 15 types
  b. There are 20 of each type of sandwich. You receive one sandwich at random. Find the theoretical probability of getting a sandwich on bread with a meat filling. $\frac{4}{15}$

12-5 Objectives

▼ To calculate probabilities of independent events (p. 654)

▼ To calculate probabilities of dependent events (p. 656)

Independent events are events for which the occurrence of one event does not affect the probability of the occurrence of the other. If A and B are independent events, the probability that both A and B occur is $P(A \text{ and } B) = P(A) \cdot P(B)$.

Dependent events are events for which the occurrence of one event affects the probability of the occurrence of the other. If A and B are dependent events, the probability that A and then B occur is $P(A, \text{ then } B) = P(A) \cdot P(B \text{ after } A)$.

You select a card at random from those at the right. Find the probability of each event.

18. You select E, replace the card, and then select V. $\frac{2}{25}$

19. You select T, do not replace the card, and then select N. $\frac{1}{20}$

12-6 Objectives
▼ To use permutations (p. 659)
▼ To use combinations (p. 660)

An arrangement in which order is important is a **permutation.** An arrangement in which order does not matter is a **combination.**

Tell whether each question is a *permutation* or a *combination* problem. Explain. Then find each answer. 20–21. See margin.

20. In how many different ways can five people line up for a photo?

21. How many groups of three pens can you select from a box of twelve pens?

12-7 and 12-9 Objectives
▼ To find experimental probability (p. 665)
▼ To use simulations (p. 665)
▼ To solve problems by simulation (p. 674)

Experimental probability is based on experimental data. You can use a simulation to model real-world problems.

Use the survey data at the right. Write each experimental probability as a fraction in simplest form.

22. P(one notebook) $\frac{9}{20}$

23. P(at least two notebooks) $\frac{1}{2}$

Notebooks in Students' Lockers

Number of Notebooks	Frequency
0	1
1	9
2	6
3 or more	4

24. You take a 3-question multiple-choice quiz. Each question has 3 choices. You don't know any of the answers. Use a simulation to find an experimental probability that you will guess exactly 2 out of 3 correctly. See margin.

12-8 Objectives
▼ To choose a sample for a survey of a population (p. 669)
▼ To make estimates about populations (p. 670)

A **population** is a group about which you want information. A **sample** is a part of the population you use to make estimates for the population. In a **random sample** each member of the population has an equal chance to be selected.

You want to find the favorite brand of in-line skates in your town. Does each survey plan describe a good sample? Explain.
25–26. See margin.

25. You interview students in your homeroom.

26. You interview every tenth student entering the building.

---

20. permutation, since order is important; 120 ways

21. combination, since order does not matter; 220 groups

24. Answers may vary. Sample: Simulate the problem by making a spinner with 3 congruent sections. Make one section red, to represent a correct answer. Spin 60 times and organize the results into 20 groups of 3. Count the number of groups with exactly 2 red spins. Divide this number by 20 to get the experimental probability.

25. Not a good sample; it includes people not in the town's skating population.

26. Not a good sample; it includes people not in the town's skating population.

681

Chapter Test

Take It to the NET
Online chapter test at
www.PHSchool.com
Web Code: ada-1252

For Exercises 1 and 2, use the box-and-whisker plot.

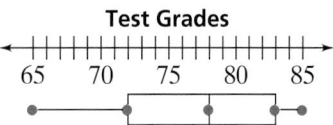

Test Grades

65   70   75   80   85

1. What is the median grade on the test? **78**

2. What is the range in grades? **20**

3. Make a box-and-whisker plot for the data. 75, 70, 80, 85, 85, 55, 60, 60, 65, 85, 75, 95, 50 **See margin.**

4. Use the data below. **a–b. See margin.**
   8, 4, 5, 1, 8, 4, 7, 9, 10, 5, 0, 5, 3, 4, 2
   a. Display the data in a frequency table.
   b. Display the data in a line plot.
   c. Find the range of the data. **10**

For Exercises 5 and 6, use the table. The table shows the money spent on movie tickets.
5–6. See back of book.

Year	Dollars (billions)
1994	5.6
1995	6.0
1996	6.3

5. Draw a graph that emphasizes the increase in money spent over time.

6. Draw a graph to suggest that the money spent has not changed much over time.

Use the word TRAIN. Find the probability of each event when a letter is drawn at random.

7. selecting an R, replacing it, and then selecting an N $\frac{1}{25}$

8. selecting an R, not replacing it, and then selecting an N $\frac{1}{20}$

9. a. Find the sample space for tossing 3 coins.
   b. Find the theoretical probability of tossing 2 heads and 1 tail. $\frac{3}{8}$

9a.
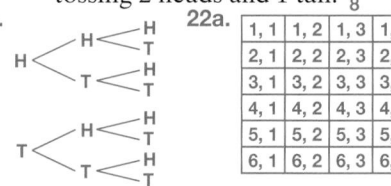

Simplify each expression.

10. $_3P_2$ **6**

11. $_5C_2$ **10**

Find the number of three-letter permutations you can make using each group of letters.

12. F, O, U, R **24**

13. L, U, N, C, H **60**

A student has 4 blue shirts and 2 white shirts. He selects one shirt at random. Without replacing the shirt, he selects a second shirt at random. Find each probability. 14–17. See below.

14. P(blue, then white)

15. P(white, then blue)

16. P(blue, then blue)

17. P(white, then white)

14. $\frac{8}{30}$, or $\frac{4}{15}$ 15. $\frac{8}{30}$, or $\frac{4}{15}$ 16. $\frac{12}{30}$, or $\frac{2}{5}$ 17. $\frac{2}{30}$, or $\frac{1}{15}$

For Exercises 18–21, use the table below. The table shows the colors of a random sample of the bicycles in a rack at school.

Color	Number of Bicycles
Black	9
Blue	10
Red	14

Find each experimental probability for a bicycle chosen at random from the rack. Write each probability as a percent, to the nearest tenth of a percent.

18. P(red)   19. P(blue)   20. P(black)
    42.4%   **30.3%**   **27.3%**

21. How many bicycles would you expect to be black if there are 50 bicycles in the rack?
    14 bicycles

22. You roll a pair of number cubes once. What is the probability of rolling doubles?
    a. Find the sample space. Then find the theoretical probability. **See below left.**
    b. Use a simulation to find the experimental probability. **See back of book.**
    c. **Writing in Math** For parts (a) and (b), how close should you expect your answers to be? Explain. **You should expect your answers to be close if your simulation has a large number of trials.**

22a.

1, 1	1, 2	1, 3	1, 4	1, 5	1, 6
2, 1	2, 2	2, 3	2, 4	2, 5	2, 6
3, 1	3, 2	3, 3	3, 4	3, 5	3, 6
4, 1	4, 2	4, 3	4, 4	4, 5	4, 6
5, 1	5, 2	5, 3	5, 4	5, 5	5, 6
6, 1	6, 2	6, 3	6, 4	6, 5	6, 6

$; \frac{6}{36}$, or $\frac{1}{6}$

682   Chapter 12   Chapter Test

3.
45 50 55 60 65 70 75 80 85 90 95 100

4a. **See back of book**

4b.
0 1 2 3 4 5 6 7 8 9 10

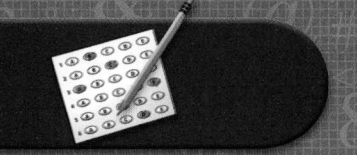

Test Prep

Multiple Choice

1. $\overleftrightarrow{MN} \parallel \overleftrightarrow{OP}$. Which angles are supplementary?
B

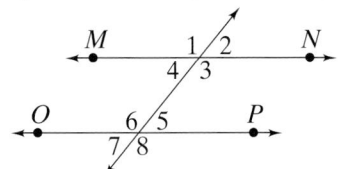

A. $\angle 1$ and $\angle 3$ **B.** $\angle 4$ and $\angle 6$
C. $\angle 2$ and $\angle 5$ **D.** $\angle 7$ and $\angle 5$

2. How many shaded triangles will exactly fill the trapezoid? **I**

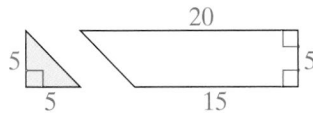

F. four   **G.** five
H. six   **I.** seven

3. Each of the six faces of a cube is painted either yellow or green. When the cube is tossed, the probability is $\frac{2}{3}$ that the cube will land with a green face up. How many faces are yellow? **B**
A. one   **B.** two
C. three   **D.** four

Gridded Response

4. Simplify $_6P_3$. **120**

5. A student has 3 blue T-shirts and 2 white T-shirts. He selects one T-shirt at random. Without replacing the T-shirt, he selects another T-shirt at random. What is the probability that the student will pick a white T-shirt and then a blue T-shirt? **3/10**

6. A shoe manufacturer checks 150 pairs of walking shoes and finds three pairs to be defective. What is the estimated percent probability that a pair of walking shoes is defective? **2**

10. [2] Not a good sample (unless your school is all girls) because it excludes boys who are part of your school population.
[1] minor error OR answer only

Short Response

7. For the data listed below, **(a)** make a box-and-whisker plot. **(b)** Label the median and the lower and upper quartiles. **See margin.**
55, 50, 60, 65, 65, 35, 40, 40, 45, 65, 55, 75, 30, 35, 55, 60, 45, 55

8. Use the data in the table. Make a graph that suggests each situation. **See back of book.**
a. sales decreasing sharply
b. sales staying about the same

Year	Sales (dollars)
1997	18.2 million
1998	17.9 million
1999	17.7 million
2000	17.5 million

In Exercises 9 and 10, (a) state whether each survey plan describes a good sample.
(b) Explain your reasoning.

9. To find how many people who buy stamps are buying them for a collection, you survey people in the post office. **See margin.**

10. To find how popular the U.S. women's soccer team is in your school, you survey all the girls in your English class. **See below left.**

11. $\angle ABC$ is an acute angle.
a. Write an inequality for x.
b. Explain your answer for part (a). **See margin.**

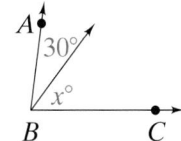

Extended Response

12. You roll two number cubes.
a. What is $P(6, \text{then } 6)$?
b. What is $P(\text{odd, then even})$?
c. Suppose you roll the two number cubes 50 times in a simulation. You roll double 3s six times. What is the experimental probability of NOT getting double 3s? **See back of book.**

Item	1	2	3	4	5	6	7	8	9	10	11	12
Lesson	9-2	10-2	12-4	12-6	12-5	12-8	12-2	12-3	12-8	12-8	9-2	12-7

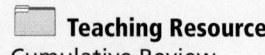

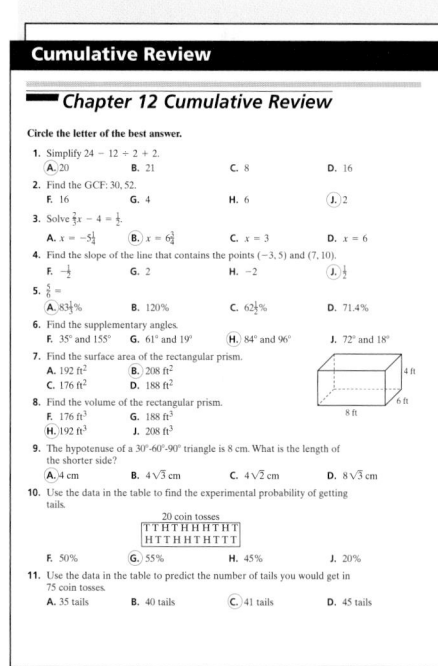

Cumulative Review

Chapter 12 Cumulative Review

Circle the letter of the best answer.

1. Simplify $24 - 12 \div 2 + 2$.
   (A.) 20   B. 21   C. 8   D. 16
2. Find the GCF: 30, 52.
   F. 16   G. 4   H. 6   (J.) 2
3. Solve $\frac{2}{3}x - 4 = \frac{1}{2}$.
   A. $x = -5\frac{1}{4}$ (B.) $x = 6\frac{3}{4}$ C. $x = 3$ D. $x = 6$
4. Find the slope of the line that contains the points $(-3, 5)$ and $(7, 10)$.
   F. $-\frac{1}{2}$ G. 2   H. -2 (J.) $\frac{1}{2}$
5. $\frac{5}{6} =$
   (A.) $83\frac{1}{3}\%$ B. 120%   C. $62\frac{1}{2}\%$ D. 71.4%
6. Find the supplementary angles.
   F. 35° and 155°   G. 61° and 19′   (H.) 84° and 96°   J. 72° and 18′
7. Find the surface area of the rectangular prism.
   A. 192 ft²   (B.) 208 ft²
   C. 176 ft²   D. 188 ft²
8. Find the volume of the rectangular prism.
   F. 176 ft³   G. 188 ft³
   (H.) 192 ft³   J. 208 ft³
9. The hypotenuse of a 30°-60°-90° triangle is 8 cm. What is the length of the shorter side?
   (A.) 4 cm   B. $4\sqrt{3}$ cm   C. $4\sqrt{2}$ cm   D. $8\sqrt{3}$ cm
10. Use the data in the table to find the experimental probability of getting tails.

20 coin tosses
T T H T H H H H T H T
H T T H H T H T T T

   F. 50%   (G.) 55%   H. 45%   J. 20%
11. Use the data in the table to predict the number of tails you would get in 75 coin tosses.
   A. 35 tails   B. 40 tails   (C.) 41 tails   D. 45 tails

9. [2] Yes; this is a good sample, with no built-in bias.
[1] minor error OR answer only

11. [2] $x < 60$; an acute angle is less than 90°, so the sum of x and 30° is less than 90°.
$$x + 30 < 90$$
$$x + 30 - 30 < 90 - 30$$
$$x < 60$$
[1] minor error OR answer only

7. [2] LQ = 40, med = 55, UQ = 60

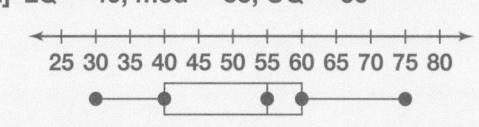

25 30 35 40 45 50 55 60 65 70 75 80

[1] correct plot; incorrect or missing labels

683

World Cup Soccer

In this activity, students use data in a table and apply their knowledge of data analysis to calculate range, mean, median, and mode.

Activating Prior Knowledge

Ask students to raise their hands if they have ever played soccer. Have volunteers explain how the game is played and how points are scored. **Answers may vary. Sample: Two teams compete to try to score goals by moving the ball with any part of their body except their hands and arms. Each team has a goaltender who tries to prevent the ball from scoring. Only these players can use their hands to stop the ball.**

Teaching Notes

Teaching Tip

Have a volunteer read the introductory paragraph. Ask: *What is the most difficult aspect of soccer?* **Answers may vary. Sample: controlling the ball without using your hands; passing the ball by using your head**

Diversity

Ask students to find out whether their grandparents played soccer or other sports when they were children. Where did their grandparents grow up? **Answers may vary. Sample: Soccer has been played around the world since the mid-1800s, but has been widespread in the U.S. only since the 1970s. Therefore, students' grandparents probably did not play soccer if they grew up in the U.S., but might have played it if they lived elsewhere.**

World Cup Soccer

Applying Data Analysis Anyone who has ever played soccer knows that controlling a rolling ball with your feet may be fun, but it isn't easy! Perhaps that's why the sport of soccer appeals to so many people of all ages all over the world. Soccer has been played in its current version since about 1863, and international competitions began before 1900. Today, Men's and Women's World Cup competitions are held every four years, one year apart.

Team Grin
Players from the United States women's soccer team pose with their gold medals after defeating China to win the 1999 Women's World Cup.

Final Gold
Mia Hamm (left) of the United States and Daniela Alves of Brazil get ready to kick the ball during the 2000 Women's Gold Cup Finals.

Take It to the NET For more information about soccer, go to **www.PHSchool.com**.
Web Code: ade-1253

684

FIFA World Cup™ Trophies
The Men's and Women's World Cup trophies are both made of gold. The United States won the FIFA Women's World Cup in 1999. Brazil won the Men's FIFA World Cup™ in 2002.

© 1998 FIFA

© 1974 FIFA

Following the Ball
Senegal midfielder Papa Bouba Diop (left) and Swedish forward Henrik Larsson go for the ball.

Activity

Use the table to answer the questions. 1–5. See margin.

1. Make a line plot of the goals scored by the players.

2. What is the range of the data in the table?

3. Find the mean, median, and mode of the data. Which measure best represents the data? Explain.

4. **a.** Based on the data at the right, make a table showing the number of goals scored by each team.

   b. Find the mean and the mode of the data in your table.

   c. Why is the mean of this data different from the mean found in Exercise 3?

5. **Number Sense** Suppose you did not know which team won the 2002 FIFA World Cup™. From the data in the table, can you determine the top two teams? Explain.

2002 FIFA Men's World Cup™ Top Goal Scorers

Flag	Player	Team	Goals Scored
	Ronaldo	Brazil	8
	Rivaldo	Brazil	5
	Miroslav Klose	Germany	5
	Jon Dahl Tomasson	Denmark	4
	Christian Vieri	Italy	4
	Marc Wilmots	Belgium	3
	Pauleta	Portugal	3
	Papa Bouba Diop	Senegal	3
	Ilhan Mansiz	Turkey	3
	Robbie Keane	Ireland	3
	Michael Ballack	Germany	3
	Fernando Morientes	Spain	3
	Raul	Spain	3
	Henrik Larsson	Sweden	3

685

1. See back of book.
2. 5 goals
3. mean = 3.8, median = 3, mode = 3; the median or mode; they are not affected by the outlier, 8.
4a. See back of book.
   b. mean = 4.8, mode = 3

c. 53 goals are divided by 11 countries instead of 14 players.
5. Answers may vary. Sample: Brazil and Germany; these two teams had the most goals from their top scorers.

Nonlinear Functions and Polynomials

Chapter at a Glance

13-1

Patterns and Sequences
pp. 688–692

Objectives
- ☑ Arithmetic Sequences
- ☑ Geometric and Other Sequences

New Vocabulary
sequence, term, arithmetic sequence, common difference, geometric sequence, common ratio

NCTM Standards
1, 2, 6, 7, 8, 9, 10

Local Standards

13-2

Graphing Nonlinear Functions
pp. 694–697

Objectives
- ☑ Graphing Quadratic Functions
- ☑ Graphing Absolute Value Functions

New Vocabulary
quadratic function, absolute value function

NCTM Standards
2, 3, 4, 6, 8, 9, 10

Local Standards

13-3

Exponential Growth and Decay
pp. 699–702

Objectives
- ☑ Exponential Growth
- ☑ Exponential Decay

NCTM Standards
2, 6, 8, 9, 10

Local Standards

✔ Checkpoint Quiz 1

13-4

Polynomials
pp. 704–707

Objectives
- ☑ Identifying Polynomials
- ☑ Evaluating Polynomials

New Vocabulary
monomial, polynomial, binomial, trinomial

NCTM Standards
2, 6, 8, 9, 10

Local Standards

13-5

Adding and Subtracting Polynomials
pp. 710–714

Objectives
- ☑ Adding Polynomials
- ☑ Subtracting Polynomials

NCTM Standards
2, 3, 7, 9, 10

Local Standards

13-6

Multiplying a Polynomial by a Monomial *pp. 715–718*

Objectives
- ☑ Using an Area Model
- ☑ Writing a Polynomial as a Product

NCTM Standards
2, 3, 4, 7, 8, 10

Local Standards

13-7

Multiplying Binomials
pp. 719–722

Objectives
- ☑ Using Models
- ☑ Using the Distributive Property

Materials
algebra tiles

NCTM Standards
2, 3, 4, 7, 8, 10

Local Standards

✔ Checkpoint Quiz 2

13-8 Problem Solving

Use Multiple Strategies
pp. 724–727

Objective
- ☑ Combining Strategies

NCTM Standards
2, 3, 4, 6, 7, 9, 10

Local Standards

Correlation to Standardized Tests

Lesson	NAEP	Terra Nova CAT/6	CTBS	ITBS	SAT10	Local Test
13-1	A1a, A1b, A1c	■	■		■	
13-2	A1e			■		
13-3	A2g					
13-4	A3b					
13-5	A3b					
13-6	A3b					
13-7	A3b	■	■			
13-8			■			

NAEP National Assessment of Educational Progress
  N = Number Sense, Properties, and Operations
  M = Measurement
  G = Geometry and Spatial Sense
  D = Data Analysis, Statistics and Probability
  A = Algebra and Functions
CAT/6 California Achievement Test, 6th Ed.
CTBS Comprehensive Test of Basic Skills
ITBS Iowa Test of Basic Skills, Form M
SAT10 Stanford Achievement Test, 10th Ed.

NCTM STANDARDS 2000

1 Number and Operations
2 Algebra
3 Geometry
4 Measurement
5 Data Analysis and Probability
6 Problem Solving
7 Reasoning and Proof
8 Communication
9 Connections
10 Representation

Pacing Options

This chart suggests pacing for only the core lessons and their parts. It is provided as a possible guide. It will help you determine how much time you have in your schedule to cover other components, such as the features, chapter projects, Chapter Review, and Chapter Test.

Day	Traditional 45-minute class periods	Two-Year 45-minute class periods	Block 90-minute class periods
1	13-1 ▼	13-1 ▼	13-1 ▼ ▼
2	13-1 ▼	13-1 ▼	13-2 ▼ ▼ / 13-3 ▼ ▼
3	13-2 ▼ ▼	13-1 ▼	13-4 ▼ ▼ / 13-5 ▼ ▼
4	13-3 ▼ ▼	13-2 ▼	13-6 ▼ ▼ / 13-7 ▼ ▼
5	13-4 ▼ ▼	13-2 ▼	13-8 ▼
6	13-5 ▼ ▼	13-2 ▼	
7	13-6 ▼ ▼	13-3 ▼	
8	13-7 ▼ ▼	13-3 ▼	
9	13-8 ▼	13-4 ▼	
10		13-4 ▼	
11		13-4 ▼	
12		13-5 ▼	
13		13-5 ▼	
14		13-5 ▼	
15		13-6 ▼	
16		13-6 ▼	
17		13-6 ▼	
18		13-7 ▼	
19		13-7 ▼	
20		13-7 ▼	
21		13-8 ▼	
22		13-8 ▼	
23			
24			

Math Background

Skills Trace

BEFORE Chapter 13

Chapter 8 developed linear functions. Students' informal work with patterns throughout this course introduced them to nonlinear functional relationships.

DURING Chapter 13

This chapter presents patterns and sequences as an introduction to nonlinear functions. Chapter 13 also introduces students to polynomials and operations with polynomials.

AFTER Chapter 13

Nonlinear functions, particularly quadratic functions, and polynomials play a large role in Algebra 1.

13-1 Patterns and Sequences

Students first encountered patterns and sequences in Lesson 1-7 when they learned about inductive reasoning. This lesson introduces arithmetic and geometric sequences, but also serves as a refresher lesson to prepare students for graphing nonlinear functions (Lessons 13-2, 13-3).

A set of numbers ordered in some specified way is called a *sequence*. Each number in a sequence is called a *term*. Consider these two sequences.

6, 9, 12, 15, 18, . . .

6, 18, 54, 162, 486, . . .

In the arithmetic sequence 6, 9, 12, 15, 18, . . . , there is a *common difference*, 3, between successive terms.

In the geometric sequence 6, 18, 54, 162, 486, . . . , there is a *common ratio*, also 3, between successive terms. You can find the common ratio by comparing any term to its predecessor.

The terms of a geometric sequence "grow" in much the same way that the values of an exponential function grow, as discussed in Lesson 13-3.

13-2, 13-3 Graphing Nonlinear Functions; Exponential Growth and Decay

In a quadratic function, the input variable x is squared. The graph of a quadratic function is always a *parabola*. A parabola is a U-shaped curve defined by an equation of the form $y = ax^2 + bx + c$. In this lesson, most of the quadratic functions have either $b = 0$ or $a = 1$ and $c = 0$, so they are of the general form $y = ax^2 + c$, or $y = x^2 + bx$.

The sign of a in ax^2 tells you whether the parabola opens upward or downward. The graph of $y = ax^2 + c$ opens upward ("holds water") when $a > 0$. When $a > 0$, the parabola has a *least* value for y. This is the lowest point on the graph, and the *vertex* of the parabola. The graph opens downward ("spills water") when $a < 0$. When $a < 0$, the parabola has a greatest value for y. That is the highest point on the graph, and the vertex of the parabola.

The graph of $y = a|x| + c$ "opens" like the graph of $y = ax^2 + c$, but the graph of this absolute value function is V-shaped instead of U-shaped.

A function of the form $y = a^x$, where $a > 1$, models *exponential growth*. The graph of such a function, for example $y = 2^x$, is shown below on the left. A function of the form $y = a^x$, where $0 < a < 1$, models *exponential decay*. The graph of such a function, for example $y = \left(\frac{1}{2}\right)^x$, is shown below on the right.

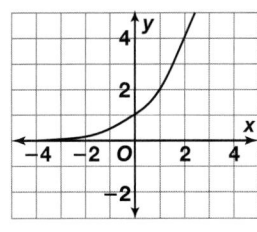

$y = 2^x$

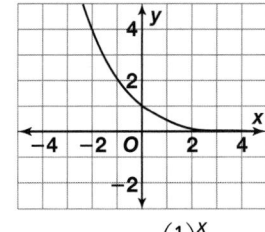

$y = \left(\frac{1}{2}\right)^x$

13-4 Polynomials

A *monomial* is a real number, a variable, or a product of a real number and variables with whole-number exponents. A simplified monomial will not have a variable in the denominator nor under a radical sign. A *polynomial* is a monomial or the sum or difference of monomials.

Students have been working with polynomials for much of the year as they evaluated or simplified expressions and solved equations. New in this chapter are second-degree polynomials in one variable. These contain the second power of a variable, such as x^2.

13-5 13-6 Adding and Subtracting Polynomials; Multiplying a Polynomial by a Monomial

You can use algebra tiles to model the addition and subtraction of polynomials. Here are the models for $2x^2 + 3x - 4$ and $x^2 + 2x + 5$.

"Adding" the tiles gives a model for the sum, $3x^2 + 5x + 1$.

When you add polynomials, you combine like terms (terms that have exactly the same variable with the same exponent). You subtract polynomials by adding the opposite of each term in the second polynomial.

$$x^2 + 2x + 5 - (2x^2 + 3x - 4) = x^2 + 2x + 5 - 2x^2 - 3x + 4$$
$$= -x^2 - x + 9$$

You can use the Distributive Property to simplify the product of a monomial and a polynomial.

$$-2x(x^3 - 4x^2 + 3x - 5) =$$
$$(-2x)(x^3) + (-2x)(-4x^2) + (-2x)(3x) + (-2x)(-5)$$
$$= -2x^4 + 8x^3 - 6x^2 + 10x$$

13-7 13-8 Multiplying Binomials; Using Multiple Strategies

To model the multiplication of binomials with algebra tiles, you can use a frame to set a length equal to one binomial and a width equal to the other binomial. Then within the frame, use tiles to build a rectangle with those dimensions. For example, a model of $(x + 1)(x + 3)$ might look like this:

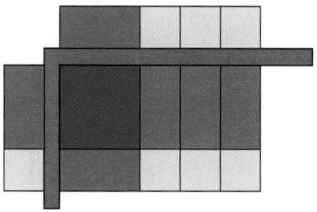

The rectangle within the frame has area $(x + 1)(x + 3)$, which is equal to $x^2 + 4x + 3$.

You can also multiply binomials by distributing each term in the first binomial to each term in the second.

$(x + 1)(x + 3) = (x + 1)(x) + (x + 1)(3)$ Distribute $(x + 1)$.

$\qquad = x^2 + x + 3x + 3$ Distribute x and 3.

$\qquad = x^2 + 4x + 3$ Simplify.

There are many strategies for problem solving. Sometimes, you may want to combine strategies to help you solve a problem. For example, it may be helpful to make a table or draw a diagram before you write an equation.

Additional Professional Development Opportunities

Chapter 13 Math Background notes: pp. 689, 695, 700, 705, 711, 716, 720, 725

Professional Development, Content Facilitator Guide: Pre-Algebra, Chapter 13

SkyLight
Professional Development

Additional resources available from SkyLight Professional Development: On-site courses, workshops, summer institutes. Online courses and chat rooms. Videocassettes and books. Visit www.skylightedu.com.

# Ongoing Assessment and Intervention

The *Prentice Hall Pre-Algebra* program provides many options for assessment in the Student Edition, Teacher's Edition, and teaching resources. From these options you may choose instructional materials and that are appropriate for your students and support your district's curriculum requirements.

Daily Assessment

Instant Check System™ in Chapter 13

Allows students to check their own learning before, during, and after each lesson.

Diagnosing Readiness before the chapter (p. 686)

Check Skills You'll Need exercises in each lesson (pp. 688, 694, 699, 704, 710, 715, 719, 724)

Check Understanding questions with each Example (pp. 688, 689, 690, 694, 695, 699, 700, 704, 705, 710, 711, 715, 716, 719, 720, 725)

Checkpoint Quiz (pp. 702, 722)

Formal Assessment

In Chapter 13 and Additional Resources

Assesses student progress throughout the *Pre-Algebra* text and with blackline masters and CD-ROM.

Student Edition
- Chapter 13 Review, with Vocabulary Skills and Concepts Review, pp. 729–731
- Chapter 13 Test, p. 732

Assessment Resources *Spanish versions available.*
- Checkpoint Quizzes 1 & 2
- Chapter Test, Forms A & B
- Chapter Alternative Assessment

Computer Test Generator CD-ROM
- Instant Chapter Tests™ — pre-made tests with items that vary every time you print.
- Online Testing allows you to give tests online and receive progress reports.
- Diagnose readiness with questions on prerequisite skills.
- Prepare students by making tests based on standardized test objectives.

Algebra Readiness Tests
- Includes Basic Skills Tests and Concept-Readiness Tests.
- Assess understanding of skills and concepts needed for success in algebra.

Standardized Test Preparation

Test Prep in Chapter 13

Teaches students strategies and gives them practice with all the test item formats they will encounter on high-stakes tests.

Test Prep exercises in each lesson (pp. 692, 697, 702, 707, 714, 718, 722, 727)

Test-Taking Strategies (p. 728: Using Mental Math)

Test Prep (p. 733: Cumulative Review)

PRENTICE HALL ASSESSMENT SYSTEM

Provides a three-step approach to preparing students for high-stakes, national, and state exams.

① Diagnose & Prescribe

② Review & Reteach

Content Diagnostic Tests
- Diagnose strengths and weaknesses with ongoing benchmark tests.
- Prescribe individualized reteaching opportunities.

Skills and Concepts Review
- Provides reteaching worksheets with instruction and practice for each skill.
- Includes course prerequisite skills.

**③ Practice & Assess**

Standardized Test Preparation
- Features practice for national standardized exams.
- Includes practice tests for NAEP, SAT9, ITBS, and Terra Nova.

Test-Taking Strategies With Transparencies
- Support the Test-Taking Strategies pages in the Student Edition.
- Provide a transparency and a worksheet for each strategy.

Reaching All Students

The textbook, the iText, and other technology components provide numerous opportunities to reach students of various ability levels and learning styles. Each Teacher's Edition lesson suggests how you can help all your students be successful and understand the mathematics in Chapter 13.

Below Level

Student Edition
- Diagnosing Readiness*: p. 686
- Check Skills You'll Need*: pp. 688, 694, 699, 704, 710, 715, 719, 724

Reteaching
Chapter 13 Grab & Go™ File: pp. 9–16

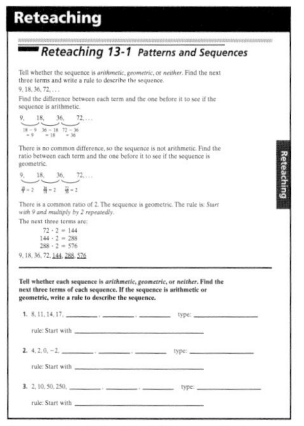

* Can be used with all ability levels to ensure mastery of prerequisite skills.

Advanced Learners

Student Edition
- Challenge exercises: pp. 692, 696, 702, 707, 713, 714, 718, 721, 727
- Extension: pp. 708, 723

Enrichment
Chapter 13 Grab & Go™ File: pp. 17–24

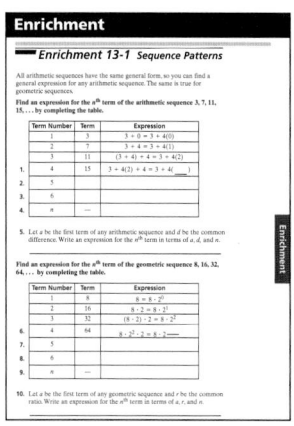

Problem Solving

Student Edition
- Strategies: pp. 724–727
- Real-World Problem Solving: pp. 689, 699, 705, 715, 724

Guided Problem Solving Masters
Chapter 13: pp. 108–115

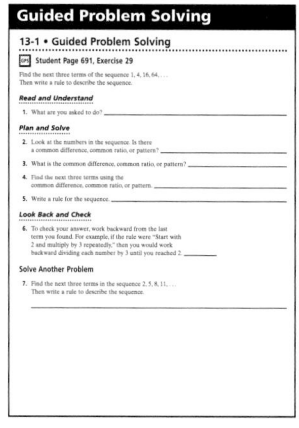

Reading and Math Literacy

Student Edition
- Vocabulary: pp. 687, 729, plus in most lessons
- Reading Math: pp. 689, 690, 695, 696, 698, 729
- Writing in Math: pp. 691, 696, 702, 706, 713, 721, 732
- Illustrated Glossary: pp. 782–826

Reading and Math Literacy Masters
Chapter 13: pp. 49–52

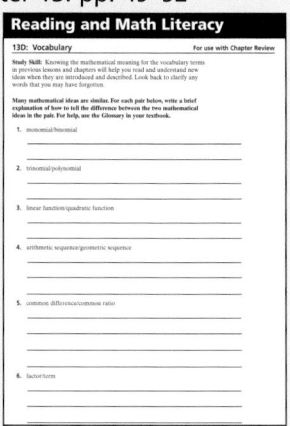

English Learners

Student Edition
- English/Spanish Illustrated Glossary: pp. 782–826

Workbook and Masters
Spanish Practice Workbook: pp. 108–115
Spanish Reading and Math Literacy Masters: pp. 49–52

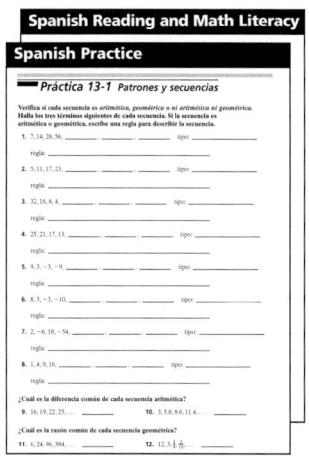

Learning Styles

Student Edition
- Investigation: pp. 688, 694
- Technology: pp. 693, 703
- DK Activities: pp. 736–737
- Chapter Project: p. 743

Activity Masters
Hands-On Activities: 32
Technology Activities: 36

Program Resources

Presentation Assistant Plus!

	Practice	Reteach	Enrich	Checkpt Quiz	Reading & Math Literacy	Technology Activities	Hands-On Activities	Guided Problem Solving	Practice	Reading & Math Literacy	Checkpt Quiz	Skills Check	Additional Examples	Answers to Exercises	Lesson Quiz	Prentice Hall Presentation Pro CD-ROM
	Resources in Grab & Go™ Files				**Resources for Reaching All Students**				**Spanish Resources**			**Transparencies**				
13-1	■	■	■		■			■	■	■		■	■	■	■	■
13-2	■	■	■			■		■	■			■	■	■	■	■
13-3	■	■	■	■	■		■	■	■	■	■	■	■	■	■	■
13-4	■	■	■					■	■			■	■	■	■	■
13-5	■	■	■					■	■			■	■	■	■	■
13-6	■	■	■					■	■			■	■	■	■	■
13-7	■	■	■	■	■			■	■	■		■	■	■	■	■
13-8	■	■	■		■			■	■	■		■	■	■	■	■
For the Chapter	Chapter Projects, Chapter Tests, Alternative Assessment, Cumulative Review, Cumulative Assessment				**On Web site only:** Home Activities, Algebra Readiness Puzzles, Interdisciplinary Activities				Spanish Chapter Tests, Alternative Assessment, Cumulative Review, Cumulative Assessment			Classroom Aid Transparencies				

Also available for use with the chapter:
- Practice Workbook
- Solution Key
- MathNotes folder
- For additional online and technology resources, see below.
- For teacher support and access to student Web site materials, use Web Code adk-5500.

PRENTICE HALL ASSESSMENT SYSTEM

Program assessment and test preparation, all in one place.

See page 686E.

Skills Intervention Kit

A *complete* system for the student who is struggling with course-level work

How to Use With Chapter 13

13-1	Operations With Fractions
13-2, 13-3, 13-4	Pre-Algebra Basics
13-5, 13-6, 13-7	
13-8	Whole Numbers

Online Intervention

Integrated within the iText, this online intervention system includes diagnostic tests and prescribed remediation, plus reports to track student mastery.

Technology

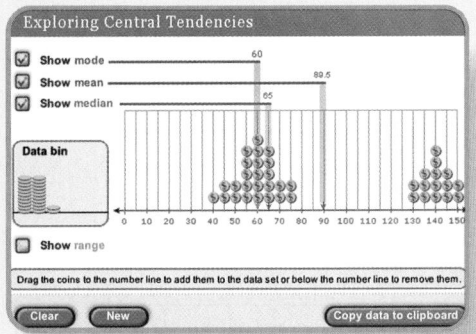

iTEXT Online and on CD-ROM

Complete Interactive Student Text online and on CD-ROM—with instant-feedback assessment, tutorial help, dynamic activities, instructional and real-world videos, audio, and additional practice.

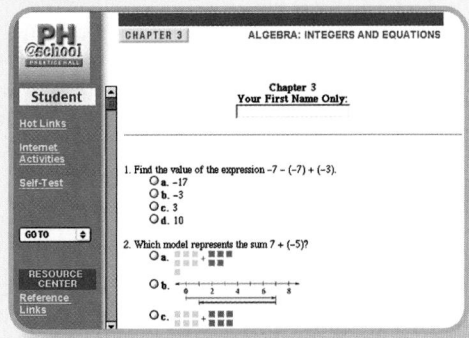

www.PHSchool.com For Students

Use Web Codes for easy access to online activities, chapter projects, self-grading lesson quizzes, chapter tests, vocabulary quizzes, updated data sources, graphing calculator procedures, and more.

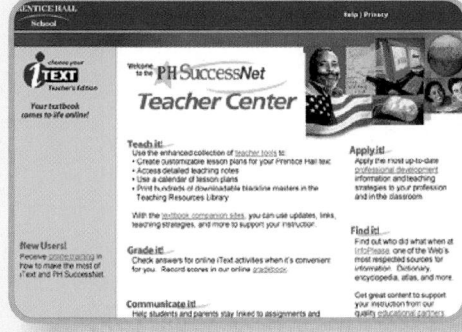

PH SuccessNet For Teachers

Online lesson planning with built-in state correlations, all the teaching resources, complete reference library, your own calendar and Teacher Web page, professional development, and more.

Presentation Assistant Plus!

The Prentice Hall *Presentation Assistant Plus!* provides you with the material you need to teach a lesson from beginning to end. Two easy-to-use formats—Transparencies and CD-ROM—allow you to present a lesson the way you are most comfortable.

 ## Transparencies

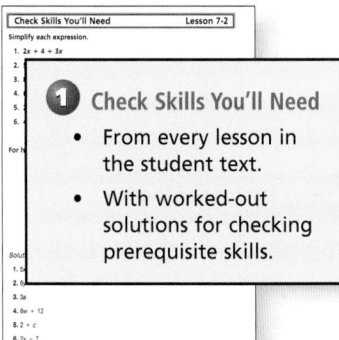

1 **Check Skills You'll Need**
- From every lesson in the student text.
- With worked-out solutions for checking prerequisite skills.

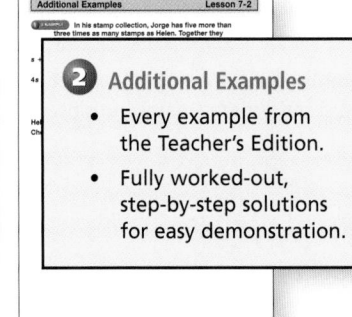

2 **Additional Examples**
- Every example from the Teacher's Edition.
- Fully worked-out, step-by-step solutions for easy demonstration.

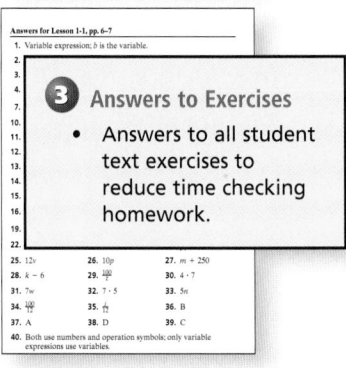

3 **Answers to Exercises**
- Answers to all student text exercises to reduce time checking homework.

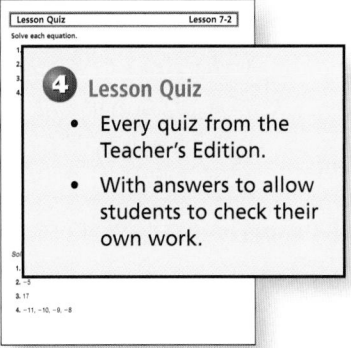

4 **Lesson Quiz**
- Every quiz from the Teacher's Edition.
- With answers to allow students to check their own work.

 **PowerPoint** Throughout the Teacher's Edition, this symbol indicates material that is available in the Presentation Assistant Plus!

PowerPoint ## Prentice Hall Presentation Pro CD-ROM

- Includes all Transparencies as PowerPoint® presentations.
- Conveniently organized by lesson so you can easily **1** Introduce, **2** Teach, **3** Check Homework, and **4** Assess each lesson.
- Animated examples allow step-by-step instruction at your own pace.
- Easy to edit so you can create custom presentations.

Teaching Chapter 13 Using Presentation Assistant Plus!

	1 Introduce	**2** Teach	**3** Check Homework	**4** Assess
	Check Skills You'll Need	Additional Examples	Student Edition Answers	Lesson Quiz
13-1	p. 111	pp. 181–182	✔	p. 111
13-2	p. 112	pp. 183–184	✔	p. 112
13-3	p. 113	p. 185	✔	p. 113
13-4	p. 114	pp. 186–187	✔	p. 114
13-5	p. 115	pp. 188–189	✔	p. 115
13-6	p. 116	p. 190	✔	p. 116
13-7	p. 117	p. 191	✔	p. 117
13-8	p. 118	p. 192	✔	p. 118

 ### Prentice Hall Presentation Pro

CD-ROM with dynamic Powerpoint® presentations for every lesson. Helps you introduce and develop concepts, check homework, and assess progress. Part of Presentation Assistant Plus! *(See above.)*

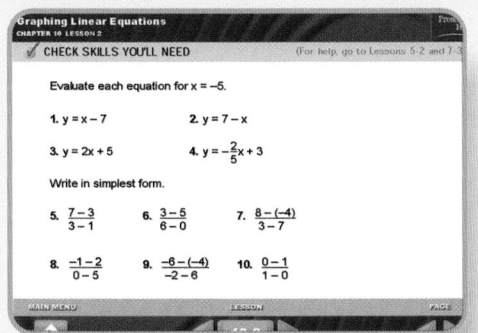

 ### Computer Test Generator

CD-ROM to create practice sheets and tests for course objectives and standardized tests. Includes Instant Chapter Tests™, online testing, and student reports. Part of the PH Assessment System. *(See page 686E.)*

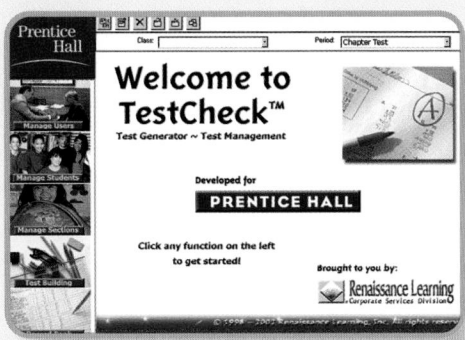

 ### Resource Pro® with Planning Express®

CD-ROM with a lesson planning tool that allows you to import state and local objectives. Includes electronic versions of all the teaching resources.

Nonlinear Functions and Polynomials

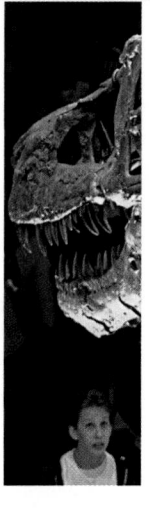

Where You've Been

● In Chapter 1, you wrote rules for patterns using inductive reasoning.

● In Chapter 2, you learned to simplify variable expressions by combining like terms.

● In Chapter 4, you learned how to multiply powers with the same base by adding the exponents.

● In Chapter 8, you graphed linear functions by making a table of values to show ordered-pair solutions.

iTEXT Instant self-check online and on CD-ROM

Diagnosing Readiness   (For help, go to the lesson in green.)

Evaluating Expressions (Lesson 1-3)

Evaluate each expression.

1. $8b$, for $b = 5$ **40**   **2.** $(-h)^5$, for $h = 2$ **−32**   **3.** $19 - (n - 6)$, for $n = 8$ **17**

4. $4a + 4$, for $a = 6$ **28**   **5.** n^2, for $n = 0.8$ **0.64**   **6.** $55 - 3mn$, for $m = 2, n = 5$ **25**

7. $\dfrac{120}{s + r}$, for $s = 25$ and $r = 35$ **2**   **8.** $\dfrac{j - k}{9}$, for $j = 75$ and $k = 12$ **7**

Using the Distributive Property (Lesson 2-2)

Simplify each expression.

9. $(d - 4)3$ **10.** $5(3x + 1)$ **11.** $3(u - 8)$ **12.** $-4(-2y - 7)$
$3d - 12$ $15x + 5$ $3u - 24$ $8y + 28$
13. $4(-3d + 1)$ **14.** $10(5 - 3s)$ **15.** $-3(7 - 2w)$ **16.** $(9 - 2b)3$
$-12d + 4$ $50 - 30s$ $-21 + 6w$ $27 - 6b$

Simplifying Variable Expressions (Lesson 2-3)

Simplify each expression.

17. $5a - 4 + 6a$ **18.** $x - 4x + 3x + 5$ **5** **19.** $g + 4 - 3g + g$
$11a - 4$ $-g + 4$
20. $5t + 5s + 5t$ **21.** $9b - 3d + 7d - 2b$ **22.** $-4(9c) + 2(-4c) - c$ **−45c**
$10t + 5s$ $7b + 4d$

Equations With Two Variables (Lesson 8-2)

Find the y values of each equation for $x = -2, 0$, and 2.

23. $y = 3x - 4$ **24.** $y = -3x$ **25.** $y = 4x - 2$ **26.** $y = \frac{3}{5}x - 5$
$-10, -4, 2$ $6, 0, -6$ $-10, -2, 6$ $-6\frac{1}{5}, -5, -3\frac{4}{5}$
27. $y = 6 - 2x$ **28.** $y = -\frac{1}{4}x - 8$ **29.** $y = \frac{1}{2}x$ **30.** $y = -3x - 1$
$10, 6, 2$ $-7\frac{1}{2}, -8, -8\frac{1}{2}$ $-1, 0, 1$ $5, -1, -7$

Nonlinear Functions and Polynomials

Where You're Going

In this chapter, you will learn how to

- Use arithmetic and geometric sequences.
- Graph nonlinear functions.
- Perform operations with polynomials.
- Solve a problem using multiple strategies.

Real-World Snapshots Applying what you learn, on pages 736–737 you will learn to solve problems about carbon-14 dating.

Key Vocabulary

- absolute value function (p. 695)
- arithmetic sequence (p. 688)
- binomial (p. 704)
- common difference (p. 688)
- common ratio (p. 689)
- geometric sequence (p. 689)
- monomial (p. 704)
- polynomial (p. 704)
- quadratic function (p. 694)
- sequence (p. 688)
- term (p. 688)
- trinomial (p. 704)

687

Chapter 13 Overview

Students begin this chapter by describing arithmetic and geometric sequences and using them to make predictions. They graph quadratic and absolute value functions. Students use tables, rules, and graphs to model exponential growth and decay. They identify and evaluate polynomials, and then add and subtract polynomials by using models and by combining like terms. Students use an area model to multiply polynomials. They use the Distributive Property to multiply two binomials and write a polynomial as the product of a monomial (GCF) and a polynomial.

Activating Prior Knowledge

Ask students how to use a table to graph a linear function. **Answers may vary. Sample: You substitute x-values to find corresponding y-values. You graph the (x, y) pairs and then draw a line through these points.**

📖 Reading Math
- Reading a Graph, p. 698
- **Vocabulary** A complete list of terms, plus vocabulary exercises, appears in the Chapter Review on p. 729.
- **Illustrated Glossary** Examples for each vocabulary term, plus definitions in both English and Spanish, appear starting on p. 782.

📝 Test-Taking Strategies
Using Mental Math, p. 728

🌐 Real-World Problem Solving
Strategy: Use Multiple Strategies, pp. 724–727
DK Real-World Snapshots: Applying Algebra, pp. 736–737
Chapter Project: Prism Building, p. 743

💻 www.PHSchool.com
Internet support includes:
- Self-grading Vocabulary and Chapter 13 Tests
- Activity Masters
- Chapter Project support
- Chapter Planner
- Chapter 13 Resources

Plus

Lesson Preview

✓ **Check Skills You'll Need**

Inductive Reasoning
Lesson 1–7: Example 2;
Exercises 3–8.
Extra Practice, p. 744.

Lesson Resources

📁 **Teaching Resources**
Practice, Reteaching, Enrichment

👥 **Reaching All Students**
Practice Workbook 13-1
Spanish Practice Workbook 13-1
Reading and Math Literacy 13A
Spanish Reading and Math
  Literacy 13AB
Guided Problem Solving 13-1

⏰ **Presentation Assistant Plus!**
Transparencies and PowerPoint™
• Check Skills You'll Need 13-1
• Additional Examples 13-1
• Student Edition Answers 13-1
• Lesson Quiz 13-1
PH Presentation Pro CD-ROM 13-1

 ASSESSMENT *SYSTEM*

Computer Test Generator CD-ROM

 Technology
Resource Pro® CD-ROM
Computer Test Generator CD-ROM
PH Presentation Pro CD-ROM

💻 **www.PHSchool.com**
Student Site
• Teacher Web Code: adk-5500
• Graphing Calculator, Procedure 3
• Self-grading Lesson Quiz
PH SuccessNet Teacher Center
• Lesson Planner
• Resources

 Plus

---

 **13-1**

Patterns and Sequences

What You'll Learn

 OBJECTIVE 1
To describe number patterns with arithmetic sequences

 OBJECTIVE 2
To describe number patterns with geometric sequences

... And Why

To use sequences in making predictions

✓ **Check Skills You'll Need**

Write a rule for each number pattern.
1–4. See below.
1. 60, 48, 36, 24, . . .

2. 7, 12, 17, 22, . . .

3. 6, 18, 54, 162, . . .

4. 60, 30, 15, $7\frac{1}{2}$, . . .

🔎 For help, go to Lesson 1-7.

New Vocabulary

• **sequence**
• **term**
• **arithmetic sequence**
• **common difference**
• **geometric sequence**
• **common ratio**

1. Start with 60 and subtract 12 repeatedly.
2. Start with 7 and add 5 repeatedly.
3. Start with 6 and multiply by 3 repeatedly.
4. Start with 60 and divide by 2 repeatedly.

📱 **TEXT** Interactive lesson includes instant self-check, tutorials, and activities.

 **In**vestigation

Discovering a Pattern

You win a contest and can choose one of two options for 30 days.

Option A	Option B
You receive $500 the first day, $550 the second, $600 the third, $650 the fourth, and so on.	You receive $1 the first day, $2 the second, $4 the third, $8 the fourth, and so on.

1. Make a table of values for both options for the first 10 days.
  a. Which option gives you more money in 10 days?
  b. Which option would you choose for 30 days? Explain.
  a–b. See back of book.

A **sequence** is a set of numbers that follow a pattern. Each number in the sequence is a **term** of the sequence. You find a term of an **arithmetic sequence** by *adding* a fixed number to the previous term. This fixed number is called the **common difference.**

Term Number	1st	2nd	3rd	4th
Arithmetic Sequence	2	6	10	14
Common Difference		+4	+4	+4

You can find the common difference for an arithmetic sequence by subtracting any term from the next term in the sequence.

1 EXAMPLE **Finding the Common Difference**

What is the common difference in the sequence 4, 2, 0, −2, . . . ?

4 → 2 → 0 → −2   **Find the common difference.**
  −2 −2 −2

● The common difference is −2.

✓ **Check Understanding** Example 1

1. What is the common difference in each sequence?

  a. 8, 13, 18, 23, . . . 5   **b.** 12, 9, 6, 3, . . . −3

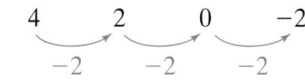 **Ongoing Assessment and Intervention**

Before the Lesson	During the Lesson	After the Lesson
Diagnose prerequisite skills using:	**Monitor progress using:**	**Assess knowledge using:**
• Check Skills You'll Need	• Check Understanding	• Lesson Quiz
	• Additional Examples	• Computer Test Generator CD-ROM
	• Test Prep	

You can continue a sequence and write a rule to describe it.

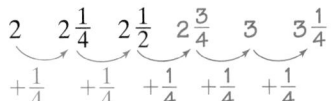

Real-World 🌐 **Problem Solving**

A runner training for a race runs 2 mi the first day, $2\frac{1}{4}$ mi the second day, $2\frac{1}{2}$ mi the third day, and so on. Find the next three terms of the sequence. Then write a rule to describe the sequence.

$$2 \quad 2\frac{1}{4} \quad 2\frac{1}{2} \quad 2\frac{3}{4} \quad 3 \quad 3\frac{1}{4}$$
$$+\frac{1}{4} \quad +\frac{1}{4} \quad +\frac{1}{4} \quad +\frac{1}{4} \quad +\frac{1}{4}$$

Find the common difference. Use it to find the next three terms.

The next three terms are $2\frac{3}{4}$, 3, and $3\frac{1}{4}$. The rule for the sequence is *Start with 2 and add $\frac{1}{4}$ repeatedly.*

✓ **Check Understanding** Example 2

2. Find the next three terms of each sequence. Then write a rule to describe the sequence. **a–b. See margin.**

   a. $23, 19, 15, 11, \ldots$ **b.** $-6, -4\frac{2}{3}, -3\frac{1}{3}, -2, \ldots$

During a two-mile run, a runner's feet strike the ground about 3,000 times.

Real-World 🌐 **Connection**

OBJECTIVE

2 Geometric and Other Sequences

You find a term of a **geometric sequence** by *multiplying* the previous term by a fixed number called the **common ratio.**

Term Number	1st	2nd	3rd	4th
Geometric Sequence	2	6	18	54
Common Ratio		×3	×3	×3

You can find the common ratio for a geometric sequence by dividing any term by the previous term in the sequence.

> **Reading Math**
>
> The word *common* means "shared." In a geometric sequence, all pairs of consecutive terms share the common ratio. In an arithmetic sequence, all pairs share the common difference.

3 EXAMPLE Finding the Common Ratio

Find the common ratio in the sequence $4, 8, 16, 32, \ldots$ Find the next three terms of the sequence. Then write a rule to describe the sequence.

$$4 \quad 8 \quad 16 \quad 32 \quad 64 \quad 128 \quad 256$$
$$\times 2 \quad \times 2 \quad \times 2 \quad \times 2 \quad \times 2 \quad \times 2$$

Find the common ratio. Use it to find the next three terms.

The next three terms are 64, 128, and 256. The rule for the sequence is *Start with 4 and multiply by 2 repeatedly.*

👥 Reaching All Students

Below Level Ask students to tell about any patterns or sequences they see in their daily lives. **Answers may vary. Sample: School buses arrive at the same time each day.**	**Advanced Learners** Ask: *If all of the terms except for the first one of a geometric sequence are the same, what is the common ratio?* **1**	**Visual Learners** See note on page 689. **English Learners** See note on page 690.

2. Teach

Professional Development

Math Background

After the first term in an arithmetic sequence, you get the other terms by adding the same number (common difference) repeatedly. After the first term in a geometric sequence, you get the other terms by multiplying by the same number (common ratio) repeatedly.

Teaching Notes

Investigation (Optional)

Point out that although $500 is significantly more than $1, students should literally "do the math" before choosing.

1 EXAMPLE Error Prevention

Point out that the common difference is always added to the previous term. The common difference is negative when the values in a sequence are decreasing and positive when the values in a sequence are increasing.

2 EXAMPLE Visual Learners

Suggest students use number lines to help find common differences and next terms in arithmetic sequences.

PowerPoint

Additional Examples

1. What is the common difference in the sequence $-6, -3, 0, 3, \ldots$? **3**

2. A swimmer training for a meet swims 5 laps the first day, $6\frac{1}{2}$ laps the next day, 8 laps the third day, and so on. Find the next three terms of the sequence. Then write a rule to describe the sequence. $9\frac{1}{2}$, 11, $12\frac{1}{2}$; Start with 5 and add $1\frac{1}{2}$ repeatedly.

3. Find the common ratio in the sequence $3, 9, 27, 81, \ldots$. Find the next three terms of the sequence. Then write a rule to describe the sequence. 3; 243, 729, 2,187; Start with 3 and multiply by 3 repeatedly.

Check Understanding 2. See back of book.

689

Additional Examples

4 Tell whether each sequence is *arithmetic, geometric,* or *neither.* Find the next three terms of each sequence.
  a. 3, 5, 9, 15, . . .
    neither; 23, 33, 45
  b. 12, 10.5, 9, 7.5, . . .
    arithmetic; 6, 4.5, 3
  c. 2, −4, 8, −16, . . .
    geometric; 32, −64, 128

English Learners

Help students distinguish when to use the different pronunciations of *arithmetic.* The accent is on the second syllable in the noun *uh RITH muh tik.* The accent is on the third syllable in the adjective *ayr ith MET ik,* as in "arithmetic sequence."

3 EXAMPLE Error Prevention

Students may assume that a *common ratio* must have the form of a fraction because the expression uses the word "ratio." Remind them that a ratio (or fraction) can simplify to the form of an integer for which a denominator is "understood" to be 1. The common ratio 2 is understood to be $\frac{2}{1}$.

Closure

Ask: *What are the two types of sequences studied in this lesson? How do they differ?* Arithmetic and geometric; for arithmetic sequences, you add a common difference to each term to find the next term. For geometric sequences, you multiply each term by a common ratio to find the next term.

3a. 3; 324, 972, 2,916; start with 4 and multiply by 3 repeatedly.

3b. 0.5; 0.25, 0.125, 0.0625; start with 4 and multiply by 0.5 repeatedly.

> ### Reading Math
>
> Read both *geometric* and *arithmetic* (ayr ith MET ik) with the emphasis on the third syllable.

4a. geometric; 243, 729, 2,187
4b. neither; 34, 45, 58
4c. geometric; −12, 12, −12
4d. arithmetic; 650, 800, 950

✔ **Check Understanding** Example 3

3. Find the common ratio and the next three terms of each sequence. Then write a rule to describe the sequence. **a–b. See left.**

  a. 4, 12, 36, 108, . . .   **b.** 4, 2, 1, 0.5, . . .

Not every sequence is arithmetic or geometric. You can determine whether any sequence of numbers is arithmetic or geometric by looking for a common difference or a common ratio. For other sequences, you can look for patterns.

4 EXAMPLE Finding the Type of Sequence

Tell whether each sequence is *arithmetic, geometric,* or *neither.* Find the next three terms of each sequence.

a. 4, 6, 8, 10, . . .

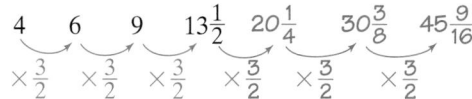

There is a common difference of 2. The sequence is arithmetic. The next three terms are 12, 14, and 16.

b. $4, 6, 9, 13\frac{1}{2}, \ldots$

The ratios for the first four terms are $\frac{6}{4}, \frac{9}{6},$ and $\frac{27}{18}.$ These equal $\frac{3}{2},$ which is the common ratio. The sequence is geometric. The next three terms are $20\frac{1}{4}, 30\frac{3}{8},$ and $45\frac{9}{16}.$

c. 4, 6, 9, 13, . . .

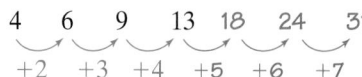

The sequence is neither arithmetic nor geometric. Following the pattern above, the next three terms are 18, 24, and 31.

✔ **Check Understanding** Example 4

4. Tell whether each sequence is *arithmetic, geometric,* or *neither.* Then find the next three terms of the sequence.

  a. 3, 9, 27, 81, . . .   **b.** 10, 13, 18, 25, . . .
  c. −12, 12, −12, 12, . . .   **d.** 50, 200, 350, 500, . . .
    a–d. See left.

3. Practice

Practice and Problem Solving

A Practice by Example

Assignment Guide

1 Objective 1
  A B Core 1–10, 18, 19, 23, 26, 28, 30, 33–35, 38
  C Extension 41

2 Objective 2
  A B Core 11–17, 20–22, 24, 25, 27, 29, 31, 32, 36, 37, 39, 40
  C Extension 42–46

Test Prep 47–50
Mixed Review 51–54

Example 1
(page 688)

What is the common difference of each arithmetic sequence?

1. 5, 4, 3, 2, . . . −1   **2.** 4, 11, 18, 25, . . . 7   **3.** 7, 1, −5, −11, . . .
                                                               −6

4. 80, 60, 40, 20, . . .   **5.** 3, 9, 15, 21, . . . 6   **6.** −6, −5, −4, −3, . . .
     −20   1

Example 2
(page 689)

7. 20, 25, 30; start with 0 and add 5 repeatedly.

8. −3, −9, −15; start with 21 and add −6 repeatedly.

9. 1, 4, 7; Start with −11 and add 3 repeatedly.

10. 56, 68, 80; start with 20 and add 12 repeatedly.

Find the next three terms of each sequence. Then write a rule to describe the sequence. 7–9. See left.

7. 0, 5, 10, 15, . . .   **8.** 21, 15, 9, 3, . . .   **9.** −11, −8, −5, −2, . . .

10. Exercising You begin doing 20 sit-ups every day in November. You do 32 sit-ups every day in December, 44 sit-ups every day in January, and so on. Find the next three terms of the sequence. Then write a rule to describe the sequence. See left.

Example 3
(page 689)

Find the common ratio and the next three terms of each sequence. Then write a rule to describe the sequence. 11–16. See margin.

11. 3, 6, 12, 24, . . .   **12.** 5, 1, $\frac{1}{5}$, $\frac{1}{25}$, . . .   **13.** 45, 90, 180, 360, . . .

14. 2, 3, 4$\frac{1}{2}$, 6$\frac{3}{4}$, . . .   **15.** 12, 4, 1$\frac{1}{3}$, $\frac{4}{9}$, . . .   **16.** 8, 40, 200, 1,000, . . .

Example 4
(page 690)

Tell whether each sequence is *arithmetic*, *geometric*, or *neither*. Find the next three terms of the sequence. 17–22. See back of book.

17. 1, 3, 9, 27, . . .   **18.** 10, 5, 0, −5, . . .   **19.** 4.5, 4, 3.5, 3, . . .

20. 2, 2, 4, 6, . . .   **21.** −1, 3, −9, 27, . . .   **22.** 0, 5, 12, 21, . . .

B Apply Your Skills

Tell whether each sequence is *arithmetic* or *geometric*. If arithmetic, give the common difference. If geometric, give the common ratio.

29. 256, 1,024, 4,096; start with 1 and multiply by 4 repeatedly.

30. −5, −7, −9; start with 3 and add −2 repeatedly.

31. 20,000, 200,000, 2,000,000; start with 2 and multiply by 10 repeatedly.

32. 144, 288, 576; start with 9 and multiply by 2 repeatedly.

33. 125, 150, 175; start with 25 and add 25 repeatedly.

34. 7.3, 7.5, 7.7; start with 6.5 and add 0.2 repeatedly.

23. 1, 1$\frac{1}{2}$, 2, 2$\frac{1}{2}$, . . .   **24.** −3, −15, −75, . . .   **25.** −4, 12, −36, 108, . . .
arithmetic; $\frac{1}{2}$ geometric; 5   geometric; −3

26. 5, 6.4, 7.8, 9.2, . . .   **27.** 5, 15, 45, 135, . . .   **28.** 8.3, 5.7, 3.1, 0.5, . . .
arithmetic; 1.4   geometric; 3   arithmetic; −2.6

Find the next three terms of each sequence. Then write a rule to describe the sequence. 29–34. See left.

GPS **29.** 1, 4, 16, 64, . . .   **30.** 3, 1, −1, −3, . . .   **31.** 2, 20, 200, 2,000, . . .

32. 9, 18, 36, 72, . . .   **33.** 25, 50, 75, 100, . . .   **34.** 6.5, 6.7, 6.9, 7.1, . . .

Tell whether each sequence is *arithmetic*, *geometric*, or *neither*. Find the next three terms of the sequence. 35–39. See back of book.

35. $\frac{1}{2}$, $\frac{5}{6}$, 1$\frac{1}{6}$, 1$\frac{1}{2}$, . . .   **36.** 1, 10, 2, 20, . . .   **37.** 13, 12, 10, 7, . . .

38. 7, 7.03, 7.06, 7.09, . . .   **39.** $-\frac{1}{5}$, $-\frac{1}{10}$, $-\frac{1}{20}$, $-\frac{1}{40}$, . . .

40. Writing in Math The first two numbers of a sequence are 4 and 8. Can you tell what kind of sequence this is? Explain.
See back of book.

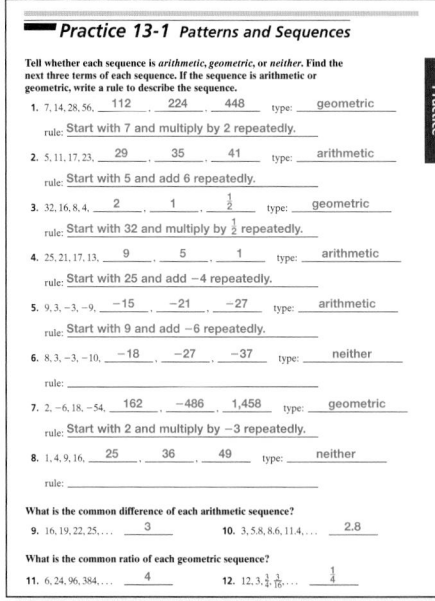

11. 2; 48, 96, 192; start with 3 and multiply by 2 repeatedly.

12. $\frac{1}{5}$; $\frac{1}{125}$, $\frac{1}{625}$, $\frac{1}{3,125}$; start with 5 and multiply by $\frac{1}{5}$ repeatedly.

13. 2; 720, 1,440, 2,880; start with 45 and multiply by 2 repeatedly.

GPS Use the Guided Problem Solving worksheet with Exercise 29.

14. 1$\frac{1}{2}$; 10$\frac{1}{8}$, 15$\frac{3}{16}$, 22$\frac{25}{32}$; start with 2 and multiply by 1$\frac{1}{2}$ repeatedly.

15–16. See back of book.

Tell whether each sequence is *arithmetic, geometric,* or *neither.* Then find the next three terms. For each arithmetic and geometric sequence, give the common difference or ratio, and write a rule to describe the sequence.

1. $9, 3, 1, \frac{1}{3}, \ldots$ geometric; $\frac{1}{9}$, $\frac{1}{27}, \frac{1}{81}$; common ratio: $\frac{1}{3}$; *Start with 9 and multiply by $\frac{1}{3}$ repeatedly.*

2. $1, 4, 9, 16, \ldots$ neither; 25, 36, 49

3. $66, 77, 88, 99, \ldots$ arithmetic; 110, 121, 132; common difference: 11; *Start with 66 and add 11 repeatedly.*

Test Prep

Resources

For additional practice with a variety of test item formats:
- Test Prep, p. 733
- Test-Taking Strategies, p. 728
- Test-Taking Strategies With Transparencies

Reteaching 13-1 *Patterns and Sequences*

Tell whether the sequence is *arithmetic, geometric,* or *neither.* Find the next three terms and write a rule to describe the sequence.
9, 18, 36, 72, . . .
Find the difference between each term and the one before it to see if the sequence is arithmetic.

9,   18,   36,   72,...

$18 - 9 \quad 36 - 18 \quad 72 - 36$
$= 9 \quad = 18 \quad = 36$

There is no common difference, so the sequence is not arithmetic. Find the ratio between each term and the one before it to see if the sequence is geometric.

9,   18,   36,   72,...

$\frac{18}{9} = 2 \quad \frac{36}{18} = 2 \quad \frac{72}{36} = 2$

There is a common ratio of 2. The sequence is geometric. The rule is: *Start with 9 and multiply by 2 repeatedly.*
The next three terms are:
$72 \cdot 2 = 144$
$144 \cdot 2 = 288$
$288 \cdot 2 = 576$
9, 18, 36, 72, 144, 288, 576

Tell whether each sequence is *arithmetic, geometric,* or *neither.* Find the next three terms of each sequence. If the sequence is arithmetic or geometric, write a rule to describe the sequence.

1. 8, 11, 14, 17, __20__, __23__, __26__ type: __arithmetic__
rule: Start with __8 and add 3 repeatedly.__

2. 4, 2, 0, −2, __−4__, __−6__, __−8__ type: __arithmetic__
rule: Start with __4 and add −2 repeatedly.__

3. 2, 10, 50, 250, __1,250__, __6,250__, __31,250__ type: __geometric__
rule: Start with __2 and multiply by 5 repeatedly.__

C Challenge — **Evaluate each expression for** $n = -2, -1, 0,$ **and 1. Is the sequence formed** *arithmetic, geometric,* **or** *neither?* 41–44. See back of book.

41. $3n$ **42.** $n(n + 1)$ **43.** 2^n **44.** n^2

Need Help?
To review compound interest, see Lesson 7-8.

45a. $2,040, $2,080.80, $2,122.42, $2,164.86
b. Geometric; each balance is about 1.02 times the previous balance.

45. Savings You open a savings account with $2,000. The account earns 4% interest compounded semiannually. a–b. See left.
  a. Write the balance in the savings account after each interest payment for two years.
  b. Does the pattern of balances form an arithmetic or geometric sequence? Explain.

46. Patterns In the Fibonacci sequence $1, 1, 2, 3, 5, 8, \ldots$, you find each term (after the first two terms) by adding the two previous terms. Write the next three terms of the sequence. 13, 21, 34

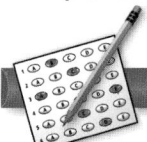
Test Prep

Multiple Choice **47.** If the first term of an arithmetic sequence is 35 and the fifth term is 67, what is the third term? B
  A. 43 **B.** 51 **C.** 59 **D.** 75

48. If the rule for a sequence is "start with −7 and multiply by −2 repeatedly," what is the fourth term in the sequence? H
  F. −112 **G.** −56 **H.** 56 **I.** 112

Reading Comprehension Read the passage below before doing Exercises 49 and 50.

Population Watch

The population of the United States in 1980 was about 226 million, in 1985 it was about 238 million, in 1990 it was about 250 million, and in 1995 it was about 263 million.

Take It to the NET
Online lesson quiz at **www.PHSchool.com**
Web Code: ada-1301

49. What intervals of time are used with the given population data?
  5 years
50. Which type of sequence, arithmetic or geometric, could you use to model the United States population data? Explain.
  See back of book.

Mixed Review

Lesson 12-8 **51. Surveys** You want to find out which presidential candidate is most popular in your city. You plan to interview people who visit the city's art museum. State whether the survey plan describes a good sample. Explain your reasoning. See margin.

Lesson 9-6 **Find the circumference of each circle rounded to the nearest tenth.**

52. radius = 8.5 m **53.** radius = 5 in. **54.** diameter = 14 cm
  53.4 m 31.4 in. 44.0 cm

Alternative Assessment

Have students write the first four terms in a sequence of their choosing. Then have them exchange papers with a partner. Partners should identify the type of sequence and the common difference or ratio, if applicable, then write the next three terms of the sequence. Have students check each other's work.

51. Not a good sample; it excludes many groups, such as people with no interest in art.

Displaying Sequences

For Use With Lesson 13-1

You can model rules for sequences mathematically and then display the sequences using graphing calculator tables.

1 EXAMPLE

Model the rule "Start with 23 and add −4 repeatedly" mathematically and then display the sequence in a calculator table.

Model: $23 + (-4)x$, or $23 - 4x$, with $x = 0, 1, 2, \ldots$

Display Method 1

Press **Y=** and enter $Y_1 = 23 - 4x$.

● In **TBLSET,** set TblStart = 0 and ΔTbl = 1, then press **TABLE.**

X	Y₁
0	23
1	19
2	15
3	11
4	7
5	3
6	−1

X=6

Move down in either column to see more terms of the sequence.

2 EXAMPLE

Model the rule "Start with 4 and multiply by 2 repeatedly" mathematically and then display the sequence in a calculator table.

Model: $4(2)^x$, with $x = 0, 1, 2, \ldots$

Display Method 2

Clear your home screen. In **STAT,** use the **OPS** menu. Select the **seq** operator, and **ENTER**. Then

enter seq(X,X,0,10) **STO▶ STAT L₁ ENTER**. In similar fashion,

enter seq(4(2)^X,X,0,10) **STO▶ STAT L₂ ENTER**.

● Press **LIST**.

L1	L2	L3	1
0	4		
1	8		
2	16		
3	32		
4	64		
5	128		
6	256		

L1(7)=6

This list ends at 10.

EXERCISES

Use a graphing calculator table to display the first 11 terms of each sequence. Record the 11th term. Use Display Method 1 for some exercises and Display Method 2 for the others.
For graphing calculator displays, check students' work.

1. Start with 0 and add 5 repeatedly. 50

2. Start with 80 and subtract 30 repeatedly. −220

3. Start with 3 and add 6 repeatedly. 63

4. Start with −4 and multiply by −3 repeatedly. −236,196

5. 7, 7.3, 7.6, 7.9, . . . 10 **6.** 3, 1, −1, −3, . . . −17 **7.** $18 - 3x; x = 0, 1, 2, \ldots$ −12 **8.** $6(3)^x$ 354,294

9. In Example 1, the model gives the desired sequence for x having values $0, 1, 2, \ldots$ Find a model using x that gives the same sequence for x having values $1, 2, 3, \ldots$ $19 - 4x$

---

1. Plan

Lesson Preview

 Check Skills You'll Need

Equations With Two Variables
Lesson 8-2: Example 1;
Exercises 1–9.
Extra Practice, p. 751.

Lesson Resources

 Teaching Resources
Practice, Reteaching, Enrichment

 Reaching All Students
Practice Workbook 13-2
Spanish Practice Workbook 13-2
Guided Problem Solving 13-2
Technology Activities 36

 Presentation Assistant Plus!
Transparencies and PowerPoint™
• Check Skills You'll Need 13-2
• Additional Examples 13-2
• Student Edition Answers 13-2
• Lesson Quiz 13-2
• Classroom Aid 3
PH Presentation Pro CD-ROM 13-2

 ASSESSMENT SYSTEM

Computer Test Generator CD-ROM

 Technology
Resource Pro® CD-ROM
Computer Test Generator CD-ROM
PH Presentation Pro CD-ROM

 www.PHSchool.com
Student Site
• Teacher Web Code: adk-5500
• Algebra Readiness Puzzles 88
• Graphing Calculator,
  Procedure 4, 5, 6, 10
• Self-grading Lesson Quiz
PH SuccessNet Teacher Center
• Lesson Planner
• Resources

Plus

What You'll Learn

OBJECTIVE 1 To graph quadratic functions

OBJECTIVE 2 To graph absolute value functions

. . . And Why

To use nonlinear functions in modeling real-world situations, such as finding the area of an enclosed space

 Check Skills You'll Need

**Find the *y* values
of each equation
for *x* = −2, 0, and 2.**

1. $y = 5x - 1$ −11, −1, 9

2. $y = \frac{1}{2}x + 3$ 2, 3, 4

3. $y = 3x + 2$ −4, 2, 8

4. $y = \frac{1}{4}x - 5$
$-5\frac{1}{2}, -5, -4\frac{1}{2}$
 For help, go to Lesson 8-2.

New Vocabulary
• quadratic function
• absolute value function

 **iTEXT** Interactive lesson includes instant self-check, tutorials, and activities.

OBJECTIVE

1 Graphing Quadratic Functions

Investigation

Graphing Data

You can graph the area of a square as a function of the length of a side of the square.

1. Copy and complete the table at the right.

2. Draw a graph of the data. Does your graph appear to be a linear function? Explain.
See back of book.

Side *x*	Area *f(x)*
1	1
2	■ 4
3	■ 9
4	■ 16
5	■ 25
6	36

In a **quadratic function,** the input variable is squared. The graph of a quadratic function is a U-shaped curve called a *parabola.* The curve may open upward or downward.

1 EXAMPLE Graphing a Quadratic Function

For the function $y = 2x^2$, make a table with integer values of *x* from −2 to 2. Then graph the function.

Make a table.

x	$2x^2 = y$	(*x, y*)
−2	$2(-2)^2 = 8$	(−2, 8)
−1	$2(-1)^2 = 2$	(−1, 2)
0	$2(0)^2 = 0$	(0, 0)
1	$2(1)^2 = 2$	(1, 2)
2	$2(2)^2 = 8$	(2, 8)

Make a graph.

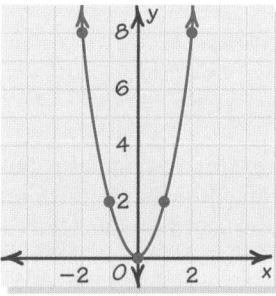

 **Check Understanding** Example 1

1. For each function, make a table with integer values of *x* from −2 to 2. Then graph each function. a–b. See back of book.

a. $y = -2x^2$

b. $y = -x^2 + 3$

INSTANT CHECK ANALYSIS **Ongoing Assessment and Intervention**

Before the Lesson	**During the Lesson**	**After the Lesson**
Diagnose prerequisite skills using:	Monitor progress using:	Assess knowledge using:
• Check Skills You'll Need	• Check Understanding	• Lesson Quiz
	• Additional Examples	• Computer Test Generator
	• Test Prep	CD-ROM

2 EXAMPLE Using a Graph to Solve a Problem

The function $A = 10x - x^2$, where x is the width in yards, gives the area A of a goat pen in square yards. Graph the function. Use the graph to find the width that gives the greatest area.

x	$10x - x^2 = y$	(x, y)
0	$10(0) - 0^2 = 0$	(0, 0)
1	$10(1) - 1^2 = 9$	(1, 9)
2	$10(2) - 2^2 = 16$	(2, 16)
3	$10(3) - 3^2 = 21$	(3, 21)
4	$10(4) - 4^2 = 24$	(4, 24)
5	$10(5) - 5^2 = 25$	(5, 25)
6	$10(6) - 6^2 = 24$	(6, 24)

The ordered pair (5, 25) shows what appears to be the highest point. So the width 5 yards gives the greatest area.

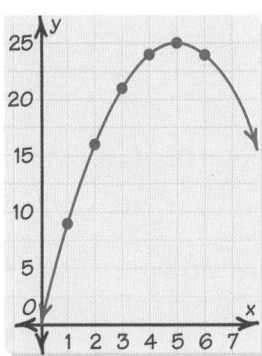

Real-World Connection

A goat pen with width 5 yd and area 25 yd^2 must have length 5 yd.

✓ Check Understanding Example 2

2. Graph each function. a–b. See back of book.

   a. $y = 3x + x^2$ **b.** $y = 6x - x^2$

OBJECTIVE

2 Graphing Absolute Value Functions

The equation $y = |x|$ is an **absolute value function.** The graph of $y = |x|$ is V-shaped.

Reading Math

Quadratic and absolute value functions are *nonlinear functions* because you cannot draw the graph of either in one line.

3 EXAMPLE Graphing an Absolute Value Function

Graph the function $y = |x|$.

x	$|x| = y$	(x, y)
-2	$|-2| = 2$	(-2, 2)
-1	$|-1| = 1$	(-1, 1)
0	$|0| = 0$	(0, 0)
1	$|1| = 1$	(1, 1)
2	$|2| = 2$	(2, 2)

✓ Check Understanding Example 3

3. Graph each function. a–b. See back of book.

   a. $y = -|x| + 1$ **b.** $y = 2|x|$

13-2 Graphing Nonlinear Functions **695**

---

2. Teach

Professional Development

Math Background

Quadratic functions and absolute value functions both have *y*-values that repeat. This gives them their U shapes and V shapes, respectively. If there is no addition or subtraction in the function rules, duplicate *y* values occur for an integer and its opposite.

Teaching Notes

Investigation (Optional)

Students may "follow the dots" and try to connect the points on this graph with segments. Help them understand that the graph of this function is actually a smooth curve.

2 EXAMPLE Visual Learners

Write the following on the board to help students remember that the graphs of quadratic functions are U-shaped, and the graphs of absolute value functions are V-shaped.

PowerPoint

📖 Additional Examples

1. For the function $y = -x^2 + 1$, make a table with integer values of x from -2 to 2. Then graph the function. **See back of book.**

2. The function $A = 12x - x^2$, where x is width in meters, gives the area A of a pond in square meters. Graph the function. Use the graph to find the width that gives the greatest area. **See back of book for graph; width of 6 meters**

3. Graph the function $y = |x| - 1$. **See back of book.**

Closure

Ask students how to recognize graphs of *quadratic* and *absolute value functions.* The graph of a quadratic function is a U-shaped curve, called a *parabola.* The graph of an absolute value function is V-shaped.

695

3. Practice

Assignment Guide

1 Objective 1
- **A B Core** 1–13, 29, 30
- **C Extension** 32

2 Objective 2
- **A B Core** 14–28, 31
- **C Extension** 33

Test Prep 34–37
Mixed Review 38–41

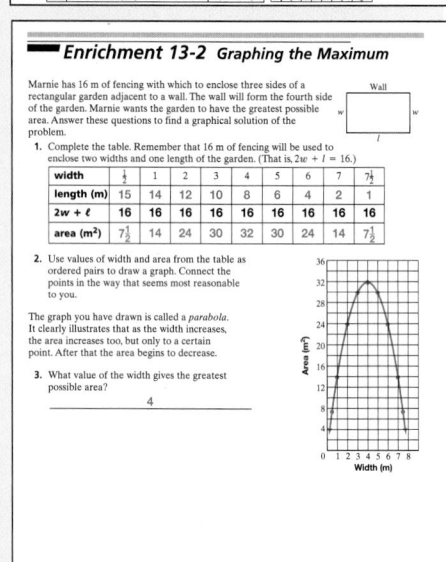

Practice 13-2 *Graphing Nonlinear Functions*

Enrichment 13-2 *Graphing the Maximum*

EXERCISES

? For more exercises, see *Extra Practice*.

Practice and Problem Solving

A **Practice by Example**

Example 1
(page 694)

For each function, make a table with integer values of x from -2 to 2. Then graph the function. 1–8. See back of book.

1. $y = 4x^2$ 2. $y = -x^2$ 3. $y = -3x^2$ 4. $y = x^2 + 1$

5. $y = -x^2 + 2$ 6. $y = x^2 - 2$ 7. $y = x^2 + 4$ 8. $y = -x^2 + 3$

Example 2
(page 695)

Graph each function. 9–12. See back of book.

9. $y = x - x^2$ 10. $y = 2x - x^2$ 11. $y = 5x - x^2$ 12. $y = 8x - x^2$

13. The function $A = 15x - x^2$, where x is the width in yards, gives the area A of a llama pen in square yards. Make a table using $\frac{1}{2}$ units from 0 to 10. Graph the function. Use the graph to find the width that gives the greatest area. **See back of book.**

Example 3
(page 695)

For each function, make a table with integer values of x from -2 to 2. Then graph the function. 14–19. See back of book.

14. $y = 3|x|$ 15. $y = |x| + 3$ 16. $y = -3|x|$

17. $y = |x| - 4$ 18. $y = -|x| - 1$ 19. $y = -2|x|$

B **Apply Your Skills**

State whether the graph of the function has a U shape or a V shape. Make a table with integer values of x from -2 to 2. Then graph the function. 20–28. See back of book.

20. $y = |x| + 1$ 21. $y = x^2 - 8$ 22. $y = 3x - x^2$

23. $y = -4x^2$ 24. $y = -|x| - 3$ 25. $y = 2x^2 - 2$

GPS 26. $y = -\frac{1}{2}|x|$ 27. $y = |x| - 2$ 28. $y = -x^2 + 5$

Reading Math

For help with reading and solving Exercise 29, see page 698.

29. **a.** Graph $y = x^2$, $y = 2x^2$, and $y = \frac{1}{2}x^2$ on the same coordinate plane.
    b. Describe how the coefficients of x^2 affect the graphs.
    a–b. See back of book.

30. **Writing in Math** Describe how the graphs of the functions $y = x^2$, $y = 2x + x^2$, and $y = 2x - x^2$ are alike and how they are different. See back of book.

31. **Open-Ended** Write an absolute value function of your own. Graph the function. **Check students' work.**

C **Challenge**

Writing in Math

How are quadratic and absolute value functions alike? How are they different?

See margin.

32. **Reasoning** For the *cubing function,* $y = x^3$, make a table with integer values of x from -2 to 2. Then graph the function. Is the cubing function a quadratic function? Explain. **See back of book.**

33. **a.** **Geometry** Make a table to show edge lengths and volumes of four cubes. Let the edge lengths be 1 m, 2 m, 3 m, and 4 m.
    b. Graph the ordered pairs from your table. **a–b. See back of book.**
    c. Using your graph from part (b), estimate the volume of a cube with edge length 3.5 m. **about 43 m³**

GPS Use the Guided Problem Solving worksheet with Exercise 26.

Writing in Math
The functions are similar because their graphs open up or down. They are different because quadratic functions are U-shaped and absolute value functions are V-shaped.

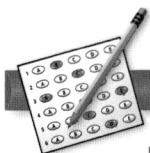

Multiple Choice For Exercises 34–36, use the graph at the right.

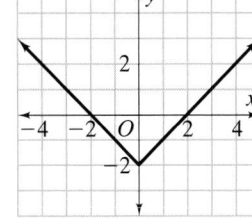

34. The graph shows what type of function? **D**
  A. quadratic   **B.** linear
  C. area   **D.** absolute value

35. Which point is NOT on the graph? **F**
  F. $(1, -2)$ **G.** $(-2, 0)$
  H. $(0, -2)$ **I.** $(1, -1)$

Take It to the NET
Online lesson quiz at
www.PHSchool.com
Web Code: ada-1302

36. Which function matches the graph? **D**
  A. $y = -2|x|$ **B.** $y = x^2 - 2$
  C. $y = |x - 2|$ **D.** $|x| - 2$

Short Response **37.** For the function $y = 3x^2$, **(a)** make a table with integer values of x from -2 to 2. **(b)** Graph the function. *See back of book.*

Mixed Review

Lesson 13-1 **Find the next three terms of each sequence. Then write a rule to describe the sequence.**

38. $\frac{1}{2}, \frac{1}{4}, \frac{1}{8}$; start with 8 and multiply by $\frac{1}{2}$ repeatedly.

38. $8, 4, 2, 1, \ldots$
See left.

39. $12, 27, 42, 57, \ldots$ **40.** $3, 4, 6, 9, \ldots$
39–40. See margin.

Lesson 12-1

41.

Price	Frequency
$6.00	1
$6.50	2
$7.00	5
$7.50	5
$8.00	3
$8.50	2

41. Statistics The table shows the prices of evening movies at 18 different theaters. Use the data to make a frequency table.
See left.

Costs of Movie Tickets

$7.00, $6.50, $7.50, $7.00, $7.50, $8.00, $7.00, $8.50, $8.00, $6.00, $7.00, $7.50, $8.00, $7.00, $7.50, $8.50, $7.50, $6.50

Math at Work

○ ··· **Systems Analyst** ●

Systems analysts are responsible for upgrading hardware and designing and installing new software. They also respond to problems users have with hardware or software. Logic skills are necessary for writing programs and solving problems.

Systems analysts have backgrounds in computer programming. Since computer technology is constantly changing, they must continue their education throughout their careers.

Take It to the NET For more information about systems analysts, go to **www.PHSchool.com**.
Web Code: adb-2031

13-2 Graphing Nonlinear Functions **697**

Alternative Assessment

Direct all students to stand. Read aloud the following in random order: $y = ax^2$, $y = b|x|$ (with various values for a and b), *quadratic, absolute value, parabola.* Have students use their arms to model the basic shapes of the graphs.

Test Prep

📁 **Resources**
For additional practice with a variety of test item formats:
• Test Prep, p. 733
• Test-Taking Strategies, p. 728
• Test-Taking Strategies With Transparencies

---

4. Assess

 Lesson Quiz 13-2

What is the shape of the graph of each function?

1. $y = 3|x| + 5$
  V; opens upward

2. $y = x - 2x^2$
  U; opens downward

3. $y = 14 + x^2$
  U; opens upward

4. $y = 25 - \frac{1}{3}|x|$
  V; opens downward

Error Prevention!

Exercises 20–28 Point out that by looking at the coefficient of $|x|$ in an absolute value function or of x^2 in a quadratic function, you can decide whether the graph of the function opens upward or downward. A positive coefficient indicates upward; a negative coefficient indicates downward. Students can use these rules to help check that graphs they draw are correct.

Error Prevention!

Exercise 22 Students may square $-x$ instead of x. Make sure they understand the difference between $-x^2$ and x^2.

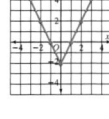

Reteaching 13-2 *Graphing Nonlinear Functions*

Complete the table and graph $y = -2x^2 + 4$.
Substitute each value for x in $y = -2x^2 + 4$ to find the corresponding value of y.

x	$y = -2x^2 + 4$	(x, y)
-2	$y = -2(-2)^2 + 4 = -2(4) + 4 = -8 + 4 = -4$	$(-2, -4)$
-1	$y = -2(-1)^2 + 4 = -2(1) + 4 = -2 + 4 = 2$	$(-1, 2)$
0	$y = -2(0)^2 + 4 = -2(0) + 4 = 0 + 4 = 4$	$(0, 4)$
1	$y = -2(1)^2 + 4 = -2(1) + 4 = -2 + 4 = 2$	$(1, 2)$
2	$y = -2(2)^2 + 4 = -2(4) + 4 = -8 + 4 = -4$	$(2, -4)$

Plot the ordered pairs in the graph. The function is of the form $y = ax^2 + b$ so it is a quadratic function. The graph of a quadratic function is a U-shaped curve called a *parabola*. Connect the plotted points with a parabola.
A function of the form $y = a|x| + b$ is an absolute value function. The graph is V-shaped.

Complete the table and graph the function for the values in the table.
$y = 2|x| - 2$

x	$y = 2|x| - 2$	(x, y)
-2	$y = 2|-2| - 2 = 4 - 2 = 2$	$(-2, 2)$
-1	$y = 2|-1| - 2 = 2 - 2 = 0$	$(-1, 0)$
0	$y = 2|0| - 2 = 0 - 2 = -2$	$(0, -2)$
1	$y = 2|1| - 2 = 2 - 2 = 0$	$(1, 0)$
2	$y = 2|2| - 2 = 4 - 2 = 2$	$(2, 2)$

39. 72, 87, 102; start with 12 and add 15 repeatedly.
40. 13, 18, 24; start with 3 and add 1, 2, 3, . . .

697

Reading a Graph

Students will learn to make a meaningful connection between a function and its graph and then go on to compare two or more graphs.

Teaching Notes

Tactile Learners
Have a volunteer stand in front of the class and model the functions with his or her arms outstretched or ask all students while sitting at their desks to model the functions as you state each function aloud.

Visual Learners
Have students use a different color of pencil for each function graphed in the Exercises.

Auditory Learners
Have students work in pairs to complete the Exercises or other similar problems. Have one student state the function and then have the other student describe the function aloud. Then have students switch roles.

Sometimes you are asked to describe a graph or compare graphs. To do so, you must be able to read the graphs.

EXAMPLE

a. Graph $y = x^2$, $y = 2x^2$, and $y = \frac{1}{2}x^2$ on the same coordinate plane.

b. Describe how the coefficients of x^2 affect the graphs.

a. By the methods of Lesson 13-2, your graphs should look like these.

b. To describe how the coefficient of x^2 affects the graphs, ask these questions. Read the graphs for the answers.

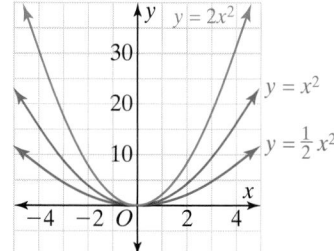

1. How are the graphs alike?

1. All three graphs are parabolas. All contain $(0, 0)$. All open upward.

2. How are the graphs different?

2. From the top down, they get wider.

3. How are the functions alike?

3. All contain x^2.

4. How are the functions different?

4. x^2 has different coefficients.

Now, make a connection and write your answer to part (b).

From the top down:
   Graphs get wider.

From the top down:
$$y = 2x^2$$
$$y = x^2$$
$$y = \frac{1}{2}x^2$$

As the coefficients of x^2 get smaller, the graphs get wider.

EXERCISES

1. For $y = -x^2$, $y = -2x^2$, and $y = -\frac{1}{2}x^2$, describe how the coefficients of x^2 affect the graphs of the functions.
See above right.

2. a. Graph $y = x^2$, $y = x^2 + 2$, and $y = x^2 - 3$ on the same coordinate plane. **a–b. See right.**

  b. Describe how the constants affect the graphs of the functions.

3. For $y = k|x|$, describe how the values of k affect the graphs.
As the coefficients of $|x|$ get closer to zero, the graphs get wider.

1. As the absolute value of the coefficients of x^2 get smaller, the graphs get wider.

2a.

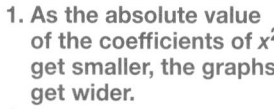
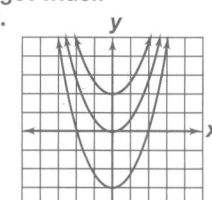

2b. Answers may vary. Sample: The graph is moved up or down the amount of the constant.

Exponential Growth and Decay 13-3

13-3

1. Plan

OBJECTIVE

1 Exponential Growth

A function like $y = 2^x$ has input, or domain, values that are exponents. It models *exponential growth*. Its graph curves upward as input values increase.

1 EXAMPLE Real-World  Problem Solving

Biology A warren of rabbits starts with one male and one female. The number of rabbits then doubles each month. The function $y = 2^x$ models the number of rabbits in the warren.

For the function $y = 2^x$, make a table with integer values of x from 2 to 5. Then graph the function.

x	2^x	y	(x, y)
2	2^2	4	(2, 4)
3	2^3	8	(3, 8)
4	2^4	16	(4, 16)
5	2^5	32	(5, 32)

✓ Check Understanding Example 1

1. For the function $y = 3^x$, make a table with integer values of x from 1 to 4. Then graph the function. **See right.**

You can multiply the power in a function by a number. For example, in $y = 0.25(4^x)$, the power 4^x is multiplied by 0.25.

What You'll Learn

OBJECTIVE 1 To use tables, rules, and graphs with functions modeling growth

OBJECTIVE 2 To use tables, rules, and graphs with functions modeling decay

. . . And Why

To model real-world situations involving population growth

✓ Check Skills You'll Need

Evaluate each expression.

1. 5^2 **2.** 4^3 **3.** 3^5 **4.** 2^8
   25   64   243   256
For help, go to Lesson 4-2.

1.

x	3^x	y	(x, y)
1	3^1	3	(1, 3)
2	3^2	9	(2, 9)
3	3^3	27	(3, 27)
4	3^4	81	(4, 81)

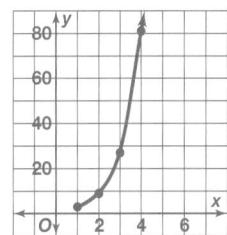

TEXT Interactive lesson includes instant self-check, tutorials, and activities.

13-3 Exponential Growth and Decay **699**

Ongoing Assessment and Intervention

Before the Lesson
Diagnose prerequisite skills using:
• Check Skills You'll Need

During the Lesson
Monitor progress using:
• Check Understanding
• Additional Examples
• Test Prep

After the Lesson
Assess knowledge using:
• Lesson Quiz
• Computer Test Generator CD-ROM
• Chapter Checkpoint 1 (p. 702)

Lesson Preview

✓ Check Skills You'll Need

Exponents
Lesson 4-2: Example 2;
Exercises 7–12.
Extra Practice, p. 747.

Lesson Resources

 Teaching Resources
Practice, Reteaching, Enrichment
Checkpoint Quiz 1

Reaching All Students
Practice Workbook 13-3
Spanish Practice Workbook 13-3
Reading and Math Literacy 13B
Spanish Reading and Math Literacy 13B
Spanish Checkpoint Quiz 1
Guided Problem Solving 13-3
Hands-On Activities 32

 Presentation Assistant Plus!
Transparencies and PowerPoint™
• Check Skills You'll Need 13-3
• Additional Examples 13-3
• Student Edition Answers 13-3
• Lesson Quiz 13-3
• Classroom Aid 2
PH Presentation Pro CD-ROM 13-3

ASSESSMENT SYSTEM

Checkpoint Quiz 1
Computer Test Generator CD-ROM

 Technology
Resource Pro® CD-ROM
Computer Test Generator CD-ROM
PH Presentation Pro CD-ROM

www.PHSchool.com
Student Site
• Teacher Web Code: adk-5500
• Graphing Calculator, Procedure 2
• Self-grading Lesson Quiz
PH SuccessNet Teacher Center
• Lesson Planner
• Resources

Plus **TEXT**

699

Math Background

Exponential functions are used to model growth and decay. The graph of an exponential-growth function rises from left to right at an ever-increasing rate, while that of an exponential-decay function falls from left to right at an ever-decreasing rate.

Teaching Notes

1 EXAMPLE English Learners

Some students may not know the meaning of *warren*. Inform them that a warren is a place where a family or group of rabbits live, such as a hole or tunnel in the ground.

1 EXAMPLE Error Prevention

Students may evaluate 2^x the same way they evaluated $2x$. Display in a table the values found by substituting 1, 2, and 3 for x in both 2^x and $2x$. Help students recognize that $y = 2^x$ and $y = 2x$ are different functions.

3 EXAMPLE Teaching Tip

Remind students that powers of fractions decrease in value as the exponent increases. For example, $\left(\frac{1}{2}\right)^1 = \frac{1}{2}$, $\left(\frac{1}{2}\right)^2 = \frac{1}{4}$, $\left(\frac{1}{2}\right)^3 = \frac{1}{8}$.

PowerPoint

Additional Examples

1 For the function $y = 4^x$, make a table with integer values of x from 1 to 4. Then graph the function.
1–3. See back of book.

2 For $y = 4(2)^x$, make a table with integer values of x from 0 to 4. Then graph the function.

3 For the function $y = 2(0.5)^x$, make a table with integer values of x from 0 to 5. Then graph the function.

Closure

Ask: *How can you distinguish an exponential-growth function from an exponential-decay function?*
See back of book.

700

---

2 For the function $y = 0.5(2)^x$, table:

x	$0.5(2)^x$	y	(x, y)
0	$0.5(2)^0$	0.5	(0, 0.5)
1	$0.5(2)^1$	1	(1, 1)
2	$0.5(2)^2$	2	(2, 2)
3	$0.5(2)^3$	4	(3, 4)
4	$0.5(2)^4$	8	(4, 8)
5	$0.5(2)^5$	16	(5, 16)

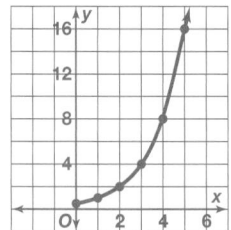

---

2 EXAMPLE Graphing Exponential Growth

For the function $y = 0.25(4)^x$, make a table with integer values of x from 0 to 4. Then graph the function.

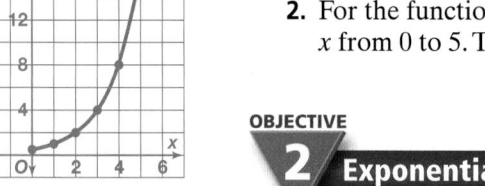

x	$0.25(4)^x$	y	(x, y)
0	$0.25(4)^0$	0.25	(0, 0.25)
1	$0.25(4)^1$	1	(1, 1)
2	$0.25(4)^2$	4	(2, 4)
3	$0.25(4)^3$	16	(3, 16)
4	$0.25(4)^4$	64	(4, 64)

✓ **Check Understanding** Example 2

2. For the function $y = 0.5(2)^x$, make a table with integer values of x from 0 to 5. Then graph the function. **See left.**

OBJECTIVE

2 Exponential Decay

A function like $y = \left(\frac{1}{2}\right)^x$ models *exponential decay*. Its graph slopes downward as input values increase.

3 EXAMPLE Graphing Exponential Decay

For $y = 60\left(\frac{1}{2}\right)^x$, make a table with integer values of x from 0 to 5. Then graph the function.

x	$60\left(\frac{1}{2}\right)^x$	y	(x, y)
0	$60\left(\frac{1}{2}\right)^0$	60	(0, 60)
1	$60\left(\frac{1}{2}\right)^1$	30	(1, 30)
2	$60\left(\frac{1}{2}\right)^2$	15	(2, 15)
3	$60\left(\frac{1}{2}\right)^3$	7.5	(3, 7.5)
4	$60\left(\frac{1}{2}\right)^4$	3.75	(4, 3.75)
5	$60\left(\frac{1}{2}\right)^5$	1.875	(5, 1.875)

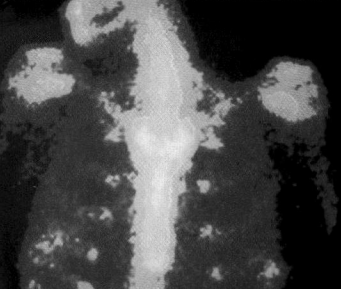

Real-World Connection

Doctors use the element technetium to make bone scans. Technetium decays exponentially. After 6 hours, only 15 mg of a 30-mg dose remain. After 12 hours, only 7.5 mg remain.

✓ **Check Understanding** Example 3

3. For the function $y = 90\left(\frac{1}{3}\right)^x$, make a table with integer values of x from 0 to 5. Then graph the function. **See back of book.**

Reaching All Students

Below Level Ask: *Would a straight line be an accurate model of a savings-account balance over 10 years if no money is withdrawn?* No; the balance increases by greater amounts each year.	**Advanced Learners** Ask: *I give one student one bean, the next student two beans, the third student four beans, etc. What function shows the number of beans each student gets?* $y = 2^{n-1}$, n = number of students	**English Learners** See note on page 700. **Error Prevention** See note on page 700.

EXERCISES

 For more exercises, see *Extra Practice*.

Practice and Problem Solving

3. Practice

Assignment Guide

1 Objective 1
Ⓐ Ⓑ Core 1–7, 13–17, 21–24
Ⓒ Extension 26

2 Objective 2
Ⓐ Ⓑ Core 8–12, 18–20, 25
Ⓒ Extension 27

Test Prep 28–33
Mixed Review 34–39

Ⓐ **Practice by Example**

Examples 1 and 2
(pages 699 and 700)

Make a table with integer values of x from 0 to 4. Then graph the function. 1–6. See back of book.

1. $y = 4^x$ **2.** $y = 5^x$ **3.** $y = 6^x$

4. $y = 0.4(2)^x$ **5.** $y = 0.5(4)^x$ **6.** $y = 0.2(5)^x$

7. Biology A bacteria culture starts with ten cells and doubles every hour. The function $y = 10(2)^x$ models the number of cells y in the culture after x hours. Make a table with integer values of x from 0 to 3. Then graph the function. See below left.

Example 3
(page 700)

Make a table with integer values of x from 0 to 5. Then graph the function. 8–10. See back of book.

8. $y = \left(\frac{1}{2}\right)^x$ **9.** $y = 30\left(\frac{1}{3}\right)^x$ **10.** $y = 100\left(\frac{1}{5}\right)^x$

Ⓑ **Apply Your Skills**

Match each graph with an equation.

7.

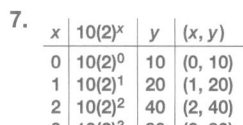

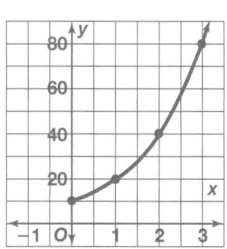

11.

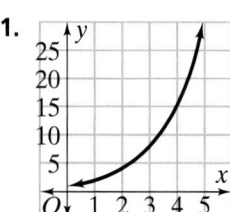

A. $y = 3^x$ **B.** $y = 2^x$

12.

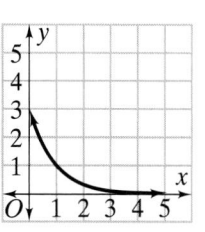

A. $y = 3\left(\frac{1}{3}\right)^x$ **B.** $y = 2\left(\frac{1}{2}\right)^x$

You put \$100 in a stock that increases in value by 20% each year. The function $v = 100(1.2)^x$ describes the value v of the stock after x years.

13. Evaluate the function for $x = 2$. What does the value represent?
144; this is the value of the stock after 2 years.

14. For the function, make a table with integer values of x from 0 to 6. Graph the function. See left.

15. Reasoning Use your graph from Exercise 14. Estimate how long it will take for the value to be twice the initial investment.
Answers may vary. Sample: 3 years 10 months

14.

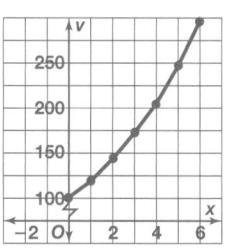

Make a table with integer values of x from 0 to 4. Then graph the function. 16–21. See back of book.

16. $y = 2 \cdot 3^x$ **17.** $y = \frac{1}{5} \cdot 5^x$ **18.** $y = 6(0.5)^x$

19. $f(x) = \frac{1}{2} \cdot 2^x$ **20.** $g(x) = 20\left(\frac{1}{2}\right)^x$ **21.** $g(x) = 3 \cdot 2^x$

Is the point (4, 16) on the graph of each function? Explain.

22. $y = 4x$ **23.** $y = 2^x$ **24.** $y = x^2$ **25.** $y = \left(\frac{1}{2}\right)^x$

yes; $4(4) = 16$ yes; $2^4 = 16$ yes; $4^2 = 16$ no; $\left(\frac{1}{2}\right)^4 \neq 16$

13-3 Exponential Growth and Decay   **701**

GPS Use the Guided Problem Solving worksheet with Exercise 7.

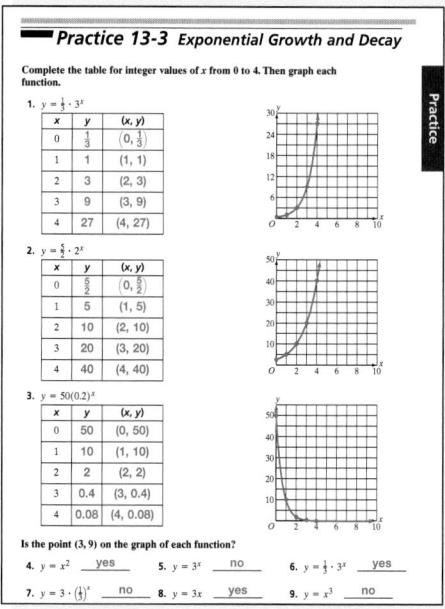

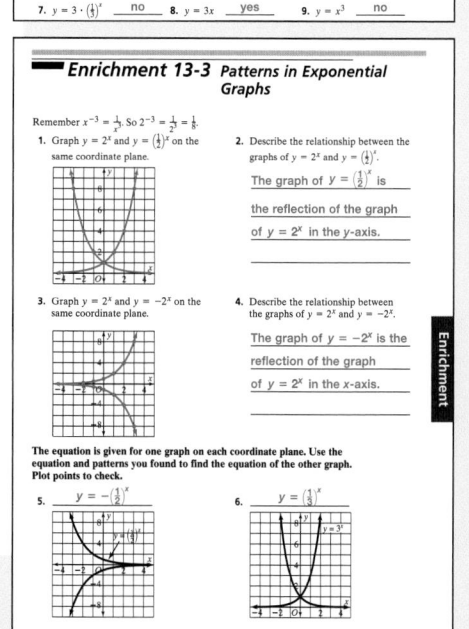

✓ Chapter Checkpoint 1

To check understanding of Lessons 13-1 to 13-3:

Checkpoint Quiz 1 (p. 702)

📁 **Teaching Resources**
Checkpoint Quiz 1 (also in Prentice Hall Assessment System)

👥 **Reaching All Students**
Reading and Math Literacy 13B

Spanish versions available.

Test Prep

📁 **Resources**
For additional practice with a variety of test item formats:
• Test Prep, p. 733
• Test-Taking Strategies, p. 728
• Test-Taking Strategies With Transparencies

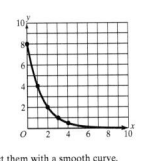

Reteaching 13-3 *Exponential Growth and Decay*

Complete the table and graph the function $y = 8\left(\frac{1}{2}\right)^x$. Substitute each value of x into the equation and find the corresponding value of y.

x	$y = 8\left(\frac{1}{2}\right)^x$	(x, y)
0	$y = 8\left(\frac{1}{2}\right)^0 = 8 \cdot 1 = 8$	(0, 8)
1	$y = 8\left(\frac{1}{2}\right)^1 = 8 \cdot \frac{1}{2} = 4$	(1, 4)
2	$y = 8\left(\frac{1}{2}\right)^2 = 8 \cdot \frac{1}{4} = 2$	(2, 2)
3	$y = 8\left(\frac{1}{2}\right)^3 = 8 \cdot \frac{1}{8} = 1$	(3, 1)
4	$y = 8\left(\frac{1}{2}\right)^4 = 8 \cdot \frac{1}{16} = \frac{1}{2}$	$\left(4, \frac{1}{2}\right)$

Plot the ordered pairs in the graph and connect them with a smooth curve. Put arrows at the end of the curve to show it continues.

Complete the table and graph the function.

$y = \frac{5}{8} \cdot 2^x$

x	$y = \frac{5}{8} \cdot 2^x$	(x, y)
0	$y = \frac{5}{8} \cdot 2^0 = \frac{5}{8} \cdot 1 = \frac{5}{8}$	$\left(0, \frac{5}{8}\right)$
1	$y = \frac{5}{8} \cdot 2^1 = \frac{5}{8} \cdot 2 = \frac{5}{4}$	$\left(1, \frac{5}{4}\right)$
2	$y = \frac{5}{8} \cdot 2^2 = \frac{5}{8} \cdot 4 = \frac{5}{2}$	$\left(2, \frac{5}{2}\right)$
3	$y = \frac{5}{8} \cdot 2^3 = \frac{5}{8} \cdot 8 = 5$	(3, 5)
4	$y = \frac{5}{8} \cdot 2^4 = \frac{5}{8} \cdot 16 = 10$	(4, 10)

Reteaching

C Challenge

26. a. For the functions $y = 2x$, $y = x^2$, and $y = 2^x$, make tables with integer values of x from 0 to 5. Then graph the functions.

b. **Writing in Math** Describe how the graphs are similar. Describe how they are different.
a–b. See back of book.

27a. growth, because $5 > 1$
b. decay, because $\frac{1}{2} < 1$
c. decay, because $0.2 < 1$
d. growth, because $2 > 1$
See left.

27. Reasoning Without graphing, predict whether each function shows exponential growth or exponential decay. Justify your prediction.

a. $y = 5^x$ **b.** $y = \left(\frac{1}{2}\right)^x$ **c.** $y = 3(0.2)^x$ **d.** $y = 3(2)^x$

Test Prep

Gridded Response For the given equation, what is the value of y for $x = 2$?

28. $y = 0.2(3)^x$ **29.** $y = 3\left(\frac{1}{3}\right)^x$ **30.** $y = 3x^2 - 6$ **31.** $y = 4|x| - 1$
1.8 · · · · · · · · · · · · · · 1/3 · · · · · · · · · · · · · · 6 · · · · · · · · · · · · · · 7

For Exercises 32 and 33, use the formula $B = p(1.08)^n$ to find the balance B (in dollars and cents) for a principal p invested at a compound interest rate of 8% for n years.

Take It to the NET
Online lesson quiz at
www.PHSchool.com
Web Code: ada-1303

32. $50 invested for 5 years
73.47

33. $25 invested for 10 years
53.97

Mixed Review

Lesson 13-2 **Graph each function.** 34–36. See back of book.

34. $y = |x| + 2$ **35.** $f(x) = 3|x|$ **36.** $g(x) = -x^2 + 1$

Lesson 12-4 🌐 **37. Shopping** Janelle is buying a sweatshirt. She has a choice of red, purple, or green; zipper or no zipper; and hooded or not hooded. How many different sweatshirt choices does she have?
12 choices

Lesson 11-3 **Find the midpoint of each segment with the given endpoints.**

38. $A(4, -6)$ and $B(-2, 5)$
(1, −0.5)

39. $X(-3, -8)$ and $Y(1, 6)$
(−1, −1)

✓ Checkpoint Quiz 1 Lessons 13-1 through 13-3

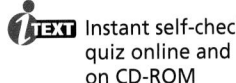

iTEXT Instant self-check quiz online and on CD-ROM

Find the next three terms of each sequence. Then write a rule to describe the sequence. 1–3. See left.

1. 40, 25, 10; start with 100 and add −15 repeatedly.
2. 45, 52, 59; start with 17 and add 7 repeatedly.
3. 208, 416, 832; start with 13 and multiply by 2 repeatedly.

1. $100, 85, 70, 55, \ldots$ **2.** $17, 24, 31, 38, \ldots$ **3.** $13, 26, 52, 104, \ldots$

4. A geometric sequence begins with 3 and has common ratio 2. Write its first five terms. 3, 6, 12, 24, 48

For each function, make a table with integer values of x. (Use −2 to 2 for Ex. 5 and 6; use 0 to 4 for Ex. 7.) Then graph the function.
5–7. See back of book.

5. $y = \frac{1}{4}x^2$ **6.** $f(x) = \frac{1}{4}|x|$ **7.** $f(x) = 0.5(3)^x$

Alternative Assessment

Have students work in pairs. Have some pairs make posters showing the graphs of $y = 1^x$, $y = 2^x$, and $y = 3^x$. Have the remaining pairs make posters showing the graphs of $y = 1^x$, $y = \left(\frac{1}{2}\right)^x$, and $y = \left(\frac{1}{3}\right)^x$.

2 EXAMPLE Naming a Polynomial

State whether the polynomial is a *monomial*, a *binomial*, or a *trinomial*.

a. $x - y$
  binomial

b. $8xyz$
  monomial

c. $y^2 + 8y + 18$
  trinomial

✓ Check Understanding Example 2

2. Is the polynomial a monomial, a binomial, or a trinomial?

a. 10
  monomial

b. $9x^2 + xy$
  binomial

c. $8 - y$
  binomial

d. $5 + x - 3y$
  trinomial

OBJECTIVE

2 Evaluating Polynomials

You evaluate polynomials by substituting values for the variables.

3 EXAMPLE Evaluating a Polynomial

Evaluate each polynomial for $m = 8$ and $p = -3$.

a. $2mp$

$$2mp = 2(8)(-3) \quad \textbf{Replace } m \textbf{ with 8 and } p \textbf{ with } -3.$$
$$= -48 \qquad \textbf{Simplify.}$$

b. $3m - 2p$

$$3m - 2p = 3(8) - 2(-3)$$
$$= 24 + 6$$
$$= 30$$

✓ Check Understanding Example 3

3. Evaluate each polynomial for $x = -2$ and $y = 5$.

a. $5xy$ -50

b. $x + 3y$ 13

c. $y^2 - 2y + x$ 13

4 EXAMPLE Real-World 🌐 Problem Solving

Physics The polynomial $-16t^2 + 140t$ gives the height, in feet, reached by fireworks in t seconds. If the fireworks explode 4 seconds after launch, at what height do they explode?

$$-16t^2 + 140t$$
$$-16(4)^2 + 140(4) \quad \textbf{Replace } t \textbf{ with 4.}$$
$$304 \qquad \textbf{Simplify.}$$

The fireworks explode at 304 feet.

✓ Check Understanding Example 4

4. Fireworks are set to explode 6 seconds after launch. At what height will they explode?   **264 ft**

Real-World 🌐 Connection

During a twenty-minute show, fireworks technicians can set off as many as 6,000 different fireworks.

13-4 Polynomials **705**

---

2. Teach

Professional Development

Math Background

A *polynomial* is an algebraic expression of one or more terms in which the simplified form has no variables in a denominator, no variables under a radical sign, and no variables with negative integer exponents. Expressions that are not polynomials include $\frac{1}{x}$, $\sqrt{x}$, and x^{-2}.

Teaching Notes

1 EXAMPLE Error Prevention

Help students understand why $\frac{m}{6}$ is a monomial, but $\frac{6}{m}$ is not. You can rewrite $\frac{m}{6}$ as $\frac{1}{6} \cdot m^1$, but $\frac{6}{m}$ is rewritten as $6 \cdot \frac{1}{m}$, or $6 \cdot m^{-1}$. The definition of a monomial requires that a variable factor in a monomial have a whole-number exponent.

2 EXAMPLE Visual Learners

Have students copy each expression, and then circle each addition or subtraction sign. Point out that these signs are the key to identifying types of polynomials.

PowerPoint

🖳 Additional Examples

1 Is each expression a monomial? Explain. **See back of book.**
a. $5 + c$ b. $\frac{7z}{3}$ c. $6ab^2$ d. $\frac{4g}{h}$

2 Tell whether each polynomial is a *monomial*, a *binomial*, or a *trinomial*.
a. $14x^2 + 2xy - 7y^2$ trinomial
b. $\frac{11a^2bc}{3}$ monomial
c. $z + 10$ binomial

3 Evaluate each polynomial for $r = 2$ and $s = 7$.
a. $5r^2 - s$ 13 b. $\frac{6rs}{3}$ 28

4 The polynomial $-16t^2 + 100t$ gives the height, in feet, reached by a fireworks shell in t seconds. If the shell explodes 5 seconds after launch, at what height did it explode? **100 ft**

Closure

Ask students: *How do you name a polynomial?*
See back of book.

👥 Reaching All Students

Below Level Ask students the difference between a bicycle and a tricycle. Discuss the meanings of the prefixes *bi-* and *tri-*.	**Advanced Learners** Ask students whether $\frac{15x^2y}{2x}$ is a polynomial and explain. **See back of book.**	**Error Prevention** See note on page 705. **Visual Learners** See note on page 705.

705

3. Practice

Assignment Guide

1 **Objective 1**
  Ⓐ Ⓑ **Core** 1–17, 28–42

2 **Objective 2**
  Ⓐ Ⓑ **Core** 18–27, 43–48
  Ⓒ **Extension** 49–53

Test Prep 54–57
Mixed Review 58–64

Practice 13-4 Polynomials

Evaluate each polynomial for $x = -1$, $y = 3$, and $z = 2$.

1. $x^2 + z$ __3__
2. $3y + x$ __8__
3. $2z + y$ __7__
4. $x + y + z$ __4__
5. $x^2 + y^2$ __10__
6. $z - x - y$ __0__

Evaluate each polynomial for $m = 21$, $n = -9$, and $p = 28$.

7. $3m - 2p$ __7__
8. $2n^2 - 5m$ __57__
9. $m^2 - n^2$ __360__
10. $n^2 + 5n - 6$ __30__
11. $5p^2 - 5p$ __3,780__
12. $7m + 6p$ __315__

Solve using the given polynomials.

13. Find the number of diagonals that can be drawn in a polygon with 24 sides.
$N = \frac{1}{2}n^2 - \frac{3}{2}n$
N = number of diagonals
n = number of sides
    252 diagonals

14. A rock thrown from the top of a cliff with an initial velocity of 3 m/s takes 6.2 s to reach the bottom. To the nearest meter, how tall is the cliff?
$d = 4.9t^2 - vt$
d = distance fallen
t = time falling
v = initial velocity
    170 m

Tell whether each polynomial is a *monomial*, a *binomial*, or a *trinomial*.

15. $36abc$ __monomial__
16. $10 - h^3$ __binomial__
17. $95xy + y$ __binomial__
18. $a^2 + b^2 + cd$ __trinomial__
19. $3k$ __monomial__
20. $-12e + 12f^2$ __binomial__

Enrichment 13-4 Interesting Polynomials

The following problem uses polynomials.
Jason is 16 years old. Each year, beginning with his 13th birthday, his mother has given him $100. He invests the money at an annual yield of 6%.

1. How much money did Jason get on his 13th birthday? __$100__

If 6% is the interest rate, we can express the interest as 100(0.06). We can express the total amount in the account at the end of the first year as $100 + 100(0.06)$. Another way is 106% of $100 or 100(1.06).

2. Money in the account after Jason's 14th birthday: 100(1.06) + __$100__

3. During the year the amount in the account earns 6% interest. Use the distributive property to write the addition expression another way so that it represents the total amount in the account.
Money in the account after earning 6% interest: 1.06[100(1.06) + 100] =
    __$100(1.06)^2 + 100(1.06)$__

4. Money in the account after Jason's 15th birthday:
$100(1.06)^2 + 100(1.06) +$ __$100__

5. Money in the account after earning 6% interest:
$1.06[100(1.06)^2 + 100(1.06) + 100] =$
    __$100(1.06)^3 + 100(1.06)^2 + 100(1.06)$__

A spreadsheet can be used to organize and evaluate the data.

	A	B	C	D
1	amount before birthday	birthday year	amount added	total
2	0	13	100	100
3	106	14	100	206

6. Write a formula for each of the following cells.
$A4 =$ __D3 * 1.06__ $D4 =$ __A4 + C4__ $A5 =$ __D4 * 1.06__
$D5 =$ __A5 + C5__ $A6 =$ __D5 * 1.06__ $D6 =$ __A6 + C6__

7. How much money is in his account after his 16th birthday?
    __$437.46__

8. Explain how the polynomial, $100y^3 + 100y^2 + 100y + 100$ represents the amount of money in Jason's account just after his 16th birthday.
    __y represents 1.06 in the expression__
    __$100(1.06)^3 + 100(1.06)^2 + 100(1.06) + 100$__

706

EXERCISES

 For more exercises, see *Extra Practice*.

Practice and Problem Solving

Ⓐ **Practice by Example**

Example 1
(page 704)

Is the expression a monomial? Explain. 1–2. See below left.

1. $2 + x$
2. $18ab^2$
3. $\frac{a}{3}$
4. $\frac{4}{b}$
5. 1
6. $0.82k$
7. $2x$
8. $-0.3y$

3–8. See margin.

Example 2
(page 705)

State whether the polynomial is a *monomial*, a *binomial*, or a *trinomial*.

9. $3xy + 4y^2$ binomial
10. $5c - 2 + a$ trinomial
11. $7y^2 + 2y - 9$ trinomial
12. 658 monomial
13. $3x^2 + 2x$ binomial
14. 21 monomial
15. $7p^2$ monomial
16. $56 - x$ binomial
17. $a^2 + 7b - 3c$ trinomial

Example 3
(page 705)

Evaluate each polynomial for $a = 2$ and $b = -4$.

18. $2ab$ −16
19. $-4ab$ 32
20. $7a + b$ 10
21. $a - 3b$ 14
22. $5a + 7b$ −18
23. $ab^2 + 5$ 37
24. $a^2 + 2b - 3$ −7
25. $2a^2 - b + 4$ 16
26. $10a + b^2 - 7$ 29

Example 4
(page 705)
GPS

27. **Sports** The polynomial $-16t^2 + 32t + 4$ gives the height, in feet, that a tossed ball reaches in t seconds. If the ball reaches a maximum height after one second, what is that height? **20 ft**

Ⓑ **Apply Your Skills**

Is the expression a monomial? Explain. 28–31. See left.

28. pq^{-3}
29. 0
30. $\frac{3}{p}$
31. $10bc + b$

28. No; a variable has an exponent that is not a whole number.
29. Yes; it is a real number.
30. No; the denominator contains a variable.
31. No; it is a sum.

State whether the polynomial is a *monomial*, a *binomial*, a *trinomial* or *none* of these. 32–39. See left.

32. $4.5 + 3.7m$
33. $2x - 4^{-1}$
34. -42
35. $x^2 + 7x + 4$
36. $3a^2 - 6a^{-3}$
37. $15 + w$
38. abc
39. $b^2 + \frac{2}{b} - 3$

32. binomial
33. binomial
34. monomial
35. trinomial
36. none of these
37. binomial
38. monomial
39. none of these

40. **Open-Ended** Write a polynomial with four terms.
Answers may vary. Sample: $3a^2 + 2b - 3c + 5$

41. **Geometry** You can write the formula for the area of a trapezoid as $A = \frac{1}{2}b_1h + \frac{1}{2}b_2h$. What kind of polynomial is $\frac{1}{2}b_1h + \frac{1}{2}b_2h$? binomial

42. a. **Writing in Math** Name other words with the prefixes *mono*, *bi*, *tri*, and *poly*. How do the prefixes help you understand the meanings of the words? a–b. See left.

  b. What would you call a polynomial with four terms?

42a. Answers may vary. Sample: monotone, bicycle, trilogy, polygon; the prefixes tell you the number of items involved.
b. Answers may vary. Sample: quadrinomial

Evaluate each polynomial for $x = -5$ and $y = 3$.

43. $2x + 2y$ −4
44. $7 + x^2y$ 82
45. $7y^2 + 6x - 20$ 13
46. $xy - y$ −18
47. $x^2 + 2x - 3$ 12
48. $\frac{x^2}{5} + x$ 0

706   Chapter 13   Nonlinear Functions and Polynomials

 Use the Guided Problem Solving worksheet with Exercise 27.

3. Yes, it is a product of the real number $\frac{1}{3}$ and the variable a.

4. No, the denominator contains a variable.

5. Yes, it is a real number.

6. Yes, it is a product of the real number 0.82 and the variable k.

7. Yes, it is the product of the real number 2 and the variable x.

8. Yes, it is the product of the real number −0.3 and the variable y.

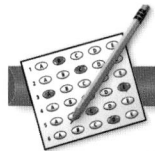

C Challenge

Reasoning Tell why each expression is not a polynomial.

49. $x^2 + 2x + \frac{1}{x}$ **50.** $2ab + b^2 + \sqrt{a}$ **51.** $(y^2 + 4) \div y$
49–51. See left.

49. The term $\frac{1}{x}$ contains a variable in the denominator.
50. $\sqrt{a}$ is not a monomial.
51. The expression is a quotient with a variable in the denominator.

52. a. Public Schools The polynomial $34x^2 - 945x + 46{,}971$ models U.S. public school enrollment, in thousands, from 1970 to 1998. The value of x for 1970 is 1 and the value of x for 1998 is 29. How many students were enrolled in public schools in 1970? In 1998?

52a. 46,060,000 students;
    48,160,000 students
b. 65,380,000 students

    b. Use the polynomial to predict enrollment in 2010.
    a–b. See left.

53. Geometry A polygon is convex if no diagonal has points outside the polygon. The polynomial $\frac{n^2}{2} - \frac{3n}{2}$ gives the number of diagonals that you can draw in a convex polygon with n sides. How many diagonals does a 20-sided convex polygon have?
170 diagonals

Test Prep

Multiple Choice

54. Which of the following statements is NOT true? **C**
    A. A monomial is a polynomial.
    B. A binomial is a sum or difference of two monomials.
    C. A polynomial must have more than one term.
    D. An integer is a monomial.

Take It to the NET
Online lesson quiz at
www.PHSchool.com
Web Code: ada-1304

55. The area of a trapezoid is $\frac{1}{2}b_1h + \frac{1}{2}b_2h$, where h is the height and b_1 and b_2 are the lengths of the bases. What is the area of a trapezoid with height 13 in., one base 4 in., and the other base twice as long? **H**
    F. 39 in.^{2} **G.** 52 in.^{2} **H.** 78 in.^{2} **I.** 130 in.^{2}

Short Response

56. Is $\frac{4}{x}$ a monomial? Explain. See back of book.

57. a. Write an example of a monomial, a binomial, and a trinomial.
    b. Explain why each is that type of polynomial.
    [2] Correct examples. Samples: monomial: $3x^2$, has one term; binomial: $8 - 2k$, has two terms; trinomial: $2b + 5 - 4z$, has three terms [1] minor error OR answers only

Mixed Review

Lesson 13-3

For each function make a table with integer values of x from 1 to 4. Then graph each function. 58–60. See back of book.

58. $y = 2 \cdot 2^x$ **59.** $f(x) = \frac{1}{3} \cdot 3^x$ **60.** $y = 18(0.2)^x$

Lesson 11-7 **61. Navigation** A plane is flying 6.3 mi above the ground. The angle of depression to an airport is 14°. How far is the plane from the airport (in ground distance)? about 25.3 mi

Lesson 2-3

Simplify each expression.

62. $m + 5 + 3m$ **63.** $2y - 1 + 6x + 5$ **64.** $4a + 10b - 7a - 2$
    $4m + 5$ $2y + 6x + 4$ $-3a + 10b - 2$

 **Lesson Quiz 13-4**

Tell whether each expression is a *monomial, binomial, trinomial,* or *not a polynomial.*

1. $\frac{14c^2}{b}$ not a polynomial

2. $s + 14 - t$ trinomial

3. 8 monomial

4. $6x + 2y$ binomial

5. Evaluate $7m - 3p$ for $m = 3$ and $p = -5$. 36

6. The polynomial $-16t^2 + 120t$ gives the height, in feet, reached by a fireworks shell in t seconds. What is the height of the shell after 5 seconds? 200 ft

Test Prep

 Resources
For additional practice with a variety of test item formats:
• Test Prep, p. 733
• Test-Taking Strategies, p. 728
• Test-Taking Strategies With Transparencies

Reteaching 13-4 *Polynomials*

The polynomial $d = 4.9t^2 - vt$ gives the distance d in meters an object has fallen after t seconds if it is thrown down with an initial velocity v. A rock is thrown from the top of a cliff with an initial velocity of 2 m/s. The rock takes 7.3 s to reach the bottom. To the nearest meter, how tall is the cliff?

$d = 4.9t^2 - vt$ Substitute 7.3 for t and 2 for v.

$d = 4.9(7.3)^2 - 2(7.3)$

$d = 4.9(53.29) - 2(7.3)$ Evaluate using the order of operations. Evaluate the power first.

$d = 261.121 - 14.6$ Multiply.

$d = 246.521$ Subtract.
$d \approx 247$ meters   Round.

Use the polynomial $d = 4.9t^2 - vt$ to find the distance each object falls for the given time and initial velocity. Round to the nearest meter.

1. $t = 7$ s, $v = 3$ m/s   **2.** $t = 6$ s, $v = 3.5$ m/s
    219 m   155 m

3. $t = 5.7$ s, $v = 2$ m/s   **4.** $t = 6.4$ s, $v = 2.8$ m/s
    148 m   183 m

Evaluate each polynomial for $x = -2$ and $y = 3$.

5. $x^2 - 2x - 5$ **6.** $xy + y^2 + 2x$
    3   −1

7. $9 - 3x^2$ **8.** $x^2 - 2xy - y^2$
    −3   7

9. The polynomial $S = 2\pi r^2 + 2\pi rh$ gives the surface area of a cylinder with radius r and height h. Find the surface area of a cylinder with radius 8 cm and height 14 cm, to the nearest cm^2.
    1,105 cm^2

Alternative Assessment

Say the words *monomial, binomial,* and *trinomial* aloud and have students write an example of each. Then have them write an expression that is not a polynomial of any type.

Degree of a Polynomial

In this Extension, students learn to identify the degree of a polynomial.

Teaching Notes

Teaching Tip

Point out that in a polynomial only one of its terms determines the degree of the polynomial. This is the term that has the greatest sum of exponents on its variables.

1 EXAMPLE Error Prevention

Stress that only the powers of the variables, not the coefficients, affect the degree of a polynomial.

 **Extension** **Degree of a Polynomial**

For Use With Lesson 13-4

Just as you can get information about a polynomial by counting the number of terms, you can get other information by looking at the exponents. The *degree of a term* is the sum of the exponents of the variables in the term. The *degree of a polynomial* is the greatest degree of its terms.

polynomial $\longrightarrow$ $x^3 + 4x^2 + xy - 5x + 9$ $\longleftarrow$ The degree of a nonzero constant is zero.

degree of each term $\longrightarrow$ 3   2   2   1   0

Degree of the polynomial is 3.

1 EXAMPLE

Identify each polynomial by name and by degree.

a. $2 - a$

    0   1 $\longleftarrow$ degree of each term

Greatest degree of the two terms is 1.

The polynomial is a binomial of degree 1.

b. $3y^3x$

    4 $\longleftarrow$ Add the exponents: $3 + 1 = 4$.

Degree of the one term is 4.

The polynomial is a monomial of degree 4.

c. $5x^2 + x + 4$

    2   1   0 $\longleftarrow$ degree of each term

Greatest degree of the three terms is 2.

The polynomial is a trinomial of degree 2.

When you write a polynomial with the terms in order of decreasing degree, the polynomial is in *standard form.* If you need to move terms to do this, you can first write subtractions as additions and then use the Commutative Property of Addition. For example, first write $4 - x^2$ as $4 + (-x^2)$. Then rewrite the polynomial as $-x^2 + 4$.

Auditory Learners

Exercises 1–8 Group students in pairs and have them take turns identifying (and explaining) aloud the polynomial and the degree.

3 EXAMPLE **Visual Learners**

Suggest that students copy each problem. Then have them circle, underline, and box to indicate and distinguish the like terms they will combine.

Additional Example

Simplify the polynomial and write it in standard form. Then identify the result as a monomial, binomial, or trinomial, and state its degree.
$8 + 7d - 2d^2 - 5 - 3d + d^2$
$-d^2 + 4d + 3$; trinomial of degree 2

2 EXAMPLE

Write each polynomial in standard form.

a. $x^4 + 2 - x^2$

$\quad$ 4 $\quad$ 0 $\quad$ 2 $\longleftarrow$ degree of each term

$\quad$ standard form: $x^4 - x^2 + 2$

b. $-2y + y^3 + y^2 - 3$

$\quad$ 1 $\quad$ 3 $\quad$ 2 $\quad$ 0 $\longleftarrow$ degree of each term

$\quad$ standard form: $y^3 + y^2 - 2y - 3$

When you simplify a polynomial, write your result in standard form.

3 EXAMPLE

Simplify each polynomial.

a. $5a + a^2 + 3a^2 + 2$

$\quad 5a + (1 + 3)a^2 + 2$ $\quad$ **Combine like terms.**

$\quad 5a + 4a^2 + 2$ $\quad$ **Simplify.**

$\quad 4a^2 + 5a + 2$ $\quad$ **Write in standard form.**

b. $3x - 8x + 2x^2 + 4x^2$

$\quad (3 - 8)x + (2 + 4)x^2$

$\quad -5x + 6x^2$

$\quad 6x^2 - 5x$

EXERCISES

Identify each polynomial by name and by degree.

1. $9c + 5$
binomial of degree 1

2. $12a^2b$
monomial of degree 3

3. $6x^2 - 3x + 2$
trinomial of degree 2

4. p^2q^3
monomial of degree 5

5. $d^4 + 6d$
binomial of degree 4

6. $4a^3 + 8a^2 - 11$
trinomial of degree 3

7. $24x^3yz$
monomial of degree 5

8. $15x - 2x^2$
binomial of degree 2

Write each polynomial in standard form.

9. $8 + 5a$ $\quad 5a + 8$

10. $3y^2 + 16 + y$ $\quad 3y^2 + y + 16$

11. $2c + 4c^2 - 7$ $\quad 4c^2 + 2c - 7$

12. $5x - 4x^2 + 3$ $\quad -4x^2 + 5x + 3$

13. $2b^2 - 2 + b^3 - b$
$b^3 + 2b^2 - b - 2$

14. $11 + 6y^2 - y$ $\quad 6y^2 - y + 11$

15. $4x^4 + 4x^5 + x^2 + 2x^3$
$4x^5 + 4x^4 + 2x^3 + x^2$

16. $p^6 - 4 + p + p^2 - 7p^3$
$p^6 - 7p^3 + p^2 + p - 4$

17. $9a - 5 + 6a^3 - 5a^2$
$6a^3 - 5a^2 + 9a - 5$

Simplify each polynomial.

18. $x + 3x^2 + x^2$ $\quad 4x^2 + x$

19. $3a + 5a^2 + 2a + 6$
$5a^2 + 5a + 6$

20. $4m^2 + m^2 + 10 + 4m$
$5m^2 + 4m + 10$

21. $6p - 5p^2 + 4p + 3p^2$
$-2p^2 + 10p$

22. $c + 9c^2 - 7c - 8$
$9c^2 - 6c - 8$

23. $-2x^2 + 5 + 3x^2 + 2x + 3$
$x^2 + 2x + 8$

24. $3b + 1 + 7b^2 - 3b - 2b^2$
$5b^2 + 1$

25. $5m^3 + 8m^2 + 11m + 14$
$5m^3 + 8m^2 + 11m + 14$

26. $3a^4 - 5a^6 - 9a + 6$
$-5a^6 + 3a^4 - 9a + 6$

27. $-11 - y^2 - 8y + 2y$
$-y^2 - 6y - 11$

28. $6p + 8p^2 + 5p + 7p^2$
$15p^2 + 11p$

29. $22x + 18x^2 + 6 + 4x$
$18x^2 + 26x + 6$

Lesson Preview

 Check Skills You'll Need

Simplifying Variable Expressions
Lesson 2-3: Example 3;
Exercises 11–16.
Extra Practice, p. 745.

Lesson Resources

 Teaching Resources
Practice, Reteaching, Enrichment

 Reaching All Students
Practice Workbook 13-5
Spanish Practice Workbook 13-5
Guided Problem Solving 13-5

 Presentation Assistant Plus!
Transparencies and PowerPoint™
• Check Skills You'll Need 13-5
• Additional Examples 13-5
• Student Edition Answers 13-5
• Lesson Quiz 13-5
PH Presentation Pro CD-ROM 13-5

 ASSESSMENT SYSTEM

Computer Test Generator CD-ROM

 Technology
Resource Pro® CD-ROM
Computer Test Generator CD-ROM
PH Presentation Pro CD-ROM

 www.PHSchool.com
Student Site
• Teacher Web Code: adk-5500
• Self-grading Lesson Quiz
PH SuccessNet Teacher Center
• Lesson Planner
• Resources
Plus

What You'll Learn

 To add polynomials

 To subtract polynomials

. . . And Why
To solve problems involving area and volume

✔ **Check Skills You'll Need**
Simplify each expression.

1. $5x - 7 - 3x$
   $2x - 7$
2. $a + 3b + 4a - 7b$
   $5a - 4b$
3. $8m - 4n - 7m - 8n$
   $m - 12n$
4. $2x + 3y - 7 - 8x + 2$
   $-6x + 3y - 5$

🔎 For help, go to Lesson 2-3.

Need Help?

Like terms are terms with the same variable(s), raised to the same power(s). You combine like terms by adding coefficients.

$3b + 12b = (3 + 12)b$
$\qquad = 15b$

iTEXT Interactive lesson includes instant self-check, tutorials, and activities.

Adding and Subtracting Polynomials

OBJECTIVE
1 Adding Polynomials

In Chapter 2, you saw models for variables and numbers. You can also model the square, x^2, of a variable x.

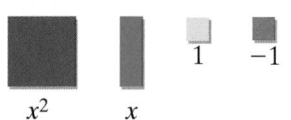
$x^2 \qquad x \qquad 1 \quad -1$

You can use models or properties to add polynomials.

1 EXAMPLE Adding Polynomials

Simplify $(2x^2 + 3x - 1) + (x^2 + x - 3)$.

Method 1 Add using tiles.

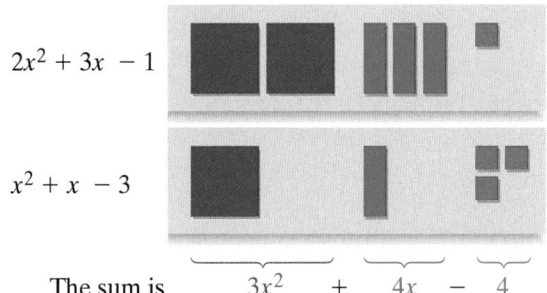

$2x^2 + 3x - 1$

$x^2 + x - 3$

The sum is $\qquad 3x^2 \qquad + \qquad 4x \qquad - \qquad 4$

Method 2 Add by combining like terms.

$(2x^2 + 3x - 1) + (x^2 + x - 3)$

$= (2x^2 + x^2) + (3x + x) - 1 - 3$ Use the Commutative and Associative Properties of Addition to group like terms.

$= (2 + 1)x^2 + (3 + 1)x - 1 - 3$ Use the Distributive Property to combine like terms.

$= 3x^2 + 4x - 4$ Simplify.

✔ **Check Understanding** Example 1

1. Simplify.

   a. $(7d^2 + 7d) + (2d^2 + 3d)$ $9d^2 + 10d$
   b. $(x^2 + 2x + 5) + (3x^2 + x + 12)$ $4x^2 + 3x + 17$

 Ongoing Assessment and Intervention

Before the Lesson
Diagnose prerequisite skills using:
• Check Skills You'll Need

During the Lesson
Monitor progress using:
• Check Understanding
• Additional Examples
• Test Prep

After the Lesson
Assess knowledge using:
• Lesson Quiz
• Computer Test Generator CD-ROM

You can also add polynomials in a column by aligning like terms and then adding their coefficients.

2 EXAMPLE   **Aligning Like Terms**

Find the sum of $z^2 + 5z + 4$ and $2z^2 - 5$.

Align like terms.

$$\begin{array}{r} z^2 + 5z + 4 \\ + \quad 2z^2 \quad\;\; - 5 \\ \hline 3z^2 + 5z - 1 \end{array}$$

Add the terms in each column.

✓ **Check Understanding**   Example 2

2. Simplify each sum.

   a. $\begin{array}{r} 4x + 9y \\ + \quad 3x - 5y \\ \hline 7x + 4y \end{array}$ **b.** $\begin{array}{r} a^2 + 6a - 4 \\ + \quad 8a^2 - 8a \\ \hline 9a^2 - 2a - 4 \end{array}$

   c. $(4g^2 - 2g + 2) + (2g^2 - 3)$ $6g^2 - 2g - 1$
   d. $(-2t^2 + t + 5) + (2t + 4)$ $-2t^2 + 3t + 9$

OBJECTIVE

2   **Subtracting Polynomials**

You subtract polynomials by adding the opposite of each term in the second polynomial.

3 EXAMPLE   **Subtracting Polynominals**

Simplify $(5x^2 + 10x) - (3x - 12)$.

$(5x^2 + 10x) - (3x - 12)$

$= 5x^2 + 10x - 3x + 12$ **Write the opposite of each term in the second polynomial.**

$= 5x^2 + (10x - 3x) + 12$ **Group like terms.**

$= 5x^2 + (10 - 3)x + 12$ **Use the Distributive Property.**

$= 5x^2 + 7x + 12$ **Simplify.**

Test-Taking Tip

After you have *written* the sum or difference of two polynomials, make a mental check of your work, term by term.

✓ **Check Understanding**   Example 3

3. Simplify each difference.

   a. $(7a^2 - 2a) - (5a^2 + 3a)$ $2a^2 - 5a$
   b. $(10z^2 + 6z + 5) - (z^2 - 8z + 7)$ $9z^2 + 14z - 2$
   c. $(3w^2 + 8 + v) - (5w^2 - 3 - 7v)$ $-2w^2 + 11 + 8v$

🎓 Reaching All Students

Below Level Ask: *Would it be easier to find the value of 100 coins by first combining all the like coins or by adding the individual values? Tell students this a real-world example of "collecting like terms."*	**Advanced Learners** Ask: *If you add two polynomials, one with two terms and the other with three terms, how many terms could the sum have? Explain.* The sum could have from 1 to 5 terms.	**Inclusion** See note on page 711. **Tactile Learners** See note on page 711.

---

2. Teach

Math Background

Using algebra tiles to model the addition and subtraction of polynomials gives students a concrete representation for the abstract mathematics. Help students connect what they do with the models to the idea of combining like terms, and eventually to the fact that when you add or subtract like terms, you are basically adding or subtracting the coefficients.

Teaching Notes

1 EXAMPLE   **Inclusion**

Allow students who may have trouble seeing or handling tiles to use larger "tiles" made from colored construction paper or poster board.

3 EXAMPLE   **Error Prevention**

Emphasize to students that to subtract a quantity, they must add the opposite of *each* term, not just the first term.

3 EXAMPLE   **Tactile Learners**

Have students model each polynomial with tiles. Then have them turn over each tile in the model of the second polynomial to reflect adding the opposite of each term.

PowerPoint

Additional Examples

1 Simplify $(4b^2 + 2b + 1) + (7b^2 + b - 3)$. $11b^2 + 3b - 2$

2 Find the sum of $2z^2 - 9z - 15$ and $8z + 11$. $2z^2 - z - 4$

3 Simplify $(12y^2 + 10y - 5) - (6y^2 + 8y - 11)$. $6y^2 + 2y + 6$

Closure

Ask students to explain how to subtract polynomials. Add the opposite of each term in the polynomial being subtracted.

Assignment Guide

▼1 **Objective 1**

Ⓐ Ⓑ **Core** 1–12, 20, 21, 23, 26–31, 38

Ⓒ **Extension** 40, 42

▼2 **Objective 2**

Ⓐ Ⓑ **Core** 13–19, 22, 24, 25, 32–37

Ⓒ **Extension** 39, 41

Test Prep 43–46

Mixed Review 47–53

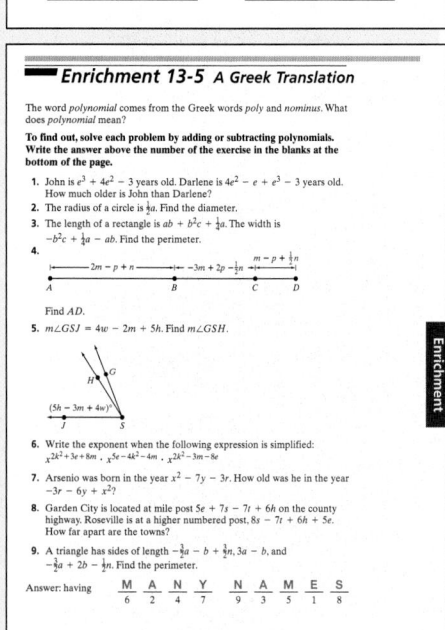

EXERCISES

For more exercises, see *Extra Practice*.

Practice and Problem Solving

Ⓐ **Practice by Example**

Write the sum modeled in each exercise. Then simplify the sum.

Example 1
(page 710)

1.

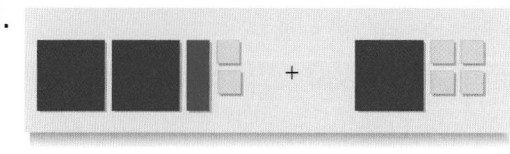

$(2x^2 + x + 2) + (x^2 + 4) = 3x^2 + x + 6$

2.

$(x^2 + 2x - 4) + (x^2 + 2x + 2) = 2x^2 + 4x - 2$

Add by combining like terms.

3. $(x^2 + 3x + 1) + (x^2 + x + 6)$
$2x^2 + 4x + 7$

4. $(x^2 + 5x + 2) + (3x^2 + x + 1)$
$4x^2 + 6x + 3$

5. $(3x + 2) + (-4x + 3)$
$-x + 5$

6. $(5x^2 + 3x + 7) + (7x - 2)$
$5x^2 + 10x + 5$

Example 2
(page 711)

Simplify each sum. 7–12. See left.

7. $2a + 9b$
8. $9x^2 + x + 5$
9. $x^4 + 10x^3 - 4x - 11$
10. $3xy + 2x - 5y - 4$
11. $2x^3 + 5x^2 + x + 4$
12. $12x^2 - 2xy - 3y + 3$

7.
$\quad 5a + 7b$
$+ \ -3a + 2b$

8.
$\quad x^2 + 4x - 2$
$+ \ 8x^2 - 3x + 7$

9.
$\quad x^4 + 3x^3 - x^2 + \ x - 2$
$+ \qquad 7x^3 + x^2 - 5x - 9$

10.
$\quad xy + 5x - 2y + 4$
$+ \ 2xy - 3x - 3y - 8$

11.
$\quad x^3 + 5x^2 + 3x - 2$
$+ \ x^3 \qquad\quad - 2x + 6$

12.
$\quad 4x^2 - 5xy \qquad + 7$
$+ \ 8x^2 + 3xy - 3y - 4$

Example 3
(page 711)

Simplify each difference.

13. $(5x + 9) - (2x + 1)$
$3x + 8$

14. $(-11a^2 + 2a - 1) - (7a^2 + 4a)$
$-18a^2 - 2a - 1$

15. $(3x - 2y) - (5x + 4y)$
$-2x - 6y$

16. $(2x^2 + 3x - 7) - (x^2 - 6x - 9)$
$x^2 + 9x + 2$

17. $(ab - 4) - (3ab - 6)$
$-2ab + 2$

18. $(-4x^2 + x - 1) - (x^2 - x + 8)$
$-5x^2 + 2x - 9$

Ⓑ **Apply Your Skills**

Simplify each sum or difference.

19. $(x^2 - 3x - 9) - (5x - 4)$
$x^2 - 8x - 5$

20. $(13a^2 - 3a) + (2a^2 + 5a)$
$15a^2 + 2a$

21. $(2x^2 + 3x) + (x^2 + 2x)$
$3x^2 + 5x$

22. $(8j - 3k + 6m) - (-2j + 3m)$
$10j - 3k + 3m$

23. $(w^2 + 5w) + (2w - 6)$
$w^2 + 7w - 6$

24. $(3x^2 + x + 7) - (2x^2 + x + 2)$
$x^2 + 5$

25. $(6y - 8) - (2y + 7)$
$4y - 15$

26. $(x^2 + 3x + 5) + (x^2 + x + 2)$
$2x^2 + 4x + 7$

27a. $x + (x + 1) + (x + 2) = 3x + 3$

27. a. Write an expression for the sum of three consecutive integers. Let x be the first integer. Then simplify the expression. See left.

GPS **b.** What three consecutive integers have the sum 108? 35, 36, 37

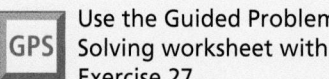 Use the Guided Problem Solving worksheet with Exercise 27.

Geometry Write the perimeter of each figure as a polynomial. Simplify.

28.

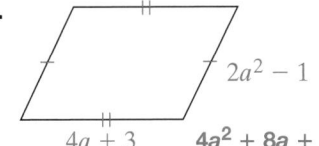

$2a^2 - 1$

$4a + 3$ $4a^2 + 8a + 4$

29.

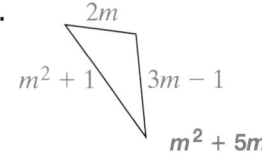

$2m$

$m^2 + 1$ $3m - 1$

$m^2 + 5m$

30.

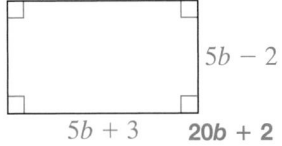

$5b - 2$

$5b + 3$ $20b + 2$

31.

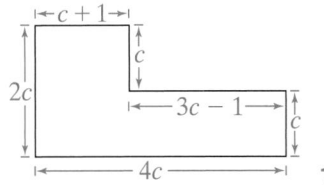

$c + 1$

c

$2c$ $3c - 1$

c

$4c$ $12c$

$5x^2 + 4x - 3$
$-\quad 2x^2 - x$
$\overline{\quad 3x^2 + 3x - 3}$

32. Error Analysis Tian simplified $(5x^2 + 4x - 3) - (2x^2 - x)$ as shown at the left. What is his error? **See below left.**

33. The perimeter of a triangle is $11y - 2$. Two of the sides are represented by the expressions $3y - 1$ and $3y + 1$. Write an expression for the third side. **$5y - 2$**

32. Answers may vary. Sample: Tian added $4x$ and $-x$. He should have added $4x$ and the opposite of $-x$, since this is a subtraction problem.

Geometry Find each missing length.

34. perimeter $= 11x + 6$ **$4x + 1$**

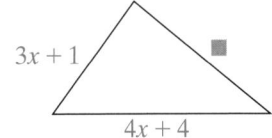

$3x + 1$

$4x + 4$

35. perimeter $= 12b - 2$ **$4b - 1$**

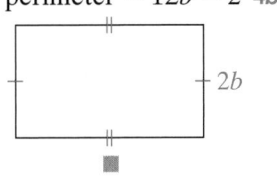

$2b$

38. Answers may vary. Sample: You add the coefficients for like terms of polynomials just as you add two integers; you may combine only like terms when adding polynomials.

36. perimeter $= 5m^2 + 3m$

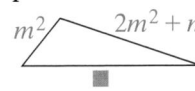

m^2 $2m^2 + m$ **$2m^2 + 2m$**

37. perimeter $= 6a + 3$ **$2a + 2$**

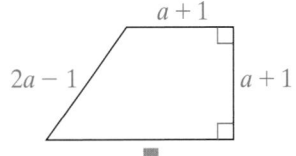

$a + 1$

$2a - 1$ $a + 1$

38. Writing in Math How is the process for adding two polynomials like the process for adding two integers? How is it different? **See left.**

C **Challenge**

39. Reasoning Justify each step.

$(x^2 + 2x + 1) - (2x^2 - 3x - 4)$

$(x^2 + 2x + 1) + (-2x^2) + 3x + 4$ To subtract, add opposites.

$(x^2 + -2x^2) + (2x + 3x) + (1 + 4)$ Commutative and Associative Properties of Addition

$(1 + -2)x^2 + (2 + 3)x + (1 + 4)$ Distributive Property

$-x^2 + 5x + 5$ Simplify.

40. Do Exercise 27 by letting x be the second integer.
$(x - 1) + x + (x + 1); 3x; 35, 36, 37$

4. Assess

Lesson Quiz 13-5

Simplify each sum or difference.

1. $(5c^2 + 4c + 2) + (3c^2 - 5c - 7)$
   $8c^2 - c - 5$

2. $(4a^2 - a + 3) - (9a^2 - 6a + 2)$
   $-5a^2 + 5a + 1$

3. $(6x^2 + 3x + 7) + (2x^2 - 4)$
   $8x^2 + 3x + 3$

Test Prep

Resources

For additional practice with a variety of test item formats:
• Test Prep, p. 733
• Test-Taking Strategies, p. 728
• Test-Taking Strategies With Transparencies

Reteaching

41a. $(3x^3 + 9) - (x^3 - 3) = 2x^3 + 12$

41c. With $x = 2$, the original volume is 33 in.^{3}, so its edge is less than 4 in. It will fit into the box.

41. **a. Geometry** The volume of a cube is $(3x^3 + 9)$ in.^{3}. A smaller cube with volume $(x^3 - 3)$ in.^{3} is cut out of the cube. Write a polynomial for the remaining volume. **See left.**
    b. Evaluate your polynomial for $x = 2$. **28 in.^{3}**
    c. Reasoning When $x = 2$, will the large cube fit into a 5 in.-by-4 in.-by-6 in. box? Explain. (*Hint:* Recall cube roots, p. 583.) **See left.**

42. **a.** What polynomial is the opposite of $2x^2 + 3x - 5$? $-2x^2 - 3x + 5$
    b. What is the sum of $2x^2 + 3x - 5$ and its opposite? **0**

Test Prep

Multiple Choice For Exercises 43 and 44 assume x is an integer.

43. What is the sum of x and the next two integers? **B**
    A. $x + 2x + 3x$ B. $x + x + 1 + x + 2$
    C. $x^3 + x^2 + x$ D. $x + y + 1 + z + 2$

44. What is the sum of x and the previous two integers? **F**
    F. $x + x - 1 + x - 2$ G. $x - x - 1 - x - 2$
    H. $x + x + 1 + x + 2$ I. $x + 2x + 3x$

45. What is the perimeter of the given figure? **C**
    A. $4a + 4b$ B. $4a + 3b$
    C. $7a + 4b$ D. $6a + 4b$

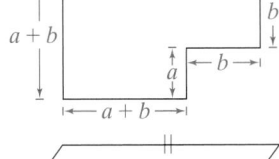

Short Response 46. The perimeter of the given figure is $8x^2 + 4$.
    a. What is the missing length?
    b. If $x = 3$ cm, what is the perimeter of the figure?
    [2] $2x^2$; 76 cm
    [1] one correct answer

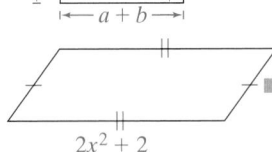

Take It to the NET
Online lesson quiz at **www.PHSchool.com**
Web Code: ada-1305

Mixed Review

Lesson 13-4   **Evaluate each polynomial for $a = 2$, $b = -1$, and $c = \frac{1}{2}$.**

47. $8ab + 1$ -15
48. $5 + 4ab - c$ $-3\frac{1}{2}$
49. $a^2 + ab + b^2$ 3

Lesson 10-2   **Find the area of each figure.**   50–52. See left.

50. 12 in.^{2}
51. 5 cm^2
52. 4.5 cm^2

50.
51.
52.

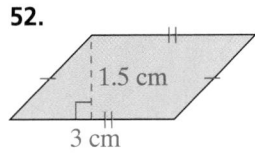

Lesson 3-6 🌐 **53. Charity** A student participated in a walk for charity. His friends pledged a total of \$3.20 for each mile he walked. The student earned \$22.40 for the charity. How many miles did he walk? **7 mi**

Alternative Assessment

Have one student state a type of polynomial. Instruct another student to give an example of such a polynomial. Write the polynomial on the board. Let another student name a type of polynomial. Ask another student to give an example of such a polynomial while you write it next to the first one.

On their own papers, have the students add the two polynomials and write the sum in standard form. Repeat for subtraction.

Multiplying a Polynomial by a Monomial

OBJECTIVE

1 Using an Area Model

You can model the product of a monomial and a polynomial using algebra tiles. You can find the area of a rectangle that is $2x$ units long and $(x + 4)$ units wide by counting the tiles.

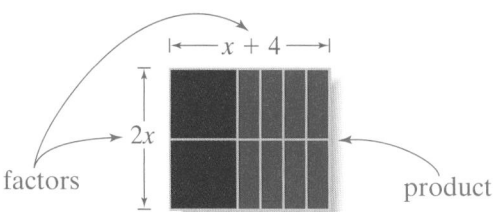

factors   product

The area is $2x^2 + 8x$. So $2x(x + 4) = 2x^2 + 8x$.

You can also use the Distributive Property to simplify a product of a monomial and a polynomial. Multiply each term of the polynomial by the monomial.

1 EXAMPLE   Real-World Problem Solving

Find the area of the garden. All measurements are in feet.

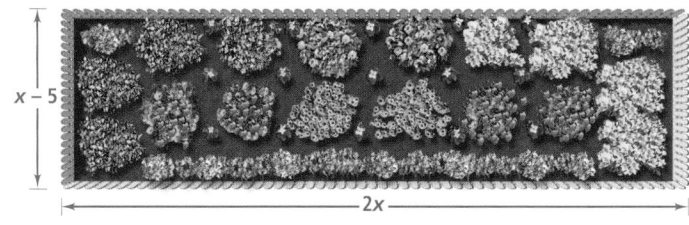

$x - 5$

$2x$

$$A = \ell w$$
$$= 2x(x - 5) \quad \textbf{Substitute.}$$
$$= 2x(x) - 2x(5) \quad \textbf{Use the Distributive Property.}$$
$$= 2x^2 - 10x \quad \textbf{Simplify.}$$

• The area of the garden is $(2x^2 - 10x)$ ft².

✔ Check Understanding   Example 1

1. Simplify each product.

   a. $3x(x + 4)$ $3x^2 + 12x$ **b.** $x(2x - 3)$ $2x^2 - 3x$

What You'll Learn

OBJECTIVE
1 To use an area model for multiplication

OBJECTIVE
2 To write a polynomial as the product of a monomial and a polynomial

. . . And Why

To use area formulas with polynomials

✔ Check Skills You'll Need

Simplify each expression.

1. $7(v + 3)$ $7v + 21$

2. $3(u - 8)$ $3u - 24$

3. $-5(6 - 3t)$ $-30 + 15t$

4. $(p + 8)9$ $9p + 72$

 For help, go to Lesson 2-3.

 TEXT Interactive lesson includes instant self-check, tutorials, and activities.

 Ongoing Assessment and Intervention

Before the Lesson
Diagnose prerequisite skills using:
• Check Skills You'll Need

During the Lesson
Monitor progress using:
• Check Understanding
• Additional Examples
• Test Prep

After the Lesson
Assess knowledge using:
• Lesson Quiz
• Computer Test Generator CD-ROM

2. Teach

Professional Development

Math Background

To add or subtract polynomials, you add or subtract only the like terms. There is no similar restriction when multiplying polynomials.

Teaching Notes

1 EXAMPLE Visual Learners

Help students see that to multiply a polynomial by a monomial, you use the Distributive Property to multiply each term of the polynomial by the monomial. In $2x(x - 5)$, have students circle the three coefficients and underline all variables. (Have them write "1" in front of x, and make sure they circle "-5".)

2 EXAMPLE Error Prevention

Have students rewrite the problem and cross out each term of the polynomial as they multiply it by $3x^2$ to help them keep track of where they are.

3 EXAMPLE Alternative Method

Help students learn to factor expressions like this mentally by scanning. They should first scan the coefficients and find their GCF. Next, they should scan for the least power of the variable.

PowerPoint

Additional Examples

1 Find the area of the rectangle. All measurements are in meters.

$v + 7$ [rectangle]

$(4v^2 + 28v)$ m² **4v**

2 Simplify $5n^2(2n^3 - 4n^2 + n)$.
$10n^5 - 20n^4 + 5n^3$

3 Write $6r^4 + 10r^3 - 14r^2$ as a product of two factors.
$2r^2(3r^2 + 5r - 7)$

Closure

Ask students how to write a polynomial as the product of two factors. See back of book.

You can often use other properties to simplify the product of a monomial and a polynomial.

2 EXAMPLE Simplifying a Product

Simplify $3x^2(8x^2 - 5x + 2)$.

$3x^2(8x^2 - 5x + 2)$

$= 3x^2(8x^2) + 3x^2(-5x) + 3x^2(2)$ **Use the Distributive Property.**

$= (3)(8)x^{2+2} + (3)(-5)x^{2+1} + (3)(2)x^2$ **Use the Commutative Property of Multiplication.**

$= (3)(8)x^4 + (3)(-5)x^3 + (3)(2)x^2$ **Add exponents.**

$= 24x^4 - 15x^3 + 6x^2$ **Simplify.**

Need Help?
To multiply powers with the same base, add exponents.

✔ **Check Understanding**   Example 2

2. Simplify each product.

   a. $x(x^2 + 2x + 4)$ **b.** $2a^2(2a^3 - 3a^2 + 3)$
      $x^3 + 2x^2 + 4x$ $4a^5 - 6a^4 + 6a^2$

OBJECTIVE

2 Writing a Polynomial as a Product

You can sometimes use the Distributive Property to write a polynomial as the product of two factors. First, find the GCF of all the terms of the polynomial and then use it as one of the factors.

3 EXAMPLE Finding Factors of a Polynomial

Write $6x^3 + 3x^2 + 9x$ as a product of two factors.

$\left.\begin{array}{l} 6x^3 = 2 \cdot 3 \cdot x \cdot x \cdot x \\ 3x^2 = 3 \cdot x \cdot x \\ 9x = 3 \cdot 3 \cdot x \end{array}\right\}$ **Write the prime factorization of each term.**

$GCF = 3x$ **Find the GCF.**

Write each term as the product of $3x$ and another factor.

$6x^3 = 3x \cdot 2x^2$ $3x^2 = 3x \cdot x$ $9x = 3x \cdot 3$

$6x^3 + 3x^2 + 9x = 3x(2x^2 + x + 3)$ **Use the Distributive Property.**

Need Help?
To review prime factorization, see Lesson 4-3.

✔ **Check Understanding**   Example 3

3. Use the GCF of the terms to write each polynomial as the product of two factors.

   a. $2x^2 + x$ $x(2x + 1)$ **b.** $2b^3 + 6b^2 - 12b$
                                      $2b(b^2 + 3b - 6)$

👥 Reaching All Students

Below Level You may want to review finding the Greatest Common Factor (GCF) in Lesson 4-3.	**Advanced Learners** Have students simplify $9c^5(7c^2 + 4cd + 11d^2)$. $63c^7 + 36c^6d + 99c^5d^2$	**Visual Learners** See note on page 716. **Error Prevention** See note on page 716.

For more exercises, see *Extra Practice*.

Practice and Problem Solving

A Practice by Example

Simplify each product. Use an area model as needed.

Example 1
(page 715)

1. $3x(x + 1)$ $3x^2 + 3x$ **2.** $x(x + 5)$ $x^2 + 5x$ **3.** $2x(x + 4)$ $2x^2 + 8x$

4. $2x(x + 3)$ $2x^2 + 6x$ **5.** $3y(y + 7)$ $3y^2 + 21y$ **6.** $2x(3x + 1)$ $6x^2 + 2x$

7. $2x(x + 6)$ $2x^2 + 12x$ **8.** $x(2x + 6)$ $2x^2 + 6x$ **9.** $3x(3x - 1)$ $9x^2 - 3x$

10. $3x(2x + 4)$ $6x^2 + 12x$ **11.** $5x(x + 3)$ $5x^2 + 15x$ **12.** $7c(4 + c)$ $28c + 7c^2$

13. City Property Find the area of the city lot shown. All measurements are in feet. $(3x^2 - 135x)$ ft^2

3x

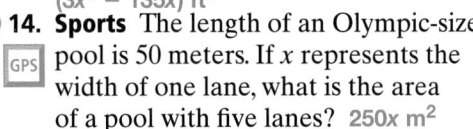
x−45

14. Sports The length of an Olympic-size pool is 50 meters. If x represents the width of one lane, what is the area of a pool with five lanes? $250x$ m^2

Example 2
(page 716)

Simplify each product.

15. $5x(-3x^2 + 2x)$ $-15x^3 + 10x^2$ **16.** $x(5x^2 + x - 4)$ $5x^3 + x^2 - 4x$ **17.** $3a(a^2 + 2a + 1)$ $3a^3 + 6a^2 + 3a$

18. $3b(2b^2 - b + 4)$ $6b^3 - 3b^2 + 12b$ **19.** $a^3(a + a^2 + 5)$ $a^4 + a^5 + 5a^3$ **20.** $-3(2c^2 - 3c - 1)$ $-6c^2 + 9c + 3$

21. $5c(c + 5 - c^2)$ $5c^2 + 25c - 5c^3$ **22.** $4x^2(x^3 + x^2 - x)$ $4x^5 + 4x^4 - 4x^3$ **23.** $7b^2(2b^2 + b - 3)$ $14b^4 + 7b^3 - 21b^2$

Example 3
(page 716)

Use the GCF of the terms to write each polynomial as the product of two factors.

24. $3d^4 + d^2$ $d^2(3d^2 + 1)$ **25.** $4y^3 - 8y^2 - 12y$ $4y(y^2 - 2y - 3)$ **26.** $10x^5 - 5x^3 + 10x$ $5x(2x^4 - x^2 + 2)$

27. $7x^2 - 14x$ $7x(x - 2)$ **28.** $14a^2 + 7a - 7$ $7(2a^2 + a - 1)$ **29.** $24y^3 + 6y^2 - 20y$ $2y(12y^2 + 3y - 10)$

30. $7p^2 + p$ $p(7p + 1)$ **31.** $5z^2 - 20z$ $5z(z - 4)$ **32.** $15x^3 + 4x^2 - 7x$ $x(15x^2 + 4x - 7)$

B Apply Your Skills

Simplify each product. 33–41. See left.

33. $12y^2 - 3y$
34. $a^3 + 3a$
35. $-14a^3 - 42a^2 + 56a$
36. $\frac{1}{2}b^2 - 4b$
37. $-16y^2 - 24y$
38. $6y^4 - 12y^3 - 2y^2$
39. $60x^3 + 24x^2$
40. $2x^2 - 5x$
41. $34y^3 - 136y^2 + 153y$
44. $3b(-3b - 1)$ or $-3b(3b + 1)$
45. $4x^2(x^3 - x^2 + 2)$
46. $3g^2(6g^5 - 2g^2 + 1)$
47. $2a(a^2 - 3a - 2)$
48. $y^3(6y^3 + 32y - 1)$
49. $2m^2(2m^7 + 3m^3 - 1)$
50. $a(2a + b)$
51. $2mn(m^2 - 3mn + 4)$

33. $3y(4y - 1)$ **34.** $a(a^2 + 3)$ **35.** $-14a(a^2 + 3a - 4)$

36. $\frac{1}{2}b(b - 8)$ **37.** $-8y(2y + 3)$ **38.** $6y^2\left(y^2 - 2y - \frac{1}{3}\right)$

39. $12x^2(5x + 2)$ **40.** $x(2x - 5)$ **41.** $17y(2y^2 - 8y + 9)$

42. Open-Ended Write a monomial and a polynomial with 4 terms. Multiply them and then simplify the product. See margin.

43. Open-Ended Write a polynomial whose terms have a GCF $\neq 1$. Then write the polynomial as the product of two factors. Answers may vary. Sample: $2x^2 + 4x + 6; 2(x^2 + 2x + 3)$

Write each polynomial as the product of two factors. 44–51. See left.

44. $-9b^2 - 3b$ **45.** $4x^5 - 4x^4 + 8x^2$ **46.** $18g^7 - 6g^4 + 3g^2$

47. $2a^3 - 6a^2 - 4a$ **48.** $6y^6 + 32y^4 - y^3$ **49.** $4m^9 + 6m^5 - 2m^2$

50. $2a^2 + ab$ **51.** $2m^3n - 6m^2n^2 + 8mn$

13-6 Multiplying a Polynomial by a Monomial **717**

42. Answers may vary. Sample:
$6x, x^3 + x^2 + x + 1;$
$6x^4 + 6x^3 + 6x^2 + 6x$

 Use the Guided Problem Solving worksheet with Exercise 14.

 Lesson Quiz 13-6

Simplify each product.

1. $6q(8q + 3)$ $48q^2 + 18q$

2. $12p^2(2p^2 - p - 3)$
$24p^4 - 12p^3 - 36p^2$

3. Write $27y^3 - 18y^2 + 81y$ as a product of two factors.
$9y(3y^2 - 2y + 9)$

Error Prevention!

Exercises 33–41 Caution students to double-check the signs in the product, especially if the distributed monomial has a negative sign.

Test Prep

 **Resources**
For additional practice with a variety of test item formats:
• Test Prep, p. 733
• Test-Taking Strategies, p. 728
• Test-Taking Strategies With Transparencies

Reteaching 13-6 Multiplying a Polynomial by a Monomial

Use the GCF to write $36x^2y - 90x^2y^2$ as the product of two factors. Multiply to check.
Write the prime factorization of each term to find the GCF.
$36x^2y = 2 \cdot 2 \cdot 3 \cdot 3 \cdot x \cdot x \cdot y$
$90x^2y^2 = 2 \cdot 3 \cdot 3 \cdot 5 \cdot x \cdot x \cdot y \cdot y$
$GCF = 2 \cdot 3 \cdot 3 \cdot x \cdot x \cdot y = 18x^2y$
Write each term as the product of $18x^2y$ and another factor.
$36x^2y - 90x^2y^2 = 18x^2y(2) - 18x^2y(5y)$
$= 18x^2y(2 - 5y)$ Use the Distributive Property.
Thus $36x^2y - 90x^2y^2 = 18x^2y(2 - 5y)$.
Check by multiplying $18x^2y(2 - 5y)$.
$18x^2y(2 - 5y) = (18x^2y)(2) - (18x^2y)5y$ Use the Distributive Property.
$= (2 \cdot 18x^2y) - 5(18)x^2y \cdot y$ Use the Commutative and Associative Properties to rearrange terms.
$= 36x^2y - 90x^2y^2$ Simplify.
The solution checks.

Complete to show how the given expression can be written as the product of two factors.
1. $5x + 5y = 5(\underline{x} + \underline{y})$ **2.** $-3m - 3n = -3(\underline{m} + \underline{n})$
3. $4x^3 + 4x^2y = \underline{4x^2}(x + y)$ **4.** $6ab + 12b = \underline{6b}(a + 2)$

Use the GCF of the terms to write each expression as the product of two factors.
5. $12x - 16y$ $\underline{4(3x - 4y)}$ **6.** $6a + 9b$ $\underline{3(2a + 3b)}$
7. $-9x^2 - 9y^2$ $\underline{-9(x^2 + y^2)}$ **8.** $20m + 25n - 35k$ $\underline{5(4m + 5n - 7k)}$

Simplify each product.
9. $y(4x + y - 2x^2)$ $\underline{4xy + y^2 - 2x^2y}$
10. $3y(5y - 2x + 4xy)$ $\underline{15y^2 - 6xy + 12xy^2}$

Simplify each product.

52. $4z(2z^6 - 3z^5 - 12z^2 + 8)$
$8z^7 - 12z^6 - 48z^3 + 32z$

53. $-3xy(2x^2y + xy + y^2 - 3)$
$-6x^3y^2 - 3x^2y^2 - 3xy^3 + 9xy$

Geometry In Exercises 54–59, write an expression to represent the area of each figure. Then simplify the expression.

54.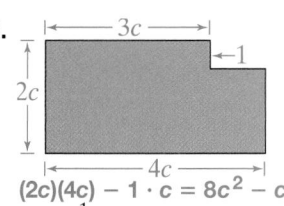
$(2a)^2 + 1 \cdot a = 4a^2 + a$

55.
$(2c)(4c) - 1 \cdot c = 8c^2 - c$

56. $\ell\left(\frac{1}{2}\ell + 7\right) = \frac{1}{2}\ell^2 + 7\ell$

Explain how to use the GCF to write the polynomial $15a^3 + 20a^2 + 45a$ as the product of two factors.

See back of book.

56. The width of a rectangle is 7 more than $\frac{1}{2}$ its length.
See above left.
57. The length of a rectangle is 5 less than 4 times its width.
$w(4w - 5) = 4w^2 - 5w$
58. The base length of a triangle is $8x$. The triangle's height is twice the base length plus 5. $\frac{1}{2} \cdot 8x(2 \cdot 8x + 5) = 64x^2 + 20x$

59. The height of an isosceles triangle is 3 less than $\frac{1}{3}$ its base.
$\frac{1}{2}b\left(\frac{1}{3}b - 3\right) = \frac{1}{6}b^2 - \frac{3}{2}b$

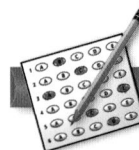

Test Prep

Multiple Choice

 **Take It to the NET**
Online lesson quiz at
www.PHSchool.com
Web Code: ada-1306

60. The length of a rectangular table is 35 inches greater than twice the width. If x is the width, what is the area of the table? **A**
A. $2x^2 + 35x$ **B.** $x + 35$ **C.** $2x + 35$ **D.** $2x^2 + 35$

61. Which polynomial is the simplified form of $-3y(-6y^2 - 5y + 1)$? **H**
F. $18y^3 - 15y^2 - 3y$ **G.** $18y^2 + 15y - 3$
H. $18y^3 + 15y^2 - 3y$ **I.** $18y^2 - 15y - 3$

Extended Response

62. The length of a rectangle is 2 inches more than the width w.
(a) What expression in terms of w could you use for the length of the rectangle? **(b)** Explain. **(c)** Draw a diagram of the rectangle and label it. **(d)** Find the area.
See back of book.

Mixed Review

Lesson 13-5 **Find each sum or difference.**

63. $(2x + 8) + (3x^2 + 5x - 2)$ $3x^2 + 7x + 6$

64. $(-7x^2 - 8x + 4) - (2x^2 - 3x - 9)$ $-9x^2 - 5x + 13$

Lesson 12-1 **Display each set of data in a line plot.** 65–66. See back of book.

65. 1.7, 2.1, 1.9, 2.1, 2.2, 2.4,
2.3, 2.1, 1.9

66. 13, 17, 15, 14, 12, 14,
11, 13, 15

Lesson 5-6 🌐 **67. Banking** A college student received a bank statement. The new balance was $200. It showed deposits of $400, interest of $1, and checks totaling $650. What was the beginning balance? $449

Alternative Assessment

Organize students in groups of three. Have each group write a monomial on one index card, a binomial on a second card, and the product of these polynomials on a third card. For example, write $2x$ and $3x - 2$, each on their own card, and then write $6x^2 - 4x$ on a third card. Collect all the cards from the class and shuffle them. Randomly redistribute the cards. Have students then exchange cards until they have a three-card "match." Since some factors may be the same, some new sets of cards may not be the same as the original sets, but they should be correct, nonetheless.

Multiplying Binomials 13-7

Lesson Preview

✓ **Check Skills You'll Need**

Simplifying Variable Expressions
Lesson 2-2: Example 5;
Exercises 22–29.
Extra Practice, p. 745.

Lesson Resources

📁 **Teaching Resources**
Practice, Reteaching, Enrichment
Checkpoint Quiz 2

👥 **Reaching All Students**
Practice Workbook 13-7
Spanish Practice Workbook 13-7
Reading and Math Literacy 13C
Spanish Reading and Math
  Literacy 13C
Spanish Checkpoint Quiz 2
Guided Problem Solving 13-7

⏱ **Presentation Assistant Plus!**
Transparencies and PowerPoint™
• Check Skills You'll Need 13-7
• Additional Examples 13-7
• Student Edition Answers 13-7
• Lesson Quiz 13-7
PH Presentation Pro CD-ROM 13-7

ASSESSMENT SYSTEM
Checkpoint Quiz 2
Computer Test Generator CD-ROM

💻 **Technology**
Resource Pro® CD-ROM
Computer Test Generator CD-ROM
PH Presentation Pro CD-ROM

💻 **www.PHSchool.com**
Student Site
• Teacher Web Code: adk-5500
• Algebra Readiness Puzzles 76, 77
• Self-grading Lesson Quiz
PH SuccessNet Teacher Center
• Lesson Planner
• Resources

Plus **iTEXT**

OBJECTIVE

1 Using Models

You can use tiles to model the product of two binomials.

1 EXAMPLE **Using a Model**

Simplify $(x + 2)(x + 4)$.

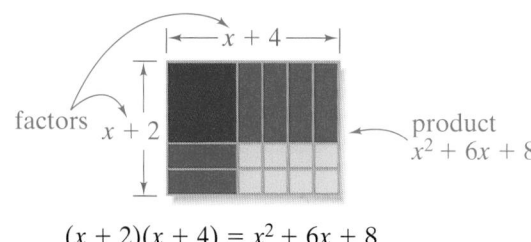

factors $x + 2$

$x + 4$

product $x^2 + 6x + 8$

$(x + 2)(x + 4) = x^2 + 6x + 8$

• The area is $x^2 + 6x + 8$.

✓ **Check Understanding** Example 1

1. Simplify each product using models.

a. $(x + 2)(x + 3)$ $x^2 + 5x + 6$ **b.** $(y + 1)(y + 4)$ $y^2 + 5y + 4$

OBJECTIVE

2 Multiplying Binomials

To simplify the product of two binomials, you can think of one binomial as a single expression and use the Distributive Property. Then you use the Distributive Property a second time.

2 EXAMPLE **Multiplying Two Binomials**

Simplify $(x + 4)(x - 3)$.

$(x + 4)(x - 3)$
$= x(x - 3) + 4(x - 3)$ **Use the Distributive Property.**
$= x^2 - 3x + 4x - 12$ **Use the Distributive Property again!**
$= x^2 + x - 12$ **Simplify.**

Check $(x + 4)(x - 3) = (x + 4)x - (x + 4)3$
$= x^2 + 4x - 3x - 12$
$= x^2 + x - 12$

What You'll Learn

OBJECTIVE 1 To use models in multiplying binomials

OBJECTIVE 2 To multiply two binomials

... And Why

To find the areas of geometric figures

✓ **Check Skills You'll Need**
Simplify each expression.

1. $-2(2x + 1)$ $-4x - 2$

2. $3(7 + 4y)$ $21 + 12y$

3. $(2a - b)5$ $10a - 5b$

4. $(3m - 2n)4$ $12m - 8n$

❓ For help, go to Lesson 2-2.

iTEXT Interactive lesson includes instant self-check, tutorials, and activities.

📋 Ongoing Assessment and Intervention

Before the Lesson
Diagnose prerequisite skills using:
• Check Skills You'll Need

During the Lesson
Monitor progress using:
• Check Understanding
• Additional Examples
• Test Prep

After the Lesson
Assess knowledge using:
• Lesson Quiz
• Computer Test Generator CD-ROM
• Chapter Checkpoint 2 (p. 722)

Math Background

The FOIL method (described below and in the Test-Taking Strategies on page 728) is a shortcut for distributing the terms in the first binomial to each term of the second, and then adding like terms.

Teaching Notes

2 EXAMPLE Error Prevention

Help students see that when using the Distributive Property to multiply binomials, you multiply both terms in the first binomial by both terms in the second. You may want to suggest that students draw arrows from each term in the first binomial to each term in the second.

2 EXAMPLE Tactile Learners

Write the binomials on the board or a transparency. Explain the FOIL method to students, pointing out and using the phrases "First terms, Outside terms, Inside terms, and Last terms." Then demonstrate by having four students stand facing the class with their backs to the board. Write one term of the two binomials on the board above each student. Demonstrate the FOIL method by having the First students shake hands; Outer students shake hands; Inner students shake hands; then Last students shake hands. Have students say aloud the FOIL step they are performing as they shake hands.

PowerPoint
Additional Examples

1 Simplify $(x + 3)(x + 5)$.
$x^2 + 8x + 15$

2 Simplify $(b + 2)(3b - 1)$.
$3b^2 + 5b - 2$

Closure

Ask students to explain two processes for multiplying two binomials. You can use tiles to model the product. You can also use the Distributive Property twice, and then combine like terms.

720

---

2. Simplify each product.

a. $(x + 2)(x - 5)$ $x^2 - 3x - 10$ **b.** $(m + 2)(2m + 3)$
$2m^2 + 7m + 6$

More Than One Way

Write a polynomial to express the area of the square at the right.

$(2x + 1)$ in.

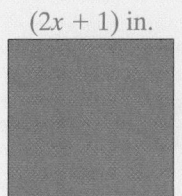

Eric's Method

Use a model.

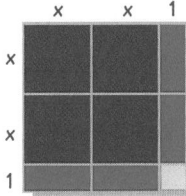

The area of the square is $(4x^2 + 4x + 1)$ in.^{2}.

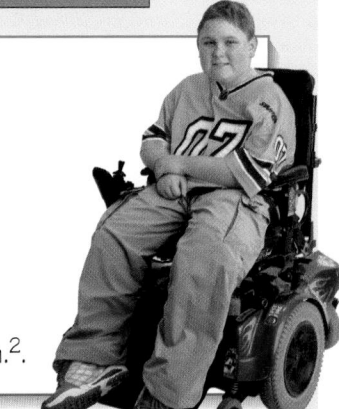

Jasmine's Method

Use the formula for the area of a square and the Distributive Property.

$$\text{Area} = \text{side}^2$$
$$A = (2x + 1)^2$$
$$= (2x + 1)(2x + 1)$$
$$= 2x(2x + 1) + 1(2x + 1)$$
$$= 2x(2x) + 2x(1) + 1(2x) + 1(1)$$
$$= 4x^2 + 2x + 2x + 1$$
$$= 4x^2 + 4x + 1$$

The area of the square is $(4x^2 + 4x + 1)$ in.^{2}.

1. Answers may vary. Sample: Eric's Method; it helps to see the relationship between the polynomial and the area.
2. Answers may vary. Sample: Jasmine's Method; Eric's Method requires too many pieces.

Choose a Method   1–2. See left.

1. Which method do you prefer to use? Explain.

2. Which method would you use to simplify $(3x + 4)(3x + 4)$?

👥 Reaching All Students

| Below Level Ask: *Why can you say that each side of an x^2-tile has length x?* Then ask: *Why do the sides of an x-tile have lengths x and 1?*

A square with area x^2 must have sides of length x. A rectangle with area x and one side-length x must have 1 as its other side length. | Advanced Learners Challenge students to simplify $(x + y)(a + b + c)$.
$xa + xb + xc + ya + yb + yc$ | Error Prevention See note on page 720.
Tactile Learners See note on page 720. |

Practice by Example

Example 1
(page 719)

Simplify each product using models. Sketch and label your models.

1. $(x + 2)(x + 1)$
$x^2 + 3x + 2$

2. $(y + 2)(y + 2)$
$y^2 + 4y + 4$

3. $(w + 3)(w + 1)$
$w^2 + 4w + 3$

4. $(k + 3)(k + 4)$
$k^2 + 7k + 12$

5. $(x + 4)(x + 5)$
$x^2 + 9x + 20$

6. $(m + 9)(m + 3)$
$m^2 + 12m + 27$

7. $(s + 3)(s + 6)$
$s^2 + 9s + 18$

8. $(t + 2)(t + 5)$
$t^2 + 7t + 10$

9. $(m + 1)(m + 6)$
$m^2 + 7m + 6$

Example 2
(page 719)

Simplify each product using the Distributive Property.

10. $(x + 2)(x - 1)$
$x^2 + x - 2$

11. $(c + 7)(c + 9)$
$c^2 + 16c + 63$

12. $(x - 5)(x + 3)$
$x^2 - 2x - 15$

13. $(a - 4)(a - 2)$
$a^2 - 6a + 8$

14. $(x + 5)(x + 5)$
$x^2 + 10x + 25$

15. $(b + 6)(b - 6)$
$b^2 - 36$

16. $(c + 3)(c - 4)$
$c^2 - c - 12$

17. $(x + 3)(x - 2)$
$x^2 + x - 6$

18. $(y + 3)(y + 8)$
$y^2 + 11y + 24$

 **Apply Your Skills**

Find the area of each rectangle. **19–22.** See left.

19. $2x^2 + 7x + 3$
20. $12n^2 - 11n - 5$
21. $10c^2 + 26c + 12$
22. $9x^2 - 9$

19.

$x + 3$
$2x + 1$

20.
$4n - 5$
$3n + 1$

21.
GPS $2c + 4$
$5c + 3$

22.
$3x + 3$
$3x - 3$

28. $8ac + 4bc - 4ad - 2bd$

32. The student did not distribute the 5 to the -3. The third line should read $x^2 - 3x + 5x - 15$.

33. Answers may vary. Sample: Both can be done using the distributive property; one term is distributed when multiplying by a monomial, and two terms are distributed when multiplying two binomials.

Simplify each product.

23. $(x + 4)(2x + 1)$
$2x^2 + 9x + 4$

24. $(n - 16)(n + 20)$
$n^2 + 4n - 320$

25. $(x + 2)(x + 8)$
$x^2 + 10x + 16$

26. $(b + 1)^2$
$b^2 + 2b + 1$

27. $(m - 8)(m - 3)$
$m^2 - 11m + 24$

28. $(2a + b)(4c - 2d)$
See left.

29. $(3c + 1)(2c - 4)$
$6c^2 - 10c - 4$

30. $(3 + x)(5 - x)$
$15 + 2x - x^2$

31. $\left(\frac{1}{2}x + 9\right)(4x + 8)$
$2x^2 + 40x + 72$

32. Error Analysis A student simplifies $(x + 5)(x - 3)$ as shown at the right. Find the error in the student's work.
See above left.

$(x + 5)(x - 3)$
$x(x - 3) + 5(x - 3)$
$x^2 - 3x + 5x - 3$
$x^2 + 2x - 3$

33. Writing in Math Explain the similarities between multiplying two binomials and multiplying a polynomial by a monomial.
See above left.

 **Challenge**

Patterns Simplify the expressions. What pattern do you see?

34. $(y + 2)^2, (y + 3)^2, (y + 4)^2$ **34–35.** See margin.

35. $(y + 1)(y - 1), (y + 2)(y - 2), (y + 5)(y - 5)$

36. Geometry The base of a parallelogram is $(w + 5)$ cm. The height is 2 cm less than the base. Find the area of the parallelogram.
$(w^2 + 8w + 15)$cm^2

37. Suppose x is an odd integer. What is the product of x and the next two odd integers? $x^3 + 6x^2 + 8x$

13-7 Multiplying Binomials **721**

34. $y^2 + 4y + 4; y^2 + 6y + 9; y^2 + 8y + 16.$ The product is the square of the first term added to twice the product of the two terms, added to the square of the second term.

35. $y^2 - 1; y^2 - 4; y^2 - 25.$ The product is a binomial consisting of the square of the first term minus the square of the second term.

 Use the Guided Problem Solving worksheet with Exercise 21.

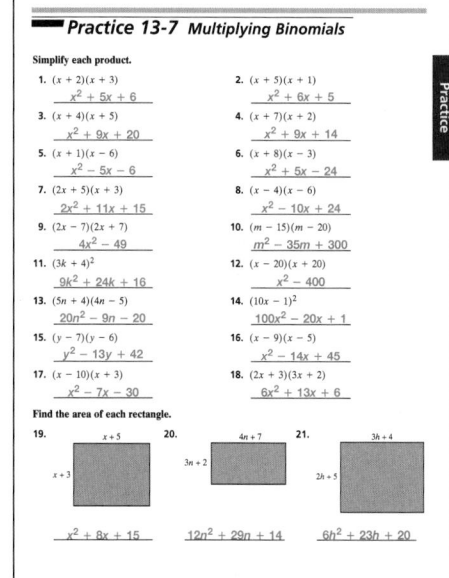

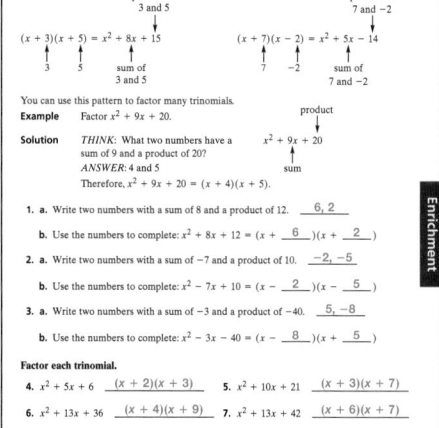

Simplify each product.

1. $(r + 7)(r - 8)$ $r^2 - r - 56$

2. $(4g - 2)(g - 5)$
$4g^2 - 22g + 10$

3. $(9 + z)(1 + 2z)$
$9 + 19z + 2z^2$

4. $(n - 15)(n + 16)$
$n^2 + n - 240$

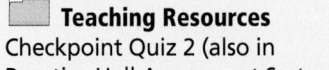

✔ **Chapter Checkpoint 2**

To check understanding of
Lessons 13-4 to 13-7:

Checkpoint Quiz 2 (p. 722)

📁 **Teaching Resources**
Checkpoint Quiz 2 (also in
Prentice Hall Assessment System)

👥 **Reaching All Students**
Reading and Math Literacy 13C

Spanish versions available.

■ Reteaching 13-7 *Multiplying Binomials*

Simplify $(2x - 7)(x + 5)$.
$(2x - 7)(x + 5)$
    $= 2x(x + 5) - 7(x + 5)$ Use the Distributive Property, treating $(x + 5)$ as one number.
    $= 2x \cdot x + 2x \cdot 5 - 7 \cdot x - 7 \cdot 5$ Use the Distributive Property two more times.
    $= 2x^2 + 10x - 7x - 35$ Simplify.
    $= 2x^2 + 3x - 35$ Subtract $10x - 7x = 3x$.
So, $(2x - 7)(x + 5) = 2x^2 + 3x - 35$.

Simplify each product.

1. $(4x - 1)(2x + 7)$ **2.** $(x + a)(x + b)$
    $8x^2 + 26x - 7$ $x^2 + ax + bx + ab$

3. $(y - 9)^2$ **4.** $(x - 4)(x + 4)$
    $y^2 - 18y + 81$ $x^2 - 16$

5. $(3m - n)(m + n)$ **6.** $(a - 14)(a + 8)$
    $3m^2 + 2mn - n^2$ $a^2 - 6a - 112$

7. $(k - 6)(k + 6)$ **8.** $(p + 5)^2$
    $k^2 - 36$ $p^2 + 10p + 25$

9. $(a + b)(a - b)$ **10.** $(x + 1)^2$
    $a^2 - b^2$ $x^2 + 2x + 1$

11. $(a - b)(a - b)$ **12.** $(x + 4)(x - 4)$
    $a^2 - 2ab + b^2$ $x^2 - 16$

13. A rectangle has length $4x + 3$ and height $3x - 7$. Find the area of the rectangle.
    $12x^2 - 19x - 21$ units^2

46.

Test Prep

Multiple Choice

38. Suppose m is an even integer. What is the product of the next two consecutive even integers? **B**
   A. $m^2 + 3m + 2$ **B.** $m^2 + 6m + 8$
   C. $m^2 + 2m$ **D.** $2m + 6$

Take It to the NET
Online lesson quiz at
www.PHSchool.com
Web Code: ada-1307

39. If the length of a rectangular picture is $(2x + 3)$ inches and the width is $(x - 4)$ inches, which expression represents the area of the picture? **I**
   F. $(2x^2 + 5x - 12)$ in.^{2} **G.** $(2x^2 + 3x - 12)$ in.^{2}
   H. $(2x^2 - 8x - 12)$ in.^{2} **I.** $(2x^2 - 5x - 12)$ in.^{2}

Short Response

40. a. Simplify $(3c - 1)(4c + 2)$ using the Distributive Property.
   b. Justify each step in part (a). See back of book.

Mixed Review

Lesson 13-6   **Find each product.**

41. $7a(a + 5b + 2c)$
    $7a^2 + 35ab + 14ac$

42. $-3xy(2x + 9y - 6)$
    $-6x^2y - 27xy^2 + 18xy$

43. $8m^2(-4m^3 + mp + 2p^4)$
    $-32m^5 + 8m^3p + 16m^2p^4$

44. $2pq(5p + 8pq + 2)$
    $10p^2q + 16p^2q^2 + 4pq$

Lesson 12-6   **45.** Does the problem below require *permutations* or *combinations*? Explain.

      You select three colors from a choice of eight colors to paint a picture. How many 3-color choices are possible?
      Combinations, since the order of the colors is not important.

Lesson 12-2   **Make a box-and-whisker plot for the data.**

46. $8, 9, 27, 39, 14, 17, 13, 25, 15, 8, 11, 29, 36, 10, 15, 25$ See margin.

✔ **Checkpoint Quiz 2**   **Lessons 13-4 through 13-7**

📱 **iTEXT** Instant self-check
quiz online and
on CD-ROM

Tell whether each polynomial is a *monomial*, a *binomial*, or a *trinomial*.

1. 178 **2.** $x + 15y$ **3.** $7pq$ **4.** $m^2 + 4m - 12$
   monomial   binomial   monomial   trinomial

Evaluate each polynomial for $x = -1$ and $y = 3$.

5. $5x - y$ -8 **6.** $x + 3y$ 8 **7.** $-7x + x^2y$ **8.** $4y^2 + 11x - 16$
                                                 10 9

Simplify each expression.

9. $(4a - b) + (3a - 5b)$ **10.** $(x^2 + 7x - 4) + (x^2 + 9)$
    $7a - 6b$ $2x^2 + 7x + 5$

11. $(g + 6)(g + 4)$ **12.** $3m(-6m - 2m^2p - 10p)$
    $g^2 + 10g + 24$ $-18m^2 - 6m^3p - 30mp$

13. Open-Ended Write a binomial expression for the length of a side of a square. Use it to write a polynomial for the area of the square.
   Answers may vary. Sample: $x + 3$; $x^2 + 6x + 9$

Alternative Assessment

Group your students in pairs. Instruct each student to write a binomial. Then have both students multiply their two binomials, working independently. Have them check their results with each other and discuss any discrepancies.

Test Prep

📁 **Resources**
For additional practice with a variety of test item formats:
- Test Prep, p. 733
- Test-Taking Strategies, p. 728
- Test-Taking Strategies With Transparencies

Binomial Factors of a Trinomial

For Use With Lesson 13-7

You can sometimes write a trinomial as the product of two binomial factors. You can use algebra tiles to find the factors. Use tiles to form a rectangle. The lengths of the sides of the rectangle are the factors of the trinomial.

EXAMPLE

Write $x^2 + 4x + 3$ as the product of two binomial factors.

$$x^2 + 4x + 3$$

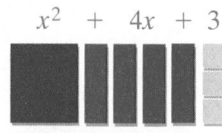

Model the trinomial.

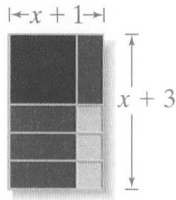

Use the tiles to form a rectangle. The length is $(x + 3)$ and the width is $(x + 1)$.

$x^2 + 4x + 3 = (x + 3)(x + 1)$

EXERCISES

Use tiles to find binomial factors of each trinomial.

1. $x^2 + 2x + 1$ $(x + 1)^2$

2. $x^2 + 5x + 6$ $(x + 2)(x + 3)$

3. $x^2 + 7x + 10$ $(x + 2)(x + 5)$

4. $x^2 + 6x + 5$ $(x + 5)(x + 1)$

5. $x^2 + 4x + 4$ $(x + 2)^2$

6. $x^2 + 5x + 4$ $(x + 4)(x + 1)$

7. $x^2 + 9x + 8$ $(x + 8)(x + 1)$

8. $2x^2 + 5x + 3$ $(2x + 3)(x + 1)$

9. $2x^2 + 7x + 3$
$(2x + 1)(x + 3)$

10. $2x^2 + 9x + 4$ $(2x + 1)(x + 4)$

11. $2x^2 + 9x + 9$
$(2x + 3)(x + 3)$

12. $2x^2 + 9x + 10$
$(2x + 5)(x + 2)$

13. Reasoning Complete $x^2 + \blacksquare x + 12$ with three different integers so that each trinomial has two binomial factors. For each trinomial, write the binomial factors.

$x^2 + 13x + 12 = (x + 12)(x + 1)$
$x^2 + 8x + 12 = (x + 6)(x + 2)$
$x^2 + 7x + 12 = (x + 3)(x + 4)$

14. a. What two numbers have a sum of 11 and a product of 30? 5 and 6

   b. Reasoning Use your answer to part (a) to find the binomial factors of $x^2 + 11x + 30$. $(x + 5)(x + 6)$

15. $(x + 3)^2 = x^2 + 6x + 9$ is a *perfect-square trinomial*. What properties of a trinomial would reveal it as a perfect-square trinomial? Show how a perfect-square trinomial can be factored.
The constant is a perfect square and the coefficient of the x-term is twice the square root of the constant (if the coefficient of x^2 is 1); $x^2 + 6x + 9$; $(x + 3)(x + 3)$. Find the square root of the constant.

Extension

Binomial Factors of a Trinomial

This Extension introduces students to factoring trinomials by modeling with algebra tiles.

Teaching Notes

Factoring a trinomial reverses the process of multiplying two binomial factors. There are a number of ways to teach the factoring of trinomials. No matter which algebraic techniques students ultimately use, they often develop a better understanding of why those techniques work if they first meet the idea by using area models made from algebra tiles.

EXAMPLE Inclusion

Provide enlarged versions of algebra tiles made from colored construction paper or poster board to help those students with impaired vision.

EXAMPLE Error Prevention

Students may think x-tiles all represent the same number since they are all the same length. Remind them that x can represent any number. Also, an x-tile is about the same length as a few unit tiles. Make sure students do not assume that this number of unit tiles is the length (value) of the x-tile.

Additional Example

Use tiles to find the binomial factors of $3x^2 + 4x + 1$.
$(3x + 1)(x + 1)$

13-8

Lesson Preview

 Check Skills You'll Need

Variables and Equations
Lesson 2-4: Example 2;
Exercises 10 and 11.
Extra Practice, p. 745

Lesson Resources

 **Teaching Resources**
Practice, Reteaching, Enrichment

 Reaching All Students
Practice Workbook 13-8
Spanish Practice Workbook 13-8
Guided Problem Solving 13-8

 Presentation Assistant Plus!
Transparencies and PowerPoint™
• Check Skills You'll Need 13-8
• Additional Examples 13-8
• Student Edition Answers 13-8
• Lesson Quiz 13-8
PH Presentation Pro CD-ROM 13-8

ASSESSMENT SYSTEM

Computer Test Generator CD-ROM

Technology
Resource Pro® CD-ROM
Computer Test Generator CD-ROM
PH Presentation Pro CD-ROM

www.PHSchool.com

Student Site
• Teacher Web Code: adk-5500
• Self-grading Lesson Quiz
PH SuccessNet Teacher Center
• Lesson Planner
• Resources

Plus **iTEXT**

724

13-8 Problem Solving: Use Multiple Strategies

OBJECTIVE

1 Combining Strategies

What You'll Learn

OBJECTIVE 1 To solve problems by combining strategies

. . . And Why

To solve problems about building a kite

 **Check Skills You'll Need**

Write an equation for each statement.

1. Seven times the opposite of twelve is negative 84.
$7(-12) = -84$
2. Eleven times a number is 132.
$11x = 132$
3. A number divided by 45 is three. $\frac{x}{45} = 3$

4. A number squared is 64. $x^2 = 64$

For help, go to Lesson 2-4.

Math Strategies in Action
After a natural disaster such as an earthquake, a tornado, or a flood, relief workers help to rescue survivors. They also bring food, clothing, and blankets to people who need them. Relief organizers use multiple strategies as they plan and coordinate their efforts.

In many situations in your own life, you have already combined multiple strategies. Remember when you learned how to ride a bike or fly a kite. The more you practiced, the less you had to think about the steps required to be successful.

In mathematics, you can combine strategies to solve problems. The more strategies you learn and the more you use them, the better problem solver you will be. Solving problems can become as easy as riding a bike or flying a kite!

1 EXAMPLE **Real-World** **Problem Solving**

Hobbies Suppose you receive instructions for building a kite. The writer of the instructions presents them as a puzzle:

I fly above the clouds with my tail flowing behind me. My tail is 12 ft plus twice my length. Together, our length is 21 ft. How long am I? How long is my tail?

Read and Understand

Read the problem carefully.

1. What do you want to find? the length of the kite and the length of the tail
2. What is the relationship between the length of the kite's tail and the length of the kite's body? The tail is 12 ft plus twice the length of the kite. Together, the two lengths total 21 ft.

iTEXT Interactive lesson includes instant self-check, tutorials, and activities.

724 Chapter 13 Nonlinear Functions and Polynomials

Ongoing Assessment and Intervention

Before the Lesson	During the Lesson	After the Lesson
Diagnose prerequisite skills using:	Monitor progress using:	Assess knowledge using:
• Check Skills You'll Need	• Check Understanding	• Lesson Quiz
	• Additional Examples	• Computer Test Generator CD-ROM
	• Test Prep	

Plan and Solve

To get a visual picture of the problem, draw a diagram. Then write an equation to solve the problem.

Draw a diagram.

Let b = length of the body of the kite.

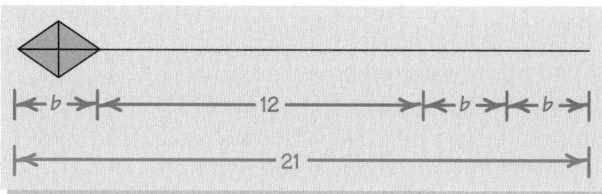

Write an equation.

$3b + 12 = 21$	**Use the diagram to write an equation.**
$3b + 12 - 12 = 21 - 12$	**Subtract 12 from each side.**
$3b = 9$	**Simplify.**
$\frac{3b}{3} = \frac{9}{3}$	**Divide each side by 3.**
$b = 3$	

The kite is 3 ft long. Now find the length of the tail.

length of tail = $2b + 12$	**Use the diagram to write an expression for the length of the tail.**
$= 2(3) + 12$	**Replace b with the length of the kite's body.**
$= 18$	**Simplify.**

The tail is 18 ft long.

Look Back and Check

It is always good procedure to check your result in the context of the original problem.

✓ Check Understanding

3. The original problem says that the tail must be 12 ft plus twice the length of the kite's body. Show that the lengths found meet this condition. $18 = 12 + 2 \cdot 3$

4. The length of the kite's body plus the length of its tail must be 21 ft. Show that the lengths found meet this condition. $3 + 18 = 21$

👥 Reaching All Students

Below Level You may want to review the problem-solving strategies *Draw a Diagram* (Lesson 9-4) and *Write an Equation* (Lesson 7-4).	**Advanced Learners** Ask a volunteer to discuss a problem that he or she solved using multiple strategies and explain the reason for using the strategies.	**Diversity** See note on page 725. **Auditory Learners** See note on page 727.

Math Background

It is often helpful to use more than one problem-solving strategy. You may want to *Make a Table, Make a Model,* or *Draw a Diagram* to help understand the situation and what is needed to solve the problem. Or, you might want to *Work Backward, Simplify the Problem, Write an Equation,* or *Look for a Pattern.*

Teaching Notes

Diversity

Some students may have experienced one or more of the natural disasters listed at the beginning of the lesson. If there is class discussion on these disasters, encourage the class to be sensitive to the feelings of others.

① EXAMPLE History Connection

There is no written record of when the first kite was invented. People in Asia have been flying kites for countless centuries. By the beginning of the 20th century, militaries were experimenting with large kites for aerial observations. However, they never fully developed this use because of the invention of the airplane.

PowerPoint

📷 Additional Examples

① A grocer stacks apples in the shape of a square pyramid. He wants to make the pyramid have six "layers." How many apples does the grocer need? **91 apples**

Closure

Ask students why they should understand the idea of using multiple strategies when solving problems. The more strategies you know, the better problem solver you are likely to be.

3. Practice

Assignment Guide

▼ Objective 1
  Ⓐ Ⓑ Core 1–12
  Ⓒ Extension 13, 14

Test Prep 15–18
Mixed Review 19–25

Practice 13-8 *Use Multiple Strategies*

Use multiple strategies to solve each problem.

1. A rectangle has length $(x - 3)^2$ and width 4. The perimeter of the rectangle is 40. Find the length.

    16

2. A rectangular prism has length $x + 2$, width $x + 1$, height 4, and volume 24. Find the length and the width.

    3 and 2

3. A piece of cardboard measures 12 ft by 12 ft. Corners are to be cut from it as shown by the broken lines, and the sides folded up to make a box with an open top. What size corners should be cut from the cardboard to make a box with the greatest possible volume?

    2 ft by 2 ft

4. What size corners should be cut from a piece of cardboard that measures 30 in. by 30 in. to make an open-top box with the greatest possible volume?

    5 in. by 5 in.

5. What is the maximum number of small boxes that can fit inside the large box?

    64 boxes

6. The perimeter of a right triangle is 24 in. Find the dimensions of the triangle if the sides are all whole-number lengths.

    6 in., 8 in., 10 in.

Enrichment 13-8 *Free Fall*

Because of gravity, a free falling object falls faster and faster, or *accelerates*, as it descends. The distance (d) in feet that an object falls in t seconds is given by the equation $d = 16t^2$.

1. A penny thrown into a wishing well takes 3 s to reach the bottom. How deep is the well?

    144 ft

2. Complete the table showing how far an object falls each of the first 8 s.

t (s)	1	2	3	4	5	6	7	8
d (ft)	16	64	144	256	400	576	784	1,024

3. How far does an object fall during the fifth second (from $t = 4$ to $t = 5$)?

    144 ft

  during the sixth second? **176 ft**

  during the seventh second? **208 ft**

4. How much farther does an object fall during the eighth second than it falls during the seventh second?

    32 ft

  during the fifth second than during the fourth second? **32 ft**

  during the third second than during the second second? **32 ft**

You can use the division property to write a new free-fall equation.

5. Complete: If $d = 16t^2$, then $t^2 = \frac{d}{16}$.

Use your new equation to solve. You may wish to use a calculator.

6. A rock fell from the top of a 2,304-ft cliff to the base of the cliff. For how long did the rock fall?

    12 s

7. A rivet falls off an airplane from 28,224 ft. How long does it take the rivet to hit the ground?

    42 s

EXERCISES

🔖 For more exercises, see *Extra Practice*.

Practice and Problem Solving

Ⓐ Practice by Example

Combine multiple strategies to solve each problem.

Example 1
(page 724)

1. **Travel** A bus traveling 40 mi/h left Freetown at noon. A car following the bus at 60 mi/h left Freetown at 1:30 P.M.
  a. At what time did the car catch up with the bus? **4:30 P.M.**
  b. How many miles were the car and the bus from Freetown when the car caught up with the bus? **180 mi**

2. **Chess** A student playing a computer chess game gets 5 points every time he wins a round. The computer gets 3 points every time it wins a round. They play 64 rounds and end with a tied score. How many rounds did the computer win? **40 rounds**

3. **⟮Algebra⟯** A kite and its tail total 36 ft in length. The tail is five times the length of the body. How long is the kite's tail? **30 ft**

Ⓑ Apply Your Skills

Solve using any strategy.

4. A student has $8 to spend on a phone call. The cost of a call is $.34 for the first minute and $.24 for each additional minute. How long can the student talk on the phone? **32 min**

5. **Painting** A painter places an 8.5-ft-long ladder against a wall. The bottom of the ladder is 4 ft from the base of the wall. How high up the wall does the ladder reach? **7.5 ft**

6. **Geometry** A room has a floor area of 1,025 ft^2 and a 10-ft-high ceiling. The Housing Code requires at least 200 ft^3 per person. What is the maximum number of people allowed in the room?
  51 people

7. **Pets** A student weighs her hamsters two at a time. Sandy and White Ears weigh 209 g together. White Ears and Sport weigh 223 g together. Sandy and Sport weigh 216 g together. How much does each hamster weigh? **Sandy 101 g, White Ears 108 g, Sport 115 g**

8. **Geometry** There are 27 white cubes assembled to form a large cube. The outside surface of the large cube is painted red. The large cube is then separated into the 27 smaller cubes. How many of the small cubes will have red paint on exactly the following number of faces?
  a. three faces **b.** two faces **c.** one face **d.** no face
    8 cubes   **12 cubes**   **6 cubes**   **1 cube**

9. You decide to purchase a new telephone. You can choose from 8 different models, 2 different cord lengths, and 4 different colors. How many possible choices do you have? **64 choices**

10. **Geometry** A lot measures 50 ft by 100 ft. The house on the lot measures 25 ft by 50 ft. What is the area of the lawn? **3,750 ft^2**

11. **⟮Algebra⟯** A student spends $\frac{1}{3}$ of her money on a movie and $\frac{1}{4}$ of the remaining amount on a snack after the movie. She now has $12 left. How much money did she have originally? **$24**

Strategies

- Account for All Possibilities
- Draw a Diagram
- Look for a Pattern
- Make a Model
- Make a Table
- Simplify the Problem
- Simulate the Problem
- Solve by Graphing
- Try, Test, Revise
- Use Multiple Strategies
- Work Backward
- Write an Equation
- Write a Proportion

GPS Use the Guided Problem Solving worksheet with Exercise 10.

12. **Salaries** A clerk starts working at a beginning salary of $10,400 with an annual increase of $400. An assistant clerk who starts at the same time has a starting salary of $9,600 per year with an annual increase of $600.

    a. Who earns more after 3 years? the clerk

    b. After how many years will the assistant be earning more money than the clerk? after 5 years

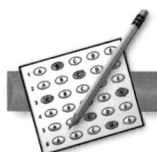 **Challenge**

13. Areas in order:
circle: about 287 cm²;
square: 225 cm²;
triangle: about 173 cm²

13. **Geometry** You have three pieces of string, each 60 cm long. You form a circle with one piece, a square with another, and an equilateral triangle with the third piece. How do the areas of the three figures compare? Explain. See left.

14. Each face of a cube can be painted either red or yellow. How many different ways can you paint the cube? 10 ways

 **Test Prep**

Multiple Choice

15. What is the product of $(x - 3)(x + 3)$? C

    A. $x^2 + 6x - 9$ **B.** $x^2 - 6x + 9$

    C. $x^2 - 9$ **D.** $x^2 + 9$

16. A house lot measures 75 ft by 100 ft. It is all lawn except for the house on the lot. The house measures 30 ft by 50 ft. What is the area of the lawn? G

    F. 1,500 ft²   **G.** 6,000 ft²   **H.** 7,500 ft²   **I.** 8,000 ft²

Short Response

Take It to the NET
Online lesson quiz at
www.PHSchool.com
Web Code: ada-1308

17. A square has a perimeter of 24 inches and a rectangle has an area of 36 sq. inches. **(a)** Which figure has the greater area? **(b)** Explain.
See margin.

18. Aaron receives his allowance of $25. He spends $\frac{1}{5}$ of it on food, $\frac{1}{4}$ of it on magazines, and $\frac{11}{20}$ of it on movies. **(a)** How much of his allowance does Aaron have left? **(b)** Show your work.

[2] $0; $1 - \frac{1}{5} - \frac{1}{4} - \frac{11}{20} = \frac{20}{20} - \frac{4}{20} - \frac{5}{20} - \frac{11}{20} = 0$
[1] minor error OR answer only

Mixed Review

Lesson 13-7

Simplify each product.

19. $(x + 1)(x - 3)$ 20. $(d + 2)(2d + 5)$ 21. $(x + 3)^2$
    $x^2 - 2x - 3$ $2d^2 + 9d + 10$ $x^2 + 6x + 9$

Lesson 12-6

22. GO, GA, GT, OA, OT, AT; 6
23. AP, AE, PE; 3
24. HY, HE, HN, HA, YE, YN, YA, EN, EA, NA; 10

Make a list to find the number of two-letter combinations you can form from each group of letters. 22–24. See left.

22. G, O, A, T   23. A, P, E   24. H, Y, E, N, A

Lesson 5-1  25. **Jogging** A boy jogs in the park every other day. His sister jogs every third day. They both jogged together on April 2. On how many more of the 30 days in April will they jog together if they maintain this schedule? four more days

---

PowerPoint **Lesson Quiz 13-8**

Solve.

1. Emilio's age is four years more than half the age of his sister Rosa. The sum of their ages is 28. How old are Emilio and Rosa? Emilio is 12 and Rosa is 16.

2. Marie sells magazine subscriptions. She earns $15 a week plus $3 for each subscription she sells. How many subscriptions must she sell to earn $90 in one week? 25 subscriptions

3. Paper plates come in packages of 15 or 20. George bought 10 packages and had a total of 170 plates. How many of each package did he buy?
6 packages of 15,
4 packages of 20

Auditory Learners
Exercises 1–3 Suggest students discuss with a partner the problem-solving strategies that they could use with these problems before solving the problems.

Reteaching 13-8 *Use Multiple Strategies*

A rectangular prism has length 5 cm, width $(x + 1)$ cm, height $(x + 3)$ cm, and volume 120 cm³. Find the width and the height.
To get a visual picture of the problem, draw a diagram. Label the dimensions. Next, write an equation.

$V = Bh, B = lw,$ so $V = lwh$ Use the formulas for the volume of a prism and the area of a rectangle.

$V = lwh$
$120 = 5(x + 1)(x + 3)$ Substitute 120 for V, 5 for l, $x + 1$ for w and $x + 3$ for h.

$\frac{120}{5} = \frac{5(x + 1)(x + 3)}{5}$ Divide each side by 5.

$24 = (x + 1)(x + 3)$ Simplify.

Use Try, Test, Revise to find x. Organize tests in a table.

x	$x + 1$	$x + 3$	$(x + 1)(x + 3)$	Comment
2	3	5	15	Too low
4	5	7	35	Too high
3	4	6	24	$x = 3$

If $x = 3, x + 1 = 3 + 1 = 4$
     $x + 3 = 3 + 3 = 6$
The width of the prism is 4 cm and the height is 6 cm.
Check: $V = 5 \cdot 4 \cdot 6 = 120$ cm³ ✓

Use multiple strategies to solve each problem.

1. The product of two whole numbers is 36. What is the greatest possible sum that the numbers can have?
37 (1 and 36)

2. The sum of two numbers is 14. What is the greatest possible product that the numbers can have?
49 (7 and 7)

3. A rectangle has length $k + 6$ and width $k - 6$. The area of the rectangle is 64. Find the length and the width.
16 and 4

Alternative Assessment

Have each student devise and write a problem that may be solved by using multiple strategies. Have students exchange problems with a partner and solve.

Test Prep

📁 **Resources**

For additional practice with a variety of test item formats:
• Test Prep, p. 733
• Test-Taking Strategies, p. 728
• Test-Taking Strategies With Transparencies

17. [2] The areas are the same; square: perimeter = $4s = 24$; $s = 6$ in. area = $s^2 = (6)^2 = 36$ in.²
[1] minor error OR answer only

Using Mental Math

This strategy helps students save time when taking tests.

Resources

ASSESSMENT *SYSTEM*

Test-Taking Strategies With Transparencies
- Transparency 13
- Practice sheet, p. 13

Teaching Notes

Error Prevention!

Remind students to check their work and make sure that they completed all of the steps of the FOIL method.

Visual Learners

Have four volunteers stand in front of the class and model the FOIL method. Give the two volunteers that represent the first binomial two strings each, and have them hold each string at one end. Have the volunteers that represent the second binomial each take hold of the other ends of two strings, one from each of the first "binomial." The strings link the quantities that are multiplied.

728

You can solve many problems quickly using mental math and proven "shortcut" methods. One well-known shortcut is the FOIL method for multiplying binomials. With it, you multiply each term of the first binomial with each term of the second binomial, just as you did when you used the Distributive Property in Lesson 13-7.

EXAMPLE

Simplify the product $(2x + 3)(x + 6)$.

First Last
$(2x+3)(x+6)$
Inner
Outer

Think First terms, Outer terms,
      Inner terms, Last terms.
Notice that the first letters spell FOIL.

Identify the *First* terms in each binomial.	$2x$ and x	
Multiply them.	$2x \cdot x =$	$2x^2$
Identify the *Outer* terms.	$2x$ and 6	
Multiply them.	$2x \cdot 6 = 12x$	
Identify the *Inner* terms.	3 and x	
Multiply them.	$3 \cdot x = 3x$	
Add the outer and inner products.	$12x + 3x =$	$15x$
Identify the *Last* terms in each binomial.	3 and 6	
Multiply them.	$3 \cdot 6 =$	18

Your FOIL result will look like this: $(2x + 3)(x + 6) = 2x^2 + 15x + 18$

EXERCISES

Use FOIL and mental math to simplify the following.

1. $(x + 2)(x + 3)$
  $x^2 + 5x + 6$
2. $(x + 6)(x + 6)$
  $x^2 + 12x + 36$
3. $(x + 3)(x + 4)$
  $x^2 + 7x + 12$
4. $(x + 2)^2$
  $x^2 + 4x + 4$
5. $(x - 8)(x - 2)$
  $x^2 - 10x + 16$
6. $(x - 6)(x - 3)$
  $x^2 - 9x + 18$
7. $(x - 5)(x - 5)$
  $x^2 - 10x + 25$
8. $(x - 4)^2$
  $x^2 - 8x + 16$
9. $(x - 9)(x + 9)$
  $x^2 - 81$
10. $(x + 4)(x - 7)$
  $x^2 - 3x - 28$
11. $(x - 5)(x + 8)$
  $x^2 + 3x - 40$
12. $(x + 6)(x - 6)$
  $x^2 - 36$
13. $(2x + 2)(x + 6)$
  $2x^2 + 14x + 12$
14. $(7x + 7)(x + 3)$
  $7x^2 + 28x + 21$
15. $(6x - 5)(4x - 10)$
  $24x^2 - 80x + 50$
16. $(3x + 1)^2$
  $9x^2 + 6x + 1$
17. $(5x - 2)(4x + 3)$
  $20x^2 + 7x - 6$
18. $(8x + 5)(3x - 1)$
  $24x^2 + 7x - 5$
19. $(6x + 5)(4x - 10)$
  $24x^2 - 40x - 50$
20. $(3x - 2)(4x + 3)$
  $12x^2 + x - 6$
21. $(4x + 6)(4x - 6)$
  $16x^2 - 36$
22. $(3 - 3x)(5 + 4x)$
  $15 - 3x - 12x^2$
23. $(7 + 2x)(1 - x)$
  $7 - 5x - 2x^2$
24. $\left(\frac{1}{2}x + 5\right)(4x + 10)$
  $2x^2 + 25x + 50$

Chapter Review

Vocabulary

absolute value function (p. 695)
arithmetic sequence (p. 688)
binomial (p. 704)
common difference (p. 688)

common ratio (p. 689)
geometric sequence (p. 689)
monomial (p. 704)
polynomial (p. 704)

quadratic function (p. 694)
sequence (p. 688)
term (p. 688)
trinomial (p. 704)

 **Reading Math**
Understanding Vocabulary

Match the vocabulary terms on the right with their descriptions on the left.

1. A monomial or a sum or difference of monomials **d**

2. The graph of this is a parabola. **e**

3. A sequence in which you find the terms by adding a fixed number to previous terms **a**

4. An equation of the type $y = |x|$ **f**

5. A polynomial with two terms **b**

6. A polynomial with three terms **h**

7. Each number in a sequence **g**

8. A set of numbers that follow a pattern **i**

9. A real number, a variable, or a product of a real number and variables with whole-number exponents **c**

a. arithmetic sequence
b. binomial
c. monomial
d. polynomial
e. quadratic function
f. absolute value function
g. term
h. trinomial
i. sequence

 **Take It to the NET**
Online vocabulary quiz
at **www.PHSchool.com**
Web Code: adj-1351

Skills and Concepts

13-1 Objectives

▼ To describe number patterns with arithmetic sequences (p. 688)

▼ To describe number patterns with geometric sequences (p. 689)

10. 17, 21, 25; start with 1 and add 4 repeatedly.
11. −3.75, −1.875, −0.9375; start with −60 and multiply by $\frac{1}{2}$ repeatedly.
12. 128, 135, 142; start with 100 and add 7 repeatedly.
13. −20, −25, −30; start with 0 and add −5 repeatedly.

A **sequence** is a set of numbers that follow a pattern. Each number in the sequence is a **term** of the sequence. You find a term of an **arithmetic sequence** by adding a fixed number, called the **common difference,** to the previous term.

You find a term of a **geometric sequence** by multiplying the previous term by a fixed number. This fixed number is the **common ratio.**

Find the next three terms of each sequence. Then write a rule to describe the sequence. 10–13. See left.

10. 1, 5, 9, 13, . . .

11. −60, −30, −15, −7.5, . . .

12. 100, 107, 114, 121, . . .

13. 0, −5, −10, −15, . . .

14. 26, 15, 4, −7, . . . See below.

15. $\frac{1}{10}, \frac{1}{2}, 2\frac{1}{2}, 12\frac{1}{2}, \ldots$ See below.

14. −18, −29, −40; start with 26 and add −11 repeatedly.

15. $62\frac{1}{2}, 312\frac{1}{2}, 1,562\frac{1}{2}$; start with $\frac{1}{10}$ and multiply by 5 repeatedly.

23.

x	$\frac{1}{2}x^2$	y	(x, y)
-2	$\frac{1}{2} \cdot (-2)^2$	2	$(-2, 2)$
-1	$\frac{1}{2} \cdot (-1)^2$	$\frac{1}{2}$	$(-1, \frac{1}{2})$
0	$\frac{1}{2} \cdot (0)^2$	0	$(0, 0)$
1	$\frac{1}{2} \cdot (1)^2$	$\frac{1}{2}$	$(1, \frac{1}{2})$
2	$\frac{1}{2} \cdot (2)^2$	2	$(2, 2)$

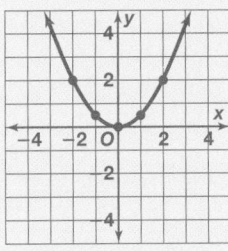

24.

x	$2|x|$	y	(x, y)
-2	$2|-2|$	4	$(-2, 4)$
-1	$2|-1|$	2	$(-1, 2)$
0	$2|0|$	0	$(0, 0)$
1	$2|1|$	2	$(1, 2)$
2	$2|2|$	4	$(2, 4)$

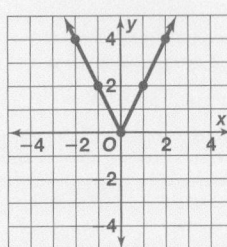

25.

x	$|x| + 1$	y	(x, y)
-2	$|-2| + 1$	3	$(-2, 3)$
-1	$|-1| + 1$	2	$(-1, 2)$
0	$|0| + 1$	1	$(0, 1)$
1	$|1| + 1$	2	$(1, 2)$
2	$|2| + 1$	3	$(2, 3)$

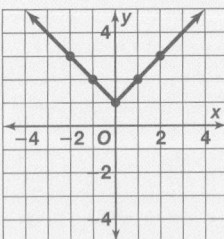

26.

x	$x^2 + 5$	y	(x, y)
-2	$(-2)^2 + 5$	9	$(-2, 9)$
-1	$(-1)^2 + 5$	6	$(-1, 6)$
0	$0^2 + 5$	5	$(0, 5)$
1	$1^2 + 5$	6	$(1, 6)$
2	$2^2 + 5$	9	$(2, 9)$

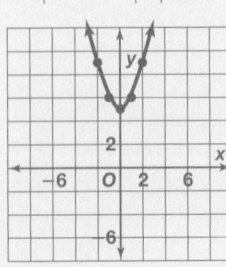

Tell whether each sequence is *arithmetic*, *geometric*, or *neither*. Find the next three terms of the sequence.

17. geometric; $-\frac{1}{2}, -\frac{1}{4}, -\frac{1}{8}$

19. arithmetic; 22, 33, 44

21. geometric; $\frac{2}{25}, \frac{4}{25}, \frac{8}{25}$

16. $9, 13, 17, 21, \ldots$
arithmetic; 25, 29, 33

18. $3, 4, 5, 6, \ldots$
arithmetic; 7, 8, 9

20. $10, 1, 20, 2, \ldots$
neither; 30, 3, 40

17. $-8, -4, -2, -1, \ldots$ See left.

19. $-22, -11, 0, 11, \ldots$ See left.

21. $\frac{1}{200}, \frac{1}{100}, \frac{1}{50}, \frac{1}{25}, \ldots$ See left.

22. Open-Ended Describe a situation that you can represent with an arithmetic sequence. Write a sequence of numbers for that situation and identify the common difference.
Sample: A club starts with 10 members and adds 1 new member every week; 10, 11, 12, . . . ; 1

13-2 and 13-3 Objectives

▼ To graph quadratic functions (p. 694)

▼ To graph absolute value functions (p. 695)

▼ To use tables, rules, and graphs with functions modeling growth (p. 699)

▼ To use tables, rules, and graphs with functions modeling decay (p. 700)

Two types of nonlinear functions are **quadratic functions** and **absolute value functions.** The graph of a quadratic function is a U-shaped curve called a *parabola* that opens upward or downward. The graph of an absolute value function is V-shaped.

A function like $y = 2^x$ models *exponential growth*. Its graph curves upward as input values increase. A function like $y = \left(\frac{1}{2}\right)^x$ models *exponential decay*. Its graph slopes downward as input values increase.

For each function, make a table with integer values of x from -2 to 2. Then graph the function. 23–30. See margin.

23. $y = \frac{1}{2}x^2$ **24.** $y = 2|x|$ **25.** $y = |x| + 1$ **26.** $y = x^2 + 5$

27. $y = -|x|$ **28.** $y = \frac{1}{2}|x|$ **29.** $y = -x^2 - 3$ **30.** $y = -x^2 + 4$

For each function, make a table with integer values of x from 0 to 4. Then graph the function. 31–34. See back of book.

31. $y = \left(\frac{1}{4}\right)^x$ **32.** $y = \frac{1}{2} \cdot 2^x$ **33.** $y = 3^x$ **34.** $y = \left(\frac{1}{2}\right)^x$

13-4 Objectives

▼ To identify polynomials (p. 704)

▼ To evaluate polynomials (p. 705)

35. monomial
36. binomial
37. monomial
38. trinomial
39. monomial
40. monomial
41. binomial
42. binomial
43. binomial
44. trinomial

A **monomial** is a real number, a variable, or a product of a real number and variables with whole-number exponents. A **polynomial** is a monomial or a sum or difference of monomials. You can name a polynomial by the number of its terms. A **binomial** has two terms and a **trinomial** has three terms.

Tell whether each polynomial is a *monomial*, a *binomial*, or a *trinomial*. 35–44. See left.

35. $3x$ **36.** $2x^2 - 1$ **37.** $\frac{2}{3}x$ **38.** $x^4 - x^3 + 2$ **39.** 15

40. mn **41.** $z^2 + z$ **42.** $7d + f$ **43.** $-2x^2 - 12$ **44.** $3 + 2x - x^2$

Evaluate each polynomial for $x = -3$ and $y = 2$.

45. y^5 **46.** $x^2 - y$ **47.** $y^2 - x - 1$ **48.** $2xy$ **49.** $3 - xy$
  32   7   6 -12 9

27.

x	$-|x|$	y	(x, y)
-2	$-|-2|$	-2	$(-2, -2)$
-1	$-|-1|$	-1	$(-1, -1)$
0	$-|0|$	0	$(0, 0)$
1	$-|1|$	-1	$(1, -1)$
2	$-|2|$	-2	$(2, -2)$

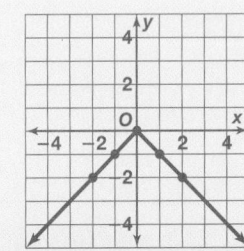

28.

x	$\frac{1}{2}|x|$	y	(x, y)
-2	$\frac{1}{2}|-2|$	1	$(-2, 1)$
-1	$\frac{1}{2}|-1|$	$\frac{1}{2}$	$(-1, \frac{1}{2})$
0	$\frac{1}{2}|0|$	0	$(0, 0)$
1	$\frac{1}{2}|1|$	$\frac{1}{2}$	$(1, \frac{1}{2})$
2	$\frac{1}{2}|2|$	1	$(2, 1)$

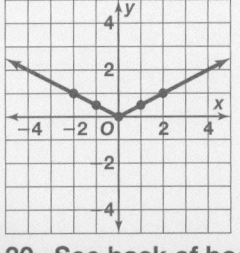

29–30. See back of book.

730

13-5 Objectives

▼ To add polynomials (p. 710)

▼ To subtract polynomials (p. 711)

You can add polynomials by using models, combining like terms, or aligning like terms vertically and then adding their coefficients. You can subtract polynomials by adding the opposite of each term in the second polynomial.

Simplify each sum or difference.

50. $(a^2 + a + 1) + (2a^2 + a + 7)$ $3a^2 + 2a + 8$

51. $(m^2 - 5m - 2) + (3m^2 + 3m - 10)$ $4m^2 - 2m - 12$

52. $(3x^2 - 4) + (x^2 - 2x + 6)$ $4x^2 - 2x + 2$

53. $(7p - 5q + 2) - (3p + 2q + 4)$ $4p - 7q - 2$

54. $(10w^2 + 6w) - (7w^2 - 3w + 5)$ $3w^2 + 9w - 5$

55. $(9x - 3y) - (3x - 9y)$ $6x + 6y$

13-6 and 13-7 Objectives

▼ To use an area model for multiplication (p. 715)

▼ To write a polynomial as the product of a monomial and a polynomial (p. 716)

▼ To use models in multiplying binomials (p. 719)

▼ To multiply two binomials (p. 719)

56. $2a^2 + 5a$
57. $12c^2 - 28c$
58. $-30y^2 - 18y$
59. $3x^3 - 3x^2 - 15x$
60. $x^3 + 7x^2$
61. $2x^4 - 6x^3 - 12x^2$
62. $x^2 + 7x + 12$
63. $x^2 - 4x - 5$
64. $x^2 - 6x + 8$

You can use properties to simplify the product of a monomial and a polynomial. You can sometimes use the Distributive Property to write a polynomial as the product of two factors.

You can use tiles to model the product of two binomials. When you use the Distributive Property to find the product of two binomials, you use the Distributive Property twice.

Simplify each product.   56–64. See below left.

56. $a(2a + 5)$ **57.** $4c(3c - 7)$ **58.** $-6y(5y + 3)$

59. $3x(x^2 - x - 5)$ **60.** $x^2(x + 7)$ **61.** $2x^2(x^2 - 3x - 6)$

62. $(x + 3)(x + 4)$ **63.** $(x + 1)(x - 5)$ **64.** $(x - 2)(x - 4)$

Use the GCF of the terms to write each expression as the product of two factors.

65. $x^2 - x$
$x(x - 1)$

66. $9p^2 + 27$
$9(p^2 + 3)$

67. $3x^3 - 9x^2 + 6x$
$3x(x^2 - 3x + 2)$

68. $5b^5 + 20b^3 - 30$
$5(b^5 + 4b^3 - 6)$

69. $8x^3 + 2x^2 + 4x$
$2x(4x^2 + x + 2)$

70. $28a^2 - 4ab$
$4a(7a - b)$

13-8 Objectives

▼ To solve problems by combining strategies (p. 724)

You can combine multiple strategies to solve problems.

71. A gardener plans to use 196 feet of fencing to enclose a garden. What is the largest possible area of the garden? $2,401 \text{ ft}^2$

72. Explain your choice of strategies for Exercise 71.

Answers may vary. Sample: A diagram gives a visual picture of the problem. A table organizes possible dimensions and their related areas. Looking for a pattern leads to the answer.

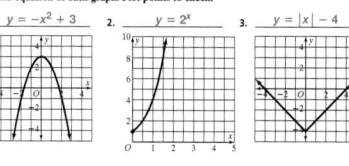
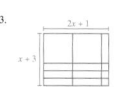

 **Chapter 13**

Chapter Test

 **Take It to the NET**
Online chapter test at
www.PHSchool.com
Web Code: ada-1352

Find the next three terms of each sequence. Then write a rule to describe the sequence.
1–4. See margin.
1. $5, 8, 11, 14, \ldots$
2. $-1.5, -3, -6, \ldots$
3. $50, 10, 2, 0.4, \ldots$
4. $100, 93, 86, 79, \ldots$

Tell whether each sequence is *arithmetic, geometric,* or *neither.* Find the next three terms of the sequence.
5. $5, 2, -1, -4, \ldots$
   See margin.
6. $1, 1, 2, 3, 5, \ldots$
   neither; 8, 13, 21
7. $15, 13, 11, 9, \ldots$
   arithmetic; 7, 5, 3
8. $-48, -12, -3, \ldots$
   See margin.
9. $2, 4, 8, 16, \ldots$
   See margin.
10. $0, 7, 14, 21, \ldots$
   arithmetic; 28, 35, 42

For each function, make a table with integer values of x from -2 to 2. Then graph the function. 11–16. See margin.
11. $y = x^2$
12. $y = x^2 - 1$
13. $y = -x^2 + 1$
14. $y = -x^2 - 2$
15. $y = |x| - 1$
16. $y = \frac{1}{2}|x|$

For each function, make a table with integer values of x from 0 to 4. Then graph the function. 17–20. See margin.
17. $y = 2^x$
18. $y = 3^x$
19. $y = 2\left(\frac{1}{2}\right)^x$
20. $y = \left(\frac{1}{3}\right)^x$

Tell whether each polynomial is a *monomial,* a *binomial,* or a *trinomial.*
21. $4x - 1$ binomial
22. $c^2 + c + 1$ trinomial
23. xyz monomial
24. $a^5 - 7$ binomial
25. $h^4 - h^3 - h$ trinomial
26. ab monomial

Evaluate each polynomial for $x = 4$ and $y = 10$.
27. $x + y$ 14
28. $y - x^2$ -6
29. $xy - 15$ 25
30. $x^2 + xy - y^2$ -44

31. **Open-Ended** Write a polynomial with two different variables. Assign a value to each variable. Evaluate your polynomial for those values. **Check students' work.**

Simplify each sum or difference.
32. $(x^2 + 4x + 3) + (x^2 - 3x + 7)$ $2x^2 + x + 10$
33. $(2x^2 - 3) + (x + 4)$ $2x^2 + x + 1$
34. $(3x^2 + 2x + 4) + (x^2 + 3)$ $4x^2 + 2x + 7$
35. $(x^2 + 10x + 9) - (x^2 + x + 1)$ $9x + 8$
36. $(3x^2 - x + 3) - (2x^2 - 2x - 4)$ $x^2 + x + 7$
37. $(2x^2 - 4x) - (x^2 - 3x - 5)$ $x^2 - x + 5$

Simplify each product.
38. $x(x - 4)$ $x^2 - 4x$
39. $2x(x^2 - x + 2)$ $2x^3 - 2x^2 + 4x$
40. $x^2(3x^2 + 2x - 5)$ $3x^4 + 2x^3 - 5x^2$
41. $(x + 2)(x + 4)$ $x^2 + 6x + 8$
42. $(x + 1)(x + 5)$ $x^2 + 6x + 5$
43. $(x + 3)(x - 1)$ $x^2 + 2x - 3$
44. $(x + 2)(x - 4)$ $x^2 - 2x - 8$
45. $(x - 1)(x - 6)$ $x^2 - 7x + 6$
46. $(x - 2)(x - 3)$ $x^2 - 5x + 6$

Write each expression as the product of a monomial and a polynomial.
47. $2x^3 + 4x^2 + 12x$ $2x(x^2 + 2x + 6)$
48. $x^2 - x$ $x(x - 1)$
49. $9x^3 - 18x^2 - 3x$ $3x(3x^2 - 6x - 1)$

50. **Writing in Math** Explain how you can use the Distributive Property to write the expression $3x^2 + 6x$ as the product of a monomial and a polynomial. **See below.**

51. A customer gives a clerk a $100 bill for a $76 purchase. In how many ways can the clerk give change without using coins? in ten ways

50. Answers may vary. Sample: After finding the GCF of $3x$, use the Distributive Property to bring $3x$ to the front as a factor. This gives you $3x(x + 2)$, which is the product of a monomial and a binomial.

1. 17, 20, 23; start with 5 and add 3 repeatedly.
2. $-12, -24, -48$; start with -1.5 and multiply by 2 repeatedly.
3. 0.08, 0.016, 0.0032; start with 50 and multiply by 0.2 repeatedly.
4. 72, 65, 58; start with 100 and add -7 repeatedly.
5. arithmetic; $-7, -10, -13$
8. geometric; $-\frac{3}{4}, -\frac{3}{16}, -\frac{3}{64}$
9. geometric; 32, 64, 128
11–20. See back of book.

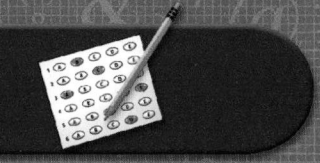
Test Prep

CUMULATIVE REVIEW
CHAPTERS 1–13

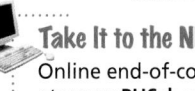
Take It to the NET
Online end-of-course test
at **www.PHSchool.com**
Web Code: ada-1154

Multiple Choice

1. What is the solution of $-3x + 1 < 25$? **C**
A. $x > 8$ B. $x < -8$
C. $x > -8$ D. $x < 8$

2. 32% of b is 8,000. What is b? **H**
F. 250   G. 2,560
H. 25,000   I. 25,600

3. What is the distance Joe traveled if he drove for $2\frac{1}{2}$ h at a rate of 62 mi/h? **D**
A. 24.8 mi   B. 124 mi
C. 154 mi   D. 155 mi

4. Which decimal is between $(-0.1)^2$ and 0.05? **F**
F. 0.03   G. 0.2
H. 0.3   I. -0.02

5. What is $\frac{a^5 b^3 c}{a^6 b^2}$ if $a = 2$, $b = -3$, and $c = -4$? **C**
A. -6 B. -2 C. 6   D. 12

6. An artist created this scale drawing of a lighthouse. About how tall is the actual lighthouse? Use your centimeter ruler. **G**

Scale:
1 cm = 12 m

F. 36 m   G. 42 m
H. 72 m   I. 120 m

7. Which ordered pair is a solution of $x - 2y = 3$ and $3x + y = 2$? **A**
A. $(1, -1)$ B. $(-1, 1)$
C. $(3, 2)$ D. $\left(2, -\frac{1}{2}\right)$

8. What number is next in the pattern?
$-1, \sqrt{1}, -2, \sqrt{4}, -3, \ldots$ **I**
F. $\sqrt{3}$ G. $\sqrt{5}$
H. $\sqrt{7}$ I. $\sqrt{9}$

9. In $\triangle ABC$, $m\angle A = 55°$, and $m\angle C = 15°$. What type of triangle is $\triangle ABC$? **D**
A. acute   B. equilateral
C. right   D. obtuse

10. If $\triangle ABC \sim \triangle DEF$. What is AC? **F**

F. 15.11 in.   G. 17.25 in.
H. 24 in.   I. 76.5 in.

11. $ABCD$ is a rectangle. Which statement is NOT true? **D**

A. $\overline{AC} \cong \overline{DB}$ B. $\angle ADC \cong \angle CBA$
C. $\triangle DAE \cong \triangle BCE$ D. $\angle CBD \cong \angle DAB$

12. A cone has $r = 4$ and $h = 12$. What is its volume? **G**
F. 16π G. 64π
H. 96π I. 192π

13. Which inequality represents *The number t is at least 35*? **C**
A. $t > 35$ B. $t < 35$
C. $t \geq 35$ D. $t \leq 35$

14. What is the area of the shaded region? **G**

2 ft

F. 2.4 ft²   G. 3.4 ft²
H. 4.2 ft²   I. 4.3 ft²

15. What is the area of $\triangle CDE$? **B**

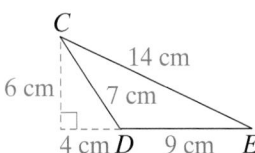

A. 12 cm²   B. 27 cm²
C. 36 cm²   D. 39 cm²

Item	1	2	3	4	5	6	7	8	9	10	11	12	13	14	15
Lesson	7-6	6-7	6-1	4-2	4-8	6-3	8-7	13-1	9-3	6-3	9-3	10-9	2-8	10-3	10-2

37. [2] $125,000; $8,750
    [1] one answer only

38. [2] $5b + 5b + 5b + 5b$; $20b$
    [1] minor error OR
    one answer only

39. [2] $(3x - 1) + (2x + 1) + 2x$;
    $7x$
    [1] minor error OR
    one answer only

40. [2] Yes; for each sale
    price there is one
    amount for the
    commission.
    [1] minor error OR
    one answer only

41. [4]

x	3^x	y	(x, y)
0	3^0	1	$(0, 1)$
1	3^1	3	$(1, 3)$
2	3^2	9	$(2, 9)$
3	3^3	27	$(3, 27)$
4	3^4	81	$(4, 81)$

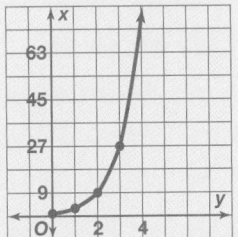

Exponential growth; the
graph curves upward
as x-values increase.

[3] correct table of values,
but incorrect graph
[2] error in table causes
error in graph
[1] multiple errors in table
and graph OR missing
table or graph

16. A bicycle company makes 3 different bicycle styles. Each style comes in 4 colors. Each style is made in 6 frame sizes with a choice of 2 types of seat. The bicycle shop would like to order one of each type of bicycle. How many bicycles is that? **H**
    F. 60 bicycles
    G. 120 bicycles
    H. 144 bicycles
    I. 240 bicycles

17. In a box filled with 60 colored chips, $\frac{1}{6}$ are blue, $\frac{1}{12}$ are white, $\frac{1}{4}$ are yellow, and $\frac{1}{2}$ are purple. What is the probability of picking at random a purple chip or a white chip? **B**
    A. $\frac{1}{24}$ **B.** $\frac{7}{12}$ **C.** $\frac{3}{5}$ **D.** $\frac{2}{3}$

18. If the first term in an arithmetic sequence is 15 and the fifth term is 39, what is the fourth term in the sequence? **G**
    F. 32 **G.** 33 **H.** 34 **I.** 35

19. What is the simplest form $6z(4 - 2z^2)$? **A**
    A. $24z - 12z^3$ **B.** $24z - 12z^2$
    C. $24z - 2z^2$ **D.** $24z + 12z^3$

20. Which expression is represented by the model shown below? **I**

    F. $2(x^2 + 2x) + 3$ **G.** $2x^2 + 2 + 3^2$
    H. $x^2 + 2x + 3$ **I.** $2x^2 + 2x + 3$

21. What is $(x^4 + 2x^3 - x^2 + x - 3) + 6x^3 + x^2 - 4x - 8$? **D**

    A. $x^4 + 4x^3 - 2x^2 - 5x - 5$
    B. $x^4 + 8x^3 - 4x - 5$
    C. $x^4 + 8x^3 + 2x^2 - 3x - 11$
    D. $x^4 + 8x^3 - 3x - 11$

22. What is $(5r - 4s) - (2r - s)$? **G**
    F. $10r - 4s$ **G.** $3r - 3s$
    H. $10r^2 - 4s^2$ **I.** $3r - 5s$

23. Which phrase best describes the expression $9xyz$? **A**
    A. monomial **B.** binomial
    C. trinomial **D.** polynomial

24. Which equation matches the graph? **F**

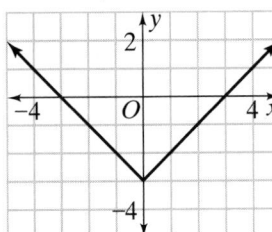

    F. $y = |x| - 3$ **G.** $y = x^2 - 3$
    H. $y = -3|x|$ **I.** $y = |x - 3|$

25. A submarine dove to a depth of 540 ft, then rose 84 ft. Which integer represents the final depth of the submarine? **B**
    A. -624 **B.** -456
    C. 456 **D.** 624

26. Which property does $7(w + 8) = 7w + 56$ show? **I**
    F. Commutative Property of Addition
    G. Associative Property of Multiplication
    H. Identity Property of Addition
    I. Distributive Property

27. Which of the following equations would you use to find out how far a satellite will travel in 2 minutes if it is traveling at a rate of 8 km per second? **A**
    A. $d = 8(120)$ **B.** $d = \frac{8}{120}$
    C. $d = 8(2)$ **D.** $d = \frac{8}{2}$

28. What is the GCF of $18x^3y^4$ and $48xy^5$? **H**
    F. $12xy^4$ **G.** $12x^2y$
    H. $6xy^4$ **I.** $6x^2y$

29. Which of the following is the simplified form of $\left(\frac{3a}{6b}\right)^3$? **D**
    A. $\frac{a^3}{2b^3}$ **B.** $\frac{a^3}{6b^3}$
    C. $\frac{a^3}{8b^2}$ **D.** $\frac{a^3}{8b^3}$

734 Chapter 13 Test Prep

Item	16	17	18	19	20	21	22	23	24	25	26	27	28	29
Lesson	12-6	12-4	13-1	13-6	13-4	13-5	13-5	13-4	13-2	1-5	2-1	6-1	4-3	4-8

30. Which of the following is a rule for the function described in the table? **F**

x	f(x)
−2	−7
0	−3
2	1
4	5

F. $f(x) = 2x - 3$ **G.** $f(x) = 3x - 2$
H. $f(x) = 2x + 3$ **I.** $f(x) = 3x + 2$

31. Between which two integers is the value of $\sqrt{70}$? **B**
A. 3 and 4   **B.** 8 and 9
C. 36 and 49   **D.** 64 and 81

32. Which polynomial is the product of the binomials $(x + 2)$ and $(x - 13)$? **G**
F. $x^2 + 15x + 26$ **G.** $x^2 - 11x - 26$
H. $x^2 - 11x + 26$ **I.** $x^2 - 15x - 26$

Gridded Response

33. If $m\angle 2 = 110°$, what is $m\angle 3$ in degrees? **70**

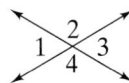

34. Small pieces of paper with the letters SKATES are placed in a bag. What is the probability of selecting a T from the bag at random, not replacing it, and then selecting an A? **1/30**

35. A truck leaves a rest stop and travels at a steady rate of 65 mi/h. Later, a car leaves the rest stop, travels at a steady rate of 75 mi/h, and catches up with the truck in 3.25 hours. For how many hours had the truck been traveling? **15/4 or 3.75**

36. What is the surface area of the figure to the nearest whole number of square feet? **402**

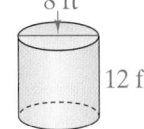
8 ft
12 ft

Short Response

37. An agent made a $7,500 commission for selling a house. The commission rate is 6%.
   a. What was the price of the house?
   b. If the commission rate is raised to 7%, what commission would the agent make for the house price in part (a)?
   See page 734 margin.

In Exercises 38 and 39, (a) write the perimeter of each figure as a polynomial.   (b) Then simplify.
38–39. See page 734 margin.

38.

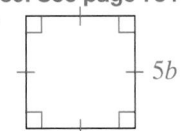
5b

39.
3x − 1
2x + 1
2x

40. A salesperson receives a 5% commission for each computer sold. **(a)** Is the value of the commission a function of the final sales price of each computer?   **(b)** Explain.
   See margin.

Extended Response

For each function, (a) make a table with integer values of x from 0 to 4.   (b) Graph the function. (c) What exponential change does the graph show, growth or decay? Explain your answer.
41–42. See pp. 734–735 margins.
41. $y = 3^x$ **42.** $y = 20\left(\frac{1}{2}\right)^x$

43. Two electronics stores have the same television model on sale. The price of the television at Store A is $299 before a 25% discount. The price of the television at Store B is $279 before a 20% discount.
   a. Which store has the greater discount?
   b. Which store has the lower sale price?
   c. What is the difference between the two sale prices? See margin.

42. [4]

x	$20\left(\frac{1}{2}\right)^x$	y	(x, y)
0	$20\left(\frac{1}{2}\right)^0$	20	(0, 20)
1	$20\left(\frac{1}{2}\right)^1$	10	(1, 10)
2	$20\left(\frac{1}{2}\right)^2$	5	(2, 5)
3	$20\left(\frac{1}{2}\right)^3$	2.5	(3, 2.5)
4	$20\left(\frac{1}{2}\right)^4$	1.25	(4, 1.25)

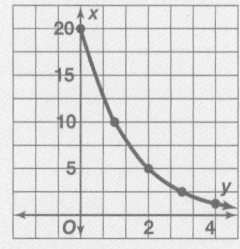

Exponential decay; the graph curves downward as x-values increase.

[3] correct table of values, but incorrect graph
[2] error in table causes error in graph
[1] multiple errors in table and graph OR missing table or graph

43. [4] Store A has the greater discount, which is $74.75, as compared to the discount of $55.80 at Store B. The final price of the television is lowest at Store B, because 279 − 55.80 = 223.20 and 299 − 74.75 = 224.25. The difference between the two sale prices is 224.25 − 223.20 = $1.05.
[3] correct prediction and lowest final price, but no work shown
[2] correct prediction, but one error in work finding lowest final price
[1] correct prediction, but incorrect final price and no work shown

Item	30	31	32	33	34	35	36	37	38	39	40	41	42	43
Lesson	8-4	11-1	13-7	9-2	12-5	7-7	10-5	6-7	13-5	13-5	8-1	13-3	13-3	6-9

735

Carbon Dating

In this activity, students complete a table and apply their knowledge of algebra and estimation to solve problems related to carbon-14 dating of fossils.

Activating Prior Knowledge

Ask students whether they have seen fossils in museums or in their local area. Invite volunteers to name places where fossils may be found. Answers may vary. Sample: archaeological sites, the seaside, ploughed fields, old quarries, riverbanks; these are places where wind and water may expose sedimentary rock, in which fossils are often found.

Teaching Notes

Teaching Tip

Have a volunteer read the introductory paragraph. Ask: *Why is it important that scientists be able to accurately date fossils?* Answers may vary. Sample: Accurate dating of fossils enables scientists to learn when different species lived and died and how life has evolved on Earth.

Inclusion

Ask students to define *fossil.* Have a volunteer look up *fossil* in a dictionary and read the definition aloud. Answers may vary. Sample: Fossils are remains of plants and animals that lived a long time ago or traces of these living things or their activities.

Connection to Geography

Ask: *Why are fossils important to the study of dinosaurs?* Have students research and locate on a world map some sites of major fossil discoveries. Answers may vary. Sample: Our knowledge of dinosaurs has come from the study of fossils because dinosaurs became extinct long before people existed; some major fossil finds occurred at La Brea Tar Pits (California), Mazon Creek (Illinois), Ediacara Hills (Australia), Burgess Shale (Canada), and Solnhofen (Germany).

736

Carbon Dating

Applying Algebra Have you ever wondered how a scientist can estimate the age of a fossil? When an organism is alive, it maintains carbon-14 in the same proportion as the atmosphere. When the organism dies, it stops replenishing its carbon-14. A scientist finds the amount of carbon-14 currently present in the fossil and calculates how long the amount that was present at death has been decaying.

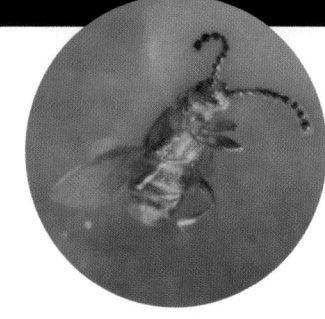

Amber Insects
Sometimes bees, flies, and other insects get stuck in the sap from a tree. Over time, the sap hardens and turns into amber.

How Old Is That?
Carbon-14 has a half-life of 5,730 years. Scientists use it to determine the age of bone, cloth, wood, and plant fibers.

Mammoth Model
The "woolly mammoth" was about 11 ft tall and weighed 4 to 6 tons, the same as an African elephant today, but had very small ears, a sloping back, and much longer tusks.

Shoulder hump

Mammoth hair was up to 3 ft long.

736

Activity

1. Copy and complete the table. **1–4. See margin.**

2. **Estimation** About how old is a fossil that has 40% carbon-14 present?

3. **Estimation** What percent of carbon-14 would you hope to find in a fossil that you think is 20,000 years old?

4. **Reasoning** Why do you think carbon-14 dating works only on fossils less than 60,000 years old?

Carbon-14 Dating

Percent of Carbon-14 Present	Age of Fossil (years)
100	0
50	5,730
■	11,460
12.5	■
■	22,920
3.125	■
■	34,380
0.78125	■

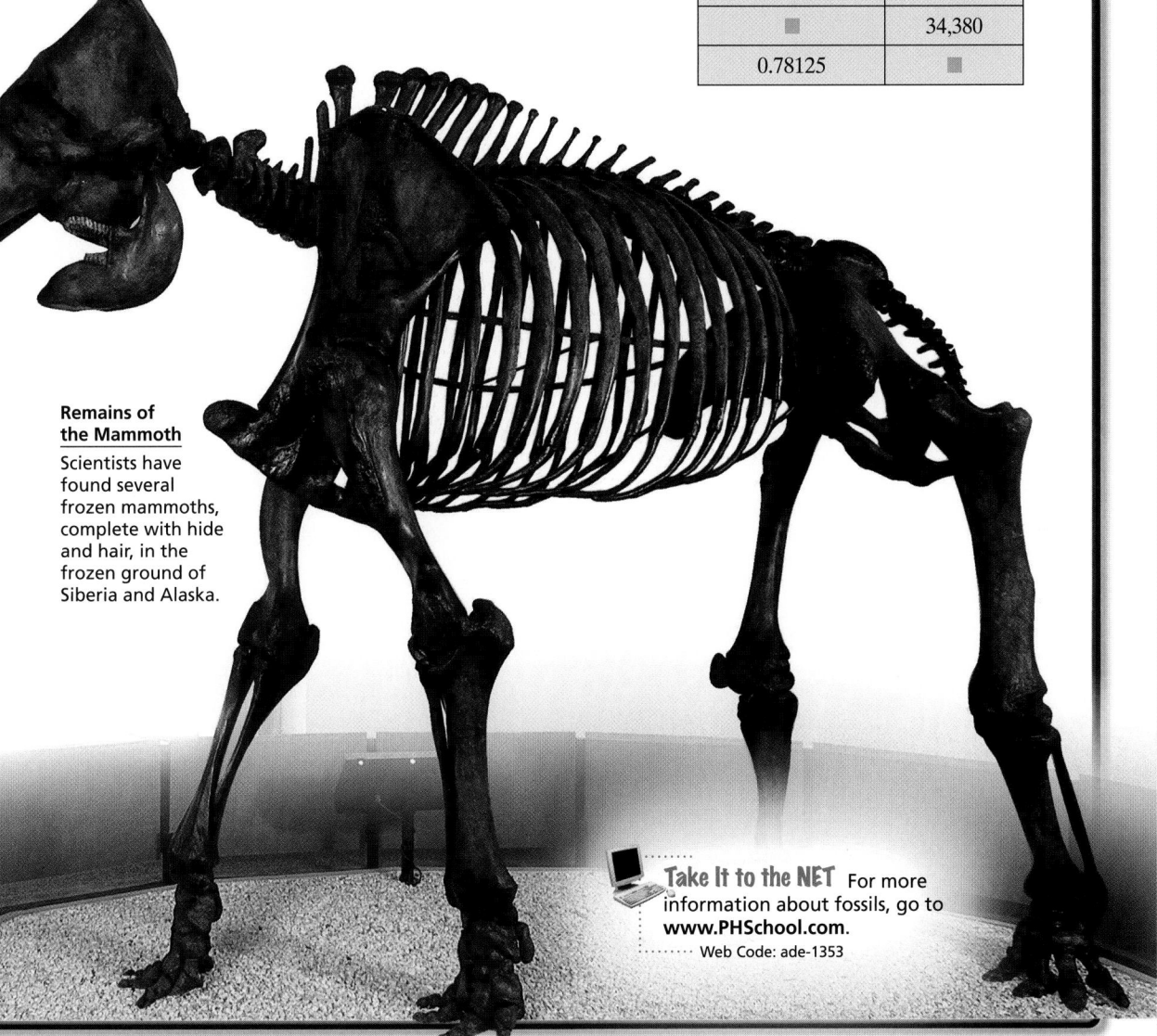

Remains of the Mammoth

Scientists have found several frozen mammoths, complete with hide and hair, in the frozen ground of Siberia and Alaska.

Take It to the NET For more information about fossils, go to www.PHSchool.com.
Web Code: ade-1353

737

1. See back of book.
2. about 8,000 years old
3. about 9%

4. Answers may vary. Sample: After ten half-lives there is about one tenth of one percent of carbon-14 present. This small percent is difficult to measure.

Chapter Projects

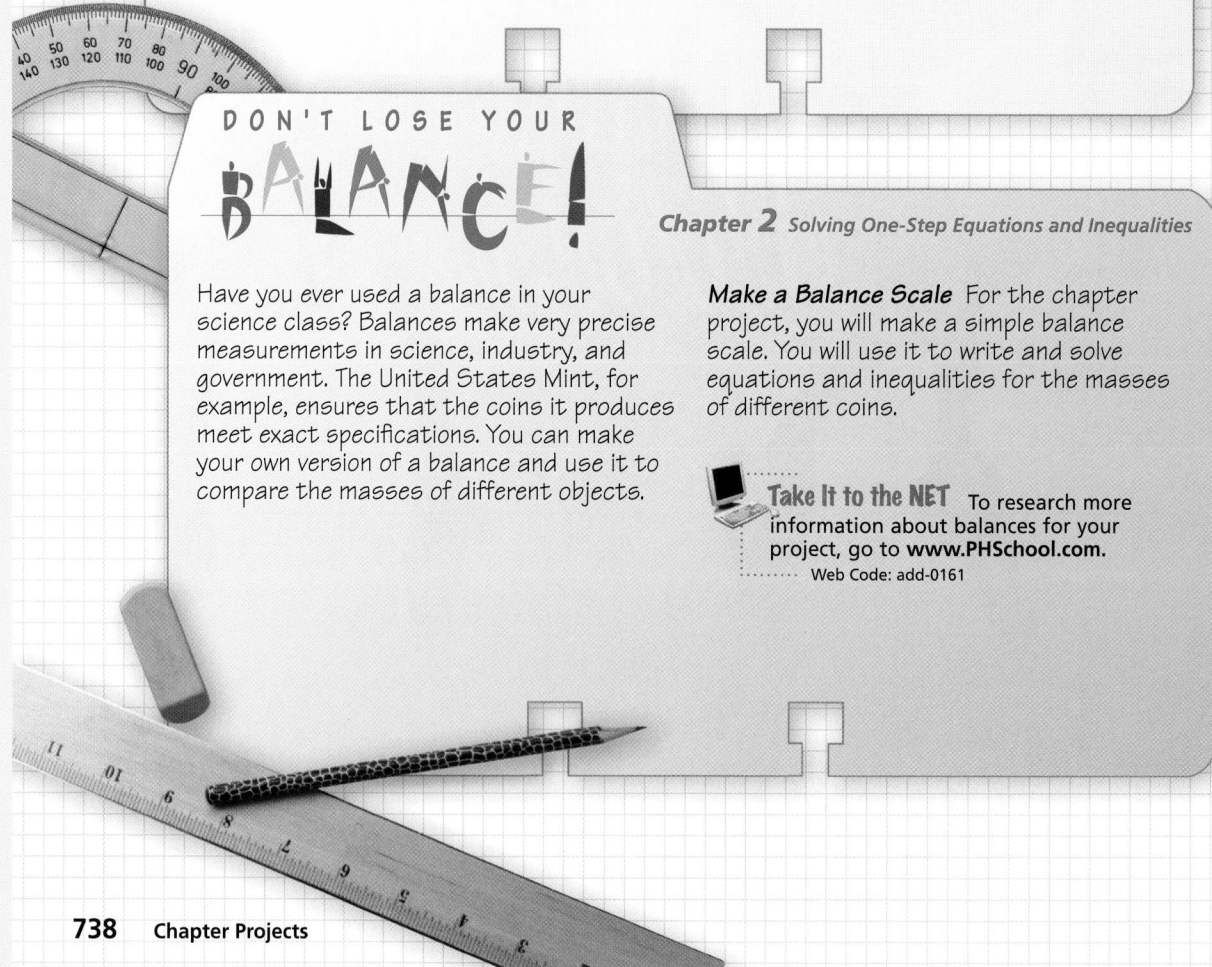

Cure for the Common Code

A special sculpture stands outside the headquarters of the United States Central Intelligence Agency (CIA) in Langley, Virginia. Carved in the copper sculpture is a message in secret code. The code is so complex that for many years even CIA agents could not figure it out. The sculptor, James Sandborn, provided the secret agents with a challenge they could appreciate.

Chapter 1 *Algebraic Expressions and Integers*

Invent a Secret Code For the chapter project, you will decode computer writing and write in a code used by Julius Caesar. Then you'll invent a code of your own.

Take It to the NET To research more information about secret codes for your project, go to **www.PHSchool.com**.
Web Code: add-0161

DON'T LOSE YOUR BALANCE!

Have you ever used a balance in your science class? Balances make very precise measurements in science, industry, and government. The United States Mint, for example, ensures that the coins it produces meet exact specifications. You can make your own version of a balance and use it to compare the masses of different objects.

Chapter 2 *Solving One-Step Equations and Inequalities*

Make a Balance Scale For the chapter project, you will make a simple balance scale. You will use it to write and solve equations and inequalities for the masses of different coins.

Take It to the NET To research more information about balances for your project, go to **www.PHSchool.com**.
Web Code: add-0161

CURRENCY EVENTS

Chapter 3 *Decimals and Equations*

When you are shopping, of course you want to know how much an item costs before you decide to buy it! When you travel in another country, you need to "translate" the cost into its value in U.S. dollars.

Compare Currencies For the chapter project, you will research currency exchange rates and calculate prices in different currencies. You will make a poster that shows prices in U.S. dollars and in the currencies of three other countries.

 Take It to the NET To research more information about currencies for your project, go to **www.PHSchool.com**.
Web Code: add-0161

TIME AFTER TIME

Chapter 4 *Factors, Fractions, and Exponents*

On the morning of the summer solstice, the sun rises directly over one of the stones at Stonehenge in southern England. Just as a sundial tells the time of day, Stonehenge tells the time of year.

A calendar may involve several astronomical events. For example, our day is based on Earth's rotation, whereas our year is based on Earth's movement around the sun. Over the centuries, people have come up with many different calendars.

Design a Calendar For the chapter project, you will investigate calendars and adjustments to calendars. Then you will design your own calendar. Your final project will be a sample and an explanation of your calendar.

 Take It to the NET To research more information about calendars for your project, go to **www.PHSchool.com**.
Web Code: add-0161

Chapter Projects **739**

If the Shoe Fits

What size shoe do you wear? As you grow, your shoe size can change rapidly. If your foot grows half an inch, does that mean you should get shoes that are a half-size larger?

The scale we use for sizing shoes is from the *duodecimal,* or base 12, number system. For that reason, a size chart could come in handy.

Make a Comparison Chart For the chapter project, you will make measurements and calculations that relate women's shoe sizes, men's shoe sizes, and shoe lengths. Your final project will be a convenient comparison chart that you can distribute to your friends and family and to shoe stores.

Take It to the NET To research more information about shoe sizes for your project, go to **www.PHSchool.com**.
Web Code: add-0161

STRING BAND

Guitars, fiddles, harps . . . people have been enjoying stringed instruments for thousands of years. The music from a stringed instrument follows rules of mathematics that you will learn in this chapter.

Make a Musical Instrument For the chapter project, you will construct and play a simple stringed instrument. You will make measurements that can be applied to a real instrument. Your final project will consist of drawings that show how to play notes on both instruments.

Take It to the NET To research more information about stringed instruments for your project, go to **www.PHSchool.com**.
Web Code: add-0161

740 Chapter Projects

The Intensity of DENSITY

Have you ever wondered why some objects sink while others float? People float in the salt water of the Dead Sea. Pebbles sink when tossed into a river. The densities of a liquid and an object influence whether the object sinks or floats in the liquid. Similarly, the densities of two liquids influence whether they combine or separate.

Chapter 7 *Solving Equations and Inequalities*

Find the Densities of Liquids For the chapter project, you will measure the masses and volumes of several liquids. You will use your measurements and an equation to calculate the density of each liquid.

Take It to the NET To research more information about densities for your project, go to **www.PHSchool.com**.
Web Code: add-0161

Rental Math

Your school is planning its graduation ceremony. Hundreds of people will be coming, and they need places to sit. Your school has some chairs, but not enough for this crowd! Better call a rental company.

Chapter 8 *Linear Functions and Graphing*

Compare Prices For the chapter project, you will research the cost of renting folding chairs. You do not yet know how many chairs you will need, so you will investigate the price per chair, as well as delivery charges. For your report to the graduation committee, you will write and graph equations to show the total costs of renting chairs from different companies.

Take It to the NET To research more information about chair rentals for your project, go to **www.PHSchool.com**.
Web Code: add-0161

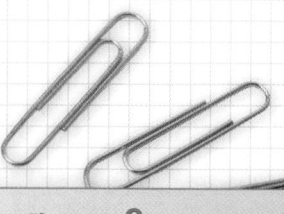

TREASURE HUNT!

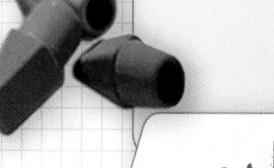

A mysterious map has come into your possession. The map shows the Sea Islands off the coast of Georgia. But that's not all! The map also contains three clues that tell where a treasure is supposedly buried.

Draw a Treasure Map Your project for this chapter will be to find the location of the treasure. Trace the map provided, and then add to the drawing by following the clues in the activities.

 Take It to the NET To research more information about treasure maps for your project, go to **www.PHSchool.com**.
Web Code: add-0161

MAKING A SPLASH

When you jump into a pool or step into a bathtub, you cause the water level to rise. That's an example of water displacement. The volume of water displaced is equal to the volume of the object submerged—you.

Use Water Displacement to Find Volume For your chapter project, you will build a prism and a cylinder. You will calculate their volumes by using formulas. Then you will find their volumes by using water displacement.

 Take It to the NET To research more information about water displacement for your project, go to **www.PHSchool.com**.
Web Code: add-0161

Tree Angles

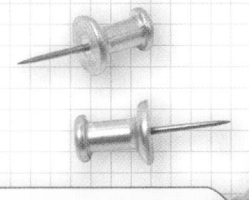

A giant sequoia in California is the largest living thing on Earth. It weighs about as much as 15 blue whales. What is the largest tree in your neighborhood? Maybe it is the largest of its species. You could nominate it to be in the National Register of Big Trees.

Measure a Big Tree The National Register of Big Trees has a formula to compare the sizes of trees of the same species: Big Tree Points = $C + H + \frac{S}{4}$, where C is the circumference in inches of the trunk at $4\frac{1}{2}$ feet above the ground, H is the tree's height in feet, and S is the average spread in feet of the tree's crown of branches.

For the chapter project, you will measure a tree and calculate its score in Big Tree Points.

Take It to the NET To research more information about tree sizes for your project, go to **www.PHSchool.com**.
Web Code: add-0161

The Good Times POLL

Do you participate in an organized extracurricular activity, such as a sport or a club? How much time do you devote to such activities each week? How does the amount of time you spend compare to the averages for students in your class and your school?

Conduct a Survey For the chapter project, you will do a survey of your class and a survey of your school. You will use statistical measures and graphs to analyze and display the results.

Take It to the NET To research more information about surveys for your project, go to **www.PHSchool.com**.
Web Code: add-0161

PRISM BUILDING

The prismatic shapes of tall buildings can be described using mathematical expressions such as $(a + b)^3$. Is $(a + b)^3$ equal to $a^3 + b^3$? No, but many students make that mistake. Sometimes it helps to have a concrete representation of a mathematical expression.

Make a 3-D Polynomial Model For the chapter project, you will make a three-dimensional model of a polynomial. You will analyze the model and its parts. You will use the model to see how polynomials can represent real-world objects.

Take It to the NET To research more information about polynomials for your project, go to **www.PHSchool.com**.
Web Code: add-0161

Chapter Projects 743

31. Start with −12, and add
9 to the previous term.
33, 42, 51
32. Start with 0.15, and add
0.15 to the previous
term. 0.75, 0.90, 1.05
42–50.

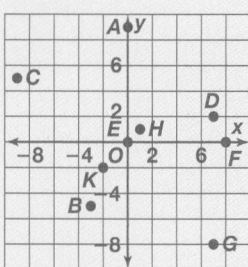

● Lesson 1-1 **Write a variable expression for each word phrase.**

1. 6 less than x $x − 6$

2. y less than 12 $12 − y$

3. the sum of z and 2 $z + 2$

4. a number m increased by 34 $m + 34$

5. the product of 8 and p $8p$

6. t divided by 5 $\frac{t}{5}$

● Lesson 1-2 **Simplify each expression.**

7. $15 + 20 \cdot 3$ 75

8. $46 − 4(2 + 8)$ 6

9. $16 ÷ 4 + 10 ÷ 2$ 9

10. $100 ÷ (30 + 20)$ 2

11. $5(8 + 4) ÷ 6 ÷ 2$ 5

12. $9 \cdot 6 − 12 ÷ 2$ 48

● Lesson 1-3 **Evaluate each expression.**

13. $3x + 6$, for $x = 12$ 42

14. $15a − 2a$, for $a = 20$ 260

15. $38 − 3y$, for $y = 9$ 11

16. $25 − (t + 18)$, for $t = 7$ 0

17. $\frac{x + y}{10}$, for $x = 35$ and $y = 65$ 10

● Lesson 1-4 **Compare. Use >, <, or = to complete each statement.**

18. $−12$ ■ $−9$ <

19. $|−4|$ ■ $|4|$ =

20. $−|−7|$ ■ $|−7|$ <

21. 0 ■ $−100$ >

● Lessons 1-5 and 1-6 **Simplify each expression.**

22. $−56 + 60$ 4

23. $18 + (−25)$ −7

24. $−34 + (−36)$ −70

25. $19 − (−5)$ 24

26. $80 − (−125)$ 205

27. $−82 − (−50)$ −32

28. $−7 + 35 + (−22)$ 6

29. $−44 − 20 − 80$ −144

30. $−8 + (−13) − (24)$ −45

● Lesson 1-7 **Write a rule for continuing each pattern. Find the next three numbers in the pattern.**

31. $−12, −3, 6, 15, 24, \ldots$
See margin.

32. $0.15, 0.3, 0.45, 0.6, \ldots$
See margin.

33. $1, 1, 2, 3, 5, 8, 13, \ldots$
Add the two previous
terms. 21, 34, 55

● Lesson 1-9 **Simplify each expression.**

34. $−4 \cdot 12$ −48

35. $−15(−8)$ 120

36. $30 \cdot (−5)$ −150

37. $−1(−2)(−3)(−4)$ 24

38. $−78 ÷ (−3)$ 26

39. $−150 ÷ 25$ −6

40. $\frac{120}{−15}$ −8

41. $−1,125 ÷ (−125)$ 9

● Lesson 1-10 **Draw a coordinate plane. Graph each point.** 42–50. See margin.

42. $A(0, 9)$

43. $B(−3, −5)$

44. $C(−9, 5)$

45. $D(7, 2)$

46. $E(0, 0)$

47. $F(8, 0)$

48. $G(7, −8)$

49. $H(1, 1)$

50. $K(−2, −2)$

Extra Practice

● **Lesson 2-1 Simplify each expression. Justify each step.** 1–6. See margin.

1. $99 + (-46) + (-99) + 45$

2. $225 + 320 + 75$

3. $18 + 12 + (-25) + 13$

4. $5 \cdot 678 \cdot 2$

5. $58 \cdot 2 \cdot 50$

6. $20 \cdot 4 \cdot 5 \cdot 25$

● **Lessons 2-2 and 2-3 Use the Distributive Property to simplify.**

7. $7(5) - 3(5)$ 20

8. $3 \cdot 6 + 7 \cdot 6$ 60

9. $15 \cdot 32 - 12 \cdot 32$ 96

10. $7b + 25 - 4b$ 3b + 25

11. $3(a - 2c)$ 3a − 6c

12. $3q + 2(q + 1)$ 5q + 2

13. $-3(4y - 1) + 5(7 - y)$
−17y + 38

14. $41 - 2(m + 1) - m$
−3m + 39

15. $12 + 5x - 2(3x + 5)$ −x + 2

● **Lesson 2-4 Write an equation for each sentence. Is each equation *true*, *false*, or an *open sentence*?**

16. Twice the sum of a number and one is twenty-two. $2(x + 1) = 22$; open sentence

17. Negative three divided by negative one is three. $\frac{-3}{-1} = 3$; true

18. Forty-five plus five equals negative fifty. $45 + 5 = -50$; false

● **Lessons 2-5 and 2-6 Solve each equation.**

19. $40 + x = 25$ −15

20. $-5 = y - 12$ 7

21. $z + (-23) = -47$ −24

22. $14 = a - 9$ 23

23. $t - 453 = -520$ −67

24. $78 = b + 100$ −22

25. $4k = 96$ 24

26. $300 = -15j$ −20

27. $-12c = 180$ −15

28. $\frac{d}{7} = -14$ −98

29. $-4 = \frac{w}{6}$ −24

30. $\frac{k}{-9} = -20$ 180

● **Lesson 2-8 Graph the solutions of each inequality.** 31–36. See margin.

31. $x > -12$

32. $y \leq 3$

33. $0 \geq z$

34. $p < -9$

35. $7 < n$

36. $f \leq -3$

● **Lessons 2-9 and 2-10 Solve each inequality.**

37. $a + 3 < -1$ a < −4

38. $-2 > b - 4$ 2 > b

39. $5 + x > -8$ x > −13

40. $-12 < -2 + y$ −10 < y

41. $w - 32 \leq 15$ w ≤ 47

42. $-20 \geq z - 13$ −7 ≥ z

43. $\frac{c}{5} \leq -3$ c ≤ −15

44. $8p \geq -96$ p ≥ −12

45. $0 < 8r$ 0 < r

46. $\frac{t}{-6} < -3$ t > 18

47. $\frac{a}{11} > -22$ a > −242

48. $-12k \geq -144$ k ≤ 12

Extra Practice

Extra Practice

1. $99 + (-99) + 45 + (-46)$
Commutative Property of Addition
$0 + 45 + (-46)$
additive inverse
-1

2. $225 + 75 + 320$
Commutative Property of Addition
$300 + 320$
Add from left to right.
620

3. $18 + 12 + 13 + (-25)$
Commutative Property of Addition
$18 + -25 + (12 + 13)$
Associative Property of Addition
$18 + -25 + 25$
Commutative Property of Addition
18

4. $5 \cdot 2 \cdot 678$
Commutative Property of Multiplication
$10 \cdot 678$
Multiply from left to right.
$6,780$

5. $2 \cdot 50 \cdot 58$
Commutative Property of Multiplication
$100 \cdot 58$
Multiply from left to right.
$5,800$

6. $20 \cdot 5 \cdot 4 \cdot 25$
Commutative Property of Multiplication
$100 \cdot 4 \cdot 25$
$100 \cdot 100$
Associative Property of Multiplication
$10,000$

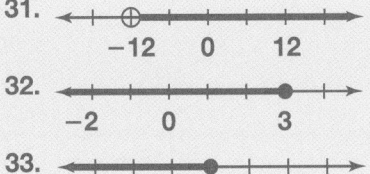

31.

−12   0   12

32.

−2   0   3

33.

−3   0   3

34.

−9   0

35.

−2 0   7

36.

−3 0   4

13. mean: 12.9; median: 12;
   modes: 10 and 12;
   outlier: 19
14. mean: 81.8; median:
   85.5; modes: 85 and 90;
   outlier: 50

Chapter 3 Extra Practice

● **Lesson 3-1 Estimate. State the method you used.** 1–6. Answers may vary. Samples are given.

1. $5.35 + 7.953$
about 13; rounding

2. $25.68 - 3.7$
about 22; rounding

3. $6.877 + 3.521 + 8.5$
about 19; front-end

4. $103.890 - 25.6$
about 70; rounding

5. $42.875 + 36.982 + 45.7$
about 120; clustering

6. $42.651 - 12.8$
about 30; rounding

● **Lesson 3-2 Estimate each product or quotient.**

7. $9.5(12.31)$ about 120

8. $24.8 \div 5.03$ about 5

9. $2.8 \cdot 6.11$ about 18

10. $-5.78 \div 1.95$ about -3

11. $(-2.468)(-9.031)$ about 18

12. $-19.32 \div 4.025$ about -5

● **Lesson 3-3 Find the mean, median, and mode. When the answer is not an integer, round to the nearest tenth. Identify any outliers.**

13. 10 13 10 15 12 11 12 19 14 See margin.

14. 85 86 80 85 90 90 50 88 See margin.

15. \$25 \$30 \$32 \$28 \$30 \$15 \$28 \$30
mean: \$27.30; median: \$29; mode: \$30;
outlier: \$15

16. 6.2 4.5 4.8 12.3 5.7 4.8 6.0
mean: 6.3; median: 5.7; mode: 4.8; outlier: 12.3

● **Lesson 3-4 Evaluate each formula for the values given.**

17. perimeter of a rectangle: $P = 2\ell + 2w$
when $\ell = 45$ yd and $w = 20$ yd 130 yd

18. circumference of a circle: $C = 2\pi r$
when $r = 6.8$ in.; use 3.14 for π about 42.7 in.

19. distance traveled: $d = rt$
when $r = 50$ mi/h and $t = 3.5$ h 175 mi

20. perimeter of a square: $P = 4s$
when $s = 12$ cm 48 cm

● **Lessons 3-5 and 3-6 Solve each equation.**

21. $t + 4.5 = 17.2$ 12.7

22. $15.5 + y = 10.5$ -5

23. $x - 70.2 = 23.6$ 93.8

24. $1.2b = 6$ 5

25. $c \div 5.3 = 12$ 63.6

26. $-21.2 = p - 12.7$ -8.5

27. $f \div 5.25 = 7.8$ 40.95

28. $6.4m = 38.4$ 6

29. $-3.1 = -31a$ 0.1

30. $h + 25.8 = 76$ 50.2

31. $101.5 = j - 82.8$ 184.3

32. $-50.8 = d + 36.2$ -87

33. $4.5v = 13.5$ 3

34. $s \div 10.5 = 42$ 441

35. $26.2 = z - 6.55$ 32.75

● **Lesson 3-7 Complete each statement.**

36. 0.95 m = ▨ cm 95

37. 250 mL = ▨ L 0.25

38. 2.5 kg = ▨ g 2,500

39. 60 g = ▨ kg 0.060

40. 0.54 L = ▨ mL 540

41. 5.62 m = ▨ cm 562

42. 58 cm = ▨ m 0.58

43. 564 mm = ▨ m 0.564

44. 345 g = ▨ mg 345,000

45. 36 mg = ▨ g 0.036

46. 234 cm = ▨ m 2.34

47. 567 mg = ▨ g 0.567

Extra Practice

Extra Practice

Extra Practice

13. composite; 5^2
14. composite; $2^2 \cdot 3^2$
15. prime
16. composite; $2 \cdot 19$
17. neither
18. composite; $3^2 \cdot 13$

1. 1, 2, 3, 4, 5, 6, 10, 12, 15, 20, 30, 60
6. 1, 2, 4, 5, 10, 20, 25, 50, 100

● **Lesson 4-1** List all the factors of each number.

1. 60 See above right.
2. 45 1, 3, 5, 9, 15, 45
3. 64 1, 2, 4, 8, 16, 32, 64
4. 46 1, 2, 23, 46
5. 36 1, 2, 3, 4, 6, 9, 12, 18, 36
6. 100 See above.

● **Lesson 4-2** Evaluate each expression.

7. x^2, for $x = 8$ 64
8. $-2v^3$, for $v = 2$ −16
9. $5t^2 - 4$, for $t = 4$ 76

10. $a^3 + 10$, for $a = -5$ −115
11. mn^2, for $m = 3$ and $n = 4$ 48
12. $6(2r - 4)^2$, for $r = 7$ 600

● **Lesson 4-3** Is each number *prime*, *composite*, or *neither*? For each composite number, write the prime factorization. Use exponents where possible. 13–18. See margin.

13. 25
14. 36
15. 47
16. 38
17. 1
18. 117

Find the GCF.

19. 20, 30 10
20. 8, 12, 18 2
21. $5x, 40x$ $5x$
22. $6y, 108$ 6

● **Lesson 4-4** Write in simplest form.

23. $\frac{12}{20}$ $\frac{3}{5}$
24. $\frac{4}{20}$ $\frac{1}{5}$
25. $\frac{35}{80}$ $\frac{7}{16}$
26. $\frac{18}{36}$ $\frac{1}{2}$

27. $\frac{13}{52}$ $\frac{1}{4}$
28. $\frac{75}{100}$ $\frac{3}{4}$
29. $\frac{16}{50}$ $\frac{8}{25}$
30. $\frac{5x}{65x^2}$ $\frac{1}{13x}$

31. $\frac{3x^2}{45x}$ $\frac{x}{15}$
32. $\frac{50a^2}{5a}$ $10a$
33. $\frac{36x}{16}$ $\frac{9x}{4}$
34. $\frac{100pq}{625q}$ $\frac{4p}{25}$

● **Lesson 4-6** Graph each rational number on one number line. 35–39. See margin.

35. 0.2
36. $\frac{3}{10}$
37. −2
38. −1
39. $-\frac{1}{2}$

Evaluate each expression for $a = 10$ and $b = -4$. Write in simplest form.

40. $\frac{a + b}{a}$ $\frac{3}{5}$
41. $\frac{b}{a}$ $-\frac{2}{5}$
42. $\frac{a - b}{3a}$ $\frac{7}{15}$
43. $\frac{b^2}{a^2}$ $\frac{4}{25}$

● **Lessons 4-7 and 4-8** Simplify each expression.

44. $8a^2 \cdot 3a^4$ $24a^6$
45. $3y^2 \cdot 2y^3$ $6y^5$
46. $(p^5)^6$ p^{30}
47. $(x^3)(y)(x^5)$ x^8y

48. $\frac{6x^2}{2x^5}$ $\frac{3}{x^3}$
49. $\frac{18t^{20}}{6t^5}$ $3t^{15}$
50. $\frac{b^2}{b^3}$ $\frac{1}{b}$
51. 12^0 1

● **Lesson 4-9** Multiply. Express each result in scientific notation.

52. $(5 \times 10^4)(8 \times 10^9)$
4×10^{14}
53. $(1.1 \times 10^6)(6 \times 10^{10})$
6.6×10^{16}
54. $(3 \times 10^{12})(4 \times 10^8)$
1.2×10^{21}

35–39.

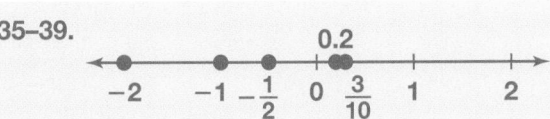

● **Lesson 5-1** Find the LCM of each group of numbers or expressions.

1. $15, 30$ 30   **2.** $4, 8, 10$ 40   **3.** $8x, 12y$ 24xy   **4.** $3t^2, 5t$ $15t^2$

Compare. Use $>$, $<$, or $=$ to complete each statement.

5. $\frac{5}{8} \blacksquare \frac{3}{5}$ >   **6.** $\frac{3}{10} \blacksquare \frac{1}{3}$ <   **7.** $\frac{3}{4} \blacksquare \frac{6}{8}$ =   **8.** $-\frac{1}{5} \blacksquare -\frac{1}{4}$ >

● **Lesson 5-2** Write each fraction or mixed number as a decimal.

9. $\frac{7}{8}$ 0.875   **10.** $2\frac{3}{5}$ 2.6   **11.** $\frac{3}{11}$ $0.\overline{27}$ **12.** $\frac{16}{5}$ 3.2   **13.** $-\frac{7}{10}$ -0.7 **14.** $-2\frac{1}{9}$ $-2.\overline{1}$

Write each decimal as a fraction or mixed number in
simplest form.

15. 1.3 $1\frac{3}{10}$ **16.** 0.605 $\frac{121}{200}$ **17.** $0.\overline{6}$ $\frac{2}{3}$ **18.** $-0.\overline{15}$ $-\frac{5}{33}$ **19.** 0.35 $\frac{7}{20}$ **20.** 5.4 $5\frac{2}{5}$

● **Lesson 5-3** Add or subtract.

21. $\frac{2}{5} + \frac{3}{5}$ 1   **22.** $3\frac{3}{4} - 1\frac{5}{6}$ $1\frac{11}{12}$ **23.** $-\frac{5}{8} + \frac{1}{4}$ $-\frac{3}{8}$ **24.** $\frac{10}{x} - \frac{12}{x}$ $-\frac{2}{x}$

25. $\frac{1}{2} - \frac{3}{4}$ $-\frac{1}{4}$ **26.** $4\frac{5}{6} + 5\frac{2}{9}$ $10\frac{1}{18}$ **27.** $\frac{5}{t} + \frac{3}{4}$ $\frac{20 + 3t}{4t}$ **28.** $5\frac{1}{3} - \frac{7}{8}$ $4\frac{11}{24}$

● **Lesson 5-4** Find each product or quotient.

29. $\frac{3}{5} \cdot \frac{2}{3}$ $\frac{2}{5}$ **30.** $\frac{5}{6} \div 1\frac{2}{3}$ $\frac{1}{2}$ **31.** $-\frac{7}{10} \cdot 1\frac{3}{7}$ -1 **32.** $\frac{5y}{6} \div \frac{2y}{3}$ $\frac{5}{4}$ **33.** $-\frac{2}{3} \cdot \left(-\frac{9}{22}\right)$ $\frac{3}{11}$

34. $10\frac{5}{8} \div \frac{5}{8}$ 17   **35.** $\frac{5x}{7} \cdot \frac{1}{5}$ $\frac{x}{7}$ **36.** $\left(-\frac{1}{2}\right)\left(-\frac{3}{4}\right)$ $\frac{3}{8}$ **37.** $\frac{2}{5} \div \left(-\frac{1}{5}\right)$ -2 **38.** $\frac{6}{7} \cdot \frac{3}{7}$ $\frac{18}{49}$

● **Lesson 5-5** Complete each statement.

39. $60 \text{ in.} = \blacksquare \text{ ft}$ 5 ft   **40.** $15 \text{ qt} = \blacksquare \text{ pt}$ 30 pt   **41.** $4 \text{ lb} = \blacksquare \text{ oz}$ 64 oz

● **Lessons 5-7 and 5-8** Solve each equation.

42. $\frac{3}{5} + a = 1\frac{2}{3}$ $1\frac{1}{15}$ **43.** $b - 3\frac{1}{2} = 5$ $8\frac{1}{2}$ **44.** $-\frac{4}{5}c = \frac{7}{10}$ $-\frac{7}{8}$

45. $5d = \frac{3}{4}$ $\frac{3}{20}$ **46.** $1\frac{4}{7} = f + \frac{3}{14}$ $1\frac{5}{14}$ **47.** $\frac{7}{8} = g - \frac{2}{3}$ $1\frac{13}{24}$

● **Lesson 5-9** Simplify each expression.

48. $(8a^3)^2$ $64a^6$ **49.** $(x^2y^3)^4$ x^8y^{12} **50.** $(-2v)^3$ $-8v^3$ **51.** $(abc^3)^5$ $a^5b^5c^{15}$ **52.** $(f^2g^3)^6$ $f^{12}g^{18}$

53. $(2xy)^3$ $8x^3y^3$ **54.** $\left(\frac{2}{5}\right)^3$ $\frac{8}{125}$ **55.** $\left(\frac{2c}{d^3}\right)^2$ $\frac{4c^2}{d^6}$ **56.** $\left(\frac{3t}{4v}\right)^2$ $\frac{9t^2}{16v^2}$ **57.** $\left(\frac{1}{4}\right)^3$ $\frac{1}{64}$

6

Extra Practice

● **Lesson 6-1 Write each ratio as a fraction in simplest form.**

1. 15 : 30 $\frac{1}{2}$ **2.** 25 to 10 $\frac{5}{2}$ **3.** 4 out of 16 $\frac{1}{4}$ **4.** $\frac{15}{35}$ $\frac{3}{7}$

Find each unit rate.

5. 40 mi/h = ▦ ft/s 58.$\overline{6}$ ft/s   **6.** 8 cm/s = ▦ m/h 288 m/h   **7.** 5.5 qt/min = ▦ gal/h 82.5 gal/h

● **Lesson 6-2 Solve each proportion. Round to the nearest tenth where necessary.**

8. $\frac{3}{5} = \frac{a}{60}$ 36   **9.** $\frac{8}{7} = \frac{96}{b}$ 84   **10.** $\frac{8}{c} = \frac{40}{85}$ 17   **11.** $\frac{d}{36} = \frac{2}{3}$ 24

12. $\frac{105}{200} = \frac{x}{40}$ 21   **13.** $\frac{8}{15} = \frac{y}{50}$ 26.7   **14.** $\frac{z}{40} = \frac{11}{15}$ 29.3   **15.** $\frac{t}{2} = \frac{1.5}{8}$ 0.4

● **Lesson 6-3 The scale of a map is 4 in. : 25 mi. Find the actual distance for each map distance. Round to the nearest tenth where necessary.**

16. 10 in. 62.5 mi   **17.** 5.5 in. 34.4 mi   **18.** $\frac{1}{2}$ in. 3.1 mi   **19.** 3 in. 18.8 mi

● **Lesson 6-4 Find each probability for one roll of a number cube. Then find the odds in favor of the event.**

20. $P(4)$ $\frac{1}{6}$; 1 to 5   **21.** $P(8)$ 0; 0 to 6   **22.** P(even number) $\frac{3}{6}$, or $\frac{1}{2}$; 1 to 1   **23.** $P(1$ or $2)$ $\frac{2}{6}$, or $\frac{1}{3}$; 1 to 2

● **Lesson 6-5 Write each percent as a fraction in simplest form and as a decimal.**

24. 10% $\frac{1}{10}$; 0.1   **25.** 200% $\frac{2}{1}$; 2   **26.** 6% $\frac{3}{50}$; 0.06   **27.** 1.75% $\frac{7}{400}$; 0.0175   **28.** 8.5% $\frac{17}{200}$; 0.085

Write each number as a percent. Where necessary, round to the nearest tenth of a percent.

29. 0.15 15%   **30.** 1.2 120%   **31.** $\frac{5}{12}$ 41.7%   **32.** $\frac{1}{8}$ 12.5%   **33.** 0.345 34.5%

● **Lessons 6-6 and 6-7 Solve each percent problem by using a proportion or an equation.**

34. Find 12% of 80. 9.6   **35.** 30% of x is 12. What is x? 40

36. What percent of 50 is 2.5? 5%   **37.** Find 30% of 121. 36.3

● **Lesson 6-8 Find each percent of change. Tell whether the change is an increase or a decrease.**

38. 120 to 80 33.3% decrease   **39.** 40 to 100 150% increase   **40.** 175 to 231 32% increase   **41.** $4 to $3.50 12.5% decrease

● **Lesson 6-9 Find each sale price.**

42. regular price, $100; discount, 20% $80   **43.** regular price, $60; discount, 25% $45

Chapter 6   Extra Practice **749**

22.

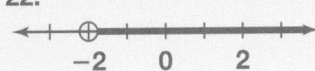

23.

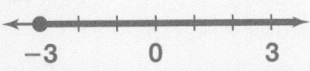

24.

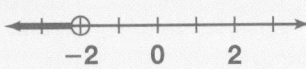

25.

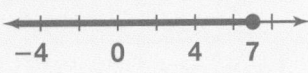

26.

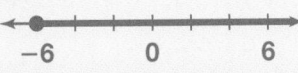

27.

28.

29.

30.

● **Lessons 7-1, 7-2, 7-3, and 7-5** **Solve and check each equation.**

1. $10 - 5x = 15$ −1   **2.** $3y + 17 = -13$ −10   **3.** $62 = -12z + 14$ −4

4. $6x - 2x = 12$ 3   **5.** $t + 5 - 2t = -10$ 15   **6.** $24 = 2(b - 2) - 4b$ −14

7. $5 - 2(y - 5) = 27$ −6   **8.** $-56a + 90 + 58a = 92$ 1   **9.** $8 = 3(c + 8)$ $-5\frac{1}{3}$

10. $8 - \frac{t}{2} = 53$ −90   **11.** $75 = \frac{m}{3} + 10$ 195   **12.** $\frac{3}{5}p + 18 = 24$ 10

13. $0.05x - 0.08 + x = 0.97$ 1   **14.** $2.5y + 3.5 = -1.5$ −2   **15.** $6.3p + 1.2p = 22.5$ 3

16. $2x + 6 = 5x$ 2   **17.** $3a + 2 = a - 8$ −5   **18.** $3(b - 2) = 9b$ −1

19. $8(f + 3) = 10f - 32$ 28   **20.** $\frac{1}{4}(x - 8) = \frac{3}{4}x$ −4   **21.** $4(w - 2.1) = w + 0.6$ 3

● **Lesson 7-6** **Solve and graph each inequality.** 22–30. For graphs, see margin.

22. $3x + 18 > 12$ $x > -2$ **23.** $4 + 9a \geq -23$ $a \geq -3$ **24.** $10.5 < -4y + 2.5$ $-2 > y$

25. $19 - 3x \geq -2$ $x \leq 7$ **26.** $-5(a - 3) \leq 45$ $a \geq -6$ **27.** $\frac{1}{2}(t - 6) \leq 22$ $t \leq 50$

28. $\frac{y}{4} - 6 < -9$ $y < -12$ **29.** $-31.4 \leq 2x + 1$ $x \geq -16.2$ **30.** $5.8 > 1 + 0.2m$ $m < 24$

● **Lesson 7-7** **Solve for the variable indicated in red.**

31. $s = p + c$ $p = s - c$ **32.** $x + y = 180$ **33.** $a - b = c$ $a = c + b$ **34.** $I = prt$ $\frac{I}{rt} = p$
$y = 180 - x$

● **Lesson 7-8** **Find the simple interest.**

35. $450 deposited at an interest rate of 2% for 4 years $36

36. $3,000 deposited at an interest rate of 3% for 10 years $900

37. $10,000 deposited at an interest rate of 9% for 5 years $4,500

Find each balance.

38. $9,000 at 6% compounded annually for 5 years $12,044.03

39. $25,000 at 7% compounded semiannually for 10 years $49,744.72

40. $12,000 at 3% compounded semiannually for 8 years $15,227.83

41. $1,000 at 4% compounded annually for 10 years $1,480.24

42. $500 at 1.5% compounded annually for 4 years $530.68

43. $2,000 at 5% compounded semiannually for 2 years $2,207.63

Extra Practice

● **Lesson 8-1 Is each relation a function? Explain.** 1–4. See margin.

1. $\{(3, 5), (4, 7), (4, 8), (6, 10)\}$

2. $\{(0, -1), (1, 3), (-2, 4), (3, 6)\}$

3. $\{(4, 5), (5, 2), (1, -3), (-2, -3), (0, 2)\}$

4. $\{(1.5, 0.6), (1.5, 1.1), (2, 1.9), (1, 3.2)\}$

● **Lesson 8-2 Find the solution of each equation for $x = -3, 0,$ and 2.** 5–12. See margin.

5. $y = 3x - 2$

6. $y = 2x + 5$

7. $y = \frac{1}{2}x + 8$

8. $x = 3 - y$

9. $y = -4$

10. $2y = 6x - 10$

11. $x - 2y = 3$

12. $y = -x - 1.5$

● **Lesson 8-3 Find the slope and y-intercept of the graph of each equation.**

13. $y = 5x - 4$ 5, -4

14. $y = 10 - 3x$ -3, 10

15. $2y = 3x + 12$ $\frac{3}{2}$, 6

16. $4x + y = 16$ -4, 16

17. $y = \frac{3}{5}x - 1$ $\frac{3}{5}$, -1

18. $12x - 6y = 30$ 2, -5

19. $y = x - \frac{1}{2}$ 1, $-\frac{1}{2}$

20. $x - y = -2$ 1, 2

Graph each line. 21–26. See margin.

21. slope 3, through $(0, -5)$

22. slope -1, through $(3, 5)$

23. no slope, through $(2, -1)$

24. $y = 2x + 1$

25. $x + y = 4$

26. $y = \frac{1}{2}x - 1$

● **Lesson 8-4 Write a rule for each linear function.**

27.

x	y
0	-1
1	2
2	5
3	8

$y = 3x - 1$

28.

x	y
-1	4
0	6
1	8
2	10

$y = 2x + 6$

29.

x	y
-2	-6
0	4
2	14
4	24

$y = 5x + 4$

30. The graph has slope $-\frac{1}{2}$ and y-intercept 3. $y = -\frac{1}{2}x + 3$

31. The graph has slope 2 and contains the point $(-1, 1)$. $y = 2x + 3$

32. The graph contains the points $(-3, -2)$ and $(3, 0)$. $y = \frac{1}{3}x - 1$

● **Lesson 8-5 Use the table to complete Exercises 33 and 34.**

33. Make a scatter plot of (time studying, test grade). See margin.

Study Time

Time Spent Studying (minutes)	40	30	20	50	75
Test Grade	85	80	60	80	90

34. Is there a positive correlation, negative correlation, or no correlation between the sets of data? Explain. Positive correlation; as you move to the right, most scores increase.

● **Lessons 8-7 and 8-8 Solve each system by graphing.** 37–38. See back of book for graphs.

35. $y = x + 3$
    $3x - y = 1$ $(2, 5)$

36. $x + y = -7$
    $x - y = 1$ $(-3, -4)$

37. $y > 2x - 4$
    $y < -3x + 6$

38. $x + y < 10$
    $x - y < -5$

21.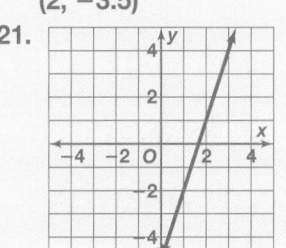

22.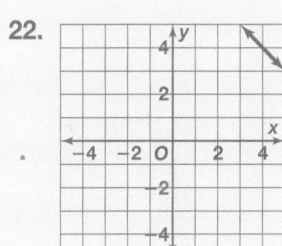

23.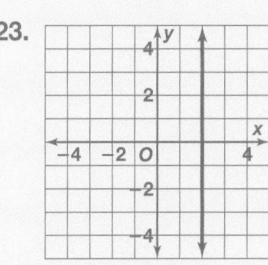

24.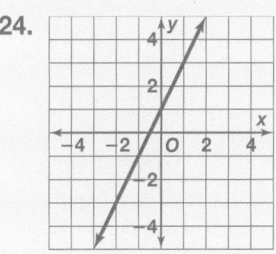

25.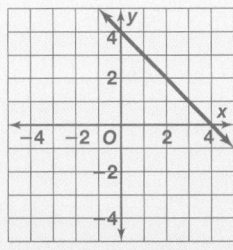

26.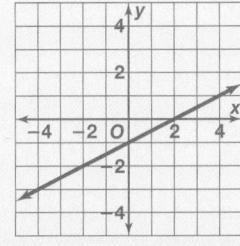

33.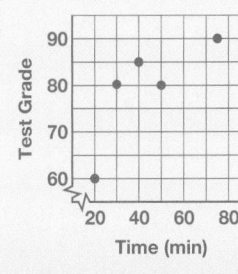

16.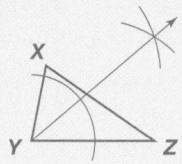

17.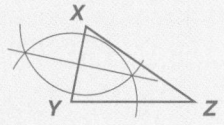

18.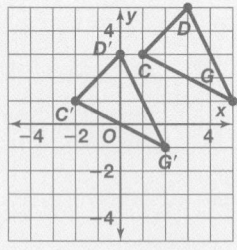

19.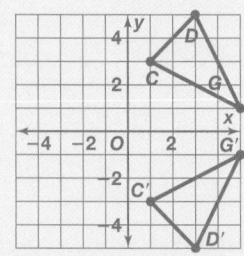

20.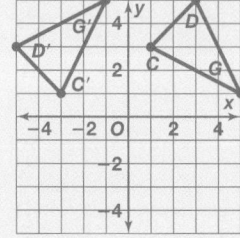

● **Lesson 9-1** Use the figure at the right.

1. Name the line in three ways.
$\overleftrightarrow{AB}$, $\overleftrightarrow{AC}$, $\overleftrightarrow{BC}$

2. Name four different rays.
$\overrightarrow{AC}$, $\overrightarrow{BC}$, $\overrightarrow{CA}$, $\overrightarrow{BA}$

Use the figure at the right. Name each of the following.

3. four segments that intersect $\overline{MR}$
$\overline{RS}$, $\overline{MQ}$, $\overline{MN}$, $\overline{UR}$

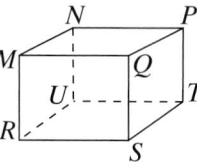

4. three segments parallel to $\overline{MR}$
$\overline{NU}$, $\overline{PT}$, $\overline{QS}$

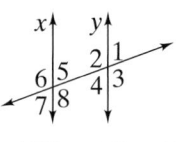

5. three segments skew to $\overline{MR}$
$\overline{UT}$, $\overline{NP}$, $\overline{ST}$

● **Lesson 9-2** In the figure at the right, $x \parallel y$.

6. List all angles that are congruent to $\angle 1$.
$\angle 4$, $\angle 5$, $\angle 7$

7. If $m\angle 5 = 67°$, what are the measures of the other angles? $m\angle 7 = 67°$; $m\angle 4 = 67°$; $m\angle 1 = 67°$; $m\angle 8 = 113°$; $m\angle 6 = 113°$; $m\angle 2 = 113°$; $m\angle 3 = 113°$

● **Lesson 9-3** Classify each figure.

8. 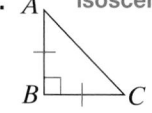 isosceles right triangle

9. 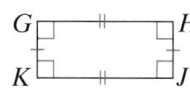 rectangle

10. 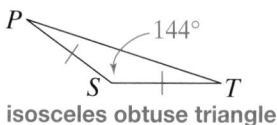 isosceles obtuse triangle

● **Lesson 9-5**

11. $\triangle XYZ \cong \triangle STU$. Which of the following must be true? a
a. $\overline{YZ} \cong \overline{TU}$ **b.** $\angle X \cong \angle T$ **c.** $\overline{ZX} \cong \overline{TS}$
d. $\angle YZX \cong \angle STU$ **e.** $\triangle YZX \cong \triangle UTS$

● **Lesson 9-6** Find the circumference of each circle with the given radius or diameter. Use 3.14 for π. Round to the nearest tenth.

12. radius = 4 in.
25.1 in.

13. diameter = 25 ft
78.5 ft

14. radius = 7.8 cm
49.0 cm

15. diameter = 100 m
314 m

● **Lesson 9-7** Draw $\triangle XYZ$ with acute $\angle Y$. 16–17. See margin.

16. Construct the angle bisector of $\angle Y$.   **17.** Construct a bisector of $\overline{XY}$.

● **Lessons 9-8, 9-9 and 9-10** Graph the image of $\triangle CDG$ with vertices $C(1, 3)$, $D(3, 5)$, and $G(5, 1)$ after each transformation. 18–20. See margin.

18. 3 units left, 2 units down   **19.** reflected over the x-axis   **20.** rotated 90° about the origin

10.

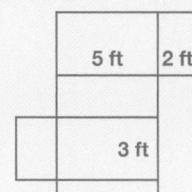

● **Lessons 10-1 and 10-2** Find the area of each figure.

1.

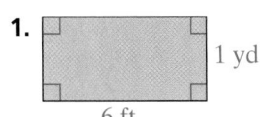

1 yd
6 ft

18 ft² or 2 yd²

2.

7.5 in.
15 in.

56.25 in.²

3.

5 m
15 m

75 m²

4.

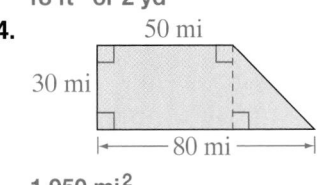

50 mi
30 mi
80 mi

1,950 mi²

5.

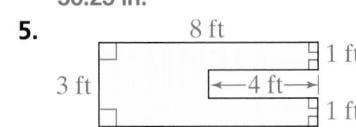

8 ft
1 ft
3 ft
4 ft
1 ft

20 ft²

6.

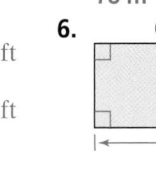

6 in.
3 in.
8 in.

21 in.²

● **Lesson 10-3** Find the area of each figure. Give an exact answer, and an approximate answer to the nearest tenth using 3.14 for π.

7.

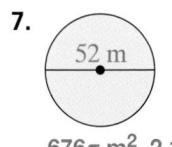

52 m

676π m², 2,122.6 m²

8.

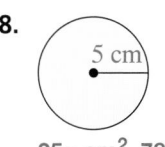

5 cm

25π cm², 78.5 cm²

9.

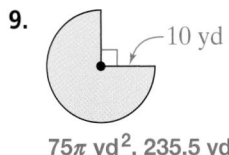

10 yd

75π yd², 235.5 yd²

● **Lesson 10-4**

10. Draw a net to represent a rectangular box that is 3 ft long, 5 ft wide, and 2 ft high. Label dimensions on the net and find the surface area. **For sketch, see margin; 62 ft²**

● **Lessons 10-5, 10-6, 10-7, and 10-9** Find the surface area and volume of each space figure, to the nearest tenth. Use 3.14 for π.

11.

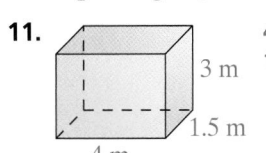

3 m
1.5 m
4 m

45 m²
18 m³

12.

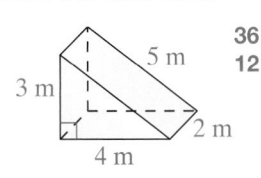

5 m
3 m
2 m
4 m

36 m²
12 m³

13.

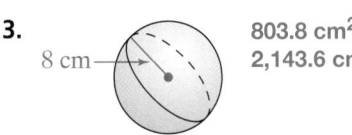

8 cm

803.8 cm²
2,143.6 cm³

14.

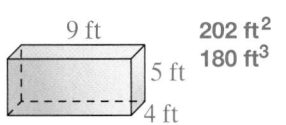

3 in.
5 in.

150.7 in.²
141.3 in.³

15.

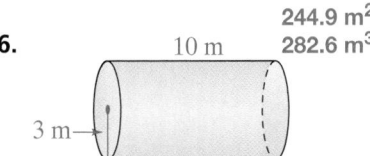

9 ft
5 ft
4 ft

202 ft²
180 ft³

16.

10 m
3 m

244.9 m²
282.6 m³

17.

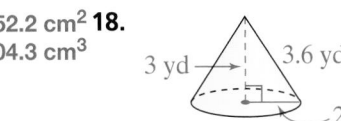

12 cm

452.2 cm²
904.3 cm³

18.

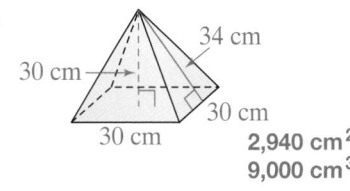

3 yd
3.6 yd
2 yd

35.2 yd²
12.6 yd³

19.

34 cm
30 cm
30 cm
30 cm

2,940 cm²
9,000 cm³

● **Lesson 11-1 Simplify each square root.**

1. $\sqrt{4}$ 2   **2.** $\sqrt{100}$ 10   **3.** $-\sqrt{36}$ −6   **4.** $\sqrt{121}$ 11   **5.** $\sqrt{25}$ 5

Estimate to the nearest integer.

6. $\sqrt{50}$ 7   **7.** $\sqrt{12}$ 3   **8.** $\sqrt{40}$ 6   **9.** $\sqrt{105}$ 10   **10.** $\sqrt{55}$ 7

Identify each number as rational or irrational.

11. $\sqrt{9}$ rational **12.** 0.6 rational   **13.** $\sqrt{5}$ irrational **14.** $0.\overline{6}$ rational   **15.** $0.010010001\ldots$
 irrational

● **Lesson 11-2 Find each missing length, to the nearest tenth of a unit.**

16. 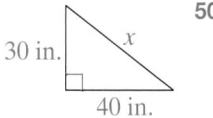 50 in.   **17.** 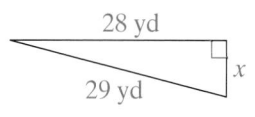 7.5 yd **18.** 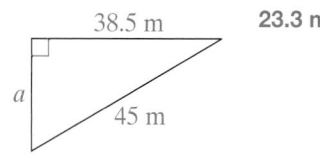 23.3 m

● **Lesson 11-3 Find the distance between each pair of points. Round to the nearest tenth.**

19. $(4, 6), (8, 2)$ 5.7   **20.** $(0, -4), (-5, 1)$ 7.1   **21.** $(20, -5), (10, -8)$ 10.4

Find the midpoint of each segment with the given endpoints.

22. $A(5, 4)$ and $B(3, 0)$ (4, 2)   **23.** $C(-2, -4)$ and $D(3, 1)$ **24.** $E(-1, 5)$ and $F(2, -1)$ $\left(\frac{1}{2}, 2\right)$
$\left(\frac{1}{2}, -\frac{3}{2}\right)$

● **Lesson 11-5 Find the missing lengths.**

25. 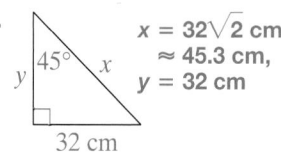 $x = 32\sqrt{2}$ cm
≈ 45.3 cm,
$y = 32$ cm

26. 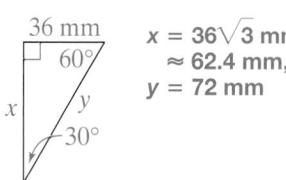 $x = 36\sqrt{3}$ mm
≈ 62.4 mm,
$y = 72$ mm

27. 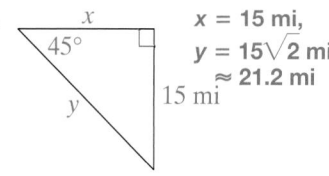 $x = 15$ mi,
$y = 15\sqrt{2}$ mi
≈ 21.2 mi

● **Lessons 11-6 and 11-7 Find each value. Round to four decimal places.**

28. $\sin 10°$ 0.1736   **29.** $\tan 85°$ 11.4301   **30.** $\cos 33°$ 0.8387

31. $\tan 5°$ 0.0875   **32.** $\sin 78°$ 0.9781   **33.** $\cos 65°$ 0.4226

34. $\cos 52°$ 0.6157   **35.** $\tan 50°$ 1.1918   **36.** $\sin 30°$ 0.5

37. A right triangle has one leg of 10 cm and an angle whose measure is
    25°. What lengths are possible for the other leg and the hypotenuse,
    to the nearest tenth? 4.7 cm and 11.0 cm, or 21.4 cm and 23.7 cm

Extra Practice

● **Lesson 12-1** Display each set of data in a frequency table. Then draw a line plot for each frequency table. Find the range. 1–2. See margin for tables and line plots.

1. 21 22 20 21 21 20 23 22 21 21
range = 3

2. 95 100 95 95 90 80 85 80 95 100
range = 20

● **Lesson 12-2** Use box-and-whisker plots to compare data sets. Use a single number line. See margin.

3. 1st set: 26 60 36 44 62 24 29 50 37 52 40 41 18 39 64 42
2nd set: 78 22 29 67 10 62 50 72 8 63 35 80 52 60 18 65 61

● **Lesson 12-3** Use the graph at the right for Exercises 4 and 5.

4. The graph suggests that the number of farms in 1982 was three times the number in 1992. Is this true? Explain. See margin.

5. Redraw the graph without a break. See margin.

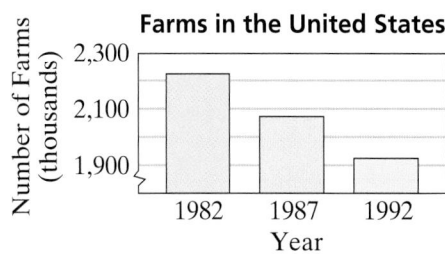

Farms in the United States

● **Lesson 12-4**

6. A menu shows that you can pick one vegetable from four choices, one potato dish from five choices, and one main dish from two choices. How many different choices of meals do you have? **40 choices**

● **Lesson 12-5** You select letters at random from the word **MATHEMATICS**.

7. Find the probability that you select A and then, after replacing A, select T. $\frac{4}{121}$

8. Find the probability that you select A and then, without replacing A, select T. $\frac{2}{55}$

● **Lesson 12-6** Simplify each expression.

9. $_3C_2$ 3   **10.** $_3P_2$ 6   **11.** $_5P_2$ 20   **12.** $_7C_3$ 35   **13.** $_{10}C_3$ 120   **14.** $_8P_3$ 336

● **Lessons 12-7 and 12-8** Some students were surveyed about the number of books in their lockers. The table shows the results.

15. Find the experimental probability that a locker will have 3 books. $\frac{1}{6}$

16. In a school of 600 students, how many lockers would you expect to have one book? **120 lockers**

Number of Books in Students' Lockers

Number of Books	1	2	3	4	5
Number of Students	12	21	10	7	10

1.

Number	Frequency
20	2
21	5
22	2
23	1

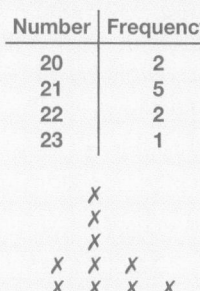

2.

Number	Frequency
80	2
85	1
90	1
95	4
100	2

3.

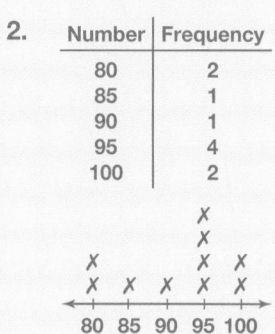

4. No; in 1992, there were about 1,900 thousand farms. Three times 1,900 thousand is 5,700 thousand. The graph shows that in 1982 there were about 2,200 thousand farms.

5.

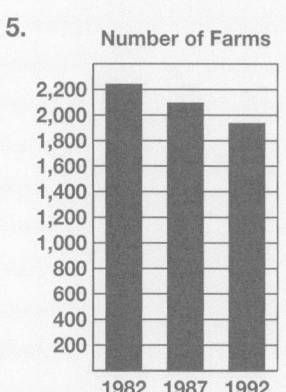

Number of Farms

4. 500,000, 5,000,000, 50,000,000; start with 50 and multiply by 10 repeatedly.

7.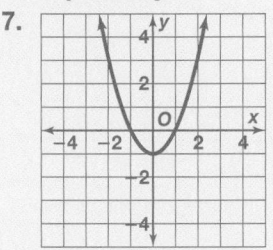

8.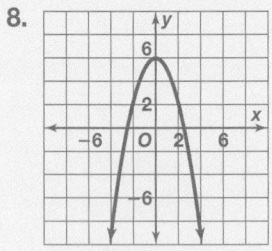

9.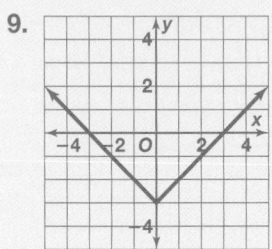

10.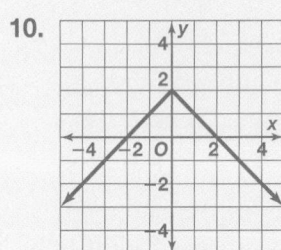

11.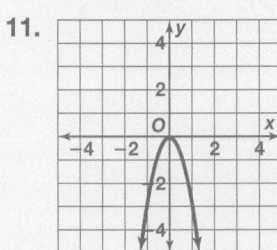

12.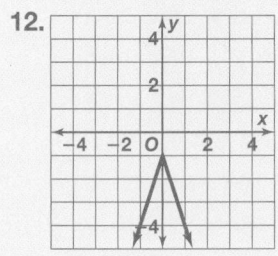

Extra Practice

● **Lesson 13-1** Find the next three terms of each sequence. Then write a rule to describe each sequence.

1. 100, 80, 60, 40, . . . 20, 0, −20; start with 100 and add −20 repeatedly.
2. 6, 12, 18, 24, . . . 30, 36, 42; start with 6 and add 6 repeatedly.
3. 8, 16, 24, 32, . . . 40, 48, 56; start with 8 and add 8 repeatedly.
4. 50, 500, 5,000, 50,000, . . . See margin.
5. −5, 25, −125, 625, . . . −3,125, 15,625, −78,125; start with −5 and multiply by −5 repeatedly.
6. 50, 10, −30, −70, . . . −110, −150, −190; start with 50 and add −40 repeatedly.

● **Lesson 13-2** Graph each function, for x values from **−2 to 2.** 7–14. See margin.

7. $y = x^2 - 1$ **8.** $y = -x^2 + 6$ **9.** $y = |x| - 3$ **10.** $y = -|x| + 2$

11. $y = -3x^2$ **12.** $y = -3|x| - 1$ **13.** $y = 2x^2 - 2$ **14.** $y = \frac{1}{2}|x|$

● **Lesson 13-3** For each function, make a table with integer values of x from 0 to 4. Then graph each function. 15–18. See back of book.

15. $y = 4^x$ **16.** $y = \frac{1}{2} \cdot 10^x$ **17.** $y = 10(0.5)^x$ **18.** $y = 2^x$

● **Lesson 13-4** Tell whether each polynomial is a *monomial*, a *binomial*, or a *trinomial*.

19. $2x^2 - 3x - 1$ trinomial   **20.** $3xy$ monomial   **21.** $5x^3 - 15$ binomial   **22.** $10 - 2x + 5y$ trinomial
23. xyz^2 monomial   **24.** $56 - y$ binomial   **25.** $3ab - a^2 - b$ trinomial   **26.** 80 monomial

● **Lesson 13-5** Simplify each sum or difference.

27. $(5y - 12) + (2y + 10)$ $7y - 2$ **28.** $(x^2 + 3x + 4) + (2x^2 + x + 6)$ $3x^2 + 4x + 10$
29. $(x^2 - 7x + 2) + (-x^2 + 6x - 2)$ $-x$ **30.** $(4a^2 - 3a - 2) - (2a^2 + 5a + 10)$ $2a^2 - 8a - 12$
31. $(5x - 3) + (6x^2 - 9)$ $6x^2 + 5x - 12$ **32.** $(15y^2 + 12y) - (12y^2 - 20)$ $3y^2 + 12y + 20$
33. $(3ab + a^2 + b^2) - (a^2 - 3b^2 - 5ab)$ $4b^2 + 8ab$ **34.** $(10t - t^2 - 15) + (3t^2 + 12)$ $2t^2 + 10t - 3$

● **Lessons 13-6 and 13-7** Simplify each product.

35. $2x(5x^2 + 6)$ $10x^3 + 12x$ **36.** $y^2(x + y)$ $xy^2 + y^3$ **37.** $6t^2(2t^2 - 3 + 8t)$ $12t^4 - 18t^2 + 48t^3$
38. $(x - 8)(x + 1)$ $x^2 - 7x - 8$ **39.** $(y + 6)(2y + 4)$ $2y^2 + 16y + 24$ **40.** $3b(5ab + 2ab^2 + 6b)$ $15ab^2 + 6ab^3 + 18b^2$

Use the GCF of the terms to write each expression as the product of two factors.

41. $4x^2 - 12$ $4(x^2 - 3)$ **42.** $5z^2 - 20z + 30$ $5(z^2 - 4z + 6)$ **43.** $2a^2b - 4a + 6b$ $2(a^2b - 2a + 3b)$
44. $t^2 - 3t$ $t(t - 3)$ **45.** $6xy + 2x + 3x^2y$ $x(6y + 2 + 3xy)$ **46.** $5w^3 + 6w^2 - 3w$ $w(5w^2 + 6w - 3)$

756   Chapter 13   Extra Practice

13.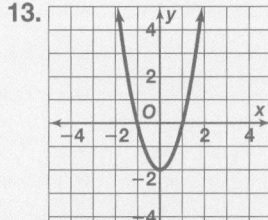

14.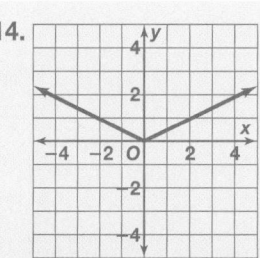

Skills Handbook

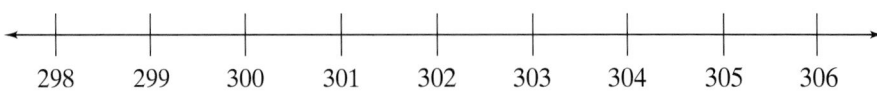

Comparing and Ordering Whole Numbers

The numbers on a number line are in order from least to greatest.

298 299 300 301 302 303 304 305 306

You can use a number line to compare whole numbers. Use the symbols > (is greater than) and < (is less than).

1 EXAMPLE

Use > or < to compare the numbers.

a. 303 ▨ 299
303 is to the right of 299.
303 > 299

b. 301 ▨ 305
301 is to the left of 305.
301 < 305

The value of a digit depends on its place in a number. Compare digits starting from the left.

2 EXAMPLE

Use > or < to compare the numbers.

a. 12,060,012,875 ▨ 12,060,012,675
8 hundreds > 6 hundreds, so
12,060,012,875 > 12,060,012,675.

b. 465,320 ▨ 4,653,208
0 millions < 4 millions, so
465,320 < 4,653,208.

EXERCISES

Use > or < to compare the numbers.

1. 3,660 ▨ 360
   >

2. 74,328 ▨ 74,238
   >

3. 88,010 ▨ 8,101
   >

4. 87,524 ▨ 9,879
   >

5. 295,286 ▨ 295,826
   <

6. 829,631 ▨ 842,832
   <

7. 932,401 ▨ 932,701
   <

8. 60,000 ▨ 500,009
   <

9. 1,609,372,002 ▨ 609,172,002
   >

10. 45,248,315,150 ▨ 45,283,718,150
   <

Write the numbers from least to greatest.

11. 3,747; 3,474; 3,774; 3,347; 3,734
   3,347; 3,474; 3,734; 3,747; 3,774

12. 70,903; 70,309; 73,909; 73,090
   70,309; 70,903; 73,090; 73,909

13. 32,056,403; 302,056,403; 30,265,403; 30,256,403
   30,256,403; 30,265,403; 32,056,403; 302,056,403

14. 884,172; 881,472; 887,142; 881,872
   881,472; 881,872; 884,172; 887,142

Skills Handbook **757**

Rounding Whole Numbers

You can use number lines to help you round numbers.

1 EXAMPLE

a. Round 7,510 to the nearest thousand.

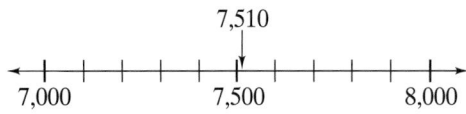

7,510 is between 7,000 and 8,000
and closer to 8,000.
7,510 rounds to 8,000.

b. Round 237 to the nearest ten.

237 is between 230 and 240
and closer to 240.
237 rounds to 240.

To round a number to a particular place, look at the digit to the right
of that place. If the digit is less than 5, round down. If the digit is 5 or
greater, round up.

2 EXAMPLE

Round to the place of the underlined digit.

a. 3,4<u>6</u>3,280

The digit to the right of the 6 is 3, so
3,463,280 rounds down to 3,460,000.

b. 28<u>9</u>,543

The digit to the right of the 9 is 5, so
289,543 rounds up to 290,000.

EXERCISES

Round to the nearest ten.

1. 42 40
2. 89 90
3. 671 670
4. 3,482 3,480
5. 7,029 7,030
6. 661,423
   661,420

Round to the nearest thousand.

7. 5,800 6,000
8. 3,100 3,000
9. 44,280
   44,000
10. 9,936
    10,000
11. 987 1,000
12. 313,591
    314,000
13. 5,641 6,000
14. 37,896
    38,000
15. 82,019
    82,000
16. 808,155
    808,000
17. 34,501
    35,000
18. 650,828
    651,000

Round to the place of the underlined digit.

19. 68,<u>8</u>52
    68,900
20. 4<u>5</u>1,006
    500,000
21. 3,40<u>7</u>,481
    3,407,000
22. 2<u>8</u>,512,030
    29,000,000
23. 71,2<u>2</u>5,003
    71,230,000
24. 96,<u>4</u>49
    96,400
25. 4<u>0</u>1,223 400,000
26. <u>8</u>,902 9,000
27. 3,6<u>7</u>7 3,680
28. 2,551,<u>7</u>50
    2,551,800
29. 68,<u>6</u>63
    69,000
30. 7<u>0</u>1,803,229
    702,000,000
31. 56<u>5</u>,598 566,000
32. 32,<u>8</u>10 32,800
33. 1,<u>4</u>46,300
    1,400,000

Multiplying Whole Numbers

When you multiply by a two-digit number, first multiply by the ones and then multiply by the tens. Add the products.

① EXAMPLE

Multiply 62 × 704.

Step 1	Step 2	Step 3
704	704	704
× 62	× 62	× 62
1408	1408	1 408
	42240	+ 42 240
		43,648

② EXAMPLE

Find each product.

a. **93 × 6**

```
   93
 ×  6
  558
```

b. **25 × 48**

```
    48
  × 25
   240
 + 960
 1,200
```

c. **80 × 921**

```
   921
 ×  80
73,680
```

EXERCISES

Find each product.

1.
```
  74
×  6
 444
```

2.
```
  35
×  9
 315
```

3.
```
  53
×  7
 371
```

4.
```
  80
×  8
 640
```

5.
```
  98
×  4
 392
```

6.
```
  65
×  8
 520
```

7.
```
 512
×  3
1,536
```

8.
```
 407
×  9
3,663
```

9.
```
 225
×  6
1,350
```

10.
```
 340
×  5
1,700
```

11.
```
 816
×  7
5,712
```

12.
```
 603
×  3
1,809
```

13.
```
  70
× 36
2,520
```

14.
```
  41
× 55
2,255
```

15.
```
  38
× 49
1,862
```

16.
```
  601
×  87
52,287
```

17.
```
 271
× 34
9,214
```

18.
```
  450
×  67
30,150
```

19. 6 × 82
   492

20. 405 × 5
   2,025

21. 81 × 9
   729

22. 3 × 274
   822

23. 552 × 4
   2,208

24. 60 × 84
   5,040

25. 52 × 17
   884

26. 31 × 90
   2,790

27. 78 × 52
   4,056

28. 43 × 66
   2,838

29. 826 × 3
   2,478

30. 702 × 4
   2,808

31. 8 × 180
   1,440

32. 6 × 339
   2,034

33. 781 × 7
   5,467

Dividing Whole Numbers

First estimate the quotient by rounding the divisor, the dividend, or both. When you divide, after you bring down a digit, you must write a digit in the quotient.

EXAMPLE

Find each quotient.

a. 741 ÷ 8

Estimate:

$720 \div 8 \approx 90$

$$
\begin{array}{r}
92 \text{ R5} \\
8\overline{)741} \\
-72 \\
\hline
21 \\
-16 \\
\hline
5
\end{array}
$$

b. 838 ÷ 43

Estimate:

$800 \div 40 \approx 20$

$$
\begin{array}{r}
19 \text{ R21} \\
43\overline{)838} \\
-43 \\
\hline
408 \\
-387 \\
\hline
21
\end{array}
$$

c. 367 ÷ 9

Estimate:

$360 \div 9 \approx 40$

$$
\begin{array}{r}
40 \text{ R7} \\
9\overline{)367} \\
-360 \\
\hline
7
\end{array}
$$

EXERCISES

Divide.

1. $4\overline{)61}$ 15 R1
2. $8\overline{)53}$ 6 R5
3. $7\overline{)90}$ 12 R6
4. $3\overline{)84}$ 28
5. $6\overline{)81}$ 13 R3

6. $6\overline{)469}$ 78 R1
7. $3\overline{)653}$ 217 R2
8. $8\overline{)645}$ 80 R5
9. $9\overline{)231}$ 25 R6
10. $4\overline{)415}$ 103 R3

11. $60\overline{)461}$ 7 R41
12. $40\overline{)213}$ 5 R13
13. $70\overline{)517}$ 7 R27
14. $30\overline{)432}$ 14 R12
15. $80\overline{)276}$ 3 R36

16. $43\overline{)273}$ 6 R15
17. $52\overline{)281}$ 5 R21
18. $69\overline{)207}$ 3
19. $38\overline{)121}$ 3 R7
20. $81\overline{)433}$ 5 R28

21. $94\overline{)1,368}$ 14 R52
22. $62\overline{)1,147}$ 18 R31
23. $55\overline{)2,047}$ 37 R12
24. $85\overline{)1,450}$ 17 R5
25. $46\overline{)996}$ 21 R30

26. $94 \div 4$ 23 R2
27. $66 \div 9$ 7 R3
28. $90 \div 5$ 18
29. $69 \div 6$ 11 R3
30. $58 \div 8$ 7 R2

31. $323 \div 5$ 64 R3
32. $849 \div 7$ 121 R2
33. $404 \div 8$ 50 R4
34. $934 \div 3$ 311 R1
35. $619 \div 6$ 103 R1

36. $777 \div 50$ 15 R27
37. $528 \div 20$ 26 R8
38. $443 \div 70$ 6 R23
39. $312 \div 40$ 7 R32
40. $335 \div 60$ 5 R35

41. $382 \div 72$ 5 R22
42. $580 \div 68$ 8 R36
43. $279 \div 43$ 6 R21
44. $232 \div 27$ 8 R16
45. $331 \div 93$ 3 R52

46. $614 \div 35$ 17 R19
47. $423 \div 28$ 15 R3
48. $489 \div 15$ 32 R9
49. $1,134 \div 51$ 22 R12
50. $1,103 \div 26$ 42 R11

Decimals and Place Value

Each digit in a whole number or a decimal has both a place and a value.
The value of any place is one tenth the value of the place to its left. The
chart below can help you read and write decimals.

Billions	Hundred millions	Ten millions	Millions	Hundred thousands	Ten thousands	Thousands	Hundreds	Tens	Ones	.	Tenths	Hundredths	Thousandths	Ten-thousandths	Hundred-thousandths	Millionths
2	4	0	1	2	6	2	8	3	0	.	7	5	0	1	9	1

Skills Handbook

EXAMPLE

a. What is the value of the digit 8 in the number above?
The digit 8 is in the hundreds place.
So, its value is 8 hundreds.

b. Write 2.006 in words.
The digit 6 is in the thousandths place.
So, 2.006 is read two and six thousandths.

c. Write five and thirty-four ten-thousandths as a decimal.
Ten-thousandths is 4 places to the right of the decimal point.
So, the decimal will have 4 places after the decimal point.
The answer is 5.0034.

EXERCISES

Use the chart above. Write the value of each digit.

1. the digit 9   9 hundred-thousandths

2. the digit 7   7 tenths

3. the digit 5   5 hundredths

4. the digit 6   6 ten thousands

5. the digit 4   4 hundred millions

6. the digit 3   3 tens

Write a decimal for the given words.

7. forty-one ten-thousandths   0.0041

8. eighteen and five hundred four thousandths   18.504

9. eight millionths   0.000008

10. seven and sixty-three hundred-thousandths   7.00063

11. thirteen thousandths   0.013

12. sixty-five and two hundred one thousandths   65.201

Write each decimal in words.

13. 0.06   six hundredths

14. 4.7   four and seven tenths

15. 0.00011   eleven hundred-thousandths

16. 0.9   nine tenths

17. 0.012   twelve thousandths

18. 0.000059   fifty-nine millionths

19. 0.0042   forty-two ten-thousandths

20. 6.020   six and twenty thousandths

Comparing and Ordering Decimals

To compare two decimals, use the symbols > (is greater than),
< (is less than), or = (is equal to). When you compare, start at the left
and compare the digits.

1 ⟩ EXAMPLE

Use >, <, or = to compare the decimals.

a. 0.1 ▨ 0.06

1 tenth > 0 tenths, so
0.1 > 0.06.

b. 2.4583 ▨ 2.48

5 hundredths < 8 hundredths,
so 2.4583 < 2.48.

c. 0.30026 ▨ 0.03026

3 tenths > 0 tenths, so
0.30026 > 0.03026.

2 ⟩ EXAMPLE

Draw number lines to compare the decimals.

a. 0.1 ▨ 0.06

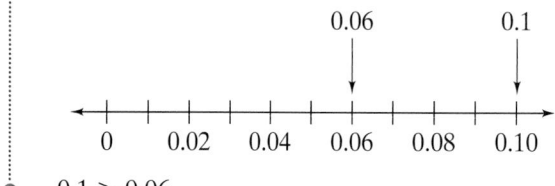

0.1 > 0.06

b. 2.4583 ▨ 2.48

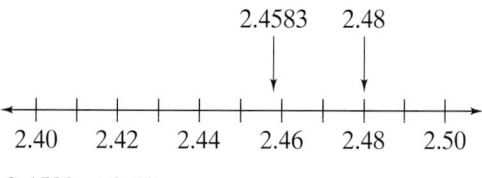

2.4583 < 2.48

EXERCISES

**Use >, <, or = to compare the decimals. Draw number
lines if you wish.**

1. 0.003 ▨ 0.02
     <

2. 84.2 ▨ 842
    <

3. 0.162 ▨ 0.106
     >

4. 0.0659 ▨ 0.6059
      <

5. 2.13 ▨ 2.99
   <

6. 3.53 ▨ 3.529
    >

7. 2.01 ▨ 2.010
    =

8. 0.00072 ▨ 0.07002
      <

9. 0.458 ▨ 0.4589
    <

10. 8.627 ▨ 8.649
     <

11. 0.0019 ▨ 0.0002
      >

12. 0.19321 ▨ 0.19231
       >

Write the decimals in order from least to greatest.

13. 2.31, 0.231, 23.1, 0.23, 3.21
0.23, 0.231, 2.31, 3.21, 23.1

14. 1.02, 1.002, 1.2, 1.11, 1.021
1.002, 1.02, 1.021, 1.11, 1.2

15. 0.02, 0.002, 0.22, 0.222, 2.22
0.002, 0.02, 0.22, 0.222, 2.22

16. 55.5, 555.5, 55.555, 5.5555
5.5555, 55.5, 55.555, 555.5

17. 0.07, 0.007, 0.7, 0.71, 0.72
0.007, 0.07, 0.7, 0.71, 0.72

18. 2.78, 2.7001, 2.701, 2.71, 2.7
2.7, 2.7001, 2.701, 2.71, 2.78

19. 7, 7.3264, 7.3, 7.3246, 7.0324
7, 7.0324, 7.3, 7.3246, 7.3264

20. 0.0101, 0.0099, 0.011, 0.00019
0.00019, 0.0099, 0.0101, 0.011

Rounding

When you round to a particular place, look at the digit to the right of that place. If it is 5 or greater, you increase the digit in the place you are rounding to by 1. If it is less than 5, you leave the digit in the place you are rounding to unchanged.

EXAMPLE

a. **Round 1.627 to the nearest whole number.**
The digit to the right of the units place is 6, so 1.627 rounds up to 2.

b. **Round 12,034 to the nearest thousand.**
The digit to the right of the thousands place is 0, so 12,034 rounds down to 12,000.

c. **Round 2.7195 to the nearest hundredth.**
The digit to the right of the hundredths place is 9, so 2.7195 rounds up to 2.72.

d. **Round 0.060521 to the nearest thousandth.**
The digit to the right of the thousandths place is 5, so 0.060521 rounds up to 0.061.

EXERCISES

Round to the nearest thousand.

1. 105,099
   105,000

2. 10,400
   10,000

3. 79,527,826
   79,528,000

4. 79,932
   80,000

5. 4,312,349
   4,312,000

Round to the nearest whole number.

6. 135.91 136
7. 3.001095 3
8. 96.912 97
9. 101.167 101
10. 299.9 300

Round to the nearest tenth.

11. 82.01 82.0
12. 4.67522 4.7
13. 20.397 20.4
14. 399.95 400.0
15. 129.98 130.0

Round to the nearest hundredth.

16. 13.458 13.46
17. 96.4045 96.40
18. 0.699 0.70
19. 4.234 4.23
20. 12.09531 12.10

Round to the place of the underlined digit.

21. 7.0615 7.06
22. 5.77125 6
23. 1,522 1,520
24. 0.91952 0.9195
25. 4.243 4.2

26. 236.001 240
27. 352 400
28. 3.495366
    3.49537
29. 8.07092 8.1
30. 0.6008 1

31. 409 410
32. 23,951,888
    24,000,000
33. 2.5784 2.58
34. 862 860
35. 19.32 19

36. 918 900
37. 7,735 7,700
38. 25.66047 25.66
39. 983,240,631
    980,000,000
40. 27 30

41. 0.003771
    0.00377
42. 0.0649 0.1
43. 12.777 12.8
44. 1,759,230
    1,759,000
45. 20,908 21,000

Adding and Subtracting Decimals

You add or subtract decimals just as you do whole numbers. You line up the decimal points and then add or subtract. If you wish, you can use zeros to make the columns even.

EXAMPLE

Find each sum or difference.

a. 37.6 + 8.431

$$\begin{array}{r} 37.6 \\ + 8.431 \\ \hline \end{array} \rightarrow \begin{array}{r} 37.600 \\ + 8.431 \\ \hline 46.031 \end{array}$$

b. 8 − 4.593

$$\begin{array}{r} 8 \\ - 4.593 \\ \hline \end{array} \rightarrow \begin{array}{r} 8.000 \\ - 4.593 \\ \hline 3.407 \end{array}$$

c. 8.3 + 2.99 + 17.5

$$\begin{array}{r} 8.3 \\ 2.99 \\ + 17.5 \\ \hline \end{array} \rightarrow \begin{array}{r} 8.30 \\ 2.99 \\ + 17.50 \\ \hline 28.79 \end{array}$$

EXERCISES

Find each sum or difference.

1.	2.	3.	4.	5.
$\begin{array}{r} 39.7 \\ - 36.03 \\ \hline 3.67 \end{array}$	$\begin{array}{r} 1.08 \\ - 0.9 \\ \hline 0.18 \end{array}$	$\begin{array}{r} 6.784 \\ + 0.528 \\ \hline 7.312 \end{array}$	$\begin{array}{r} 5.01 \\ - 0.87 \\ \hline 4.14 \end{array}$	$\begin{array}{r} 13.02 \\ + 23.107 \\ \hline 36.127 \end{array}$

6.	7.	8.	9.	10.
$\begin{array}{r} 8.634 \\ + 1.409 \\ \hline 10.043 \end{array}$	$\begin{array}{r} 2.1 \\ - 0.5 \\ \hline 1.6 \end{array}$	$\begin{array}{r} 8.23 \\ - 3.1 \\ \hline 5.13 \end{array}$	$\begin{array}{r} 1.05 \\ + 12.9 \\ \hline 13.95 \end{array}$	$\begin{array}{r} 2.6 \\ + 0.003 \\ \hline 2.603 \end{array}$

11.	12.	13.	14.	15.
$\begin{array}{r} 0.1 \\ 58.21 \\ + 1.9 \\ \hline 60.21 \end{array}$	$\begin{array}{r} 12.2 \\ 3.06 \\ + 0.5 \\ \hline 15.76 \end{array}$	$\begin{array}{r} 9.42 \\ 3.6 \\ + 21.003 \\ \hline 34.023 \end{array}$	$\begin{array}{r} 15.22 \\ 7.4 \\ + 8.125 \\ \hline 30.745 \end{array}$	$\begin{array}{r} 3.7 \\ 20.06 \\ + 16.19 \\ \hline 39.95 \end{array}$

16. 76.39 − 8.47 67.92   **17.** 8.7 + 17.03 25.73   **18.** 32.403 + 12.06 44.463   **19.** 20.5 + 11.45 31.95

20. 8.9 − 4.45 4.45   **21.** 1.245 + 5.8 7.045   **22.** 3.9 + 6.57 10.47   **23.** 14.81 − 8.6 6.21

24. 11.9 − 2.06 9.84   **25.** 3.45 + 4.061 7.511   **26.** 8.29 + 4.3 12.59   **27.** 7.06 − 4.235 2.825

28. 6.02 + 4.005 10.025   **29.** 7.05 − 3.5 3.55   **30.** 1.18 + 3.015 4.195   **31.** 2.304 − 0.87 1.434

32. 5.002 − 3.45 1.552   **33.** 6.8 + 3.57 10.37   **34.** 0.23 + 0.091 0.321   **35.** 0.5 − 0.18 0.32

36. 8.3 + 2.99 + 17.52 28.81   **37.** 9.5 + 12.32 + 6.4 28.22   **38.** 4.521 + 1.8 + 3.07 9.391

39. 3.602 + 9.4 + 24 37.002   **40.** 11.6 + 8.05 + 5.13 24.78   **41.** 7.023 + 1.48 + 3.9 12.403

42. 57 + 0.6327 + 189.007 246.6397   **43.** 741 + 6.08 + 0.0309 747.1109   **44.** 0.045 + 16.32 + 8.6 24.965

45. 4.27 + 6.18 + 0.91 11.36   **46.** 3.856 + 14.01 + 1.72 19.586   **47.** 11.45 + 3.79 + 23.861 39.101

Multiplying Decimals

Multiply decimals as you would whole numbers. Then place the decimal point in the product. To do this, add the number of decimal places in the factors.

Skills Handbook

1 EXAMPLE

Multiply 0.068 × 2.3.

Step 1 Multiply.

$$\begin{array}{r} 0.068 \\ \times\ 2.3 \\ \hline 204 \\ +\ 1360 \\ \hline 1564 \end{array}$$

Step 2 Place the decimal point.

$$\begin{array}{r} 0.068 \\ \times\ 2.3 \\ \hline 204 \\ +\ 1360 \\ \hline 0.1564 \end{array}$$

0.068 ← **three decimal places**
× 2.3 ← **one decimal place**

0.1564 ← **four decimal places**

2 EXAMPLE

Find each product.

a. 3.12 × 0.9

$$\begin{array}{r} 3.12 \\ \times\ 0.9 \\ \hline 2.808 \end{array}$$

b. 5.75 × 42

$$\begin{array}{r} 5.75 \\ \times\ 42 \\ \hline 11\ 50 \\ +\ 230\ 00 \\ \hline 241.50 \end{array}$$

c. 0.964 × 0.28

$$\begin{array}{r} 0.964 \\ \times\ 0.28 \\ \hline 7712 \\ +\ 19280 \\ \hline 0.26992 \end{array}$$

EXERCISES

Multiply.

1. $\begin{array}{r} 1.48 \\ \times\ 3.6 \\ \hline 5.328 \end{array}$

2. $\begin{array}{r} 191.2 \\ \times\ 3.4 \\ \hline 650.08 \end{array}$

3. $\begin{array}{r} 0.05 \\ \times\ 43 \\ \hline 2.15 \end{array}$

4. $\begin{array}{r} 0.27 \\ \times\ 5 \\ \hline 1.35 \end{array}$

5. $\begin{array}{r} 1.36 \\ \times\ 3.8 \\ \hline 5.168 \end{array}$

6. $\begin{array}{r} 6.23 \\ \times\ 0.21 \\ \hline 1.3083 \end{array}$

7. $\begin{array}{r} 0.512 \\ \times\ 0.76 \\ \hline 0.38912 \end{array}$

8. $\begin{array}{r} 0.04 \\ \times\ 7 \\ \hline 0.28 \end{array}$

9. $\begin{array}{r} 0.136 \\ \times\ 8.4 \\ \hline 1.1424 \end{array}$

10. $\begin{array}{r} 3 \\ \times\ 0.05 \\ \hline 0.15 \end{array}$

11. 2.07 × 1.004 2.07828

12. 0.12 × 6.1 0.732

13. 3.2 × 0.15 0.48

14. 0.74 × 0.23 0.1702

15. 2.6 × 0.14 0.364

16. 0.77 × 51 39.27

17. 9.3 × 0.706 6.5658

18. 71.13 × 0.4 28.452

19. 0.42 × 98 41.16

20. 6.3 × 85 535.5

21. 45 × 0.028 1.26

22. 76 × 3.3 250.8

23. 9 × 1.35 12.15

24. 4.56 × 7 31.92

25. 5 × 2.41 12.05

26. 704 × 0.3 211.2

27. 8.003 × 0.6 4.8018

28. 42.2 × 0.9 37.98

29. 0.6 × 30.02 18.012

30. 0.05 × 11.8 0.59

Zeros in a Product

When you multiply with decimals, you may have to write one or more zeros to the left of a product before you can place the decimal point.

1 EXAMPLE

Multiply 0.06 × 0.015.

Step 1 Multiply.

$$\begin{array}{r} 0.015 \\ \times\ 0.06 \\ \hline 90 \end{array}$$

Step 2 Place the decimal point.

$$\begin{array}{r} 0.015 \\ \times\ 0.06 \\ \hline 0.00090 \end{array}$$ ← **The product should have 5 decimal places, so you must write three zeros before placing the decimal point**

2 EXAMPLE

a. **0.02 × 1.3**

$$\begin{array}{r} 1.3 \\ \times\ 0.02 \\ \hline 0.026 \end{array}$$

b. **0.012 × 2.4**

$$\begin{array}{r} 2.4 \\ \times\ 0.012 \\ \hline 48 \\ +\ 240 \\ \hline 0.0288 \end{array}$$

c. **0.022 × 0.051**

$$\begin{array}{r} 0.051 \\ \times\ 0.022 \\ \hline 102 \\ +\ 1020 \\ \hline 0.001122 \end{array}$$

EXERCISES

Multiply.

1. $\begin{array}{r} 0.03 \\ \times\ 0.9 \\ \hline 0.027 \end{array}$

2. $\begin{array}{r} 0.06 \\ \times\ 0.5 \\ \hline 0.03 \end{array}$

3. $\begin{array}{r} 2.4 \\ \times\ 0.03 \\ \hline 0.072 \end{array}$

4. $\begin{array}{r} 7 \\ \times\ 0.01 \\ \hline 0.07 \end{array}$

5. $\begin{array}{r} 0.05 \\ \times\ 0.05 \\ \hline 0.0025 \end{array}$

6. $\begin{array}{r} 0.016 \\ \times\ 0.12 \\ \hline 0.00192 \end{array}$

7. $\begin{array}{r} 0.031 \\ \times\ 0.08 \\ \hline 0.00248 \end{array}$

8. $\begin{array}{r} 0.03 \\ \times\ 0.2 \\ \hline 0.006 \end{array}$

9. $\begin{array}{r} 0.27 \\ \times\ 0.033 \\ \hline 0.00891 \end{array}$

10. $\begin{array}{r} 0.014 \\ \times\ 0.25 \\ \hline 0.0035 \end{array}$

11. 0.003 × 0.55
0.00165

12. 0.01 × 0.74
0.0074

13. 0.47 × 0.08
0.0376

14. 0.76 × 0.1
0.076

15. 0.3 × 0.27
0.081

16. 0.19 × 0.05
0.0095

17. 0.018 × 0.04
0.00072

18. 0.43 × 0.2
0.086

19. 0.03 × 0.03
0.0009

20. 4.003 × 0.02
0.08006

21. 0.5 × 0.08
0.04

22. 0.06 × 0.7
0.042

23. 0.047 × 0.008
0.000376

24. 0.05 × 0.06
0.003

25. 0.03 × 0.4
0.012

26. 0.05 × 0.036
0.0018

27. 0.4 × 0.23
0.092

28. 0.3 × 0.017
0.0051

29. 0.3 × 0.24
0.072

30. 0.67 × 0.09
0.0603

31. 3.02 × 0.006
0.01812

32. 0.31 × 0.08
0.0248

33. 0.14 × 0.05
0.007

34. 0.07 × 0.85
0.0595

Dividing Decimals by Whole Numbers

When you divide a decimal by a whole number, the decimal point in the quotient goes directly above the decimal point in the dividend. You may need extra zeros to place the decimal point.

1 EXAMPLE

Divide 2.432 ÷ 32.

Step 1 Divide.

```
      76
32)2.432
  − 2 24
     192
   − 192
       0
```

Step 2 Place the decimal point.

```
    0.076      ← Put extra zeros to the left.
32)2.432          Then place the decimal point.
  − 2 24
     192
   − 192
       0
```

2 EXAMPLE

a. **37.6 ÷ 8**

```
   4.7
8)37.6
 − 32
   5 6
 − 5 6
     0
```

b. **39.33 ÷ 69**

```
    0.57
69)39.33
  − 34 5
    4 83
  − 4 83
      0
```

c. **4.482 ÷ 54**

```
    0.083
54)4.482
  − 4 32
    162
  − 162
      0
```

EXERCISES

Divide.

1. 7)17.92 2.56
2. 5)16.5 3.3
3. 9)6.984 0.776
4. 6)91.44 15.24
5. 4)35.16 8.79

6. 56)8.848 0.158
7. 22)2.42 0.11
8. 26)1,723.8 66.3
9. 83)15.272 0.184
10. 39)26.91 0.69

11. 14.49 ÷ 7 2.07
12. 10.53 ÷ 9 1.17
13. 17.52 ÷ 2 8.76
14. 37.14 ÷ 6 6.19

15. 0.1352 ÷ 8 0.0169
16. 0.0324 ÷ 9 0.0036
17. 0.0882 ÷ 6 0.0147
18. 0.8682 ÷ 6 0.1447

19. 12.342 ÷ 22 0.561
20. 29.792 ÷ 32 0.931
21. 22.568 ÷ 26 0.868
22. 11.340 ÷ 36 0.315

23. 45.918 ÷ 18 2.551
24. 79.599 ÷ 13 6.123
25. 58.5 ÷ 15 3.9
26. 74.664 ÷ 12 6.222

27. 21.0 ÷ 84 0.25
28. 89.378 ÷ 67 1.334
29. 0.0672 ÷ 48 0.0014
30. 171.031 ÷ 53 3.227

Multiplying and Dividing by Powers of Ten

You can use shortcuts to multiply or divide by powers of ten.

When you multiply by	Move the decimal point	When you divide by	Move the decimal point
10,000	4 places to the right	10,000	4 places to the left
1,000	3 places to the right	1,000	3 places to the left
100	2 places to the right	100	2 places to the left
10	1 place to the right	10	1 place to the left
0.1	1 place to the left	0.1	1 place to the right
0.01	2 places to the left	0.01	2 places to the right
0.001	3 places to the left	0.001	3 places to the right

EXAMPLE

Multiply or divide.

a. 0.7×0.001

Move the decimal point 3 places to the left.

0.000.7

$0.7 \times 0.001 = 0.0007$

b. $0.605 \div 100$

Move the decimal point 2 places to the left.

0.00.605

$0.605 \div 100 = 0.00605$

EXERCISES

Multiply or divide.

1. $10,000 \times 0.056$ 560 **2.** 0.001×0.09 0.00009 **3.** 5.2×10 52 **4.** $0.03 \times 1,000$ 30

5. $236.7 \div 0.1$ 2,367 **6.** $45.28 \div 10$ 4.528 **7.** $0.9 \div 1,000$ 0.0009 **8.** $1.07 \div 0.01$ 107

9. 100×0.08 8 **10.** $1.03 \times 10,000$ 10,300 **11.** 1.803×0.001 0.001803 **12.** 4.1×100 410

13. $13.7 \div 0.001$ 13,700 **14.** $203.05 \div 0.01$ 20,305 **15.** $4.7 \div 10$ 0.47 **16.** $0.05 \div 100$ 0.0005

17. 23.6×0.01 0.236 **18.** $1,000 \times 0.12$ 120 **19.** 0.41×0.001 0.00041 **20.** 0.01×6.2 0.062

21. $42.3 \div 0.1$ 423 **22.** $0.4 \div 10,000$ 0.00004 **23.** $5.02 \div 0.01$ 502 **24.** $16.5 \div 100$ 0.165

25. $0.27 \div 0.01$ 27 **26.** 1.05×0.001 0.00105 **27.** 10×0.04 0.4 **28.** $2.09 \div 100$ 0.0209

29. 0.65×0.1 0.065 **30.** $0.03 \div 100$ 0.0003 **31.** $2.6 \div 0.1$ 26 **32.** $12.6 \times 10,000$ 126,000

33. $0.3 \div 1,000$ 0.0003 **34.** 0.01×6.7 0.067 **35.** 100×0.158 15.8 **36.** $23.1 \div 10$ 2.31

Dividing Decimals by Decimals

To divide with a decimal divisor, multiply it by the smallest power of ten that will make the divisor a whole number. Then multiply the dividend by that same power of ten.

EXAMPLE

Find each quotient.

a. 3.348 ÷ 6.2
Multiply by 10.

$$
\begin{array}{r}
0.54 \\
6.2\overline{)3\,3.48} \\
-3\,1\,0 \\
\hline
2\,48 \\
-2\,48 \\
\hline
0
\end{array}
$$

b. 2.4885 ÷ 0.35
Multiply by 100.

$$
\begin{array}{r}
7.11 \\
0.35\overline{)2.48.85} \\
-2\,45 \\
\hline
3\,8 \\
-3\,5 \\
\hline
35 \\
-35 \\
\hline
0
\end{array}
$$

c. 0.0576 ÷ 0.012
Multiply by 1,000.

$$
\begin{array}{r}
4.8 \\
0.012\overline{)0.057.6} \\
-48 \\
\hline
96 \\
-96 \\
\hline
0
\end{array}
$$

EXERCISES

Divide.

1. $3.2\overline{)268.8}$ 84 **2.** $1.9\overline{)123.5}$ 65   **3.** $0.3\overline{)135.6}$ 452   **4.** $2.3\overline{)170.2}$ 74   **5.** $7.9\overline{)252.8}$ 32

6. $5.7\overline{)10.26}$ 1.8 **7.** $2.3\overline{)71.53}$ 31.1 **8.** $3.1\overline{)16.12}$ 5.2   **9.** $7.8\overline{)24.18}$ 3.1 **10.** $6.3\overline{)14.49}$ 2.3

11. $134.42 \div 5.17$ 26 **12.** $89.96 \div 3.46$ 26 **13.** $160.58 \div 5.18$ 31 **14.** $106.59 \div 6.27$ 17

15. $62.4 \div 3.9$ 16 **16.** $260.4 \div 8.4$ 31 **17.** $316.8 \div 7.2$ 44 **18.** $162.4 \div 2.9$ 56

19. $1.512 \div 0.54$ 2.8 **20.** $3.225 \div 0.43$ 7.5 **21.** $2.484 \div 0.69$ 3.6 **22.** $511.5 \div 5.5$ 93

23. $0.992 \div 0.8$ 1.24 **24.** $4.53 \div 0.05$ 90.6 **25.** $3.498 \div 0.06$ 58.3 **26.** $59.2 \div 0.8$ 74

27. $2.198 \div 0.07$ 31.4 **28.** $14.28 \div 0.7$ 20.4 **29.** $1.98 \div 0.5$ 3.96 **30.** $26.36 \div 0.04$ 659

31. $3.922 \div 7.4$ 0.53 **32.** $23.52 \div 0.98$ 24 **33.** $71.25 \div 7.5$ 9.5 **34.** $114.7 \div 3.7$ 31

35. $0.832 \div 0.52$ 1.6 **36.** $1.125 \div 0.09$ 12.5 **37.** $9.666 \div 2.7$ 3.58 **38.** $1.456 \div 9.1$ 0.16

39. $0.4374 \div 1.8$ 0.243 **40.** $2.3414 \div 0.46$ 5.09 **41.** $0.07224 \div 0.021$ 3.44 **42.** $0.1386 \div 0.18$ 0.77

43. $0.16926 \div 0.091$ 1.86 **44.** $0.6042 \div 5.3$ 0.114 **45.** $2.3374 \div 0.62$ 3.77 **46.** $1.0062 \div 0.078$ 12.9

Skills Handbook   **769**

Zeros in Decimal Division

When you are dividing by a decimal, sometimes you need to use extra zeros in the dividend or the quotient, or both.

1 EXAMPLE

Divide 0.045 ÷ 3.6.

Step 1 Multiply by 10.

$$3.\underset{\curvearrowright}{6.)\overline{0.0.45}}$$

Step 2 Divide.

$$
\begin{array}{r}
125 \\
3.6.)\overline{0.0.4500} \\
-36 \\
\hline
90 \\
-72 \\
\hline
180 \\
-180 \\
\hline
0
\end{array}
$$

Step 3 Place the decimal point.

$$
\begin{array}{r}
0.0125 \\
3.6.)\overline{0.0.4500} \\
-36 \\
\hline
90 \\
-72 \\
\hline
180 \\
-180 \\
\hline
0
\end{array}
$$

2 EXAMPLE

Find each quotient.

a. **0.4428 ÷ 8.2**
  Multiply by 10.
$$
\begin{array}{r}
0.054 \\
8.2.)\overline{0.4.428}
\end{array}
$$

b. **0.00434 ÷ 0.07**
  Multiply by 100.
$$
\begin{array}{r}
0.062 \\
0.07.)\overline{0.00.434}
\end{array}
$$

c. **0.00306 ÷ 0.072**
  Multiply by 1,000.
$$
\begin{array}{r}
0.0425 \\
0.072.)\overline{0.003.0600}
\end{array}
$$

EXERCISES

Divide.

1. $0.05)\overline{0.0023}$ 0.046
2. $0.02)\overline{0.000162}$ 0.0081
3. $0.12)\overline{0.009}$ 0.075
4. $2.5)\overline{0.021}$ 0.0084

5. $0.0019 \div 0.2$ 0.0095
6. $0.9 \div 0.8$ 1.125
7. $0.000175 \div 0.07$ 0.0025
8. $0.142 \div 0.04$ 3.55

9. $0.0017 \div 0.02$ 0.085
10. $0.003 \div 0.6$ 0.005
11. $0.0105 \div 0.7$ 0.015
12. $0.034 \div 0.05$ 0.68

13. $0.00056 \div 0.16$ 0.0035
14. $0.0612 \div 7.2$ 0.0085
15. $0.217 \div 3.1$ 0.07
16. $0.052 \div 0.8$ 0.065

17. $0.000924 \div 0.44$ 0.0021
18. $0.05796 \div 0.63$ 0.092
19. $0.00123 \div 8.2$ 0.00015
20. $0.0954 \div 0.09$ 1.06

21. $0.0084 \div 1.4$ 0.006
22. $0.259 \div 3.5$ 0.074
23. $0.00468 \div 0.52$ 0.009
24. $0.104 \div 0.05$ 2.08

25. $0.00063 \div 0.18$ 0.0035
26. $0.011 \div 0.25$ 0.044
27. $0.3069 \div 9.3$ 0.033
28. $0.00045 \div 0.3$ 0.0015

Writing Equivalent Fractions

If you multiply or divide both the numerator and the denominator of a fraction by the same number, you get an equivalent fraction.

1 EXAMPLE

a. Find the missing number in $\frac{5}{6} = \frac{20}{\blacksquare}$.

$$\overset{\times 4}{\frac{5}{6} = \frac{20}{\blacksquare}}$$

$$\underset{\times 4}{\frac{5}{6} = \frac{20}{24}}$$

b. Find the missing number in $\frac{12}{30} = \frac{\blacksquare}{15}$.

$$\overset{\div 2}{\frac{12}{30} = \frac{\blacksquare}{15}}$$

$$\underset{\div 2}{\frac{12}{30} = \frac{6}{15}}$$

To write a fraction in simplest form, divide both the numerator and the denominator by the greatest common factor.

2 EXAMPLE

a. Write $\frac{6}{15}$ in simplest form.

3 is the greatest common factor.

$$\frac{6}{15} = \frac{6 \div 3}{15 \div 3} = \frac{2}{5}$$

The simplest form of $\frac{6}{15}$ is $\frac{2}{5}$.

b. Write $\frac{36}{42}$ in simplest form.

6 is the greatest common factor.

$$\frac{36}{42} = \frac{36 \div 6}{42 \div 6} = \frac{6}{7}$$

The simplest form of $\frac{36}{42}$ is $\frac{6}{7}$.

EXERCISES

Find each missing number.

1. $\frac{1}{3} = \frac{\blacksquare}{6}$ 2

2. $\frac{3}{4} = \frac{\blacksquare}{16}$ 12

3. $\frac{18}{30} = \frac{6}{\blacksquare}$ 10

4. $\frac{2}{3} = \frac{\blacksquare}{21}$ 14

5. $\frac{3}{4} = \frac{9}{\blacksquare}$ 12

6. $\frac{3}{10} = \frac{9}{\blacksquare}$ 30

7. $\frac{4}{5} = \frac{\blacksquare}{30}$ 24

8. $\frac{2}{3} = \frac{8}{\blacksquare}$ 12

9. $\frac{33}{55} = \frac{\blacksquare}{5}$ 3

10. $\frac{27}{72} = \frac{9}{\blacksquare}$ 24

11. $\frac{2}{3} = \frac{\blacksquare}{24}$ 16

12. $\frac{11}{12} = \frac{55}{\blacksquare}$ 60

13. $\frac{3}{5} = \frac{18}{\blacksquare}$ 30

14. $\frac{60}{72} = \frac{10}{\blacksquare}$ 12

15. $\frac{7}{8} = \frac{\blacksquare}{24}$ 21

Write each fraction in simplest form.

16. $\frac{12}{36}$ $\frac{1}{3}$

17. $\frac{25}{30}$ $\frac{5}{6}$

18. $\frac{14}{16}$ $\frac{7}{8}$

19. $\frac{27}{36}$ $\frac{3}{4}$

20. $\frac{21}{35}$ $\frac{3}{5}$

21. $\frac{40}{50}$ $\frac{4}{5}$

22. $\frac{24}{40}$ $\frac{3}{5}$

23. $\frac{32}{64}$ $\frac{1}{2}$

24. $\frac{15}{45}$ $\frac{1}{3}$

25. $\frac{27}{63}$ $\frac{3}{7}$

26. $\frac{44}{77}$ $\frac{4}{7}$

27. $\frac{45}{75}$ $\frac{3}{5}$

28. $\frac{60}{72}$ $\frac{5}{6}$

29. $\frac{77}{84}$ $\frac{11}{12}$

30. $\frac{12}{24}$ $\frac{1}{2}$

31. $\frac{24}{32}$ $\frac{3}{4}$

32. $\frac{7}{21}$ $\frac{1}{3}$

33. $\frac{18}{42}$ $\frac{3}{7}$

Mixed Numbers and Improper Fractions

A fraction, such as $\frac{10}{7}$, in which the numerator is greater than or equal to the denominator is an improper fraction. You can write an improper fraction as a mixed number that shows the sum of a whole number and a fraction.

Sometimes it is necessary to do the opposite and write a mixed number as an improper fraction.

EXAMPLE

a. Write $\frac{11}{5}$ as a mixed number.

$$\frac{11}{5} \rightarrow \begin{array}{r} 2 \\ 5\overline{)11} \\ -10 \\ \hline 1 \end{array}$$ ← whole number

← remainder

$\frac{11}{5} = 2\frac{1}{5}$ ← whole number + $\frac{\text{remainder}}{\text{denominator}}$

b. Write $2\frac{5}{6}$ as an improper fraction.

$$2\frac{5}{6} = 2 + \frac{5}{6}$$

$$= \frac{12}{6} + \frac{5}{6}$$ ← Write 2 as $\frac{12}{6}$.

$$= \frac{12 + 5}{6}$$ ← Add the numerators.

$$2\frac{5}{6} = \frac{17}{6}$$

EXERCISES

Write each improper fraction as a mixed number.

1. $\frac{7}{5}$ $1\frac{2}{5}$
2. $\frac{9}{2}$ $4\frac{1}{2}$
3. $\frac{13}{4}$ $3\frac{1}{4}$
4. $\frac{21}{5}$ $4\frac{1}{5}$
5. $\frac{13}{10}$ $1\frac{3}{10}$
6. $\frac{49}{5}$ $9\frac{4}{5}$

7. $\frac{21}{8}$ $2\frac{5}{8}$
8. $\frac{13}{7}$ $1\frac{6}{7}$
9. $\frac{17}{5}$ $3\frac{2}{5}$
10. $\frac{49}{6}$ $8\frac{1}{6}$
11. $\frac{17}{4}$ $4\frac{1}{4}$
12. $\frac{5}{2}$ $2\frac{1}{2}$

13. $\frac{27}{5}$ $5\frac{2}{5}$
14. $\frac{12}{9}$ $1\frac{1}{3}$
15. $\frac{30}{8}$ $3\frac{3}{4}$
16. $\frac{37}{12}$ $3\frac{1}{12}$
17. $\frac{8}{6}$ $1\frac{1}{3}$
18. $\frac{19}{12}$ $1\frac{7}{12}$

19. $\frac{45}{10}$ $4\frac{1}{2}$
20. $\frac{15}{12}$ $1\frac{1}{4}$
21. $\frac{11}{2}$ $5\frac{1}{2}$
22. $\frac{20}{6}$ $3\frac{1}{3}$
23. $\frac{34}{8}$ $4\frac{1}{4}$
24. $\frac{21}{9}$ $2\frac{1}{3}$

Write each mixed number as an improper fraction.

25. $1\frac{1}{2}$ $\frac{3}{2}$
26. $2\frac{2}{3}$ $\frac{8}{3}$
27. $1\frac{1}{12}$ $\frac{13}{12}$
28. $3\frac{1}{5}$ $\frac{16}{5}$
29. $2\frac{2}{7}$ $\frac{16}{7}$
30. $4\frac{1}{2}$ $\frac{9}{2}$

31. $2\frac{7}{8}$ $\frac{23}{8}$
32. $1\frac{2}{9}$ $\frac{11}{9}$
33. $5\frac{1}{5}$ $\frac{26}{5}$
34. $4\frac{7}{9}$ $\frac{43}{9}$
35. $9\frac{1}{4}$ $\frac{37}{4}$
36. $2\frac{3}{8}$ $\frac{19}{8}$

37. $7\frac{7}{8}$ $\frac{63}{8}$
38. $1\frac{5}{12}$ $\frac{17}{12}$
39. $3\frac{3}{7}$ $\frac{24}{7}$
40. $6\frac{1}{2}$ $\frac{13}{2}$
41. $3\frac{1}{10}$ $\frac{31}{10}$
42. $4\frac{6}{7}$ $\frac{34}{7}$

Adding and Subtracting Fractions With Like Denominators

When you add or subtract fractions with the same denominator, add or subtract the numerators and then write the answer over the denominator.

1 **EXAMPLE**

Add or subtract. Write each answer in simplest form.

a. $\frac{5}{8} + \frac{7}{8}$

$$\frac{5}{8} + \frac{7}{8} = \frac{5 + 7}{8}$$

$$= \frac{12}{8} = 1\frac{4}{8} = 1\frac{1}{2}$$

b. $\frac{11}{12} - \frac{2}{12}$

$$\frac{11}{12} - \frac{2}{12} = \frac{11 - 2}{12}$$

$$= \frac{9}{12} = \frac{3}{4}$$

To add or subtract mixed numbers, add or subtract the fractions first. Then add or subtract the whole numbers.

2 **EXAMPLE**

Add or subtract. Write each answer in simplest form.

a. $3\frac{4}{6} + 2\frac{5}{6}$

$$3\frac{4}{6}$$
$$+ 2\frac{5}{6}$$
$$\overline{5\frac{9}{6}} = 5 + 1 + \frac{3}{6} = 6\frac{1}{2}$$

b. $6\frac{1}{4} - 1\frac{3}{4}$

$$6\frac{1}{4} \rightarrow \quad 5\frac{5}{4} \quad \leftarrow \text{Rewrite 1 unit as } \frac{4}{4} \text{ and add it to } \frac{1}{4}.$$
$$- 1\frac{3}{4} \quad - 1\frac{3}{4}$$
$$\overline{\quad\quad\quad 4\frac{2}{4}} = 4\frac{1}{2}$$

EXERCISES

Add or subtract. Write each answer in simplest form.

1. $\frac{4}{5} + \frac{3}{5}$ $1\frac{2}{5}$ 2. $\frac{2}{6} - \frac{1}{6}$ $\frac{1}{6}$ 3. $\frac{2}{7} + \frac{2}{7}$ $\frac{4}{7}$ 4. $\frac{7}{8} + \frac{2}{8}$ $1\frac{1}{8}$ 5. $1\frac{2}{5} - \frac{1}{5}$ $1\frac{1}{5}$

6. $\frac{3}{6} - \frac{1}{6}$ $\frac{1}{3}$ 7. $\frac{6}{8} - \frac{3}{8}$ $\frac{3}{8}$ 8. $\frac{2}{9} + \frac{1}{9}$ $\frac{1}{3}$ 9. $\frac{4}{5} - \frac{1}{5}$ $\frac{3}{5}$ 10. $\frac{5}{9} + \frac{7}{9}$ $1\frac{1}{3}$

11. $9\frac{1}{3} - 8\frac{1}{3}$ 1 12. $8\frac{6}{7} - 4\frac{2}{7}$ $4\frac{4}{7}$ 13. $3\frac{1}{10} + 1\frac{3}{10}$ $4\frac{2}{5}$ 14. $2\frac{2}{9} + 3\frac{4}{9}$ $5\frac{2}{3}$

15. $4\frac{5}{12} - 3\frac{1}{12}$ $1\frac{1}{3}$ 16. $9\frac{5}{9} + 6\frac{7}{9}$ $16\frac{1}{3}$ 17. $5\frac{7}{8} + 2\frac{3}{8}$ $8\frac{1}{4}$ 18. $4\frac{4}{7} - 2\frac{1}{7}$ $2\frac{3}{7}$

19. $9\frac{3}{4} + 1\frac{3}{4}$ $11\frac{1}{2}$ 20. $8\frac{2}{3} - 4\frac{1}{3}$ $4\frac{1}{3}$ 21. $8\frac{7}{10} + 2\frac{3}{10}$ 11 22. $1\frac{4}{5} + 3\frac{3}{5}$ $5\frac{2}{5}$

23. $7\frac{1}{5} - 2\frac{3}{5}$ $4\frac{3}{5}$ 24. $4\frac{1}{3} - 1\frac{2}{3}$ $2\frac{2}{3}$ 25. $4\frac{3}{8} - 3\frac{5}{8}$ $\frac{3}{4}$ 26. $5\frac{1}{12} - 2\frac{7}{12}$ $2\frac{1}{2}$

Multiplying and Dividing Fractions

To multiply fractions, multiply the numerators and the denominators.
To divide fractions, multiply by the reciprocal of the divisor.

EXAMPLE

Multiply. Write each answer in simplest form.

a. $\dfrac{8}{9} \times \dfrac{3}{10} = \dfrac{\overset{4}{\cancel{8}}}{\underset{3}{\cancel{9}}} \times \dfrac{\overset{1}{\cancel{3}}}{\underset{5}{\cancel{10}}} = \dfrac{4}{15}$

b. $3\dfrac{1}{8} \times 1\dfrac{3}{4} = \dfrac{25}{8} \times \dfrac{7}{4}$

$= \dfrac{175}{32} = 5\dfrac{15}{32}$ ← Rewrite as a mixed number.

Divide. Write each answer in simplest form.

c. $\dfrac{2}{3} \div \dfrac{4}{5} = \dfrac{2}{3} \times \dfrac{5}{4}$

$= \dfrac{\overset{1}{\cancel{2}}}{3} \times \dfrac{5}{\underset{2}{\cancel{4}}} = \dfrac{5}{6}$

d. $3\dfrac{1}{8} \div 1\dfrac{3}{4} = \dfrac{25}{8} \div \dfrac{7}{4}$

$= \dfrac{25}{\underset{2}{\cancel{8}}} \times \dfrac{\overset{1}{\cancel{4}}}{7} = \dfrac{25}{14} = 1\dfrac{11}{14}$ ← Rewrite as a mixed number.

EXERCISES

Multiply. Write each answer in simplest form.

1. $\dfrac{3}{4} \times \dfrac{3}{5}$ $\dfrac{9}{20}$
2. $\dfrac{2}{3} \times \dfrac{3}{4}$ $\dfrac{1}{2}$
3. $6 \times \dfrac{2}{3}$ 4

4. $\dfrac{3}{4} \times \dfrac{5}{6}$ $\dfrac{5}{8}$
5. $\dfrac{5}{8} \times \dfrac{2}{3}$ $\dfrac{5}{12}$
6. $\dfrac{9}{16} \times \dfrac{2}{3}$ $\dfrac{3}{8}$

7. $\dfrac{3}{10} \times \dfrac{2}{15}$ $\dfrac{1}{25}$
8. $\dfrac{3}{4} \times \dfrac{1}{6}$ $\dfrac{1}{8}$
9. $\dfrac{1}{4} \times \dfrac{5}{20}$ $\dfrac{1}{16}$

10. $\dfrac{9}{10} \times \dfrac{1}{3}$ $\dfrac{3}{10}$
11. $1\dfrac{1}{3} \times 2\dfrac{2}{3}$ $3\dfrac{5}{9}$
12. $\dfrac{3}{5} \times 2\dfrac{3}{4}$ $1\dfrac{13}{20}$

13. $2\dfrac{1}{4} \times 3\dfrac{1}{3}$ $7\dfrac{1}{2}$
14. $\dfrac{1}{4} \times 3\dfrac{1}{3}$ $\dfrac{5}{6}$
15. $6\dfrac{1}{4} \times 7$ $43\dfrac{3}{4}$

16. $1\dfrac{3}{4} \times 2\dfrac{1}{5}$ $3\dfrac{17}{20}$
17. $2\dfrac{3}{4} \times \dfrac{1}{2}$ $1\dfrac{3}{8}$
18. $3\dfrac{4}{5} \times 2\dfrac{1}{3}$ $8\dfrac{13}{15}$

Divide. Write each answer in simplest form.

19. $\dfrac{5}{8} \div \dfrac{5}{7}$ $\dfrac{7}{8}$
20. $\dfrac{5}{7} \div \dfrac{5}{8}$ $1\dfrac{1}{7}$
21. $\dfrac{3}{4} \div \dfrac{6}{11}$ $1\dfrac{3}{8}$

22. $\dfrac{1}{9} \div \dfrac{1}{9}$ 1
23. $\dfrac{1}{9} \div 9$ $\dfrac{1}{81}$
24. $\dfrac{9}{10} \div \dfrac{3}{5}$ $1\dfrac{1}{2}$

25. $\dfrac{2}{3} \div \dfrac{1}{9}$ 6
26. $\dfrac{4}{5} \div \dfrac{5}{6}$ $\dfrac{24}{25}$
27. $\dfrac{1}{5} \div \dfrac{8}{9}$ $\dfrac{9}{40}$

28. $\dfrac{7}{8} \div \dfrac{1}{3}$ $2\dfrac{5}{8}$
29. $4\dfrac{1}{5} \div 2\dfrac{2}{5}$ $1\dfrac{3}{4}$
30. $6\dfrac{1}{4} \div 4\dfrac{3}{8}$ $1\dfrac{3}{7}$

31. $2\dfrac{1}{3} \div 5\dfrac{5}{6}$ $\dfrac{2}{5}$
32. $1\dfrac{1}{2} \div 4\dfrac{1}{2}$ $\dfrac{1}{3}$
33. $15\dfrac{2}{3} \div 1\dfrac{1}{3}$ $11\dfrac{3}{4}$

34. $10\dfrac{1}{3} \div 2\dfrac{1}{5}$ $4\dfrac{23}{33}$
35. $6\dfrac{1}{4} \div 1\dfrac{3}{4}$ $3\dfrac{4}{7}$
36. $6\dfrac{2}{3} \div 3\dfrac{1}{8}$ $2\dfrac{2}{15}$

Working With Integers

Quantities less than zero can be written using negative integers. For example, a temperature of 5 degrees below zero can be written as −5. Positive integers are used for quantities greater than zero.

Skills Handbook

1 EXAMPLE

Write an integer for each situation.

a. 10 degrees above zero
+10, or 10

b. a loss of $20
−20

c. 15 yards lost
−15

A number line can be used to compare integers. The integer to the right is greater.

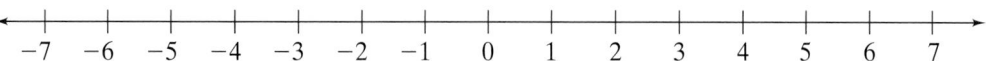

2 EXAMPLE

Compare. Use >, <, or = to complete each statement.

a. 0 ■ −3
0 is to the right, so it is greater.
0 > −3

b. −2 ■ −6
−2 is to the right, so it is greater.
−2 > −6

c. −7 ■ 3
−7 is to the left, so it is less.
−7 < 3

EXERCISES

Write an integer for each situation.

1. 6 yards gained 6 **2.** 10 yards lost −10 **3.** 5 steps forward 5 **4.** 4 steps backward −4

5. find $3 3 **6.** lose $8 −8 **7.** 12 floors up 12 **8.** 4 floors down −4

Compare. Use >, <, or = to complete each statement.

9. 0 ■ −1
>
10. −9 ■ 0
<
11. −3 ■ 3
<
12. 7 ■ −3
>
13. 0 ■ 1
<

14. 3 ■ 0
>
15. 1 ■ −4
>
16. −2 ■ −9
>
17. 6 ■ −1
>
18. 3 ■ −10
>

19. −7 ■ 3
<
20. 4 ■ 6
<
21. −16 ■ −25
>
22. −15 ■ −12
<
23. 7 ■ −8
>

24. 2 ■ 3
<
25. −7 ■ −8
>
26. 35 ■ −40
>
27. −30 ■ −20
<
28. 25 ■ −25
>

29. 9 ■ −9
>
30. −6 ■ −5
<
31. −23 ■ −15
<
32. −17 ■ −19
>
33. −15 ■ −25
>

Skills Handbook

Tables

Table 1 Measures

Metric

Length
10 millimeters (mm) = 1 centimeter (cm)
100 cm = 1 meter (m)
1,000 m = 1 kilometer (km)

Area
100 square millimeters (mm²) =
   1 square centimeter (cm²)
10,000 cm² = 1 square meter (m²)
1,000,000 m² = 1 square kilometer (km²)

Volume
1,000 cubic millimeters (mm³) =
   1 cubic centimeter (cm³)
1,000,000 cm³ = 1 cubic meter (m³)

Mass
1,000 milligrams (mg) = 1 gram (g)
1,000 g = 1 kilogram (kg)

Volume (Capacity)
1,000 milliliters (mL) = 1 liter (L)
1 mL = 1 cm³

Customary

Length
12 inches (in.) = 1 foot (ft)
3 ft = 1 yard (yd)
36 in. = 1 yd
5,280 ft = 1 mile (mi)
1,760 yd = 1 mi

Area
144 square inches (in.²) = 1 square foot (ft²)
9 ft² = 1 square yard (yd²)
4,840 yd² = 1 acre

Volume
1,728 cubic inches (in.³) = 1 cubic foot (ft³)
27 ft³ = 1 cubic yard (yd³)

Weight
16 ounces (oz) = 1 pound (lb)
2,000 lb = 1 ton (t)

Volume (Capacity)
8 fluid ounces (fl oz) = 1 cup (c)
2 c = 1 pint (pt)
2 pt = 1 quart (qt)
4 qt = 1 gallon (gal)

Time
1 minute (min) = 60 seconds (s)
1 hour (h) = 60 min
1 day (d) = 24 h
1 year (yr) = 365 d

Table 2 Reading Math Symbols

Symbol	Meaning	Page
$>$	is greater than	p. 103
$<$	is less than	p. 103
$\geq$	is greater than or equal to	p. 103
$\leq$	is less than or equal to	p. 103
$=$	is equal to	p. 80
$\neq$	is not equal to	p. 80
$\approx$	is approximately equal to	p. 128
$\stackrel{?}{=}$	is this statement true?	p. 81
$+$	plus (addition)	p. 5
$-$	minus (subtraction)	p. 5
$\times, \cdot$	times (multiplication)	p. 5
$\div, \overline{)}$	divide (division)	p. 5
$\sqrt{x}$	nonnegative square root of x	p. 580
$\circ$	degrees	p. 464
$\%$	percent	p. 310
$(\ )$	parentheses for grouping	p. 9
$|a|$	absolute value of a	p. 19
$a : b, \frac{a}{b}$	ratio of a to b	p. 288
(a, b)	ordered pair with x-coordinate a and y-coordinate b	p. 50
$\cong$	is congruent to	p. 465
$\sim$	is similar to	p. 299
$\parallel$	is parallel to	p. 459
π	pi, an irrational number approximately equal to 3.14	p. 486
$f(n)$	function value at n, f of n	p. 418
b	y-intercept	p. 413
m	slope of a line	p. 413
$\begin{bmatrix} 1 & 3 \\ 2 & 4 \end{bmatrix}$	matrix	p. 502
$-a$	opposite of a	p. 19
$\frac{1}{a}$	reciprocal of a	p. 250
a^n	nth power of a	p. 182
d	diameter	p. 486
	distance	pp. 143, 592
A'	image of A, A prime	p. 497
A	Area	p. 522

Symbol	Meaning	Page
b_1, b_2	base lengths of a trapezoid	p. 529
b	base length	p. 523
h	height	p. 523
p or P	perimeter	p. 144
ℓ	length	p. 144
	slant height	p. 552
w	width	p. 144
C	circumference	p. 486
S.A.	surface area	p. 545
L.A.	lateral area	p. 546
B	area of a base	p. 546
V	volume	p. 557
r	rate	p. 143
	radius	p. 487
$\overline{AB}$	segment AB	p. 458
$\overrightarrow{AB}$	ray AB	p. 458
$\overleftrightarrow{AB}$	line AB	p. 458
$\triangle ABC$	triangle with vertices A, B, and C	p. 299
$\angle A$	angle with vertex A	p. 464
$\angle ABC$	angle with sides $\overrightarrow{BA}$ and $\overrightarrow{BC}$	p. 464
$m\angle ABC$	measure of angle ABC	p. 465
AB	length of segment $\overline{AB}$	p. 458
$\sin A$	sine of $\angle A$	p. 609
$\cos A$	cosine of $\angle A$	p. 609
$\tan A$	tangent of $\angle A$	p. 609
$P(\text{event})$	probability of an event	p. 305
$_nP_r$	number of permutations of n things taken r at a time	p. 659
$_nC_r$	number of combinations of n things taken r at a time	p. 660
$\wedge$	raised to a power (in software or a calculator)	p. 209
$*$	multiply (in software or a calculator)	p. 147
$/$	divide (in software or a calculator)	p. 147

Table 3 Squares and Square Roots

N	N²	√N	N	N²	√N
1	1	1	51	2,601	7.141
2	4	1.414	52	2,704	7.211
3	9	1.732	53	2,809	7.280
4	16	2	54	2,916	7.348
5	25	2.236	55	3,025	7.416
6	36	2.449	56	3,136	7.483
7	49	2.646	57	3,249	7.550
8	64	2.828	58	3,364	7.616
9	81	3	59	3,481	7.681
10	100	3.162	60	3,600	7.746
11	121	3.317	61	3,721	7.810
12	144	3.464	62	3,844	7.874
13	169	3.606	63	3,969	7.937
14	196	3.742	64	4,096	8
15	225	3.873	65	4,225	8.062
16	256	4	66	4,356	8.124
17	289	4.123	67	4,489	8.185
18	324	4.243	68	4,624	8.246
19	361	4.359	69	4,761	8.307
20	400	4.472	70	4,900	8.367
21	441	4.583	71	5,041	8.426
22	484	4.690	72	5,184	8.485
23	529	4.796	73	5,329	8.544
24	576	4.899	74	5,476	8.602
25	625	5	75	5,625	8.660
26	676	5.099	76	5,776	8.718
27	729	5.196	77	5,929	8.775
28	784	5.292	78	6,084	8.832
29	841	5.385	79	6,241	8.888
30	900	5.477	80	6,400	8.944
31	961	5.568	81	6,561	9
32	1,024	5.657	82	6,724	9.055
33	1,089	5.745	83	6,889	9.110
34	1,156	5.831	84	7,056	9.165
35	1,225	5.916	85	7,225	9.220
36	1,296	6	86	7,396	9.274
37	1,369	6.083	87	7,569	9.327
38	1,444	6.164	88	7,744	9.381
39	1,521	6.245	89	7,921	9.434
40	1,600	6.325	90	8,100	9.487
41	1,681	6.403	91	8,281	9.539
42	1,764	6.481	92	8,464	9.592
43	1,849	6.557	93	8,649	9.644
44	1,936	6.633	94	8,836	9.695
45	2,025	6.708	95	9,025	9.747
46	2,116	6.782	96	9,216	9.798
47	2,209	6.856	97	9,409	9.849
48	2,304	6.928	98	9,604	9.899
49	2,401	7	99	9,801	9.950
50	2,500	7.071	100	10,000	10

Table 4 Trigonometric Ratios

Angle	Sine	Cosine	Tangent	Angle	Sine	Cosine	Tangent
1°	0.0175	0.9998	0.0175	46°	0.7193	0.6947	1.0355
2°	0.0349	0.9994	0.0349	47°	0.7314	0.6820	1.0724
3°	0.0523	0.9986	0.0524	48°	0.7431	0.6691	1.1106
4°	0.0698	0.9976	0.0699	49°	0.7547	0.6561	1.1504
5°	0.0872	0.9962	0.0875	50°	0.7660	0.6428	1.1918
6°	0.1045	0.9945	0.1051	51°	0.7771	0.6293	1.2349
7°	0.1219	0.9925	0.1228	52°	0.7880	0.6157	1.2799
8°	0.1392	0.9903	0.1405	53°	0.7986	0.6018	1.3270
9°	0.1564	0.9877	0.1584	54°	0.8090	0.5878	1.3764
10°	0.1736	0.9848	0.1763	55°	0.8192	0.5736	1.4281
11°	0.1908	0.9816	0.1944	56°	0.8290	0.5592	1.4826
12°	0.2079	0.9781	0.2126	57°	0.8387	0.5446	1.5399
13°	0.2250	0.9744	0.2309	58°	0.8480	0.5299	1.6003
14°	0.2419	0.9703	0.2493	59°	0.8572	0.5150	1.6643
15°	0.2588	0.9659	0.2679	60°	0.8660	0.5000	1.7321
16°	0.2756	0.9613	0.2867	61°	0.8746	0.4848	1.8040
17°	0.2924	0.9563	0.3057	62°	0.8829	0.4695	1.8807
18°	0.3090	0.9511	0.3249	63°	0.8910	0.4540	1.9626
19°	0.3256	0.9455	0.3443	64°	0.8988	0.4384	2.0503
20°	0.3420	0.9397	0.3640	65°	0.9063	0.4226	2.1445
21°	0.3584	0.9336	0.3839	66°	0.9135	0.4067	2.2460
22°	0.3746	0.9272	0.4040	67°	0.9205	0.3907	2.3559
23°	0.3907	0.9205	0.4245	68°	0.9272	0.3746	2.4751
24°	0.4067	0.9135	0.4452	69°	0.9336	0.3584	2.6051
25°	0.4226	0.9063	0.4663	70°	0.9397	0.3420	2.7475
26°	0.4384	0.8988	0.4877	71°	0.9455	0.3256	2.9042
27°	0.4540	0.8910	0.5095	72°	0.9511	0.3090	3.0777
28°	0.4695	0.8829	0.5317	73°	0.9563	0.2924	3.2709
29°	0.4848	0.8746	0.5543	74°	0.9613	0.2756	3.4874
30°	0.5000	0.8660	0.5774	75°	0.9659	0.2588	3.7321
31°	0.5150	0.8572	0.6009	76°	0.9703	0.2419	4.0108
32°	0.5299	0.8480	0.6249	77°	0.9744	0.2250	4.3315
33°	0.5446	0.8387	0.6494	78°	0.9781	0.2079	4.7046
34°	0.5592	0.8290	0.6745	79°	0.9816	0.1908	5.1446
35°	0.5736	0.8192	0.7002	80°	0.9848	0.1736	5.6713
36°	0.5878	0.8090	0.7265	81°	0.9877	0.1564	6.3138
37°	0.6018	0.7986	0.7536	82°	0.9903	0.1392	7.1154
38°	0.6157	0.7880	0.7813	83°	0.9925	0.1219	8.1443
39°	0.6293	0.7771	0.8098	84°	0.9945	0.1045	9.5144
40°	0.6428	0.7660	0.8391	85°	0.9962	0.0872	11.4301
41°	0.6561	0.7547	0.8693	86°	0.9976	0.0698	14.3007
42°	0.6691	0.7431	0.9004	87°	0.9986	0.0523	19.0811
43°	0.6820	0.7314	0.9325	88°	0.9994	0.0349	28.6363
44°	0.6947	0.7193	0.9657	89°	0.9998	0.0175	57.2900
45°	0.7071	0.7071	1.0000				

Formulas and Properties

Geometric Formulas

Perimeter and Circumference

Rectangle
$P = 2\ell + 2w$

Circle
$C = \pi d$ or $C = 2\pi r$

Area

Square
$A = s^2$

Parallelogram and Rectangle
$A = bh$

Triangle
$A = \frac{1}{2}bh$

Trapezoid
$A = \frac{1}{2}h(b_1 + b_2)$

Circle
$C = \pi r^2$

Triangle Formulas

Pythagorean Theorem
In a right triangle with legs of lengths a and b and hypotenuse of length c, $a^2 + b^2 = c^2$.

Trigonometric Ratios

sine of $\angle A = \dfrac{\text{length of leg opposite } \angle A}{\text{length of hypotenuse}}$

cosine of $\angle A = \dfrac{\text{length of leg adjacent to } \angle A}{\text{length of hypotenuse}}$

tangent of $\angle A = \dfrac{\text{length of leg opposite } \angle A}{\text{length of leg adjacent to } \angle A}$

Triangle Angle Sum
For any $\triangle ABC$,
$m\angle A + m\angle B + m\angle C = 180°$.

Surface Area

Rectangular Prism
L.A. $= ph$
S.A. $=$ L.A. $+ 2B$

Cylinder
L.A. $= 2\pi rh$
S.A. $=$ L.A. $+ 2B$

Pyramid
L.A. $= \frac{1}{2}p\ell = n\left(\frac{1}{2}b\ell\right)$, where n is the number of faces
S.A. $=$ L.A. $+ B$

Cone
L.A. $= \pi r\ell$
S.A. $=$ L.A. $+ B$

Sphere
S.A. $= 4\pi r^2$

Volume

Prism
$V = Bh$

Cylinder
$V = Bh$, or $\pi r^2 h$

Pyramid
$V = \frac{1}{3}Bh$

Cone
$V = \frac{1}{3}Bh$, or $\frac{1}{3}\pi r^2 h$

Sphere
$V = \frac{4}{3}\pi r^3$

Properties of Real Numbers

Unless otherwise stated, a, b, c, and d are real numbers.

Identity Properties

Addition $a + 0 = a$ and $0 + a = a$

Multiplication $a \cdot 1 = a$ and $1 \cdot a = a$

Commutative Properties

Addition $a + b = b + a$

Multiplication $a \cdot b = b \cdot a$

Associative Properties

Addition $(a + b) + c = a + (b + c)$

Multiplication $(a \cdot b) \cdot c = a \cdot (b \cdot c)$

Inverse Properties

Addition
$a + (-a) = 0$ and $-a + a = 0$

Multiplication
$a \cdot \frac{1}{a} = 1$ and $\frac{1}{a} \cdot a = 1 (a \neq 0)$

Distributive Properties

$a(b + c) = ab + ac$ $(b + c)a = ba + ca$
$a(b - c) = ab - ac$ $(b - c)a = ba - ca$

Properties of Equality

Addition If $a = b$, then $a + c = b + c$.

Subtraction If $a = b$, then $a - c = b - c$.

Multiplication If $a = b$, then $a \cdot c = b \cdot c$.

Division If $a = b$, and $c \neq 0$, then $\frac{a}{c} = \frac{b}{c}$.

Substitution If $a = b$, then b can replace a in any expression.

Reflexive $a = a$

Symmetric If $a = b$, then $b = a$.

Transitive If $a = b$ and $b = c$, then $a = c$.

Zero-Product Property

If $ab = 0$ then $a = 0$ or $b = 0$.

Zero Property of Multiplication

$a \cdot 0 = 0 \cdot a = 0$

Cross Product Property

$\frac{a}{b} = \frac{c}{d}$ is equivalent to $ad = bc$.

Closure Properties

$a + b$ is a unique real number.
ab is a unique real number.

Density Property

Between any two rational numbers, there is at least one other rational number.

Properties of Inequality

Addition If $a > b$, then $a + c > b + c$.
If $a < b$, then $a + c < b + c$.

Subtraction If $a > b$, then $a - c > b - c$.
If $a < b$, then $a - c < b - c$.

Multiplication
If $a > b$ and $c > 0$, then $ac > bc$.
If $a < b$ and $c > 0$, then $ac < bc$.
If $a > b$ and $c < 0$, then $ac < bc$.
If $a < b$ and $c < 0$, then $ac > bc$.

Division
If $a > b$ and $c > 0$, then $\frac{a}{c} > \frac{b}{c}$.
If $a < b$ and $c > 0$, then $\frac{a}{c} < \frac{b}{c}$.
If $a > b$ and $c < 0$, then $\frac{a}{c} < \frac{b}{c}$.
If $a < b$ and $c < 0$, then $\frac{a}{c} > \frac{b}{c}$.

Transitive If $a > b$ and $b > c$, then $a > c$.

Comparison If $a = b + c$ and $c > 0$, then $a > b$.

Properties of Exponents

For $a \neq 0$ and any integers m and n:

Zero Exponent $a^0 = 1$

Negative Exponent $a^{-n} = \frac{1}{a^n}$

Product of Powers $a^m \cdot a^n = a^{m+n}$

Quotient of Powers $\frac{a^m}{a^n} = a^{m-n}$

Power of a Power $(a^m)^n = a^{m \cdot n}$

Formulas and Properties

Formulas and Properties

English/Spanish Illustrated Glossary

A

Absolute value (p. 19) Absolute value is the distance of a number from zero on a number line. You write *the absolute value* of -3 as $|-3|$.

The absolute value of -3 is 3 because -3 is 3 units from zero on a number line.

Valor absoluto (p. 19) El valor absoluto de un número es la distancia desde cero hasta ese número en una recta numérica. Escribe "el valor absoluto de 23" como $|-3|$.

Absolute value function (p. 695) An absolute value function is a function with a graph that is V-shaped and opens up or down.
EXAMPLE The absolute value function $y = |x| - 3$ has the graph shown here.

Función de valor absoluto (p. 695) Una función de valor absoluto es una función con una gráfica en forma de V abierta hacia arriba o hacia abajo.

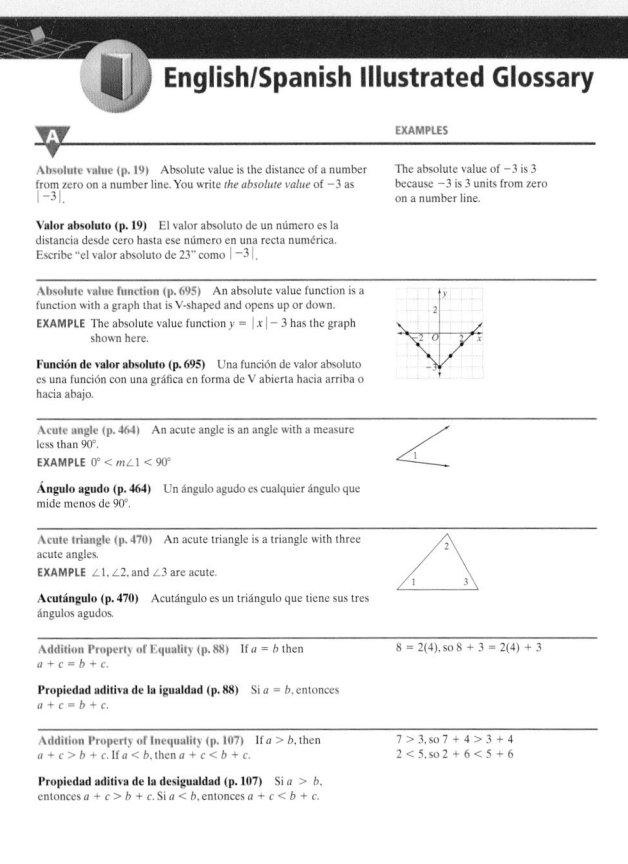

Acute angle (p. 464) An acute angle is an angle with a measure less than 90°.
EXAMPLE $0° < m\angle 1 < 90°$

Ángulo agudo (p. 464) Un ángulo agudo es cualquier ángulo que mide menos de 90°.

Acute triangle (p. 470) An acute triangle is a triangle with three acute angles.
EXAMPLE $\angle 1$, $\angle 2$, and $\angle 3$ are acute.

Acutángulo (p. 470) Acutángulo es un triángulo que tiene sus tres ángulos agudos.

Addition Property of Equality (p. 88) If $a = b$ then $a + c = b + c$.

$8 = 2(4)$, so $8 + 3 = 2(4) + 3$

Propiedad aditiva de la igualdad (p. 88) Si $a = b$, entonces $a + c = b + c$.

Addition Property of Inequality (p. 107) If $a > b$, then $a + c > b + c$. If $a < b$, then $a + c < b + c$.

$7 > 3$, so $7 + 4 > 3 + 4$
$2 < 5$, so $2 + 6 < 5 + 6$

Propiedad aditiva de la desigualdad (p. 107) Si $a > b$, entonces $a + c > b + c$. Si $a < b$, entonces $a + c < b + c$.

Additive identity (p. 67) The additive identity is zero. When you add a number and 0, the sum equals the original number.

$a + 0 = a$

Identidad aditiva (p. 67) La identidad aditiva es cero. Cuando se suman un número y 0, la suma es idéntica al número original.

Additive inverses (p. 24) Additive inverses are two numbers with a sum of zero.

23 and -23 are additive inverses because $-23 + 23 = 0$.

Inversos aditivos (p. 24) Se llaman inversos aditivos a los números cuya suma es igual a cero.

Adjacent angles (p. 465) Adjacent angles are two angles that share a vertex and a side but no points in their interiors.

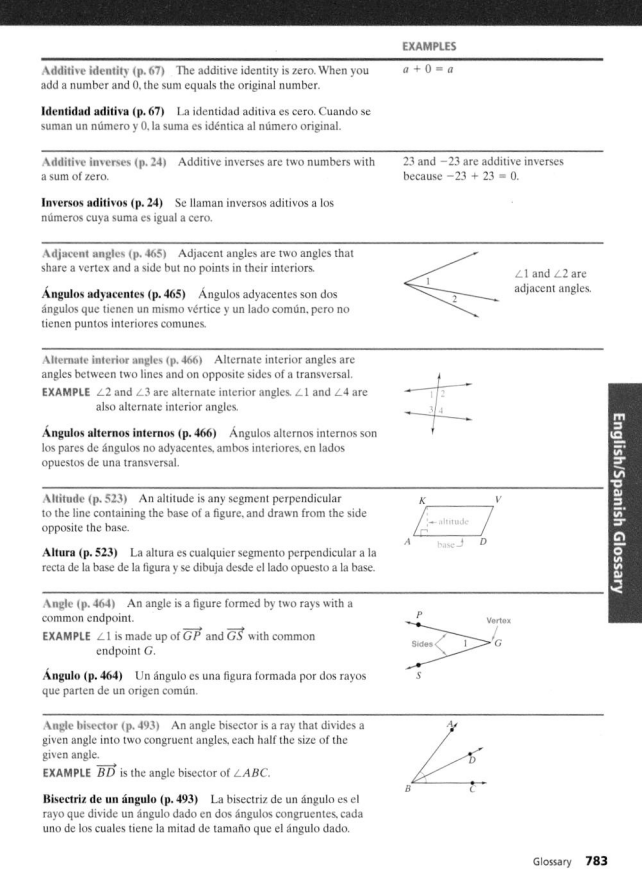

$\angle 1$ and $\angle 2$ are adjacent angles.

Ángulos adyacentes (p. 465) Ángulos adyacentes son dos ángulos que tienen un mismo vértice y un lado común, pero no tienen puntos interiores comunes.

Alternate interior angles (p. 466) Alternate interior angles are angles between two lines and on opposite sides of a transversal.
EXAMPLE $\angle 2$ and $\angle 3$ are alternate interior angles. $\angle 1$ and $\angle 4$ are also alternate interior angles.

Ángulos alternos internos (p. 466) Ángulos alternos internos son los pares de ángulos no adyacentes, ambos interiores, en lados opuestos de una transversal.

Altitude (p. 523) An altitude is any segment perpendicular to the line containing the base of a figure, and drawn from the side opposite the base.

Altura (p. 523) La altura es cualquier segmento perpendicular a la recta de la base de la figura y se dibuja desde el lado opuesto a la base.

Angle (p. 464) An angle is a figure formed by two rays with a common endpoint.
EXAMPLE $\angle 1$ is made up of $\overrightarrow{GP}$ and $\overrightarrow{GS}$ with common endpoint G.

Ángulo (p. 464) Un ángulo es una figura formada por dos rayos que parten de un origen común.

Angle bisector (p. 493) An angle bisector is a ray that divides a given angle into two congruent angles, each half the size of the given angle.
EXAMPLE $\overrightarrow{BD}$ is the angle bisector of $\angle ABC$.

Bisectriz de un ángulo (p. 493) La bisectriz de un ángulo es el rayo que divide un ángulo dado en dos ángulos congruentes, cada uno de los cuales tiene la mitad de tamaño que el ángulo dado.

Angle of depression (p. 616) An angle of depression is an angle formed by a horizontal line and a line of sight below it.
EXAMPLE $\angle XYZ$ is an angle of depression.

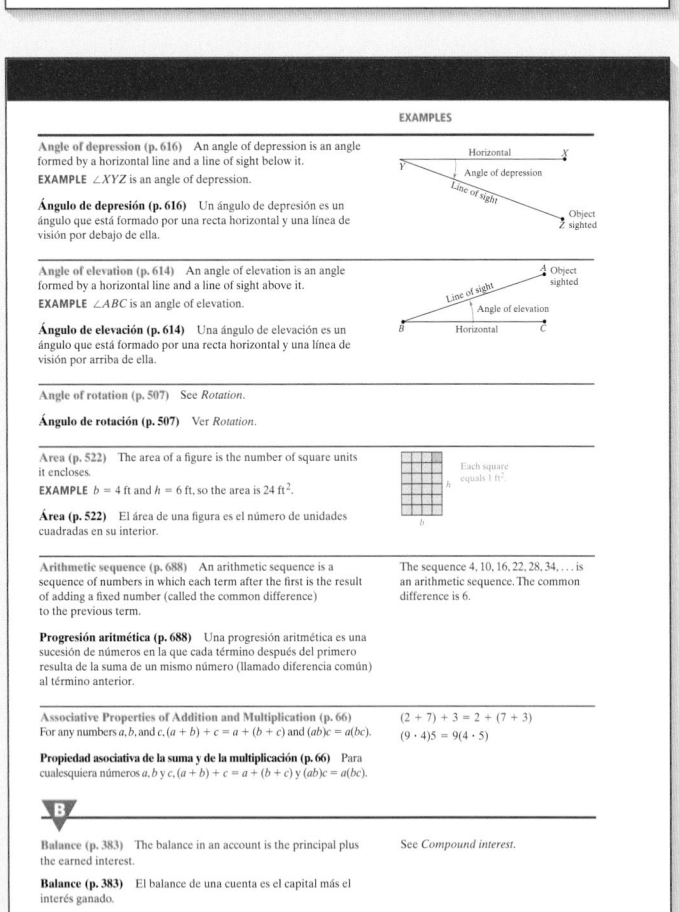

Ángulo de depresión (p. 616) Un ángulo de depresión es un ángulo que está formado por una recta horizontal y una línea de visión por debajo de ella.

Angle of elevation (p. 614) An angle of elevation is an angle formed by a horizontal line and a line of sight above it.
EXAMPLE $\angle ABC$ is an angle of elevation.

Ángulo de elevación (p. 614) Un ángulo de elevación es un ángulo que está formado por una horizontal y una línea de visión por arriba de ella.

Angle of rotation (p. 507) See *Rotation*.

Ángulo de rotación (p. 507) Ver *Rotation*.

Area (p. 522) The area of a figure is the number of square units it encloses.
EXAMPLE $b = 4$ ft and $h = 6$ ft, so the area is 24 ft².

Each square equals 1 ft².

Área (p. 522) El área de una figura es el número de unidades cuadradas en su interior.

Arithmetic sequence (p. 688) An arithmetic sequence is a sequence of numbers in which each term after the first is the result of adding a fixed number (called the common difference) to the previous term.

The sequence 4, 10, 16, 22, 28, 34, ... is an arithmetic sequence. The common difference is 6.

Progresión aritmética (p. 688) Una progresión aritmética es una sucesión de números en la que cada término después del primero resulta de la suma de un mismo número (llamado diferencia común) al término anterior.

Associative Properties of Addition and Multiplication (p. 66) For any numbers a, b, and c, $(a + b) + c = a + (b + c)$ and $(ab)c = a(bc)$.

$(2 + 7) + 3 = 2 + (7 + 3)$
$(9 \cdot 4)5 = 9(4 \cdot 5)$

Propiedad asociativa de la suma y de la multiplicación (p. 66) Para cualesquiera números a, b y c, $(a + b) + c = a + (b + c)$ y $(ab)c = a(bc)$.

B

Balance (p. 383) The balance in an account is the principal plus the earned interest.

See *Compound interest*.

Balance (p. 383) El balance de una cuenta es el capital más el interés ganado.

Bar graph (p. 101) A bar graph is a graph that compares amounts.
EXAMPLE This bar graph compares the numbers of students in grades 6, 7, and 8.

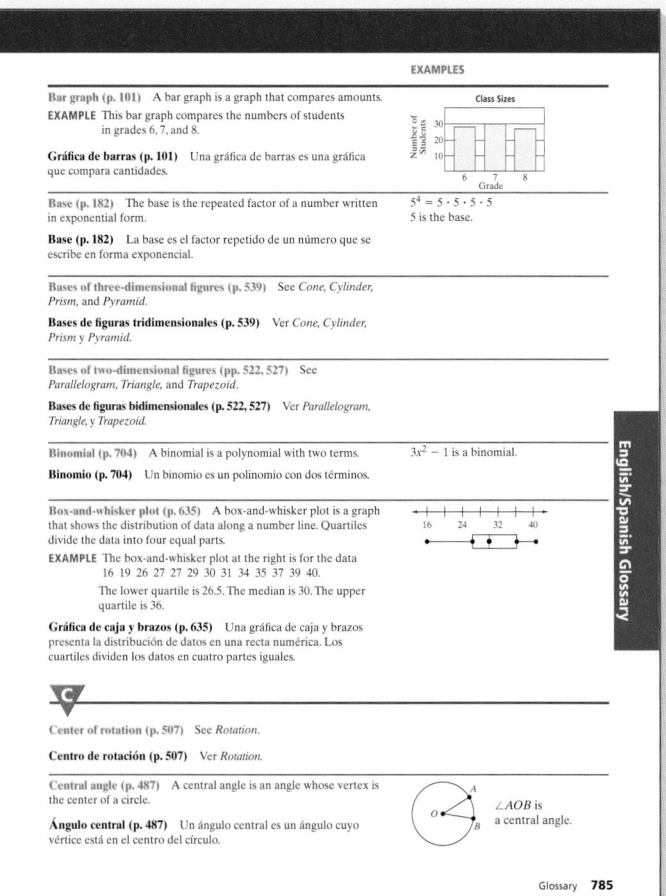

Gráfica de barras (p. 101) Una gráfica de barras es una gráfica que compara cantidades.

Base (p. 182) The base is the repeated factor of a number written in exponential form.

$5^4 = 5 \cdot 5 \cdot 5 \cdot 5$
5 is the base.

Base (p. 182) La base es el factor repetido de un número que se escribe en forma exponencial.

Bases of three-dimensional figures (p. 539) See *Cone*, *Cylinder*, *Prism*, and *Pyramid*.

Bases de figuras tridimensionales (p. 539) Ver *Cone*, *Cylinder*, *Prism* y *Pyramid*.

Bases of two-dimensional figures (pp. 522, 527) See *Parallelogram*, *Triangle*, and *Trapezoid*.

Bases de figuras bidimensionales (p. 522, 527) Ver *Parallelogram*, *Triangle*, y *Trapezoid*.

Binomial (p. 704) A binomial is a polynomial with two terms.

$3x^2 - 1$ is a binomial.

Binomio (p. 704) Un binomio es un polinomio con dos términos.

Box-and-whisker plot (p. 635) A box-and-whisker plot is a graph that shows the distribution of data along a number line. Quartiles divide the data into four equal parts.
EXAMPLE The box-and-whisker plot at the right is for the data 16 19 26 27 27 29 30 31 34 35 37 39 40. The lower quartile is 26.5. The median is 30. The upper quartile is 36.

Gráfica de caja y brazos (p. 635) Una gráfica de caja y brazos presenta la distribución de datos en una recta numérica. Los cuartiles dividen los datos en cuatro partes iguales.

C

Center of rotation (p. 507) See *Rotation*.

Centro de rotación (p. 507) Ver *Rotation*.

Central angle (p. 487) A central angle is an angle whose vertex is the center of a circle.

$\angle AOB$ is a central angle.

Ángulo central (p. 487) Un ángulo central es un ángulo cuyo vértice está en el centro del círculo.

Chord (p. 486) A chord of a circle is a segment whose endpoints are on the circle.
EXAMPLE $\overline{AB}$ is a chord of circle O.

Cuerda (p. 486) Una cuerda es un segmento cuyos extremos se hallan en un círculo.

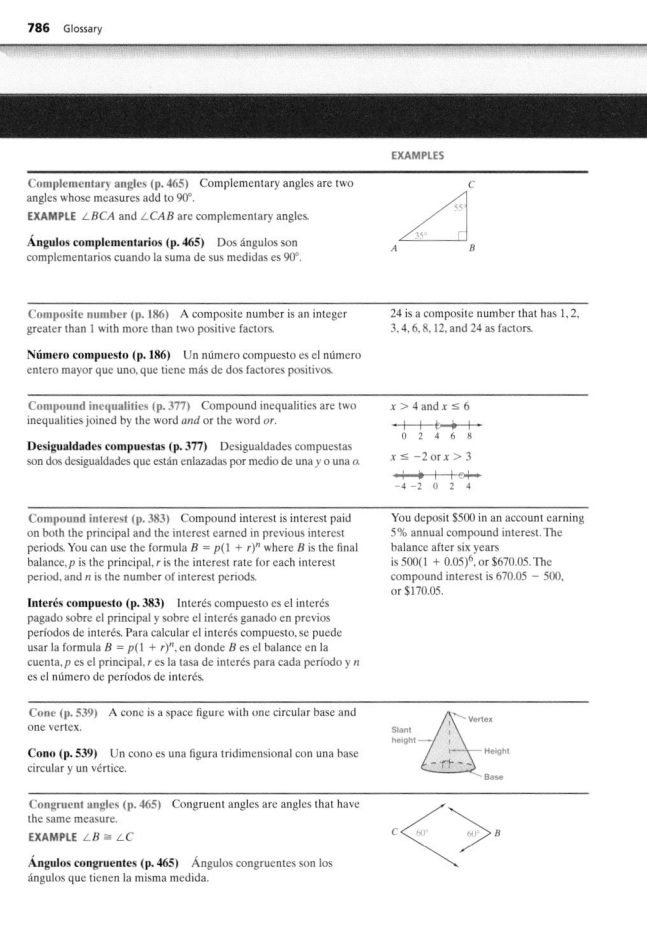

Circle (p. 486) A circle is the set of all points in a plane that are equidistant from a given point, called the center.
EXAMPLE Circle O

Círculo (p. 486) Un círculo es un conjunto de puntos en un plano que se hallan a la misma distancia de un punto dado llamado el centro.

Circle graph (p. 487) A circle graph is a graph that represents parts of a whole. The total must be 100% or 1.
EXAMPLE This circle graph represents the different types of the plays that William Shakespeare wrote.

Gráfica circular (p. 487) Una gráfica circular es la gráfica que representa partes de un todo. El total debe ser cien por ciento o uno.

Shakespeare's Plays
Histories 26%
Tragedies 26%
Romances 13%
Comedies 35%

Circumference (p. 486) Circumference is the distance around a circle. You calculate the circumference of a circle by multiplying the diameter by π.

Circunferencia (p. 486) La circunferencia es la distancia alrededor de un círculo. La circunferencia de un círculo se calcula multiplicando el diámetro por π.

10 cm, about 31.4 cm
O
The circumference of the circle is 10π cm, or approximately 31.4 cm.

Coefficient (p. 76) A coefficient is a number that multiplies a variable.

Coeficiente (p. 76) Coeficiente es el número que multiplica una variable.

In the expression $2x + 3y - 16$, 2 is the coefficient of x and 3 is the coefficient of y.

Combination (p. 660) A combination is a group of items in which the order of the items is *not* important. You can use the notation $_nC_r$ to express the number of combinations of n objects chosen r at a time.

Combinación (p. 660) Una combinación es un conjunto de datos en el cual el orden de sus componentes no es importante. Se puede usar la notación $_nC_r$ para expresar el número de combinaciones de n objetos elegidos r veces a la vez.

The combination (pots and pans) is the same as the combination (pans and pots).

Commission (p. 321) Commission is pay that is equal to a percent of sales.

Comisión (p. 321) Una comisión es un pago que equivale a un porcentaje de las ventas.

A saleswoman received a 5% commission on sales of $120. Her commission was $6.

Common difference (p. 688) See *Arithmetic sequence*.

Diferencia común (p. 688) Ver *Arithmetic sequence*.

Common ratio (p. 689) See *Geometric sequence*.

Razón común (p. 689) Ver *Geometric sequence*.

Commutative Properties of Addition and Multiplication (p. 66) For any numbers a and b, $a + b = b + a$ and $ab = ba$.

Propiedad conmutativa de la suma (p. 66) Para cualquier número a y b, $a + b = b + a$, y $ab = ba$.

$6 + 4 = 4 + 6$
$9 \cdot 5 = 5 \cdot 9$

Compass (p. 491) A compass is a geometric tool used to draw circles and arcs.

Compás (p. 491) Un compás es un instrumento de geometría que se emplea para trazar círculos y arcos.

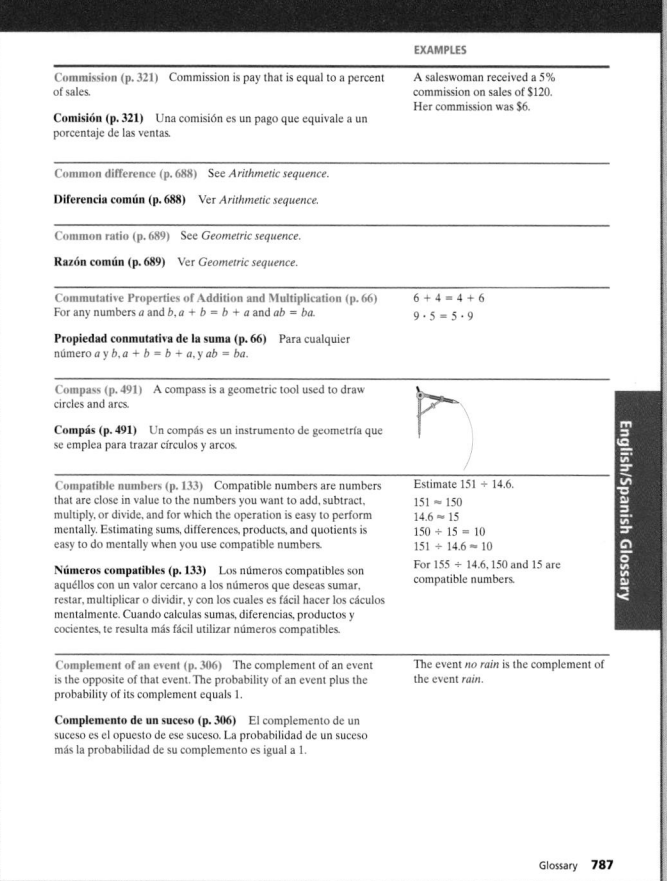

Compatible numbers (p. 133) Compatible numbers are numbers that are close in value to the numbers you want to add, subtract, multiply, or divide, and for which the operation is easy to perform mentally. Estimating sums, differences, products, and quotients is easy to do mentally when you use compatible numbers.

Números compatibles (p. 133) Los números compatibles son aquéllos con un valor cercano a los números que deseas sumar, restar, multiplicar o dividir, y con los cuales es fácil hacer los cálculos mentalmente. Cuando calculas sumas, diferencias, productos y cocientes, te resulta más fácil utilizar números compatibles.

Estimate $151 + 14.6$.
$151 \approx 150$
$14.6 \approx 15$
$150 \div 15 = 10$
$151 \div 14.6 \approx 10$
For $155 \div 14.6$, 150 and 15 are compatible numbers.

Complement of an event (p. 306) The complement of an event is the opposite of that event. The probability of an event plus the probability of its complement equals 1.

Complemento de un suceso (p. 306) El complemento de un suceso es el opuesto de ese suceso. La probabilidad de un suceso más la probabilidad de su complemento es igual a 1.

The event *no rain* is the complement of the event *rain*.

Complementary angles (p. 465) Complementary angles are two angles whose measures add to 90°.
EXAMPLE $\angle BCA$ and $\angle CAB$ are complementary angles.

Ángulos complementarios (p. 465) Dos ángulos son complementarios cuando la suma de sus medidas es 90°.

Composite number (p. 186) A composite number is an integer greater than 1 with more than two positive factors.

Número compuesto (p. 186) Un número compuesto es el número entero mayor que uno, que tiene más de dos factores positivos.

24 is a composite number that has 1, 2, 3, 4, 6, 8, 12, and 24 as factors.

Compound inequalities (p. 377) Compound inequalities are two inequalities joined by the word *and* or the word *or*.

Desigualdades compuestas (p. 377) Desigualdades compuestas son dos desigualdades que están enlazadas por medio de una *y* o una *o*.

$x > 4$ and $x \leq 6$
0 2 4 6 8
$x \leq -2$ or $x > 3$
−4 −2 0 2 4

Compound interest (p. 383) Compound interest is interest paid on both the principal and the interest earned in previous interest periods. You can use the formula $B = p(1 + r)^n$ where B is the final balance, p is the principal, r is the interest rate for each interest period, and n is the number of interest periods.

Interés compuesto (p. 383) Interés compuesto es el interés pagado sobre el principal y sobre el interés ganado en previos períodos de interés. Para calcular el interés compuesto, se puede usar la fórmula $B = p(1 + r)^n$, en donde B es el balance en la cuenta, p es el principal, r es la tasa de interés para cada período y n es el número de períodos de interés.

You deposit $500 in an account earning 5% annual compound interest. The balance after six years is $500(1 + 0.05)^6$, or $670.05. The compound interest is 670.05 − 500, or $170.05.

Cone (p. 539) A cone is a space figure with one circular base and one vertex.

Cono (p. 539) Un cono es una figura tridimensional con una base circular y un vértice.

Vertex
Slant height
Height
Base

Congruent angles (p. 465) Congruent angles are angles that have the same measure.
EXAMPLE $\angle B \cong \angle C$

Ángulos congruentes (p. 465) Ángulos congruentes son los ángulos que tienen la misma medida.

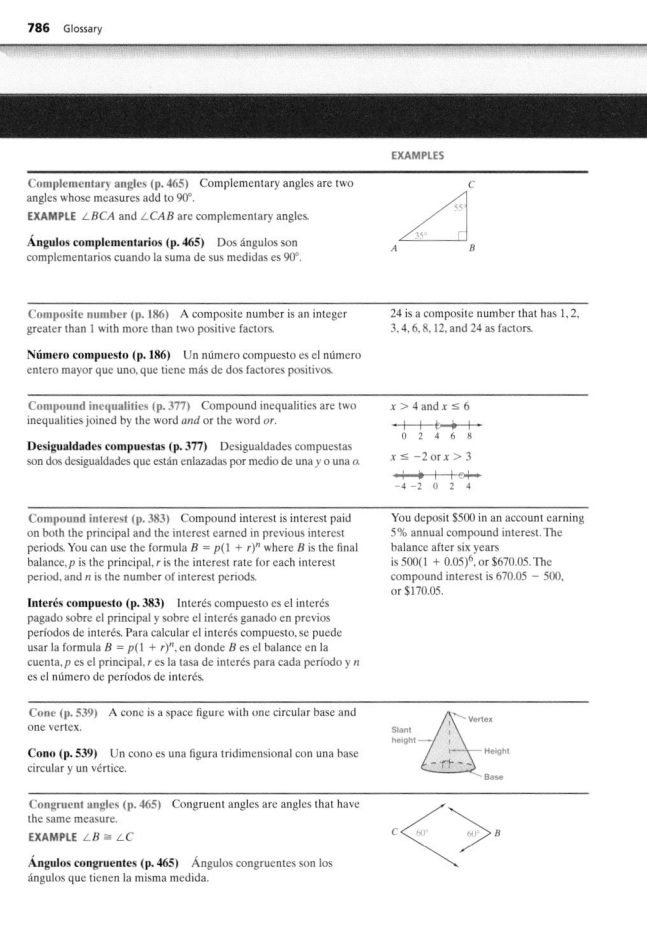

Congruent figures (p. 480) Congruent figures are figures that have the same size and shape. Congruent polygons have congruent corresponding sides and congruent corresponding angles. The symbol $\cong$ means "is congruent to."
EXAMPLE $\overline{AB} \cong \overline{QS}$, $\overline{BC} \cong \overline{SR}$, and $\overline{AC} \cong \overline{QR}$.
$\angle A \cong \angle Q$, $\angle B \cong \angle S$, and $\angle C \cong \angle R$.
Triangles ABC and QSR are congruent.
$\triangle ABC \cong \triangle QSR$

Figuras congruentes (p. 480) Figuras congruentes son las figuras que tienen el mismo tamaño y la misma forma. Los polígonos congruentes tienen lados correspondientes congruentes y ángulos correspondientes congruentes. El símbolo $\cong$ significa "es congruente con."

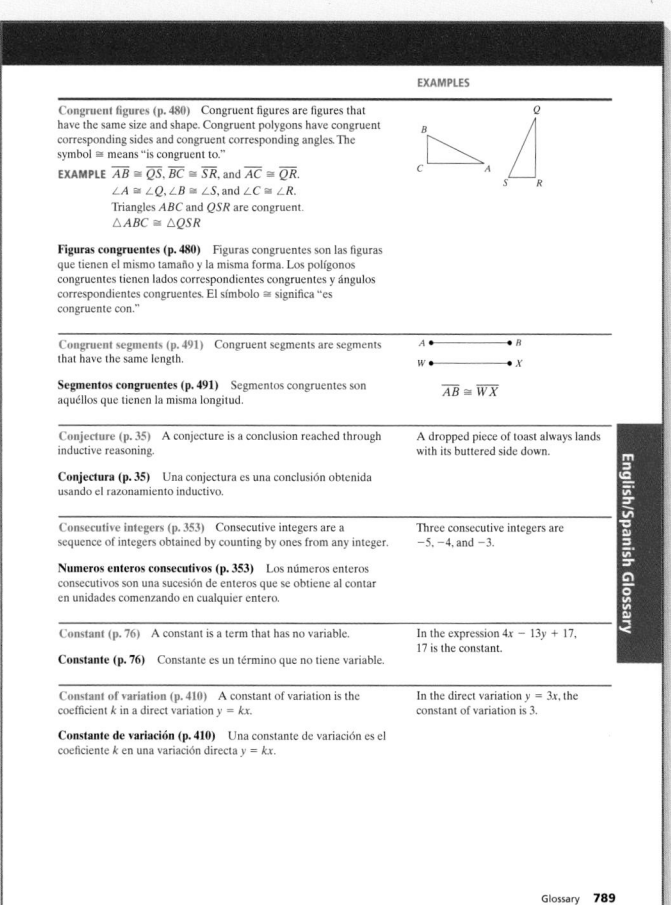

Congruent segments (p. 491) Congruent segments are segments that have the same length.

Segmentos congruentes (p. 491) Segmentos congruentes son aquéllos que tienen la misma longitud.

A • ———— • B
W • ———— • X
$\overline{AB} \cong \overline{WX}$

Conjecture (p. 35) A conjecture is a conclusion reached through inductive reasoning.

Conjetura (p. 35) Una conjetura es una conclusión obtenida usando el razonamiento inductivo.

A dropped piece of toast always lands with its buttered side down.

Consecutive integers (p. 353) Consecutive integers are a sequence of integers obtained by counting by ones from any integer.

Números enteros consecutivos (p. 353) Los números enteros consecutivos son una sucesión de enteros que se obtiene al contar en unidades comenzando en cualquier entero.

Three consecutive integers are −5, −4, and −3.

Constant (p. 76) A constant is a term that has no variable.

Constante (p. 76) Constante es un término que no tiene variable.

In the expression $4x - 13y + 17$, 17 is the constant.

Constant of variation (p. 410) A constant of variation is the coefficient k in a direct variation $y = kx$.

Constante de variación (p. 410) Una constante de variación es el coeficiente k en una variación directa $y = kx$.

In the direct variation $y = 3x$, the constant of variation is 3.

Coordinate plane (p. 50) The coordinate plane is the plane formed by two number lines that intersect at their zero points. The horizontal number line is called the *x*-axis. The vertical number line is called the *y*-axis. The two axes meet at the origin, $O(0, 0)$, and divide the coordinate plane into four quadrants.

Plano de coordenadas (p. 50) El plano de coordenadas está formado por la intersección de una recta numérica horizontal, llamada el eje de *x*, y una recta numérica vertical, llamada el eje de *y*. Los dos ejes se intersecan en el origen, $O(0, 0)$, y divide el plano de coordenadas en cuatro cuadrantes.

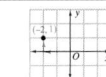

Coordinates (p. 50) Coordinates are ordered pairs (x, y) that identify points in a coordinate plane. The *x*-coordinate (the first coordinate) shows the horizontal position. The *y*-coordinate (the second coordinate) shows the vertical position.

Coordenadas (p. 50) Las coordenadas son pares ordenados (x, y), que identifican puntos en el plano de coordenadas. La coordenada *x*, (la primera coordenada) muestra la posición horizontal. La coordenada *y* (la segunda coordenada) muestra la posición vertical.

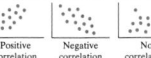

The ordered pair $(-2, 1)$ describes the point that is found by moving 2 units to the left from the origin and one unit up from the *x*-axis.

Correlation (p. 425) A correlation is a relation between two sets of data. The data have a *positive correlation* if, as one set of values increases, the other set tends to increase. The data have a *negative correlation* if, as one set of values increases, the other set tends to decrease. The data have little or *no correlation* if the values show no relationship.

Correlación (p. 425) Una correlación es la relación que hay entre dos conjuntos de datos. Los datos tienen una *correlación positiva* si, a medida que aumenta un conjunto de valores, el otro conjunto tiende a aumentar. Los datos tienen una *correlación negativa* si, a medida que aumenta un conjunto de valores, el otro conjunto tiende a disminuir. Los datos tienen correlación débil o *no tienen correlación* si los valores no muestran relación entre ellos.

Positive correlation   Negative correlation   No correlation

Corresponding angles (p. 466) Corresponding angles are pairs of nonadjacent angles that lie on the same side of a transversal of two lines and in corresponding positions.
EXAMPLE $\angle 1$ and $\angle 3$ are corresponding angles.
$\angle 2$ and $\angle 4$ are corresponding angles.

Ángulos correspondientes (p. 466) Ángulos correspondientes son los pares de ángulos no adyacentes, uno interior y el otro exterior, en el mismo lado de la transversal.

Corresponding angles of polygons (p. 480) Corresponding angles are matching angles of similar or congruent figures.

Ángulos correspondientes de polígonos (p. 480) Ángulos correspondientes son los ángulos equivalentes de figuras semejantes o congruentes.

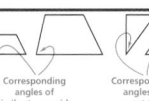
Corresponding angles of similar trapezoids   Corresponding angles of congruent triangles

Corresponding sides of polygons (p. 480) Corresponding sides are matching sides of similar or congruent figures.

Lados correspondientes de polígonos (p. 480) Lados correspondientes son los lados equivalentes de figuras semejantes o congruentes.

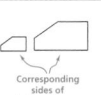
Corresponding sides of similar polygons   Corresponding sides of congruent triangles

Cosine (p. 608) See *Trigonometric ratios.*

Razón coseno (p. 608) Ver *Trigonometric ratios.*

Counterexample (p. 37) A counterexample is an example that proves a statement false.

Contraejemplo (p. 37) Contraejemplo es todo ejemplo que pruebe la falsedad de un enunciado.

Statement: Motor vehicles have four wheels.
Counterexample: A motorcycle is a motor vehicle with two wheels.

Counting Principle (p. 650) If there are *m* ways of making one choice and *n* ways of making a second choice, then there are $m \times n$ ways of making the first choice followed by the second.

Principio de conteo (p. 650) Si hay *m* maneras de realizar una elección y *n* maneras de realizar una segunda elección, por lo tanto hay $m \times n$ maneras de realizar la primera elección seguida de la segunda elección.

There are 26 possible choices for each letter of a monogram. Thus, there are $26 \cdot 26$, or 676, possible two-letter monograms.

Cross products (p. 294) Cross products are products formed from a proportion. They are the product of the numerator of the first ratio and the denominator of the second ratio, and the product of the denominator of the first ratio and the numerator of the second ratio. For a proportion, these products are equal.

Productos cruzados (p. 294) Los productos cruzados son los productos formados a partir de una proporción. Son el producto del numerador de la primera razón y el denominador de la segunda razón, y el producto del denominador de la primera razón y del numerador de la segunda razón. Para una proporción, estos productos son iguales.

The cross products for the proportion $\frac{3}{4} = \frac{6}{8}$ are $3 \cdot 8$ and $4 \cdot 6$.
$3 \cdot 8 = 24$ and $4 \cdot 6 = 24$.

English/Spanish Glossary

Cross section (p. 544) A cross section is the intersection of a plane and a space figure.

Sección de corte (p. 544) Una sección de corte es la intersección de un plano y una figura tridimensional.

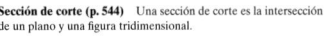

Cube (p. 540) A cube is rectangular prism with six congruent faces.

Cubo (p. 540) Un cubo es un prisma rectangular con seis caras congruentes.

Face

Cube root (p. 583) The cube root of a given number is a number whose third power is the given number. The symbol for the cube root of a number is $\sqrt[3]{\ }$.

Raíz cúbica (p. 583) La raíz cúbica de un número dado es un número cuya tercera potencia es el número dado. El símbolo de la raíz cúbica de un número es $\sqrt[3]{\ }$.

$\sqrt[3]{8} = 2$ because $2^3 = 8$.
$\sqrt[3]{-8} = -2$ because $(-2)^3 = -8$.

Cubic unit (p. 557) A cubic unit is the amount of space occupied by a cube with edges one unit long.

Unidad cúbica (p. 557) Una unidad cúbica es el espacio que ocupa un cubo cuyos lados tienen una unidad de longitud.

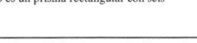

Cylinder (p. 539) A cylinder is a space figure with two circular, parallel, and congruent bases.

Cilindro (p. 539) Un cilindro es una figura tridimensional con dos bases circulares, paralelas y congruentes.

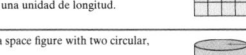
Bases
Height

D

Decagon (p. 474) A decagon is a polygon with ten sides.

Decágono (p. 474) Un decágono es un polígono que tiene diez lados.

See *Polygon.*

Deductive reasoning (p. 77) Deductive reasoning is the process of reasoning logically from given facts to a conclusion.
EXAMPLE Deductive reasoning is used to simplify the expression $4c + 3(3 + c)$.

Razonamiento deductivo (p. 77) El razonamiento deductivo es el proceso de razonar lógicamente para llegar a una conclusión a partir de datos dados.

$$\begin{aligned} 4c + 3(3 + c) &= 4c + 9 + 3c \\ &= 4c + 3c + 9 \\ &= (4 + 3)c + 9 \\ &= 7c + 9 \end{aligned}$$

Dependent events (p. 656) Dependent events are events for which the occurrence of one event affects the probability of the occurrence of the other.

Sucesos dependientes (p. 656) Cuando el resultado de un seceso afecta el resultado de un segundo suceso, los sucesos son dependientes.

A bag contains 10 pieces of paper and on each piece is a different number from 1 to 10. A paper is picked and not returned to the bag. The probability of the outcome of the second pick is dependent on the outcome of the first pick.

Diagonal (p. 476) A diagonal of a polygon is a segment that connects two nonconsecutive vertices.

Diagonal (p. 476) Una diagonal de un polígono es un segmento que conecta dos vértices no consecutivos.

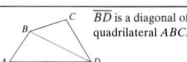
$\overline{BD}$ is a diagonal of quadrilateral $ABCD$.

Diameter (p. 486) A diameter of a circle is a chord that passes through the center of the circle.
EXAMPLE $\overline{RS}$ is a diameter of circle O.

Diámetro (p. 486) Un diámetro de un círculo es una cuerda que pasa a través del centro de un círculo.

Dilation (p. 304) A dilation is a transformation that results in a size change. The scale factor, *r*, describes the size of the change from the original figure to its image. If $r > 1$, the dilation is an enlargement. If *r* is positive and $r < 1$, the dilation is a reduction.

Dilatación (p. 304) Una dilatación es una transformación que da como resultado un cambio de tamaño. El factor de escala *r* describe el tamaño del cambio de la figura original a su reproducción. Si $r > 1$, la dilatación es un agrandamiento. Si $r < 1$, la dilatación es una reducción.

The blue triangle is an enlargement of the red triangle. The red triangle is a reduction of the blue triangle.

Dimensional analysis (p. 254) Dimensional analysis is a process of analyzing units to decide which conversion factors to use.

Análisis dimensional (p. 254) El análisis dimensional es el proceso de analizar unidades para decidir qué factores de conversión usar.

$0.5 \text{ mi} = \frac{0.5 \text{ mi}}{1} \cdot \frac{5,280 \text{ ft}}{1 \text{ mi}} = 2,640 \text{ ft}$

Direct variation (p. 410) A direct variation is a linear function modeled by the equation $y = kx$, where $k \neq 0$.

Variación directa (p. 410) Una variación directa es una función lineal representada por una ecuación $y = kx$, donde $k \neq 0$.

$y = 3x$

Discount (p. 329) A discount is the amount by which a price is decreased.

Descuento (p. 329) Descuento es la cantidad en la cual un precio es reducido.

The price of a $10 book is reduced by a discount of $1.50 to sell for $8.50.

English/Spanish Glossary

Distance Formula (p. 592) The distance d between any two points (x_1, y_1) and (x_2, y_2) is $d = \sqrt{(x_2 - x_1)^2 + (y_2 - y_1)^2}$.

Fórmula de distancia (p. 592) La distancia d entre cualesquiera dos puntos (x_1, y_1) y (x_2, y_2) es $d = \sqrt{(x_2 - x_1)^2 + (y_2 - y_1)^2}$.

The distance between $(6, 3)$ and $(1, 9)$ is d:
$$d = \sqrt{(1 - 6)^2 + (9 - 3)^2}$$
$$= \sqrt{(-5)^2 + 6^2}$$
$$= \sqrt{61}$$
$$\approx 7.8$$

Distributive Property (p. 71) For any numbers a, b, and c, $a(b + c) = ab + ac$ and $a(b - c) = ab - ac$.

Propiedad distributiva (p. 71) Para cualquier número a, b y c, $a(b + c) = ab + ac$ y $a(b - c) = ab - ac$

$2\left(3 + \frac{1}{2}\right) = 2 \cdot 3 + 2 \cdot \frac{1}{2}$
$8(5 - 3) = 8(5) - 8(3)$

Divisible (p. 178) Divisible means that the remainder is 0 when you divide one integer by another.

Divisible (p. 178) Un número entero es divisible por otro número si el residuo es cero.

15 is divisible by 5 because $15 \div 5 = 3$ with remainder 0.

Division Property of Equality (p. 92) If $a = b$ and $c \neq 0$, then $\frac{a}{c} = \frac{b}{c}$.

Propiedad de igualdad en la división (p. 92) Si $a = b$ y $c \neq 0$, entonces $\frac{a}{c} = \frac{b}{c}$.

$6 = 3(2)$, so $\frac{6}{3} = \frac{3(2)}{3}$

Division Properties of Inequality (p. 110) If $a < b$ and c is positive, then $\frac{a}{c} < \frac{b}{c}$. If $a > b$ and c is positive, then $\frac{a}{c} > \frac{b}{c}$.
If you divide each side of an inequality by a negative number, you reverse the inequality symbol.
If $a < b$ and c is negative, then $\frac{a}{c} > \frac{b}{c}$.
If $a > b$ and c is negative, then $\frac{a}{c} < \frac{b}{c}$.

Propiedad de división de la desigualdad (p. 110) Si $a < b$ y c es positivo, entonces $\frac{a}{c} < \frac{b}{c}$. Si $a > b$ y c es positivo, entonces $\frac{a}{c} > \frac{b}{c}$. Si se divide cada lado de una desigualdad por un número negativo, se invierte la dirección del símbolo de desigualdad.
Si $a < b$, y c es negativo, entonces $\frac{a}{c} > \frac{b}{c}$.
Si $a > b$, y c es negativo, entonces $\frac{a}{c} < \frac{b}{c}$.

$3 < 6$, so $\frac{3}{3} < \frac{6}{3}$
$8 > 2$, so $\frac{8}{2} > \frac{2}{2}$
$6 < 12$, so $\frac{6}{-3} > \frac{12}{-3}$
$16 > 8$, so $\frac{16}{-4} < \frac{8}{-4}$

Domain (p. 400) A domain is the set of first coordinates of the ordered pairs of a relation.

Dominio (p. 400) Un dominio es el conjunto que comprende todas las primeras coordenadas de los pares ordenados de una relación.

In the relation $\{(0, 1), (-3, 2), (0, 2)\}$, the domain is $\{0, -3\}$.

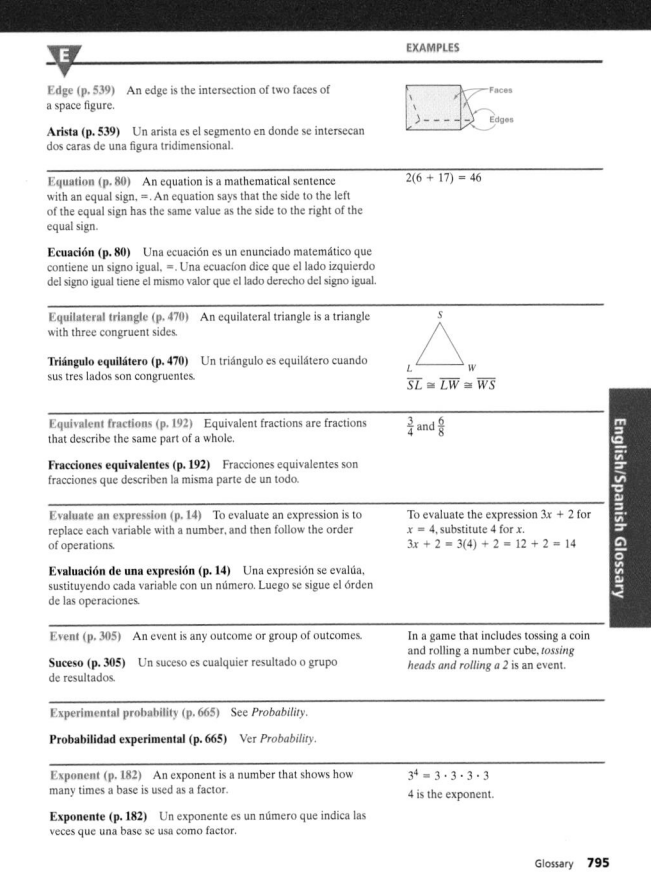

E

Edge (p. 539) An edge is the intersection of two faces of a space figure.

Arista (p. 539) Un arista es el segmento en donde se intersecan dos caras de una figura tridimensional.

Equation (p. 80) An equation is a mathematical sentence with an equal sign, =. An equation says that the side to the left of the equal sign has the same value as the side to the right of the equal sign.

Ecuación (p. 80) Una ecuación es un enunciado matemático que contiene un signo igual, =. Una ecuación dice que el lado izquierdo del signo igual tiene el mismo valor que el lado derecho del signo igual.

$2(6 + 17) = 46$

Equilateral triangle (p. 470) An equilateral triangle is a triangle with three congruent sides.

Triángulo equilátero (p. 470) Un triángulo es equilátero cuando sus tres lados son congruentes.

$\overline{SL} \cong \overline{LW} \cong \overline{WS}$

Equivalent fractions (p. 192) Equivalent fractions are fractions that describe the same part of a whole.

Fracciones equivalentes (p. 192) Fracciones equivalentes son fracciones que describen la misma parte de un todo.

$\frac{3}{4}$ and $\frac{6}{8}$

Evaluate an expression (p. 14) To evaluate an expression is to replace each variable with a number, and then follow the order of operations.

Evaluación de una expresión (p. 14) Una expresión se evalúa, sustituyendo cada variable con un número. Luego se sigue el órden de las operaciones.

To evaluate the expression $3x + 2$ for $x = 4$, substitute 4 for x.
$3x + 2 = 3(4) + 2 = 12 + 2 = 14$

Event (p. 305) An event is any outcome or group of outcomes.

Suceso (p. 305) Un suceso es cualquier resultado o grupo de resultados.

In a game that includes tossing a coin and rolling a number cube, *tossing heads and rolling a 2* is an event.

Experimental probability (p. 665) See *Probability*.

Probabilidad experimental (p. 665) Ver *Probability*.

Exponent (p. 182) An exponent is a number that shows how many times a base is used as a factor.

Exponente (p. 182) Un exponente es un número que indica las veces que una base se usa como factor.

$3^4 = 3 \cdot 3 \cdot 3 \cdot 3$
4 is the exponent.

Exponential decay (p. 700) Exponential decay is any function of the form $y = b^x$, where $0 < b < 1$. The graph of the function slopes downward as input values increase.
EXAMPLE The function $y = 10\left(\frac{1}{2}\right)^x$ is graphed for integer values of x from 1 to 5.

Decremento exponencial (p. 700) Decremento exponencial es cualquier función de la forma $y = b^x$, donde $0 < b < 1$. La gráfica de la función tiene pendiente hacia abajo a medida que aumentan los valores de entrada.

Exponential growth (p. 699) Exponential growth is any function of the form $y = b^x$, where $b > 1$. The graph of the function curves upward as input values increase.
EXAMPLE The function $y = 2^x$ is graphed for integer values of x from 0 to 4.

Incremento exponencial (p. 699) Incremento exponencial es cualquier función de la forma $y = b^x$, donde $b > 1$. La gráfica de la función se curva hacia arriba a medida que aumentan los valores de entrada.

F

Face (p. 539) A face is a surface of a space figure.

Cara (p. 539) Cara es la superficie plana de una figura tridimensional.

Factor (p. 179) A factor of a nonzero integer is an integer that divides the nonzero integer with remainder zero.

Factor (p. 179) Un número entero es factor de otro número entero distinto de cero, cuando lo divide y el residuo es cero.

1, 2, 3, 4, 6, 9, 12, 18, and 36 are factors of 36.

Formula (p. 143) A formula is an equation that shows a relationship between quantities that are represented by variables.

Fórmula (p. 143) Una fórmula es una ecuación que muestra una relación entre las cantidades que representan las variables.

The formula $P = 4s$ gives the perimeter of a square in terms of the length s of a side.

Frequency table (p. 630) A frequency table is a list of items that shows the number of times, or frequency, with which they occur.
EXAMPLE This frequency table shows the number of household telephones for the students in one school class.

Tabla de frecuencia (p. 630) Una tabla de frecuencia registra el número de veces, o frecuencia, con que se ha producido un determinado tipo de resultado.

Household Telephones

Phones	Tally	Frequency
1	JHI IIII	8
2	JHI I	6
3	IIII	4

Front-end estimation (p. 128) Front-end estimation is a way to estimate a sum. First add the front-end digits. Round to estimate the sum of the remaining digits. Then combine estimates.

Estimación por la izquierda (p. 128) La estimación por la izquierda se emplea para estimar sumas. Primero, se suman los dígitos delanteros. Luego, se redondea para estimar la suma de los dígitos restantes. Por último se combinan las estimaciones.

Estimate $\$3.49 + \$2.29$.
$3 + 2 = 5$
$0.49 + 0.29 \approx 0.50 + 0.30 = 0.80$
$\$3.49 + \$2.29 \approx \$5 + \$0.80 = \$5.80$

Function (p. 400) A function is a relationship in which each member of the domain is paired with exactly one member of the range. A number of the domain is an input and the related number of the range is an output.

Función (p. 400) Una función es una relación en la que a cada miembro de un dominio le corresponde exactamente un miembro dominio. Un número del dominio es el valor de entrada y el número relacionado del dominio es el valor de salida.

Earned income is a function of the number of hours worked (n). If you earn $\$5$/h, then your income is expressed by the function $f(n) = 5n$.

Function notation (p. 418) Function notation is notation that represents a function as $f(x)$ instead of y.

Notación de una función (p. 418) La notación de una función es aquélla que representa una función $f(x)$ en vez de y.

$f(x) = -2x + 1$

Function rule (p. 418) A function rule is an equation that describes a function.

Regla de una función (p. 418) La regla de una función es la ecuación que describe una función.

$y = 2x + 5, f(x) = -4x + 3$

G

Geometric sequence (p. 689) A geometric sequence is a sequence of numbers in which each term after the first is the result of multiplying the previous term by a fixed number (called the common ratio).

Progresión geométrica (p. 689) Una progresión geométrica es una sucesión de números en la que cada término, después del primero, es el resultado de la multiplicación del término anterior por un número fijo (llamando razón común).

The sequence 1, 3, 9, 27, 81, ... is a geometric sequence. The common ratio is 3.

Greatest common factor (GCF) (p. 187) The greatest common factor of two or more numbers is the greatest factor that the numbers have in common.

Máximo común divisor (MCD) (p. 187) El máximo común divisor de dos o más números es el mayor divisor que los números tienen en común.

The greatest common factor (GCF) of 12 and 30 is 6.

Greatest possible error (p. 258)   The greatest possible error of a measurement is half the unit used for measuring.

The measurement 400 kg is rounded to the nearest hundred kilograms. So, the greatest possible error is 50 kg.

Máximo error posible (p. 258)   El máximo error posible de una medida es la mitad de la unidad usada para medir.

H

Height of a three-dimensional figure (pp. 546, 547, 566)   See *Cone, Cylinder, Prism,* and *Pyramid.*

Altura de figuras tridimensionales (pp. 546, 547, 566)   Ver *Cone, Cylinder, Prism* y *Pyramid.*

Height of a two-dimensional figure (pp. 523, 527, 529)   See *Parallelogram, Triangle,* and *Trapezoid.*

Altura de figuras bidimensionales (pp. 523, 527, 529)   Ver *Parallelogram, Triangle* y *Trapezoid.*

Hexagon (p. 472)   A hexagon is a polygon with six sides.

See *Polygon.*

Hexágono (p. 472)   Un hexágono es un polígono que tiene seis lados.

Histogram (p. 634)   A histogram is a bar graph in which the heights of the bars give the frequencies of the data. There are no spaces between bars.
EXAMPLE This histogram gives the frequencies of board-game purchases at a local toy store.

Board-Game Purchases (bar graph: Frequency vs Games Bought, 1–2, 3–4, 5–6, 7–8)

Histograma (p. 634)   Un histograma es una gráfica de barras en la cual la altura de las barras representa la frecuencia de los datos. No hay espacio entre las barras.

Hypotenuse (p. 584)   In a right triangle, the hypotenuse is the longest side, which is opposite the right angle.

See *Right triangle.*

Hipotenusa (p. 584)   La hipotenusa es el lado más largo de un triángulo rectángulo. Es el lado opuesto al ángulo recto.

I

Identity Properties of Addition and Multiplication (p. 67)   For any number *a,* the sum of *a* and 0 is *a.* The product of *a* and 1 is 1.

$za + 0 = a$
$a \cdot 1 = a$

Propiedad de identidad de la suma y de la multiplicación (p. 67)   La suma de cero y cualquier número *a* es *a.* El producto de cualquier número *a* y uno es *a.*

Image (p. 497)   An image is the result of the transformation of a point, line, or figure to a new set of coordinates.

See *Transformation.*

Imagen (p. 497)   Una imagen es el resultado de la transformación de un punto, una recta o una figura a un nuevo conjunto de coordenadas.

Improper fraction (p. 244)   An improper fraction is a fraction with a numerator that is greater than or equal to the denominator.

$\frac{24}{15}$ and $\frac{16}{16}$ are improper fractions.

Fracción impropia (p. 244)   Una fracción impropia es una fracción cuyo numerador es mayor o igual que su denominador.

Independent events (p. 654)   Two events are independent events if the occurrence of one event does not affect the probability of the occurrence of the other.

When a number cube is rolled twice, the events rolling 6 and then rolling 3 are independent.

Sucesos independientes (p. 654)   Dos sucesos son independientes si el acontecimiento de uno no afecta la probabilidad de que el otro suceso ocurra.

Indirect measurement (p. 300)   Indirect measurement is a method of determining length or distance without measuring directly.
EXAMPLE By using the distances shown in the diagram and using properties of similar figures, you can find the height of the taller tower.

$\frac{240}{540} = \frac{x}{1,192} \rightarrow x \approx 529.8$ ft

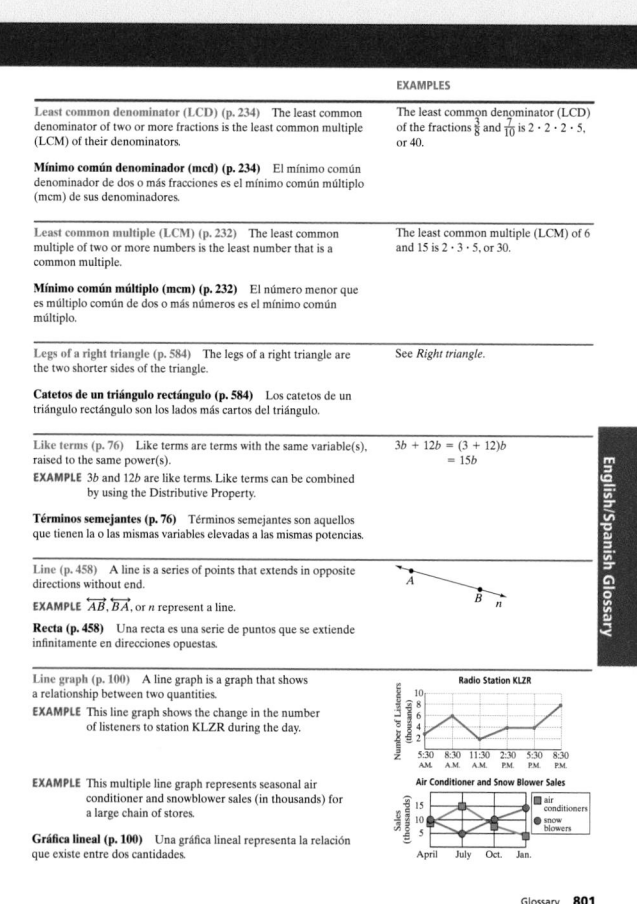

240 ft
540 ft   1192 ft

Medición indirecta (p. 300)   La medición indirecta es un método para determinar la longitud o distancia sin medir directamente.

Inductive reasoning (p. 35)   Inductive reasoning is making conclusions based on patterns you observe.

By inductive reasoning, the next number in the pattern 2, 4, 6, 8, . . . is 10.

Razonamiento inductivo (p. 35)   El razonamiento inductivo es sacar conclusiones a partir de patrones observados.

Inequality (p. 102)   An inequality is a sentence that uses one of the symbols $>, <, \geq, \leq,$ or $\neq.$

$0 \leq 2, k > -3, 10 < t$

Desigualdad (p. 102)   Una desigualdad es un enunciado que usa uno de los siguientes símbolos $>, <, \geq, \leq,$ o $\neq.$

Integer (p. 19)   The integers are the whole numbers and their opposites.

$-45, 0,$ and 289 are integers.

Números enteros (p. 19)   Los números enteros son el conjunto de los números enteros positivos (naturales) y sus opuestos.

English/Spanish Glossary

Interest (p. 382)   See *Compound interest* and *Simple interest.*

Interés (p. 382)   Ver *Compound interest* y *Simple interest.*

Interest rate (p. 382)   An interest rate is the percentage of the balance that an account or investment earns in a fixed period of time.

A savings account pays $2\frac{1}{4}\%$ per year.

Tasa de interés (p. 382)   Una tasa de interés es el porcentaje del saldo que gana una cuenta o inversión durante un período fijo.

Inverse operations (p. 86)   Inverse operations are operations that undo each other.

Multiplication and division are inverse operations.

Operaciones inversas (p. 86)   Operaciones inversas son las operaciones que se cancelan una a la otra.

Irrational number (p. 581)   An irrational number is a number whose decimal form neither terminates nor repeats.

The number $\pi,$ which is approximately equal to 3.141592654, is an irrational number.

Número irracional (p. 581)   Un número irracional es aquél cuyas cifras decimales son infinitas y no se repiten.

Isosceles triangle (p. 470)   An isosceles triangle is a triangle with at least two congruent sides.
EXAMPLE $\overline{LM} \cong \overline{LB}$
$\triangle MLB$ is an isosceles triangle.

(triangle diagram with vertices L, M, B)

Triángulo isósceles (p. 470)   Un triángulo isósceles es aquel que tiene al menos dos lados congruentes.

L

Lateral area (p. 546)   The lateral area of a prism is the sum of the areas of the lateral faces.

(diagram: perimeter of base $a + b + c + d$; prism; Lateral Area = *ph*)

Área lateral (p. 546)   El área lateral de un prisma es la suma de las áreas de las caras laterales.

Lateral face (p. 539)   See *Prism* and *Pyramid.*

Cara lateral (p. 539)   Ver *Prism* y *Pyramid.*

Least common denominator (LCD) (p. 234)   The least common denominator of two or more fractions is the least common multiple (LCM) of their denominators.

The least common denominator (LCD) of the fractions $\frac{5}{8}$ and $\frac{7}{10}$ is $2 \cdot 2 \cdot 2 \cdot 5,$ or 40.

Mínimo común denominador (mcd) (p. 234)   El mínimo común denominador de dos o más fracciones es el mínimo común múltiplo (mcm) de sus denominadores.

Least common multiple (LCM) (p. 232)   The least common multiple of two or more numbers is the least number that is a common multiple.

The least common multiple (LCM) of 6 and 15 is $2 \cdot 3 \cdot 5,$ or 30.

Mínimo común múltiplo (mcm) (p. 232)   El número menor que es múltiplo común de dos o más números es el mínimo común múltiplo.

Legs of a right triangle (p. 584)   The legs of a right triangle are the two shorter sides of the triangle.

See *Right triangle.*

Catetos de un triángulo rectángulo (p. 584)   Los catetos de un triángulo rectángulo son los lados más cortos del triángulo.

Like terms (p. 76)   Like terms are terms with the same variable(s), raised to the same power(s).
EXAMPLE $3b$ and $12b$ are like terms. Like terms can be combined by using the Distributive Property.

$3b + 12b = (3 + 12)b$
$= 15b$

Términos semejantes (p. 76)   Términos semejantes son aquellos que tienen la o las mismas variables elevadas a las mismas potencias.

Line (p. 458)   A line is a series of points that extends in opposite directions without end.
EXAMPLE $\overleftrightarrow{AB}, \overleftrightarrow{BA},$ or *n* represent a line.

(line through points A, B labeled *n*)

Recta (p. 458)   Una recta es una serie de puntos que se extiende infinitamente en direcciones opuestas.

Line graph (p. 100)   A line graph is a graph that shows a relationship between two quantities.
EXAMPLE This line graph shows the change in the number of listeners to station KLZR during the day.

Radio Station KLZR (line graph: Number of Listeners (thousands) vs time 5:30 A.M.–8:30 P.M.)

EXAMPLE This multiple line graph represents seasonal air conditioner and snowblower sales (in thousands) for a large chain of stores.

Air Conditioner and Snow Blower Sales (line graph: Sales (thousands) vs April, July, Oct., Jan.; air conditioners, snow blowers)

Gráfica lineal (p. 100)   Una gráfica lineal representa la relación que existe entre dos cantidades.

English/Spanish Glossary

Line of reflection (p. 504) A line of reflection is a line across which a figure is reflected.

See *Reflection*.

Eje de reflexión (p. 504) Un eje de reflexión es una recta sobre la cual una figura es reflejada.

Line of symmetry (p. 503) A line of symmetry is a line that divides a figure with reflectional symmetry into two congruent halves.

Eje de simetría (p. 503) Un eje de simetría es una recta que divide una figura que tiene simetría de reflexión en dos mitades congruentes.

Line plot (p. 631) A line plot is a graph that displays data by using X's above a number line.

EXAMPLE This line plot shows the numbers of girls on a field hockey team who are at the indicated heights.

Heights of Girls

Diagrama de puntos (p. 631) Un diagrama de puntos es una gráfica que muestra datos marcando una X sobre una recta numérica.

Linear equation (p. 406) A linear equation is any equation whose graph is a line.

EXAMPLE $y = \frac{1}{2}x + 3$ is linear because its graph is a line.

$y = \frac{1}{2}x + 3$

Ecuación lineal (p. 406) Una ecuación lineal es cualquier ecuación cuya gráfica de todas sus soluciones es una recta.

Linear inequality (p. 441) A linear inequality is a number sentence in which the equal sign of a linear equation is replaced with $>$, $<$, $\geq$, or $\leq$.

$y \geq 2x + 3$
$y < -4x - 1$

Desigualdad lineal (p. 441) Una desigualdad lineal es una proposición numérica en la cual el signo igual de una ecuación lineal se reemplaza con un signo $>$, $<$, $\geq$ o $\leq$.

Lower quartile (p. 635) The lower quartile is the median of the lower half of a data set.

See *Box-and-whisker plot*.

Cuartil inferior (p. 635) El cuartil inferior es la mediana de la mitad inferior del conjunto de datos.

M

Markup (p. 329) Markup is the amount of increase in price. Markup is added to the cost of merchandise to arrive at the selling price.

A store buys a coat for $60 and sells it for $100. The markup is $40.

Sobrecosto (p. 329) El sobrecosto es la cantidad que se aumenta en precio. El sobrecosto se agrega al costo de la mercadería y eso da el precio de venta.

Matrix (p. 502) A matrix is a rectangular arrangement of numbers.

$\begin{bmatrix} 0 & -1 & -4 \\ 0 & 4 & 0 \end{bmatrix}$

Matriz (p. 502) Una matriz es una organización de números dispuestos en forma rectangular.

Mean (p. 137) The mean of a collection of data is the sum of the data items divided by the number of data items.

The mean temperature (°F) for the temperatures 44, 52, 48, 55, 61, 67, and 58 is 55.

Media (p. 137) La media de un conjunto de datos resulta de la suma de los datos dividida entre el número de componentes de los datos.

Measures of central tendency (p. 137) Measures of central tendency in statistics are *mean*, *median*, and *mode*.

See *Mean*, *Median*, and *Mode*.

Medidas de tendencia central (p. 137) En estadistia, la *media*, la *mediana* y la *moda* son medidas de tendencia central en la estadística.

Median (p. 137) The median of a collection of data is the middle number when there is an odd number of data items and they are written in order. For an even number of data items, the median is the mean of the two middle numbers.

The median temperature (°F) for the temperatures 44, 48, 52, 55, 58, 61, and 67 is 55.

Mediana (p. 137) La mediana es el número central de un conjunto de datos, cuando hay un número impar de datos y éstos están dispuestos en orden. Si hay un número par de datos, la mediana es la media de los dos números centrales.

Midpoint Formula (p. 594) The midpoint of a line segment with endpoints $A(x_1, y_1)$ and $B(x_2, y_2)$ is $\left(\frac{x_1 + x_2}{2}, \frac{y_1 + y_2}{2}\right)$.

The midpoint of $A(-3, 2)$ and $B(7, -2)$ is $\left(\frac{-3 + 7}{2}, \frac{2 + -2}{2}\right)$, or $(2, 0)$.

Fórmula del punto medio (p. 594) El punto medio de un segmento con puntos extremos $A(x_1, y_1)$ y $B(x_2, y_2)$ es $\left(\frac{x_1 + x_2}{2}, \frac{y_1 + y_2}{2}\right)$.

Mixed number (p. 237) A mixed number is the sum of a whole number and a fraction.

$3\frac{11}{16}$ is a mixed number.
$3\frac{11}{16} = 3 + \frac{11}{16}$

Número mixto (p. 237) Un número mixto es la suma de un número entero y una fracción.

Mode (p. 137) The mode of a collection of data is the data item that occurs most often. There can be no mode, one mode, or more than one mode.

The mode of the collection of numbers 3, 4, 1, 3, 2, 2, 5, 3 is 3.

Moda (p. 137) La moda de un conjunto de datos es el dato que se presenta con mayor frecuencia. Puede no haber moda, una moda o más de una moda.

Monomial (p. 704) A monomial is a real number, a variable, or a product of a real number and variables with whole number exponents.

$5x$, -4, and y^3 are all monomials.

Monomio (p. 704) Un monomio es un número real, una variable o el producto de un número real y variables con exponentes que sean números enteros.

Multiple (p. 232) A multiple of a number is the product of that number and any nonzero whole number.

The multiples of 13 are 13, 26, 39, 52, and so on.

Múltiplo (p. 232) El múltiplo de un número es el producto de dicho número y cualquier otro número entero distinto de cero.

Multiple line graph (p. 100) A multiple line graph is a graph that shows more than one data set changing over time.

See *Line graph*.

Gráfica multilineal (p. 100) Una gráfica multilineal representa las variaciones de más de un conjunto de datos en el tiempo.

Multiplication Property of Equality (p. 93) If $a = b$, then $ac = bc$.

$12 = 3(4)$, so $12 \cdot 2 = 3(4) \cdot 2$

Propiedad multiplicativa de la igualdad (p. 93) Si $a = b$, entonces $ac = bc$.

Multiplication Properties of Inequality (p. 111) If $a < b$, and c is positive, then $ac < bc$. If $a > b$, and c is positive, then $ac > bc$. If you multiply each side of an inequality by a negative number, you reverse the inequality symbol.
If $a < b$, and c is negative, then $ac > bc$. If $a > b$, and c is negative, then $ac < bc$.

$3 < 4$, so $3(5) < 4(5)$
$7 > 2$, so $7(6) > 2(6)$

$6 < 9$, so $6(-2) > 9(-2)$
$7 > 5$, so $7(-3) < 5(-3)$

Propiedad multiplicativa de la desigualdad (p. 111) Si $a < b$, y c es positivo, entonces $ac < bc$. Si $a > b$, y c es positivo, entonces $ac > bc$. Si se multiplica cada lado de una desigualdad por un número negativo, se invierte la dirección del signo de la desigualdad. Si $a < b$, y c es negativo, entonces $ac > bc$. Si $a > b$, y c es negativo, entonces $ac < bc$.

Multiplicative identity (p. 67) The multiplicative identity is 1. For any number a, the product of a and 1 is a.

$a \cdot 1 = a$

Identidad multiplicativa (p. 67) La identidad multiplicativa es 1. Cuando se multiplica un número por uno, el producto es igual al número original.

Multiplicative inverse (p. 250) The multiplicative inverse of a number is its reciprocal.

The multiplicative inverse of $\frac{4}{9}$ is $\frac{9}{4}$.

Inverso multiplicativo (p. 250) El inverso multiplicativo de un número es su recíproco.

N

Negative correlation (p. 425) See *Correlation*.

Correlación negativa (p. 425) Ver *Correlation*.

Net (p. 540) A net is a pattern that can be folded to form a space figure.

EXAMPLE This net can be folded to form a cube.

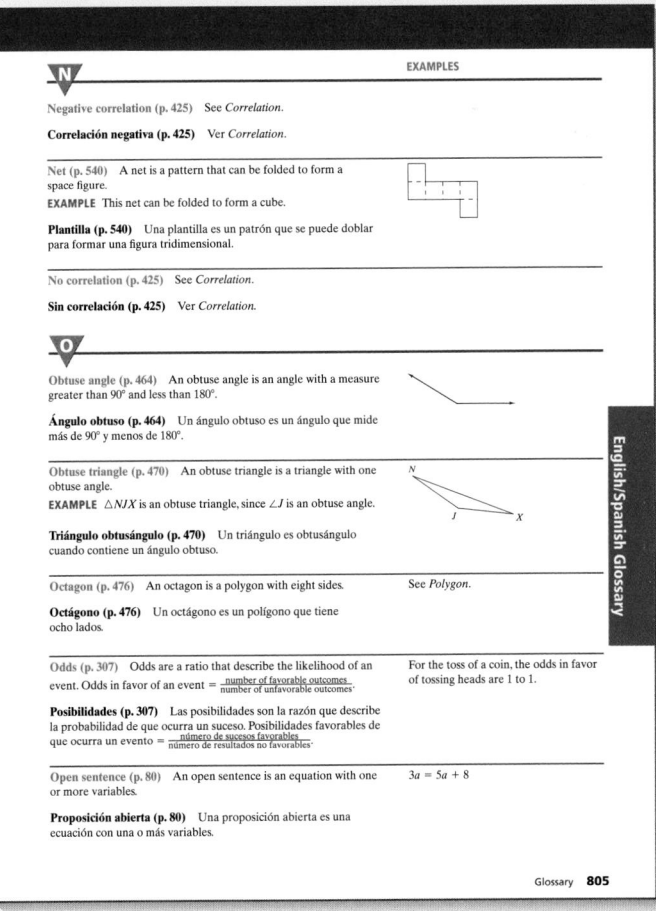

Plantilla (p. 540) Una plantilla es un patrón que se puede doblar para formar una figura tridimensional.

No correlation (p. 425) See *Correlation*.

Sin correlación (p. 425) Ver *Correlation*.

O

Obtuse angle (p. 464) An obtuse angle is an angle with a measure greater than 90° and less than 180°.

Ángulo obtuso (p. 464) Un ángulo obtuso es un ángulo que mide más de 90° y menos de 180°.

Obtuse triangle (p. 470) An obtuse triangle is a triangle with one obtuse angle.

EXAMPLE $\triangle NJX$ is an obtuse triangle, since $\angle J$ is an obtuse angle.

Triángulo obtusángulo (p. 470) Un triángulo es obtusángulo cuando contiene un ángulo obtuso.

Octagon (p. 476) An octagon is a polygon with eight sides.

See *Polygon*.

Octágono (p. 476) Un octágono es un polígono que tiene ocho lados.

Odds (p. 307) Odds are a ratio that describe the likelihood of an event. Odds in favor of an event = $\frac{\text{number of favorable outcomes}}{\text{number of unfavorable outcomes}}$.

For the toss of a coin, the odds in favor of tossing heads are 1 to 1.

Posibilidades (p. 307) Las posibilidades son la razón que describe la probabilidad de que ocurra un suceso. Posibilidades favorables de que ocurra un evento = $\frac{\text{número de sucesos favorables}}{\text{número de resultados no favorables}}$.

Open sentence (p. 80) An open sentence is an equation with one or more variables.

$3a = 5a + 8$

Proposición abierta (p. 80) Una proposición abierta es una ecuación con una o más variables.

English/Spanish Glossary

T783

Opposites (p. 19) Opposites are numbers that are the same distance from zero on the number line but in opposite directions.

−17 and 17 are opposites because they are both 17 units from zero on the number line.

Números opuestos (p. 19) Números opuestos son los números que se hallan a la misma distancia de cero en una recta, numérica pero en direcciones opuestas.

Order of operations (pp. 9, 183)
1. Work inside grouping symbols.
2. Simplify any terms with exponents.
3. Multiply and divide in order from left to right.
4. Add and subtract in order from left to right.

$2^3(7 − 4) = 2^3(3) = 8 \cdot 3 = 24$

Orden de las operaciones (pp. 9, 183)
1. Efectúa las operaciones que están dentro de los signos de agrupación.
2. Trabaja con los exponentes.
3. Multiplica y divide en orden de izquierda a derecha.
4. Suma y resta en orden de izquierda a derecha.

Ordered pair (p. 50) An ordered pair is a pair of numbers that gives the location of a point in a coordinate plane. The first number is the x-coordinate and the second number is the y-coordinate.

See *Coordinates*.

Par ordenado (p. 50) Un par ordenado es un par de números que describe la localización de un punto en un plano de coordenadas. El primer número es la coordenada x y el segundo número es la coordenada y.

Origin (p. 50) The origin is the intersection of the x-axis and the y-axis in a coordinate plane. The ordered pair $(0, 0)$ describes the origin.

See *Coordinate plane*.

Origen (p. 50) El origen el punto de intersección de los ejes de x y de y en un plano de coordenadas. El par ordenado $(0, 0)$ describe el origen.

Outcomes (p. 305) Outcomes are the possible results of an action.

Heads is an outcome of tossing a coin.

Resultados (p. 305) Se llama resultados a los posibles efectos o consecuencias de una acción.

Outlier (p. 138) An outlier is a data value that is much higher or lower than the other data values in a collection of data.

An outlier in the data 1, 1, 2, 3, 4, 4, 6, 7, 7, 52 is 52.

Extremo (p. 138) Un extremo es el valor de un conjunto de datos que es mucho mayor o menor que el resto de los datos.

P

Parabola (p. 694) A parabola is the graph of a quadratic function. It is U-shaped.
EXAMPLE This parabola is the graph of the equation $y = x^2 − 2$.

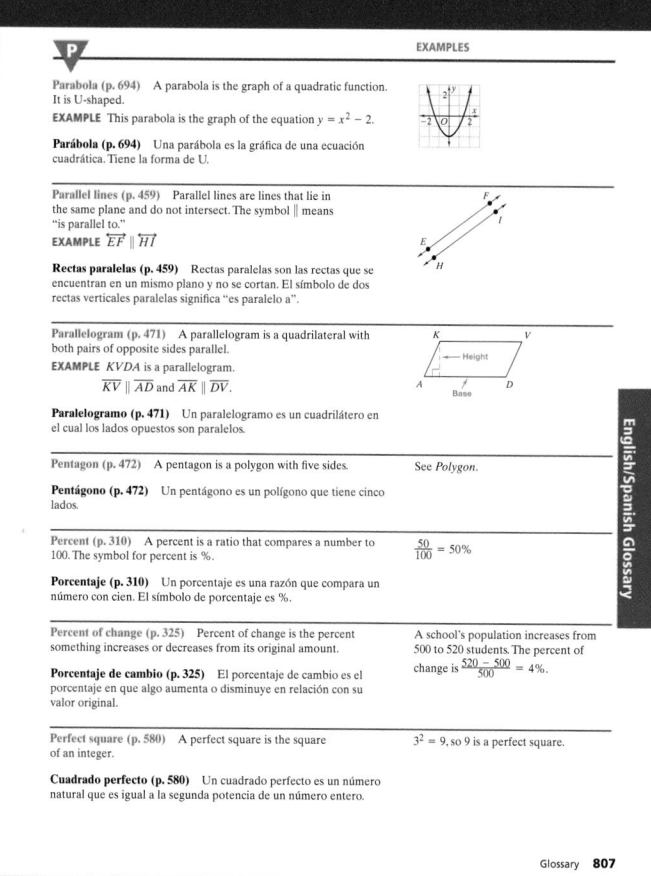

Parábola (p. 694) Una parábola es la gráfica de una ecuación cuadrática. Tiene la forma de U.

Parallel lines (p. 459) Parallel lines are lines that lie in the same plane and do not intersect. The symbol $\parallel$ means "is parallel to."
EXAMPLE $\overleftrightarrow{EF} \parallel \overleftrightarrow{HI}$

Rectas paralelas (p. 459) Rectas paralelas son las rectas que se encuentran en un mismo plano y no se cortan. El símbolo de dos rectas verticales paralelas significa "es paralelo a".

Parallelogram (p. 471) A parallelogram is a quadrilateral with both pairs of opposite sides parallel.
EXAMPLE $KVDA$ is a parallelogram.
$\overline{KV} \parallel \overline{AD}$ and $\overline{AK} \parallel \overline{DV}$.

Paralelogramo (p. 471) Un paralelogramo es un cuadrilátero en el cual los lados opuestos son paralelos.

Pentagon (p. 472) A pentagon is a polygon with five sides.

See *Polygon*.

Pentágono (p. 472) Un pentágono es un polígono que tiene cinco lados.

Percent (p. 310) A percent is a ratio that compares a number to 100. The symbol for percent is %.

$\frac{50}{100} = 50\%$

Porcentaje (p. 310) Un porcentaje es una razón que compara un número con cien. El símbolo de porcentaje es %.

Percent of change (p. 325) Percent of change is the percent something increases or decreases from its original amount.

A school's population increases from 500 to 520 students. The percent of change is $\frac{520 − 500}{500} = 4\%$.

Porcentaje de cambio (p. 325) El porcentaje de cambio es el porcentaje en que algo aumenta o disminuye en relación con su valor original.

Perfect square (p. 580) A perfect square is the square of an integer.

$3^2 = 9$, so 9 is a perfect square.

Cuadrado perfecto (p. 580) Un cuadrado perfecto es un número natural que es igual a la segunda potencia de un número entero.

Perimeter (p. 144) The perimeter of a figure is the distance around the figure. To find the perimeter of a rectangle, find the sum of the lengths of all its sides, or use the formula $P = 2\ell + 2w$.
EXAMPLE The perimeter of $ABCD$ is 12 ft.

Perímetro (p. 144) El perímetro de una figura es la suma de las longitudes de sus lados. Para hallar el perímetro de un rectángulo, halla la suma de los largos de todos los lados o usa la fórmula $P = 2\ell + 2w$.

Permutation (p. 659) A permutation is an arrangement of items in a particular order. You can use the notation $_nP_r$ to express the number of permutations of n objects chosen r at a time.

The seating plans (Judith, Ann, Adrian) and (Ann, Judith, Adrian) are two different permutations.

Permutación (p. 659) Una permutación es una colocación de objetos en un determinado orden. Se puede usar la notación $_nP_r$ para expresar el número de permutaciones de n objetos elegidos r a la vez.

Perpendicular bisector (p. 492) A perpendicular bisector is a line, segment, or ray that is perpendicular to a segment at its midpoint.
EXAMPLE $\overleftrightarrow{FG}$ is the perpendicular bisector of $\overline{DE}$.

Mediatriz (p. 492) Una mediatriz es una recta, segmento o rayo que es perpendicular a un segmento en su punto medio.

Perpendicular lines (p. 492) Perpendicular lines are lines that intersect to form right angles.

Rectas perpendiculares (p. 492) Rectas perpendiculares son aquellas que se cortan para formar ángulos rectos.

$\overleftrightarrow{DE} \perp \overleftrightarrow{RS}$

Pi (p. 486) Pi (π) is the name for the ratio of the circumference C to the diameter d of a circle.

$\pi = \frac{C}{d}$

Pi (p. 486) Pi (π) es el nombre de la razón de la circunferencia C al diámetro d de un círculo.

Plane (p. 458) A plane is a flat surface that has no thickness and extends without end in the directions of all the lines it contains.

Plano (p. 458) Un plano es una superficie plana que no tiene grosor y que se extiende indefinidamente en las direcciones de todas las líneas que contiene.

$ABCD$ or M is a plane.

Point (p. 458) A point is a location in space that has no size.

$\cdot A$

Punto (p. 458) Un punto es una posición en el espacio. No tiene dimensiones, solamente tiene localización.

A is a point.

Polygon (p. 470) A polygon is a closed plane figure with at least three sides.

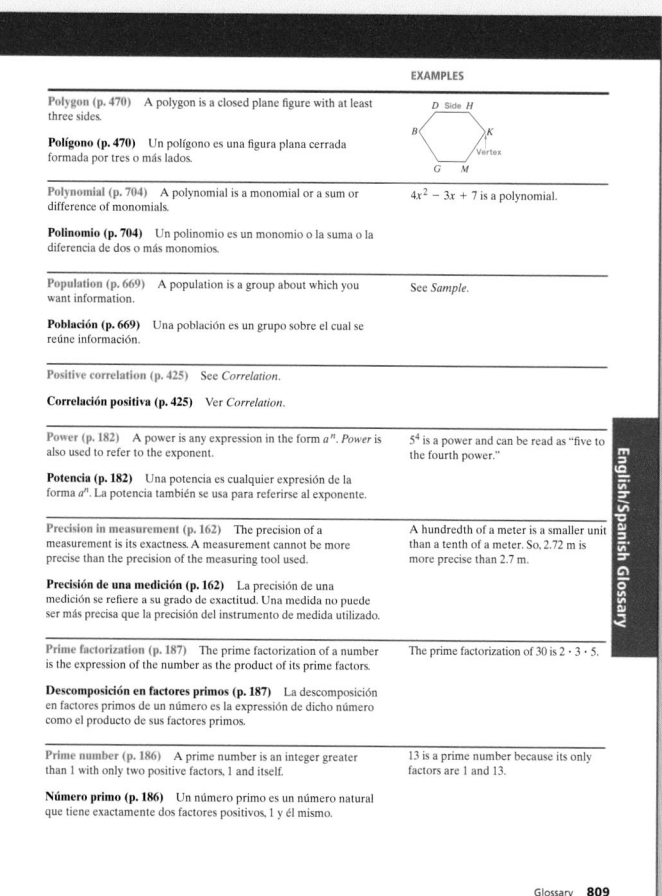

Polígono (p. 470) Un polígono es una figura plana cerrada formada por tres o más lados.

Polynomial (p. 704) A polynomial is a monomial or a sum or difference of monomials.

$4x^2 − 3x + 7$ is a polynomial.

Polinomio (p. 704) Un polinomio es un monomio o la suma o la diferencia de dos o más monomios.

Population (p. 669) A population is a group about which you want information.

See *Sample*.

Población (p. 669) Una población es un grupo sobre el cual se reúne información.

Positive correlation (p. 425) See *Correlation*.

Correlación positiva (p. 425) Ver *Correlation*.

Power (p. 182) A power is any expression in the form a^n. *Power* is also used to refer to the exponent.

5^4 is a power and can be read as "five to the fourth power."

Potencia (p. 182) Una potencia es cualquier expresión de la forma a^n. La potencia también se usa para referirse al exponente.

Precision in measurement (p. 162) The precision of a measurement is its exactness. A measurement cannot be more precise than the precision of the measuring tool used.

A hundredth of a meter is a smaller unit than a tenth of a meter. So, 2.72 m is more precise than 2.7 m.

Precisión de una medición (p. 162) La precisión de una medición se refiere a su grado de exactitud. Una medida no puede ser más precisa que la precisión del instrumento de medida utilizado.

Prime factorization (p. 187) The prime factorization of a number is the expression of the number as the product of its prime factors.

The prime factorization of 30 is $2 \cdot 3 \cdot 5$.

Descomposición en factores primos (p. 187) La descomposición en factores primos de un número es la expresión de dicho número como el producto de sus factores primos.

Prime number (p. 186) A prime number is an integer greater than 1 with only two positive factors, 1 and itself.

13 is a prime number because its only factors are 1 and 13.

Número primo (p. 186) Un número primo es un número natural que tiene exactamente dos factores positivos, 1 y él mismo.

Principal (p. 382) The principal is the initial amount of an investment or loan. | See *Simple interest.*

Capital (p. 382) El capital es el monto inicial de una inversión o préstamo.

Prism (p. 539) A prism is a space figure with two parallel and congruent polygonal faces, called bases, and lateral faces that are parallelograms. A prism is named for the shape of its base.

Prisma (p. 539) Un prisma es una figura tridimensional con dos caras poligonales congruentes y paralelas llamadas bases, y caras laterales paralelas. Un prisma recibe su nombre de acuerdo a la forma de las bases.

Probability (p. 305) The *theoretical probability* of an event E is $P(E) = \frac{\text{number of favorable outcomes}}{\text{number of possible outcomes}}$ when outcomes are equally likely. The *experimental probability* of an event E is $P(E) = \frac{\text{number of times an event occurs}}{\text{number of times experiment is done}}$. Experimental probability is based on experimental data. | The theoretical probability of spinning the number 4 is $\frac{1}{8}$.

In 100 trials, you spin the number 4 ten times. The experimental probability of spinning 4 is $\frac{10}{100}$, or $\frac{1}{10}$.

Probabilidad (p. 305) La *probabilidad teórica* de un suceso E es $P(E) = \frac{\text{número de resultados favorables}}{\text{número de resultados posibles}}$ cuando los resultados tienen la misma posibilidad de producirse. La *probabilidad experimental* de un suceso E es $P(E) = \frac{\text{número de veces que ocurre un suceso}}{\text{número de veces que se realiza un experimento}}$. La probabilidad experimental se basa en datos experimentales.

Proportion (p. 294) A proportion is an equality of two ratios. | $\frac{3}{12} = \frac{12}{48}$ is a proportion.

Proporción (p. 294) Una proporción es una igualdad de dos razones.

Pyramid (p. 539) A pyramid is a space figure with triangular faces that meet at a vertex, and a base that is a polygon. A pyramid is named for the shape of its base.

Pirámide (p. 539) Una pirámide es una figura tridimensional con caras triangulares que convergen en un vértice, y una base que es un polígono. Una pirámide recibe su nombre de acuerdo a la forma de la base.

Pythagorean Theorem (p. 584) In any right triangle, the sum of the squares of the lengths of the legs (a and b) is equal to the square of the length of the hypotenuse (c): $a^2 + b^2 = c^2$.

Teorema de Pitágoras (p. 584) Para cualquier triángulo rectángulo, la suma del cuadrado de las longitudes de los catetos (a y b) es igual al cuadrado de la longitud de la hipotenusa (c): $a^2 + b^2 = c^2$.

$3^2 + 4^2 = 5^2$

Q

Quadrants (p. 50) Quadrants are the four regions determined by the x- and y-axes of the coordinate plane. | See *Coordinate plane.*

Cuadrante (p. 50) El eje de x y el eje de y dividen el plano de coordenadas en cuatro regiones llamadas cuadrantes.

Quadratic function (p. 694) A quadratic function is a function based on squaring the input variable. The graph of a quadratic function is a parabola. | See *Parabola.*

Función cuadrática (p. 694) Una función cuadrática es la función que tiene una variable elevada a la segunda potencia. La gráfica de una función cuadrática es una parábola.

Quadrilateral (p. 471) A quadrilateral is a polygon with four sides. | See *Polygon.*

Cuadrilátero (p. 471) Un cuadrilátero es un polígono con cuatro lados.

Quartiles (p. 635) Quartiles are numbers that divide a data set into four equal parts. | See *Box-and-whisker plot.*

Cuartiles (p. 635) Los cuartiles son números que dividen un conjunto de datos en cuatro partes iguales.

R

Radius (plural is radii) (p. 486) A radius of a circle is a segment that has one endpoint at the center of the circle and the other endpoint on the circle.
EXAMPLE $\overline{OA}$ is a radius of circle O.

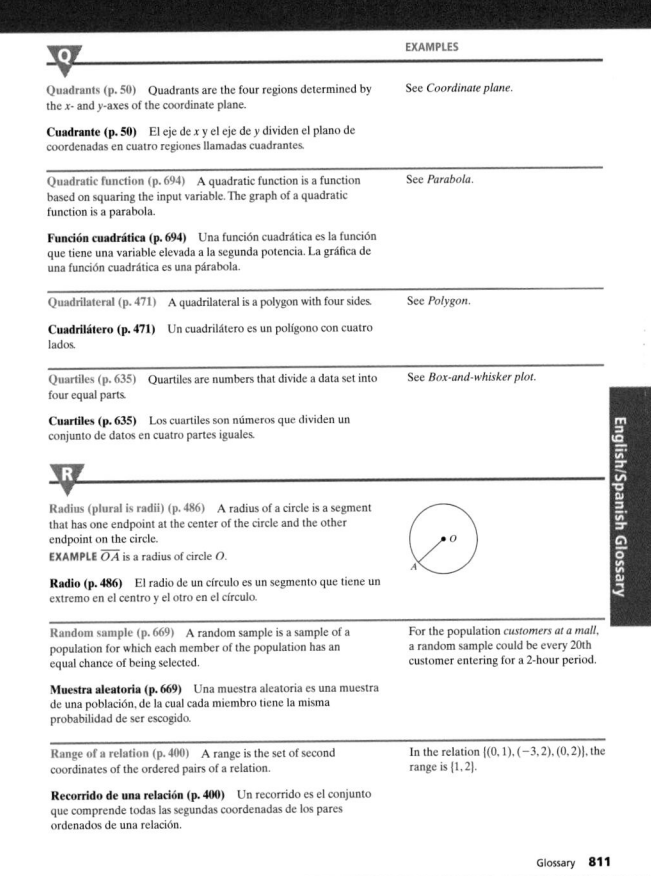

Radio (p. 486) El radio de un círculo es un segmento que tiene un extremo en el centro y el otro en el círculo.

Random sample (p. 669) A random sample is a sample of a population for which each member of the population has an equal chance of being selected. | For the population *customers at a mall*, a random sample could be every 20th customer entering for a 2-hour period.

Muestra aleatoria (p. 669) Una muestra aleatoria es una muestra de una población, de la cual cada miembro tiene la misma probabilidad de ser escogido.

Range of a relation (p. 400) A range is the set of second coordinates of the ordered pairs of a relation. | In the relation $\{(0,1),(-3,2),(0,2)\}$, the range is $\{1,2\}$.

Recorrido de una relación (p. 400) Un recorrido es el conjunto que comprende todas las segundas coordenadas de los pares ordenados de una relación.

Range of a set of data (p. 631) The range is the difference between the greatest and least values in a set of data. | The range of the data 7 9 15 3 18 2 16 14 14 20 is $20 - 2 = 18$.

Amplitud de un conjunto de datos (p. 631) La amplitud es la diferencia entre los valores mayor y menor de un conjunto de datos.

Rate (p. 289) A rate is a ratio that compares quantities measured in different units. | A student typed 1,100 words in 50 minutes for a typing rate of 1,100 words per 50 minutes, or 22 words/minute.

Tasa (p. 289) Una tasa es una razón que compara dos cantidades medidas en unidades diferentes.

Ratio (p. 288) A ratio is a comparison of two quantities by division. | There are three ways to write a ratio: 72 to 100, 72 : 100, and $\frac{72}{100}$.

Razón (p. 288) Una razón es la comparación de dos números mediante una división.

Rational number (p. 201) A rational number is any number you can write as a quotient of two integers $\frac{a}{b}$, where b is not zero. | $\frac{3}{5}, -8, 8.7, 0.333\ldots, -5\frac{3}{11}, 0$, and $\frac{17}{4}$ are rational numbers.

Número racional (p. 201) Un número racional es cualquier número que puede escribirse como el cociente de dos enteros $\frac{a}{b}$, donde b es distinto de cero.

Ray (p. 458) A ray is a part of a line. It has exactly one endpoint. Its endpoint is named first. | $\overrightarrow{SW}$ represents a ray.

Rayo (p. 458) Un rayo es una parte de una recta. Tiene exactamente un extremo. El extremo se nombre primero.

Real number (p. 581) A real number is a rational number or an irrational number. | $3, -5.25, 3.141592653\ldots$, and $\frac{7}{8}$ are real numbers.

Números reales (p. 581) Un número real es un número racional o un número irracional.

Reciprocal (p. 250) Reciprocals are two numbers with a product of 1. | $\frac{4}{9}$ and $\frac{9}{4}$ are reciprocals. $\frac{4}{9} \cdot \frac{9}{4} = 1$.

Recíprocos (p. 250) Dos números son recíprocos cuando su producto es 1.

Rectangle (p. 471) A rectangle is a parallelogram with four right angles.
EXAMPLE *RSWH* is a rectangle.

Rectángulo (p. 471) Un rectángulo es un paralelogramo con cuatro ángulos rectos.

Reflection (p. 504) A reflection is a transformation that flips a figure over a line of reflection.
EXAMPLE $K'L'M'N'$ is the reflection of *KLMN* across the y-axis. The y-axis is the line of reflection.

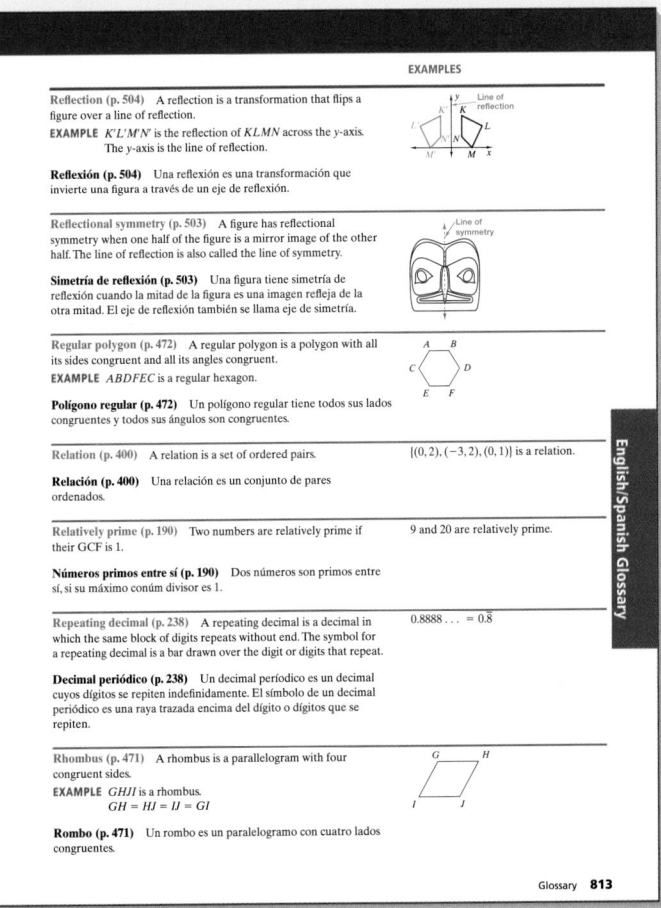

Reflexión (p. 504) Una reflexión es una transformación que invierte una figura a través de un eje de reflexión.

Reflectional symmetry (p. 503) A figure has reflectional symmetry when one half of the figure is a mirror image of the other half. The line of reflection is also called the line of symmetry.

Simetría de reflexión (p. 503) Una figura tiene simetría de reflexión cuando la mitad de la figura es una imagen refleja de la otra mitad. El eje de reflexión también se llama eje de simetría.

Regular polygon (p. 472) A regular polygon is a polygon with all its sides congruent and all its angles congruent.
EXAMPLE *ABDFEC* is a regular hexagon.

Polígono regular (p. 472) Un polígono regular tiene todos sus lados congruentes y todos sus ángulos son congruentes.

Relation (p. 400) A relation is a set of ordered pairs. | $\{(0,2),(-3,2),(0,1)\}$ is a relation.

Relación (p. 400) Una relación es un conjunto de pares ordenados.

Relatively prime (p. 190) Two numbers are relatively prime if their GCF is 1. | 9 and 20 are relatively prime.

Números primos entre sí (p. 190) Dos números son primos entre sí, si su máximo común divisor es 1.

Repeating decimal (p. 238) A repeating decimal is a decimal in which the same block of digits repeats without end. The symbol for a repeating decimal is a bar drawn over the digit or digits that repeat. | $0.8888\ldots = 0.\overline{8}$

Decimal periódico (p. 238) Un decimal periódico es un decimal cuyos dígitos se repiten indefinidamente. El símbolo de un decimal periódico es una raya trazada encima del dígito o dígitos que se repiten.

Rhombus (p. 471) A rhombus is a parallelogram with four congruent sides.
EXAMPLE *GHJI* is a rhombus. $GH = HJ = IJ = GI$

Rombo (p. 471) Un rombo es un paralelogramo con cuatro lados congruentes.

English/Spanish Glossary

T785

Right angle (p. 464)   A right angle is an angle with a measure of 90°.
EXAMPLE ∠CDE is a right angle.

Ángulo recto (p. 464)   Un ángulo recto es un ángulo que mide 90°.

Right triangle (p. 470)   A right triangle is a triangle with one right angle.
EXAMPLE △ABC is a right triangle, since ∠B is a right angle.

Triángulo rectángulo (p. 470)   Un triángulo rectángulo es aquél que posee un ángulo recto.

Rotation (p. 507)   A rotation is a transformation that turns a figure about a fixed point, called the center of rotation. The angle measure of the rotation is the angle of rotation.
EXAMPLE The image of △PQR after a 90° rotation is △PQ'R'. Point P is the center of rotation.

Rotación (p. 507)   Una rotación es una transformación en la cual una figura se mueve sin deformación alrededor de un punto fijo, llamado centro de rotación. La medida del ángulo de la rotación es el ángulo de rotación.

Rotational symmetry (p. 508)   A figure has rotational symmetry if the figure can be rotated 180° or less and match the original figure.

Simetría rotacional (p. 508)   Una figura tiene simetría rotacional si la figura se puede rotar 180° o menos y coincide exactamente con la figura original.

This figure has 60° rotational symmetry.

S

Sample (p. 669)   A sample is a part of a population.

Muestra (p. 669)   Una muestra es una parte de una población.

A class of 25 students is a sample of the population of a large school.

Sample space (p. 650)   A sample space is all possible outcomes of an experiment.

Espacio muestral (p. 650)   Un espacio muestral es el conjunto de todos los resultados posibles de un experimento.

The sample space for tossing two coins is HH, HT, TH, TT.

Scale drawing (p. 300)   A scale drawing is an enlarged or reduced drawing that is similar to an actual object or place.

Dibujo a escala (p. 300)   Un dibujo a escala es un dibujo aumentado o reducido que es similar al objeto o lugar real.

A map is a scale drawing.

Scalene triangle (p. 470)   A scalene triangle is a triangle with no congruent sides.
EXAMPLE △NPO is a scalene triangle.

Triángulo escaleno (p. 470)   Un triángulo escaleno es un triángulo que no tiene lados congruentes.

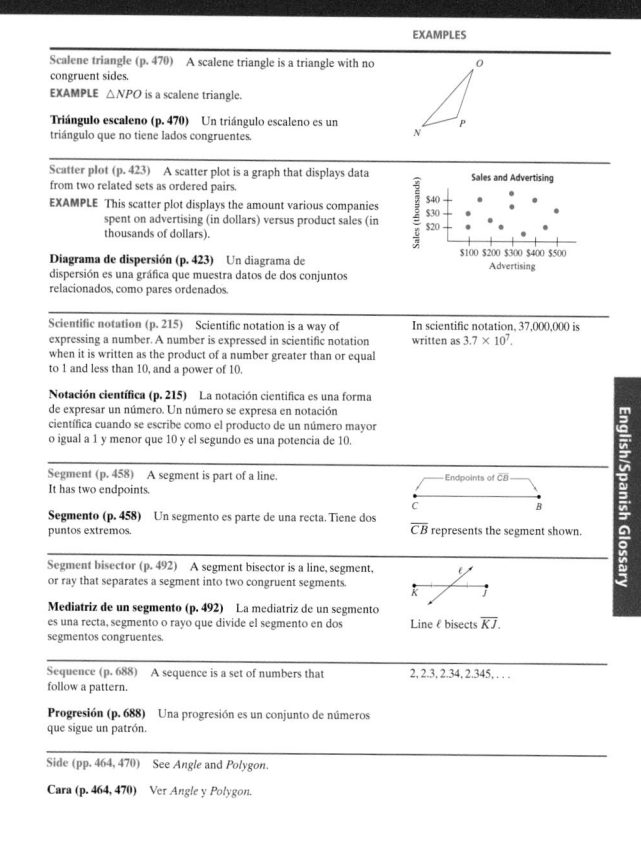

Scatter plot (p. 423)   A scatter plot is a graph that displays data from two related sets as ordered pairs.
EXAMPLE This scatter plot displays the amount various companies spent on advertising (in dollars) versus product sales (in thousands of dollars).

Diagrama de dispersión (p. 423)   Un diagrama de dispersión es una gráfica que muestra datos de dos conjuntos relacionados, como pares ordenados.

Scientific notation (p. 215)   Scientific notation is a way of expressing a number. A number is expressed in scientific notation when it is written as the product of a number greater than or equal to 1 and less than 10, and a power of 10.

Notación científica (p. 215)   La notación científica es una forma de expresar un número. Un número se expresa en notación científica cuando se escribe como el producto de un número mayor o igual a 1 y menor que 10 y el segundo es una potencia de 10.

In scientific notation, 37,000,000 is written as 3.7×10^7.

Segment (p. 458)   A segment is part of a line. It has two endpoints.

Segmento (p. 458)   Un segmento es parte de una recta. Tiene dos puntos extremos.

$\overline{CB}$ represents the segment shown.

Segment bisector (p. 492)   A segment bisector is a line, segment, or ray that separates a segment into two congruent segments.

Mediatriz de un segmento (p. 492)   La mediatriz de un segmento es una recta, segmento o rayo que divide el segmento en dos segmentos congruentes.

Line ℓ bisects $\overline{KJ}$.

Sequence (p. 688)   A sequence is a set of numbers that follow a pattern.

Progresión (p. 688)   Una progresión es un conjunto de números que sigue un patrón.

2, 2.3, 2.34, 2.345, ...

Side (pp. 464, 470)   See Angle and Polygon.

Cara (p. 464, 470)   Ver Angle y Polygon.

English/Spanish Glossary

Significant digits (p. 162)   Significant digits are the digits that represent an actual measurement.

Dígitos significativos (p. 162)   Dígitos significativos son los dígitos que representan una medida real.

Similar figures (p. 299)   Similar figures are figures with corresponding angles that have equal measures and corresponding sides that have proportional lengths. The symbol ~ means "is similar to."
EXAMPLE △ABC ~ △RTS

Figuras semejantes (p. 299)   Figuras semejantes son figuras con ángulos correspondientes que tienen la misma medida y lados correspondientes que tienen longitudes proporcionales. El símbolo ~ significa "es semejante a."

Simple interest (p. 382)   Simple interest is interest paid only on the principal, the initial amount of money invested or borrowed. The formula for simple interest is I = prt, where I is the interest, p is the principal, r is the interest rate per year, and t is the time in years.

Interés simple (p. 382)   Interés simple es aquel que se paga sólo por el capital, el monto inicial de dinero que se invierte o se pide prestado. La fórmula de interés simple es I = prt, donde I es el interés, p es el capital, r es la tasa de interés anual y t es el tiempo en años.

The simple interest on $1,000 at 5% for 2 years is $1,000 · 0.05 · 2, or $100.

Simplest form of a fraction (p. 192)   The simplest form of a fraction is the form in which the only common factor of the numerator and denominator is 1.

Mínima expresión de una fracción (p. 192)   La mínima expresión de una fracción es la expresión en que el único factor común del numerador y del denominador es 1.

The simplest form of the fraction $\frac{15}{20}$ is $\frac{3}{4}$.

Simplify a variable expression (p. 76)   To simplify a variable expression is to replace it with an equivalent expression having as few terms as possible.

Simplificar una expresión variable (p. 76)   Se simplifica una expresión variable al reemplazarla con una expresión equivalente que tiene el menor número posible de términos.

$2x + 5 + 4x$ simplifies to $6x + 5$.

Simulation (p. 665)   A simulation is a model used to find experimental probability.

Simulación (p. 665)   Una simulación es un modelo que se usa para hallar la probabilidad experimental.

Your baseball team has an equal chance of winning or losing each of its next five games. You can toss a coin to simulate the outcomes of the next five games.

Sine (p. 608)   See Trigonometric ratios.

Razón del seno (p. 608)   Ver Trigonometric ratios.

Skew lines (p. 459)   Skew lines are lines in space that do not intersect and are not parallel. They do not lie in the same plane. Skew segments must be parts of skew lines.

Rectas cruzadas (p. 459)   Las rectas cruzadas son rectas en el espacio, que no se intersecan y que no son paralelas. No están en el mismo plano. Los segmentos cruzados son partes de rectas cruzadas.

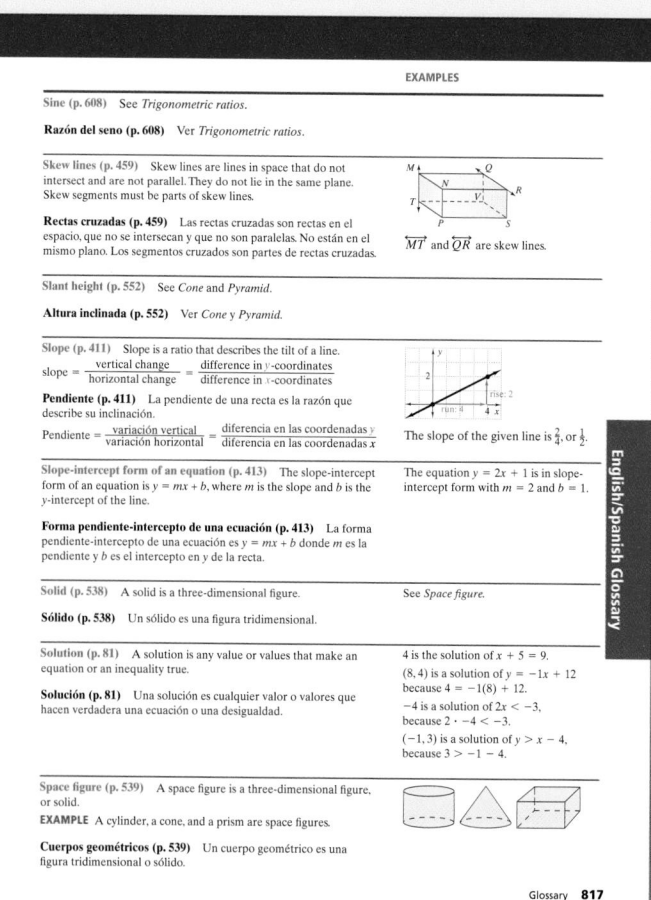

$\overline{MT}$ and $\overline{QR}$ are skew lines.

Slant height (p. 552)   See Cone and Pyramid.

Altura inclinada (p. 552)   Ver Cone y Pyramid.

Slope (p. 411)   Slope is a ratio that describes the tilt of a line.
$$\text{slope} = \frac{\text{vertical change}}{\text{horizontal change}} = \frac{\text{difference in } y\text{-coordinates}}{\text{difference in } x\text{-coordinates}}$$

Pendiente (p. 411)   La pendiente de una recta es la razón que describe su inclinación.
$$\text{Pendiente} = \frac{\text{variación vertical}}{\text{variación horizontal}} = \frac{\text{diferencia en las coordenadas } y}{\text{diferencia en las coordenadas } x}$$

The slope of the given line is $\frac{2}{4}$, or $\frac{1}{2}$.

Slope-intercept form of an equation (p. 413)   The slope-intercept form of an equation is y = mx + b, where m is the slope and b is the y-intercept of the line.

Forma pendiente-intercepto de una ecuación (p. 413)   La forma pendiente-intercepto de una ecuación es y = mx + b donde m es la pendiente y b es el intercepto en y de la recta.

The equation $y = 2x + 1$ is in slope-intercept form with m = 2 and b = 1.

Solid (p. 538)   A solid is a three-dimensional figure.

Sólido (p. 538)   Un sólido es una figura tridimensional.

See Space figure.

Solution (p. 81)   A solution is any value or values that make an equation or an inequality true.

Solución (p. 81)   Una solución es cualquier valor o valores que hacen verdadera una ecuación o una desigualdad.

4 is the solution of $x + 5 = 9$.
(8, 4) is a solution of $y = -1x + 12$ because $4 = -1(8) + 12$.
−4 is a solution of $2x < -3$, because $2 \cdot -4 < -3$.
(−1, 3) is a solution of $y > x - 4$, because $3 > -1 - 4$.

Space figure (p. 539)   A space figure is a three-dimensional figure, or solid.
EXAMPLE A cylinder, a cone, and a prism are space figures.

Cuerpos geométricos (p. 539)   Un cuerpo geométrico es una figura tridimensional o sólido.

English/Spanish Glossary

Sphere (p. 539) A sphere is the set of points in space that are a given distance from a point, called the center.

Esfera (p. 539) Una esfera es el conjunto de todos los puntos del espacio que se hallan a una misma distancia de un punto dado llamado el centro.

Square (p. 471) A square is a parallelogram with four right angles and four congruent sides.
EXAMPLE $QRTS$ is a square.
$\angle Q, \angle R, \angle T,$ and $\angle S$ are right angles.
$QR = RT = ST = SQ$

Cuadrado (p. 471) Un cuadrado es un paralelogramo con cuatro ángulos rectos y cuatro lados congruentes.

Square root (p. 580) The square root of a given number is a number that when multiplied by itself equals the given number. The symbol for the nonnegative square root of a number is $\sqrt{}$.

$\sqrt{25} = 5$ because $5^2 = 25$.

Raíz cuadrada (p. 580) La raíz cuadrada de un número dado es un número que cuando es multiplicado por sí mismo, es igual al número dado.

Standard form (p. 708) Standard form of a polynomial is the form in which the terms are in order of decreasing degree.

$3y^2 + 8y - 2$ is in standard form.

Forma general de un polinomio (p. 708) Un polinomio está en forma general cuando sus términos están en orden descendente.

Standard notation (p. 216) Standard notation is the usual form for representing a number.

The standard notation of 8.9×10^5 is 890,000.

Notación normal (p. 216) La notación normal es la forma común de representar un número.

Stem-and-leaf plot (p. 640) A stem-and-leaf plot is a display that shows numeric data arranged in order. The leaf of each data item is its last digit. The stem is its other digits. The stems are stacked in order and the leaves are arranged in order to the side of each stem.
EXAMPLE This stem-and-leaf plot displays recorded times in a race. The stem records the whole number of seconds. The leaf represents tenths of a second. So, 27 | 7 represents 27.7 seconds.

Stem | Leaf
27 | 7
28 | 5 6 8
29 | 6 9
30 | 8

27 | 7 means 27.7.

Diagrama de tallo y hojas (p. 640) Un diagrama de tallo y hojas es una representación que muestra datos numéricos en orden de valor relativo. La hoja de cada dato es su último dígito. El tallo son sus otros dígitos. Los tallos están organizados en columnas ordenadas y las hojas están organizadas en orden al lado de cada tallo.

Straight angle (p. 464) A straight angle is an angle with a measure of 180°.

Ángulo llano (p. 464) Un ángulo llano es un ángulo cuya medida es 180°.

Subtraction Property of Equality (p. 86) If $a = b$, then $a - c = b - c$.

$10 = 2(5)$, so $10 - 5 = 2(5) - 5$

Propiedad sustrativa de la igualdad (p. 86) Si $a = b$, entonces $a - c = b - c$.

Subtraction Property of Inequality (p. 106) If $a > b$, then $a - c > b - c$. If $a < b$, then $a - c < b - c$.

$7 > 4$, so $7 - 3 > 4 - 3$
$6 < 9$, so $6 - 2 < 9 - 2$

Propiedad sustractiva de la desigualdad (p. 106) Si $a > b$, entonces $a - c > b - c$. Si $a < b$, entonces $a - c < b - c$.

Supplementary angles (p. 465) Supplementary angles are two angles whose measures add to 180°.

$\angle A$ and $\angle D$ are supplementary.

Ángulos suplementarios (p. 465) Dos ángulos son suplementarios si la suma de sus medidas es 180°.

Surface area (p. 545) Surface area is the sum of the areas of the base(s) and lateral faces of a space figure.
EXAMPLE The surface area of the prism is the sum of the areas of its faces.
$(12 + 12 + 12 + 12 + 9 + 9)$ in.$^2 = 66$ in.^{2}

Each square = 1 in.^{2}

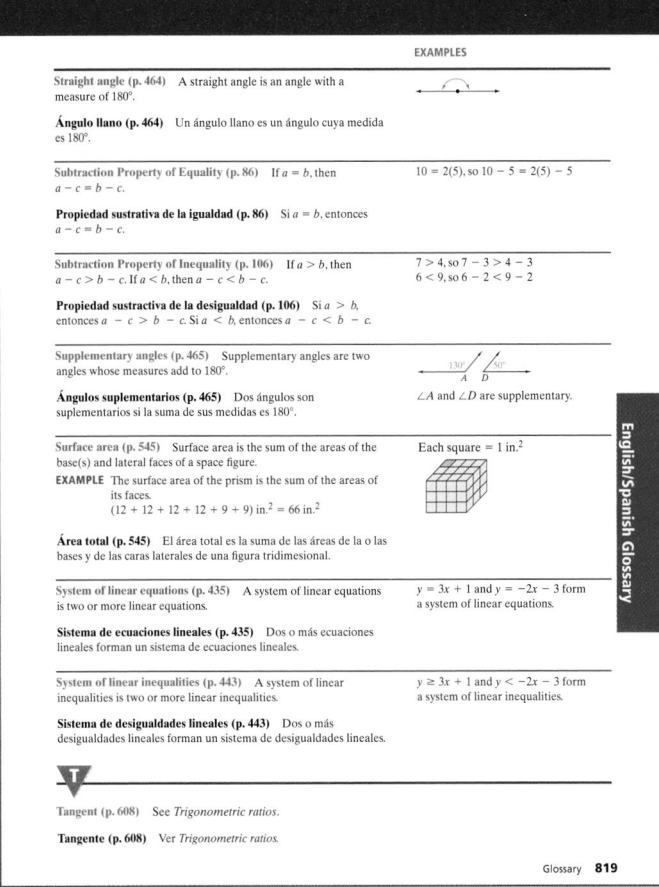

Área total (p. 545) El área total es la suma de las áreas de la o las bases y de las caras laterales de una figura tridimesional.

System of linear equations (p. 435) A system of linear equations is two or more linear equations.

$y = 3x + 1$ and $y = -2x - 3$ form a system of linear equations.

Sistema de ecuaciones lineales (p. 435) Dos o más ecuaciones lineales forman un sistema de ecuaciones lineales.

System of linear inequalities (p. 443) A system of linear inequalities is two or more linear inequalities.

$y \geq 3x + 1$ and $y < -2x - 3$ form a system of linear inequalities.

Sistema de desigualdades lineales (p. 443) Dos o más desigualdades lineales forman un sistema de desigualdades lineales.

Tangent (p. 608) See *Trigonometric ratios*.

Tangente (p. 608) Ver *Trigonometric ratios*.

Term of an expression (p. 76) A term is a number, a variable, or the product of a number and variable(s).

The expression $7x + 12 + (-9y)$ has three terms: $7x$, 12, and $-9y$.

Término de una expresión (p. 76) Un término es un número, una variable o el producto de un número y una o mas variables.

Term of a sequence (p. 688) A term of a sequence is any number in the sequence.
EXAMPLE In this sequence, 1 is the first term, 2 is the second term, 3 is the third term, and 4 is the fourth term.

$1, 2, 3, 4, \ldots$

Término de una progresión (p. 688) Un término de una progresión es cualquier número de la progresión.

Terminating decimal (p. 237) A terminating decimal is a decimal with a finite number of digits.

Both 0.6 and 0.7265 are terminating decimals.

Decimal finito (p. 237) Un decimal finito es un decimal que tiene un número finito de dígitos.

Tessellation (p. 511) A tessellation is a repeated pattern of figures that completely covers a plane without gaps or overlaps.

Teselación (p. 511) Una teselación es un patrón repetido de figuras que cubre completamente un plano sin dejar espacios ni sobreponerse.

This tessellation consists of small squares and large squares.

Theoretical Probability (p. 650) See *Probability*.

Probabilidad teórica (p. 650) Ver *Probability*.

Three-dimensional figure (p. 539) A three-dimensional figure is a figure that does not lie in a plane.

See *Space figure*.

Figura tridimensional (p. 539) Una figura tridimensional es una figura que no está situada en un plano.

Transformation (p. 497) A transformation is a change of position or size of a figure. Four types of transformations are translations, reflections, rotations, and dilations.
EXAMPLE $K'L'M'N'$ is a reflection of $KLMN$ across the y-axis.

Transformación (p. 497) Una transformación es un cambio de posición o tamaño de una figura. Una transformación puede ser una traslacion, una reflexión, una rotación o una dilatación.

Translation (p. 497) A translation is a transformation that moves points the same distance and in the same direction.
EXAMPLE $A'B'C'D'$ is the translation image of $ABCD$.

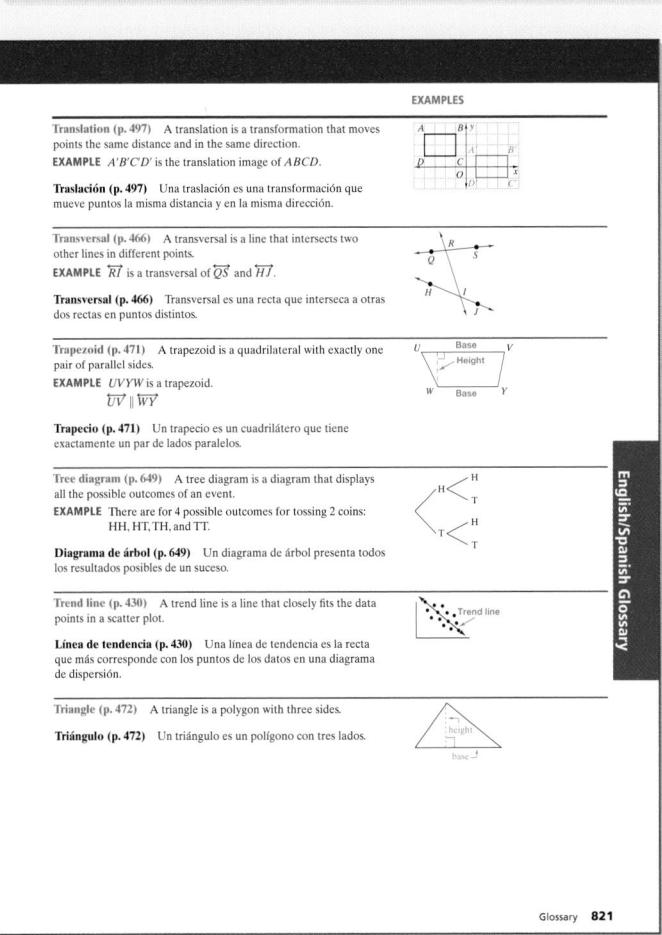

Traslación (p. 497) Una traslación es una transformación que mueve puntos la misma distancia y en la misma dirección.

Transversal (p. 466) A transversal is a line that intersects two other lines in different points.
EXAMPLE $\overleftrightarrow{RI}$ is a transversal of $\overleftrightarrow{QS}$ and $\overleftrightarrow{HJ}$.

Transversal (p. 466) Transversal es una recta que interseca a otras dos rectas en puntos distintos.

Trapezoid (p. 471) A trapezoid is a quadrilateral with exactly one pair of parallel sides.
EXAMPLE $UVYW$ is a trapezoid.
$\overline{UV} \parallel \overline{WY}$

Trapecio (p. 471) Un trapecio es un cuadrilátero que tiene exactamente un par de lados paralelos.

Tree diagram (p. 649) A tree diagram is a diagram that displays all the possible outcomes of an event.
EXAMPLE There are for 4 possible outcomes for tossing 2 coins: HH, HT, TH, and TT.

Diagrama de árbol (p. 649) Un diagrama de árbol presenta todos los resultados posibles de un suceso.

Trend line (p. 430) A trend line is a line that closely fits the data points in a scatter plot.

Línea de tendencia (p. 430) Una línea de tendencia es la recta que más corresponde con los puntos de los datos en una diagrama de dispersión.

Triangle (p. 472) A triangle is a polygon with three sides.

Triángulo (p. 472) Un triángulo es un polígono con tres lados.

Trigonometric ratios (p. 608) Trigonometric ratios are the sine, cosine, and tangent. In $\triangle ABC$ with right $\angle C$,

sine $\angle A = \dfrac{\text{length of leg opposite } \angle A}{\text{length of hypotenuse}} = \dfrac{a}{c}$,

cosine $\angle A = \dfrac{\text{length of leg adjacent to } \angle A}{\text{length of hypotenuse}} = \dfrac{b}{c}$,

tangent $\angle A = \dfrac{\text{length of leg opposite } \angle A}{\text{length of leg adjacent to } \angle A} = \dfrac{a}{b}$.

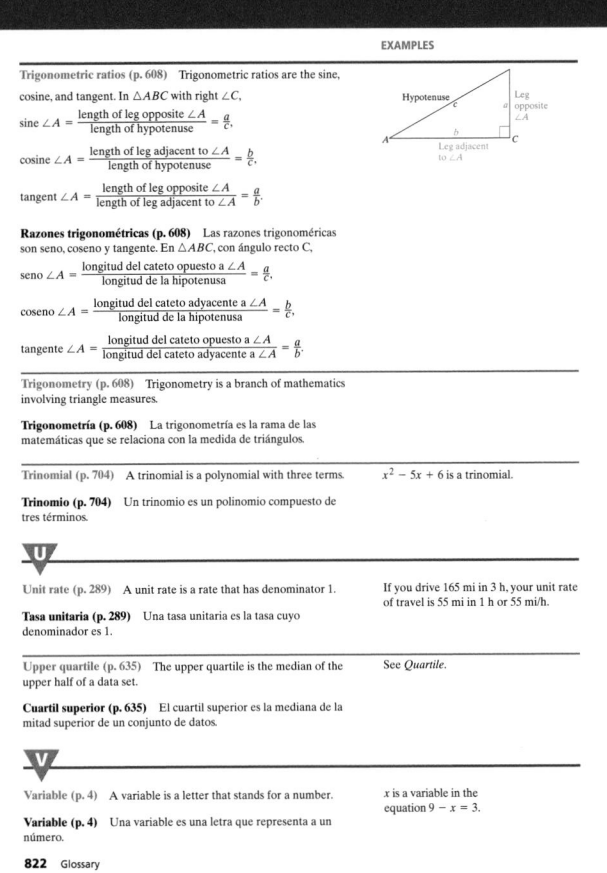

Razones trigonométricas (p. 608) Las razones trigonoméricas son seno, coseno y tangente. En $\triangle ABC$, con ángulo recto C,

seno $\angle A = \dfrac{\text{longitud del cateto opuesto a } \angle A}{\text{longitud de la hipotenusa}} = \dfrac{a}{c}$,

coseno $\angle A = \dfrac{\text{longitud del cateto adyacente a } \angle A}{\text{longitud de la hipotenusa}} = \dfrac{b}{c}$,

tangente $\angle A = \dfrac{\text{longitud del cateto opuesto a } \angle A}{\text{longitud del cateto adyacente a } \angle A} = \dfrac{a}{b}$.

Trigonometry (p. 608) Trigonometry is a branch of mathematics involving triangle measures.

Trigonometría (p. 608) La trigonometría es la rama de las matemáticas que se relaciona con la medida de triángulos.

Trinomial (p. 704) A trinomial is a polynomial with three terms.

Trinomio (p. 704) Un trinomio es un polinomio compuesto de tres términos.

$x^2 - 5x + 6$ is a trinomial.

U

Unit rate (p. 289) A unit rate is a rate that has denominator 1.

Tasa unitaria (p. 289) Una tasa unitaria es la tasa cuyo denominador es 1.

If you drive 165 mi in 3 h, your unit rate of travel is 55 mi in 1 h or 55 mi/h.

Upper quartile (p. 635) The upper quartile is the median of the upper half of a data set.

Cuartil superior (p. 635) El cuartil superior es la mediana de la mitad superior de un conjunto de datos.

See *Quartile*.

V

Variable (p. 4) A variable is a letter that stands for a number.

Variable (p. 4) Una variable es una letra que representa a un número.

x is a variable in the equation $9 - x = 3$.

Variable expression (p. 4) A variable expression is a mathematical phrase that uses variables, numbers, and operation symbols.

Expresión algebraica (p. 4) Una expresión algebraica es una expresión en la que se usan variables, números y símbolos de operaciones.

$7 + x, 2y - 4, \frac{3}{5}g,$ and $\frac{7}{k}$ are variable expressions.

Venn diagram (p. 191) A Venn diagram is a diagram that illustrates the relationships among collections of objects or numbers. The intersection, or overlap, of two circles indicates what is common to both collections.
EXAMPLE The Venn diagram shows the activities of 67 music students.

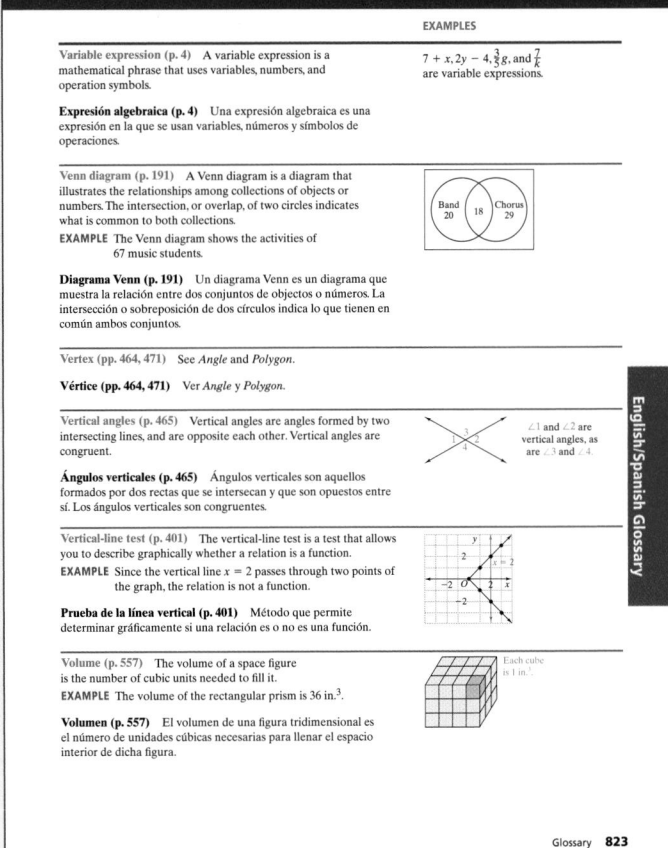

Diagrama Venn (p. 191) Un diagrama Venn es un diagrama que muestra la relación entre dos conjuntos de objetos o números. La intersección o sobreposición de dos círculos indica lo que tienen en común ambos conjuntos.

Vertex (pp. 464, 471) See *Angle* and *Polygon*.

Vértice (pp. 464, 471) Ver *Angle* y *Polygon*.

Vertical angles (p. 465) Vertical angles are angles formed by two intersecting lines, and are opposite each other. Vertical angles are congruent.

$\angle 1$ and $\angle 2$ are vertical angles, as are $\angle 3$ and $\angle 4$.

Ángulos verticales (p. 465) Ángulos verticales son aquellos formados por dos rectas que se intersecan y que son opuestos entre sí. Los ángulos verticales son congruentes.

Vertical-line test (p. 401) The vertical-line test is a test that allows you to describe graphically whether a relation is a function.
EXAMPLE Since the vertical line $x = 2$ passes through two points of the graph, the relation is not a function.

Prueba de la línea vertical (p. 401) Método que permite determinar gráficamente si una relación es o no es una función.

Volume (p. 557) The volume of a space figure is the number of cubic units needed to fill it.
EXAMPLE The volume of the rectangular prism is 36 in.^{3}.

Each cube is 1 in.^{3}.

Volumen (p. 557) El volumen de una figura tridimensional es el número de unidades cúbicas necesarias para llenar el espacio interior de dicha figura.

English/Spanish Glossary

X

x-axis (p. 50) The *x*-axis is the horizontal number line that, together with the *y*-axis, establishes the coordinate plane.

See *Coordinate plane*.

Eje de *x* (p. 50) El eje de *x* es la recta numérica horizontal que, junto al eje de *y*, forma el plano de coordenadas.

x-coordinate (p. 50) The *x*-coordinate is the horizontal position of a point in the coordinate plane.

See *Coordinates*.

Coordenada *x* (p. 50) La coordenada *x* muestra la ubicación horizontal de un punto en el plano de coordenadas.

x-intercept (p. 409) The *x*-intercept of a line is the *x*-coordinate of the point where the line crosses the *x*-axis.
EXAMPLE The *x*-intercept is 2. The *y*-intercept is −3.

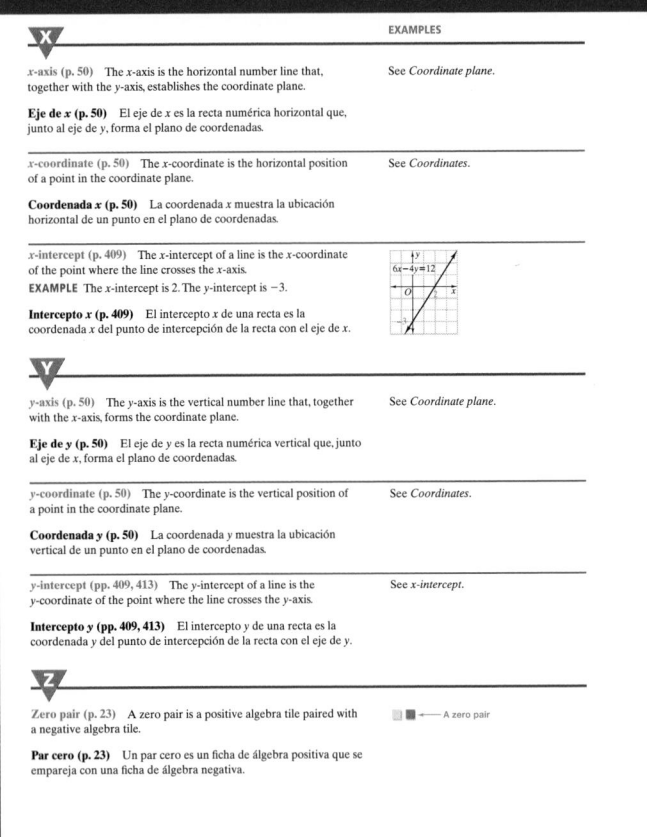

Intercepto *x* (p. 409) El intercepto *x* de una recta es la coordenada *x* del punto de intercepción de la recta con el eje de *x*.

Y

y-axis (p. 50) The *y*-axis is the vertical number line that, together with the *x*-axis, forms the coordinate plane.

See *Coordinate plane*.

Eje de *y* (p. 50) El eje de *y* es la recta numérica vertical que, junto al eje de *x*, forma el plano de coordenadas.

y-coordinate (p. 50) The *y*-coordinate is the vertical position of a point in the coordinate plane.

See *Coordinates*.

Coordenada *y* (p. 50) La coordenada *y* muestra la ubicación vertical de un punto en el plano de coordenadas.

y-intercept (pp. 409, 413) The *y*-intercept of a line is the *y*-coordinate of the point where the line crosses the *y*-axis.

See *x-intercept*.

Intercepto *y* (pp. 409, 413) El intercepto *y* de una recta es la coordenada *y* del punto de intercepción de la recta con el eje de *y*.

Z

Zero pair (p. 23) A zero pair is a positive algebra tile paired with a negative algebra tile.

← A zero pair

Par cero (p. 23) Un par cero es una ficha de álgebra positiva que se empareja con una ficha de álgebra negativa.

Answers to Instant Check System™

Chapter 1

Diagnosing Readiness p. 2

1. 1 **2.** 11 **3.** 11 **4.** 19 **5.** 13 **6.** 40 **7.** 17 **8.** 43 **9.** 176 **10.** 28 **11.** 166 **12.** 75 **13.** > **14.** > **15.** < **16.** < **17.** < **18.** = **19.** 12 **20.** 30 **21.** 28 **22.** 5 **23.** 96 **24.** 5 **25.** 200 **26.** 80 **27.** 31 **28.** 13 **29.** 480 **30.** 12 **31.** 1 **32.** 4 **33.** 7 **34.** 10

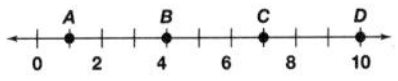

Lesson 1-1 pp. 4–7

Check Skills You'll Need **1.** 7 **2.** 12 **3.** 5 **4.** 4 **5.** 3

Check Understanding **1a.** Variable expression; x is the variable. **b.** numerical expression **c.** Variable expression.; d is the variable **2a.** $0.50b$ **b.** $\frac{m}{60}$

Lesson 1-2 pp. 8–12

Check Skills You'll Need **1.** 82 **2.** 43 **3.** 71 **4.** 19 **5.** 14 **6.** 26

Check Understanding **1a.** 17 **b.** 3 **c.** 3 **2a.** 4 **b.** 12 **3a.** 6 **b.** 3

Lesson 1-3 pp. 14–17

Check Skills You'll Need **1.** 60 **2.** 18 **3.** 29 **4.** 32

Check Understanding **1a.** 28 **b.** 45 **2a.** 90 **b.** 23 **c.** 12 **3.** $29c$; \$145 **4.** \$104

Lesson 1-4 pp. 18–22

Check Skills You'll Need **1.** −7 **2.** 9 **3.** 8 **4.** 3 **5.** −5

Check Understanding **1.** −2

2. 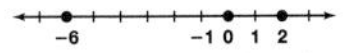

−6, 0, 2 **3.** the absolute value of negative ten; 10

Checkpoint Quiz 1 **1.** $f + 23$ **2.** $\frac{g}{34}$ **3.** $9p$ **4.** 20 **5.** 2 **6.** 19 **7.** 0 **8.** 54 **9.** 15

10a. 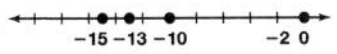

b. Tuesday, Wednesday, Monday, Thursday

Lesson 1-5 pp. 24–29

Check Skills You'll Need **1.** < **2.** > **3.** < **4.** = **5.** > **6.** >

Check Understanding **1a.** 3 **b.** 4 **c.** −4 **2a.** −4 **b.** 5 **c.** −6 **3a.** −38 **b.** 47 **c.** −90 **4.** 1,280 m **5a.** −10 **b.** 70

Lesson 1-6 pp. 30–34

Check Skills You'll Need **1.** −1 **2.** −29 **3.** −10 **4.** 11 **5.** 0 **6.** −23

Check Understanding **1a.** −5 **b.** −1 **c.** −3 **2a.** −4 **b.** −6 **c.** 5 **3a.** 35 **b.** −106 **c.** −46 **3d.** −81°C

Lesson 1-7 pp. 35–39

Check Skills You'll Need **1.** −7 **2.** −11 **3.** −15 **4.** −19

Check Understanding **1.** A six-sided figure with all vertices on a circle. **2a.** Start with 4 and add 5 repeatedly. **b.** Start with 3 and multiply by 3 readily **c.** Start with 1, 1. Then each number is the sum of the previous two numbers. **3.** Start with 1 and add 2 repeatedly; 9, 11. **4.** No; if the coin is fair, the coin can come up tails on any toss. **5a.** correct **b.** Incorrect; 8 and |8| are not opposites. **c.** correct

Lesson 1-8 pp. 40–43

Check Skills You'll Need **1.** Start with 8 and add 3 repeatedly; 20, 23, 26 **2.** Start with 1, then alternately add 4 and subtract 1; 11, 10, 14 **3.** Start with 3, then alternately add 2 and multiply by 2; 26, 52, 54 **4.** Start with 1, then add 3 repeatedly; 13, 16, 19

Check Understanding **8.** 127

Lesson 1-9 pp. 44–49

Check Skills You'll Need **1.** 20 **2.** 24 **3.** 25 **4.** 28 **5.** 30 **6.** 140

Check Understanding **1a.** −12 **b.** −12 **c.** −14 **2.** 12 **3a.** 64 **b.** −90 **c.** 0 **4a.** −4 **b.** 8 **c.** 14 **d.** −2

Checkpoint Quiz 2 **1.** −8 **2.** 20 **3.** −45 **4.** 8 **5.** −12 **6.** 72 **7–9.** Answers may vary. Samples are given. **7.** −7 **8.** 22 **9.** −40 **10.** 13, 18, 23 **11.** 81, 243, 729

Lesson 1-10 pp. 50–54

Check Skills You'll Need

1. 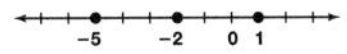

2. 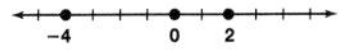

3. 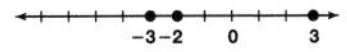

4. 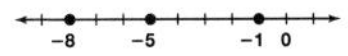

Check Understanding **1a.** (2, −3); (3, 3) **b.** Quadrant IV; Quadrant I

2a–b. 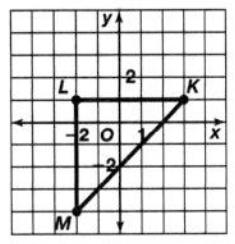

b. a triangle

Chapter 2

Diagnosing Readiness p. 64

1. 11, 11 **2.** 5, 5 **3.** −3, −3 **4.** −19, −19 **5.** 25, 25 **6.** 6, 6 **7.** 6, 6 **8.** 7, 7 **9.** < **10.** > **11.** < **12.** > **13.** < **14.** = **15.** = **16.** < **17.** > **18.** < **19.** < **20.** > **21.** 25 **22.** 28 **23.** 15 **24.** −110 **25.** 36 **26.** 16 **27.** −24 **28.** 45 **29.** −20 **30.** −27 **31.** −5 **32.** −45

Lesson 2-1 pp. 66–70

Check Skills You'll Need **1.** −25 **2.** 35 **3.** −7 **4.** −46

Check Understanding

1. \$18; 6 + 8 + 4
= 6 + (8 + 4)   Assoc. Prop. of Add.
= 6 + (4 + 8)   Comm. Prop. of Add.
= (6 + 4) + 8   Assoc. Prop. of Add.
= 10 + 8   Add within parentheses.
= 18   Add.

2a. Comm. Prop. of Add **b.** Ident. Prop of Mult. **c.** Assoc. Prop. of Mult. **3a.** 27 **b.** 3 **c.** 40 **d.** 10 **4.** \$6.30 **5a.** 300 **b.** −120 **c.** 240 **d.** 540

Lesson 2-2 pp. 71–75

Check Skills You'll Need **1.** 12 **2.** 24 **3.** 20 **4.** 6 **5.** 8 **6.** 4

Check Understanding **1a.** 2,650 **b.** 3,120 **c.** 1,791 **2.** \$1,428 **3a.** 210 **b.** −120 **c.** 35 **4a.** $8x - 12$ **b.** $3x + 12$ **c.** $6x + 2$ **5a.** $14 - 6d$ **b.** $18m + 3$ **c.** $-15t + 6$

Lesson 2-3 pp. 76–79

Check Skills You'll Need **1.** $5b + 20$ **2.** $-6x - 15$ **3.** $-32 - 12q$ **4.** $-12b + 42$

Check Understanding **1a.** 2, 4; $2s$, $4s$; 6 **b.** −4; none; none **c.** 9, 2, −2, 1; $9m$ and $-2m$, $2r$ and r; none **2.** $7a + 1$ **3a.** $2b$ **b.** $-13m$ **c.** $3p$ **4a.** $-y + 5m$ **b.** $2x - 7$

Checkpoint Quiz 1 **1.** Comm. Prop of Mult. **2.** Assoc. Prop. of Mult. **3.** Ident. Prop. of Mult. **4.** Comm. Prop. of Add. **5.** Comm. Prop. of Mult. **6.** Dist. Prop. **7.** $9a$ **8.** $18y$ **9.** $16w - 6$

Lesson 2-4 pp. 80–83

Check Skills You'll Need **1.** $x + 46$ **2.** $g - 4$ **3.** $t - 5$ **4.** $\frac{z}{26}$

Check Understanding **1a.** false; $2 \neq 3$ **b.** open; has a variable **c.** true; 20 = 20 **2.** $20 - x = 3$; open because there is a variable **3a.** no **b.** yes **4.** b + 6 = 33; 27 + 6 = 33; Yes, the backpack weighs 27 lb.

Lesson 2-5 pp. 86–90

Check Skills You'll Need **1.** 3 **2.** 9 **3.** 8 **4.** 6

Check Understanding **1a.** −5 **b.** 4 **c.** −1 **2.** $123 = r + 55$; 68 beats/min **3a.** 13 **b.** 72 **c.** 112 **4.** $5 = h - 17$; \$22

Lesson 2-6 pp. 92–95

Check Skills You'll Need **1.** 1 **2.** −1 **3.** −1 **4.** 1

Check Understanding **1a.** 21 **b.** 13 **c.** 9 **2a.** −8 **b.** −12 **c.** 14 **3a.** −50 **b.** 324 **c.** −600

Lesson 2-7 pp. 96–99

Check Skills You'll Need **1.** 178 **2.** 188 **3.** 183 **4.** 180

Check Understanding **6.** 53 adult tickets, 80 student tickets

Lesson 2-8 pp. 102–105

Check Skills You'll Need

1. 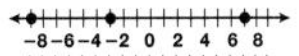

2. 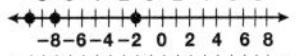

3. 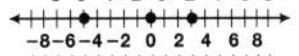

4. 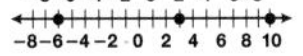

Check Understanding

1a. 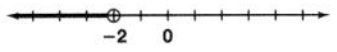

b. 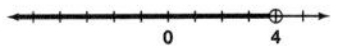

c. 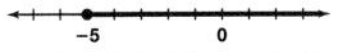

d. 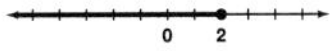

2. $x \geq 3$ **3.** $n < 5$

Lesson 2-9 pp. 106–109

Check Skills You'll Need **1.** −2 **2.** 19 **3.** 9 **4.** 29

Check Understanding **1a.** $m > 3$

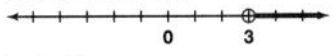

b. $t < 7$ 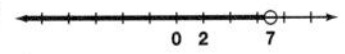

c. $x \geq -10$ 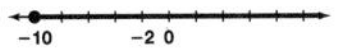

2. ≤ 28 lb **3a.** $m > 42$ **b.** $v \leq 11$ **c.** $t \geq 16$

Checkpoint Quiz 2 **1.** true; 19 = 19 **2.** open; variable **3.** false; $1 \neq -1$ **4.** −4 **5.** 4 **6.** 6 **7.** −32 **8.** −9 **9.** $a \geq 6$ **10.** $r < 19$ **11.** $m > -19$ **12.** 1 quarter, 5 dimes, 2 pennies

Lesson 2-10 pp. 110–114

Check Skills You'll Need **1.** 4 **2.** −9 **3.** −20 **4.** 288

Check Understanding **1a.** $x > 10$ **b.** $m < -7$ **c.** $t > -4$ **2a.** $m \geq 8$ **b.** $t > -21$ **c.** $r > 35$

Chapter 3

Diagnosing Readiness p.124

1. 40 **2.** 10 **3.** 0 **4.** 600 **5.** 830 **6.** 6,010 **7.** < **8.** > **9.** < **10.** < **11.** > **12.** > **13.** 8,349, 8.35, 8.351, 9.25 **14.** 0.017, 0.02, 0.0201, 0.201 **15.** −14.1, −1.401, −1.4, −1.04 **16.** −3.2, −3.19, −2.8, −2.3 **17.** 11.49 **18.** 3.07 **19.** 3.65 **20.** 1.206 **21.** 6.7067 **22.** 6.9 **23.** 55.12 **24.** 10.6 **25.** 98.7 **26.** 532 **27.** 300 **28.** 154,070 **29.** 0.08 **30.** 0.0842 **31.** 0.0161 **32.** 0.001209

Lesson 3-1 pp. 127–131

Check Skills You'll Need **1.** 2 tens **2.** 3 tenths **3.** 8 hundredths **4.** 6 thousandths

Check Understanding **1a.** tenths; 38.4 **b.** ones; 1 **c.** tenths; 7,098.6 **d.** thousandths; 274.943 **e.** tenths; 5.0 **f.** hundredths; 9.85 **2a.** about 560 **b.** about 220 **3a.** about 18.6 **b.** about \$11 **4a.** about \$15 **b.** about 125

Lesson 3-2 pp. 132–135

Check Skills You'll Need **1.** 146 **2.** 199 **3.** 101 **4.** 28

Check Understanding **1a.** about 10 **b.** about 68 **c.** about 160 **2.** about \$40 **3a.** about 20 **b.** about 6 **c.** about 20 **4a.** Yes; 0.68 is close to an estimate of 0.8. **b.** No; 52.3 is not close to an estimate of 5.

Lesson 3-3 pp. 137–141

Check Skills You'll Need **1.** 3, 4, 5, 6, 6, 8, 9 **2.** 68, 69, 71, 72, 72 **3.** 98, 101, 101, 112, 120 **4.** 3, 3.3, 3.7, 3.74, 37

Check Understanding **1.** 2.95, 2.8, 2.3 **2a.** 3 modes **b.** 1 mode **3a.** 31; raises the mean by 2.6 **b.** 1; lowers the mean by 2.8 **4a.** \$25.25, \$23.50, \$20 **b.** Answers may vary. Sample: Median; the mode is equal to two of the smaller data values, and the outlier (\$42) affects the mean too much.

Lesson 3-4 pp. 143–146

Check Skills You'll Need **1.** 14 **2.** 10 **3.** 14 **4.** 3.5

Check Understanding **1a.** r = 28 mi/h **b.** t = 51.5 yr **2a.** 61°F **b.** 59°F **c.** 53.5°F **3a.** 88.2 cm **b.** 52 in.

Checkpoint Quiz 1 **1.** 15.66 **2.** 0.891 **3.** 7,023 **4.** 345.7 **5.** about 32 **6.** about 24 **7.** about −1 **8.** about 6 **9.** 56, 57, no mode **10.** 2, 2, 1 **11.** 8.5 h

Lesson 3-5 pp. 148–151

Check Skills You'll Need **1.** 9.86 **2.** 2.45 **3.** 2.04 **4.** 3.08

Check Understanding **1a.** 13.9 **b.** 38.96 **2.** $35.48 + m = 70$; \$34.52 **3a.** 21.1 **b.** −7.4 **4.** $x - 14.95 = 12.48$; \$27.43

Lesson 3-6 pp. 152–155

Check Skills You'll Need **1.** 11.7 **2.** 0.48 **3.** 6.618 **4.** 4.8018

Check Understanding **1a.** −2 **b.** 0.5 **c.** 90.9 **2.** $5.5p = 7.70$; \$1.40 **3a.** −3 **b.** 12.5 **c.** −360 **4.** 12 hits

Lesson 3-7 pp. 156–161

Check Skills You'll Need **1.** 500 **2.** 0.01406 **3.** 2.94 **4.** 0.009

Check Understanding **1a.** Centimeter; a meter is too large unless you use fractional parts of a meter; millimeters are too small. **b.** Gram; an energy bar has a mass of several grams, but it is much less than 1 kilogram. **c.** Kilogram; a horse is very heavy, so grams are too small. **d.** Liter; a gas tank holds several liters, so milliliters are too small. **2a.** 50 km; millimeters are used to measure very small lengths. **b.** 10 mL; the eyedropper holds several drops of water but much less than a quart. **3a.** 0.035 **b.** 250,000 **c.** 6,000 **4a.** 3,800 m **b.** 250 mL

Checkpoint Quiz 2 **1.** 0.25 **2.** 8.55 **3.** 130 **4.** 3.05 **5.** 6.5 **6.** 129.6 **7.** 1.5 m; 1.5 cm is a little wider than the width of a thumbnail. **8.** 500 mL; 500 L would be about 500 qt. **9.** 0.095 **10.** 7,650,000 **11.** 0.675 **12.** 7,100 **13.** 9,100 g

Lesson 3-8 pp. 164–167

Check Skills You'll Need **1.** Start with 0 and add 6 repeatedly; 24, 30, 36 **2.** Start with −18 and add 9 repeatedly; 18, 27, 36 **3.** Start with 0. Alternately add 2 and subtract 1; 5, 4, 6 **4.** Start with 7. Alternately subtract 1 and add 2; 9, 11, 10

Check Understanding

6. 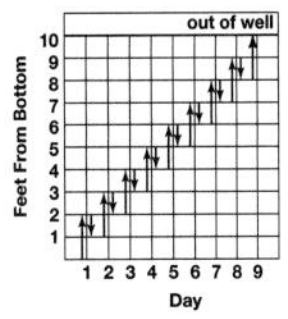

Chapter 4

Diagnosing Readiness p. 176

1. 1,728 **2.** −64 **3.** 6,561 **4.** 15,625 **5.** 512 **6.** 64 **7.** 2, 6 **8.** 9, 5 **9.** 3, 6 **10.** 9, 7 **11.** 6, 4 **12.** 2, 25 **13.** 16, 2 **14.** 9, 9 **15.** 6, 9 **16.** 6, 10 **17.** 4, 7 **18.** 7, 8 **19.** 4, 11 **20.** 9, 4 **21.** 8, 9 **22.** 90 **23.** 900 **24.** 22 **25.** 49 **26.** 21 **27.** 45 **28.** 212 **29.** 140 **30.** 23 **31.** 27 **32.** 91 **33.** 130

Lesson 4-1 pp. 178–181

Check Skills You'll Need **1.** 160 **2.** 73 **3.** 51 **4.** 48 **5.** 177 **6.** 118

Check Understanding **1a.** Yes; 160 ends in 0. **b.** No; 56 does not end in 0. **c.** No; 53 does no end in 0, 2, 4, 6, or 8. **d.** Yes; 1,118 ends in 8. **2a.** No; the sum of the digits, 10, is not divisible by 9. **b.** No; the sum of the digits, 13, is not divisible by 3. **c.** Yes; the sum of the digits, 12, is divisible by 3. **d.** Yes; the sum of the digits, 18, is divisible by 9. **3a.** 1, 2, 5, 10 **b.** 1, 3, 7, 21 **c.** 1, 2, 3, 4, 6, 8, 12, 24 **d.** 1, 31 **e.** 1 row of 36 students, 2 rows of 18 students, 3 rows of 12 students, 4 rows of 9 students, or 6 rows of 6 students

Lesson 4-2 pp. 182–185

Check Skills You'll Need **1.** 81 **2.** 144 **3.** −64 **4.** 10,000

Check Understanding **1a.** 6^3 **b.** $4xy^2$ **c.** $(-3)^4$ **2a.** 49 **b.** −16, 16 **3a.** −58 **b.** 81

Lesson 4-3 pp. 186–190

Check Skills You'll Need **1.** 1, 3, 5, 15 **2.** 1, 5, 7, 35 **3.** 1, 7 **4.** 1, 2, 4, 5, 10, 20 **5.** 1, 2, 4, 5, 10, 20, 25, 50, 100 **6.** 1, 11, 121

Check Understanding **1a.** 11, 13, 17, 19 **b.** 10, 12, 14, 15, 16, 18, 20 **2a.** $2^3 \cdot 3^2$ **b.** 11^2 **c.** $3^2 \cdot 5^2$ **b.** $2^2 \cdot 59$ **3a.** 4 **b.** 3 **c.** $4r$ **d.** $15m$

Lesson 4-4 pp. 192–195

Check Skills You'll Need **1.** 7 **2.** 12 **3.** $5mn$ **4.** 3

Check Understanding **1a–c.** Answers may vary. Samples are given. **1a.** $\frac{1}{3}, \frac{10}{30}$ **b.** $\frac{5}{6}, \frac{20}{24}$ **c.** $\frac{7}{10}, \frac{28}{40}$ **2a.** $\frac{3}{4}$ **b.** $\frac{3}{4}$ **c.** $\frac{4}{5}$ **3a.** $\frac{1}{ac}$ **b.** $\frac{n}{3}$ **c.** $3x$

Checkpoint Quiz 1 **1.** 2, 3, 5, 10 **2.** 2, 3, 9 **3.** 2, 3 **4.** none **5.** 3, 9 **6.** 64 **7.** 125 **8.** −18 **9.** $\frac{1}{2}$ **10.** $\frac{2}{3}$ **11.** $\frac{4}{7}$ **12.** $\frac{1}{4}$ **13.** $2y$ **14.** Answers may vary. Samples: $5a^2$, $10a^2$; $25a^3b$, $30a^2$

Lesson 4-5 pp. 197–200

Check Skills You'll Need **1.** > **2.** > **3.** < **4.** <

Check Understanding **7.** 45 pictures

Lesson 4-6 pp. 201–204

Check Skills You'll Need **1.** $\frac{1}{5}$ **2.** $\frac{2}{3}$ **3.** $\frac{4}{5}$ **4.** $\frac{3}{4}$

Check Understanding **1a–d.** Answers may vary. Samples are given. **1a.** $\frac{2}{6}, \frac{-2}{-6}, \frac{-1}{-3}$ **b.** $-\frac{8}{10}, \frac{-4}{5}, \frac{4}{-5}$ **c.** $\frac{10}{16}, \frac{-10}{-16}, \frac{-5}{-8}$ **d.** $-\frac{2}{4}, \frac{-1}{2}, \frac{1}{-2}$

2a–d. 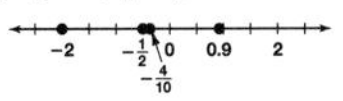

3a. $-\frac{1}{3}$ **b.** $\frac{2}{3}$ **c.** −3

Lesson 4-7 pp. 205–208

Check Skills You'll Need **1.** k^4 **2.** m^2n^2 **3.** 2^4 **4.** 5^3

Check Understanding **1a.** 32 **b.** m^{12} **c.** x^5y^5 **2a.** $18a^4$ **b.** $15c^9$ **c.** $12x^6$ **3a.** 256 **b.** c^{20} **c.** m^6

Lesson 4-8 pp. 210–214

Check Skills You'll Need **1.** x **2.** $\frac{1}{y}$ **3.** $\frac{2x}{3}$ **4.** $\frac{ab}{4}$

Check Understanding **1a.** 1,000 **b.** x^7 **c.** $4m^4$ **2a.** 1 **b.** 5 **c.** y^3 **d.** 5 **3a.** $\frac{1}{16}$ **b.** $\frac{1}{a^2}$ **c.** $\frac{1}{3y^4}$ **4a.** b^{-6} **b.** $m^{-3}n^{-6}$ **c.** $x^{-4}y^2$

Checkpoint Quiz 2 **1–5.** Answers may vary. Samples are given. **1.** $\frac{1}{4}, \frac{-1}{-4}, \frac{2}{8}$ **2.** $\frac{1}{3}, \frac{-1}{-3}, \frac{2}{6}$ **3.** $\frac{7}{10}, \frac{-7}{-10}, \frac{14}{20}$ **4.** $\frac{9}{14}, \frac{-9}{-14}, \frac{-18}{-28}$ **5.** $\frac{8}{10}, \frac{-8}{-10}, \frac{-4}{-5}$ **6.** $-\frac{1}{3}$ **7.** $-\frac{1}{2}$ **8.** $\frac{2}{3}$ **9.** $-\frac{5}{8}$ **10.** $\frac{1}{4}$

11–15.

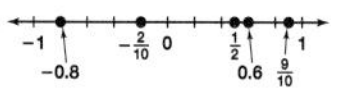

16. 128 **17.** x^{50} **18.** $6a^2$ **19.** $\frac{1}{x^5}$ **20.** $\frac{1}{a^6}$ **21.** $\frac{3}{4}$

Lesson 4-9 pp. 215–220

Check Skills You'll Need **1.** 10^8 **2.** 10^{16} **3.** 10^2 **4.** 10^{-3}

Check Understanding **1a.** 5.45×10^7 **b.** 7.23×10^5 **c.** 6.02×10^{11} **2a.** 2.1×10^{-4} **b.** 5×10^{-8} **c.** 8.03×10^{-11} **3a.** 32,100,000 **b.** 0.000000059 **c.** 10,060,000,000 **4a.** 1.6×10^6 **b.** 2.03×10^5 **c.** 7.243×10^{15} **5a.** 18.3×10^6, 0.098×10^9, 526×10^7 **b.** 0.22×10^{-10}, 8×10^{-9}, 14.7×10^{-7} **6a.** 2.4×10^{11} **b.** 5.68×10^{-3}

Chapter 5

Diagnosing Readiness p. 230

1. 1.2 **2.** 60 **3.** −45 **4.** −40 **5.** 1.5 **6.** 74 **7.** 8 **8.** −1.78 **9.** 3 **10.** 4 **11.** 12 **12.** 1 **13.** 10 **14.** 5 **15.** 9 **16.** 1 **17.** 10 **18.** 14 **19–21.** Answers may vary. Samples are given. **19.** $\frac{1}{2}, \frac{3}{6}$ **20.** $\frac{8}{12}, \frac{2}{3}$ **21.** $\frac{3}{4}, \frac{6}{8}$ **22.** $\frac{5}{6}$ **23.** $\frac{2}{5}$ **24.** −2 **25.** $\frac{1}{4}$ **26.** $-\frac{24}{25}$ **27.** $\frac{1}{3}$ **28.** $\frac{4}{15}$ **29.** $\frac{4}{31}$ **30.** $-\frac{2}{9}$ **31.** $-\frac{2}{13}$ **32.** $\frac{1}{6}$ **33.** $\frac{5}{7}$ **34.** 5.4 **35.** 0.6 **36.** 0.625 **37.** 0.75 **38.** 0.375

Lesson 5-1 pp. 232–236

Check Skills You'll Need **1.** $2^2 \cdot 5$ **2.** 5^3 **3.** $3^2 \cdot 5$ **4.** $2 \cdot 3 \cdot 31$ **5.** $3^3 \cdot 23$ **6.** $3^2 \cdot 5^2 \cdot 7$

Check Understanding **1a.** 12 **b.** 20 **c.** 60 **2a.** 48 **b.** 45 **c.** 180 **3a.** $60xy$ **b.** $56m^4$ **c.** $75xy^2$ **4a.** $\frac{4}{9} > \frac{2}{9}$ **b.** $-\frac{4}{9} < -\frac{2}{9}$ **c.** $-\frac{4}{9} < \frac{2}{9}$ **5a.** $\frac{6}{7} > \frac{4}{5}$ **b.** $\frac{2}{3} < \frac{3}{4}$ **c.** $-\frac{3}{4} < -\frac{7}{10}$ **6a.** $\frac{1}{6} < \frac{5}{12} < \frac{2}{3}$ **b.** $\frac{1}{5} < \frac{3}{10} < \frac{1}{2} < \frac{7}{12}$

Lesson 5-2 pp. 237–241

Check Skills You'll Need **1.** 0.241, 2.41, 12.4, 24.1 **2.** 1.003, 1.030, 1.300, 13.03 **3.** −0.1, −0.01, 0.01, 0.1

Check Understanding **1a.** 0.25 **b.** 1.875 **c.** 3.3 **d.** 0.6 **2a.** $0.\overline{7}$; repeating 7 **b.** $0.9\overline{54}$; repeating; 54 **c.** 1.375; terminating **d.** $0.\overline{72}$; repeating; 72 **3a.** 0.2, 0.5, $\frac{7}{10}$, $\frac{4}{5}$ **b.** −0.75, −0.375, $-\frac{1}{4}$, $-\frac{1}{8}$ **4a.** $1\frac{3}{4}$ **b.** $2\frac{8}{25}$ **c.** $\frac{13}{20}$ **5a.** $\frac{7}{9}$ **b.** $\frac{6}{11}$ **c.** $\frac{71}{333}$

Lesson 5-3 pp. 243–247

Check Skills You'll Need **1.** 8 **2.** 18 **3.** $10n$ **4.** 18 **5.** 40 **6.** $10n$

Check Understanding **1a.** $\frac{4}{7}$ **b.** $\frac{5}{k}$ **c.** $\frac{2}{5}$ **d.** $\frac{6}{y}$ **2a.** $\frac{7}{15}$ **b.** $-\frac{1}{8}$ **c.** $\frac{3m-14}{7m}$ **3a.** $6\frac{5}{8}$ **b.** $2\frac{1}{2}$ **c.** $3\frac{1}{4}$ **d.** $3\frac{1}{2}$ qt

Checkpoint Quiz 1 **1.** > **2.** = **3.** < **4.** < **5.** 0.51 **6.** $\frac{3}{250}$ **7.** 1.25 **8.** $\frac{1}{3}$ **9.** $0.8\overline{3}$ **10.** $\frac{17}{33}$ **11.** $\frac{11}{13}$ **12.** $\frac{5}{36}$ **13.** $4\frac{19}{40}$ **14.** $\frac{2}{3}$

Lesson 5-4 pp. 248–252

Check Skills You'll Need **1.** $\frac{7}{3}$ **2.** $\frac{33}{10}$ **3.** $\frac{13}{9}$ **4.** $\frac{24}{5}$ **5.** $\frac{63}{8}$ **6.** $\frac{36}{7}$

Check Understanding **1a.** $\frac{2}{15}$ **b.** $-\frac{5}{9}$ **c.** $\frac{35}{72}$ **d.** $\frac{3}{32}$ **2a.** $\frac{4}{7}$ **b.** $-\frac{7}{25}$ **c.** $\frac{x}{6}$ **3a.** $1\frac{1}{2}$ **b.** $\frac{6}{7}$ **c.** $-4\frac{8}{15}$ **4a.** $-\frac{1}{2}$ **b.** $\frac{15a}{16}$ **c.** $\frac{b}{2}$ **5a.** $1\frac{3}{5}$ **b.** $-1\frac{1}{3}$ **c.** $7\frac{1}{2}$

Lesson 5-5 pp. 253–257

Check Skills You'll Need **1.** $\frac{1}{3}$ **2.** 52 **3.** 10 **4.** $1\frac{1}{2}$

Check Understanding **1a.** Feet; inches are too small and miles are too large. **b.** Pounds; the weight is too great to measure in ounces. **c.** Inches; the pencil is too small to measure in feet. **d.** Fluid ounces; the capacity of a cup is too large. **2a.** $\frac{7}{8}$ **b.** $1\frac{1}{6}$ **c.** 7 **3a.** 56 **b.** $10\frac{1}{2}$ **c.** 7

Lesson 5-6 pp. 259–262

Check Skills You'll Need **1.** $\frac{1}{10}, \frac{1}{5}, \frac{1}{4}, \frac{1}{3}, \frac{1}{2}$ **2.** $\frac{3}{3}, \frac{5}{3}, \frac{7}{3}, \frac{13}{3}$ **3.** $\frac{3}{13}, \frac{3}{7}, \frac{3}{5}, \frac{3}{3}$ **4.** $-\frac{3}{3}, -\frac{3}{5}, -\frac{3}{7}, -\frac{3}{13}$

Check Understanding **7.** 3 h 55 min

Lesson 5-7 pp. 264–267

Check Skills You'll Need **1.** $-1\frac{1}{8}$ **2.** $8\frac{5}{24}$ **3.** $2\frac{5}{8}$ **4.** $-7\frac{7}{18}$

Check Understanding **1a.** $-\frac{1}{3}$ **b.** $\frac{1}{15}$ **c.** $\frac{13}{30}$ **2a.** $\frac{4}{5}$ **b.** $1\frac{1}{7}$ **3a.** $7\frac{5}{12}$ **b.** $2\frac{1}{18}$

Lesson 5-8 pp. 268–272

Check Skills You'll Need **1.** $\frac{5}{14}$ **2.** $-1\frac{1}{2}$ **3.** $6\frac{1}{4}$ **4.** 3

Check Understanding **1a.** $\frac{5}{56}$ **b.** $\frac{7}{18}$ **c.** $\frac{4}{15}$ **2a.** $3\frac{3}{4}$ **b.** $1\frac{5}{27}$ **c.** 1 **3a.** $-\frac{7}{8}$ **b.** $\frac{13}{15}$ **c.** $-\frac{1}{14}$ **4a.** 8 **b.** $-\frac{3}{10}$ **c.** $4\frac{6}{11}$

Checkpoint Quiz 2 **1.** 14 **2.** $\frac{1}{2}$ **3.** $-\frac{4}{27}$ **4.** $1\frac{1}{3}$ **5.** −2 **6.** 34 **7.** $2\frac{1}{4}$ **8.** 90 **9.** $1\frac{1}{2}$ **10.** $\frac{1}{3}$ **11.** $\frac{1}{5}$ **12.** $1\frac{5}{8}$ **13.** $11\frac{1}{4}$ **14.** $\frac{6}{35}$ **15.** $\frac{7}{15}$ **16.** $-17\frac{1}{3}$ **17.** $-\frac{27}{40}$ **18.** $3\frac{3}{5}$ **19.** $\frac{5}{33}$ **20.** 6 miles **21.** 55 mi/h **22.** $12 **23.** Answers may vary. Sample: A desktop can be measured in inches; 48 inches.

Lesson 5-9 pp. 274–277

Check Skills You'll Need **1.** 64 **2.** 81 **3.** 1 **4.** x^{18} **5.** b^{10} **6.** a^{28}

Check Understanding **1a.** 216 **b.** $16p^4$ **c.** x^5y^{10} **d.** $25x^6$ **2a.** $16y^4$ **b.** $-16y^4$ **c.** $-125a^6b^3$ **3a.** $\frac{1}{8}$ **b.** $\frac{16}{81}$ **c.** $\frac{8x^6}{27}$

Chapter 6

Diagnosing Readiness p. 286

1. 16 **2.** 13.5 **3.** $\frac{7}{8}$ **4.** 2.5 **5.** $1\frac{1}{4}$ **6.** 27.5 **7–12.** Answers may vary. Samples are given. **7.** $\frac{2}{8}, \frac{4}{16}$ **8.** $\frac{2}{5}, \frac{8}{20}$ **9.** $\frac{3}{7}, \frac{12}{28}$ **10.** $\frac{4}{18}, \frac{6}{27}$ **11.** $\frac{6}{16}, \frac{9}{24}$ **12.** $\frac{10}{12}, \frac{15}{18}$ **13.** $\frac{1}{4}$ **14.** $\frac{1}{4}$ **15.** $\frac{4}{5}$ **16.** $\frac{3}{8}$ **17.** $\frac{3}{7}$ **18.** $\frac{1}{8}$ **19.** $\frac{5}{6}$ **19.** $\frac{5}{6}$ **20.** $\frac{1}{25}$ **21.** 0.35 **22.** $\frac{3}{50}$ **23.** 3.75 **24.** $\frac{7}{20}$ **25.** $\frac{7}{8}$ **26.** 3.6 **27.** $1\frac{7}{100}$ **28.** $0.\overline{6}$ **29.** $11.\overline{1}$ **30.** $\frac{1}{3}$ **31.** 6.25 **32.** $3\frac{49}{50}$

Lesson 6-1 pp. 288–291

Check Skills You'll Need **1.** $\frac{6}{7}$ **2.** $\frac{3}{5}$ **3.** $\frac{9}{10}$ **4.** $\frac{4}{5}$ **5.** $\frac{1}{3}$ **6.** $\frac{5}{3}$, or $1\frac{2}{3}$

Check Understanding **1a.** $\frac{2}{5}$ **b.** $\frac{3}{2}$ **2a.** $.99/L **b.** 34 mi/gal **3a.** 52.5 **b.** 432

Lesson 6-2 pp. 294–298

Check Skills You'll Need **1.** 13 **2.** 6 **3.** 15 **4.** 3

Check Understanding **1a.** 6 **b.** 44 **c.** 77 **2a.** yes, cross products equal **b.** no, cross products not equal **c.** yes, cross products equal **3.** 87 nautical miles

Lesson 6-3 pp. 299–303

Check Skills You'll Need **1.** 14 **2.** 133.3 **3.** 6.7 **4.** 3.6

Check Understanding **1.** 15.8 **2.** 28 ft

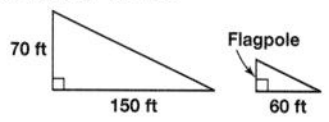

3. $1\frac{7}{8}$ in.

Lesson 6-4 pp. 305–309

Check Skills You'll Need **1.** $\frac{5}{8}$ **2.** $\frac{3}{20}$ **3.** $\frac{5}{11}$ **4.** $\frac{11}{12}$

Check Understanding **1a.** $\frac{3}{6}$, or $\frac{1}{2}$ **b.** $\frac{1}{6}$ **c.** $\frac{2}{6}$, or $\frac{1}{3}$ **2a.** $\frac{5}{6}$ **b.** a certain event **3a.** 1 to 4 **b.** 4 to 1 **ci.** 2 to 3 **cii.** 3 to 2

Checkpoint Quiz 1 **1.** 4 mi/h **2.** 6 gal/min **3.** 48 ft/s **4.** 4.5 **5.** 42 times **6.** $\frac{2}{6}$, or $\frac{1}{3}$

Lesson 6-5 pp. 310–314

Check Skills You'll Need **1.** 0.625 **2.** 0.45 **3.** 0.75 **4.** $0.8\overline{3}$ **5.** $0.\overline{6}$ **6.** $0.\overline{72}$

Check Understanding **1a.** $\frac{29}{50}$ **b.** $\frac{18}{25}$ **c.** $1\frac{11}{25}$ **2a.** 0.16 **b.** 0.625 **c.** 1.2 **d.** 0.45, $\frac{9}{20}$ **3a.** 40% **b.** 2.3% **c.** 175% **4.** 27%

Lesson 6-6 pp. 315–319

Check Skills You'll Need **1.** 7 **2.** 230 **3.** 25 **4.** 18

Check Understanding

1a.

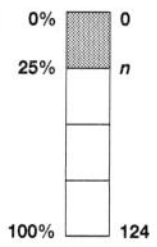

$\frac{25}{100} = \frac{n}{124}$; 31

b.

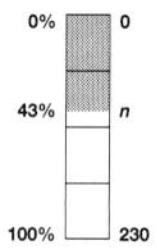

$\frac{43}{100} = \frac{n}{230}$; 98.9

c.

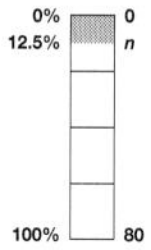

$\frac{12.5}{100} = \frac{n}{80}$; 10

2a. 55.2% **b.** 93.3% **3a.** 25.3 **b.** 313.1 **4.** about 3,567 screens

Lesson 6-7 pp. 320–323

Check Skills You'll Need **1.** 0.48 **2.** 0.05 **3.** 0.238 **4.** 0.7225 **5.** 1.36 **6.** 1.785

Check Understanding **1a.** $0.96 = n \cdot 10$; 9.6% **b.** $19.2 = 0.32 \cdot n$; 60 **2a.** $n = 1.455 \cdot 20$; 29.1 **b.** $380 = 1.25n$; 304 **3.** $.85 **4.** 1,344 people

Lesson 6-8 pp. 325–328

Check Skills You'll Need **1.** 46% **2.** 247% **3.** 3% **4.** 523.6%

Check Understanding **1a.** 14% **b.** 60% **c.** 112.5% **2.** 26% **3a.** 50% **b.** 5.0% **c.** 92.9%

Lesson 6-9 pp. 329–332

Check Skills You'll Need **1.** $61.50 **2.** $71.40 **3.** $1.32 **4.** $12.79

Check Understanding **1.** $42 **2.** $8.50 **3.** $3.30

Checkpoint Quiz 2 **1.** = **2.** < **3.** > **4.** $0.33 \cdot 120 = n$; 39.6 **5.** $1.25 \cdot 42 = n$; 52.5 **6.** $n \cdot 5.6 = 1.4$; 25% **7.** $0.15 \cdot q = 9.75$; 65 **8.** $9,600

Lesson 6-10 pp. 334–337

Check Skills You'll Need **1.** $163.83

Check Understanding **11.** about 299 million people

Chapter 7

Diagnosing Readiness p. 346

1. $p + 3$ **2.** $q - 6$ **3.** $12y$ **4.** $10d$ **5.** $2b$ **6.** $n - 8$ **7.** $4n$ **8.** $-3b + 10$ **9.** $19c + 13$ **10.** $-7x - 5y$ **11.** $2a + 6$ **12.** $9m - 35$ **13.** 11 **14.** −21 **15.** −98 **16.** 5 **17.** 8 **18.** 9 **19.** −32 **20.** −8 **21.** $c \geq 1$ **22.** $y < 2$ **23.** $b < 4$ **24.** $x > 0$ **25.** $x \geq -6$ **26.** $x \leq 15$ **27.** $b \leq 19$ **28.** $m \geq 80$

Lesson 7-1 pp. 348–351

Check Skills You'll Need **1.** 8 **2.** 11 **3.** 1 **4.** −12 **5.** −10

Check Understanding **1a.** 3 **b.** 16 **c.** −6 **d.** −1 **2a.** −2 **b.** 21 **c.** −3 **3.** $11

Lesson 7-2 pp. 352–356

Check Skills You'll Need **1.** $5x + 4$ **2.** $6y$ **3.** $3a$ **4.** $2 + c$ **5.** $2x - 7$

Check Understanding **1.** 92 points **2a.** 88, 89, 90, 91 **b.** 32, 34 **3a.** $4\frac{2}{3}$ **b.** −14

Lesson 7-3 pp. 357–361

Check Skills You'll Need **1.** −3 **2.** $2\frac{1}{4}$ **3.** −4 **4.** $\frac{2}{3}$

Check Understanding **1a.** 50 **b.** $10\frac{1}{2}$ **2a.** $\frac{3}{4}$ **b.** $5\frac{1}{2}$ **3a.** 4 **b.** 3.5

Lesson 7-4 pp. 362–365

Check Skills You'll Need **1.** $p - 21 = 48$ **2.** $b + 6 = 33$ **3.** $140 + d = 192$

Check Understanding **6.** Answers may vary. Sample: Write and solve an equation because it is faster. **7.** 122 mi

Checkpoint Quiz 1 **1.** 20 **2.** 11 **3.** −18 **4.** 4 **5.** 28 **6.** −48 **7.** 2 **8.** 1.3 **9.** −6 **10.** 0 **11.** 1 **12.** 6 **13.** $p - 0.25p = 82.50$; $110 **14.** $n + (n + 1) + (n + 2) = 132$; 43, 44, 45

Lesson 7-5 pp. 367–371

Check Skills You'll Need **1.** 5 **2.** 7 **3.** −10 **4.** 8

Check Understanding **1a.** 16 **b.** 2 **2.** 6 h

Lesson 7-6 pp. 373–376

Check Skills You'll Need

1. $w \geq -9$

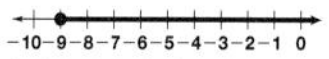

2. $z > 10$

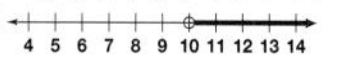

3. $a < 2$

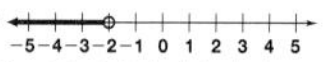

4. $x \leq -1$

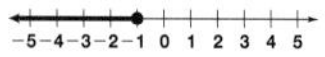

Check Understanding

1a. $a > 4$

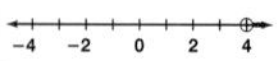

1b. $x \leq -8$

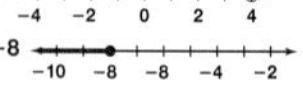

1c. $c < -6$

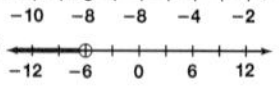

2a. $m \geq -15$

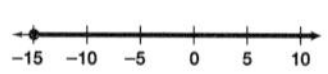

2b. $x < 3$

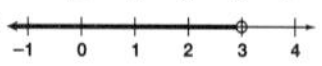

2c. $b < -22$

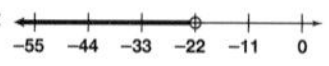

3. ≥ $7,500

Lesson 7-7 pp. 378–381

Check Skills You'll Need **1.** 320 km **2.** 32 m **3.** 48 ft^2

Check Understanding **1a.** $s = p + c$ **b.** $k = hj$ **c.** $p = \frac{I}{rt}$ **2a.** $a = \frac{1}{5}b - \frac{7}{5}$ **b.** $w = \frac{1}{2}P - \ell$ **c.** $x = 3(y - 8)$ **3.** $r = \frac{d}{t}$ **4.** $h = an$; 11 hits

Checkpoint Quiz 2 **1.** −2 **2.** −6 **3.** $\frac{2}{9}$ **4.** 4 **5.** 3 **6.** 5 **7.** $y > -\frac{9}{10}$ **8.** $x > -56$ **9.** $x > 5$ **10.** $h = s - g$ **11.** $r = \frac{1}{3}k - \frac{4}{3}$ **12.** $t = \frac{I}{pr}$

Lesson 7-8 pp. 382–386

Check Skills You'll Need **1.** $24 **2.** $1,100 **3.** $31.50 **4.** $17.88

Check Understanding **1a.** $30 **b.** $4.38

2a.

Bal. at Yr Start	Interest	Bal. at Yr End
$500.00	$15.00	$515.00
$515.00	$15.45	$530.45

2b.

Bal. at Yr Start	Interest	Bal. at Yr End
$625.00	$12.50	$637.50
$637.50	$12.75	$650.25
$650.25	$13.01	$663.26
$663.26	$13.27	$676.53

3a. $955.09 **b.** $955.37

Chapter 8

Diagnosing Readiness p. 396

1. −4, −7 **2.** 19, 13 **3.** 10.5, 12 **4.** −11, −13 **5.** (5, 2) **6.** (−3, 4) **7.** (4, 0) **8.** (6, −3) **9.** (−4, −3) **10.** (0, 3) **11–16.**

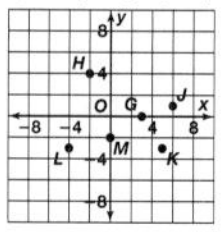

17. $-\frac{1}{18}$ **18.** 3 **19.** 1 **20.** $\frac{1}{3}$ **21.** $y = -4x + 3$ **22.** $y = -2x + 4$ **23.** $y = 2x - 6$ **24.** $y = -6x - 8$ **25.** $y = -x + 12$ **26.** $y = -\frac{1}{2}x + \frac{5}{2}$ **27.** $y = \frac{1}{5}x + 4$ **28.** $y = -\frac{3}{4}x + 3$

Lesson 8-1 pp. 400–404

Check Skills You'll Need **1–6.**

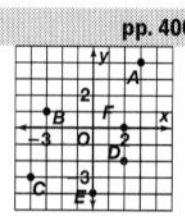

Check Understanding **1a.** No; there are two range values for the domain value 2. **b.** Yes; there is one range value for each domain value. **2a.** No; a specific postage cost (domain value) can mail packages of different weights (range values). **b.** Yes; for each package weight (domain value) there is one postage cost to the same zip code (range value).

3a. A function; no vertical line passes through two graphed points.

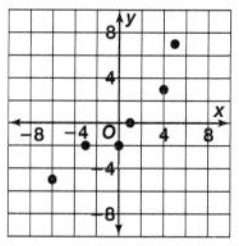

b. Not a function; a vertical line passes through both (−1, 1) and (−1, 3).

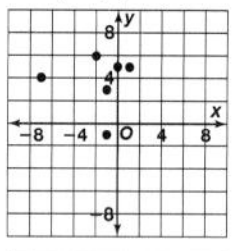

c. A function; no vertical line passes through two graphed points.

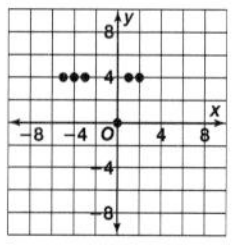

Lesson 8-2 pp. 405–409

Check Skills You'll Need **1.** 4 **2.** −10 **3.** 3 **4.** 6

Check Understanding **1a.** (−3, −5) **b.** (−3, 15) **c.** (−3, −4) **2.** 14°C

3a.

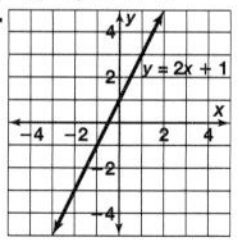

b.

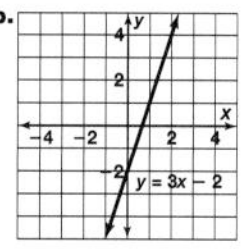

c.

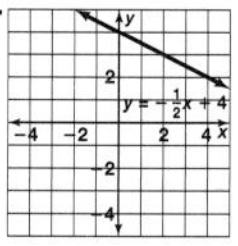

4a. no

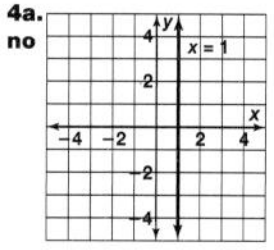

b. yes

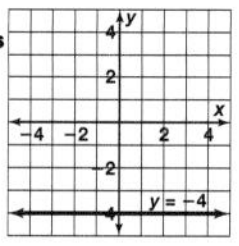

c. no

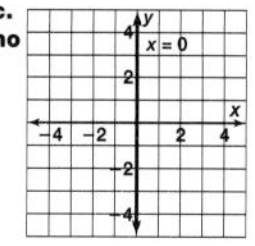

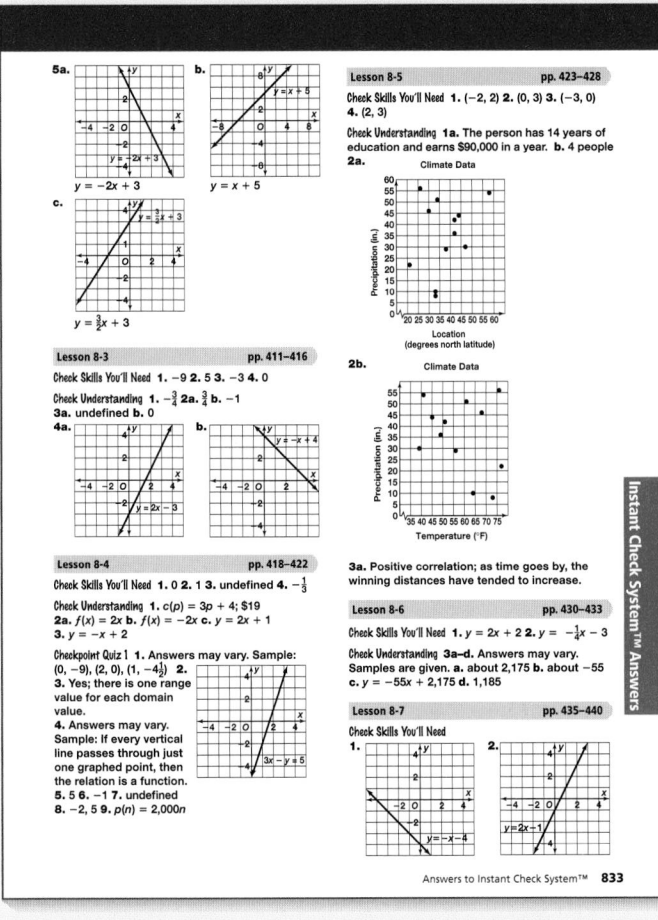

5a. [graph] **b.** [graph]
$y = -2x + 3$ $y = x + 5$
c. [graph]
$y = \frac{3}{4}x + 3$

Lesson 8-3 pp. 411–416
Check Skills You'll Need 1. -9 **2.** 5 **3.** -3 **4.** 0
Check Understanding 1. $-\frac{3}{4}$ **2a.** $\frac{3}{4}$ **b.** -1
3a. undefined **b.** 0
4a. [graph] $y = 2x - 3$ **b.** [graph] $y = -x + 4$

Lesson 8-4 pp. 418–422
Check Skills You'll Need 1. 0 **2.** 1 **3.** undefined **4.** $-\frac{1}{3}$
Check Understanding 1. $c(p) = 3p + 4$; $19
2a. $f(x) = 2x$ **b.** $f(x) = -2x$ **c.** $y = 2x + 1$
3. $y = -x + 2$
Checkpoint Quiz 1 1. Answers may vary. Sample:
$(0, -9)$, $(2, 0)$, $(1, -4\frac{1}{2})$ **2.** [graph]
3. Yes; there is one range value for each domain value.
4. Answers may vary. Sample: If every vertical line passes through just one graphed point, then the relation is a function.
5. 5 **6.** -1 **7.** undefined
8. $-2, 5$ **9.** $p(n) = 2,000n$

Lesson 8-5 pp. 423–428
Check Skills You'll Need 1. $(-2, 2)$ **2.** $(0, 3)$ **3.** $(-3, 0)$
4. $(2, 3)$
Check Understanding 1a. The person has 14 years of education and earns $90,000 in a year. **b.** 4 people
2a. [Climate Data scatterplot]
Precipitation (in.) vs. Location (degrees north latitude)
2b. [Climate Data scatterplot]
Precipitation (in.) vs. Temperature (°F)
3a. Positive correlation; as time goes by, the winning distances have tended to increase.

Lesson 8-6 pp. 430–433
Check Skills You'll Need 1. $y = 2x + 2$ **2.** $y = -\frac{1}{3}x - 3$
Check Understanding 3a–d. Answers may vary. Samples are given. **a.** about 2,175 **b.** about -55
c. $y = -55x + 2,175$ **d.** 1,185

Lesson 8-7 pp. 435–440
Check Skills You'll Need
1. [graph] **2.** [graph] $y = 2x + 1$

Answers to Instant Check System™ **833**

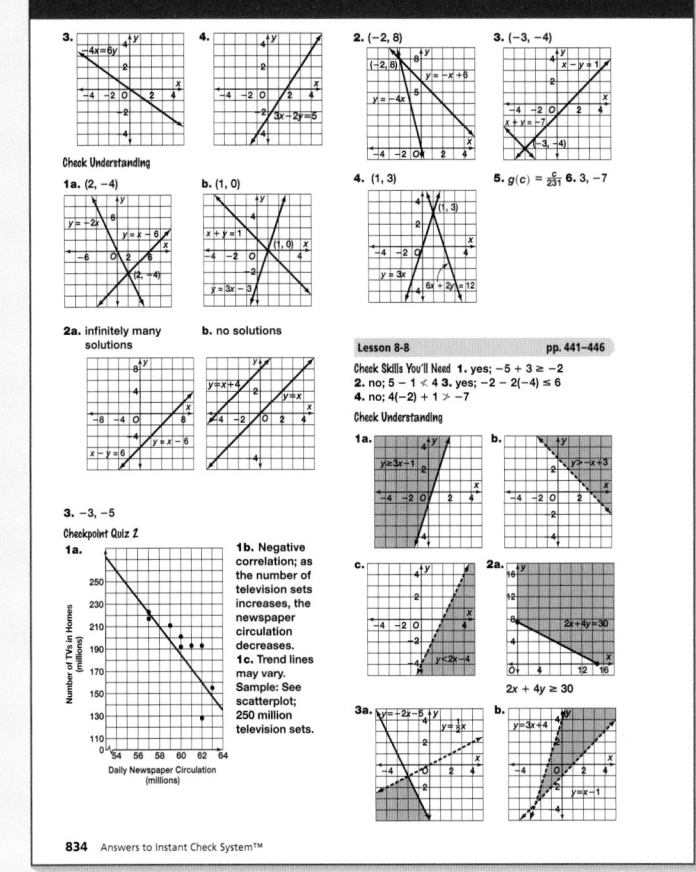

3. [graph] $-4x = 6y$ **4.** [graph] **2.** $(-2, 8)$ [graph] $y = -x + 5$ **3.** $(-3, -4)$ [graph] $x - y + 1$

Check Understanding
1a. $(2, -4)$ [graph] **b.** $(1, 0)$ [graph] **4.** $(1, 3)$ [graph] **5.** $g(c) = \frac{5}{231}$ **6.** $3, -7$
2a. infinitely many solutions **b.** no solutions [graphs]
3. $-3, -5$

Checkpoint Quiz 2
1a. [scatterplot: Number of TVs in Homes (millions) vs. Daily Newspaper Circulation (millions)]
1b. Negative correlation; as the number of television sets increases, the newspaper circulation decreases.
1c. Trend lines may vary. Sample: See scatterplot; 250 million television sets.

Lesson 8-8 pp. 441–446
Check Skills You'll Need 1. yes; $-5 + 3 \geq -2$
2. no; $5 - 1 \not< 4$ **3.** yes; $-2 - 2(-4) \leq 6$
4. no; $4(-2) + 1 \not> -7$
Check Understanding
1a. [graph] $y \geq 3x - 1$ **b.** [graph] $y > -x + 3$
c. [graph] $y < 2x - 4$ **2a.** [graph] $2x + 4y \geq 30$
3a. [graph] $y = -2x - 5$, $y = \frac{1}{2}x$ **b.** [graph] $y = 3x + 4$, $y = x - 1$

834 Answers to Instant Check System™

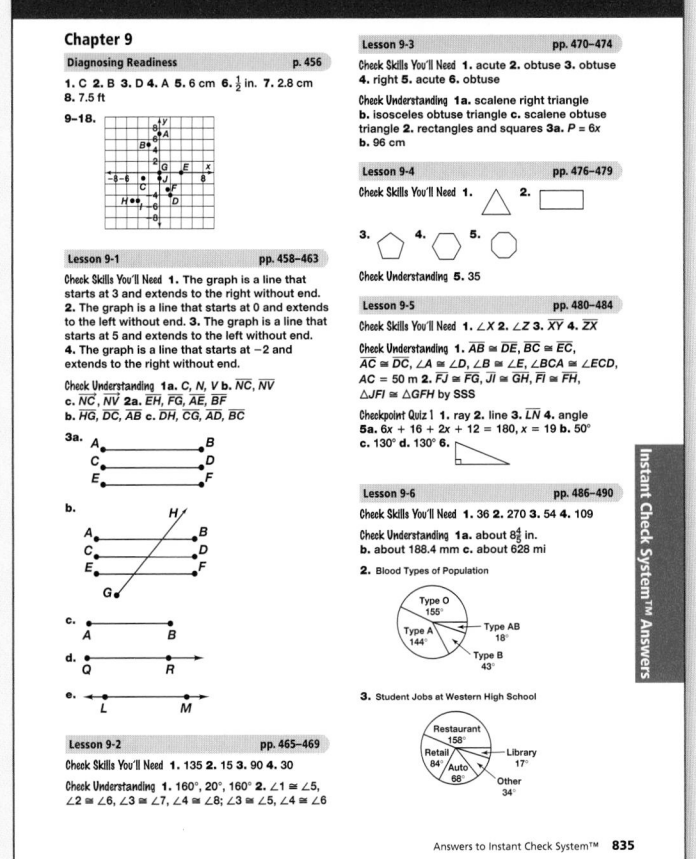

Chapter 9

Diagnosing Readiness p. 456
1. C **2.** B **3.** D **4.** A **5.** 6 cm **6.** $1\frac{1}{2}$ in. **7.** 2.8 cm
8. 7.5 ft
9–18. [graph]

Lesson 9-1 pp. 458–463
Check Skills You'll Need 1. The graph is a line that starts at 3 and extends to the right without end.
2. The graph is a line that starts at 0 and extends to the left without end. **3.** The graph is a line that starts at 5 and extends to the left without end.
4. The graph is a line that starts at -2 and extends to the right without end.
Check Understanding 1a. C, N, V **b.** $\overline{NC}$, $\overline{NV}$
c. $\overrightarrow{NC}$, $\overrightarrow{NV}$ **2a.** $\overline{EH}$, $\overline{FG}$, $\overline{AE}$, $\overline{BF}$
b. $\overline{HG}$, $\overline{DC}$, $\overline{AB}$ **c.** $\overline{DH}$, $\overline{CG}$, $\overline{AD}$, $\overline{BC}$
3a. [diagram] **b.** [diagram] **c.** [diagram] **d.** [diagram] **e.** [diagram]

Lesson 9-2 pp. 465–469
Check Skills You'll Need 1. 135 **2.** 15 **3.** 90 **4.** 30
Check Understanding 1. 160°, 20°, 160° **2.** $\angle 1 \cong \angle 5$, $\angle 2 \cong \angle 6$, $\angle 3 \cong \angle 7$, $\angle 4 \cong \angle 8$; $\angle 3 \cong \angle 5$, $\angle 4 \cong \angle 6$

Lesson 9-3 pp. 470–474
Check Skills You'll Need 1. acute **2.** obtuse **3.** obtuse
4. right **5.** acute **6.** obtuse
Check Understanding 1a. scalene right triangle
b. isosceles obtuse triangle **c.** scalene obtuse triangle **2.** obtuse triangle **3a.** $P = 6x$
b. 96 cm

Lesson 9-4 pp. 476–479
Check Skills You'll Need 1. [triangle] **2.** [rectangle]
3. [pentagon] **4.** [hexagon] **5.** [heptagon]
Check Understanding 5. 35

Lesson 9-5 pp. 480–484
Check Skills You'll Need 1. $\angle X$ **2.** $\angle Z$ **3.** $\overline{XY}$ **4.** $\overline{ZX}$
Check Understanding 1. $\overline{AB} \cong \overline{DE}$, $\overline{BC} \cong \overline{EC}$, $\overline{AC} \cong \overline{DC}$, $\angle A \cong \angle D$, $\angle B \cong \angle E$, $\angle BCA \cong \angle ECD$, $AC = 50$ m **2.** $\overline{FJ} \cong \overline{FG}$, $\overline{JI} \cong \overline{GH}$, $\overline{FI} \cong \overline{FH}$, $\triangle JFI \cong \triangle GFH$ by SSS
Checkpoint Quiz 1 1. ray **2.** line **3.** $\overline{LN}$ **4.** angle
5a. $6x + 16 + 2x + 12 = 180$, $x = 19$ **b.** 50°
c. 130° **d.** 130° **6.** [triangle]

Lesson 9-6 pp. 486–490
Check Skills You'll Need 1. 36 **2.** 270 **3.** 54 **4.** 109
Check Understanding 1a. about $8\frac{4}{9}$ in.
b. about 188.4 mm **c.** about 628 mi
2. Blood Types of Population [pie chart]
Type O 155°, Type A 144°, Type AB 18°, Type B 43°
3. Student Jobs at Western High School [pie chart]
Restaurant 158°, Retail 84°, Auto 68°, Library 17°, Other 34°

Answers to Instant Check System™ **835**

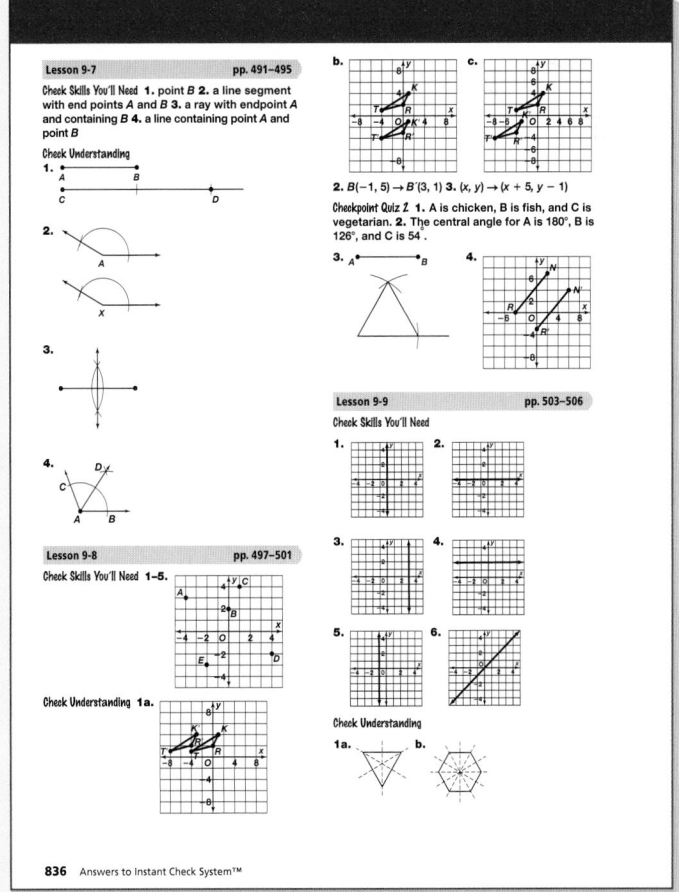

Lesson 9-7 pp. 491–495
Check Skills You'll Need 1. point B **2.** a line segment with end points A and B **3.** a ray with endpoint A and containing B **4.** a line containing point A and point B
Check Understanding
1. [diagram] **2.** [diagram] **3.** [diagram] **4.** [diagram]

Lesson 9-8 pp. 497–501
Check Skills You'll Need 1–5. [graph]
Check Understanding 1a. [graph]
b. [graph] **c.** [graph]
2. $B(-1, 5) \to B'(3, 1)$ **3.** $(x, y) \to (x + 5, y - 1)$
Checkpoint Quiz 2 1. A is chicken, B is fish, and C is vegetarian. **2.** The central angle for A is 180°, B is 126°, and C is 54°.
3. [diagram] **4.** [graph]

Lesson 9-9 pp. 503–506
Check Skills You'll Need
1. [graph] **2.** [graph]
3. [graph] **4.** [graph]
5. [graph] **6.** [graph]
Check Understanding
1a. [diagram] **b.** [diagram]

836 Answers to Instant Check System™

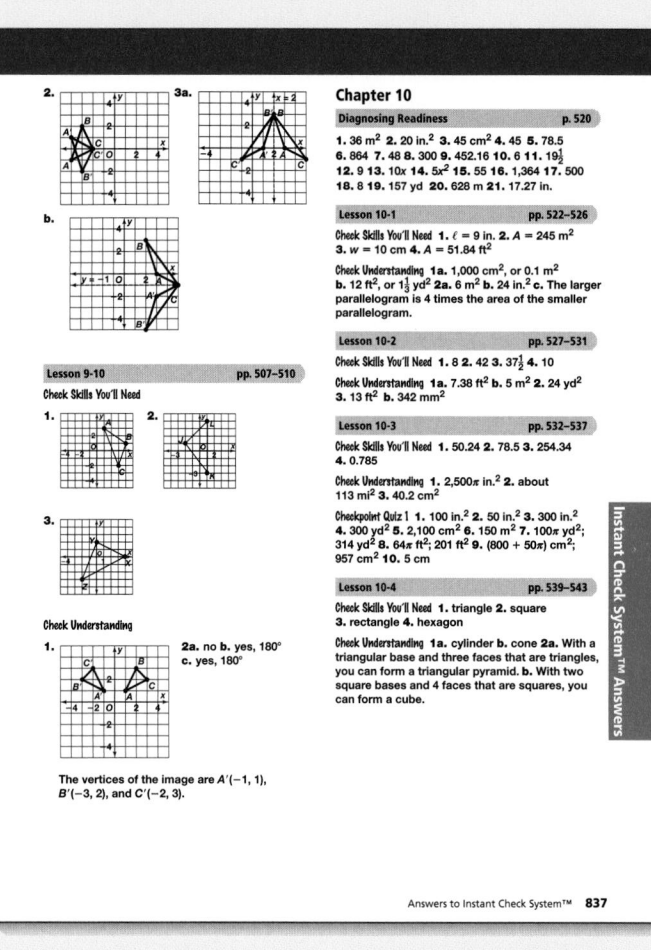

2. **3a.**

b.

Lesson 9-10 pp. 507–510

Check Skills You'll Need

1. **2.**

3.

Check Understanding

1.

2a. no **b.** yes, 180°
c. yes, 180°

The vertices of the image are $A'(-1, 1)$, $B'(-3, 2)$, and $C'(-2, 3)$.

Chapter 10

Diagnosing Readiness p. 520
1. 36 m² 2. 20 in.² 3. 45 cm² 4. 45 5. 78.5
6. 864 7. 48 8. 300 9. 452.16 10. 6 11. $19\frac{1}{2}$
12. 9 13. $10x$ 14. $5x^2$ 15. 55 16. 1,364 17. 500
18. 8 19. 157 yd 20. 628 m 21. 17.27 in.

Lesson 10-1 pp. 522–526
Check Skills You'll Need 1. $\ell = 9$ in. 2. $A = 245$ m²
3. $w = 10$ cm 4. $A = 51.84$ ft²
Check Understanding 1a. 1,000 cm², or 0.1 m²
b. 12 ft², or $1\frac{1}{3}$ yd² 2a. 6 m² b. 24 in.² c. The larger
parallelogram is 4 times the area of the smaller
parallelogram.

Lesson 10-2 pp. 527–531
Check Skills You'll Need 1. 8 2. 42 3. $37\frac{1}{2}$ 4. 10
Check Understanding 1a. 7.38 ft² b. 5 m² 2. 24 yd²
3. 13 ft² b. 342 cm²

Lesson 10-3 pp. 532–537
Check Skills You'll Need 1. 50.24 2. 78.5 3. 254.34
4. 0.785
Check Understanding 1. $2,500\pi$ in.² 2. about
113 mi² 3. 40.2 cm²
Checkpoint Quiz 1 1. 100 in.² 2. 50 in.² 3. 300 in.²
4. 300 yd² 5. 2,100 cm² 6. 150 m² 7. 100π yd²;
314 yd² 8. 64π ft²; 201 ft² 9. $(800 + 50\pi)$ cm²;
957 cm² 10. 5 cm

Lesson 10-4 pp. 539–543
Check Skills You'll Need 1. triangle 2. square
3. rectangle 4. hexagon
Check Understanding 1a. cylinder b. cone 2a. With a
triangular base and three faces that are triangles,
you can form a triangular pyramid. b. With two
square bases and 4 faces that are squares, you
can form a cube.

Lesson 10-5 pp. 545–550
Check Skills You'll Need
1. 31.4 in.
2. 26.4 cm
3. 25.1 ft
4. 21.3 in.
Check Understanding 1a. 84 yd² b. 336 yd² c. The
surface area of the larger prism is 4 times the
surface area of the smaller prism. 2. 108 m²
3. about 785 cm²

Lesson 10-6 pp. 552–556
Check Skills You'll Need 1. 10π 2. 15π 3. 5π 4. 22π
Check Understanding 1. 720 ft² 2. about 1,011 ft²
3. about 452 cm²

Lesson 10-7 pp. 557–560
Check Skills You'll Need 1. about 201 cm²
2. about 452 cm² 3. about 314 cm²
Check Understanding 1. 216 ft³ 2a. 1,900 ft³
b. The volume of the larger cylinder is 8 times the
volume of the smaller cylinder.

Lesson 10-8 pp. 562–565
Check Skills You'll Need
1. 2.
3.
Check Understanding 8a. 66 in.³; 52.5 in.³; 21 in.³
b. Yes; $5\frac{1}{2}$ in. by 8 in. by $1\frac{1}{2}$ in.
Checkpoint Quiz 1 1. square prism, 56 cm²
2. cylinder, 207 in.² 3. square pyramid,
85 cm² 4. 78.1 cm³ 5. 169.6 in.³
6. Check students' work.

Lesson 10-9 pp. 566–569
Check Skills You'll Need
1. $20.9\overline{3}$ 2. 32 3. $33.49\overline{3}$ 4. $0.52\overline{3}$
Check Understanding 1. 21 cm³ 2. 167 ft³
3a. 14,130 m³ b. 180 mi³

Chapter 11

Diagnosing Readiness p. 578
1. G 2. K 3. H 4. D 5. B 6. F 7. (−5, 4) 8. (2, 1)
9. (7, 0) 10. (−7, 1) 11. (4, −2) 12. (−6, −3)
13. 100 14. 36 15. 4 16. 81 17. 121 18. 0.04
19. 49 20. 5.29 21. 16 22. 25 23. 4 24. 25. 1
26. 10 27. 2 28. 60 29. 77 30. 26 31. 10 32. 32
33. 17 34. 8

Lesson 11-1 pp. 580–583
Check Skills You'll Need 1. 1, 4, 9, 16, 25, 36, 49, 64, 81,
100, 121, 144 2. 100; 400; 900; 1,600; 2,500; 3,600;
4,900; 6,400; 8,100, 10,000; 12,100; 14,400
Check Understanding 1a. 10 b. −10 c. 4 d. −4 2a. 5
b. −8 c. 7 d. −5 3a. irrational; because 2 is
not a perfect square b. rational; because 81 is a
perfect square c. rational; because it is a
terminating decimal d. irrational; because 42 is
not a perfect square

Lesson 11-2 pp. 584–589
Check Skills You'll Need 1. 52 2. 89 3. 130 4. 90
Check Understanding 1a. 5 ft b. 9 m 2. 12.7 m
3. 8.7 ft 4a. Yes, $7^2 + 8^2 = 113$.
b. No, $5^2 + 6^2 \neq 10^2$.

Lesson 11-3 pp. 592–596
Check Skills You'll Need 1. (−3, 4) 2. (0, 3) 3. (−4, −2)
4. (3, −1)
Check Understanding 1a. 4.1 b. 9.5 2. 17.5
3a. (4, 3) b. (−1, 0.5)
Checkpoint Quiz 1 1. −2 2. 4 3. 5 4. 9 5. −7 6. 10
7. 10 ft 8. 16.1 m 9. 25 yd 10. 7.1 cm 11. 9.2;
(−3, −5.5) 12. 15.8; (1.5, 6.5) 13. Answers may
vary.
Sample: $\sqrt{120}$, $\sqrt{299}$, 15.010010001 . . .

Lesson 11-4 pp. 598–601
Check Skills You'll Need 1. 4 2. 4 3. 32 4. 10
Check Understanding 3. $\overline{RQ}$ and $\overline{RP}$, $\overline{ST}$ and $\overline{SP}$
4. It allows you to draw the entire $40 + x$ side to
complete the larger triangle.

Lesson 11-5 pp. 602–606
Check Skills You'll Need 1. 10 m 2. 12 m 3. 45 m
4. 36 m
Check Understanding 1. 5.9 cm 2. 17 m
3a. $a \approx 6.9$ cm, $b = 8$ cm b. $e = 6$ in., $f \approx 10.4$ in.

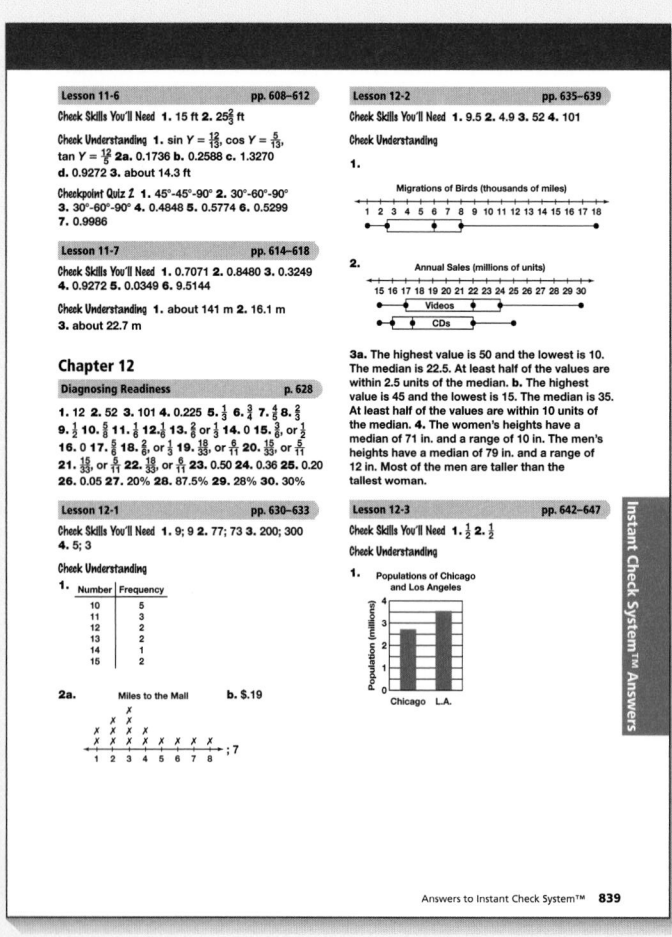

Lesson 11-6 pp. 608–612
Check Skills You'll Need 1. 15 ft 2. $25\frac{2}{3}$ ft
Check Understanding 1. $\sin Y = \frac{12}{13}$, $\cos Y = \frac{5}{13}$,
$\tan Y = \frac{12}{5}$ 2a. 0.1736 b. 0.2588 c. 1.3270
d. 0.9272 3. about 14.3 ft
Checkpoint Quiz 1 1. 45°-45°-90° 2. 30°-60°-90°
3. 30°-60°-90° 4. 0.4848 5. 0.5774 6. 0.5299
7. 0.9986

Lesson 11-7 pp. 614–618
Check Skills You'll Need 1. 0.7071 2. 0.8480 3. 0.3249
4. 0.9272 5. 0.0349 6. 9.5144
Check Understanding 1. about 141 m 2. 16.1 m
3. about 22.7 m

Chapter 12

Diagnosing Readiness p. 628
1. 12 2. 52 3. 101 4. 0.225 5. $\frac{5}{6}$ 6. $\frac{3}{4}$ 7. $\frac{5}{8}$ 8. $\frac{2}{3}$
9. $\frac{1}{2}$ 10. $\frac{7}{8}$ 11. $\frac{3}{8}$ 12. $\frac{4}{5}$ 13. $\frac{2}{3}$ 14. 0 15. $\frac{9}{10}$, or $\frac{9}{10}$
16. 0 17. 18. $\frac{8}{9}$ 19. $\frac{18}{33}$, or $\frac{6}{11}$ 20. $\frac{15}{33}$, or $\frac{5}{11}$
21. $\frac{13}{15}$, or $\frac{11}{15}$ 22. 23. 0.36 24. 0.36 25. 0.20
26. 0.05 27. 20% 28. 87.5% 29. 28% 30. 30%

Lesson 12-1 pp. 630–633
Check Skills You'll Need 1. 9; 2. 77; 73 3. 200; 300
4. 5; 3
Check Understanding

1.

Number	Frequency
10	5
11	3
12	2
13	2
14	1
15	2

2a. Miles to the Mall ; 7   b. $.19

Lesson 12-2 pp. 635–639
Check Skills You'll Need 1. 9.5 2. 4.9 3. 52 4. 101
Check Understanding

1.

Migrations of Birds (thousands of miles)

2.

Annual Sales (millions of units)
Videos
CDs

3a. The highest value is 50 and the lowest is 10.
The median is 22.5. At least half of the values are
within 2.5 units of the median. b. The highest
value is 45 and the lowest is 15. The median is 35.
At least half of the values are within 10 units of
the median. 4. The women's heights have a
median of 71 in. and a range of 10 in. The men's
heights have a median of 79 in. and a range of
12 in. Most of the men are taller than the
tallest woman.

Lesson 12-3 pp. 642–647
Check Skills You'll Need 1. $\frac{1}{2}$ 2. $\frac{1}{2}$
Check Understanding

1. Populations of Chicago and Los Angeles

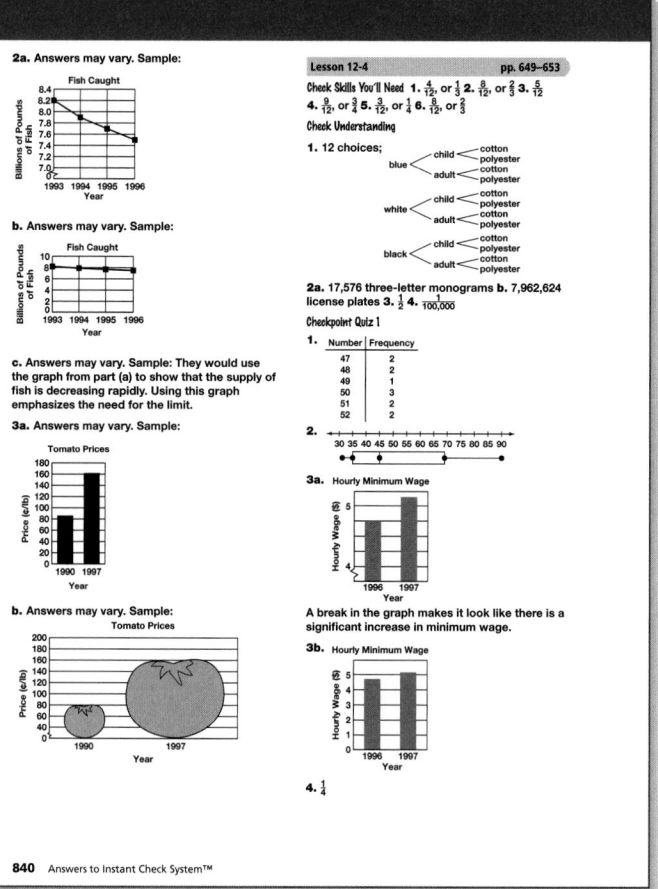

2a. Answers may vary. Sample:

Fish Caught

b. Answers may vary. Sample:

Fish Caught

c. Answers may vary. Sample: They would use
the graph from part (a) to show that the supply of
fish is decreasing rapidly. Using this graph
emphasizes the need for the limit.

3a. Answers may vary. Sample:

Tomato Prices

b. Answers may vary. Sample:

Tomato Prices

Lesson 12-4 pp. 649–653
Check Skills You'll Need 1. $\frac{4}{12}$, or $\frac{1}{3}$ 2. $\frac{2}{12}$, or $\frac{1}{6}$ 3. $\frac{5}{12}$
4. $\frac{9}{12}$, or $\frac{3}{4}$ 5. $\frac{3}{12}$, or $\frac{1}{4}$ 6. $\frac{8}{12}$, or $\frac{2}{3}$
Check Understanding

1. 12 choices;
blue → child: cotton, polyester; adult: cotton, polyester
white → child: cotton, polyester; adult: cotton, polyester
black → child: cotton, polyester; adult: cotton, polyester

2a. 17,576 three-letter monograms b. 7,962,624
license plates 3. $\frac{1}{2}$ 4. $\frac{1}{100,000}$

Checkpoint Quiz 1

1.

Number	Frequency
47	2
48	2
49	3
50	3
51	2
52	2

2. [line plot 30–90]

3a. Hourly Minimum Wage

A break in the graph makes it look like there is a
significant increase in minimum wage.

3b. Hourly Minimum Wage

4. $\frac{1}{4}$

Lesson 12-5 — pp. 654–658

Check Skills You'll Need 1. $\frac{9}{25}$ 2. $\frac{1}{9}$ 3. $\frac{2}{25}$ 4. $\frac{1}{9}$ 5. $\frac{2}{7}$ 6. $\frac{4}{5}$

Check Understanding 1. $\frac{1}{4}$ 2. 9% 3a. $\frac{3}{10}$ b. $\frac{3}{10}$

Lesson 12-6 — pp. 659–663

Check Skills You'll Need 1. 36 outcomes 2. 15,600 outcomes 3. 84 outcomes 4. 16 outcomes

Check Understanding 1. 120 2a. 20 b. 60 c. 120 d. 120 3. 20 ways 4a. 28 b. 56 c. 70 d. 56 5a. Combinations; the order in which the teacher selects the students does not matter. b. Permutations; the order in which students are chosen matters.

Lesson 12-7 — pp. 665–668

Check Skills You'll Need 1. 80% 2. 53% 3. 62.5% 4. 60% 5. 58.3% 6. 62.5%

Check Understanding 1. 52% 2a. The experimental probability is less than the theoretical probability. b. The experimental probability is likely to get closer to the theoretical probability of $\frac{1}{2}$.

Lesson 12-8 — pp. 669–672

Check Skills You'll Need 1. 112.5 2. 6,720 3. 400 4. 5,760

Check Understanding 1a. Not a good sample; these students would be most interested in racing bikes. b. Not a good sample; this sample would not include teens who do not rent videos. c. This is a good sample, because there is little built-in bias for or against any cereal. 2a. 200 calculators b. Less accurate; a larger sample is likely to be more representative of the population. c. The entire population might be too large to be surveyed. Also, the testing might be destructive, as would occur in testing light-bulb life.

Checkpoint Quiz 2 1. $\frac{2}{9}$ 2a. 380 outcomes b. 190 committees 3. $\frac{2}{15}$; 3 goals 4. 9,444 premium oranges

Lesson 12-9 — pp. 674–677

Check Skills You'll Need

letter	tally	frequency
a	┼┼┼	5
c	|	1
d	|	1
e	┼┼┼ |	6
f	|	1
i	||||	4
l	|||	3
m	||	2
n	||	2
o	|||	3
p	|	1
r	||	2
s	||	2
t	|	1
u	|	1
x	|	1

Check Understanding 6. Check students' work. 7. Check students' work.

Chapter 13

Diagnosing Readiness — p. 686

1. 40 2. -32 3. 17 4. 28 5. 0.64 6. 25 7. 2 8. 7 9. $3d - 12$ 10. $15x + 5$ 11. $3u - 24$ 12. $8y + 28$ 13. $-12d + 4$ 14. $50 - 30s$ 15. $-21 + 6w$ 16. $27 - 6b$ 17. $11a - 4$ 18. 5 19. $-g + 4$ 20. $10t + 5s$ 21. $7b + 4d$ 22. $-45c$ 23. $-10, -4, 2$ 24. $6, 0, -6$ 25. $-10, -2, 6$ 26. $-6\frac{1}{3}, -5, -3\frac{2}{3}$ 27. $10, 6, 2$ 28. $-7\frac{1}{2}, -8, -8\frac{1}{2}$ 29. $-1, 0, 1$ 30. $5, -1, -7$

Lesson 13-1 — pp. 688–692

Check Skills You'll Need 1. Start with 60 and subtract 12 repeatedly. 2. Start with 7 and add 5 repeatedly. 3. Start with 6 and multiply by 3 repeatedly. 4. Start with 60 and divide by 2 repeatedly.

Check Understanding 1a. 5 b. -3 2a. 7, 3, -1; start with 23 and add -4 repeatedly. b. $-\frac{2}{3}, \frac{2}{3}, 2$; start with -6 and add $1\frac{1}{3}$ repeatedly. 3a. 3; 324, 972, 2,916; start with 4 and multiply by 3 repeatedly. b. 0.5; 0.25, 0.125, 0.0625; start with 4 and multiply by 0.5 repeatedly. 4a. geometric; 243, 729, 2,187 b. neither; 34, 45, 58 c. geometric; -12, 12, -12 d. arithmetic; 650, 800, 950

Lesson 13-2 — pp. 694–697

Check Skills You'll Need 1. $-11, -1, 9$ 2. $2, 3, 4$ 3. $-4, 2, 8$ 4. $-5\frac{1}{2}, -5, -4\frac{1}{2}$

Check Understanding

1a.

x	$-2x^2 = y$	(x, y)
-2	$-2(-2)^2 = -8$	(-2, -8)
-1	$-2(-1)^2 = -2$	(-1, -2)
0	$-2(0)^2 = 0$	(0, 0)
1	$-2(1)^2 = -2$	(1, -2)
2	$-2(2)^2 = -8$	(2, -8)

1b.

x	$-x^2 + 3 = y$	(x, y)
-2	$-(-2)^2 + 3 = -1$	(-2, -1)
-1	$-(-1)^2 + 3 = 2$	(-1, 2)
0	$-0^2 + 3 = 3$	(0, 3)
1	$-1^2 + 3 = 2$	(1, 2)
2	$-2^2 + 3 = -1$	(2, -1)

2a. 2b. 3a. 3b.

Lesson 13-3 — pp. 699–702

Check Skills You'll Need 1. 25 2. 64 3. 243 4. 256

Check Understanding

1.

x	3^x	y	(x, y)
1	3^1	3	(1, 3)
2	3^2	9	(2, 9)
3	3^3	27	(3, 27)
4	3^4	81	(4, 81)

2.

x	$0.5(2)^x$	y	(x, y)
0	$0.5(2)^0$	0.5	(0, 0.5)
1	$0.5(2)^1$	1	(1, 1)
2	$0.5(2)^2$	2	(2, 2)
3	$0.5(2)^3$	4	(3, 4)
4	$0.5(2)^4$	8	(4, 8)
5	$0.5(2)^5$	16	(5, 16)

3.

x	$90\left(\frac{1}{3}\right)^x$	y	(x, y)
0	$90\left(\frac{1}{3}\right)^0$	90	(0, 90)
1	$90\left(\frac{1}{3}\right)^1$	30	(1, 30)
2	$90\left(\frac{1}{3}\right)^2$	10	(2, 10)
3	$90\left(\frac{1}{3}\right)^3$	$3\frac{1}{3}$	$(3, 3\frac{1}{3})$
4	$90\left(\frac{1}{3}\right)^4$	$1\frac{1}{9}$	$(4, 1\frac{1}{9})$
5	$90\left(\frac{1}{3}\right)^5$	$\frac{10}{27}$	$(5, \frac{10}{27})$

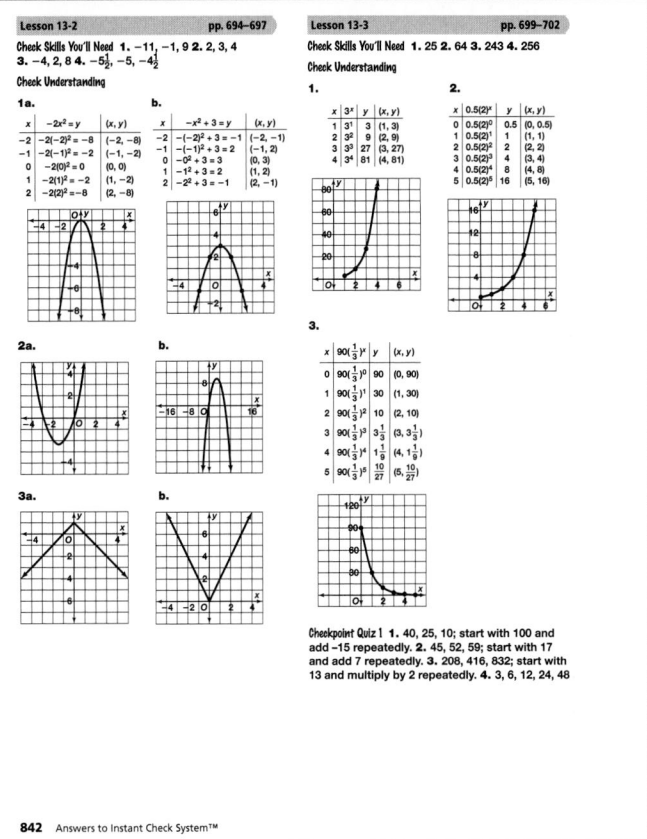

Checkpoint Quiz 1 1. 40, 25, 10; start with 100 and add -15 repeatedly. 2. 45, 52, 59; start with 17 and add 7 repeatedly. 3. 208, 416, 832; start with 13 and multiply by 2 repeatedly. 4. 3, 6, 12, 24, 48

5.

x	$\frac{1}{4}x^2$	y	(x, y)
-2	$\frac{1}{4}\cdot(-2)^2$	1	(-2, 1)
-1	$\frac{1}{4}\cdot(-1)^2$	$\frac{1}{4}$	$(-1, \frac{1}{4})$
0	$\frac{1}{4}\cdot 0^2$	0	(0, 0)
1	$\frac{1}{4}\cdot 1^2$	$\frac{1}{4}$	$(1, \frac{1}{4})$
2	$\frac{1}{4}\cdot 2^2$	1	(2, 1)

6.

x	$\frac{1}{4}\lvert x\rvert$	y	(x, y)
-2	$\frac{1}{4}\cdot\lvert-2\rvert$	$\frac{1}{2}$	$(-2, \frac{1}{2})$
-1	$\frac{1}{4}\cdot\lvert-1\rvert$	$\frac{1}{4}$	$(-1, \frac{1}{4})$
0	$\frac{1}{4}\cdot\lvert0\rvert$	0	(0, 0)
1	$\frac{1}{4}\cdot\lvert1\rvert$	$\frac{1}{4}$	$(1, \frac{1}{4})$
2	$\frac{1}{4}\cdot\lvert2\rvert$	$\frac{1}{2}$	$(2, \frac{1}{2})$

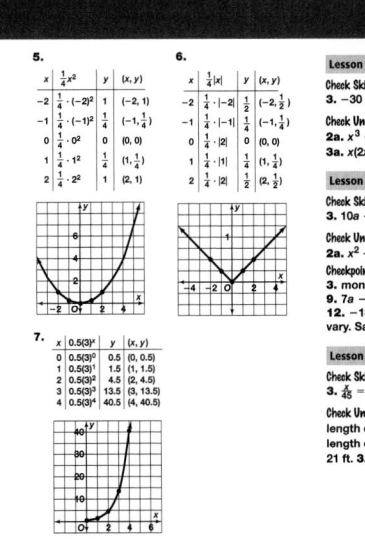

7.

x	$0.5(3)^x$	y	(x, y)
0	$0.5(3)^0$	0.5	(0, 0.5)
1	$0.5(3)^1$	1.5	(1, 1.5)
2	$0.5(3)^2$	4.5	(2, 4.5)
3	$0.5(3)^3$	13.5	(3, 13.5)
4	$0.5(3)^4$	40.5	(4, 40.5)

Lesson 13-4 — pp. 704–707

Check Skills You'll Need 1. -40 2. -24 3. -2 4. 28

Check Understanding 1a. No; the denominator contains a variable. b. Yes; it is the product of the variable m and the real number $\frac{1}{8}$. c. Yes, it is a real number. d. No, it is a sum. 2a. monomial b. binomial c. binomial d. trinomial 3a. -50 b. 13 c. 13 4. 264 ft

Lesson 13-5 — pp. 710–714

Check Skills You'll Need 1. $2x - 7$ 2. $5a - 4b$ 3. $m - 12n$ 4. $-6x + 3y - 5$

Check Understanding 1a. $9d^2 + 10d$ b. $4x^2 + 3x + 17$ 2a. $7x + 4y$ b. $9a^2 - 2a - 4$ c. $6g^2 - 2g - 1$ d. $-2t^2 + 3t + 9$ 3a. $2a^2 - 5a$ b. $9z^2 + 14z - 2$ c. $-2w^2 + 11 + 8v$

Lesson 13-6 — pp. 715–718

Check Skills You'll Need 1. $7v + 21$ 2. $3u - 24$ 3. $-30 + 15t$ 4. $9p + 72$

Check Understanding 1a. $3x^2 + 12x$ b. $2x^2 - 3x$ 2a. $x^3 + 2x^2 + 4x$ b. $4a^5 - 6a^4 + 6a^2$ 3a. $x(2x + 1)$ b. $2b(b^2 + 3b - 6)$

Lesson 13-7 — pp. 719–722

Check Skills You'll Need 1. $-4x - 2$ 2. $21 + 12y$ 3. $10a - 5b$ 4. $12m - 8n$

Check Understanding 1a. $x^2 + 5x + 6$ b. $y^2 + 5y + 4$ 2a. $x^2 - 3x - 10 + 4x$ b. $2m^2 + 7m + 6$

Checkpoint Quiz 2 1. monomial 2. binomial 3. monomial 4. trinomial 5. -8 6. 8 7. 10 8. 9 9. $7a - 6b$ 10. $2x^2 + 7x + 5$ 11. $g^2 + 10g + 24$ 12. $-18m^2 - 6m^3p - 30mp$ 13. Answers may vary. Sample: $x + 3$; $x^2 + 6x + 9$

Lesson 13-8 — pp. 724–727

Check Skills You'll Need 1. $7(-12) = -84$ 2. $11x = 132$ 3. $\frac{4}{45} = 3$ 4. $x^2 = 64$

Check Understanding 1. the length of the kite and the length of the tail 2. The tail is 12 ft plus twice the length of the kite. Together, the two lengths total 21 ft. 3. $18 = 12 + 2 \cdot 3$ 4. $3 + 18 = 21$

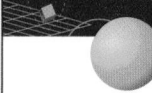

Selected Answers

Chapter 1

Lesson 1-1 pp. 6–7

EXERCISES **3.** Variable expression; n is the variable. **5.** Variable expression; x is the variable. **11.** $3b$ **15.** $2 - x$ **17.** $2 \cdot 12$ **21.** $4 \cdot 3$ **23.** Variable expression; d is the variable. **25.** Variable expression; g is the variable. **29.** $\frac{160}{16}$ **31.** $\frac{100}{12}$ **35.** $70a + 100b$ **37.** C **39.** A **47.** 72 **51.** 9,563

Lesson 1-2 pp. 11–12

EXERCISES **15.** 49 **23.** We must agree on an order of operations to ensure that everyone gets the same value for an expression. **25.** 24 **31.** 22 **33.** > **37.** > **39.** $(7 + 4) \cdot 6 = 66$ **41.** $(3 + 8 - 2) \cdot 5 = 45$ **43.** $4 \cdot 9 + 5$; 41 **45.** $17 - (25 \div 5)$; 12 **57.** $\frac{k}{20}$ **59.** $10d$

Lesson 1-3 pp. 16–17

EXERCISES **1.** 35 **5.** 1 **9.** 4 **13.** 14 **15a.** $55m$ **b.** 1,100 words **23.** 99 **29.** Answers may vary. Sample: You did not work within the grouping symbols first. **39.** 53 **41.** $19 - t$ **43.** $8 + n$

Lesson 1-4 pp. 20–22

EXERCISES **3.** −45 **5.** −50 **11.** 5 **13.** −9, −2, 8 **15.** −6, 0, 6 **17.** 2, 2 **21.** 4, 4 **23.** 9 **27.** 2 **29.** Answers may vary. Sample: 28 golf strokes over par **31.** 6 **33.** 2 **37.** −13 **39.** −23 **43.** < **45.** < **47.** $10h$ **49.** $r + n$ **51.** Answers may vary. Sample: My friend did not take into account the signs of the numbers. **53.** negative **55.** negative **67.** 24 **69.** > **71.** $c + 6$

Lesson 1-5 pp. 27–29

EXERCISES **1.** $-4 + 7$; 3 **3.** $-4 + (-2)$; −6 **7.** 3 **11.** −1 **15.** −13 **19.** 100 **23.** 23 **25.** −61 **27.** Negative; both numbers are negative. **29.** Zero; the numbers are opposites. **31.** 0 **35.** −40 **39.** > **41.** > **43.** −8 **45.** $-20 + 18$; −2 **47.** $120 + (-25)$; 95 **49.** 1 **53.** $158 **65.** > **69.** < **71.** $25 + 10n$; $55

Lesson 1-6 pp. 32–34

EXERCISES **1.** $-9 - (-2) = -7$ **5.** 1 **13.** −6 **21.** $2 + (-6)$; −4 **31.** −15 **35.** 170 **39.** −68 **41.** −30 **43.** 10 **45–47.** Answers may vary. Samples are given. **45.** $3 - 3 = 0$; $(-4) - (-4) = 0$ **47.** $1 - 7 = -6$; $-10 - (-4) = -6$ **51.** It decreases. **53.** −8°C **55.** −60 **59.** 66 **61.** −40 **87.** 7 **89–92.** Answers may vary. Samples are given. **89.** −7 **91.** 0 **93.** $100 + 6 \cdot 9$; 154

Lesson 1-7 pp. 38–39

EXERCISES **1.** 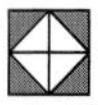 a square with four shaded corners

5. Start with 2 and add 5 repeatedly; 22, 27 **7.** Start with 1 and add 3 repeatedly; 13, 16 **11.** correct **13.** 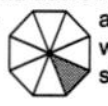 an eight-sided figure with bottom right eighth shaded

15. Start with 1 and add 0.5 repeatedly; 3.5, 4, 4.5 **17.** Start with 6 and add −2 repeatedly; −2, −4, −6 **19.** Incorrect; $8 + (-6)$ is 2, $2 < 8$. **27.** −7 **29.** 103 **31.** −2 **33.** $1{,}500n$; 36,000

Lesson 1-8 pp. 42–43

EXERCISES **1.** 36 laps/day **3.** $10.23 **5.** 11 pieces; 16 pieces **7a.** $59; $21 **b.** 10 people **13.** a circle divided into 5 pieces 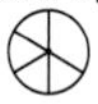 **15.** 0 **17.** 25

Lesson 1-9 pp. 47–49

EXERCISES **1.** $5 \cdot (-2) = -10$ **3.** $5(-5)$; −25 **9.** −18 **17.** −360 **23.** −7 **27.** −12 **29.** −2°C **31.** 0 **33.** Positive; the integers have the same sign. **35.** Negative; the integers have opposite signs. **37.** *A* **39.** *C* **43.** 4,661 **47.** −76 **53.** > **55.** = **57.** 12 **59.** −27 **73.** < **75.** < **77.** $60y$ **78.** $x + y$

Lesson 1-10 pp. 52–54

EXERCISES **1.** III **5.** II **9.** (−2, 4) **11.** (−8, 3) **15, 18.**

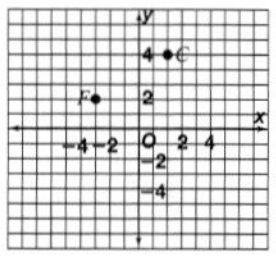

33. *P* **37.** (6, 6) **39.** (0, −4) **41.** IV **43.** II **47.** III **49.** y-axis **51.** triangle **53.** parallelogram

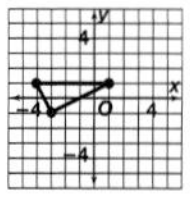

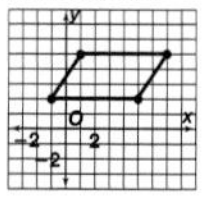

55. (0, −5) **57.** about 90° W, 32° N **59.** Frankfort, Kentucky **61.** 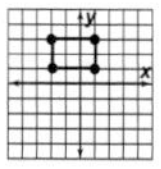

63. Answers may vary. Sample: 62a flips the figure across the y-axis. 62b flips the figure across the x-axis. 62c flips the figure across one axis and then the other. 62d doubles the lengths of the sides. **73.** −9 **75.** −925 ft **77.** −95 **81.** 3

Chapter 1 Review pp. 57–59

1. origin **2.** variable **3.** y-axis **4.** quadrants **5.** integers **6.** x-coordinate **7.** absolute value **8.** $x - 25$ **9.** $3n$ **10.** $10 - t$ **11.** $\frac{x}{4}$ **12.** $n + 5$ **13.** $y + 2$ **14.** 24 **15.** 12 **16.** 37 **17.** 19 **18.** 17 **19.** 20 **20.** 40 **21.** 450 **22.** 16 **23.** −17 **24.** 1,000 **25.** 9 **26.** −12 **27.** > **28.** > **29.** < **30.** = **31.** −30 **32.** −7 **33.** 12 **34.** 14 **35.** −15 **36.** −27 **37.** −11 **38.** −1 **39.** −20 ft **40.** Start with 0 and add 6 repeatedly; 24, 30, 36 **41.** Start with −18 and add 9 repeatedly; 18, 27, 36 **42.** Start with $\frac{1}{2}$ and add $\frac{1}{2}$ repeatedly; $2\frac{1}{2}$, 3, $3\frac{1}{2}$ **43.** 8 weeks **44.** $112 **45.** −42 **46.** −5 **47.** 72 **48.** 7 **49.** −3 **50.** −165 **51.** −8 **52.** 35 **53.** 102 **54.** (1, −3) **55.** (−2, 1) **56.** (−3, −3) **57.** (2, 2)

Chapter 2

Lesson 2-1 pp. 69–70

EXERCISES **1.** $(1 + 3) + 25$; $1 + (3 + 25)$ **3.** $215; Answers may vary.
Sample: $120 + 15 + 80$
$= 120 + (15 + 80)$ Assoc. Prop. of Add.
$= 120 + (80 + 15)$ Comm. Prop. of Add.
$= (120 + 80) + 15$ Assoc. Prop. of Add.
$= 200 + 15$ Add within parentheses.
$= 215$ Add.
5. Ident. Prop. of Add. **9.** Comm. Prop. of Mult. **15.** 3 **19.** 7.88 **23.** 90 **25.** 800 **27.** Assoc. Prop. of Mult. **31.** Ident. Prop. of Add. **35.** −10,000 **37.** $352 **47.** III **49.** II **51.** 12 h **53.** 72

Lesson 2-2 pp. 74–75

EXERCISES **7.** 784 **9.** 1,176 people **11.** −9 **13.** 21 **17.** $3(3x - 1)$; $9x - 3$ **19.** $4v - 12$ **21.** $-14z - 6$ **23.** $12a + 36$ **27.** $-7t + 28$ **31.** −55 **35.** −104 **37.** 1,792 miles **43.** $-15y - 24$ **45.** My friend didn't distribute the 7 to the t. **55.** Comm. Prop. of Mult. **57.** Assoc. Prop. of Mult. **59.** 1 **61.** −3

Lesson 2-3 pp. 78–79

EXERCISES **1.** 3, 5; none; −3 **5.** −3; none; none **7.** $7x + 10$ **9.** $4x + 2$ **13.** b **15.** $8r - 5$ **17.** $5g + 15$ **19.** $-m + 4d$ **25.** $-5a - 12$ **33.** Answers may vary. Sample: My friend added $x + y$ to get xy.

Lesson 2-4 pp. 82–83

EXERCISES **5.** false; $7 \neq 8$ **7.** true; $20 = 20$ **11.** $25 = v + 15$; open; variable **15.** yes **19.** no **21.** $140 + d = 192$; yes **23.** True; for example $3 + 2 = 7$. **25.** True; by definition, an open sentence is one that contains a variable. **29.** open; variable **31.** true; $12 = 12$ **33.** $(-20)(9) = -11$; false; $-180 \neq -11$ **35.** $48 \div 12 = 3$; false; $4 \neq 3$ **37.** yes; $-9 = -9$ **39.** no; $-6 \neq 6$ **47.** $4m + 7$ **49.** $6k - w$ **51.** 16 **53.** 8

Lesson 2-5 pp. 89–90

EXERCISES **5.** 28 **11.** $5{,}200 = s + 2{,}520$; 2,680 m/s **13.** 54 **21.** $108 = d - 42$; 150 million km **23.** 35; 35; −125 **31.** −49 **35.** Answers may vary. Sample: This year the Tigers won 22 games in all. **37.** 100 **39.** The student subtracted (rather than added) 6 on the right side. **53.** open; variable **55.** false; $2 \neq 3$ **57.** 48 **59.** 400

Selected Answers

Lesson 2-6 pp. 94–95

EXERCISES **17.** 23 **19.** 36 h **23.** 105 **27.** 40 **33.** 300 **37.** Dividing by 0 would result in $4 = 5$, which is not a true statement. **39.** no; $\frac{-18}{-3} \neq -6$ **41.** $-20y = 100$; −5 **43.** $7k = -168$; −24 **49.** −15,000 **61.** −11 **63.** −19 **65.** increase of 1,765 ft **67.** $7n$

Lesson 2-7 pp. 98–99

EXERCISES **1.** Answers may vary. Samples: 14 dimes, 2 nickels; 2 quarters, 6 dimes, 8 nickels **3.** 11 years and 12 years **5.** 16 ft^2 11. 2 CDs, 3 books **19.** −6 **21.** 2 **23.** Ident. Prop. of Mult. **25.** Comm. Prop. of Add.

Lesson 2-8 pp. 104–105

EXERCISES **1.** 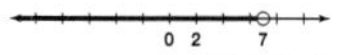

3. 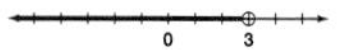

13. $x \le -2$

15. $x < 0$ **17.** $t \le 3$ **23.** $t > 7$ **27.** Use a solid dot for ≥ and ≤; use an open dot for > and <. **29.** $x \le -10$ **31.** $x < -\frac{1}{2}$ **43.** 5 **45.** $9 - s$ **47.** $52y$

Lesson 2-9 pp. 108–109

EXERCISES **3.** $x \ge 1$ 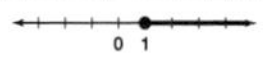

9. 64,000 lb **15.** $c > 14$ **19.** $y \le 8$ **21.** Add 3 to each side.

23. $y > -13$ 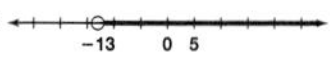

29. $b > 5$ 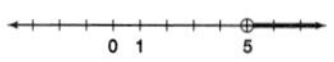

31. $13 + n > 15$; $n > 2$ **33.** ≤ $49

41. 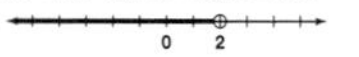

43. 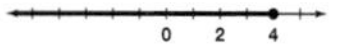

45. $2x + 12$ **47.** −35

Lesson 2-10 pp. 113–114

EXERCISES **7.** $k \le -8$ **11.** $f \ge -3$ **19.** $q > -18$ **25.** $h < 80$ **27.** unchanged **29.** reverses

31. $r \le -21$ **37.** $x \ge 4$ **41.** $7t \le 21$; $t \le 3$ **45.** You have to divide by −4 instead of 4. The direction of each inequality sign is different when you solve each inequality. **55.** $t > 11$ **57.** $r \le -14$ **59.** Dist. Prop. **61.** Assoc. Prop. of Add.

Chapter 2 Review pp. 117–119

1. d **2.** b **3.** e **4.** a **5.** c **6.** h **7.** j **8.** f **9.** g **10.** i **11.** 80 **12.** 700 **13.** 547 **14.** 6,500 **15.** 300 **16.** 105 **17.** 864 **18.** 496 **19.** 387 **20.** $4w + 36$ **21.** $24 + 48a$ **22.** $-42 + 14m$ **23.** You can write 15 as $5 \cdot 3$. $5x + 5 \cdot 3 = 5(x + 3)$ by the Distributive Property. **24.** $-3a + 7$ **25.** $7w + 9$ **26.** $9 - 3x$ **27.** $15 - 24n$ **28.** k **29.** $-17r + 31$ **30.** They have the same variable or no variable and are separated by addition or subtraction signs. **31.** $32 + 5 = 6 \cdot 6$; false **32.** $\frac{t}{17} = -3$; open **33.** $4 \cdot 20 = 80$; true **34.** $p + 1.75 = 6.50$ **35.** 11 **36.** 8 **37.** −5 **38.** 27 **39.** 128 **40.** −8 **41.** $6.50 **42.** 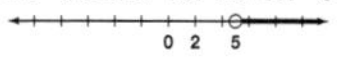

43. 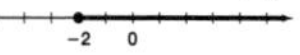

44. 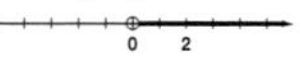

45. 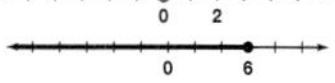

46. $t < 0$ **47.** $h > 12$ **48.** $n > 14$ **49.** $k \ge 2$ **50.** $s \le 3$ **51.** $m < -6$ **52.** $d < -14$ **53.** $c \le 36$

Chapter 3

Lesson 3-1 pp. 130–131

EXERCISES **1.** hundredths; 27.39 **3.** ones; 1,046 **5.** 345.7 **7.** 215 **11.** about 40 **13.** about $28 **15.** about $13.90 **19.** about 7.10 miles **21.** about $27 **23.** about 80 **27.** about 400 **33.** about 22,000 mi^2 **37, 39.** Answers may vary. Samples are given. **37.** about 30; rounding **39.** about 90; front-end **47.** $x \le 3$ **49.** $y \ge 0$ **51.** 7 bikes; 3 trucks **53.** −12 **55.** −30

Lesson 3-2 pp. 134–135

EXERCISES **1.** about 35 **5.** about 180 **7.** about $18 **9.** about 2 **15.** about $2.00 per pound **19.** about 380 **23.** about $6 **25.** Answers may vary: Samples are given. physical therapist: about $18/h in Dallas, about $16/h in Washington, D.C.; pharmacist: about $20/h in Dallas, about $21/h in Washington, D.C.; nurse: about $15/h in Dallas, about $18/h in Washington, D.C. **27.** about $2 **29.** reasonable; $72 \div 12 = 6$ **41.** about 39 **43.** about 12 **45.** Quadrant I **47.** Quadrant IV

Lesson 3-3 pp. 140–141

EXERCISES **1.** 58.9, 56, 56 **5.** 1.8 h, 1.8 h, 1.5 h **7.** 1 mode **9.** 1 mode **11.** 115; lowers mean by about 1.9 **13.** Mean; there likely are no outliers.

15. Mean; there likely are no outliers. **17.** Mean, median, or mode **19.** 5.8, 6.5, 6.5; median (or mode); the outlier (1.2) affects the mean too much. **21.** 7.8, 8, none; there is no mode and the mean and median are nearly the same. **23.** Mode; the data are not numerical. **25.** Median; there could easily be outliers. **33.** about 6 **35.** about $39.00 **37.** $6x + 10$ **39.** $x - 2t + 5$

Lesson 3-4 pp. 145–146

EXERCISES **1.** $d = 481.25$ m **3.** $t = 259.3$ s **5.** 67°F **7.** 60°F **9.** 55.4 mm **11.** 136.4°F **13.** 161.6°F **17.** 21 m; 24.5 m^2 **29.** 306 mL, 303 mL, 250 mL; mean **31.** −13 **33.** $n = 2t$; each n value is twice the t value below it.

Lesson 3-5 pp. 150–151

EXERCISES **3.** 26.1 **7.** $s + 599.01 = 686.98$; 87.97 days **9.** 23.7 **15.** $x - 13.50 = 26.50$; $40 **17.** 13.8 **19.** $r - 23.86 = 19.32$; 43.18 s **21.** 7.285 **25.** −10.5 **27.** 1.2 **31.** Add −1.8 to each side. **39.** 38.5 cm^2 **41.** −30 **43.** $1.30

Lesson 3-6 pp. 154–155

EXERCISES **5.** −25.1 **11.** $2.5m = 5.30$; $2.12 **13.** −1.94 **21.** 179 hits **23.** 2.3 **27.** −5.4 **29.** $-7.3n = 30.66$; −4.2 **31.** $\frac{n}{-2.35} = 400.9$; −942.115 **41.** − 5.3 **43.** 7.285 **45.** no; $8 \neq 3$

Lesson 3-7 pp. 159–161

EXERCISES **1.** C **5.** A **7.** 5 kg; the mass of a dog is much greater than the mass of 5 paper clips. **9.** 350 g; 350 mg is less than the mass of a paper clip. **13.** 3,010 **19.** 5.18 m **23.** Centimeter; the length is much less than a meter and much more than a millimeter, so meters are too large and millimeters are too small. **27.** Camille multiplied 6,392 g by 1,000, so she changed grams to milligrams. To change grams to kilograms she should have *divided* 6,392 by 1,000 to get 6.392 kg. **29.** mm **31.** cm **33.** 150 cm; 150 m is greater than the length of a football field. **35.** 1 g; 1 mg is closer to the mass of a speck of sawdust. **43.** 301,000,000 **45.** 3.068 kg **51.** A **53a.** 33,580 mm **b.** 0.03358 km **61.** $6t = 8.1$ or $t = \frac{8.1}{6}$; 1.35 s/knot **63.** about 90 **65.** $a \ge 21$ **67.** $r \ge -7$

Lesson 3-8 pp. 166–167

EXERCISES **1.** 107 digits **3.** 13 triangles **5.** 3.25 ft **7.** 80 sketches **17.** 0.27 **21.** 300 **23.** 91 **25.** about $12

Chapter 3 Review pp. 169–171

1. mean **2.** compatible numbers **3.** mode **4.** outlier **5.** median **6.** formula **7.** measures of central tendency **8.** perimeter **9–18.** Answers may vary. Samples are given. **9.** about 10; front-end **10.** about 4; rounding **11.** about 24; rounding **12.** about 10; rounding **13.** about 60; clustering **14.** about 7; rounding **15.** about 11.7; front-end **16.** about 6; rounding **17.** about 18; clustering **18.** about 6; rounding **19.** Answers may vary. Sample: You use rounding when only a rough answer is needed and the numbers are not clustered. You use front-end estimation when you need a better estimate of a sum. You use clustering when there are 3 or more numbers and there is one number that they are all close to. **20.** about 40 feet **21.** about 48 **22.** about 4 **23.** about 10 **24.** about 5 **25.** about 12 **26.** about 5 **27.** about −8 **28.** about −6 **29.** about 12 **30.** 5.4, 5, 2 and 5; no outliers **31.** 16.1, 16.2, 16.3; no outliers **32.** 36, 33, none; outlier: 57 **33.** 1.0, 0.2, 0.1; outlier: 7.9 **34–36.** Answers may vary. Samples are given. **34.** Mode; the data are not numerical. **35.** Median; there could easily be outliers. **36.** Mean; there likely are no outliers. **37.** 70 mi **38.** 384 mm^2 **39.** 37.68 in. **40.** 52 cm **41.** 7.1 **42.** 9.25 **43.** −2.01 **44.** 26.2 **45.** −9.1 **46.** 10.6 **47.** 2.5 **48.** 40.817 **49.** 11.3 **50.** 968.75 **51.** −19.4 **52.** −185.0125 **53a.** $3.2 + x = 2.64$ **b.** −$.56 **54.** Meter; a kilometer is too large unless you use fractional parts of a kilometer; centimeters are too small. **55.** Kilogram; a bicycle is heavy, so grams are too small. **56.** Milliliter; a liter is about the same as a quart, so liters are too large. **57.** 85 **58.** 0.16 **59.** 230 **60.** 1,600 **61.** 620 **62.** 0.08 **63.** A mature oak tree would be a number of meters tall. Centimeters is too small a unit. **64.** 1, 4, 9, 16, 25, 36, 49, 64, 81, 100

Chapter 4

Lesson 4-1 pp. 180–181

EXERCISES **5.** yes; ends in 0 **15.** yes; sum of digits is divisible by 3 **17.** 1, 2, 4 **21.** 1 row of 32; 2 rows of 16; 4 rows of 8 **23.** none **27.** 3, 9; $8 + 9 + 1 = 18$; 18 is divisible by 3 and 9 **33.** $1 \cdot 32, 2 \cdot 16, 4 \cdot 8$ **37.** $1 \cdot 53$ **39.** 7 **43.** Explanations may vary. Sample: Yes; a number divisible by 9 has 3 as a factor. **55.** cm **57.** 27

Selected Answers

Lesson 4-2 pp. 184–185

EXERCISES **1.** 8^3 **5.** 9^5 **9.** 64 **13.** 1,000,000 **15.** −15 **19.** 42 **21.** −212 **23.** 22 **25.** d^3 **27.** The student didn't multiply $a \cdot a \cdot a$. **29.** −16 and 16 **31.** −288 **37.** 243 **41.** Yes; $-a^2 = (-a)^2$ only when $a = 0$. **59.** none **63a.** 83 **b.** 82 **65.** $-3w - 7$

Lesson 4-3 pp. 189–190

EXERCISES **3.** Prime; it has only two factors, 1 and 31. **7.** Composite; it has more than two factors, 1, 3, 29, and 87. **11.** $2 \cdot 17$ **15.** $2 \cdot 3 \cdot 31$ **19.** 25 **23.** $6c^3$ **25.** prime **29.** 8 groups **33.** 4 **43.** Answers may vary. Sample: 6, 30 **63.** 20 **65.** 29 **67.** 1.8 **71.** 81 books

Lesson 4-4 pp. 194–195

EXERCISES **1.** $\frac{1}{4}, \frac{4}{16}$ **5.** $\frac{1}{3}, \frac{12}{36}$ **9.** $\frac{1}{4}$ **13.** $\frac{1}{3}$ **17.** $\frac{3x}{2}$ **21.** $8b$ **25.** $\frac{5}{8}, \frac{20}{32}$ **27.** $\frac{1}{4}, \frac{2}{8}$ **31.** $\frac{3}{4}$ **41.** Answers may vary. Sample: $\frac{6x}{10}, \frac{3xy}{5y}$ **51.** 2 **53.** $7a$ **55.** 2.62 **57.** −6.33

Lesson 4-5 pp. 199–200

EXERCISES
1. 15 days;

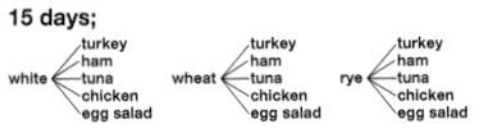

3. 15 pizzas **5.** 28 handshakes **7.** 36 blocks **17.** $\frac{1}{2}$ **19.** $\frac{2a^2}{5}$ **21.** Start with 10; add 10 repeatedly. **23.** Start with 2; multiply by 3 repeatedly.

Lesson 4-6 pp. 203–204

EXERCISES **1.** $\frac{4}{8}, \frac{5}{10}, \frac{6}{12}$ **5, 7.** Answers may vary. Samples are given. **5.** $-\frac{10}{18}, \frac{-5}{9}, \frac{5}{-9}$ **7.** $\frac{-4}{6}, \frac{-2}{3}, \frac{2}{-3}$

9, 13.

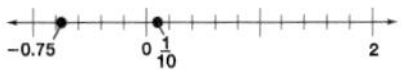

15. $\frac{2}{3}$ **21.** 44 ft/s^2 **25, 27, 29.** Answers may vary. Samples are given. **25.** $-\frac{4}{9}, \frac{-12}{27}, \frac{12}{-27}$ **27.** $\frac{-10}{26}, \frac{-5}{13}, \frac{10}{-26}$ **29.** $\frac{8}{8}$ **33.** $-\frac{1}{4}$ **37.** $\frac{4}{-5}, \frac{-12}{15}, -\frac{16}{20}$ **57.** −28 **59.** 31 **61.** −1 **63.** −4

Lesson 4-7 pp. 207–208

EXERCISES **9.** x^6y^5 **21.** m^{24} **29.** 7 **33.** 3 **35.** < **39.** $2x^4$; the two terms are being added, not multiplied. **49.** −4 **53.**

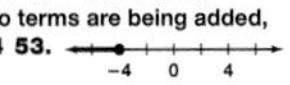

55. 8(1.50) + 10(1.25); $24.50

Lesson 4-8 pp. 213–214

EXERCISES **3.** $\frac{5y^5}{3}$ **23.** $\frac{1}{1{,}296}$ **25.** y^{-3} **27.** $m^{-2}n^{-2}$ **31.** 5 **35.** 900 times as much **39.** x^{-2} **41.** m^7n^{-7} **51.** 125 **53.** $16a^{16}$ **55.** about 20.2 **57.** 87, 88, 89

Lesson 4-9 pp. 219–220

EXERCISES **5.** 2.09×10^{-1} **7.** 5×10^9 km **9.** 0.00000002104 **13.** 0.0060502 **15.** 7.2×10^{-5} **17.** 3.508×10^{-4} **19.** 3.7×10^{-8}, 253×10^{-9}, 12.9×10^{-7} **21.** 3×10^9 **25.** 2×10^{10} lb **27.** 8,430,000 **29.** 5,880,000,000,000 mi **31.** $10^{-8}, 10^{-6}, 10^0, 10^5, 10^9$ **33a–b.** Answers may vary. Samples are given. Move the decimal point 4 places to the right and write 4.3×10^{-4}. Write $523.4 \times 10^5 = 5.234 \times 10^2 \times 10^5 = 5.234 \times 10^7$. **41.** x^2 **43.** $\frac{3m^2}{n}$ **45.** 0.9 ft/h **47.** 78 chimes

Chapter 4 Review pp. 223–225

1. factor **2.** simplest form **3.** rational number **4.** scientific notation **5.** exponents **6.** prime number **7.** 1, 2, 3, 4, 6, 12 **8.** 1, 2, 3, 5, 6, 10, 15, 30 **9.** 1, 2, 3, 6, 7, 14, 21, 42 **10.** 1, 2, 3, 4, 6, 8, 9, 12, 18, 24, 36, 72 **11.** 1, 3, 37, 111 **12.** 1, 2, 3, 4, 6, 7, 9, 12, 14, 18, 21, 28, 36, 42, 63, 84, 126, 252 **13.** 8 **14.** 27 **15.** 172 **16.** −25 **17.** 121 **18.** 58 **19.** 49 **20.** 16 **21.** prime **22.** composite; $2^2 \cdot 5$ **23.** prime **24.** composite; $2 \cdot 5 \cdot 11$ **25.** composite; $3 \cdot 29$ **26.** 4 **27.** 9 **28.** 1 **29.** $3x^2$ **30.** $2ab$ **31.** $3cd$ **32.** No factor of a positive integer is greater than the integer. **33.** $\frac{1}{5}$ **34.** $\frac{1}{2}$ **35.** $\frac{4}{13}$ **36.** $\frac{7}{10}$ **37.** $\frac{7}{11}$ **38.** $\frac{1}{6}$ **39.** x **40.** 5 **41.** $\frac{1}{4}$ **42.** $\frac{2}{5}$ **43.** $\frac{x}{3}$ **44.** $4b$ **45.** 24 days

46–49.

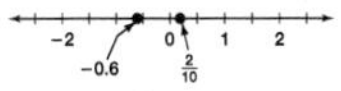

50. $\frac{2}{5}$ **51.** $\frac{7}{8}$ **52.** −1 **53.** $-\frac{4}{5}$ **54.** 128 **55.** $21a^6$ **56.** b^7c^4 **57.** x^{15} **58.** y^{20} **59.** 4,096 **60.** $\frac{1}{b^2}$ **61.** $\frac{7}{8y^5}$ **62.** 2×10^6 **63.** 4.58×10^8 **64.** 7×10^{-7} **65.** 5.9×10^{-9} **66.** 800,000,000,000 **67.** 0.0000032 **68.** 11,190,000 **69.** 0.000000000005 **70.** 4.3×10^{10}, 12×10^{11},

$3{,}644 \times 10^9$ **71.** 8×10^{-10}, 58×10^{-10}, 716×10^{-10} **72.** 2.4×10^{16} **73.** 1.8×10^{11}

Chapter 5

Lesson 5-1 pp. 235–236

EXERCISES **1.** 90 **9.** in 21 days **13.** 60 **17.** $24a^3$ **19.** $\frac{-2}{3} < -\frac{1}{3}$

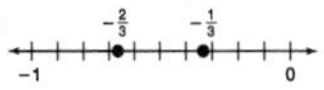

21. $\frac{11}{12} > \frac{7}{12}$

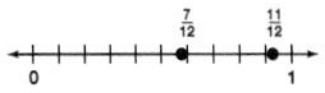

23. < **25.** > **27.** $\frac{3}{9} < \frac{5}{9} < \frac{7}{9}$ **29.** $\frac{2}{7} < \frac{2}{5} < \frac{2}{3}$ **35.** = **39.** Yes; $\frac{2}{3} > \frac{5}{8}$ **41.** 1,800 **45.** $72xy$ **49.** = **57.** Answers may vary. Sample: I would prefer Fran's method. The LCD of $\frac{5}{8}$ and $\frac{9}{12}$ is 24. It would be easier to work with smaller numbers. **65.** 1.394×10^{-3} **67.** 5×10^{-6} **69.** 4 **71.** $45x$

Lesson 5-2 pp. 240–241

EXERCISES **1.** 0.28 **5.** Yes, $\frac{5}{16} = 5 \div 16 = 0.3125$, so $10\frac{5}{16} = 10.3125$. **7.** $-0.1\overline{6}$; repeating; 6 **9.** $0.\overline{81}$ repeating; 81 **13.** 0.06, $\frac{2}{5}, \frac{6}{5}, \frac{3}{2}$ **15.** $\frac{22}{11}$, 2.01, 2.1, $\frac{22}{10}$ **21.** $6\frac{37}{100}$ **27.** $-\frac{1}{3}$ **29.** = **31.** < **33.** 5.375 **37.** −0.31 **39.** $\frac{7}{20}$ **43a.** Sarah: 0.286; Lizzie: 0.302 **b.** Lizzie; 0.302 > 0.286 **55.** $-\frac{5}{6}, -\frac{1}{3}, \frac{1}{6}, \frac{2}{3}$ **57.** $-\frac{6}{7}, -\frac{4}{7}, -\frac{3}{14}, -\frac{1}{14}$ **61.** $\frac{73}{7}$ **63.** $\frac{47}{10}$

Lesson 5-3 pp. 246–247

EXERCISES **3.** $\frac{7}{q}$ **7.** $-\frac{2}{5}$ **9.** $\frac{1}{12}$ **11.** $-\frac{7}{20}$ **15.** $13\frac{7}{8}$ **21.** $3\frac{13}{20}$ h **23.** Sample answer: 15 **27.** $1\frac{7}{8}$ in. **29.** $\frac{30 - 3n}{10n}$ **31.** $1\frac{11}{18}$ **33.** $7\frac{2}{5}$ **35.** $20\frac{3}{4}$ **45.** $\frac{3}{6}, \frac{4}{7}, \frac{5}{8}$ **47.** $-\frac{10}{9}, -\frac{9}{10}, \frac{9}{10}, \frac{10}{9}$ **49.** x^{12}

Lesson 5-4 pp. 251–252

EXERCISES **5.** $\frac{7}{10}$ **13.** $1\frac{1}{4}$ hours **17.** $-1\frac{1}{21}$ **25.** $1\frac{1}{2}$ **31.** $-\frac{3}{5}$ **37.** $\frac{35}{72}$ **41.** $-1\frac{7}{8}$ **45.** $\frac{2}{3w}$ **49.** $2\frac{1}{2}$ **57.** 4 mi; $2\frac{2}{15}$ mi **67.** $1\frac{23}{35}$ **69.** $\frac{3}{10}$ **73.** $4\frac{1}{2}$ **77.** 24 years old

Lesson 5-5 pp. 255–257

EXERCISES **1.** Ounces; it is closest to the weight of a paper clip. **3.** Miles; distances to continents would be measured in miles. **7.** $\frac{1}{2}$ **9.** $1\frac{1}{2}$ **13.** C **17.** E **21.** 78 **25.** 7 **31.** C **37.** 9,560 ft **39.** weight **43.** volume **45.** Pounds or ounces; tons are too large. **49a.** mile; about 3,740 mi **51.** yes **55.** no; 1 lb **59.** 10,000 **67.** $3\frac{1}{8}$ **85.** $\frac{9}{29}$ **87.** $1\frac{1}{5}$ **89.** $x + 3y$ **91.** $-3y$

Lesson 5-6 pp. 261–262

EXERCISES **1.** 8:30 A.M. **3.** the 12:15 P.M. bus **5.** 6 different amounts; \$.40, \$.45, \$.50, \$.55, \$.60, and \$.65 **7.** \$30 **19.** $\frac{3}{32}$ **27.** about \$48

Lesson 5-7 pp. 266–267

EXERCISES **5.** $\frac{1}{8}$ **7.** $\frac{1}{6}$ of the book **11.** $1\frac{1}{8}$ **15.** $2\frac{3}{4}$ **21.** Negative; $\frac{9}{10} > \frac{1}{2}$, so $\frac{1}{2} - \frac{9}{10} < 0$. **23b.** $60\frac{7}{8}$ in. **27.** $-\frac{7}{9}$ **33.** $13\frac{3}{8}$ lb. **45.** c **49.** yd **51.** 2.5 **53.** −28.125

Lesson 5-8 pp. 270–272

EXERCISES **13.** $\frac{1}{2}$ **21.** $\frac{3}{4}s = 9$; 12 sheets **25.** $\frac{7}{15}$ **29.** $7\frac{7}{15}$ **31.** Positive; a positive product means the two factors have the same sign. **35.** 20 weeks **39.** $3\frac{9}{13}$ **47.** 4 **63.** $\frac{1}{8}$ **65.** $3\frac{5}{8}$ **67.** $3r^5$ **71.** x^{13}

Lesson 5-9 pp. 276–277

EXERCISES **7.** $8x^6$ **21a.** $25s^4$ cm^2 **b.** Yes; The area of the tablecloth is $25s^4$ cm^2 which is greater than $20s^4$ cm^2. **25.** $\frac{81x^8}{10{,}000}$ **31.** $\frac{9t^4}{25}$ **33.** 1 **37.** 3 **39.** $-\frac{1}{27}$ **43.** $(3x^2)_2 = 9x^4$ ft^2 **49.** $-\frac{125}{512}$ **55.** $-\frac{1}{32y^{15}}$ **69.** $3\frac{1}{16}$ **73.** \$15.99 **75.** (4, 2) **77.** (4, 0) **79.** *H* **81.** *G*

Chapter 5 Review pp. 279–281

1. f **2.** c **3.** a **4.** b **5.** g **6.** d **7.** e **8.** 36 **9.** $56m^2$ **10.** 105 **11.** $30xy$ **12.** > **13.** < **14.** > **15.** = **16.** 0.6 **17.** $0.1\overline{6}$ **18.** 0.625 **19.** 0.3 **20.** 0.07 **21.** $\frac{1}{4}$ **22.** $\frac{5}{6}$ **23.** $5\frac{3}{5}$ **24.** $2\frac{4}{99}$ **25.** $3\frac{1}{12}$ **26.** $7\frac{2}{15}$ **27.** $\frac{30 + 3x}{5x}$ **28.** $\frac{7}{8}$ **29.** $\frac{7}{12}$ ft, or 7 in. **30.** $\frac{7}{40}$ **31.** $-\frac{4}{5}$ **32.** $1\frac{1}{5}$ **33.** $3\frac{3}{4}$ **34.** $\frac{1}{2}$ **35.** $2\frac{1}{2}$ **36.** $3\frac{3}{8}$ **37.** 60 **38.** 24 **39.** 96 **40.** 5,500 **41.** 2:30 P.M. **42.** 15 buses **43.** \$45.50 **44.** $2\frac{3}{8}$ **45.** $1\frac{2}{15}$ **46.** $1\frac{1}{3}$ **47.** $\frac{1}{54}$ **48.** $-\frac{8}{21}$ **49.** $\frac{2}{9}$ **50.** $16d^4$ **51.** 36 **52.** $a^{10}b^5$ **53.** $-\frac{1}{8}$ **54.** $\frac{x^2}{9}$ **55.** $\frac{16a^4}{c^8}$

Chapter 6

Lesson 6-1 pp. 290–291

EXERCISES **5.** $\frac{1}{10}$ **11.** $\frac{14}{25}$ **13.** 48 ft/s **15.** 52 mi/h **17.** $\frac{1}{2}$ **21.** $117\frac{1}{3}$ **25.** $\frac{4}{3}$ **27.** Anna; $\frac{3}{8}$ mi/h **31.** class A **39.** −1,728 **41.** $\frac{b^6}{a^3}$ **43.** =

Lesson 6-2 pp. 296–298

EXERCISES **5.** 8 **11.** 20 **17.** no, cross products not equal **23.** 15 posters **25.** no, cross products not equal **27.** no, cross products not equal **29.** 10 **31.** 72 **35.** 19.2 **39.** 17.5 **47.** 1 **51.** 40 defective chips **55.** $\frac{3}{1.65} = \frac{5}{x}$; \$2.75 **57.** $\frac{25}{2.5} = \frac{100}{x}$; 10 s **73.** $\frac{1}{100}$ **75.** $\frac{25}{14}$ **77.** true

Lesson 6-3 pp. 301–303

EXERCISES **1.** $2\frac{2}{5}$ ft **3.** $3\frac{1}{3}$ ft **7.** 5.6 ft **9.** 51 cm **11.** 144 km **13.** 99.6 cm **15.** 4 in. **19.** 1.2 m **21.** 45 km **23.** 7.5 km **25.** HO model; N model **27.** 4.5 in. **29.** 2 in. **31.** $1\frac{3}{4}$ in. **35.** 1 in. : 350 mi **37.** 1 in. : 10 ft **39.** 2.5 ft **51.** $5\frac{5}{8}$ **53.** 136 **55.** 0.375 **57.** 0.4375 **59.** 9, 9.5, 10

Lesson 6-4 pp. 308–309

EXERCISES **3.** $\frac{3}{6}$, or $\frac{1}{2}$ **5.** $\frac{2}{6}$, or $\frac{1}{3}$ **9.** $\frac{2}{8}$, or $\frac{1}{4}$ **13a.** $\frac{2}{3}$ **b.** not choosing green **15.** 3 to 2; 2 to 3 **17.** 0 **21.** $\frac{6}{11}$ **23.** $\frac{7}{11}$ **27.** 1 to 2; 2 to 1 **31.** 1 to 3; 3 to 1 **41.** $6\frac{2}{3}$mi **43.** 70 mi **45.** $\frac{2}{3}$ **47.** $5\frac{3}{20}$

Lesson 6-5 pp. 312–314

EXERCISES **5.** $\frac{1}{5}$ **9.** $2\frac{1}{5}$ **17.** 3.5 **21.** 0.4; $\frac{2}{5}$ **23.** 36% **29.** 111% **41.** 38.9% **43.** 64% **45.** 83.3% **47.** 450% **49.** about 80% **51.** 16.7% **53.** 33.3% **55.** 0.8, 80% **59.** $\frac{67}{100}$, 0.67 **61.** Yes; 100% − 17% = 83% **63.** Yes; the runner ran $1\frac{1}{2}$ times as far as she ran yesterday. **69.** < **75a.** 19 questions **b.** 20% **87.** $\frac{3}{8}$ **89.** $\frac{6}{8}$ or $\frac{3}{4}$ **91.** −0.175 **93.** −45

Lesson 6-6 pp. 318–319

EXERCISES **5.** 37.1 **23.** 627,000 people **25.** 150 **31.** 80% **47.** 8% **49.** $58.\overline{3}$% **51.** $10^{-2}, 10^{-1}, 10^0, 10^3$ **53.** $4 - c$

Lesson 6-7 pp. 322–323

EXERCISES **9.** $n = 1.5 \cdot 90$; 135 **17.** \$.96 **19.** about 83 million households **25.** $n \cdot 8 = 20$; 250% **29.** \$120 **31.** 50% **35.** 48 **45.** $\frac{35}{100} = \frac{n}{60}$; 21 **47.** Thursday

Lesson 6-8 pp. 327–328

EXERCISES **5.** 137.5% **9.** 20% **13.** 40% **21.** 43.7% **27.** 20.8% decrease **31.** Eva should compare 8 − 7 to 7, not 8. **33.** 20% increase **37.** 50% decrease **47.** 94% **49.** $-1\frac{5}{6}$ **51.** 75 **53.** 1

Lesson 6-9 pp. 331–332

EXERCISES **3.** \$55.50 **5.** \$8.55 **7.** \$3.99 **9.** \$73.92 **11.** \$27; \$73 **15.** \$37.50; \$87.50 **19.** \$17.25 **21.** store B; \$.11 **29.** 22.2%

34.

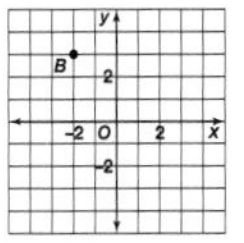

35. 7%

Lesson 6-10 pp. 336–337

EXERCISES **1.** about 8,934 people **3.** 6 orders **5.** 16 outfits **7.** 8 and 26 **11.** 3.5 cm **17.** \$27.30 **19.** $\frac{1}{2}$ **21.** $\frac{2}{13}$ **23.** $\frac{4x}{3y}$

Chapter 6 Review pp. 339–341

1. c **2.** b **3.** a **4.** d **5.** g **6.** e **7.** f **8.** $\frac{3}{8}$ **9.** $\frac{4}{7}$ **10.** $\frac{3}{4}$ **11.** $\frac{10}{13}$ **12.** 50 mi/h **13.** \$1.89/lb **14.** 90 words/min **15.** 35 **16.** 0.7 **17.** 49 **18.** 126 **19.** 45 **20.** 35 **21.** 0.5 cm **22.** $\frac{1}{8}$; 1 to 7 **23.** $\frac{2}{8}$, or $\frac{1}{4}$; 1 to 3 **24.** $\frac{3}{8}$; 3 to 5 **25.** $\frac{6}{25}$; 0.24 **26.** $\frac{18}{25}$; 0.72 **27.** $\frac{2}{25}$; 0.08 **28.** $\frac{1}{200}$; 0.005 **29.** 30% **30.** 33% **31.** 33.3% **32.** 35% **33.** 88.9% **34.** 2.1% **35.** 240% **36.** 0.6% **37.** $\frac{15}{100} = \frac{n}{48}$; 7.2 **38.** $\frac{20}{100} = \frac{30}{x}$; 150 **39.** $\frac{n}{100} = \frac{90}{300}$; 30% **40.** $\frac{125}{100} = \frac{100}{y}$; 80 **41.** $0.35 \cdot a = 70$; 200 **42.** $n = 0.68 \cdot 300$; 204 **43.** $n \cdot 180 = 9$; 5% **44.** $n \cdot 56 = 3.5$; 6.25% **45.** 25% decrease **46.** 75% decrease **47.** 20% increase **48.** 75% decrease **49.** \$8.75 **50.** \$1.70/lb **51.** 30 mi **52.** Check students' work.

Chapter 7

Lesson 7-1 pp. 350–351

EXERCISES **1.** Subtract 9 from each side. **3.** Add 6 to each side. **7.** −3 **13.** 16 weeks **19.** 6 **21.** \$4.45 **23.** −60 **25.** 15 **31.** 2 **33.** 14 **39.** 25% **41.** 3 to 4 **43.** $-3c + 8$

Lesson 7-2 pp. 355–356

EXERCISES **1.** 12 **7.** Jasmine: 30 marbles, Bill: 64 marbles **9.** 18, 20, 22 **11.** 10 **15.** 1 **19.** −12 **21.** 18 **25.** −15, −14, −13, −12, −11 **29.** First, use the Distributive Property and combine like terms. Next, subtract 8 from each side. Finally, divide each side by 12. **31.** 2 **41.** $\frac{2}{5}$ **43.** 48

Lesson 7-3 pp. 360–361

EXERCISES **1.** Subtract 3 from each side or multiply each side by 4. **3.** Multiply each side by 2. **5.** 10 **7.** 8 **9.** 10 **11.** 74 **15.** 6.5 **19.** 6 pencils **21.** $\frac{1}{2}$ **25.** −7 **33.** Answers may vary. Sample: First, combine like terms. Then divide each side by 0.85. **45.** 0 **47.** 12 gal **49.** c^4d

Lesson 7-4 pp. 364–365

EXERCISES **1.** \$60 **3.** 20 cm by 12 cm **7.** 28 posts **9.** 8 quarters and 8 dimes **17.** 60 **19.** $\frac{41}{200}$, 0.205 **21.** $\frac{41}{20}$, or $2\frac{1}{20}$; 2.05

Lesson 7-5 pp. 369–371

EXERCISES **1.** $a, -3a, -3a, -3a, \frac{-3a}{-3}, 5$ **9.** 3 **17.** 3 h **19.** −2 **23.** 2.9 **27.** The student subtracted $4x$ from the left side of the equation instead of adding $4x$; $x = -\frac{2}{3}$ **41.** \$11.25 **43.** \$41.28

45. $x > -8$

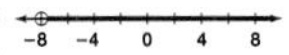

47. $y > -4$

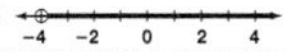

Lesson 7-6 pp. 375–376

EXERCISES **1.** Add 2 to each side, simplify, divide each side by 4, and simplify.

3. $a < -4$

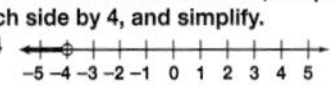

7. $a \geq 9$

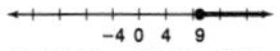

13. $y \leq -5$ **15.** $8t \geq 420$; $t \geq 52.5$; at least 52.5 mi/h **17.** $c \leq 72$ **19.** $y > 4\frac{4}{5}$ **35.** 3 **37.** 146.25 mi **39.** 48 cm/h

Lesson 7-7 pp. 380–381

EXERCISES **1.** 3; 3; 6, 6; 6, c **3.** $w = \frac{V}{\ell h}$ **9.** \$4,900 **11.** $h = \frac{2V}{\pi r^2}$ **15.** Answers may vary. Sample: Solve the equation for h and substitute the known values. **23.** $a \leq -3$ **25.** 6 weeks **27.** 31.3

Lesson 7-8 pp. 385–386

EXERCISES **1.** \$28; \$228 **3.** \$120.00 \$3,120.00 \$3,120.00 \$124.80 \$3,244.80 \$3,244.80 \$129.79 \$3,374.59 **7.** \$2,207.63 **9a.** 2%, **b.** 12 periods, **c.** \$760.95 **13.** \$13,821.43 **17.** Answers may vary. Sample: \$10,000 at 6%; \$13,000; \$13,382.26 **27.** $x = \frac{1}{4}y + \frac{9}{4}$ **29.** 3 in.

31.

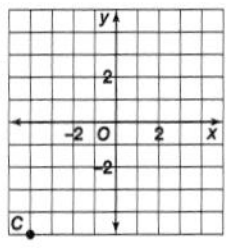

Chapter 7 Review pp. 389–391

EXERCISES **1.** compound interest **2.** principal **3.** balance **4.** consecutive integers **5.** interest rate **6.** simple interest **7.** interest **8.** −4 **9.** 2 **10.** 48 **11.** 3 **12.** 21 **13.** $1\frac{2}{3}$ **14.** $\frac{4}{5}$ **15.** −2 **16.** $-6\frac{3}{8}$ **17.** 39 **18.** 3.5 **19.** 8 **20.** −18, −17, −16, −15 **21.** $p - 0.15p = 29.74$; \$34.99 **22.** $10n + 20n + 147 = 1{,}167$; 34 tens, 34 twenties **23.** $a + 0.08a = 1{,}296$; \$1,200 **24.** 3 **25.** −4 **26.** $1\frac{1}{5}$ **27.** 4 **28.** −7 **29.** $\frac{2}{3}$ **30.** 2 h

31. $a > 7$

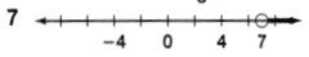

32. $y \leq -3$

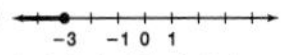

33. $c \leq \frac{2}{3}$

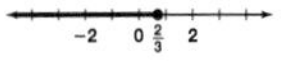

34. $x < -4$

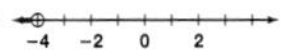

35. $x < -9$

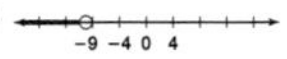

36. $b < 2$

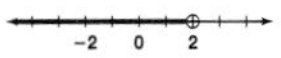

37. $x < 6$

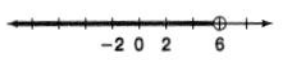

38. $x \geq -\frac{3}{5}$

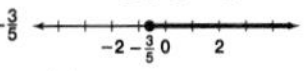

39. $799 + 25\left(\frac{c}{8}\right) \leq 1{,}000$; about 64 megabytes **40.** $m = \frac{r}{6k}$ **41.** $y = \frac{4}{3}x$ **42.** $g = \frac{Q}{p}$ **43.** $b = a + 2c$ **44.** $a = \frac{1}{3}w - \frac{5}{3}n$ **45.** $h = 6e - 66$ **46.** \$27 **47.** \$252.50 **48.** \$90.00 **49.** \$11,239.42 **50.** \$44,890.37 **51.** \$35,303.54 **52.** \$80,016.89 **53.** Answers may vary. Sample: Yes; with more interest periods, the interest would start earning interest earlier.

Chapter 8

Lesson 8-1   pp. 403–404

EXERCISES 1a. Yes; there is one range value for each domain value. **7.** No; subscribers of a specific age (domain value) may pay different subscription prices (range values).

11.   **13.**

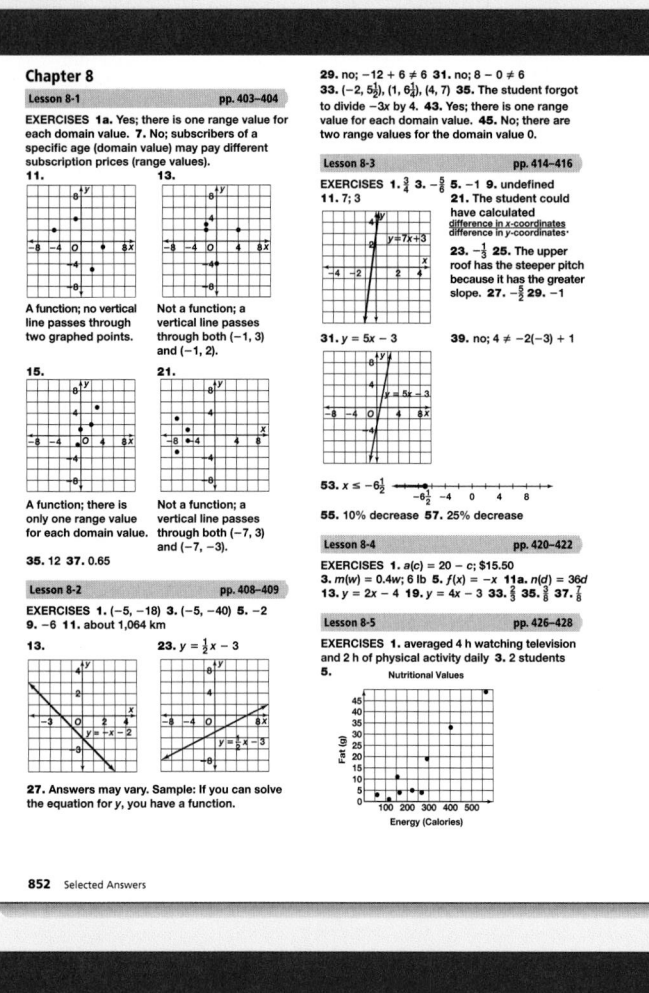

A function; no vertical line passes through two graphed points.

Not a function; a vertical line passes through both (−1, 3) and (−1, 2).

15.   **21.**

A function; there is only one range value for each domain value.

Not a function; a vertical line passes through both (−7, 3) and (−7, −3).

35. 12 **37.** 0.65

Lesson 8-2   pp. 408–409

EXERCISES 1. (−5, −18) **3.** (−5, −40) **5.** −2 **9.** −6 **11.** about 1,064 km

13.   **23.** $y = \frac{1}{2}x - 3$

27. Answers may vary. Sample: If you can solve the equation for *y*, you have a function.

---

29. no; −12 + 6 ≠ 6 **31.** no; 8 − 0 ≠ 6
33. (−2, 5½), (1, 6¼), (4, 7) **35.** The student forgot to divide −3x by 4. **43.** Yes; there is one range value for each domain value. **45.** No; there are two range values for the domain value 0.

Lesson 8-3   pp. 414–416

EXERCISES 1. $\frac{3}{4}$ **3.** $-\frac{5}{2}$ **5.** −1 **9.** undefined **11.** 7; 3 **21.** The student could have calculated ~~difference in x-coordinates~~ difference in y-coordinates. **23.** $-\frac{1}{3}$ **25.** The upper roof has the steeper pitch because it has the greater slope. **27.** $-\frac{5}{2}$ **29.** −1

31. $y = 5x - 3$ **39.** no; 4 ≠ −2(−3) + 1

53. $x \le -6\frac{1}{2}$

55. 10% decrease **57.** 25% decrease

Lesson 8-4   pp. 420–422

EXERCISES 1. $a(c) = 20 - c$; $15.50
3. $m(w) = 0.4w$; 6 lb **5.** $f(x) = -x$ **11a.** $n(d) = 36d$
13. $y = 2x - 4$ **19.** $y = 4x - 3$ **33.** $\frac{2}{3}$ **35.** $\frac{3}{2}$ **37.** $\frac{7}{8}$

Lesson 8-5   pp. 426–428

EXERCISES 1. averaged 4 h watching television and 2 h of physical activity daily **3.** 2 students
5.

Nutritional Values

---

7. No correlation; there is no apparent relationship. **11.** Negative; as one set of values increases, the other set tends to decrease. **13.** 10 min **15.** 3 students **17.** Negative; the lower the temperature, the more layers of clothing you wear. **21.** No correlation; the sets of data are not related. **31.** $y = \frac{5}{2}x$

33. $f(x) = -x + 7$ **35.** $h = \frac{2A}{b+c}$ **37.** $41.54

Lesson 8-6   pp. 432–433

EXERCISES 1a–b. Trend lines may vary. Sample is given.

State Populations and Cars

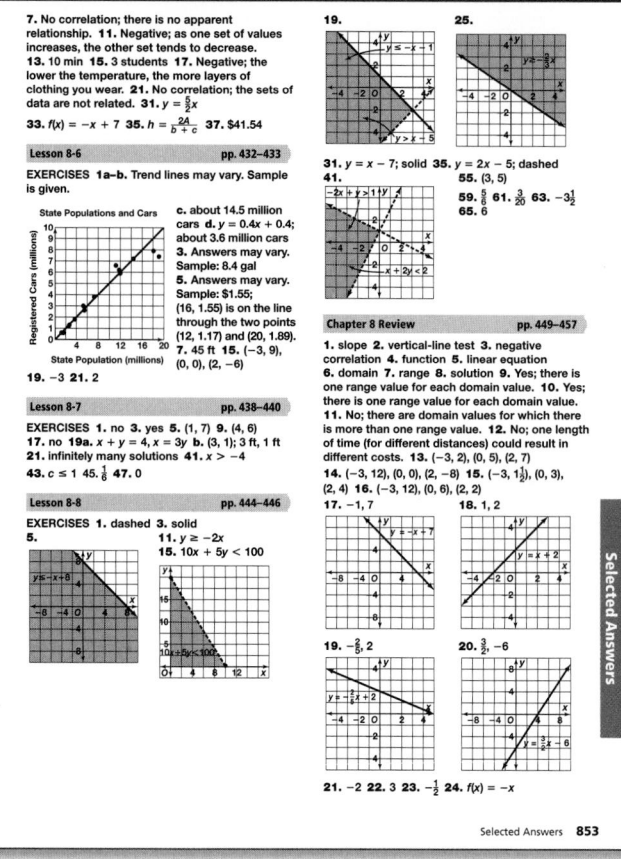

c. about 14.5 million cars **d.** $y = 0.4x + 0.4$; about 3.6 million cars
3. Answers may vary. Sample: 8.4 gal
5. Answers may vary. Sample: $1.55; (16, 1.55) is on the line through the two points (12, 1.17) and (20, 1.89).
7. 45 ft **15.** (−3, 9), (0, 0), (2, −6)

19. −3 **21.** 2

Lesson 8-7   pp. 438–440

EXERCISES 1. no **3.** yes **5.** (1, 7) **9.** (4, 6)
17. no **19a.** $x + y = 4$, $x = 3y$ **b.** (3, 1); 3 ft, 1 ft
21. infinitely many solutions **41.** $x > -4$
43. $c \le 1$ **45.** $\frac{1}{8}$ **47.** 0

Lesson 8-8   pp. 444–446

EXERCISES 1. dashed **3.** solid
5.

11. $y \ge -2x$
15. $10x + 5y < 100$

---

19.   **25.**

31. $y = x - 7$; solid **35.** $y = 2x - 5$; dashed
41.

55. (3, 5)

59. $\frac{5}{2}$ **61.** $\frac{3}{20}$ **63.** $-3\frac{1}{2}$
65. 6

Chapter 8 Review   pp. 449–457

1. slope **2.** vertical-line test **3.** negative correlation **4.** function **5.** linear equation **6.** domain **7.** range **8.** solution **9.** Yes; there is one range value for each domain value. **10.** Yes; there is one range value for each domain value. **11.** No; there are domain values for which there is more than one range value. **12.** No; one length of time (for different distances) could result in different costs. **13.** (−3, 2), (0, 5), (2, 7) **14.** (−3, 12), (0, 0), (2, −8) **15.** (−3, 1½), (0, 3), (2, 4) **16.** (−3, 12), (0, 6), (2, 2)
17. −1, 7 **18.** 1, 2

19. $-\frac{2}{3}$, 2   **20.** $\frac{3}{2}$, −6

21. −2 **22.** 3 **23.** $-\frac{1}{2}$ **24.** $f(x) = -x$

---

25. $y = 2x + 1$ **26.** $y = -x + 4$ **27.** $c(t) = 14t + 2$
28. 30 min **29.** about 620 calories **30.** Positive correlation; as the time bicycling increases, the calories used increases.
31. about 800 calories
32.   **33.**

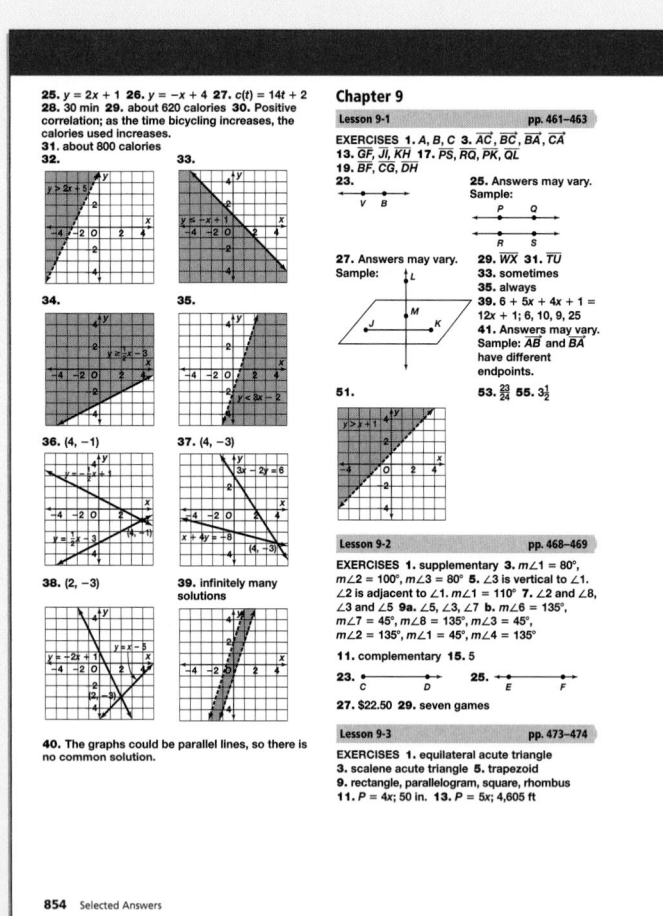

34.   **35.**

36. (4, −1) **37.** (4, −3)

38. (2, −3) **39.** infinitely many solutions

40. The graphs could be parallel lines, so there is no common solution.

Chapter 9

Lesson 9-1   pp. 461–463

EXERCISES 1. A, B, C **3.** $\overrightarrow{AC}$, $\overrightarrow{BC}$, $\overrightarrow{BA}$, $\overrightarrow{CA}$
13. $\overrightarrow{GF}$, $\overrightarrow{JI}$, $\overrightarrow{KH}$ **17.** $\overrightarrow{PS}$, $\overrightarrow{RQ}$, $\overrightarrow{PK}$, $\overrightarrow{QL}$
19. $\overrightarrow{BF}$, $\overrightarrow{CG}$, $\overrightarrow{DH}$
23.   **25.** Answers may vary. Sample:

27. Answers may vary. Sample: **29.** $\overrightarrow{WX}$ **31.** $\overrightarrow{TU}$
33. sometimes **35.** always
39. 6 + 5x + 4x + 1 = 12x + 1; 6, 10, 9, 25
41. Answers may vary. Sample: $\overrightarrow{AB}$ and $\overrightarrow{BA}$ have different endpoints.

51.   **53.** $\frac{23}{24}$ **55.** $3\frac{1}{2}$

Lesson 9-2   pp. 468–469

EXERCISES 1. supplementary **3.** $m\angle 1 = 80°$, $m\angle 2 = 100°$, $m\angle 3 = 80°$ **5.** ∠3 is vertical to ∠1. ∠2 is adjacent to ∠1. $m\angle 1 = 110°$ **7.** ∠2 and ∠8, ∠3 and ∠5 **9a.** ∠5, ∠3, ∠7 **b.** $m\angle 6 = 135°$, $m\angle 7 = 45°$, $m\angle 8 = 135°$, $m\angle 3 = 45°$, $m\angle 2 = 135°$, $m\angle 1 = 45°$, $m\angle 4 = 135°$
11. complementary **15.** 5
23.   **25.**

27. $22.50 **29.** seven games

Lesson 9-3   pp. 473–474

EXERCISES 1. equilateral acute triangle
3. scalene acute triangle **5.** trapezoid
9. rectangle, parallelogram, square, rhombus
11. P = 4x; 50 in. **13.** P = 5x; 4,605 ft

---

15.   **19.**

23. 19.5 in. **25.** trapezoid, parallelogram, rhombus **37.** 8 antique cycles **39.** 10

Lesson 9-4   pp. 478–479

EXERCISES 1. 4 mi **5.** 8 students **7.** 5 cm **11.** the dog **21.** equilateral triangle **23.** isosceles right triangle **25.** $\frac{7}{50}$, 14%
29. $\frac{1}{8}$, 12.5%

Lesson 9-5   pp. 482–484

EXERCISES 1. ∠D **5.** $m\angle D$, or 53°
15. $\overline{EB} \cong \overline{JF} \cong \overline{IL} \cong \overline{DH}$, $\overline{BD} \cong \overline{FE} \cong \overline{LJ} \cong \overline{HI}$, $\overline{DE} \cong \overline{EJ} \cong \overline{JI} \cong \overline{ID}$ **17.** $\overline{BC} \cong \overline{HG}$, $\overline{AB} \cong \overline{KH}$, ∠B ≅ ∠H, △ABC ≅ △KHG by SAS **19.** $\overline{ON} \cong \overline{RQ}$, $\overline{OM} \cong \overline{RP}$, $\overline{NM} \cong \overline{QP}$, △ONM ≅ △RQP by SSS **21.** $\overline{AB} \cong \overline{XY}$, $\overline{BC} \cong \overline{YZ}$, $\overline{AC} \cong \overline{XZ}$ **23.** $\overline{NL} \cong \overline{QR}$, $\overline{NM} \cong \overline{QP}$, ∠N ≅ ∠Q, △LNM ≅ △RQP by SAS **25.** $\overline{KM} \cong \overline{JM}$, $\overline{ML} \cong \overline{ML}$, ∠KML ≅ ∠JML, △KML ≅ △JML by SAS **27.** Incorrect; ∠R does not correspond with ∠N. **31.** Incorrect; ∠V and ∠C are not corresponding angles. **41.** 14 students
43. 0.15 · x = 12, 80 **45.** $\frac{3}{8}$, $\frac{1}{2}$, $\frac{5}{8}$ **47.** $\frac{1}{7}$, $\frac{1}{6}$, $\frac{1}{4}$

Lesson 9-6   pp. 489–490

EXERCISES 1. about 314 in. **3.** about 19.8 cm **5.** about 29$\frac{1}{3}$ m **7.** about 113 in. **11.** 180° **15.** 270° **19.** about 14.4 yd **29.** $\overline{AD} \cong \overline{CD}$, $\overline{BD} \cong \overline{BD}$, ∠ADB ≅ ∠CDB, △ADB ≅ △CDB by SAS **31.** Yes; there is one range value for each domain value. **33.** 256 times

Lesson 9-7   pp. 494–495

EXERCISES
1.

5.

9.   **11.**

13.

17. Answers may vary. Sample: In both constructions, you use the compass to draw intersecting arcs, and then use the points of intersection to draw the bisectors. **25.** 43° **27.** 18° **29.** 5 and 20 **31.** $3

Lesson 9-8   pp. 499–501

EXERCISES
3.   **7.**

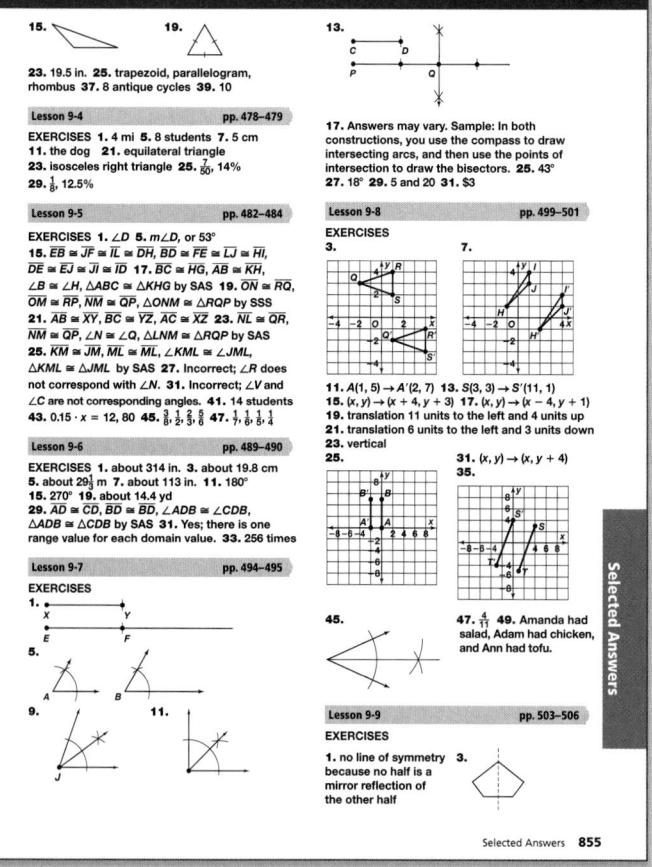

11. A(1, 5) → A′(2, 7) **13.** S(3, 3) → S′(11, 1)
15. (x, y) → (x + 4, y + 3) **17.** (x, y) → (x − 4, y + 1)
19. translation 11 units to the left and 4 units up
21. translation 6 units to the right and 3 units down
23. vertical
25.   **31.** (x, y) → (x, y + 4)
35.

45.   **47.** $\frac{4}{11}$ **49.** Amanda had salad, Adam had chicken, and Ann had tofu.

Lesson 9-9   pp. 503–506

EXERCISES
1. no line of symmetry because no half is a mirror reflection of the other half **3.**

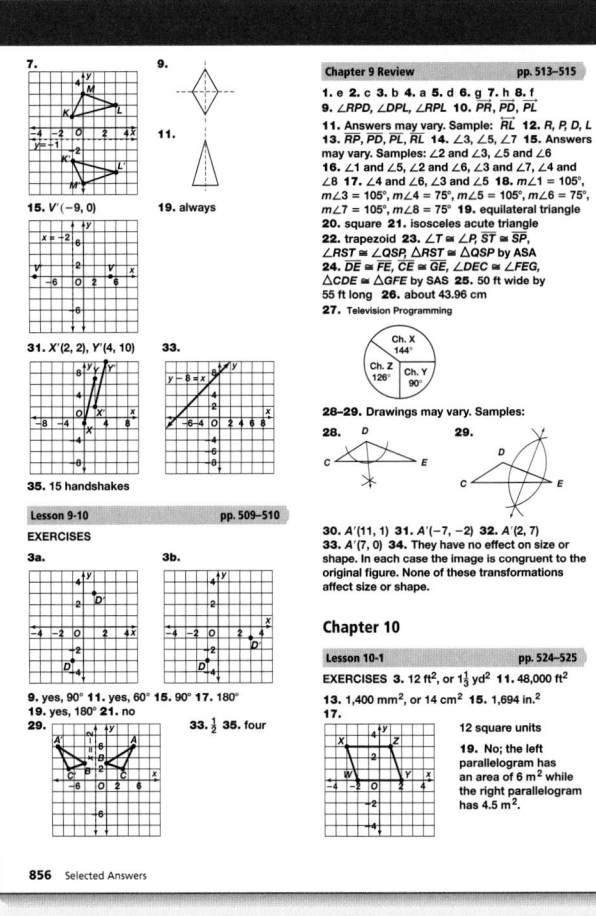

7.

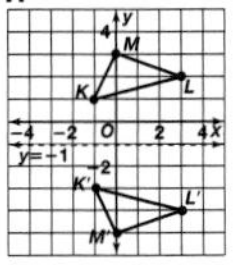

9.

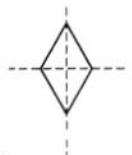

11.

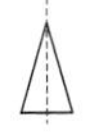

15. $V'(-9, 0)$

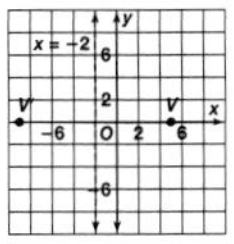

19. always

31. $X'(2, 2)$, $Y'(4, 10)$

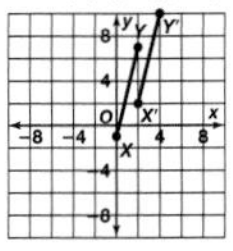

33.

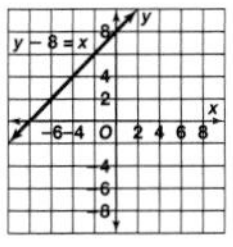
y − 8 = x

35. 15 handshakes

Lesson 9-10 pp. 509–510

EXERCISES

3a.

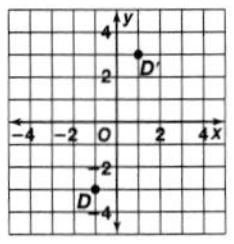

3b.

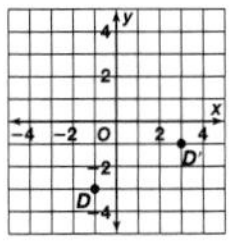

9. yes, 90° **11.** yes, 60° **15.** 90° **17.** 180° **19.** yes, 180° **21.** no

29.

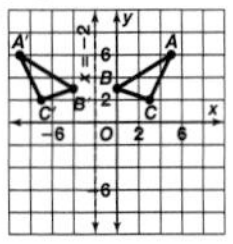

33. $\frac{1}{2}$ **35.** four

Chapter 9 Review pp. 513–515

1. e **2.** c **3.** b **4.** a **5.** d **6.** g **7.** h **8.** f **9.** $\angle RPD$, $\angle DPL$, $\angle RPL$ **10.** $\overrightarrow{PR}$, $\overrightarrow{PD}$, $\overrightarrow{PL}$

11. Answers may vary. Sample: $\overleftrightarrow{RL}$ **12.** *R, P, D, L* **13.** $\overline{RP}$, $\overline{PD}$, $\overline{PL}$, $\overline{RL}$ **14.** $\angle 3$, $\angle 5$, $\angle 7$ **15.** Answers may vary. Samples: $\angle 2$ and $\angle 3$, $\angle 5$ and $\angle 6$ **16.** $\angle 1$ and $\angle 5$, $\angle 2$ and $\angle 6$, $\angle 3$ and $\angle 7$, $\angle 4$ and $\angle 8$ **17.** $\angle 4$ and $\angle 6$, $\angle 3$ and $\angle 5$ **18.** $m\angle 1 = 105°$, $m\angle 3 = 105°$, $m\angle 4 = 75°$, $m\angle 5 = 105°$, $m\angle 6 = 75°$, $m\angle 7 = 105°$, $m\angle 8 = 75°$ **19.** equilateral triangle **20.** square **21.** isosceles acute triangle **22.** trapezoid **23.** $\angle T \cong \angle P$, $\overline{ST} \cong \overline{SP}$, $\angle RST \cong \angle QSP$, $\triangle RST \cong \triangle QSP$ by ASA **24.** $\overline{DE} \cong \overline{FE}$, $\overline{CE} \cong \overline{GE}$, $\angle DEC \cong \angle FEG$, $\triangle CDE \cong \triangle GFE$ by SAS **25.** 50 ft wide by 55 ft long **26.** about 43.96 cm

27. Television Programming

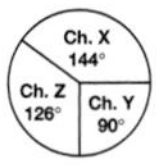
Ch. X
144°
Ch. Z
126°
Ch. Y
90°

28–29. Drawings may vary. Samples:

28.

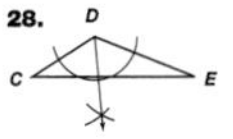
D
C
E

29.

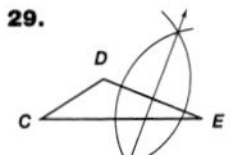
D
C
E

30. $A'(11, 1)$ **31.** $A'(-7, -2)$ **32.** $A'(2, 7)$ **33.** $A'(7, 0)$ **34.** They have no effect on size or shape. In each case the image is congruent to the original figure. None of these transformations affect size or shape.

Chapter 10

Lesson 10-1 pp. 524–525

EXERCISES **3.** 12 ft², or $1\frac{1}{3}$ yd² **11.** 48,000 ft²

13. 1,400 mm², or 14 cm² **15.** 1,694 in.²

17.

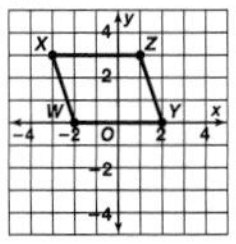

12 square units

19. No; the left parallelogram has an area of 6 m² while the right parallelogram has 4.5 m².

856 Selected Answers

32.

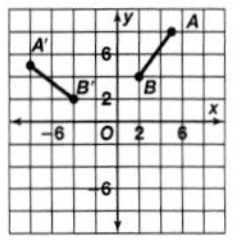

37. $\frac{4}{25}$ **39.** $4\frac{8}{9}$

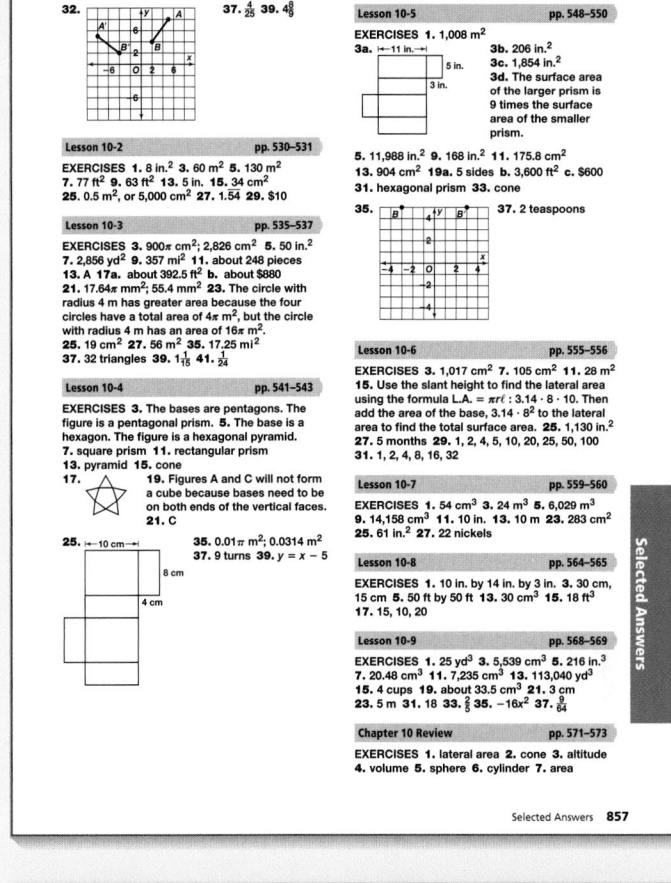

Lesson 10-2 pp. 530–531

EXERCISES **1.** 8 in.² **3.** 60 m² **5.** 130 m² **7.** 77 ft² **9.** 63 ft² **13.** 5 in. **15.** 34 cm² **25.** 0.5 m², or 5,000 cm² **27.** $1.\overline{54}$ **29.** $10

Lesson 10-3 pp. 535–537

EXERCISES **3.** 900π cm²; 2,826 cm² **5.** 50 in.² **7.** 2,856 yd² **9.** 357 mi² **11.** about 248 pieces **13.** A **17a.** about 392.5 ft² **b.** about $880 **21.** 17.64π mm²; 55.4 mm² **23.** The circle with radius 4 m has greater area because the four circles have a total area of 4π m², but the circle with radius 4 m has an area of 16π m². **25.** 19 cm² **27.** 56 m² **35.** 17.25 mi² **37.** 32 triangles **39.** $1\frac{1}{15}$ **41.** $\frac{1}{24}$

Lesson 10-4 pp. 541–543

EXERCISES **3.** The bases are pentagons. The figure is a pentagonal prism. **5.** The base is a hexagon. The figure is a hexagonal pyramid. **7.** square prism **11.** rectangular prism **13.** pyramid **15.** cone

17.

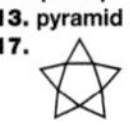

19. Figures A and C will not form a cube because bases need to be on both ends of the vertical faces. **21.** C

25.

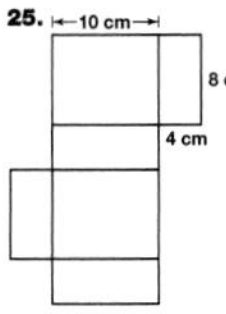
10 cm
8 cm
4 cm

35. 0.01π m²; 0.0314 m² **37.** 9 turns **39.** $y = x - 5$

Lesson 10-5 pp. 548–550

EXERCISES **1.** 1,008 m²

3a.

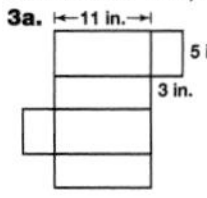
11 in.
5 in.
3 in.

3b. 206 in.² **3c.** 1,854 in.² **3d.** The surface area of the larger prism is 9 times the surface area of the smaller prism.

5. 11,988 in.² **9.** 168 in.² **11.** 175.8 cm² **13.** 904 cm² **19a.** 5 sides **b.** 3,600 ft² **c.** $600 **31.** hexagonal prism **33.** cone

35.

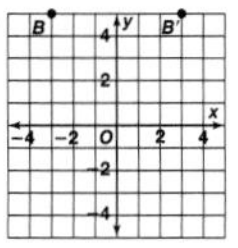

37. 2 teaspoons

Lesson 10-6 pp. 555–556

EXERCISES **3.** 1,017 cm² **7.** 105 cm² **11.** 28 m² **15.** Use the slant height to find the lateral area using the formula L.A. $= \pi r\ell$: $3.14 \cdot 8 \cdot 10$. Then add the area of the base, $3.14 \cdot 8^2$ to the lateral area to find the total surface area. **25.** 1,130 in.² **27.** 5 months **29.** 1, 2, 4, 5, 10, 20, 25, 50, 100 **31.** 1, 2, 4, 8, 16, 32

Lesson 10-7 pp. 559–560

EXERCISES **1.** 54 cm³ **3.** 24 m³ **5.** 6,029 m³ **9.** 14,158 cm³ **11.** 10 in. **13.** 10 m **23.** 283 cm² **25.** 61 in.² **27.** 22 nickels

Lesson 10-8 pp. 564–565

EXERCISES **1.** 10 in. by 14 in. by 3 in. **3.** 30 cm, 15 cm **5.** 50 ft by 50 ft **13.** 30 cm³ **15.** 18 ft³ **17.** 15, 10, 20

Lesson 10-9 pp. 568–569

EXERCISES **1.** 25 yd³ **3.** 5,539 cm³ **5.** 216 in.³ **7.** 20.48 cm³ **11.** 7,235 cm³ **13.** 113,040 yd³ **15.** 4 cups **19.** about 33.5 cm³ **21.** 3 cm **23.** 5 m **31.** 18 **33.** $\frac{2}{5}$ **35.** $-16x^2$ **37.** $\frac{9}{64}$

Chapter 10 Review pp. 571–573

EXERCISES **1.** lateral area **2.** cone **3.** altitude **4.** volume **5.** sphere **6.** cylinder **7.** area

Selected Answers

Selected Answers 857

8. 189 m² **9.** 14 cm² **10.** 6.25 yd² **11.** 79 m² **12.** 201 mm² **13.** 57 m² **14.** 31 in.² **15.** triangular prism **16.** square pyramid **17.** cylinder **18.** 164 cm² **19.** 205,513 m² **20.** 84 cm² **21.** 63 in.² **22.** 84 cm² **23.** 85 cm² **24.** 314 ft² **25.** 27 ft² **26.** 24 in. by 18 in. **27.** Find the area of the walk and garden, and then subtract the area of the garden. **28.** 384 units³ **29.** 18 units³ **30.** 311 units³ **31.** 268 units³

Chapter 11

Lesson 11-1 pp. 582–583

EXERCISES **3.** 1 **7.** −3 **9.** 3 **13.** 27 mi **17.** rational; because it is a repeating decimal **21.** irrational; it neither terminates nor repeats **23.** $\frac{2}{3}$ **25.** $\frac{3}{4}$ **31.** −10 **33.** 10 **35.** rational; repeating decimal **37.** x **41.** 5, −5 **43.** 2, −2 **57.** about 113 cm³ **59.** Yes; $\frac{17}{25}$ is 0.68, or 68%. Since 68% ≥ 65%, Shannon passed the test. **61.** 1, 2, 11, 22 **63.** 1, 3, 5, 9, 15, 45

Lesson 11-2 pp. 587–589

EXERCISES **1.** 13 cm **3.** 8 in. **5.** 20 in. **7.** 14 ft **9.** about 15.2 ft; about 30.4 ft **11.** 6.7 km **15.** yes; $6^2 + 7^2 = 85$ **17.** yes; $5^2 + 12^2 = 13^2$ **19.** 3.1 m **21.** 2.1 km **23.** yes; $3^2 + 4^2 = 5^2$ **25.** no; $10^2 + 24^2 \neq 25^2$ **29.** yes; $(\sqrt{2})^2 + (\sqrt{3})^2 = (\sqrt{5})^2$ **31.** about 131.9 in. **43.** irrational; because 12 is not a perfect square **45.** rational; because it is a terminating decimal **47.** $16x^8$ **51.** 2.1756×10^6 km²

Lesson 11-3 pp. 595–596

EXERCISES **1.** 5 **5.** 17.7 **7.** 19.3 **9.** (1.5, 2) **11.** 30; (0, 0) **13.** The student used subtraction in the numerators instead of addition. **15.** No; addition is commutative. **17a.** (−0.5, 3)

b. $AM = \sqrt{(-3-(-0.5))^2 + (5-3)^2}$

$MB = \sqrt{(2-(-0.5))^2 + (1-3)^2}$

$\sqrt{10.5} = \sqrt{10.5}$

23. yes; $8^2 + 15^2 = 17^2$ **25.** yes; $12^2 + 16^2 = 20^2$ **27.** 9 **29.** 12.5

Lesson 11-4 pp. 600–601

EXERCISES **1.** $\frac{20}{x+20} = \frac{13}{21}$; 12.3 m **3.** 1.2 mi **7.** $20 **11.** 6.3 ft² **17.** (0.5, 4)

19.

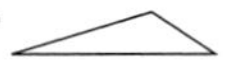

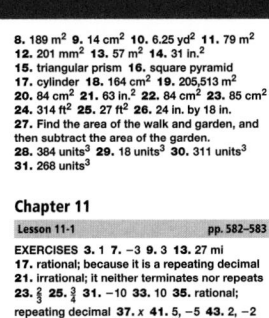

Lesson 11-5 pp.605–606

EXERCISES **3.** 7.6 in. **7.** 17 in. **11.** $x \approx 18.4$ cm, $y = 13$ cm **13.** Answers may vary. Sample: The hypotenuse is twice the shorter leg. Since the shorter leg is 10 ft, the hypotenuse is 20 ft. The longer leg is $\sqrt{3}$ times the shorter leg, which is $10\sqrt{3}$, or about 17.3 ft. **26.** 33 m **27.** about 25.1 in. **31.** Yes; for each domain value there is only one range value.

Lesson 11-6 pp. 611–612

EXERCISES **1.** 4 **3.** 5 **5.** $\frac{9}{15}$ or $\frac{3}{5}$, $\frac{12}{15}$ or $\frac{4}{5}$, $\frac{9}{12}$ or $\frac{3}{4}$ **9.** 0.9703 **15.** 19.3 ft

17. 1

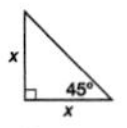
x
45°
x

21. Both are correct. The ratios include h, a known side length, and a known angle measure.

29. $4\sqrt{2}$ m, or about 5.7 m **31.** $13\sqrt{3}$ in., or about 22.5 in. **33.** 5, 2, −7

Lesson 11-7 pp. 617–618

EXERCISES **1.** about 30 yd **3.** 26.7 m **5.** about 71.6 mi **7.** angle of elevation = $\angle ADC$, angle of depression = $\angle BAD$ **13.** about 1,293.8 m **21.** 0.9848 **23.** 0.9703 **27.** 100π mm²; 314.0 mm² **29.** $3\frac{3}{4}$ c

Chapter 11 Review pp. 621–623

EXERCISES **1.** c **2.** f **3.** d **4.** e **5.** a **6.** b **7.** 1 **8.** −4 **9.** 7 **10.** 8 **11.** −6 **12.** 2 **13.** 3 **14.** 6 **15.** 8 **16.** 10 **17.** rational; because it is a terminating decimal **18.** rational; because 64 is a perfect square **19.** rational; because it is a repeating decimal **20.** irrational; because 15 is not a perfect square **21.** rational; because it is a repeating decimal **22.** It is irrational because the decimal neither terminates nor repeats. **23.** no; $1^2 + 3^2 \neq 3^2$ **24.** yes; $8^2 + 15^2 = 17^2$ **25.** yes; $(\sqrt{6})^2 + (\sqrt{10})^2 = 4^2$ **26.** yes; $30^2 + 40^2 = 50^2$ **27.** 3.6 **28.** 5 **29.** 12.6 **30.** 2.2 **31.** 9.2 **32.** 13.4 **33.** (2, 4) **34.** (3, 4) **35.** (−2, 2) **36.** (4.5, 10) **37.** (−12, −8) **38.** (2.5, −0.5) **39.** about 337.5 ft **40.** $a = 6$ in., $b \approx 10.4$ in. **41.** $y \approx 9.9$ m **42.** $f = 4$ ft, $c \approx 3.5$ ft **43.** $g \approx 10.6$ mm **44.** 0.2756 **45.** 7.1154 **46.** 0.9063 **47.** 0.0524 **48.** 0.9986 **49.** 0.2924 **50.** 0.6947 **51.** 1.0000 **52.** 0.9816 **53.** 0.2309 **54.** 8 ft **55.** 99 ft

858 Selected Answers

Chapter 12

Lesson 12-1 pp. 632–633

EXERCISES

1.

Number	Frequency
0	2
1	2
2	2
3	2
4	2

5. Rolls of a Number Cube

Number	Frequency
1	4
2	3
3	3
4	2
5	3
6	2

7.

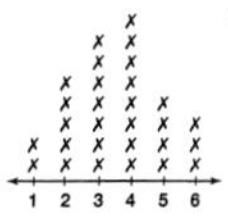

9.

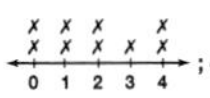
; 4

13. Numbers of Letters

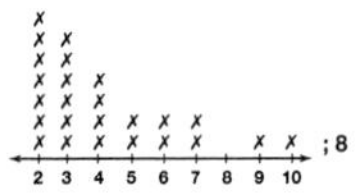
; 8

15. Ages of Club Members

Age	Frequency
12	3
13	1
14	4
15	4
16	3

Ages of Club Members

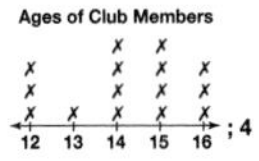
; 4

21. 4, 8, 12; 8 **23.** 400; 400 **25.** 25; 25 **33.** $\angle R$ **35.** LM **37.** 13.875, 13, no mode

Lesson 12-2 pp. 638–639

EXERCISES **1.** Maximum Speeds of Animals (mi/h)

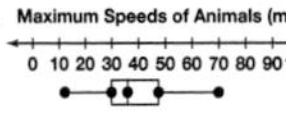

3.

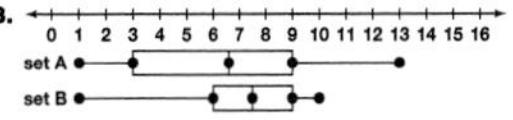
set A
set B

5. $60; $70; $85 **7.** Answers may vary. Sample: The orca weights have a median of 3,000 lb and a range of 2,000 lb. The hippopotamus weights have a median of 2,500 lb and a range of 1,800 lb. A significant number of the orcas and hippos in this comparison fall within the same weight range.

9. The acreages vary considerably, from about 25 acres to about 650 acres. However, about half of the parks are between 50 and 250 acres, with a median of 125 acres. **11.** Answers may vary. Sample: The student assumed that the lower value, the upper value, and the quartiles are equally spaced.

17.

Number	Frequency
4	2
5	3
6	5
7	4
8	4

19. 7.2 **23a.** 7,650 blades of grass **23b.** about 2.18×10^{15} blades of grass

Lesson 12-3 pp. 645–647

EXERCISES **1.** *American Ampersand* **3.** You might compare the lengths of the bars without noticing the break in the scale. **5.** It suggests that the percent is rising rapidly, by putting 1989 and 1993 very close together.

7.

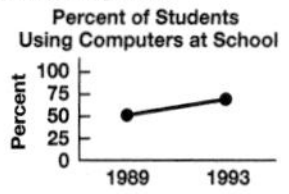
Percent of Students
Using Computers at School
Percent
1989
1993

11a.

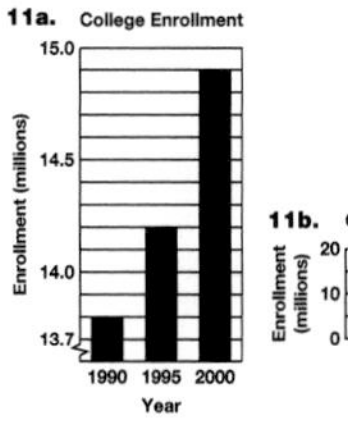
College Enrollment
Enrollment (millions)
Year

11b.

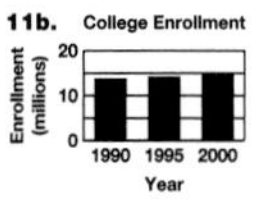
College Enrollment
Enrollment (millions)
Year

13. nearly 2 to 1; about 1.14 to 1

23.

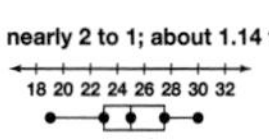

25.

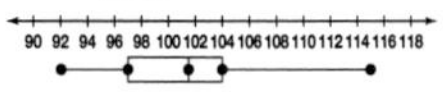

27. $\frac{3}{10}$ **29.** $\frac{7}{10}$

Selected Answers

Selected Answers 859

Selected Answers

T797

Lesson 12-4 pp. 652–653

EXERCISES
1. 10 choices

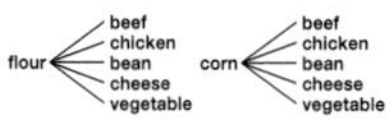

3. 28 routes **5.** $\frac{1}{8}$ **7.** $\frac{7}{8}$ **9.** $\frac{1}{125{,}000}$
11. 15 sweaters **13.** $\frac{3}{15}$, or $\frac{1}{3}$ **15.** $\frac{5}{104}$
21.

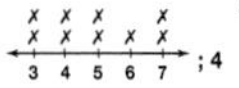

; 4 **23.** (0, 2)

Lesson 12-5 pp. 657–658

EXERCISES **3.** $\frac{2}{30}$, or $\frac{1}{18}$ **7.** about 83% **11.** $\frac{4}{90}$, or $\frac{2}{45}$
13. $\frac{24}{90}$, or $\frac{4}{15}$ **15.** Independent; the possibilities on the second roll are the same as on the first.
17. $\frac{9}{100}$ **19.** $\frac{6}{100}$, or $\frac{3}{50}$ **21.** $\frac{20}{72}$, or $\frac{5}{18}$ **23.** $\frac{20}{72}$, or $\frac{5}{18}$
33. $\frac{6}{10}$ or $\frac{3}{5}$, $\frac{8}{10}$, or $\frac{4}{5}$, $\frac{6}{8}$, or $\frac{3}{4}$

Lesson 12-6 pp. 662–663

EXERCISES **1.** 6 **3.** 120 **5.** 360 **7.** 1,814,400
9. 3; CA, CT, AT **11.** 10; VA, VL, VU, VE, AL, AU, AE, LU, LE, UE **15.** 45 **17.** 20 sandwiches
19. Combinations; the order of the shirts selected does not matter. **21.** 720 **27.** 2 **31.** 20 **37.** $\frac{1}{25}$
39. 120 $in.^2$

Lesson 12-7 pp. 667–668

EXERCISES **3.** 13.2% **5.** 77.9% **9.** $\frac{1}{2}$ **11.** $\frac{3}{8}$
21. 720 **23.** 20 **25.** $(x, y) \rightarrow (x + 7, y + 4)$

Lesson 12-8 pp. 671–672

EXERCISES **3.** Not a good sample; it excludes students not interested in basketball.
5. 2,240 pairs **7.** Not a good sample; it excludes people who dislike that particular restaurant.
9a. The cold virus may be passed from student to student in that class so that more of them have colds than in the total school population.
9b. Answers may vary. Sample: Survey students as they enter the school cafeteria.
17. $\frac{9}{26}$ **21.** 495 combinations
23. 506.25π $in.^2$; 1,590 $in.^2$

Lesson 12-9 pp. 676–677

EXERCISES **1.** Answers may vary. Sample: Simulate the problem by tossing a coin. Let heads be a girl and tails be a boy. Toss the coin 100 times and organize the results into 20 groups of five. Count the number of groups with exactly three tails. Divide this number by 20 to get the experimental probability. **5.** \$67.50 **9.** $\frac{1}{10{,}000}$
15. 2,960 wrenches **17.** 4 **19.** 7

Chapter 12 Review pp. 679–681

EXERCISES **1.** combination **2.** sample
3. theoretical probability **4.** permutation
5. range **6.** frequency table **7.** dependent events
8. random sample

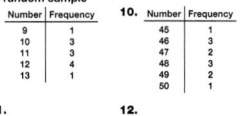

9.

Number	Frequency
9	1
10	3
11	3
12	4
13	1

10.

Number	Frequency
45	1
46	3
47	2
48	3
49	2
50	1

11.

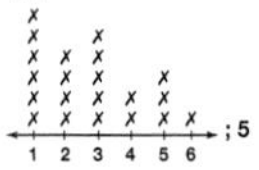

; 5

12.

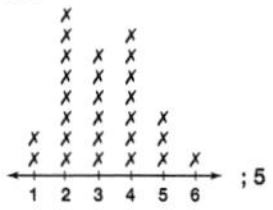

; 5

13.

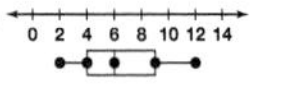

14.

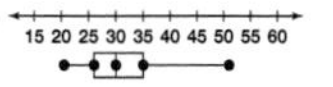

15. It increased gradually. **16.** Answers may vary. Sample: Break the vertical axis and mark a scale from 50 to 60 above the break.
17a. 15 types **b.** $\frac{4}{15}$ **18.** $\frac{2}{25}$ **19.** $\frac{1}{20}$
20. permutation, since order is important; 120 ways **21.** combination, since order does not matter; 220 groups **22.** $\frac{9}{20}$ **23.** $\frac{1}{2}$ **24.** Answers may vary. Sample: Simulate the problem by making a spinner with 3 congruent sections. Make one section red, to represent a correct answer. Spin 60 times and organize the results into 20 groups of 3. Count the number of groups with exactly 2 red spins. Divide this number by 20 to get the experimental probability. **25.** Not a good sample; it includes people not in the town's skating population. **26.** Not a good sample; it includes people not in the town's skating population.

Chapter 13

Lesson 13-1 pp. 691–692

EXERCISES **1.** −1 **3.** −6 **7.** 20, 25, 30; start with 0 and add 5 repeatedly. **9.** 1, 4, 7; Start with −11

and add 3 repeatedly. **11.** 2; 48, 96, 192; start with 3 and multiply by 2 repeatedly. **13.** 2; 720, 1440, 2880; start with 45 and multiply by 2 repeatedly.
17. geometric; 81, 243, 729 **21.** geometric; −81, 243, −729 **23.** arithmetic; $\frac{1}{2}$ **27.** geometric; 3
29. 256, 1,024, 4,096; start with 1 and multiply by 4 repeatedly. **33.** 125, 150, 175; start with 25 and add 25 repeatedly. **35.** arithmetic; $1\frac{5}{6}$, $2\frac{1}{6}$, $2\frac{1}{2}$ **39.** geometric; $-\frac{1}{80}$, $-\frac{1}{160}$, $-\frac{1}{320}$
51. Not a good sample; it excludes many groups, such as people with no interest in art. **53.** 31.4 in.

Lesson 13-2 pp. 696–697

EXERCISES

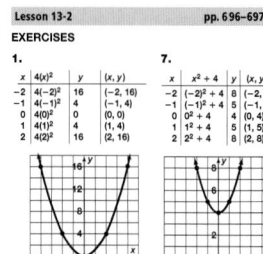

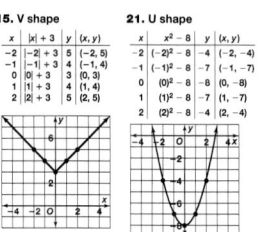

1.

x	$4(x)^2$	y	(x, y)
−2	$4(-2)^2$	16	(−2, 16)
−1	$4(-1)^2$	4	(−1, 4)
0	$4(0)^2$	0	(0, 0)
1	$4(1)^2$	4	(1, 4)
2	$4(2)^2$	16	(2, 16)

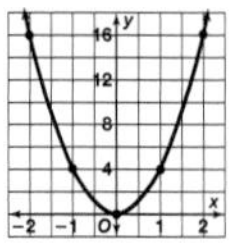

7.

x	$x^2 + 4$	y	(x, y)
−2	$(-2)^2 + 4$	8	(−2, 8)
−1	$(-1)^2 + 4$	5	(−1, 5)
0	$0^2 + 4$	4	(0, 4)
1	$1^2 + 4$	5	(1, 5)
2	$2^2 + 4$	8	(2, 8)

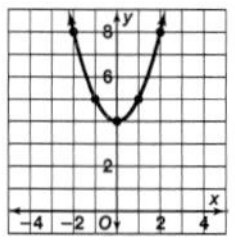

15. V shape

x	$\lvert x\rvert + 3$	y	(x, y)
−2	$\lvert -2\rvert + 3$	5	(−2, 5)
−1	$\lvert -1\rvert + 3$	4	(−1, 4)
0	$\lvert 0\rvert + 3$	3	(0, 3)
1	$\lvert 1\rvert + 3$	4	(1, 4)
2	$\lvert 2\rvert + 3$	5	(2, 5)

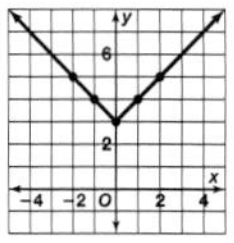

21. U shape

x	$x^2 - 8$	y	(x, y)
−2	$(-2)^2 - 8$	−4	(−2, −4)
−1	$(-1)^2 - 8$	−7	(−1, −7)
0	$(0)^2 - 8$	−8	(0, −8)
1	$(1)^2 - 8$	−7	(1, −7)
2	$(2)^2 - 8$	−4	(2, −4)

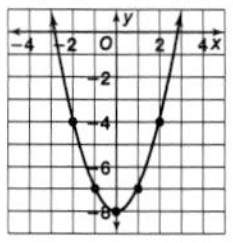

30. The graphs of the functions have the same shape, but $y = x^2 + 2$ is shifted up 2 from the origin and $y = x^2 - 3$ is shifted down 3 from the origin.
38. $\frac{1}{2}$, $\frac{1}{4}$, $\frac{1}{8}$; start with 8 and multiply by $\frac{1}{2}$ repeatedly.
40. 15, 18, 21; start with 3 and add 3 repeatedly.

Lesson 13-3 pp. 701–702

EXERCISES

1.

x	4^x	y	(x, y)
0	4^0	1	(0, 1)
1	4^1	4	(1, 4)
2	4^2	16	(2, 16)
3	4^3	64	(3, 64)
4	4^4	256	(4, 256)

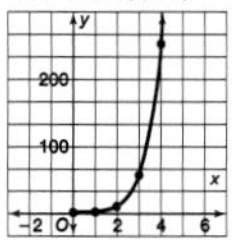

9.

x	$30(\frac{1}{3})^x$	y	(x, y)
0	$30(\frac{1}{3})^0$	30	(0, 30)
1	$30(\frac{1}{3})^1$	10	(1, 10)
2	$30(\frac{1}{3})^2$	$3\frac{1}{3}$	$(2, 3\frac{1}{3})$
3	$30(\frac{1}{3})^3$	$1\frac{1}{9}$	$(3, 1\frac{1}{9})$
4	$30(\frac{1}{3})^4$	$\frac{10}{27}$	$(4, \frac{10}{27})$
5	$30(\frac{1}{3})^5$	$\frac{10}{81}$	$(5, \frac{10}{81})$

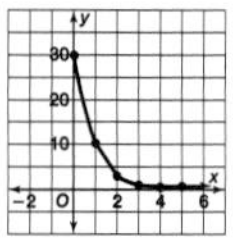

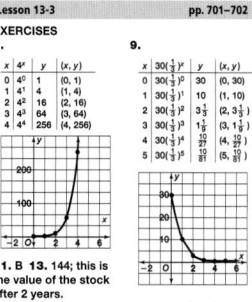

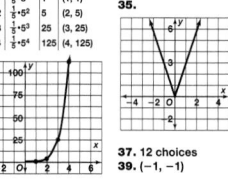

11. B **13.** 144; this is the value of the stock after 2 years.
15. Answers may vary. Sample: 3 yr 10 months

17.

x	$\frac{1}{5} \cdot 5^x$	y	(x, y)
0	$\frac{1}{5} \cdot 5^0$	$\frac{1}{5}$	$(0, \frac{1}{5})$
1	$\frac{1}{5} \cdot 5^1$	1	(1, 1)
2	$\frac{1}{5} \cdot 5^2$	5	(2, 5)
3	$\frac{1}{5} \cdot 5^3$	25	(3, 25)
4	$\frac{1}{5} \cdot 5^4$	125	(4, 125)

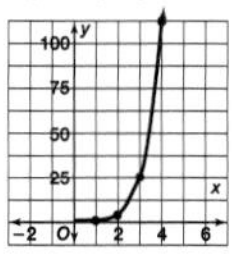

23. yes; $2^4 = 16$
25. no; $\left(\frac{1}{2}\right)^4 \neq 16$
35.

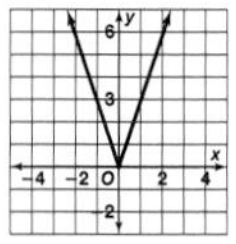

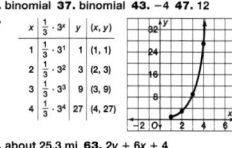

37. 12 choices
39. (−1, −1)

Lesson 13-4 pp. 706–707

EXERCISES **1.** No; it is a sum. **3.** Yes; it is a product of the real number $\frac{1}{3}$ and the variable a.
9. binomial **15.** monomial **19.** 32 **23.** 37
29. Yes; it is a real number. **31.** No; it is a sum.
33. binomial **37.** binomial **43.** −4 **47.** 12
59.

x	$\frac{1}{3} \cdot 3^x$	y	(x, y)
1	$\frac{1}{3} \cdot 3^1$	1	(1, 1)
2	$\frac{1}{3} \cdot 3^2$	3	(2, 3)
3	$\frac{1}{3} \cdot 3^3$	9	(3, 9)
4	$\frac{1}{3} \cdot 3^4$	27	(4, 27)

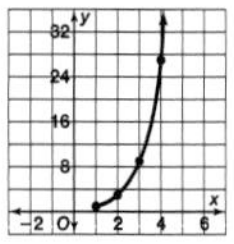

61. about 25.3 mi **63.** $2y + 6x + 4$

Lesson 13-5 pp. 712–714

EXERCISES **1.** $(2x^2 + x + 2) + (x^2 + 4) = 3x^2 + x + 6$ **3.** $2x^2 + 4x + 7$ **5.** $-x + 5$
7. $2a + 9b$ **11.** $2x^3 + 5x^2 + x + 4$ **13.** $3x + 8$
17. $-2ab + 2$ **19.** $x^2 - 8x - 5$ **23.** $w^2 + 7w - 6$
29. $m^2 + 5m$ **33.** $5y - 2$ **35.** $4b - 1$ **37.** $2a + 2$
47. −15 **49.** 3 **51.** 5 cm^2 **53.** 7 mi

Lesson 13-6 pp. 717–718

EXERCISES **5.** $3y^2 + 21y$ **13.** $(3x^2 - 135x)$ ft^2
15. $-15x^3 + 10x^2$ **19.** $a^4 + a^5 + 5a^3$
25. $4y(y^2 - 2y - 3)$ **31.** $5z(z - 4)$
35. $-14a^3 - 42a^2 + 56a$ **39.** $60x^3 + 24x^2$
45. $4x^2(x^3 - x^2 + 2)$ **51.** $2mn(m^2 - 3mn + 4)$
63. $3x^2 + 7x + 6$
65.

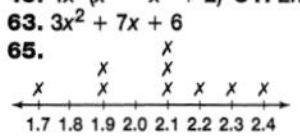

67. \$449

Lesson 13-7 pp. 721–722

EXERCISES **1.** $x^2 + 3x + 2$ **5.** $x^2 + 9x + 20$
11. $c^2 + 16c + 63$ **17.** $x^2 + x - 6$
19. $2x^2 + 7x + 3$ **21.** $10c^2 + 26c + 12$
25. $x^2 + 10x + 16$ **29.** $6c^2 - 10c - 4$
41. $7a^2 + 35ab + 14ac$
43. $-32m^5 + 8m^3p + 16m^2p^4$
45. Combinations, since the order of the colors is not important.

Lesson 13-8 pp. 726–727

EXERCISES **1a.** 4:30 P.M. **b.** 180 mi **3.** 30 ft
7. Sandy 101 g, White Ears 108 g, Sport 115 g
9. 64 choices **19.** $x^2 - 2x - 3$ **21.** $x^2 + 6x + 9$
23. AP, AE, PE; 3 **25.** four more days

Chapter 13 Review pp. 729–731

EXERCISES **1.** d **2.** e **3.** a **4.** f **5.** b **6.** h **7.** g **8.** i **9.** c **10.** 17, 21, 25; start with 1 and add 4 repeatedly. **11.** −3.75, −1.875, −0.9375; start with −60 and multiply by 0.5 repeatedly. **12.** 128, 135, 142; start with 100 and add 7 repeatedly.
13. −20, −25, −30; start with 0 and add −5 repeatedly. **14.** 14. −18, −29, −40; start with 26 and add −11 repeatedly. **15.** $62\frac{1}{2}$, $312\frac{1}{2}$, $1{,}562\frac{1}{2}$; start with $\frac{1}{10}$ and multiply by 5 repeatedly.
16. arithmetic; 25, 29, 33 **17.** geometric; $-\frac{1}{2}$, $-\frac{1}{4}$, $-\frac{1}{8}$ **18.** arithmetic; 7, 8, 9 **19.** arithmetic; 22, 33, 44 **20.** neither; 30, 3, 40 **21.** geometric; $\frac{2}{25}$, $\frac{4}{25}$, $\frac{8}{25}$
22. Sample: A club starts with 10 members and adds 1 new member every week; 10, 11, 12, . . .; 1

23.

x	$\frac{1}{2}x^2$	y	(x, y)
−2	$\frac{1}{2} \cdot (-2)^2$	2	(−2, 2)
−1	$\frac{1}{2} \cdot (-1)^2$	$\frac{1}{2}$	$(-1, \frac{1}{2})$
0	$\frac{1}{2} \cdot (0)^2$	0	(0, 0)
1	$\frac{1}{2} \cdot (1)^2$	$\frac{1}{2}$	$(1, \frac{1}{2})$
2	$\frac{1}{2} \cdot (2)^2$	2	(2, 2)

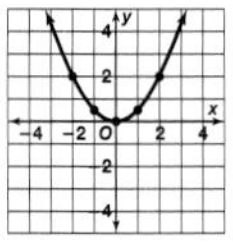

24.

x	$2\lvert x\rvert$	y	(x, y)
−2	$2\lvert -2\rvert$	4	(−2, 4)
−1	$2\lvert -1\rvert$	2	(−1, 2)
0	$2\lvert 0\rvert$	0	(0, 0)
1	$2\lvert 1\rvert$	2	(1, 2)
2	$2\lvert 2\rvert$	4	(2, 4)

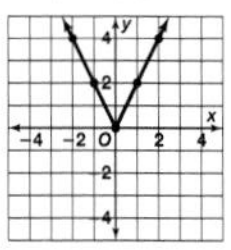

25.

x	$\lvert x\rvert + 1$	y	(x, y)
−2	$\lvert -2\rvert + 1$	3	(−2, 3)
−1	$\lvert -1\rvert + 1$	2	(−1, 2)
0	$\lvert 0\rvert + 1$	1	(0, 1)
1	$\lvert 1\rvert + 1$	2	(1, 2)
2	$\lvert 2\rvert + 1$	3	(2, 3)

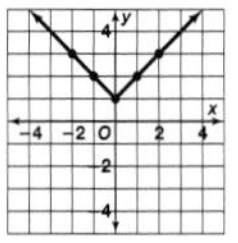

26.

x	$x^2 + 5$	y	(x, y)
−2	$(-2)^2 + 5$	9	(−2, 9)
−1	$(-1)^2 + 5$	6	(−1, 6)
0	$0^2 + 5$	5	(0, 5)
1	$1^2 + 5$	6	(1, 6)
2	$2^2 + 5$	9	(2, 9)

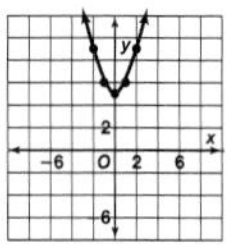

27.

x	$-\lvert x\rvert$	y	(x, y)
−2	$-\lvert -2\rvert$	−2	(−2, −2)
−1	$-\lvert -1\rvert$	−1	(−1, −1)
0	$-\lvert 0\rvert$	0	(0, 0)
1	$-\lvert 1\rvert$	−1	(1, −1)
2	$-\lvert 2\rvert$	−2	(2, −2)

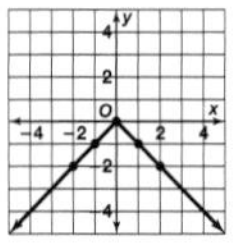

28.

x	$\frac{1}{2}\lvert x\rvert$	y	(x, y)
−2	$\frac{1}{2}\lvert -2\rvert$	1	(−2, 1)
−1	$\frac{1}{2}\lvert -1\rvert$	$\frac{1}{2}$	$(-1, \frac{1}{2})$
0	$\frac{1}{2}\lvert 0\rvert$	0	(0, 0)
1	$\frac{1}{2}\lvert 1\rvert$	$\frac{1}{2}$	$(1, \frac{1}{2})$
2	$\frac{1}{2}\lvert 2\rvert$	1	(2, 1)

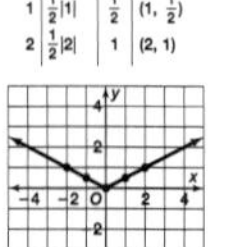

29.

x	$-x^2 - 3$	y	(x, y)
−2	$-(-2)^2 - 3$	−7	(−2, −7)
−1	$-(-1)^2 - 3$	−4	(−1, −4)
0	$-(0)^2 - 3$	−3	(0, −3)
1	$-(1)^2 - 3$	−4	(1, −4)
2	$-(2)^2 - 3$	−7	(2, −7)

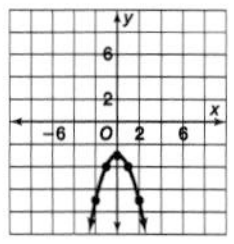

30.

x	$-x^2 + 4$	y	(x, y)
−2	$-(-2)^2 + 4$	0	(−2, 0)
−1	$-(-1)^2 + 4$	3	(−1, 3)
0	$-(0)^2 + 4$	4	(0, 4)
1	$-(1)^2 + 4$	3	(1, 3)
2	$-(2)^2 + 4$	0	(2, 0)

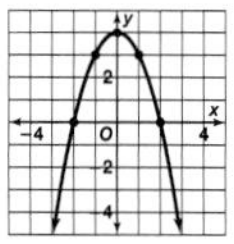

31.

x	$\left(\frac{1}{4}\right)^x$	y	(x, y)
0	$\left(\frac{1}{4}\right)^0$	1	(0, 1)
1	$\left(\frac{1}{4}\right)^1$	$\frac{1}{4}$	$(1, \frac{1}{4})$
2	$\left(\frac{1}{4}\right)^2$	$\frac{1}{16}$	$(2, \frac{1}{16})$
3	$\left(\frac{1}{4}\right)^3$	$\frac{1}{64}$	$(3, \frac{1}{64})$
4	$\left(\frac{1}{4}\right)^4$	$\frac{1}{256}$	$(4, \frac{1}{256})$

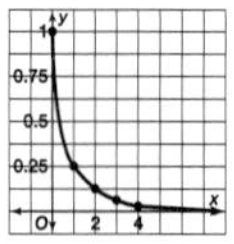

32.

x	$\frac{1}{2} \cdot 2^x$	y	(x, y)
0	$\frac{1}{2} \cdot 2^0$	$\frac{1}{2}$	$(0, \frac{1}{2})$
1	$\frac{1}{2} \cdot 2^1$	1	(1, 1)
2	$\frac{1}{2} \cdot 2^2$	2	(2, 2)
3	$\frac{1}{2} \cdot 2^3$	4	(3, 4)
4	$\frac{1}{2} \cdot 2^4$	8	(4, 8)

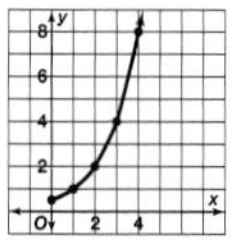

33.

x	3^x	y	(x, y)
0	3^0	1	(0, 1)
1	3^1	3	(1, 3)
2	3^2	9	(2, 9)
3	3^3	27	(3, 27)
4	3^4	81	(4, 81)

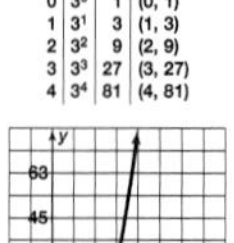

34.

x	$\left(\frac{1}{2}\right)^x$	y	(x, y)
0	$\left(\frac{1}{2}\right)^0$	1	(0, 1)
1	$\left(\frac{1}{2}\right)^1$	$\frac{1}{2}$	$(1, \frac{1}{2})$
2	$\left(\frac{1}{2}\right)^2$	$\frac{1}{4}$	$(2, \frac{1}{4})$
3	$\left(\frac{1}{2}\right)^3$	$\frac{1}{8}$	$(3, \frac{1}{8})$
4	$\left(\frac{1}{2}\right)^4$	$\frac{1}{16}$	$(4, \frac{1}{16})$

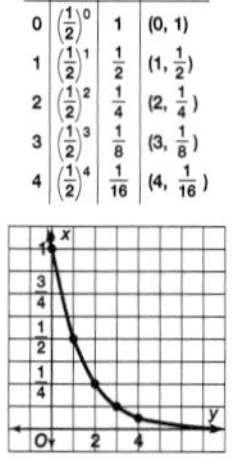

35. monomial **36.** binomial **37.** monomial
38. trinomial **39.** monomial **40.** monomial
41. binomial **42.** binomial **43.** binomial
44. trinomial **45.** 32 **46.** 7 **47.** 6 **48.** −12 **49.** 9
50. $3a^2 + 2a + 8$ **51.** $4m^2 - 2m - 12$
52. $4x^2 - 2x + 2$ **53.** $4p - 7q - 2$
54. $3w^2 + 9w - 5$ **55.** $6x + 6y$ **56.** $2a^2 + 5a$
57. $12c^2 - 28c$ **58.** $-30y^2 - 18y$
59. $3x^3 - 3x^2 - 15x$ **60.** $x^3 + 7x^2$
61. $2x^4 - 6x^3 - 12x^2$ **62.** $x^2 + 7x + 12$
63. $x^2 - 4x - 5$ **64.** $x^2 - 6x + 8$ **65.** $x(x - 1)$
66. $9(p^2 + 3)$ **67.** $3x(x^2 - 3x + 2)$
68. $5(b^5 + 4b^3 - 6)$ **69.** $2x(4x^2 + x + 2)$
70. $4a(7a - b)$ **71.** 2,401 ft^2 **72.** Answers may vary. Sample: A diagram gives a visual picture of the problem. A table organizes possible dimensions and their related areas. Looking for a pattern leads to the answer.

Extra Practice

Chapter 1 p. 744

1. $x - 6$ **5.** $8p$ **9.** 9 **11.** 5 **13.** 42 **15.** 11
19. = **21.** > **23.** −7 **27.** −32 **31.** Start with −12, and add 9 to the previous term. 33, 42, 51
33. Add the two previous terms. 21, 34, 55 **37.** 24
41. 9 **42–50.**

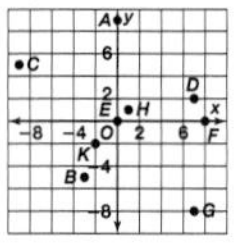

Chapter 2 p. 745

1. 99 + (−99) + 45 + (−46)
Commutative Property of Addition
0 + 45 + (−46)
additive inverse
−1
5. 2 • 50 • 58
Commutative Property of Multiplication
100 • 58
Multiply from left to right.
5,800
7. 20 **13.** $-17y + 38$ **17.** $\frac{-3}{-1} = 3$; true **21.** −24
25. 24 **33.**

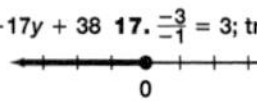

35.

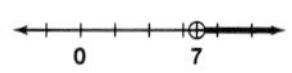

39. $x > -13$ **43.** $c \leq -15$

Chapter 3   p. 746

1. about 13; rounding 5. about 120; clustering
7. about 120 11. about 18 13. mean: 12.9;
median: 12; modes: 10 and 12; outlier: 19
15. mean: $27.30; median: $29; mode: $30; outlier:
$15 17. 130 yd 19. 175 mi 25. 63.6 33. 3
37. 0.25 45. 0.036

Chapter 4   p. 747

3. 1, 2, 4, 8, 16, 32, 64 5. 1, 2, 3, 4, 6, 9, 12, 18, 36
7. 64 11. 48 13. composite; 5^2 15. prime 19. 10
21. $5x$ 25. $\frac{7}{16}$ 31. $\frac{x}{15}$

35–39.

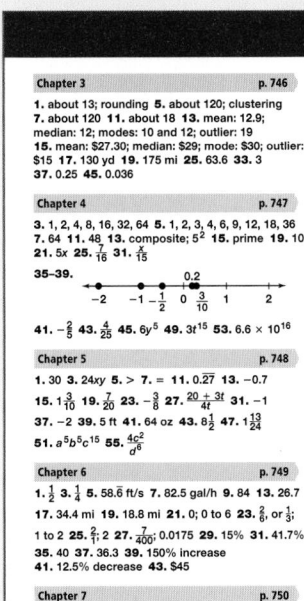

41. $-\frac{2}{25}$ 43. $\frac{4}{25}$ 45. $6y^5$ 49. $3t^{15}$ 53. 6.6×10^{16}

Chapter 5   p. 748

1. 30 3. $24xy$ 5. > 7. = 11. $0.\overline{27}$ 13. −0.7
15. $1\frac{3}{10}$ 19. $\frac{7}{20}$ 23. $-\frac{3}{8}$ 27. $\frac{20 + 3t}{4t}$ 31. −1
37. −2 39. 5 ft 41. 64 oz 43. $8\frac{1}{2}$ 47. $1\frac{13}{24}$
51. a^5b^5c 55. $\frac{4c^2}{d^6}$

Chapter 6   p. 749

1. $\frac{1}{3}$ 3. $\frac{1}{4}$ 5. $58.\overline{6}$ ft/s 7. 82.5 gal/h 9. 84 13. 26.7
17. 34.4 mi 19. 18.8 mi 21. 0; 0 to 6 23. $\frac{2}{8}$, or $\frac{1}{3}$;
1 to 2 25. $\frac{2}{1}$; 2 27. $\frac{7}{400}$; 0.0175 29. 15% 31. 41.7%
35. 40 37. 36.3 39. 150% increase
41. 12.5% decrease 43. $45

Chapter 7   p. 750

9. $-5\frac{1}{3}$ 17. −5
23. $a \geq -3$

-3   0

27. $t \leq 50$

0   50

31. $p = s - c$ 33. $a = c + b$
37. $4,500 41. $1,480.24

Chapter 8   p. 751

1. No; there are two range values for the domain
value 4. 3. Yes; there is one range value for each
domain value. 5. (−3, −11), (0, −2), (2, 4)
9. (−3, −4), (0, −4), (2, −4) 13. 5, −4 17. $\frac{3}{5}$, −1

21.   23.

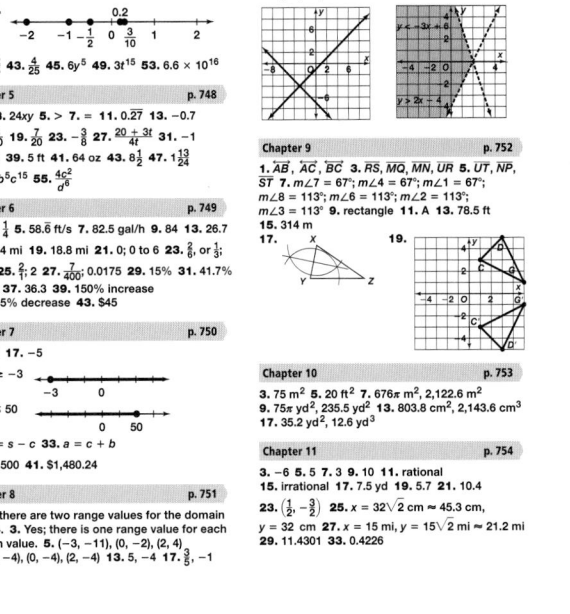

27. $y = 3x - 1$ 29. $y = 5x + y$ 31. $y = 2x + 3$
34. Positive correlation; as you move to the right,
most scores increase.
35. (−3, −4) 37.

Chapter 9   p. 752

1. $\overline{AB}$, $\overline{AC}$, $\overline{BC}$ 3. $\overline{RS}$, $\overline{MQ}$, $\overline{MN}$, $\overline{UR}$ 5. $\overline{UT}$, $\overline{NP}$,
$\overline{ST}$ 7. $m\angle 7 = 67°$; $m\angle 4 = 67°$; $m\angle 1 = 67°$;
$m\angle 8 = 113°$; $m\angle 6 = 113°$; $m\angle 2 = 113°$;
$m\angle 3 = 113°$ 9. rectangle 11. A 13. 78.5 ft
15. 314 m
17.   19.

Chapter 10   p. 753

3. 75 m² 5. 20 ft² 7. 676π m², 2,122.6 m²
9. 75π yd², 235.5 yd² 13. 803.8 cm², 2,143.6 cm³
17. 35.2 yd², 12.6 yd³

Chapter 11   p. 754

3. −6 5. 5 7. 3 9. 10 11. rational
15. irrational 17. 7.5 yd 19. 5.7 21. 10.4
23. $\left(\frac{1}{2}, -\frac{3}{2}\right)$ 25. $x = 32\sqrt{2}$ cm ≈ 45.3 cm,
$y = 32$ cm 27. $x = 15$ mi, $y = 15\sqrt{2}$ mi ≈ 21.2 mi
29. 11.4301 33. 0.4226

Chapter 12   p. 755

1. range = 3

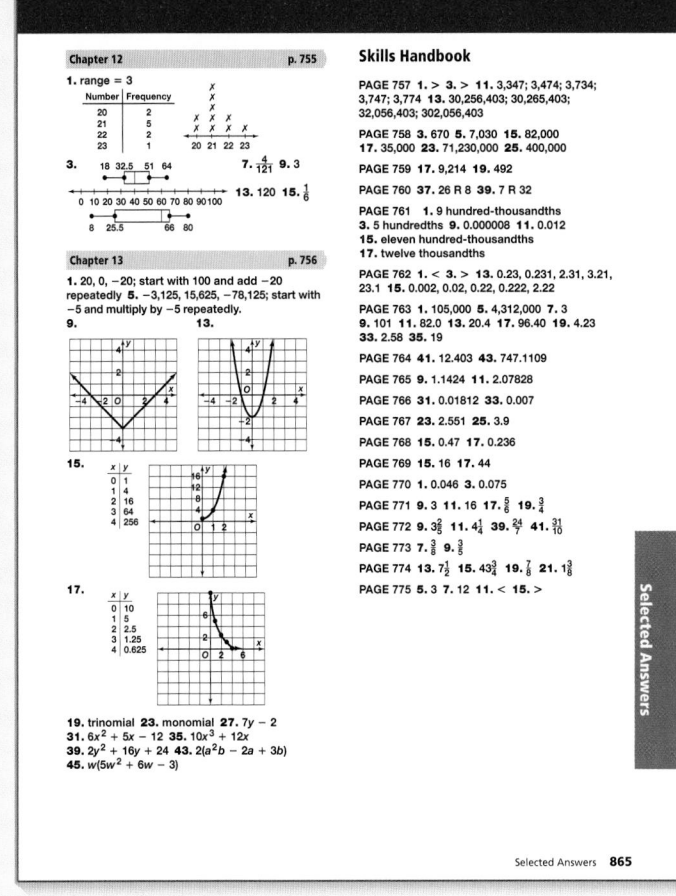

Number	Frequency
20	2
21	5
22	2
23	1

3.   7. $\frac{4}{121}$ 9. 3
13. 120 15. $\frac{1}{6}$

Chapter 13   p. 756

1. 20, 0, −20; start with 100 and add −20
repeatedly. 5. −3,125, 15,625, −78,125; start with
−5 and multiply by −5 repeatedly.
9.   13.

15.

x	y
0	1
1	4
2	16
3	64
4	256

17.

x	y
0	10
1	5
2	2.5
3	1.25
4	0.625

19. trinomial 23. monomial 27. $7y - 2$
31. $6x^2 + 5x - 12$ 35. $10x^3 + 12x$
39. $2y^2 + 16y + 24$ 43. $2(a^2b - 2a + 3b)$
45. $w(5w^2 + 6w - 3)$

Skills Handbook

PAGE 757 1. > 3. > 11. 3,347; 3,474; 3,734;
3,747; 3,774 13. 30,256,403; 30,265,403;
32,056,403; 302,056,403

PAGE 758 3. 670 5. 7,030 15. 82,000
17. 35,000 23. 71,230,000 25. 400,000

PAGE 759 17. 9,214 19. 492

PAGE 760 37. 26 R 8 39. 7 R 32

PAGE 761 1. 9 hundred-thousandths
3. 5 hundredths 9. 0.000008 11. 0.012
15. eleven hundred-thousandths
17. twelve thousandths

PAGE 762 1. < 3. > 13. 0.23, 0.231, 2.31, 3.21,
23.1 15. 0.002, 0.02, 0.22, 0.222, 2.22

PAGE 763 1. 105,000 5. 4,312,000 7. 3
9. 101 11. 82.0 13. 20.4 17. 96.40 19. 4.23
33. 2.58 35. 19

PAGE 764 41. 12.403 43. 747.1109

PAGE 765 9. 1.1424 11. 2.07828

PAGE 766 31. 0.01812 33. 0.007

PAGE 767 23. 2.551 25. 3.9

PAGE 768 15. 0.47 17. 0.236

PAGE 769 15. 16 17. 44

PAGE 770 1. 0.046 3. 0.075

PAGE 771 9. 3 11. 16 17. $\frac{5}{8}$ 19. $\frac{3}{4}$

PAGE 772 9. $3\frac{5}{8}$ 11. $4\frac{1}{4}$ 39. $\frac{24}{7}$ 41. $\frac{31}{10}$

PAGE 773 7. $\frac{3}{8}$ 9. $\frac{2}{3}$

PAGE 774 13. $7\frac{1}{2}$ 15. $43\frac{3}{4}$ 19. $\frac{7}{8}$ 21. $1\frac{3}{8}$

PAGE 775 5. 3 7. 12 11. < 15. >

Additional Answers

CHAPTER 1

LESSON 1-9

page 44 Investigation

1. $-4 + (-4) + (-4) + (-4) + (-4)$
   -20

   $-8 + (-8) -16$

   $-10 + (-10) + (-10) + (-10) -40$

LESSON 1-10

page 50 Check Skills You'll Need

1.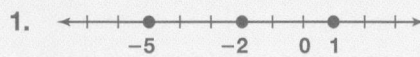

2.

3.

4.

CHAPTER 2

LESSON 2-1

**page 67 Check Understanding
Example 1**

1. Explanations may vary. Sample:
   $6 + 8 + 4$
   $= 6 + (8 + 4)$ Assoc. Prop. of Add.
   $= 6 + (4 + 8)$ Comm. Prop. of Add.
   $= (6 + 4) + 8$ Assoc. Prop. of Add.
   $= 10 + 8$ Add within parentheses.
   $= 18$ Add.

LESSON 2-8

TE page 103 Additional Example 1

1a.

b.

c.

d.

TE page 103 Closure

The closed dot shows that a number is included in the solution. Otherwise, you use an open dot.

**page 104 Practice and
Problem Solving**

6.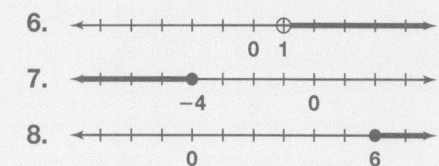

7.

8.

9.

10.

11.

12.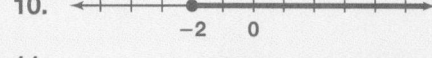

19.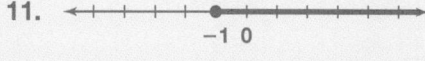

20.

21.

22.

23.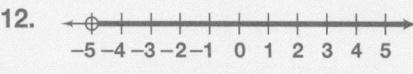

24.

25.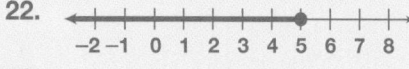

26.

LESSON 2-9

**page 106 Check Understanding
Example 1**

1a.

1b.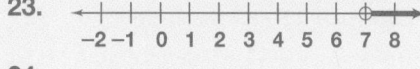

1c.

TE page 107 Additional Example 1

1a.

1b.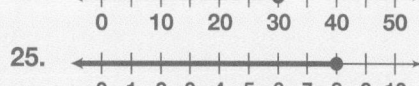

TE page 107 Closure

In both cases, you must add the same amount to or subtract the same amount from each side of the inquality or equation.

**page 108 Practice and
Problem Solving**

1.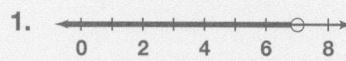

2.

3.

4.

5.

6.

7.

8.

25.

26.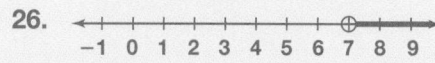

27.

28.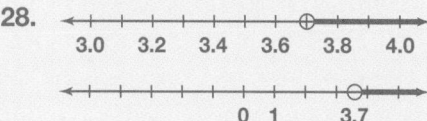

29.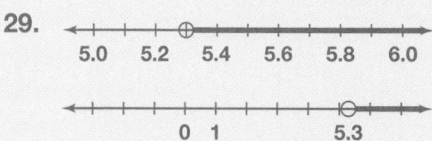

30.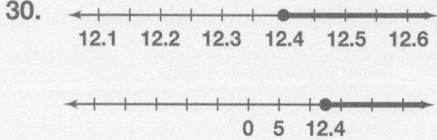

page 109　Mixed Review

41.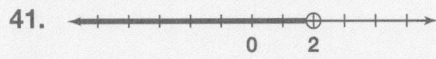
    number line with open circle at 2, shaded left; marks at 0, 2

42. number line with closed dot at −5, shaded right; marks at −5, 0, 1

43. number line with closed dot at 4, shaded left; marks at 0, 2, 4

44. number line with open circle at 1, shaded right; marks at 0, 1

page 116　Test-Taking Strategies

1. Answers may vary. Sample: The correct original price of the calculator is given, and the equation and the solution are correct with all work shown.

2. Answers may vary. Sample: An incorrect original price is given and there is work shown with minimal errors.

3. Answers may vary. Sample: An incorrect original price is given and no work is shown.

4. x is the original price.
   $x + 17 = 62$
   $x + 17 - 17 = 62 - 17$
   $x = 45$
   The original price was $45.
   2-point response

5. x is the height of each story.
   $15x = 135$
   $\frac{15x}{15} = \frac{135}{15}$
   $x = 9$
   The height of each story is 9 ft.
   2-point response

page 121　Test Prep
　　　　Cumulative Review

13. [2] $3c - 4c + 1$
    $-c + 1$, OR $1 - c$
    [1] minor error OR answer only

14. [2] $6(t + 7) + t$
    $6(t) + 6(7) + t$
    $6t + 42 + t$
    $7t + 42$
    [1] minor error OR answer only

15. [2] $-5(n + 9) - n$
    $-5(n) + (-5)(9) - n$
    $-5n - 45 - n$
    $-6n - 45$
    [1] minor error OR answer only

16. [2] $8 - 4(s + 2) - s$
    $8 - 4(s) - 4(2) - s$
    $8 - 4s - 8 - s$
    $-5s$
    [1] minor error OR answer only

17. [2] $24 > b + 17$
    $24 - 17 > b + 17 - 17$
    $7 > b$ OR $b < 7$
    [1] minor error OR answer only

18. [2] $x - 9 < -14$
    $x - 9 + 9 < -14 + 9$
    $x < -5$
    [1] minor error OR answer only

19. [2] $\frac{r}{13} \geq 3$
    $(13) \cdot \frac{r}{13} \geq 3(13)$
    $r \geq 39$
    [1] minor error OR answer only

20. [2] $-4s \geq -56$
    $\frac{-4s}{-4} \leq \frac{-56}{-4}$
    $s \leq 14$
    [1] minor error OR answer only

21. [2] They are alike except that to multiply or divide each side of an inequality by a negative number, you must reverse the inequality symbol.
    [1] Describes similarity only OR difference only.

22. [2] 700; Use the Commutative Property to write $25 \cdot 4 \cdot 7$. Then use the Associative Property to write $(25 \cdot 4) \cdot 7$. Then simplify $25 \cdot 4 = 100$. The expression is then a simple multiplication of $100 \cdot 7$.
    [1] minor error OR answer only

23. [2] $\$3.25 + \$5.25 + 5x$
    $\$8.50 + 5x$
    $8.50 + 5x$
    [1] minor error OR answer only

24. [2] $6b + 2p + 5b + 12$
    $11b + 2p + 12$
    [1] minor error OR answer only

CHAPTER 3

LESSON 3-2

page 133　Check Understanding
　　　　Example 4

4a. Yes; 0.68 is close to an estimate of 0.8.

4b. No; 52.3 is not close to an estimate of 5.

TE page 135　Alternative Assessment

Answers may vary. Sample: Round the divisor, 6.83, to 7. Then round 22.83 to a nearby multiple of 7, namely 21. Divide 21 by 7. The estimate is 3.

LESSON 3-4

page 146　Test Prep

27. [2] 5.84 mi, about 1.1 mi
    [1] one answer only

LESSON 3-7

page 156　Check Understanding
　　　　Example 1

1a. Centimeter; a meter is too large unless you use fractional parts of a meter; millimeters are too small.

1b. Gram; an energy bar has a mass of several grams, but it is much less than 1 kilogram.

1c. Kilogram; a horse is very heavy, so grams are too small.

1d. Liter; a gas tank holds several liters, so milliliters are too small.

TE page 157　Additional Example 1

1a. Centimeter; the width of this textbook is much less than the distance from a doorknob to the floor.

1b. Gram; glasses have about the same mass as many paperclips, but less than this textbook.

1c. Milliliter; a thimble will hold only a small amount of water.

Additional Example 2

2a. 500 mL; a drinking glass holds less than a quart of milk.

2b. 5 cm; the length of a hair clip would be about 5 widths of a thumbnail.

2c. 1 kg; the mass is about one half the mass of this math book.

page 167　Practice and
　　　　Problem Solving

16. [2] $4d = 60$
    $\frac{4d}{4} = \frac{60}{4}$
    $d = 15$
    There are 15 fence posts that are used.
    [1] minor error OR answer only

CHAPTER 4

LESSON 4-1

page 180　Practice and
　　　　Problem Solving

13. no; sum of digits is not divisible by 9

14. yes; sum of digits is divisible by 9

15. yes; sum of digits is divisible by 3

16. yes; sum of digits is divisible by 3

44a. 2 plates of 21 cookies, 3 plates of 14 cookies, 6 plates of 7 cookies

44b. 2 plates of 28 cookies, 4 plates of 14 cookies, 7 plates of 8 cookies, 8 plates of 7 cookies

44c. 2 plates of 30 cookies, 3 plates of 20 cookies, 4 plates of 15 cookies, 5 plates of 12 cookies, 6 plates of 10 cookies

44d. 2 plates of 72 cookies, 3 plates of 48 cookies, 4 plates of 36 cookies, 6 plates of 24 cookies, 8 plates of 18 cookies, 9 plates of 16 cookies, 12 plates of 12 cookies, 16 plates of 9 cookies, 18 plates of 8 cookies

LESSON 4-2

page 185 Practice and Problem Solving

48. Answers may vary. Sample: A number *squared* is the area of a square. A number *cubed* is the volume of a cube.

49. $x = y$ or $x = 0$ or $y = 0$;
$5(-2)^2(-2) = 5(-2)(-2)^2$ or
$5(0)^2y = 5(0)y^2$ or $5x^2(0) = 5x(0)^2$

page 185 Test Prep

54. [2] No; sample: for $a = -2$, $(-2)^3 < -2$; correct explanation with correct example.
[1] minor error OR answer only

LESSON 4-3

page 190 Test Prep

62. [4] No; explanation includes the fact that the product of the two primes has the primes themselves as factors that are different from 1 and the product. Sample: $3 \cdot 5 = 15$. 15 has more than two factors; 1, 3, 5 and 15.
[3] correct explanation, minor error in example.
[2] incomplete explanation, correct example.
[1] incorrect explanation and no example.

LESSON 4-5

TE page 198 Closure

Answers may vary. Sample: Make an organized list or a carefully drawn diagram that will force the consideration of all possibilities.

page 200 Practice and Problem Solving

8.

LESSON 4-6

TE page 202 Additional Examples

1.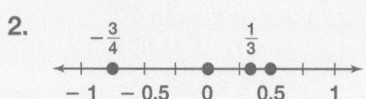

2.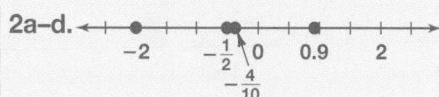

page 202 Check Understanding Example 2

2a–d.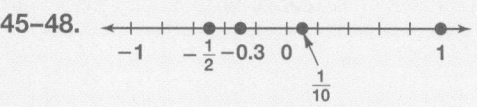

page 203 Practice and Problem Solving

38a. Answers may vary. Sample: $\frac{1}{3}, \frac{1}{4}$

38b. Infinitely many. Between any two rational numbers, you can find another rational number.

39. Answers may vary. Sample: $\frac{-a}{-b}, \frac{2a}{2b}$, and $\frac{-2a}{-2b}$ all simplify to $\frac{a}{b}$ so they are equivalent to $\frac{a}{b}$.

41. Whole numbers are integers because the integers include all the whole numbers and their opposites. Integers are rational numbers because you can write any integer as itself divided by 1.

page 226 Chapter Test

45–48.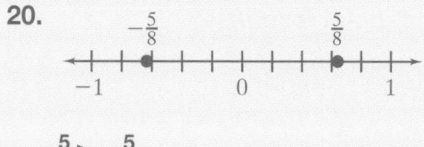

page 227 Cumulative Review

19. [2] $-6.2k = -70.68$; 11.4
[1] correct equation OR solution only

20. [2] 9; $1 \cdot (3^2) \cdot 5$
$1 \cdot 3^3 \cdot 5$
[1] minor error OR answer only

21. [2] $4a$; $4(7) = 28$
[1] Correct variable expression OR answer only

22. [4] four ways

$.05	$.10	$.15
4	0	0
2	1	0
1	0	1
0	2	0

[3] lists three solutions
[2] lists two solutions
[1] answer only OR lists one solution

CHAPTER 5

LESSON 5-1

page 235 Practice and Problem Solving

20.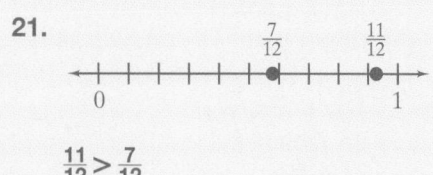

$\frac{5}{8} > -\frac{5}{8}$

21.

$\frac{11}{12} > \frac{7}{12}$

LESSON 5-3

page 247 Test Prep

43. [2] Yes; $\frac{3}{4} + \frac{3}{8} = 1\frac{1}{8}$, and $1\frac{1}{8}$ oz > 1 oz.
[1] minor error OR answer only

44. [2] Yes; $5\frac{3}{8} + 2\frac{5}{7} = 8\frac{5}{56}$, which is greater than 8 mi.
[1] minor error OR answer only

LESSON 5-8

page 271   Practice and Problem Solving

50. Answers may vary. Sample:

Multiply each side by $\frac{3}{2}$. This gives $x = \frac{9}{2}$, or $4\frac{1}{2}$. To check, substitute $\frac{9}{2}$ for x: $\frac{2}{3}\left(\frac{9}{2}\right) \stackrel{?}{=} 3$. $3 = 3$ ✔

CHAPTER 6

LESSON 6-2

page 298   Test Prep

72. [4] correct ratios $\left(\frac{3x - 5}{x + 5}, \frac{2}{1}\right)$; correct proportion $\left(\frac{3x - 5}{x + 5} = \frac{2}{1}\right)$; $x = 15$; Tara had \$45 on Monday and Seth had \$15.
    [3] correct ratios, proportion, and value for x; minor calculation error
    [2] incomplete explanation with correct answer
    [1] answer only

LESSON 6-3

page 300   Check Understanding Example 2

2. 28 ft (See diagram.)

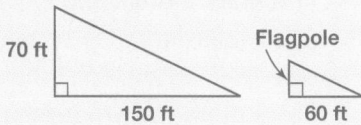

page 303   Test Prep

48. [2] Yes; to scale, the mural will measure $8\frac{1}{3}$ in. by 10 in.
    [1] correct answer; minor error in explanation

page 309   Practice and Problem Solving

35. Answers may vary. Sample: If the odds in favor of an event are $a:b$, then the probability of the event is $\frac{a}{a + b}$. Example: The odds in favor of a number less than 6 on a number cube are 5 to 1. The probability is $\frac{5}{5 + 1}$, or $\frac{5}{6}$.

page 309   Test Prep

39. [2] No; the number of favorable outcomes is always less than or equal to the number of possible outcomes.
    [1] correct answer; minor error in explanation

LESSON 6-6

page 315   Check Understanding Example 1

a. 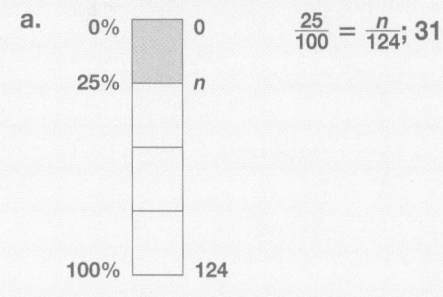 $\frac{25}{100} = \frac{n}{124}$; 31

b. 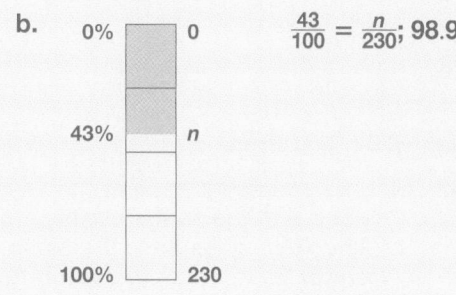 $\frac{43}{100} = \frac{n}{230}$; 98.9

c. 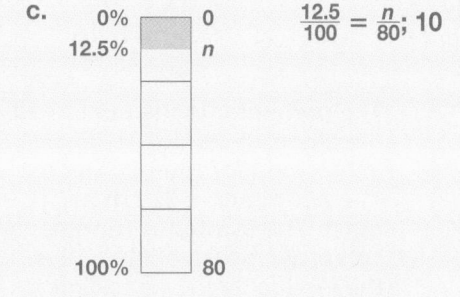 $\frac{12.5}{100} = \frac{n}{80}$; 10

LESSON 6-7

page 323   Writing in Math

Answers may vary. Sample: The method in this lesson. Writing and solving an equation is easier than writing a proportion.

LESSON 6-8

page 328   Test Prep

46. [4] 200 decreased by 5% is $200 - 200(0.05) = 190$. The result, 190, increased by 5% is $190 + 190(0.05) = 199.5$. The result is less than 200 because 5% of 200 is larger than 5% of 190, so the decrease is larger than the increase.
    [3] 1 computational error with work shown
    [2] 2 computational errors with work shown
    [1] correct answer with no work shown

LESSON 6-9

page 330   More Than One Way

1. Answers may vary. Sample: Michelle's method; the subtraction is done earlier with simpler numbers.

page 332   Test Prep

28. [2] The printers at Store B; the selling price at Store A is \$67.96, and the selling price at Store B is \$67.16.
    [1] correct answer with no explanation

33–35.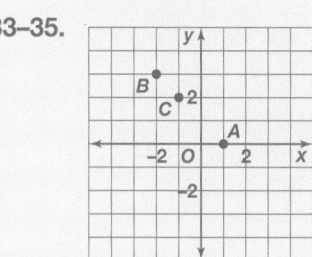

CUMULATIVE REVIEW

page 343   Test Prep

32. [2] \$31.90; first, find 45% of 58. $0.45(58) = 26.1$. Then, subtract 26.1 from 58 to get the sale price. $58 - 26.1 = 31.90$.
    [1] correct answer with no explanation

33. [2] \$3.20; first, find 80% of 15.98. $0.80(15.98) \approx 12.78$. Then, subtract 12.78 from 15.98 to get the sale price. $15.98 - 12.78 = 3.20$.
    [1] correct answer with no explanation

34. [4] Brand B; \$.09; $15.98 - 15.98(.30) \approx 11.19$ and $18.50 - 18.50(.40) = 11.10$, which is 0.09 less than 11.19.
    [3] 1 computational error
    [2] 2 computational errors with work shown
    [1] correct answer; no work shown

CHAPTER 7

LESSON 7-1

page 351   Test Prep

38. [2] $0.25x + 7.5 = 14$
    $0.25x + 7.5 - 7.5 = 14 - 7.5$
    $0.25x = 6.5$
    $\frac{0.25x}{0.25} = \frac{6.25}{0.25}$
    $x = 26$
    Brett bought 26 tokens.
    [1] minor error OR answer only

LESSON 7-4

page 365   Test Prep

15. [2] $2b + 2(2b + 3) = 15$
$2b + 4b + 6 = 15$
$6b + 6 = 15$
$6b + 6 - 6 = 15 - 6$
$6b = 9$
$\frac{6n}{6} = \frac{9}{6}$
$b = 1.5$
$h = 2b + 3 = 2(1.5) + 3 = 6$
$h = 6$ ft

[1] minor error OR answer only

LESSON 7-6

page 373   Check Skills You'll Need

1. $w > -9$

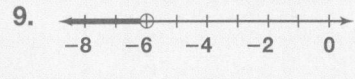

2. $z > 10$

3. $a < -2$

4. $x \le -1$

page 373   Check Understanding Example 1

1a.

1b.

1c.

page 373   Check Understanding Example 2

2a.

2b.

2c.

page 375   Practice and Problem Solving

9.

10.

11.

12.

13.

14.

page 376   Test Prep

33. [4] Let s represent each of the sides with the same length. Since two sides have the same length, $2s$ represents them both.

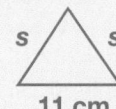
11 cm

The perimeter is the sum of all the sides, so $2s + 11$ is an expression for the perimeter. The perimeter is 32 cm at most. The symbol $\le$ represents "at most," so $2s + 11 \le 32$ is the inequality to use to find s.

$2s + 11 \le 32$
$2s + 11 - 11 \le 32 - 11$
$2s \le 21$
$\frac{2s}{2} \le \frac{21}{2}$
$s \le 10\frac{1}{2}$

The sides that are the same length must be $10\frac{1}{2}$ cm or less.

[3] correct diagram and work shown; one computational error

[2] correct lengths; either diagram or work is not shown

[1] correct lengths; no diagram and no work is shown

LESSON 7-7

page 381   Test Prep

21. [4] $A = \frac{1}{2}(a + b)h$

$2(A) = 2[\frac{1}{2}(a + b)h]$	Multiply each side by 2.
$2(A) = (a + b)h$	Simplify.
$\frac{2A}{a + b} = \frac{(a + b)h}{(a + b)}$	Divide each side by $(a + b)$
$\frac{2A}{(a + b)} = h$	Simplify.

$A = \frac{1}{2}(a + b)h$

$2(A) = 2[\frac{1}{2}(a + b)h]$	Multiply each side by 2.
$2(A) = (a + b)h$	Simplify.
$\frac{2A}{h} = \frac{(a + b)h}{h}$	Divide each side by h.
$\frac{2A}{h} = (a + b)$	Simplify.
$\frac{2A}{h} - a = a + b - a$	Subtract a from each side.
$\frac{2A}{h} - a = b$	Simplify.

The two processes are similar in that they both have the same first step: multiplying by two (the reciprocal of $\frac{1}{2}$) on each side to undo multiplication by $\frac{1}{2}$.

From there the processes are different. The first process has just one more step: dividing each side by $(a + b)$. The second process has two more steps: dividing each side by h, and then subtracting a from each side.

[3] 1 minor error with work shown
[2] 2 minor errors with work shown
[1] answer only with no work shown

LESSON 7-8

page 386   Writing in Math

Answers may vary. Sample: When a bank compounds interest daily, interest is found using a daily interest rate. The bank account balance has daily interest added to the principal balance.

page 386 Mixed Review

30–32.

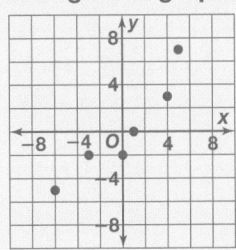

page 388 Test-Taking Strategies

4. The area of a rectangle is the product of the length and width. The area is increased, therefore the product must be greater than 64. The choices 6 in. by 8 in. and 8 in. by 8 in. do not have products greater than 64. You can eliminate choices A and D.

CHAPTER 8

LESSON 8-1

TE page 401 Additional Example 1

1a. Yes; there is one range value for each domain value.
1b. Yes; there is one range value for each domain value.
1c. No; there are two range values for the domain value 0.

TE page 401 Additional Example 2

2. No; two lawns of the same size (domain value) can require different lengths of time (range values) for mowing.

page 402 Check Understanding Example 3

3a. A function; no vertical line passes through two graphed points.

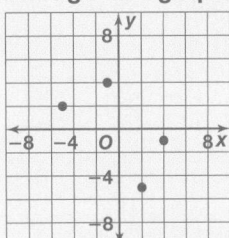

3b. Not a function; a vertical line passes through both (−1, 1) and (−1, 3).

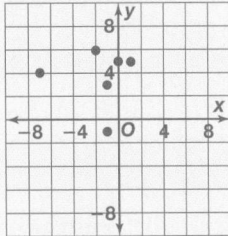

3c. A function; no vertical line passes through two graphed points.

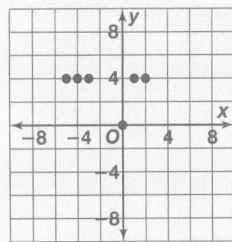

pages 403–404 Practice and Problem Solving

6–10. Answers may vary. Samples are given.

6. No; each distance (domain value) may take you different lengths of times (range values).

7. No; subscribers of a specific age (domain value) may pay different subscription prices (range values).

8. Yes; for each length of cloth (domain value), there is one price (range value).

10. Yes; for each number of students (domain value), there is a desired number of buses (range value).

11. A function; no vertical line passes through two graphed points.

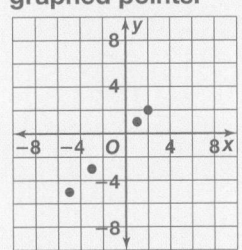

12. A function; no vertical line passes through two graphed points.

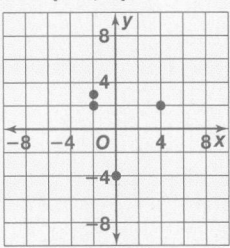

13. Not a function; a vertical line passes through both (−1, 3) and (−1, 2).

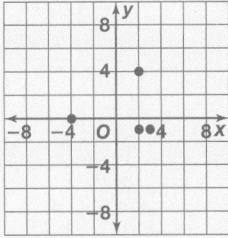

14. Not a function; a vertical line passes through both (2, −1) and (2, 4).

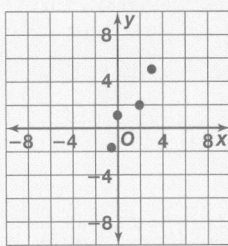

15. A function; there is only one range value for each domain value.

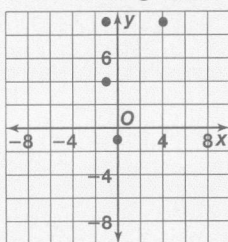

16. Not a function; domain value −1 has two range values 4 and 9.

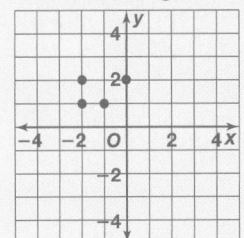

17. Not a function; domain value −2 has two range values 2 and 3.

18. Not a function; domain value of 4 has two range values −8 and 6; domain value 1 has range values of 2, 5, and −6.

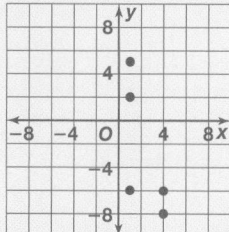

19. A function; no vertical line passes through two points on the graph.

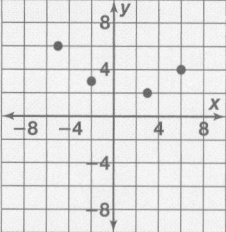

20. A function; no vertical line passes through two points on the graph.

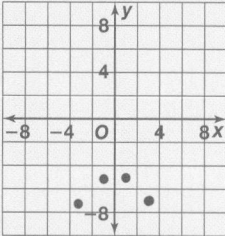

21. Not a function; a vertical line passes through both (−7, 3) and (−7, −3) and through both (−5, 1) and (−5, −1).

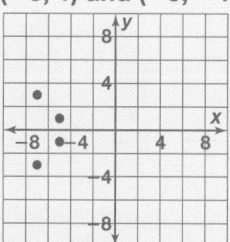

22. A function; no vertical line passes through two points on the graph.

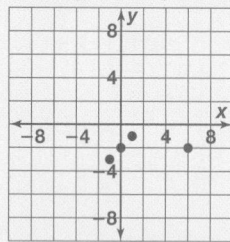

23. No; yes; a relation can have more than one range value for a domain value and thereby not be a function. A function is a relation by definition.

26. Each range value is two greater than its domain value.

27. Each range value is the absolute value of its domain value.

28. Each range value is 0.5 times its domain value.

29. Each range value is the square of its domain value.

30a. Answers may vary. Sample: {(−1, 1), (0, 2), (1, 2)}, {(−1, 1), (0, 1), (0, 2), (1, 1)}

30b. For samples in 30a: Function; no vertical line passes through two graphed points.

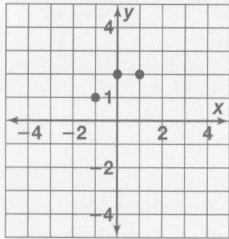

Not a function; a vertical line passes through both (0, 1) and (0, 2).

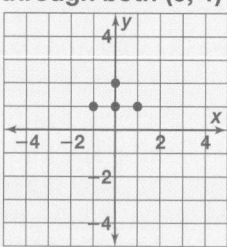

33. [2] (a) No; a specific number of sandwiches (domain value) does not determine the number of people who attend (range value).
(b) Yes; the number of people who attend determines the number of sandwiches made.
[1] minor error OR answers only

LESSON 8-2

pages 408–409 Practice and Problem Solving

14.

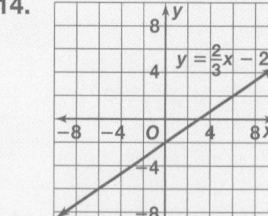

15.

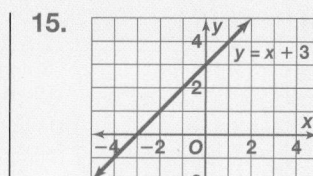

16.

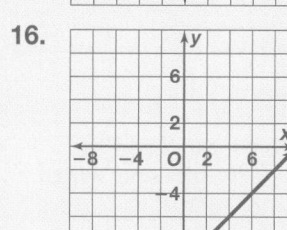

17.

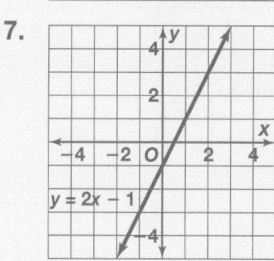

18.

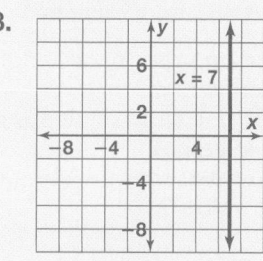

19.

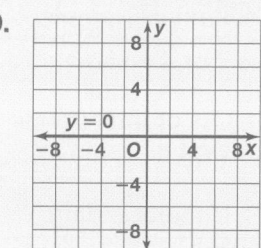

20.

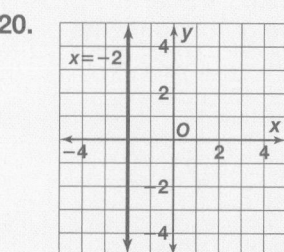

21. $y = 4x + 16$

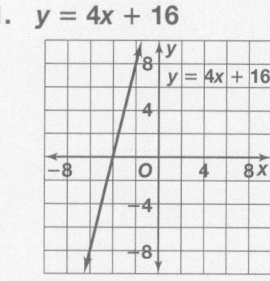

22. $y = -x + 3$

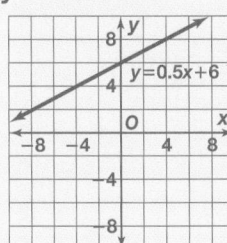

23. $y = \frac{1}{2}x - 3$

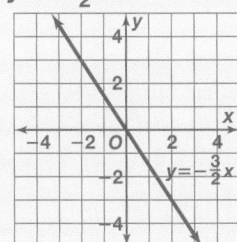

24. $y = 0.5x + 6$

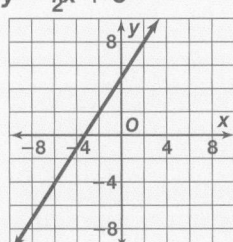

25. $y = -\frac{3}{2}x$

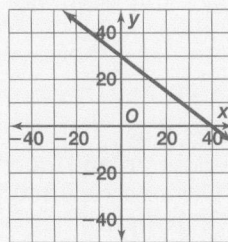

26. $y = \frac{3}{2}x + 5$

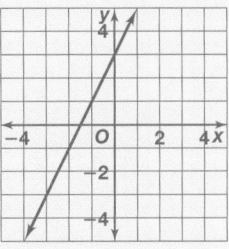

37b.

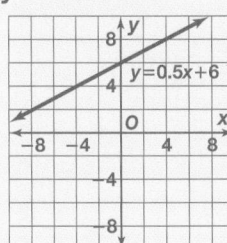

page 409   Mixed Review

42. Yes; there is one range value for each domain value.

---

43. Yes; there is one range value for each domain value.

44. No; there are two range values for the domain value 3.

45. No; there are two range values for the domain value 0.

TE page 409 Lesson Quiz 8-2

4.

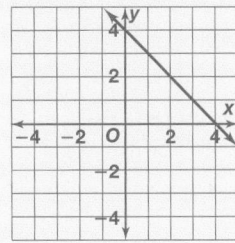

5.

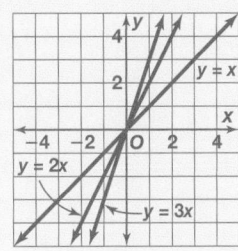

LESSON 8-3

page 411   Investigation

1a.

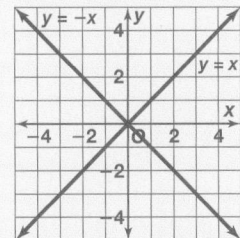

2a.

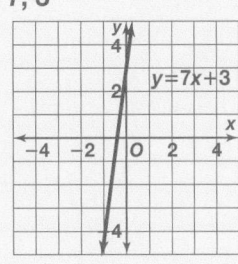

pages 414–416   Practice and Problem Solving

11. 7; 3

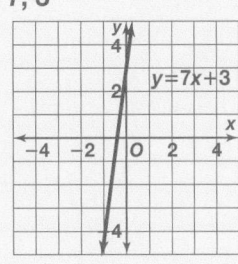

---

12. −1; 0

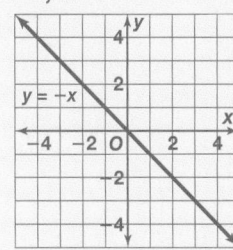

13. $\frac{1}{2}$; −8

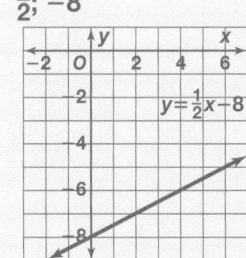

14. 2; 1

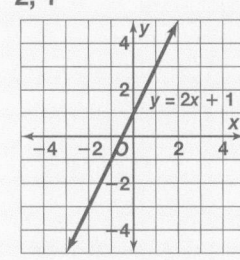

15. −3; −1

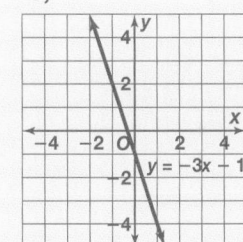

16. 1; −4

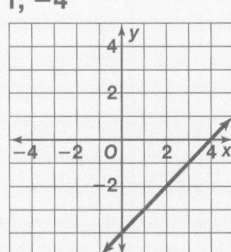

17. 0; 4

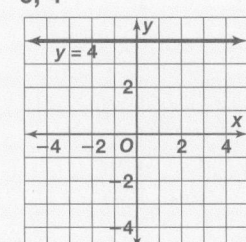

18. −3; 3

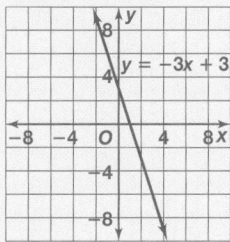

19. $-\frac{3}{2}$; 6

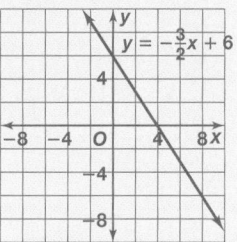

20.

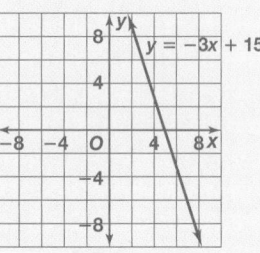

35. $y = -3$

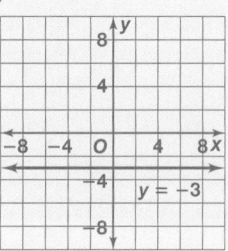

36. $y = \frac{1}{2}x - 4$

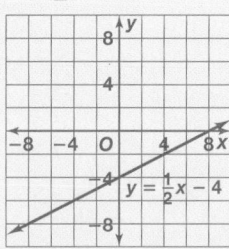

37. $y = -\frac{1}{4}x - 12$

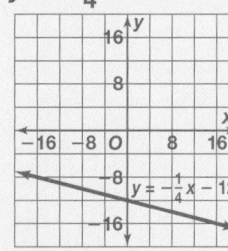

38. $y = \frac{2}{3}x + 5$

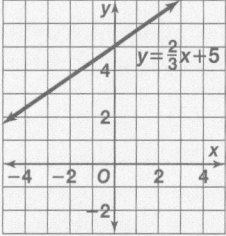

41.

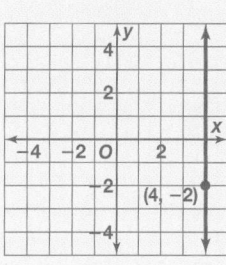

42.

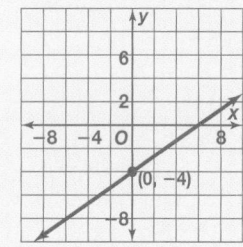

43a.

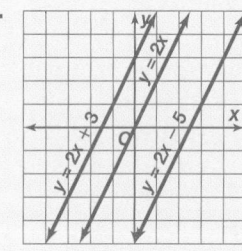

page 416   Mixed Review

52. $x < 3$

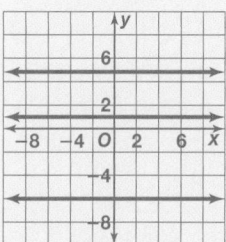

53. $x \leq -6\frac{1}{2}$

54. $x < -25$

page 417   Technology

6.

7.

8.

9.

TE page 419   Closure

First, find the slope by writing the difference of $f(x)$-values over the difference of corresponding x-values. Then find the y-intercept by finding the value of $f(x)$ when $x = 0$. Write the rule in $f(x) = mx + b$ form.

page 422   Test Prep

31.   [2] $q(g) = 4g$; 68 qt
   [1] correct function and incorrect answer OR incorrect function and correct answer

page 422   Checkpoint Quiz 1

2.
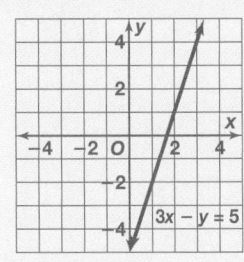
$3x - y = 5$

LESSON 8-5

page 426   **Practice and Problem Solving**

4.
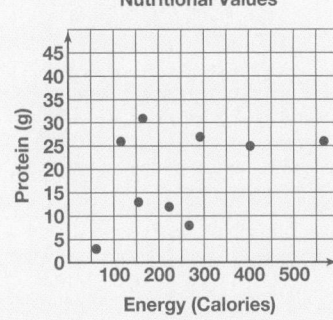
Nutritional Values

5.
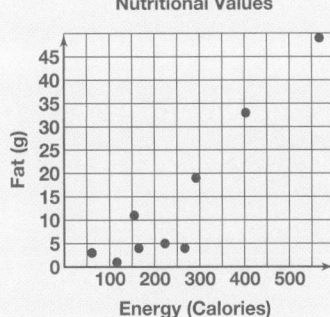
Nutritional Values

6.
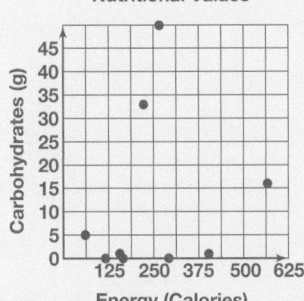
Nutritional Values

page 428   Test Prep

29. [2] In a graph with a negative correlation, the *y*-values decrease as the *x*-values increase; correct graph
     [1] correct description; incorrect or no sketch

30. [2] In a graph with no correlation, there is no relationship between the two data sets; correct graph
     [1] correct description; incorrect or no sketch

LESSON 8-6

page 432   **Practice and Problem Solving**

1a–b.   Trend lines may vary. Sample given.

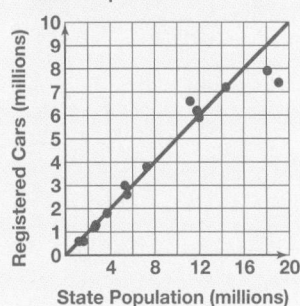
State Populations and Cars

LESSON 8-7

page 435   **Check Skills You'll Need**

1.
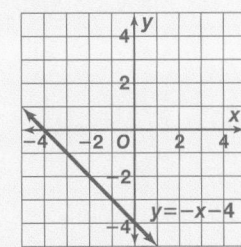
$y = -x - 4$

2.
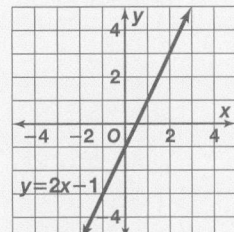
$y = 2x - 1$

3.
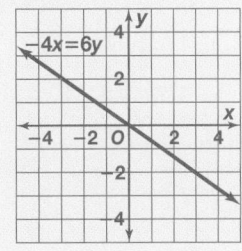
$-4x = 6y$

4.
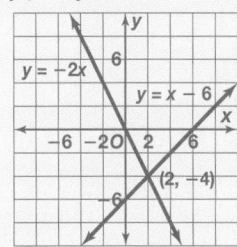
$3x - 2y = 5$

page 435   Check Understanding Example 1

1a. $(2, -4)$
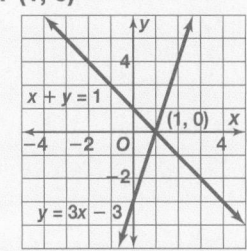
$y = -2x$ $y = x - 6$ $(2, -4)$

1b. $(1, 0)$
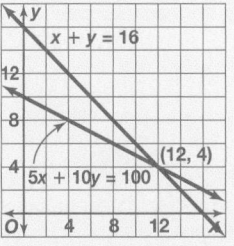
$x + y = 1$ $(1, 0)$ $y = 3x - 3$

page 439   **Practice and Problem Solving**

39. [4] $x + y = 16$; $5x + 10y = 100$;

$x + y = 16$ $5x + 10y = 100$ $(12, 4)$

   12 five-point questions, 4 ten-point questions
   [3] correct equations, but graph or solution contains computational errors
   [2] correct equations, but graph or solution is missing
   [1] correct equations, but graph and solution are missing

page 440   Checkpoint Quiz 2

1a.
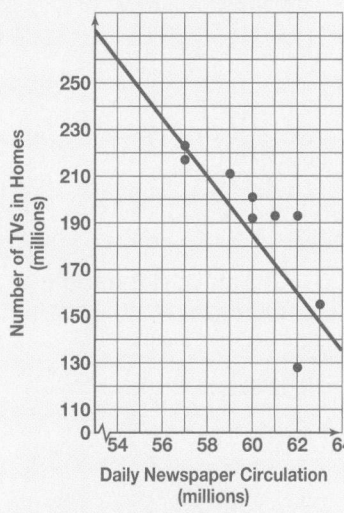

1b. Negative correlation; as the number of television sets increases, the newspaper circulation decreases.

1c. Trend lines may vary. Sample: See scatterplot; 250 million television sets

LESSON 8-8

page 442   Check Understanding
Example 1

1c.
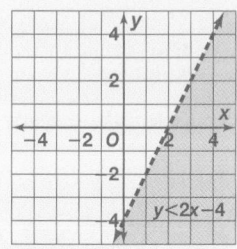

pages 444–445   Practice and Problem Solving

6.
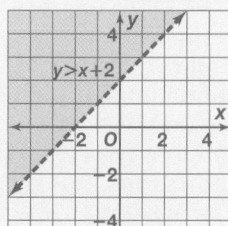

7.
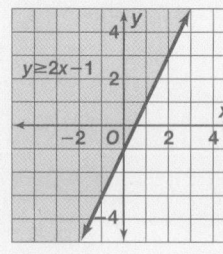

8.
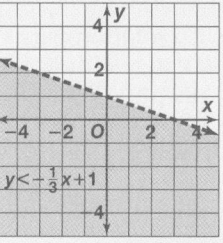

9.
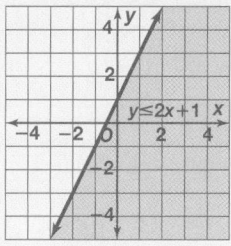

13. $x + y > 3$
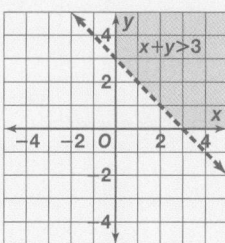

14. $y \geq 3x$
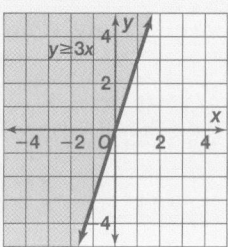

15. $10x + 5y < 100$
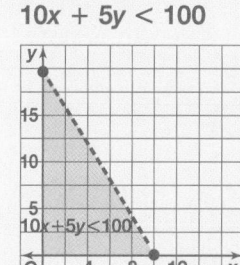

16.
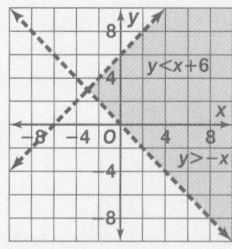

17.
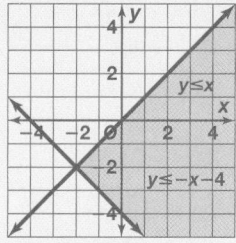

18.
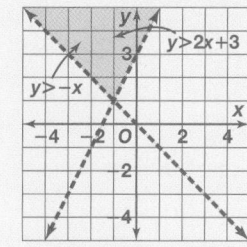

19.
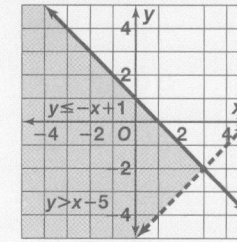

37.
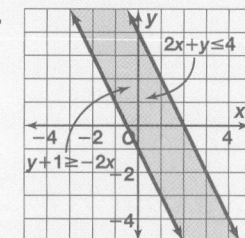

38.
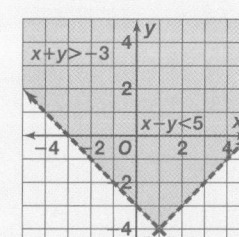

39.
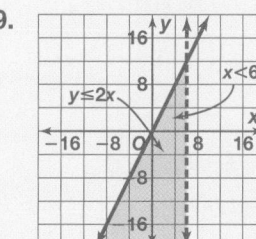

40.
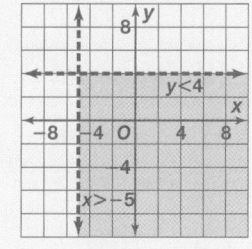

T810

41.

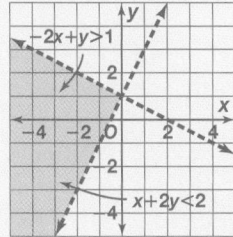

42.

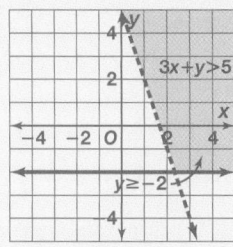

page 446   Test Prep

54. [2] The *y*-intercept is 3, so draw
   a point at (0, 3). The slope is 2,
   so rise 2 and run 1, and draw
   another point. Because the
   inequality symbol is ≥, draw a
   solid line through the points.
   The point (1, 6) satisfies the
   inequality, so shade above the
   boundary line, the side that
   contains (1, 6). (Test points
   may vary.)

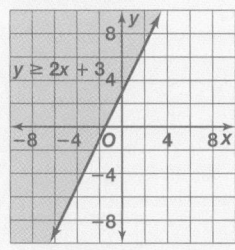

[1] incorrect or incomplete
   explanation; correct graph

page 452   Chapter Test

17.

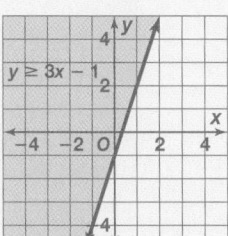

18.

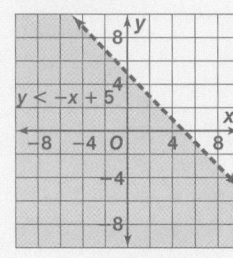

22.

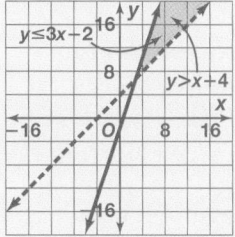

23. Yes; for each labeled price there is
   one amount of sales tax.

24. No; for each height, there are
   people of different ages.

25a.

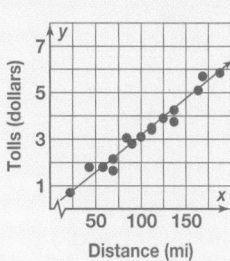

25b. See part (a) for trend line.
   Predictions may vary.
   Sample: $6.25

25c. Predictions may vary. Sample:
   145 mi

25d. Equations may vary. Sample: *t* =
   3*d* + 5 where *t* is the toll in cents
   and *d* is the distance in miles.

page 453   Test Prep

12. [2] (−3, 9), (0, 12) and (2, 14);
   $y = -3 + 12 = 9$
   $y = 0 + 12 = 12$
   [1] minor error OR answers only

13. [2] (0, −2), (2, 0), and (4, 2);
   $4(0) - 4y = 8$
   $-4y = 8$
   $y = -2$
   $4(2) - 4y = 8$
   $-4y = 0$
   $y = 0$
   [1] minor error OR answers only

14. [4] $y = -2x + 8$; −2; 8; and (2, 0)

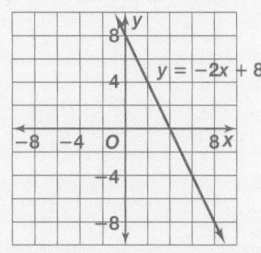

[3] 1 minor error with work shown
[2] 2 minor errors with work shown
[1] correct answer with no work
   shown

CHAPTER 9

LESSON 9-1

page 458   Check Skills You'll Need

1. The graph starts at 3 and extends
   to the right without end.

2. The graph starts at 0 and extends
   to the left without end.

3. The graph starts at 5 and extends
   to the left without end.

4. The graph starts at −2 and
   extends to the right without end.

TE page 460   Additional Examples

3.

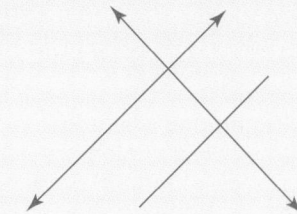

page 463   Test Prep

49. [2]

A line is a series of points
   extending in opposite
   directions, so $\overleftrightarrow{AB}$ is the same
   as $\overleftrightarrow{BA}$. Answers may vary.
   Sample: $\overleftrightarrow{BC}$.
   [1] minor error OR sketch only

page 463   Mixed Review

50.

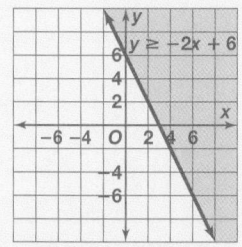

51.

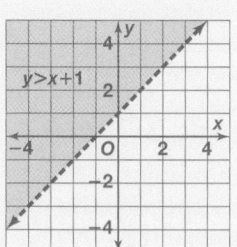

52.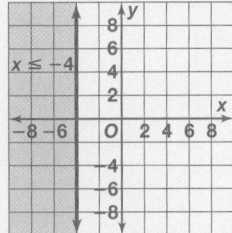

$x \leq -4$

LESSON 9-2

TE page 467　Closure

Adjacent angles share a vertex and a side, but no points in their interiors. Vertical angles are formed by intersecting lines and are not adjacent, but they are congruent. The sum of the measures of two supplementary angles is 180°. The sum of the measures of two complementary angles is 90°. If parallel lines are crossed by a transversal, the corresponding angles are congruent and alternate interior angles are also congruent. Check students' drawings.

page 469　Mixed Review

22.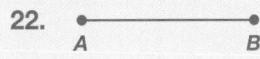
A　　　　B

23.
C　　　　D

24.
D　　　　C

25.
E　　　F

26.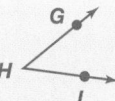
G
H
I

LESSON 9-3

page 474　Practice and Problem Solving

29. The congruent sides must be 12 cm, so the perimeter is 29 cm. If the congruent sides were 5 cm, then the base could not be 12 cm because the third side would have to be less than 10 cm to form a triangle.

30. The perimeter cannot be determined because the third side is unknown.

page 474　Writing in Math

Yes; equilateral triangles have three congruent sides, so at least two of the sides are congruent. No; some isosceles triangles may not have three congruent sides.

page 474　Test Prep

34. [2] Yes; a square has four congruent sides.
[1] minor error OR answer only

35. [2] Yes; a square has four right angles.
[1] minor error OR answer only

page 474　Mixed Review

36. Sketches may vary. Sample:

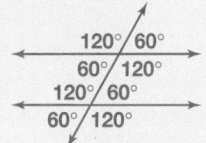
120° / 60°
60° / 120°
120° / 60°
60° / 120°

LESSON 9-4

page 479　Practice and Problem Solving

24. $8x + 5y \geq 1,000$

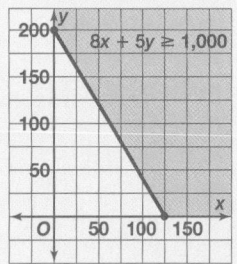
$8x + 5y \geq 1,000$

LESSON 9-5

TE page 481　Additional Examples

1. a. $\angle T \cong \angle W$, $\angle V \cong \angle X$, $\angle TUV \cong \angle WUX$

b. $\overline{TV} \cong \overline{WX}$, $\overline{TU} \cong \overline{WU}$, $\overline{VU} \cong \overline{XU}$

c. 300 m

2. a. $\angle ACB \cong \angle ECD$, $\overline{AC} \cong \overline{EC}$, $\angle CAB \cong \angle CED$, $\triangle ACB \cong \triangle ECD$ by ASA

b. $\overline{MK} \cong \overline{LJ}$, $\angle MJK \cong \angle LJK$, $\overline{JK} \cong \overline{JK}$, $\triangle MKJ \cong \triangle LJK$ by SAS.

TE page 481　Closure

Side-Side-Side, Side-Angle-Side, Angle-Side-Angle

TE page 487　Additional Example 2

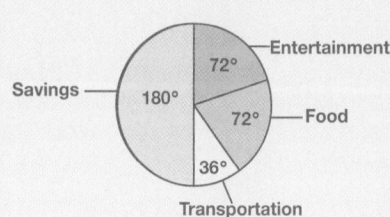
Entertainment
72°
Savings
180°
72° — Food
36°
Transportation

LESSON 9-6

page 490　Practice and Problem Solving

25a–b.
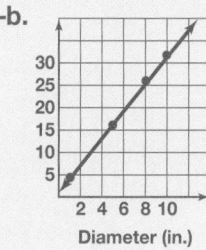
Diameter (in.)

LESSON 9-7

page 492　Check Understanding Example 2

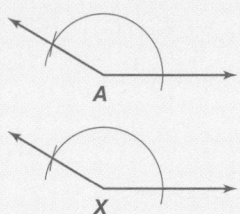
A

X

pages 494–495　Practice and Problem Solving

3.
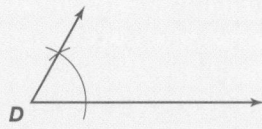
D

4.
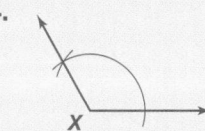
X

5.
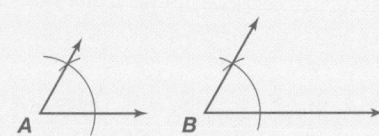
A　　　B

9.
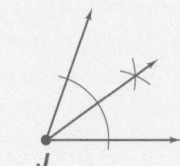
J

10.
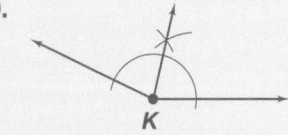
K

11.

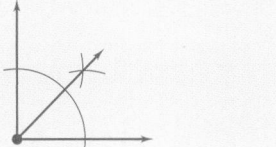

12.

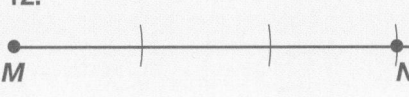

13.

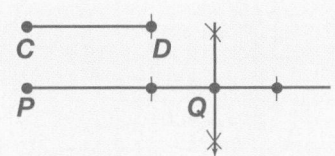

14.

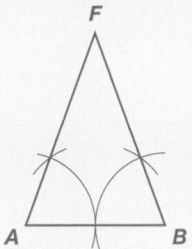

15.

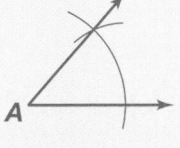

16.

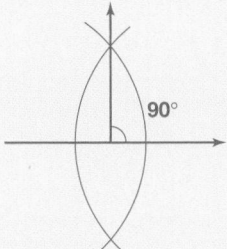

20a.

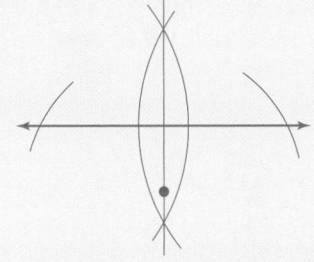

21.

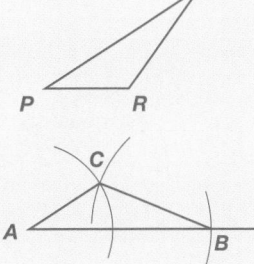

24. **[4]** First, draw a segment. Second, construct the perpendicular bisector of the segment. Third, construct an angle bisector of the 90° angle formed by the segment and its perpendicular bisector.

For part (b), construct an angle bisector of the 45° angle from part (a). For part (c), construct an angle bisector of a 90° angle. Then construct a bisector of one of the 45° angles. The $67\frac{1}{2}°$ angle is the sum of 45° and $22\frac{1}{2}°$.

[3] correct construction, but only two of the three above steps of the explanation complete

[2] correct construction, but only one of the three above steps of the explanation complete

[1] correct construction, but missing explanation

45° Sample:

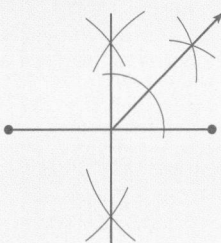

LESSON 9-8

page 497   Check Skills You'll Need

1–5.

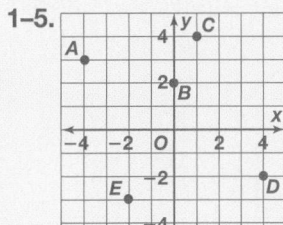

page 497   Check Understanding
            Example 1

1a.

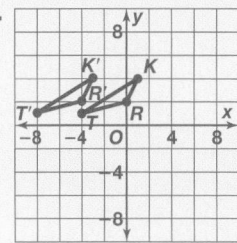

1b.

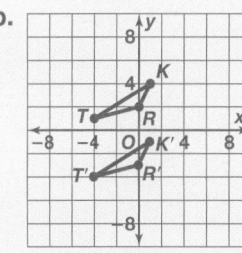

1c.

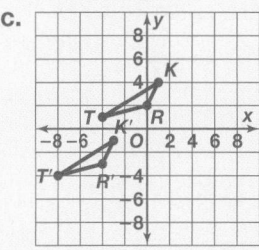

pages 499–500   Practice and
                 Problem Solving

25.

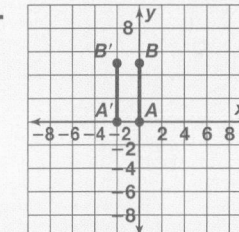

26.

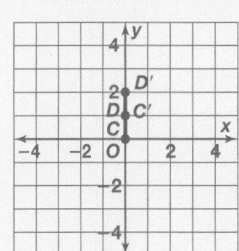

27.

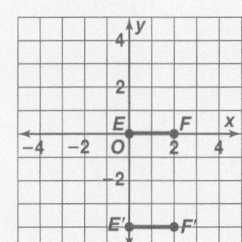

T813

28.

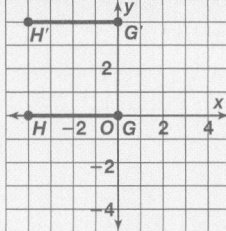

29.

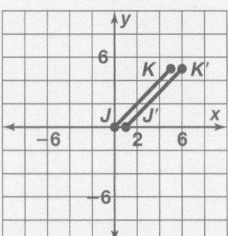

30.

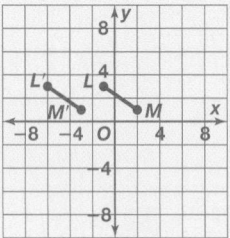

33.

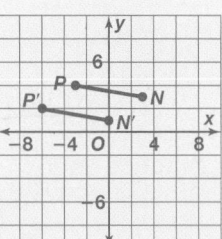

34.

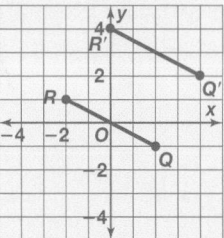

35.

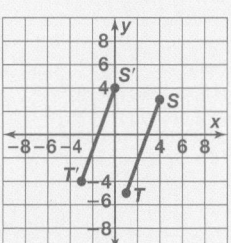

36.

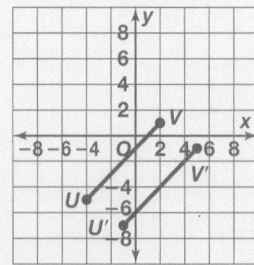

page 501   Mixed Review

45.

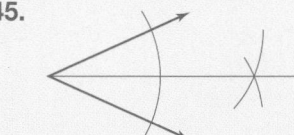

page 501   Checkpoint Quiz 2

4.

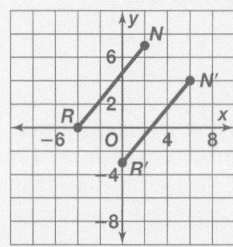

TE page 501   Lesson Quiz 9-8

1.

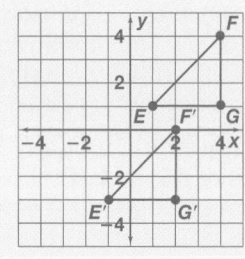

LESSON 9-9

page 503   Check Skills You'll Need

1.

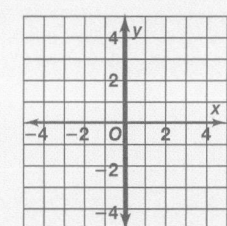

2.

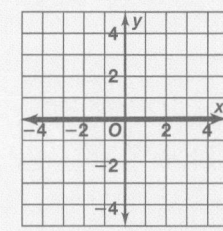

3.

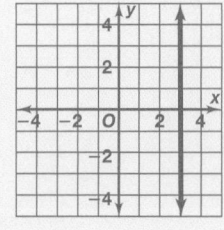

4.

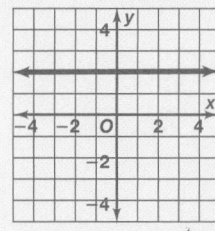

5.

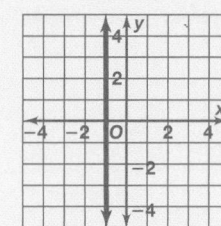

6.

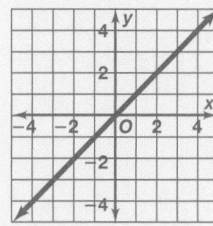

TE page 504   Additional Example 2

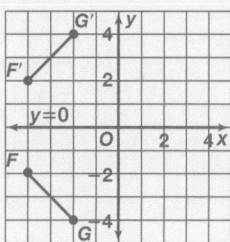

TE page 504   Additional Example 3

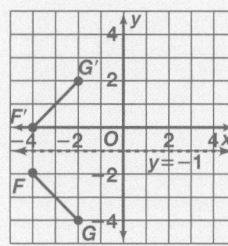

TE page 504   Closure

A reflection is a transformation that flips a figure over a line.

A line of symmetry divides a figure into two congruent halves that are reflection images of each other.

pages 505–506 Practice and
Problem Solving

6.
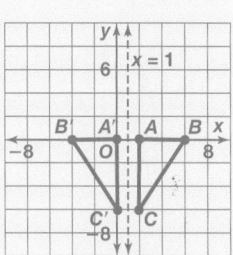

7.
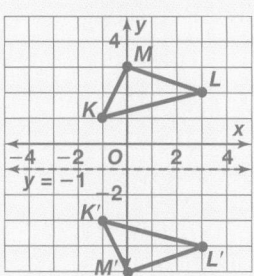

8.
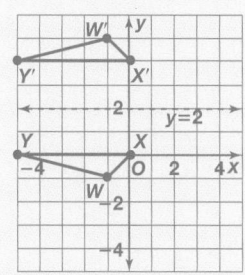

13. $H'(-8, 5)$
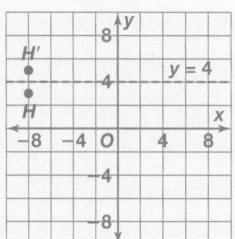

14. $J'(-8, 1)$
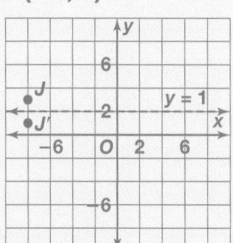

15. $V'(-9, 0)$
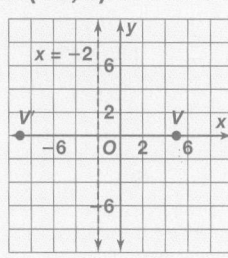

16. $A'(5, 2)$
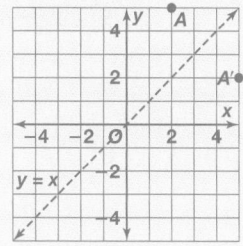

17. $B'(0, -3)$
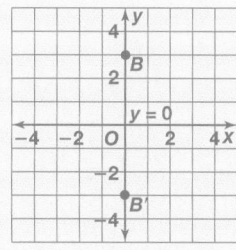

18. $C'(-4, 0)$
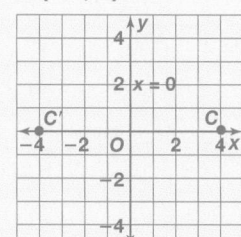

25a–b.
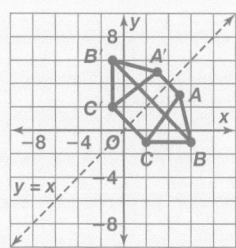

c. They are perpendicular.

page 506 Test Prep

28. [2] Always true; when a point is
reflected over a horizontal line,
the y-coordinate changes
because the vertical position
changes, but the x-coordinate
remains the same.
[1] minor error OR answer only

29. [2] Never true; when a point is
reflected over a horizontal line,
the y-coordinate changes
because the vertical position
changes.
[1] minor error OR answer only

page 506 Mixed Review

30. $A'(1, 1), B'(2, 5)$
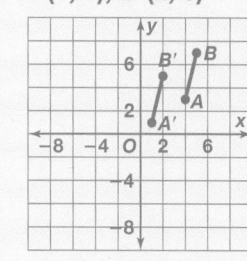

31. $X'(2, 2), Y'(4, 10)$
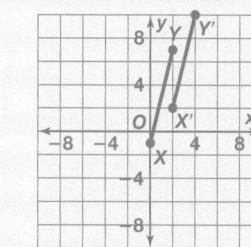

32.
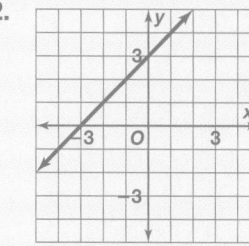

33.
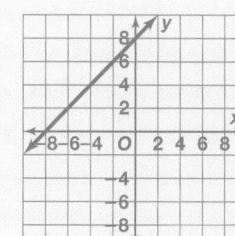

34.
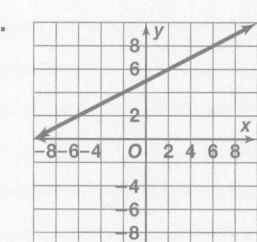

LESSON 9-10

page 507 Check Skills You'll Need

1.
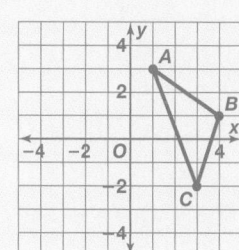

2.

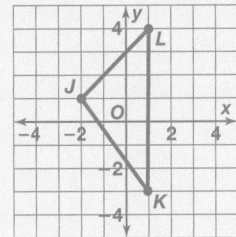

3.

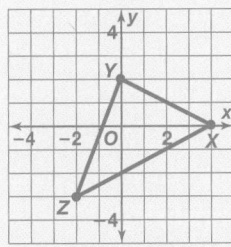

page 508　Check Understanding
　　　　　Example 1

1.

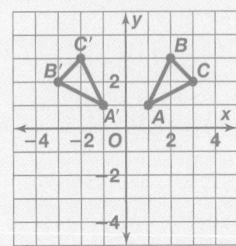

The vertices of the image are
A' (−1, 1), B' (−3, 2), and C' (−2, 3).

pages 509–510　Practice and
　　　　　　　Problem Solving

2a.

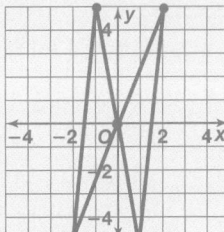

2b.

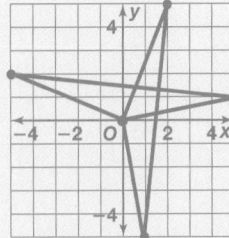

3a.

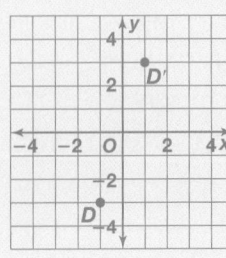

3b.

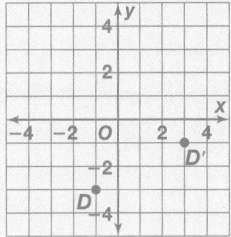

4a.

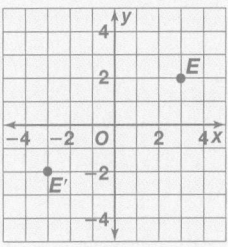

4b.

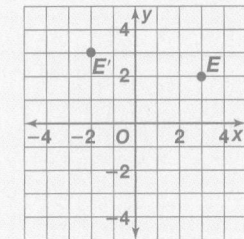

5a.

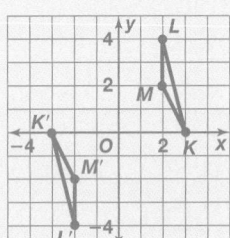

5b.

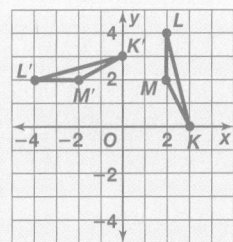

6a.

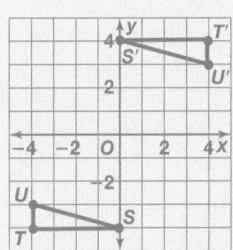

6b.

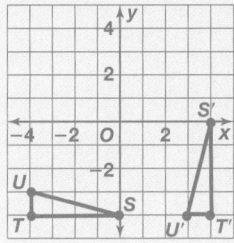

7a.

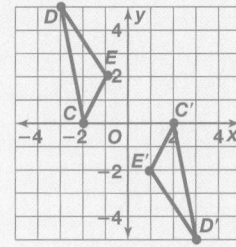

7b.

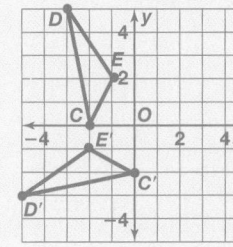

8a.

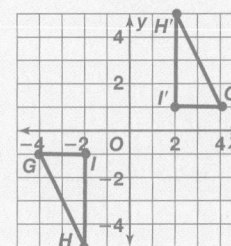

8b.

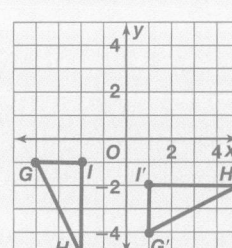

13a.

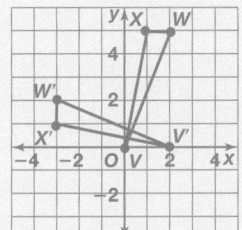

T816

13b.

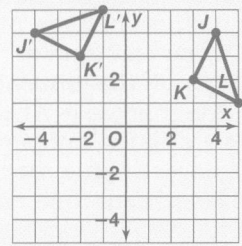

23a. $J'(-4, 4)$, $K'(-2, 3)$, $L'(-1, 5)$

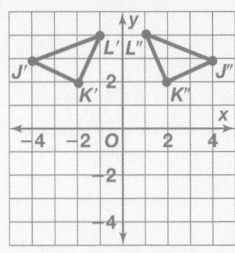

23b.

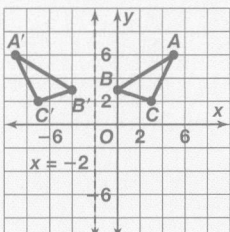

page 510   Test Prep

28. [2] Equilateral triangle; an equilateral triangle has an angle of rotation of 120°.
[1] minor error OR answer only

29.

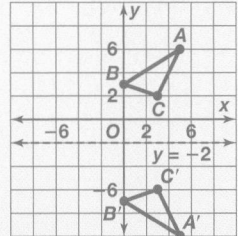

30.

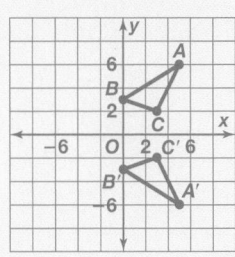

31.

CHAPTER 10

LESSON 10-2

page 531   Practice and Problem Solving

22. [2] $A = \frac{1}{2}bh$
$= \frac{1}{2}(9)(8)$
$= 36$ units^2
[1] minor error OR answer only

23. [2] $A = \frac{1}{2}h(b_1 + b_2)$
$= \frac{1}{2}(14)(14 + 24.5)$
$= 269.5$ units^2
[1] minor error OR answer only

page 538   Extension

2.

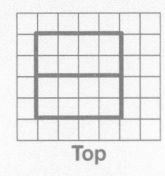
Top

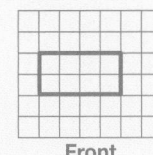
Front

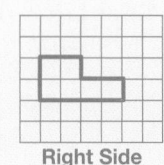
Right Side

3.

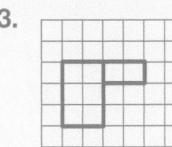
Top

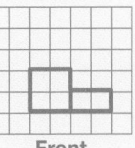
Front

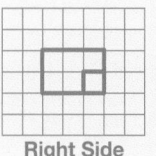
Right Side

4.

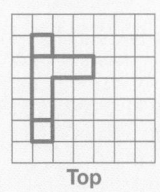
Top

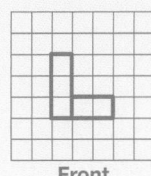
Front

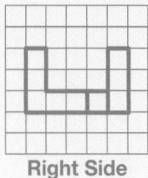
Right Side

LESSON 10-5

page 550   Mixed Review

36.

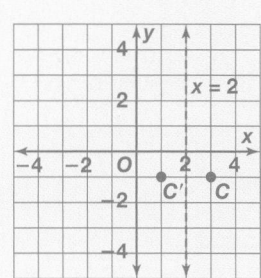

LESSON 10-6

page 556   Test Prep

24. [4] 215π ft^2 or about 675.1 ft^2; the radius of the tank is $\frac{1}{2} \cdot 10 = 5$. The lateral surface area of the cylindrical part of the tank is $2 \cdot \pi \cdot 5 \cdot 15 = 150\pi$ ft^2. The lateral area of the conical roof is $\pi \cdot 5 \cdot 8 = 40\pi$ ft^2. The area of the base of the cylindrical part of the tank is $\pi \cdot 5^2 = 25\pi$ ft^2. Add the areas for a total surface area of 215π ft^2.
[3] 1 computational error with work shown
[2] 2 computational errors with work shown
[1] correct answer with no work shown

LESSON 10-7

page 560   Test Prep

22. [4] cylinder volume = 678.24 cm^3
prism volume = 661.5 cm^3
cylinder surface area = 439.6 cm^2
prism surface area = 476 cm^2
The cylinder is the better package because it holds more than the prism and there is less cardboard in the packaging.
[3] 1 computational error with work shown
[2] 2 computational errors with work shown
[1] correct answer with no work shown

LESSON 10-8

page 562   Check Skills You'll Need

1.

2.

3.

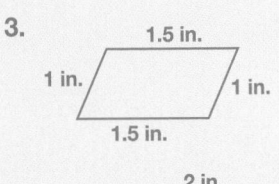

page 564 Practice and Problem Solving

2. Answers may vary. Sample:

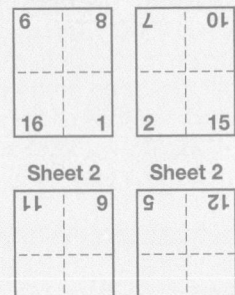

7. Answers may vary. Sample: Fold a sheet of paper in quarters. Imagine the fold is the spine of a book. Letter the "pages" *A* through *H.* Unfold the paper.

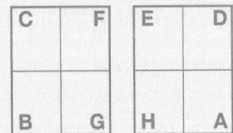

page 575 Test Prep

16. [2] $V = Bh$
$= (10 \cdot 8.5)(6)$
$= 510 \text{ mm}^3$
[1] minor error OR answer only

17. [2] $V = Bh$
$= \left(\frac{1}{2} \cdot 5 \cdot 8\right)(12)$
$= 240 \text{ m}^3$
[1] minor error OR answer only

18. [2] $V = \frac{1}{3}Bh$
$= \frac{1}{3} \cdot \pi \cdot 37.5^2(40)$
$= \frac{1}{3} \cdot (3.14) \cdot 37.5^2(40)$
$\approx 58,875 \text{ ft}^3$
[1] minor error OR answer only

19. [2] $V = \frac{1}{3}Bh$
$= \frac{1}{3}(8 \cdot 8)(5.5)$
$= \frac{1}{3}(352)$
$= 117.\overline{3}, \text{ or } 117 \text{ m}^3$
[1] minor error OR answer only

20. [2] $V = Bh$
$= (\pi \cdot 15^2)(60)$
$\approx (3.14)(225)(60)$
$\approx 42,390 \text{ yd}^3$
[1] minor error OR answer only

21. [2] $V = \frac{4}{3}\pi r^3$
$= \frac{4}{3}(3.14)(6)^3$
$\approx 904.32, \text{ or } 904 \text{ yd}^3$
[1] minor error OR answer only

22. [4]

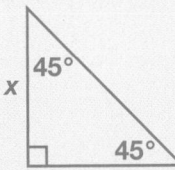

$SA = \text{L.A.} + 2B$
$= 2\pi rh + 2(\pi r^2)$
$= 2\pi(1.5)(6) + 2\pi(1.5)^2$
$\approx 71 \text{ cm}^2$
$V = Bh$
$= \pi r^2 h$
$\approx 3.14(1.5)^2(6)$
$\approx 42.39 \text{ cm}^3$
[3] 1 computational error with work shown
[2] 2 computational errors with work shown
[1] correct answers with no work shown

CHAPTER 11

LESSON 11-1

page 580   Check Skills You'll Need

1. 1, 4, 9, 16, 25, 36, 49, 64, 81, 100, 121, 144

2. 100; 400; 900; 1,600; 2,500; 3,600; 4,900; 6,400; 8,100, 10,000; 12,100; 14,400

LESSON 11-2

page 589   Test Prep

40. [4] a. Yes; since $3^2 + 4^2 = 5^2$, by the Converse of the Pythagorean Theorem, the sides can form a right triangle.
b. You place 3 segments of rope along the wall to one side of the corner. Place 4 segments along the other wall. If you can form a triangle with the remaining rope, the triangle is a right triangle with the right angle in the corner of the room.
c. The 12-segment rope can be used to check if corners are right angles because a triangle with side lengths 3, 4, and 5 (totaling 12) is a right triangle.
[3] one minor error in explanation
[2] two minor errors in explanation
[1] one part only with no explanation

LESSON 11-4

page 601   Test Prep

15. [2] $\frac{x}{x + 1.5} = \frac{64}{72}$
$72 \cdot x = 64(x + 1.5)$
$72x = 64x + 96$
$72x - 64x = 64x - 64x + 96$
$8x = 96$
$\frac{8x}{8} = \frac{96}{8}$
$x = 12$
[1] minor error OR answer only

LESSON 11-5

page 606   Writing in Math

Answers may vary. Sample:

The length of the other leg is *x* because the legs in a 45°-45°-90° triangle are equal. The length of the hypotenuse is $x\sqrt{2}$.

page 606 Practice and
Problem Solving

20a. Answers may vary. Sample:

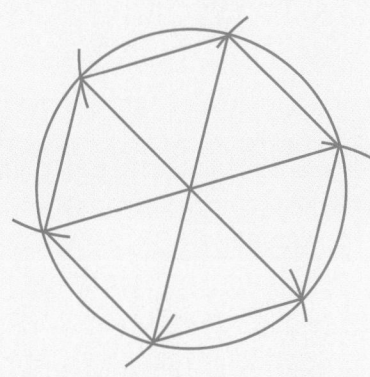

20b. Answers may vary. Sample: If the diameter of the circle is 2 in., one side of each triangle is 1 in. The height of one triangle is $0.5 \cdot \sqrt{3}$ or about 0.87 in. The area of one triangle is $\frac{1}{2} \cdot 1 \cdot 0.87$, or about 0.44 in.^{2}. The area of the hexagon is $6 \cdot 0.44$, or about 2.6 in.^{2}.

page 606   Test Prep

23. [2] Neither; in a 45°-45°-90° triangle two sides are congruent. In a 30°-60°-90° triangle the hypotenuse is twice the shorter leg.
[1] minor error OR answer only

24. [2] 45°-45°-90°; this is a 45°-45°-90° triangle because two sides are congruent and the hypotenuse is $\sqrt{2}$ times a leg.
[1] minor error OR answer only

25. [2] 30°-60°-90°; this is a 30°-60°-90° triangle because the hypotenuse is twice the shorter leg and the longer leg is $\sqrt{3}$ times the shorter leg.
[1] minor error OR answer only

page 606   Mixed Review

30. Yes; for each domain value there is only one range value.

31. Yes; for each domain value there is only one range value.

LESSON 11-6

page 611   Practice and
Problem Solving

20. $\frac{\sqrt{3}}{2}x$, $2x$, 30°, $\sqrt{3}x$

21. Both are correct. Both ratios include h, a known number, and a known angle.

TE page 627   Real-World Snapshots

1a.

Side a	Side $a + b$	$\dfrac{a}{b}$	$\dfrac{(a + b)}{a}$	Golden Ratio?
5	8	$\frac{5}{3} = 1.\overline{6} \approx 1.67$	$\frac{8}{5} = 1.6$	Yes
3	4	$\frac{3}{1} = 3$	$\frac{4}{3} \approx 1.3$	No
6	10	$\frac{6}{4} = 1.5$	$\frac{10}{6} \approx 1.7$	No
14	22	$\frac{14}{8} \approx 1.8$	$\frac{22}{14} \approx 1.6$	No
12	16	$\frac{12}{4} = 3$	$\frac{16}{12} \approx 1.3$	No
15	24	$\frac{15}{9} \approx 1.7$	$\frac{24}{15} = 1.6$	Yes
18	26	$\frac{18}{8} \approx 2.3$	$\frac{26}{18} \approx 1.4$	No
21	33	$\frac{21}{12} \approx 1.8$	$\frac{33}{21} \approx 1.6$	No

CHAPTER 12

LESSON 12-1

TE page 631 Additional Examples

1.

Number	Tally	Frequency
1	JHT I	6
2	JHT I	6
3	JHT II	7
4	III	3

2.

```
      x       x
      x x x x
    x x x x x
    x x x x x
    x x x x x
    0 1 2 3 4
```

TE page 631   Closure

A frequency table lists each data item together with the number of times it occurs. A line plot uses marks above a number line to represent the frequency of each data item.

pages 632–633 Practice and
Problem Solving

2.

Number	Frequency
1	1
2	2
3	1
4	3
5	1
6	2
7	1
8	2
9	1

4.

Number	Frequency
25	2
26	2
27	1
28	3
29	2
30	2

5.   Rolls of a Number Cube

Number	Frequency
1	4
2	3
3	3
4	2
5	3
6	2

6.   Test Scores

Score	Frequency
60	1
65	1
70	4
75	2
80	1
85	2
90	2
95	1
100	2

7.
```
          x
        x x
        x x
      x x x
      x x x x
    x x x x x x
  x x x x x x
  x x x x x x
  1 2 3 4 5 6
```

8.
```
          x x
          x x
          x x
      x x x x
      x x x x
    x x x x x
    x x x x x
  x x x x x x
  1 2 3 4 5 6
```

9.
```
  x x x     x
  x x x x x
  0 1 2 3 4   ; 4
```

10.
```
      x x x x
  x x x x x x
  1 2 3 4 5 6   ; 5
```

11.
```
            x
  x     x x
  x   x x x x
  x x x x x x   ; 5
  0 1 2 3 4 5
```

12.

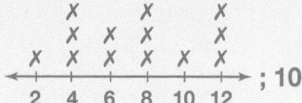

; 10

13. Numbers of Letters

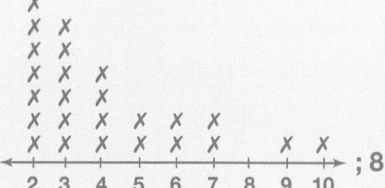

; 8

15. Ages of Club Members

Age	Frequency
12	3
13	1
14	4
15	4
16	3

Ages of Club Members

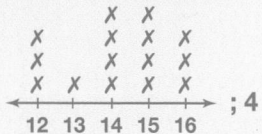

; 4

16. Heights of Plants (inches)

Heights	Frequency
16	1
20	2
25	5
26	1
28	1
30	2
31	1

Heights of Plants (inches)

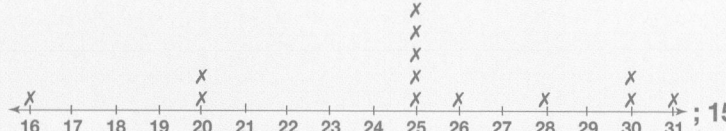

; 15

17.

Number	7	8	9	10	11
Frequency	2	2	2	2	4

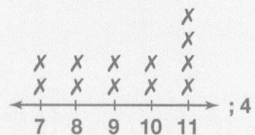

; 4

18.

Number	16	17	18	19	20
Frequency	1	5	4	2	2

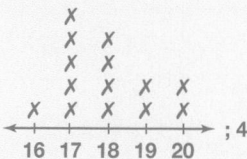

; 4

19. World Series Games, 1970–2002

Number of Games	Frequency
0	1
1	0
2	0
3	0
4	5
5	6
6	8
7	13

; 7

26b. Answers may vary. Sample: For mode, find the value of the stack with the most x's. For median, find the middle value or the average of the two middle values. For mean, multiply the number of x's in a stack by the value of each stack. Find the sum of the products. Divide by the number of x's from part (a).

page 633 Test Prep

30. [2] 27 students; the plot contains 27 x's and each x represents 1 student
[1] minor error OR answer only

TE page 633 Lesson Quiz

1.

Pets	Tally	Frequency
0	IIII	5
1	IIII II	7
2	III	3
3	II	2

2. Books Read

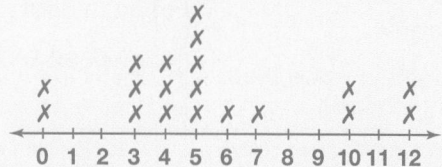

LESSON 12-2

page 636 Check Understanding Example 1

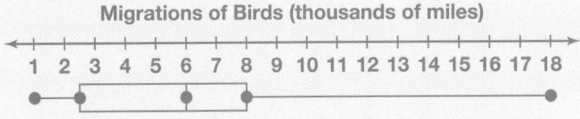

Migrations of Birds (thousands of miles)

page 636 Check Understanding Example 2

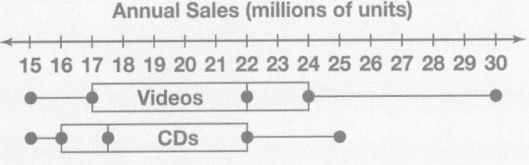

Annual Sales (millions of units)

TE page 637 Closure

Answers may vary. Sample: A box-and-whisker plot displays the distribution of data items along a number line. Quartiles divide the data into four parts. The median is the middle quartile. The middle two fourths of the data are grouped inside a box. You show the first and last fourths as whiskers extending from the sides of the box, which indicate the upper and lower quartiles.

pages 638–639 Practice and Problem Solving

2.

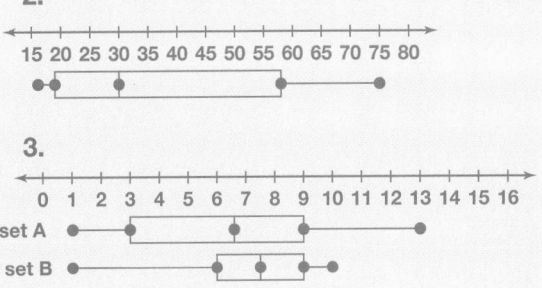

3.

8a.

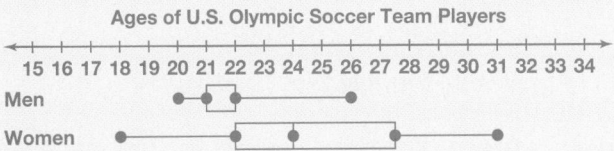

Ages of U.S. Olympic Soccer Team Players

8b. Answers may vary. Sample: The men are all from 20 to 26 years old, and about 67% are aged 21 to 22. The women's ages are much more spread out, ranging from 18 to 31. The median age for women is two years greater than the median age for men.

11. Answers may vary. Sample: The student assumed that the lower value, the upper value, and the quartiles are equally spaced.

13. The median can be determined from the vertical line in the box. The mean and mode are not indicated, and the data values to find them are not shown in the plot.

page 639 Test Prep

16. [2]

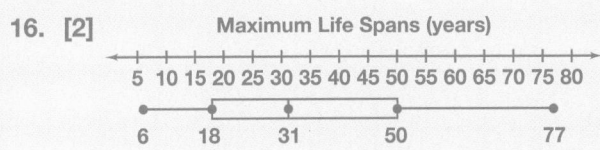

Maximum Life Spans (years)

median = 31 yr, upper quartile = 50 yr, lower quartile = 18 yr, least value = 6 yr, greatest value = 77 yr

[1] incorrect plot with correct labels OR correct plot with no labels

page 639 Mixed Review

18.

Number	Frequency
29	1
30	1
31	3
32	4
33	2
34	0
35	1

TE page 639 Lesson Quiz 12-2

1.

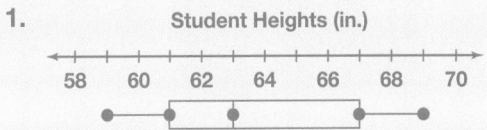

Student Heights (in.)

2. Answers may vary. Sample: prices at the discount store are more tightly grouped around the median price of $25. Half the items cost from $18 to $45. For less expensive items, there is not much difference in the prices at the two stores. For more expensive items, the discount store offers lower prices.

pages 640–641 Extension

3.

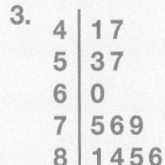

4	1 7
5	3 7
6	0
7	5 6 9
8	1 4 5 6

7 | 5 means 75

75.5; no mode; 45

5.

```
0 | 2 8 8
1 | 4
2 | 6
3 | 5
4 | 3 3 5
5 |
6 | 0
```

4 | 3 means 4.3

3.05; 0.8 and 4.3; 5.8

7.

Set D		Set C
	23	6 7
8 3	24	1 2
7 1	25	0
2	26	

means 251 ⟵ 1 | 25 | 0 ⟶ means 250

Set C: 241; no mode
Set D: 251; no mode

8.

Videos (millions)		CDs (millions)
7 6 5	1	5 6 6 6 7 8 8
8 4 4 2 2 1	2	2 4 5
0	3	

means 21 → 1 | 2 | 2 ← means 22

Median for videos: 22   Median for CDs: 17.5
Modes for videos: 24 and 22   Modes for CDs: 16

LESSON 12–3

page 642   Check Understanding Example 1

1.

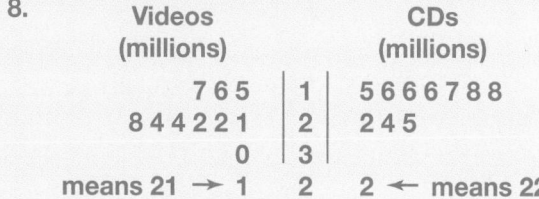

Populations of Chicago and Los Angeles

TE page 643   Additional Examples

1. "Areas of Texas and California." Because of the break in the vertical axis, the bar for Texas appears to be more than six times the height of the bar for California. Actually, the area of Texas is about 267,000 mi², which is not even two times the area of California, which is about 159,000 mi².

page 643   Check Understanding
Example 2

2a. Answers may vary. Sample:

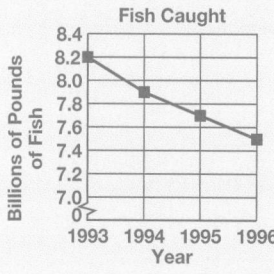

Fish Caught

2b. Answers may vary. Sample:

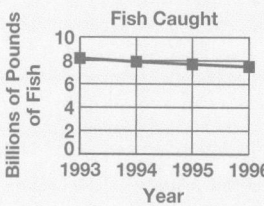

Fish Caught

TE page 644   Closure

Check the graph to see that the representation of data is accurate and honest.

page 644   Check Understanding
Example 3

3a. Answers may vary. Sample:

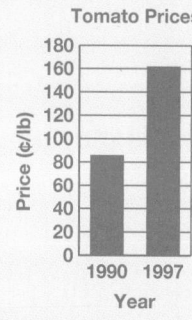

Tomato Prices

3b. Answers may vary. Sample:

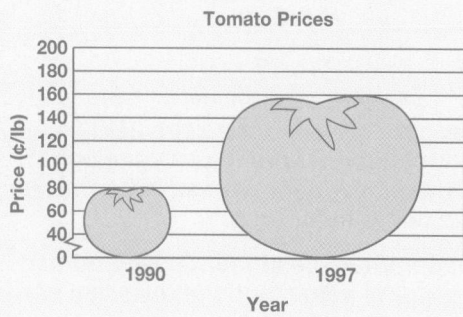

Tomato Prices

4.

Magazine Circulation

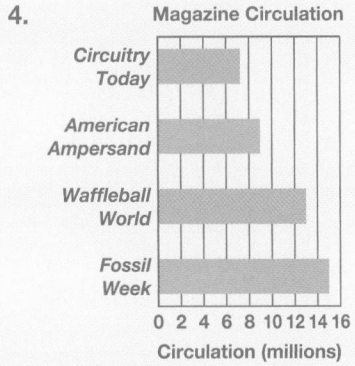

7.

Percent of Students Using Computers at School

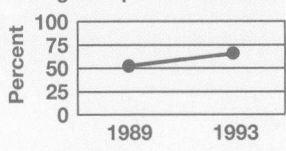

9.

Milk Sales in the School Cafeteria

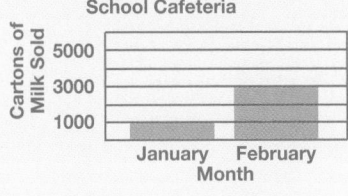

10.

Milk Sales in the School Cafeteria

15.

Average Annual Tuition and Fees for Four-Year Public Colleges

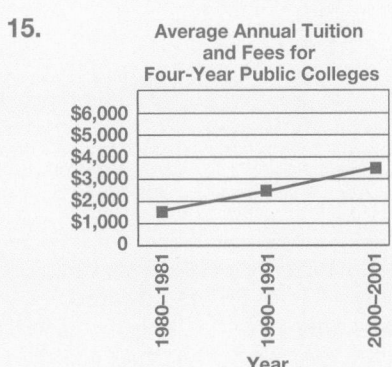

17. Answers may vary. Sample:

Percent of Milk Sold That Was Low-Fat

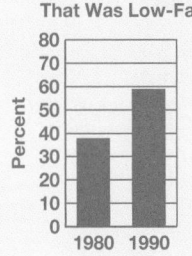

Percent of Milk Sold That Was Low-Fat

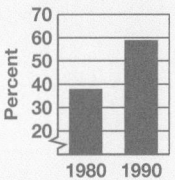

page 647   Test Prep

22. [2]

Annual Sales

Annual Sales

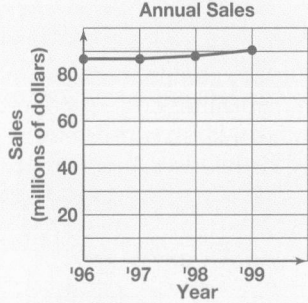

[1] one correct graph

page 647   Mixed Review

23.

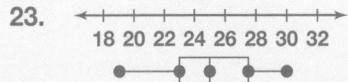

24.

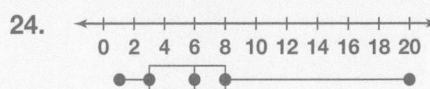

25.

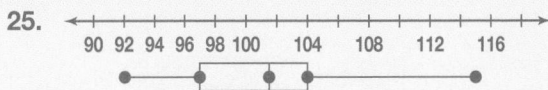

LESSON 12-4

page 649 Check Understanding Example 1

1. 12 choices;

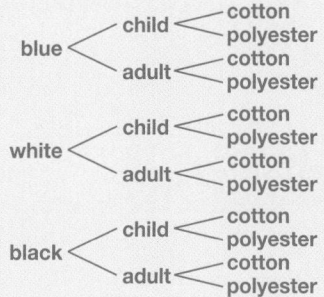

page 652 Practice and Problem Solving

1. 10 choices;

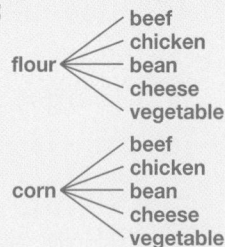

2. 12 choices;

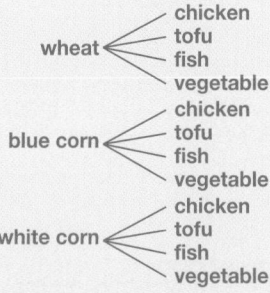

10. 9 choices; vanilla, red/blue; vanilla, red/green; vanilla, blue/green; chocolate, red/blue; chocolate, red/green; chocolate, blue/green; strawberry, red/blue; strawberry, red/green; strawberry, blue/green

page 653 Test Prep

20. [4] a. $\frac{2}{36}$, or $\frac{1}{18}$ b. $\frac{6}{36}$, or $\frac{1}{6}$ c. $\frac{30}{36}$, or $\frac{5}{6}$

1, 1	1, 2	1, 3	1, 4	1, 5	1, 6
2, 1	2, 2	2, 3	2, 4	2, 5	2, 6
3, 1	3, 2	3, 3	3, 4	3, 5	3, 6
4, 1	4, 2	4, 3	4, 4	4, 5	4, 6
5, 1	5, 2	5, 3	5, 4	5, 5	5, 6
6, 1	6, 2	6, 3	6, 4	6, 5	6, 6

[3] 3 out of 4 answers correct
[2] 2 out of 4 answers correct
[1] 1 out of 4 answers correct

page 653 Mixed Review

21. 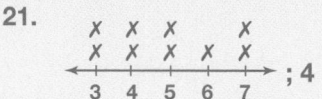 ; 4

22. 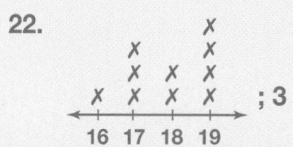 ; 3

page 653 Checkpoint Quiz 1

1.

Number	Frequency
47	2
48	2
49	1
50	3
51	2
52	2

2.

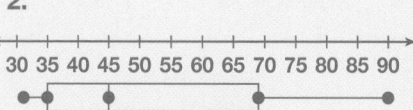

3a.

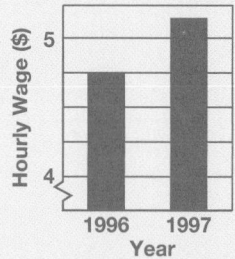

A break in the graph makes it look like there is a significant increase in the minimum wage.

3b.

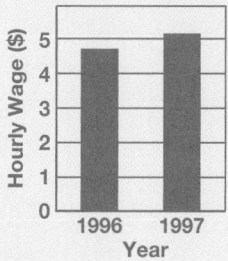

LESSON 12-5

page 658 Test Prep

31. [2] Dependent; when the letters are discarded, the probability of selecting a "T" or "H" is affected.
[1] minor error OR answer only

T824

LESSON 12-8

TE page 670   Additional Examples

1a. This is not a good sample. It may be that people leaving a restaurant are more likely to own computers.

b. This is a good sample. It is selected at random from the population you want to study.

c. This is not a good sample. This sample will be primarily students, but the population you are investigating is the whole community.

2. about 133 calculators

TE page 670   Closure

Answers may vary. Sample: Select every tenth student from class lists.

TE page 670   Advanced Learners

Answers may vary. Sample: You may have surveyed people who were not representative of the people who attend Track and Field Day.

page 671   Practice and Problem Solving

2. This is a good sample, since there is no bias built into the sample.

9a. The cold virus may be passed from student to student in that class so that more of them have colds than in the total school population.

9b. Answers may vary. Sample: Survey students as they enter the school cafeteria.

page 672   Test Prep

15. [2] No; barbershop customers will tend to be male and will include adults, so the sample is not taken from the population you want to study.
[1] minor error OR answer only

16. [2] Yes; it is a random sample from the population you want to study and no bias built into the study.
[1] minor error OR answer only

LESSON 12-9

page 674   Check Skills You'll Need

letter	tally	frequency
a	⊮	5
c	I	1
d	I	1
e	⊮ I	6
f	I	1
i	IIII	4
l	III	3
m	II	2
n	II	2
o	III	3
p	I	1
r	II	2
s	II	2
t	I	1
u	I	1
x	I	1

TE page 675   Closure

Answers may vary. Sample: you can use simulations to model real-world problems or situations for which "real" experiments would be too dangerous. For example, automakers crash test cars and trucks to see how safe their seat belts are.

pages 676–677   Practice and Problem Solving

2. Answers may vary. Sample: simulate the problem by constructing a spinner with four congruent sections. Make one section red, to represent a correct answer. Spin 60 times and organize the results into 20 groups of three. Count the number of groups with exactly two red spins. Divide this number by 20 to get the experimental probability.

10a. Answers may vary. Sample: simulate the problem by using one marked index card and two unmarked index cards. Let the marked card be the prize door. Choose one of the three cards 50 times at random. Count the number of times you chose the marked card. Divide this number by 50 to get the experimental probability.

b. Answers may vary. Sample: Simulate the problem by using one marked index card and two unmarked index cards. Let the marked card be the prize door. Choose one of the three cards at random, discard it, and discard

one of the remaining unchosen, unmarked cards. Note whether the remaining card is marked. Repeat 50 times. Count the number of times the remaining card is the marked card. Divide this number by 50 to get the experimental probability.

c. Answers may vary. Sample: Switch; switching has the greater experimental probability. (Theoretical probability of winning by switching is $\frac{2}{3}$, given the assumptions in part (b). Theoretical probability of winning by not switching is $\frac{1}{3}$.)

page 682   Chapter Test

4a.

Number	Frequency
0	1
1	1
2	1
3	1
4	3
5	3
6	0
7	1
8	2
9	1
10	1

5. Answers may vary. Sample:

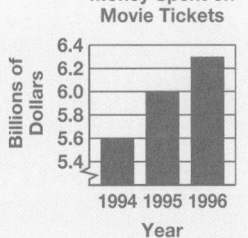

Money Spent on Movie Tickets

6. Answers may vary. Sample:

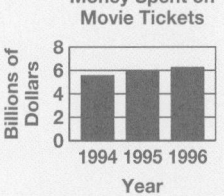

Money Spent on Movie Tickets

22b. Answers will vary. Sample: Make a set of 36 index cards. Write one of the possible rolls on each card. Draw a card at random and replace it. Repeat 50 times. Count the number of doubles drawn and divide by 50 to find the experimental probability.

8. [2]

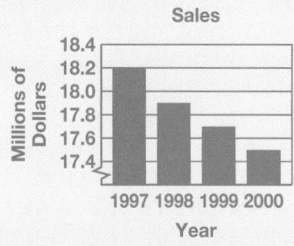

[1] 1 correct graph

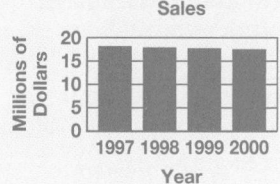

12. [4] a. $\frac{1}{36}$

b. $\frac{9}{36}$, or $\frac{1}{4}$

c. $\frac{44}{50}$, or $\frac{22}{25}$

[3] parts (a) and (b) correct

[2] part (c) and (a) or (b) correct

[1] 1 correct answer

TE page 685   Real-World Snapshots

1.

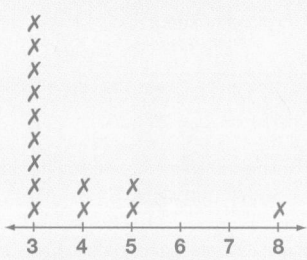

4a.

Team	Goals Scored
Brazil	13
Germany	8
Spain	6
Denmark	4
Italy	4
Belgium	3
Ireland	3
Portugal	3
Senegal	3
Sweden	3
Turkey	3

CHAPTER 13

LESSON 13–1

page 688   Check Skills You'll Need

1. Start with 60 and subtract 12 repeatedly.

2. Start with 7 and add 5 repeatedly.

3. Start with 6 and multiply by 3 repeatedly.

4. Start with 60 and divide by 2 repeatedly.

page 688   Investigation

1.

Day	Option A	Option B
1	$500	$1
2	$550	$2
3	$600	$4
4	$650	$8
5	$700	$16
6	$750	$32
7	$800	$64
8	$850	$128
9	$900	$256
10	$950	$512

1a. Option A; in 10 days, the Option A total is $7,250 and the Option B total is $1,023.

1b. Option B. Option A increases at a steady $50 a day. From day 7 on, Option B is increasing faster, and will soon pass Option A.

page 689   Check Understanding Example 2

2a. 7, 3, −1; start with 23 and add −4 repeatedly.

2b. $-\frac{2}{3}, \frac{2}{3}, 2$; start with −6 and add $1\frac{1}{3}$ repeatedly.

pages 691–692   Practice and Problem Solving

15. $\frac{1}{3}, \frac{4}{27}, \frac{4}{81}, \frac{4}{243}$; start with 12 and multiply by $\frac{1}{3}$ repeatedly.

16. 5; 5,000, 25,000, 125,000; start with 8 and multiply by 5 repeatedly.

17. geometric; 81, 243, 729

18. arithmetic; −10, −15, −20

19. arithmetic; 2.5, 2, 1.5

20. neither; 10, 16, 26

21. geometric; −81, 243, −729

22. neither; 32, 45, 60

35. arithmetic; $1\frac{5}{6}, 2\frac{1}{6}, 2\frac{1}{2}$

36. neither; 3, 30, 4

37. neither; 3, −2, −8

38. arithmetic; 7.12, 7.15, 7.18

39. geometric; $-\frac{1}{80}, -\frac{1}{160}, -\frac{1}{320}$

40. No; it could be arithmetic, such as 4, 8, 12, 16, . . . , or it could be geometric, such as 4, 8, 16, 32, . . . , or it could be neither, such as 4, 8, 13, 19, 26, . . .

41. −6, −3, 0, 3; arithmetic

42. 2, 0, 0, 2; neither

43. $\frac{1}{4}, \frac{1}{2}$, 1, 2; geometric

44. 4, 1, 0, 1; neither

page 692 Test Prep

50. Either; the differences between the values and the ratios between the values are close.

LESSON 13–2

page 694   Investigation

2.

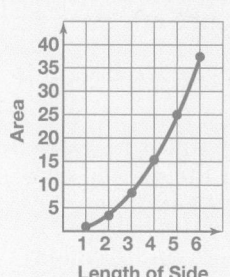

This is not a linear function because its graph is a curve.

page 694   Check Understanding Example 1

1a.

x	$-2x^2 = y$	(x, y)
−2	$-2(-2)^2 = -8$	$(-2, -8)$
−1	$-2(-1)^2 = -2$	$(-1, -2)$
0	$-2(0)^2 = 0$	$(0, 0)$
1	$-2(1)^2 = -2$	$(1, -2)$
2	$-2(2)^2 = -8$	$(2, -8)$

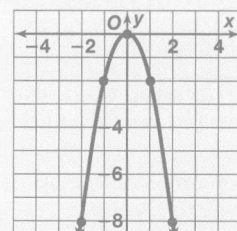

1b.

x	$-x^2 + 3 = y$	(x, y)
-2	$-(-2)^2 + 3 = -1$	$(-2, -1)$
-1	$-(-1)^2 + 3 = 2$	$(-1, 2)$
0	$-0^2 + 3 = 3$	$(0, 3)$
1	$-1^2 + 3 = 2$	$(1, 2)$
2	$-2^2 + 3 = -1$	$(2, -1)$

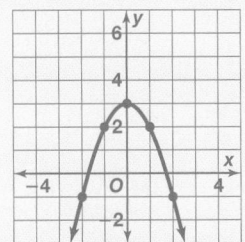

page 695   Check Understanding
Example 2

2a.

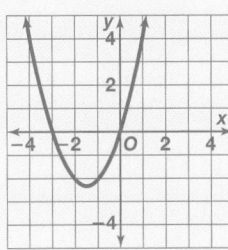

2b.

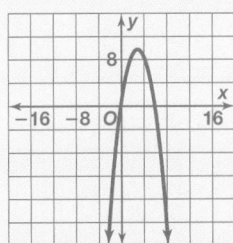

Check Understanding Example 3

3a.

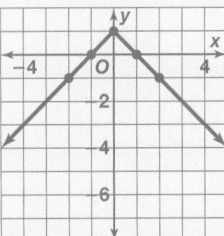

3b.

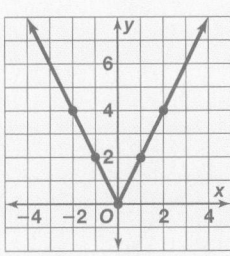

TE page 695   Additional Example 1

1.

x	$-x^2 + 1 = y$	(x, y)
-2	$-(-2)^2 + 1 = -3$	$(-2, -3)$
-1	$-(-1)^2 + 1 = 0$	$(-1, 0)$
0	$-(0)^2 + 1 = 1$	$(0, 1)$
1	$-(1)^2 + 1 = 0$	$(1, 0)$
2	$-(2)^2 + 1 = -3$	$(2, -3)$

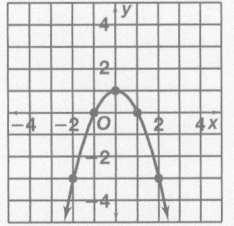

Additional Example 2

2.

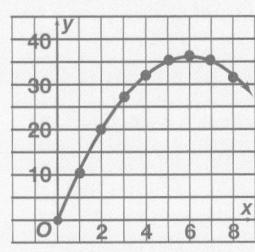

Additional Example 3

3.

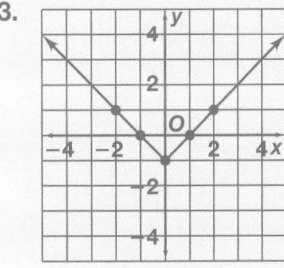

page 696   Practice and
Problem Solving

1.

x	$4(x)^2$	y	(x, y)
-2	$4(-2)^2$	16	$(-2, 16)$
-1	$4(-1)^2$	4	$(-1, 4)$
0	$4(0)^2$	0	$(0, 0)$
1	$4(1)^2$	4	$(1, 4)$
2	$4(2)^2$	16	$(2, 16)$

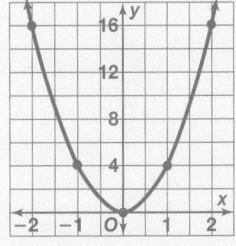

2.

x	$-x^2$	y	(x, y)
-2	$-(-2)^2$	-4	$(-2, -4)$
-1	$-(-1)^2$	-1	$(-1, -1)$
0	$-(0)^2$	0	$(0, 0)$
1	$-(1)^2$	-1	$(1, -1)$
2	$-(2)^2$	-4	$(2, -4)$

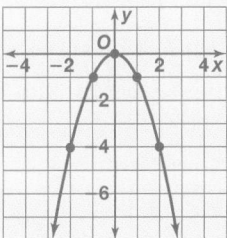

3.

x	$-3x^2$	y	(x, y)
-2	$-3(-2)^2$	-12	$(-2, -12)$
-1	$-3(-1)^2$	-3	$(-1, -3)$
0	$-3(0)^2$	0	$(0, 0)$
1	$-3(1)^2$	-3	$(1, -3)$
2	$-3(2)^2$	-12	$(2, -12)$

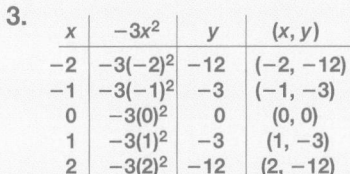
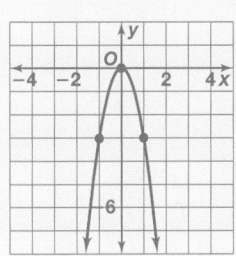

4.

x	$x^2 + 1$	y	(x, y)
-2	$(-2)^2 + 1$	5	$(-2, 5)$
-1	$(-1)^2 + 1$	2	$(-1, 2)$
0	$0^2 + 1$	1	$(0, 1)$
1	$1^2 + 1$	2	$(1, 2)$
2	$2^2 + 1$	5	$(2, 5)$

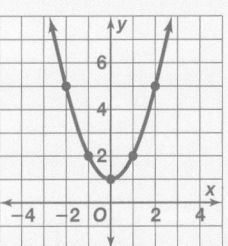

5.

x	$-x^2 + 2$	y	(x, y)
-2	$-(-2)^2 + 2$	-2	$(-2, -2)$
-1	$-(-1)^2 + 2$	1	$(-1, 1)$
0	$-0^2 + 2$	2	$(0, 2)$
1	$-1^2 + 2$	1	$(1, 1)$
2	$-2^2 + 2$	-2	$(2, -2)$

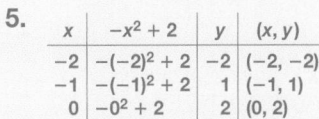
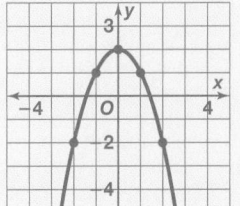

6.

x	$x^2 - 2$	y	(x, y)
-2	$(-2)^2 - 2$	2	$(-2, 2)$
-1	$(-1)^2 - 2$	-1	$(-1, -1)$
0	$0^2 - 2$	-2	$(0, -2)$
1	$1^2 - 2$	-1	$(1, -1)$
2	$2^2 - 2$	2	$(2, 2)$

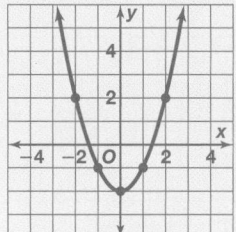

7.

x	$x^2 + 4$	y	(x, y)
-2	$(-2)^2 + 4$	8	$(-2, 8)$
-1	$(-1)^2 + 4$	5	$(-1, 5)$
0	$0^2 + 4$	4	$(0, 4)$
1	$1^2 + 4$	5	$(1, 5)$
2	$2^2 + 4$	8	$(2, 8)$

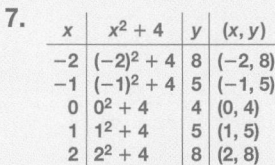

8.

x	$-x^2 + 3$	y	(x, y)
-2	$-(-2)^2$	-1	$(-2, -1)$
-1	$-(-1)^2$	2	$(-1, 2)$
0	$-(0)^2 + 3$	3	$(0, 3)$
1	$-(1)^2 + 3$	2	$(1, 2)$
2	$-(2)^2 + 3$	-1	$(2, -1)$

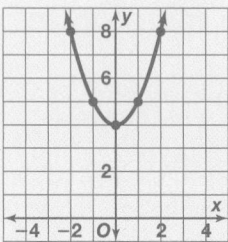

9.

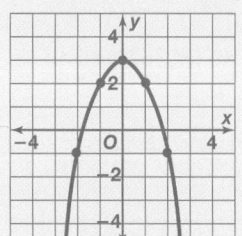

10.

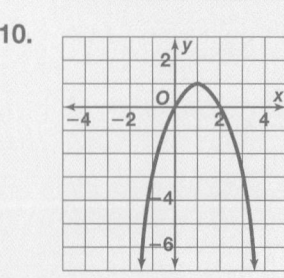

11.

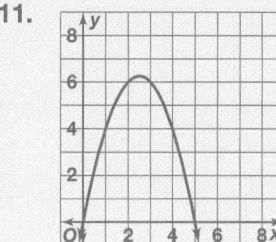

12.

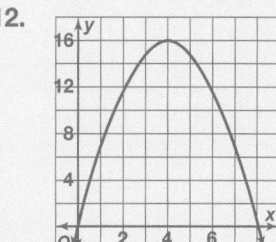

13.

x	$15x - x^2$	y	(x, y)
0	$15(0) - (0)^2$	0	$(0, 0)$
1	$15(1) - (1)^2$	14	$(1, 14)$
2	$15(2) - (2)^2$	26	$(2, 26)$
3	$15(3) - (3)^2$	36	$(3, 36)$
4	$15(4) - (4)^2$	44	$(4, 44)$
5	$15(5) - (5)^2$	50	$(5, 50)$
6	$15(6) - (6)^2$	54	$(6, 54)$
7	$15(7) - (7)^2$	56	$(7, 56)$
8	$15(8) - (8)^2$	56	$(8, 56)$
9	$15(9) - (9)^2$	54	$(9, 54)$
10	$15(10) - (10)^2$	50	$(10, 50)$

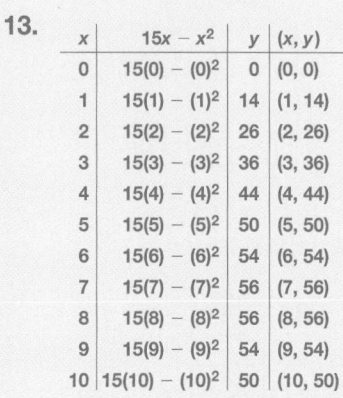

A width of 7.5 yd gives the greatest area.

14.

x	$3\lvert x \rvert$	y	(x, y)
-2	$3\lvert -2 \rvert$	6	$(-2, 6)$
-1	$3\lvert -1 \rvert$	3	$(-1, 3)$
0	$3\lvert 0 \rvert$	0	$(0, 0)$
1	$3\lvert 1 \rvert$	3	$(1, 3)$
2	$3\lvert 2 \rvert$	6	$(2, 6)$

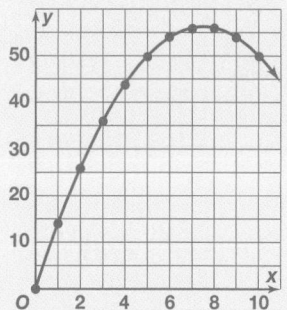

15.

x	$\lvert x \rvert + 3$	y	(x, y)
-2	$\lvert -2 \rvert + 3$	5	$(-2, 5)$
-1	$\lvert -1 \rvert + 3$	4	$(-1, 4)$
0	$\lvert 0 \rvert + 3$	3	$(0, 3)$
1	$\lvert 1 \rvert + 3$	4	$(1, 4)$
2	$\lvert 2 \rvert + 3$	5	$(2, 5)$

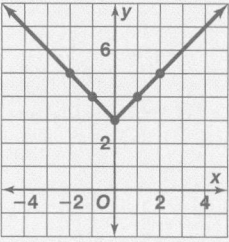

16.

x	$-3\lvert x \rvert$	y	(x, y)
-2	$-3\lvert -2 \rvert$	-6	$(-2, -6)$
-1	$-3\lvert -1 \rvert$	-3	$(-1, -3)$
0	$-3\lvert 0 \rvert$	0	$(0, 0)$
1	$-3\lvert 1 \rvert$	-3	$(1, -3)$
2	$-3\lvert 2 \rvert$	-6	$(2, -6)$

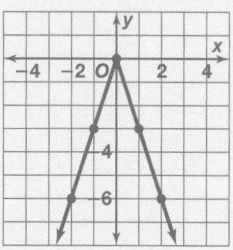

17.

x	$\lvert x \rvert - 4$	y	(x, y)
-2	$\lvert -2 \rvert - 4$	-2	$(-2, -2)$
-1	$\lvert -1 \rvert - 4$	-3	$(-1, -3)$
0	$\lvert 0 \rvert - 4$	-4	$(0, -4)$
1	$\lvert 1 \rvert - 4$	-3	$(1, -3)$
2	$\lvert 2 \rvert - 4$	-2	$(2, -2)$

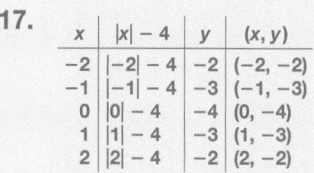

18.

x	$-\lvert x \rvert - 1$	y	(x, y)
-2	$-\lvert -2 \rvert - 1$	-3	$(-2, -3)$
-1	$-\lvert -1 \rvert - 1$	-2	$(-1, -2)$
0	$-\lvert 0 \rvert - 1$	-1	$(0, -1)$
1	$-\lvert 1 \rvert - 1$	-2	$(1, -2)$
2	$-\lvert 2 \rvert - 1$	-3	$(2, -3)$

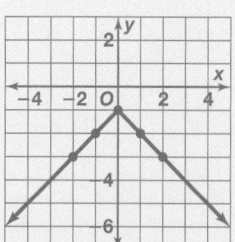

19.

x	$-2\lvert x\rvert$	y	(x, y)
-2	$-2\lvert-2\rvert$	-4	$(-2, -4)$
-1	$-2\lvert-1\rvert$	-2	$(-1, -2)$
0	$-2\lvert0\rvert$	0	$(0, 0)$
1	$-2\lvert1\rvert$	-2	$(1, -2)$
2	$-2\lvert2\rvert$	-4	$(2, -4)$

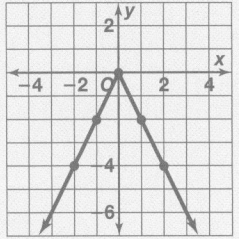

20. V shape

x	$\lvert x\rvert + 1$	y	(x, y)
-2	$\lvert-2\rvert + 1$	3	$(-2, 3)$
-1	$\lvert-1\rvert + 1$	2	$(-1, 2)$
0	$\lvert0\rvert + 1$	1	$(0, 1)$
1	$\lvert1\rvert + 1$	2	$(1, 2)$
2	$\lvert2\rvert + 1$	3	$(2, 3)$

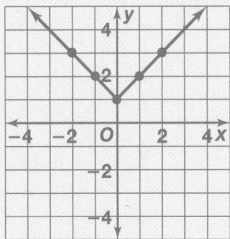

21. U shape

x	$x^2 - 8$	y	(x, y)
-2	$(-2)^2 - 8$	-4	$(-2, -4)$
-1	$(-1)^2 - 8$	-7	$(-1, -7)$
0	$(0)^2 - 8$	-8	$(0, -8)$
1	$(1)^2 - 8$	-7	$(1, -7)$
2	$(2)^2 - 8$	-4	$(2, -4)$

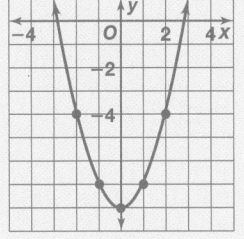

22. U shape

x	$3x - x^2$	y	(x, y)
-2	$3(-2) - (-2)^2$	-10	$(-2, -10)$
-1	$3(-1) - (-1)^2$	-4	$(-1, -4)$
0	$3(0) - (0)^2$	0	$(0, 0)$
1	$3(1) - (1)^2$	2	$(1, 2)$
2	$3(2) - (2)^2$	2	$(2, 2)$

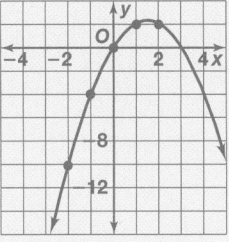

23. U shape

x	$-4x^2$	y	(x, y)
-2	$-4(-2)^2$	-16	$(-2, -16)$
-1	$-4(-1)^2$	-4	$(-1, -4)$
0	$-4(0)^2$	0	$(0, 0)$
1	$-4(1)^2$	-4	$(1, -4)$
2	$-4(1)^2$	-16	$(2, -16)$

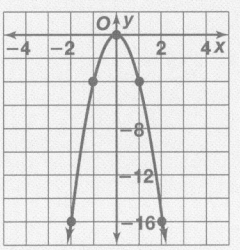

24. V shape

x	$-\lvert x\rvert - 3$	y	(x, y)
-2	$-\lvert-2\rvert - 3$	-5	$(-2, -5)$
-1	$-\lvert-1\rvert - 3$	-4	$(-1, -4)$
0	$-\lvert0\rvert - 3$	-3	$(0, -3)$
1	$-\lvert1\rvert - 3$	-4	$(1, -4)$
2	$-\lvert2\rvert - 3$	-5	$(2, -5)$

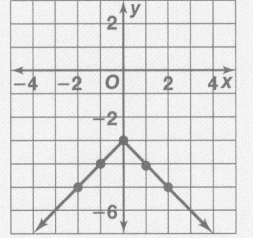

25. U shape

x	$2x^2 - 2$	y	(x, y)
-2	$2(-2)^2 - 2$	6	$(-2, 6)$
-1	$2(-1)^2 - 2$	0	$(-1, 0)$
0	$2(0)^2 - 2$	-2	$(0, -2)$
1	$2(1)^2 - 2$	0	$(1, 0)$
2	$2(2)^2 - 2$	6	$(2, 6)$

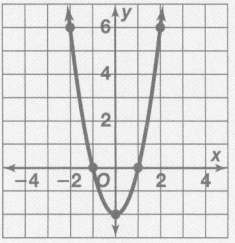

26. V shape

x	$-\tfrac{1}{2}\lvert x\rvert$	y	(x, y)
-2	$-\tfrac{1}{2}\lvert-2\rvert$	-1	$(-2, -1)$
-1	$-\tfrac{1}{2}\lvert-1\rvert$	$-\tfrac{1}{2}$	$(-1, -\tfrac{1}{2})$
0	$-\tfrac{1}{2}\lvert0\rvert$	0	$(0, 0)$
1	$-\tfrac{1}{2}\lvert1\rvert$	$-\tfrac{1}{2}$	$(1, -\tfrac{1}{2})$
2	$-\tfrac{1}{2}\lvert2\rvert$	-1	$(2, -1)$

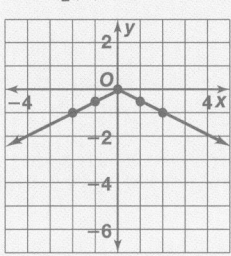

27. V shape

x	$\lvert x\rvert - 2$	y	(x, y)
-2	$\lvert-2\rvert - 2$	0	$(-2, 0)$
-1	$\lvert-1\rvert - 2$	-1	$(-1, -1)$
0	$\lvert0\rvert - 2$	-2	$(0, -2)$
1	$\lvert1\rvert - 2$	-1	$(1, -1)$
2	$\lvert2\rvert - 2$	0	$(2, 0)$

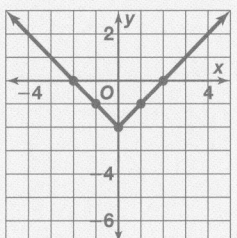

28. U shape

x	$-x^2 + 5$	y	(x, y)
−2	$-(-2)^2 + 5$	1	(−2, 1)
−1	$-(-1)^2 + 5$	4	(−1, 4)
0	$-0^2 + 5$	5	(0, 5)
1	$-1^2 + 5$	4	(1, 4)
2	$-2^2 + 5$	1	(2, 1)

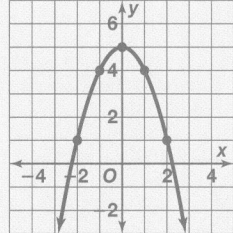

29a.

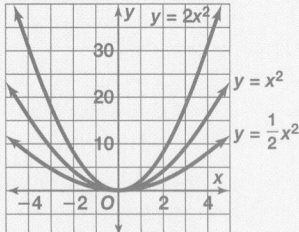

29b. The greater the coefficient of x^2, the narrower the graph.

30. The graphs of $y = x^2$ and $y = 2x + x^2$ have the same shape and both open upward. The lowest point of the graph of $y = 2x + x^2$ is to the left and below the lowest point of $y = x^2$. The graph of $y = 2x - x^2$ has the same shape as the other two graphs but it opens downward.

32.

x	x^3	y	(x, y)
−2	$(-2)^3$	−8	(−2, −8)
−1	$(-1)^3$	−1	(−1, −1)
0	0^3	0	(0, 0)
1	1^3	1	(1, 1)
2	2^3	8	(2, 8)

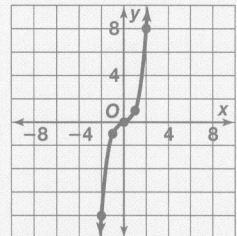

No; the graph of the function is not a parabola.

33a–b.

Edge Length	Volume
1 m	1 m³
2 m	8 m³
3 m	27 m³
4 m	64 m³

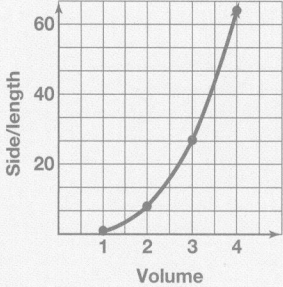

page 697   Test Prep

37. [2]

x	$-3x^2 = y$	(x, y)
−2	$-3(-2)^2 = -12$	(−2, −12)
−1	$-3(-1)^2 = -3$	(−1, −3)
0	$-3(0)^2 = 0$	(0, 0)
1	$-3(1)^2 = -3$	(1, −3)
2	$-3(2)^2 = -12$	(2, −12)

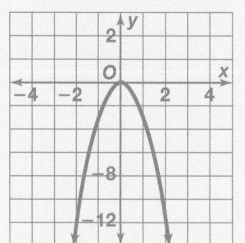

[1] minor error OR table only

LESSON 13–3

TE page 700 Closure

For exponential growth, the base of the exponent is greater than 1. For exponential growth, the base is less than 1.

Additional Example 1

1.

x	4^x	y	(x, y)
1	4^1	4	(1, 4)
2	4^2	16	(2, 16)
3	4^3	64	(3, 64)
4	4^4	256	(4, 256)

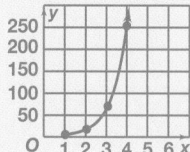

Additional Example 2

2.

x	$4(2)^x$	y	(x, y)
0	$4(2)^0$	4	(0, 4)
1	$4(2)^1$	8	(1, 8)
2	$4(2)^2$	16	(2, 16)
3	$4(2)^3$	32	(3, 32)
4	$4(2)^4$	64	(4, 64)

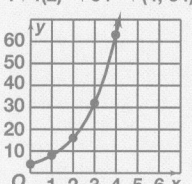

Check Understanding Example 3

3.

x	$90(\frac{1}{3})^x$	y	(x, y)
0	$90(\frac{1}{3})^0$	90	(0, 90)
1	$90(\frac{1}{3})^1$	30	(1, 30)
2	$90(\frac{1}{3})^2$	10	(2, 10)
3	$90(\frac{1}{3})^3$	$3\frac{1}{3}$	$(3, 3\frac{1}{3})$
4	$90(\frac{1}{3})^4$	$1\frac{1}{9}$	$(4, 1\frac{1}{9})$
5	$90(\frac{1}{3})^5$	$\frac{10}{27}$	$(5, \frac{10}{27})$

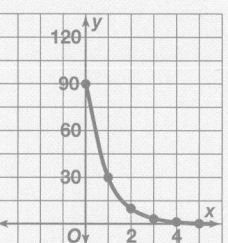

Additional Example 3

3.

x	$2(0.5)^x$	y	(x, y)
0	$2(0.5)^0$	2	(0, 2)
1	$2(0.5)^1$	1	(1, 1)
2	$2(0.5)^2$	0.5	(2, 0.5)
3	$2(0.5)^3$	0.25	(3, 0.25)
4	$2(0.5)^4$	0.125	(4, 0.125)
5	$2(0.5)^5$	0.0625	(5, 0.0625)

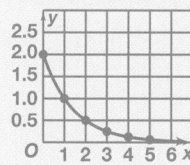

pages 701–702 Practice and Problem Solving

1.

x	4^x	y	(x, y)
0	4^0	1	(0, 1)
1	4^1	4	(1, 4)
2	4^2	16	(2, 16)
3	4^3	64	(3, 64)
4	4^4	256	(4, 256)

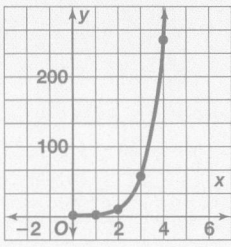

2.

x	5^x	y	(x, y)
0	5^0	1	(0, 1)
1	5^1	25	(1, 5)
2	5^2	25	(2, 25)
3	5^3	125	(3, 125)
4	5^4	625	(4, 625)

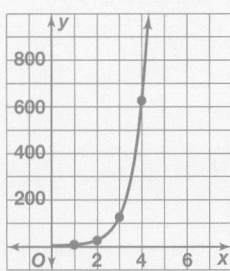

3.

x	6^x	y	(x, y)
0	6^0	1	(0, 1)
1	6^1	6	(1, 6)
2	6^2	36	(2, 36)
3	6^3	216	(3, 216)
4	6^4	1296	(4, 1296)

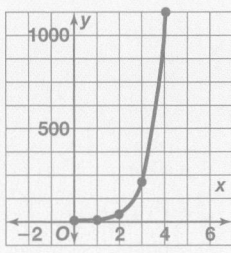

4.

x	$0.4(2)^x$	y	(x, y)
0	$0.4(2)^0$	0.4	(0, 0.4)
1	$0.4(2)^1$	0.8	(1, 0.8)
2	$0.4(2)^2$	1.6	(2, 1.6)
3	$0.4(2)^3$	3.2	(3, 3.2)
4	$0.4(2)^4$	6.4	(4, 6.4)

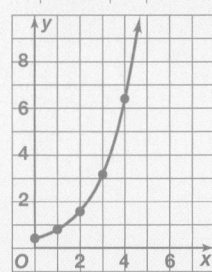

5.

x	$0.5(4)^x$	y	(x, y)
0	$0.5(4)^0$	0.5	(0, 0.5)
1	$0.5(4)^1$	2	(1, 2)
2	$0.5(4)^2$	8	(2, 8)
3	$0.5(4)^3$	32	(3, 32)
4	$0.5(4)^4$	128	(4, 128)

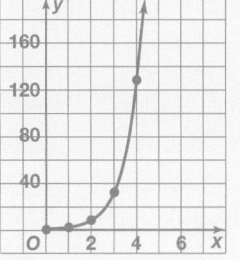

6.

x	$0.2(5)^x$	y	(x, y)
0	$0.2(5)^0$	0.2	(0, 0.2)
1	$0.2(5)^1$	1	(1, 1)
2	$0.2(5)^2$	5	(2, 5)
3	$0.2(5)^3$	25	(3, 25)
4	$0.2(5)^4$	125	(4, 125)

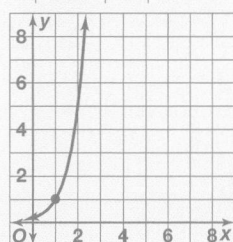

8.

x	$\left(\frac{1}{2}\right)^x$	y	(x, y)
0	$\left(\frac{1}{2}\right)^0$	1	(0, 1)
1	$\left(\frac{1}{2}\right)^1$	$\frac{1}{2}$	$(1, \frac{1}{2})$
2	$\left(\frac{1}{2}\right)^2$	$\frac{1}{4}$	$(2, \frac{1}{4})$
3	$\left(\frac{1}{2}\right)^3$	$\frac{1}{8}$	$(3, \frac{1}{8})$
4	$\left(\frac{1}{2}\right)^4$	$\frac{1}{16}$	$(4, \frac{1}{16})$
5	$\left(\frac{1}{2}\right)^5$	$\frac{1}{32}$	$(5, \frac{1}{32})$

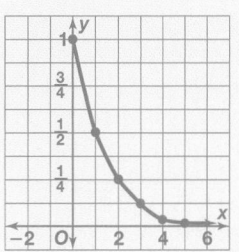

9.

x	$30\left(\frac{1}{3}\right)^x$	y	(x, y)
0	$30\left(\frac{1}{3}\right)^0$	30	(0, 30)
1	$30\left(\frac{1}{3}\right)^1$	10	(1, 10)
2	$30\left(\frac{1}{3}\right)^2$	$3\frac{1}{3}$	$(2, 3\frac{1}{3})$
3	$30\left(\frac{1}{3}\right)^3$	$1\frac{1}{9}$	$(3, 1\frac{1}{9})$
4	$30\left(\frac{1}{3}\right)^4$	$\frac{10}{27}$	$(4, \frac{10}{27})$
5	$30\left(\frac{1}{3}\right)^5$	$\frac{10}{81}$	$(5, \frac{10}{81})$

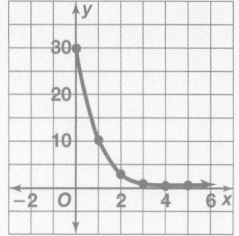

10.

x	$100\left(\frac{1}{5}\right)^x$	y	(x, y)
0	$100\left(\frac{1}{5}\right)^0$	100	(0, 100)
1	$100\left(\frac{1}{5}\right)^1$	20	(1, 20)
2	$100\left(\frac{1}{5}\right)^2$	4	(2, 4)
3	$100\left(\frac{1}{5}\right)^3$	0.8	(3, 0.8)
4	$100\left(\frac{1}{5}\right)^4$	0.16	(4, 0.16)
5	$100\left(\frac{1}{5}\right)^5$	0.032	(5, 0.032)

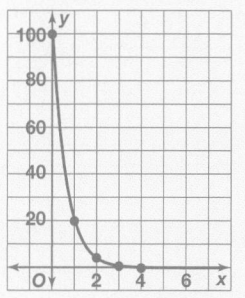

16.

x	$2 \cdot 3^x$	y	(x, y)
0	$2 \cdot 3^0$	2	(0, 2)
1	$2 \cdot 3^1$	6	(1, 6)
2	$2 \cdot 3^2$	18	(2, 18)
3	$2 \cdot 3^3$	54	(3, 54)
4	$2 \cdot 3^4$	162	(4, 162)

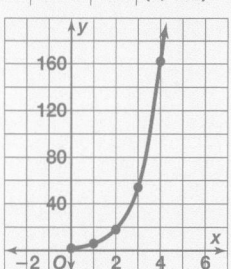

17.

x	$\frac{1}{5} \cdot 5^x$	y	(x, y)
0	$\frac{1}{5} \cdot 5^0$	$\frac{1}{5}$	$(0, \frac{1}{5})$
1	$\frac{1}{5} \cdot 5^1$	1	$(1, 1)$
2	$\frac{1}{5} \cdot 5^2$	5	$(2, 5)$
3	$\frac{1}{5} \cdot 5^3$	25	$(3, 25)$
4	$\frac{1}{5} \cdot 5^4$	125	$(4, 125)$

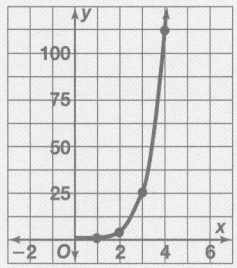

18.

x	$6(0.5)^x$	y	(x, y)
0	$6(0.5)^0$	6	$(0, 6)$
1	$6(0.5)^1$	3	$(1, 3)$
2	$6(0.5)^2$	1.5	$(2, 1.5)$
3	$6(0.5)^3$	0.75	$(3, 0.75)$
4	$6(0.5)^4$	0.375	$(4, 0.375)$

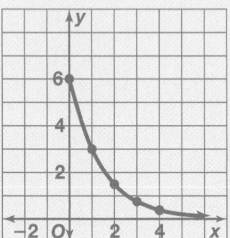

19.

x	$\frac{1}{2} \cdot 2^x$	y	(x, y)
0	$\frac{1}{2} \cdot 2^0$	$\frac{1}{2}$	$(0, \frac{1}{2})$
1	$\frac{1}{2} \cdot 2^1$	1	$(1, 1)$
2	$\frac{1}{2} \cdot 2^2$	2	$(2, 2)$
3	$\frac{1}{2} \cdot 2^3$	4	$(3, 4)$
4	$\frac{1}{2} \cdot 2^4$	8	$(4, 8)$

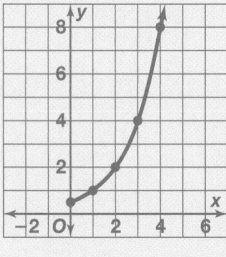

20.

x	$20(\frac{1}{2})^x$	y	(x, y)
0	$20(\frac{1}{2})^0$	20	$(0, 20)$
1	$20(\frac{1}{2})^1$	10	$(1, 10)$
2	$20(\frac{1}{2})^2$	5	$(2, 5)$
3	$20(\frac{1}{2})^3$	2.5	$(3, 2.5)$
4	$20(\frac{1}{2})^4$	1.25	$(4, 1.25)$

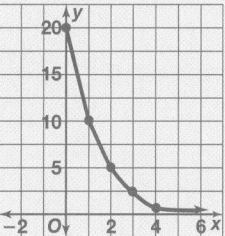

21.

x	$3 \cdot 2^x$	y	(x, y)
0	$3 \cdot 2^0$	3	$(0, 3)$
1	$3 \cdot 2^1$	6	$(1, 6)$
2	$3 \cdot 2^2$	12	$(2, 12)$
3	$3 \cdot 2^3$	24	$(3, 24)$
4	$3 \cdot 2^4$	48	$(4, 48)$

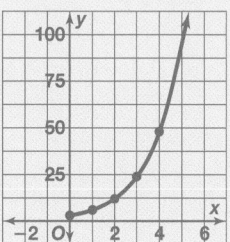

26a.

x	$2x$	y	(x, y)
0	$2 \cdot 0$	0	$(0, 0)$
1	$2 \cdot 1$	2	$(1, 2)$
2	$2 \cdot 2$	4	$(2, 4)$
3	$2 \cdot 3$	6	$(3, 6)$
4	$2 \cdot 4$	8	$(4, 8)$
5	$2 \cdot 5$	10	$(5, 10)$

x	x^2	y	(x, y)
0	0^2	0	$(0, 0)$
1	1^2	1	$(1, 1)$
2	2^2	4	$(2, 4)$
3	3^2	9	$(3, 9)$
4	4^2	16	$(4, 16)$
5	5^2	25	$(5, 25)$

x	2^x	y	(x, y)
0	2^0	1	$(0, 1)$
1	2^1	2	$(1, 2)$
2	2^2	4	$(2, 4)$
3	2^3	8	$(3, 8)$
4	2^4	16	$(4, 16)$
5	2^5	32	$(5, 32)$

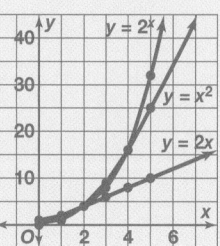

26b. They are similar because they all are increasing functions and they all pass through (2, 4). They are different because $y = 2x$ increases at a constant rate while $y = x^2$ and $y = 2^x$ increase at different rates.

page 702   Mixed Review

34.

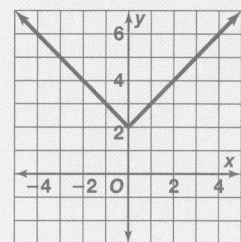

35.

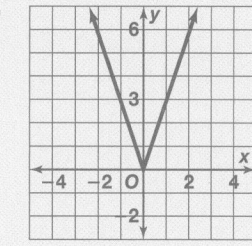

36.

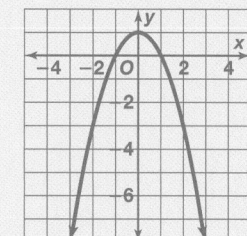

page 702   Checkpoint Quiz 1

5.

x	$\frac{1}{4}x^2$	y	(x, y)
-2	$\frac{1}{4} \cdot -2^2$	1	$(-2, 1)$
-1	$\frac{1}{4} \cdot -1^2$	$\frac{1}{4}$	$(-1, \frac{1}{4})$
0	$\frac{1}{4} \cdot 0^2$	0	$(0, 0)$
1	$\frac{1}{4} \cdot 1^2$	$\frac{1}{4}$	$(1, \frac{1}{4})$
2	$\frac{1}{4} \cdot 2^2$	1	$(2, 1)$

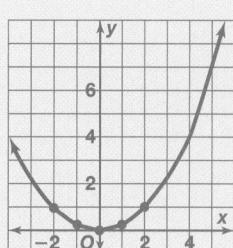

6.

x	$\frac{1}{4}\lvert x\rvert$	y	(x, y)
-2	$\frac{1}{4}\cdot\lvert-2\rvert$	$\frac{1}{2}$	$(-2, \frac{1}{2})$
-1	$\frac{1}{4}\cdot\lvert-1\rvert$	$\frac{1}{4}$	$(-1, \frac{1}{4})$
0	$\frac{1}{4}\cdot\lvert0\rvert$	0	$(0, 0)$
1	$\frac{1}{4}\cdot\lvert1\rvert$	$\frac{1}{4}$	$(1, \frac{1}{4})$
2	$\frac{1}{4}\cdot\lvert2\rvert$	$\frac{1}{2}$	$(2, \frac{1}{2})$

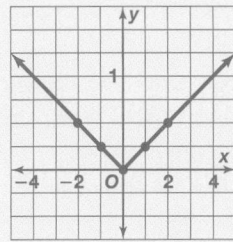

7.

x	$0.5(3)^x$	y	(x, y)
0	$0.5(3)^0$	0.5	$(0, 0.5)$
1	$0.5(3)^1$	1.5	$(1, 1.5)$
2	$0.5(3)^2$	4.5	$(2, 4.5)$
3	$0.5(3)^3$	13.5	$(3, 13.5)$
4	$0.5(3)^4$	40.5	$(4, 40.5)$

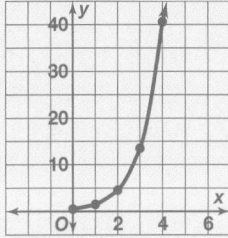

page 703   Technology

1.

x	y
-5	10
-4	8
-3	6
-2	4
-1	2
0	0
1	2
2	4
3	6
4	8
5	10

2.

x	y
-5	-10
-4	-8
-3	-6
-2	-4
-1	-2
0	0
1	-2
2	-4
3	-6
4	-8
5	-10

3.

x	y
-5	11
-4	9
-3	7
-2	5
-1	3
0	1
1	3
2	5
3	7
4	9
5	11

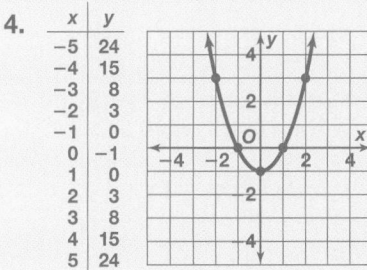

4.

x	y
-5	24
-4	15
-3	8
-2	3
-1	0
0	-1
1	0
2	3
3	8
4	15
5	24

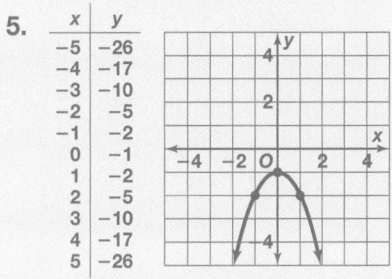

5.

x	y
-5	-26
-4	-17
-3	-10
-2	-5
-1	-2
0	-1
1	-2
2	-5
3	-10
4	-17
5	-26

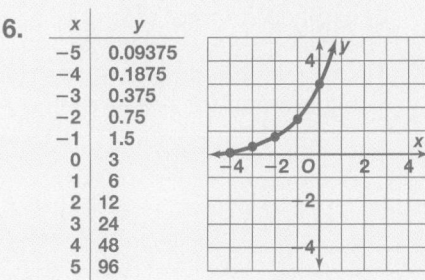

6.

x	y
-5	0.09375
-4	0.1875
-3	0.375
-2	0.75
-1	1.5
0	3
1	6
2	12
3	24
4	48
5	96

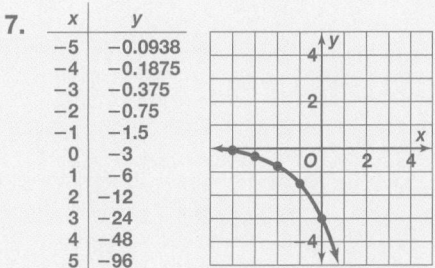

7.

x	y
-5	-0.0938
-4	-0.1875
-3	-0.375
-2	-0.75
-1	-1.5
0	-3
1	-6
2	-12
3	-24
4	-48
5	-96

8.

x	y
-5	96
-4	48
-3	24
-2	12
-1	6
0	3
1	1.5
2	0.75
3	0.375
4	0.1875
5	0.09375

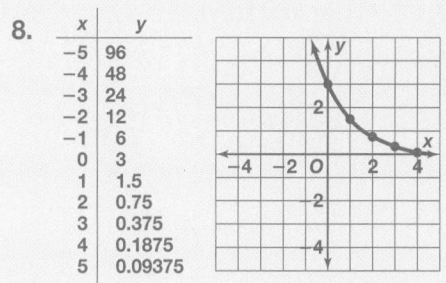

9.

x	y
-5	-96
-4	-48
-3	-24
-2	-12
-1	-6
0	-3
1	-1.5
2	-0.75
3	-0.375
4	-0.1875
5	-0.0938

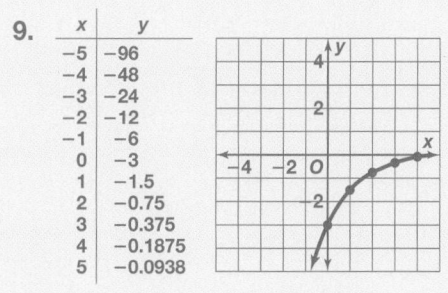

LESSON 13-4

TE page 705   Additional Examples

1a. No; the expression is a sum.

1b. Yes; the expression is the product of the real number $\frac{7}{3}$ and the variable z.

1c. Yes; the expression is the product of the real number 6 and the variables a, b, and b.

1d. No; the denominator contains a variable.

TE page 705   Closure

You name a polynomial by the number of terms it has. A monomial has one term, a binomial has two, and a trinomial has three.

TE page 705   Reaching All Students/Advanced Learners

It is a polynomial because it simplifies to $\frac{15xy}{2}$, which is a polynomial. Recall $\frac{15x^2y}{2x}$ has no meaning if $x = 0$.

page 707   Test Prep

56. [2] No; it is not the product of a real number and a variable with a whole number exponent.
[1] minor error OR answer only

page 707 Mixed Review

58.

x	$2 \cdot 2^x$	y	(x, y)
1	$2 \cdot 2^1$	4	(1, 4)
2	$2 \cdot 2^2$	8	(2, 8)
3	$2 \cdot 2^3$	16	(3, 16)
4	$2 \cdot 2^4$	32	(4, 32)

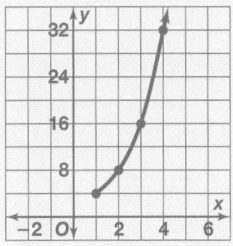

59.

x	$\frac{1}{3} \cdot 3^x$	y	(x, y)
1	$\frac{1}{3} \cdot 3^1$	1	(1, 1)
2	$\frac{1}{3} \cdot 3^2$	3	(2, 3)
3	$\frac{1}{3} \cdot 3^3$	9	(3, 9)
4	$\frac{1}{3} \cdot 3^4$	27	(4, 27)

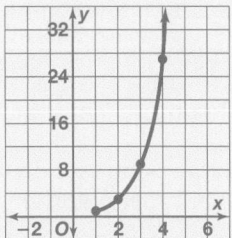

60.

x	$18(0.2)^x$	y	(x, y)
1	$18(0.2)^1$	0.36	(1, 0.36)
2	$18(0.2)^2$	0.0072	(2, 0.0072)
3	$18(0.2)^3$	1.44×10^{-4}	$(3, 1.44 \times 10^{-4})$
4	$18(0.2)^4$	2.88×10^{-6}	$(4, 2.88 \times 10^{-6})$

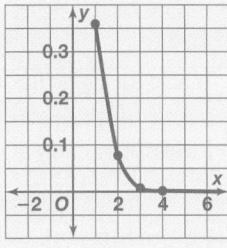

LESSON 13-6

TE page 716 Closure

Find the GCF of the terms by finding the factors common to all terms. Write each term as the product of the GCF and another factor. Use the Distributive Property to write the polynomial as the product of the GCF and the sum of the other factors.

page 718 Writing in Math

First, you write the prime factorization of each term. Then find the GCF, which is 5a. Write each term as the product of 5a and use the Distributive Property.

page 718 Test Prep

62. [4] (a) $w + 2$.
   (b) The length of the rectangle is $w + 2$ because the description says the length is 2 inches greater than the width w.
   (c)

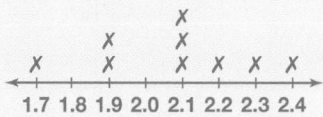

   (d) The area is $w(w + 2)$ or $w^2 + 2w$.

   [3] explanation missing
   [2] explanation and diagram missing
   [1] explanation, diagram, and expression for area missing

page 718 Mixed Review

65.

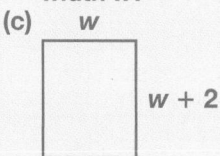

66.

LESSON 13–7

page 722 Test Prep

40. [2] $(3c - 1)(4c + 2)$

   $3c(4c + 2)$ Use the
   $- 1(4c + 2)$ Distributive Property

   $3c \cdot 4c + 3c \cdot 2$ Use the
   $- 1 \cdot 4c - 1 \cdot 2$ Distributive Property

   $12c^2 + 6c - 4c - 2$ Simplify
   $12c^2 + 2c - 2$ Simplify
   [1] minor error OR answer only

page 730 Chapter Review

29.

x	$-x^2 - 3$	y	(x, y)
-2	$-(-2)^2 - 3$	-7	(-2, -7)
-1	$-(-1)^2 - 3$	-4	(-1, -4)
0	$-(0)^2 - 3$	-3	(0, -3)
1	$-(1)^2 - 3$	-4	(1, -4)
2	$-(2)^2 - 3$	-7	(2, -7)

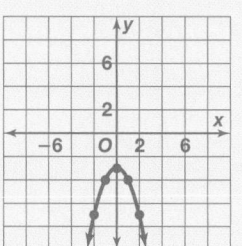

30.

x	$-x^2 + 4$	y	(x, y)
-2	$-(-2)^2 + 4$	0	(-2, 0)
-1	$-(-1)^2 + 4$	3	(-1, 3)
0	$-(0)^2 + 4$	4	(0, 4)
1	$-(1)^2 + 4$	3	(1, 3)
2	$-(2)^2 + 4$	0	(2, 0)

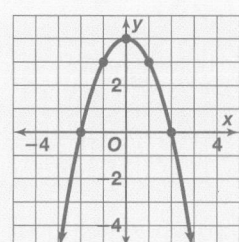

31.

x	$\left(\frac{1}{4}\right)^x$	y	(x, y)
0	$\left(\frac{1}{4}\right)^0$	1	$(0, 1)$
1	$\left(\frac{1}{4}\right)^1$	$\frac{1}{4}$	$\left(1, \frac{1}{4}\right)$
2	$\left(\frac{1}{4}\right)^2$	$\frac{1}{16}$	$\left(2, \frac{1}{16}\right)$
3	$\left(\frac{1}{4}\right)^3$	$\frac{1}{64}$	$\left(3, \frac{1}{64}\right)$
4	$\left(\frac{1}{4}\right)^4$	$\frac{1}{256}$	$\left(4, \frac{1}{256}\right)$

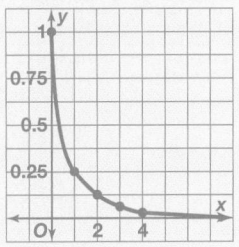

32.

x	$\frac{1}{2} \cdot 2^x$	y	(x, y)
0	$\frac{1}{2} \cdot 2^0$	$\frac{1}{2}$	$\left(0, \frac{1}{2}\right)$
1	$\frac{1}{2} \cdot 2^1$	1	$(1, 1)$
2	$\frac{1}{2} \cdot 2^2$	2	$(2, 2)$
3	$\frac{1}{2} \cdot 2^3$	4	$(3, 4)$
4	$\frac{1}{2} \cdot 2^4$	8	$(4, 8)$

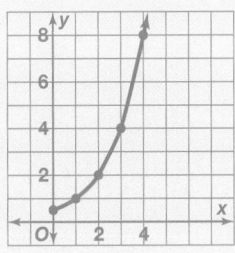

33.

x	3^x	y	(x, y)
0	3^0	1	$(0, 1)$
1	3^1	3	$(1, 3)$
2	3^2	9	$(2, 9)$
3	3^3	27	$(3, 27)$
4	3^4	81	$(4, 81)$

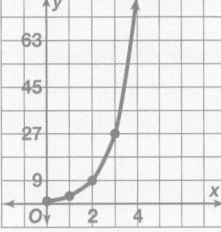

34.

x	$\left(\frac{1}{2}\right)^x$	y	(x, y)
0	$\left(\frac{1}{2}\right)^0$	1	$(0, 1)$
1	$\left(\frac{1}{2}\right)^1$	$\frac{1}{2}$	$\left(1, \frac{1}{2}\right)$
2	$\left(\frac{1}{2}\right)^2$	$\frac{1}{4}$	$\left(2, \frac{1}{4}\right)$
3	$\left(\frac{1}{2}\right)^3$	$\frac{1}{8}$	$\left(3, \frac{1}{8}\right)$
4	$\left(\frac{1}{2}\right)^4$	$\frac{1}{16}$	$\left(4, \frac{1}{16}\right)$

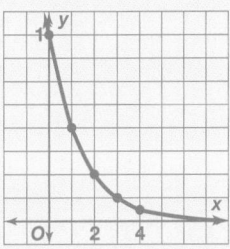

page 732 Chapter Test

11.

x	x^2	y	(x, y)
-2	$(-2)^2$	4	$(-2, 4)$
-1	$(-1)^2$	1	$(-1, 1)$
0	0^2	0	$(0, 0)$
1	1^2	1	$(1, 1)$
2	2^2	4	$(2, 4)$

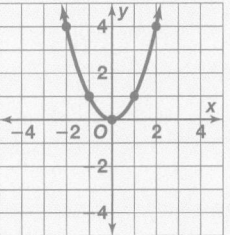

12.

x	$x^2 - 1$	y	(x, y)
-2	$(-2)^2 - 1$	3	$(-2, 3)$
-1	$(-1)^2 - 1$	0	$(-1, 0)$
0	$0^2 - 1$	-1	$(0, -1)$
1	$1^2 - 1$	0	$(1, 0)$
2	$2^2 - 1$	3	$(2, 3)$

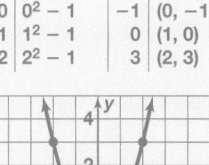
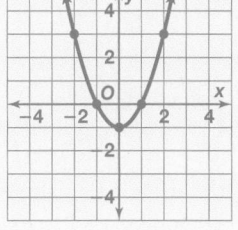

13.

x	$-x^2 + 1$	y	(x, y)
-2	$-(-2)^2 + 1$	-3	$(-2, -3)$
-1	$-(-1)^2 + 1$	0	$(-1, 0)$
0	$-(0)^2 + 1$	1	$(0, 1)$
1	$-(1)^2 + 1$	0	$(1, 0)$
2	$-(2)^2 + 1$	-3	$(2, -3)$

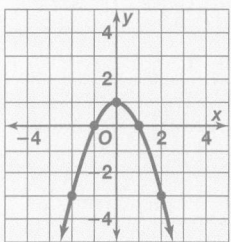

14.

x	$-x^2 - 2$	y	(x, y)
-2	$-(-2)^2 - 2$	-6	$(-2, -6)$
-1	$-(-1)^2 - 2$	-3	$(-1, -3)$
0	$-(0)^2 - 2$	-2	$(0, -2)$
1	$-(1)^2 - 2$	-3	$(1, -3)$
2	$-(2)^2 - 2$	-6	$(2, -6)$

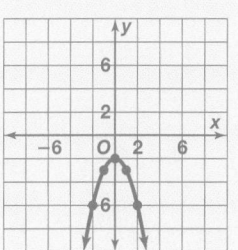

15.

x	$\lvert x\rvert-1$	y	(x,y)
-2	$\lvert-2\rvert-1$	1	$(-2,1)$
-1	$\lvert-1\rvert-1$	0	$(-1,0)$
0	$\lvert0\rvert-1$	-1	$(0,-1)$
1	$\lvert1\rvert-1$	0	$(1,0)$
2	$\lvert2\rvert-1$	1	$(2,1)$

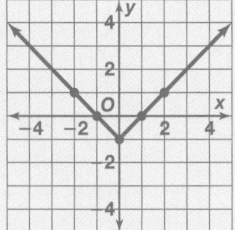

16.

x	$\frac{1}{2}\lvert x\rvert$	y	(x,y)
-2	$\frac{1}{2}\lvert-2\rvert$	1	$(-2,1)$
-1	$\frac{1}{2}\lvert-1\rvert$	$\frac{1}{2}$	$(-1,\frac{1}{2})$
0	$\frac{1}{2}\lvert0\rvert$	0	$(0,0)$
1	$\frac{1}{2}\lvert1\rvert$	$\frac{1}{2}$	$(1,\frac{1}{2})$
2	$\frac{1}{2}\lvert2\rvert$	1	$(2,1)$

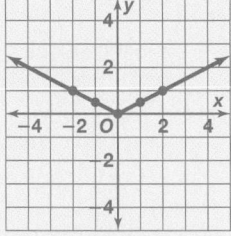

17.

x	2^x	y	(x,y)
0	2^0	1	$(0,1)$
1	2^1	2	$(1,2)$
2	2^2	4	$(2,4)$
3	2^3	8	$(3,8)$
4	2^4	16	$(4,16)$

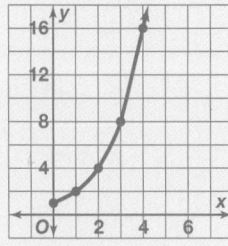

18.

x	3^x	y	(x,y)
0	3^0	1	$(0,1)$
1	3^1	3	$(1,3)$
2	3^2	9	$(2,9)$
3	3^3	27	$(3,27)$
4	3^4	81	$(4,81)$

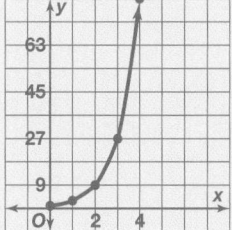

19.

x	$2\left(\frac{1}{2}\right)^x$	y	(x,y)
0	$2\left(\frac{1}{2}\right)^0$	2	$(0,2)$
1	$2\left(\frac{1}{2}\right)^1$	1	$(1,1)$
2	$2\left(\frac{1}{2}\right)^2$	$\frac{1}{2}$	$(2,\frac{1}{2})$
3	$2\left(\frac{1}{2}\right)^3$	$\frac{1}{4}$	$(3,\frac{1}{4})$
4	$2\left(\frac{1}{2}\right)^4$	$\frac{1}{8}$	$(4,\frac{1}{8})$

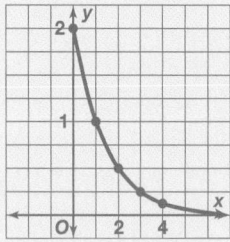

20.

x	$\left(\frac{1}{3}\right)^x$	y	(x,y)
0	$\left(\frac{1}{3}\right)^0$	1	$(0,1)$
1	$\left(\frac{1}{3}\right)^1$	$\frac{1}{3}$	$(1,\frac{1}{3})$
2	$\left(\frac{1}{3}\right)^2$	$\frac{1}{9}$	$(2,\frac{1}{9})$
3	$\left(\frac{1}{3}\right)^3$	$\frac{1}{27}$	$(3,\frac{1}{27})$
4	$\left(\frac{1}{3}\right)^4$	$\frac{1}{81}$	$(4,\frac{1}{81})$

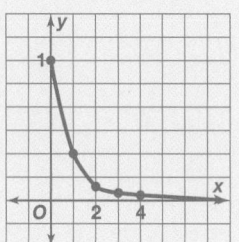

TE page 737   Real-World Snapshots

1.

Percent of Carbon-14 Present	Age of Fossil (years)
100	0
50	5,730
25	11,460
12.5	17,190
6.25	22,920
3.125	28,650
1.5625	34,380
0.78125	40,110

EXTRA PRACTICE

CHAPTER 8

page 751 Extra Practice

37.

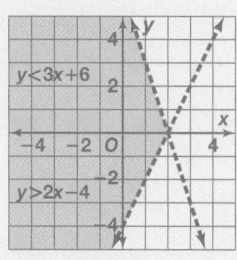

38.

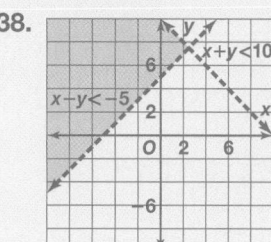

CHAPTER 13

page 756 Extra Practice

15.

x	y
0	1
1	4
2	16
3	64
4	256

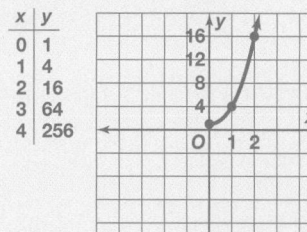

16.

x	y
0	0.5
1	5
2	50
3	500
4	5,000

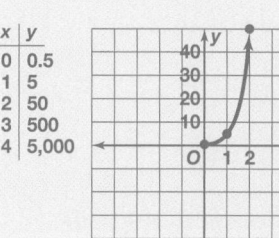

17.

x	y
0	10
1	5
2	2.5
3	1.25
4	0.625

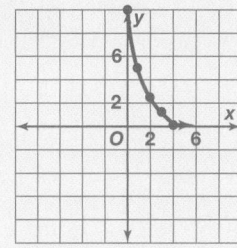

18.

x	y
0	1
1	2
2	4
3	8
4	16

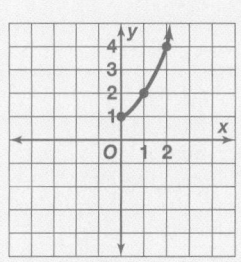

Index

Index

Like denominators, 243, 773

Like terms
aligning, 711
combining, 77, 352–353
defined, 76
Distributive Property and, 77

Line
defined, 458, 513
drawing, 460
graph of. *See* Line graph.
graphing, 406–409, 435–440
horizon, 542
intersecting, 459–463
parallel, 459–463
perpendicular, 492
of reflection, 504–506
shape of, 411–417, 450
of sight, 614–615
skew, 459–461, 463
of symmetry, 503, 505–506
trend, 430–433
vanishing, 542
y-intercept of, 413

Linear equations, 450
defined, 406, 450
graphing, 406, 413–417
problem-solving with, 430–433
slope-intercept form, 413
solutions of, 405, 450
writing, 418–421
from tables or graphs, 419
from words, 418
See also Systems of linear equations.

Linear functions
graphing and, 397–455. *See also* Graphing.
rules for. *See* Function rules.
writing rules for, 418–422

Linear inequalities, 441–443. *See also* Inequality.

Line graph, 406–409, 417, 642–647

Line plot, 631, 679

Line of reflection, 504

Line of sight, 614, 615

Line of symmetry, 503, 505–506

Line segment, congruent, 458–462

Longitude, 51, 53

Literacy. See Math Literacy; Reading Literacy; Writing in Math.

***Look for a Pattern* problem solving strategy,** 40–43

Lower quartile, 635

Lowest common denominator. *See* Least common denominator.

M

***Make a Model* problem solving strategy,** 562–565

***Make a Table* problem solving strategy,** 334–337

Manipulatives
algebra tiles. *See* Algebra tiles; Modeling.
calculator, 9, 221, 238, 384, 585, 609, 613, 673
centimeter ruler, 162, 258
coins, 307
compass, 491–496
graphing calculator, 55, 142, 209, 333, 417, 447, 609, 613, 634, 661, 673, 693, 703
graph paper, 584
isometric dot paper, 538

number cubes, 305–306
paper cutting/folding, 248
protractor, 464
straightedge, 491–495
tape measure, 162, 258, 300

Mapping
diagram, 400
of figure onto its image, 400, 498

Map, scale of, 300–302

Markup, 149, 329–332, 341

Mass, 156–161, 212, 776

Math at Work
air-traffic controller, 589
architect, 562
caterer, 337
choreographer, 463
city planner, 371
earthquake-monitor technician, 26
geophysicist, 208
lifeguard, 581
meteorologist, 96
movie-camera operator, 416
nurse, 99
oceanographer, 44
pharmacist, 526
pilot, 674
relief worker, 724
scuba diver, 81
stock trader, 345
systems analyst, 697
technical artist, 257
weaver, 29
wildlife statistician, 663
woodworker, 167

Math Background, 2C–D, 64C–D, 124C–D, 176C–D, 230C–D, 286C–D, 346C–D, 396C–D, 456C–D, 520C–D, 578C–D, 628C–D, 686C–D, Teacher's Edition pages 5, 9, 15, 19, 25, 31, 36, 41, 45, 51, 67, 72, 77, 81, 87, 93, 97, 103, 107, 111, 128, 133, 138, 144, 149, 153, 157, 165, 179, 183, 187, 193, 198, 202, 206, 211, 216, 233, 238, 244, 249, 254, 260, 265, 269, 275, 289, 295, 300, 306, 311, 316, 321, 326, 330, 335, 349, 353, 358, 363, 368, 374, 379, 383, 401, 406, 412, 419, 424, 431, 436, 442, 459, 466, 471, 477, 481, 487, 492, 498, 504, 508, 523, 528, 533, 540, 546, 553, 558, 563, 567, 581, 585, 593, 599, 603, 609, 615, 631, 636, 643, 650, 655, 660, 666, 670, 675, 689, 695, 700, 705, 711, 716, 720, 725

Mathematics Connections. *See also* Geometry, Patterns.
algebra, 402, 414, 415, 433, 462, 468, 469, 473, 474, 484, 595, 601, 712, 726
data analysis, 16, 21, 42, 101, 134, 172, 194, 240, 247, 421, 427, 432, 440
estimation, 160, 255, 262, 296, 332, 671
geometry, 42, 53, 98, 166, 185, 199, 200, 207, 236, 249, 258, 261, 275, 276, 277, 297, 304, 309, 336, 356, 361, 364, 404, 420, 438, 439, 478, 502, 583, 588, 595, 596, 606, 612, 625, 647, 668, 672, 676, 677, 689, 696, 706, 707, 713, 714, 718, 721, 726, 727
geometry (coordinate), 524
measurement, 5, 6, 133, 144, 155, 218, 235, 356, 408, 420, 440, 478, 480, 633

mental math, 27, 33, 47, 52, 67–68, 69, 70, 74, 75, 90, 94, 95, 150, 158, 159, 160, 171, 184, 235, 240, 296, 323, 327, 350, 360, 370, 385, 728

number sense, 12, 42, 105, 133, 134, 155, 158, 160, 214, 240, 241, 251, 255, 262, 266, 270, 276, 282, 336, 353, 355, 364, 365, 369, 392, 495, 510, 535, 600

patterns, 33, 49, 90, 110, 146, 155, 199, 204, 215, 220, 252, 404, 421, 582, 692, 721

probability, 240, 351, 440

trigonometry, 608–612

Math Connections, Teacher's Edition pages 249, 356, 379, 590, 603

Math Literacy, 2F–G, 64F–G, 124F–G, 176F–G, 230F–G, 286F–G, 346F–G, 396F–G, 456F–G, 520F–G, 578F–G, 628F–G, 686F–G, Teacher's Edition pages 4, 18, 22, 44, 57, 66, 76, 79, 106, 109, 117, 127, 143, 146, 156, 161, 169, 178, 192, 195, 210, 214, 223, 232, 243, 247, 268, 272, 279, 288, 305, 309, 329, 332, 339, 348, 362, 365, 378, 381, 389, 400, 418, 422, 435, 440, 449, 458, 480, 484, 497, 501, 513, 522, 532, 537, 562, 565, 571, 580, 592, 596, 608, 612, 621, 630, 649, 653, 669, 672, 679, 688, 699, 702, 719, 722, 729

Math symbols, 777

Matrix, 502

Matrix entry, 502

Mean, 137–142, 170
from graphing calculator, 142
outlier effects on, 138–140

Measurement, 480, 633
of angles of polygon, 475
of angles of triangle, 475
of capacity. *See* Capacity.
converting between systems, 292–293
customary units of, 253–257, 420, 440, 776
estimating, 133–135, 145, 255, 256
expression for, 5, 6
greatest possible error in, 258
handbreadth, 256
historical, 256
identifying approximate, 156–159, 253, 255–256
indirect, 300, 301, 600, 615
of length, 16, 25, 148, 156–163, 235, 253–257, 408
of mass, 133, 156–163, 212, 253–257, 738
metric system of. *See* Metric system of measurement.
of perimeter, 144
precision in, 162–163, 258
real-world application of, 5, 25, 49, 133, 146, 148, 158, 164, 212, 218, 249, 254, 256, 259, 409, 480
rod, 256
rounding, 258
significant digits in, 162–163
span, 256
table of customary and metric, 776
of temperature, 18, 21, 29, 31, 33, 144
units of, 156, 253
of volume. *See* Volume.
of weight, 218

Measures of central tendency, 137–139, 170

Median, 137–142, 170
box-and-whisker plot, 635, 637, 639

Number line
absolute value on, 19
adding integers, 25, 44
comparing fractions, 233–234
graphing inequalities on, 102–105, 208, 373, 375–377, 390
graphing integers on, 18–21
horizontal and vertical, 50–54
line plots, 630–633
multiplying integers on, 44–45, 47
opposites on, 635–638
rational numbers on, 202–204, 225
repeated addition on, 44
Number patterns, 36, 40–43. *See also* Patterns.
Numbers
classifying, 201–204, 581–582
comparing and ordering, 18, 29, 49, 217, 234–236, 241, 247, 282, 291, 313
compatible, 133–135, 170
composite, 186, 189, 224, 226
even, 178
factoring, 179–181, 223
irrational, 581–582, 589, 621, 624
negative, 17–21
odd, 178
positive, 17–21
prime, 186, 189, 190, 224, 226
properties of, 66–75, 117, 118
random, 673
rational, 201–204, 225, 581–582, 589, 621
real, 581–583
relatively prime, 190
rounding. *See* Rounding.
See also Integers; Mixed numbers; Properties; Rational numbers; Whole numbers.
Number sense, problems involving, 6, 42, 105, 133, 134, 155, 158, 160, 214, 240, 241, 251, 255, 262, 266, 270, 276, 282, 336, 353, 355, 364, 365, 369, 392, 495, 510, 535, 600
Number square, 34
Number theory, 98
divisibility tests and, 178–179, 223
factors and common factors in, 179–181, 187–190, 223
multiples and common multiples in, 232, 279
prime and composite numbers in, 186–190, 224
Numerator
adding and subtracting, 243–247
comparing to denominator, 242
multiplying and dividing, 248–252
rounding, 242
simplest form of, 192–195
Numerical expressions, 4–7, 71–72

O _____

Object, three views of, 538
Oblique cylinder, 545
Oblique prism, 545
Observation, 35
Obtuse angle, 464, 492, 516
Obtuse triangle, 470
Octagon, angles of, 472, 475
Odd number, 178
Odds, 307–309

One-point perspective, 542
One-step equations, solving, 65–123
One-step inequalities, solving
by adding, 107–109
by dividing, 110–111
by multiplying, 111–112
by subtraction, 106–109
Ongoing Assessment and Intervention, 2E, 64E, 124E, 176E, 230E, 286E, 346E, 396E, 456E, 520E, 578E, 628E, 686E, Teacher's Edition pages 4, 8, 14, 18, 24, 30, 35, 40, 44, 50, 66, 71, 76, 80, 86, 92, 96, 102, 106, 110, 127, 132, 137, 143, 148, 152, 156, 164, 178, 182, 186, 192, 197, 201, 205, 210, 215, 232, 237, 243, 248, 253, 259, 264, 268, 274, 288, 294, 299, 305, 310, 315, 320, 325, 329, 334, 348, 352, 357, 362, 367, 373, 378, 382, 400, 405, 411, 418, 423, 430, 435, 441, 458, 465, 470, 476, 480, 486, 491, 497, 503, 507, 522, 527, 532, 539, 545, 552, 557, 562, 566, 580, 584, 592, 598, 602, 608, 614, 630, 635, 642, 649, 654, 659, 665, 669, 674, 688, 694, 699, 704, 710, 715, 719, 724
Online Intervention. See Intervention.
Open-Ended exercises, 12, 20, 21, 32, 34, 48, 49, 54, 78, 85, 90, 95, 114, 120, 131, 147, 181, 189, 194, 195, 203, 207, 213, 252, 256, 272, 302, 308, 314, 319, 369, 385, 404, 414, 439, 445, 452, 473, 484, 495, 501, 516, 517, 525, 530, 536, 541, 549, 574, 596, 639, 646, 653, 668, 671, 696, 703, 706, 717, 722, 730, 732
Open sentence, 80
Operations. *See also* Fractions, Order of operations.
with fractions, 231–285
undoing, 348–349, 373
Opposites, 19
Order, 8
Ordered pair, 50, 59
Ordering
decimals, 282, 762
fractions, 232–236
numbers, 217, 757
whole numbers, 2, 757
Order of operations, 8–12, 57
calculator and, 9
with exponents, 183
grouping symbols in, 9
with integers, 26
defined, 8
using, 9
Origin, 50, 507
Outcome, 305–306, 309, 340
counting, 649–650
defined, 305
in sample space, 649
Outlier
defined, 138
effect on mean, 138–140, 170

P _____

Pacing Options (Traditional, Two-Year, Block), 2B, 64B, 124B, 176B, 230B, 286B, 346B, 396B, 456B, 520B, 578B, 628B, 686B

Pairs of angles, 465–469
Parabola, 694, 697, 730
Parallel lines, 459–462, 466
Parallelogram, 471
area of, 523–525, 531, 571, 574
formula for, 780
perimeter of, 525, 593
similar, 299
Parentheses ( )
as grouping symbol, 9
using, on calculator, 384
Part. *See* Proportions.
Pascal's Triangle, 664
Patterns, 110
addition, 36–39
angles of polygons, 475
arithmetic, 688–689, 690–692, 729–730
discovering, 688
extending, 36
geometric, 689–692, 721
in Inductive Reasoning, 35–39, 40, 45, 48, 59
looking for, 35–43, 404, 408
multiplying integers, 45
number, 36, 40–43
predictions and, 36–39
problems involving, 33, 40–43, 49, 90, 146, 155, 199, 204, 215, 220, 252, 404, 421, 582, 692, 721
in quotients, 252
sequences and, 688–692
similar figures, 299
tables to find, 40–43, 215
visual, 35, 38
writing rules for, 35–36, 38–39, 59, 200
See also Nets.
Pentagon, 472
Percent, 340
of change, 325–326, 334–337, 341, 416
of circle graph, 488–489
of commission, 321–323
of decrease, 326–328, 341
defined, 310, 340
of discount, 330–332
equations and, 320–323
of increase, 325–328, 334–335, 341
of markup, 330–332
of number, 315–323
proportions and, 315–319
reading percent problems, 324
of whole, 316–323
writing
as decimal, 310, 312–314
decimal as, 311–314
as fraction or mixed number, 310, 312–314
fraction as, 311–314
See also Decimals; Fractions; Percent equations.
Percent equations
percents greater than 100, 320, 322–323
to solve percent problems, 321–323
writing and solving, 320
Perfect square, 580, 621
Perimeter
adding polynomials to find, 710–714
defined, 144, 170
distance formula for, 593
of equilateral triangle, 473
formulas for, 144, 378, 780

music sales, 329
national parks, 488
navigation, 295, 616, 617, 618, 624, 707
number theory, 98
nutrition, 103, 105, 141, 160, 351, 426
octagons, 476
oil spills, 195
Olympics, 638
online purchasing, 16
online shopping, 15
organization, 189
packaging, 461, 549, 558, 562, 564, 568
painting, 549
parades, 474, 522
party planning, 208
personal finance, 149, 150, 252, 298, 428, 489
petroleum, 152
pets, 130, 311, 564, 726
pet supplies, 78
photocopies, 296
photography, 132, 197, 375
physical fitness, 160, 490
plants, 568
population, 642
populations, 312, 318, 334, 336
postage, 154
profit, 319
projection, 301
public schools, 707
publishing, 564
purchasing, 7, 15, 88, 296, 319
quality control, 297, 670, 671, 677
quilting, 132, 588
ramps, 610
reading, 266
reasoning, 644
recipes, 332, 550
recreation, 330, 535
recycling, 669
relay races, 98
remodeling, 240
renting, 380
reptiles, 172
retail delivery, 478
retailing, 329
retail sales, 141
rock climbing, 79
routes, 200
royalties, 321, 322
runners, 689
running, 150
salaries, 727
sales, 360
sales commissions, 418
sales tax, 319, 376
savings, 42, 94, 98, 349, 350, 382, 385, 692
scale drawings, 313
schedules, 235
school, 224
school computers, 645
school supplies, 68, 119
schoolwork, 440
scientific notation, 216
scuba diving, 81
seating arrangements, 189, 200
servings, 236
sewing, 403
shipping, 530
shopping, 98, 108, 149, 172, 331, 702

snacks, 272, 568, 652
snow spheres, 567
soccer games, 478
softball, 200, 257
solar system, 219
sports, 166, 232, 322, 422, 425, 524, 671, 706, 717
sports equipment, 134
storage, 559
surveying, 598, 606, 618
surveys, 288, 321, 631, 692
telephone service, 129
television programming, 515
temperature, 18, 22, 379
test scores, 167, 314, 375
theaters, 317
ticket prices, 427
tickets, 105
ticket sales, 74, 96, 309, 336, 416, 479
time, 259
track and field, 98, 235, 255
transportation, 108, 261, 290
travel, 69, 135, 143, 261, 368, 375, 379, 390, 392, 658, 726
travel time, 368, 390, 392
typesetting, 166
urban planning, 10
unit prices, 289
unit pricing, 134
utilities, 155
vacation, 291
video rental, 370
video sales, 331
viewing distance, 582
vital statistics, 306
walking, 403
waste management, 326
water resources, 336
waterskiing, 611
weather, 31, 34, 43, 47, 99, 114, 131, 169, 246
weather forecasting, 657
weight, 82
white-water rafting, 360
wildlife, 430
word processing, 16
See also Interdisciplinary Connections; Math at Work; Real-World Snapshots.

Real-World Snapshots
applying algebra, 736–737
applying area, 576–577
applying circles, 518–519
applying data, 454–455
applying data analysis, 684–685
applying decimals, 174–175
applying equations, 122–123, 394–395
applying factors and multiples, 228–229
applying fractions, 284–285
applying integers, 62–63
applying percents, 344–345
applying ratios, 626–627

Real-World Snapshots, Teacher's Edition pages 62, 122, 174, 228, 284, 344, 394, 454, 518, 576, 626, 684, 736

Reasonableness, 133

Reasoning, 28, 33, 39, 42, 48, 54, 75, 94, 104, 105, 108, 114, 139, 155, 171, 180, 181, 185, 189, 203, 204, 207, 241, 252, 257, 271, 297, 302, 308, 313, 314, 318, 322, 323, 328, 332, 370, 387, 399, 415, 423, 427, 439, 445, 468, 473, 483, 490, 510, 525, 531, 550, 556, 560, 564,

583, 587, 606, 611, 633, 639, 644, 652, 655, 664, 670, 671, 696, 713, 714, 723. *See also* Conjecture; Critical Thinking; Deductive reasoning; Error Analysis; Inductive reasoning.

Reciprocal, 250, 268–269, 357

Rectangle
area of, 10, 12, 71, 145, 172, 207, 249, 356, 438, 522–526, 721
classifying, 471
defined, 471
formulas for, 780
modeling factors, 179, 186, 248
perimeter of, 144–147, 172, 380, 516

Rectangular graph, 538

Rectangular graph paper, 538

Reduction. *See* Dilation.

Reflection, 503–506

Reflectional symmetry, 503, 505

Reflexive property of equality, 781

Regular polygon, 472
angles of, 475
defined, 472
diagonals in, 476–479

Regular pyramid, 552

Relations
defined, 400, 449
graphing, 401–404

Relatively prime numbers, 190

Repeated addition, 44–49

Repeated multiplication, 182–184

Repeating decimal, 238, 239, 280

Reteaching, 2F–G, 64F–G, 124F–G, 176F–G, 230F–G, 286F–G, 346F–G, 396F–G, 456F–G, 520F–G, 578F–G, 628F–G, 686F–G, Teacher's Edition pages 7, 12, 17, 22, 29, 34, 39, 43, 49, 54, 70, 75, 79, 83, 90, 95, 99, 105, 109, 114, 130, 135, 141, 146, 151, 155, 161, 167, 181, 185, 190, 195, 200, 204, 208, 214, 220, 236, 241, 247, 252, 257, 262, 267, 272, 277, 291, 298, 303, 309, 314, 319, 323, 328, 332, 337, 351, 356, 361, 365, 371, 376, 381, 386, 404, 409, 416, 422, 428, 433, 440, 446, 463, 469, 474, 479, 484, 490, 495, 501, 506, 510, 526, 531, 537, 543, 550, 556, 560, 565, 569, 583, 589, 596, 601, 606, 612, 618, 633, 639, 647, 653, 658, 663, 668, 672, 677, 692, 697, 702, 707, 714, 718, 722, 727

Review. *See* Assessment (Chapter Review and Cumulative Review); Mixed Review; Skills Handbook.

Rhombus, 471

Right angle, 464

Right cylinder, 545

Right prism, 545

Right triangle, 470
angles of, 613
defined, 450
45°-45°-90°, 602, 603
hypotenuse in, 584–589, 601–605
identifying, 586–587
isosceles, 602–603
legs of, 584–585
Pythagorean Theorem, 584–589

Acknowledgments

Staff Credits

The people who made up the Pre-Algebra team—representing editorial, editorial services, education technology, design services, market research, marketing, marketing services, project office, production services, and publishing processes—are listed below. Bold type denotes the core team members.

Leora Adler, Carolyn Artin, Peter Brooks, Judith D. Buice, Justin Collins, Sheila DeFazio, Marian DeLollis, **Emily Ellen,** Jayne Holman, Karen Holtzman, Kate House, Lisa LaVallee, **James Lonergan,** Cheryl Mahan, Constance McCarty, Eve Melnechuk, Terri Mitchell, Janet Morris, Cindy Noftle, Michael Oster, Rashid Ross, Dennis Slattery, Lisa Smith-Ruvalcaba, Nancy Smith, Deborah Sommer, Mark Tricca, **Joe Will,** Mathew Wilson, Helen Young

Cover Design

Brainworx Studio

Cover Image

Peacock, Charles Philip/Corbis; Ferris wheel, PhotoDisc, Inc./Getty Images, Inc.

Technical Illustration

Nesbitt Graphics, Inc.

Illustration

Suzanne Biron: 42, 256, 482, 738t, 739t, 740t, 741t, 742t, 743t, 743b; photocompositing—6, 51, 128, 162, 258, 260, 460, 464, 467, 473, 480, 481, 483, 498, 503, 508t
DLF Group: 613
Ortelius Design, Inc.: 31, 53, 145, 158, 218, 241, 244, 249, 300b, 349, 379, 529, 598t
Pat Packer-Williams: 300b, 738b, 739b, 740b, 741b, 742b, 743m; photocompositing—87, 289, 300b, 411, 426, 635, 642, 643
Wendy Simpson: photocompositing—300b, 411, 508b, 635
J/B Woolsey Associates: 33, 36, 46, 51, 68, 72, 75, 92, 129, 130, 137, 138, 148, 199, 245, 247, 248, 253, 261, 300t, 312, 317, 321, 326, 355, 375, 421, 462, 469, 472, 488, 498, 511, 532, 534, 535, 568, 586, 588, 598b, 600, 601, 610, 614, 616, 617, 624, 640, 642, 644, 645, 646, 667, 715

Photo Research

Sharon Donahue

Photography

Picture Research: Toni Michaels
Front Matter: Page v, ©Royal Tyrrell Museum of Palaeontology/Alberta Community Development; **vi,** Jose L./Palaez; **vii,** Stone/Doug Armand; **viii,** Russell C. Hansen/Peter Arnold, Inc.; **ix,** Stone/Jason Hawkes; **x,** Stone/ Renee Lynn; **xi,** Jose Carillo/PhotoEdit; **xii,** Joe Sohm/The Image Works; **xiii,** Alfred Pasteka/Science Photo Library/Photo Researchers; **xiv,** Sara Krulwich/NYT Pictures; **xv,** Stone/Hideo Kurihara; **xvi,** Marilyn Kazmers/Peter Arnold, Inc.; **xvii,** Bob Burch/Bruce Coleman; **xxviii, xix, xx, xxi,** Richard Haynes.

Chapter One: Pages 2–3, Stephen Frink/Index Stock Imagery Inc.; **5,** ©Royal Tyrrell Museum of Palaeontology/Alberta Community Development; **6,** PhotoDisc, Inc.; **10 tl,** Minnesota Dept. of Natural Resources; **10 bl,** Richard Haynes; **10 mr,** Richard Haynes; **15,** Russ Lappa; **16,** Stone/Stuart Westmorland; **26,** Albuquerque Seismological Lab, USGS; **29,** Patrick Somelet/DIAF/The Stock Market; **31,** ©Sowers/Penn State University; **33,** Index Stock Imagery; 40, Michael Simpson/FPG International; **42 t,** PhotoDisc, Inc.; **42 b,** Russ Lappa; **44,** OAR/National Undersea Research Program (NURP); **51,** Tom Van Sant/The Stock Market; **62 bl,** Dorling Kindersley/Charlestown Shipwreck Heritage Centre; **62 tr,** Corbis Digital Stock; **62 br,** EyeWire/Getty Images, Inc.; **63 tl,** AP/Wide World Photos; **63 r,** Stephen Frink/Getty Images, Inc.

Chapter Two: Pages 64–65, Mark Richards/PhotoEdit; **68,** Russ Lappa; **70,** Mark Kelley/Stock Boston; **72,** Tony Freeman/ PhotoEdit; **81,** Stone/Chris Simpson; **84 all,** Ken O'Donoghue; **86 both,** Anthony Neste; **87,** David R. Frazier Photolibrary; **96,** Superstock; **99,** Jose L./Palaez; **103 l,** D. & J. Heaton/Stock Boston; **103 m,** Superstock; **103 r,** Spencer Grant/PhotoEdit; **107,** Russ Lappa; **111,** Andrew Yates/Image Bank; **112 both,** Richard Haynes; **122 t,** Dennis Galante/Getty Images, Inc.; **122 bl,** Arthur Tilley/Getty Images, Inc.; **122 m,** Davies & Starr/Getty Images, Inc.; **123 tl,** www.Merlin-Net.com; **123,** Doug Menuez/Getty Images, Inc.

Chapter Three: Pages 124–125, Alan Goldsmith/Corbis; **128,** Russ Lappa; **129 both,** Richard Haynes; **132,** Russ Lappa; **133,** G. Cigolini/Image Bank; **143,** Alvin Staffan/Photo Researchers; **148,** Corel Corp.; **150,** Kevin Schafer/Peter Arnold, Inc.; **151,** Dilbert reprinted by permission of United Features Syndicate, Inc.; **153,** Corbis/Bettmann; **158,** Stone/Ed Simpson; **160,** Stone/ Doug Armand; **162 both,** Russ Lappa; **164,** Stone/I. Burgum/ P. Boorman; **167,** Bob Daemmrich/Stock Boston; **174 t,** Smithsonian Institution/National Numismatic Collection/ Douglas Mudd; **174 ml,** Equity Management, Inc.; **174 l,** Stamp from the private collection of Professor C.M. Lang, photography by Gary J. Shulfer, University of Wisconsin, Stevens Point; **174 mr,** U.S. Postal Service; **174 b,** Eric Meola/ Getty Images, Inc.; **175 tl,** Getty Images, Inc.-Hulton Archive Photos; **175 mr,** Phil Banko/Getty Images, Inc.

Chapter Four: Pages 176–177, John Mitchell/Photo Researchers, Inc.; **179,** Russ Lappa; **183 all,** ©Bruce Iverson; **186,** Russ Lappa; **188 both,** Richard Haynes; **193,** Bob Daemmrich/Stock Boston; **197,** Russ Lappa; **202,** AP/Dusan Vranic/Wide World Photos; **208,** Peggy Yoram Kahana/Peter Arnold, Inc.; **212,** Russell C. Hansen/Peter Arnold, Inc.; **213,** Mark Downey/ Liaison Agency; **216,** Tim Barnwell/Stock Boston; **218,** K & G Photo/FPG International; **228 t,** Breck P Kent/Animals Animals/Earth Scenes; **228 b,** Colin Keates/Dorling Kindersley; **229 br,** Gary C. Will/Visuals Unlimited.

Chapter Five: Pages 230–231, Gary Noland/Seeley Swan/ Pathfinder; **234,** Monkmeyer/Grant Pix; **237 both,** Ken Karp; **244,** Mark Gibson/Corbis; **245 both,** Richard Haynes; **249,** Alan Schen; **250,** Russ Lappa; **257,** Photri/The Stock Market; **258,** Russ Lappa; **259,** Stone/Jason Hawkes; **260 all,** Russ Lappa; **266,** Jim Corwim/Photo Researchers; **270,** Daniel Lyons/Bruce Coleman; **275,** Dirk Weisheit/DDB Stock Photo; **284 t,** ROBERT KIRKHAM/Buffalo News; **284 b,** New England Quilt Museum. Gift of The Brinney Family, 1995.20. Photo by Greg Heins.; **285 br,** Pilgrim/Roy Quilt Collection Warner, NH.

Chapter Six: Pages 286–287, Michael Paras/Image State; **289,** Russ Lappa; **291,** Stone/Kindra Clineff; **295,** NASA; **297,** REAL LIFE ADVENTURES ©1999 GarLanco. Reprinted with permission of Universal Press Syndicate. All rights reserved.; **302,** Richard Haynes; **304, 305,** Russ Lappa; **307 all,** The United States Mint; **311,** Stone/Renee Lynn; **313,** Jay Syverson/Stock Boston; **317,** Cincinnati Zoo; **330 both,** Richard Haynes; **334,** Joseph Sohm/Stock Boston; **336,** Tek Image/Science Photo Library/Photo Researchers; **337,** Spencer Grant/Stock Boston; **344 tr,** Rafael Macia/Photo Researchers, Inc.; **344 b,** 1997 ChromoSohm/Sohm; **345 tr,** Charles Thatcher/Getty Images, Inc.; **345 m,** Bruno Joachim/Index Stock Imagery/PictureQuest.

Chapter Seven: Pages 346–347, Marc Romanelli/Getty Images, Inc.; **349,** Stone/Mark Lewis; **359 both,** Richard Haynes; **360,** Tim Barnell/Stock Boston; **362,** The Granger Collection, New York; **368,** James Frank/Stock Connection/PNI; **371,** Michael Heron/The Stock Market; **374,** Jose Carrillo/PhotoEdit; **379,** Stone/David Schultz; **394 tl,** Russ Lappa; **394 bl,** Dieceland Technologies Corp; **394 tr,** Bob Mitchell/Corbis; **394 br,** Dieceland Technologies Corp; **395 bl,** The Boston Globe via www.Merlin-Net.com; **395 br,** The Boston Globe via www.Merlin-Net.com.

Chapter Eight: Pages 396–397, Dana White/PhotoEdit; **401,** David Young Wolff; **402,** Corel Corp.; **405,** Lester Lefkowitz/ The Stock Market; **411,** Stone/Jess Stock; **415 t,** Bob Daemmrich/The Image Works; **415 b,** Donald Dietz/Stock Boston; **416,** Stone/Don Smetzer; **426,** Russ Lappa; **430,** Erwin & Peggy Bauer/Bruce Coleman Inc.; **437 both,** Richard Haynes; **442,** Joe Sohm/The Image Works; **454 t,** Haruyoshi Yamaguchi/ Corbis; **454–455 b,** Raoul Minsart/Corbis; **455 tl,** Yoshida-Fujifotos/The Image Works; **455 tr,** Lester Lefkowitz/Getty Images, Inc.

Chapter Nine: Pages 456–457, Jim Corwin/Stock Boston; **458,** Photo Researchers; **460,** James Marshall/The Stock Market; **463,** AP/Paul Warner/Wide World Photos; **464,** Jon Chomitz; **467 r,** Courtesy of J.C. Guillois/Santa Fe Stained Glass; **467 mr,** Richard Haynes; **467 br,** Richard Haynes; **472,** Peter Gridley/ FPG International; **473,** Gianalberto Cigolini/Image Bank; **476,** Alfred Pasteka/Science Photo Library/Photo Researchers; **480,** Georg Gerster/Photo Researchers; **481,** John Heiney/ Sportschrome; **483,** R. Wahhlstrom/Image Bank; **486, 491,** Russ Lappa; **492,** Jon Chomitz; **498, 503 tl,** Russ Lappa; **503 bl,** Patti Murray/Animals Animals; **503 tr,** Russ Lappa; **503 br,** C. Zeiss/ Bruce Coleman; **508 t,** Russ Lappa; **508 b,** Danilo G. Donadoni/ Bruce Coleman; **509 tl,** Steve Solum/Bruce Coleman; **509 tr,** Adam Peiperl/The Stock Market; **509 bl,** Larry West/Bruce Coleman; **509 br,** John Gerlach/Tom Stack & Associates; **518 tr,** C. Kropp, Publ. Milwaukee No 331; **518–519 b,** Ray Juno/ Corbis; **518 l,** B.W. Kilburn/Corbis; **519 tr,** Kyodo News International, Inc.

Chapter Ten: Pages 520–521, Barth Falkenberg/Stock Boston; **522,** Leslye Borden/PhotoEdit; **526,** Ken Chernus/FPG/PNI; **528,** Pascal Quittemelle/Stock Boston; **529,** Corbis-Bettmann; **533,** Alan Carey/Photo Researchers, Inc.; **540,** Ellis Herwig/ Stock Boston; **542 all, 544, 547,** Russ Lappa; **554 tl,** Russ Lappa; **554 ml,** J. Sapinsky/The Stock Market; **554 bl,** Richard Haynes; **554 mr,** Richard Haynes; **556,** Sara Krulwich/NYT Pictures; **558, 560,** Russ Lappa; **562,** Stone/Steven Peters; **567,** Jeff Foott/ Bruce Coleman; **576 l,** Jim Cummins/Getty Images, Inc.; **576–577 b,** Eyewire/ Getty Images, Inc.; **577 tl,** Bill Sikes AP Wide World Photo; **577 tm,** Steve Lipofsky/Index Stock Imagery; **577 tr,** Jamie Squire/Getty Images News & Sport.

Chapter Eleven: Pages 578–579, Steve Casimiro/Getty Images, Inc.; **581,** Alese/Mort PECHTER/The Stock Market; **582,** Telegraph Colour Library/FPG International; **589,** Stone/Chad Slattery; **598,** Stone/Hideo Kurihara; **601,** H.P. Merten/The Stock Market; **603,** Landslides; **610 all,** Richard Haynes; **612,** Lance Nelson/The Stock Market; **626 b,** Ping Amranand/ Superstock; **627 tl,** Sydney McGinley, credit: Collection of the Artist; **627 tr,** ©ARS, NY Anthony Scibilia/Art Resource, NY.

Chapter Twelve: Pages 628–629, Zoran Milich/Getty Images, Inc.; **635,** Stone; **636 t,** Marilyn Kazmers/Peter Arnold, Inc.; **636 b,** David Madison/Bruce Coleman; **642 l,** Brent Jones/Stock Boston; **642 r,** Nik Wheeler/Corbis; **643,** Gerard Lacz/Peter Arnold, Inc.; **650,** Russ Lappa; **655,** John Lemker/Earth Scenes; **660,** Corel Corp.; **663,** Lynn Rogers/Peter Arnold, Inc.; **666 both,** Richard Haynes; **674,** Stone/Greg Pease; **684 tr,** AFP/Corbis; **684 b,** Al Bello/Getty Images News & Sport; **685 tm,** Andy Crawford/Dorling Kindersley; **685 tl,** AP/Wide World Photos/FIFA; **685 tr,** AFP/Corbis.

Chapter Thirteen: Pages 686–687, Tannen Maury/The Image Works; **689,** Marc Romanelli/Image Bank; **695,** Sydney Thompson/Animals Animals; **697,** Bob Daemmrich/Stock Boston; **699,** Andrew Henley/Auscape; **700,** Peter Berndt, M.D., P.A.; **705,** Bob Burch/Bruce Coleman; **720 both,** Richard Haynes; **724,** John Davenport/Liaison Agency; **736 tr,** SuperStock, Inc.; **736 bl,** Dorling Kindersley/Royal British Columbia Museum; **736 l,** James King-Holmes/Photo Researchers, Inc.; **737,** Malcolm Macgregor/Dorling Kindersley.

Teacher's Edition

Design Coordination: Susan Gerould/Perspectives
Editorial and Production Services: Laurel Technical Services